The College Blue Book®

44th Edition

Tabular Data

The College Blue Book®

44th Edition

Tabular Data

MACMILLAN REFERENCE USA
A part of Gale, Cengage Learning

GALE
CENGAGE Learning®

Farmington Hills, Mich • San Francisco • New York • Waterville, Maine
Meriden, Conn • Mason, Ohio • Chicago

The College Blue Book, 44th Edition Volume 2

Project Editor: Bohdan Romaniuk

Editorial Support Services: Wayne Fong

Composition and Electronic Prepress: Gary Leach

Manufacturing: Rita Wimberley

For product information and technology assistance, contact us at **Gale Customer Support, 1-800-877-4253.**
For permission to use material from this text or product, submit all requests online at **www.cengage.com/permissions.**
Further permissions questions can be emailed to **permissionrequest@cengage.com**

Gale
27500 Drake Rd.
Farmington Hills, MI, 48331-3535

ISBN-13: 978-0-02-866306-7 (6 vol. set)
ISBN-13: 978-0-02-866308-1 (vol. 2)

ISSN 1082-7056

This title is also available as an e-book.
ISBN-13: 978-0-02-866314-2 (set)
Contact your Gale sales representative for ordering information.

Printed in the United States of America
1 2 3 4 5 6 7 20 19 18 17 16

Contents

The College Blue Book® has been a standard, professional reference on higher education since it was first published in 1923. New features have been added during the intervening years to keep pace with the changing needs for information about our educational facilities. The information, especially in the areas of tuition, room and board, enrollment figures, library holdings, is constantly changing. It is difficult to maintain up-to-date figures in these areas, as many schools change tuition and related costs on an ongoing basis. We therefore urge our readers to check directly with the schools for the most current cost information.

CONTENTS OF EACH VOLUME

Volume 1: Narrative Descriptions

More than 4,300 colleges in the United States and Canada are fully described. Entrance requirements are detailed and campus facilities and costs are described. A map of each U.S. state and Canadian province is included and each college has a grid index for easy location. Web sites are also listed.

Volume 2: Tabular Data

Colleges are listed alphabetically by state or province. Information about costs, accreditation, enrollment figures, faculty, and names of the chief administrative officers are given for each school.

Volume 3: Degrees Offered by College and Subject

In Part I, the name of each college is listed alphabetically by state or province, with a list of the subject areas for which degrees are offered. Part II includes an alphabetical listing of subject areas for which degrees are granted by one or more institutions of higher education.

Volume 4: Occupational Education

More than 6,500 schools in the United States that provide occupational or technical training are fully described,

offering such information as tuition costs, enrollment figures, and entrance requirements. Two indexes are provided: an alphabetical listing of schools in the "Index of Occupational Education Schools," in addition to the "Curricula and Areas of Instruction" index.

Volume 5: Scholarships, Fellowships, Grants, and Loans

This volume provides a listing of more than 6,000 sources of financial aid for students wishing to further their education. Split alphabetically into eight broad subject areas (each containing several more specialized concentrations of study), as well as a general section, each listing provides basic information about a specific award, including eligibility requirements, amount of award, and application deadlines.

Volume 6: Distance Learning Programs

Responding to this rapidly growing trend in post-secondary education, this volume features comprehensive profiles of nearly 1,000 institutions offering distance learning programs within the United States and Canada.

FOR MORE INFORMATION

We are always open to suggestions and recommendations for improvement of The College Blue Book® from our readers and from the educational professions. Please contact: Editor, The College Blue Book

Macmillan Reference USA

27500 Drake Rd.

Farmington Hills, MI 48331-3535 Phone: (248)699-4253

Toll-free: 800-877-4253

Fax: (248)699-8075

Email: bob.romaniuk@cengage.com

Web site: www.gale.cengage.com

The decision to continue education beyond high school years, the selection of a collegiate institution, and the area of study to be pursued are some of the essential experiences necessary for students to determine their futures. Alternatives of choice institutions, work selection, job opportunities, professional training, or even discontinuing any further education are all selective decisions open to the students.

Nearly all students today have opportunities to continue education beyond high school. There are more schools accepting wider ranges of student ability and interest than ever before. This means more effort, more planning, and more personal study in making the college choice.

Self Appraisal

The best place to begin is with oneself. An appraisal with objective, honest answers is necessary. What are the personal potentials as a student? Where has the best performance been? What are the probabilities for improvement? What are the reasons for really wanting to go to college; is it for intellectual development, vocational preparation, or simply to satisfy a desire for status? What are the personal ideas of college? What is expected from the college experience? Have career plans been made? Where are the academic abilities? What subjects are preferred? What is the quality of performance in the preferred areas of study? What is the overall grade average? What is the class rank in high school? In what subject areas is there the greatest interest? What is the quality of work in these areas? Are interests and performance generally consistent? Are the expressed and recorded interests truly and accurately reflecting the inward wishes? What was liked best about the high school experience? Has the college preparatory program been followed in high school? What were the social and cultural experiences during high school years that were most meaningful? What was considered, if anything, to be lacking?

Well-thought-out answers to these and similar questions are helpful. Discussions of such topics with counselors, parents, and teachers increases the probability of success in college selection, attendance, and completion.

The counselor today is an extremely valued resource person available to assist the student. When an effective working team of counselor-student-parent actually exists, the probabilities for the student making selective choices that prove to be the "right" ones are unquestionably the greatest. The better the student and the counselor know one another, the more effective the guidance and counseling program will be. For this to occur, the opportunity for face-to-face student-counselor discussion needs to start in the latter elementary school years and continue through high school and college.

College Appraisals

Research is continuing in the areas of college admissions and student success. The identification and understanding of causes of success and failure need professional study. However, one thing is apparent: the more careful the preparations and planning by the student, the better the chances of college admission and success.

Systemized planning should begin early. The more self-understanding and knowledge about available colleges one has, the better one can plan with corresponding success. Certainly, early in the high school career, students should be reviewing detailed information on colleges and universities with the counselor, noting academic requirements such as scholastic performance, course requirements, costs and other particular qualities of individual collegiate institutions. There is no single one-and-only college for the student. Colleges have personalities just as the students do. There are always several colleges with academic and social climates compatible and acceptable to each student.

Entrance requirements, courses available, costs, size of student body, academic pressure, special programs, geographical location, and specialty schools are some of the considerations of every student in appraising available colleges.

The College Blue Book® is dedicated to providing detailed information regarding collegiate institutions throughout the United States and Canada. Students and counselors should browse through The College Blue Book® and become familiar with the colleges of our country and neighboring Canada. As interest sharpens and narrows, a more selective and in-depth study of institutions should be made.

Where feasible, students should plan visits to college campuses. Campus visiting may begin during the summer between the sophomore and junior years of high school. The best time to be on a college campus, however, is during the regular term with a carefully planned visit in the spring semester of the junior year. Preparatory plans should be made with the high school counselor, reviewing discussions of earlier personal conferences. Advance arrangements should be made with admission officers of the colleges the student expects to visit. The admission officer's name and telephone number will be found in most instances in *The College Blue Book®* volume entitled *Tabular Data*. The admissions officer in many cases will want to know whether the student has actually applied for admission and probably the areas the student may plan to major in or other special interests the student has in the particular institution. The student should have prepared a summary of personal data. If possible, high school students should also talk to students of the colleges they wish to attend.

The growth of community colleges has opened up another avenue for students, especially those of limited finances or those who have not decided on their ultimate educational goals. Students will find many of these community colleges offer an excellent opportunity to gain a solid college background. Then one can choose a four-year institution to complete an undergraduate degree.

Any regular high school graduate can find a school that will accept him. Many students need to be encouraged to consider the smaller, private and public colleges of good standing.

Students entering professional training such as engineering or law might consider small schools that have cooperative programs with major universities. A knowledgeable student, through planning and guidance, can avoid unnecessary disappointment. A college career can be quite beneficial to the student who spends three to four years on a small campus and one, two, or three additional years of graduate work on another, larger campus.

Costs

Costs are continuing to rise. Tuition charges as listed herein should only be used as a guide. It would be wise to check with the institution of interest to be sure of having the most up-to-date information available.

Should the need for financial aid be a factor in selecting a college, a college-bound student should be aware that the best single source of financial assistance and information is the financial aid officer or admission director at the college. It is most important for the student to contact the finance office as early as possible during the student's senior year in high school. A principal source of financial assistance is the major federal undergraduate aid programs. Applications can be obtained from the college. Most colleges and universities also offer financial assistance in several forms including academic and general scholarships, grants-in-aid, student loans, and part-time work. For more information, see volume 5 of *The College Blue Book®*: *Scholarships, Fellowships, Grants, and Loans.*

Two-Year Colleges

Two-year colleges, referred to as junior colleges or community colleges, both public and private, offer programs that prepare students for technical and semiprofessional careers in business and technology fields, and for transfer to senior colleges. There are hundreds of two-year colleges providing comprehensive programs meeting the lower division requirements of virtually all four-year colleges and universities.

There are decided advantages for some students to enroll in a two-year college. Some of these are: less cost, home residence, availability of highly specialized programs, opportunity for the student to mature, a smaller student body, and generally a closer relationship to the faculty. The development of two-year colleges across the nation is one of the most vital forces in education today. The two-year college is neither an extension of high school, nor a little senior college. It has its own identity, sphere of service, and contribution to make to American education. The comprehensive community college is considered one of the best means of accommodating the demands of higher education, embracing the increasing variety of abilities of students graduating from high schools, preparing students in the technological and semiprofessional occupations, and all in an economical manner.

One very important caution needs to be heeded by students enrolling in two-year colleges who are planning to continue their work through a bachelor's program. Students expecting to transfer should very carefully study the requirements of the institution they ultimately plan to attend. In conference with the junior college counselor, a careful review of the planned program should be made to be sure the contemplated courses at the junior college will satisfy the requirements of the senior institution. Students who depart from prescribed courses stated by the senior institution or fail in any of these courses may experience difficulty with admission or normal progress toward the bachelor degree.

Liberal Arts Colleges

The liberal arts colleges offer four years of college and award the Bachelor of Arts and the Bachelor of Science degrees. The curriculum for the first two years is usually broad with an emphasis in the humanities, natural sciences, and cultural history of our society. The last two years may provide a concentration of specific programs such as premedicine or pre-law leading to graduate professional training.

Students considering professional training at the graduate level should keep this in mind as they plan their work at the liberal arts college. Graduate schools in some cases have strict preparatory requirements. Familiarity with these requirements can greatly assist in making the transfer to graduate level without loss of credit or time.

Specialized Institutions

Four-year institutions of technology are examples of the more specialized schools where concentration in a specialty is intensively pursued throughout the college career. Most of these institutions are quite selective in admission practice and may require more high school mathematics and science than most other schools for entrance. These programs lead to engineering degrees in many fields emphasizing technology and science. Recently there has been a broadening of the program of the first two years, but, in general, such a program is not nearly as comprehensive and varied as the liberal arts college. The demand for engineers and scientists with specially developed skills creates great competition for entrance into schools of technology.

There are other specialized institutions such as conservatories of music, seminaries, medical and law schools, institutions specializing in teacher training, or schools of the fine arts, most of which require specialized preparation for entrance.

Universities

The university is generally composed of a number of degree-granting colleges and schools where both bachelor and graduate degrees are grouped under one administrative head. Bachelor degrees at the university may be earned in liberal arts or one of the professions such as engineering or the physical sciences. The university, to some extent, combines what is available at the liberal arts college with the specialized institution. Complete professional training in such areas as law, medicine, and science is available on the university campus.

As a rule, universities have much larger student bodies than colleges. In order to meet the demand, most state universities have established several campuses. Many state universities are very selective in admitting students. This is particularly true for a student who is applying for admission from out- of-state.

Entrance Examinations

There are more applicants than there is room for students on many campuses. As this demand increases, colleges and universities attempt to identify those applicants who are most likely to succeed on their campuses. A quality scholastic record has more influence on acceptance and admission than any other single factor. High school grades predict with better accuracy than any other single measurement what college grades and success will be. The more selective colleges and universities may choose students who come out highest on quantitative criteria, that is, high school scholastic averages combined with test scores. Some institutions have far more applicants (whose scholastic records and test scores are of a maximum quality) than they can accept. In such cases, applicants are sometimes screened and accepted on the basis of categories according to residence in the state or region, special talents, minority groups, or relationship to alumni. Such procedures are used in an attempt to influence the makeup of the enrollment.

When investigating several schools, one of the most accurate ways for evaluation of an institution is to consider test scores and the high school rank order of the students actually on campus. In many instances this is more informative than the announced admission policies.

College testing is required by many colleges and universities for entering students; some have developed their own tests and over the years have established norms for such tests. Most institutions requiring tests for entrance, however, now use either the test of the American College Testing Program (ACT) or the examinations of the College Entrance Examination Board. The College Entrance Examination Board offers the Preliminary Scholastic Assessment Test/National Merit Scholarship Qualifying Test (PSAT/ NM-SQT), the Scholastic Assessment Test I: Reasoning Test (Verbal and Math), and the SAT II: Subject Tests.

Coaching, tutoring, drill, and memorization of facts can do little to improve the scores of the standardized examinations. It is recommended that students not invest time and money in cramming in hopes of improving test scores. Students can do their best preparation in general reading, completing their school assignments, and arriving on the proper day of the test rested and refreshed.

American College Testing Assessment (ACT)

The ACT Assessment provided by the American College Testing Program covers four subject areas: English, mathematics, reading, and science reasoning. The ACT test is scored on a range of 1 to 36. The ACT is administered at various test sites in the United States and other countries on specified dates throughout the year. Many colleges and universities recommend that prospective students take the examination early in the senior year.

The tests provide estimates of the students' current level of educational development in knowledge skill areas often required in college work. The ACT college testing program was founded in 1959. It is a nonprofit educational service offering programs in testing and financial need analysis.

Scholastic Assessment Tests (SAT)

The SAT I: Reasoning Test is an examination to measure the verbal and mathematics abilities students have developed both in and out of school. The SAT II: Subject Tests, which some colleges require for admission or placement purposes, consist of 22 separate tests that cover subjects such as literature, history, math, languages, chemistry, biology, and physics. Unlike the SAT I, which measures more general abilities, the SAT II tests measure the students' knowledge of a particular subject and their ability to apply that knowledge. Because of this, students should try to take a SAT II Test as soon as possible after completion of their last course in that subject.

The SAT I and II tests are given on certain dates throughout the year at various test centers in the United States and foreign countries. The combination of the student's academic record and the SAT scores, along with other pertinent secondary information enables admissions officers to estimate how well the student will perform on a particular college campus. The SAT is scored on a scale of 200 minimum to 800 maximum.

Admission Policies

One of the most important considerations in planning is to note when colleges and universities request applications, and to be sure that the applications are complete and forwarded during the appropriate periods. Failure in any way in this procedure will usually automatically disqualify a student from acceptance.

Counselors can provide students with freshman profiles on many of the institutions. Studying *The College Blue Book*®, particularly the volume *Tabular Data,* provides a great amount of information on the kind of student bodies found on the campuses of American institutions. There are four general classifications of admission policies. An understanding of these provides valuable guidelines in identifying colleges for consideration.

Most Selective: Many more students apply who meet the announced admission requirements than the college could possibly accept. In addition to requiring outstanding academic records, personal recommendations are required from the high school, and identification of any special qualities of the student should be made known. In this regard, the high school recommendation made to the collegiate institution requires special attention.

Many times, particularly at selective institutions, the high school recommendation actually provides the necessary edge for admission. The recommendation should be on time, carefully providing all information called for, and finally, be precise and detailed in citing personal qualities of the applicant.

All these qualities, however, do not guarantee acceptance. It is strongly recommended that qualified students apply to more than one institution of this type, and that not all applications should be made to the same type of institution.

Very Selective: Colleges having a very selective procedure in accepting students require ACT scores of 23 or over, or an SAT I score of 600 or more. Students should rank in the top 10 to 12 percent of their high school graduating classes. In addition, strong recommendations stressing particular talents and achievements are necessary. Applications should be made to several institutions of this type.

Selective: An ACT of 20 or over, or an SAT I score of 550 or more is generally necessary. Applications for admission to selective colleges and universities are usually called for in the spring prior to fall entry. In many situations, applications may be submitted in the fall of the senior year with final confirmation to be made after all grades are recorded and confirmed upon graduation from high school.

Least Selective: The fourth classification represents those institutions that will accept students with a C average on their high school work. In certain unusual instances, and under special situations, even the selective institutions may accept students who are in this category, particularly if the scores on the ACT are in the mid-20's or are in excess of 500 on the SAT I. Generally, for acceptance in the less selective schools, students should have an ACT composite score of 17 or a SAT I score of 450.

Entrance examinations may or may not be required. Occasionally, if examinations are required, the results are used for student placement rather than admission. Most high school graduates can meet the requirements for entry and will be accepted. It should be pointed out, however, that in some cases an institution may be liberal in acceptance but carefully screens candidates for graduation. In such an institution, a high attrition rate may occur.

Open Enrollment Policy: This is becoming more common, particularly with the public community colleges. Many students will find this privilege most helpful in continuing their formal education beyond high school. Such a policy enables those students to have a second chance who have failed to perform up to their ability during their high school years. Enrollment and attendance may enable the student to complete a most rewarding vocational program or to later transfer and complete the Bachelor degree, which otherwise might not have been possible because of the deficiency in the high school scholastic record.

A number of colleges and universities, particularly the publicly supported ones, have adopted the open enrollment policy. In response to a feeling of community responsibility, they accept any student who has a diploma (or G.E.D. equivalency certificate) from an accredited high school. This procedure allows students from disadvantaged and minority backgrounds, who might otherwise be denied such an opportunity, to acquire a college education and prepare for a meaningful occupation. These institutions have not lowered their graduation requirements; they have, instead, created opportunities for more students to satisfy these requirements.

Do not assume the erroneous generality that the tougher it is to get into an institution, the better the quality; or the easier to enter, the poorer the school. In fact, there is research evidence available indicating that it may be wise to re-examine some of our traditional notions and attitudes regarding admissions. Not all degree programs on any particular campus are equally outstanding. Every institution has its particular strengths in programs available. Certain institutions are excellent places for some kinds of students in some kinds of programs, but no institution is the one most suited for everyone.

More than 4,300 educational institutions of the United States and Canada are presented in this volume. The information presented has been collected by questionnaires submitted to these institutions. In addition the most recent college catalogs were often consulted.

ORGANIZATION

All institutions are arranged in alpha-geographic order. Beginning with the state of Alabama, each institution is listed in alphabetical order within each state. The states are followed by schools in Canada listed by province.

For easier, more comprehensive use this volume is in a ready-reference format that gives statistical data available on each institution. Another use for this volume is to provide easy comparisons of schools as to enrollment, tuition, and other data. Additional information may be obtained from consulting the individual school listing in the *Narrative Descriptions* volume.

USE

Most of the data in this volume are self-explanatory. A few elements, however, need some clarification:

Costs Per Year

Tuition charges are constantly changing and information reported here is as correct as possible. However, it is recommended that the institutions be contacted for the most cur-

rent information on charges for tuition, room and board, and miscellaneous fees. Many schools will have several tuitions: in-district, instate, nonresident. See *Narrative Descriptions* volume for a more complete breakdown.

Athletics

An Index on Intercollegiate Athletics listed alphabetically by sport and then by school follows the main section of this volume.

Professional Accreditations

Due to space constraints, acronyms have been used. A list of these acronyms follows this section. An Index of Professional Accreditations follows the athletics index in this volume.

Admission Plans

Early admission: Exceptionally able students are admitted before high school graduation. *Early action plan:* Students apply and are notified of admission early; if accepted, the candidate is not committed to enroll. *Early decision:* The school accepts well-qualified students who are notified earlier than usual, generally by mid-December. *Rolling admission:* An admission decision will be given as soon as possible after all application materials are received. *Deferred admission:* A student who wants to work, travel, study abroad, etc., for one year, will be accepted for the following year. *Open admission:* Students are admitted without the usual record for standard qualifications. Almost all students with a high school diploma or equivalent are admitted.

AABB	American Association of Blood Banks
AABI	Aviation Accrditation Board International
AACN	American Association of Colleges of Nursing
AACSB	AACSB International-The Association to Advance Collegiate Schools of Business
AAFCS	American Association of Family and Consumer Sciences
AALE	American Academy for Liberal Education
AALS	Association of American Law Schools
AAMAE	American Association of Medical Assistants Endowment
AAMFT	American Association for Marriage and Family Therapy
AANA	American Association of Nurse Anesthetists
AARTS	Association of Advanced Rabbinical and Talmudic Schools
ABA	American Bar Association
ABET	Accreditation Board for Engineering and Technology, Inc.
ABFSE	American Board of Funeral Service Education
ABHE	Association for Biblical Higher Education
ABHES	Accrediting Bureau of Health Education Schools
ACA	American Counseling Association
ACAOM	Accredition Commission for Acupuncture and Oriental Medicine
ACBSP	Accreditation Council for Business Schools and Programs
ACCE	American Council for Construction Education
ACCSC	Accrediting Commission of Career Schools and Colleges
ACEJMC	Accrediting Council on Education in Journalism and Mass Communications
ACEN	Accreditation commission for Education in Nursing
ACF	American Culinary Federation, Inc.
ACICS	Accrediting Council for Independent Colleges and Schools
ACIPE	Association for Clinical Pastoral Education, Inc.
ACNM	American College of Nurse-Midwives
ACPeE	Accreditation Committee for Perfusion Education
ACPE	American Council for Pharmacy Education
ACSP	American Institute of Certified Planners/Association of Collegiate Schools of Planning
ADA	American Dental Association
AHIMA	American Health Information Management Association
ALA	American Library Association
AND	Academy of Nutrition and Dietetics
AOA	American Optometric Association
AOsA	American Osteopathic Association
AOTA	American Occupational Therapy Association
APA	American Psychological Association
APMA	American Podiatric Medical Association
APTA	American Physical Therapy Association
ARCEAA	Accreditation Review Commission on Education for the Anesthesiologist Assistant
ARCMI	Accreditation Review Committee for the Medical Illustrator
ARCST	Accreditation Review Committee on Education in Surgical Technology
ASC	American Society of Cytopathology
ASHA	American Speech-Language-Hearing Association
ASLA	American Society of Landscape Architects
ATMAE	Association of Technology, Management, and Applied Engineering
ATS	Association of Theological Schools in the United States and Canada
AVMA	American Veterinary Medical Association
CAHME	Commission on Accreditation of Healthcare Management Education
CCE	Council on Chiropractic Education
CEPH	Council on Education for Public Health
CIDA	Council for Interior Design Accreditation
CoA-KT	Committee on Accreditation of Education Programs in Kinesiotherapy
CoARC	Committee on Accreditation for Respiratory Care
COA	Commission on Opticianry Accreditation
COE	Council on Occupational Education
CORE	Council on Rehabilitation Education
CSWE	Council on Social Work Education
DEAC	Distance Education Acedditing Commission
JCAHPO	Joint Commission on Allied Health Personnel in Ophthalmology
JRCAT	Joint Review Committee on Educational Programs in Athletic Training
JRCECT	Joint Review Committee on Education in Cardiovascular Technology
JRCEDMS	Joint Review Committee on Education in Diagnostic Medical Sonography
JRCEMTP	Joint Review Committee on Educational Programs for the EMT-Paramedic
JRCEND	Joint Review Committee on Education in Electroneurodiagnostic Technology
JRCERT	Joint Review Committee on Education in Radiologic Technology
JRCNMT	Joint Review Committee on Educational Programs in Nuclear Medicine Technology
LCME/AMA	Liaison Committee on Medical Education/American Medical Association

MACTE	Montessori Accreditation Council for Teacher Education
MEAC	Midwifery Education Accreditation Council
NAACLS	National Accrediting Agency for Clinical Laboratory Sciences
NASAD	National Association of Schools of Art and Design
NASD	National Association of Schools of Dance
NASM	National Association of Schools of Music
NASPAA	Network of Schools of Public Policy, Affairs and Administration
NAST	National Association of Schools of Theatre
NCATE	National Council for Accreditation of Teacher Education

NCCU	Northwest Commission on Colleges and Universities
NCOPE	National Commission on Orthotic and Prosthetic Education
NLN	National League for Nursing
NPWH	National Association of Nurse Practitioners in Women's Health
NRPA	National Recreation and Park Association
NYSBR	New York State Board of Regents
SAF	Society of American Foresters
TEAC	Teacher Education Accreditation Council
TRACS	Transnational Association of Christian Colleges and Schools

ACT	American College Testing Program		PT	Part-time
FT	Full-time		SAT I	Scholastic Assessment Test: Reasoning Test
GED	General Education Development		SAT II	Scholastic Assessment Test: Subject Tests
Grad	Graduate level		V	Verbal
M	Math (SAT); Men		W	Women

ALABAMA AGRICULTURAL AND MECHANICAL UNIVERSITY

4900 Meridian St.
Huntsville, AL 35811
Tel: (256)372-5000; Free: 800-553-0816
Fax: (256)372-5881
Web Site: www.aamu.edu
President/CEO: Dr. Andrew Hugine, Jr.
Admissions: Dr. Evelyn Ellis
Financial Aid: Deborah Gordon

Type: University **Sex:** Coed **Scores:** 64% SAT V 400+; 62% SAT M 400+; 43% ACT 18-23; 4% ACT 24-29 **% Accepted:** 51 **Admission Plans:** Deferred Admission **Application Deadline:** June 15 **Application Fee:** $10.00 **H.S. Requirements:** High school diploma required; GED accepted **Costs Per Year:** Application fee: $10. State resident tuition: $7770 full-time, $259 per credit hour part-time. Nonresident tuition: $15,540 full-time, $518 per credit hour part-time. Mandatory fees: $1596 full-time, $1590 per term part-time. Full-time tuition and fees vary according to course load. Part-time tuition and fees vary according to course load. College room and board: $8140. College room only: $3140. Room and board charges vary according to board plan, housing facility, and location. **Scholarships:** Available. **Calendar System:** Semester, Summer session available **Enrollment:** Full-time 4,592, Graduate full-time 433, Graduate part-time 441, Part-time 348 **Faculty:** Full-time 289, Part-time 1 **Student-Faculty Ratio:** 20:1 **Exams:** ACT. **% Receiving Financial Aid:** 90 **Regional Accreditation:** Southern Association of Colleges and Schools **Credit Hours For Degree:** 128 semester hours, Bachelors **ROTC:** Army **Professional Accreditation:** AAFCS, ABET, ACSP, ASHA, CORE, CSWE, NCATE, SAF. **Intercollegiate Athletics:** Baseball M; Basketball M & W; Cross-Country Running M & W; Football M; Golf M; Soccer M; Tennis M & W; Track and Field M & W; Volleyball W

ALABAMA SOUTHERN COMMUNITY COLLEGE

PO Box 2000
Monroeville, AL 36461
Tel: (251)575-3156
E-mail: jhorton@ascc.edu
Web Site: www.ascc.edu
President/CEO: Dr. Reginald Sykes
Admissions: Jana S. Horton

Type: Two-Year College **Sex:** Coed **Affiliation:** Alabama Community College System. **Admission Plans:** Early Admission; Open Admission; Preferred Admission **Application Deadline:** September 10 **Application Fee:** $0.00 **H.S. Requirements:** High school diploma required; GED accepted **Costs Per Year:** Application fee: $0. State resident tuition: $3680 full-time. Nonresident tuition: $7360 full-time. Mandatory fees: $928 full-time. Full-time tuition and fees vary according to course load. **Scholarships:** Available. **Calendar System:** Semester, Summer session available **Student-Faculty Ratio:** 17:1 **Exams:** ACT. **Final Year or Final Semester Residency Requirement:** No **Regional Accreditation:** Southern Association of Colleges and Schools **Credit Hours For Degree:** 60 semester hours, Associates **Professional Accreditation:** ACEN. **Intercollegiate Athletics:** Baseball M; Basketball M & W; Softball W

ALABAMA STATE UNIVERSITY

915 S Jackson St.
Montgomery, AL 36101-0271

Tel: (334)229-4100; Free: 800-253-5037
Fax: (334)229-4984
E-mail: wesmith@alasu.edu
Web Site: www.alasu.edu
President/CEO: Dr. Gwendolyn E. Boyd
Admissions: Dr. William E. Smith
Financial Aid: Marcus Byrd

Type: Comprehensive **Sex:** Coed **Affiliation:** Alabama Commission on Higher Education. **Scores:** 64% SAT V 400+; 63% SAT M 400+; 42.49% ACT 18-23; 6.84% ACT 24-29 **% Accepted:** 48 **Admission Plans:** Deferred Admission; Early Admission **Application Deadline:** July 31 **Application Fee:** $25.00 **H.S. Requirements:** High school diploma required; GED accepted **Costs Per Year:** Application fee: $25. One-time mandatory fee: $150. State resident tuition: $6936 full-time, $289 per credit hour part-time. Nonresident tuition: $13,872 full-time, $578 per credit hour part-time. Mandatory fees: $1784 full-time, $446. Full-time tuition and fees vary according to course load and degree level. Part-time tuition and fees vary according to course load and degree level. College room and board: $5422. College room only: $3346. Room and board charges vary according to board plan and housing facility. **Scholarships:** Available. **Calendar System:** Semester, Summer session available **Enrollment:** Full-time 4,377, Graduate full-time 290, Graduate part-time 329, Part-time 387 **Faculty:** Full-time 254, Part-time 155 **Exams:** ACT essay component not used; SAT I or ACT; SAT essay component not used; SAT Reasoning; SAT Subject. **% Receiving Financial Aid:** 96 **% Residing in College-Owned, -Operated, or -Affiliated Housing:** 34 **Final Year or Final Semester Residency Requirement:** No **Regional Accreditation:** Southern Association of Colleges and Schools **Credit Hours For Degree:** 129 credit hours, Bachelors **ROTC:** Air Force, Army **Professional Accreditation:** ACBSP, AOTA, APTA, CORE, CSWE, NASM, NCATE. **Intercollegiate Athletics:** Baseball M; Basketball M & W; Bowling W; Cheerleading M & W; Cross-Country Running M & W; Football M; Golf M & W; Soccer W; Softball W; Tennis M & W; Track and Field M & W; Volleyball W

AMRIDGE UNIVERSITY

1200 Taylor Rd.
Montgomery, AL 36117
Tel: (334)387-3877; Free: 888-790-8080
Fax: (334)387-3878
E-mail: registrar@amridgeuniversity.edu
Web Site: www.amridgeuniversity.edu
President/CEO: Dr. Michael C. Turner
Admissions: Elaine Tarence
Financial Aid: Starr Fain

Type: University **Sex:** Coed **Affiliation:** Church of Christ. **Admission Plans:** Early Admission **Application Deadline:** Rolling **Application Fee:** $50.00 **H.S. Requirements:** High school diploma required; GED accepted **Costs Per Year:** Application fee: $50. Tuition: $9960 full-time. Mandatory fees: $900 full-time. Full-time tuition and fees vary according to course load, program, and student level. Tuition guaranteed not to increase for student's term of enrollment. **Scholarships:** Available. **Calendar System:** Semester, Summer session available **Enrollment:** Full-time 171, Graduate full-time 140, Graduate part-time 181, Part-time 144 **Faculty:** Full-time 38, Part-time 26 **Student-Faculty Ratio:** 10:1 **Exams:** ACT essay component not used; SAT I or ACT; SAT essay component not used. **% Receiving Financial Aid:** 89 **Final Year or Final Semester Residency Requirement:** No **Regional**

Accreditation: Southern Association of Colleges and Schools **Credit Hours For Degree:** 64 semester hours, Associates; 128 semester hours, Bachelors

ATHENS STATE UNIVERSITY
300 N Beaty St.
Athens, AL 35611
Tel: (256)233-8100; Free: 800-522-0272
Fax: (256)233-8164
E-mail: necedah.henderson@athens.edu
Web Site: www.athens.edu
President/CEO: Dr. Robert Glenn
Admissions: Necedah Henderson
Financial Aid: Mary Chambliss

Type: Two-Year Upper Division **Sex:** Coed **Admission Plans:** Deferred Admission; Open Admission **Application Fee:** $30.00 **H.S. Requirements:** High school diploma required; GED accepted **Costs Per Year:** Application fee: $30. State resident tuition: $5520 full-time. Nonresident tuition: $11,040 full-time. Mandatory fees: $750 full-time. **Scholarships:** Available. **Calendar System:** Semester, Summer session available **Enrollment:** Full-time 1,226, Part-time 1,816 **Faculty:** Full-time 80, Part-time 111 **Student-Faculty Ratio:** 17:1 **% Receiving Financial Aid:** 55 **Regional Accreditation:** Southern Association of Colleges and Schools **Credit Hours For Degree:** 124 credit hours, Bachelors **Professional Accreditation:** ACBSP, NCATE.

AUBURN UNIVERSITY
Auburn University, AL 36849
Tel: (334)844-4000; Free: 800-AUBURN9
E-mail: admissions@auburn.edu
Web Site: www.auburn.edu
President/CEO: Dr. Jay Gogue, PhD
Admissions: Cindy Singley
Financial Aid: Mike Reynolds

Type: University **Sex:** Coed **Scores:** 99% SAT V 400+; 100% SAT M 400+; 15.01% ACT 18-23; 53.2% ACT 24-29 **% Accepted:** 78 **Admission Plans:** Deferred Admission; Early Admission; Early Decision Plan **Application Deadline:** February 1 **Application Fee:** $50.00 **H.S. Requirements:** High school diploma required; GED accepted **Costs Per Year:** Application fee: $50. State resident tuition: $8808 full-time, $367 per semester hour part-time. Nonresident tuition: $26,424 full-time, $1101 per semester hour part-time. Mandatory fees: $1616 full-time, $808 per term part-time. Full-time tuition and fees vary according to program and reciprocity agreements. Part-time tuition and fees vary according to course load, program, and reciprocity agreements. College room and board: $12,584. College room only: $7298. Room and board charges vary according to board plan and housing facility. **Scholarships:** Available. **Calendar System:** Semester, Summer session available **Enrollment:** Full-time 19,738, Graduate full-time 3,177, Graduate part-time 2,324, Part-time 2,048 **Faculty:** Full-time 1,216, Part-time 183 **Student-Faculty Ratio:** 19:1 **Exams:** SAT I or ACT; SAT Reasoning. **% Receiving Financial Aid:** 38 **% Residing in College-Owned, -Operated, or -Affiliated Housing:** 21 **Regional Accreditation:** Southern Association of Colleges and Schools **Credit Hours For Degree:** 120 semester hours, Bachelors **ROTC:** Air Force, Army, Navy **Professional Accreditation:** AABI, AACN, AACSB, AAFCS, AAMFT, ABET, ACA, ACCE, ACEJMC, ACPE, APA, ASHA, ASLA, AVMA, CIDA, CORE, CSWE, NAAB, NASAD, NASM, NASPAA, NAST, NCATE, SAF. **Intercollegiate Athletics:** Baseball M; Basketball M & W; Cross-Country Running M & W; Equestrian Sports W; Football M; Golf M & W; Gymnastics W; Soccer W; Softball W; Swimming and Diving M & W; Tennis M & W; Track and Field M & W; Volleyball W

AUBURN UNIVERSITY AT MONTGOMERY
PO Box 244023
Montgomery, AL 36124-4023
Tel: (334)244-3000; Free: 800-227-2649
Fax: (334)244-3795
E-mail: admissions@aum.edu
Web Site: www.aum.edu
President/CEO: Dr. John G. Veres, III
Financial Aid: Anthony Richey

Type: Comprehensive **Sex:** Coed **Affiliation:** Auburn University. **Scores:** 75.2% ACT 18-23; 23.7% ACT 24-29 **% Accepted:** 79 **Admission Plans:** Deferred Admission **Application Deadline:** Rolling **H.S. Requirements:** High school diploma required; GED accepted **Costs Per Year:** State resident tuition: $8700 full-time, $290 per credit hour part-time. Nonresident tuition: $19,560 full-time, $652 per credit hour part-time. Mandatory fees:

$650 full-time. Full-time tuition and fees vary according to course load and degree level. Part-time tuition varies according to course load and degree level. College room and board: $5520. College room only: $4320. Room and board charges vary according to housing facility. **Scholarships:** Available. **Calendar System:** Semester, Summer session available **Enrollment:** Full-time 3,083, Graduate full-time 217, Graduate part-time 445, Part-time 1,174 **Faculty:** Full-time 191, Part-time 155 **Student-Faculty Ratio:** 16:1 **Exams:** ACT essay component not used; SAT I or ACT; SAT essay component not used. **% Receiving Financial Aid:** 67 **% Residing in College-Owned, -Operated, or -Affiliated Housing:** 20 **Final Year or Final Semester Residency Requirement:** No **Regional Accreditation:** Southern Association of Colleges and Schools **Credit Hours For Degree:** 120 semester hours, Bachelors **ROTC:** Air Force, Army **Professional Accreditation:** AACN, AACSB, ACA, NAACLS, NASPAA, NCATE. **Intercollegiate Athletics:** Baseball M; Basketball M & W; Cheerleading M & W; Cross-Country Running M & W; Soccer M & W; Softball W; Tennis M & W

BEVILL STATE COMMUNITY COLLEGE
1411 Indiana Ave.
Jasper, AL 35501
Tel: (205)387-0511
Web Site: www.bscc.edu
President/CEO: Dr. Larry Ferguson, PhD
Admissions: Melissa Stowe

Type: Two-Year College **Sex:** Coed **Affiliation:** Alabama Community College System. **Admission Plans:** Deferred Admission; Early Admission; Open Admission **Application Deadline:** Rolling **H.S. Requirements:** High school diploma required; GED accepted **Costs Per Year:** State resident tuition: $2760 full-time, $115 per credit hour part-time. Nonresident tuition: $5520 full-time, $230 per credit hour part-time. Mandatory fees: $711 full-time. Full-time tuition and fees vary according to course load and program. Part-time tuition varies according to course load and program. College room and board: $1850. Room and board charges vary according to board plan and location. **Scholarships:** Available. **Calendar System:** Semester, Summer session available **Enrollment:** Full-time 1,838, Part-time 1,771 **Faculty:** Full-time 117, Part-time 169 **Student-Faculty Ratio:** 17:1 **Final Year or Final Semester Residency Requirement:** No **Regional Accreditation:** Southern Association of Colleges and Schools **Professional Accreditation:** ACEN, NAACLS.

BIRMINGHAM-SOUTHERN COLLEGE
900 Arkadelphia Rd.
Birmingham, AL 35254
Tel: (205)226-4600; Free: 800-523-5793
Fax: (205)226-3074
E-mail: jwaters@bsc.edu
Web Site: www.bsc.edu
President/CEO: Gen. Charles Krulak
Admissions: Jennifer Waters

Type: Four-Year College **Sex:** Coed **Affiliation:** Methodist. **Scores:** 100% SAT V 400+; 100% SAT M 400+; 26.99% ACT 18-23; 52.25% ACT 24-29 **% Accepted:** 65 **Admission Plans:** Deferred Admission; Early Decision Plan **Application Fee:** $40.00 **H.S. Requirements:** High school diploma required; GED accepted **Costs Per Year:** Application fee: $40. One-time mandatory fee: $200. Comprehensive fee: $44,478 includes full-time tuition ($31,954), mandatory fees ($1174), and college room and board ($11,350). College room only: $6600. Full-time tuition and fees vary according to program and reciprocity agreements. Room and board charges vary according to board plan and housing facility. **Scholarships:** Available. **Calendar System:** 4-1-4, Summer session available **Enrollment:** Full-time 1,208, Part-time 23 **Faculty:** Full-time 86, Part-time 28 **Student-Faculty Ratio:** 13:1 **Exams:** ACT essay component used as validity check; SAT I or ACT; SAT essay component used as validity check; SAT Reasoning; SAT Subject. **% Receiving Financial Aid:** 58 **% Residing in College-Owned, -Operated, or -Affiliated Housing:** 85 **Final Year or Final Semester Residency Requirement:** No **Regional Accreditation:** Southern Association of Colleges and Schools **Credit Hours For Degree:** 32 courses, Bachelors **ROTC:** Air Force, Army **Professional Accreditation:** AACSB, NASM, NCATE. **Intercollegiate Athletics:** Baseball M; Basketball M & W; Cheerleading M & W; Cross-Country Running M & W; Football M; Golf M & W; Lacrosse M & W; Soccer M & W; Softball W; Swimming and Diving M & W; Tennis M & W; Track and Field M & W; Volleyball W

BISHOP STATE COMMUNITY COLLEGE
351 N Broad St.
Mobile, AL 36603-5898

Tel: (251)405-7000
Fax: (251)438-5403
E-mail: admiss@bishop.edu
Web Site: www.bishop.edu
President/CEO: James Lowe, PhD
Type: Two-Year College **Sex:** Coed **Affiliation:** Alabama Community College System. **Admission Plans:** Deferred Admission; Early Admission; Open Admission **Application Deadline:** Rolling **Application Fee:** $0.00 **H.S. Requirements:** High school diploma required; GED accepted **Scholarships:** Available. **Calendar System:** Semester, Summer session available **Enrollment:** Full-time 2,171, Part-time 1,725 **Faculty:** Full-time 118, Part-time 69 **Student-Faculty Ratio:** 23:1 **Final Year or Final Semester Residency Requirement:** Yes **Regional Accreditation:** Southern Association of Colleges and Schools **Credit Hours For Degree:** 60 credit hours, Associates **Professional Accreditation:** ABFSE, ACBSP, ACEN, ACF, AHIMA, APTA. **Intercollegiate Athletics:** Baseball M & W; Basketball M & W; Cheerleading W; Softball W

CALHOUN COMMUNITY COLLEGE

PO Box 2216
Decatur, AL 35609-2216
Tel: (256)306-2500
Fax: (256)306-2877
E-mail: admissions@calhoun.edu
Web Site: www.calhoun.edu
President/CEO: Marilyn C. Beck
Type: Two-Year College **Sex:** Coed **Affiliation:** Alabama College System. **Admission Plans:** Open Admission **Application Deadline:** Rolling **Application Fee:** $0.00 **H.S. Requirements:** High school diploma required; GED accepted **Scholarships:** Available. **Calendar System:** Semester, Summer session available **Student-Faculty Ratio:** 26:1 **Exams:** SAT I or ACT. **Regional Accreditation:** Southern Association of Colleges and Schools **Credit Hours For Degree:** 64 semester hours, Associates **Professional Accreditation:** ACBSP, ACEN, ADA. **Intercollegiate Athletics:** Baseball M; Softball W

CENTRAL ALABAMA COMMUNITY COLLEGE

1675 Cherokee Rd.
Alexander City, AL 35011-0699
Tel: (256)234-6346
Fax: (256)234-0384
Web Site: www.cacc.edu
President/CEO: Dr. Stephen Franks
Admissions: Donna Whaley
Financial Aid: Cindy Entrekin
Type: Two-Year College **Sex:** Coed **Affiliation:** Alabama College System. **Admission Plans:** Early Admission; Open Admission **Application Deadline:** September 9 **Application Fee:** $0.00 **H.S. Requirements:** High school diploma required; GED accepted **Scholarships:** Available. **Calendar System:** Semester, Summer session available **Enrollment:** Full-time 1,304, Part-time 873 **Faculty:** Full-time 52, Part-time 141 **Student-Faculty Ratio:** 15:1 **Exams:** SAT I or ACT. **Regional Accreditation:** Southern Association of Colleges and Schools **Professional Accreditation:** ACEN. **Intercollegiate Athletics:** Baseball M; Golf M; Softball W; Tennis M & W; Volleyball W

CHATTAHOOCHEE VALLEY COMMUNITY COLLEGE

2602 College Dr.
Phenix City, AL 36869-7928
Tel: (334)291-4900
Fax: (334)291-4994
E-mail: admissions@cv.edu
Web Site: www.cv.edu
President/CEO: Dr. Glen Cannon
Financial Aid: Joan B. Waters
Type: Two-Year College **Sex:** Coed **Affiliation:** Alabama College System. **% Accepted:** 100 **Admission Plans:** Early Admission; Open Admission; Preferred Admission **Application Deadline:** Rolling **Application Fee:** $0.00 **H.S. Requirements:** High school diploma required; GED accepted **Scholarships:** Available. **Calendar System:** Semester, Summer session available **Enrollment:** Full-time 944, Part-time 753 **Faculty:** Full-time 35, Part-time 89 **Student-Faculty Ratio:** 20:1 **Regional Accreditation:** Southern Association of Colleges and Schools **Intercollegiate Athletics:** Baseball M; Basketball M & W; Softball W

COLUMBIA SOUTHERN UNIVERSITY

21982 University Ln.
Orange Beach, AL 36561
Tel: (251)981-3771; Free: 800-977-8449
Fax: (251)981-3815
E-mail: admissions@columbiasouthern.edu
Web Site: www.columbiasouthern.edu
President/CEO: Robert G. Mayes, Jr.
Type: Comprehensive **Sex:** Coed **Admission Plans:** Open Admission **Application Deadline:** Rolling **Application Fee:** $0.00 **H.S. Requirements:** High school diploma required; GED accepted **Costs Per Year:** Application fee: $0. One-time mandatory fee: $135. Tuition: $210 per credit part-time. Part-time tuition varies according to course load. **Calendar System:** Miscellaneous, Summer session not available **Enrollment:** Full-time 6,705, Graduate full-time 5,282, Part-time 7,806 **Faculty:** Full-time 138, Part-time 361 **Student-Faculty Ratio:** 57:1 **Final Year or Final Semester Residency Requirement:** No **Credit Hours For Degree:** 60 credit hours, Associates; 120 credit hours, Bachelors **Professional Accreditation:** DEAC.

COMMUNITY COLLEGE OF THE AIR FORCE

CCAF/DESS
100 S Turner Blvd.
Maxwell Gunter Air Force Base, AL 36114-3011
Tel: (334)649-5000
E-mail: gwendolyn.ford@us.af.mil
Web Site: www.au.af.mil/au/ccaf
President/CEO: Lt. Col. Nathan J. Leap
Admissions: Gwendolyn Ford
Type: Two-Year College **Sex:** Coed **Affiliation:** Air University. **% Accepted:** 100 **Admission Plans:** Open Admission **Application Deadline:** Rolling **Application Fee:** $0.00 **H.S. Requirements:** High school diploma required; GED accepted **Calendar System:** Continuous **Enrollment:** Full-time 286,450 **Faculty:** Full-time 6,144 **Exams:** Other. **Regional Accreditation:** Southern Association of Colleges and Schools **Credit Hours For Degree:** 64 semester hours, Associates **Professional Accreditation:** APTA.

CONCORDIA COLLEGE ALABAMA

1712 Broad St.
Selma, AL 36701
Tel: (334)874-5700
Fax: (334)874-3728
E-mail: prichardson@ccal.edu
Web Site: www.ccal.edu
President/CEO: Dr. Tiahun M. Mendedo
Admissions: Phyllis Richardson
Financial Aid: T. H. Bridges
Type: Four-Year College **Sex:** Coed **Affiliation:** Lutheran; Concordia University System. **Admission Plans:** Deferred Admission **Application Deadline:** August 15 **Application Fee:** $10.00 **H.S. Requirements:** High school diploma required; GED accepted **Costs Per Year:** Application fee: $10. Comprehensive fee: $15,720 includes full-time tuition ($9920), mandatory fees ($200), and college room and board ($5600). College room only: $2300. Room and board charges vary according to housing facility. Part-time tuition: $415 per credit hour. Part-time tuition varies according to course load. **Scholarships:** Available. **Calendar System:** Semester, Summer session available **Enrollment:** Full-time 565, Part-time 46 **Faculty:** Full-time 22, Part-time 24 **Student-Faculty Ratio:** 19:1 **Exams:** ACT essay component not used; SAT I or ACT; SAT essay component not used. **% Receiving Financial Aid:** 79 **Final Year or Final Semester Residency Requirement:** Yes **Regional Accreditation:** Southern Association of Colleges and Schools **Credit Hours For Degree:** 64 credits, Associates; 126 credits, Bachelors **ROTC:** Army **Intercollegiate Athletics:** Baseball M; Basketball M & W; Cheerleading M; Football M; Soccer M; Softball W; Track and Field M & W; Volleyball M & W

ENTERPRISE STATE COMMUNITY COLLEGE

PO Box 1300
Enterprise, AL 36331-1300
Tel: (334)347-2623
E-mail: gdeas@eocc.edu
Web Site: www.escc.edu
President/CEO: Dr. Cynthia Anthony
Admissions: Gary Deas
Financial Aid: Dr. Henry L. Quisenberry, Jr.

Type: Two-Year College Sex: Coed Affiliation: Alabama College System. Admission Plans: Deferred Admission; Early Admission; Open Admission Application Deadline: Rolling Application Fee: $0.00 H.S. Requirements: High school diploma required; GED accepted Scholarships: Available. Calendar System: Semester, Summer session available Regional Accreditation: Southern Association of Colleges and Schools Intercollegiate Athletics: Baseball M; Basketball M & W; Cheerleading M & W; Softball W

FAULKNER UNIVERSITY

5345 Atlanta Hwy.
Montgomery, AL 36109-3398
Tel: (334)386-7324; Free: 800-879-9816
Fax: (334)386-7268
E-mail: nscott@faulkner.edu
Web Site: www.faulkner.edu
President/CEO: Pres. Billy D. Hilyer
Admissions: Neil Scott
Financial Aid: William G. Jackson, II

Type: University Sex: Coed Affiliation: Church of Christ. Scores: 93% SAT V 400+; 87% SAT M 400+; 51% ACT 18-23; 22% ACT 24-29 % Accepted: 57 Admission Plans: Deferred Admission; Early Admission Application Deadline: Rolling Application Fee: $0.00 H.S. Requirements: High school diploma required; GED accepted Costs Per Year: Application fee: $0. Comprehensive fee: $26,410 includes full-time tuition ($17,500), mandatory fees ($1780), and college room and board ($7130). College room only: $3380. Full-time tuition and fees vary according to class time, course load, location, and program. Room and board charges vary according to board plan and housing facility. Part-time tuition: $590 per semester hour. Part-time mandatory fees: $315 per term. Part-time tuition and fees vary according to class time, course load, location, and program. Scholarships: Available. Calendar System: Semester, Summer session available Enrollment: Full-time 1,771, Graduate full-time 612, Graduate part-time 86, Part-time 793 Faculty: Full-time 120, Part-time 180 Student-Faculty Ratio: 15:1 Exams: SAT I or ACT; SAT Reasoning; SAT Subject. % Receiving Financial Aid: 36 % Residing in College-Owned, -Operated, or -Affiliated Housing: 50 Final Year or Final Semester Residency Requirement: Yes Regional Accreditation: Southern Association of Colleges and Schools Credit Hours For Degree: 64 semester hours, Associates; 126 semester hours, Bachelors ROTC: Air Force, Army Professional Accreditation: ABA, NCATE. Intercollegiate Athletics: Baseball M; Basketball M & W; Cheerleading M & W; Football M; Golf M & W; Soccer M & W; Softball W; Volleyball W

FORTIS COLLEGE (MOBILE)

7033 Airport Blvd.
Mobile, AL 36608
Tel: (334)344-1203; Free: 855-4-FORTIS
Fax: (334)344-1299
Web Site: www.fortis.edu
Type: Two-Year College Sex: Coed Professional Accreditation: ABHES.

FORTIS COLLEGE (MONTGOMERY)

3470 Eastdale Cir.
Montgomery, AL 36117
Tel: (334)244-1827; Free: 855-4-FORTIS
Web Site: www.fortis.edu
Type: Two-Year College Sex: Coed Professional Accreditation: ABHES.

FORTIS COLLEGE (MONTGOMERY)

3736 Atlanta Hwy.
Montgomery, AL 36109
Tel: (334)272-3857; Free: 855-4-FORTIS
Web Site: www.fortis.edu
Type: Two-Year College Sex: Coed Professional Accreditation: ABHES.

FORTIS INSTITUTE

100 London Pky.
Ste. 150
Birmingham, AL 35211
Tel: (205)940-7800; Free: 855-4-FORTIS
Web Site: www.fortis.edu
Type: Two-Year College Sex: Coed Professional Accreditation: ACICS.

GADSDEN STATE COMMUNITY COLLEGE

PO Box 227
Gadsden, AL 35902-0227
Tel: (256)549-8200; Free: 800-226-5563
Fax: (256)549-8444
E-mail: info@gadsdenstate.edu
Web Site: www.gadsdenstate.edu
President/CEO: Dr. Martha G. Lavender
Admissions: Jennie Dobson
Financial Aid: Kelly D'Eath

Type: Two-Year College Sex: Coed Affiliation: Alabama Community College System. Admission Plans: Deferred Admission; Early Admission; Open Admission Application Deadline: Rolling Application Fee: $0.00 H.S. Requirements: High school diploma required; GED accepted. For auto collision repair, automotive service technology, basic carpentry, advanced carpentry, construction management, cosmetology, diesel mechanics, welding programs: High school diploma required; GED accepted Costs Per Year: Application fee: $0. State resident tuition: $2760 full-time, $115 per credit hour part-time. Nonresident tuition: $5520 full-time, $230 per credit hour part-time. Mandatory fees: $456 full-time, $19 per credit hour part-time. Full-time tuition and fees vary according to reciprocity agreements. Part-time tuition and fees vary according to reciprocity agreements. College room and board: $3600. Scholarships: Available. Calendar System: Semester, Summer session available Enrollment: Full-time 2,576, Part-time 2,442 Faculty: Full-time 149, Part-time 154 Student-Faculty Ratio: 17:1 % Residing in College-Owned, -Operated, or -Affiliated Housing: 2 Final Year or Final Semester Residency Requirement: No Regional Accreditation: Southern Association of Colleges and Schools Credit Hours For Degree: 60 credit hours, Associates ROTC: Army Professional Accreditation: ACBSP, ACEN, JRCEMTP, JRCERT, NAACLS. Intercollegiate Athletics: Basketball M & W; Softball W; Tennis M; Volleyball W

GEORGE C. WALLACE COMMUNITY COLLEGE

1141 Wallace Dr.
Dothan, AL 36303-9234
Tel: (334)983-3521; Free: 800-543-2426
Fax: (334)983-3600
E-mail: ksaulsberry@wallace.edu
Web Site: www.wallace.edu
President/CEO: Dr. Linda C. Young
Admissions: Keith Saulsberry

Type: Two-Year College Sex: Coed Affiliation: The Alabama Community College System. % Accepted: 100 Admission Plans: Early Admission; Open Admission Application Deadline: Rolling Application Fee: $0.00 H.S. Requirements: High school diploma required; GED accepted. For some technical programs: High school diploma required; GED not accepted Costs Per Year: Application fee: $0. State resident tuition: $3450 full-time, $115 per credit hour part-time. Nonresident tuition: $6900 full-time, $230 per credit hour part-time. Mandatory fees: $810 full-time, $27 per credit hour part-time. Full-time tuition and fees vary according to reciprocity agreements. Part-time tuition and fees vary according to reciprocity agreements. Scholarships: Available. Calendar System: Semester, Summer session not available Enrollment: Full-time 2,161, Part-time 2,608 Faculty: Full-time 130, Part-time 99 Student-Faculty Ratio: 19:1 Exams: SAT I or ACT. Regional Accreditation: Southern Association of Colleges and Schools Professional Accreditation: AAMAE, ACEN, APTA, CoARC, JRCEMTP, JRCERT. Intercollegiate Athletics: Baseball M; Softball W

GEORGE CORLEY WALLACE STATE COMMUNITY COLLEGE

PO Box 2530
Selma, AL 36702
Tel: (334)876-9227
Fax: (334)876-9250
Web Site: www.wccs.edu
President/CEO: Dr. James M. Mitchell
Admissions: Sunette Newman

Type: Two-Year College Sex: Coed Affiliation: Alabama College System. Admission Plans: Deferred Admission; Early Admission; Open Admission Application Deadline: Rolling Application Fee: $0.00 H.S. Requirements: High school diploma required; GED accepted Scholarships: Available. Calendar System: Semester, Summer session available Regional Accreditation: Southern Association of Colleges and Schools Credit Hours For Degree: 64 semester hours, Associates Professional Accreditation: ACEN. Intercollegiate Athletics: Baseball M; Basketball M

H. COUNCILL TRENHOLM STATE COMMUNITY COLLEGE

1225 Air Base Blvd.
Montgomery, AL 36108-2699
Tel: (334)420-4200; Free: 866-753-4544
Fax: (334)420-4201
E-mail: tmcbryde@trenholmstate.edu
Web Site: www.trenholmstate.edu
President/CEO: Sam Munnerlyn
Admissions: Tennie McBryde
Type: Two-Year College **Sex:** Coed **Affiliation:** Alabama Community College System. **% Accepted:** 29 **Admission Plans:** Early Admission; Open Admission **Application Deadline:** Rolling **Application Fee:** $0.00 **H.S. Requirements:** High school diploma required; GED accepted **Costs Per Year:** Application fee: $0. State resident tuition: $3432 full-time, $117 per credit hour part-time. Nonresident tuition: $6240 full-time, $234 per credit hour part-time. Mandatory fees: $780 full-time, $26 per credit hour part-time. **Scholarships:** Available. **Calendar System:** Semester, Summer session available **Faculty:** Full-time 53, Part-time 44 **Student-Faculty Ratio:** 15:1 **Exams:** ACT. **Regional Accreditation:** Southern Association of Colleges and Schools **Credit Hours For Degree:** 62 credit hours, Associates **Professional Accreditation:** ACF, COE.

HERITAGE CHRISTIAN UNIVERSITY

PO Box HCU
Florence, AL 35630
Tel: (256)766-6610; Free: 800-367-3565
Fax: (256)760-0981
E-mail: bmckinnon@hcu.edu
Web Site: www.hcu.edu
President/CEO: Dennis Jones
Admissions: Brad McKinnon
Financial Aid: Mechelle R. Thompson
Type: Comprehensive **Sex:** Coed **Affiliation:** Church of Christ. **% Accepted:** 100 **Admission Plans:** Deferred Admission; Early Admission; Open Admission; Preferred Admission **Application Deadline:** Rolling **Application Fee:** $25.00 **H.S. Requirements:** High school diploma required; GED accepted **Scholarships:** Available. **Calendar System:** Semester, Summer session available **Enrollment:** Full-time 27, Graduate full-time 5, Graduate part-time 20, Part-time 36 **Faculty:** Full-time 5, Part-time 15 **Student-Faculty Ratio:** 5:1 **Exams:** Other. **% Receiving Financial Aid:** 100 % **Residing in College-Owned, -Operated, or -Affiliated Housing:** 60 **Final Year or Final Semester Residency Requirement:** Yes **Credit Hours For Degree:** 65 semester hours, Associates; 128 semester hours, Bachelors **Professional Accreditation:** ABHE.

HERZING UNIVERSITY

280 W Valley Ave.
Birmingham, AL 35209
Tel: (205)916-2800; Free: 800-596-0724
Fax: (205)916-2807
E-mail: admiss@bhm.herzing.edu
Web Site: www.herzing.edu/birmingham
President/CEO: Tommy Dennis
Admissions: Tess Anderson
Type: Four-Year College **Sex:** Coed **Affiliation:** Herzing Institutes, Inc. **H.S. Requirements:** High school diploma required; GED accepted **Scholarships:** Available. **Calendar System:** Semester, Summer session available **Regional Accreditation:** North Central Association of Colleges and Schools **Professional Accreditation:** ACCSC.

HUNTINGDON COLLEGE

1500 E Fairview Ave.
Montgomery, AL 36106-2148
Tel: (334)833-4497; Free: 800-763-0313
Fax: (334)833-4347
E-mail: admiss@hawks.huntingdon.edu
Web Site: www.huntingdon.edu
President/CEO: Rev. J. Cameron West
Financial Aid: Brittany Nicole Davis
Type: Four-Year College **Sex:** Coed **Affiliation:** United Methodist. **Scores:** 88% SAT V 400+; 94% SAT M 400+; 65% ACT 18-23; 20% ACT 24-29 **Costs Per Year:** Comprehensive fee: $33,900 includes full-time tuition ($24,000), mandatory fees ($1050), and college room and board ($8850). Full-time tuition and fees vary according to course load, program, and

student level. Room and board charges vary according to housing facility. Part-time tuition: $1000 per credit hour. Part-time tuition varies according to course load and program. Tuition guaranteed not to increase for student's term of enrollment. **Scholarships:** Available. **Calendar System:** Semester, Summer session available **Enrollment:** Full-time 896, Part-time 270 **Faculty:** Full-time 45, Part-time 77 **Student-Faculty Ratio:** 14:1 **Exams:** ACT essay component not used; SAT I or ACT; SAT II; SAT essay component not used. **% Receiving Financial Aid:** 75 **% Residing in College-Owned, -Operated, or -Affiliated Housing:** 62 **Final Year or Final Semester Residency Requirement:** Yes **Regional Accreditation:** Southern Association of Colleges and Schools **Credit Hours For Degree:** 120 semester credit hours, Bachelors **ROTC:** Air Force, Army **Professional Accreditation:** NASM. **Intercollegiate Athletics:** Baseball M; Basketball M & W; Football M; Golf M & W; Lacrosse M & W; Soccer M & W; Softball W; Tennis M & W; Volleyball W; Wrestling M

HUNTSVILLE BIBLE COLLEGE

904 Oakwood Ave.
Huntsville, AL 35811-1632
Tel: (256)539-0834
Web Site: www.hbc1.edu
Type: Comprehensive **Sex:** Coed **Professional Accreditation:** ABHE.

J. F. DRAKE STATE COMMUNITY AND TECHNICAL COLLEGE

3421 Meridian St. N
Huntsville, AL 35811-1584
Tel: (256)539-8161; Free: 888-413-7253
E-mail: kristin.treadway@drakestate.edu
Web Site: www.drakestate.edu
President/CEO: Dr. Kemba Chambers, EdD
Admissions: Kristin Treadway
Financial Aid: Jennifer O'Linger
Type: Two-Year College **Sex:** Coed **Affiliation:** Alabama Community College System. **Admission Plans:** Deferred Admission; Open Admission **Application Deadline:** Rolling **Application Fee:** $0.00 **H.S. Requirements:** High school diploma required; GED accepted **Scholarships:** Available. **Calendar System:** Semester, Summer session not available **Enrollment:** Full-time 484, Part-time 512 **Faculty:** Full-time 31, Part-time 48 **Student-Faculty Ratio:** 15:1 **Final Year or Final Semester Residency Requirement:** No **Regional Accreditation:** Southern Association of Colleges and Schools **Credit Hours For Degree:** 72 semester hours, Associates **Professional Accreditation:** COE.

J F INGRAM STATE TECHNICAL COLLEGE

5375 Ingram Rd.
Deatsville, AL 36022
Web Site: www.istc.edu
Type: Two-Year College **Sex:** Coed **Professional Accreditation:** COE.

JACKSONVILLE STATE UNIVERSITY

700 Pelham Rd., N
Jacksonville, AL 36265-1602
Tel: (256)782-5781; Free: 800-231-5291
Fax: (256)782-5291
E-mail: info@jsu.edu
Web Site: www.jsu.edu
President/CEO: Dr. John M. Beehler
Admissions: Andrew Green
Financial Aid: Vickie Adams
Type: Comprehensive **Sex:** Coed **Scores:** 94% SAT V 400+; 88% SAT M 400+; 53.51% ACT 18-23; 40.31% ACT 24-29 **% Accepted:** 80 **Admission Plans:** Deferred Admission; Early Admission **Application Deadline:** Rolling **Application Fee:** $35.00 **H.S. Requirements:** High school diploma required; GED accepted **Costs Per Year:** Application fee: $35. State resident tuition: $9000 full-time, $300 per credit hour part-time. Nonresident tuition: $18,000 full-time, $600 per credit hour part-time. Mandatory fees: $300 full-time, $150 per term part-time. College room and board: $7128. Room and board charges vary according to board plan and housing facility. **Scholarships:** Available. **Calendar System:** Semester, Summer session available **Enrollment:** Full-time 5,461, Graduate full-time 179, Graduate part-time 752, Part-time 1,922 **Faculty:** Full-time 317, Part-time 139 **Student-Faculty Ratio:** 18:1 **Exams:** ACT essay component not used; SAT I or ACT; SAT essay component not used. **% Receiving Financial Aid:** 88 % **Residing in College-Owned, -Operated, or -Affiliated Housing:** 25 **Final**

Year or Final Semester Residency Requirement: No **Regional Accreditation:** Southern Association of Colleges and Schools **Credit Hours For Degree:** 120 semester hours, Bachelors **ROTC:** Army **Professional Accreditation:** AACN, AACSB, AAFCS, ABET, ACA, ATMAE, CSWE, NASAD, NASM, NAST, NCATE. **Intercollegiate Athletics:** Baseball M; Basketball M & W; Cross-Country Running M & W; Football M; Golf M & W; Riflery M & W; Soccer W; Softball W; Tennis M & W; Volleyball W

JAMES H. FAULKNER STATE COMMUNITY COLLEGE

1900 Hwy. 31 S
Bay Minette, AL 36507
Tel: (251)580-2100; Free: 800-231-3752
Fax: (251)580-2285
E-mail: cmikkelsen@faulknerstate.edu
Web Site: www.faulknerstate.edu
President/CEO: Gary L. Branch
Admissions: Carmelita Mikkelsen

Type: Two-Year College **Sex:** Coed **Affiliation:** Alabama Community College System. **Admission Plans:** Deferred Admission; Early Admission; Open Admission **Application Deadline:** Rolling **Application Fee:** $0.00 **H.S. Requirements:** High school diploma required; GED accepted **Costs Per Year:** Application fee: $0. State resident tuition: $4320 full-time, $115 per hour part-time. Nonresident tuition: $7770 full-time, $230 per hour part-time. Mandatory fees: $850 full-time, $29 per hour part-time, $29. Full-time tuition and fees vary according to course level, course load, program, and student level. Part-time tuition and fees vary according to course level, course load, program, and student level. College room and board: $5800. Room and board charges vary according to board plan and housing facility. **Scholarships:** Available. **Calendar System:** Semester, Summer session not available **Enrollment:** Full-time 2,139, Part-time 1,184 **Faculty:** Full-time 86, Part-time 141 **Student-Faculty Ratio:** 15:1 **% Residing in College-Owned, -Operated, or -Affiliated Housing:** 9 **Regional Accreditation:** Southern Association of Colleges and Schools **Credit Hours For Degree:** 60 semester hours, Associates **Professional Accreditation:** ACEN, ACF, ADA, ARCST. **Intercollegiate Athletics:** Baseball M; Basketball M & W; Golf M; Softball W; Tennis M & W; Volleyball W

JEFFERSON DAVIS COMMUNITY COLLEGE

PO Box 958
Brewton, AL 36427-0958
Tel: (251)867-4832
Fax: (251)809-0178
Web Site: www.jdcc.edu
President/CEO: Camille P. Cochrane
Admissions: Robin Sessions

Type: Two-Year College **Sex:** Coed **Admission Plans:** Early Admission; Open Admission **Application Deadline:** Rolling **Application Fee:** $0.00 **H.S. Requirements:** High school diploma required; GED accepted **Scholarships:** Available. **Calendar System:** Semester, Summer session available **Regional Accreditation:** Southern Association of Colleges and Schools **Credit Hours For Degree:** 60 credit hours, Associates **Professional Accreditation:** ACEN. **Intercollegiate Athletics:** Baseball M; Basketball M; Softball W; Volleyball W

JEFFERSON STATE COMMUNITY COLLEGE

2601 Carson Rd.
Birmingham, AL 35215-3098
Tel: (205)853-1200; Free: 800-239-5900
Fax: (205)856-8547
E-mail: lowens@jeffstateonline.com
Web Site: www.jeffstateonline.com
President/CEO: Keith Brown
Admissions: Lillian Owens
Financial Aid: Theresa Mays

Type: Two-Year College **Sex:** Coed **Affiliation:** Alabama Community College System. **Admission Plans:** Deferred Admission; Early Admission; Open Admission **Application Deadline:** Rolling **Application Fee:** $0.00 **H.S. Requirements:** High school diploma required; GED accepted **Costs Per Year:** Application fee: $0. State resident tuition: $4440 full-time, $148 per semester hour part-time. Nonresident tuition: $7950 full-time, $265 per semester hour part-time. Full-time tuition varies according to course load. Part-time tuition varies according to course load. **Scholarships:** Available. **Calendar System:** Semester, Summer session available **Enrollment:** Full-time 2,842, Part-time 5,984 **Student-Faculty Ratio:** 20:1 **Regional Ac-**

creditation: Southern Association of Colleges and Schools **Credit Hours For Degree:** 60 semester hours, Associates **ROTC:** Air Force, Army **Professional Accreditation:** ABFSE, ACBSP, ACCE, ACEN, ACF, APTA, JRCERT, NAACLS.

JUDSON COLLEGE

302 Bibb St.
Marion, AL 36756
Tel: (334)683-5100; Free: 800-447-9472
Fax: (334)683-5158
E-mail: admissions@judson.edu
Web Site: www.judson.edu
President/CEO: Dr. David E. Potts
Admissions: Layne Hoggle
Financial Aid: Ashley D. Clemons

Type: Four-Year College **Sex:** Coed **Affiliation:** Baptist. **Scores:** 100% SAT V 400+; 100% SAT M 400+; 62% ACT 18-23; 30% ACT 24-29 **% Accepted:** 63 **Admission Plans:** Deferred Admission; Early Admission **Application Deadline:** Rolling **Application Fee:** $42.00 **H.S. Requirements:** High school diploma required; GED accepted **Costs Per Year:** Application fee: $42. Comprehensive fee: $26,524 includes full-time tuition ($15,744), mandatory fees ($1094), and college room and board ($9686). Part-time tuition: $534 per unit. Part-time mandatory fees: $547 per term. **Scholarships:** Available. **Calendar System:** Semester, Summer session available **Enrollment:** Full-time 249, Part-time 125 **Faculty:** Full-time 30, Part-time 15 **Student-Faculty Ratio:** 8:1 **Exams:** ACT essay component not used; SAT I or ACT; SAT essay component not used; SAT Reasoning. **% Residing in College-Owned, -Operated, or -Affiliated Housing:** 51 **Final Year or Final Semester Residency Requirement:** No **Regional Accreditation:** Southern Association of Colleges and Schools **Credit Hours For Degree:** 71 Hours in the Associate Degree in Nursing, Associates; 128 semester hours, Bachelors **ROTC:** Army **Professional Accreditation:** NASM. **Intercollegiate Athletics:** Basketball W; Equestrian Sports W; Soccer W; Softball W; Tennis W; Volleyball W

LAWSON STATE COMMUNITY COLLEGE

3060 Wilson Rd., SW
Birmingham, AL 35221-1798
Tel: (205)925-2515
Fax: (205)929-6316
E-mail: jshelley@lawsonstate.edu
Web Site: www.lawsonstate.edu
President/CEO: Dr. Perry W. Ward
Admissions: Jeff Shelley

Type: Two-Year College **Sex:** Coed **Affiliation:** Alabama Community College System. **% Accepted:** 82 **Admission Plans:** Open Admission **Application Deadline:** Rolling **Application Fee:** $0.00 **H.S. Requirements:** High school diploma required; GED accepted **Scholarships:** Available. **Calendar System:** Semester, Summer session available **Faculty:** Full-time 82, Part-time 127 **Student-Faculty Ratio:** 17:1 **% Residing in College-Owned, -Operated, or -Affiliated Housing:** 1 **Final Year or Final Semester Residency Requirement:** No **Regional Accreditation:** Southern Association of Colleges and Schools **Credit Hours For Degree:** 60 credit hours, Associates **Professional Accreditation:** ACBSP, ACEN. **Intercollegiate Athletics:** Baseball M; Basketball M & W; Volleyball W

LURLEEN B. WALLACE COMMUNITY COLLEGE

PO Box 1418
Andalusia, AL 36420-1418
Tel: (334)222-6591
E-mail: jriley@lbwcc.edu
Web Site: www.lbwcc.edu
President/CEO: Dr. Herbert H. J. Riedel
Admissions: Jan Riley
Financial Aid: Donna Bass

Type: Two-Year College **Sex:** Coed **Affiliation:** Alabama Community College System. **Admission Plans:** Open Admission **Application Deadline:** Rolling **Application Fee:** $0.00 **H.S. Requirements:** High school diploma required; GED accepted. For automotive mechanics, diesel and heavy equipment mechanics, welding, cosmetology, esthetics, nail technology programs: High school diploma or equivalent not required **Costs Per Year:** Application fee: $0. State resident tuition: $3450 full-time, $115 per credit hour part-time. Nonresident tuition: $6900 full-time, $230 per credit hour part-time. Mandatory fees: $870 full-time, $29 per credit hour part-time. Full-time tuition and fees vary according to course load. Part-time tuition and fees vary according to course load. **Scholarships:** Available. **Calendar System:** Semester, Summer session available **Enrollment:** Full-time 1,034, Part-time 698 **Faculty:** Full-time 54, Part-time 50 **Student-Faculty Ratio:** 18:1 **Exams:** Other. **Final Year or Final Semester Residency Requirement:** No **Regional Accreditation:** Southern Association of Colleges and Schools **Credit Hours For Degree:** 60 credits, Associates **Professional Accreditation:** ACEN, JRCEMTP. **Intercollegiate Athletics:** Baseball M; Basketball M & W; Softball W

MARION MILITARY INSTITUTE

1101 Washington St.
Marion, AL 36756
Tel: (334)683-2300; Free: 800-664-1842
Fax: (334)683-2380
E-mail: bcrawford@marionmilitary.edu
Web Site: www.marionmilitary.edu
President/CEO: Col. David J. Mollahan, Retd.
Admissions: Brittany Crawford
Type: Two-Year College **Sex:** Coed **Affiliation:** Alabama Community College System. **Scores:** 94% SAT V 400+; 95% SAT M 400+; 49.07% ACT 18-23; 34.58% ACT 24-29 **% Accepted:** 30 **Admission Plans:** Deferred Admission **Application Deadline:** Rolling **Application Fee:** $30.00 **H.S. Requirements:** High school diploma required; GED accepted **Costs Per Year:** Application fee: $30. State resident tuition: $6000 full-time. Nonresident tuition: $12,000 full-time. Mandatory fees: $2778 full-time. College room and board: $4450. **Scholarships:** Available. **Calendar System:** Semester, Summer session not available **Enrollment:** Full-time 449, Part-time 8 **Faculty:** Full-time 20, Part-time 18 **Student-Faculty Ratio:** 17:1 **Exams:** SAT I or ACT; SAT Reasoning; SAT Subject. **% Residing in College-Owned, -Operated, or -Affiliated Housing:** 100 **Final Year or Final Semester Residency Requirement:** Yes **Regional Accreditation:** Southern Association of Colleges and Schools **Credit Hours For Degree:** 64 credit hours, Associates **ROTC:** Air Force, Army **Intercollegiate Athletics:** Baseball M; Basketball M; Softball W; Tennis M & W

MILES COLLEGE

5500 Myron Massey Blvd.
Fairfield, AL 35064
Tel: (205)929-1000; Free: 800-445-0708
E-mail: admissions@miles.edu
Web Site: www.miles.edu
President/CEO: Dr. George T. French
Admissions: Christopher Robertson
Financial Aid: P. N. Lanier
Type: Four-Year College **Sex:** Coed **Affiliation:** Christian Methodist Episcopal. **Scores:** 10% ACT 18-23; 1% ACT 24-29 **% Accepted:** 26 **Admission Plans:** Open Admission **Application Deadline:** August 23 **Application Fee:** $0.00 **H.S. Requirements:** High school diploma required; GED accepted **Scholarships:** Available. **Calendar System:** Semester, Summer session available **Enrollment:** Full-time 1,589, Part-time 149 **Faculty:** Full-time 105, Part-time 42 **Student-Faculty Ratio:** 14:1 **Exams:** ACT; Other. **% Receiving Financial Aid:** 99 **% Residing in College-Owned, -Operated, or -Affiliated Housing:** 40 **Regional Accreditation:** Southern Association of Colleges and Schools **Credit Hours For Degree:** 124 semester hours, Bachelors **ROTC:** Air Force, Army **Professional Accreditation:** CSWE, NCATE. **Intercollegiate Athletics:** Baseball M; Basketball M & W; Cheerleading W; Cross-Country Running M; Football M; Softball W; Track and Field M

NORTHEAST ALABAMA COMMUNITY COLLEGE

PO Box 159
Rainsville, AL 35986-0159
Tel: (256)228-6001
E-mail: graces@nacc.edu
Web Site: www.nacc.edu
President/CEO: Dr. David Campbell
Admissions: Sherie Grace
Type: Two-Year College **Sex:** Coed **Affiliation:** Alabama Community College System. **Admission Plans:** Open Admission **Application Deadline:** Rolling **Application Fee:** $0.00 **H.S. Requirements:** High school diploma required; GED accepted **Costs Per Year:** Application fee: $0. State resident tuition: $3450 full-time, $115 per credit hour part-time. Nonresident tuition: $6900 full-time, $230 per credit hour part-time. Mandatory fees: $870 full-

time, $29 per credit hour part-time, $29. **Calendar System:** Semester, Summer session available **Enrollment:** Full-time 1,193, Part-time 1,511 **Faculty:** Full-time 42, Part-time 106 **Student-Faculty Ratio:** 22:1 **Final Year or Final Semester Residency Requirement:** No **Regional Accreditation:** Southern Association of Colleges and Schools **Credit Hours For Degree:** 60 semester hours, Associates **Professional Accreditation:** ACEN, JRCEMTP.

NORTHWEST-SHOALS COMMUNITY COLLEGE

PO Box 2545
Muscle Shoals, AL 35662
Tel: (256)331-5200
Fax: (256)331-5366
E-mail: tom.carter@nwscc.edu
Web Site: www.nwscc.edu
President/CEO: Dr. Humphrey Lee
Admissions: Tom Carter
Financial Aid: Lindsey Peck
Type: Two-Year College **Sex:** Coed **Affiliation:** Alabama Community College System. **% Accepted:** 100 **Admission Plans:** Open Admission **Application Deadline:** Rolling **Application Fee:** $0.00 **H.S. Requirements:** High school diploma required; GED accepted **Costs Per Year:** Application fee: $0. State resident tuition: $3450 full-time, $115 per credit hour part-time. Nonresident tuition: $6900 full-time, $230 per credit hour part-time. Mandatory fees: $841 full-time, $27 per credit hour part-time. Full-time tuition and fees vary according to course load. Part-time tuition and fees vary according to course load. **Scholarships:** Available. **Calendar System:** Semester, Summer session available **Enrollment:** Full-time 1,638, Part-time 2,029 **Faculty:** Full-time 78, Part-time 75 **Student-Faculty Ratio:** 25:1 **Regional Accreditation:** Southern Association of Colleges and Schools **Credit Hours For Degree:** 64 credit hours, Associates **Professional Accreditation:** ACEN.

OAKWOOD UNIVERSITY

7000 Adventist Blvd.
Huntsville, AL 35896
Tel: (256)726-7000; Free: 800-824-5312
Fax: (256)726-7404
E-mail: admission@oakwood.edu
Web Site: www.oakwood.edu
President/CEO: Dr. Delbert W. Baker
Admissions: Jason McCracken
Type: Comprehensive **Sex:** Coed **Affiliation:** Seventh-day Adventist. **Scores:** 82% SAT V 400+; 70% SAT M 400+; 41% ACT 18-23; 11% ACT 24-29 **% Accepted:** 57 **Admission Plans:** Deferred Admission; Early Decision Plan **Application Deadline:** Rolling **Application Fee:** $25.00 **H.S. Requirements:** High school diploma required; GED accepted **Costs Per Year:** Application fee: $25. Comprehensive fee: $26,032 includes full-time tuition ($15,714), mandatory fees ($1006), and college room and board ($9312). College room only: $4354. Room and board charges vary according to board plan and housing facility. Part-time tuition: $678 per semester hour. **Scholarships:** Available. **Calendar System:** Semester, Summer session not available **Enrollment:** Full-time 1,712, Part-time 112 **Faculty:** Full-time 103, Part-time 68 **Student-Faculty Ratio:** 14:1 **Exams:** SAT I or ACT. **% Receiving Financial Aid:** 90 **% Residing in College-Owned, -Operated, or -Affiliated Housing:** 64 **Regional Accreditation:** Southern Association of Colleges and Schools **Credit Hours For Degree:** 64 semester hours, Associates; 128 semester hours, Bachelors **Professional Accreditation:** ACBSP, ACEN, AND, CSWE, NCATE. **Intercollegiate Athletics:** Basketball M & W

REID STATE TECHNICAL COLLEGE

100 Hwy. 83
Evergreen, AL 36401-0588
Tel: (251)578-1313
Fax: (251)578-5355
E-mail: akstuart@rstc.edu
Web Site: www.rstc.edu
President/CEO: Dr. David J. Rhodes
Admissions: Dr. Alesia Stuart
Type: Two-Year College **Sex:** Coed **Affiliation:** Alabama Community College System. **% Accepted:** 100 **Admission Plans:** Early Admission; Open Admission **Application Deadline:** Rolling **Application Fee:** $0.00 **H.S. Requirements:** High school diploma or equivalent not required. For industrial electricity/electronics, administration, computer information

systems, child care and development, practical nursing programs: High school diploma required; GED accepted **Costs Per Year:** Application fee: $0. State resident tuition: $4212 full-time, $117 per credit part-time. Nonresident tuition: $8424 full-time, $234 per credit part-time. Mandatory fees: $1080 full-time, $30 per credit part-time. Full-time tuition and fees vary according to course load and program. Part-time tuition and fees vary according to course load and program. **Scholarships:** Available. **Calendar System:** Semester, Summer session available **Enrollment:** Full-time 250, Part-time 321 **Faculty:** Full-time 24, Part-time 6 **Student-Faculty Ratio:** 12:1 **Professional Accreditation:** COE.

REMINGTON COLLEGE–MOBILE CAMPUS

828 Downtowner Loop W
Mobile, AL 36609-5404
Tel: (251)343-8200; Free: 800-560-6192
Fax: (251)343-0577
E-mail: david.helveston@remingtoncollege.edu
Web Site: www.remingtoncollege.edu
President/CEO: Steve Backman
Admissions: David Helveston
Financial Aid: Linda Calvanese

Type: Two-Year College **Sex:** Coed **H.S. Requirements:** High school diploma required; GED accepted **Scholarships:** Available. **Calendar System:** Quarter, Summer session not available **Professional Accreditation:** ACCSC.

SAMFORD UNIVERSITY

800 Lakeshore Dr.
Birmingham, AL 35229
Tel: (205)726-2011; Free: 800-888-7218
Fax: (205)726-2171
E-mail: blkenned@samford.edu
Web Site: www.samford.edu
President/CEO: Dr. T. Andrew Westmoreland
Admissions: Brian L. Kennedy
Financial Aid: Lane Smith

Type: University **Sex:** Coed **Affiliation:** Baptist. **Scores:** 99% SAT V 400+; 98% SAT M 400+; 28.2% ACT 18-23; 53.8% ACT 24-29 **% Accepted:** 93 **Admission Plans:** Deferred Admission; Early Admission **Application Deadline:** June 30 **Application Fee:** $40.00 **H.S. Requirements:** High school diploma required; GED accepted **Costs Per Year:** Application fee: $40. Comprehensive fee: $39,232 includes full-time tuition ($28,552), mandatory fees ($850), and college room and board ($9830). College room only: $5108. Full-time tuition and fees vary according to course load and program. Room and board charges vary according to board plan and housing facility. Part-time tuition: $955 per credit hour. Part-time mandatory fees: $325 per term. Part-time tuition and fees vary according to course load and program. **Scholarships:** Available. **Calendar System:** 4-1-4, Summer session available **Enrollment:** Full-time 3,040, Graduate full-time 1,845, Graduate part-time 193, Part-time 128 **Faculty:** Full-time 333, Part-time 182 **Student-Faculty Ratio:** 12:1 **Exams:** ACT essay component used for placement; SAT I or ACT; SAT essay component used for placement; SAT Reasoning; SAT Subject. **% Receiving Financial Aid:** 41 **% Residing in College-Owned, -Operated, or -Affiliated Housing:** 72 **Final Year or Final Semester Residency Requirement:** No **Regional Accreditation:** Southern Association of Colleges and Schools **Credit Hours For Degree:** 128 credit hours, Bachelors **ROTC:** Air Force, Army **Professional Accreditation:** AACN, AACSB, AAFCS, AALS, AANA, ABA, ACPE, ATS, CIDA, JRCAT, NASM, NCATE. **Intercollegiate Athletics:** Baseball M; Basketball M & W; Cross-Country Running M & W; Football M; Golf M & W; Soccer W; Softball W; Tennis M & W; Track and Field M & W; Volleyball W

SELMA UNIVERSITY

1501 Lapsley St.
Selma, AL 36701-5299
Tel: (334)872-2533
Web Site: www.selmauniversity.edu
President/CEO: Dr. Alvin A. Cleveland
Admissions: Collette Fikes

Type: Comprehensive **Sex:** Coed **Affiliation:** Baptist. **Costs Per Year:** Comprehensive fee: $9125 includes full-time tuition ($6480), mandatory fees ($145), and college room and board ($2500). Full-time tuition and fees vary according to program. Part-time tuition: $250 per credit hour. Part-time tuition varies according to program. **Calendar System:** Semester, Summer

session available **Enrollment:** Full-time 333, Graduate full-time 12, Graduate part-time 10, Part-time 65 **Faculty:** Full-time 15, Part-time 21 **Student-Faculty Ratio:** 12:1 **Exams:** ACT essay component used for advising; ACT essay component used for placement; SAT I or ACT; SAT essay component used for advising; SAT essay component used for placement. **% Residing in College-Owned, -Operated, or -Affiliated Housing:** 85 **Final Year or Final Semester Residency Requirement:** No **Credit Hours For Degree:** 66 semester hours, Associates; 126 semester hours, Bachelors **Professional Accreditation:** ABHE. **Intercollegiate Athletics:** Baseball M; Basketball M & W

SHELTON STATE COMMUNITY COLLEGE

9500 Old Greensboro Rd.
Tuscaloosa, AL 35405
Tel: (205)391-2211
Fax: (205)391-2426
E-mail: schastine@sheltonstate.edu
Web Site: www.sheltonstate.edu
President/CEO: Joan Y. Davis, JD
Admissions: Sharon Chastine
Financial Aid: Cindy Green

Type: Two-Year College **Sex:** Coed **Affiliation:** Alabama Community College System. **Admission Plans:** Open Admission **Application Deadline:** Rolling **Application Fee:** $0.00 **H.S. Requirements:** High school diploma required; GED accepted **Scholarships:** Available. **Calendar System:** Semester, Summer session available **Enrollment:** Full-time 2,468, Part-time 2,600 **Faculty:** Full-time 91, Part-time 131 **Student-Faculty Ratio:** 25:1 **Final Year or Final Semester Residency Requirement:** No **Regional Accreditation:** Southern Association of Colleges and Schools **Credit Hours For Degree:** 64 semester hours, Associates **ROTC:** Air Force, Army **Professional Accreditation:** ACEN, CoARC. **Intercollegiate Athletics:** Baseball M; Basketball M & W; Cheerleading M & W; Softball W

SNEAD STATE COMMUNITY COLLEGE

220 N Walnut St.
Boaz, AL 35957-0734
Tel: (256)593-5120
Fax: (256)593-7180
E-mail: jwatts@snead.edu
Web Site: www.snead.edu
President/CEO: Dr. Robert Exley
Admissions: Dr. Jason Watts

Type: Two-Year College **Sex:** Coed **Affiliation:** Alabama College System. **Admission Plans:** Deferred Admission; Early Admission; Open Admission **Application Fee:** $0.00 **H.S. Requirements:** High school diploma required; GED accepted **Scholarships:** Available. **Calendar System:** Semester, Summer session available **Enrollment:** Full-time 1,538, Part-time 623 **Student-Faculty Ratio:** 23:1 **Regional Accreditation:** Southern Association of Colleges and Schools **Credit Hours For Degree:** 62 semester hours, Associates **Professional Accreditation:** ACEN. **Intercollegiate Athletics:** Baseball M; Basketball M & W; Softball W; Tennis W; Volleyball W

SOUTH UNIVERSITY

5355 Vaughn Rd.
Montgomery, AL 36116-1120
Tel: (334)395-8800; Free: 866-629-2962
Fax: (334)395-8859
Web Site: www.southuniversity.edu/montgomery
President/CEO: Victor K. Biebighauser

Type: Comprehensive **Sex:** Coed **Affiliation:** Education Management Corporation. **Calendar System:** Quarter **Regional Accreditation:** Southern Association of Colleges and Schools **Professional Accreditation:** AAMAE, ACBSP, APTA.

SOUTHEASTERN BIBLE COLLEGE

2545 Valleydale Rd.
Birmingham, AL 35244-2083
Tel: (205)970-9200; Free: 800-749-8878
Fax: (205)970-9207
E-mail: jscott@sebc.edu
Web Site: www.sebc.edu
President/CEO: Dr. Alexander Granados
Admissions: Josh Scott
Financial Aid: Joanne Belin

Type: Four-Year College **Sex:** Coed **Affiliation:** nondenominational. **Scores:** 100% SAT V 400+; 100% SAT M 400+; 45% ACT 18-23; 44% ACT 24-29 **% Accepted:** 100 **Admission Plans:** Deferred Admission **Application Fee:** $30.00 **H.S. Requirements:** High school diploma required; GED accepted **Costs Per Year:** Application fee: $30. Comprehensive fee: $16,040 includes full-time tuition ($11,340), mandatory fees ($450), and college room and board ($4250). Full-time tuition and fees vary according to program. Part-time tuition: $405 per semester hour. Part-time mandatory fees: $225 per term. Part-time tuition and fees vary according to program. **Scholarships:** Available. **Calendar System:** Semester, Summer session available **Enrollment:** Full-time 109, Part-time 42 **Faculty:** Full-time 10, Part-time 20 **Student-Faculty Ratio:** 7:1 **Exams:** ACT essay component not used; SAT I or ACT; SAT essay component not used; SAT Reasoning; SAT Subject. **% Residing in College-Owned, -Operated, or -Affiliated Housing:** 25 **Final Year or Final Semester Residency Requirement:** Yes **Credit Hours For Degree:** 65 semester hours, Associates; 128 semester hours, Bachelors **Professional Accreditation:** ABHE.

SOUTHERN UNION STATE COMMUNITY COLLEGE

PO Box 1000, Roberts St.
Wadley, AL 36276
Tel: (256)395-2211
Fax: (256)395-2215
E-mail: info@suscc.edu
Web Site: www.suscc.edu
President/CEO: Glenda Colagross
Type: Two-Year College **Sex:** Coed **Affiliation:** Alabama College System. **Admission Plans:** Deferred Admission; Early Admission; Open Admission **Application Deadline:** Rolling **H.S. Requirements:** High school diploma required; GED accepted **Scholarships:** Available. **Calendar System:** Semester, Summer session available **Student-Faculty Ratio:** 25:1 **Regional Accreditation:** Southern Association of Colleges and Schools **Credit Hours For Degree:** 96 quarter hours, Associates **ROTC:** Air Force **Professional Accreditation:** ACEN, JRCEMTP, JRCERT.

SPRING HILL COLLEGE

4000 Dauphin St.
Mobile, AL 36608-1791
Tel: (251)380-4000; Free: 800-SHC-6704
Fax: (251)460-2186
E-mail: bfinley@shc.edu
Web Site: www.shc.edu
President/CEO: Dr. Christopher Puto
Admissions: Britney Finley
Financial Aid: Jim V. Love
Type: Comprehensive **Sex:** Coed **Affiliation:** Roman Catholic (Jesuit). **Scores:** 101% SAT V 400+; 100% SAT M 400+; 43% ACT 18-23; 50% ACT 24-29 **% Accepted:** 41 **Admission Plans:** Deferred Admission; Early Admission **Application Deadline:** July 15 **Application Fee:** $25.00 **H.S. Requirements:** High school diploma required; GED accepted **Costs Per Year:** Application fee: $25. Comprehensive fee: $46,318 includes full-time tuition ($32,032), mandatory fees ($2060), and college room and board ($12,226). College room only: $6636. Room and board charges vary according to board plan and housing facility. Part-time tuition: $975 per credit hour. Part-time mandatory fees: $50 per credit hour. **Scholarships:** Available. **Calendar System:** Semester, Summer session available **Enrollment:** Full-time 1,341, Graduate full-time 6, Graduate part-time 120, Part-time 29 **Faculty:** Full-time 84, Part-time 51 **Student-Faculty Ratio:** 14:1 **Exams:** ACT essay component used for advising; SAT I or ACT; SAT essay component used for advising; SAT Reasoning. **% Receiving Financial Aid:** 68 **% Residing in College-Owned, -Operated, or -Affiliated Housing:** 77 **Final Year or Final Semester Residency Requirement:** Yes **Regional Accreditation:** Southern Association of Colleges and Schools **Credit Hours For Degree:** 128 semester hours, Bachelors **ROTC:** Air Force, Army **Professional Accreditation:** AACN. **Intercollegiate Athletics:** Baseball M; Basketball M & W; Cross-Country Running M & W; Golf M & W; Soccer M & W; Softball W; Tennis M & W; Track and Field M & W; Volleyball W

STILLMAN COLLEGE

PO Drawer 1430, 3600 Stillman Blvd.
Tuscaloosa, AL 35403-9990
Tel: (205)349-4240; Free: 800-841-5722
Fax: (205)366-8996
E-mail: vboman@stillman.edu

Web Site: www.stillman.edu
President/CEO: Dr. Ernest McNealey
Admissions: Victoria Boman
Financial Aid: Jacqueline S. Morris
Type: Four-Year College **Sex:** Coed **Affiliation:** Presbyterian Church (U.S.A.). **Scores:** 59% SAT V 400+; 78% SAT M 400+; 43% ACT 18-23; 7% ACT 24-29 **% Accepted:** 44 **Admission Plans:** Deferred Admission; Early Action; Early Admission **Application Deadline:** Rolling **Application Fee:** $15.00 **H.S. Requirements:** High school diploma required; GED accepted **Scholarships:** Available. **Calendar System:** Semester, Summer session available **Enrollment:** Full-time 1,032, Part-time 40 **Faculty:** Full-time 54, Part-time 7 **Student-Faculty Ratio:** 18:1 **Exams:** ACT; SAT I; SAT I and SAT II or ACT; SAT I or ACT; SAT II. **% Receiving Financial Aid:** 95 **% Residing in College-Owned, -Operated, or -Affiliated Housing:** 63 **Regional Accreditation:** Southern Association of Colleges and Schools **Credit Hours For Degree:** 124 semester hours, Bachelors **ROTC:** Army **Professional Accreditation:** AACN, NASM, NCATE. **Intercollegiate Athletics:** Baseball M; Basketball M & W; Cross-Country Running M & W; Football M; Softball W; Tennis M & W; Track and Field M & W; Volleyball W

STRAYER UNIVERSITY–BIRMINGHAM CAMPUS

3570 Grandview Pky.
Ste. 200
Birmingham, AL 35243
Tel: (205)453-6300
Fax: (205)453-6330
Web Site: www.strayer.edu/alabama/birmingham
President/CEO: Brian W. Jones
Type: Comprehensive **Sex:** Coed **Regional Accreditation:** Middle States Association of Colleges and Schools

STRAYER UNIVERSITY–HUNTSVILLE CAMPUS

4955 Corporate Dr., NW
Ste. 200
Huntsville, AL 35805
Tel: (256)665-9800
Fax: (256)665-9730
Web Site: www.strayer.edu/alabama/huntsville
President/CEO: Brian W. Jones
Type: Comprehensive **Sex:** Coed **Regional Accreditation:** Middle States Association of Colleges and Schools

TALLADEGA COLLEGE

627 W Battle St.
Talladega, AL 35160-2354
Tel: (256)362-0206; Free: 866-540-3956
Fax: (256)362-2268
E-mail: fapolydore@talladega.edu
Web Site: www.talladega.edu
President/CEO: Dr. Billy C. Hawkins
Admissions: Felicia Polydore
Financial Aid: K. Michael Francois
Type: Four-Year College **Sex:** Coed **% Accepted:** 15 **Admission Plans:** Early Admission **Application Deadline:** Rolling **Application Fee:** $25.00 **H.S. Requirements:** High school diploma required; GED accepted **Costs Per Year:** Application fee: $25. Comprehensive fee: $19,014 includes full-time tuition ($11,192), mandatory fees ($1318), and college room and board ($6504). College room only: $3020. Full-time tuition and fees vary according to course load. Part-time tuition: $466.33 per credit hour. Part-time mandatory fees: $659 per credit hour. **Scholarships:** Available. **Calendar System:** Semester, Summer session available **Enrollment:** Full-time 846, Part-time 143 **Faculty:** Full-time 49, Part-time 9 **Student-Faculty Ratio:** 20:1 **Exams:** SAT I or ACT. **% Receiving Financial Aid:** 92 **% Residing in College-Owned, -Operated, or -Affiliated Housing:** 80 **Final Year or Final Semester Residency Requirement:** No **Regional Accreditation:** Southern Association of Colleges and Schools **Credit Hours For Degree:** 65 credit hours, Associates; 124 credit hours, Bachelors **ROTC:** Army **Professional Accreditation:** CSWE. **Intercollegiate Athletics:** Baseball M; Basketball M; Golf M; Soccer M & W; Softball W; Tennis W; Track and Field M & W

TROY UNIVERSITY

University Ave.
Troy, AL 36082
Tel: (334)670-3000; Free: 800-551-9716

Fax: (334)670-3815
E-mail: bstar@troy.edu
Web Site: www.troy.edu
President/CEO: Dr. Jack Hawkins, Jr.
Admissions: Buddy Starling
Financial Aid: Carol Ballard
Type: Comprehensive **Sex:** Coed **Affiliation:** Troy University System. **Scores:** 92% SAT V 400+; 88% SAT M 400+; 49.94% ACT 18-23; 32.7% ACT 24-29 **% Accepted:** 92 **Admission Plans:** Deferred Admission **Application Deadline:** Rolling **Application Fee:** $30.00 **H.S. Requirements:** High school diploma required; GED accepted **Costs Per Year:** Application fee: $30. State resident tuition: $8610 full-time, $287 per credit hour part-time. Nonresident tuition: $17,220 full-time, $574 per credit hour part-time. Mandatory fees: $1036 full-time, $39 per credit hour part-time, $50. Full-time tuition and fees vary according to location and program. Part-time tuition and fees vary according to location and program. College room and board: $6525. College room only: $3724. Room and board charges vary according to board plan and housing facility. **Scholarships:** Available. **Calendar System:** Semester, Summer session available **Enrollment:** Full-time 8,951, Graduate full-time 1,930, Graduate part-time 2,436, Part-time 5,113 **Faculty:** Full-time 543, Part-time 580 **Student-Faculty Ratio:** 14:1 **Exams:** SAT I or ACT. **% Receiving Financial Aid:** 62 **% Residing in College-Owned, -Operated, or -Affiliated Housing:** 35 **Final Year or Final Semester Residency Requirement:** No **Regional Accreditation:** Southern Association of Colleges and Schools **Credit Hours For Degree:** 62 credit hours, Associates; 120 credit hours, Bachelors **ROTC:** Air Force, Army **Professional Accreditation:** ABET, ACA, ACBSP, ACEN, CORE, CSWE, JRCAT, NASM, NASPAA, NCATE. **Intercollegiate Athletics:** Baseball M; Basketball M & W; Cross-Country Running M & W; Football M; Golf M & W; Soccer W; Softball W; Tennis M & W; Track and Field M & W; Volleyball W

TUSKEGEE UNIVERSITY

1200 W Montgomery Rd.
Tuskegee, AL 36088
Tel: (334)727-8011; Free: 800-622-6531
E-mail: cgriffin@mytu.tuskegee.edu
Web Site: www.tuskegee.edu
President/CEO: Dr. Brian L. Johnson
Admissions: Hon. Courtney L. Griffin
Financial Aid: A. D. James, Jr.
Type: Comprehensive **Sex:** Coed **Scores:** 90% SAT V 400+; 83% SAT M 400+; 66% ACT 18-23; 20% ACT 24-29 **% Accepted:** 53 **Admission Plans:** Early Admission **Application Deadline:** April 15 **Application Fee:** $25.00 **H.S. Requirements:** High school diploma required; GED accepted **Costs Per Year:** Application fee: $25. Comprehensive fee: $29,460 includes full-time tuition ($18,560), mandatory fees ($1760), and college room and board ($9140). College room only: $4300. Full-time tuition and fees vary according to course load. Room and board charges vary according to board plan and housing facility. Part-time tuition: $5135 per term. Part-time tuition varies according to course load. **Scholarships:** Available. **Calendar System:** Semester, Summer session available **Enrollment:** Full-time 2,430, Graduate full-time 449, Graduate part-time 61, Part-time 55 **Faculty:** Full-time 194, Part-time 13 **Student-Faculty Ratio:** 14:1 **Exams:** ACT essay component used for placement; SAT I; SAT I or ACT; SAT essay component used for placement. **% Receiving Financial Aid:** 72 **% Residing in College-Owned, -Operated, or -Affiliated Housing:** 63 **Final Year or Final Semester Residency Requirement:** No **Regional Accreditation:** Southern Association of Colleges and Schools **Credit Hours For Degree:** 124 credit hours, Bachelors **ROTC:** Air Force, Army, Navy **Professional Accreditation:** AACSB, AAFCS, ABET, ACEN, AOTA, AVMA, CSWE, NAAB, NAACLS, NCATE. **Intercollegiate Athletics:** Baseball M; Basketball M & W; Cross-Country Running M & W; Football M; Golf M; Riflery M & W; Soccer M; Tennis M & W; Track and Field M & W; Volleyball W

UNITED STATES SPORTS ACADEMY

One Academy Dr.
Daphne, AL 36526-7055
Tel: (251)626-3303; Free: 800-223-2668
Fax: (251)621-2527
E-mail: sbutler@ussa.edu
Web Site: www.ussa.edu
President/CEO: Dr. Thomas P. Rosandich
Admissions: Dr. Stephen Butler
Type: Two-Year Upper Division **Sex:** Coed **% Accepted:** 37 **Application**

Fee: $50.00 **H.S. Requirements:** High school diploma required; GED accepted **Costs Per Year:** Application fee: $50. Tuition: $360 per course part-time. **Scholarships:** Available. **Calendar System:** Continuous **Enrollment:** Full-time 17, Graduate full-time 73, Graduate part-time 167, Part-time 82 **Faculty:** Full-time 7, Part-time 27 **Student-Faculty Ratio:** 12:1 **% Receiving Financial Aid:** 73 **Regional Accreditation:** Southern Association of Colleges and Schools **Credit Hours For Degree:** 120 credits, Bachelors

THE UNIVERSITY OF ALABAMA

Tuscaloosa, AL 35487
Tel: (205)348-6010; Free: 800-933-BAMA
Fax: (205)348-9046
E-mail: admissions@ua.edu
Web Site: www.ua.edu
President/CEO: Dr. Stuart R. Bell
Admissions: Mary K. Spiegel
Financial Aid: Helen Allen
Type: University **Sex:** Coed **Affiliation:** University of Alabama System. **Scores:** 99% SAT V 400+; 100% SAT M 400+; 33% ACT 18-23; 31% ACT 24-29 **% Accepted:** 54 **Admission Plans:** Early Admission **Application Deadline:** May 1 **Application Fee:** $40.00 **H.S. Requirements:** High school diploma required; GED accepted **Costs Per Year:** Application fee: $40. State resident tuition: $10,170 full-time. Nonresident tuition: $25,950 full-time. Mandatory fees: $27 full-time. Full-time tuition and fees vary according to course load. College room and board: $9030. College room only: $5600. Room and board charges vary according to board plan and housing facility. **Scholarships:** Available. **Calendar System:** Semester, Summer session available **Enrollment:** Full-time 28,689, Graduate full-time 3,321, Graduate part-time 1,819, Part-time 3,269 **Faculty:** Full-time 1,284, Part-time 515 **Exams:** ACT essay component used for admission; SAT I or ACT; SAT essay component used for admission; SAT Reasoning. **% Receiving Financial Aid:** 42 **% Residing in College-Owned, -Operated, or -Affiliated Housing:** 26 **Final Year or Final Semester Residency Requirement:** No **Regional Accreditation:** Southern Association of Colleges and Schools **Credit Hours For Degree:** 120 semester hours, Bachelors **ROTC:** Air Force, Army **Professional Accreditation:** AACN, AACSB, AAFCS, AALS, ABA, ABET, ACA, ACEJMC, ALA, AND, APA, ASHA, CIDA, CORE, CSWE, JRCAT, NASAD, NASD, NASM, NAST, NCATE. **Intercollegiate Athletics:** Badminton M & W; Baseball M; Basketball M & W; Cheerleading M & W; Crew M & W; Cross-Country Running M & W; Equestrian Sports M & W; Field Hockey W; Football M; Golf M & W; Gymnastics W; Ice Hockey M; Lacrosse M & W; Racquetball M & W; Rugby M & W; Soccer M & W; Softball W; Swimming and Diving M & W; Table Tennis M & W; Tennis M & W; Track and Field M & W; Triathlon M & W; Ultimate Frisbee M & W; Volleyball M & W; Weight Lifting M & W; Wrestling M

THE UNIVERSITY OF ALABAMA AT BIRMINGHAM

1720 2nd Ave. S
Birmingham, AL 35294
Tel: (205)934-4011; Free: 800-421-8743
Fax: (205)975-7114
E-mail: chooseuab@uab.edu
Web Site: www.uab.edu
President/CEO: Dr. Ray L. Watts
Admissions: Tyler Peterson
Financial Aid: Helen M. McIntyre
Type: University **Sex:** Coed **Affiliation:** University of Alabama System. **Scores:** 42% ACT 18-23; 43% ACT 24-29 **% Accepted:** 60 **Admission Plans:** Deferred Admission; Early Admission **Application Deadline:** June 1 **Application Fee:** $30.00 **H.S. Requirements:** High school diploma required; GED accepted **Costs Per Year:** Application fee: $30. State resident tuition: $9596 full-time, $305 per credit hour part-time. Nonresident tuition: $21,956 full-time, $717 per contact hour part-time. Full-time tuition varies according to course load, degree level, program, and reciprocity agreements. Part-time tuition varies according to course load, degree level, program, and reciprocity agreements. College room only: $5900. Room charges vary according to housing facility. **Scholarships:** Available. **Calendar System:** Semester, Summer session available **Enrollment:** Full-time 8,416, Graduate full-time 3,515, Graduate part-time 3,307, Part-time 3,304 **Faculty:** Full-time 726, Part-time 39 **Student-Faculty Ratio:** 18:1 **Exams:** ACT essay component not used; SAT I or ACT; SAT essay component not used; SAT Reasoning. **% Receiving Financial Aid:** 56 **% Residing in College-Owned, -Operated, or -Affiliated Housing:** 21 **Final Year or Final Semester Residency Requirement:** Yes **Regional Ac-**

creditation: Southern Association of Colleges and Schools **Credit Hours For Degree:** 120 hours, Bachelors **ROTC:** Air Force, Army **Professional Accreditation:** AACN, AACSB, AANA, ABET, ACA, ACIPE, ADA, AHIMA, AND, AOA, AOTA, APA, APTA, ASC, CAHME, CEPH, CORE, CSWE, CoARC, JRCEMTP, JRCERT, JRCNMT, LCME/AMA, NAACLS, NASAD, NASM, NASPAA, NCATE. **Intercollegiate Athletics:** Baseball M; Basketball M & W; Cross-Country Running W; Golf M & W; Soccer M & W; Softball W; Tennis M & W; Track and Field W; Volleyball W

THE UNIVERSITY OF ALABAMA IN HUNTSVILLE

301 Sparkman Dr.
Huntsville, AL 35899
Tel: (256)824-1000; Free: 800-UAH-CALL
Fax: (256)824-6073
E-mail: uahadmissions@uah.edu
Web Site: www.uah.edu
President/CEO: Dr. Robert A. Altenkirch
Admissions: Peggy Masters
Financial Aid: Patrick James
Type: University **Sex:** Coed **Affiliation:** University of Alabama System. **Scores:** 98% SAT V 400+; 100% SAT M 400+; 23% ACT 18-23; 42.6% ACT 24-29 **% Accepted:** 81 **Admission Plans:** Deferred Admission **Application Deadline:** August 17 **Application Fee:** $30.00 **H.S. Requirements:** High school diploma required; GED accepted **Costs Per Year:** Application fee: $30. State resident tuition: $9128 full-time, $367 per credit hour part-time. Nonresident tuition: $20,622 full-time, $826 per credit hour part-time. Full-time tuition varies according to course load and program. Part-time tuition varies according to course load and program. College room and board: $9205. College room only: $6285. Room and board charges vary according to board plan and housing facility. **Scholarships:** Available. **Calendar System:** Semester, Summer session available **Enrollment:** Full-time 4,774, Graduate full-time 708, Graduate part-time 1,145, Part-time 1,239 **Faculty:** Full-time 319, Part-time 234 **Student-Faculty Ratio:** 16:1 **Exams:** ACT essay component not used; SAT I or ACT; SAT essay component not used; SAT Reasoning. **% Receiving Financial Aid:** 52 **% Residing in College-Owned, -Operated, or -Affiliated Housing:** 24 **Final Year or Final Semester Residency Requirement:** Yes **Regional Accreditation:** Southern Association of Colleges and Schools **Credit Hours For Degree:** 120 semester hours, Bachelors **ROTC:** Army **Professional Accreditation:** AACN, AACSB, ABET, NASAD, NASM, NCATE. **Intercollegiate Athletics:** Baseball M; Basketball M & W; Cheerleading M & W; Crew M & W; Cross-Country Running M & W; Ice Hockey M; Lacrosse M & W; Soccer M & W; Softball W; Tennis M & W; Track and Field M & W; Volleyball W

UNIVERSITY OF MOBILE

5735 College Pky.
Mobile, AL 36613
Tel: (251)442-2773; Free: 800-946-7267
Fax: (251)442-2498
E-mail: cwittner@umobile.edu
Web Site: www.umobile.edu
President/CEO: Dr. Mark R. Foley
Admissions: Charity Wittner
Financial Aid: Marie Thomas Batson
Type: Comprehensive **Sex:** Coed **Affiliation:** Southern Baptist. **Scores:** 86% SAT V 400+; 95% SAT M 400+; 54.8% ACT 18-23; 32.4% ACT 24-29 **% Accepted:** 61 **Admission Plans:** Deferred Admission **Application Deadline:** Rolling **Application Fee:** $25.00 **H.S. Requirements:** High school diploma required; GED accepted **Costs Per Year:** Application fee: $25. Comprehensive fee: $29,630 includes full-time tuition ($19,470), mandatory fees ($1000), and college room and board ($9160). College room only: $5200. Full-time tuition and fees vary according to course load. Room and board charges vary according to housing facility. Part-time tuition: $695 per credit hour. Part-time mandatory fees: $400 per year. Part-time tuition and fees vary according to course load. **Scholarships:** Available. **Calendar System:** Semester, Summer session available **Enrollment:** Full-time 1,283, Graduate full-time 33, Graduate part-time 91, Part-time 159 **Faculty:** Full-time 80, Part-time 90 **Student-Faculty Ratio:** 13:1 **Exams:** ACT essay component not used; SAT I or ACT; SAT essay component not used; SAT Reasoning; SAT Subject. **% Receiving Financial Aid:** 70 **% Residing in College-Owned, -Operated, or -Affiliated Housing:** 50 **Final Year or Final Semester Residency Requirement:** No **Regional Accreditation:** Southern Association of Colleges and Schools **Credit Hours For Degree:** 61 semester hours, Associates; 123 semester hours, Bachelors **ROTC:** Air

Force, Army **Professional Accreditation:** AACN, ACBSP, ACEN, APTA, NASM. **Intercollegiate Athletics:** Baseball M; Basketball M & W; Cheerleading W; Cross-Country Running M & W; Golf M & W; Soccer M & W; Softball W; Tennis M & W; Track and Field M & W; Volleyball W

UNIVERSITY OF MONTEVALLO

Station 6001
Montevallo, AL 35115
Tel: (205)665-6000; Free: 800-292-4349
E-mail: admissions@montevallo.edu
Web Site: www.montevallo.edu
President/CEO: Dr. John W. Stewart, III, PhD
Admissions: Greg Embry
Financial Aid: Bob Walker
Type: Comprehensive **Sex:** Coed **Scores:** 48% ACT 18-23; 43% ACT 24-29 **% Accepted:** 70 **Admission Plans:** Deferred Admission; Early Admission **Application Deadline:** August 1 **Application Fee:** $30.00 **H.S. Requirements:** High school diploma required; GED accepted **Costs Per Year:** Application fee: $30. State resident tuition: $10,740 full-time, $358 per credit hour part-time. Nonresident tuition: $22,110 full-time, $737 per credit hour part-time. Mandatory fees: $670 full-time. College room and board: $6900. College room only: $4300. Room and board charges vary according to housing facility. **Scholarships:** Available. **Calendar System:** Semester, Summer session available **Enrollment:** Full-time 2,302, Graduate full-time 186, Graduate part-time 281, Part-time 264 **Faculty:** Full-time 146, Part-time 78 **Student-Faculty Ratio:** 16:1 **Exams:** ACT; SAT I or ACT. **% Receiving Financial Aid:** 65 **% Residing in College-Owned, -Operated, or -Affiliated Housing:** 47 **Regional Accreditation:** Southern Association of Colleges and Schools **Credit Hours For Degree:** 130 semester hours, Bachelors **ROTC:** Air Force, Army **Professional Accreditation:** AACSB, AAFCS, ACA, ASHA, CSWE, NASAD, NASM, NCATE. **Intercollegiate Athletics:** Baseball M; Basketball M & W; Cheerleading W; Cross-Country Running M & W; Golf M & W; Lacrosse W; Soccer M & W; Softball W; Tennis W; Track and Field M & W; Volleyball W

UNIVERSITY OF NORTH ALABAMA

One Harrison Plz.
Florence, AL 35632-0001
Tel: (256)765-4100; Free: 800-TALK-UNA
Fax: (256)765-4329
E-mail: admissions@una.edu
Web Site: www.una.edu
President/CEO: Dr. Kenneth D. Kitts
Admissions: Julie Taylor
Financial Aid: Shauna L. James
Type: Comprehensive **Sex:** Coed **Scores:** 76% SAT V 400+; 79% SAT M 400+; 52.52% ACT 18-23; 32.66% ACT 24-29 **% Accepted:** 58 **Admission Plans:** Deferred Admission; Early Admission **Application Deadline:** Rolling **Application Fee:** $25.00 **H.S. Requirements:** High school diploma required; GED accepted **Costs Per Year:** Application fee: $25. State resident tuition: $7620 full-time, $254 per credit hour part-time. Nonresident tuition: $15,240 full-time, $508 per credit hour part-time. Mandatory fees: $1888 full-time. Full-time tuition and fees vary according to course load and program. Part-time tuition varies according to course load and program. College room and board: $6516. Room and board charges vary according to board plan and housing facility. **Scholarships:** Available. **Calendar System:** Semester, Summer session available **Enrollment:** Full-time 4,983, Graduate full-time 321, Graduate part-time 665, Part-time 1,109 **Faculty:** Full-time 243, Part-time 118 **Student-Faculty Ratio:** 21:1 **Exams:** ACT essay component not used; SAT I or ACT; SAT essay component not used. **% Receiving Financial Aid:** 50 **% Residing in College-Owned, -Operated, or -Affiliated Housing:** 26 **Final Year or Final Semester Residency Requirement:** No **Regional Accreditation:** Southern Association of Colleges and Schools **Credit Hours For Degree:** 120 semester hours, Bachelors **ROTC:** Army **Professional Accreditation:** AACN, AAFCS, ABET, ACA, ACBSP, CSWE, NASAD, NASM, NCATE. **Intercollegiate Athletics:** Baseball M; Basketball M & W; Cheerleading M & W; Cross-Country Running M & W; Football M; Golf M; Soccer W; Softball W; Tennis M & W; Volleyball W

UNIVERSITY OF SOUTH ALABAMA

307 University Blvd.
Mobile, AL 36688-0002
Tel: (251)460-6101; Free: 800-872-5247

Fax: (251)460-7025
E-mail: recruitment@southalabama.edu
Web Site: www.southalabama.edu
President/CEO: Dr. Tony G. Waldrop
Admissions: Christopher A. Lynch
Type: University **Sex:** Coed **Scores:** 91% SAT V 400+; 85% SAT M 400+; 53% ACT 18-23; 35% ACT 24-29 **% Accepted:** 78 **Admission Plans:** Early Admission; Preferred Admission **Application Deadline:** July 15 **Application Fee:** $45.00 **H.S. Requirements:** High school diploma required; GED accepted **Costs Per Year:** Application fee: $45. State resident tuition: $8790 full-time, $293 per credit hour part-time. Nonresident tuition: $17,580 full-time, $586 per credit hour part-time. Full-time tuition varies according to course load and program. Part-time tuition varies according to course load and program. College room and board: $7250. College room only: $3850. Room and board charges vary according to board plan and housing facility. **Scholarships:** Available. **Calendar System:** Semester, Summer session available **Enrollment:** Full-time 9,380, Graduate full-time 4,101, Graduate part-time 586, Part-time 2,144 **Faculty:** Full-time 568, Part-time 473 **Student-Faculty Ratio:** 20:1 **Exams:** ACT essay component not used; SAT I or ACT; SAT essay component not used; SAT Reasoning; SAT Subject. **% Receiving Financial Aid:** 63 **% Residing in College-Owned, -Operated, or -Affiliated Housing:** 29 **Regional Accreditation:** Southern Association of Colleges and Schools **Credit Hours For Degree:** 120 semester hours, Bachelors **ROTC:** Air Force, Army **Professional Accreditation:** AACN, AACSB, ABET, AOTA, APTA, ASHA, CoARC, JRCEMTP, LCME/AMA, NAACLS, NASM, NCATE. **Intercollegiate Athletics:** Baseball M; Basketball M & W; Cross-Country Running M & W; Football M; Golf M & W; Soccer W; Softball W; Tennis M & W; Track and Field M & W; Volleyball W

THE UNIVERSITY OF WEST ALABAMA
Livingston, AL 35470
Tel: (205)652-3400; Free: 888-636-8800
E-mail: belliott@uwa.edu
Web Site: www.uwa.edu
President/CEO: Dr. Ken Tucker
Admissions: Brenda Edwards
Financial Aid: Don Rainer
Type: Comprehensive **Sex:** Coed **Scores:** 59% ACT 18-23; 23% ACT 24-29 **% Accepted:** 73 **Admission Plans:** Deferred Admission **Application Deadline:** Rolling **Application Fee:** $40.00 **H.S. Requirements:** High school diploma required; GED accepted **Costs Per Year:** Application fee: $40. State resident tuition: $7144 full-time, $304 per hour part-time. Nonresident tuition: $14,288 full-time, $608 per hour part-time. Mandatory fees: $1590 full-time. Full-time tuition and fees vary according to course load. Part-time tuition varies according to course load. College room and board: $6460. College room only: $3920. Room and board charges vary according to board plan, housing facility, and student level. **Scholarships:** Available. **Calendar System:** Semester, Summer session available **Enrollment:** Full-time 1,704, Graduate full-time 1,952, Graduate part-time 165, Part-time 211 **Faculty:** Full-time 126, Part-time 124 **Student-Faculty Ratio:** 13:1 **Exams:** SAT I or ACT; SAT Reasoning; SAT Subject. **% Receiving Financial Aid:** 76 **% Residing in College-Owned, -Operated, or -Affiliated Housing:** 46 **Final Year or Final Semester Residency Requirement:** No **Regional Accreditation:** Southern Association of Colleges and Schools **Credit Hours For Degree:** 60 credit hours, Associates; 120 credit hours, Bachelors **ROTC:** Air Force **Professional Accreditation:** ACBSP, ACEN, JRCAT, NCATE. **Intercollegiate Athletics:** Baseball M; Basketball M & W; Cross-Country Running M & W; Football M; Golf M & W; Soccer M & W; Softball W; Tennis M & W; Track and Field M & W; Triathlon W; Volleyball W

VIRGINIA COLLEGE IN BIRMINGHAM
488 Palisades Blvd.
Birmingham, AL 35209
Tel: (205)802-1200
Fax: (205)802-1597
Web Site: www.vc.edu
President/CEO: Khaled Sakalla
Type: Comprehensive **Sex:** Coed **Application Deadline:** Rolling **Application Fee:** $100.00 **H.S. Requirements:** High school diploma required; GED accepted **Scholarships:** Available. **Calendar System:** Quarter **Credit Hours For Degree:** 96 quarter hours, Associates **Professional Accreditation:** ACF, ACICS.

VIRGINIA COLLEGE IN HUNTSVILLE
2021 Drake Ave. SW
Huntsville, AL 35801
Tel: (256)533-7387
Fax: (256)533-7785
Web Site: www.vc.edu
President/CEO: James D. Foster
Type: Two-Year College **Sex:** Coed **Application Deadline:** Rolling **Application Fee:** $100.00 **H.S. Requirements:** High school diploma required; GED accepted **Scholarships:** Available. **Calendar System:** Quarter **Credit Hours For Degree:** 90 quarter hours, Associates **Professional Accreditation:** ACICS.

VIRGINIA COLLEGE IN MOBILE
3725 Airport Blvd.
Ste. 165
Mobile, AL 36608
Tel: (251)343-7227
Web Site: www.vc.edu
Type: Two-Year College **Sex:** Coed **Professional Accreditation:** ACICS.

VIRGINIA COLLEGE IN MONTGOMERY
6200 Atlanta Hwy.
Montgomery, AL 36117-2800
Tel: (334)277-2901
Web Site: www.vc.edu
Type: Two-Year College **Sex:** Coed **Professional Accreditation:** ACICS.

WALLACE STATE COMMUNITY COLLEGE
801 Main St.
Hanceville, AL 35077-2000
Tel: (256)352-8000; Free: 866-350-9722
Fax: (256)352-8228
Web Site: www.wallacestate.edu
President/CEO: Vicki Hawsey
Admissions: Jennifer Hill
Type: Two-Year College **Sex:** Coed **Admission Plans:** Deferred Admission; Early Admission; Open Admission **Application Deadline:** Rolling **H.S. Requirements:** High school diploma required; GED accepted **Scholarships:** Available. **Calendar System:** Semester, Summer session available **Student-Faculty Ratio:** 23:1 **Regional Accreditation:** Southern Association of Colleges and Schools **Credit Hours For Degree:** 60 semester hours, Associates **Professional Accreditation:** AAMAE, ACBSP, ACEN, ADA, AHIMA, AOTA, APTA, CoARC, JRCEDMS, JRCEMTP, JRCERT, NAACLS. **Intercollegiate Athletics:** Baseball M; Basketball M & W; Cross-Country Running M & W; Golf M; Soccer M & W; Softball W; Tennis M & W; Track and Field M & W; Volleyball W

ALASKA BIBLE COLLEGE
200 College Rd.
Glennallen, AK 99588-0289
Tel: (907)822-3201; Free: 800-478-7884
Fax: (907)822-5027
E-mail: npalmer@akbible.edu
Web Site: www.akbible.edu
President/CEO: Nick Ringger
Admissions: Nikki Palmer
Financial Aid: Sandy Anderson
Type: Four-Year College **Sex:** Coed **Affiliation:** nondenominational. **Admission Plans:** Deferred Admission; Open Admission **Application Deadline:** July 1 **Application Fee:** $35.00 **H.S. Requirements:** High school diploma required; GED accepted **Scholarships:** Available. **Calendar System:** Semester, Summer session not available **Enrollment:** Full-time 21, Part-time 10 **Faculty:** Full-time 8, Part-time 3 **Student-Faculty Ratio:** 3:1 **Exams:** SAT I or ACT; SAT Subject. **% Residing in College-Owned, -Operated, or -Affiliated Housing:** 93 **Final Year or Final Semester Residency Requirement:** No **Credit Hours For Degree:** 61 credits, Associates; 120 credits, Bachelors **Professional Accreditation:** ABHE.

ALASKA CAREER COLLEGE
1415 E Tudor Rd.
Anchorage, AK 99507
Tel: (907)563-7575
Web Site: www.alaskacareercollege.edu
Type: Two-Year College **Sex:** Coed **H.S. Requirements:** High school diploma required; GED accepted **Calendar System:** Continuous **Exams:** ACT; SAT I; SAT I and SAT II or ACT; SAT I or ACT; SAT II.

ALASKA CHRISTIAN COLLEGE
35109 Royal Pl.
Soldotna, AK 99669
Tel: (907)260-7422
Web Site: www.akcc.org
Type: Two-Year College **Sex:** Coed **Professional Accreditation:** ABHE.

ALASKA PACIFIC UNIVERSITY
4101 University Dr.
Anchorage, AK 99508-4672
Tel: (907)561-1266; Free: 800-252-7528
Fax: (907)564-8317
E-mail: admissions@alaskapacific.edu
Web Site: www.alaskapacific.edu
President/CEO: Dr. Don Bantz
Admissions: Carter Caywood
Financial Aid: Katie Bishop
Type: Comprehensive **Sex:** Coed **Scores:** 100% SAT V 400+; 90% SAT M 400+; 60% ACT 18-23; 30% ACT 24-29 **% Accepted:** 42 **Admission Plans:** Deferred Admission **Application Deadline:** August 1 **Application Fee:** $25.00 **H.S. Requirements:** High school diploma required; GED accepted **Costs Per Year:** Application fee: $25. Comprehensive fee: $26,680 includes full-time tuition ($19,500), mandatory fees ($180), and college room and board ($7000). Full-time tuition and fees vary according to course load, degree level, program, and reciprocity agreements. Room and board

charges vary according to board plan and housing facility. Part-time tuition: $812 per semester hour. Part-time tuition varies according to course load, degree level, and program. **Scholarships:** Available. **Calendar System:** Semester, Summer session available **Enrollment:** Full-time 215, Graduate full-time 79, Graduate part-time 201, Part-time 111 **Faculty:** Full-time 47, Part-time 47 **Student-Faculty Ratio:** 7:1 **Exams:** SAT I or ACT; SAT Reasoning; SAT Subject. **% Receiving Financial Aid:** 68 **% Residing in College-Owned, -Operated, or -Affiliated Housing:** 26 **Final Year or Final Semester Residency Requirement:** Yes **Credit Hours For Degree:** 64 semester hours, Associates; 128 semester hours, Bachelors **ROTC:** Air Force, Army **Professional Accreditation:** NCATE, NCCU.

CHARTER COLLEGE
2221 E Northern Lights Blvd.
Ste. 120
Anchorage, AK 99508
Tel: (907)277-1000; Free: 888-200-9942
Fax: (907)274-3342
Web Site: www.chartercollege.edu
President/CEO: Larry Capps
Admissions: Lily Sirianni
Type: Two-Year College **Sex:** Coed **Admission Plans:** Open Admission **Application Deadline:** Rolling **Application Fee:** $20.00 **H.S. Requirements:** High school diploma required; GED accepted **Scholarships:** Available. **Calendar System:** Quarter, Summer session available **Faculty:** Full-time 10, Part-time 33 **Student-Faculty Ratio:** 15:1 **Credit Hours For Degree:** 90 credit hours, Associates **Professional Accreditation:** ACICS.

ILISAGVIK COLLEGE
UIC/Narl
Barrow, AK 99723
Tel: (907)852-3333
Fax: (907)852-2729
E-mail: tennessee.judkins@ilisagvik.edu
Web Site: www.ilisagvik.edu
President/CEO: Pres. Pearl Kiyawn Brower
Admissions: Tennessee Judkins
Type: Two-Year College **Sex:** Coed **% Accepted:** 100 **Admission Plans:** Deferred Admission; Open Admission **Application Deadline:** August 14 **Application Fee:** $0.00 **H.S. Requirements:** High school diploma required; GED accepted **Costs Per Year:** Application fee: $0. State resident tuition: $125 per credit part-time. Nonresident tuition: $125 per year part-time. Mandatory fees: $60 per term part-time, $60 per term part-time. Part-time tuition and fees vary according to course load and program. **Calendar System:** Semester, Summer session available **Faculty:** Full-time 11, Part-time 24 **Student-Faculty Ratio:** 7:1 **Exams:** ACT essay component not used; Other; SAT essay component not used. **% Residing in College-Owned, -Operated, or -Affiliated Housing:** 10 **Final Year or Final Semester Residency Requirement:** No **Credit Hours For Degree:** 60 credit hours, Associates **Professional Accreditation:** NCCU.

UNIVERSITY OF ALASKA ANCHORAGE
3211 Providence Dr.
Anchorage, AK 99508
Tel: (907)786-1800

Fax: (907)786-4888
E-mail: enroll@uaa.alaska.edu
Web Site: www.uaa.alaska.edu
President/CEO: Tom Case
Financial Aid: Sonya F. Stein
Type: Comprehensive **Sex:** Coed **Affiliation:** University of Alaska System.
Scores: 90% SAT V 400+; 90% SAT M 400+; 45% ACT 18-23; 27% ACT
24-29 **% Accepted:** 80 **Admission Plans:** Deferred Admission; Open
Admission **Application Deadline:** June 15 **Application Fee:** $50.00 **H.S.**
Requirements: High school diploma required; GED accepted. For ap-
plicants to associate degree programs, 18 or over, may be admitted through
an Ability to Benefit Process: High school diploma or equivalent not required
Scholarships: Available. **Calendar System:** Semester, Summer session
available **Enrollment:** Full-time 7,485, Graduate full-time 226, Graduate
part-time 632, Part-time 8,978 **Faculty:** Full-time 678, Part-time 728
Student-Faculty Ratio: 12:1 **% Receiving Financial Aid:** 48 **Credit Hours**
For Degree: 60 semester credits, Associates; 120 semester credits,
Bachelors **ROTC:** Air Force, Army **Professional Accreditation:** AACSB,
AAMAE, ABET, ACEJMC, ACEN, ADA, AND, CSWE, NAACLS, NASAD,
NASM, NCATE, NCCU. **Intercollegiate Athletics:** Basketball M & W;
Cross-Country Running M & W; Gymnastics W; Ice Hockey M; Skiing
(Cross-Country) M & W; Skiing (Downhill) M & W; Track and Field M & W;
Volleyball W

UNIVERSITY OF ALASKA ANCHORAGE, KENAI PENINSULA COL-
LEGE
156 College Rd.
Soldotna, AK 99669-9798
Tel: (907)262-0300; Free: 877-262-0330
Fax: (907)262-0322
E-mail: jmcotterell@kpc.alaska.edu
Web Site: www.kpc.alaska.edu
President/CEO: Gary J. Turner
Admissions: Julie Cotterell
Type: Two-Year College **Sex:** Coed **Affiliation:** University of Alaska System.
Admission Plans: Open Admission **Application Deadline:** Rolling **Ap-**
plication Fee: $40.00 **H.S. Requirements:** High school diploma required;
GED accepted **Costs Per Year:** Application fee: $40. State resident tuition:
$5568 full-time, $183 per credit hour part-time. Nonresident tuition: $16,488
full-time, $649 per credit hour part-time. Mandatory fees: $1153 full-time.
Full-time tuition and fees vary according to course load, degree level, location, and program. Part-time tuition varies according to course load, degree
level, location, and program. College room and board: $9290. College room
only: $7040. Room and board charges vary according to board plan. Tuition
guaranteed not to increase for student's term of enrollment. **Scholarships:**
Available. **Calendar System:** Semester, Summer session not available
Exams: Other; SAT essay component used for admission. **Final Year or**
Final Semester Residency Requirement: Yes **Credit Hours For Degree:**
60 credits, Associates **Professional Accreditation:** NCCU.

UNIVERSITY OF ALASKA ANCHORAGE, KODIAK COLLEGE
117 Benny Benson Dr.
Kodiak, AK 99615-6643
Tel: (907)486-4161; Free: 800-486-7660
Fax: (907)486-1257
E-mail: jmyrick@kodiak.alaska.edu
Web Site: www.koc.alaska.edu
President/CEO: Barbara Bolson
Admissions: Jennifer Myrick Pedersen
Type: Two-Year College **Sex:** Coed **Affiliation:** University of Alaska System.
% Accepted: 77 **Admission Plans:** Open Admission **Application**
Deadline: Rolling **Application Fee:** $40.00 **H.S. Requirements:** High
school diploma required; GED accepted **Calendar System:** Semester, Sum-
mer session available **Enrollment:** Full-time 148, Part-time 331 **Faculty:**
Full-time 11 **Student-Faculty Ratio:** 13:1 **Exams:** Other. **Final Year or**
Final Semester Residency Requirement: No **Credit Hours For Degree:**
60 credits, Associates **Professional Accreditation:** NCCU.

UNIVERSITY OF ALASKA ANCHORAGE, MATANUSKA-SUSITNA
COLLEGE
PO Box 2889
Palmer, AK 99645-2889
Tel: (907)745-9774
Fax: (907)745-9747

E-mail: info@matsu.alaska.edu
Web Site: www.matsu.alaska.edu
President/CEO: Dennis Clark
Admissions: Sandra Gravley
Financial Aid: Korry M. Dunham
Type: Two-Year College **Sex:** Coed **Affiliation:** University of Alaska System.
Admission Plans: Open Admission **Application Deadline:** September 15
Application Fee: $40.00 **H.S. Requirements:** High school diploma
required; GED accepted **Scholarships:** Available. **Calendar System:**
Semester, Summer session available **Enrollment:** Full-time 452, Part-time
1,330 **Faculty:** Full-time 26, Part-time 90 **Student-Faculty Ratio:** 16:1
Credit Hours For Degree: 60 credits, Associates **Professional Accredita-**
tion: NCCU.

UNIVERSITY OF ALASKA FAIRBANKS
PO Box 757500
Fairbanks, AK 99775-7520
Tel: (907)474-7211; Free: 800-478-1823
Fax: (907)474-5379
E-mail: admissions@uaf.edu
Web Site: www.uaf.edu
President/CEO: Brian Rogers
Admissions: Libby Eddy
Financial Aid: Deanna Dieringer
Type: University **Sex:** Coed **Affiliation:** University of Alaska System.
Scores: 95% SAT V 400+; 91% SAT M 400+; 42% ACT 18-23; 33% ACT
24-29 **% Accepted:** 74 **Admission Plans:** Deferred Admission **Application**
Deadline: June 15 **Application Fee:** $50.00 **H.S. Requirements:** High
school diploma required; GED not accepted. For High school diploma is
required and GED is accepted for associate programs: High school diploma
or equivalent not required **Costs Per Year:** Application fee: $50. State
resident tuition: $6060 full-time, $183 per credit part-time. Nonresident
tuition: $20,040 full-time, $649 per credit part-time. Mandatory fees: $1314
full-time. Full-time tuition and fees vary according to course level, course
load, location, and reciprocity agreements. Part-time tuition varies according
to course level, course load, location, and reciprocity agreements. College
room and board: $8380. College room only: $4060. Room and board
charges vary according to board plan, housing facility, and location.
Scholarships: Available. **Calendar System:** Semester, Summer session
available **Enrollment:** Full-time 3,491, Graduate full-time 579, Graduate
part-time 558, Part-time 4,072 **Faculty:** Full-time 379, Part-time 614
Student-Faculty Ratio: 11:1 **Exams:** ACT essay component used for advising; ACT essay component used for placement; SAT I or ACT; SAT essay
component used for advising; SAT essay component used for placement;
SAT Reasoning. **% Receiving Financial Aid:** 52 **% Residing in College-**
Owned, -Operated, or -Affiliated Housing: 29 **Final Year or Final**
Semester Residency Requirement: No **Credit Hours For Degree:** 60
credits, Associates; 120 credits, Bachelors **ROTC:** Army **Professional Ac-**
creditation: AACSB, AAMAE, ABET, ACEJMC, CSWE, NASM, NCATE,
NCCU, SAF. **Intercollegiate Athletics:** Basketball M & W; Cross-Country
Running M & W; Ice Hockey M; Riflery M & W; Skiing (Cross-Country) M &
W; Swimming and Diving W; Volleyball W

UNIVERSITY OF ALASKA, PRINCE WILLIAM SOUND COLLEGE
PO Box 97
Valdez, AK 99686-0097
Tel: (907)834-1600; Free: 800-478-8800
Fax: (907)834-1627
E-mail: drunge@pwscc.edu
Web Site: www.pwsc.alaska.edu
President/CEO: Dr. J. Daniel O'Connor
Admissions: Dr. Denise Runge
Financial Aid: Susan Love
Type: Two-Year College **Sex:** Coed **Affiliation:** University of Alaska System.
% Accepted: 78 **Admission Plans:** Early Admission; Open Admission **Ap-**
plication Deadline: Rolling **Application Fee:** $25.00 **H.S. Requirements:**
High school diploma required; GED accepted **Costs Per Year:** Application
fee: $25. One-time mandatory fee: $40. State resident tuition: $4032 full-
time, $168 per credit part-time. Nonresident tuition: $4032 full-time, $168 per
credit part-time. Mandatory fees: $350 full-time, $100 per term part-time.
College room only: $2527. Room charges vary according to housing facility.
Scholarships: Available. **Calendar System:** Semester, Summer session
available **Student-Faculty Ratio:** 5:1 **Exams:** Other; SAT I or ACT. **%**
Residing in College-Owned, -Operated, or -Affiliated Housing: 2 **Final**

Year or Final Semester Residency Requirement: No **Credit Hours For Degree:** 60 credits, Associates **Professional Accreditation:** NCCU.

UNIVERSITY OF ALASKA SOUTHEAST

11120 Glacier Hwy.
Juneau, AK 99801
Tel: (907)796-6457; Free: 877-465-4827
Fax: (907)796-6365
E-mail: admissions@uas.alaska.edu
Web Site: www.uas.alaska.edu
President/CEO: John Pugh
Admissions: Deema Ferguson
Financial Aid: Corinne Soltis
Type: Comprehensive **Sex:** Coed **Affiliation:** University of Alaska System. **Scores:** 89% SAT V 400+; 86% SAT M 400+ **Admission Plans:** Deferred Admission; Open Admission **Application Deadline:** September 9 **Application Fee:** $50.00 **H.S. Requirements:** High school diploma required; GED accepted **Scholarships:** Available. **Calendar System:** Semester, Summer session available **Enrollment:** Full-time 860, Graduate full-time 96, Graduate part-time 289, Part-time 2,213 **Faculty:** Full-time 102, Part-time 127 **Student-Faculty Ratio:** 9:1 **Exams:** ACT essay component used for placement; SAT I or ACT; SAT essay component used for placement. **% Receiving Financial Aid:** 60 **% Residing in College-Owned, -Operated, or -Affiliated Housing:** 17 **Final Year or Final Semester Residency Requirement:** No **Credit Hours For Degree:** 60 credits, Associates; 120 credits, Bachelors **Professional Accreditation:** NCATE, NCCU. **Intercollegiate Athletics:** Riflery M & W

UNIVERSITY OF ALASKA SOUTHEAST, KETCHIKAN CAMPUS

2600 7th Ave.
Ketchikan, AK 99901-5798
Tel: (907)225-6177
Fax: (907)225-3624
E-mail: ketch.info@uas.alaska.edu
Web Site: www.ketch.alaska.edu
Type: Two-Year College **Sex:** Coed **Affiliation:** University of Alaska System. **Application Deadline:** Rolling **Application Fee:** $50.00 **H.S. Requirements:** High school diploma required; GED accepted **Scholarships:** Available. **Calendar System:** Semester, Summer session not available **Credit Hours For Degree:** 60 credits, Associates **Professional Accreditation:** NCCU.

UNIVERSITY OF ALASKA SOUTHEAST, SITKA CAMPUS

1332 Seward Ave.
Sitka, AK 99835-9418
Tel: (907)747-6653; Free: 800-478-6653
Fax: (907)747-7747
E-mail: ktgordon@uas.alaska.edu
Web Site: www.uas.alaska.edu
President/CEO: Dr. Jeff Johnston
Admissions: Teal Gordon
Type: Two-Year College **Sex:** Coed **Affiliation:** University of Alaska Southeast; University of Alaska System. **Admission Plans:** Deferred Admission; Early Admission; Open Admission **Application Deadline:** Rolling **Application Fee:** $35.00 **H.S. Requirements:** High school diploma required; GED accepted **Costs Per Year:** Application fee: $35. One-time mandatory fee: $50. State resident tuition: $4224 full-time, $176 per credit part-time. Nonresident tuition: $4224 full-time, $176 per credit part-time. Mandatory fees: $856 full-time, $35.50 per credit part-time. Full-time tuition and fees vary according to degree level, location, and program. Part-time tuition and fees vary according to degree level, location, and program. College room only: $4800. **Calendar System:** Semester, Summer session available **Faculty:** Full-time 19, Part-time 40 **Student-Faculty Ratio:** 13:1 **Final Year or Final Semester Residency Requirement:** No **Credit Hours For Degree:** 60 credits, Associates; 120 credits, Bachelors **Professional Accreditation:** AHIMA, NCCU.

ARGOSY UNIVERSITY, PHOENIX

2233 W Dunlap Ave.
Phoenix, AZ 85021
Tel: (602)216-2600; Free: 866-216-2777
Fax: (602)216-2601
Web Site: www.argosy.edu/phoenix-arizona/default.aspx
President/CEO: Hugh Jensen
Type: University **Sex:** Coed **Calendar System:** Semester **Regional Accreditation:** Western Association of Colleges and Schools **Professional Accreditation:** ACBSP, APA.

ARIZONA AUTOMOTIVE INSTITUTE

6829 N 46th Ave.
Glendale, AZ 85301-3597
Tel: (602)934-7273; Free: 800-321-5961
Fax: (602)937-5000
E-mail: info@azautoinst.com
Web Site: www.aai.edu
President/CEO: Darin Bargen
Type: Two-Year College **Sex:** Coed **Admission Plans:** Open Admission **Application Deadline:** Rolling **Application Fee:** $100.00 **Professional Accreditation:** ACCSC.

ARIZONA CHRISTIAN UNIVERSITY

2625 E Cactus Rd.
Phoenix, AZ 85032-7042
Tel: (602)489-5300; Free: 800-247-2697
E-mail: lambert.cruz@arizonachristian.edu
Web Site: arizonachristian.edu
President/CEO: Pres. Len Munsil
Admissions: Lambert Cruz
Financial Aid: Steven Young
Type: Four-Year College **Sex:** Coed **Affiliation:** Conservative Baptist. **Scores:** 82% SAT V 400+; 86% SAT M 400+; 70% ACT 18-23; 16% ACT 24-29 **Costs Per Year:** Comprehensive fee: $33,484 includes full-time tuition ($22,986), mandatory fees ($910), and college room and board ($9588). College room only: $5180. Full-time tuition and fees vary according to class time, course load, and program. Room and board charges vary according to board plan. Part-time mandatory fees: $455 per term. Part-time fees vary according to class time, course load, and program. **Scholarships:** Available. **Calendar System:** Miscellaneous, Summer session available **Enrollment:** Full-time 628, Part-time 151 **Faculty:** Full-time 14, Part-time 83 **Student-Faculty Ratio:** 15:1 **Exams:** ACT essay component not used; Other; SAT I or ACT; SAT II; SAT essay component not used. **% Receiving Financial Aid:** 77 **% Residing in College-Owned, -Operated, or -Affiliated Housing:** 28 **Final Year or Final Semester Residency Requirement:** No **Regional Accreditation:** North Central Association of Colleges and Schools **Credit Hours For Degree:** 61 credits, Associates; 120 credits, Bachelors **ROTC:** Air Force **Intercollegiate Athletics:** Baseball M; Basketball M & W; Cross-Country Running M & W; Football M; Golf M & W; Soccer M & W; Softball W; Tennis M & W; Track and Field M & W; Volleyball W

ARIZONA COLLEGE

4425 W Olive Ave.
Ste. 300

Glendale, AZ 85302-3843
Tel: (602)222-9300
Fax: (602)200-8726
E-mail: lhicks@arizonacollege.edu
Web Site: www.arizonacollege.edu
President/CEO: C. Larkin Hicks
Type: Two-Year College **Sex:** Coed **Application Fee:** $25.00 **Calendar System:** Quarter **Student-Faculty Ratio:** 16:1 **Professional Accreditation:** ABHES.

ARIZONA COLLEGE–MESA

163 N Dobson Rd.
Mesa, AZ 85201
Web Site: www.arizonacollege.edu
Type: Four-Year College **Sex:** Coed **Professional Accreditation:** ABHES.

ARIZONA STATE UNIVERSITY AT THE DOWNTOWN PHOENIX CAMPUS

411 N Central Ave.
Phoenix, AZ 85004
Tel: (602)496-4636
E-mail: admissions@asu.edu
Web Site: campus.asu.edu/downtown
President/CEO: Dr. Michael M. Crow
Type: University **Sex:** Coed **Affiliation:** Arizona State University. **Scores:** 97% SAT V 400+; 97% SAT M 400+; 45% ACT 18-23; 42.4% ACT 24-29 **% Accepted:** 78 **Application Deadline:** Rolling **Application Fee:** $50.00 **H.S. Requirements:** High school diploma required; GED accepted **Costs Per Year:** Application fee: $50. One-time mandatory fee: $320. State resident tuition: $9484 full-time, $677 per credit hour part-time. Nonresident tuition: $24,784 full-time, $1033 per credit hour part-time. Mandatory fees: $674 full-time. Full-time tuition and fees vary according to program. Part-time tuition varies according to program. College room and board: $13,000. College room only: $8500. Room and board charges vary according to board plan and housing facility. **Scholarships:** Available. **Calendar System:** Miscellaneous, Summer session available **Enrollment:** Full-time 8,235, Graduate full-time 1,293, Graduate part-time 484, Part-time 940 **Faculty:** Full-time 436, Part-time 115 **Student-Faculty Ratio:** 22:1 **Exams:** SAT I or ACT; SAT II. **% Receiving Financial Aid:** 70 **% Residing in College-Owned, -Operated, or -Affiliated Housing:** 17 **Final Year or Final Semester Residency Requirement:** No **Regional Accreditation:** North Central Association of Colleges and Schools **Credit Hours For Degree:** 120 credits, Bachelors **ROTC:** Air Force, Army, Navy **Intercollegiate Athletics:** Baseball M; Basketball M & W; Cross-Country Running M & W; Football M; Golf M & W; Gymnastics W; Ice Hockey M; Lacrosse W; Soccer W; Softball W; Swimming and Diving M & W; Tennis W; Track and Field M & W; Triathlon W; Volleyball W; Water Polo W; Wrestling M

ARIZONA STATE UNIVERSITY AT THE POLYTECHNIC CAMPUS

7001 E Williams Field Rd.
Mesa, AZ 85212
Tel: (480)727-1585
Fax: (480)727-1008
E-mail: admissions@asu.edu
Web Site: campus.asu.edu/polytechnic

President/CEO: Dr. Michael M. Crow
Type: University **Sex:** Coed **Affiliation:** Arizona State University. **Scores:** 97% SAT V 400+; 99% SAT M 400+; 41.4% ACT 18-23; 45% ACT 24-29 **% Accepted:** 80 **Application Deadline:** Rolling **Application Fee:** $50.00 **H.S. Requirements:** High school diploma required; GED accepted **Costs Per Year:** Application fee: $50. One-time mandatory fee: $320. State resident tuition: $9010 full-time, $677 per credit hour part-time. Nonresident tuition: $23,545 full-time, $1033 per credit hour part-time. Mandatory fees: $674 full-time. Full-time tuition and fees vary according to program. Part-time tuition varies according to program. College room and board: $11,760. College room only: $7260. Room and board charges vary according to board plan and housing facility. **Scholarships:** Available. **Calendar System:** Miscellaneous, Summer session available **Enrollment:** Full-time 3,210, Graduate full-time 292, Graduate part-time 106, Part-time 470 **Faculty:** Full-time 195, Part-time 14 **Student-Faculty Ratio:** 19:1 **Exams:** SAT I or ACT; SAT II. **% Receiving Financial Aid:** 64 **% Residing in College-Owned, -Operated, or -Affiliated Housing:** 25 **Final Year or Final Semester Residency Requirement:** No **Regional Accreditation:** North Central Association of Colleges and Schools **Credit Hours For Degree:** 120 semester hours, Bachelors **ROTC:** Air Force, Army, Navy **Professional Accreditation:** AABI, ABET, AND, ATMAE. **Intercollegiate Athletics:** Baseball M; Basketball M & W; Cross-Country Running M & W; Football M; Golf M & W; Gymnastics W; Ice Hockey M; Lacrosse W; Soccer W; Softball W; Swimming and Diving M & W; Tennis W; Track and Field M & W; Triathlon W; Volleyball W; Water Polo W; Wrestling M

ARIZONA STATE UNIVERSITY AT THE TEMPE CAMPUS

Tempe, AZ 85287
Tel: (480)965-2100
Fax: (482)965-1608
E-mail: admissions@asu.edu
Web Site: www.asu.edu
President/CEO: Dr. Michael M. Crow
Type: University **Sex:** Coed **Affiliation:** Arizona State University. **Scores:** 97% SAT V 400+; 98% SAT M 400+; 31.3% ACT 18-23; 49.7% ACT 24-29 **% Accepted:** 83 **Application Deadline:** Rolling **Application Fee:** $50.00 **H.S. Requirements:** High school diploma required; GED accepted **Costs Per Year:** Application fee: $50. One-time mandatory fee: $320. State resident tuition: $9484 full-time, $677 per credit hour part-time. Nonresident tuition: $24,784 full-time, $1033 per credit hour part-time. Mandatory fees: $674 full-time. Full-time tuition and fees vary according to program. Part-time tuition varies according to program. College room and board: $11,061. College room only: $6561. Room and board charges vary according to board plan and housing facility. **Scholarships:** Available. **Calendar System:** Miscellaneous, Summer session available **Enrollment:** Full-time 38,212, Graduate full-time 7,694, Graduate part-time 2,462, Part-time 3,616 **Faculty:** Full-time 2,065, Part-time 164 **Student-Faculty Ratio:** 23:1 **Exams:** SAT I or ACT; SAT II. **% Receiving Financial Aid:** 57 **% Residing in College-Owned, -Operated, or -Affiliated Housing:** 22 **Final Year or Final Semester Residency Requirement:** No **Regional Accreditation:** North Central Association of Colleges and Schools **Credit Hours For Degree:** 120 credits, Bachelors **ROTC:** Air Force, Army, Navy **Professional Accreditation:** AACN, AACSB, AALS, ABA, ABET, ACA, ACCE, ACEJMC, ACSP, AOTA, APA, ASHA, ASLA, CAHME, CEPH, CIDA, CSWE, NAAB, NAACLS, NASAD, NASM, NASPAA, NRPA. **Intercollegiate Athletics:** Baseball M; Basketball M & W; Cross-Country Running M & W; Football M; Golf M & W; Gymnastics M & W; Ice Hockey M; Lacrosse W; Soccer W; Softball W; Swimming and Diving M & W; Tennis W; Track and Field M & W; Triathlon W; Volleyball W; Water Polo W; Wrestling M

ARIZONA STATE UNIVERSITY AT THE WEST CAMPUS

4701 W Thunderbird Rd.
Glendale, AZ 85306
Tel: (602)543-5500
E-mail: admissions@asu.edu
Web Site: campus.asu.edu/west
President/CEO: Dr. Michael M. Crow
Type: Comprehensive **Sex:** Coed **Affiliation:** Arizona State University. **Scores:** 94% SAT V 400+; 95% SAT M 400+; 44.6% ACT 18-23; 40.2% ACT 24-29 **% Accepted:** 76 **Application Deadline:** Rolling **Application Fee:** $50.00 **H.S. Requirements:** High school diploma required; GED accepted **Costs Per Year:** Application fee: $50. One-time mandatory fee: $320. State resident tuition: $9010 full-time, $677 per credit hour part-time. Nonresident tuition: $23,545 full-time, $1033 per credit hour part-time. Mandatory fees:

$674 full-time. Full-time tuition and fees vary according to program. Part-time tuition varies according to program. College room and board: $10,474. College room only: $5974. Room and board charges vary according to board plan and housing facility. **Scholarships:** Available. **Calendar System:** Miscellaneous, Summer session available **Enrollment:** Full-time 2,724, Graduate full-time 233, Graduate part-time 150, Part-time 512 **Faculty:** Full-time 247, Part-time 43 **Student-Faculty Ratio:** 12:1 **Exams:** SAT I or ACT; SAT II. **% Receiving Financial Aid:** 76 **% Residing in College-Owned, -Operated, or -Affiliated Housing:** 12 **Final Year or Final Semester Residency Requirement:** No **Regional Accreditation:** North Central Association of Colleges and Schools **Credit Hours For Degree:** 120 credits, Bachelors **ROTC:** Air Force, Army, Navy **Professional Accreditation:** CSWE, NRPA. **Intercollegiate Athletics:** Baseball M; Basketball M & W; Cross-Country Running M & W; Football M; Golf M & W; Gymnastics W; Ice Hockey M; Lacrosse W; Soccer W; Softball W; Swimming and Diving M & W; Tennis W; Track and Field M & W; Triathlon W; Volleyball W; Water Polo W; Wrestling M

ARIZONA WESTERN COLLEGE

2020 S Ave. 8E
Yuma, AZ 85365
Tel: (928)317-6000; Free: 888-293-0392
Fax: (928)344-7730
E-mail: nicole.harral@azwestern.edu
Web Site: www.azwestern.edu
President/CEO: Dr. Glenn Mayle
Admissions: Nicole D. Harral
Type: Two-Year College **Sex:** Coed **Affiliation:** Arizona State Community College System. **Admission Plans:** Deferred Admission; Early Admission; Open Admission **Application Deadline:** Rolling **Application Fee:** $0.00 **H.S. Requirements:** High school diploma or equivalent not required. For applicants 18 or over: High school diploma required; GED accepted **Costs Per Year:** Application fee: $0. State resident tuition: $2400 full-time, $80 per credit part-time. Nonresident tuition: $9390 full-time, $313 per credit part-time. Full-time tuition varies according to course load, program, and reciprocity agreements. Part-time tuition varies according to course load, program, and reciprocity agreements. College room and board: $6464. College room only: $2240. Room and board charges vary according to board plan and housing facility. **Scholarships:** Available. **Calendar System:** Semester, Summer session available **Enrollment:** Full-time 2,653, Part-time 4,861 **Faculty:** Full-time 111, Part-time 432 **Student-Faculty Ratio:** 21:1 **Exams:** SAT I or ACT. **% Residing in College-Owned, -Operated, or -Affiliated Housing:** 7 **Final Year or Final Semester Residency Requirement:** No **Regional Accreditation:** North Central Association of Colleges and Schools **Credit Hours For Degree:** 64 credit hours, Associates **Professional Accreditation:** ACEN. **Intercollegiate Athletics:** Baseball M; Basketball M & W; Football M; Soccer M & W; Softball W; Volleyball W

THE ART INSTITUTE OF PHOENIX

2233 W Dunlap Ave.
Phoenix, AZ 85021-2859
Tel: (602)331-7500; Free: 800-474-2479
Fax: (602)331-5301
Web Site: www.artinstitutes.edu/phoenix
President/CEO: Chad Williams
Type: Four-Year College **Sex:** Coed **Affiliation:** Education Management Corporation. **Calendar System:** Quarter **Regional Accreditation:** Southern Association of Colleges and Schools **Professional Accreditation:** ACF, ACICS.

THE ART INSTITUTE OF TUCSON

5099 E Grant Rd., Ste. 100
Tucson, AZ 85712
Tel: (520)318-2700; Free: 866-690-8850
Fax: (520)881-4234
Web Site: www.artinstitutes.edu/tucson
President/CEO: Chad Williams
Type: Four-Year College **Sex:** Coed **Regional Accreditation:** Southern Association of Colleges and Schools **Professional Accreditation:** ACICS.

BROOKLINE COLLEGE (PHOENIX)

2445 W Dunlap Ave., Ste. 100
Phoenix, AZ 85021
Tel: (602)242-6265; Free: 800-793-2428

Fax: (602)973-2572
E-mail: tdean@brooklinecollege.edu
Web Site: brooklinecollege.edu
President/CEO: Michael Adkins
Admissions: Theresa Dean

Type: Four-Year College **Sex:** Coed **Admission Plans:** Open Admission **Application Deadline:** Rolling **H.S. Requirements:** High school diploma required; GED accepted **Calendar System:** Continuous, Summer session not available **Faculty:** Full-time 22, Part-time 21 **Student-Faculty Ratio:** 25:1 **Credit Hours For Degree:** 60 credits, Associates; 120 credits, Bachelors **Professional Accreditation:** ACICS.

BROOKLINE COLLEGE (TEMPE)

1140-1150 S Priest Dr.
Tempe, AZ 85281
Tel: (480)545-8755; Free: 888-886-2428
Fax: (480)926-1371
E-mail: ckindred@brooklinecollege.edu
Web Site: brooklinecollege.edu
President/CEO: Cheryl Kindred
Admissions: Cheryl Kindred

Type: Four-Year College **Sex:** Coed **Admission Plans:** Open Admission **Application Deadline:** Rolling **Application Fee:** $0.00 **H.S. Requirements:** High school diploma required; GED accepted **Calendar System:** Continuous **Enrollment:** Full-time 415 **Faculty:** Full-time 15, Part-time 22 **Student-Faculty Ratio:** 11:1 **Credit Hours For Degree:** 60 credits, Associates **Professional Accreditation:** ACICS.

BROOKLINE COLLEGE (TUCSON)

5441 E 22nd St.
Ste. 125
Tucson, AZ 85711
Tel: (520)748-9799; Free: 888-292-2428
Fax: (520)748-9355
E-mail: lpechota@brooklinecollege.edu
Web Site: brooklinecollege.edu
President/CEO: Leigh Anne Pechota
Admissions: Leigh Anne Pechota

Type: Four-Year College **Sex:** Coed **Admission Plans:** Open Admission **Application Deadline:** Rolling **H.S. Requirements:** High school diploma required; GED accepted **Costs Per Year:** Tuition: $15,225 full-time. Full-time tuition varies according to degree level and program. Tuition guaranteed not to increase for student's term of enrollment. **Calendar System:** Continuous **Student-Faculty Ratio:** 16:1 **Credit Hours For Degree:** 60 credits, Associates **Professional Accreditation:** ACICS.

CARRINGTON COLLEGE–MESA

1001 W Southern Ave.
Ste. 130
Mesa, AZ 85210
Tel: (480)212-1600
Web Site: carrington.edu
President/CEO: Steven Temple

Type: Two-Year College **Sex:** Coed **Affiliation:** Carrington Colleges Group, Inc. **Application Fee:** $0.00 **H.S. Requirements:** High school diploma required; GED accepted **Costs Per Year:** Application fee: $0. Tuition: $14,265 full-time. Mandatory fees: $679 full-time. Full-time tuition and fees vary according to program. **Scholarships:** Available. **Calendar System:** Semester **Enrollment:** Full-time 572, Part-time 61 **Faculty:** Full-time 6, Part-time 30 **Student-Faculty Ratio:** 37:1 **Credit Hours For Degree:** 66 credit hours, Associates **Professional Accreditation:** ABHES, CoARC.

CARRINGTON COLLEGE–PHOENIX NORTH

8503 N 27th Ave.
Phoenix, AZ 85051
Tel: (602)393-5900
Web Site: carrington.edu
President/CEO: Valentina Colmone

Type: Two-Year College **Sex:** Coed **Affiliation:** Carrington Colleges Group, Inc. **H.S. Requirements:** High school diploma required; GED accepted **Costs Per Year:** Tuition: $14,265 full-time. Mandatory fees: $679 full-time. Full-time tuition and fees vary according to program. Tuition guaranteed not to increase for student's term of enrollment. **Scholarships:** Available. **Calendar System:** Continuous, Summer session not available **Enrollment:**

Full-time 676 **Faculty:** Full-time 14, Part-time 6 **Student-Faculty Ratio:** 37:1 **Professional Accreditation:** ABHES, CoARC.

CARRINGTON COLLEGE–PHOENIX WEST

2701 W Bethany Home Rd.
Phoenix, AZ 85017
Tel: (602)433-1333
Web Site: carrington.edu
President/CEO: Valentina Colmone

Type: Two-Year College **Sex:** Coed **Affiliation:** Carrington Colleges Group, Inc. **Admission Plans:** Open Admission **Application Fee:** $0.00 **H.S. Requirements:** High school diploma required; GED accepted **Costs Per Year:** Application fee: $0. Tuition: $52,594 per degree program. **Scholarships:** Available. **Calendar System:** Semester **Enrollment:** Full-time 266, Part-time 80 **Faculty:** Full-time 14, Part-time 29 **Student-Faculty Ratio:** 12:1 **Professional Accreditation:** ABHES.

CARRINGTON COLLEGE–TUCSON

201 N Bonita Ave.
Ste. 101
Tucson, AZ 85745
Tel: (520)888-5885
Web Site: carrington.edu
President/CEO: Antonio Thompson

Type: Two-Year College **Sex:** Coed **Affiliation:** Carrington Colleges Group, Inc. **Application Fee:** $0.00 **H.S. Requirements:** High school diploma required; GED accepted **Costs Per Year:** Application fee: $0. Tuition: $14,265 full-time. Mandatory fees: $679 full-time. Full-time tuition and fees vary according to program. **Calendar System:** Semester **Enrollment:** Full-time 357 **Faculty:** Full-time 6, Part-time 6 **Student-Faculty Ratio:** 45:1 **Professional Accreditation:** ABHES.

CENTRAL ARIZONA COLLEGE

8470 N Overfield Rd.
Coolidge, AZ 85128
Tel: (520)494-5444; Free: 800-237-9814
Fax: (520)426-4234
E-mail: james.moore@centralaz.edu
Web Site: www.centralaz.edu
President/CEO: Doris Helmich
Admissions: Dr. James Moore

Type: Two-Year College **Sex:** Coed **Admission Plans:** Deferred Admission; Early Admission; Open Admission **Application Deadline:** Rolling **Application Fee:** $0.00 **H.S. Requirements:** High school diploma or equivalent not required **Scholarships:** Available. **Calendar System:** Semester, Summer session available **Enrollment:** Full-time 2,976, Part-time 4,937 **Faculty:** Full-time 94, Part-time 116 **Student-Faculty Ratio:** 14:1 **% Residing in College-Owned, -Operated, or -Affiliated Housing:** 17 **Final Year or Final Semester Residency Requirement:** No **Regional Accreditation:** North Central Association of Colleges and Schools **Credit Hours For Degree:** 64 credits, Associates **Professional Accreditation:** ACEN. **Intercollegiate Athletics:** Baseball M; Basketball M & W; Cross-Country Running M & W; Equestrian Sports M & W; Softball W; Track and Field M & W

CHAMBERLAIN COLLEGE OF NURSING

2149 W Dunlap Ave.
Phoenix, AZ 85021
Tel: (602)331-2720; Free: 877-751-5783
Fax: (602)749-4653
Web Site: www.chamberlain.edu
President/CEO: Pam Fuller

Type: Four-Year College **Sex:** Coed **Costs Per Year:** Tuition: $17,560 full-time, $665 per credit hour part-time. Mandatory fees: $600 full-time, $300 per term part-time. Full-time tuition and fees vary according to course load and program. Part-time tuition and fees vary according to course load and program. **Calendar System:** Semester **Enrollment:** Full-time 344, Part-time 225 **Faculty:** Full-time 13, Part-time 70 **Student-Faculty Ratio:** 12:1 **Exams:** ACT essay component used for admission; SAT I or ACT; SAT essay component used for admission. **Professional Accreditation:** AACN.

CHANDLER-GILBERT COMMUNITY COLLEGE

2626 E Pecos Rd.
Chandler, AZ 85225-2479
Tel: (480)732-7000

E-mail: ryan.cain@cgc.edu
Web Site: www.cgc.maricopa.edu
President/CEO: William Guerriero, EdD
Admissions: Ryan Cain
Type: Two-Year College **Sex:** Coed **Affiliation:** Maricopa County Community College District System. **Admission Plans:** Open Admission **Application Fee:** $0.00 **H.S. Requirements:** High school diploma or equivalent not required **Costs Per Year:** Application fee: $0. State resident tuition: $2016 full-time, $84 per credit hour part-time. Nonresident tuition: $7800 full-time, $325 per credit hour part-time. Mandatory fees: $30 full-time, $15 per term part-time. Full-time tuition and fees vary according to reciprocity agreements. Part-time tuition and fees vary according to reciprocity agreements. **Calendar System:** Semester, Summer session available **Enrollment:** Full-time 4,193, Part-time 10,461 **Faculty:** Full-time 133, Part-time 495 **Student-Faculty Ratio:** 25:1 **Regional Accreditation:** North Central Association of Colleges and Schools **Credit Hours For Degree:** 64 credits, Associates **Professional Accreditation:** ACEN. **Intercollegiate Athletics:** Baseball M; Basketball M & W; Golf M & W; Soccer M & W; Softball W; Volleyball W

COCHISE COUNTY COMMUNITY COLLEGE DISTRICT
4190 W Hwy. 80
Douglas, AZ 85607-6190
Tel: (520)364-7943; Free: 800-593-9567
Fax: (520)364-0236
E-mail: quickd@cochise.edu
Web Site: www.cochise.edu
President/CEO: Dr. James Dale Rottweiler
Admissions: Debbie Quick
Financial Aid: Karen Emmer
Type: Two-Year College **Sex:** Coed **% Accepted:** 100 **Admission Plans:** Deferred Admission; Open Admission **Application Deadline:** Rolling **H.S. Requirements:** High school diploma or equivalent not required **Costs Per Year:** State resident tuition: $2370 full-time, $79 per credit hour part-time. Nonresident tuition: $7500 full-time, $250 per credit hour part-time. Full-time tuition varies according to course load, program, and reciprocity agreements. Part-time tuition varies according to course load, program, and reciprocity agreements. College room and board: $6564. Room and board charges vary according to housing facility. **Scholarships:** Available. **Calendar System:** Semester, Summer session available **Enrollment:** Full-time 1,786, Part-time 2,723 **Faculty:** Full-time 86, Part-time 239 **Student-Faculty Ratio:** 17:1 **Exams:** ACT essay component used for placement; SAT essay component used for placement. **% Residing in College-Owned, -Operated, or -Affiliated Housing:** 2 **Final Year or Final Semester Residency Requirement:** No **Regional Accreditation:** North Central Association of Colleges and Schools **Credit Hours For Degree:** 64 credits, Associates **Intercollegiate Athletics:** Baseball M; Basketball M & W; Soccer W

COCONINO COMMUNITY COLLEGE
2800 S Lonetree Rd.
Flagstaff, AZ 86001
Tel: (928)527-1222; Free: 800-350-7122
Fax: (928)526-1821
E-mail: veronica.hipolito@coconino.edu
Web Site: www.coconino.edu
President/CEO: Dr. Leah Bornstein
Admissions: Veronica Hipolito
Type: Two-Year College **Sex:** Coed **Admission Plans:** Open Admission **Application Deadline:** Rolling **Application Fee:** $0.00 **H.S. Requirements:** High school diploma or equivalent not required **Costs Per Year:** Application fee: $0. State resident tuition: $2208 full-time, $92 per credit hour part-time. Nonresident tuition: $7728 full-time, $322 per credit hour part-time. Mandatory fees: $168 full-time. Full-time tuition and fees vary according to course level and program. Part-time tuition varies according to course level and program. **Scholarships:** Available. **Calendar System:** Semester, Summer session available **Enrollment:** Full-time 1,009, Part-time 2,689 **Faculty:** Full-time 39, Part-time 168 **Student-Faculty Ratio:** 18:1 **Regional Accreditation:** North Central Association of Colleges and Schools **Credit Hours For Degree:** 60 credit hours, Associates **ROTC:** Air Force, Army

COLLEGEAMERICA–FLAGSTAFF
399 S Malpais Ln.
Flagstaff, AZ 86001
Tel: (928)774-1934; Free: 800-622-2894

Fax: (928)526-3468
E-mail: doreen.evans@collegeamerica.edu
Web Site: www.collegeamerica.edu
President/CEO: Kathy Turner
Admissions: Doreen Evans
Type: Two-Year College **Sex:** Coed **Admission Plans:** Open Admission **Application Fee:** $0.00 **H.S. Requirements:** High school diploma required; GED accepted **Scholarships:** Available. **Calendar System:** Quarter **Enrollment:** Full-time 205 **Faculty:** Full-time 9, Part-time 5 **Student-Faculty Ratio:** 15:1 **Credit Hours For Degree:** 100.5 credits for Associates of Occupational Studies, Associates; 181.5 Credits for Bachelor of Science, Bachelors **Professional Accreditation:** ABHES, ACCSC.

COLLEGEAMERICA–PHOENIX
9801 N Metro Pky. E
Phoenix, AZ 85051
Tel: (602)257-7522; Free: 800-622-2894
Fax: (602)246-3063
Web Site: www.collegeamerica.edu
Type: Two-Year College **Sex:** Coed **Professional Accreditation:** ACCSC.

DEVRY UNIVERSITY (MESA)
1201 S Alma School Rd., Ste. 5450
Mesa, AZ 85210-2011
Tel: (480)827-1511; Free: 866-338-7941
Fax: (480)827-2552
Web Site: www.devry.edu
Type: Comprehensive **Sex:** Coed **Costs Per Year:** Tuition: $17,052 full-time, $609 per credit hour part-time. Mandatory fees: $80 full-time, $40 per term part-time. **Calendar System:** Semester **Regional Accreditation:** North Central Association of Colleges and Schools **Professional Accreditation:** ACBSP.

DEVRY UNIVERSITY (PHOENIX)
2149 W Dunlap Ave.
Phoenix, AZ 85021-2995
Tel: (602)749-7301; Free: 866-338-7941
Web Site: www.devry.edu
Type: Comprehensive **Sex:** Coed **Affiliation:** DeVry University. **Application Fee:** $40.00 **H.S. Requirements:** High school diploma required; GED accepted **Costs Per Year:** Application fee: $40. Tuition: $17,052 full-time, $609 per credit hour part-time. Mandatory fees: $80 full-time, $40 per term part-time. **Scholarships:** Available. **Calendar System:** Semester **Enrollment:** Full-time 375, Graduate full-time 9, Graduate part-time 111, Part-time 355 **Faculty:** Full-time 26, Part-time 97 **Student-Faculty Ratio:** 9:1 **Exams:** ACT essay component used for admission; ACT essay component used for placement; SAT essay component used for admission; SAT essay component used for placement. **Regional Accreditation:** North Central Association of Colleges and Schools **Professional Accreditation:** ABET.

DINÉ COLLEGE
PO Box 98
Tsaile, AZ 86556
Tel: (520)724-6600; Free: 877-988-DINE
Fax: (520)724-3349
E-mail: louise@dinecollege.edu
Web Site: www.dinecollege.edu
President/CEO: Ferlin Clark
Admissions: Louise Litzin
Type: Two-Year College **Sex:** Coed **Admission Plans:** Early Admission; Open Admission; Preferred Admission **Application Deadline:** Rolling **Application Fee:** $20.00 **H.S. Requirements:** High school diploma required; GED accepted **Costs Per Year:** Application fee: $20. One-time mandatory fee: $20. State resident tuition: $660 full-time, $55 per credit hour part-time. Nonresident tuition: $660 full-time, $55 per credit hour part-time. Mandatory fees: $90 full-time, $45 per unit part-time. College room and board: $4940. College room only: $1280. Room and board charges vary according to board plan and location. Tuition guaranteed not to increase for student's term of enrollment. **Scholarships:** Available. **Calendar System:** Semester, Summer session available **Enrollment:** Full-time 815, Part-time 842 **Regional Accreditation:** North Central Association of Colleges and Schools **Credit Hours For Degree:** 64 credit hours, Associates **Intercollegiate Athletics:** Archery M & W; Cross-Country Running M & W

DUNLAP-STONE UNIVERSITY

19820 N 7th St.
Ste. No.100
Phoenix, AZ 85024
Tel: (602)648-5750; Free: 800-474-8013
Fax: (602)648-5755
E-mail: director@expandglobal.com
Web Site: www.dunlap-stone.edu
Admissions: Dr. Donald N. Burton

Type: Comprehensive **Sex:** Coed **Admission Plans:** Deferred Admission; Open Admission **Application Deadline:** Rolling **Application Fee:** $0.00 **H.S. Requirements:** High school diploma required; GED accepted **Costs Per Year:** Application fee: $0. Tuition: $8000 full-time. **Calendar System:** Semester, Summer session not available **Faculty:** Part-time 100 **Student-Faculty Ratio:** 15:1 **Final Year or Final Semester Residency Requirement:** No **Professional Accreditation:** DEAC.

EASTERN ARIZONA COLLEGE

615 N Stadium Ave.
Thatcher, AZ 85552-0769
Tel: (928)428-8472; Free: 800-678-3808
Fax: (928)428-8462
E-mail: admissions@eac.edu
Web Site: www.eac.edu
President/CEO: Pres. Mark Bryce, JD
Admissions: Suzette Udall
Financial Aid: Bill Osborn

Type: Two-Year College **Sex:** Coed **Affiliation:** Arizona State Community College System. **% Accepted:** 100 **Admission Plans:** Deferred Admission; Early Admission; Open Admission **Application Deadline:** Rolling **Application Fee:** $0.00 **H.S. Requirements:** High school diploma or equivalent not required **Costs Per Year:** Application fee: $0. State resident tuition: $2080 full-time, $100 per credit hour part-time. Nonresident tuition: $9580 full-time, $235 per credit hour part-time. Full-time tuition varies according to program. Part-time tuition varies according to program. College room and board: $6125. Room and board charges vary according to board plan. **Scholarships:** Available. **Calendar System:** Semester, Summer session available **Enrollment:** Full-time 1,783, Part-time 4,596 **Faculty:** Full-time 93, Part-time 269 **Student-Faculty Ratio:** 18:1 **% Residing in College-Owned, -Operated, or -Affiliated Housing:** 5 **Regional Accreditation:** North Central Association of Colleges and Schools **Credit Hours For Degree:** 64 semester hours, Associates **Intercollegiate Athletics:** Baseball M; Basketball M & W; Football M; Golf M & W; Softball W; Volleyball W

EMBRY-RIDDLE AERONAUTICAL UNIVERSITY–PRESCOTT

3700 Willow Creek Rd.
Prescott, AZ 86301-3720
Tel: (928)777-3728; Free: 800-888-3728
Fax: (928)777-3740
E-mail: pradmit@erau.edu
Web Site: www.embryriddle.edu
President/CEO: Dr. John R. Watret
Financial Aid: Debra Hintz

Type: Comprehensive **Sex:** Coed **Scores:** 96% SAT V 400+; 97% SAT M 400+; 26.42% ACT 18-23; 53.14% ACT 24-29 **% Accepted:** 79 **Admission Plans:** Deferred Admission **Application Deadline:** Rolling **Application Fee:** $50.00 **H.S. Requirements:** High school diploma required; GED accepted **Costs Per Year:** Application fee: $50. Comprehensive fee: $44,054 includes full-time tuition ($32,592), mandatory fees ($1234), and college room and board ($10,228). College room only: $5700. Room and board charges vary according to board plan and housing facility. Part-time tuition: $1358 per credit hour. Part-time mandatory fees: $617 per term. **Scholarships:** Available. **Calendar System:** Semester, Summer session available **Enrollment:** Full-time 2,082, Graduate full-time 51, Graduate part-time 9, Part-time 123 **Exams:** ACT; SAT I; SAT I and SAT II or ACT; SAT I or ACT; SAT II; SAT Subject. **% Receiving Financial Aid:** 61 **% Residing in College-Owned, -Operated, or -Affiliated Housing:** 41 **Final Year or Final Semester Residency Requirement:** Yes **Regional Accreditation:** Southern Association of Colleges and Schools **Credit Hours For Degree:** 120 credit hours, Bachelors **ROTC:** Air Force, Army **Professional Accreditation:** AABI, ABET, ACBSP. **Intercollegiate Athletics:** Basketball M & W; Cross-Country Running M & W; Golf M & W; Soccer M & W; Softball W; Track and Field M & W; Volleyball W; Wrestling M

ESTRELLA MOUNTAIN COMMUNITY COLLEGE

3000 N Dysart Rd.
Avondale, AZ 85392
Tel: (623)935-8000
E-mail: debbie.kushibab@emcmail.maricopa.edu
Web Site: www.estrellamountain.edu
President/CEO: Dr. Ernesto Lara
Admissions: Dr. Debbie Kushibab
Financial Aid: Rosanna Short

Type: Two-Year College **Sex:** Coed **Affiliation:** Maricopa County Community College District System. **% Accepted:** 100 **Admission Plans:** Open Admission **Scholarships:** Available. **Calendar System:** Semester, Summer session available **Enrollment:** Full-time 3,015, Part-time 6,149 **Student-Faculty Ratio:** 22:1 **Regional Accreditation:** North Central Association of Colleges and Schools **Credit Hours For Degree:** 60 credits, Associates **ROTC:** Air Force **Professional Accreditation:** ACEN. **Intercollegiate Athletics:** Cross-Country Running M & W; Golf M & W

FORTIS COLLEGE

555 N 18th St., Ste. 110
Phoenix, AZ 85006
Tel: (602)254-3099; Free: 855-4-FORTIS
Web Site: www.fortis.edu

Type: Two-Year College **Sex:** Coed **Professional Accreditation:** ACCSC.

GATEWAY COMMUNITY COLLEGE

108 N 40th St.
Phoenix, AZ 85034-1795
Tel: (602)286-8000
Fax: (602)286-8003
E-mail: enroll@gatewaycc.edu
Web Site: www.gatewaycc.edu
President/CEO: Dr. Eugene Giovannini

Type: Two-Year College **Sex:** Coed **Affiliation:** GateWay Community College; Maricopa County Community College District System. **% Accepted:** 100 **Admission Plans:** Deferred Admission; Early Admission; Open Admission **Application Deadline:** Rolling **Application Fee:** $0.00 **H.S. Requirements:** High school diploma or equivalent not required. For health science, nursing programs: High school diploma required; GED accepted **Scholarships:** Available. **Calendar System:** Semester, Summer session available **Faculty:** Full-time 99, Part-time 391 **Student-Faculty Ratio:** 18:1 **Final Year or Final Semester Residency Requirement:** No **Regional Accreditation:** North Central Association of Colleges and Schools **Credit Hours For Degree:** 60 credit hours, Associates **ROTC:** Air Force, Army **Professional Accreditation:** ACEN, APTA, CoARC, JRCERT. **Intercollegiate Athletics:** Baseball M; Cross-Country Running M & W; Golf M & W; Soccer M & W; Softball W

GLENDALE COMMUNITY COLLEGE

6000 W Olive Ave.
Glendale, AZ 85302-3090
Tel: (623)845-3000
Fax: (623)845-3329
E-mail: admissions.recruitment@gccaz.edu
Web Site: www.gc.maricopa.edu
President/CEO: Dr. Irene Kovola
Admissions: Mary Blackwell

Type: Two-Year College **Sex:** Coed **Affiliation:** Maricopa County Community College District System. **Admission Plans:** Open Admission **Application Deadline:** August 20 **Application Fee:** $0.00 **H.S. Requirements:** High school diploma or equivalent not required **Scholarships:** Available. **Calendar System:** Semester, Summer session available **Enrollment:** Full-time 7,335, Part-time 14,026 **Faculty:** Full-time 277, Part-time 646 **Regional Accreditation:** North Central Association of Colleges and Schools **Credit Hours For Degree:** 60 credit hours, Associates **ROTC:** Air Force, Army **Professional Accreditation:** ACEN. **Intercollegiate Athletics:** Baseball M; Basketball M & W; Cross-Country Running M & W; Football M; Golf M; Soccer M & W; Softball W; Tennis M & W; Track and Field M & W; Volleyball W

GOLF ACADEMY OF AMERICA

2031 N Arizona Ave.
Ste. 2
Chandler, AZ 85225

Tel: (480)857-1574
Web Site: www.golfacademy.edu
Type: Two-Year College **Sex:** Coed **Calendar System:** Semester **Professional Accreditation:** ACICS.

GRAND CANYON UNIVERSITY

3300 W Camelback Rd.
Phoenix, AZ 85017-1097
Tel: (602)249-3300; Free: 800-800-9776
Fax: (602)589-2580
E-mail: admissionsonline@gcu.edu
Web Site: www.gcu.edu
President/CEO: Brent Richardson
Type: Comprehensive **Sex:** Coed **Affiliation:** Southern Baptist. **Admission Plans:** Deferred Admission; Early Admission **Application Deadline:** Rolling **H.S. Requirements:** High school diploma required; GED accepted **Scholarships:** Available. **Calendar System:** Semester, Summer session available **Exams:** SAT I or ACT. **% Residing in College-Owned, -Operated, or -Affiliated Housing:** 40 **Regional Accreditation:** North Central Association of Colleges and Schools **Credit Hours For Degree:** 128 semester hours, Bachelors **ROTC:** Air Force, Army **Professional Accreditation:** AACN, ACBSP, NCATE. **Intercollegiate Athletics:** Baseball M; Basketball M & W; Cross-Country Running M & W; Golf M & W; Lacrosse M; Soccer M & W; Softball W; Swimming and Diving M & W; Tennis M & W; Track and Field M & W; Volleyball M & W; Wrestling M

HARRISON MIDDLETON UNIVERSITY

1105 E Broadway
Tempe, AZ 85282
Tel: (480)317-5955; Free: 877-248-6724
Fax: (480)829-4999
E-mail: information@hmu.edu
Web Site: www.hmu.edu
President/CEO: Dr. David W. Curd
Admissions: Lauren Guthrie
Type: Comprehensive **Sex:** Coed **Admission Plans:** Open Admission **Application Deadline:** Rolling **Application Fee:** $50.00 **H.S. Requirements:** High school diploma required; GED accepted **Costs Per Year:** Application fee: $50. One-time mandatory fee: $400. Tuition: $5400 full-time, $300 per credit hour part-time. **Calendar System:** Continuous, Summer session available **Enrollment:** Full-time 69, Graduate full-time 78 **Faculty:** Full-time 17, Part-time 6 **Student-Faculty Ratio:** 1:1 **Final Year or Final Semester Residency Requirement:** No **Credit Hours For Degree:** 60 credit hours, Associates; 120 credit hours, Bachelors **Professional Accreditation:** DEAC.

INTERNATIONAL BAPTIST COLLEGE AND SEMINARY

2211 W Germann Rd.
Chandler, AZ 85286
Tel: (480)245-7903; Free: 800-422-4858
E-mail: admissions@ibconline.edu
Web Site: www.ibcs.edu
President/CEO: David Brock
Type: Comprehensive **Sex:** Coed **Affiliation:** Baptist. **Admission Plans:** Early Admission; Open Admission **Application Deadline:** August 20 **Application Fee:** $35.00 **H.S. Requirements:** High school diploma or equivalent not required **Scholarships:** Available. **Calendar System:** 4-1-4 **Student-Faculty Ratio:** 7:1 **Credit Hours For Degree:** 67 semester hours, Associates; 133 semester hours, Bachelors **Professional Accreditation:** TRACS.

MESA COMMUNITY COLLEGE

1833 W Southern Ave.
Mesa, AZ 85202-4866
Tel: (480)461-7000; Free: 866-532-4983
Fax: (480)461-7805
E-mail: admissionsandrecords@mesacc.edu
Web Site: www.mesacc.edu
President/CEO: Dr. Shouan Pan
Admissions: Dr. Barbara Boros
Type: Two-Year College **Sex:** Coed **Affiliation:** Maricopa County Community College District System. **Admission Plans:** Deferred Admission; Early Admission; Open Admission **Application Deadline:** August 18 **Application Fee:** $0.00 **H.S. Requirements:** High school diploma or

equivalent not required **Costs Per Year:** Application fee: $0. State resident tuition: $2016 full-time. Nonresident tuition: $7800 full-time. Mandatory fees: $30 full-time. Full-time tuition and fees vary according to course load and reciprocity agreements. **Scholarships:** Available. **Calendar System:** Semester, Summer session available **Final Year or Final Semester Residency Requirement:** No **Regional Accreditation:** North Central Association of Colleges and Schools **Credit Hours For Degree:** 60 credit hours, Associates **ROTC:** Air Force, Army **Professional Accreditation:** ABFSE, ACEN. **Intercollegiate Athletics:** Baseball M; Basketball M & W; Cross-Country Running M; Football M; Golf M & W; Soccer M & W; Softball W; Tennis M & W; Track and Field M & W; Volleyball W; Wrestling M

MOHAVE COMMUNITY COLLEGE

1971 Jagerson Ave.
Kingman, AZ 86409
Tel: (928)757-4331; Free: 888-664-2832
Fax: (928)757-0808
E-mail: amasterson@mohave.edu
Web Site: www.mohave.edu
President/CEO: Dr. Michael J. Kearns
Admissions: Ana Masterson
Financial Aid: Shannon Sheaff
Type: Two-Year College **Sex:** Coed **Admission Plans:** Deferred Admission; Early Admission; Open Admission **Application Deadline:** Rolling **H.S. Requirements:** High school diploma or equivalent not required **Costs Per Year:** State resident tuition: $2430 full-time, $81 per credit hour part-time. Nonresident tuition: $8505 full-time, $283.50 per credit hour part-time. Mandatory fees: $210 full-time, $7 per credit hour part-time. Full-time tuition and fees vary according to program. Part-time tuition and fees vary according to program. **Scholarships:** Available. **Calendar System:** Semester, Summer session available **Enrollment:** Full-time 938, Part-time 3,422 **Faculty:** Full-time 79, Part-time 230 **Student-Faculty Ratio:** 13:1 **Regional Accreditation:** North Central Association of Colleges and Schools **Credit Hours For Degree:** 60 semester hours, Associates **Professional Accreditation:** ACEN.

NATIONAL PARALEGAL COLLEGE

717 E Maryland Ave., Ste. 115
Phoenix, AZ 85014
Tel: (845)371-9101; Free: 800-371-6105
E-mail: info@nationalparalegal.edu
Web Site: nationalparalegal.edu
President/CEO: Avi Katz
Type: Comprehensive **Sex:** Coed **Admission Plans:** Open Admission **Application Deadline:** Rolling **Application Fee:** $0.00 **H.S. Requirements:** High school diploma required; GED accepted **Costs Per Year:** Application fee: $0. One-time mandatory fee: $195. Tuition: $7800 full-time, $325 per credit part-time. Tuition guaranteed not to increase for student's term of enrollment. **Calendar System:** Continuous, Summer session available **Enrollment:** Full-time 895, Graduate full-time 98, Graduate part-time 1, Part-time 44 **Faculty:** Full-time 5, Part-time 28 **Credit Hours For Degree:** 60 credits, Associates; 120 credits, Bachelors **Professional Accreditation:** DEAC.

NORTHCENTRAL UNIVERSITY

8667 E Hartford Dr.
Ste. 100
Scottsdale, AZ 85255
Tel: (928)541-7777; Free: 866-776-0331
Fax: (928)541-7817
E-mail: Information@ncu.edu
Web Site: www.ncu.edu
President/CEO: George Burnett
Admissions: Ken Boutelle
Type: Two-Year Upper Division **Sex:** Coed **Application Deadline:** Rolling **Application Fee:** $0.00 **H.S. Requirements:** High school diploma required; GED accepted **Costs Per Year:** Application fee: $0. One-time mandatory fee: $350. Tuition: $10,368 full-time, $1296 per course part-time. **Calendar System:** Continuous **Enrollment:** Full-time 32, Graduate full-time 5,212, Graduate part-time 5,649, Part-time 136 **Faculty:** Full-time 114, Part-time 356 **Final Year or Final Semester Residency Requirement:** No **Regional Accreditation:** North Central Association of Colleges and Schools **Credit Hours For Degree:** 120 credits, Bachelors **Professional Accreditation:** ACBSP.

NORTHERN ARIZONA UNIVERSITY

S San Francisco St.
Flagstaff, AZ 86011
Tel: (928)523-9011; Free: 888-MORE-NAU
Fax: (928)523-0226
E-mail: admissions@nau.edu
Web Site: www.nau.edu
President/CEO: Dr. Rita Cheng

Type: University **Sex:** Coed **Affiliation:** Arizona University System. **Scores:** 94% SAT V 400+; 93% SAT M 400+; 51% ACT 18-23; 37% ACT 24-29 **% Accepted:** 78 **Admission Plans:** Deferred Admission **Application Deadline:** Rolling **Application Fee:** $25.00 **H.S. Requirements:** High school diploma required; GED accepted **Costs Per Year:** Application fee: $25. State resident tuition: $9462 full-time, $676 per credit hour part-time. Nonresident tuition: $22,452 full-time, $936 per credit hour part-time. Mandatory fees: $896 full-time, $331 per credit hour part-time. Full-time tuition and fees vary according to course load, location, and reciprocity agreements. Part-time tuition and fees vary according to course load, location, and reciprocity agreements. College room and board: $9132. College room only: $4990. Room and board charges vary according to board plan and housing facility. Tuition guaranteed not to increase for student's term of enrollment. **Scholarships:** Available. **Calendar System:** Semester, Summer session available **Enrollment:** Full-time 20,357, Graduate full-time 1,863, Graduate part-time 2,048, Part-time 4,763 **Faculty:** Full-time 1,068, Part-time 553 **Student-Faculty Ratio:** 20:1 **Exams:** ACT; ACT essay component not used; Other; SAT I; SAT I and SAT II or ACT; SAT I or ACT; SAT II; SAT essay component not used. **% Receiving Financial Aid:** 60 **% Residing in College-Owned, -Operated, or -Affiliated Housing:** 29 **Final Year or Final Semester Residency Requirement:** No **Regional Accreditation:** North Central Association of Colleges and Schools **Credit Hours For Degree:** 120 semester hours, Bachelors **ROTC:** Air Force, Army **Professional Accreditation:** AACN, AACSB, ABET, ACA, ACBSP, ACCE, ADA, APTA, ASHA, CEPH, CSWE, NASM, NCATE, NRPA, SAF. **Intercollegiate Athletics:** Basketball M & W; Cross-Country Running M & W; Football M; Golf W; Soccer W; Swimming and Diving W; Tennis M & W; Track and Field M & W; Volleyball W

NORTHLAND PIONEER COLLEGE

PO Box 610
Holbrook, AZ 86025
Tel: (928)524-7311; Free: 800-266-7845
Fax: (928)524-7612
Web Site: www.npc.edu
President/CEO: Dr. Jeanne Swarthout
Admissions: Suzette Willis

Type: Two-Year College **Sex:** Coed **Affiliation:** Arizona State Community College System. **Admission Plans:** Early Admission; Open Admission **Application Deadline:** Rolling **Application Fee:** $0.00 **H.S. Requirements:** High school diploma or equivalent not required **Scholarships:** Available. **Calendar System:** Semester, Summer session available **Enrollment:** Full-time 946, Part-time 3,690 **Faculty:** Full-time 73, Part-time 153 **Student-Faculty Ratio:** 17:1 **Final Year or Final Semester Residency Requirement:** No **Regional Accreditation:** North Central Association of Colleges and Schools **Credit Hours For Degree:** 64 semester hours, Associates **Professional Accreditation:** ACEN.

PARADISE VALLEY COMMUNITY COLLEGE

18401 N 32nd St.
Phoenix, AZ 85032-1200
Tel: (602)787-6500
Fax: (602)787-6625
E-mail: shirley.green@pvmail.maricopa.edu
Web Site: www.pvc.maricopa.edu
President/CEO: Dr. Paul Dale
Admissions: Dr. Shirley Green

Type: Two-Year College **Sex:** Coed **Affiliation:** Maricopa County Community College District System. **Admission Plans:** Early Admission; Open Admission **Application Deadline:** Rolling **Application Fee:** $0.00 **H.S. Requirements:** High school diploma or equivalent not required **Scholarships:** Available. **Calendar System:** Semester, Summer session available **Enrollment:** Full-time 3,043, Part-time 6,908 **Faculty:** Full-time 98, Part-time 444 **Regional Accreditation:** North Central Association of Colleges and Schools **Credit Hours For Degree:** 60 credit hours, Associates **ROTC:** Army **Professional Accreditation:** ACEN. **Intercollegiate Athletics:** Baseball M; Cross-Country Running M & W; Golf M & W; Soccer M & W; Softball W; Tennis M & W; Track and Field M & W

THE PARALEGAL INSTITUTE AT BRIGHTON COLLEGE

8777 E Via de Ventura, Ste. 300
Scottsdale, AZ 85258
Tel: (602)212-0501; Free: 800-354-1254
E-mail: paralegalinst@mindspring.com
Web Site: www.theparalegalinstitute.edu
Admissions: Patricia Yancy

Type: Two-Year College **Sex:** Coed **% Accepted:** 25 **Faculty:** Full-time 1, Part-time 3 **Credit Hours For Degree:** 60 credits, Associates **Professional Accreditation:** DEAC.

PENN FOSTER COLLEGE

14300 N Northsight Blvd.
Ste. 120
Scottsdale, AZ 85260
Tel: (480)947-6644; Free: 800-471-3232
Web Site: www.pennfostercollege.edu

Type: Two-Year College **Sex:** Coed **Admission Plans:** Open Admission **Application Deadline:** Rolling **Application Fee:** $75.00 **H.S. Requirements:** High school diploma required; GED accepted **Costs Per Year:** Application fee: $75. Tuition: $79 per credit part-time. Part-time tuition varies according to course load and program. **Calendar System:** Continuous **Faculty:** Full-time 40, Part-time 163 **Final Year or Final Semester Residency Requirement:** No **Credit Hours For Degree:** 60 credits, Associates; 120 credits, Bachelors **Professional Accreditation:** DEAC.

PHOENIX COLLEGE

1202 W Thomas Rd.
Phoenix, AZ 85013-4234
Tel: (602)285-7800
Fax: (602)285-7700
E-mail: kathy.french@pcmail.maricopa.edu
Web Site: www.pc.maricopa.edu
President/CEO: Dr. Anna Solley
Admissions: Brenda Stark

Type: Two-Year College **Sex:** Coed **Affiliation:** Maricopa County Community College District System. **Admission Plans:** Deferred Admission; Early Admission; Open Admission **Application Deadline:** Rolling **Application Fee:** $0.00 **H.S. Requirements:** High school diploma or equivalent not required **Costs Per Year:** Application fee: $0. Area resident tuition: $2016 full-time, $84 per credit hour part-time. State resident tuition: $8784 full-time, $366 per credit hour part-time. Mandatory fees: $30 full-time, $15 per term part-time. Full-time tuition and fees vary according to reciprocity agreements. Part-time tuition and fees vary according to course load and reciprocity agreements. **Scholarships:** Available. **Calendar System:** Semester, Summer session available **Enrollment:** Full-time 3,421, Part-time 9,255 **Faculty:** Full-time 161, Part-time 605 **Student-Faculty Ratio:** 17:1 **Final Year or Final Semester Residency Requirement:** No **Regional Accreditation:** North Central Association of Colleges and Schools **Credit Hours For Degree:** 60 credit hours, Associates **ROTC:** Air Force, Army, Navy **Professional Accreditation:** ACEN, ADA, AHIMA. **Intercollegiate Athletics:** Baseball M; Basketball M & W; Football M; Soccer M & W; Softball W; Volleyball W

PIMA COMMUNITY COLLEGE

4905 E Broadway Blvd.
Tucson, AZ 85709-1010
Tel: (520)206-4666
Fax: (520)884-6728
E-mail: tbenson@pima.edu
Web Site: www.pima.edu
President/CEO: Dr. Lee Lambert
Admissions: Terra Benson

Type: Two-Year College **Sex:** Coed **Admission Plans:** Open Admission **Application Fee:** $0.00 **H.S. Requirements:** High school diploma or equivalent not required **Costs Per Year:** Application fee: $0. State resident tuition: $2265 full-time, $75.50 per credit hour part-time. Nonresident tuition: $10,560 full-time, $352 per credit hour part-time. **Scholarships:** Available. **Calendar System:** Semester, Summer session available **Final Year or Final Semester Residency Requirement:** No **Regional Accreditation:**

North Central Association of Colleges and Schools **ROTC:** Air Force, Army, Navy **Professional Accreditation:** ACEN, ADA, CoARC, JRCERT.

PIMA MEDICAL INSTITUTE (MESA)

2160 S Power Rd.
Mesa, AZ 85209
Tel: (480)898-9898
E-mail: sbuckley@pmi.edu
Web Site: www.pmi.edu
President/CEO: Bill Wiechertjes
Admissions: Steve Buckley

Type: Two-Year College **Sex:** Coed **Exams:** Other. **Professional Accreditation:** ABHES.

PIMA MEDICAL INSTITUTE (MESA)

957 S Dobson Rd.
Mesa, AZ 85202
Tel: (480)644-0267; Free: 888-477-PIMA
Fax: (480)649-5249
Web Site: www.pmi.edu
President/CEO: Kristen Torres

Type: Two-Year College **Sex:** Coed **Affiliation:** Vocational Training Institutes, Inc. **Calendar System:** Miscellaneous **Exams:** Other. **Professional Accreditation:** ABHES, ACCSC, CoARC, JRCERT.

PIMA MEDICAL INSTITUTE (TUCSON)

3350 E Grant Rd.
Tucson, AZ 85716
Tel: (520)326-1600; Free: 888-477-PIMA
Fax: (520)326-4125
Web Site: www.pmi.edu
President/CEO: Dale Berg

Type: Two-Year College **Sex:** Coed **Affiliation:** Vocational Training Institutes, Inc. **Admission Plans:** Early Admission **H.S. Requirements:** High school diploma required; GED accepted **Calendar System:** Miscellaneous, Summer session not available **Exams:** Other. **Credit Hours For Degree:** 66 credits, Associates **Professional Accreditation:** ABHES, CoARC, JRCERT.

PRESCOTT COLLEGE

220 Grove Ave.
Prescott, AZ 86301
Tel: (928)350-2100; Free: 877-350-2100
Fax: (928)776-5157
E-mail: admissions@prescott.edu
Web Site: www.prescott.edu
President/CEO: John Flicker
Admissions: Nancy Simmons
Financial Aid: Mary Frances Causey

Type: Comprehensive **Sex:** Coed **Scores:** 91% SAT V 400+; 35.3% ACT 18-23; 35.3% ACT 24-29 **% Accepted:** 68 **Admission Plans:** Deferred Admission; Early Action **Application Deadline:** August 15 **Application Fee:** $0.00 **H.S. Requirements:** High school diploma required; GED accepted **Costs Per Year:** Application fee: $0. One-time mandatory fee: $775. Comprehensive fee: $33,929 includes full-time tuition ($26,088), mandatory fees ($641), and college room and board ($7200). College room only: $6800. Room and board charges vary according to board plan. Part-time tuition: $1087 per credit hour. Part-time mandatory fees: $320 per term. **Scholarships:** Available. **Calendar System:** Semester, Summer session available **Enrollment:** Full-time 371, Graduate full-time 132, Graduate part-time 252, Part-time 93 **Faculty:** Full-time 63, Part-time 46 **Student-Faculty Ratio:** 9:1 **Exams:** SAT I or ACT; SAT Reasoning. **% Receiving Financial Aid:** 70 **% Residing in College-Owned, -Operated, or -Affiliated Housing:** 16 **Final Year or Final Semester Residency Requirement:** No **Regional Accreditation:** North Central Association of Colleges and Schools **Credit Hours For Degree:** 120 semester credits, Bachelors

THE REFRIGERATION SCHOOL

4210 E Washington St.
Phoenix, AZ 85034-1816
Tel: (602)275-7133; Free: 888-943-4822
E-mail: info@rsiaz.edu
Web Site: www.refrigerationschool.com
President/CEO: Stephen Malutich

Admissions: Heather Haskell

Type: Two-Year College **Sex:** Coed **Scholarships:** Available. **Calendar System:** Continuous **Student-Faculty Ratio:** 27:1 **Professional Accreditation:** ACCSC.

RIO SALADO COLLEGE

2323 W 14th St.
Tempe, AZ 85281-6950
Tel: (480)517-8000; Free: 800-729-1197
Fax: (480)517-8199
E-mail: admission@riomail.maricopa.edu
Web Site: www.rio.maricopa.edu
President/CEO: Dr. Chris Bustamante
Admissions: Laurel Redman

Type: Two-Year College **Sex:** Coed **Affiliation:** Maricopa County Community College District System. **Admission Plans:** Deferred Admission; Early Admission; Open Admission **Application Deadline:** Rolling **Application Fee:** $0.00 **H.S. Requirements:** High school diploma or equivalent not required **Costs Per Year:** Application fee: $0. State resident tuition: $2016 full-time, $84 per credit hour part-time. Nonresident tuition: $5160 full-time, $215 per credit hour part-time. Mandatory fees: $30 full-time, $15 per term part-time. Full-time tuition and fees vary according to course load and reciprocity agreements. Part-time tuition and fees vary according to course load and reciprocity agreements. **Scholarships:** Available. **Calendar System:** Semester, Summer session available **Student-Faculty Ratio:** 25:1 **Regional Accreditation:** North Central Association of Colleges and Schools **Credit Hours For Degree:** 64 credit hours, Associates **Professional Accreditation:** ADA.

SCOTTSDALE COMMUNITY COLLEGE

9000 E Chaparral Rd.
Scottsdale, AZ 85256-2626
Tel: (480)423-6000
Fax: (480)423-6200
E-mail: fran.Vitale@scottsdalecc.edu
Web Site: www.scottsdalecc.edu
President/CEO: Dr. Jan L. Gehler
Admissions: Fran Vitale

Type: Two-Year College **Sex:** Coed **Affiliation:** Maricopa County Community College District System. **Admission Plans:** Early Admission; Open Admission **Application Deadline:** Rolling **Application Fee:** $0.00 **H.S. Requirements:** High school diploma or equivalent not required **Costs Per Year:** Application fee: $0. Area resident tuition: $1260 full-time. State resident tuition: $2520 full-time, $84 per credit part-time. Nonresident tuition: $9750 full-time, $325 per credit part-time. Mandatory fees: $30 full-time, $15 per term part-time. Full-time tuition and fees vary according to program and reciprocity agreements. Part-time tuition and fees vary according to program and reciprocity agreements. **Scholarships:** Available. **Calendar System:** Semester, Summer session available **Enrollment:** Full-time 2,745, Part-time 7,338 **Faculty:** Full-time 172, Part-time 398 **Student-Faculty Ratio:** 17:1 **Final Year or Final Semester Residency Requirement:** No **Regional Accreditation:** North Central Association of Colleges and Schools **Credit Hours For Degree:** 64 credit hours, Associates **Professional Accreditation:** ACEN, ACF. **Intercollegiate Athletics:** Baseball M; Basketball M & W; Cross-Country Running M & W; Football M; Golf M & W; Soccer M & W; Softball W; Volleyball W

SESSIONS COLLEGE FOR PROFESSIONAL DESIGN

350 S Mill Ave., Ste. B-104
Tempe, AZ 85281
Tel: (480)212-1704; Free: 800-258-4115
Fax: (480)212-1705
E-mail: admissions@sessions.edu
Web Site: www.sessions.edu
President/CEO: Gordon Drummond
Admissions: Mhelanie Hernandez

Type: Two-Year College **Sex:** Coed **Admission Plans:** Early Admission **Application Deadline:** July 15 **Application Fee:** $50.00 **H.S. Requirements:** High school diploma required; GED accepted **Professional Accreditation:** DEAC.

SOUTH MOUNTAIN COMMUNITY COLLEGE

7050 S Twenty-fourth St.
Phoenix, AZ 85040

Tel: (602)243-8000
Fax: (602)243-8329
Web Site: www.southmountaincc.edu
President/CEO: Dr. Kenneth Atwater
Type: Two-Year College **Sex:** Coed **Affiliation:** Maricopa County Community College District System. **Admission Plans:** Open Admission **Application Deadline:** August 22 **Scholarships:** Available. **Calendar System:** Semester, Summer session available **Student-Faculty Ratio:** 20:1 **Regional Accreditation:** North Central Association of Colleges and Schools **Credit Hours For Degree:** 62 credit hours, Associates **ROTC:** Air Force **Intercollegiate Athletics:** Baseball M; Basketball M & W; Golf M & W; Soccer M; Softball W; Volleyball W

SOUTHWEST INSTITUTE OF HEALING ARTS
1100 E Apache Blvd.
Tempe, AZ 85281
Tel: (480)994-9244; Free: 888-504-9106
Fax: (480)994-3228
E-mail: joannl@swiha.net
Web Site: www.swiha.org
President/CEO: K. C. Miller
Admissions: Katie Yearous
Type: Two-Year College **Sex:** Coed **Application Fee:** $75.00 **Calendar System:** Quarter **Professional Accreditation:** ACCSC.

SOUTHWEST UNIVERSITY OF VISUAL ARTS
2525 N Country Club Rd.
Tucson, AZ 85716-2505
Tel: (520)325-0123; Free: 800-825-8753
Fax: (520)325-5535
Web Site: www.suva.edu
President/CEO: Pres. Sharmon Woods
Admissions: Robert Mairs
Type: Comprehensive **Sex:** Coed **Costs Per Year:** Tuition: $22,944 full-time, $5736 per term part-time. Mandatory fees: $125 full-time. Full-time tuition and fees vary according to course load and location. Part-time tuition varies according to course load and location. **Scholarships:** Available. **Calendar System:** Miscellaneous, Summer session available **Enrollment:** Full-time 133, Graduate full-time 11, Part-time 44 **Faculty:** Full-time 11, Part-time 17 **Exams:** Other. **Final Year or Final Semester Residency Requirement:** No **Regional Accreditation:** North Central Association of Colleges and Schools **Credit Hours For Degree:** 150 credits, Bachelors **ROTC:** Army **Professional Accreditation:** ACCSC, CIDA.

TOHONO O'ODHAM COMMUNITY COLLEGE
PO Box 3129
Sells, AZ 85634
Tel: (520)383-8401
Fax: (520)383-8403
E-mail: jhill@tocc.edu
Web Site: www.tocc.edu
President/CEO: Pres. Paul Robertson
Admissions: Jennifer Hill
Type: Two-Year College **Sex:** Coed **Costs Per Year:** State resident tuition: $2070 full-time, $69 per credit hour part-time. Nonresident tuition: $3696 full-time, $69 per credit hour part-time. Mandatory fees: $20 full-time, $10 per course part-time. Full-time tuition and fees vary according to class time, course level, course load, degree level, location, program, and student level. Part-time tuition and fees vary according to class time, course level, course load, degree level, location, program, and student level. College room and board: $2400. **Calendar System:** Semester, Summer session available **Enrollment:** Full-time 89, Part-time 117 **Faculty:** Full-time 17, Part-time 31 **Student-Faculty Ratio:** 10:1 **Exams:** ACT essay component not used; SAT essay component not used. **% Residing in College-Owned, -Operated, or -Affiliated Housing:** 10 **Regional Accreditation:** North Central Association of Colleges and Schools **Credit Hours For Degree:** 60 credits, Associates **Intercollegiate Athletics:** Basketball M & W

TRINE UNIVERSITY
14100 N 83rd. Ave.
Ste. 100
Peoria, AZ 85381
Tel: (855)997-7701
Web Site: www.trine.edu/peoria

Type: Comprehensive **Sex:** Coed **Regional Accreditation:** North Central Association of Colleges and Schools

UNIVERSAL TECHNICAL INSTITUTE
10695 W Pierce St.
Avondale, AZ 85323
Tel: (602)264-4164; Free: 800-510-5072
Fax: (602)264-6412
Web Site: www.uti.edu
President/CEO: Mike Romano
Type: Two-Year College **Sex:** Coed **Admission Plans:** Open Admission **H.S. Requirements:** High school diploma required; GED accepted **Scholarships:** Available. **Student-Faculty Ratio:** 23:1 **Professional Accreditation:** ACCSC.

UNIVERSITY OF ADVANCING TECHNOLOGY
2625 W Baseline Rd.
Tempe, AZ 85283-1042
Tel: (602)383-8228; Free: 800-658-5744
Fax: (602)383-8222
E-mail: admissions@uat.edu
Web Site: www.uat.edu
President/CEO: Jason Pistillo
Type: Comprehensive **Sex:** Coed **Application Deadline:** Rolling **Application Fee:** $0.00 **H.S. Requirements:** High school diploma required; GED accepted **Costs Per Year:** Application fee: $0. Tuition: $23,150 full-time. **Scholarships:** Available. **Calendar System:** Semester, Summer session available **Enrollment:** Full-time 1,013, Graduate full-time 55, Graduate part-time 5 **Faculty:** Full-time 31, Part-time 29 **Student-Faculty Ratio:** 14:1 **Exams:** SAT I or ACT. **% Receiving Financial Aid:** 56 **% Residing in College-Owned, -Operated, or -Affiliated Housing:** 22 **Regional Accreditation:** North Central Association of Colleges and Schools **Credit Hours For Degree:** 60 credits, Associates; 120 credits, Bachelors **Professional Accreditation:** ACICS.

THE UNIVERSITY OF ARIZONA
Tucson, AZ 85721
Tel: (520)621-2211
Fax: (520)621-9799
E-mail: admissions@arizona.edu
Web Site: www.arizona.edu
President/CEO: Dr. Ann Weaver Hart
Admissions: Kasey Urquidez
Financial Aid: Elizabeth Acree
Type: University **Sex:** Coed **Affiliation:** Arizona Board of Regents. **Scores:** 95% SAT V 400+; 96% SAT M 400+; 37.85% ACT 18-23; 42.93% ACT 24-29 **% Accepted:** 76 **Admission Plans:** Early Admission; Preferred Admission **Application Deadline:** May 1 **Application Fee:** $50.00 **H.S. Requirements:** High school diploma required; GED accepted **Costs Per Year:** Application fee: $50. State resident tuition: $9864 full-time, $705 per credit hour part-time. Nonresident tuition: $29,017 full-time, $1209 per credit hour part-time. Mandatory fees: $1013 full-time, $88 per credit hour part-time. Full-time tuition and fees vary according to class time, course level, course load, degree level, location, program, reciprocity agreements, and student level. Part-time tuition and fees vary according to class time, course level, course load, degree level, location, program, reciprocity agreements, and student level. College room and board: $9840. College room only: $7140. Room and board charges vary according to board plan and housing facility. Tuition guaranteed not to increase for student's term of enrollment. **Scholarships:** Available. **Calendar System:** Semester, Summer session available **Enrollment:** Full-time 29,804, Graduate full-time 7,036, Graduate part-time 2,320, Part-time 3,928 **Faculty:** Full-time 1,614, Part-time 289 **Exams:** SAT I or ACT; SAT Reasoning; SAT Subject. **% Receiving Financial Aid:** 52 **% Residing in College-Owned, -Operated, or -Affiliated Housing:** 20 **Regional Accreditation:** North Central Association of Colleges and Schools **Credit Hours For Degree:** 120 semester hours, Bachelors **ROTC:** Air Force, Army, Navy **Professional Accreditation:** AACN, AACSB, AAFCS, AALS, ABA, ABET, ACA, ACEJMC, ACPE, ACSP, ALA, AND, APA, ASHA, ASLA, CEPH, CORE, LCME/AMA, NAAB, NAACLS, NASAD, NASD, NASM, NASPAA, NAST. **Intercollegiate Athletics:** Badminton M & W; Baseball M; Basketball M & W; Cheerleading M & W; Cross-Country Running M & W; Football M; Golf M & W; Gymnastics W; Ice Hockey M; Lacrosse M & W; Racquetball M & W; Rugby M & W; Soccer M & W; Softball

W; Swimming and Diving M & W; Tennis M & W; Track and Field M & W; Ultimate Frisbee M & W; Volleyball M & W; Water Polo M & W

UNIVERSITY OF PHOENIX–ONLINE CAMPUS

3157 E Elwood St.
Phoenix, AZ 85034-7209
Tel: (602)387-7000; Free: 866-766-0766
Web Site: www.phoenix.edu
President/CEO: Timothy P. Slottow
Admissions: Marc Booker

Type: Comprehensive **Sex:** Coed **Admission Plans:** Deferred Admission; Open Admission **Application Deadline:** Rolling **Application Fee:** $0.00 **H.S. Requirements:** High school diploma required; GED accepted **Scholarships:** Available. **Calendar System:** Continuous, Summer session not available **Enrollment:** Full-time 236,109 **Faculty:** Full-time 158, Part-time 11,319 **Regional Accreditation:** North Central Association of Colleges and Schools **Credit Hours For Degree:** 60 credits, Associates; 120 credits, Bachelors **Professional Accreditation:** AACN, ACBSP.

UNIVERSITY OF PHOENIX–PHOENIX CAMPUS

1625 W Fountainhead Pky.
Tempe, AZ 85282-2371
Tel: (602)557-2000; Free: 866-766-0766
Web Site: www.phoenix.edu
President/CEO: Timothy P. Slottow
Admissions: Marc Booker

Type: Comprehensive **Sex:** Coed **Admission Plans:** Deferred Admission; Open Admission **Application Deadline:** Rolling **Application Fee:** $0.00 **H.S. Requirements:** High school diploma required; GED accepted **Scholarships:** Available. **Calendar System:** Continuous, Summer session not available **Enrollment:** Full-time 3,718 **Faculty:** Full-time 76, Part-time 909 **Regional Accreditation:** North Central Association of Colleges and Schools **Credit Hours For Degree:** 60 credits, Associates; 120 credits, Bachelors **Professional Accreditation:** AACN, ACA, ACBSP, ACEN.

UNIVERSITY OF PHOENIX–SOUTHERN ARIZONA CAMPUS

300 S Craycroft Rd.
Tucson, AZ 85711
Tel: (520)881-6512; Free: 866-766-0766
Fax: (520)795-6177
Web Site: www.phoenix.edu
President/CEO: Timothy P. Slottow
Admissions: Marc Booker

Type: Comprehensive **Sex:** Coed **Admission Plans:** Deferred Admission; Open Admission **Application Deadline:** Rolling **Application Fee:** $0.00

H.S. Requirements: High school diploma required; GED accepted **Scholarships:** Available. **Calendar System:** Continuous, Summer session not available **Enrollment:** Full-time 1,631 **Faculty:** Full-time 14, Part-time 270 **Regional Accreditation:** North Central Association of Colleges and Schools **Credit Hours For Degree:** 60 credits, Associates; 120 credits, Bachelors **Professional Accreditation:** ACA, ACBSP.

WESTERN INTERNATIONAL UNIVERSITY

9215 N Black Canyon Hwy.
Phoenix, AZ 85021-2718
Tel: (602)943-2311
E-mail: melissa.machuca@west.edu
Web Site: www.west.edu
President/CEO: Tracy Lorenz, CPA
Admissions: Melissa Machuca
Financial Aid: Ella Owen

Type: Comprehensive **Sex:** Coed **Affiliation:** Apollo Global and Apollo Group. **Admission Plans:** Deferred Admission **Application Deadline:** Rolling **Application Fee:** $25.00 **H.S. Requirements:** High school diploma required; GED accepted **Calendar System:** Continuous, Summer session available **Enrollment:** Full-time 2,322, Graduate full-time 671 **Faculty:** Full-time 2 **Student-Faculty Ratio:** 24:1 **% Receiving Financial Aid:** 80 **Regional Accreditation:** North Central Association of Colleges and Schools **Credit Hours For Degree:** 60 credit hours, Associates; 126 credit hours, Bachelors

YAVAPAI COLLEGE

1100 E Sheldon St.
Prescott, AZ 86301-3297
Tel: (928)445-7300; Free: 800-922-6787
Fax: (928)776-2151
E-mail: registration@yc.edu
Web Site: www.yc.edu
President/CEO: Dr. James Horton
Admissions: Sheila Jarrell

Type: Two-Year College **Sex:** Coed **Affiliation:** Arizona State Community College System. **Admission Plans:** Deferred Admission; Early Admission; Open Admission **Application Deadline:** Rolling **H.S. Requirements:** High school diploma required; GED accepted **Scholarships:** Available. **Calendar System:** Semester, Summer session available **Enrollment:** Full-time 1,917, Part-time 6,359 **Faculty:** Full-time 112, Part-time 292 **Student-Faculty Ratio:** 15:1 **% Residing in College-Owned, -Operated, or -Affiliated Housing:** 5 **Regional Accreditation:** North Central Association of Colleges and Schools **Credit Hours For Degree:** 64 credits, Associates **ROTC:** Air Force, Army **Professional Accreditation:** ACEN. **Intercollegiate Athletics:** Baseball M; Soccer M; Softball W; Volleyball W

ARKANSAS BAPTIST COLLEGE

1621 Dr. Martin Luther King, Jr. Dr.
Little Rock, AR 72202-6067
Tel: (501)374-7856
Web Site: www.arkansasbaptist.edu
President/CEO: Fitzgerald Hill
Type: Four-Year College **Sex:** Coed **Affiliation:** Baptist. **Admission Plans:** Deferred Admission; Open Admission **Application Deadline:** Rolling **Application Fee:** $25.00 **H.S. Requirements:** High school diploma required; GED accepted **Scholarships:** Available. **Calendar System:** Semester, Summer session available **Enrollment:** Full-time 495, Part-time 131 **Faculty:** Full-time 18, Part-time 20 **Student-Faculty Ratio:** 22:1 **Exams:** ACT; Other. **% Residing in College-Owned, -Operated, or -Affiliated Housing:** 13 **Regional Accreditation:** North Central Association of Colleges and Schools **Credit Hours For Degree:** 124 semester hours, Bachelors **Intercollegiate Athletics:** Baseball M; Basketball M & W; Cheerleading W; Football M

ARKANSAS NORTHEASTERN COLLEGE

PO Box 1109
Blytheville, AR 72316-1109
Tel: (870)762-1020
Fax: (870)763-3704
Web Site: www.anc.edu
President/CEO: Dr. James Shemwell
Type: Two-Year College **Sex:** Coed **% Accepted:** 100 **Admission Plans:** Deferred Admission; Open Admission **Application Deadline:** Rolling **Application Fee:** $0.00 **H.S. Requirements:** High school diploma required; GED accepted **Costs Per Year:** Application fee: $0. Area resident tuition: $1820 full-time, $65 per credit hour part-time. State resident tuition: $2100 full-time, $75 per credit hour part-time. Nonresident tuition: $3500 full-time, $125 per credit hour part-time. Mandatory fees: $330 full-time, $10 per credit hour part-time, $25 per term part-time. Full-time tuition and fees vary according to course load. Part-time tuition and fees vary according to course load. **Scholarships:** Available. **Calendar System:** Semester, Summer session available **Enrollment:** Full-time 538, Part-time 887 **Regional Accreditation:** North Central Association of Colleges and Schools **Credit Hours For Degree:** 62 semester hours, Associates **Professional Accreditation:** ACEN.

ARKANSAS STATE UNIVERSITY

PO Box 600
State University, AR 72467
Tel: (870)972-2100; Free: 800-382-3030
Fax: (870)972-2090
E-mail: admissions@astate.edu
Web Site: www.astate.edu
President/CEO: Dr. Tim Hudson
Admissions: Tracy Finch
Financial Aid: Terry Finney
Type: Comprehensive **Sex:** Coed **Affiliation:** Arkansas State University System. **Scores:** 88% SAT V 400+; 92% SAT M 400+; 48.2% ACT 18-23; 43.7% ACT 24-29 **% Accepted:** 70 **Admission Plans:** Early Admission **Application Deadline:** Rolling **Application Fee:** $15.00 **H.S. Requirements:** High school diploma required; GED accepted **Costs Per Year:** Application

fee: $15. State resident tuition: $6000 full-time, $200 per credit hour part-time. Nonresident tuition: $12,000 full-time, $400 per credit hour part-time. Mandatory fees: $2050 full-time, $66 per credit hour part-time, $35 per term part-time. Full-time tuition and fees vary according to course load, location, and program. Part-time tuition and fees vary according to course load, location, and program. College room and board: $8140. Room and board charges vary according to board plan, housing facility, and student level. **Scholarships:** Available. **Calendar System:** Semester, Summer session available **Enrollment:** Full-time 7,295, Graduate full-time 736, Graduate part-time 3,082, Part-time 2,297 **Faculty:** Full-time 505, Part-time 206 **Student-Faculty Ratio:** 17:1 **Exams:** ACT; ACT essay component not used; Other; SAT I or ACT; SAT essay component not used; SAT Reasoning; SAT Subject. **% Receiving Financial Aid:** 85 **% Residing in College-Owned, -Operated, or -Affiliated Housing:** 30 **Final Year or Final Semester Residency Requirement:** Yes **Regional Accreditation:** North Central Association of Colleges and Schools **Credit Hours For Degree:** 62 credit hours, Associates; 120-136 credit hours (depending upon the degree program), Bachelors **ROTC:** Army **Professional Accreditation:** AACSB, AANA, ABET, ACA, ACEJMC, ACEN, APTA, ASHA, CORE, CSWE, JRCAT, JRCERT, NAACLS, NASAD, NASM, NASPAA, NCATE. **Intercollegiate Athletics:** Baseball M; Basketball M & W; Bowling W; Cross-Country Running M & W; Football M; Golf M & W; Soccer W; Tennis W; Track and Field M & W; Volleyball W

ARKANSAS STATE UNIVERSITY MID-SOUTH

2000 W Broadway
West Memphis, AR 72301
Tel: (870)733-6722; Free: 866-733-6722
Fax: (870)733-6719
E-mail: jreece@midsouthcc.edu
Web Site: www.asumidsouth.edu
President/CEO: Dr. Glen F. Fenter
Admissions: Jeremy Reece
Type: Two-Year College **Sex:** Coed **% Accepted:** 100 **Admission Plans:** Early Admission; Open Admission **Application Deadline:** Rolling **Application Fee:** $0.00 **H.S. Requirements:** High school diploma required; GED accepted **Scholarships:** Available. **Calendar System:** Semester, Summer session available **Enrollment:** Full-time 703, Part-time 1,090 **Faculty:** Full-time 35, Part-time 69 **Student-Faculty Ratio:** 14:1 **Exams:** ACT essay component not used; Other; SAT essay component not used. **Regional Accreditation:** North Central Association of Colleges and Schools **Credit Hours For Degree:** 60-63 credit hours, Associates

ARKANSAS STATE UNIVERSITY–BEEBE

PO Box 1000
Beebe, AR 72012-1000
Tel: (501)882-3600; Free: 800-632-9985
Fax: (501)882-8370
E-mail: rdhudson@asub.edu
Web Site: www.asub.edu
President/CEO: Dr. Eugene McKay
Admissions: Ronald Hudson
Financial Aid: Linda Yelder
Type: Two-Year College **Sex:** Coed **Affiliation:** Arkansas State University System. **% Accepted:** 54 **Admission Plans:** Deferred Admission; Open

Admission **Application Deadline:** Rolling **Application Fee:** $0.00 **H.S. Requirements:** High school diploma required; GED accepted **Scholarships:** Available. **Calendar System:** Semester, Summer session available **Enrollment:** Full-time 2,601, Part-time 1,890 **Faculty:** Full-time 63, Part-time 34 **Student-Faculty Ratio:** 30:1 **% Residing in College-Owned, -Operated, or -Affiliated Housing:** 12 **Regional Accreditation:** North Central Association of Colleges and Schools **Credit Hours For Degree:** 62 credit hours, Associates **ROTC:** Army **Professional Accreditation:** ABET, NAACLS.

ARKANSAS STATE UNIVERSITY–MOUNTAIN HOME

1600 S College St.
Mountain Home, AR 72653
Tel: (870)508-6100
E-mail: dparrish@asumh.edu
Web Site: www.asumh.edu
President/CEO: Dr. William Edward Coulter
Admissions: Delba Parrish
Financial Aid: Clay S. Berry

Type: Two-Year College **Sex:** Coed **Affiliation:** Arkansas State University System. **Admission Plans:** Open Admission **Application Fee:** $0.00 **H.S. Requirements:** High school diploma required; GED accepted **Scholarships:** Available. **Calendar System:** Semester, Summer session available **Exams:** ACT essay component not used; Other; SAT I or ACT. **Final Year or Final Semester Residency Requirement:** No **Regional Accreditation:** North Central Association of Colleges and Schools **Credit Hours For Degree:** 60 credits, Associates **ROTC:** Army **Professional Accreditation:** ABFSE.

ARKANSAS STATE UNIVERSITY–NEWPORT

7648 Victory Blvd.
Newport, AR 72112
Tel: (870)512-7800; Free: 800-976-1676
E-mail: candace_gross@asun.edu
Web Site: www.asun.edu
President/CEO: Dr. Sandra Massey
Admissions: Candace L. Gross
Financial Aid: Deana Tims

Type: Two-Year College **Sex:** Coed **Affiliation:** Arkansas State University System. **Admission Plans:** Open Admission **Application Deadline:** Rolling **Application Fee:** $0.00 **H.S. Requirements:** High school diploma required; GED accepted **Scholarships:** Available. **Calendar System:** Semester, Summer session available **Enrollment:** Full-time 963, Part-time 1,094 **Faculty:** Full-time 62, Part-time 82 **Student-Faculty Ratio:** 14:1 **Exams:** Other. **Final Year or Final Semester Residency Requirement:** No **Regional Accreditation:** North Central Association of Colleges and Schools **Credit Hours For Degree:** 62 credits, Associates

ARKANSAS TECH UNIVERSITY

Russellville, AR 72801
Tel: (479)968-0389; Free: 800-582-6953
Fax: (479)964-0522
E-mail: tech.enroll@atu.edu
Web Site: www.atu.edu
President/CEO: Dr. Robin E. Bowen
Admissions: Shauna Donnell

Type: Comprehensive **Sex:** Coed **Scores:** 100% SAT V 400+; 94% SAT M 400+; 43.33% ACT 18-23; 34.25% ACT 24-29 **% Accepted:** 89 **Admission Plans:** Deferred Admission; Early Decision Plan **Application Fee:** $0.00 **H.S. Requirements:** High school diploma required; GED accepted **Costs Per Year:** Application fee: $0. State resident tuition: $6450 full-time, $215 per credit hour part-time. Nonresident tuition: $12,900 full-time, $430 per credit hour part-time. Mandatory fees: $1290 full-time, $43 per credit hour part-time. Full-time tuition and fees vary according to course load and location. Part-time tuition and fees vary according to course load and location. College room and board: $6918. College room only: $4290. Room and board charges vary according to board plan, housing facility, and location. **Scholarships:** Available. **Calendar System:** Semester, Summer session available **Enrollment:** Full-time 7,065, Graduate full-time 225, Graduate part-time 638, Part-time 4,126 **Faculty:** Full-time 349, Part-time 230 **Student-Faculty Ratio:** 19:1 **Exams:** ACT essay component used for advising; SAT I or ACT; SAT essay component used for advising; SAT Reasoning; SAT Subject. **% Receiving Financial Aid:** 67 **% Residing in College-Owned, -Operated, or -Affiliated Housing:** 32 **Final Year or Final**

Semester Residency Requirement: Yes **Regional Accreditation:** North Central Association of Colleges and Schools **Credit Hours For Degree:** 60 semester hours, Associates; 120 semester hours, Bachelors **ROTC:** Army **Professional Accreditation:** AACSB, AAMAE, ABET, ACEN, AHIMA, NASM, NCATE, NRPA. **Intercollegiate Athletics:** Baseball M; Basketball M & W; Cheerleading M & W; Cross-Country Running W; Football M; Golf M & W; Softball W; Tennis W; Volleyball W

BAPTIST HEALTH COLLEGE LITTLE ROCK

11900 Colonel Glenn Rd.
Ste. 100
Little Rock, AR 72210-2820
Tel: (501)202-7415
Fax: (501)202-7406
Web Site: www.bhclr.edu
Type: Two-Year College **Sex:** Coed **Affiliation:** Baptist Church.

BLACK RIVER TECHNICAL COLLEGE

1410 Hwy. 304 E
Pocahontas, AR 72455
Tel: (870)248-4000
Fax: (870)248-4100
Web Site: www.blackrivertech.edu
President/CEO: Eric Turner

Type: Two-Year College **Sex:** Coed **Admission Plans:** Open Admission **Application Deadline:** Rolling **H.S. Requirements:** High school diploma required; GED accepted **Scholarships:** Available. **Calendar System:** Semester, Summer session available **Exams:** Other. **Regional Accreditation:** North Central Association of Colleges and Schools **Credit Hours For Degree:** 62 credit hours, Associates **Professional Accreditation:** CoARC.

BRYAN UNIVERSITY

3704 W Walnut St.
Rogers, AR 72756
Tel: (479)899-6644
Web Site: www.bryanu.edu
Type: Two-Year College **Sex:** Coed **Professional Accreditation:** ACICS.

CENTRAL BAPTIST COLLEGE

1501 College Ave.
Conway, AR 72032
Tel: (501)329-6872; Free: 800-205-6872
E-mail: jpoole@cbc.edu
Web Site: www.cbc.edu
President/CEO: Terry Kimbrow
Admissions: Jason Poole
Financial Aid: Christi Bell

Type: Four-Year College **Sex:** Coed **Affiliation:** Baptist. **% Accepted:** 47 **Admission Plans:** Early Admission **Application Deadline:** August 15 **Application Fee:** $0.00 **H.S. Requirements:** High school diploma required; GED accepted **Costs Per Year:** Application fee: $0. Comprehensive fee: $21,900 includes full-time tuition ($12,900), mandatory fees ($1500), and college room and board ($7500). Part-time tuition: $430 per credit hour. Part-time mandatory fees: $1500 per year. **Scholarships:** Available. **Calendar System:** Semester, Summer session available **Enrollment:** Full-time 635, Part-time 246 **Faculty:** Full-time 30, Part-time 54 **Student-Faculty Ratio:** 11:1 **Exams:** SAT I or ACT. **Regional Accreditation:** North Central Association of Colleges and Schools **Credit Hours For Degree:** 64 credit hours, Associates; 127 credit hours, Bachelors **ROTC:** Army **Intercollegiate Athletics:** Baseball M; Basketball M & W; Golf M & W; Soccer M & W; Softball W; Volleyball W; Wrestling M

COLLEGE OF THE OUACHITAS

One College Cir.
Malvern, AR 72104
Tel: (501)337-5000
Fax: (501)337-9382
E-mail: snelson@coto.edu
Web Site: www.coto.edu
President/CEO: Dr. Stephen Schoonmaker
Admissions: Shanea Nelson

Type: Two-Year College **Sex:** Coed **Scores:** 53% ACT 18-23; 9% ACT 24-29 **Admission Plans:** Deferred Admission; Early Admission; Open Admission **Application Deadline:** Rolling **H.S. Requirements:** High school diploma required; GED accepted **Costs Per Year:** State resident tuition: $2790 full-time, $93 per credit hour part-time. Nonresident tuition: $5580 full-time, $186 per credit hour part-time. Mandatory fees: $1180 full-time, $24 per credit hour part-time, $28 per term part-time. Full-time tuition and fees vary according to program. Part-time tuition and fees vary according to program. Tuition guaranteed not to increase for student's term of enrollment. **Scholarships:** Available. **Calendar System:** Semester, Summer session available **Enrollment:** Full-time 584, Part-time 917 **Faculty:** Full-time 39, Part-time 59 **Exams:** Other; SAT I or ACT. **Regional Accreditation:** North Central Association of Colleges and Schools **Credit Hours For Degree:** 60 credit hours, Associates

COSSATOT COMMUNITY COLLEGE OF THE UNIVERSITY OF ARKANSAS
183 College Dr.
De Queen, AR 71832
Tel: (870)584-4471; Free: 800-844-4471
E-mail: tcobb@cccua.edu
Web Site: www.cccua.edu
President/CEO: Steve L. Cole, EdD
Admissions: Tommi Cobb
Financial Aid: Denise Hammond
Type: Two-Year College **Sex:** Coed **Affiliation:** University of Arkansas System. **Admission Plans:** Open Admission **Application Fee:** $0.00 **H.S. Requirements:** High school diploma required; GED accepted **Scholarships:** Available. **Calendar System:** Semester, Summer session available **Faculty:** Full-time 36, Part-time 48 **Student-Faculty Ratio:** 15:1 **Final Year or Final Semester Residency Requirement:** No **Regional Accreditation:** North Central Association of Colleges and Schools **Credit Hours For Degree:** 60 credit hours, Associates **Professional Accreditation:** ACBSP. **Intercollegiate Athletics:** Soccer M & W

CROWLEY'S RIDGE COLLEGE
100 College Dr.
Paragould, AR 72450-9731
Tel: (870)236-6901; Free: 800-264-1096
Fax: (870)236-7748
E-mail: njoneshi@crc.pioneer.paragould.ar.us
Web Site: www.crc.edu
President/CEO: Ken Hoppe
Admissions: Amanda Drake
Type: Two-Year College **Sex:** Coed **Affiliation:** Church of Christ. **Admission Plans:** Open Admission **Application Deadline:** Rolling **Application Fee:** $0.00 **H.S. Requirements:** High school diploma required; GED accepted **Scholarships:** Available. **Calendar System:** Semester, Summer session available **Regional Accreditation:** North Central Association of Colleges and Schools **Credit Hours For Degree:** 64 credit hours, Associates

EAST ARKANSAS COMMUNITY COLLEGE
1700 Newcastle Rd.
Forrest City, AR 72335-2204
Tel: (870)633-4480; Free: 877-797-3222
Fax: (870)633-7222
E-mail: dadams@eacc.edu
Web Site: www.eacc.edu
President/CEO: Dr. Coy Grace
Admissions: Sharon Collier
Type: Two-Year College **Sex:** Coed **Admission Plans:** Deferred Admission; Early Admission; Open Admission **Application Deadline:** Rolling **Application Fee:** $0.00 **H.S. Requirements:** High school diploma required; GED accepted. For applicants 18 or over who demonstrate ability to benefit from college: High school diploma or equivalent not required **Costs Per Year:** Application fee: $0. One-time mandatory fee: $50. Area resident tuition: $2460 full-time, $82 per credit hour part-time. State resident tuition: $2760 full-time, $92 per credit hour part-time. Nonresident tuition: $3270 full-time, $109 per credit hour part-time. Mandatory fees: $330 full-time, $11 per credit hour part-time. Full-time tuition and fees vary according to course load, location, and program. Part-time tuition and fees vary according to course load, location, and program. **Scholarships:** Available. **Calendar System:** Semester, Summer session available **Enrollment:** Full-time 779, Part-time 768 **Faculty:** Full-time 39, Part-time 56 **Student-Faculty Ratio:** 18:1 **Regional Accreditation:** North Central Association of Colleges and Schools **Credit Hours For Degree:** 64 credits, Associates **Professional Accreditation:** ACEN.

ECCLESIA COLLEGE
9653 Nations Dr.
Springdale, AR 72762
Tel: (479)248-7236
E-mail: myfuture@ecollege.edu
Web Site: www.ecollege.edu
President/CEO: Oren N. Paris, III
Admissions: Titus Hofer
Type: Four-Year College **Sex:** Coed **Affiliation:** Christian. **Application Fee:** $35.00 **H.S. Requirements:** High school diploma required; GED accepted **Calendar System:** Semester, Summer session not available **Student-Faculty Ratio:** 10:1 **Exams:** Other; SAT I or ACT. **Final Year or Final Semester Residency Requirement:** No **Credit Hours For Degree:** 64 credits, Associates; 128 credits, Bachelors **Professional Accreditation:** ABHE. **Intercollegiate Athletics:** Baseball M; Basketball M & W

HARDING UNIVERSITY
915 E Market Ave.
Searcy, AR 72149-0001
Tel: (501)279-4000; Free: 800-477-4407
Fax: (501)279-4865
E-mail: admissions@harding.edu
Web Site: www.harding.edu
President/CEO: Dr. Bruce D. McLarty
Admissions: Glenn Dillard
Financial Aid: Dr. Jonathan C. Roberts
Type: University **Sex:** Coed **Affiliation:** Church of Christ. **Scores:** 98% SAT V 400+; 97% SAT M 400+; 36% ACT 18-23; 44% ACT 24-29 **% Accepted:** 76 **Admission Plans:** Deferred Admission; Early Admission; Early Decision Plan **Application Deadline:** Rolling **Application Fee:** $50.00 **H.S. Requirements:** High school diploma required; GED accepted **Costs Per Year:** Application fee: $50. Comprehensive fee: $24,433 includes full-time tuition ($17,130), mandatory fees ($675), and college room and board ($6628). College room only: $3398. Full-time tuition and fees vary according to course load. Room and board charges vary according to board plan and housing facility. Part-time tuition: $571 per credit hour. Part-time mandatory fees: $25 per credit hour. Part-time tuition and fees vary according to course load. **Scholarships:** Available. **Calendar System:** Semester, Summer session available **Enrollment:** Full-time 4,105, Graduate full-time 667, Graduate part-time 892, Part-time 345 **Faculty:** Full-time 332, Part-time 157 **Student-Faculty Ratio:** 15:1 **Exams:** ACT essay component not used; SAT I or ACT; SAT essay component not used; SAT Reasoning. **% Receiving Financial Aid:** 61 **% Residing in College-Owned, -Operated, or -Affiliated Housing:** 74 **Final Year or Final Semester Residency Requirement:** No **Regional Accreditation:** North Central Association of Colleges and Schools **Credit Hours For Degree:** 128 semester hours, Bachelors **Professional Accreditation:** AAFCS, AAMFT, ABET, ACBSP, ACEN, ACPE, APTA, CSWE, NASM, NCATE. **Intercollegiate Athletics:** Baseball M; Basketball M & W; Cheerleading W; Cross-Country Running M & W; Football M; Golf M & W; Lacrosse M; Rugby M; Soccer M & W; Tennis M & W; Track and Field M & W; Ultimate Frisbee M & W; Volleyball W

HENDERSON STATE UNIVERSITY
1100 Henderson St.
Arkadelphia, AR 71999-0001
Tel: (870)230-5000; Free: 800-228-7333
Fax: (870)230-5144
E-mail: hardwrv@hsu.edu
Web Site: www.hsu.edu
President/CEO: Dr. Glen Jones
Admissions: Vikita Hardwrick
Financial Aid: Vicki Taylor
Type: Comprehensive **Sex:** Coed **Scores:** 96% SAT V 400+; 96% SAT M 400+; 45% ACT 18-23; 31% ACT 24-29 **% Accepted:** 64 **Admission Plans:** Deferred Admission **Application Deadline:** July 15 **Application Fee:** $0.00 **H.S. Requirements:** High school diploma required; GED accepted **Costs Per Year:** Application fee: $0. State resident tuition: $6210 full-time, $207 per credit hour part-time. Nonresident tuition: $12,810 full-time, $427 per credit hour part-time. Mandatory fees: $1598 full-time. Full-time tuition and fees vary according to course load. Part-time tuition varies according to course load. College room and board: $6862. Room and board charges vary according to board plan and housing facility. **Scholarships:** Available. **Calendar System:** Semester, Summer session available **Enrollment:** Full-time 2,747, Graduate full-time 75, Graduate part-time 353, Part-time 352

Faculty: Full-time 178, Part-time 66 **Student-Faculty Ratio:** 14:1 **Exams:** ACT; ACT essay component not used; SAT I or ACT; SAT essay component not used. **% Receiving Financial Aid:** 82 **% Residing in College-Owned, -Operated, or -Affiliated Housing:** 43 **Final Year or Final Semester Residency Requirement:** No **Regional Accreditation:** North Central Association of Colleges and Schools **Credit Hours For Degree:** 60 semester hours, Associates; 124 semester hours, Bachelors **ROTC:** Army **Professional Accreditation:** AACN, AACSB, AAFCS, ACA, NASM, NCATE. **Intercollegiate Athletics:** Baseball M; Basketball M & W; Cross-Country Running W; Football M; Golf M & W; Softball W; Swimming and Diving M & W; Tennis W; Volleyball W

HENDRIX COLLEGE
1600 Washington Ave.
Conway, AR 72032-3080
Tel: (501)329-6811; Free: 800-277-9017
Fax: (501)450-3843
E-mail: baker@hendrix.edu
Web Site: www.hendrix.edu
President/CEO: Dr. William M. Tsutsui
Admissions: Fred Baker
Financial Aid: Kristina Burford
Type: Comprehensive **Sex:** Coed **Affiliation:** United Methodist. **Scores:** 99% SAT V 400+; 99% SAT M 400+; 13.5% ACT 18-23; 46.3% ACT 24-29 **% Accepted:** 82 **Admission Plans:** Early Decision Plan **Application Deadline:** June 1 **Application Fee:** $40.00 **H.S. Requirements:** High school diploma required; GED accepted **Costs Per Year:** Application fee: $40. Comprehensive fee: $54,020 includes full-time tuition ($42,090), mandatory fees ($350), and college room and board ($11,580). College room only: $5962. Full-time tuition and fees vary according to course load and student level. Room and board charges vary according to board plan and housing facility. Part-time tuition: $5261 per course. Part-time tuition varies according to course load and student level. **Scholarships:** Available. **Calendar System:** Semester, Summer session not available **Enrollment:** Full-time 1,318, Graduate full-time 11, Part-time 9 **Faculty:** Full-time 107, Part-time 33 **Student-Faculty Ratio:** 11:1 **Exams:** ACT essay component used for advising; ACT essay component used for placement; SAT I or ACT; SAT essay component used for advising; SAT essay component used for placement; SAT Reasoning; SAT Subject. **% Receiving Financial Aid:** 64 **% Residing in College-Owned, -Operated, or -Affiliated Housing:** 90 **Final Year or Final Semester Residency Requirement:** Yes **Regional Accreditation:** North Central Association of Colleges and Schools **Credit Hours For Degree:** 32 courses, Bachelors **ROTC:** Army **Professional Accreditation:** NASM, NCATE. **Intercollegiate Athletics:** Baseball M; Basketball M & W; Cross-Country Running M & W; Field Hockey W; Football M; Golf M & W; Lacrosse M & W; Soccer M & W; Softball W; Swimming and Diving M & W; Tennis M & W; Track and Field M & W; Volleyball W

JEFFERSON REGIONAL MEDICAL CENTER SCHOOL OF NURSING
1600 W 40th Ave.
Pine Bluff, AR 71603
Tel: (870)541-7850
Web Site: www.jrmc.org
Type: Two-Year College **Sex:** Coed **Professional Accreditation:** ABHES.

JOHN BROWN UNIVERSITY
2000 W University St.
Siloam Springs, AR 72761-2121
Tel: (479)524-9500; Free: 877-JBU-INFO
Fax: (479)524-9548
E-mail: jburgess@jbu.edu
Web Site: www.jbu.edu
President/CEO: Dr. Charles W. Pollard
Admissions: Jared Burgess
Financial Aid: Kim Eldridge
Type: Comprehensive **Sex:** Coed **Affiliation:** interdenominational. **Scores:** 99% SAT V 400+; 100% SAT M 400+; 28.73% ACT 18-23; 52.99% ACT 24-29 **% Accepted:** 69 **Admission Plans:** Deferred Admission **Application Deadline:** Rolling **Application Fee:** $25.00 **H.S. Requirements:** High school diploma required; GED accepted **Costs Per Year:** Application fee: $25. Comprehensive fee: $33,132 includes full-time tuition ($23,398), mandatory fees ($1070), and college room and board ($8664). Full-time tuition and fees vary according to course load. Room and board charges vary according to board plan and housing facility. Part-time tuition: $752 per

credit hour. Part-time tuition varies according to course load. **Scholarships:** Available. **Calendar System:** Semester, Summer session not available **Enrollment:** Full-time 1,565, Graduate full-time 145, Graduate part-time 474, Part-time 216 **Faculty:** Full-time 78, Part-time 122 **Student-Faculty Ratio:** 14:1 **Exams:** SAT I or ACT. **% Receiving Financial Aid:** 69 **% Residing in College-Owned, -Operated, or -Affiliated Housing:** 77 **Final Year or Final Semester Residency Requirement:** No **Regional Accreditation:** North Central Association of Colleges and Schools **Credit Hours For Degree:** 62 semester hours, Associates; 124 semester hours, Bachelors **ROTC:** Air Force, Army **Professional Accreditation:** ABET, ACBSP, ACCE, NCATE. **Intercollegiate Athletics:** Basketball M & W; Cheerleading M & W; Cross-Country Running M & W; Golf M; Soccer M & W; Tennis M & W; Volleyball W

LYON COLLEGE
PO Box 2317
Batesville, AR 72503-2317
Tel: (870)793-9813; Free: 800-423-2542
Fax: (870)698-4622
E-mail: admissions@lyon.edu
Web Site: www.lyon.edu
President/CEO: Dr. Donald V. Weatherman
Financial Aid: Tommy Tucker
Type: Four-Year College **Sex:** Coed **Affiliation:** Presbyterian. **Scores:** 100% SAT V 400+; 93% SAT M 400+; 44% ACT 18-23; 41.5% ACT 24-29 **% Accepted:** 59 **Admission Plans:** Deferred Admission; Early Admission **Application Deadline:** Rolling **Application Fee:** $25.00 **H.S. Requirements:** High school diploma required; GED accepted **Costs Per Year:** Application fee: $25. Comprehensive fee: $33,390 includes full-time tuition ($25,040), mandatory fees ($240), and college room and board ($8110). Full-time tuition and fees vary according to course load. Room and board charges vary according to board plan and housing facility. Part-time tuition: $835 per credit hour. **Scholarships:** Available. **Calendar System:** Semester, Summer session available **Enrollment:** Full-time 698, Part-time 17 **Faculty:** Full-time 42, Part-time 40 **Exams:** ACT; ACT essay component not used; SAT I; SAT I and SAT II or ACT; SAT I or ACT; SAT II; SAT essay component not used. **% Receiving Financial Aid:** 75 **% Residing in College-Owned, -Operated, or -Affiliated Housing:** 74 **Final Year or Final Semester Residency Requirement:** Yes **Regional Accreditation:** North Central Association of Colleges and Schools **Credit Hours For Degree:** 120 credits, Bachelors **Professional Accreditation:** NCATE. **Intercollegiate Athletics:** Baseball M; Basketball M & W; Cross-Country Running M & W; Football M; Golf M & W; Soccer M & W; Softball W; Volleyball W; Wrestling M & W

NATIONAL PARK COLLEGE
101 College Dr.
Hot Springs, AR 71913
Tel: (501)760-4222
Fax: (501)760-4100
E-mail: bmoody@npcc.edu
Web Site: www.np.edu
President/CEO: John Hogan
Admissions: Dr. Allen B. Moody
Type: Two-Year College **Sex:** Coed **Affiliation:** Arkansas Department of Higher Education. **% Accepted:** 100 **Admission Plans:** Deferred Admission; Early Admission; Open Admission **Application Deadline:** Rolling **Application Fee:** $0.00 **H.S. Requirements:** High school diploma required; GED accepted **Scholarships:** Available. **Calendar System:** Semester, Summer session available **Enrollment:** Full-time 1,237, Part-time 1,759 **Faculty:** Full-time 64, Part-time 83 **Student-Faculty Ratio:** 21:1 **Exams:** Other; SAT I and SAT II or ACT. **Regional Accreditation:** North Central Association of Colleges and Schools **Credit Hours For Degree:** 60 semester hours, Associates **Professional Accreditation:** ACEN, AHIMA, JRCERT, NAACLS.

NORTH ARKANSAS COLLEGE
1515 Pioneer Dr.
Harrison, AR 72601
Tel: (870)743-3000; Free: 800-679-6622
Fax: (870)391-3339
E-mail: charlam@northark.edu
Web Site: www.northark.edu
President/CEO: Dr. Jeff Olson
Admissions: Charla Jennings

Financial Aid: Jennifer Haddock

Type: Two-Year College **Sex:** Coed **Scores:** 60% ACT 18-23; 19.3% ACT 24-29 **% Accepted:** 100 **Admission Plans:** Deferred Admission; Open Admission **Application Deadline:** Rolling **Application Fee:** $0.00 **H.S. Requirements:** High school diploma required; GED accepted **Scholarships:** Available. **Calendar System:** Semester, Summer session available **Enrollment:** Full-time 1,491, Part-time 938 **Student-Faculty Ratio:** 19:1 **Final Year or Final Semester Residency Requirement:** No **Regional Accreditation:** North Central Association of Colleges and Schools **Credit Hours For Degree:** 62 credit hours, Associates **Professional Accreditation:** ACBSP, ACEN, ARCST, JRCERT, NAACLS. **Intercollegiate Athletics:** Baseball M; Basketball M & W; Softball W

NORTHWEST ARKANSAS COMMUNITY COLLEGE

One College Dr.
Bentonville, AR 72712
Tel: (479)636-9222; Free: 800-995-6922
Fax: (479)619-4116
E-mail: admissions@nwacc.edu
Web Site: www.nwacc.edu
President/CEO: Dr. Evelyn Jorgenson

Type: Two-Year College **Sex:** Coed **Scores:** 57.4% ACT 18-23; 16.1% ACT 24-29 **Admission Plans:** Open Admission **Application Deadline:** Rolling **Application Fee:** $10.00 **H.S. Requirements:** High school diploma required; GED accepted **Costs Per Year:** Application fee: $10. Area resident tuition: $2250 full-time, $75 per credit hour part-time. State resident tuition: $3675 full-time, $122.50 per credit hour part-time. Nonresident tuition: $3750 full-time, $125 per credit hour part-time. Mandatory fees: $958 full-time, $28.50 per credit hour part-time, $55 per term part-time. **Scholarships:** Available. **Calendar System:** Semester, Summer session available **Faculty:** Full-time 144, Part-time 326 **Student-Faculty Ratio:** 18:1 **Final Year or Final Semester Residency Requirement:** No **Regional Accreditation:** North Central Association of Colleges and Schools **Credit Hours For Degree:** 60 credits, Associates **ROTC:** Air Force, Army **Professional Accreditation:** ACBSP, CoARC, JRCEMTP.

OUACHITA BAPTIST UNIVERSITY

410 Ouachita St.
Arkadelphia, AR 71998-0001
Tel: (870)245-5000; Free: 800-342-5628
Fax: (870)245-5500
E-mail: motll@obu.edu
Web Site: www.obu.edu
President/CEO: Dr. Charles W. Wright
Admissions: Lori Motl
Financial Aid: Susan Hurst

Type: Four-Year College **Sex:** Coed **Affiliation:** Baptist. **Scores:** 94% SAT V 400+; 97% SAT M 400+; 41% ACT 18-23; 40% ACT 24-29 **% Accepted:** 60 **Admission Plans:** Deferred Admission **Application Deadline:** August 15 **Application Fee:** $0.00 **H.S. Requirements:** High school diploma required; GED accepted **Costs Per Year:** Application fee: $0. Comprehensive fee: $24,940 includes full-time tuition ($24,400), mandatory fees ($540), and college room and board ($0). Full-time tuition and fees vary according to degree level. Part-time tuition: $675 per semester hour. Part-time tuition varies according to degree level. **Scholarships:** Available. **Calendar System:** Semester, Summer session available **Enrollment:** Full-time 1,455, Part-time 83 **Faculty:** Full-time 107, Part-time 52 **Student-Faculty Ratio:** 12:1 **Exams:** ACT essay component not used; SAT I or ACT; SAT essay component not used; SAT Reasoning; SAT Subject. **% Receiving Financial Aid:** 61 **% Residing in College-Owned, -Operated, or -Affiliated Housing:** 96 **Final Year or Final Semester Residency Requirement:** Yes **Regional Accreditation:** North Central Association of Colleges and Schools **Credit Hours For Degree:** 60 semester hours, Associates; 120 semester hours, Bachelors **ROTC:** Army **Professional Accreditation:** AACSB, AAFCS, NASM, NCATE. **Intercollegiate Athletics:** Baseball M; Basketball M & W; Cheerleading M & W; Cross-Country Running W; Football M; Soccer M & W; Softball W; Swimming and Diving M & W; Tennis M & W; Volleyball W; Wrestling M

OZARKA COLLEGE

PO Box 10
Melbourne, AR 72556
Tel: (870)368-7371; Free: 800-821-4335
Fax: (870)368-4733

E-mail: dmmowery@ozarka.edu
Web Site: www.ozarka.edu
President/CEO: Dr. Richard Dawe
Admissions: Dylan Mowery
Financial Aid: Laura Lawrence

Type: Two-Year College **Sex:** Coed **Admission Plans:** Deferred Admission; Open Admission **Application Deadline:** August 19 **Application Fee:** $0.00 **H.S. Requirements:** High school diploma required; GED accepted **Scholarships:** Available. **Calendar System:** Semester, Summer session available **Faculty:** Full-time 31, Part-time 40 **Student-Faculty Ratio:** 20:1 **Regional Accreditation:** North Central Association of Colleges and Schools **Credit Hours For Degree:** 62 credit hours, Associates

PHILANDER SMITH COLLEGE

900 W Daisy Bates Dr.
Little Rock, AR 72202-3799
Tel: (501)375-9845; Free: 800-446-6772
Fax: (501)370-5225
Web Site: www.philander.edu
President/CEO: Dr. Johnny Moore
Admissions: Bertha Owens
Financial Aid: Kisa L. Hinton

Type: Four-Year College **Sex:** Coed **Affiliation:** United Methodist. **Scores:** 81% SAT V 400+; 71% SAT M 400+; 51.4% ACT 18-23; 13.1% ACT 24-29 **% Accepted:** 52 **Admission Plans:** Deferred Admission; Open Admission **Application Fee:** $25.00 **H.S. Requirements:** High school diploma required; GED accepted **Costs Per Year:** Application fee: $25. One-time mandatory fee: $150. Comprehensive fee: $20,814 includes full-time tuition ($11,804), mandatory fees ($760), and college room and board ($8250). Full-time tuition and fees vary according to course load and program. **Scholarships:** Available. **Calendar System:** Semester, Summer session available **Enrollment:** Full-time 521, Part-time 46 **Faculty:** Full-time 46, Part-time 10 **Student-Faculty Ratio:** 11:1 **Exams:** SAT I or ACT; SAT Reasoning. **% Receiving Financial Aid:** 88 **% Residing in College-Owned, -Operated, or -Affiliated Housing:** 40 **Final Year or Final Semester Residency Requirement:** No **Regional Accreditation:** North Central Association of Colleges and Schools **Credit Hours For Degree:** 124 semester hours, Bachelors **ROTC:** Army **Professional Accreditation:** ACBSP, CSWE, NCATE. **Intercollegiate Athletics:** Basketball M & W; Track and Field M & W; Volleyball W

PHILLIPS COMMUNITY COLLEGE OF THE UNIVERSITY OF ARKANSAS

PO Box 785
Helena, AR 72342-0785
Tel: (870)338-6474
Fax: (870)338-7542
Web Site: www.pccua.edu
President/CEO: Dr. Steven Murray
Admissions: Lynn Boone

Type: Two-Year College **Sex:** Coed **Affiliation:** University of Arkansas System. **Admission Plans:** Early Admission; Open Admission **Application Deadline:** August 25 **H.S. Requirements:** High school diploma required; GED accepted **Scholarships:** Available. **Calendar System:** Semester, Summer session available **Regional Accreditation:** North Central Association of Colleges and Schools **Credit Hours For Degree:** 64 semester hours, Associates **Professional Accreditation:** ACBSP, ACEN, NAACLS.

PULASKI TECHNICAL COLLEGE

3000 W Scenic Dr.
North Little Rock, AR 72118
Tel: (501)812-2200
Fax: (501)812-2316
E-mail: catkins@pulaskitech.edu
Web Site: www.pulaskitech.edu
President/CEO: Dr. Dan Bakke
Admissions: Clark Atkins

Type: Two-Year College **Sex:** Coed **% Accepted:** 100 **Admission Plans:** Open Admission **Application Deadline:** Rolling **Application Fee:** $0.00 **H.S. Requirements:** High school diploma required; GED accepted **Scholarships:** Available. **Calendar System:** Semester, Summer session available **Enrollment:** Full-time 4,856, Part-time 5,399 **Faculty:** Full-time 153, Part-time 320 **Student-Faculty Ratio:** 25:1 **Final Year or Final Semester Residency Requirement:** Yes **Regional Accreditation:** North Central Association of Colleges and Schools **Credit Hours For Degree:** 62 semester hours, Associates **Professional Accreditation:** ACF, ADA, CoARC.

REMINGTON COLLEGE–LITTLE ROCK CAMPUS

19 Remington Dr.
Little Rock, AR 72204
Tel: (501)312-0007
Fax: (501)225-3819
E-mail: brian.maggio@remingtoncollege.edu
Web Site: www.remingtoncollege.edu
President/CEO: Edna Higgins
Admissions: Brian Maggio
Type: Two-Year College **Sex:** Coed **Professional Accreditation:** ACCSC.

RICH MOUNTAIN COMMUNITY COLLEGE

1100 College Dr.
Mena, AR 71953
Tel: (479)394-7622
Fax: (479)394-2628
Web Site: www.rmcc.edu
President/CEO: Phillip Wilson
Admissions: Dr. Steve Rook
Type: Two-Year College **Sex:** Coed **Admission Plans:** Early Admission; Open Admission **Application Deadline:** August 25 **Application Fee:** $0.00 **H.S. Requirements:** High school diploma required; GED accepted **Costs Per Year:** Application fee: $0. Area resident tuition: $1728 full-time, $72 per credit hour part-time. State resident tuition: $2064 full-time, $86 per credit hour part-time. Nonresident tuition: $4680 full-time, $195 per credit hour part-time. Mandatory fees: $720 full-time, $30 per credit hour part-time. Full-time tuition and fees vary according to course load. Part-time tuition and fees vary according to course load. **Scholarships:** Available. **Calendar System:** Semester, Summer session available **Regional Accreditation:** North Central Association of Colleges and Schools **Credit Hours For Degree:** 60 credits, Associates

SHORTER COLLEGE

604 Locust St.
North Little Rock, AR 72114-4885
Tel: (501)374-6305
Fax: (501)374-9333
Web Site: www.shortercollege.edu
Admissions: Keith Hunter
Type: Two-Year College **Sex:** Coed **Affiliation:** African Methodist Episcopal. **Admission Plans:** Deferred Admission; Early Admission; Open Admission **Application Deadline:** Rolling **H.S. Requirements:** High school diploma required; GED accepted **Scholarships:** Available. **Calendar System:** Semester, Summer session available **Faculty:** Full-time 9, Part-time 15 **Exams:** ACT. **Credit Hours For Degree:** 64 credits, Associates **Professional Accreditation:** TRACS. **Intercollegiate Athletics:** Basketball M & W

SOUTH ARKANSAS COMMUNITY COLLEGE

PO Box 7010
El Dorado, AR 71731-7010
Tel: (870)862-8131; Free: 800-955-2289
Fax: (870)864-7122
E-mail: dinman@southark.edu
Web Site: www.southark.edu
President/CEO: Dr. Alan Rasro
Admissions: Dr. Stephanie Tully-Dartez
Financial Aid: Veronda C. Tatum
Type: Two-Year College **Sex:** Coed **Affiliation:** Arkansas Department of Higher Education. **Admission Plans:** Deferred Admission; Early Admission; Open Admission **Application Deadline:** August 25 **H.S. Requirements:** High school diploma or equivalent not required **Scholarships:** Available. **Calendar System:** Semester, Summer session available **Enrollment:** Full-time 612, Part-time 756 **Exams:** Other; SAT I or ACT. **Regional Accreditation:** North Central Association of Colleges and Schools **Credit Hours For Degree:** 60 semester hours, Associates **Professional Accreditation:** AOTA, APTA, JRCERT, NAACLS.

SOUTHEAST ARKANSAS COLLEGE

1900 Hazel St.
Pine Bluff, AR 71603
Tel: (870)543-5900; Free: 888-SEARC TC

E-mail: bdunn@seark.edu
Web Site: www.seark.edu
President/CEO: Dr. Stephan Hilterbran
Admissions: Barbara Dunn
Financial Aid: Donna Cox
Type: Two-Year College **Sex:** Coed **Admission Plans:** Early Admission; Open Admission **Application Fee:** $0.00 **H.S. Requirements:** High school diploma required; GED accepted **Scholarships:** Available. **Calendar System:** Semester, Summer session available **Enrollment:** Full-time 1,157, Part-time 1,030 **Faculty:** Full-time 63, Part-time 78 **Student-Faculty Ratio:** 16:1 **Exams:** ACT; Other; SAT I and SAT II or ACT; SAT I or ACT; SAT II. **Final Year or Final Semester Residency Requirement:** No **Regional Accreditation:** North Central Association of Colleges and Schools **Credit Hours For Degree:** 62 credits, Associates **Professional Accreditation:** ACEN, ARCST, JRCERT.

SOUTHERN ARKANSAS UNIVERSITY TECH

6415 Spellman Rd.
Camden, AR 71701
Tel: (870)574-4500
Fax: (870)574-4520
E-mail: bellis@sautech.edu
Web Site: www.sautech.edu
President/CEO: Dr. Corbet Lamkin
Admissions: Beverly Ellis
Financial Aid: Jennifer Williams
Type: Two-Year College **Sex:** Coed **Affiliation:** Southern Arkansas University System. **Scores:** 100% SAT V 400+; 67% SAT M 400+; 57% ACT 18-23; 1% ACT 24-29 **% Accepted:** 100 **Admission Plans:** Deferred Admission; Open Admission **Application Deadline:** August 15 **Application Fee:** $0.00 **H.S. Requirements:** High school diploma required; GED accepted **Costs Per Year:** Application fee: $0. State resident tuition: $3240 full-time, $108 per credit hour part-time. Nonresident tuition: $4680 full-time, $156 per credit hour part-time. Mandatory fees: $1560 full-time, $47 per credit hour part-time, $10. Full-time tuition and fees vary according to course load, location, program, and reciprocity agreements. Part-time tuition and fees vary according to course load, location, program, and reciprocity agreements. College room and board: $5691. College room only: $3250. Room and board charges vary according to housing facility. **Scholarships:** Available. **Calendar System:** Semester, Summer session available **Enrollment:** Full-time 589, Part-time 1,228 **Faculty:** Full-time 29, Part-time 76 **Student-Faculty Ratio:** 19:1 **% Residing in College-Owned, -Operated, or -Affiliated Housing:** 2 **Regional Accreditation:** North Central Association of Colleges and Schools **Credit Hours For Degree:** 62 semester hours, Associates

SOUTHERN ARKANSAS UNIVERSITY–MAGNOLIA

100 E University
Magnolia, AR 71753
Tel: (870)235-4000; Free: 800-332-7286
Fax: (870)235-5005
E-mail: sejennings@saumag.edu
Web Site: www.saumag.edu
President/CEO: Dr. Trey Berry
Admissions: Sarah Jennings
Financial Aid: Marcela D. Brunson
Type: Comprehensive **Sex:** Coed **Affiliation:** Southern Arkansas University System. **Scores:** 76% SAT V 400+; 84% SAT M 400+; 52% ACT 18-23; 27% ACT 24-29 **% Accepted:** 67 **Admission Plans:** Deferred Admission; Early Admission **Application Deadline:** August 27 **Application Fee:** $0.00 **H.S. Requirements:** High school diploma required; GED accepted **Costs Per Year:** Application fee: $0. State resident tuition: $6510 full-time, $217 per credit hour part-time. Nonresident tuition: $10,080 full-time, $336 per credit hour part-time. Mandatory fees: $1371 full-time, $44 per credit hour part-time, $18 per term part-time. Full-time tuition and fees vary according to course load. Part-time tuition and fees vary according to course load. College room and board: $5704. College room only: $2900. Room and board charges vary according to board plan and housing facility. **Scholarships:** Available. **Calendar System:** Semester, Summer session available **Enrollment:** Full-time 2,691, Graduate full-time 336, Graduate part-time 636, Part-time 432 **Faculty:** Full-time 161, Part-time 119 **Student-Faculty Ratio:** 17:1 **Exams:** ACT; SAT I or ACT. **% Receiving Financial Aid:** 78 **% Residing in College-Owned, -Operated, or -Affiliated Housing:** 40 **Final Year or Final Semester Residency Requirement:** Yes **Regional Accreditation:** North

Central Association of Colleges and Schools **Credit Hours For Degree:** 65 semester hours, Associates; 120 semester hours, Bachelors **Professional Accreditation:** AACSB, ACEN, CSWE, NASM, NCATE. **Intercollegiate Athletics:** Baseball M; Basketball M & W; Cheerleading M & W; Cross-Country Running M & W; Football M; Golf M & W; Softball W; Tennis W; Track and Field M & W; Volleyball W

STRAYER UNIVERSITY–LITTLE ROCK CAMPUS

10825 Financial Centre Pky.
Ste. 131
Little Rock, AR 72211
Web Site: www.strayer.edu/arkansas/little-rock
President/CEO: Brian W. Jones
Type: Comprehensive **Sex:** Coed **Regional Accreditation:** Middle States Association of Colleges and Schools

UNIVERSITY OF ARKANSAS

800 Hotz Hall
Fayetteville, AR 72701-1201
Tel: (479)575-2000; Free: 800-377-8632
Fax: (479)575-7515
E-mail: uofa@uark.edu
Web Site: www.uark.edu
President/CEO: Joseph E. Steinmetz
Admissions: Cliff Murphy
Financial Aid: Wendy Stouffer
Type: University **Sex:** Coed **Affiliation:** University of Arkansas System. **Scores:** 99% SAT V 400+; 99% SAT M 400+; 26% ACT 18-23; 55.3% ACT 24-29 **% Accepted:** 60 **Admission Plans:** Early Decision Plan **Application Deadline:** August 1 **Application Fee:** $40.00 **H.S. Requirements:** High school diploma required; GED accepted **Costs Per Year:** Application fee: $40. State resident tuition: $7028 full-time, $234.26 per credit hour part-time. Nonresident tuition: $20,332 full-time, $677.73 per credit hour part-time. Mandatory fees: $1494 full-time. Full-time tuition and fees vary according to course load, location, and program. Part-time tuition varies according to course load, location, and program. College room and board: $9880. College room only: $6314. Room and board charges vary according to board plan, housing facility, and location. **Scholarships:** Available. **Calendar System:** Semester, Summer session available **Enrollment:** Full-time 19,607, Graduate full-time 1,802, Graduate part-time 2,793, Part-time 2,552 **Faculty:** Full-time 1,137, Part-time 183 **Student-Faculty Ratio:** 19:1 **Exams:** ACT essay component not used; SAT I or ACT; SAT essay component not used; SAT Reasoning; SAT Subject. **% Receiving Financial Aid:** 41 **% Residing in College-Owned, -Operated, or -Affiliated Housing:** 26 **Final Year or Final Semester Residency Requirement:** No **Regional Accreditation:** North Central Association of Colleges and Schools **Credit Hours For Degree:** 120 credit hours, Bachelors **ROTC:** Air Force, Army **Professional Accreditation:** AACN, AACSB, AAFCS, AALS, ABA, ABET, ACA, ACEJMC, APA, ASHA, ASLA, CIDA, CORE, CSWE, NAAB, NASM, NCATE, NRPA. **Intercollegiate Athletics:** Baseball M; Basketball M & W; Cross-Country Running M & W; Football M; Golf M & W; Gymnastics W; Soccer W; Softball W; Swimming and Diving W; Tennis M & W; Track and Field M & W; Volleyball W

UNIVERSITY OF ARKANSAS COMMUNITY COLLEGE AT BATESVILLE

PO Box 3350
Batesville, AR 72503
Tel: (870)612-2000; Free: 800-508-7878
Fax: (870)793-4988
E-mail: amy.foree@uaccb.edu
Web Site: www.uaccb.edu
President/CEO: Deborah Frazier
Admissions: Amy Foree
Type: Two-Year College **Sex:** Coed **Affiliation:** University of Arkansas System. **Admission Plans:** Open Admission **Application Deadline:** Rolling **Application Fee:** $0.00 **H.S. Requirements:** High school diploma required; GED accepted **Scholarships:** Available. **Calendar System:** Semester, Summer session available **Enrollment:** Full-time 750, Part-time 565 **Student-Faculty Ratio:** 19:1 **Exams:** ACT essay component not used; Other; SAT essay component not used. **Regional Accreditation:** North Central Association of Colleges and Schools **Credit Hours For Degree:** 60 credits, Associates **Professional Accreditation:** ACEN.

UNIVERSITY OF ARKANSAS COMMUNITY COLLEGE AT HOPE

PO Box 140
Hope, AR 71802
Tel: (870)777-5722
Fax: (870)722-5957
E-mail: judy.anderson@uacch.edu
Web Site: www.uacch.edu
President/CEO: Chris Thomason
Admissions: Judy Anderson
Financial Aid: Becky Wilson
Type: Two-Year College **Sex:** Coed **Affiliation:** University of Arkansas System. **% Accepted:** 100 **Admission Plans:** Early Admission; Open Admission **Application Deadline:** Rolling **Application Fee:** $0.00 **H.S. Requirements:** High school diploma or equivalent not required **Costs Per Year:** Application fee: $0. Area resident tuition: $1860 full-time, $60.50 per credit part-time. State resident tuition: $2040 full-time, $65.50 per credit part-time. Nonresident tuition: $4080 full-time, $131 per credit part-time. Mandatory fees: $520 full-time, $15 per term part-time, $8 per term part-time. **Scholarships:** Available. **Calendar System:** Semester, Summer session available **Enrollment:** Full-time 666, Part-time 694 **Faculty:** Full-time 40, Part-time 51 **Student-Faculty Ratio:** 15:1 **Exams:** ACT essay component not used; Other; SAT I or ACT; SAT essay component not used. **Regional Accreditation:** North Central Association of Colleges and Schools **Credit Hours For Degree:** 60 credits, Associates **Professional Accreditation:** ABFSE, CoARC.

UNIVERSITY OF ARKANSAS COMMUNITY COLLEGE AT MORRILTON

1537 University Blvd.
Morrilton, AR 72110
Tel: (501)977-2000; Free: 800-264-1094
Fax: (501)354-9948
E-mail: mullins@uaccm.edu
Web Site: www.uaccm.edu
President/CEO: Dr. Larry Davis
Admissions: Terry McCoy
Financial Aid: Teresa Y. Cash
Type: Two-Year College **Sex:** Coed **Affiliation:** University of Arkansas System. **Scores:** 54.3% ACT 18-23; 15.6% ACT 24-29 **% Accepted:** 66 **Admission Plans:** Deferred Admission; Early Admission; Open Admission **Application Deadline:** Rolling **Application Fee:** $0.00 **H.S. Requirements:** High school diploma required; GED accepted **Costs Per Year:** Application fee: $0. Area resident tuition: $2535 full-time, $84.50 per credit hour part-time. State resident tuition: $2745 full-time, $91.50 per credit hour part-time. Nonresident tuition: $3840 full-time, $128 per credit hour part-time. Mandatory fees: $1040 full-time, $34 per credit hour part-time, $10 per term part-time. Full-time tuition and fees vary according to course load and program. Part-time tuition and fees vary according to course load and program. **Scholarships:** Available. **Calendar System:** Semester, Summer session available **Enrollment:** Full-time 1,354, Part-time 688 **Faculty:** Full-time 62, Part-time 13 **Student-Faculty Ratio:** 24:1 **Exams:** ACT essay component not used; Other; SAT I or ACT; SAT essay component not used. **Final Year or Final Semester Residency Requirement:** No **Regional Accreditation:** North Central Association of Colleges and Schools **Credit Hours For Degree:** 60 credit hours, Associates

UNIVERSITY OF ARKANSAS AT LITTLE ROCK

2801 S University Ave.
Little Rock, AR 72204-1099
Tel: (501)569-3000; Free: 800-482-8892
Fax: (501)569-8915
E-mail: twharrison@ualn.edu
Web Site: www.ualr.edu
President/CEO: Dr. Joel E. Anderson
Admissions: Tammy Harrison
Type: University **Sex:** Coed **Affiliation:** University of Arkansas System. **Scores:** 80% SAT V 400+; 93% SAT M 400+ **% Accepted:** 59 **Admission Plans:** Deferred Admission; Early Admission **Application Fee:** $40.00 **H.S. Requirements:** High school diploma required; GED accepted **Costs Per Year:** Application fee: $40. One-time mandatory fee: $40. State resident tuition: $6180 full-time, $206 per credit hour part-time. Nonresident tuition: $17,250 full-time, $575 per credit hour part-time. Mandatory fees: $1928 full-time. Full-time tuition and fees vary according to course load, degree level, and program. Part-time tuition varies according to course load, degree level,

and program. College room and board: $5708. Room and board charges vary according to board plan and housing facility. **Scholarships:** Available. **Calendar System:** Semester, Summer session available **Enrollment:** Full-time 4,921, Graduate full-time 1,059, Graduate part-time 1,202, Part-time 4,463 **Faculty:** Full-time 453, Part-time 287 **Student-Faculty Ratio:** 13:1 **Exams:** ACT essay component not used; SAT I or ACT; SAT essay component not used. **% Residing in College-Owned, -Operated, or -Affiliated Housing:** 2 **Final Year or Final Semester Residency Requirement:** Yes **Regional Accreditation:** North Central Association of Colleges and Schools **ROTC:** Army **Professional Accreditation:** AACSB, AALS, ABA, ABET, ACCE, ACEN, ASHA, CAHME, CORE, CSWE, NASAD, NASM, NASPAA, NAST, NCATE. **Intercollegiate Athletics:** Baseball M; Basketball M & W; Cross-Country Running M & W; Golf M & W; Soccer M & W; Swimming and Diving W; Track and Field M & W; Volleyball W

UNIVERSITY OF ARKANSAS FOR MEDICAL SCIENCES

4301 W Markham
Little Rock, AR 72205-7199
Tel: (501)686-5000
Web Site: www.uams.edu
President/CEO: Dr. Dan Rahn
Financial Aid: Gloria Kemp

Type: University **Sex:** Coed **Affiliation:** University of Arkansas System. **% Accepted:** 29 **H.S. Requirements:** High school diploma required; GED accepted **Scholarships:** Available. **Calendar System:** Semester, Summer session not available **Enrollment:** Full-time 575, Graduate full-time 1,557, Graduate part-time 690, Part-time 199 **Faculty:** Full-time 464, Part-time 52 **Regional Accreditation:** North Central Association of Colleges and Schools **ROTC:** Army **Professional Accreditation:** AACN, ACPE, ACIPE, ADA, AND, APA, ARCST, ASC, CEPH, CoARC, JRCEMTP, JRCERT, JRCNMT, LCME/AMA, NAACLS. **Intercollegiate Athletics:** Ultimate Frisbee M & W; Volleyball M & W

UNIVERSITY OF ARKANSAS AT MONTICELLO

Monticello, AR 71656
Tel: (870)367-6811; Free: 800-844-1826
Fax: (870)460-1321
E-mail: admissions@uamont.edu
Web Site: www.uamont.edu
President/CEO: Dr. Jack Lassiter
Admissions: Mary Whiting
Financial Aid: Susan Brewer

Type: Comprehensive **Sex:** Coed **Affiliation:** University of Arkansas System. **Scores:** 42% ACT 18-23; 15% ACT 24-29 **% Accepted:** 46 **Admission Plans:** Deferred Admission; Early Admission; Open Admission **Application Deadline:** August 1 **Application Fee:** $0.00 **H.S. Requirements:** High school diploma required; GED accepted **Scholarships:** Available. **Calendar System:** Semester, Summer session available **Enrollment:** Full-time 2,676, Graduate full-time 21, Graduate part-time 97, Part-time 1,126 **Faculty:** Full-time 172, Part-time 68 **Student-Faculty Ratio:** 16:1 **% Residing in College-Owned, -Operated, or -Affiliated Housing:** 25 **Final Year or Final Semester Residency Requirement:** Yes **Regional Accreditation:** North Central Association of Colleges and Schools **Credit Hours For Degree:** 62 hours, Associates; 124 hours, Bachelors **ROTC:** Army **Professional Accreditation:** ACBSP, ACEN, CSWE, NASM, NCATE, SAF. **Intercollegiate Athletics:** Baseball M; Basketball M & W; Cross-Country Running W; Football M; Golf M; Softball W; Tennis W

UNIVERSITY OF ARKANSAS AT PINE BLUFF

1200 N University Dr.
Pine Bluff, AR 71601-2799
Tel: (870)575-8000; Free: 800-264-6585
Fax: (870)543-2021
E-mail: owasoyop@uapb.edu
Web Site: www.uapb.edu
President/CEO: Dr. Laurence B. Alexander, PhD
Admissions: Philomena Owasoyo
Financial Aid: Carolyn Iverson

Type: Comprehensive **Sex:** Coed **Affiliation:** University of Arkansas System. **Scores:** 71% SAT V 400+; 80% SAT M 400+; 45% ACT 18-23; 7% ACT 24-29 **% Accepted:** 46 **Admission Plans:** Deferred Admission; Early Admission; Open Admission **Application Deadline:** Rolling **Application Fee:** $0.00 **H.S. Requirements:** High school diploma required; GED accepted **Costs Per Year:** Application fee: $0. State resident tuition: $6271

full-time, $151 per credit hour part-time. Nonresident tuition: $11,941 full-time, $340 per credit hour part-time. Full-time tuition varies according to course level, degree level, and location. Part-time tuition varies according to course level, degree level, and location. College room and board: $7270. Room and board charges vary according to board plan and housing facility. **Scholarships:** Available. **Calendar System:** Semester, Summer session available **Enrollment:** Full-time 2,312, Graduate full-time 43, Graduate part-time 70, Part-time 233 **Faculty:** Full-time 161, Part-time 38 **Student-Faculty Ratio:** 15:1 **Exams:** SAT I or ACT. **% Receiving Financial Aid:** 96 **% Residing in College-Owned, -Operated, or -Affiliated Housing:** 41 **Final Year or Final Semester Residency Requirement:** No **Regional Accreditation:** North Central Association of Colleges and Schools **Credit Hours For Degree:** 62 semester hours, Associates; 120 semester hours, Bachelors **ROTC:** Army **Professional Accreditation:** AAFCS, ACEN, ATMAE, CSWE, NASAD, NASM, NCATE. **Intercollegiate Athletics:** Baseball M; Basketball M & W; Cross-Country Running M & W; Football M; Golf M; Track and Field M & W; Volleyball W

UNIVERSITY OF ARKANSAS–FORT SMITH

PO Box 3649
Fort Smith, AR 72913-3649
Tel: (479)788-7000; Free: 888-512-5466
Fax: (479)788-7003
E-mail: kelly.westeen@uafortsmith.edu
Web Site: uafs.edu
President/CEO: Dr. Paul B. Beran
Admissions: Kelly Westeen
Financial Aid: Tammy Malone

Type: Four-Year College **Sex:** Coed **Affiliation:** University of Arkansas System. **Scores:** 51% ACT 18-23; 33% ACT 24-29 **% Accepted:** 56 **Admission Plans:** Deferred Admission **Application Deadline:** Rolling **Application Fee:** $0.00 **H.S. Requirements:** High school diploma required; GED accepted **Scholarships:** Available. **Calendar System:** Semester, Summer session available **Enrollment:** Full-time 4,581, Part-time 2,242 **Faculty:** Full-time 236, Part-time 176 **Student-Faculty Ratio:** 18:1 **Exams:** ACT essay component not used; Other; SAT essay component not used; SAT Reasoning. **% Receiving Financial Aid:** 57 **% Residing in College-Owned, -Operated, or -Affiliated Housing:** 13 **Final Year or Final Semester Residency Requirement:** Yes **Regional Accreditation:** North Central Association of Colleges and Schools **Credit Hours For Degree:** 60 credit hours, Associates; 120 credit hours, Bachelors **ROTC:** Air Force, Army **Professional Accreditation:** ACEN, ADA, ARCST, JRCERT, NASM, NCATE. **Intercollegiate Athletics:** Baseball M; Basketball M & W; Cross-Country Running M & W; Golf M & W; Tennis M & W; Volleyball W

UNIVERSITY OF CENTRAL ARKANSAS

201 Donaghey Ave.
Conway, AR 72035-0001
Tel: (501)450-5000; Free: 800-243-8245
Fax: (501)450-5228
E-mail: admissions@uca.edu
Web Site: www.uca.edu
President/CEO: Tom Courtway
Financial Aid: Cheryl Lyons

Type: University **Sex:** Coed **Scores:** 92% SAT V 400+; 98% SAT M 400+; 46.9% ACT 18-23; 38.1% ACT 24-29 **% Accepted:** 92 **Admission Plans:** Deferred Admission; Early Admission **Application Deadline:** Rolling **Application Fee:** $25.00 **H.S. Requirements:** High school diploma required; GED accepted **Costs Per Year:** Application fee: $25. State resident tuition: $5,918 full-time, $197.25 per credit hour part-time. Nonresident tuition: $11,835 full-time, $394.50 per credit hour part-time. Mandatory fees: $1,971 full-time. Full-time tuition and fees vary according to course load. Part-time tuition varies according to course load. College room and board: $5982. Room and board charges vary according to board plan and housing facility. **Scholarships:** Available. **Calendar System:** Semester, Summer session available **Enrollment:** Full-time 8,281, Graduate full-time 762, Graduate part-time 1,105, Part-time 1,606 **Faculty:** Full-time 547, Part-time 188 **Exams:** SAT I or ACT. **% Residing in College-Owned, -Operated, or -Affiliated Housing:** 36 **Final Year or Final Semester Residency Requirement:** No **Regional Accreditation:** North Central Association of Colleges and Schools **Credit Hours For Degree:** 60 credit hours, Associates; 124 credit hours, Bachelors **ROTC:** Army **Professional Accreditation:** AACN,

AACSB, AAFCS, ABET, AND, AOTA, APTA, ASHA, NASAD, NASM, NAST, NCATE. **Intercollegiate Athletics:** Baseball M; Basketball M & W; Cheerleading M & W; Cross-Country Running M & W; Football M; Golf M & W; Soccer M & W; Softball W; Tennis W; Track and Field M & W; Volleyball W

UNIVERSITY OF THE OZARKS

415 N College Ave.
Clarksville, AR 72830-2880
Tel: (479)979-1000; Free: 800-264-8636
Fax: (479)979-1355
E-mail: admiss@ozarks.edu
Web Site: www.ozarks.edu
President/CEO: Dr. Rick Niece
Admissions: Jana Hart
Financial Aid: Jana D. Hart
Type: Four-Year College **Sex:** Coed **Affiliation:** Presbyterian. **% Accepted:** 97 **Admission Plans:** Deferred Admission **H.S. Requirements:** High school diploma required; GED accepted **Costs Per Year:** Comprehensive fee: $30,850 includes full-time tuition ($23,750) and college room and board ($7100). College room only: $3200. **Scholarships:** Available. **Calendar System:** Semester **Student-Faculty Ratio:** 13:1 **Exams:** SAT I or ACT; SAT Reasoning. **% Residing in College-Owned, -Operated, or -Affiliated Housing:** 76 **Final Year or Final Semester Residency Requirement:** Yes **Regional Accreditation:** North Central Association of Colleges and Schools **Professional Accreditation:** NCATE.

WILLIAMS BAPTIST COLLEGE

60 W Fulbright Ave.
Walnut Ridge, AR 72476
Tel: (870)886-6741; Free: 800-722-4434
E-mail: awatson@wbcoll.edu
Web Site: www.wbcoll.edu
President/CEO: Dr. Tom Jones
Admissions: Andrew Watson
Financial Aid: Barbara Turner
Type: Four-Year College **Sex:** Coed **Affiliation:** Southern Baptist. **Scores:** 66% ACT 18-23; 19% ACT 24-29 **% Accepted:** 64 **Application Deadline:** Rolling **Application Fee:** $0.00 **H.S. Requirements:** High school diploma required; GED accepted **Costs Per Year:** Application fee: $0. Comprehensive fee: $24,720 includes full-time tuition ($16,200), mandatory fees ($1120), and college room and board ($7400). Room and board charges vary according to board plan. Part-time tuition: $675 per credit hour. Part-time tuition varies according to course load. **Scholarships:** Available. **Calendar System:** Semester, Summer session available **Enrollment:** Full-time 483, Part-time 58 **Faculty:** Full-time 26, Part-time 24 **Student-Faculty Ratio:** 14:1 **Exams:** ACT essay component not used; SAT I or ACT; SAT essay component not used. **% Receiving Financial Aid:** 67 **% Residing in College-Owned, -Operated, or -Affiliated Housing:** 65 **Final Year or Final Semester Residency Requirement:** Yes **Regional Accreditation:** North Central Association of Colleges and Schools **Credit Hours For Degree:** 60 hours, Associates; 123 hours, Bachelors **ROTC:** Army **Professional Accreditation:** NCATE. **Intercollegiate Athletics:** Baseball M; Basketball M & W; Cross-Country Running M & W; Golf M; Soccer M & W; Softball W; Track and Field M & W; Volleyball W; Wrestling M

ACADEMY OF ART UNIVERSITY

79 New Montgomery St.
San Francisco, CA 94105-3410
Tel: (415)274-2200; Free: 800-544-ARTS
Fax: (415)263-4130
E-mail: info@academyart.edu
Web Site: www.academyart.edu
President/CEO: Dr. Elisa Stephens
Financial Aid: Joe Vollaro
Type: Comprehensive **Sex:** Coed **% Accepted:** 100 **Admission Plans:** Deferred Admission; Early Admission; Open Admission **Application Deadline:** Rolling **Application Fee:** $100.00 **H.S. Requirements:** High school diploma required; GED accepted **Costs Per Year:** Application fee: $100. Comprehensive fee: $41,740 includes full-time tuition ($26,190), mandatory fees ($300), and college room and board ($15,250). Full-time tuition and fees vary according to course load. Room and board charges vary according to board plan and housing facility. Part-time tuition: $873 per unit. Part-time tuition varies according to course load. **Scholarships:** Available. **Calendar System:** Semester, Summer session available **Enrollment:** Full-time 5,339, Graduate full-time 2,962, Graduate part-time 1,721, Part-time 3,778 **Faculty:** Full-time 287, Part-time 1,147 **Student-Faculty Ratio:** 15:1 **% Receiving Financial Aid:** 42 **% Residing in College-Owned, -Operated, or -Affiliated Housing:** 15 **Final Year or Final Semester Residency Requirement:** No **Regional Accreditation:** Western Association of Colleges and Schools **Credit Hours For Degree:** 66 units, Associates; 132 units, Bachelors **Professional Accreditation:** ACICS, CIDA, NASAD. **Intercollegiate Athletics:** Baseball M; Basketball M & W; Cross-Country Running M & W; Golf M & W; Soccer M & W; Softball W; Tennis W; Track and Field M & W; Volleyball W

ACADEMY OF COUTURE ART

8484 Wilshire Blvd., Ste. 730
Beverly Hills, CA 90211
Tel: (310)360-8888
Fax: (310)857-6974
Web Site: www.academyofcoutureart.edu
President/CEO: Sonia Ete
Admissions: Jennifer Park Zerkel
Financial Aid: Adrian Sarmiento
Type: Two-Year College **Sex:** Coed **Admission Plans:** Early Admission; Open Admission **Application Fee:** $40.00 **H.S. Requirements:** High school diploma required; GED accepted **Costs Per Year:** Application fee: $40. One-time mandatory fee: $100. Tuition: $19,998 full-time, $620.50 per credit part-time. Mandatory fees: $2340 full-time. Full-time tuition and fees vary according to class time, course level, course load, degree level, location, program, reciprocity agreements, and student level. Part-time tuition varies according to class time, course level, course load, degree level, location, program, reciprocity agreements, and student level. Tuition guaranteed not to increase for student's term of enrollment. **Scholarships:** Available. **Faculty:** Full-time 3, Part-time 1 **Exams:** SAT I or ACT. **Professional Accreditation:** ACICS.

ADVANCED COLLEGE

13180 Paramount Blvd.
South Gate, CA 90280
Tel: (562)408-6969
Web Site: www.advancedcollege.edu
Type: Two-Year College **Sex:** Coed **Professional Accreditation:** COE.

ADVANCED COMPUTING INSTITUTE

3470 Wilshire Blvd. 11th Fl.
Los Angeles, CA 90010-3911
Web Site: www.advancedcomputinginstitute.edu
Type: Two-Year College **Sex:** Coed **Professional Accreditation:** COE.

ADVANCED TRAINING ASSOCIATES

1810 Gillespie Way
Ste. 104
El Cajon, CA 92020
Tel: (619)596-2766; Free: 800-720-2125
Fax: (619)596-4526
Web Site: www.advancedtraining.edu
Type: Two-Year College **Sex:** Coed **Professional Accreditation:** COE.

ALLAN HANCOCK COLLEGE

800 S College Dr.
Santa Maria, CA 93454-6399
Tel: (805)922-6966; Free: 866-342-5242
Fax: (805)596-3477
Web Site: www.hancockcollege.edu
President/CEO: Dr. Kevin Walthers
Admissions: Adela Esquivel Swinson
Type: Two-Year College **Sex:** Coed **Admission Plans:** Open Admission **Application Deadline:** Rolling **Application Fee:** $0.00 **H.S. Requirements:** High school diploma or equivalent not required **Scholarships:** Available. **Calendar System:** Semester, Summer session available **Enrollment:** Full-time 2,996, Part-time 7,391 **Faculty:** Full-time 152, Part-time 442 **Student-Faculty Ratio:** 17:1 **Final Year or Final Semester Residency Requirement:** No **Regional Accreditation:** Western Association of Colleges and Schools **Credit Hours For Degree:** 60 units, Associates **Intercollegiate Athletics:** Baseball M; Basketball M & W; Cross-Country Running M & W; Football M; Golf M; Soccer M & W; Softball W; Tennis M & W; Track and Field M & W; Volleyball W

ALLIANT INTERNATIONAL UNIVERSITY–SAN DIEGO

10455 Pomerado Rd.
San Diego, CA 92131-1799
Tel: (858)271-4300; Free: 866-825-5426
Fax: (858)635-4739
E-mail: admissions@alliant.edu
Web Site: www.alliant.edu
President/CEO: Geoffrey Cox, PhD
Admissions: Kevin McMackin
Financial Aid: Deborah Spindler
Type: University **Sex:** Coed **Affiliation:** Alliant International University. **Admission Plans:** Deferred Admission **Application Fee:** $65.00 **H.S. Requirements:** High school diploma required; GED accepted **Scholarships:** Available. **Calendar System:** Semester, Summer session available **Enrollment:** Full-time 152, Graduate full-time 1,866, Graduate part-time 1,420, Part-time 85 **Faculty:** Full-time 234, Part-time 392 **Student-Faculty

Ratio: 9:1 % Receiving Financial Aid: 64 % Residing in College-Owned, -Operated, or -Affiliated Housing: 40 Regional Accreditation: Western Association of Colleges and Schools Credit Hours For Degree: 120 semester units, Bachelors Professional Accreditation: AAMFT.

ALLIED AMERICAN UNIVERSITY
22952 Alcade Dr.
Laguna Hills, CA 92653
Free: 888-384-0849
Fax: (949)707-2978
E-mail: info@allied.edu
Web Site: allied.edu
President/CEO: Charlotte Hislop
Admissions: Lindsay Oglesby
Type: Four-Year College Sex: Coed Application Fee: $50.00 Regional Accreditation: Western Association of Colleges and Schools Professional Accreditation: DEAC.

AMERICAN ACADEMY OF DRAMATIC ARTS–LOS ANGELES
1336 N La Brea Ave.
Hollywood, CA 90028
Tel: (323)464-2777; Free: 800-222-2867
Fax: (323)464-1250
E-mail: shong@aada.edu
Web Site: www.aada.edu
President/CEO: John Polsky
Admissions: Steven Hong
Type: Two-Year College Sex: Coed % Accepted: 20 Admission Plans: Deferred Admission Application Deadline: Rolling Application Fee: $50.00 H.S. Requirements: High school diploma required; GED accepted Costs Per Year: Application fee: $50. Tuition: $32,440 full-time. Mandatory fees: $750 full-time. Scholarships: Available. Calendar System: Semester, Summer session not available Enrollment: Full-time 282 Faculty: Full-time 9, Part-time 41 Student-Faculty Ratio: 12:1 Credit Hours For Degree: 77 units, Associates Professional Accreditation: NAST.

AMERICAN CAREER COLLEGE (ANAHEIM)
1200 N Magnolia Ave.
Anaheim, CA 92801
Tel: (714)763-9066; Free: 877-832-0790
E-mail: info@americancareer.com
Web Site: americancareercollege.edu
President/CEO: Tom McNamara
Admissions: Susan Pailet
Type: Two-Year College Sex: Coed % Accepted: 77 Student-Faculty Ratio: 16:1 Professional Accreditation: ABHES.

AMERICAN CAREER COLLEGE (LOS ANGELES)
4021 Rosewood Ave.
Los Angeles, CA 90004-2932
Tel: (323)668-7555; Free: 877-832-0790
E-mail: info@americancareer.com
Web Site: americancareercollege.edu
President/CEO: Tom McNamara
Admissions: Tamra Adams
Type: Two-Year College Sex: Coed % Accepted: 86 Student-Faculty Ratio: 15:1

AMERICAN CAREER COLLEGE (ONTARIO)
3130 E Sedona Ct.
Ontario, CA 91764
Tel: (909)218-3253; Free: 877-832-0790
E-mail: info@americancareer.com
Web Site: americancareercollege.edu
President/CEO: Tom McNamara
Admissions: Juan Tellez
Type: Two-Year College Sex: Coed % Accepted: 76 Student-Faculty Ratio: 31:1 Professional Accreditation: ABHES.

AMERICAN JEWISH UNIVERSITY
15600 Mulholland Dr.
Bel Air, CA 90077-1599
Tel: (310)476-9777; Free: 888-853-6763
Fax: (310)471-3657

E-mail: admissions@aju.edu
Web Site: www.aju.edu
President/CEO: Dr. Robert Wexler
Admissions: Yosef Funke
Financial Aid: Larisa Zadoyen
Type: Comprehensive Sex: Coed Affiliation: Jewish. Scores: 87% SAT V 400+; 75% SAT M 400+; 33% ACT 18-23; 34% ACT 24-29 % Accepted: 61 Admission Plans: Deferred Admission Application Deadline: May 31 Application Fee: $35.00 H.S. Requirements: High school diploma required; GED accepted Scholarships: Available. Calendar System: Semester, Summer session not available Enrollment: Full-time 108, Graduate full-time 80, Graduate part-time 37, Part-time 4 Faculty: Full-time 8, Part-time 30 Student-Faculty Ratio: 3:1 Exams: ACT essay component not used; SAT I or ACT; SAT essay component not used; SAT Reasoning; SAT Subject. % Receiving Financial Aid: 87 % Residing in College-Owned, -Operated, or -Affiliated Housing: 34 Final Year or Final Semester Residency Requirement: Yes Regional Accreditation: Western Association of Colleges and Schools Credit Hours For Degree: 120 units, Bachelors

AMERICAN MEDICAL SCIENCES CENTER
225 W Broadway, Ste. 115
Glendale, CA 91204-5108
Web Site: www.amsc.edu
Type: Two-Year College Sex: Coed Professional Accreditation: ABHES.

AMERICAN MUSICAL AND DRAMATIC ACADEMY, LOS ANGELES
6305 Yucca St.
Los Angeles, CA 90028
Tel: (323)469-3300; Free: 888-474-9444
Fax: (323)469-3350
E-mail: kjackson@amda.edu
Web Site: www.amda.edu
President/CEO: David Martin
Admissions: Karen Jackson
Type: Four-Year College Sex: Coed Application Fee: $50.00 Professional Accreditation: NAST.

AMERICAN RIVER COLLEGE
4700 College Oak Dr.
Sacramento, CA 95841-4286
Tel: (916)484-8011
E-mail: nealr@arc.losrios.edu
Web Site: www.arc.losrios.edu
President/CEO: Thomas Greene
Admissions: Dr. Robin Neal
Type: Two-Year College Sex: Coed Affiliation: Los Rios Community College District System. Admission Plans: Deferred Admission; Early Admission; Open Admission Application Deadline: Rolling H.S. Requirements: High school diploma or equivalent not required. For nursing, respiratory therapy programs; applicants under 18: High school diploma required; GED accepted Costs Per Year: State resident tuition: $0 full-time. Nonresident tuition: $4800 full-time, $200 per unit part-time. Mandatory fees: $1104 full-time, $46 per unit part-time. Full-time tuition and fees vary according to course load. Part-time tuition and fees vary according to course load. Scholarships: Available. Calendar System: Semester, Summer session available Final Year or Final Semester Residency Requirement: No Regional Accreditation: Western Association of Colleges and Schools Credit Hours For Degree: 60 units, Associates Professional Accreditation: ABFSE, CoARC. Intercollegiate Athletics: Baseball M; Basketball M & W; Cross-Country Running M & W; Football M; Golf M & W; Soccer M & W; Softball W; Swimming and Diving M & W; Tennis M & W; Track and Field M & W; Volleyball W; Water Polo M & W

AMERICAN UNIVERSITY OF HEALTH SCIENCES
1600 E Hill St.
Bldg. No.1
Signal Hill, CA 90755
Tel: (562)988-2278
Fax: (562)988-1791
Web Site: www.auhs.edu
Type: Comprehensive Sex: Coed Professional Accreditation: ACICS.

ANGELES COLLEGE
3440 Wilshire Blvd., Ste. 310
Los Angeles, CA 90010
Tel: (213)487-2211
Web Site: www.angelescollege.edu
Type: Four-Year College **Sex:** Coed **Professional Accreditation:** ABHES.

ANTELOPE VALLEY COLLEGE
3041 W Ave. K
Lancaster, CA 93536-5426
Tel: (661)722-6300
Fax: (661)943-5573
Web Site: www.avc.edu
President/CEO: Pres. Ed Knudson
Type: Two-Year College **Sex:** Coed **Affiliation:** California Community College System. **% Accepted:** 100 **Admission Plans:** Early Admission; Open Admission **Application Deadline:** Rolling **Application Fee:** $0.00 **H.S. Requirements:** High school diploma or equivalent not required **Costs Per Year:** Application fee: $0. State resident tuition: $1104 full-time, $46 per credit part-time. Nonresident tuition: $6768 full-time, $236 per credit part-time. Mandatory fees: $40 full-time, $20 per term part-time. **Scholarships:** Available. **Calendar System:** Semester, Summer session available **Faculty:** Full-time 174, Part-time 448 **Final Year or Final Semester Residency Requirement:** No **Regional Accreditation:** Western Association of Colleges and Schools **Credit Hours For Degree:** 60 units, Associates **ROTC:** Air Force, Army, Navy **Intercollegiate Athletics:** Baseball M; Basketball M & W; Cross-Country Running M & W; Football M; Golf M; Soccer W; Softball W; Tennis W; Track and Field M & W; Volleyball W

ANTIOCH UNIVERSITY LOS ANGELES
400 Corporate Pointe
Culver City, CA 90230
Tel: (310)578-1080; Free: 800-726-8462
Fax: (310)827-4742
E-mail: admissions@antiochla.edu
Web Site: www.antiochla.edu
President/CEO: Neal King
Type: Two-Year Upper Division **Sex:** Coed **Affiliation:** Antioch University. **Admission Plans:** Deferred Admission **Application Fee:** $60.00 **H.S. Requirements:** High school diploma required; GED accepted **Costs Per Year:** Application fee: $60. Tuition: $26,256 full-time. Mandatory fees: $400 full-time. Full-time tuition and fees vary according to course load and program. **Calendar System:** Quarter, Summer session available **Enrollment:** Full-time 57, Graduate full-time 349, Graduate part-time 71, Part-time 115 **Regional Accreditation:** North Central Association of Colleges and Schools **Credit Hours For Degree:** 180 units, Bachelors

ANTIOCH UNIVERSITY SANTA BARBARA
602 Anacapa St.
Santa Barbara, CA 93101-1581
Tel: (805)962-8179; Free: 866-526-8462
Fax: (805)962-4786
E-mail: jporcaro@antioch.edu
Web Site: www.antiochsb.edu
President/CEO: Dr. Nancy Leffert
Admissions: Jessica Porcaro
Financial Aid: Heather Nguyen
Type: Two-Year Upper Division **Sex:** Coed **Affiliation:** Antioch University. **Admission Plans:** Deferred Admission **Application Fee:** $60.00 **H.S. Requirements:** High school diploma required; GED accepted **Costs Per Year:** Application fee: $60. Tuition: $17,820 full-time, $495 per credit part-time. Mandatory fees: $300 full-time. Full-time tuition and fees vary according to course load, degree level, and program. Part-time tuition varies according to course load, degree level, and program. **Scholarships:** Available. **Calendar System:** Quarter, Summer session available **Faculty:** Full-time 9, Part-time 69 **Exams:** Other. **Regional Accreditation:** North Central Association of Colleges and Schools **Credit Hours For Degree:** 180 quarter hours, Bachelors

APT COLLEGE
5751 Palmer Way, Ste. D
Carlsbad, CA 92013
Free: 800-431-8488
Fax: (888)431-8588

E-mail: aptc@aptc.com
Web Site: www.aptc.edu
President/CEO: Steven W. Blume
Admissions: Monica Hoffman
Type: Two-Year College **Sex:** Coed **Application Fee:** $50.00 **Professional Accreditation:** DEAC.

ARGOSY UNIVERSITY, INLAND EMPIRE
3401 Centre Lake Dr., Ste. 200
Ontario, CA 91761
Tel: (909)472-0800; Free: 866-217-9075
Web Site: www.argosy.edu/locations/inland-empire
President/CEO: Deborah Markos
Type: University **Sex:** Coed **Regional Accreditation:** Western Association of Colleges and Schools **Professional Accreditation:** ACBSP.

ARGOSY UNIVERSITY, LOS ANGELES
5230 Pacific Concourse, Ste. 200
Los Angeles, CA 90045
Tel: (310)531-9700; Free: 866-505-0332
Web Site: www.argosy.edu/locations/los-angeles
President/CEO: Deborah Markos
Type: University **Sex:** Coed **Regional Accreditation:** Western Association of Colleges and Schools **Professional Accreditation:** ACBSP.

ARGOSY UNIVERSITY, ORANGE COUNTY
601 S Lewis St.
Orange, CA 92868
Tel: (714)620-3700; Free: 800-716-9598
Web Site: www.argosy.edu/locations/los-angeles-orange-county
President/CEO: Deborah Markos
Type: University **Sex:** Coed **H.S. Requirements:** High school diploma required; GED accepted **Calendar System:** Semester **Regional Accreditation:** Western Association of Colleges and Schools **Professional Accreditation:** ACBSP.

ARGOSY UNIVERSITY, SAN DIEGO
1615 Murray Canyon Rd., Ste. 100
San Diego, CA 92108
Tel: (619)321-3000; Free: 866-505-0333
Web Site: www.argosy.edu/locations/san-diego
President/CEO: Deborah Markos
Type: University **Sex:** Coed **Regional Accreditation:** Western Association of Colleges and Schools **Professional Accreditation:** ACBSP.

ARGOSY UNIVERSITY, SAN FRANCISCO BAY AREA
1005 Atlantic Ave.
Alameda, CA 94501
Tel: (510)217-4700; Free: 866-215-2777
Fax: (510)217-4806
Web Site: www.argosy.edu/locations/san-francisco
President/CEO: Lance Garrison
Type: University **Sex:** Coed **Affiliation:** Education Management Corporation. **Calendar System:** Semester **Regional Accreditation:** Western Association of Colleges and Schools **Professional Accreditation:** ACBSP, APA.

ART CENTER COLLEGE OF DESIGN
1700 Lida St.
Pasadena, CA 91103
Tel: (626)396-2200
Fax: (626)795-0578
E-mail: kit.baron@artcenter.edu
Web Site: www.artcenter.edu
President/CEO: Lorne Buchman, PhD
Admissions: Kit Baron
Financial Aid: Clema McKenzie
Type: Comprehensive **Sex:** Coed **% Accepted:** 80 **Admission Plans:** Deferred Admission **Application Fee:** $50.00 **H.S. Requirements:** High school diploma required; GED accepted **Costs Per Year:** Application fee: $50. Tuition: $40,046 full-time, $1669 per credit part-time. Mandatory fees: $550 full-time. **Scholarships:** Available. **Calendar System:** Semester, Summer session available **Enrollment:** Full-time 1,613, Graduate full-time 161, Graduate part-time 57, Part-time 302 **Exams:** ACT; ACT essay component

not used; SAT I; SAT I or ACT; SAT essay component not used. **Final Year or Final Semester Residency Requirement:** Yes **Regional Accreditation:** Western Association of Colleges and Schools **Credit Hours For Degree:** 120 credits, Bachelors **Professional Accreditation:** NASAD.

THE ART INSTITUTE OF CALIFORNIA–HOLLYWOOD, A CAMPUS OF ARGOSY UNIVERSITY
5250 Lankershim Blvd.
North Hollywood, CA 91601
Tel: (818)299-5100; Free: 877-468-6232
Web Site: www.artinstitutes.edu/hollywood
President/CEO: Matthew Madrid
Type: Four-Year College **Sex:** Coed **Affiliation:** Education Management Corporation. **Calendar System:** Quarter **Regional Accreditation:** Western Association of Colleges and Schools **Professional Accreditation:** ACICS.

THE ART INSTITUTE OF CALIFORNIA–INLAND EMPIRE, A CAMPUS OF ARGOSY UNIVERSITY
674 E Brier Dr.
San Bernardino, CA 92408
Tel: (909)915-2100; Free: 800-353-0812
Web Site: www.artinstitutes.edu/inlandempire
President/CEO: Matthew Madrid
Type: Four-Year College **Sex:** Coed **Affiliation:** Education Management Corporation. **Regional Accreditation:** Western Association of Colleges and Schools

THE ART INSTITUTE OF CALIFORNIA–LOS ANGELES, A CAMPUS OF ARGOSY UNIVERSITY
2900 31st St.
Santa Monica, CA 90405-3035
Tel: (310)752-4700; Free: 888-646-4610
Fax: (310)752-4708
Web Site: www.artinstitutes.edu/losangeles
President/CEO: Claude Brown
Type: Four-Year College **Sex:** Coed **Affiliation:** Education Management Corporation. **Calendar System:** Quarter **Regional Accreditation:** Western Association of Colleges and Schools **Professional Accreditation:** ACICS.

THE ART INSTITUTE OF CALIFORNIA–ORANGE COUNTY, A CAMPUS OF ARGOSY UNIVERSITY
3601 W Sunflower Ave.
Santa Ana, CA 92704
Tel: (714)830-0200; Free: 888-549-3055
Web Site: www.artinstitutes.edu/orangecounty
President/CEO: John Andersen
Type: Four-Year College **Sex:** Coed **Affiliation:** Education Management Corporation. **Calendar System:** Quarter **Regional Accreditation:** Western Association of Colleges and Schools **Professional Accreditation:** ACICS.

THE ART INSTITUTE OF CALIFORNIA–SACRAMENTO, A CAMPUS OF ARGOSY UNIVERSITY
2850 Gateway Oaks Dr., Ste. 100
Sacramento, CA 95833
Tel: (916)830-6320; Free: 800-477-1957
Web Site: www.artinstitutes.edu/sacramento
President/CEO: Elden Monday
Type: Four-Year College **Sex:** Coed **Regional Accreditation:** Western Association of Colleges and Schools **Professional Accreditation:** ACICS.

THE ART INSTITUTE OF CALIFORNIA–SAN DIEGO, A CAMPUS OF ARGOSY UNIVERSITY
7650 Mission Valley Rd.
San Diego, CA 92108
Tel: (858)598-1200; Free: 866-275-2422
Web Site: www.artinstitutes.edu/sandiego
President/CEO: AJ Antun
Financial Aid: Monica McCormick
Type: Four-Year College **Sex:** Coed **Affiliation:** Education Management Corporation. **Calendar System:** Quarter **Regional Accreditation:** Western Association of Colleges and Schools **Professional Accreditation:** ACCSC, ACF.

THE ART INSTITUTE OF CALIFORNIA–SAN FRANCISCO, A CAMPUS OF ARGOSY UNIVERSITY
1170 Market St.
San Francisco, CA 94102
Tel: (415)865-0198; Free: 888-493-3261
Fax: (415)863-6344
Web Site: www.artinstitutes.edu/sanfrancisco
President/CEO: Byron Chung
Type: Comprehensive **Sex:** Coed **Affiliation:** Education Management Corporation. **Calendar System:** Quarter **Regional Accreditation:** Western Association of Colleges and Schools **Professional Accreditation:** ACICS.

ASHFORD UNIVERSITY
8620 Spectrum Ctr. Blvd.
San Diego, CA 92123
Free: 866-711-1700
E-mail: admissns@tfu.edu
Web Site: www.ashford.edu
President/CEO: Dr. Jane McAuliffe
Admissions: Waunita M. Sullivan
Financial Aid: Lisa Kramer
Type: Comprehensive **Sex:** Coed **Scores:** 49% ACT 18-23; 9% ACT 24-29 **Admission Plans:** Deferred Admission; Early Admission **Application Deadline:** Rolling **Application Fee:** $20.00 **H.S. Requirements:** High school diploma required; GED accepted **Scholarships:** Available. **Calendar System:** Semester, Summer session available **Enrollment:** Full-time 9,761, Part-time 105 **Faculty:** Full-time 45, Part-time 703 **Student-Faculty Ratio:** 37:1 **Exams:** SAT I or ACT. **Regional Accreditation:** Western Association of Colleges and Schools **Credit Hours For Degree:** 62 credit hours, Associates; 122 credit hours, Bachelors **Intercollegiate Athletics:** Baseball M; Basketball M & W; Cross-Country Running M & W; Golf M & W; Soccer M & W; Softball W; Track and Field M & W; Volleyball W

AVIATION & ELECTRONIC SCHOOLS OF AMERICA
111 S Railroad St.
Colfax, CA 95713-1810
Tel: (530)346-6792; Free: 800-345-2742
Fax: (530)346-8466
E-mail: aesa@aesa.com
Web Site: www.aesa.com
President/CEO: James P. Doyle
Type: Two-Year College **Sex:** Coed **Calendar System:** Continuous **Professional Accreditation:** COE.

AZUSA PACIFIC UNIVERSITY
901 E Alosta Ave.
Azusa, CA 91702-7000
Tel: (626)969-3434; Free: 800-TALK-APU
E-mail: admissions@apu.edu
Web Site: www.apu.edu
President/CEO: Dr. Jon R. Wallace
Admissions: Lynnette Barnes
Financial Aid: Todd Ross
Type: University **Sex:** Coed **Affiliation:** nondenominational. **Scores:** 98% SAT V 400+; 96% SAT M 400+; 41.7% ACT 18-23; 43.9% ACT 24-29 **% Accepted:** 81 **Admission Plans:** Early Decision Plan **Application Deadline:** June 1 **Application Fee:** $45.00 **H.S. Requirements:** High school diploma required; GED accepted **Costs Per Year:** Application fee: $45. Tuition: $34,174 full-time, $1424 per credit hour part-time. Mandatory fees: $580 full-time. Full-time tuition and fees vary according to course load and degree level. Part-time tuition varies according to course load and degree level. College room only: $5438. Room charges vary according to housing facility. **Scholarships:** Available. **Calendar System:** Semester, Summer session available **Enrollment:** Full-time 5,356, Graduate full-time 1,915, Graduate part-time 2,177, Part-time 527 **Faculty:** Full-time 456, Part-time 725 **Student-Faculty Ratio:** 12:1 **Exams:** ACT essay component used for advising; ACT essay component used for placement; SAT I or ACT; SAT essay component used for advising; SAT essay component used for placement. **% Receiving Financial Aid:** 76 **% Residing in College-Owned, -Operated, or -Affiliated Housing:** 62 **Final Year or Final Semester Residency Requirement:** No **Regional Accreditation:** Western Association of Colleges and Schools **Credit Hours For Degree:** 120 units, Bachelors **ROTC:** Air Force, Army **Professional Accreditation:** AACN, APA, APTA, ATS, CSWE, JRCAT, NASAD, NASM, NCATE. **Intercollegiate**

Athletics: Baseball M; Basketball M & W; Cross-Country Running M & W; Football M; Gymnastics W; Soccer M & W; Softball W; Swimming and Diving W; Tennis M & W; Track and Field M & W; Volleyball W; Water Polo W

BAKERSFIELD COLLEGE

1801 Panorama Dr.
Bakersfield, CA 93305-1299
Tel: (661)395-4011
Fax: (661)395-4230
E-mail: svaughn@bakersfieldcollege.edu
Web Site: www.bakersfieldcollege.edu
President/CEO: Sonya Christian
Admissions: Sue Vaughn

Type: Two-Year College **Sex:** Coed **Affiliation:** California Community College System. **Admission Plans:** Open Admission; Preferred Admission **Application Deadline:** Rolling **Application Fee:** $0.00 **H.S. Requirements:** High school diploma or equivalent not required. For applicants under 18: High school diploma required; GED accepted **Scholarships:** Available. **Calendar System:** Semester, Summer session available **Regional Accreditation:** Western Association of Colleges and Schools **Credit Hours For Degree:** 60 units, Associates **Professional Accreditation:** JRCERT. **Intercollegiate Athletics:** Baseball M; Basketball M & W; Cross-Country Running M & W; Football M; Golf M; Soccer W; Softball W; Tennis M & W; Track and Field M & W; Volleyball W; Wrestling M

BARSTOW COMMUNITY COLLEGE

2700 Barstow Rd.
Barstow, CA 92311-6699
Tel: (760)252-2411
Fax: (760)252-1875
E-mail: hcaldon@barstow.edu
Web Site: www.barstow.edu
President/CEO: Thom Armstrong
Admissions: Heather Caldon

Type: Two-Year College **Sex:** Coed **Affiliation:** California Community College System. **Admission Plans:** Deferred Admission; Early Admission; Open Admission **Application Deadline:** Rolling **H.S. Requirements:** High school diploma or equivalent not required. For applicants under 18: High school diploma required; GED accepted **Scholarships:** Available. **Calendar System:** Semester, Summer session available **Student-Faculty Ratio:** 35:1 **Regional Accreditation:** Western Association of Colleges and Schools **Credit Hours For Degree:** 60 units, Associates **Intercollegiate Athletics:** Baseball M; Basketball M & W; Cross-Country Running M & W

BERGIN UNIVERSITY OF CANINE STUDIES

5860 Labath Ave.
Rohnert Park, CA 94928
Tel: (707)545-3647
Web Site: www.berginu.edu
Type: Comprehensive **Sex:** Coed **Calendar System:** Semester **Professional Accreditation:** ACICS.

BERKELEY CITY COLLEGE

2050 Ctr. St.
Berkeley, CA 94704-5102
Tel: (510)981-2800
Fax: (510)841-7333
E-mail: mrivas@peralta.edu
Web Site: www.berkeleycitycollege.edu
President/CEO: Dr. Deborah Budd
Admissions: Dr. May Kuang-chi Chen
Financial Aid: Loan Nguyen

Type: Two-Year College **Sex:** Coed **Affiliation:** Peralta Community College District; California Community College System. **Scholarships:** Available. **Calendar System:** Semester, Summer session available **Faculty:** Full-time 62, Part-time 250 **Student-Faculty Ratio:** 35:1 **Regional Accreditation:** Western Association of Colleges and Schools **Credit Hours For Degree:** 60 semester hours, Associates

BETHESDA UNIVERSITY

730 N Euclid St.
Anaheim, CA 92801
Tel: (714)517-1945
Fax: (714)517-1948

E-mail: admission@bcu.edu
Web Site: www.buc.edu
President/CEO: Dr. Young Gull Lee
Admissions: Jacquie Ha
Financial Aid: Grace Choi
Type: Comprehensive **Sex:** Coed **Affiliation:** Full Gospel World Mission. **% Accepted:** 95 **Admission Plans:** Early Admission; Open Admission **Application Deadline:** August 11 **Application Fee:** $35.00 **H.S. Requirements:** High school diploma required; GED accepted **Scholarships:** Available. **Calendar System:** Semester, Summer session available **% Receiving Financial Aid:** 33 **Credit Hours For Degree:** 125 units, Bachelors **Professional Accreditation:** ABHE, TRACS.

BIOLA UNIVERSITY

13800 Biola Ave.
La Mirada, CA 90639-0001
Tel: (562)903-6000; Free: 800-652-4652
Fax: (562)903-4709
E-mail: admissions@biola.edu
Web Site: www.biola.edu
President/CEO: Dr. Barry H. Corey
Admissions: Michelle Reider

Type: University **Sex:** Coed **Affiliation:** interdenominational. **Scores:** 97% SAT V 400+; 96% SAT M 400+; 40.9% ACT 18-23; 43.7% ACT 24-29 **% Accepted:** 73 **Admission Plans:** Deferred Admission; Early Action; Early Decision Plan **Application Deadline:** March 1 **Application Fee:** $45.00 **H.S. Requirements:** High school diploma required; GED accepted **Costs Per Year:** Application fee: $45. Comprehensive fee: $46,400 includes full-time tuition ($36,696) and college room and board ($9704). College room only: $5424. Full-time tuition varies according to course load and degree level. Room and board charges vary according to board plan. Part-time tuition: $1529 per unit. Part-time tuition varies according to course load and degree level. **Scholarships:** Available. **Calendar System:** 4-1-4, Summer session available **Enrollment:** Full-time 4,073, Graduate full-time 873, Graduate part-time 1,124, Part-time 152 **Faculty:** Full-time 271, Part-time 284 **Student-Faculty Ratio:** 15:1 **Exams:** ACT essay component not used; SAT I or ACT; SAT essay component not used; SAT Reasoning. **% Receiving Financial Aid:** 68 **% Residing in College-Owned, -Operated, or -Affiliated Housing:** 63 **Final Year or Final Semester Residency Requirement:** Yes **Regional Accreditation:** Western Association of Colleges and Schools **Credit Hours For Degree:** 130 degree applicable units (minimum), Bachelors **ROTC:** Air Force, Army **Professional Accreditation:** AACN, ACBSP, APA, ATS, NASAD, NASM. **Intercollegiate Athletics:** Baseball M; Basketball M & W; Cross-Country Running M & W; Golf M & W; Soccer M & W; Softball W; Swimming and Diving M & W; Tennis M & W; Track and Field M & W; Volleyball W

BLAKE AUSTIN COLLEGE

611-K Orange Dr.
Vacaville, CA 95687
Tel: (707)0557
Web Site: www.blakeaustincollege.edu
Type: Two-Year College **Sex:** Coed **Professional Accreditation:** COE.

BRANDMAN UNIVERSITY

16355 Laguna Canyon Rd.
Irvine, CA 92618
Tel: (949)753-4774; Free: 800-746-0082
Fax: (949)753-7875
E-mail: apply@brandman.edu
Web Site: www.brandman.edu/irvine
President/CEO: Pres. Gary Brahm
Type: Comprehensive **Sex:** Coed **Calendar System:** Trimester, Summer session available **Enrollment:** Full-time 1,208, Graduate full-time 1,518, Graduate part-time 2,660, Part-time 2,618 **Faculty:** Full-time 73, Part-time 703 **Student-Faculty Ratio:** 16:1 **Exams:** ACT essay component not used; SAT essay component not used. **Final Year or Final Semester Residency Requirement:** Yes **Regional Accreditation:** Western Association of Colleges and Schools **Credit Hours For Degree:** 60 credit hours, Associates; 120 credit hours, Bachelors

BRIGHTWOOD COLLEGE, BAKERSFIELD CAMPUS

1914 Wible Rd.
Bakersfield, CA 93304

Tel: (661)836-6300; Free: 800-935-1857
Web Site: www.brightwood.edu
President/CEO: Jacki Rupe
Type: Two-Year College **Sex:** Coed **H.S. Requirements:** High school diploma required; GED accepted **Professional Accreditation:** ACICS.

BRIGHTWOOD COLLEGE, CHULA VISTA CAMPUS
555 Broadway
Chula Vista, CA 91910
Free: 800-935-1857
Web Site: www.brightwood.edu
President/CEO: Kevin Prehn
Type: Two-Year College **Sex:** Coed **H.S. Requirements:** High school diploma required; GED accepted **Professional Accreditation:** ACCSC, ACICS.

BRIGHTWOOD COLLEGE, FRESNO CAMPUS
44 Shaw Ave.
Fresno, CA 93612
Tel: (559)325-5100; Free: 800-935-1857
Web Site: www.brightwood.edu
President/CEO: Noha Elbaz
Type: Two-Year College **Sex:** Coed **H.S. Requirements:** High school diploma required; GED accepted **Professional Accreditation:** ACCSC, ACICS.

BRIGHTWOOD COLLEGE, MODESTO CAMPUS
5172 Kiernan Ct.
Salida, CA 95368
Tel: (209)543-7000; Free: 800-935-1857
Fax: (209)571-9836
Web Site: www.brightwood.edu
President/CEO: Bill Jones
Type: Two-Year College **Sex:** Coed **H.S. Requirements:** High school diploma required; GED accepted **Calendar System:** Semester **Professional Accreditation:** ACICS.

BRIGHTWOOD COLLEGE, NORTH HOLLYWOOD CAMPUS
6180 Laurel Canyon Blvd.
Ste. 101
North Hollywood, CA 91606
Tel: (818)754-6000; Free: 800-935-1857
E-mail: rcodner@mariccollege.edu
Web Site: www.brightwood.edu
Admissions: Renee Codner
Type: Two-Year College **Sex:** Coed **Calendar System:** Quarter **Professional Accreditation:** ACCSC, ACICS.

BRIGHTWOOD COLLEGE, PALM SPRINGS CAMPUS
2475 E Tahquitz Canyon Way
Palm Springs, CA 92262
Tel: (760)778-3540; Free: 800-935-1857
Web Site: www.brightwood.edu
President/CEO: Kevin Quirk
Type: Two-Year College **Sex:** Coed **H.S. Requirements:** High school diploma required; GED accepted **Professional Accreditation:** ACCSC, ACICS.

BRIGHTWOOD COLLEGE, RIVERSIDE CAMPUS
4040 Vine St.
Riverside, CA 92507
Tel: (951)276-1704; Free: 800-935-1857
Web Site: www.brightwood.edu
President/CEO: Jacki Rupe
Type: Two-Year College **Sex:** Coed **H.S. Requirements:** High school diploma required; GED accepted **Professional Accreditation:** ACCSC, ACICS.

BRIGHTWOOD COLLEGE, SACRAMENTO CAMPUS
4330 Watt Ave.
Ste. 400
Sacramento, CA 95821
Tel: (916)649-8168; Free: 800-935-1857
Fax: (916)649-8344

Web Site: www.brightwood.edu
President/CEO: Rob Dillman
Type: Two-Year College **Sex:** Coed **H.S. Requirements:** High school diploma required; GED accepted **Calendar System:** Semester **Professional Accreditation:** ACICS.

BRIGHTWOOD COLLEGE, SAN DIEGO CAMPUS
9055 Balboa Ave.
San Diego, CA 92123
Tel: (858)279-4500; Free: 800-935-1857
Fax: (858)279-4885
Web Site: www.brightwood.edu
President/CEO: David Movsesian
Type: Two-Year College **Sex:** Coed **H.S. Requirements:** High school diploma required; GED accepted **Calendar System:** Semester **Professional Accreditation:** ACCSC, ACICS.

BRIGHTWOOD COLLEGE, VISTA CAMPUS
2022 University Dr.
Vista, CA 92083
Tel: (760)630-1555; Free: 800-935-1857
Fax: (760)630-1656
Web Site: www.brightwood.edu
President/CEO: Laura Stinson
Type: Two-Year College **Sex:** Coed **H.S. Requirements:** High school diploma required; GED accepted **Professional Accreditation:** ACICS.

BRISTOL UNIVERSITY
2390 Orangewood Ave.
Ste. 485
Anaheim, CA 92806
Tel: (714)542-8086
Fax: (714)245-2425
Web Site: bristoluniversity.edu
Type: Comprehensive **Sex:** Coed **Professional Accreditation:** ACICS.

BROOKS INSTITUTE
5301 N Ventura Ave.
Ventura, CA 93001
Tel: (805)585-8000; Free: 888-276-4999
Fax: (805)585-8099
E-mail: admissions@brooks.edu
Web Site: www.brooks.edu
President/CEO: Roger Andersen
Financial Aid: Stacey Eymann
Type: Comprehensive **Sex:** Coed **Affiliation:** Career Education Corporation. **Application Fee:** $100.00 **H.S. Requirements:** High school diploma required; GED accepted **Scholarships:** Available. **Calendar System:** Trimester, Summer session not available **Student-Faculty Ratio:** 22:1 **Regional Accreditation:** Western Association of Colleges and Schools **Credit Hours For Degree:** 153 credits, Bachelors **Professional Accreditation:** ACICS.

BRYAN COLLEGE
2339 Gold Meadow Way
Ste. 111
Gold River, CA 95670
Tel: (916)649-2400; Free: 866-649-2400
E-mail: studentinfo@bryancollege.edu
Web Site: www.bryancollege.edu
President/CEO: Jeff Horton
Type: Two-Year College **Sex:** Coed **% Accepted:** 63 **Application Fee:** $25.00 **Scholarships:** Available. **Student-Faculty Ratio:** 11:1 **Professional Accreditation:** ACCSC.

BRYAN UNIVERSITY
3580 Wilshire Blvd.
Los Angeles, CA 90010
Tel: (213)484-8850
Fax: (213)483-3936
Web Site: losangeles.bryanuniversity.edu
Type: Two-Year College **Sex:** Coed **Professional Accreditation:** ACICS.

BUTTE COLLEGE
3536 Butte Campus Dr.
Oroville, CA 95965-8399
Tel: (530)895-2511
Fax: (530)895-2345
Web Site: www.butte.edu
President/CEO: Dr. Kimberly Perry
Admissions: Brad Zuniga
Type: Two-Year College **Sex:** Coed **Affiliation:** California Community College System. **% Accepted:** 100 **Admission Plans:** Deferred Admission; Early Admission; Open Admission **Application Deadline:** Rolling **Application Fee:** $0.00 **H.S. Requirements:** High school diploma or equivalent not required. For applicants under 18: High school diploma required; GED accepted **Scholarships:** Available. **Calendar System:** Semester, Summer session available **Enrollment:** Full-time 5,330, Part-time 6,960 **Student-Faculty Ratio:** 25:1 **Final Year or Final Semester Residency Requirement:** No **Regional Accreditation:** Western Association of Colleges and Schools **Credit Hours For Degree:** 60 semester hours, Associates **Professional Accreditation:** CoARC. **Intercollegiate Athletics:** Baseball M; Basketball M & W; Cross-Country Running M & W; Football M; Golf M & W; Soccer M & W; Softball W; Track and Field M & W; Volleyball W

CABRILLO COLLEGE
6500 Soquel Dr.
Aptos, CA 95003-3194
Tel: (831)479-6100
Fax: (831)479-6425
E-mail: tabolton@cabrillo.edu
Web Site: www.cabrillo.edu
President/CEO: Brian King
Admissions: Tama Bolton
Type: Two-Year College **Sex:** Coed **Affiliation:** California Community College System. **Admission Plans:** Early Admission; Open Admission **Application Deadline:** Rolling **Application Fee:** $0.00 **H.S. Requirements:** High school diploma or equivalent not required. For applicants under 18: High school diploma required; GED accepted **Scholarships:** Available. **Calendar System:** Semester, Summer session available **Student-Faculty Ratio:** 26:1 **Regional Accreditation:** Western Association of Colleges and Schools **Credit Hours For Degree:** 60 semester hours, Associates **Professional Accreditation:** AAMAE, ADA, JRCERT. **Intercollegiate Athletics:** Baseball M; Basketball M & W; Football M; Golf M; Soccer M & W; Softball W; Swimming and Diving M & W; Tennis M & W; Volleyball W; Water Polo M & W

CALIFORNIA BAPTIST UNIVERSITY
8432 Magnolia Ave.
Riverside, CA 92504-3206
Tel: (951)689-5771; Free: 877-228-8866
E-mail: admissions@calbaptist.edu
Web Site: www.calbaptist.edu
President/CEO: Dr. Ronald L. Ellis
Admissions: Allen Johnson
Financial Aid: Joshua Morey
Type: Comprehensive **Sex:** Coed **Affiliation:** Southern Baptist. **Scores:** 83% SAT V 400+; 81% SAT M 400+; 45.96% ACT 18-23; 24.44% ACT 24-29 **% Accepted:** 65 **Admission Plans:** Deferred Admission; Early Decision Plan **Application Deadline:** Rolling **Application Fee:** $45.00 **H.S. Requirements:** High school diploma required; GED accepted **Costs Per Year:** Application fee: $45. One-time mandatory fee: $310. Comprehensive fee: $42,052 includes full-time tuition ($29,562), mandatory fees ($1810), and college room and board ($10,680). College room only: $5260. Full-time tuition and fees vary according to course load, location, and program. Room and board charges vary according to board plan and housing facility. Part-time tuition: $1137 per unit. Part-time mandatory fees: $175 per term. Part-time tuition and fees vary according to course load, location, and program. **Scholarships:** Available. **Calendar System:** Miscellaneous, Summer session available **Enrollment:** Full-time 5,674, Graduate full-time 932, Graduate part-time 979, Part-time 956 **Faculty:** Full-time 289, Part-time 383 **Student-Faculty Ratio:** 17:1 **Exams:** ACT essay component used for admission; ACT essay component used for placement; SAT I and SAT II or ACT; SAT I or ACT; SAT essay component used for admission; SAT essay component used for placement; SAT Reasoning; SAT Subject. **% Receiving Financial Aid:** 82 **% Residing in College-Owned, -Operated, or -Affiliated Housing:** 39 **Final Year or Final Semester Residency Requirement:** No **Regional Accreditation:** Western Association of Colleges and Schools

Credit Hours For Degree: 60 units, Associates; 124 units, Bachelors **ROTC:** Air Force, Army **Professional Accreditation:** AACN, ACBSP, NASM. **Intercollegiate Athletics:** Baseball M; Basketball M & W; Cheerleading W; Cross-Country Running M & W; Golf M & W; Soccer M & W; Softball W; Swimming and Diving M & W; Track and Field M & W; Volleyball M & W; Water Polo M & W; Wrestling M

CALIFORNIA CHRISTIAN COLLEGE
5364 E Belmont Ave.
Fresno, CA 93727
Tel: (559)251-4215
E-mail: cccadmissions@sbcglobal.net
Web Site: www.calchristiancollege.edu
President/CEO: Pres. Wendell Walley
Admissions: Trent Walley
Financial Aid: Mindy Scroggins
Type: Four-Year College **Sex:** Coed **Affiliation:** Free Will Baptist. **% Accepted:** 100 **Admission Plans:** Open Admission **Application Deadline:** Rolling **Application Fee:** $40.00 **H.S. Requirements:** High school diploma required; GED accepted **Costs Per Year:** Application fee: $40. Comprehensive fee: $13,550 includes full-time tuition ($8160), mandatory fees ($590), and college room and board ($4800). Part-time tuition: $340 per unit. **Scholarships:** Available. **Calendar System:** Semester, Summer session not available **Enrollment:** Full-time 11, Part-time 7 **Faculty:** Part-time 7 **Exams:** Other; SAT I or ACT. **% Receiving Financial Aid:** 91 **% Residing in College-Owned, -Operated, or -Affiliated Housing:** 25 **Credit Hours For Degree:** 64 units, Associates; 128 units, Bachelors **Professional Accreditation:** TRACS.

CALIFORNIA COAST UNIVERSITY
925 N Spurgeon St.
Santa Ana, CA 92701
Tel: (714)547-9625; Free: 888-CCU-UNIV
E-mail: admissions@calcoast.edu
Web Site: www.calcoast.edu
President/CEO: Thomas Neal
Admissions: Damien McMenamin
Type: Comprehensive **Sex:** Coed **Application Fee:** $75.00 **H.S. Requirements:** High school diploma required; GED accepted **Professional Accreditation:** DEAC.

CALIFORNIA COLLEGE OF THE ARTS
1111 Eighth St.
San Francisco, CA 94107
Tel: (415)703-9500; Free: 800-447-1ART
Fax: (415)703-9539
E-mail: enroll@cca.edu
Web Site: www.cca.edu
President/CEO: Stephen Beal
Admissions: Arnold Icasiano
Financial Aid: Dewayne J. Barnes
Type: Comprehensive **Sex:** Coed **Scores:** 92% SAT V 400+; 90% SAT M 400+; 44% ACT 18-23; 40% ACT 24-29 **Costs Per Year:** Tuition: $43,248 full-time. Mandatory fees: $460 full-time. Full-time tuition and fees vary according to degree level. College room only: $460. Room charges vary according to housing facility. **Scholarships:** Available. **Calendar System:** Semester, Summer session available **Enrollment:** Full-time 1,446, Graduate full-time 419, Graduate part-time 36, Part-time 87 **Faculty:** Full-time 99, Part-time 400 **Student-Faculty Ratio:** 7:1 **Exams:** ACT essay component not used; SAT essay component not used. **% Receiving Financial Aid:** 54 **% Residing in College-Owned, -Operated, or -Affiliated Housing:** 22 **Final Year or Final Semester Residency Requirement:** Yes **Regional Accreditation:** Western Association of Colleges and Schools **Credit Hours For Degree:** 126 until fall 2016 when it drops to 120 units, Bachelors **Professional Accreditation:** CIDA, NAAB, NASAD.

CALIFORNIA COLLEGE SAN DIEGO (NATIONAL CITY)
22 W 35th St.
National City, CA 91950
Tel: (619)680-4421; Free: 800-622-3188
Web Site: www.cc-sd.edu
Type: Four-Year College **Sex:** Coed **Professional Accreditation:** ACCSC.

CALIFORNIA COLLEGE SAN DIEGO (SAN DIEGO)
6602 Convoy Ct.
Ste. 100
San Diego, CA 92111
Tel: (619)293-0190; Free: 800-622-3188
E-mail: tana.sanderson@cc-sd.edu
Web Site: www.cc-sd.edu
President/CEO: David Parker
Admissions: Tana Sanderson
Financial Aid: Raul Rivera
Type: Four-Year College **Sex:** Coed **Admission Plans:** Open Admission **Scholarships:** Available. **Student-Faculty Ratio:** 19:1 **Professional Accreditation:** ACCSC.

CALIFORNIA COLLEGE SAN DIEGO (SAN MARCOS)
277 Rancheros Dr., Ste. 200
San Marcos, CA 92069
Tel: (760)621-4333; Free: 800-622-3188
Web Site: www.cc-sd.edu
Type: Four-Year College **Sex:** Coed **Professional Accreditation:** ACCSC.

CALIFORNIA INSTITUTE OF THE ARTS
24700 McBean Pky.
Valencia, CA 91355-2340
Tel: (661)255-1050; Free: 800-545-2787
E-mail: admiss@calarts.edu
Web Site: www.calarts.edu
President/CEO: Steven D. Lavine
Admissions: Molly Ryan
Financial Aid: Dr. Robin Bailey-Chen
Type: Comprehensive **Sex:** Coed **% Accepted:** 25 **Application Deadline:** January 5 **Application Fee:** $70.00 **H.S. Requirements:** High school diploma required; GED accepted **Costs Per Year:** Application fee: $70. Tuition: $45,030 full-time. **Scholarships:** Available. **Calendar System:** Semester, Summer session available **Enrollment:** Full-time 943, Graduate full-time 493, Graduate part-time 6, Part-time 6 **Faculty:** Full-time 160, Part-time 180 **Student-Faculty Ratio:** 7:1 **% Receiving Financial Aid:** 69 **% Residing in College-Owned, -Operated, or -Affiliated Housing:** 40 **Final Year or Final Semester Residency Requirement:** Yes **Regional Accreditation:** Western Association of Colleges and Schools **Credit Hours For Degree:** 120 units, Bachelors **Professional Accreditation:** NASAD, NASD, NASM, NAST.

CALIFORNIA INSTITUTE OF INTEGRAL STUDIES
1453 Mission St.
San Francisco, CA 94103
Tel: (415)575-6100
Fax: (415)575-1264
E-mail: admissions@ciis.edu
Web Site: www.ciis.edu
President/CEO: Joseph L. Subbiondo
Type: Two-Year Upper Division **Sex:** Coed **Application Fee:** $65.00 **Costs Per Year:** Application fee: $65. Tuition: $27,987 full-time, $778 per unit part-time. Mandatory fees: $705 full-time. **Scholarships:** Available. **Calendar System:** Semester, Summer session not available **Enrollment:** Full-time 87, Graduate full-time 1,090, Graduate part-time 303, Part-time 15 **Faculty:** Full-time 66, Part-time 165 **Student-Faculty Ratio:** 11:1 **% Receiving Financial Aid:** 99 **Regional Accreditation:** Western Association of Colleges and Schools **Credit Hours For Degree:** 120 credits, Bachelors **Professional Accreditation:** APA.

CALIFORNIA INSTITUTE OF TECHNOLOGY
1200 E California Blvd.
Pasadena, CA 91125-0001
Tel: (626)395-6811
Fax: (626)683-3026
Web Site: www.caltech.edu
President/CEO: Dr. Thomas F. Rosenbaum
Admissions: Jarrid James Whitney
Financial Aid: Don Crewell
Type: University **Sex:** Coed **Scores:** 100% SAT V 400+; 100% SAT M 400+ **% Accepted:** 9 **Admission Plans:** Deferred Admission; Early Admission; Early Decision Plan **Application Deadline:** January 3 **Application Fee:** $75.00 **H.S. Requirements:** High school diploma or equivalent not required

Costs Per Year: Application fee: $75. One-time mandatory fee: $500. Comprehensive fee: $58,761 includes full-time tuition ($43,710), mandatory fees ($1680), and college room and board ($13,371). College room only: $7536. Room and board charges vary according to housing facility. **Scholarships:** Available. **Calendar System:** Miscellaneous, Summer session not available **Enrollment:** Full-time 1,001, Graduate full-time 1,254 **Faculty:** Full-time 330, Part-time 27 **Student-Faculty Ratio:** 3:1 **Exams:** SAT I and SAT II or ACT; SAT I or ACT; SAT Reasoning; SAT Subject. **% Receiving Financial Aid:** 52 **% Residing in College-Owned, -Operated, or -Affiliated Housing:** 86 **Final Year or Final Semester Residency Requirement:** No **Regional Accreditation:** Western Association of Colleges and Schools **Credit Hours For Degree:** 486 units, Bachelors **ROTC:** Air Force, Army **Professional Accreditation:** ABET. **Intercollegiate Athletics:** Baseball M; Basketball M & W; Cross-Country Running M & W; Fencing M & W; Soccer M & W; Swimming and Diving M & W; Tennis M & W; Track and Field M & W; Volleyball M & W; Water Polo M & W

CALIFORNIA INTERCONTINENTAL UNIVERSITY
17310 Red Hill Ave. No.200
Irvine, CA 92614
Tel: (909)396-6090; Free: 866-687-2258
Fax: (909)804-5151
E-mail: admissions@caluniversity.com
Web Site: caluniversity.edu
President/CEO: Senthil Kumar
Admissions: John Ramsay
Type: Comprehensive **Sex:** Coed **Application Fee:** $75.00 **Professional Accreditation:** DEAC.

CALIFORNIA LUTHERAN UNIVERSITY
60 W Olsen Rd.
Thousand Oaks, CA 91360-2787
Tel: (805)492-2411; Free: 877-258-3678
Fax: (805)493-3114
E-mail: cluadm@clunet.edu
Web Site: www.callutheran.edu
President/CEO: Dr. Christopher Kimball
Admissions: Dr. Michael Elgarico
Financial Aid: Jerry McKeen
Type: Comprehensive **Sex:** Coed **Affiliation:** Lutheran. **Scores:** 98% SAT V 400+; 100% SAT M 400+; 44% ACT 18-23; 46% ACT 24-29 **% Accepted:** 62 **Admission Plans:** Deferred Admission; Early Decision Plan **Application Deadline:** January 1 **Application Fee:** $25.00 **H.S. Requirements:** High school diploma required; GED accepted **Costs Per Year:** Application fee: $25. Comprehensive fee: $52,820 includes full-time tuition ($39,310), mandatory fees ($450), and college room and board ($13,060). College room only: $7010. Room and board charges vary according to board plan and housing facility. Part-time tuition: $1265 per unit. **Scholarships:** Available. **Calendar System:** Semester, Summer session available **Enrollment:** Full-time 2,675, Graduate full-time 1,005, Graduate part-time 311, Part-time 135 **Faculty:** Full-time 193, Part-time 244 **Student-Faculty Ratio:** 15:1 **Exams:** ACT essay component used for admission; SAT I or ACT; SAT essay component used for admission; SAT Reasoning. **% Receiving Financial Aid:** 69 **% Residing in College-Owned, -Operated, or -Affiliated Housing:** 52 **Final Year or Final Semester Residency Requirement:** Yes **Regional Accreditation:** Western Association of Colleges and Schools **Credit Hours For Degree:** 124 units, Bachelors **ROTC:** Air Force, Army **Professional Accreditation:** ATS, NCATE. **Intercollegiate Athletics:** Baseball M; Basketball M & W; Cheerleading M & W; Cross-Country Running M & W; Football M; Golf M & W; Soccer M & W; Softball W; Swimming and Diving M & W; Tennis M & W; Track and Field M & W; Volleyball M & W; Water Polo M & W

CALIFORNIA MARITIME ACADEMY
200 Maritime Academy Dr.
Vallejo, CA 94590
Tel: (707)654-1000; Free: 800-561-1945
Fax: (707)648-4204
E-mail: admission@csum.edu
Web Site: www.csum.edu
President/CEO: Dr. William B. Eisenhardt
Admissions: Marc McGee
Financial Aid: Nicole Hill
Type: Comprehensive **Sex:** Coed **Affiliation:** California State University

System. **Scores:** 98% SAT V 400+; 98% SAT M 400+; 37.7% ACT 18-23; 52.6% ACT 24-29 **% Accepted:** 82 **Admission Plans:** Preferred Admission **Application Fee:** $55.00 **H.S. Requirements:** High school diploma required; GED accepted **Costs Per Year:** Application fee: $55. State resident tuition: $5472 full-time. Mandatory fees: $1314 full-time. Full-time tuition and fees vary according to course load. College room and board: $11,756. Room and board charges vary according to board plan and housing facility. **Scholarships:** Available. **Calendar System:** Semester, Summer session available **Enrollment:** Full-time 1,038, Graduate part-time 74, Part-time 37 **Faculty:** Full-time 64, Part-time 26 **Student-Faculty Ratio:** 15:1 **Exams:** ACT essay component not used; SAT I or ACT; SAT essay component not used; SAT Reasoning. **% Receiving Financial Aid:** 80 **% Residing in College-Owned, -Operated, or -Affiliated Housing:** 67 **Final Year or Final Semester Residency Requirement:** Yes **Regional Accreditation:** Western Association of Colleges and Schools **Credit Hours For Degree:** 126 units, Bachelors **ROTC:** Air Force, Navy **Professional Accreditation:** ABET. **Intercollegiate Athletics:** Basketball M & W; Crew M & W; Golf M & W; Rugby M; Sailing M & W; Soccer M; Volleyball W; Water Polo M & W

CALIFORNIA MIRAMAR UNIVERSITY

3550 Camino Del Rio N
Ste. 208
San Diego, CA 92108
Tel: (858)653-3000; Free: 877-570-5678
Fax: (858)653-6786
E-mail: admissions@calmu.edu
Web Site: www.calmu.edu
President/CEO: Dr. Dominic Mwenja
Admissions: Jean Van Slyke
Type: Comprehensive **Sex:** Coed **Application Fee:** $25.00 **Professional Accreditation:** ACICS.

CALIFORNIA NATIONAL UNIVERSITY FOR ADVANCED STUDIES

8550 Balboa Blvd., Ste. 210
Northridge, CA 91325
Tel: (818)830-2411; Free: 800-782-2422
Fax: (818)830-2418
E-mail: cnuadms@mail.cnuas.edu
Web Site: www.cnuas.edu
Admissions: Stephanie Smith
Type: Comprehensive **Sex:** Coed **Admission Plans:** Deferred Admission; Open Admission **Application Deadline:** Rolling **Application Fee:** $75.00 **H.S. Requirements:** High school diploma required; GED accepted **Calendar System:** Trimester **Faculty:** Part-time 98 **Student-Faculty Ratio:** 10:1 **Professional Accreditation:** DEAC.

CALIFORNIA POLYTECHNIC STATE UNIVERSITY, SAN LUIS OBISPO

1 Grand Ave.
San Luis Obispo, CA 93407
Tel: (805)756-1111
E-mail: admissions@calpoly.edu
Web Site: www.calpoly.edu
President/CEO: Dr. Jeffrey D. Armstrong
Admissions: James Maraviglia
Financial Aid: Lois Kelly
Type: Comprehensive **Sex:** Coed **Affiliation:** California State University System. **Scores:** 100% SAT V 400+; 100% SAT M 400+; 10.5% ACT 18-23; 53.6% ACT 24-29 **% Accepted:** 31 **Admission Plans:** Early Action; Early Admission **Application Deadline:** November 30 **Application Fee:** $55.00 **H.S. Requirements:** High school diploma required; GED accepted **Costs Per Year:** Application fee: $55. State resident tuition: $5472 full-time, $3174 per year part-time. Nonresident tuition: $16,632 full-time, $7638 per year part-time. Mandatory fees: $3528 full-time, $3075 per year part-time. Full-time tuition and fees vary according to course load, degree level, and program. Part-time tuition and fees vary according to course load, degree level, and program. College room and board: $12,009. College room only: $7176. Room and board charges vary according to housing facility. **Scholarships:** Available. **Calendar System:** Quarter, Summer session available **Enrollment:** Full-time 19,318, Graduate full-time 664, Graduate part-time 231, Part-time 731 **Faculty:** Full-time 889, Part-time 522 **Student-Faculty Ratio:** 19:1 **Exams:** ACT essay component not used; SAT I or ACT; SAT essay component not used; SAT Reasoning. **% Receiving Financial Aid:**

40 **% Residing in College-Owned, -Operated, or -Affiliated Housing:** 36 **Regional Accreditation:** Western Association of Colleges and Schools **Credit Hours For Degree:** 180 units, Bachelors **ROTC:** Army **Professional Accreditation:** AACSB, ABET, ACA, ACCE, ACSP, ASLA, ATMAE, NAAB, NASAD, NASM, NCATE, NRPA, SAF. **Intercollegiate Athletics:** Baseball M; Basketball M & W; Cross-Country Running M & W; Football M; Golf M & W; Soccer M & W; Softball W; Swimming and Diving M & W; Tennis M & W; Track and Field M & W; Volleyball W; Wrestling M

CALIFORNIA STATE POLYTECHNIC UNIVERSITY, POMONA

3801 W Temple Ave.
Pomona, CA 91768-2557
Tel: (909)869-7659
Fax: (909)869-4529
E-mail: awright@cpp.edu
Web Site: www.cpp.edu
President/CEO: Dr. Soraya M. Coley
Admissions: Andrew M. Wright
Financial Aid: Diana Minor
Type: Comprehensive **Sex:** Coed **Affiliation:** California State University System. **Scores:** 92% SAT V 400+; 94% SAT M 400+; 36.39% ACT 18-23; 40.42% ACT 24-29 **% Accepted:** 39 **Application Deadline:** November 30 **Application Fee:** $55.00 **H.S. Requirements:** High school diploma required; GED accepted. For applicants out of high school 5 years or more: High school diploma or equivalent not required **Costs Per Year:** Application fee: $55. State resident tuition: $5472 full-time. Nonresident tuition: $16,632 full-time. Mandatory fees: $1504 full-time, $248 per credit part-time. Full-time tuition and fees vary according to course load, degree level, and program. Part-time fees vary according to course load, degree level, and program. College room and board: $15,238. College room only: $9858. Room and board charges vary according to board plan and housing facility. **Scholarships:** Available. **Calendar System:** Quarter, Summer session available **Enrollment:** Full-time 19,619, Graduate full-time 641, Graduate part-time 919, Part-time 2,538 **Faculty:** Full-time 573, Part-time 652 **Student-Faculty Ratio:** 25:1 **Exams:** ACT essay component used for admission; ACT essay component used for placement; SAT I or ACT; SAT essay component used for admission; SAT essay component used for placement; SAT Reasoning. **% Receiving Financial Aid:** 66 **% Residing in College-Owned, -Operated, or -Affiliated Housing:** 10 **Final Year or Final Semester Residency Requirement:** Yes **Regional Accreditation:** Western Association of Colleges and Schools **Credit Hours For Degree:** 180 units, Bachelors **ROTC:** Army **Professional Accreditation:** AACSB, ABET, ACSP, AND, ASLA, CIDA, NAAB, NASAD, NASPAA. **Intercollegiate Athletics:** Baseball M; Basketball M & W; Cross-Country Running M & W; Soccer M & W; Track and Field M & W; Volleyball W

CALIFORNIA STATE UNIVERSITY, BAKERSFIELD

9001 Stockdale Hwy.
Bakersfield, CA 93311
Tel: (661)664-2011; Free: 800-788-2782
Fax: (661)664-3188
E-mail: admissions@csub.edu
Web Site: www.csub.edu
President/CEO: Horace Mitchell
Admissions: Debra Blowers
Financial Aid: Dr. Ron Radney
Type: Comprehensive **Sex:** Coed **Affiliation:** California State University System. **Scores:** 74% SAT V 400+; 78% SAT M 400+; 42.56% ACT 18-23; 13.64% ACT 24-29 **% Accepted:** 100 **Admission Plans:** Deferred Admission; Preferred Admission **Application Fee:** $55.00 **H.S. Requirements:** High school diploma required; GED not accepted **Costs Per Year:** Application fee: $55. State resident tuition: $5472 full-time. Nonresident tuition: $17,071 full-time. Mandatory fees: $1339 full-time. Full-time tuition and fees vary according to course load and degree level. College room and board: $12,561. College room only: $7971. Room and board charges vary according to board plan and housing facility. **Scholarships:** Available. **Calendar System:** Quarter **Enrollment:** Full-time 6,655, Graduate full-time 997, Graduate part-time 203, Part-time 1,370 **Faculty:** Full-time 272, Part-time 201 **Student-Faculty Ratio:** 28:1 **Exams:** SAT I or ACT. **% Receiving Financial Aid:** 81 **Regional Accreditation:** Western Association of Colleges and Schools **Credit Hours For Degree:** 186 quarter units, Bachelors **Professional Accreditation:** AACN, AACSB, CSWE, NASPAA, NCATE. **Intercollegiate Athletics:** Basketball M; Golf M; Soccer M; Softball W; Swimming and Diving M & W; Tennis W; Track and Field M & W; Volleyball W; Water Polo W; Wrestling M

CALIFORNIA STATE UNIVERSITY, CHANNEL ISLANDS
One University Dr.
Camarillo, CA 93012
Tel: (805)437-8400
Fax: (805)437-8951
E-mail: prospective.student@csuci.edu
Web Site: www.csuci.edu
President/CEO: Richard R. Rush
Admissions: Ginger Reyes
Type: Comprehensive **Sex:** Coed **Affiliation:** California State University System. **% Accepted:** 53 **Application Fee:** $50.00 **Faculty:** Full-time 89, Part-time 205 **Student-Faculty Ratio:** 15:1 **Exams:** SAT I or ACT. **% Residing in College-Owned, -Operated, or -Affiliated Housing:** 23 **Regional Accreditation:** Western Association of Colleges and Schools **Professional Accreditation:** AACN.

CALIFORNIA STATE UNIVERSITY, CHICO
400 W First St.
Chico, CA 95929-0722
Tel: (530)898-4636; Free: 800-542-4426
Fax: (530)898-6456
E-mail: info@csuchico.edu
Web Site: www.csuchico.edu
President/CEO: Dr. Paul J. Zingg, PhD
Financial Aid: Dan Reed
Type: Comprehensive **Sex:** Coed **Affiliation:** California State University System. **Scores:** 90% SAT V 400+; 89% SAT M 400+; 48% ACT 18-23; 31% ACT 24-29 **% Accepted:** 65 **Admission Plans:** Deferred Admission **Application Deadline:** November 30 **Application Fee:** $55.00 **H.S. Requirements:** High school diploma required; GED accepted **Costs Per Year:** Application fee: $55. State resident tuition: $7026 full-time. Nonresident tuition: $18,182 full-time. Mandatory fees: $5472 full-time. Full-time tuition and fees vary according to degree level. College room and board: $12,234. Room and board charges vary according to board plan and housing facility. **Scholarships:** Available. **Calendar System:** Semester, Summer session available **Enrollment:** Full-time 14,552, Part-time 1,575 **Faculty:** Full-time 479, Part-time 503 **Student-Faculty Ratio:** 24:1 **Exams:** ACT essay component not used; SAT I or ACT; SAT essay component not used; SAT Reasoning; SAT Subject. **% Receiving Financial Aid:** 65 **% Residing in College-Owned, -Operated, or -Affiliated Housing:** 13 **Regional Accreditation:** Western Association of Colleges and Schools **Credit Hours For Degree:** 120 units, Bachelors **Professional Accreditation:** AACN, AACSB, ABET, ACCE, ACEJMC, AND, ASHA, ATMAE, CSWE, NASAD, NASM, NASPAA, NCATE, NRPA. **Intercollegiate Athletics:** Baseball M; Basketball M & W; Cross-Country Running M & W; Golf M & W; Soccer M & W; Softball W; Track and Field M & W; Volleyball W

CALIFORNIA STATE UNIVERSITY, DOMINGUEZ HILLS
1000 E Victoria St.
Carson, CA 90747-0001
Tel: (310)243-3300
E-mail: info@csudh.edu
Web Site: www.csudh.edu
President/CEO: Dr. Willie J. Hagan
Financial Aid: Delores S. Lee
Type: Comprehensive **Sex:** Coed **Affiliation:** California State University System. **Scores:** 66% SAT V 400+; 66% SAT M 400+; 36.16% ACT 18-23; 5.54% ACT 24-29 **% Accepted:** 58 **Admission Plans:** Preferred Admission **Application Deadline:** Rolling **Application Fee:** $55.00 **H.S. Requirements:** High school diploma required; GED accepted **Costs Per Year:** Application fee: $55. State resident tuition: $5472 full-time. Nonresident tuition: $16,632 full-time. Mandatory fees: $802 full-time. **Scholarships:** Available. **Calendar System:** Semester, Summer session available **Enrollment:** Full-time 9,172, Graduate full-time 1,064, Graduate part-time 1,009, Part-time 3,390 **Faculty:** Full-time 289, Part-time 677 **Student-Faculty Ratio:** 23:1 **Exams:** ACT essay component not used; SAT I or ACT; SAT essay component not used; SAT Reasoning. **% Receiving Financial Aid:** 74 **% Residing in College-Owned, -Operated, or -Affiliated Housing:** 5 **Final Year or Final Semester Residency Requirement:** No **Regional Accreditation:** Western Association of Colleges and Schools **Credit Hours For Degree:** 120 semester units, Bachelors **ROTC:** Air Force, Army **Professional Accreditation:** AACN, ABET, ACBSP, AOTA, CSWE, NAACLS,

NASM, NASPAA, NAST, NCATE, NCOPE. **Intercollegiate Athletics:** Baseball M; Basketball M & W; Golf M; Soccer M & W; Softball W; Track and Field W; Volleyball W

CALIFORNIA STATE UNIVERSITY, EAST BAY
25800 Carlos Bee Blvd.
Hayward, CA 94542-3000
Tel: (510)885-3000
Fax: (510)885-3816
E-mail: dave.vasquez@csueastbay.edu
Web Site: www.csueastbay.edu
President/CEO: Dr. Leroy Morishita
Admissions: Dave Vasques
Type: Comprehensive **Sex:** Coed **Affiliation:** California State University System. **Scores:** 75% SAT V 400+; 76% SAT M 400+; 46.9% ACT 18-23; 10.6% ACT 24-29 **% Accepted:** 74 **Application Deadline:** November 30 **Application Fee:** $55.00 **H.S. Requirements:** High school diploma required; GED accepted **Costs Per Year:** Application fee: $55. State resident tuition: $5472 full-time. Nonresident tuition: $16,632 full-time. Mandatory fees: $1092 full-time. Full-time tuition and fees vary according to course load, program, and reciprocity agreements. College room and board: $14,183. Room and board charges vary according to board plan and housing facility. **Scholarships:** Available. **Calendar System:** Quarter, Summer session available **Enrollment:** Full-time 11,110, Graduate full-time 1,232, Graduate part-time 1,288, Part-time 1,898 **Faculty:** Full-time 354, Part-time 485 **Student-Faculty Ratio:** 23:1 **Exams:** SAT I or ACT; SAT Reasoning. **% Receiving Financial Aid:** 59 **Final Year or Final Semester Residency Requirement:** No **Regional Accreditation:** Western Association of Colleges and Schools **Credit Hours For Degree:** 186 units, Bachelors **Professional Accreditation:** AACSB, ABET, ACEN, ASHA, CSWE, NASAD, NASM, NASPAA, NCATE. **Intercollegiate Athletics:** Baseball M; Basketball M & W; Cross-Country Running M & W; Soccer M & W; Softball W; Swimming and Diving W; Volleyball W; Water Polo W

CALIFORNIA STATE UNIVERSITY, FRESNO
5241 N Maple Ave.
Fresno, CA 93740-8027
Tel: (559)278-4240
Fax: (559)278-4715
E-mail: andyhe@csufresno.edu
Web Site: www.csufresno.edu
President/CEO: Dr. Joseph Castro
Admissions: Andy Hernandez
Financial Aid: Denise Tardell
Type: Comprehensive **Sex:** Coed **Affiliation:** California State University System. **Scores:** 73% SAT V 400+; 76% SAT M 400+; 42% ACT 18-23; 12% ACT 24-29 **% Accepted:** 52 **Admission Plans:** Preferred Admission **Application Fee:** $55.00 **H.S. Requirements:** High school diploma required; GED accepted **Costs Per Year:** Application fee: $55. State resident tuition: $6298 full-time. Nonresident tuition: $17,446 full-time. College room and board: $10,604. Room and board charges vary according to board plan. **Scholarships:** Available. **Calendar System:** Semester, Summer session available **Enrollment:** Full-time 17,806, Graduate full-time 1,858, Graduate part-time 796, Part-time 3,676 **Faculty:** Full-time 657, Part-time 650 **Student-Faculty Ratio:** 22:1 **Exams:** ACT essay component not used; SAT I or ACT; SAT essay component not used; SAT Reasoning; SAT Subject. **% Receiving Financial Aid:** 74 **% Residing in College-Owned, -Operated, or -Affiliated Housing:** 5 **Final Year or Final Semester Residency Requirement:** Yes **Regional Accreditation:** Western Association of Colleges and Schools **Credit Hours For Degree:** 120 units, Bachelors **ROTC:** Air Force, Army **Professional Accreditation:** AACN, AACSB, AAFCS, ABET, ACA, ACCE, AND, APTA, ASHA, CEPH, CIDA, CORE, CSWE, JRCAT, NASM, NASPAA, NAST, NCATE, NRPA. **Intercollegiate Athletics:** Baseball M; Basketball M & W; Cross-Country Running M & W; Equestrian Sports W; Football M; Golf M & W; Lacrosse W; Soccer W; Softball W; Swimming and Diving W; Tennis M & W; Track and Field M & W; Volleyball W

CALIFORNIA STATE UNIVERSITY, FULLERTON
PO Box 34080
Fullerton, CA 92834-9480
Tel: (657)278-2011
E-mail: admissions@fullerton.edu
Web Site: www.fullerton.edu

President/CEO: Dr. Mildred Garcia
Admissions: Nancy J. Dority
Financial Aid: Cecilia Schouwe

Type: Comprehensive **Sex:** Coed **Affiliation:** California State University System. **Scores:** 93% SAT V 400+; 95% SAT M 400+; 55% ACT 18-23; 27% ACT 24-29 **% Accepted:** 44 **Admission Plans:** Preferred Admission **Application Deadline:** November 30 **Application Fee:** $55.00 **H.S. Requirements:** High school diploma required; GED accepted **Costs Per Year:** Application fee: $55. State resident tuition: $5472 full-time, $3174 per year part-time. Nonresident tuition: $16,632 full-time, $7638 per year part-time. Mandatory fees: $969 full-time, $968.92 per year part-time. Full-time tuition and fees vary according to course load. Part-time tuition and fees vary according to course load. College room and board: $14,574. Room and board charges vary according to board plan and housing facility. **Scholarships:** Available. **Calendar System:** Semester, Summer session available **Enrollment:** Full-time 26,762, Graduate full-time 2,462, Graduate part-time 2,940, Part-time 5,964 **Faculty:** Full-time 944, Part-time 1,100 **Student-Faculty Ratio:** 25:1 **Exams:** SAT I; SAT I or ACT; SAT Reasoning. **% Receiving Financial Aid:** 51 **% Residing in College-Owned, -Operated, or -Affiliated Housing:** 6 **Final Year or Final Semester Residency Requirement:** No **Regional Accreditation:** Western Association of Colleges and Schools **Credit Hours For Degree:** 120 semester units, Bachelors **ROTC:** Army **Professional Accreditation:** AACN, AACSB, AANA, ABET, ACA, ACEJMC, ACNM, ASHA, CSWE, JRCAT, NASAD, NASD, NASM, NASPAA, NAST, NCATE. **Intercollegiate Athletics:** Archery M & W; Baseball M; Basketball M & W; Bowling M & W; Cross-Country Running M & W; Equestrian Sports M & W; Golf M & W; Ice Hockey M & W; Lacrosse M & W; Rugby M & W; Sailing M & W; Skiing (Downhill) M & W; Soccer M & W; Softball W; Tennis W; Track and Field M & W; Ultimate Frisbee M & W; Volleyball M & W; Water Polo M & W

CALIFORNIA STATE UNIVERSITY, LONG BEACH

1250 Bellflower Blvd.
Long Beach, CA 90840
Tel: (562)985-4111
E-mail: janice.miller@csulb.edu
Web Site: www.csulb.edu
President/CEO: Dr. Jane Close Conoley
Admissions: Janice Miller
Financial Aid: Nicolas Valdivia

Type: Comprehensive **Sex:** Coed **Affiliation:** California State University System. **Scores:** 94% SAT M 400+; 41.5% ACT 18-23; 41.5% ACT 24-29 **% Accepted:** 34 **Admission Plans:** Preferred Admission **Application Deadline:** November 30 **Application Fee:** $55.00 **H.S. Requirements:** High school diploma required; GED accepted **Costs Per Year:** Application fee: $55. State resident tuition: $5472 full-time. Nonresident tuition: $15,144 full-time. Mandatory fees: $980 full-time. Full-time tuition and fees vary according to degree level and program. College room and board: $12,382. Room and board charges vary according to board plan. **Scholarships:** Available. **Calendar System:** Semester, Summer session available **Enrollment:** Full-time 26,727, Graduate full-time 3,097, Graduate part-time 2,270, Part-time 5,352 **Faculty:** Full-time 960, Part-time 1,290 **Student-Faculty Ratio:** 25:1 **Exams:** SAT I or ACT; SAT Reasoning. **% Receiving Financial Aid:** 73 **% Residing in College-Owned, -Operated, or -Affiliated Housing:** 30 **Regional Accreditation:** Western Association of Colleges and Schools **Credit Hours For Degree:** 120 units, Bachelors **ROTC:** Army **Professional Accreditation:** AACN, AACSB, AAFCS, ABET, AND, APA, APTA, ASHA, CAHME, CEPH, CSWE, CoA-KT, JRCERT, NASAD, NASD, NASM, NASPAA, NAST, NCATE, NRPA. **Intercollegiate Athletics:** Archery M & W; Badminton M & W; Basketball M & W; Bowling M & W; Crew M & W; Cross-Country Running M & W; Fencing M & W; Golf M & W; Rugby M; Sailing M & W; Skiing (Downhill) M & W; Soccer M & W; Softball W; Table Tennis M; Tennis W; Track and Field M & W; Volleyball M & W; Water Polo M & W

CALIFORNIA STATE UNIVERSITY, LOS ANGELES

5151 State University Dr.
Los Angeles, CA 90032-8530
Tel: (323)343-3000
Fax: (323)343-2670
E-mail: admission@calstatela.edu
Web Site: www.calstatela.edu
President/CEO: Dr. William A. Covino
Admissions: Vince Lopez

Financial Aid: Tamie L. Nguyen
Type: Comprehensive **Sex:** Coed **Affiliation:** California State University System. **Scores:** 69% SAT V 400+; 75% SAT M 400+; 41% ACT 18-23; 6.5% ACT 24-29 **% Accepted:** 61 **Admission Plans:** Early Admission **Application Deadline:** November 30 **Application Fee:** $55.00 **H.S. Requirements:** High school diploma required; GED accepted **Costs Per Year:** Application fee: $55. State resident tuition: $5472 full-time. Nonresident tuition: $14,400 full-time. Mandatory fees: $881 full-time. Full-time tuition and fees vary according to course level and course load. College room and board: $12,833. Room and board charges vary according to board plan and housing facility. **Scholarships:** Available. **Calendar System:** Quarter, Summer session available **Enrollment:** Full-time 17,741, Graduate full-time 1,730, Graduate part-time 2,090, Part-time 2,927 **Faculty:** Full-time 450, Part-time 670 **Student-Faculty Ratio:** 31:1 **Exams:** SAT I or ACT; SAT Reasoning; SAT Subject. **% Receiving Financial Aid:** 84 **% Residing in College-Owned, -Operated, or -Affiliated Housing:** 4 **Regional Accreditation:** Western Association of Colleges and Schools **Credit Hours For Degree:** 186 quarter units, Bachelors **ROTC:** Air Force, Army **Professional Accreditation:** AACN, AACSB, ABET, ACA, AND, ASHA, CORE, CSWE, NASAD, NASM, NASPAA, NCATE. **Intercollegiate Athletics:** Baseball M; Basketball M & W; Cross-Country Running W; Soccer M & W; Tennis W; Track and Field M & W; Volleyball W

CALIFORNIA STATE UNIVERSITY, MONTEREY BAY

100 Campus Ctr.
Seaside, CA 93955-8001
Tel: (831)582-3000
Fax: (831)582-3540
E-mail: admissions@csumb.edu
Web Site: www.csumb.edu
President/CEO: Dr. Eduardo Ochoa, PhD
Admissions: John Larsen

Type: Comprehensive **Sex:** Coed **Affiliation:** California State University System. **Scores:** 87% SAT V 400+; 85% SAT M 400+; 50% ACT 18-23; 22% ACT 24-29 **% Accepted:** 49 **Admission Plans:** Deferred Admission **Application Fee:** $55.00 **H.S. Requirements:** High school diploma required; GED accepted **Costs Per Year:** Application fee: $55. State resident tuition: $0 full-time. Nonresident tuition: $11,160 full-time, $372 per credit hour part-time. Mandatory fees: $5963 full-time. Full-time tuition and fees vary according to course load and degree level. Part-time tuition varies according to course load and degree level. College room and board: $10,112. Room and board charges vary according to board plan and housing facility. **Scholarships:** Available. **Calendar System:** Semester, Summer session available **Enrollment:** Full-time 6,171, Graduate full-time 298, Graduate part-time 147, Part-time 486 **Faculty:** Full-time 152, Part-time 345 **Student-Faculty Ratio:** 25:1 **Exams:** ACT essay component not used; SAT I or ACT; SAT essay component used for placement; SAT Reasoning; SAT Subject. **% Receiving Financial Aid:** 62 **% Residing in College-Owned, -Operated, or -Affiliated Housing:** 46 **Final Year or Final Semester Residency Requirement:** No **Regional Accreditation:** Western Association of Colleges and Schools **Credit Hours For Degree:** 120 units, Bachelors **Professional Accreditation:** NCATE. **Intercollegiate Athletics:** Baseball M; Basketball M & W; Cross-Country Running M & W; Golf M & W; Sailing M & W; Soccer M & W; Softball W; Volleyball W; Water Polo W

CALIFORNIA STATE UNIVERSITY, NORTHRIDGE

18111 Nordhoff St.
Northridge, CA 91330
Tel: (818)677-1200
Fax: (818)677-3766
E-mail: outreach.recruitment@csun.edu
Web Site: www.csun.edu
President/CEO: Dr. Dianne F. Harrison
Admissions: Juana Maria Valdivia
Financial Aid: Lili Vidal

Type: Comprehensive **Sex:** Coed **Affiliation:** California State University System. **Scores:** 76% SAT V 400+; 75% SAT M 400+ **% Accepted:** 46 **Admission Plans:** Preferred Admission **Application Fee:** $55.00 **H.S. Requirements:** High school diploma required; GED accepted **Costs Per Year:** Application fee: $55. State resident tuition: $5472 full-time. Nonresident tuition: $16,632 full-time. Mandatory fees: $1097 full-time. College room and board: $10,996. Room and board charges vary according to board plan and housing facility. **Scholarships:** Available. **Calendar System:** Semester, Summer session available **Enrollment:** Full-time 30,115, Graduate full-time 2,371, Graduate part-time 2,260, Part-time 6,802 **Faculty:** Full-time 909, Part-time 1,179 **Student-Faculty Ratio:** 27:1 **Exams:** ACT essay component used for advising; ACT essay component used for placement; SAT I or ACT; SAT essay component used for advising; SAT essay component used for placement; SAT Reasoning. **% Receiving Financial Aid:** 79 **Regional Accreditation:** Western Association of Colleges and Schools **ROTC:** Air Force, Army **Professional Accreditation:** AACN, AACSB, AAFCS, ABET, ACA, ACEJMC, AND, APTA, ASHA, CEPH, CIDA, CSWE, JRCAT, JRCERT, NASAD, NASM, NAST, NCATE, NRPA. **Intercollegiate Athletics:** Baseball M; Basketball M & W; Cross-Country Running M & W; Football M; Golf M; Soccer M; Softball W; Swimming and Diving M & W; Tennis W; Track and Field M & W; Volleyball M & W

CALIFORNIA STATE UNIVERSITY, SACRAMENTO

6000 J St.
Sacramento, CA 95819
Tel: (916)278-6011
E-mail: admissions@csus.edu
Web Site: www.csus.edu
President/CEO: Alexander Gonzalez
Admissions: Emiliano Diaz
Financial Aid: Caryl Vickers-Harper

Type: Comprehensive **Sex:** Coed **Affiliation:** California State University System. **Scores:** 86% SAT M 400+; 52% ACT 18-23; 16% ACT 24-29 **% Accepted:** 100 **Admission Plans:** Deferred Admission; Early Action; Early Decision Plan **Application Fee:** $55.00 **H.S. Requirements:** High school diploma required; GED accepted **Scholarships:** Available. **Calendar System:** Semester **Enrollment:** Full-time 19,812, Graduate full-time 1,670, Graduate part-time 1,031, Part-time 6,836 **Faculty:** Full-time 661, Part-time 830 **Student-Faculty Ratio:** 26:1 **Exams:** ACT essay component not used; SAT I or ACT; SAT essay component not used. **% Receiving Financial Aid:** 73 **% Residing in College-Owned, -Operated, or -Affiliated Housing:** 4 **Regional Accreditation:** Western Association of Colleges and Schools **Credit Hours For Degree:** 124 units, Bachelors **ROTC:** Air Force, Army **Professional Accreditation:** AACN, AACSB, ABET, ACA, ACCE, AND, APTA, ASHA, CIDA, CORE, CSWE, JRCAT, NASAD, NASM, NAST, NRPA. **Intercollegiate Athletics:** Baseball M; Basketball M & W; Bowling M & W; Cheerleading M & W; Crew M & W; Cross-Country Running M & W; Football M; Golf M & W; Gymnastics W; Ice Hockey M; Lacrosse M & W; Racquetball M & W; Rugby M; Skiing (Downhill) M & W; Soccer M & W; Softball W; Tennis M & W; Track and Field M & W; Volleyball M & W

CALIFORNIA STATE UNIVERSITY, SAN BERNARDINO

5500 University Pky.
San Bernardino, CA 92407
Tel: (909)537-5000
E-mail: moreinfo@mail.csusb.edu
Web Site: www.csusb.edu
President/CEO: Dr. Tomas Morales
Admissions: Julie Rogers
Financial Aid: Roseanna Ruiz

Type: Comprehensive **Sex:** Coed **Affiliation:** California State University System. **Scores:** 75% SAT V 400+; 76% SAT M 400+; 45.4% ACT 18-23; 5.2% ACT 24-29 **% Accepted:** 65 **Admission Plans:** Early Admission; Early Decision Plan **Application Deadline:** Rolling **Application Fee:** $55.00 **H.S. Requirements:** High school diploma required; GED accepted **Costs Per Year:** Application fee: $55. State resident tuition: $5472 full-time. Nonresident tuition: $11,160 full-time, $248 per credit hour part-time. Mandatory fees: $1105 full-time. College room and board: $9372. Room and board charges vary according to board plan and housing facility. **Scholarships:** Available. **Calendar System:** Quarter, Summer session available **Enrollment:** Full-time 15,859, Graduate full-time 977, Graduate part-time 1,326, Part-time 1,862 **Faculty:** Full-time 441, Part-time 545 **Student-Faculty Ratio:** 29:1 **Exams:** SAT I or ACT; SAT Reasoning; SAT Subject. **% Receiving Financial Aid:** 81 **% Residing in College-Owned, -Operated, or -Affiliated Housing:** 8 **Final Year or Final Semester Residency Requirement:** No **Regional Accreditation:** Western Association of Colleges and Schools **Credit Hours For Degree:** 180 quarter units, Bachelors **ROTC:** Air Force, Army **Professional Accreditation:** AACN, AACSB, ABET, CORE, CSWE, NASAD, NASM, NASPAA, NAST, NCATE. **Intercollegiate Athletics:** Baseball M; Basketball M & W; Cross-Country Running W; Golf M; Soccer M & W; Softball W; Track and Field W; Volleyball W

CALIFORNIA STATE UNIVERSITY, SAN MARCOS

333 S Twin Oaks Valley Rd.
San Marcos, CA 92096-0001

Tel: (760)750-4000
Fax: (760)750-4030
E-mail: apply@csusm.edu
Web Site: www.csusm.edu
President/CEO: Dr. Karen S. Haynes
Admissions: Scott Hagg

Type: Comprehensive **Sex:** Coed **Affiliation:** California State University System. **Scores:** 88% SAT M 400+; 61.9% ACT 18-23; 17.2% ACT 24-29 **% Accepted:** 67 **Application Deadline:** November 30 **Application Fee:** $55.00 **H.S. Requirements:** High school diploma required; GED accepted **Costs Per Year:** Application fee: $55. State resident tuition: $0 full-time. Nonresident tuition: $14,400 full-time, $372 per unit part-time. Mandatory fees: $1792 full-time. Part-time tuition varies according to course load. College room and board: $13,240. Room and board charges vary according to housing facility. **Scholarships:** Available. **Calendar System:** Semester, Summer session available **Enrollment:** Full-time 9,578, Graduate full-time 403, Graduate part-time 213, Part-time 2,599 **Faculty:** Full-time 254, Part-time 503 **Student-Faculty Ratio:** 25:1 **Exams:** ACT essay component not used; SAT I or ACT; SAT essay component not used; SAT Reasoning. **% Residing in College-Owned, -Operated, or -Affiliated Housing:** 80 **Regional Accreditation:** Western Association of Colleges and Schools **Credit Hours For Degree:** 124 units, Bachelors **ROTC:** Air Force, Army, Navy **Professional Accreditation:** NCATE. **Intercollegiate Athletics:** Baseball M; Basketball M & W; Cross-Country Running M & W; Golf M & W; Soccer M & W; Softball W; Track and Field M & W; Volleyball W

CALIFORNIA STATE UNIVERSITY, STANISLAUS

One University Cir.
Turlock, CA 95382
Tel: (209)667-3122; Free: 800-300-7420
Fax: (209)667-3333
E-mail: outreach_help_desk@csustan.edu
Web Site: www.csustan.edu
President/CEO: Dr. Joseph Sheley

Type: Comprehensive **Sex:** Coed **Affiliation:** California State University System. **Scores:** 77% SAT V 400+; 77% SAT M 400+; 47.7% ACT 18-23; 11.3% ACT 24-29 **% Accepted:** 61 **Application Deadline:** November 30 **Application Fee:** $55.00 **H.S. Requirements:** High school diploma required; GED accepted **Scholarships:** Available. **Calendar System:** Semester, Summer session available **Enrollment:** Full-time 6,781, Graduate full-time 734, Graduate part-time 449, Part-time 1,318 **Faculty:** Full-time 269, Part-time 280 **Student-Faculty Ratio:** 20:1 **Exams:** SAT I or ACT; SAT Reasoning. **% Receiving Financial Aid:** 78 **% Residing in College-Owned, -Operated, or -Affiliated Housing:** 8 **Regional Accreditation:** Western Association of Colleges and Schools **Credit Hours For Degree:** 120 units, Bachelors **Professional Accreditation:** AACN, AACSB, CSWE, NASAD, NASM, NASPAA, NAST, NCATE. **Intercollegiate Athletics:** Baseball M; Basketball M & W; Cross-Country Running M & W; Golf M; Soccer M & W; Softball W; Tennis W; Track and Field M & W; Volleyball W

CALIFORNIA UNIVERSITY OF MANAGEMENT AND SCIENCES

721 N Euclid St.
Anaheim, CA 92801
Tel: (714)533-3946
Web Site: www.calums.edu

Type: Comprehensive **Sex:** Coed **Costs Per Year:** Tuition: $9360 full-time. Mandatory fees: $320 full-time. **Calendar System:** Quarter **Professional Accreditation:** ACICS.

CAMBRIDGE JUNIOR COLLEGE

990-A Klamath Ln.
Yuba City, CA 95993
Tel: (530)674-9199
Web Site: www.cambridge.edu
President/CEO: Daniel Flores

Type: Two-Year College **Sex:** Coed **Application Fee:** $100.00 **H.S. Requirements:** High school diploma required; GED accepted **Enrollment:** Full-time 162 **Professional Accreditation:** ACICS.

CAÑADA COLLEGE

4200 Farm Hill Blvd.
Redwood City, CA 94061-1099
Tel: (650)306-3100
Fax: (650)306-3457

E-mail: miller@smccd.edu
Web Site: www.canadacollege.edu
President/CEO: Lawrence Buckley
Admissions: Ruth Miller
Financial Aid: Margie L. Carrington
Type: Two-Year College **Sex:** Coed **Affiliation:** San Mateo County Community College District System. **Admission Plans:** Open Admission **Application Deadline:** Rolling **Application Fee:** $0.00 **H.S. Requirements:** High school diploma required; GED accepted **Costs Per Year:** Application fee: $0. State resident tuition: $1380 full-time, $46 per unit part-time. Nonresident tuition: $8070 full-time, $269 per unit part-time. Mandatory fees: $56 full-time, $28 per term part-time. Full-time tuition and fees vary according to course load. Part-time tuition and fees vary according to course load. **Scholarships:** Available. **Calendar System:** Semester, Summer session available **Enrollment:** Full-time 406, Part-time 5,027 **Faculty:** Full-time 81, Part-time 160 **Student-Faculty Ratio:** 16:1 **Final Year or Final Semester Residency Requirement:** No **Regional Accreditation:** Western Association of Colleges and Schools **Credit Hours For Degree:** 60 credits, Associates **ROTC:** Air Force, Army, Navy **Professional Accreditation:** JRCERT. **Intercollegiate Athletics:** Baseball M; Basketball M; Golf W; Soccer M & W; Tennis W

CARRINGTON COLLEGE–CITRUS HEIGHTS

7301 Greenback Ln.
Ste. A
Citrus Heights, CA 95621
Tel: (916)722-8200
Web Site: carrington.edu
President/CEO: Michelle Kreuzer-Moore
Type: Two-Year College **Sex:** Coed **Affiliation:** Carrington Colleges Group, Inc. **Application Fee:** $0.00 **H.S. Requirements:** High school diploma required; GED accepted **Costs Per Year:** Application fee: $0. Tuition: $32,266 full-time. Mandatory fees: $1653 full-time. **Enrollment:** Full-time 521, Part-time 47 **Faculty:** Full-time 11, Part-time 14 **Student-Faculty Ratio:** 34:1 **Regional Accreditation:** Western Association of Colleges and Schools

CARRINGTON COLLEGE–PLEASANT HILL

380 Civic Dr.
Ste. 300
Pleasant Hill, CA 94523
Tel: (925)609-6650
Web Site: carrington.edu
President/CEO: La Shawn B. Wells
Type: Two-Year College **Sex:** Coed **Affiliation:** Carrington Colleges Group, Inc. **H.S. Requirements:** High school diploma required; GED accepted **Costs Per Year:** Tuition: $34,166 per degree program. Part-time tuition varies according to program. **Calendar System:** Semester **Enrollment:** Full-time 519, Part-time 97 **Faculty:** Full-time 19, Part-time 17 **Student-Faculty Ratio:** 22:1 **Regional Accreditation:** Western Association of Colleges and Schools **Professional Accreditation:** AAMAE.

CARRINGTON COLLEGE–POMONA

901 Corporate Ctr. Dr.
Ste. 300
Pomona, CA 91768
Tel: (909)868-5800; Free: 877-206-2106
Web Site: carrington.edu
Type: Two-Year College **Sex:** Coed **H.S. Requirements:** High school diploma required; GED accepted **Costs Per Year:** Tuition: $34,166 per degree program. Part-time tuition varies according to program. **Enrollment:** Full-time 278, Part-time 128 **Faculty:** Full-time 15, Part-time 2 **Student-Faculty Ratio:** 20:1 **Regional Accreditation:** Western Association of Colleges and Schools

CARRINGTON COLLEGE–SACRAMENTO

8909 Folsom Blvd.
Sacramento, CA 95826
Tel: (916)361-1660
Web Site: carrington.edu
President/CEO: Sue Smith
Type: Two-Year College **Sex:** Coed **Affiliation:** Carrington Colleges Group, Inc. **Application Deadline:** Rolling **H.S. Requirements:** High school diploma required; GED accepted **Costs Per Year:** Tuition: $44,490 per

degree program. Part-time tuition varies according to program. **Calendar System:** Semester **Enrollment:** Full-time 1,048, Part-time 224 **Faculty:** Full-time 36, Part-time 44 **Student-Faculty Ratio:** 16:1 **Exams:** Other. **Regional Accreditation:** Western Association of Colleges and Schools **Professional Accreditation:** AAMAE.

CARRINGTON COLLEGE–SAN JOSE

5883 Rue Ferrari
Ste. 125
San Jose, CA 95138
Tel: (408)960-0161
Web Site: carrington.edu
President/CEO: Frederick Holland
Type: Two-Year College **Sex:** Coed **Affiliation:** Carrington Colleges Group, Inc. **H.S. Requirements:** High school diploma required; GED accepted **Costs Per Year:** Tuition: $17,603 full-time. Mandatory fees: $760 full-time. Full-time tuition and fees vary according to program. **Calendar System:** Semester, Summer session not available **Enrollment:** Full-time 739, Part-time 52 **Faculty:** Full-time 22, Part-time 29 **Student-Faculty Ratio:** 24:1 **Exams:** Other. **Regional Accreditation:** Western Association of Colleges and Schools **Professional Accreditation:** ACCSC.

CARRINGTON COLLEGE–SAN LEANDRO

15555 E 14th St.
Ste. 500
San Leandro, CA 94578
Tel: (510)276-3888
Web Site: carrington.edu
President/CEO: Kristina Lopez
Type: Two-Year College **Sex:** Coed **Affiliation:** Carrington Colleges Group, Inc. **Application Deadline:** Rolling **H.S. Requirements:** High school diploma required; GED accepted **Costs Per Year:** Tuition: $17,603 full-time. Mandatory fees: $760 full-time. Full-time tuition and fees vary according to program. **Calendar System:** Semester **Enrollment:** Full-time 436, Part-time 42 **Faculty:** Full-time 12, Part-time 11 **Student-Faculty Ratio:** 28:1 **Exams:** Other. **Regional Accreditation:** Western Association of Colleges and Schools **Professional Accreditation:** AAMAE, AOTA.

CARRINGTON COLLEGE–STOCKTON

1313 W Robinhood Dr.
Ste. B
Stockton, CA 95207
Tel: (209)956-1240
Web Site: carrington.edu
Type: Two-Year College **Sex:** Coed **Application Fee:** $0.00 **H.S. Requirements:** High school diploma required; GED accepted **Costs Per Year:** Application fee: $0. Tuition: $32,266 full-time. Mandatory fees: $1653 full-time. Full-time tuition and fees vary according to program. **Enrollment:** Full-time 550, Part-time 33 **Faculty:** Full-time 7, Part-time 9 **Student-Faculty Ratio:** 56:1 **Regional Accreditation:** Western Association of Colleges and Schools

CASA LOMA COLLEGE–VAN NUYS

6725 Kester Ave.
Van Nuys, CA 91405
Tel: (818)785-2726
Web Site: www.casalomacollege.edu
Type: Two-Year College **Sex:** Coed **Professional Accreditation:** ABHES.

CERRITOS COLLEGE

11110 Alondra Blvd.
Norwalk, CA 90650-6298
Tel: (562)860-2451
E-mail: smurguia@cerritos.edu
Web Site: www.cerritos.edu
President/CEO: Dr. Jose Fierro, PhD
Admissions: Stephanie Murguia
Type: Two-Year College **Sex:** Coed **Affiliation:** California Community College System. **% Accepted:** 88 **Admission Plans:** Deferred Admission; Early Admission; Open Admission **Application Deadline:** Rolling **Application Fee:** $0.00 **H.S. Requirements:** High school diploma or equivalent not required. For applicants under 18: High school diploma required; GED accepted **Costs Per Year:** Application fee: $0. State resident tuition: $0 full-time. Nonresident tuition: $4972 full-time, $259 per unit part-time. Mandatory fees: $1346 full-time, $46 per unit part-time, $342 per term part-time. Full-

time tuition and fees vary according to course load. Part-time tuition and fees vary according to course load. **Scholarships:** Available. **Calendar System:** Semester, Summer session available **Enrollment:** Full-time 5,107, Part-time 14,673 **Faculty:** Full-time 269, Part-time 576 **Final Year or Final Semester Residency Requirement:** No **Regional Accreditation:** Western Association of Colleges and Schools **Credit Hours For Degree:** 60 units, Associates **Professional Accreditation:** ACEN, ADA, APTA. **Intercollegiate Athletics:** Baseball M; Basketball M & W; Cross-Country Running M & W; Football M; Golf M; Soccer M & W; Softball W; Swimming and Diving M & W; Tennis M & W; Track and Field M & W; Volleyball W; Water Polo M; Wrestling M

CERRO COSO COMMUNITY COLLEGE

3000 College Heights Blvd.
Ridgecrest, CA 93555-9571
Tel: (760)384-6100
Fax: (760)375-4776
E-mail: hostash@cerrocoso.edu
Web Site: www.cerrocoso.edu
President/CEO: A. Jill Board
Admissions: Heather Ootash

Type: Two-Year College **Sex:** Coed **Affiliation:** Kern Community College District System. **Admission Plans:** Early Admission; Open Admission **Application Deadline:** Rolling **Application Fee:** $0.00 **H.S. Requirements:** High school diploma or equivalent not required. For nursing program: High school diploma required; GED accepted **Scholarships:** Available. **Calendar System:** Semester, Summer session available **Regional Accreditation:** Western Association of Colleges and Schools **Credit Hours For Degree:** 60 semester hours, Associates **Intercollegiate Athletics:** Baseball M; Basketball W

CHABOT COLLEGE

25555 Hesperian Blvd.
Hayward, CA 94545-5001
Tel: (510)723-6600
Web Site: www.chabotcollege.edu
President/CEO: Susan Sperling
Admissions: Paulette Lino
Financial Aid: Refugio Franco

Type: Two-Year College **Sex:** Coed **Affiliation:** California Community College System. **Admission Plans:** Open Admission; Preferred Admission **Application Fee:** $0.00 **H.S. Requirements:** High school diploma required; GED accepted **Scholarships:** Available. **Calendar System:** Semester, Summer session available **Regional Accreditation:** Western Association of Colleges and Schools **Credit Hours For Degree:** 60 semester hours, Associates **ROTC:** Air Force, Army **Professional Accreditation:** AAMAE, ADA, AHIMA. **Intercollegiate Athletics:** Baseball M; Basketball M & W; Cross-Country Running M & W; Football M; Golf M; Soccer M & W; Softball W; Swimming and Diving M & W; Tennis M & W; Track and Field M & W; Volleyball W; Water Polo W; Wrestling M

CHAFFEY COLLEGE

5885 Haven Ave.
Rancho Cucamonga, CA 91737-3002
Tel: (909)652-6000
E-mail: erlinda.martinez@chaffey.edu
Web Site: www.chaffey.edu
President/CEO: Henry D. Shannon
Admissions: Erlinda Martinez
Financial Aid: Karen Sanders

Type: Two-Year College **Sex:** Coed **Affiliation:** California Community College System. **Admission Plans:** Early Admission; Open Admission **Application Deadline:** Rolling **Application Fee:** $0.00 **H.S. Requirements:** High school diploma or equivalent not required. For applicants under 18: High school diploma required; GED accepted **Scholarships:** Available. **Calendar System:** Semester, Summer session available **Student-Faculty Ratio:** 24:1 **Regional Accreditation:** Western Association of Colleges and Schools **Credit Hours For Degree:** 60 units, Associates **ROTC:** Army **Professional Accreditation:** ACEN, ADA, JRCERT. **Intercollegiate Athletics:** Baseball M; Basketball M & W; Football M; Soccer M & W; Softball W; Swimming and Diving M & W; Track and Field M & W; Volleyball W; Water Polo M & W

CHAPMAN UNIVERSITY

One University Dr.
Orange, CA 92866
Tel: (714)997-6815; Free: 888-CUAPPLY
Fax: (714)997-6713
E-mail: admit@chapman.edu
Web Site: www.chapman.edu
President/CEO: Dr. James L. Doti
Admissions: Marcela Mejía-Martinez
Financial Aid: Jim Whitaker

Type: Comprehensive **Sex:** Coed **Affiliation:** Christian Church (Disciples of Christ); Brandman University. **Scores:** 100% SAT V 400+; 100% SAT M 400+; 12% ACT 18-23; 58% ACT 24-29 **% Accepted:** 48 **Admission Plans:** Early Decision Plan **Application Deadline:** January 15 **Application Fee:** $65.00 **H.S. Requirements:** High school diploma required; GED accepted **Costs Per Year:** Application fee: $65. Comprehensive fee: $63,078 includes full-time tuition ($48,310), mandatory fees ($400), and college room and board ($14,368). College room only: $9812. Room and board charges vary according to board plan and housing facility. Part-time tuition: $1500 per credit. Part-time tuition varies according to course load. **Scholarships:** Available. **Calendar System:** 4-1-4, Summer session available **Enrollment:** Full-time 6,080, Graduate full-time 1,422, Graduate part-time 520, Part-time 283 **Faculty:** Full-time 417, Part-time 534 **Student-Faculty Ratio:** 14:1 **Exams:** SAT I or ACT; SAT II; SAT Reasoning; SAT Subject. **% Receiving Financial Aid:** 59 **% Residing in College-Owned, -Operated, or -Affiliated Housing:** 34 **Final Year or Final Semester Residency Requirement:** No **Regional Accreditation:** Western Association of Colleges and Schools **Credit Hours For Degree:** 124 semester credits, Bachelors **ROTC:** Air Force, Army **Professional Accreditation:** AACSB, AAMFT, ABA, APTA, NASD, NASM, TEAC. **Intercollegiate Athletics:** Baseball M; Basketball M & W; Cheerleading W; Crew M & W; Cross-Country Running M & W; Football M; Golf M; Ice Hockey M; Lacrosse M & W; Soccer M & W; Softball W; Swimming and Diving M & W; Tennis M & W; Track and Field M & W; Volleyball M & W; Water Polo M & W

CHARLES R. DREW UNIVERSITY OF MEDICINE AND SCIENCE

1731 E 120th St.
Los Angeles, CA 90059
Tel: (323)563-4800
E-mail: yvettelane@cdrewu.edu
Web Site: www.cdrewu.edu
President/CEO: David Carlisle, MD
Admissions: Yvette Lane

Type: Comprehensive **Sex:** Coed **% Accepted:** 21 **Application Deadline:** April 30 **Application Fee:** $35.00 **H.S. Requirements:** High school diploma required; GED accepted **Scholarships:** Available. **Calendar System:** Semester **Enrollment:** Full-time 126, Graduate full-time 20, Graduate part-time 11, Part-time 104 **Faculty:** Full-time 22, Part-time 3 **Student-Faculty Ratio:** 9:1 **Exams:** SAT I or ACT. **Regional Accreditation:** Western Association of Colleges and Schools **Professional Accreditation:** AAMAE, ACNM, AHIMA, JRCERT.

CHARTER COLLEGE

19034 Soledad Canyon Rd.
Canyon Country, CA 91351
Tel: (661)252-1864
Web Site: www.chartercollege.edu
Type: Two-Year College **Sex:** Coed **Professional Accreditation:** ACICS.

CITRUS COLLEGE

1000 W Foothill Blvd.
Glendora, CA 91741-1899
Tel: (626)963-0323
E-mail: admissions@citruscollege.edu
Web Site: www.citruscollege.edu
President/CEO: Geraldine M. Perri, PhD

Type: Two-Year College **Sex:** Coed **Affiliation:** California Community College System. **% Accepted:** 100 **Admission Plans:** Early Action; Open Admission **Application Deadline:** Rolling **Application Fee:** $0.00 **H.S. Requirements:** High school diploma required; GED accepted **Costs Per Year:** Application fee: $0. State resident tuition: $1380 full-time, $46 per unit part-time. Nonresident tuition: $8100 full-time, $224 per unit part-time. Mandatory fees: $87 full-time. Full-time tuition and fees vary according to course load. Part-time tuition varies according to course load. **Scholarships:** Available. **Calendar System:** Semester, Summer session available **Enrollment:** Full-time 4,921, Part-time 7,859 **Faculty:** Full-time 155, Part-time 354 **Student-Faculty Ratio:** 30:1 **Regional Accreditation:** Western

Association of Colleges and Schools **Credit Hours For Degree:** 60 units, Associates **Professional Accreditation:** ADA. **Intercollegiate Athletics:** Baseball M; Basketball M & W; Cross-Country Running M & W; Football M; Golf M & W; Soccer M & W; Softball W; Swimming and Diving W; Volleyball W; Water Polo M & W

CITY COLLEGE OF SAN FRANCISCO

50 Phelan Ave.
San Francisco, CA 94112-1821
Tel: (415)239-3000
Fax: (415)239-3936
E-mail: mleyba@ccsf.edu
Web Site: www.ccsf.edu
President/CEO: Arthur Q. Tyler
Admissions: Mary Lou Leyba-Frank

Type: Two-Year College **Sex:** Coed **Affiliation:** California Community College System. **Admission Plans:** Early Admission; Open Admission **Application Deadline:** August 9 **H.S. Requirements:** High school diploma or equivalent not required. For applicants under 18: High school diploma required; GED accepted **Scholarships:** Available. **Calendar System:** Semester, Summer session available **Student-Faculty Ratio:** 23:1 **Regional Accreditation:** Western Association of Colleges and Schools **Credit Hours For Degree:** 60 units, Associates **Professional Accreditation:** AAMAE, ACF, ADA, AHIMA, JRCERT. **Intercollegiate Athletics:** Badminton W; Baseball M; Basketball M & W; Football M; Soccer M & W; Softball W; Tennis W; Track and Field M & W; Volleyball W

CLAREMONT MCKENNA COLLEGE

500 E 9th St.
Claremont, CA 91711
Tel: (909)621-8000
E-mail: jennifer.sandoval@cmc.edu
Web Site: www.claremontmckenna.edu
President/CEO: Hiram E. Chodosh
Admissions: Jennifer Sandoval-Dancs
Financial Aid: Georgette R. DeVeres

Type: Comprehensive **Sex:** Coed **Scores:** 100% SAT V 400+; 100% SAT M 400+; 19% ACT 24-29 **% Accepted:** 11 **Admission Plans:** Deferred Admission; Early Action **Application Deadline:** January 1 **Application Fee:** $70.00 **H.S. Requirements:** High school diploma required; GED accepted **Costs Per Year:** Application fee: $70. Comprehensive fee: $64,825 includes full-time tuition ($48,800), mandatory fees ($745), and college room and board ($15,280). College room only: $8220. Room and board charges vary according to board plan and housing facility. **Scholarships:** Available. **Calendar System:** Semester, Summer session not available **Enrollment:** Full-time 1,326, Graduate full-time 21, Part-time 2 **Faculty:** Full-time 150, Part-time 15 **Student-Faculty Ratio:** 8:1 **Exams:** Other; SAT I or ACT; SAT II; SAT essay component used as validity check. **% Receiving Financial Aid:** 40 **% Residing in College-Owned, -Operated, or -Affiliated Housing:** 97 **Final Year or Final Semester Residency Requirement:** Yes **Regional Accreditation:** Western Association of Colleges and Schools **Credit Hours For Degree:** 32 courses, Bachelors **ROTC:** Air Force, Army **Intercollegiate Athletics:** Archery M & W; Baseball M; Basketball M & W; Cheerleading M & W; Cross-Country Running M & W; Equestrian Sports M & W; Fencing M & W; Field Hockey M & W; Football M; Golf M & W; Lacrosse M & W; Rugby M & W; Sailing M & W; Skiing (Downhill) M & W; Soccer M & W; Softball W; Swimming and Diving M & W; Tennis M & W; Track and Field M & W; Volleyball M & W; Water Polo M & W

COASTLINE COMMUNITY COLLEGE

11460 Warner Ave.
Fountain Valley, CA 92708-2597
Tel: (714)546-7600
Fax: (714)241-6288
Web Site: www.coastline.edu
President/CEO: Dr. Lori Adrian
Admissions: Jennifer McDonald

Type: Two-Year College **Sex:** Coed **Affiliation:** Coast Community College District System. **Admission Plans:** Early Admission; Open Admission **Application Deadline:** Rolling **Application Fee:** $0.00 **H.S. Requirements:** High school diploma or equivalent not required. For applicants under 18: High school diploma required; GED accepted **Costs Per Year:** Application fee: $0. State resident tuition: $1104 full-time, $46 per unit part-time. Nonresident tuition: $6648 full-time, $231 per unit part-time. Mandatory fees:

$32 full-time. Tuition guaranteed not to increase for student's term of enrollment. **Scholarships:** Available. **Calendar System:** Semester, Summer session available **Enrollment:** Full-time 2,488, Part-time 8,943 **Faculty:** Full-time 41, Part-time 241 **Student-Faculty Ratio:** 32:1 **Final Year or Final Semester Residency Requirement:** No **Regional Accreditation:** Western Association of Colleges and Schools **Credit Hours For Degree:** 60 units, Associates

COGSWELL POLYTECHNICAL COLLEGE

191 Baypointe Pky.
San Jose, CA 95134
Tel: (408)541-0100; Free: 800-264-7955
Fax: (408)747-0764
E-mail: akark@cogswell.edu
Web Site: www.cogswell.edu
President/CEO: Dr. Deborah Snyder
Admissions: Aaron Kark
Financial Aid: Lisa Mandy

Type: Comprehensive **Sex:** Coed **Scores:** 97% SAT V 400+; 97% SAT M 400+; 71% ACT 18-23; 29% ACT 24-29 **% Accepted:** 61 **Admission Plans:** Deferred Admission **Application Deadline:** Rolling **Application Fee:** $0.00 **H.S. Requirements:** High school diploma required; GED accepted **Costs Per Year:** Application fee: $0. Tuition: $18,096 full-time, $754 per credit part-time. Mandatory fees: $1000 full-time. Full-time tuition and fees vary according to course load, degree level, and program. Part-time tuition varies according to course load, degree level, and program. College room only: $8000. Room charges vary according to housing facility. **Scholarships:** Available. **Calendar System:** Semester, Summer session available **Enrollment:** Full-time 528, Part-time 105 **Faculty:** Full-time 17, Part-time 74 **Student-Faculty Ratio:** 13:1 **Exams:** ACT essay component used for advising; ACT essay component used for placement; SAT I or ACT; SAT essay component used for advising; SAT essay component used for placement. **% Residing in College-Owned, -Operated, or -Affiliated Housing:** 30 **Final Year or Final Semester Residency Requirement:** No **Regional Accreditation:** Western Association of Colleges and Schools **Credit Hours For Degree:** 120 semester hours, Bachelors

THE COLBURN SCHOOL CONSERVATORY OF MUSIC

200 S Grand Ave.
Los Angeles, CA 90012
Tel: (213)621-2200
Fax: (213)621-2110
E-mail: admissions@colburnschool.edu
Web Site: www.colburnschool.edu
President/CEO: Adrian Daly
Admissions: Jessica Cameron
Financial Aid: Carrie Wade

Type: Comprehensive **Sex:** Coed **% Accepted:** 10 **Admission Plans:** Deferred Admission **Application Deadline:** December 1 **Application Fee:** $120.00 **H.S. Requirements:** High school diploma required; GED accepted **Costs Per Year:** Application fee: $120. Tuition: $0 full-time. Mandatory fees: $3000 full-time. Full scholarships covering tuition, room and board are awarded to all students enrolled in the Conservatory (to the extent that this amount is not underwritten by outside scholarships). **Scholarships:** Available. **Calendar System:** Semester **Enrollment:** Full-time 55, Graduate full-time 60 **Student-Faculty Ratio:** 3:1 **Exams:** SAT I or ACT. **% Receiving Financial Aid:** 28 **% Residing in College-Owned, -Operated, or -Affiliated Housing:** 100 **Final Year or Final Semester Residency Requirement:** No **Credit Hours For Degree:** 120 credits, Bachelors **Professional Accreditation:** NASM.

COLEMAN UNIVERSITY

8888 Balboa Ave.
San Diego, CA 92123
Tel: (858)499-0202; Free: 800-430-2030
Fax: (858)499-0233
E-mail: jschafer@cts.com
Web Site: www.coleman.edu
President/CEO: Scott Rhude

Type: Comprehensive **Sex:** Coed **% Accepted:** 100 **Admission Plans:** Deferred Admission **Application Deadline:** August 1 **Application Fee:** $100.00 **H.S. Requirements:** High school diploma required; GED accepted **Scholarships:** Available. **Calendar System:** Quarter, Summer session available **Regional Accreditation:** Western Association of Colleges and

Schools **Credit Hours For Degree:** 108 quarter hours, Associates; 180 quarter hours, Bachelors **Professional Accreditation:** ACICS.

COLLEGE OF ALAMEDA

555 Ralph Appezzato Memorial Pky.
Alameda, CA 94501-2109
Tel: (510)522-7221
E-mail: kcompton@peralta.edu
Web Site: alameda.peralta.edu
President/CEO: George Herring
Admissions: Kerry Compton
Type: Two-Year College **Sex:** Coed **Affiliation:** Peralta Community College District System. **Admission Plans:** Open Admission **Application Deadline:** Rolling **Application Fee:** $0.00 **H.S. Requirements:** High school diploma required; GED accepted. For applicants 18 or over: High school diploma or equivalent not required **Scholarships:** Available. **Calendar System:** Semester, Summer session available **Student-Faculty Ratio:** 32:1 **Regional Accreditation:** Western Association of Colleges and Schools **Credit Hours For Degree:** 60 semester hours, Associates **Professional Accreditation:** ADA. **Intercollegiate Athletics:** Basketball M; Volleyball W

COLLEGE OF THE CANYONS

26455 Rockwell Canyon Rd.
Santa Clarita, CA 91355
Tel: (661)259-7800
Fax: (661)362-5300
E-mail: jasmine.ruys@canyons.edu
Web Site: www.canyons.edu
President/CEO: Dr. Dianne G. Van Hook
Admissions: Dr. Jasmine Ruys
Financial Aid: Tom Bilbruck
Type: Two-Year College **Sex:** Coed **Affiliation:** California Community College System. **Admission Plans:** Open Admission **Application Deadline:** Rolling **Application Fee:** $0.00 **H.S. Requirements:** High school diploma or equivalent not required **Costs Per Year:** Application fee: $0. State resident tuition: $1154 full-time, $46 per credit hour part-time. Mandatory fees: $50 full-time. Full-time tuition and fees vary according to course load. Part-time tuition varies according to course load. **Scholarships:** Available. **Calendar System:** Semester, Summer session available **Faculty:** Full-time 175, Part-time 549 **Regional Accreditation:** Western Association of Colleges and Schools **Credit Hours For Degree:** 60 units, Associates **Professional Accreditation:** ACEN. **Intercollegiate Athletics:** Baseball M; Basketball M & W; Cross-Country Running M & W; Football M; Golf M & W; Ice Hockey M; Soccer M & W; Softball W; Swimming and Diving M & W; Track and Field M & W; Volleyball W

COLLEGE OF THE DESERT

43-500 Monterey Ave.
Palm Desert, CA 92260-9305
Tel: (760)346-8041
E-mail: srodriguez@collegeofthedesert.edu
Web Site: www.collegeofthedesert.edu
President/CEO: Dr. Joel L. Kinnamon
Admissions: Sally Rodriguez
Financial Aid: Ken Lira
Type: Two-Year College **Sex:** Coed **Affiliation:** California Community College System. **% Accepted:** 100 **Admission Plans:** Open Admission; Preferred Admission **Application Deadline:** Rolling **Application Fee:** $0.00 **H.S. Requirements:** High school diploma required; GED accepted. For applicants 18 or over: High school diploma or equivalent not required **Scholarships:** Available. **Calendar System:** Semester, Summer session available **Enrollment:** Full-time 3,629, Part-time 5,630 **Faculty:** Full-time 103, Part-time 320 **Student-Faculty Ratio:** 29:1 **Final Year or Final Semester Residency Requirement:** No **Regional Accreditation:** Western Association of Colleges and Schools **Credit Hours For Degree:** 60 units, Associates **Professional Accreditation:** ACEN. **Intercollegiate Athletics:** Baseball M; Basketball M & W; Cross-Country Running M & W; Fencing M & W; Football M; Golf M & W; Soccer M & W; Softball W; Tennis M & W; Track and Field M & W; Volleyball W

COLLEGE OF MARIN

835 College Ave.
Kentfield, CA 94904
Tel: (415)457-8811

Fax: (415)883-2632
E-mail: diane.traversi@marin.edu
Web Site: www.marin.edu
President/CEO: David Wain Coon
Admissions: Diane Traversi
Financial Aid: David Cook
Type: Two-Year College **Sex:** Coed **Affiliation:** California Community College System. **Admission Plans:** Early Admission; Open Admission **Application Deadline:** Rolling **H.S. Requirements:** High school diploma or equivalent not required **Costs Per Year:** State resident tuition: $1380 full-time, $46 per credit hour part-time. Nonresident tuition: $7530 full-time, $205 per credit hour part-time. Full-time tuition varies according to course load. Part-time tuition varies according to course load. **Scholarships:** Available. **Calendar System:** Semester, Summer session available **Regional Accreditation:** Western Association of Colleges and Schools **Credit Hours For Degree:** 60 credits, Associates **Professional Accreditation:** ACEN, ADA. **Intercollegiate Athletics:** Baseball M; Basketball M & W; Soccer M & W; Softball W; Swimming and Diving M & W; Track and Field M & W; Volleyball W; Water Polo M & W

COLLEGE OF THE REDWOODS

7351 Tompkins Hill Rd.
Eureka, CA 95501-9300
Tel: (707)476-4100; Free: 800-641-0400
Web Site: www.redwoods.edu
President/CEO: Jeff Marsee
Type: Two-Year College **Sex:** Coed **Affiliation:** California Community College System. **Admission Plans:** Early Admission; Open Admission **Application Deadline:** Rolling **Application Fee:** $0.00 **H.S. Requirements:** High school diploma required; GED accepted. For applicants 18 or over: High school diploma or equivalent not required **Scholarships:** Available. **Calendar System:** Semester, Summer session available **Student-Faculty Ratio:** 23:1 **Regional Accreditation:** Western Association of Colleges and Schools **Credit Hours For Degree:** 60 units, Associates **Professional Accreditation:** ADA, ATMAE. **Intercollegiate Athletics:** Baseball M; Basketball M & W; Football M; Soccer W; Softball W; Volleyball W

COLLEGE OF SAN MATEO

1700 W Hillsdale Blvd.
San Mateo, CA 94402-3784
Tel: (650)574-6161
E-mail: csmadmission@smccd.edu
Web Site: www.collegeofsanmateo.edu
President/CEO: Michael E. Claire
Admissions: Henry Villareal
Type: Two-Year College **Sex:** Coed **Affiliation:** California Community College System. **Admission Plans:** Early Admission; Open Admission **Application Deadline:** Rolling **Application Fee:** $0.00 **H.S. Requirements:** High school diploma or equivalent not required. For applicants under 18: High school diploma required; GED accepted **Calendar System:** Semester, Summer session available **Student-Faculty Ratio:** 26:1 **Regional Accreditation:** Western Association of Colleges and Schools **Credit Hours For Degree:** 60 semester hours, Associates **ROTC:** Air Force, Army, Navy **Professional Accreditation:** ADA. **Intercollegiate Athletics:** Baseball M; Basketball W; Cross-Country Running M & W; Football M; Softball W; Swimming and Diving M & W; Track and Field M & W; Water Polo W

COLLEGE OF THE SEQUOIAS

915 S Mooney Blvd.
Visalia, CA 93277-2234
Tel: (559)730-3700
Web Site: www.cos.edu
President/CEO: Dr. William Scroggins
Admissions: Lisa Hott
Type: Two-Year College **Sex:** Coed **Affiliation:** California Community College System. **Admission Plans:** Open Admission **Application Deadline:** August 15 **Application Fee:** $0.00 **H.S. Requirements:** High school diploma or equivalent not required. For applicants under 18: High school diploma required; GED accepted **Scholarships:** Available. **Calendar System:** Semester, Summer session available **Enrollment:** Full-time 5,147, Part-time 8,302 **Faculty:** Full-time 185, Part-time 325 **Student-Faculty Ratio:** 27:1 **Regional Accreditation:** Western Association of Colleges and Schools **Credit Hours For Degree:** 60 units, Associates **ROTC:** Air Force **Intercollegiate Athletics:** Baseball M; Basketball M & W; Cross-Country

Running M & W; Football M; Golf M; Soccer W; Softball W; Swimming and Diving M & W; Tennis M & W; Track and Field M & W; Volleyball W; Water Polo M

COLLEGE OF THE SISKIYOUS

800 College Ave.
Weed, CA 96094-2899
Tel: (530)938-5555; Free: 888-397-4339
Fax: (530)938-5227
E-mail: admissions-weed@siskiyous.edu
Web Site: www.siskiyous.edu
President/CEO: Randall Lawrence
Financial Aid: Andrea Castro
Type: Two-Year College **Sex:** Coed **Affiliation:** California Community College System. **Admission Plans:** Deferred Admission; Early Admission; Open Admission **Application Deadline:** Rolling **H.S. Requirements:** High school diploma or equivalent not required. For applicants under 18: High school diploma required; GED accepted **Costs Per Year:** State resident tuition: $1154 full-time, $46 per unit part-time. Nonresident tuition: $6194 full-time, $256 per unit part-time. Mandatory fees: $50 full-time. Full-time tuition and fees vary according to course load and reciprocity agreements. Part-time tuition varies according to reciprocity agreements. College room and board: $8925. Room and board charges vary according to board plan. **Scholarships:** Available. **Calendar System:** Semester, Summer session available **Student-Faculty Ratio:** 20:1 **Regional Accreditation:** Western Association of Colleges and Schools **Credit Hours For Degree:** 60 units, Associates **Intercollegiate Athletics:** Baseball M; Basketball M & W; Football M; Softball W; Track and Field M & W; Volleyball W

COLUMBIA COLLEGE

11600 Columbia College Dr.
Sonora, CA 95370
Tel: (209)588-5100
E-mail: ccadmissions@yosemite.edu
Web Site: www.gocolumbia.edu
President/CEO: Dr. Angela Fairchilds
Financial Aid: Marnie Shively
Type: Two-Year College **Sex:** Coed **Affiliation:** Yosemite Community College District System. **Admission Plans:** Early Admission; Open Admission; Preferred Admission **Application Deadline:** Rolling **Application Fee:** $0.00 **H.S. Requirements:** High school diploma required; GED accepted **Costs Per Year:** Application fee: $0. State resident tuition: $0 full-time. Nonresident tuition: $6406 full-time. Mandatory fees: $1150 full-time. Full-time tuition and fees vary according to course load. **Scholarships:** Available. **Calendar System:** Semester, Summer session available **Enrollment:** Full-time 717, Part-time 1,707 **Faculty:** Full-time 44, Part-time 7 **Student-Faculty Ratio:** 19:1 **Final Year or Final Semester Residency Requirement:** No **Regional Accreditation:** Western Association of Colleges and Schools **Credit Hours For Degree:** 55-60 credit units (degrees vary in unit requirements - please check the current Columbia College Catalog), Associates **Professional Accreditation:** ACF, JRCEMTP. **Intercollegiate Athletics:** Basketball M; Volleyball W

COLUMBIA COLLEGE HOLLYWOOD

18618 Oxnard St.
Tarzana, CA 91356
Tel: (818)345-8414; Free: 800-785-0585
Fax: (818)345-9053
E-mail: admissions@columbiacollege.edu
Web Site: www.columbiacollege.edu
President/CEO: Richard Kobritz
Admissions: Carmen Munoz
Financial Aid: Jan Hastings
Type: Four-Year College **Sex:** Coed **% Accepted:** 57 **Admission Plans:** Deferred Admission **Application Deadline:** Rolling **Application Fee:** $50.00 **H.S. Requirements:** High school diploma required; GED accepted **Scholarships:** Available. **Calendar System:** Quarter, Summer session available **Enrollment:** Full-time 359 **Faculty:** Full-time 52 **Student-Faculty Ratio:** 33:1 **% Receiving Financial Aid:** 68 **Regional Accreditation:** Western Association of Colleges and Schools **Credit Hours For Degree:** 96 units, Associates; 192 units, Bachelors **Professional Accreditation:** ACCSC, NASAD.

COMMUNITY CHRISTIAN COLLEGE

251 Tennessee St.
Redlands, CA 92373
Tel: (909)335-8863
Fax: (909)335-9101
E-mail: emelendez@cccollege.edu
Web Site: www.cccollege.edu
President/CEO: Robert Johnson
Admissions: Enrique D. Melendez
Type: Two-Year College **Sex:** Coed **Affiliation:** Christian. **Admission Plans:** Open Admission **Application Fee:** $25.00 **Student-Faculty Ratio:** 5:1 **Professional Accreditation:** TRACS.

CONCORDE CAREER COLLEGE (GARDEN GROVE)

12951 Euclid St.
Ste. 101
Garden Grove, CA 92840
Tel: (714)703-1900
Fax: (714)530-4737
E-mail: cbecker@concorde.edu
Web Site: www.concorde.edu
President/CEO: Kurt Schake
Admissions: Chris Becker
Type: Two-Year College **Sex:** Coed **% Accepted:** 100 **Student-Faculty Ratio:** 22:1 **Professional Accreditation:** ACCSC.

CONCORDE CAREER COLLEGE (NORTH HOLLYWOOD)

12412 Victory Blvd.
North Hollywood, CA 91606
Tel: (818)766-8151
Fax: (818)766-1587
E-mail: mvolker@concorde.edu
Web Site: www.concorde.edu
President/CEO: Carmen Bowen
Admissions: Madeline Volker
Type: Two-Year College **Sex:** Coed **% Accepted:** 100 **Student-Faculty Ratio:** 20:1 **Professional Accreditation:** ACCSC, CoARC.

CONCORDE CAREER COLLEGE (SAN BERNARDINO)

201 E Airport Dr.
San Bernardino, CA 92408
Tel: (909)884-8891
Web Site: www.concorde.edu
Type: Two-Year College **Sex:** Coed **Professional Accreditation:** ACCSC.

CONCORDE CAREER COLLEGE (SAN DIEGO)

4393 Imperial Ave.
Ste. 100
San Diego, CA 92113
Tel: (619)688-0800
Web Site: www.concorde.edu
Type: Two-Year College **Sex:** Coed **Professional Accreditation:** ACCSC.

CONCORDIA UNIVERSITY IRVINE

1530 Concordia W
Irvine, CA 92612-3299
Tel: (949)854-8002; Free: 800-229-1200
Fax: (949)854-6894
E-mail: admission@cui.edu
Web Site: www.cui.edu
President/CEO: Dr. Kurt J. Krueger
Admissions: Doug Wible
Financial Aid: Lori McDonald
Type: Comprehensive **Sex:** Coed **Affiliation:** Lutheran Church–Missouri Synod; The Concordia University System. **Scores:** 91% SAT V 400+; 93% SAT M 400+; 49.1% ACT 18-23; 30.8% ACT 24-29 **% Accepted:** 59 **Admission Plans:** Deferred Admission; Early Decision Plan **Application Deadline:** Rolling **Application Fee:** $50.00 **H.S. Requirements:** High school diploma required; GED accepted. For home-schooled applicants (documentation of home school structure, courses, grades, state high school equivalency, and/or personal recommendations may be requested): High school diploma or equivalent not required **Costs Per Year:** Application fee: $50. Comprehensive fee: $43,020 includes full-time tuition ($32,130), mandatory fees ($650), and college room and board ($10,240). College

room only: $5900. Full-time tuition and fees vary according to course load. Room and board charges vary according to board plan and housing facility. Part-time tuition: $930 per unit. Part-time tuition varies according to course load. **Scholarships:** Available. **Calendar System:** Semester, Summer session available **Enrollment:** Full-time 1,721, Graduate full-time 1,680, Graduate part-time 886, Part-time 218 **Faculty:** Full-time 115, Part-time 305 **Student-Faculty Ratio:** 17:1 **Exams:** ACT essay component not used; SAT I or ACT; SAT essay component not used; SAT Reasoning. **% Receiving Financial Aid:** 70 % **Residing in College-Owned, -Operated, or -Affiliated Housing:** 49 **Final Year or Final Semester Residency Requirement:** Yes **Regional Accreditation:** Western Association of Colleges and Schools **Credit Hours For Degree:** 64 semester hours, Associates; 128 semester hours, Bachelors **Professional Accreditation:** AACN. **Intercollegiate Athletics:** Baseball M; Basketball M & W; Cross-Country Running M & W; Lacrosse M & W; Soccer M & W; Softball W; Swimming and Diving M & W; Tennis M & W; Track and Field M & W; Volleyball M & W; Water Polo M & W

CONTRA COSTA COLLEGE

2600 Mission Bell Dr.
San Pablo, CA 94806-3195
Tel: (510)235-7800
E-mail: a&r@contracosta.edu
Web Site: www.contracosta.edu
President/CEO: McKinley Williams

Type: Two-Year College **Sex:** Coed **Affiliation:** Contra Costa Community College District and California Community College System. **Admission Plans:** Early Admission; Open Admission **Application Deadline:** Rolling **Application Fee:** $0.00 **H.S. Requirements:** High school diploma or equivalent not required. For dental assisting, nursing programs: High school diploma required; GED accepted **Scholarships:** Available. **Calendar System:** Semester, Summer session available **Student-Faculty Ratio:** 26:1 **Regional Accreditation:** Western Association of Colleges and Schools **Credit Hours For Degree:** 60 units, Associates **Professional Accreditation:** ADA, MACTE. **Intercollegiate Athletics:** Baseball M; Basketball M & W; Football M; Soccer M & W; Softball W; Volleyball W

COPPER MOUNTAIN COLLEGE

6162 Rotary Way
Joshua Tree, CA 92252
Tel: (760)366-3791; Free: 866-366-3791
E-mail: gbrown@cmccd.edu
Web Site: www.cmccd.edu
President/CEO: Dr. Roger Wagner
Admissions: Greg Brown

Type: Two-Year College **Sex:** Coed **% Accepted:** 90 **Admission Plans:** Open Admission; Preferred Admission **Application Deadline:** Rolling **Application Fee:** $0.00 **H.S. Requirements:** High school diploma or equivalent not required **Calendar System:** Semester, Summer session available **Enrollment:** Full-time 1,712, Part-time 788 **Faculty:** Full-time 21, Part-time 91 **Final Year or Final Semester Residency Requirement:** No **Regional Accreditation:** Western Association of Colleges and Schools **Credit Hours For Degree:** 60 credits, Associates

COSUMNES RIVER COLLEGE

8401 Ctr. Pky.
Sacramento, CA 95823-5799
Tel: (916)691-7344
Fax: (916)691-7375
Web Site: www.crc.losrios.edu
President/CEO: Deborah Travis

Type: Two-Year College **Sex:** Coed **Affiliation:** Los Rios Community College District System. **Admission Plans:** Early Admission; Open Admission **Application Deadline:** August 1 **Application Fee:** $0.00 **H.S. Requirements:** High school diploma required; GED accepted. For applicants 18 or over: High school diploma or equivalent not required **Scholarships:** Available. **Calendar System:** Semester, Summer session available **Enrollment:** Full-time 14,545 **Student-Faculty Ratio:** 34:1 **Final Year or Final Semester Residency Requirement:** Yes **Regional Accreditation:** Western Association of Colleges and Schools **Credit Hours For Degree:** 60 units, Associates **Professional Accreditation:** AAMAE, AHIMA.

CRAFTON HILLS COLLEGE

11711 Sand Canyon Rd.
Yucaipa, CA 92399-1799

Tel: (909)794-2161
Fax: (909)389-9141
E-mail: laycock@craftonhills.edu
Web Site: www.craftonhills.edu
President/CEO: Gloria Macias Harrison
Admissions: Larry Aycock

Type: Two-Year College **Sex:** Coed **Affiliation:** California Community College System. **Admission Plans:** Deferred Admission; Early Admission; Open Admission; Preferred Admission **Application Deadline:** Rolling **Application Fee:** $0.00 **H.S. Requirements:** High school diploma required; GED accepted **Scholarships:** Available. **Calendar System:** Semester, Summer session available **Student-Faculty Ratio:** 33:1 **Regional Accreditation:** Western Association of Colleges and Schools **Credit Hours For Degree:** 60 credits, Associates **Professional Accreditation:** CoARC, JRCEMTP.

CUESTA COLLEGE

PO Box 8106
San Luis Obispo, CA 93403-8106
Tel: (805)546-3100
E-mail: jchamber@cuesta.edu
Web Site: www.cuesta.edu
President/CEO: Gil Stork
Admissions: Joy Chambers

Type: Two-Year College **Sex:** Coed **Affiliation:** San Luis Obispo County Community College District. **Admission Plans:** Deferred Admission; Early Admission; Open Admission; Preferred Admission **Application Deadline:** Rolling **Application Fee:** $0.00 **H.S. Requirements:** High school diploma or equivalent not required **Scholarships:** Available. **Calendar System:** Semester, Summer session available **Student-Faculty Ratio:** 27:1 **Regional Accreditation:** Western Association of Colleges and Schools **Credit Hours For Degree:** 60 units, Associates **ROTC:** Army **Intercollegiate Athletics:** Baseball M; Basketball M & W; Cross-Country Running M & W; Soccer W; Softball W; Swimming and Diving M & W; Tennis W; Track and Field M & W; Volleyball W; Water Polo M & W; Wrestling M

CUYAMACA COLLEGE

900 Rancho San Diego Pky.
El Cajon, CA 92019-4304
Tel: (619)660-4000
E-mail: susan.topham@gcccd.edu
Web Site: www.cuyamaca.net
President/CEO: Tim O'Hare
Admissions: Susan Topham

Type: Two-Year College **Sex:** Coed **Affiliation:** Grossmont-Cuyamaca Community College District. **Admission Plans:** Early Admission; Open Admission **Application Deadline:** Rolling **Application Fee:** $0.00 **H.S. Requirements:** High school diploma required; GED accepted. For applicants 18 or over: High school diploma or equivalent not required **Scholarships:** Available. **Calendar System:** Semester, Summer session available **Enrollment:** Full-time 1,636, Part-time 6,070 **Faculty:** Full-time 84, Part-time 561 **Regional Accreditation:** Western Association of Colleges and Schools **Credit Hours For Degree:** 60 units, Associates **ROTC:** Air Force, Army **Intercollegiate Athletics:** Basketball M & W; Cross-Country Running M & W; Golf M; Soccer M & W; Tennis W; Track and Field M & W; Volleyball W

CYPRESS COLLEGE

9200 Valley View
Cypress, CA 90630-5897
Tel: (714)484-7000
Fax: (714)761-3934
E-mail: admissions@cypresscollege.edu
Web Site: www.cypresscollege.edu
President/CEO: Michael J. Kasler

Type: Two-Year College **Sex:** Coed **Affiliation:** California Community College System. **Admission Plans:** Open Admission **Application Deadline:** August 25 **Application Fee:** $0.00 **H.S. Requirements:** High school diploma or equivalent not required **Scholarships:** Available. **Calendar System:** Semester, Summer session available **Student-Faculty Ratio:** 26:1 **Regional Accreditation:** Western Association of Colleges and Schools **Credit Hours For Degree:** 60 units, Associates **Professional Accreditation:** ABFSE, ACEN, ADA, AHIMA, JRCERT. **Intercollegiate Athletics:**

Baseball M; Basketball M & W; Golf M; Soccer M & W; Softball W; Swimming and Diving M & W; Tennis M & W; Volleyball W; Water Polo W

DE ANZA COLLEGE

21250 Stevens Creek Blvd.
Cupertino, CA 95014-5793
Tel: (408)864-5678
Fax: (408)864-8329
E-mail: webregda@mercury.fhda.edu
Web Site: www.deanza.fhda.edu
President/CEO: Dr. Brian Murphy
Admissions: Kathleen Moberg
Type: Two-Year College **Sex:** Coed **Affiliation:** California Community College System. **Costs Per Year:** State resident tuition: $0 full-time. Nonresident tuition: $6048 full-time, $149 per credit hour part-time. Mandatory fees: $167 full-time, $31 per credit part-time, $49 per term part-time. Full-time tuition and fees vary according to course load. Part-time tuition and fees vary according to course load. **Scholarships:** Available. **Calendar System:** Quarter, Summer session available **Enrollment:** Full-time 10,365, Part-time 13,468 **Faculty:** Full-time 285, Part-time 453 **Student-Faculty Ratio:** 36:1 **Final Year or Final Semester Residency Requirement:** No **Regional Accreditation:** Western Association of Colleges and Schools **Credit Hours For Degree:** 90 units, Associates **ROTC:** Air Force, Army **Professional Accreditation:** AAMAE, APTA. **Intercollegiate Athletics:** Baseball M; Basketball M & W; Cross-Country Running M & W; Football M; Golf M & W; Soccer M & W; Softball W; Swimming and Diving M & W; Tennis M & W; Track and Field M & W; Volleyball M & W; Water Polo M

DEEP SPRINGS COLLEGE

HC 72, Box 45001
Deep Springs, CA 89010-9803
Tel: (760)872-2000
E-mail: apcom@deepsprings.edu
Web Site: www.deepsprings.edu
President/CEO: David Neidorf
Admissions: Jack Davis
Type: Two-Year College **Sex:** Men **Scores:** 100% SAT V 400+; 100% SAT M 400+ **Calendar System:** Miscellaneous, Summer session available **Enrollment:** Full-time 28 **Faculty:** Full-time 3, Part-time 13 **Student-Faculty Ratio:** 4:1 **Exams:** ACT essay component not used; SAT I or ACT; SAT essay component not used. **% Residing in College-Owned, -Operated, or -Affiliated Housing:** 100 **Final Year or Final Semester Residency Requirement:** Yes **Regional Accreditation:** Western Association of Colleges and Schools **Credit Hours For Degree:** 60 credit hours, Associates

DESIGN INSTITUTE OF SAN DIEGO

8555 Commerce Ave.
San Diego, CA 92121-2685
Tel: (858)566-1200; Free: 800-619-4337
Fax: (858)566-2711
E-mail: admissions@disd.edu
Web Site: www.disd.edu
President/CEO: Margot Doucette, JD
Admissions: Amelie Racicot
Type: Four-Year College **Sex:** Coed **Costs Per Year:** Tuition: $19,623 full-time, $711 per unit part-time. Mandatory fees: $10 full-time, $10 per year part-time. Full-time tuition and fees vary according to class time, course load, and program. Part-time tuition and fees vary according to class time, course load, and program. **Scholarships:** Available. **Calendar System:** Semester, Summer session available **Enrollment:** Full-time 83, Part-time 65 **Faculty:** Full-time 5, Part-time 20 **Student-Faculty Ratio:** 9:1 **Credit Hours For Degree:** 132 credits, Bachelors **Professional Accreditation:** ACICS, CIDA.

DEVRY UNIVERSITY (ALHAMBRA)

1000 S Freemont Ave., Bldg. A-11
Alhambra, CA 91803
Tel: (626)293-4300; Free: 866-338-7941
Web Site: www.devry.edu
Type: Comprehensive **Sex:** Coed **Application Deadline:** Rolling **Regional Accreditation:** North Central Association of Colleges and Schools **Professional Accreditation:** ACBSP.

DEVRY UNIVERSITY (ANAHEIM)

1900 S State College Blvd., Ste. 150
Anaheim, CA 92806-6136
Tel: (714)935-3200; Free: 866-338-7941
Web Site: www.devry.edu
Type: Comprehensive **Sex:** Coed **Application Deadline:** Rolling **Costs Per Year:** Tuition: $17,052 full-time, $609 per credit hour part-time. Mandatory fees: $80 full-time, $40 per term part-time. **Regional Accreditation:** North Central Association of Colleges and Schools **Professional Accreditation:** ACBSP.

DEVRY UNIVERSITY (BAKERSFIELD)

3000 Ming Ave.
Bakersfield, CA 93304-4136
Tel: (661)833-7120; Free: 866-338-7941
Web Site: www.devry.edu
Type: Four-Year College **Sex:** Coed **Application Deadline:** Rolling **Costs Per Year:** Tuition: $17,052 full-time, $609 per credit hour part-time. Mandatory fees: $80 full-time, $40 per term part-time. **Regional Accreditation:** North Central Association of Colleges and Schools

DEVRY UNIVERSITY (FREMONT)

6600 Dumbarton Cir.
Fremont, CA 94555
Tel: (510)574-1100; Free: 866-338-7941
Fax: (510)742-0868
Web Site: www.devry.edu
Financial Aid: Kim Kane
Type: Comprehensive **Sex:** Coed **Application Deadline:** Rolling **Costs Per Year:** Tuition: $17,052 full-time, $609 per credit hour part-time. Mandatory fees: $80 full-time, $40 per term part-time. **Scholarships:** Available. **Calendar System:** Semester **% Receiving Financial Aid:** 80 **Regional Accreditation:** North Central Association of Colleges and Schools **Credit Hours For Degree:** 67 credit hours, Associates; 122 credit hours, Bachelors **Professional Accreditation:** ABET, ACBSP.

DEVRY UNIVERSITY (LONG BEACH)

3880 Kilroy Airport Way
Long Beach, CA 90806
Tel: (562)427-0861; Free: 866-338-7941
Web Site: www.devry.edu
Financial Aid: Kathy Odom
Type: Comprehensive **Sex:** Coed **Affiliation:** DeVry University. **Application Deadline:** Rolling **Costs Per Year:** Tuition: $17,052 full-time, $609 per credit hour part-time. Mandatory fees: $80 full-time, $40 per term part-time. **Scholarships:** Available. **Calendar System:** Semester **% Receiving Financial Aid:** 75 **Regional Accreditation:** North Central Association of Colleges and Schools **Professional Accreditation:** ABET, ACBSP.

DEVRY UNIVERSITY (OAKLAND)

505 14th St., Ste. 100
Oakland, CA 94612
Tel: (866)473-3879; Free: 866-338-7941
Web Site: www.devry.edu
Type: Comprehensive **Sex:** Coed **Application Deadline:** Rolling **Costs Per Year:** Tuition: $17,052 full-time, $609 per credit hour part-time. Mandatory fees: $80 full-time, $40 per term part-time. **Regional Accreditation:** North Central Association of Colleges and Schools **Professional Accreditation:** ACBSP.

DEVRY UNIVERSITY (OXNARD)

300 E Esplanade Dr.
Ste. 100
Oxnard, CA 93036
Tel: (805)604-3350; Free: 866-338-7941
Web Site: www.devry.edu
Type: Comprehensive **Sex:** Coed **Application Deadline:** Rolling **Calendar System:** Semester **Regional Accreditation:** North Central Association of Colleges and Schools **Professional Accreditation:** ACBSP.

DEVRY UNIVERSITY (PALMDALE)

39115 Trade Ctr. Dr., Ste. 100
Palmdale, CA 93551
Free: 866-338-7941

Web Site: www.devry.edu
Financial Aid: Ann Logan
Type: Comprehensive **Sex:** Coed **Affiliation:** DeVry University. **Application Deadline:** Rolling **Costs Per Year:** Tuition: $17,052 full-time, $609 per credit hour part-time. Mandatory fees: $80 full-time, $40 per term part-time. **Scholarships:** Available. **Calendar System:** Semester **% Receiving Financial Aid:** 74 **Regional Accreditation:** North Central Association of Colleges and Schools **Credit Hours For Degree:** 66 credit hours, Associates; 122 credit hours, Bachelors **Professional Accreditation:** ABET, ACBSP.

DEVRY UNIVERSITY (POMONA)
901 Corporate Ctr. Dr.
Pomona, CA 91768-2642
Tel: (909)622-8866; Free: 866-338-7941
Fax: (909)623-5666
Web Site: www.devry.edu
Type: Comprehensive **Sex:** Coed **Affiliation:** DeVry University. **Application Fee:** $40.00 **H.S. Requirements:** High school diploma required; GED accepted **Costs Per Year:** Application fee: $40. Tuition: $17,052 full-time, $609 per credit hour part-time. Mandatory fees: $80 full-time, $40 per term part-time. **Scholarships:** Available. **Calendar System:** Semester **Enrollment:** Full-time 574, Graduate full-time 44, Graduate part-time 184, Part-time 927 **Faculty:** Full-time 20, Part-time 76 **Student-Faculty Ratio:** 22:1 **Exams:** ACT essay component used for admission; ACT essay component used for placement; SAT essay component used for admission; SAT essay component used for placement. **Regional Accreditation:** North Central Association of Colleges and Schools **Credit Hours For Degree:** 66 credit hours, Associates; 122 credit hours, Bachelors **Professional Accreditation:** ABET.

DEVRY UNIVERSITY (SAN DIEGO)
2655 Camino Del Rio N, Ste. 350
San Diego, CA 92108-1633
Tel: (619)683-2446; Free: 866-338-7941
Fax: (619)683-2448
Web Site: www.devry.edu
Type: Comprehensive **Sex:** Coed **Application Deadline:** Rolling **Costs Per Year:** Tuition: $17,052 full-time, $609 per credit hour part-time. Mandatory fees: $80 full-time, $40 per term part-time. **Calendar System:** Semester **Regional Accreditation:** North Central Association of Colleges and Schools **Professional Accreditation:** ACBSP.

DEVRY UNIVERSITY (SHERMAN OAKS)
15301 Ventura Blvd., D-100
Sherman Oaks, CA 91403
Tel: (888)610-0800; Free: 866-338-7941
Web Site: www.devry.edu
Type: Comprehensive **Sex:** Coed **Application Deadline:** Rolling **Costs Per Year:** Tuition: $17,052 full-time, $609 per credit hour part-time. Mandatory fees: $80 full-time, $40 per term part-time. **Scholarships:** Available. **% Receiving Financial Aid:** 65 **Regional Accreditation:** North Central Association of Colleges and Schools

DIABLO VALLEY COLLEGE
321 Golf Club Rd.
Pleasant Hill, CA 94523
Tel: (925)685-1230
Fax: (925)685-1551
E-mail: idorn@dvc.edu
Web Site: www.dvc.edu
President/CEO: Judy Walters
Admissions: Ileana Dorn
Financial Aid: Adm. Brenda Jerez
Type: Two-Year College **Sex:** Coed **Affiliation:** Contra Costa Community College District. **Admission Plans:** Early Admission; Open Admission **Application Deadline:** August 15 **Application Fee:** $0.00 **H.S. Requirements:** High school diploma or equivalent not required. For applicants under 18: High school diploma required; GED accepted **Scholarships:** Available. **Calendar System:** Semester, Summer session available **Enrollment:** Full-time 7,340, Part-time 15,227 **Faculty:** Full-time 255, Part-time 550 **Student-Faculty Ratio:** 17:1 **Regional Accreditation:** Western Association of Colleges and Schools **Credit Hours For Degree:** 60 units, Associates **ROTC:** Air Force **Professional Accreditation:** ACF, ADA. **Intercollegiate Athlet-**

ics: Basketball M & W; Cross-Country Running M & W; Football M; Soccer W; Softball W; Swimming and Diving M & W; Tennis M & W; Track and Field M & W; Volleyball W; Water Polo M & W

DOMINICAN UNIVERSITY OF CALIFORNIA
50 Acacia Ave.
San Rafael, CA 94901-2298
Tel: (415)457-4440; Free: 888-323-6763
Fax: (415)485-3214
E-mail: nichelle.passanisi@dominican.edu
Web Site: www.dominican.edu
President/CEO: Dr. Mary Marcy
Admissions: Nichelle Passanisi
Financial Aid: Shanon Little
Type: Comprehensive **Sex:** Coed **Affiliation:** Roman Catholic Church. **Scores:** 99% SAT V 400+; 98% SAT M 400+; 44.44% ACT 18-23; 47.22% ACT 24-29 **% Accepted:** 79 **Admission Plans:** Deferred Admission **Application Deadline:** February 1 **Application Fee:** $0.00 **H.S. Requirements:** High school diploma required; GED accepted **Costs Per Year:** Application fee: $0. Comprehensive fee: $55,930 includes full-time tuition ($42,100), mandatory fees ($450), and college room and board ($13,380). College room only: $7880. Full-time tuition and fees vary according to course load. Room and board charges vary according to board plan. Part-time tuition: $1760 per credit. Part-time mandatory fees: $150 per term. Part-time tuition and fees vary according to course load. **Scholarships:** Available. **Calendar System:** Semester, Summer session not available **Enrollment:** Full-time 1,180, Graduate full-time 267, Graduate part-time 213, Part-time 203 **Faculty:** Full-time 111, Part-time 174 **Student-Faculty Ratio:** 9:1 **Exams:** ACT essay component used for advising; ACT essay component used for placement; SAT I or ACT; SAT essay component used for advising; SAT essay component used for placement; SAT Reasoning. **% Receiving Financial Aid:** 76 **% Residing in College-Owned, -Operated, or -Affiliated Housing:** 40 **Final Year or Final Semester Residency Requirement:** Yes **Regional Accreditation:** Western Association of Colleges and Schools **Credit Hours For Degree:** 120 units, Bachelors **Professional Accreditation:** AACN, AOTA. **Intercollegiate Athletics:** Basketball M & W; Cross-Country Running M & W; Golf M & W; Lacrosse M; Soccer M & W; Softball W; Tennis W; Volleyball W

EAST LOS ANGELES COLLEGE
1301 Avenida Cesar Chavez
Monterey Park, CA 91754
Tel: (323)265-8650
Fax: (323)265-8763
E-mail: allredjp@elac.edu
Web Site: www.elac.edu
President/CEO: Ernest H. Moreno
Admissions: Jeremy Allred
Type: Two-Year College **Sex:** Coed **Affiliation:** Los Angeles Community College District System. **Admission Plans:** Early Admission; Open Admission **Application Deadline:** Rolling **Application Fee:** $0.00 **H.S. Requirements:** High school diploma or equivalent not required **Scholarships:** Available. **Calendar System:** Semester, Summer session available **Enrollment:** Full-time 8,063, Part-time 23,686 **Faculty:** Full-time 231, Part-time 598 **Exams:** Other. **Regional Accreditation:** Western Association of Colleges and Schools **Credit Hours For Degree:** 60 units, Associates **Professional Accreditation:** AHIMA, CoARC. **Intercollegiate Athletics:** Baseball M; Basketball M & W; Cheerleading W; Cross-Country Running M & W; Football M; Soccer M & W; Softball W; Track and Field M & W; Volleyball W; Wrestling M

EAST SAN GABRIEL VALLEY REGIONAL OCCUPATIONAL PROGRAM & TECHNICAL CENTER
1501 W Del Norte Ave.
West Covina, CA 91790
Tel: (626)472-5195
Web Site: www.esgvrop.org
Type: Two-Year College **Sex:** Coed **Professional Accreditation:** COE.

EL CAMINO COLLEGE
16007 Crenshaw Blvd.
Torrance, CA 90506-0001
Tel: (310)532-3670; Free: 866-ELCAMINO
Fax: (310)660-3818

E-mail: wmulrooney@elcamino.edu
Web Site: www.elcamino.edu
President/CEO: Dr. Thomas Fallo
Admissions: William Mulrooney

Type: Two-Year College **Sex:** Coed **Affiliation:** California Community College System. **Admission Plans:** Early Admission; Open Admission **Application Deadline:** Rolling **Application Fee:** $0.00 **H.S. Requirements:** High school diploma or equivalent not required. For applicants under 18: High school diploma required; GED accepted **Calendar System:** Semester, Summer session available **Enrollment:** Full-time 7,729, Part-time 17,166 **Faculty:** Full-time 333, Part-time 650 **Student-Faculty Ratio:** 15:1 **Regional Accreditation:** Western Association of Colleges and Schools **Credit Hours For Degree:** 60 units, Associates **Professional Accreditation:** ACEN, CoARC, JRCERT. **Intercollegiate Athletics:** Baseball M; Basketball M & W; Cross-Country Running M & W; Football M; Golf M; Gymnastics W; Soccer M; Swimming and Diving M & W; Tennis M & W; Track and Field M & W; Volleyball M & W; Water Polo M; Wrestling M

EMPIRE COLLEGE
3035 Cleveland Ave.
Santa Rosa, CA 95403
Tel: (707)546-4000; Free: 877-395-8535
Fax: (707)546-4058
Web Site: www.empcol.edu
President/CEO: Roy O. Hurd
Admissions: Dahnja Barker

Type: Two-Year College **Sex:** Coed **Application Deadline:** Rolling **Application Fee:** $75.00 **H.S. Requirements:** High school diploma required; GED accepted **Scholarships:** Available. **Calendar System:** Continuous, Summer session not available **Exams:** Other. **Credit Hours For Degree:** 105 units, Associates **Professional Accreditation:** ACICS.

EPIC BIBLE COLLEGE
4330 Auburn Blvd.
Sacramento, CA 95841
Tel: (916)348-4689
Fax: (916)334-2315
E-mail: kclarke@tlbc.edu
Web Site: epic.edu
President/CEO: Ronald W. Harden
Admissions: Sheila Knoll

Type: Four-Year College **Sex:** Coed **Affiliation:** nondenominational. **Application Fee:** $50.00 **Costs Per Year:** Application fee: $50. Tuition: $8964 full-time, $249 per credit part-time. Mandatory fees: $690 full-time, $20 per credit part-time. Full-time tuition and fees vary according to course load. Part-time tuition and fees vary according to course load. **Calendar System:** Quarter **Professional Accreditation:** TRACS.

EVERGREEN VALLEY COLLEGE
3095 Yerba Buena Rd.
San Jose, CA 95135-1598
Tel: (408)274-7900
Fax: (408)223-9351
E-mail: octavio.cruz@evc.edu
Web Site: www.evc.edu
President/CEO: David Wain Coon
Admissions: Octavio Cruz

Type: Two-Year College **Sex:** Coed **Affiliation:** California Community College System. **Admission Plans:** Early Admission; Open Admission **Application Deadline:** Rolling **H.S. Requirements:** High school diploma or equivalent not required. For applicants under 18: High school diploma required; GED accepted **Scholarships:** Available. **Calendar System:** Semester, Summer session available **Student-Faculty Ratio:** 32:1 **Regional Accreditation:** Western Association of Colleges and Schools **Credit Hours For Degree:** 60 units, Associates **ROTC:** Army **Intercollegiate Athletics:** Soccer M & W

EX'PRESSION COLLEGE FOR DIGITAL ARTS
6601 Shellmound St.
Emeryville, CA 94608
Tel: (510)654-2934; Free: 877-833-8800
Web Site: www.expression.edu
President/CEO: Daniel Levinson

Type: Four-Year College **Sex:** Coed **Professional Accreditation:** ACCSC.

FEATHER RIVER COLLEGE
570 Golden Eagle Ave.
Quincy, CA 95971-9124
Tel: (530)283-0202; Free: 800-442-9799
Fax: (530)283-3757
E-mail: info@frc.edu
Web Site: www.frc.edu
President/CEO: Dr. Kevin Trutna
Admissions: Leslie Mikesell

Type: Two-Year College **Sex:** Coed **Affiliation:** California Community College System. **Admission Plans:** Open Admission **Application Fee:** $0.00 **H.S. Requirements:** High school diploma or equivalent not required **Costs Per Year:** Application fee: $0. State resident tuition: $1380 full-time, $46 per credit part-time. Nonresident tuition: $7410 full-time, $247 per credit part-time. Mandatory fees: $81 full-time, $1.50 per credit part-time, $18 per term part-time. Full-time tuition and fees vary according to course load. Part-time tuition and fees vary according to course load. College room only: $5350. Room charges vary according to housing facility. **Scholarships:** Available. **Calendar System:** Semester, Summer session available **Enrollment:** Full-time 636, Part-time 1,146 **Faculty:** Full-time 25, Part-time 81 **Student-Faculty Ratio:** 20:1 **Exams:** ACT; Other; SAT I; SAT I and SAT II or ACT; SAT I or ACT; SAT II. **% Residing in College-Owned, -Operated, or -Affiliated Housing:** 32 **Final Year or Final Semester Residency Requirement:** No **Regional Accreditation:** Western Association of Colleges and Schools **Credit Hours For Degree:** 60 units, Associates; 120 units, Bachelors **Intercollegiate Athletics:** Baseball M; Basketball M & W; Cross-Country Running W; Equestrian Sports M & W; Football M; Soccer M & W; Softball W; Track and Field W; Volleyball W

FIDM/FASHION INSTITUTE OF DESIGN & MERCHANDISING, LOS ANGELES CAMPUS
919 S Grand Ave.
Los Angeles, CA 90015-1421
Tel: (213)624-1200; Free: 800-624-1200
Fax: (213)624-4799
E-mail: saronson@fidm.edu
Web Site: www.fidm.edu
President/CEO: Tonian Hohberg
Admissions: Susan Aronson

Type: Four-Year College **Sex:** Coed **Affiliation:** FIDM/Fashion Institute of Design & Merchandising. **% Accepted:** 49 **Admission Plans:** Deferred Admission **Application Deadline:** Rolling **Application Fee:** $225.00 **H.S. Requirements:** High school diploma required; GED accepted **Costs Per Year:** Application fee: $225. Tuition: $28,965 full-time. Mandatory fees: $965 full-time. Full-time tuition and fees vary according to program. **Scholarships:** Available. **Calendar System:** Quarter, Summer session available **Enrollment:** Full-time 2,525, Part-time 289 **Faculty:** Full-time 73, Part-time 179 **Student-Faculty Ratio:** 20:1 **Exams:** SAT I or ACT. **Final Year or Final Semester Residency Requirement:** No **Regional Accreditation:** Western Association of Colleges and Schools **Credit Hours For Degree:** 90 quarter hours, Associates; 181 units, Bachelors **Professional Accreditation:** NASAD.

FIDM/FASHION INSTITUTE OF DESIGN & MERCHANDISING, ORANGE COUNTY CAMPUS
17590 Gillette Ave.
Irvine, CA 92614
Tel: (949)851-6200; Free: 888-974-3436
Fax: (949)851-6808
Web Site: www.fidm.edu
President/CEO: Tonian Hohberg
Admissions: Michael Mirabella

Type: Two-Year College **Sex:** Coed **Affiliation:** FIDM/Fashion Institute of Design & Merchandising. **% Accepted:** 58 **Admission Plans:** Deferred Admission **Application Deadline:** Rolling **Application Fee:** $225.00 **H.S. Requirements:** High school diploma required; GED accepted **Costs Per Year:** Application fee: $225. Tuition: $28,965 full-time. Mandatory fees: $965 full-time. Full-time tuition and fees vary according to program. **Calendar System:** Quarter, Summer session available **Enrollment:** Full-time 86, Part-time 6 **Faculty:** Full-time 4, Part-time 15 **Student-Faculty Ratio:** 10:1 **Exams:** SAT I or ACT. **Final Year or Final Semester Residency Requirement:** No **Professional Accreditation:** NASAD.

FIDM/FASHION INSTITUTE OF DESIGN & MERCHANDISING, SAN DIEGO CAMPUS

350 Tenth Ave.
3rd Fl.
San Diego, CA 92101
Tel: (619)235-2049; Free: 800-243-3436
Fax: (619)232-4322
E-mail: dbaca@fidm.edu
Web Site: www.fidm.edu
President/CEO: Tonian Hohberg
Admissions: Denise Baca

Type: Two-Year College **Sex:** Coed **Affiliation:** FIDM/Fashion Institute of Design & Merchandising. **% Accepted:** 56 **Admission Plans:** Deferred Admission **Application Deadline:** Rolling **Application Fee:** $225.00 **H.S. Requirements:** High school diploma required; GED accepted **Costs Per Year:** Application fee: $225. Tuition: $28,965 full-time. Mandatory fees: $965 full-time. Full-time tuition and fees vary according to program. **Calendar System:** Quarter, Summer session available **Enrollment:** Full-time 113, Part-time 6 **Faculty:** Full-time 2, Part-time 18 **Student-Faculty Ratio:** 14:1 **Exams:** SAT I or ACT. **Final Year or Final Semester Residency Requirement:** No **Credit Hours For Degree:** 90 units, Associates **Professional Accreditation:** NASAD.

FIDM/FASHION INSTITUTE OF DESIGN & MERCHANDISING, SAN FRANCISCO CAMPUS

55 Stockton St.
San Francisco, CA 94108-5829
Tel: (415)675-5200; Free: 800-422-3436
Fax: (415)296-7299
E-mail: sbadalamenti@fidm.edu
Web Site: www.fidm.edu
President/CEO: Tonian Hohberg
Admissions: Sheryl Badalamenti

Type: Four-Year College **Sex:** Coed **Affiliation:** FIDM/Fashion Institute of Design & Merchandising. **% Accepted:** 48 **Admission Plans:** Deferred Admission **Application Deadline:** Rolling **Application Fee:** $225.00 **H.S. Requirements:** High school diploma required; GED accepted **Costs Per Year:** Application fee: $225. Tuition: $28,965 full-time. Mandatory fees: $965 full-time. Full-time tuition and fees vary according to program. **Calendar System:** Quarter, Summer session available **Enrollment:** Full-time 334, Part-time 61 **Faculty:** Full-time 12, Part-time 37 **Student-Faculty Ratio:** 21:1 **Exams:** SAT I or ACT. **Final Year or Final Semester Residency Requirement:** No **Credit Hours For Degree:** 90 quarter hours, Associates **Professional Accreditation:** NASAD.

FOLSOM LAKE COLLEGE

10 College Pky.
Folsom, CA 95630
Tel: (916)608-6500
Web Site: www.flc.losrios.edu
President/CEO: Dr. Thelma Scott-Skilman

Type: Two-Year College **Sex:** Coed **Affiliation:** Los Rios Community College District System. **Application Deadline:** Rolling **Application Fee:** $0.00 **H.S. Requirements:** High school diploma or equivalent not required. For students under 18: High school diploma required; GED accepted **Faculty:** Full-time 109, Part-time 186 **Student-Faculty Ratio:** 32:1 **Regional Accreditation:** Western Association of Colleges and Schools **Credit Hours For Degree:** 60 semester units, Associates

FOOTHILL COLLEGE

12345 El Monte Rd.
Los Altos Hills, CA 94022-4599
Tel: (650)949-7777
E-mail: acedshawna@hda.edu
Web Site: www.foothill.edu
President/CEO: Dr. Judy Miner
Admissions: Shawna Aced

Type: Two-Year College **Sex:** Coed **Affiliation:** Foothill-DeAnza Community College District. **% Accepted:** 100 **Admission Plans:** Open Admission **Application Deadline:** Rolling **H.S. Requirements:** High school diploma or equivalent not required **Scholarships:** Available. **Calendar System:** Quarter, Summer session available **Enrollment:** Full-time 5,191, Part-time 10,574 **Faculty:** Full-time 184, Part-time 354 **Final Year or Final Semester Residency Requirement:** No **Regional Accreditation:** Western Associa-

tion of Colleges and Schools **Credit Hours For Degree:** 90 quarter hours, Associates **ROTC:** Air Force, Army **Professional Accreditation:** ADA, CoARC, JRCERT. **Intercollegiate Athletics:** Basketball M & W; Football M; Soccer M & W; Softball W; Swimming and Diving M & W; Tennis M & W; Volleyball W; Water Polo W

FREMONT COLLEGE (CERRITOS)

18000 Studebaker Rd., Ste. 900A
Cerritos, CA 90703
Tel: (562)809-5100; Free: 800-373-6668
Fax: (562)809-7100
E-mail: info@fremont.edu
Web Site: www.fremont.edu
Admissions: Natasha Dawson

Type: Two-Year College **Sex:** Coed **Professional Accreditation:** ACCSC.

FREMONT COLLEGE (LOS ANGELES)

3440 Wilshire Blvd., 10th Fl.
Los Angeles, CA 90010
Tel: (213)355-7777; Free: 800-373-6668
Web Site: www.fremont.edu

Type: Two-Year College **Sex:** Coed **Professional Accreditation:** ACCSC.

FRESNO CITY COLLEGE

1101 E University Ave.
Fresno, CA 93741-0002
Tel: (559)442-4600
E-mail: fcc.admissions@fresnocitycollege.edu
Web Site: www.fresnocitycollege.edu
President/CEO: Dr. Cynthia Azari
Financial Aid: Frank Ramon

Type: Two-Year College **Sex:** Coed **Affiliation:** California Community College System. **Admission Plans:** Deferred Admission; Early Admission; Open Admission **Application Deadline:** Rolling **Application Fee:** $0.00 **H.S. Requirements:** High school diploma or equivalent not required. For applicants under 18: High school diploma required; GED accepted **Scholarships:** Available. **Calendar System:** Semester, Summer session available **Student-Faculty Ratio:** 28:1 **Regional Accreditation:** Western Association of Colleges and Schools **Credit Hours For Degree:** 60 units, Associates **ROTC:** Air Force, Army **Professional Accreditation:** ADA, AHIMA, CoARC, JRCERT. **Intercollegiate Athletics:** Badminton W; Baseball M; Basketball M & W; Cross-Country Running M & W; Football M; Golf M & W; Soccer M & W; Softball W; Tennis M & W; Track and Field M & W; Volleyball W; Water Polo M; Wrestling M

FRESNO PACIFIC UNIVERSITY

1717 S Chestnut Ave.
Fresno, CA 93702-4709
Tel: (559)453-2000; Free: 800-660-6089
Fax: (559)453-2007
E-mail: andy.johnson@fresno.edu
Web Site: www.fresno.edu
President/CEO: Dr. Pete C. Menjares
Admissions: Andy Johnson
Financial Aid: April Powell

Type: Comprehensive **Sex:** Coed **Affiliation:** Mennonite Brethren Church. **Scores:** 97% SAT V 400+; 94% SAT M 400+; 69% ACT 18-23; 18% ACT 24-29 **% Accepted:** 78 **Admission Plans:** Deferred Admission; Early Admission **Application Fee:** $40.00 **H.S. Requirements:** High school diploma required; GED accepted **Scholarships:** Available. **Calendar System:** Semester, Summer session available **Enrollment:** Full-time 2,158, Graduate full-time 395, Graduate part-time 676, Part-time 254 **Faculty:** Full-time 106, Part-time 321 **Student-Faculty Ratio:** 13:1 **Exams:** ACT essay component not used; SAT I or ACT; SAT essay component not used; SAT Reasoning. **% Receiving Financial Aid:** 83 **% Residing in College-Owned, -Operated, or -Affiliated Housing:** 26 **Final Year or Final Semester Residency Requirement:** No **Regional Accreditation:** Western Association of Colleges and Schools **Credit Hours For Degree:** 60 units, Associates; 124 units, Bachelors **Professional Accreditation:** ATS. **Intercollegiate Athletics:** Baseball M; Basketball M & W; Cheerleading W; Cross-Country Running M & W; Soccer M & W; Swimming and Diving M & W; Tennis M & W; Track and Field M & W; Volleyball M & W; Water Polo M & W

FULLERTON COLLEGE

321 E Chapman Ave.
Fullerton, CA 92832-2095
Tel: (714)992-7000
E-mail: aabutin@fullcoll.edu
Web Site: www.fullcoll.edu
President/CEO: Rajen Vurdien, PhD
Admissions: Albert Abutin

Type: Two-Year College **Sex:** Coed **Affiliation:** California Community College System. **Admission Plans:** Early Admission; Open Admission **Application Deadline:** Rolling **H.S. Requirements:** High school diploma or equivalent not required **Scholarships:** Available. **Calendar System:** Semester, Summer session available **Enrollment:** Full-time 8,145, Part-time 16,468 **Student-Faculty Ratio:** 29:1 **Regional Accreditation:** Western Association of Colleges and Schools **Credit Hours For Degree:** 60 semester hours, Associates **ROTC:** Air Force, Army, Navy **Intercollegiate Athletics:** Badminton W; Baseball M; Basketball M & W; Cross-Country Running M & W; Football M; Golf W; Soccer M & W; Softball W; Swimming and Diving M & W; Tennis M & W; Track and Field M & W; Volleyball W; Water Polo M & W

GAVILAN COLLEGE

5055 Santa Teresa Blvd.
Gilroy, CA 95020-9599
Tel: (408)847-1400
Fax: (408)848-4801
E-mail: cwhitney@gavilan.edu
Web Site: www.gavilan.edu
President/CEO: Dr. Steven M. Kinsella
Admissions: Candice Whitney

Type: Two-Year College **Sex:** Coed **Affiliation:** California Community College System. **Admission Plans:** Open Admission **Application Deadline:** Rolling **Application Fee:** $0.00 **H.S. Requirements:** High school diploma required; GED accepted. For applicants 18 or over: High school diploma or equivalent not required **Costs Per Year:** Application fee: $0. State resident tuition: $0 full-time. Nonresident tuition: $6240 full-time, $260 per credit part-time. Mandatory fees: $1166 full-time, $46 per credit part-time, $31 per term part-time. **Scholarships:** Available. **Calendar System:** Semester, Summer session available **Enrollment:** Full-time 1,767, Part-time 3,500 **Faculty:** Full-time 74, Part-time 250 **Student-Faculty Ratio:** 30:1 **Regional Accreditation:** Western Association of Colleges and Schools **Credit Hours For Degree:** 60 units, Associates **Intercollegiate Athletics:** Baseball M; Basketball M; Football M; Soccer M; Softball W; Volleyball W

GLENDALE CAREER COLLEGE

240 N Brand Blvd., Lower Level
Glendale, CA 91203
Tel: (818)243-1131
Fax: (818)243-7650
Web Site: www.glendalecareer.com
Type: Two-Year College **Sex:** Coed

GLENDALE COMMUNITY COLLEGE

1500 N Verdugo Rd.
Glendale, CA 91208-2894
Tel: (818)240-1000
Fax: (818)549-9436
E-mail: scombs@glendale.edu
Web Site: www.glendale.edu
President/CEO: Dr. Dawn Lindsay
Admissions: Sharon Combs
Financial Aid: Arda Najarian

Type: Two-Year College **Sex:** Coed **Affiliation:** California Community College System. **Admission Plans:** Deferred Admission; Early Admission; Open Admission **Application Deadline:** Rolling **Application Fee:** $0.00 **H.S. Requirements:** High school diploma required; GED accepted. For applicants 18 or over: High school diploma or equivalent not required **Scholarships:** Available. **Calendar System:** Semester, Summer session available **Student-Faculty Ratio:** 28:1 **Regional Accreditation:** Western Association of Colleges and Schools **Credit Hours For Degree:** 60 units, Associates **Intercollegiate Athletics:** Baseball M; Basketball M & W; Cross-Country Running M & W; Football M; Golf M & W; Soccer M & W; Softball W; Tennis M & W; Track and Field M & W; Volleyball W

GOLDEN GATE UNIVERSITY

536 Mission St.
San Francisco, CA 94105-2968
Tel: (415)442-7000; Free: 800-448-3381
Fax: (415)442-7807
E-mail: info@ggu.edu
Web Site: www.ggu.edu
President/CEO: Dr. David Fike
Admissions: Louis D. Riccardi, Jr.
Financial Aid: Kathleen Kelly

Type: University **Sex:** Coed **Admission Plans:** Deferred Admission **Application Deadline:** Rolling **Application Fee:** $55.00 **H.S. Requirements:** High school diploma required; GED accepted **Costs Per Year:** Application fee: $55. Tuition: $15,120 full-time. Full-time tuition varies according to course load, degree level, and program. **Scholarships:** Available. **Calendar System:** Trimester, Summer session available **Enrollment:** Full-time 145, Graduate full-time 834, Graduate part-time 1,443, Part-time 313 **Faculty:** Full-time 30, Part-time 459 **Student-Faculty Ratio:** 16:1 **% Receiving Financial Aid:** 61 **Final Year or Final Semester Residency Requirement:** No **Regional Accreditation:** Western Association of Colleges and Schools **Credit Hours For Degree:** 60 units, Associates; 123 units, Bachelors **Professional Accreditation:** AALS, ABA.

GOLDEN WEST COLLEGE

PO Box 2748, 15744 Golden W St.
Huntington Beach, CA 92647-2748
Tel: (714)892-7711
E-mail: jortberg@gwc.cccd.edu
Web Site: www.goldenwestcollege.edu
President/CEO: Wes Bryan
Admissions: Jennifer Ortberg

Type: Two-Year College **Sex:** Coed **Affiliation:** Coast Community College District System. **% Accepted:** 100 **Admission Plans:** Early Admission; Open Admission **Application Deadline:** Rolling **Application Fee:** $0.00 **H.S. Requirements:** High school diploma required; GED accepted. For applicants 18 or over: High school diploma required; GED not accepted **Costs Per Year:** Application fee: $0. State resident tuition: $1104 full-time, $46 per unit part-time. Nonresident tuition: $6648 full-time, $278 per unit part-time. Mandatory fees: $72 full-time, $36 per term part-time. Full-time tuition and fees vary according to course load and program. Part-time tuition and fees vary according to course load and program. **Scholarships:** Available. **Calendar System:** Semester, Summer session available **Enrollment:** Full-time 4,394, Part-time 8,000 **Faculty:** Full-time 128, Part-time 406 **Student-Faculty Ratio:** 33:1 **Final Year or Final Semester Residency Requirement:** No **Regional Accreditation:** Western Association of Colleges and Schools **Credit Hours For Degree:** 60 units, Associates **ROTC:** Air Force **Professional Accreditation:** ACEN. **Intercollegiate Athletics:** Baseball M; Cross-Country Running M & W; Football M; Soccer M & W; Softball W; Swimming and Diving M & W; Track and Field M & W; Volleyball M & W; Water Polo M & W

GOLF ACADEMY OF AMERICA

1950 Camino Vida Roble, Ste. 125
Carlsbad, CA 92008
Tel: (760)734-1208; Free: 800-342-7342
Fax: (760)734-1642
E-mail: sdga@sdgagolf.com
Web Site: www.golfacademy.edu
President/CEO: Richard Iorio
Admissions: Deborah Wells

Type: Two-Year College **Sex:** Coed **Application Deadline:** Rolling **Application Fee:** $50.00 **H.S. Requirements:** High school diploma required; GED accepted **Scholarships:** Available. **Calendar System:** Semester **Credit Hours For Degree:** 66 credits, Associates **Professional Accreditation:** ACICS.

GRACE MISSION UNIVERSITY

1645 W Valencia Dr.
Fullerton, CA 92833
Tel: (714)525-0088
Web Site: www.gm.edu
Type: Comprehensive **Sex:** Coed **Professional Accreditation:** ABHE.

GROSSMONT COLLEGE

8800 Grossmont College Dr.
El Cajon, CA 92020-1799
Tel: (619)644-7000
Fax: (619)644-7922
Web Site: www.grossmont.edu
President/CEO: Dr. Sunita V. Cooke
Type: Two-Year College **Sex:** Coed **Affiliation:** California Community College System. **Admission Plans:** Early Admission; Open Admission **Application Deadline:** August 12 **Application Fee:** $0.00 **H.S. Requirements:** High school diploma or equivalent not required. For applicants under 18: High school diploma required; GED accepted **Scholarships:** Available. **Calendar System:** Semester, Summer session available **Student-Faculty Ratio:** 29:1 **Regional Accreditation:** Western Association of Colleges and Schools **Credit Hours For Degree:** 60 units, Associates **ROTC:** Air Force, Army **Professional Accreditation:** ACEN, AOTA, CoARC, JRCECT. **Intercollegiate Athletics:** Badminton W; Baseball M; Basketball M & W; Cross-Country Running M; Football M; Soccer W; Softball W; Swimming and Diving M & W; Tennis M & W; Track and Field M; Volleyball M & W; Water Polo M & W

GURNICK ACADEMY OF MEDICAL ARTS

2121 S El Camino Real, Bldg. C 2000
San Mateo, CA 94403
Tel: (650)685-6616
Web Site: www.gurnick.edu
Type: Two-Year College **Sex:** Coed **Professional Accreditation:** ABHES.

HARTNELL COLLEGE

411 Central Ave.
Salinas, CA 93901
Tel: (831)755-6700
Web Site: www.hartnell.edu
President/CEO: Phoebe Helm
Type: Two-Year College **Sex:** Coed **Affiliation:** California Community College System. **Admission Plans:** Deferred Admission; Early Admission; Open Admission **Application Deadline:** Rolling **Application Fee:** $0.00 **H.S. Requirements:** High school diploma required; GED accepted **Scholarships:** Available. **Calendar System:** Semester, Summer session available **Student-Faculty Ratio:** 35:1 **Regional Accreditation:** Western Association of Colleges and Schools **Credit Hours For Degree:** 60 semester hours, Associates **Professional Accreditation:** NAACLS.

HARVEY MUDD COLLEGE

301 Platt Blvd.
Claremont, CA 91711-5994
Tel: (909)621-8000
Fax: (909)621-8360
E-mail: admission@hmc.edu
Web Site: www.hmc.edu
President/CEO: Maria Klawe
Admissions: Peter Osgood
Financial Aid: Gilma Lopez
Type: Four-Year College **Sex:** Coed **Affiliation:** The Claremont Colleges Consortium. **Scores:** 100% SAT V 400+; 100% SAT M 400+; 6% ACT 24-29 **% Accepted:** 13 **Admission Plans:** Deferred Admission; Early Action; Early Admission **Application Deadline:** January 5 **Application Fee:** $70.00 **H.S. Requirements:** High school diploma or equivalent not required **Costs Per Year:** Application fee: $70. One-time mandatory fee: $100. Comprehensive fee: $67,155 includes full-time tuition ($50,368), mandatory fees ($281), and college room and board ($16,506). College room only: $8855. Room and board charges vary according to board plan. Part-time tuition: $1574 per unit. Part-time tuition varies according to course load. **Scholarships:** Available. **Calendar System:** Semester, Summer session not available **Enrollment:** Full-time 815 **Faculty:** Full-time 101, Part-time 13 **Student-Faculty Ratio:** 8:1 **Exams:** ACT essay component used for admission; Other; SAT I or ACT; SAT II; SAT essay component used for admission. **% Receiving Financial Aid:** 51 **% Residing in College-Owned, -Operated, or -Affiliated Housing:** 99 **Regional Accreditation:** Western Association of Colleges and Schools **Credit Hours For Degree:** 128 credit hours, Bachelors **ROTC:** Air Force, Army **Professional Accreditation:** ABET. **Intercollegiate Athletics:** Baseball M; Basketball M & W; Cross-Country Running M & W; Football M; Golf M & W; Lacrosse W; Soccer M & W; Softball W; Swimming and Diving M & W; Tennis M & W; Track and Field M & W; Volleyball W; Water Polo M & W

HENLEY-PUTNAM UNIVERSITY

2107 N First St., Ste. 210
San Jose, CA 95131
Tel: (408)453-9900; Free: 888-852-8746
Fax: (408)453-9700
E-mail: nreggio@henley-putnam.edu
Web Site: www.henley-putnam.edu
President/CEO: James P. Killin
Admissions: Nancy Reggio
Type: Comprehensive **Sex:** Coed **Admission Plans:** Open Admission **Application Deadline:** Rolling **Application Fee:** $0.00 **H.S. Requirements:** High school diploma required; GED accepted **Calendar System:** Continuous **Final Year or Final Semester Residency Requirement:** No **Credit Hours For Degree:** 180 quarter units, Bachelors **Professional Accreditation:** DEAC.

HOLY NAMES UNIVERSITY

3500 Mountain Blvd.
Oakland, CA 94619-1699
Tel: (510)436-1000; Free: 800-430-1321
Fax: (510)436-1325
E-mail: rocha@hnu.edu
Web Site: www.hnu.edu
President/CEO: Dr. William Hynes
Admissions: Jose Rocha
Financial Aid: Christina Miller
Type: Comprehensive **Sex:** Coed **Affiliation:** Roman Catholic. **Scores:** 68% SAT V 400+; 68% SAT M 400+; 30.4% ACT 18-23; 13.1% ACT 24-29 **% Accepted:** 44 **Admission Plans:** Deferred Admission **Application Deadline:** Rolling **Application Fee:** $20.00 **H.S. Requirements:** High school diploma required; GED accepted **Costs Per Year:** Application fee: $20. Comprehensive fee: $47,536 includes full-time tuition ($35,166), mandatory fees ($500), and college room and board ($11,870). College room only: $5966. Full-time tuition and fees vary according to course level, course load, degree level, program, and reciprocity agreements. Room and board charges vary according to board plan and housing facility. Part-time tuition: $1206 per unit. Part-time mandatory fees: $250 per term. Part-time tuition and fees vary according to course level, course load, degree level, program, and reciprocity agreements. **Scholarships:** Available. **Calendar System:** Semester, Summer session available **Enrollment:** Full-time 546, Graduate full-time 107, Graduate part-time 286, Part-time 110 **Faculty:** Full-time 47, Part-time 158 **Student-Faculty Ratio:** 12:1 **Exams:** ACT essay component not used; SAT I or ACT; SAT essay component not used. **% Receiving Financial Aid:** 41 **% Residing in College-Owned, -Operated, or -Affiliated Housing:** 51 **Final Year or Final Semester Residency Requirement:** No **Regional Accreditation:** Western Association of Colleges and Schools **Credit Hours For Degree:** 120 units, Bachelors **ROTC:** Air Force, Army **Professional Accreditation:** AACN. **Intercollegiate Athletics:** Baseball M; Basketball M & W; Cross-Country Running M & W; Golf M & W; Soccer M & W; Softball W; Tennis M & W; Volleyball M & W

HOPE INTERNATIONAL UNIVERSITY

2500 E Nutwood Ave.
Fullerton, CA 92831-3138
Tel: (714)879-3901; Free: 866-722-HOPE
Fax: (714)526-0231
E-mail: mfmadden@hiu.edu
Web Site: www.hiu.edu
President/CEO: Dr. John Derry
Admissions: Midge Madden
Financial Aid: Shannon O'Shields
Type: Comprehensive **Sex:** Coed **Affiliation:** Christian Churches and Churches of Christ. **Scores:** 71% SAT V 400+; 80% SAT M 400+; 47% ACT 18-23; 16% ACT 24-29 **% Accepted:** 34 **Application Deadline:** Rolling **Application Fee:** $40.00 **H.S. Requirements:** High school diploma required; GED accepted **Costs Per Year:** Application fee: $40. Comprehensive fee: $37,600 includes full-time tuition ($27,900), mandatory fees ($650), and college room and board ($9050). College room only: $4800. Full-time tuition and fees vary according to course level, course load, degree level, location, program, and reciprocity agreements. Room and board charges vary according to board plan. Part-time tuition: $1230 per unit. Part-time tuition varies

according to course level, course load, degree level, location, program, and reciprocity agreements. **Scholarships:** Available. **Calendar System:** 4-1-4, Summer session not available **Enrollment:** Full-time 634, Graduate full-time 247, Graduate part-time 181, Part-time 241 **Faculty:** Full-time 42, Part-time 210 **Student-Faculty Ratio:** 9:1 **Exams:** ACT essay component not used; SAT I or ACT; SAT essay component not used. **% Receiving Financial Aid:** 87 **% Residing in College-Owned, -Operated, or -Affiliated Housing:** 42 **Final Year or Final Semester Residency Requirement:** Yes **Regional Accreditation:** Western Association of Colleges and Schools **Credit Hours For Degree:** 60 units, Associates; 120 units, Bachelors **ROTC:** Army **Professional Accreditation:** AAMFT, ABHE. **Intercollegiate Athletics:** Basketball M & W; Cheerleading M & W; Cross-Country Running M & W; Golf M & W; Soccer M & W; Softball W; Tennis M & W; Track and Field M & W; Volleyball M & W

HORIZON UNIVERSITY
5331 Mt. Alifan Dr.
San Diego, CA 92111
Tel: (858)695-8587; Free: 800-553-HORIZON
Web Site: www.horizonuniversity.edu
Type: Four-Year College **Sex:** Coed **Calendar System:** Semester **Professional Accreditation:** ABHE.

HUMBOLDT STATE UNIVERSITY
1 Harpst St.
Arcata, CA 95521-8299
Tel: (707)826-3011; Free: 866-850-9556
Fax: (707)826-6194
E-mail: hsuinfo@humboldt.edu
Web Site: www.humboldt.edu
President/CEO: Dr. Lisa Rossbacher
Admissions: Steven Ladwig
Financial Aid: Peggy Metzger
Type: Comprehensive **Sex:** Coed **Affiliation:** California State University System. **Scores:** 89% SAT V 400+; 88% SAT M 400+; 47% ACT 18-23; 27% ACT 24-29 **% Accepted:** 75 **Admission Plans:** Preferred Admission **Application Deadline:** December 6 **Application Fee:** $55.00 **H.S. Requirements:** High school diploma required; GED accepted **Costs Per Year:** Application fee: $55. State resident tuition: $5472 full-time. Nonresident tuition: $16,632 full-time. Full-time tuition varies according to degree level. College room and board: $12,114. College room only: $7434. Room and board charges vary according to board plan and housing facility. **Scholarships:** Available. **Calendar System:** Semester, Summer session available **Enrollment:** Full-time 7,710, Graduate full-time 382, Graduate part-time 166, Part-time 532 **Faculty:** Full-time 226, Part-time 340 **Student-Faculty Ratio:** 25:1 **Exams:** ACT essay component not used; SAT I or ACT; SAT essay component not used; SAT Reasoning; SAT Subject. **% Receiving Financial Aid:** 77 **% Residing in College-Owned, -Operated, or -Affiliated Housing:** 9 **Final Year or Final Semester Residency Requirement:** No **Regional Accreditation:** Western Association of Colleges and Schools **Credit Hours For Degree:** 120 semester units, Bachelors **Professional Accreditation:** AACN, ABET, CSWE, NASAD, NASM, NAST, SAF. **Intercollegiate Athletics:** Basketball M & W; Cheerleading W; Crew M & W; Cross-Country Running M & W; Football M; Lacrosse M; Soccer M & W; Softball W; Track and Field M & W; Volleyball W

HUMPHREYS COLLEGE
6650 Inglewood Ave.
Stockton, CA 95207-3896
Tel: (209)478-0800
Fax: (209)478-8721
E-mail: ugadmission@humphreys.edu
Web Site: www.humphreys.edu
President/CEO: Robert Humphreys
Financial Aid: Rita Franco
Type: Comprehensive **Sex:** Coed **Admission Plans:** Deferred Admission; Early Admission; Open Admission **Application Deadline:** Rolling **Application Fee:** $35.00 **H.S. Requirements:** High school diploma required; GED accepted **Costs Per Year:** Application fee: $35. Tuition: $14,004 full-time, $389 per credit hour part-time. Full-time tuition varies according to course load. Part-time tuition varies according to course load. **Scholarships:** Available. **Calendar System:** Quarter, Summer session available **Regional Accreditation:** Western Association of Colleges and Schools **Credit Hours For Degree:** 90 units, Associates; 180 units, Bachelors

ICDC COLLEGE
6812 Pacific Blvd.
Huntington Park, CA 33409
Tel: (310)482-6996
Web Site: icdccollege.edu
Type: Two-Year College **Sex:** Coed **Professional Accreditation:** ACCSC.

IMPERIAL VALLEY COLLEGE
380 E Aten Rd.
Imperial, CA 92251-0158
Tel: (760)352-8320
Web Site: www.imperial.edu
President/CEO: Victor Jaime
Admissions: Jill Nelipovich
Financial Aid: Lisa D. Seals
Type: Two-Year College **Sex:** Coed **Affiliation:** California Community College System. **Admission Plans:** Open Admission **Application Deadline:** Rolling **Application Fee:** $23.00 **H.S. Requirements:** High school diploma or equivalent not required **Scholarships:** Available. **Calendar System:** Semester, Summer session available **Regional Accreditation:** Western Association of Colleges and Schools **Credit Hours For Degree:** 60 units, Associates **Intercollegiate Athletics:** Baseball M; Basketball M & W; Soccer M & W; Softball W; Tennis M & W

INSTITUTE OF TECHNOLOGY
564 W Herndon Ave.
Clovis, CA 93612
Tel: (559)297-4500
Web Site: www.it-colleges.edu
Type: Two-Year College **Sex:** Coed **Professional Accreditation:** ACCSC, ACF.

INTERIOR DESIGNERS INSTITUTE
1061 Camelback Rd.
Newport Beach, CA 92660
Tel: (949)675-4451
Fax: (949)759-0667
E-mail: contact@idi.edu
Web Site: www.idi.edu
President/CEO: Judy Deaton
Type: Comprehensive **Sex:** Coed **Application Fee:** $95.00 **H.S. Requirements:** High school diploma required; GED accepted **Professional Accreditation:** ACCSC, CIDA.

IRVINE VALLEY COLLEGE
5500 Irvine Ctr. Dr.
Irvine, CA 92618
Tel: (949)451-5100
Fax: (949)559-3443
Web Site: www.ivc.edu
President/CEO: Glenn R. Roquemore, PhD
Admissions: John Edwards
Type: Two-Year College **Sex:** Coed **Affiliation:** Saddleback Community College District. **Admission Plans:** Early Admission; Open Admission **Application Deadline:** Rolling **Application Fee:** $0.00 **H.S. Requirements:** High school diploma or equivalent not required **Scholarships:** Available. **Calendar System:** Semester, Summer session available **Faculty:** Full-time 94, Part-time 250 **Regional Accreditation:** Western Association of Colleges and Schools **Credit Hours For Degree:** 60 units, Associates **Intercollegiate Athletics:** Basketball M & W; Cross-Country Running M & W; Soccer M & W; Tennis M & W; Volleyball M

JOHN F. KENNEDY UNIVERSITY
100 Ellinwood Way
Pleasant Hill, CA 94523-4817
Tel: (925)969-3300; Free: 800-696-JFKU
Fax: (925)254-6964
E-mail: jmhogg@jfku.edu
Web Site: www.jfku.edu
President/CEO: Dr. Steven Stargardter
Admissions: Jen Miller-Hogg
Financial Aid: Mindy Bergeron
Type: Two-Year Upper Division **Sex:** Coed **Affiliation:** National University System. **Admission Plans:** Deferred Admission; Open Admission **Applica-

tion Fee: $60.00 **H.S. Requirements:** High school diploma required; GED accepted **Scholarships:** Available. **Calendar System:** Quarter, Summer session available **Enrollment:** Full-time 54, Part-time 233 **Student-Faculty Ratio:** 8:1 **% Receiving Financial Aid:** 22 **Regional Accreditation:** Western Association of Colleges and Schools **Credit Hours For Degree:** 180 quarter hours, Bachelors **Professional Accreditation:** APA.

JOHN PAUL THE GREAT CATHOLIC UNIVERSITY

155 W Grand Ave.
Escondido, CA 92025
Tel: (858)653-6740
E-mail: mharold@jpcatholic.com
Web Site: www.jpcatholic.com
President/CEO: Dr. Derry Connolly
Admissions: Martin Harold
Financial Aid: Lisa Williams
Type: Comprehensive **Sex:** Coed **Affiliation:** Roman Catholic Church. **Scores:** 100% SAT V 400+; 96% SAT M 400+; 15.4% ACT 18-23; 61.5% ACT 24-29 **% Accepted:** 93 **Admission Plans:** Deferred Admission **Application Deadline:** Rolling **Application Fee:** $50.00 **H.S. Requirements:** High school diploma required; GED accepted **Costs Per Year:** Application fee: $50. Tuition: $24,000 full-time, $667 per credit part-time. Mandatory fees: $900 full-time. College room only: $8100. Tuition guaranteed not to increase for student's term of enrollment. **Scholarships:** Available. **Calendar System:** Quarter, Summer session available **Enrollment:** Full-time 192, Graduate full-time 51, Graduate part-time 60, Part-time 14 **Faculty:** Full-time 6, Part-time 21 **Student-Faculty Ratio:** 21:1 **Exams:** ACT essay component not used; SAT I or ACT; SAT II; SAT essay component not used. **% Receiving Financial Aid:** 76 **% Residing in College-Owned, -Operated, or -Affiliated Housing:** 77 **Final Year or Final Semester Residency Requirement:** No **Regional Accreditation:** Western Association of Colleges and Schools **Credit Hours For Degree:** 180 credits, Bachelors

LA SIERRA UNIVERSITY

4500 Riverwalk Pky.
Riverside, CA 92515
Tel: (951)785-2000; Free: 800-874-5587
Fax: (951)785-2901
E-mail: iteheda@lasierra.edu
Web Site: www.lasierra.edu
President/CEO: Dr. Randal Wisbey
Admissions: Ivy Teheda
Financial Aid: Elina Bascomb
Type: Comprehensive **Sex:** Coed **Affiliation:** Seventh-day Adventist; Seventh-Day Adventist Education System. **Scores:** 82% SAT V 400+; 82% SAT M 400+; 44% ACT 18-23; 12% ACT 24-29 **% Accepted:** 45 **Admission Plans:** Deferred Admission; Preferred Admission **Application Deadline:** February 1 **H.S. Requirements:** High school diploma required; GED accepted **Costs Per Year:** Comprehensive fee: $38,270 includes full-time tuition ($29,340), mandatory fees ($1130), and college room and board ($7800). Full-time tuition and fees vary according to course load, degree level, and location. Room and board charges vary according to board plan and housing facility. Part-time tuition: $815 per quarter hour. Part-time tuition varies according to course load, degree level, and location. **Scholarships:** Available. **Calendar System:** Quarter, Summer session available **Enrollment:** Full-time 1,866, Graduate full-time 243, Graduate part-time 130, Part-time 237 **Faculty:** Full-time 102, Part-time 14 **Student-Faculty Ratio:** 15:1 **Exams:** ACT essay component not used; SAT I or ACT; SAT essay component not used; SAT Reasoning; SAT Subject. **% Receiving Financial Aid:** 80 **% Residing in College-Owned, -Operated, or -Affiliated Housing:** 29 **Final Year or Final Semester Residency Requirement:** Yes **Regional Accreditation:** Western Association of Colleges and Schools **Credit Hours For Degree:** 190 quarter units, Bachelors **Professional Accreditation:** ATS, CSWE, NASM. **Intercollegiate Athletics:** Basketball M & W; Golf M; Soccer M; Softball W; Volleyball W

LAGUNA COLLEGE OF ART & DESIGN

2222 Laguna Canyon Rd.
Laguna Beach, CA 92651-1136
Tel: (949)376-6000; Free: 800-255-0762
Fax: (949)376-6009
E-mail: mkeyes@lcad.edu
Web Site: www.lcad.edu

President/CEO: Jonathon Burke
Admissions: Madison Keyes
Financial Aid: Christopher Brown
Type: Comprehensive **Sex:** Coed **Scores:** 98% SAT V 400+; 100% SAT M 400+; 20% ACT 18-23; 70% ACT 24-29 **% Accepted:** 88 **Admission Plans:** Deferred Admission; Early Action; Early Admission **Application Deadline:** Rolling **Application Fee:** $45.00 **H.S. Requirements:** High school diploma required; GED accepted **Costs Per Year:** Application fee: $45. Tuition: $28,100 full-time, $1170 per credit hour part-time. Full-time tuition varies according to course load and degree level. Part-time tuition varies according to course load and degree level. College room only: $9100. **Scholarships:** Available. **Calendar System:** Semester, Summer session not available **Enrollment:** Full-time 466, Graduate full-time 25, Graduate part-time 5, Part-time 48 **Faculty:** Full-time 14, Part-time 91 **Student-Faculty Ratio:** 12:1 **Exams:** ACT essay component not used; SAT I or ACT; SAT essay component not used. **% Residing in College-Owned, -Operated, or -Affiliated Housing:** 11 **Final Year or Final Semester Residency Requirement:** No **Regional Accreditation:** Western Association of Colleges and Schools **Credit Hours For Degree:** 122 units, Bachelors **Professional Accreditation:** NASAD.

LAKE TAHOE COMMUNITY COLLEGE

One College Dr.
South Lake Tahoe, CA 96150-4524
Tel: (530)541-4660
Fax: (530)541-7852
E-mail: admissions@ltcc.edu
Web Site: www.ltcc.edu
President/CEO: Dr. Kindred Murillo
Type: Two-Year College **Sex:** Coed **Affiliation:** California Community College System. **% Accepted:** 100 **Admission Plans:** Early Admission; Open Admission **Application Deadline:** Rolling **Application Fee:** $0.00 **H.S. Requirements:** High school diploma or equivalent not required. For applicants under 18: High school diploma required; GED accepted **Scholarships:** Available. **Calendar System:** Quarter, Summer session available **Faculty:** Full-time 41, Part-time 159 **Final Year or Final Semester Residency Requirement:** No **Regional Accreditation:** Western Association of Colleges and Schools **Credit Hours For Degree:** 90 units, Associates **Intercollegiate Athletics:** Soccer M & W

LANEY COLLEGE

900 Fallon St.
Oakland, CA 94607-4893
Tel: (510)834-5740
Web Site: www.laney.edu
President/CEO: Dr. Elnora Webb
Admissions: Barbara Simmons
Type: Two-Year College **Sex:** Coed **Affiliation:** Peralta Community College District System. **Admission Plans:** Early Admission; Open Admission **Application Deadline:** Rolling **Application Fee:** $0.00 **H.S. Requirements:** High school diploma required; GED accepted. For applicants 18 or over: High school diploma or equivalent not required **Scholarships:** Available. **Calendar System:** Semester, Summer session available **Enrollment:** Full-time 2,424, Part-time 11,039 **Faculty:** Full-time 118, Part-time 333 **Regional Accreditation:** Western Association of Colleges and Schools **Credit Hours For Degree:** 60 semester hours, Associates **Intercollegiate Athletics:** Baseball M; Football M; Golf M; Softball W; Volleyball W

LAS POSITAS COLLEGE

3000 Campus Hill Dr.
Livermore, CA 94551
Tel: (925)424-1000
Fax: (925)443-0742
Web Site: www.laspositascollege.edu
President/CEO: Dr. Guy Lease
Admissions: Sylvia R. Rodriguez
Financial Aid: Andi Schreibman
Type: Two-Year College **Sex:** Coed **Affiliation:** California Community College System. **Admission Plans:** Open Admission **Application Fee:** $0.00 **H.S. Requirements:** High school diploma required; GED accepted **Scholarships:** Available. **Calendar System:** Semester, Summer session available **Regional Accreditation:** Western Association of Colleges and Schools **Credit Hours For Degree:** 60 units, Associates **Intercollegiate Athletics:** Cross-Country Running M & W; Soccer M & W

LASSEN COMMUNITY COLLEGE DISTRICT

Hwy. 139
Susanville, CA 96130
Tel: (530)257-6181
Fax: (530)257-8964
Web Site: www.lassencollege.edu
President/CEO: William Studt
Admissions: Chris J. Alberico
Type: Two-Year College **Sex:** Coed **Affiliation:** California Community College System. **Admission Plans:** Early Admission; Open Admission **Application Deadline:** Rolling **H.S. Requirements:** High school diploma or equivalent not required. For applicants under 18: High school diploma required; GED accepted **Scholarships:** Available. **Calendar System:** Semester, Summer session available **Faculty:** Full-time 44, Part-time 160 **Regional Accreditation:** Western Association of Colleges and Schools **Credit Hours For Degree:** 60 units, Associates **Intercollegiate Athletics:** Basketball M & W; Cross-Country Running M & W; Golf M & W; Riflery M & W; Softball W; Track and Field M & W; Volleyball W; Wrestling M

LAURUS COLLEGE

81 Higuera St., Ste. 110
San Luis Obispo, CA 93401
Tel: (805)267-1690
Web Site: www.lauruscollege.edu
Type: Two-Year College **Sex:** Coed **Professional Accreditation:** ACICS.

LEARNET ACADEMY

3251 W 6th St., 2nd Fl.
Los Angeles, CA 90020
Tel: (213)387-4242
Web Site: www.learnet.edu
Type: Two-Year College **Sex:** Coed **Professional Accreditation:** ACICS.

LIFE PACIFIC COLLEGE

1100 Covina Blvd.
San Dimas, CA 91773-3298
Tel: (909)599-5433; Free: 877-886-5433
Fax: (909)599-6690
E-mail: adm@lifepacific.edu
Web Site: www.lifepacific.edu
President/CEO: Dr. Robert Flores
Admissions: Dorienne Elston
Financial Aid: Luci Perez
Type: Four-Year College **Sex:** Coed **Affiliation:** International Church of the Foursquare Gospel. **Scores:** 88% SAT V 400+; 76% SAT M 400+; 42% ACT 18-23; 25% ACT 24-29 **% Accepted:** 100 **Admission Plans:** Deferred Admission **Application Deadline:** May 1 **Application Fee:** $35.00 **H.S. Requirements:** High school diploma required; GED accepted **Scholarships:** Available. **Calendar System:** Semester, Summer session available **Enrollment:** Full-time 323, Part-time 191 **Faculty:** Full-time 16, Part-time 22 **Student-Faculty Ratio:** 16:1 **Exams:** SAT I or ACT. **% Residing in College-Owned, -Operated, or -Affiliated Housing:** 50 **Regional Accreditation:** Western Association of Colleges and Schools **Credit Hours For Degree:** 64 semester hours, Associates; 128 semester hours, Bachelors **Professional Accreditation:** ABHE.

LINCOLN UNIVERSITY

401 15th St.
Oakland, CA 94612
Tel: (510)628-8010; Free: 888-810-9998
Fax: (510)628-8026
E-mail: admissions@lincolnuca.edu
Web Site: www.lincolnuca.edu
President/CEO: Dr. Mikhail Brodsky
Admissions: Vanessa Juwono
Type: Comprehensive **Sex:** Coed **% Accepted:** 57 **Admission Plans:** Deferred Admission **Application Deadline:** July 19 **Application Fee:** $75.00 **H.S. Requirements:** High school diploma required; GED accepted **Costs Per Year:** Application fee: $75. Tuition: $9960 full-time, $410 per unit part-time. Mandatory fees: $400 full-time, $400 per year part-time. Full-time tuition and fees vary according to course level, course load, degree level, and program. Part-time tuition and fees vary according to course level, course load, degree level, and program. **Calendar System:** Semester, Summer session available **Enrollment:** Full-time 138, Graduate full-time 552,

Graduate part-time 3, Part-time 41 **Faculty:** Full-time 13, Part-time 30 **Student-Faculty Ratio:** 17:1 **Final Year or Final Semester Residency Requirement:** No **Credit Hours For Degree:** 125 units, Bachelors **Professional Accreditation:** ACICS.

LOMA LINDA UNIVERSITY

Loma Linda, CA 92350
Tel: (909)558-1000; Free: 800-422-4558
Fax: (909)558-4577
Web Site: www.llu.edu
President/CEO: Richard Hart
Financial Aid: Verdell Schaefer
Type: University **Sex:** Coed **Affiliation:** Seventh-day Adventist. **Admission Plans:** Deferred Admission **Application Fee:** $60.00 **H.S. Requirements:** High school diploma required; GED accepted **Scholarships:** Available. **Calendar System:** Quarter, Summer session not available **Enrollment:** Full-time 885, Part-time 347 **Faculty:** Full-time 557, Part-time 283 **Student-Faculty Ratio:** 8:1 **% Receiving Financial Aid:** 77 **% Residing in College-Owned, -Operated, or -Affiliated Housing:** 27 **Regional Accreditation:** Western Association of Colleges and Schools **Professional Accreditation:** AACN, AAMFT, AANA, ACPE, ACIPE, ADA, AHIMA, AND, AOTA, APA, APTA, ARCST, ASC, ASHA, CEPH, CSWE, CoARC, JRCERT, LCME/AMA, NAACLS.

LONG BEACH CITY COLLEGE

4901 E Carson St.
Long Beach, CA 90808-1780
Tel: (562)938-4353
Web Site: www.lbcc.edu
President/CEO: Eloy Oakley
Admissions: Ross Miyashiro
Type: Two-Year College **Sex:** Coed **Affiliation:** California Community College System. **Admission Plans:** Early Admission; Open Admission **Application Deadline:** Rolling **Application Fee:** $0.00 **H.S. Requirements:** High school diploma or equivalent not required. For applicants under 18, international students: High school diploma required; GED accepted **Scholarships:** Available. **Calendar System:** Semester, Summer session available **Student-Faculty Ratio:** 30:1 **Regional Accreditation:** Western Association of Colleges and Schools **Credit Hours For Degree:** 60 units, Associates **Professional Accreditation:** ACEN, JRCERT. **Intercollegiate Athletics:** Baseball M; Basketball M & W; Football M; Golf M & W; Soccer M & W; Softball W; Swimming and Diving M & W; Tennis M & W; Track and Field M & W; Volleyball M & W; Water Polo M & W

LOS ANGELES CITY COLLEGE

855 N Vermont Ave.
Los Angeles, CA 90029-3590
Tel: (323)953-4000
Fax: (323)953-4536
Web Site: www.lacitycollege.edu
President/CEO: Renee Martinez
Admissions: Elaine Geismar
Type: Two-Year College **Sex:** Coed **Affiliation:** Los Angeles Community College District System. **Admission Plans:** Open Admission **Application Deadline:** September 5 **Application Fee:** $0.00 **H.S. Requirements:** High school diploma or equivalent not required **Calendar System:** Semester, Summer session available **Faculty:** Full-time 249, Part-time 323 **Regional Accreditation:** Western Association of Colleges and Schools **Credit Hours For Degree:** 60 units, Associates **ROTC:** Air Force, Army **Professional Accreditation:** ADA, JRCERT. **Intercollegiate Athletics:** Basketball M; Cross-Country Running M; Football M; Gymnastics M; Track and Field M & W; Volleyball M & W

LOS ANGELES COUNTY COLLEGE OF NURSING AND ALLIED HEALTH

1237 N Mission Rd.
Los Angeles, CA 90033
Tel: (323)226-4911
Fax: (323)226-6427
Web Site: www.ladhs.org/wps/portal/CollegeOfNursing
President/CEO: Nancy Miller
Type: Two-Year College **Sex:** Coed **Application Fee:** $5.00 **Costs Per Year:** Application fee: $5. One-time mandatory fee: $125. Area resident tuition: $4800 full-time, $240 per unit part-time. Full-time tuition varies ac-

cording to course load. Part-time tuition varies according to course load. **Scholarships:** Available. **Calendar System:** Semester **Student-Faculty Ratio:** 4:1 **Exams:** Other. **Regional Accreditation:** Western Association of Colleges and Schools

LOS ANGELES FILM SCHOOL

6363 Sunset Blvd.
Hollywood, CA 90028
Tel: (323)860-0789; Free: 877-952-3456
Web Site: www.lafilm.edu
President/CEO: Diana Derycz-Kessler

Type: Four-Year College **Sex:** Coed **Affiliation:** Full Sail University. **% Accepted:** 85 **Admission Plans:** Open Admission **Application Fee:** $75.00 **H.S. Requirements:** High school diploma required; GED accepted **Costs Per Year:** Application fee: $75. Tuition: $71,166 per degree program. **Calendar System:** Continuous **Enrollment:** Full-time 1,358 **Faculty:** Full-time 103, Part-time 13 **Professional Accreditation:** ACCSC.

LOS ANGELES HARBOR COLLEGE

1111 Figueroa Pl.
Wilmington, CA 90744-2397
Tel: (310)233-4000
Fax: (310)233-4223
E-mail: chingdm@lahc.edu
Web Site: www.lahc.edu
President/CEO: Marvin Martinez
Admissions: David Ching

Type: Two-Year College **Sex:** Coed **Affiliation:** Los Angeles Community College District System. **Admission Plans:** Deferred Admission; Early Admission; Open Admission **Application Deadline:** September 3 **Application Fee:** $0.00 **H.S. Requirements:** High school diploma or equivalent not required. For applicants under 18: High school diploma required; GED accepted **Scholarships:** Available. **Calendar System:** Semester, Summer session available **Enrollment:** Full-time 2,812, Part-time 7,369 **Faculty:** Full-time 113, Part-time 309 **Student-Faculty Ratio:** 47:1 **Regional Accreditation:** Western Association of Colleges and Schools **Credit Hours For Degree:** 60 units, Associates **Professional Accreditation:** ACEN. **Intercollegiate Athletics:** Baseball M; Basketball M; Football M; Soccer M & W; Softball W; Volleyball W

LOS ANGELES MISSION COLLEGE

13356 Eldridge Ave.
Sylmar, CA 91342-3245
Tel: (818)364-7600
Web Site: www.lamission.edu
President/CEO: Dr. Monte Perez
Financial Aid: Dennis J. Schroeder

Type: Two-Year College **Sex:** Coed **Affiliation:** Los Angeles Community College District System, California Community Colleges. **Admission Plans:** Early Admission; Open Admission **Application Deadline:** Rolling **H.S. Requirements:** High school diploma or equivalent not required. For applicants under 18: High school diploma required; GED accepted **Scholarships:** Available. **Calendar System:** Semester, Summer session available **Enrollment:** Full-time 2,338, Part-time 7,853 **Faculty:** Full-time 80, Part-time 274 **Final Year or Final Semester Residency Requirement:** Yes **Regional Accreditation:** Western Association of Colleges and Schools **Credit Hours For Degree:** 60 credits, Associates

LOS ANGELES PIERCE COLLEGE

6201 Winnetka Ave.
Woodland Hills, CA 91371-0001
Tel: (818)710-4123
Fax: (818)710-9844
Web Site: www.piercecollege.edu
President/CEO: Dr. Kathleen Burke-Kelly
Admissions: Shelley L. Gerstl

Type: Two-Year College **Sex:** Coed **Affiliation:** Los Angeles Community College District System. **% Accepted:** 100 **Admission Plans:** Early Admission; Open Admission **Application Deadline:** August 20 **Application Fee:** $0.00 **H.S. Requirements:** High school diploma or equivalent not required. For applicants under 18, nursing program: High school diploma required; GED accepted **Scholarships:** Available. **Calendar System:** Semester, Summer session available **Regional Accreditation:** Western Association of Colleges and Schools **Credit Hours For Degree:** 60 credits, Associates

Professional Accreditation: ACEN. **Intercollegiate Athletics:** Baseball M; Basketball W; Football M; Softball W; Swimming and Diving M & W; Tennis M & W; Volleyball M & W; Water Polo M

LOS ANGELES SOUTHWEST COLLEGE

1600 W Imperial Hwy.
Los Angeles, CA 90047-4810
Tel: (323)241-5225
Web Site: www.lasc.edu
President/CEO: Dr. Linda D. Rose
Admissions: Dan W. Walden

Type: Two-Year College **Sex:** Coed **Affiliation:** Los Angeles Community College District System. **Admission Plans:** Early Admission; Open Admission **Application Deadline:** September 9 **H.S. Requirements:** High school diploma or equivalent not required. For applicants under 18: High school diploma required; GED accepted **Scholarships:** Available. **Calendar System:** Semester, Summer session available **Faculty:** Full-time 75, Part-time 148 **Regional Accreditation:** Western Association of Colleges and Schools **Credit Hours For Degree:** 60 units, Associates **Intercollegiate Athletics:** Basketball M & W; Cross-Country Running M & W; Football M; Track and Field M & W

LOS ANGELES TRADE-TECHNICAL COLLEGE

400 W Washington Blvd.
Los Angeles, CA 90015-4108
Tel: (213)763-7000
Fax: (213)748-7334
E-mail: joofhl@lattc.edu
Web Site: www.lattc.edu
President/CEO: Lawrence B. Frank
Admissions: Dr. Henan Joof

Type: Two-Year College **Sex:** Coed **Affiliation:** Los Angeles Community College District System. **Application Deadline:** September 7 **Application Fee:** $0.00 **H.S. Requirements:** High school diploma or equivalent not required. For nursing program: High school diploma required; GED accepted **Scholarships:** Available. **Calendar System:** Semester, Summer session available **Enrollment:** Full-time 4,160, Part-time 9,034 **Faculty:** Full-time 200, Part-time 243 **Regional Accreditation:** Western Association of Colleges and Schools **Credit Hours For Degree:** 60 units, Associates **Professional Accreditation:** ACF. **Intercollegiate Athletics:** Basketball M & W; Swimming and Diving M & W; Volleyball M & W

LOS ANGELES VALLEY COLLEGE

5800 Fulton Ave.
Valley Glen, CA 91401
Tel: (818)947-2600
Fax: (818)947-2610
E-mail: DunnAE@lavc.edu
Web Site: www.lavc.edu
President/CEO: Dr. Erika Endrijonas
Admissions: Ashley Dunn

Type: Two-Year College **Sex:** Coed **Affiliation:** Los Angeles Community College District System. **Admission Plans:** Early Admission; Open Admission **Application Deadline:** Rolling **Application Fee:** $0.00 **H.S. Requirements:** High school diploma or equivalent not required **Scholarships:** Available. **Calendar System:** Semester, Summer session available **Regional Accreditation:** Western Association of Colleges and Schools **Credit Hours For Degree:** 60 units, Associates **Professional Accreditation:** ACEN, CoARC. **Intercollegiate Athletics:** Baseball M; Basketball M & W; Cross-Country Running M & W; Football M; Soccer W; Softball W; Swimming and Diving M & W; Track and Field M & W; Volleyball M & W; Water Polo M & W

LOS MEDANOS COLLEGE

2700 E Leland Rd.
Pittsburg, CA 94565-5197
Tel: (925)439-2181
Fax: (925)439-8797
Web Site: www.losmedanos.net
President/CEO: Robert Kratochvil
Admissions: Gail Newman

Type: Two-Year College **Sex:** Coed **Affiliation:** California Community College System. **Admission Plans:** Open Admission **Application Deadline:** August 29 **Application Fee:** $0.00 **H.S. Requirements:** High school diploma required; GED accepted. For applicants 18 or over: High school diploma or equivalent not required **Scholarships:** Available. **Calendar System:** Semester, Summer session available **Faculty:** Full-time 104, Part-time 140 **Regional Accreditation:** Western Association of Colleges and Schools **Credit Hours For Degree:** 60 units, Associates **Intercollegiate Athletics:** Baseball M; Basketball M & W; Football M; Soccer M; Softball W; Volleyball W

LOYOLA MARYMOUNT UNIVERSITY

One LMU Dr.
Los Angeles, CA 90045-2659
Tel: (310)338-2700; Free: 800-LMU-INFO
Fax: (310)338-2797
E-mail: admissions@lmu.edu
Web Site: www.lmu.edu
President/CEO: Dr. Timothy L. Snyder, PhD
Admissions: Matthew X. Fissinger
Financial Aid: Dr. Maureen Weatherall

Type: Comprehensive **Sex:** Coed **Affiliation:** Roman Catholic. **Scores:** 100% SAT V 400+; 100% SAT M 400+; 10.05% ACT 18-23; 61.06% ACT 24-29 **Costs Per Year:** One-time mandatory fee: $225. Comprehensive fee: $57,039 includes full-time tuition ($41,876), mandatory fees ($693), and college room and board ($14,470). College room only: $10,070. Full-time tuition and fees vary according to reciprocity agreements. Room and board charges vary according to board plan and housing facility. Part-time tuition: $1747 per credit hour. Part-time tuition varies according to course load. **Scholarships:** Available. **Calendar System:** Semester, Summer session available **Enrollment:** Full-time 6,030, Graduate full-time 2,234, Graduate part-time 899, Part-time 229 **Exams:** ACT essay component used as validity check; SAT I or ACT; SAT II; SAT essay component used as validity check. **% Receiving Financial Aid:** 56 **% Residing in College-Owned, -Operated, or -Affiliated Housing:** 51 **Final Year or Final Semester Residency Requirement:** No **Regional Accreditation:** Western Association of Colleges and Schools **Credit Hours For Degree:** 120 units, Bachelors **ROTC:** Air Force, Army, Navy **Professional Accreditation:** AACSB, AALS, ABA, ABET, ATS, NASAD, NASD, NASM, NAST, NCATE. **Intercollegiate Athletics:** Baseball M; Basketball M & W; Cheerleading M & W; Crew M & W; Cross-Country Running M & W; Golf M; Soccer M & W; Softball W; Swimming and Diving W; Tennis M & W; Track and Field M & W; Volleyball W; Water Polo M & W

MARYMOUNT CALIFORNIA UNIVERSITY

30800 Palos Verdes Dr. E
Rancho Palos Verdes, CA 90275-6299
Tel: (310)377-5501
Fax: (310)377-6223
E-mail: admissions@marymountcalifornia.edu
Web Site: www.marymountcalifornia.edu
President/CEO: Dr. Ariane Schauer
Admissions: Alan Liebrecht
Financial Aid: Pedro Ladino

Type: Comprehensive **Sex:** Coed **Affiliation:** Roman Catholic. **Scores:** 77% SAT V 400+; 75% SAT M 400+; 56% ACT 18-23; 11% ACT 24-29 **% Accepted:** 60 **Admission Plans:** Deferred Admission; Early Admission **Application Deadline:** July 1 **Application Fee:** $50.00 **H.S. Requirements:** High school diploma required; GED accepted **Costs Per Year:** Application fee: $50. One-time mandatory fee: $300. Comprehensive fee: $48,610 includes full-time tuition ($32,980), mandatory fees ($1700), and college room and board ($13,930). College room only: $8700. Full-time tuition and fees vary according to location and program. Room and board charges vary according to board plan and housing facility. Part-time tuition: $1430 per credit hour. Part-time mandatory fees: $600 per year. Part-time tuition and fees vary according to location and program. **Scholarships:** Available. **Calendar System:** Semester, Summer session available **Enrollment:** Full-time 1,012, Graduate full-time 29, Graduate part-time 11, Part-time 47 **Faculty:** Full-time 32, Part-time 82 **Student-Faculty Ratio:** 18:1 **Exams:** ACT essay component used for placement; SAT I or ACT; SAT essay component used for placement; SAT Reasoning. **% Receiving Financial Aid:** 58 **% Residing in College-Owned, -Operated, or -Affiliated Housing:** 37 **Final Year or Final Semester Residency Requirement:** Yes **Regional Accreditation:** Western Association of Colleges and Schools **Credit Hours For Degree:** 60 units, Associates; 120 units, Bachelors **Intercollegiate Athletics:** Baseball M; Golf M & W; Lacrosse M & W; Soccer M & W; Track and Field M

THE MASTER'S COLLEGE AND SEMINARY

21726 Placerita Canyon Rd.
Santa Clarita, CA 91321-1200

Tel: (661)259-3540; Free: 800-568-6248
E-mail: admissions@masters.edu
Web Site: www.masters.edu
President/CEO: Dr. John MacArthur
Admissions: Hollie Jackson
Financial Aid: Gary Edwards

Type: Comprehensive **Sex:** Coed **Affiliation:** nondenominational. **Scores:** 91% SAT V 400+; 95% SAT M 400+; 38% ACT 18-23; 43% ACT 24-29 **% Accepted:** 82 **Admission Plans:** Deferred Admission; Early Admission; Early Decision Plan **Application Deadline:** September 1 **Application Fee:** $40.00 **H.S. Requirements:** High school diploma required; GED accepted **Costs Per Year:** Application fee: $40. Comprehensive fee: $41,970 includes full-time tuition ($31,550), mandatory fees ($420), and college room and board ($10,000). Full-time tuition and fees vary according to class time, course load, location, and program. Room and board charges vary according to board plan. Part-time tuition: $1325 per credit hour. Part-time tuition varies according to class time, course load, location, and program. **Scholarships:** Available. **Calendar System:** Semester, Summer session available **Enrollment:** Full-time 990, Graduate full-time 231, Graduate part-time 234, Part-time 264 **Faculty:** Full-time 67, Part-time 171 **Student-Faculty Ratio:** 10:1 **Exams:** SAT I or ACT; SAT II; SAT Reasoning. **% Receiving Financial Aid:** 78 **% Residing in College-Owned, -Operated, or -Affiliated Housing:** 82 **Final Year or Final Semester Residency Requirement:** No **Regional Accreditation:** Western Association of Colleges and Schools **Credit Hours For Degree:** 122 units, Bachelors **ROTC:** Air Force, Army **Professional Accreditation:** AAFCS, NASM. **Intercollegiate Athletics:** Baseball M; Basketball M & W; Cross-Country Running M & W; Golf M; Soccer M & W; Track and Field M & W; Volleyball W

MENDOCINO COLLEGE

1000 Hensley Creek Rd.
Ukiah, CA 95482-0300
Tel: (707)468-3000
Fax: (707)468-3430
E-mail: asimpson@mendocino.edu
Web Site: www.mendocino.edu
President/CEO: Arturo Reyes
Admissions: Anastasia Simpson-Logg

Type: Two-Year College **Sex:** Coed **Affiliation:** California Community College System. **% Accepted:** 100 **Admission Plans:** Deferred Admission; Early Admission; Open Admission; Preferred Admission **Application Deadline:** Rolling **Application Fee:** $0.00 **H.S. Requirements:** High school diploma or equivalent not required **Scholarships:** Available. **Calendar System:** Semester, Summer session available **Enrollment:** Full-time 1,296, Part-time 2,318 **Faculty:** Full-time 51, Part-time 243 **Student-Faculty Ratio:** 16:1 **Final Year or Final Semester Residency Requirement:** No **Regional Accreditation:** Western Association of Colleges and Schools **Credit Hours For Degree:** 60 units, Associates **Intercollegiate Athletics:** Baseball M; Basketball M & W; Football M; Soccer W; Softball W; Volleyball W

MENLO COLLEGE

1000 El Camino Real
Atherton, CA 94027-4301
Tel: (650)688-3753; Free: 800-556-3656
Fax: (650)617-2395
E-mail: admissions@menlo.edu
Web Site: www.menlo.edu
President/CEO: Dr. Richard A. Moran
Admissions: Priscila DeSouza
Financial Aid: Jessica Ayers

Type: Four-Year College **Sex:** Coed **Scores:** 94% SAT V 400+; 98% SAT M 400+; 66% ACT 18-23; 21% ACT 24-29 **% Accepted:** 38 **Admission Plans:** Deferred Admission; Early Admission; Early Decision Plan **Application Deadline:** April 1 **Application Fee:** $40.00 **H.S. Requirements:** High school diploma required; GED accepted **Costs Per Year:** Application fee: $40. Comprehensive fee: $53,100 includes full-time tuition ($39,250), mandatory fees ($700), and college room and board ($13,150). Room and board charges vary according to housing facility. Part-time tuition: $1636 per credit. **Scholarships:** Available. **Calendar System:** Semester, Summer session available **Enrollment:** Full-time 741, Part-time 27 **Faculty:** Full-time 29, Part-time 72 **Student-Faculty Ratio:** 14:1 **Exams:** ACT essay component not used; SAT I or ACT; SAT essay component not used. **% Receiving Financial Aid:** 63 **% Residing in College-Owned, -Operated, or -Affiliated Housing:** 60 **Final Year or Final Semester Residency Require-**

ment: Yes **Regional Accreditation:** Western Association of Colleges and Schools **Credit Hours For Degree:** 124 units, Bachelors **ROTC:** Air Force **Intercollegiate Athletics:** Basketball M & W; Cross-Country Running M & W; Golf M & W; Soccer M & W; Softball W; Track and Field M & W; Volleyball W; Wrestling M & W

MERCED COLLEGE
3600 M St.
Merced, CA 95348-2898
Tel: (209)384-6000
Fax: (209)384-6339
Web Site: www.mccd.edu
President/CEO: Ron Taylor
Admissions: Cherie Davis
Financial Aid: Shawn McCall
Type: Two-Year College **Sex:** Coed **Affiliation:** California Community College System. **% Accepted:** 100 **Admission Plans:** Early Admission; Open Admission **Application Deadline:** Rolling **H.S. Requirements:** High school diploma or equivalent not required. For applicants under 18: High school diploma required; GED accepted **Scholarships:** Available. **Calendar System:** Semester, Summer session available **Enrollment:** Full-time 4,598, Part-time 7,927 **Faculty:** Full-time 145, Part-time 276 **Regional Accreditation:** Western Association of Colleges and Schools **Credit Hours For Degree:** 60 units, Associates **ROTC:** Army **Professional Accreditation:** JRCERT. **Intercollegiate Athletics:** Baseball M; Basketball M & W; Bowling M & W; Cross-Country Running M; Equestrian Sports M & W; Football M; Golf M & W; Soccer M; Softball W; Swimming and Diving M & W; Tennis M & W; Track and Field M & W; Volleyball W; Water Polo M

MERRITT COLLEGE
12500 Campus Dr.
Oakland, CA 94619-3196
Tel: (510)531-4911
E-mail: hperdue@peralta.cc.ca.us
Web Site: www.merritt.edu
President/CEO: Norma Ambriz-Galaviz
Admissions: Barbara Simmons
Type: Two-Year College **Sex:** Coed **Affiliation:** Peralta Community College District System. **Admission Plans:** Deferred Admission; Early Admission; Open Admission **Application Deadline:** August 28 **H.S. Requirements:** High school diploma required; GED accepted. For applicants 18 or over: High school diploma or equivalent not required **Calendar System:** Semester, Summer session available **Regional Accreditation:** Western Association of Colleges and Schools **Credit Hours For Degree:** 60 semester hours, Associates **Professional Accreditation:** JRCERT. **Intercollegiate Athletics:** Basketball M & W; Cross-Country Running M & W; Track and Field M & W

MILLS COLLEGE
5000 MacArthur Blvd.
Oakland, CA 94613-1000
Tel: (510)430-2255; Free: 800-87-MILLS
Fax: (510)430-3314
E-mail: admission@mills.edu
Web Site: www.mills.edu
President/CEO: Alecia A. DeCoudreaux
Admissions: Robynne Royster
Financial Aid: Larry Blair
Type: Comprehensive **Scores:** 100% SAT V 400+; 100% SAT M 400+; 24% ACT 18-23; 45% ACT 24-29 **% Accepted:** 76 **Admission Plans:** Deferred Admission; Early Admission; Early Decision Plan **Application Deadline:** January 15 **Application Fee:** $50.00 **H.S. Requirements:** High school diploma required; GED accepted **Costs Per Year:** Application fee: $50. Comprehensive fee: $59,163 includes full-time tuition ($44,322), mandatory fees ($1313), and college room and board ($13,528). College room only: $6926. Full-time tuition and fees vary according to course load. Room and board charges vary according to board plan and housing facility. Part-time tuition: $1847 per credit. Part-time tuition varies according to course load. **Scholarships:** Available. **Calendar System:** Semester, Summer session available **Enrollment:** Full-time 815, Graduate full-time 538, Part-time 44 **Faculty:** Full-time 99, Part-time 103 **Student-Faculty Ratio:** 10:1 **Exams:** ACT essay component used for admission; SAT I and SAT II or ACT; SAT essay component used for admission; SAT Reasoning. **% Receiving Financial Aid:** 85 **% Residing in College-Owned, -Operated, or**

-Affiliated Housing: 57 **Final Year or Final Semester Residency Requirement:** Yes **Regional Accreditation:** Western Association of Colleges and Schools **Credit Hours For Degree:** 120 semester course credits, Bachelors **ROTC:** Army **Intercollegiate Athletics:** Crew W; Cross-Country Running W; Soccer W; Swimming and Diving W; Tennis W; Volleyball W

MIRACOSTA COLLEGE
One Barnard Dr.
Oceanside, CA 92056
Tel: (760)757-2121; Free: 888-201-8480
Fax: (760)795-6609
E-mail: admissions@miracosta.edu
Web Site: www.miracosta.edu
President/CEO: Dr. Sunita Cooke
Admissions: Jane Sparks
Financial Aid: Michael Dear
Type: Two-Year College **Sex:** Coed **Affiliation:** California Community College System. **Admission Plans:** Deferred Admission; Early Admission; Open Admission **Application Deadline:** Rolling **Application Fee:** $0.00 **H.S. Requirements:** High school diploma or equivalent not required **Costs Per Year:** Application fee: $0. State resident tuition: $1104 full-time, $46 per unit part-time. Nonresident tuition: $5904 full-time, $246 per unit part-time. Mandatory fees: $48 full-time. Full-time tuition and fees vary according to course load. Part-time tuition varies according to course load. **Scholarships:** Available. **Calendar System:** Semester, Summer session available **Enrollment:** Full-time 5,024, Part-time 9,663 **Faculty:** Full-time 148, Part-time 486 **Student-Faculty Ratio:** 23:1 **Final Year or Final Semester Residency Requirement:** No **Regional Accreditation:** Western Association of Colleges and Schools **Credit Hours For Degree:** 60 units, Associates **Intercollegiate Athletics:** Basketball M & W; Soccer M & W

MISSION COLLEGE
3000 Mission College Blvd.
Santa Clara, CA 95054-1897
Tel: (408)988-2200
Web Site: www.missioncollege.edu
President/CEO: Daniel A. Peck
Admissions: Daniel Sanidad
Financial Aid: Rita Grogan
Type: Two-Year College **Sex:** Coed **Affiliation:** California Community College System. **Admission Plans:** Early Admission; Open Admission; Preferred Admission **Application Deadline:** Rolling **H.S. Requirements:** High school diploma or equivalent not required. For applicants under 18, nursing program: High school diploma required; GED accepted **Scholarships:** Available. **Calendar System:** Semester, Summer session available **Enrollment:** Full-time 4,000, Part-time 6,500 **Faculty:** Full-time 180, Part-time 210 **Student-Faculty Ratio:** 26:1 **Regional Accreditation:** Western Association of Colleges and Schools **Credit Hours For Degree:** 60 semester hours, Associates **ROTC:** Air Force, Army **Intercollegiate Athletics:** Badminton M & W; Baseball M; Basketball W; Soccer M & W; Softball W; Tennis M & W

MODESTO JUNIOR COLLEGE
435 College Ave.
Modesto, CA 95350-5800
Tel: (209)575-6498
E-mail: mjcadmissions@mail.yosemite.cc.ca.us
Web Site: www.mjc.edu
President/CEO: Dr. Richard Rose
Admissions: Martha Robles
Financial Aid: Peggy Lucille Fikse
Type: Two-Year College **Sex:** Coed **Affiliation:** Yosemite Community College District System. **Admission Plans:** Open Admission **Application Deadline:** Rolling **Application Fee:** $0.00 **H.S. Requirements:** High school diploma or equivalent not required. For applicants under 18: High school diploma required; GED accepted **Scholarships:** Available. **Calendar System:** Semester, Summer session available **Enrollment:** Full-time 6,874, Part-time 12,433 **Faculty:** Full-time 267, Part-time 345 **Student-Faculty Ratio:** 29:1 **Regional Accreditation:** Western Association of Colleges and Schools **Credit Hours For Degree:** 62 units, Associates **Professional Accreditation:** AAMAE, ADA, CoARC. **Intercollegiate Athletics:** Baseball M; Basketball M & W; Cross-Country Running M & W; Football M; Golf M;

Gymnastics W; Soccer M & W; Softball W; Swimming and Diving M & W; Tennis M & W; Track and Field M & W; Volleyball W; Water Polo M & W; Wrestling M

MONTEREY PENINSULA COLLEGE

980 Fremont St.
Monterey, CA 93940-4799
Tel: (831)646-4000
Fax: (831)655-2627
E-mail: vcoleman@mpc.edu
Web Site: www.mpc.edu
President/CEO: Walt Tribley
Admissions: Vera Coleman
Financial Aid: Francisco Tostado

Type: Two-Year College **Sex:** Coed **Affiliation:** California Community College System. **Admission Plans:** Early Admission; Open Admission **Application Deadline:** Rolling **Application Fee:** $0.00 **H.S. Requirements:** High school diploma or equivalent not required. For international students: High school diploma required; GED accepted **Scholarships:** Available. **Calendar System:** Semester, Summer session available **Faculty:** Full-time 136, Part-time 181 **Regional Accreditation:** Western Association of Colleges and Schools **Credit Hours For Degree:** 60 credits, Associates **Professional Accreditation:** ACEN, ADA. **Intercollegiate Athletics:** Baseball M; Basketball M; Cross-Country Running M & W; Football M; Golf M & W; Softball W; Swimming and Diving M & W; Tennis M & W; Track and Field M & W; Volleyball W

MOORPARK COLLEGE

7075 Campus Rd.
Moorpark, CA 93021-1695
Tel: (805)378-1400
Web Site: www.moorparkcollege.edu
President/CEO: Dr. Pam Eddinger
Admissions: Katherine Colborn

Type: Two-Year College **Sex:** Coed **Affiliation:** Ventura County Community College District System. **Admission Plans:** Deferred Admission; Early Admission; Open Admission **Application Deadline:** Rolling **Application Fee:** $0.00 **H.S. Requirements:** High school diploma required; GED accepted. For nursing program: High school diploma required; GED not accepted **Scholarships:** Available. **Calendar System:** Semester, Summer session available **Enrollment:** Full-time 6,021, Part-time 7,729 **Faculty:** Full-time 176, Part-time 401 **Student-Faculty Ratio:** 30:1 **Regional Accreditation:** Western Association of Colleges and Schools **Credit Hours For Degree:** 60 units, Associates **Professional Accreditation:** ACEN, JRCERT. **Intercollegiate Athletics:** Baseball M; Basketball M & W; Cross-Country Running M & W; Football M; Golf M & W; Soccer M & W; Softball W; Track and Field M & W; Volleyball M & W; Wrestling M

MORENO VALLEY COLLEGE

16130 Lasselle St.
Moreno Valley, CA 92551
Tel: (951)571-6100
E-mail: admissions@mvc.edu
Web Site: www.mvc.edu
President/CEO: Tom Harris
Admissions: Jamie Clifton

Type: Two-Year College **Sex:** Coed **Admission Plans:** Open Admission **Application Deadline:** Rolling **H.S. Requirements:** High school diploma or equivalent not required **Faculty:** Full-time 75, Part-time 362 **Regional Accreditation:** Western Association of Colleges and Schools

MOUNT SAINT MARY'S UNIVERSITY

12001 Chalon Rd.
Los Angeles, CA 90049
Tel: (310)954-4000; Free: 800-999-9893
E-mail: admissions@msmu.edu
Web Site: www.msmu.edu
President/CEO: Dr. Ann McElaney-Johnson
Admissions: Renee Rouzan-Kay
Financial Aid: La Royce Housley

Type: Comprehensive **Sex:** Coed **Affiliation:** Roman Catholic; Sisters of St. Joseph of Carondelet. **Scores:** 82% SAT V 400+; 84% SAT M 400+; 47.5% ACT 18-23; 13.4% ACT 24-29 **Costs Per Year:** Comprehensive fee: $49,173 includes full-time tuition ($36,682), mandatory fees ($1040), and

college room and board ($11,451). College room only: $6870. Full-time tuition and fees vary according to course load, degree level, and program. Room and board charges vary according to board plan and housing facility. Part-time tuition: $1528 per unit. Part-time tuition varies according to course load, degree level, and program. **Scholarships:** Available. **Calendar System:** Semester, Summer session available **Enrollment:** Full-time 2,143, Graduate full-time 496, Graduate part-time 190, Part-time 645 **Faculty:** Full-time 117, Part-time 382 **Student-Faculty Ratio:** 13:1 **Exams:** ACT essay component used for placement; SAT I or ACT; SAT II; SAT essay component used for placement. **% Receiving Financial Aid:** 91 **% Residing in College-Owned, -Operated, or -Affiliated Housing:** 22 **Final Year or Final Semester Residency Requirement:** No **Regional Accreditation:** Western Association of Colleges and Schools **Credit Hours For Degree:** 60 units, Associates; 124 units, Bachelors **Professional Accreditation:** AACN, ACBSP, APTA.

MT. SAN ANTONIO COLLEGE

1100 N Grand Ave.
Walnut, CA 91789-1399
Tel: (909)594-5611
Web Site: www.mtsac.edu
President/CEO: Dr. Irene Malmgren
Admissions: Dr. George Bradshaw
Financial Aid: Chau Dao

Type: Two-Year College **Sex:** Coed **Affiliation:** California Community College System. **Admission Plans:** Deferred Admission; Early Admission; Open Admission **H.S. Requirements:** High school diploma or equivalent not required **Costs Per Year:** State resident tuition: $1288 full-time, $46 per unit part-time. Nonresident tuition: $7364 full-time, $273 per unit part-time. Mandatory fees: $60 full-time, $60 per term part-time. Full-time tuition and fees vary according to course load and program. Part-time tuition and fees vary according to course load and program. **Scholarships:** Available. **Calendar System:** Semester, Summer session available **Faculty:** Full-time 388, Part-time 859 **Student-Faculty Ratio:** 26:1 **Regional Accreditation:** Western Association of Colleges and Schools **Credit Hours For Degree:** 60 units, Associates **ROTC:** Air Force, Army **Professional Accreditation:** CoARC, JRCERT, NAACLS. **Intercollegiate Athletics:** Badminton W; Baseball M; Basketball M & W; Cheerleading M & W; Cross-Country Running M & W; Football M; Golf M & W; Soccer M & W; Softball W; Swimming and Diving M & W; Tennis M & W; Track and Field M & W; Volleyball M & W; Water Polo M & W; Wrestling M

MT. SAN JACINTO COLLEGE

1499 N State St.
San Jacinto, CA 92583-2399
Tel: (909)487-6752
Fax: (909)654-6738
E-mail: SLoomis@msjc.edu
Web Site: www.msjc.edu
President/CEO: Roger Schultz
Admissions: Susan Loomis

Type: Two-Year College **Sex:** Coed **Affiliation:** California Community College System. **% Accepted:** 100 **Admission Plans:** Early Admission; Open Admission **Application Deadline:** Rolling **Application Fee:** $0.00 **H.S. Requirements:** High school diploma or equivalent not required **Costs Per Year:** Application fee: $0. One-time mandatory fee: $6. State resident tuition: $1380 full-time, $46 per credit part-time. Nonresident tuition: $7710 full-time, $257 per unit part-time. **Scholarships:** Available. **Calendar System:** Semester, Summer session available **Enrollment:** Full-time 5,105, Part-time 9,065 **Faculty:** Full-time 131, Part-time 540 **Student-Faculty Ratio:** 27:1 **Regional Accreditation:** Western Association of Colleges and Schools **Credit Hours For Degree:** 60 units, Associates **Intercollegiate Athletics:** Baseball M; Basketball M & W; Football M; Golf M; Soccer W; Softball W; Tennis M & W; Volleyball W

MT. SIERRA COLLEGE

101 E Huntington Dr.
Monrovia, CA 91016
Tel: (626)873-2144; Free: 888-828-8000
Fax: (626)359-5528
E-mail: enroll@mtsierra.edu
Web Site: www.mtsierra.edu
President/CEO: Dr. William J. Kakish

Type: Four-Year College **Sex:** Coed **Application Fee:** $50.00 **H.S. Requirements: High school diploma required; GED accepted Calendar System: Quarter, Summer session available Credit Hours For Degree: 199 credits, Bachelors Professional Accreditation: ACCSC.

MTI COLLEGE
5221 Madison Ave.
Sacramento, CA 95841
Tel: (916)339-1500
Fax: (916)339-0305
Web Site: www.mticollege.edu
President/CEO: John Zimmerman

Type: Two-Year College Sex: Coed % Accepted: 62 Application Fee: $50.00 H.S. Requirements: High school diploma required; GED accepted Scholarships: Available. Calendar System: Continuous Student-Faculty Ratio: 15:1 Exams: Other. Regional Accreditation: Western Association of Colleges and Schools

MUSICIANS INSTITUTE
1655 N McCadden Pl.
Hollywood, CA 90028
Tel: (323)462-1384; Free: 800-255-PLAY
Fax: (323)462-6978
E-mail: admissions@mi.edu
Web Site: www.mi.edu
President/CEO: Hisatake Shibuya
Admissions: Paul Weinstein

Type: Four-Year College Sex: Coed % Accepted: 98 Admission Plans: Deferred Admission Application Deadline: Rolling Application Fee: $100.00 H.S. Requirements: High school diploma required; GED accepted Scholarships: Available. Calendar System: Quarter, Summer session available Faculty: Full-time 108, Part-time 96 Student-Faculty Ratio: 10:1 Exams: ACT essay component used for admission; SAT I or ACT; SAT essay component used for admission; SAT Reasoning; SAT Subject. % Receiving Financial Aid: 61 Credit Hours For Degree: 90 credits, Associates; 180 credits (60 credits of General Education courses from another college or community college; 120 program-specific credits), Bachelors Professional Accreditation: NASM.

NAPA VALLEY COLLEGE
2277 Napa-Vallejo Hwy.
Napa, CA 94558-6236
Tel: (707)253-3000; Free: 800-826-1077
Fax: (707)253-3064
E-mail: odeharo@napavalley.edu
Web Site: www.napavalley.edu
President/CEO: Dr. Ronald Kraft
Admissions: Oscar De Haro

Type: Two-Year College Sex: Coed Affiliation: California Community College System. % Accepted: 100 Admission Plans: Open Admission Application Deadline: Rolling Application Fee: $0.00 H.S. Requirements: High school diploma or equivalent not required. For allied health programs: High school diploma required; GED accepted Costs Per Year: Application fee: $0. State resident tuition: $1306 full-time. Nonresident tuition: $7025 full-time. Mandatory fees: $68 full-time. Full-time tuition and fees vary according to course load and program. Scholarships: Available. Calendar System: Semester, Summer session available Enrollment: Full-time 1,909, Part-time 4,999 Faculty: Full-time 99, Part-time 212 Student-Faculty Ratio: 22:1 Regional Accreditation: Western Association of Colleges and Schools Credit Hours For Degree: 60 units, Associates Professional Accreditation: CoARC. Intercollegiate Athletics: Baseball M; Basketball M & W; Cross-Country Running M & W; Soccer M; Softball W; Swimming and Diving M & W; Tennis M & W; Volleyball W; Wrestling M

NATIONAL CAREER COLLEGE
14355 Roscoe Blvd.
Panorama City, CA 91402
Tel: (818)988-2300
Web Site: www.nccusa.edu
Type: Two-Year College Sex: Coed Professional Accreditation: ABHES.

NATIONAL POLYTECHNIC COLLEGE
6630 Telegraph Rd.
Commerce, CA 90040
Tel: (323)728-9636

Web Site: www.npcollege.edu
Type: Two-Year College Sex: Coed Professional Accreditation: ACCSC.

NATIONAL UNIVERSITY
11255 N Torrey Pines Rd.
La Jolla, CA 92037-1011
Tel: (619)563-7100; Free: 800-NAT-UNIV
Fax: (619)563-7299
E-mail: InstResearch@nu.edu
Web Site: www.nu.edu
President/CEO: Dr. Michael Cunningham
Admissions: Stephanie Thompson
Financial Aid: Valerie Ryan

Type: Comprehensive Sex: Coed Affiliation: National University System. Admission Plans: Deferred Admission; Open Admission Application Deadline: Rolling Application Fee: $60.00 H.S. Requirements: High school diploma required; GED accepted Costs Per Year: Application fee: $60. One-time mandatory fee: $60. Tuition: $12,744 full-time, $354 per credit hour part-time. Full-time tuition varies according to course load, degree level, location, and program. Part-time tuition varies according to course load, degree level, location, and program. Scholarships: Available. Calendar System: Continuous, Summer session available Enrollment: Full-time 3,241, Graduate full-time 5,289, Graduate part-time 3,349, Part-time 5,609 Exams: Other. % Receiving Financial Aid: 52 Final Year or Final Semester Residency Requirement: No Regional Accreditation: Western Association of Colleges and Schools Credit Hours For Degree: 90 quarter hours, Associates; 180 quarter hours, Bachelors ROTC: Air Force, Army Professional Accreditation: AACN.

NEW CHARTER UNIVERSITY
543 Howard St., 5th Fl.
San Francisco, CA 94105
Tel: (415)813-5970; Free: 888-639-1388
Fax: (415)813-5980
E-mail: admissions@aju.edu
Web Site: www.new.edu
President/CEO: E. Donald Kassner
Admissions: Tammy J. Kassner

Type: Comprehensive Sex: Coed % Accepted: 87 Admission Plans: Open Admission Application Fee: $75.00 H.S. Requirements: High school diploma required; GED accepted Enrollment: Graduate part-time 242, Part-time 230 Faculty: Part-time 50 Student-Faculty Ratio: 11:1 Final Year or Final Semester Residency Requirement: No Credit Hours For Degree: 60 semester hours, Associates; 120 semester hours, Bachelors Professional Accreditation: DEAC.

NEW YORK FILM ACADEMY
3300 Riverside Dr.
Burbank, CA 91505
Tel: (818)733-2600
Fax: (818)733-4074
E-mail: studios@nyfa.edu
Web Site: www.nyfa.com
President/CEO: Jerry Sherlock

Type: Comprehensive Sex: Coed Application Fee: $50.00 Exams: SAT I or ACT. Professional Accreditation: NASAD.

NEWSCHOOL OF ARCHITECTURE AND DESIGN
1249 F St.
San Diego, CA 92101-6634
Tel: (619)235-4100; Free: 800-490-7081
E-mail: knielson@newschoolarch.edu
Web Site: www.newschoolarch.edu
President/CEO: Marvin Malecha
Admissions: Kirk Nielson
Financial Aid: Matt Wakeman

Type: Comprehensive Sex: Coed % Accepted: 79 Admission Plans: Early Action Application Deadline: Rolling Application Fee: $75.00 H.S. Requirements: High school diploma required; GED accepted Scholarships: Available. Calendar System: Quarter, Summer session available Enrollment: Full-time 368, Graduate full-time 100, Graduate part-time 7, Part-time 40 Student-Faculty Ratio: 9:1 Exams: SAT I or ACT; SAT Reasoning; SAT Subject. Final Year or Final Semester Residency Requirement: Yes Regional Accreditation: Western Association of Colleges and Schools **Credit Hours For Degree:** 180 credit hours, Bachelors **Professional Accreditation:** ACICS, NAAB.

NORCO COLLEGE
2001 Third St.
Norco, CA 92860
Tel: (951)372-7000
E-mail: admissionsnorco@norcocollege.edu
Web Site: www.norcocollege.edu
President/CEO: Dr. Debbie DiThomas
Admissions: Mark DeAsis

Type: Two-Year College **Sex:** Coed **Admission Plans:** Open Admission **Application Deadline:** Rolling **H.S. Requirements:** High school diploma or equivalent not required **Faculty:** Full-time 68, Part-time 203 **Regional Accreditation:** Western Association of Colleges and Schools

NORTH-WEST COLLEGE
2121 W Garvey Ave.
West Covina, CA 91790
Tel: (626)960-5046
Fax: (626)960-7985
Web Site: www.nw.edu

Type: Two-Year College **Sex:** Coed **Professional Accreditation:** ACCSC.

NORTHWESTERN POLYTECHNIC UNIVERSITY
47671 Westinghouse Dr.
Fremont, CA 94539-7482
Tel: (510)592-9688
Fax: (510)657-8975
E-mail: admission@npu.edu
Web Site: www.npu.edu
President/CEO: George T.C. Hsieh
Admissions: Michael Tang

Type: Comprehensive **Sex:** Coed **% Accepted:** 100 **Admission Plans:** Deferred Admission **Application Deadline:** August 2 **Application Fee:** $60.00 **H.S. Requirements:** High school diploma required; GED accepted **Calendar System:** Trimester, Summer session available **Enrollment:** Full-time 142, Graduate full-time 652, Graduate part-time 111, Part-time 22 **Faculty:** Full-time 31, Part-time 56 **Student-Faculty Ratio:** 16:1 **Exams:** SAT I. **% Residing in College-Owned, -Operated, or -Affiliated Housing:** 12 **Professional Accreditation:** ACICS. **Intercollegiate Athletics:** Table Tennis M

NOTRE DAME DE NAMUR UNIVERSITY
1500 Ralston Ave.
Belmont, CA 94002-1908
Tel: (650)508-3500; Free: 800-263-0545
Fax: (650)508-3660
E-mail: jpmurray@ndnu.edu
Web Site: www.ndnu.edu
President/CEO: Dr. Judith Maxwell Greig, PhD
Admissions: Jason Murray
Financial Aid: Wilbert Lleses

Type: Comprehensive **Sex:** Coed **Affiliation:** Roman Catholic. **Scores:** 92% SAT V 400+; 92% SAT M 400+; 58.4% ACT 18-23; 19.5% ACT 24-29 **% Accepted:** 87 **Admission Plans:** Deferred Admission; Early Admission; Early Decision Plan **Application Deadline:** Rolling **Application Fee:** $50.00 **H.S. Requirements:** High school diploma required; GED accepted **Costs Per Year:** Application fee: $50. Comprehensive fee: $45,080 includes full-time tuition ($32,208) and college room and board ($12,872). Full-time tuition varies according to degree level and program. Room and board charges vary according to board plan and housing facility. Part-time tuition: $1039 per unit. Part-time tuition varies according to degree level and program. **Scholarships:** Available. **Calendar System:** Semester, Summer session available **Enrollment:** Full-time 826, Graduate full-time 245, Graduate part-time 572, Part-time 387 **Faculty:** Full-time 63, Part-time 185 **Student-Faculty Ratio:** 11:1 **Exams:** ACT essay component not used; SAT I or ACT; SAT essay component not used; SAT Reasoning. **% Receiving Financial Aid:** 90 **% Residing in College-Owned, -Operated, or -Affiliated Housing:** 37 **Final Year or Final Semester Residency Requirement:** Yes **Regional Accreditation:** Western Association of Colleges and Schools **Credit Hours For Degree:** 124 credit hours, Bachelors **ROTC:** Air Force **Professional Accreditation:** ACBSP. **Intercollegiate Athletics:**

Basketball M & W; Cross-Country Running M & W; Golf M; Lacrosse M; Soccer M & W; Softball W; Tennis W; Volleyball W

OCCIDENTAL COLLEGE
1600 Campus Rd.
Los Angeles, CA 90041-3314
Tel: (323)259-2500; Free: 800-825-5262
Fax: (323)341-4875
E-mail: admission@oxy.edu
Web Site: www.oxy.edu
President/CEO: Dr. Jonathan Veitch, PhD
Admissions: Vince Cuseo
Financial Aid: Gina Becerril

Type: Comprehensive **Sex:** Coed **Scores:** 100% SAT V 400+; 101% SAT M 400+; 2% ACT 18-23; 51% ACT 24-29 **% Accepted:** 45 **Admission Plans:** Deferred Admission; Early Action; Early Admission **Application Deadline:** January 15 **Application Fee:** $60.00 **H.S. Requirements:** High school diploma required; GED accepted **Costs Per Year:** Application fee: $60. Comprehensive fee: $63,484 includes full-time tuition ($48,690), mandatory fees ($558), and college room and board ($14,236). College room only: $7936. Room and board charges vary according to board plan. Part-time tuition: $2029 per unit. Part-time mandatory fees: $558 per year. Part-time tuition and fees vary according to course load. **Scholarships:** Available. **Calendar System:** Semester, Summer session not available **Enrollment:** Full-time 2,090, Graduate full-time 1, Graduate part-time 1, Part-time 22 **Faculty:** Full-time 172, Part-time 88 **Student-Faculty Ratio:** 10:1 **Exams:** ACT essay component used for admission; SAT I or ACT; SAT II; SAT essay component used for admission; SAT Reasoning; SAT Subject. **% Receiving Financial Aid:** 55 **% Residing in College-Owned, -Operated, or -Affiliated Housing:** 81 **Final Year or Final Semester Residency Requirement:** No **Regional Accreditation:** Western Association of Colleges and Schools **Credit Hours For Degree:** 128 units, Bachelors **ROTC:** Air Force, Army **Intercollegiate Athletics:** Baseball M; Basketball M & W; Cross-Country Running M & W; Football M; Golf M & W; Lacrosse M & W; Rugby M & W; Soccer M & W; Softball W; Swimming and Diving M & W; Tennis M & W; Track and Field M & W; Ultimate Frisbee M & W; Volleyball W; Water Polo M & W

OHLONE COLLEGE
43600 Mission Blvd.
Fremont, CA 94539-5884
Tel: (510)659-6000
E-mail: rtravenick@ohlone.edu
Web Site: www.ohlone.edu
President/CEO: Dr. Gari Browning
Admissions: Ronald Travenick

Type: Two-Year College **Sex:** Coed **Affiliation:** California Community College System. **Admission Plans:** Early Admission; Open Admission **Application Deadline:** Rolling **Application Fee:** $0.00 **H.S. Requirements:** High school diploma or equivalent not required **Costs Per Year:** Application fee: $0. State resident tuition: $1162 full-time, $46 per unit part-time. Nonresident tuition: $6730 full-time, $278 per unit part-time. Mandatory fees: $58 full-time. Full-time tuition and fees vary according to course load, program, and reciprocity agreements. Part-time tuition varies according to course load, program, and reciprocity agreements. **Scholarships:** Available. **Calendar System:** Semester, Summer session available **Enrollment:** Full-time 3,180, Part-time 8,138 **Faculty:** Full-time 115, Part-time 336 **Student-Faculty Ratio:** 27:1 **Final Year or Final Semester Residency Requirement:** No **Regional Accreditation:** Western Association of Colleges and Schools **Credit Hours For Degree:** 60 units, Associates **ROTC:** Air Force, Army **Professional Accreditation:** ACEN, APTA, CoARC. **Intercollegiate Athletics:** Baseball M; Basketball M & W; Soccer M & W; Softball W; Swimming and Diving M & W; Tennis M & W; Volleyball M & W; Water Polo M

ORANGE COAST COLLEGE
2701 Fairview Rd.
Costa Mesa, CA 92628-5005
Tel: (714)432-0202
Fax: (714)432-5072
E-mail: egalvan@occ.cccd.edu
Web Site: www.orangecoastcollege.edu
President/CEO: Dr. Dennis Harkins
Admissions: Efren Galvan

Type: Two-Year College **Sex:** Coed **Affiliation:** Coast Community College

District System. **Admission Plans:** Open Admission **Application Deadline:** Rolling **Application Fee:** $0.00 **H.S. Requirements:** High school diploma or equivalent not required **Costs Per Year:** Application fee: $0. State resident tuition: $1326 full-time, $46 per unit part-time. Nonresident tuition: $6338 full-time, $246 per unit part-time. Mandatory fees: $900 full-time, $140 per term part-time. Full-time tuition and fees vary according to program. Part-time tuition and fees vary according to program. **Scholarships:** Available. **Calendar System:** Semester, Summer session available **Enrollment:** Full-time 8,620, Part-time 13,310 **Faculty:** Full-time 242, Part-time 408 **Student-Faculty Ratio:** 35:1 **Final Year or Final Semester Residency Requirement:** No **Regional Accreditation:** Western Association of Colleges and Schools **Credit Hours For Degree:** 60 units, Associates **ROTC:** Air Force, Army **Professional Accreditation:** ACF, ADA, CoARC, JRCECT, JRCEDMS, JRCEND, JRCERT. **Intercollegiate Athletics:** Baseball M; Basketball M & W; Bowling M & W; Crew M & W; Cross-Country Running M & W; Football M; Golf M & W; Soccer M & W; Softball W; Swimming and Diving M & W; Tennis M & W; Track and Field M & W; Volleyball W; Water Polo M & W

OTIS COLLEGE OF ART AND DESIGN
9045 Lincoln Blvd.
Los Angeles, CA 90045-9785
Tel: (310)665-6800; Free: 800-527-OTIS
Fax: (310)665-6805
E-mail: admissions@otis.edu
Web Site: www.otis.edu
President/CEO: Samuel Hoi
Admissions: Brooke Randolph
Financial Aid: Jessika Huerta
Type: Comprehensive **Sex:** Coed **Scores:** 89% SAT V 400+; 94% SAT M 400+; 48% ACT 18-23; 30% ACT 24-29 **% Accepted:** 46 **Admission Plans:** Early Admission **Application Deadline:** Rolling **Application Fee:** $50.00 **H.S. Requirements:** High school diploma required; GED accepted **Scholarships:** Available. **Calendar System:** Semester, Summer session available **Enrollment:** Full-time 1,018, Graduate full-time 43, Graduate part-time 11, Part-time 14 **Faculty:** Full-time 55, Part-time 217 **Student-Faculty Ratio:** 4:1 **Exams:** ACT essay component not used; SAT I or ACT; SAT essay component not used. **% Receiving Financial Aid:** 65 **% Residing in College-Owned, -Operated, or -Affiliated Housing:** 9 **Regional Accreditation:** Western Association of Colleges and Schools **Credit Hours For Degree:** 134 credits, Bachelors **Professional Accreditation:** NASAD.

OXNARD COLLEGE
4000 S Rose Ave.
Oxnard, CA 93033-6699
Tel: (805)986-5800
Fax: (805)986-5806
E-mail: jdiaz@vcccd.edu
Web Site: www.oxnardcollege.edu
President/CEO: Dr. James Limbaugh
Admissions: Joel Diaz
Type: Two-Year College **Sex:** Coed **Affiliation:** Ventura County Community College District System. **Admission Plans:** Early Admission; Open Admission **Application Deadline:** Rolling **Application Fee:** $0.00 **H.S. Requirements:** High school diploma required; GED accepted. For applicants 18 or over: High school diploma or equivalent not required **Costs Per Year:** Application fee: $0. State resident tuition: $0 full-time. Nonresident tuition: $8164 full-time, $230 per unit part-time. Mandatory fees: $1338 full-time, $46 per unit part-time. **Scholarships:** Available. **Calendar System:** Semester, Summer session available **Enrollment:** Full-time 1,958, Part-time 5,048 **Faculty:** Full-time 88, Part-time 142 **Student-Faculty Ratio:** 30:1 **Final Year or Final Semester Residency Requirement:** No **Regional Accreditation:** Western Association of Colleges and Schools **Credit Hours For Degree:** 60 units, Associates **Professional Accreditation:** ADA. **Intercollegiate Athletics:** Baseball M; Basketball M & W; Cross-Country Running M & W; Soccer M & W; Softball W

PACIFIC COLLEGE
3160 Red Hill Ave.
Costa Mesa, CA 92626
Tel: (714)662-4402
Web Site: pacific-college.edu
Type: Four-Year College **Sex:** Coed **Costs Per Year:** One-time mandatory fee: $100. Tuition: $28,645 full-time, $295 per credit hour part-time. Full-time

tuition varies according to course level, degree level, program, and reciprocity agreements. Part-time tuition varies according to course level, degree level, program, and reciprocity agreements. Tuition guaranteed not to increase for student's term of enrollment. **Professional Accreditation:** ACCSC.

PACIFIC OAKS COLLEGE
5 Westmoreland Pl.
Pasadena, CA 91103
Tel: (626)397-1300; Free: 877-314-2380
Fax: (626)397-1317
E-mail: admissions@pacificoaks.edu
Web Site: www.pacificoaks.edu
President/CEO: Ezat Parnia
Admissions: Augusta Pickens
Financial Aid: Rosie Tristan
Type: Two-Year Upper Division **Sex:** Coed **Affiliation:** The Chicago School Education System. **% Accepted:** 77 **Admission Plans:** Deferred Admission **Application Fee:** $55.00 **H.S. Requirements:** High school diploma required; GED accepted **Scholarships:** Available. **Calendar System:** Semester, Summer session available **Enrollment:** Full-time 17, Part-time 240 **Faculty:** Full-time 27, Part-time 98 **Student-Faculty Ratio:** 22:1 **Regional Accreditation:** Western Association of Colleges and Schools **Credit Hours For Degree:** 124 units, Bachelors

PACIFIC STATES UNIVERSITY
3424 Wilshire Blvd.
12th Fl.
Los Angeles, CA 90010
Tel: (323)731-2383; Free: 888-200-0383
Fax: (323)731-7276
E-mail: admissions@psuca.edu
Web Site: www.psuca.edu
President/CEO: Hee Young Ahn
Admissions: Maawiya Ayeva
Type: Comprehensive **Sex:** Coed **Admission Plans:** Deferred Admission; Open Admission **Application Deadline:** Rolling **Application Fee:** $100.00 **H.S. Requirements:** High school diploma required; GED accepted **Calendar System:** Quarter **Enrollment:** Full-time 19, Graduate full-time 156 **Faculty:** Full-time 7, Part-time 27 **Student-Faculty Ratio:** 5:1 **Exams:** Other; SAT I or ACT. **Credit Hours For Degree:** 180 units, Bachelors **Professional Accreditation:** ACICS.

PACIFIC UNION COLLEGE
One Angwin Ave.
Angwin, CA 94508-9707
Tel: (707)965-6311; Free: 800-862-7080
Fax: (707)965-6390
E-mail: enroll@puc.edu
Web Site: www.puc.edu
President/CEO: Dr. Heather J. Knight
Admissions: Craig Philpott
Financial Aid: Laurie Wheeler
Type: Comprehensive **Sex:** Coed **Affiliation:** Seventh-day Adventist. **Scores:** 85% SAT V 400+; 84% SAT M 400+; 40% ACT 18-23; 32% ACT 24-29 **% Accepted:** 45 **Admission Plans:** Deferred Admission **Application Fee:** $30.00 **H.S. Requirements:** High school diploma required; GED accepted **Scholarships:** Available. **Calendar System:** Quarter, Summer session available **Enrollment:** Full-time 1,358, Graduate full-time 4, Graduate part-time 1, Part-time 192 **Faculty:** Full-time 97, Part-time 46 **Student-Faculty Ratio:** 13:1 **Exams:** ACT essay component not used; SAT I or ACT; SAT essay component not used; SAT Subject. **% Receiving Financial Aid:** 80 **% Residing in College-Owned, -Operated, or -Affiliated Housing:** 71 **Final Year or Final Semester Residency Requirement:** Yes **Regional Accreditation:** Western Association of Colleges and Schools **Credit Hours For Degree:** 90 quarter hours, Associates; 192 quarter hours, Bachelors **Professional Accreditation:** ACEN, CSWE, NASM. **Intercollegiate Athletics:** Basketball M & W; Cross-Country Running M & W; Soccer M; Volleyball W

PALO ALTO UNIVERSITY
1791 Arastradero Rd.
Palo Alto, CA 94304
Tel: (650)433-3800; Free: 800-818-6136

Fax: (650)493-6147
E-mail: undergrad@paloaltou.edu
Web Site: www.paloaltou.edu
President/CEO: Dr. Allen Calvin
Admissions: Michael Teodosio

Type: Two-Year Upper Division **Sex:** Coed **Costs Per Year:** Tuition: $16,374 full-time. Mandatory fees: $4974 full-time. Full-time tuition and fees vary according to class time and program. Tuition guaranteed not to increase for student's term of enrollment. **Calendar System:** Quarter **Enrollment:** Full-time 162, Graduate full-time 747, Graduate part-time 216, Part-time 6 **Final Year or Final Semester Residency Requirement:** No **Regional Accreditation:** Western Association of Colleges and Schools **Credit Hours For Degree:** 90 Units (and students must come in having already completed 90 units), Bachelors **Professional Accreditation:** APA.

PALO VERDE COLLEGE

One College Dr.
Blythe, CA 92225
Tel: (760)921-5500
Fax: (760)921-5590
E-mail: diana.rodriguez@paloverde.edu
Web Site: www.paloverde.edu
President/CEO: James W. Hottois
Admissions: Diana Rodriguez

Type: Two-Year College **Sex:** Coed **Affiliation:** California Community College System. **Admission Plans:** Early Admission; Open Admission **Application Deadline:** Rolling **Application Fee:** $0.00 **H.S. Requirements:** High school diploma or equivalent not required **Scholarships:** Available. **Calendar System:** Semester, Summer session available **Student-Faculty Ratio:** 23:1 **Regional Accreditation:** Western Association of Colleges and Schools **Credit Hours For Degree:** 60 units, Associates

PALOMAR COLLEGE

1140 W Mission Rd.
San Marcos, CA 92069-1487
Tel: (760)744-1150
Fax: (760)744-2932
E-mail: kmagnuson@palomar.edu
Web Site: www.palomar.edu
President/CEO: Adrian Gonzales
Admissions: Dr. Kendyl Magnuson

Type: Two-Year College **Sex:** Coed **Affiliation:** California Community College System. **Admission Plans:** Open Admission **Application Deadline:** Rolling **Application Fee:** $0.00 **H.S. Requirements:** High school diploma or equivalent not required **Costs Per Year:** Application fee: $0. State resident tuition: $1104 full-time, $46 per unit part-time. Nonresident tuition: $6288 full-time, $262 per unit part-time. Mandatory fees: $60 full-time, $1 per unit part-time, $19 per term part-time. **Scholarships:** Available. **Calendar System:** Semester, Summer session available **Enrollment:** Full-time 25,244 **Faculty:** Full-time 280, Part-time 1,025 **Student-Faculty Ratio:** 21:1 **Exams:** ACT essay component not used; SAT essay component not used. **Final Year or Final Semester Residency Requirement:** No **Regional Accreditation:** Western Association of Colleges and Schools **Credit Hours For Degree:** 60 units, Associates **Professional Accreditation:** ACEN, ADA. **Intercollegiate Athletics:** Baseball M; Basketball M & W; Football M; Golf M; Soccer M & W; Softball W; Swimming and Diving M & W; Tennis M & W; Track and Field M & W; Volleyball M & W; Water Polo M & W; Wrestling M

PASADENA CITY COLLEGE

1570 E Colorado Blvd.
Pasadena, CA 91106-2041
Tel: (626)585-7123
Fax: (626)585-7915
E-mail: sbricker@pasadena.edu
Web Site: www.pasadena.edu
President/CEO: Dr. Rajen Vurdien
Admissions: Susan E. Bricker

Type: Two-Year College **Sex:** Coed **Affiliation:** California Community College System. **Admission Plans:** Open Admission **Application Deadline:** Rolling **H.S. Requirements:** High school diploma or equivalent not required. For applicants under 18: High school diploma required; GED accepted **Costs Per Year:** State resident tuition: $1152 full-time, $46 per unit part-time. Nonresident tuition: $6180 full-time, $262 per unit part-time. Mandatory fees: $48 full-time, $24. **Calendar System:** Semester, Summer session

available **Enrollment:** Full-time 11,068, Part-time 15,982 **Faculty:** Full-time 351, Part-time 748 **Student-Faculty Ratio:** 25:1 **Final Year or Final Semester Residency Requirement:** No **Regional Accreditation:** Western Association of Colleges and Schools **Credit Hours For Degree:** 60 units, Associates **Professional Accreditation:** ADA, JRCERT. **Intercollegiate Athletics:** Badminton M & W; Baseball M; Basketball M & W; Cheerleading W; Cross-Country Running M & W; Football M; Soccer M & W; Softball W; Swimming and Diving M & W; Tennis M & W; Track and Field M & W; Volleyball W; Water Polo W

PATTEN UNIVERSITY

2433 Coolidge Ave.
Oakland, CA 94601-2699
Tel: (510)261-8500; Free: 877-4PATTEN
Fax: (510)534-8564
Web Site: patten.edu
President/CEO: Dr. Gary Moncher
Admissions: Kim Guerra
Financial Aid: Robert A. Olivera

Type: Comprehensive **Sex:** Coed **Affiliation:** interdenominational. **Scores:** 100% ACT 18-23 **Admission Plans:** Deferred Admission; Early Admission; Open Admission **Application Deadline:** Rolling **Application Fee:** $30.00 **H.S. Requirements:** High school diploma required; GED accepted **Scholarships:** Available. **Calendar System:** Semester, Summer session available **Enrollment:** Full-time 487, Graduate full-time 14, Graduate part-time 42, Part-time 507 **Faculty:** Full-time 26, Part-time 99 **Student-Faculty Ratio:** 17:1 **Exams:** SAT I or ACT. **% Residing in College-Owned, -Operated, or -Affiliated Housing:** 34 **Regional Accreditation:** Western Association of Colleges and Schools **Credit Hours For Degree:** 63 units, Associates; 125 units, Bachelors **Intercollegiate Athletics:** Baseball M; Softball W

PEPPERDINE UNIVERSITY

24255 Pacific Coast Hwy.
Malibu, CA 90263
Tel: (310)506-4000
Fax: (310)506-4861
E-mail: hayley.wolf@pepperdine.edu
Web Site: www.pepperdine.edu
President/CEO: Dr. Andrew K. Benton
Admissions: Wolf Hayley
Financial Aid: Janet Lockhart

Type: University **Sex:** Coed **Affiliation:** Church of Christ. **Scores:** 100% SAT V 400+; 100% SAT M 400+; 13% ACT 18-23; 53.7% ACT 24-29 **% Accepted:** 38 **Application Deadline:** January 5 **Application Fee:** $65.00 **H.S. Requirements:** High school diploma required; GED accepted **Costs Per Year:** Application fee: $65. Comprehensive fee: $62,152 includes full-time tuition ($48,090), mandatory fees ($252), and college room and board ($13,810). Room and board charges vary according to board plan and housing facility. Part-time tuition: $1510 per credit hour. **Scholarships:** Available. **Calendar System:** Semester, Summer session available **Enrollment:** Full-time 3,228, Graduate full-time 2,335, Graduate part-time 1,764, Part-time 305 **Faculty:** Full-time 381, Part-time 324 **Student-Faculty Ratio:** 13:1 **Exams:** SAT I or ACT; SAT Reasoning. **% Receiving Financial Aid:** 54 % **Residing in College-Owned, -Operated, or -Affiliated Housing:** 54 **Final Year or Final Semester Residency Requirement:** Yes **Regional Accreditation:** Western Association of Colleges and Schools **Credit Hours For Degree:** 128 units, Bachelors **ROTC:** Air Force, Army **Professional Accreditation:** AACSB, AALS, ABA, NASM. **Intercollegiate Athletics:** Baseball M; Basketball M & W; Cross-Country Running M & W; Golf M & W; Lacrosse M & W; Rugby M; Soccer M & W; Swimming and Diving W; Tennis M & W; Track and Field W; Triathlon M & W; Ultimate Frisbee M & W; Volleyball M & W; Water Polo M

PIMA MEDICAL INSTITUTE

780 Bay Blvd.
Ste. 101
Chula Vista, CA 91910
Tel: (619)425-3200; Free: 888-477-PIMA
Fax: (619)425-3450
Web Site: www.pmi.edu
President/CEO: Keever Jankovich

Type: Two-Year College **Sex:** Coed **Affiliation:** Vocational Training Institutes, Inc. **H.S. Requirements:** High school diploma required; GED accepted **Calendar System:** Miscellaneous **Exams:** Other. **Credit Hours For Degree:** 88 credits, Associates **Professional Accreditation:** ABHES.

PITZER COLLEGE

1050 N Mills Ave.
Claremont, CA 91711-6101
Tel: (909)621-8000; Free: 800-748-9371
Fax: (909)621-8770
E-mail: admission@pitzer.edu
Web Site: www.pitzer.edu
President/CEO: Dr. Tom Poon
Admissions: Jamila Everett
Financial Aid: Robin Thompson

Type: Four-Year College **Sex:** Coed **Affiliation:** The Claremont Colleges Consortium. **Scores:** 100% SAT V 400+; 100% SAT M 400+; 3.64% ACT 18-23; 34.55% ACT 24-29 **% Accepted:** 13 **Admission Plans:** Deferred Admission; Early Action **Application Deadline:** January 1 **Application Fee:** $70.00 **H.S. Requirements:** High school diploma required; GED accepted **Costs Per Year:** Application fee: $70. Comprehensive fee: $63,880 includes full-time tuition ($48,400), mandatory fees ($270), and college room and board ($15,210). College room only: $8770. Room and board charges vary according to board plan. Part-time tuition: $6050 per course. Part-time tuition varies according to course load. **Scholarships:** Available. **Calendar System:** Semester, Summer session available **Enrollment:** Full-time 1,036, Part-time 31 **Faculty:** Full-time 96, Part-time 20 **Student-Faculty Ratio:** 10:1 **Exams:** ACT essay component not used; SAT I and SAT II or ACT; SAT I or ACT; SAT II; SAT essay component not used; SAT Reasoning; SAT Subject. **% Receiving Financial Aid:** 37 **% Residing in College-Owned, -Operated, or -Affiliated Housing:** 76 **Final Year or Final Semester Residency Requirement:** No **Regional Accreditation:** Western Association of Colleges and Schools **Credit Hours For Degree:** 32 courses, Bachelors **ROTC:** Air Force, Army **Intercollegiate Athletics:** Baseball M; Basketball M & W; Cross-Country Running M & W; Football M; Golf M; Lacrosse W; Soccer M & W; Softball W; Swimming and Diving M & W; Tennis M & W; Track and Field M & W; Volleyball W; Water Polo M & W

PLATT COLLEGE (ALHAMBRA)

1000 S Fremont A9W
Alhambra, CA 91803
Tel: (636)300-5444; Free: 888-80-PLATT
Fax: (323)258-8532
Web Site: www.plattcollege.edu
President/CEO: Daryl Goldberg
Admissions: Detroit Whiteside

Type: Two-Year College **Sex:** Coed **Application Deadline:** Rolling **Application Fee:** $75.00 **H.S. Requirements:** High school diploma required; GED accepted **Calendar System:** Continuous, Summer session available **Exams:** Other. **Credit Hours For Degree:** 96 credits, Associates **Professional Accreditation:** ACCSC.

PLATT COLLEGE (ONTARIO)

3700 Inland Empire Blvd.
Ste. 400
Ontario, CA 91764
Tel: (909)941-9410; Free: 888-80-PLATT
Fax: (909)989-8974
Web Site: www.plattcollege.edu
President/CEO: Daryl Goldberg
Admissions: Jennifer Abandonato

Type: Two-Year College **Sex:** Coed **Application Deadline:** Rolling **Application Fee:** $75.00 **H.S. Requirements:** High school diploma required; GED accepted **Calendar System:** Continuous, Summer session available **Exams:** Other. **Credit Hours For Degree:** 96 credit hours, Associates **Professional Accreditation:** ACCSC.

PLATT COLLEGE (RIVERSIDE)

6465 Sycamore Canyon Blvd.
Ste. 100
Riverside, CA 92507
Tel: (951)572-4300; Free: 888-807-5288
Web Site: www.plattcollege.edu
Type: Four-Year College **Sex:** Coed **Professional Accreditation:** ACCSC.

PLATT COLLEGE SAN DIEGO

6250 El Cajon Blvd.
San Diego, CA 92115-3919
Tel: (619)265-0107; Free: 866-752-8826
Fax: (619)265-8655
E-mail: kharbert@platt.edu
Web Site: www.platt.edu
President/CEO: Robert D. Leiker
Admissions: Kimberly Harbert
Financial Aid: Matilde Aguilar

Type: Four-Year College **Sex:** Coed **Admission Plans:** Deferred Admission; Early Admission; Open Admission **Application Deadline:** Rolling **Application Fee:** $110.00 **H.S. Requirements:** High school diploma required; GED accepted **Scholarships:** Available. **Calendar System:** Continuous, Summer session not available **Enrollment:** Full-time 369 **Faculty:** Full-time 11, Part-time 16 **Student-Faculty Ratio:** 21:1 **Exams:** Other; SAT I and SAT II or ACT; SAT I or ACT; SAT II. **Final Year or Final Semester Residency Requirement:** No **Credit Hours For Degree:** 65 semester credit hours, Associates; 128 semester credit hours, Bachelors **Professional Accreditation:** ACCSC.

POINT LOMA NAZARENE UNIVERSITY

3900 Lomaland Dr.
San Diego, CA 92106-2899
Tel: (619)849-2200; Free: 800-733-7770
Fax: (619)849-2579
E-mail: admissions@pointloma.edu
Web Site: www.pointloma.edu
President/CEO: Dr. Bob Brower
Admissions: Shannon Hutchison
Financial Aid: Pam Macias

Type: Comprehensive **Sex:** Coed **Affiliation:** Nazarene. **Scores:** 100% SAT V 400+; 99% SAT M 400+; 27.9% ACT 18-23; 56% ACT 24-29 **% Accepted:** 71 **Admission Plans:** Early Decision Plan **Application Deadline:** February 15 **Application Fee:** $55.00 **H.S. Requirements:** High school diploma required; GED accepted **Costs Per Year:** Application fee: $55. Comprehensive fee: $42,200 includes full-time tuition ($31,800), mandatory fees ($600), and college room and board ($9800). Full-time tuition and fees vary according to course load. Room and board charges vary according to board plan. Part-time tuition: $1325 per credit hour. Part-time tuition varies according to course load. **Scholarships:** Available. **Calendar System:** Semester, Summer session available **Enrollment:** Full-time 2,587, Graduate full-time 290, Graduate part-time 606, Part-time 180 **Faculty:** Full-time 136, Part-time 236 **Student-Faculty Ratio:** 15:1 **Exams:** ACT; ACT essay component used as validity check; ACT essay component used for admission; ACT essay component used for placement; SAT I; SAT I or ACT; SAT essay component used as validity check; SAT essay component used for admission; SAT essay component used for placement; SAT Reasoning. **% Receiving Financial Aid:** 68 **% Residing in College-Owned, -Operated, or -Affiliated Housing:** 61 **Final Year or Final Semester Residency Requirement:** Yes **Regional Accreditation:** Western Association of Colleges and Schools **Credit Hours For Degree:** 128 semester units, Bachelors **ROTC:** Air Force, Army, Navy **Professional Accreditation:** AACN, AAFCS, ACBSP, NASM. **Intercollegiate Athletics:** Baseball M; Basketball M & W; Cross-Country Running W; Golf W; Soccer M & W; Tennis M & W; Track and Field W; Volleyball W

POMONA COLLEGE

333 N College Way
Claremont, CA 91711
Tel: (909)621-8000
Fax: (909)621-8403
E-mail: admissions@pomona.edu
Web Site: www.pomona.edu
President/CEO: Dr. David W. Oxtoby
Admissions: C. Seth Allen
Financial Aid: Mary Booker

Type: Four-Year College **Sex:** Coed **Scores:** 100% SAT V 400+; 100% SAT M 400+; 20.94% ACT 24-29 **% Accepted:** 10 **Admission Plans:** Deferred Admission; Early Action; Early Admission **Application Deadline:** January 1 **Application Fee:** $70.00 **H.S. Requirements:** High school diploma or equivalent not required **Costs Per Year:** Application fee: $70. Comprehensive fee: $62,770 includes full-time tuition ($47,280), mandatory fees ($340), and college room and board ($15,150). Room and board charges vary according to board plan. **Scholarships:** Available. **Calendar System:** Semester, Summer session not available **Enrollment:** Full-time 1,648, Part-time 15 **Faculty:** Full-time 186, Part-time 49 **Student-Faculty Ratio:** 8:1 **Exams:** ACT essay component used as validity check; ACT essay component used for admission; ACT essay component used for advising; SAT I or ACT; SAT II; SAT essay component used for admission; SAT essay component used for advising; SAT Reasoning; SAT Subject. **% Receiving Financial Aid:** 56 **% Residing in College-Owned, -Operated, or -Affiliated Housing:** 99 **Final Year or Final Semester Residency Requirement:** No **Regional Accreditation:** Western Association of Colleges and Schools **Credit Hours For Degree:** 32 credits, Bachelors **ROTC:** Air Force, Army **Intercollegiate Athletics:** Baseball M; Basketball M & W; Cross-Country Running M & W; Football M; Golf M & W; Lacrosse W; Soccer M & W; Softball W; Swimming and Diving M & W; Tennis M & W; Track and Field M & W; Ultimate Frisbee M & W; Volleyball M & W; Water Polo M & W

PORTERVILLE COLLEGE

100 E College Ave.
Porterville, CA 93257-6058
Tel: (559)791-2200
Fax: (559)791-2349
Web Site: www.pc.cc.ca.us
President/CEO: Dr. Rosa Carlson
Admissions: Judy Pope

Type: Two-Year College **Sex:** Coed **Affiliation:** Kern Community College District System. **% Accepted:** 100 **Admission Plans:** Early Admission; Open Admission **Application Deadline:** Rolling **Application Fee:** $0.00 **H.S. Requirements:** High school diploma or equivalent not required. For licensed vocational nursing program: High school diploma required; GED accepted **Calendar System:** Semester, Summer session available **Faculty:** Full-time 60, Part-time 80 **Regional Accreditation:** Western Association of Colleges and Schools **Credit Hours For Degree:** 60 units, Associates **Intercollegiate Athletics:** Baseball M; Basketball M & W; Soccer M & W; Softball W; Tennis M & W; Volleyball W

PROFESSIONAL GOLFERS CAREER COLLEGE

26109 Ynez Rd.
Temecula, CA 92591
Tel: (909)693-2963; Free: 800-877-4380
Fax: (909)693-2863
E-mail: garygilleon@golfcollege.edu
Web Site: www.golfcollege.edu
President/CEO: Dr. Tim Somerville
Admissions: Gary Gilleon

Type: Two-Year College **Sex:** Coed **% Accepted:** 100 **Admission Plans:** Deferred Admission; Early Admission; Open Admission **Application Deadline:** Rolling **Application Fee:** $75.00 **H.S. Requirements:** High school diploma required; GED accepted **Calendar System:** Semester **Enrollment:** Full-time 282 **Faculty:** Full-time 5, Part-time 18 **Student-Faculty Ratio:** 15:1 **% Residing in College-Owned, -Operated, or -Affiliated Housing:** 26 **Final Year or Final Semester Residency Requirement:** No **Credit Hours For Degree:** 66 credits, Associates **Professional Accreditation:** ACICS.

PROVIDENCE CHRISTIAN COLLEGE

1539 E Howard St.
Pasadena, CA 91124
Tel: (626)696-4000
Fax: (626)696-4040
Web Site: www.providencecc.edu
Type: Four-Year College **Sex:** Coed **Affiliation:** Christian. **Regional Accreditation:** Western Association of Colleges and Schools

REEDLEY COLLEGE

995 N Reed Ave.
Reedley, CA 93654-2099
Tel: (559)638-3641
Web Site: www.reedleycollege.edu
President/CEO: Dr. Sandra Caldwell
Type: Two-Year College **Sex:** Coed **Affiliation:** State Center Community College District System. **Admission Plans:** Open Admission **Application Deadline:** Rolling **Application Fee:** $0.00 **H.S. Requirements:** High school diploma required; GED accepted **Scholarships:** Available. **Calendar System:** Semester, Summer session available **Faculty:** Full-time 194, Part-

time 650 **Regional Accreditation:** Western Association of Colleges and Schools **Credit Hours For Degree:** 60 units, Associates **ROTC:** Air Force **Intercollegiate Athletics:** Baseball M; Basketball M & W; Football M; Golf M; Softball W; Tennis M & W; Track and Field M & W; Volleyball W

RIO HONDO COLLEGE

3600 Workman Mill Rd.
Whittier, CA 90601-1699
Tel: (562)692-0921
Fax: (562)692-9318
E-mail: LUnger@riohondo.edu
Web Site: www.riohondo.edu
President/CEO: Teresa Dreyfuss
Admissions: Leigh Ann Unger

Type: Two-Year College **Sex:** Coed **Affiliation:** California Community College System. **Admission Plans:** Open Admission **Application Deadline:** Rolling **Application Fee:** $0.00 **H.S. Requirements:** High school diploma or equivalent not required **Costs Per Year:** Application fee: $0. State resident tuition: $1104 full-time, $46 per credit part-time. Nonresident tuition: $4800 full-time, $200 per credit part-time. Mandatory fees: $72 full-time. Full-time tuition and fees vary according to course load. Part-time tuition varies according to course load. **Scholarships:** Available. **Calendar System:** Semester, Summer session available **Faculty:** Full-time 190, Part-time 370 **Final Year or Final Semester Residency Requirement:** No **Regional Accreditation:** Western Association of Colleges and Schools **Credit Hours For Degree:** 60 units, Associates **ROTC:** Air Force, Army, Navy **Intercollegiate Athletics:** Baseball M; Basketball M & W; Cross-Country Running M & W; Soccer M & W; Softball W; Swimming and Diving M & W; Tennis M & W; Track and Field M & W; Volleyball W; Water Polo M & W; Wrestling M

RIVERSIDE CITY COLLEGE

4800 Magnolia Ave.
Riverside, CA 92506-1299
Tel: (909)222-8000
Fax: (909)222-8037
E-mail: admissionsriverside@rcc.edu
Web Site: www.rcc.edu
President/CEO: Dr. Cynthia Azari
Admissions: Joy Chambers

Type: Two-Year College **Sex:** Coed **Affiliation:** California Community College System. **Admission Plans:** Open Admission **Application Deadline:** Rolling **Application Fee:** $0.00 **H.S. Requirements:** High school diploma or equivalent not required. For registered nursing program: High school diploma required; GED accepted **Scholarships:** Available. **Calendar System:** Semester **Faculty:** Full-time 222, Part-time 443 **Regional Accreditation:** Western Association of Colleges and Schools **Professional Accreditation:** ACEN, ADA.

SACRAMENTO CITY COLLEGE

3835 Freeport Blvd.
Sacramento, CA 95822-1386
Tel: (916)558-2111
Fax: (916)558-2190
Web Site: www.scc.losrios.edu
President/CEO: Kathryn E. Jeffrey
Admissions: Sam T. Sandusky

Type: Two-Year College **Sex:** Coed **Affiliation:** California Community College System. **Admission Plans:** Open Admission **Application Deadline:** Rolling **Application Fee:** $0.00 **H.S. Requirements:** High school diploma or equivalent not required **Scholarships:** Available. **Calendar System:** Semester, Summer session available **Student-Faculty Ratio:** 30:1 **Regional Accreditation:** Western Association of Colleges and Schools **Credit Hours For Degree:** 60 units, Associates **Professional Accreditation:** ADA, AOTA, APTA. **Intercollegiate Athletics:** Baseball M; Basketball M & W; Cross-Country Running M & W; Football M; Golf M & W; Soccer W; Softball W; Swimming and Diving M & W; Tennis M & W; Track and Field M & W; Volleyball W; Water Polo W; Wrestling M

SADDLEBACK COLLEGE

28000 Marguerite Pky.
Mission Viejo, CA 92692
Tel: (949)582-4500
Fax: (949)347-8315
E-mail: earaiza@saddleback.edu

Web Site: www.saddleback.edu
President/CEO: Dr. Richard D. McCullough
Type: Two-Year College **Sex:** Coed **Admission Plans:** Early Admission; Open Admission **Application Deadline:** Rolling **Application Fee:** $0.00 **H.S. Requirements:** High school diploma or equivalent not required **Scholarships:** Available. **Calendar System:** Semester, Summer session available **Enrollment:** Full-time 6,621, Part-time 11,750 **Faculty:** Full-time 215, Part-time 539 **Regional Accreditation:** Western Association of Colleges and Schools **Credit Hours For Degree:** 64 units, Associates **Professional Accreditation:** ACEN. **Intercollegiate Athletics:** Baseball M; Basketball M & W; Cross-Country Running M & W; Football M; Golf M & W; Softball W; Swimming and Diving M & W; Tennis M & W; Track and Field M & W; Volleyball W; Water Polo M & W

SAGE COLLEGE

12125 Day St., Bldg. L
Moreno Valley, CA 92557-6720
Tel: (951)781-2727; Free: 888-755-SAGE
Fax: (951)781-0570
Web Site: www.sagecollege.edu
President/CEO: Lauren Somma
Type: Two-Year College **Sex:** Coed **% Accepted:** 100 **Application Fee:** $100.00 **Calendar System:** Quarter **Professional Accreditation:** ACICS.

SAINT KATHERINE COLLEGE

1637 Capalina Rd.
San Marcos, CA 92069
Tel: (760)471-1316
Fax: (760)471-1314
E-mail: admissions@stkath.org
Web Site: www.stkath.org
President/CEO: Dr. Frank Paptheofanis
Admissions: Dean Marina Karavokiris
Type: Four-Year College **Sex:** Coed **Affiliation:** Christian. **% Accepted:** 62 **Application Deadline:** July 15 **Application Fee:** $0.00 **H.S. Requirements:** High school diploma required; GED accepted **Costs Per Year:** Application fee: $0. One-time mandatory fee: $200. Comprehensive fee: $28,000 includes full-time tuition ($19,500), mandatory fees ($400), and college room and board ($8100). Full-time tuition and fees vary according to course load and program. Part-time tuition: $14,625 per year. Part-time mandatory fees: $200 per term. Part-time tuition and fees vary according to course load and program. **Calendar System:** Semester, Summer session not available **Enrollment:** Full-time 44 **Faculty:** Full-time 2, Part-time 12 **Student-Faculty Ratio:** 9:1 **Exams:** ACT essay component used for admission; ACT essay component used for advising; ACT essay component used for placement; SAT I or ACT; SAT essay component used for admission; SAT essay component used for advising; SAT essay component used for placement; SAT Reasoning; SAT Subject. **% Residing in College-Owned, -Operated, or -Affiliated Housing:** 25 **Final Year or Final Semester Residency Requirement:** No **Regional Accreditation:** Western Association of Colleges and Schools **Credit Hours For Degree:** 120 credits, Bachelors **Intercollegiate Athletics:** Baseball M; Basketball W; Cross-Country Running M & W; Soccer M & W; Softball W

SAINT MARY'S COLLEGE OF CALIFORNIA

1928 Saint Mary's Rd.
Moraga, CA 94575
Tel: (925)631-4000; Free: 800-800-4SMC
Fax: (925)376-7193
E-mail: smcadmit@stmarys-ca.edu
Web Site: www.stmarys-ca.edu
President/CEO: James A. Donahue, PhD
Admissions: Michael McKeon
Financial Aid: Priscilla Muha
Type: Two-Year Upper Division **Sex:** Coed **Affiliation:** Roman Catholic. **Scores:** 99% SAT V 400+; 100% SAT M 400+; 38.4% ACT 18-23; 51.9% ACT 24-29 **% Accepted:** 69 **Admission Plans:** Deferred Admission; Early Decision Plan **Application Deadline:** February 1 **Application Fee:** $55.00 **H.S. Requirements:** High school diploma required; GED accepted **Costs Per Year:** Application fee: $55. Comprehensive fee: $57,420 includes full-time tuition ($42,780), mandatory fees ($150), and college room and board ($14,490). Room and board charges vary according to board plan and housing facility. Part-time tuition: $5350 per course. Part-time tuition varies according to course load and program. **Scholarships:** Available. **Calendar**

System: 4-1-4, Summer session available **Enrollment:** Full-time 2,823, Graduate full-time 667, Graduate part-time 535, Part-time 232 **Faculty:** Full-time 213, Part-time 312 **Student-Faculty Ratio:** 12:1 **Exams:** SAT I or ACT; SAT Reasoning. **% Receiving Financial Aid:** 70 **% Residing in College-Owned, -Operated, or -Affiliated Housing:** 55 **Final Year or Final Semester Residency Requirement:** No **Regional Accreditation:** Western Association of Colleges and Schools **Credit Hours For Degree:** 36 courses, Bachelors **ROTC:** Air Force, Army **Professional Accreditation:** AACSB, MACTE. **Intercollegiate Athletics:** Baseball M; Basketball M & W; Cheerleading W; Crew M & W; Cross-Country Running M & W; Golf M; Lacrosse M & W; Rugby M; Soccer M & W; Softball W; Tennis M & W; Track and Field M & W; Volleyball W; Water Polo M & W

THE SALVATION ARMY COLLEGE FOR OFFICER TRAINING AT CRESTMONT

30840 Hawthorne Blvd.
Rancho Palos Verdes, CA 90275
Tel: (310)377-0481
Fax: (310)265-6565
Web Site: www.crestmont.edu
President/CEO: Maj. Stephen Smith
Admissions: Capt. Brian Jones
Type: Two-Year College **Sex:** Coed **Affiliation:** Salvation Army; The Salvation Army. **Admission Plans:** Preferred Admission **Application Deadline:** June 1 **Application Fee:** $15.00 **H.S. Requirements:** High school diploma required; GED accepted **Costs Per Year:** Application fee: $15. Comprehensive fee: $4500. **Calendar System:** Quarter, Summer session not available **Enrollment:** Full-time 61, Part-time 63 **Faculty:** Full-time 13, Part-time 22 **Student-Faculty Ratio:** 1:1 **% Residing in College-Owned, -Operated, or -Affiliated Housing:** 100 **Final Year or Final Semester Residency Requirement:** Yes **Regional Accreditation:** Western Association of Colleges and Schools **Credit Hours For Degree:** 90 quarter units, Associates

SAMUEL MERRITT UNIVERSITY

3100 Telegraph Ave.
Oakland, CA 94609-3108
Tel: (510)869-6511; Free: 800-607-6377
Fax: (510)869-6525
E-mail: admission@samuelmerritt.edu
Web Site: www.samuelmerritt.edu
President/CEO: Dr. Sharon Diaz
Admissions: Timothy Cranford
Financial Aid: Saeng Saephanh
Type: Two-Year Upper Division **Sex:** Coed **Admission Plans:** Deferred Admission **Application Fee:** $50.00 **H.S. Requirements:** High school diploma required; GED accepted **Costs Per Year:** Application fee: $50. Tuition: $44,166 full-time, $1861 per credit part-time. Mandatory fees: $1327 full-time. Full-time tuition and fees vary according to program. Part-time tuition varies according to program. **Scholarships:** Available. **Calendar System:** Trimester, Summer session not available **Enrollment:** Full-time 489, Graduate full-time 785, Graduate part-time 252, Part-time 77 **Student-Faculty Ratio:** 9:1 **% Receiving Financial Aid:** 93 **Final Year or Final Semester Residency Requirement:** No **Regional Accreditation:** Western Association of Colleges and Schools **Credit Hours For Degree:** 128 units, Bachelors **ROTC:** Air Force, Army **Professional Accreditation:** AACN, AANA, AOTA, APTA.

SAN BERNARDINO VALLEY COLLEGE

701 S Mount Vernon Ave.
San Bernardino, CA 92410-2748
Tel: (909)384-4400
Web Site: www.valleycollege.edu
President/CEO: Dr. Gloria Fisher
Admissions: Helena Johnson
Financial Aid: Nancy Davis
Type: Two-Year College **Sex:** Coed **Affiliation:** San Bernardino Community College District System. **Admission Plans:** Open Admission **Application Deadline:** August 29 **H.S. Requirements:** High school diploma required; GED accepted **Scholarships:** Available. **Calendar System:** Semester, Summer session available **Faculty:** Full-time 175, Part-time 200 **Regional Accreditation:** Western Association of Colleges and Schools **Credit Hours For Degree:** 60 semester hours, Associates **Professional Accreditation:** ACEN. **Intercollegiate Athletics:** Basketball M & W; Cross-Country Run-

ning M & W; Football M; Golf M; Soccer M & W; Tennis M & W; Track and Field M & W; Volleyball W; Wrestling M

SAN DIEGO CHRISTIAN COLLEGE

200 Riverview Pky.
Santee, CA 92071
Tel: (619)201-8700; Free: 800-676-2242
Fax: (619)440-0209
E-mail: christine.roberts@sdcc.edu
Web Site: www.sdcc.edu
President/CEO: Dr. Paul Ague
Admissions: Christine Roberts
Financial Aid: Erin Neill

Type: Comprehensive **Sex:** Coed **Affiliation:** nondenominational. **Scores:** 78% SAT V 400+; 77% SAT M 400+; 45% ACT 18-23; 23% ACT 24-29 **% Accepted:** 52 **Admission Plans:** Deferred Admission **Application Deadline:** Rolling **Application Fee:** $25.00 **H.S. Requirements:** High school diploma required; GED accepted **Costs Per Year:** Application fee: $25. Comprehensive fee: $40,524 includes full-time tuition ($28,100), mandatory fees ($1450), and college room and board ($10,974). Full-time tuition and fees vary according to course load, location, and program. Room and board charges vary according to board plan, location, and student level. Part-time tuition: $1210 per credit. Part-time mandatory fees: $290 per term. Part-time tuition and fees vary according to course load and program. **Scholarships:** Available. **Calendar System:** Semester, Summer session available **Enrollment:** Full-time 713, Graduate full-time 25, Graduate part-time 11, Part-time 167 **Faculty:** Full-time 21, Part-time 76 **Student-Faculty Ratio:** 17:1 **Exams:** ACT essay component not used; SAT I or ACT; SAT essay component not used; SAT Reasoning. **% Residing in College-Owned, -Operated, or -Affiliated Housing:** 28 **Final Year or Final Semester Residency Requirement:** No **Regional Accreditation:** Western Association of Colleges and Schools **Credit Hours For Degree:** 62 semester credits, Associates; 124 semester credits, Bachelors **ROTC:** Air Force, Army **Intercollegiate Athletics:** Baseball M; Basketball M & W; Cross-Country Running M & W; Soccer M & W; Softball W; Tennis M & W; Volleyball W

SAN DIEGO CITY COLLEGE

1313 Park Blvd.
San Diego, CA 92101-4787
Tel: (619)388-3400
Fax: (619)388-3063
E-mail: lhumphri@sdccd.edu
Web Site: www.sdcity.edu
President/CEO: Anthony E. Beebe
Admissions: Lou Humphries
Financial Aid: Gregory Sanchez

Type: Two-Year College **Sex:** Coed **Affiliation:** San Diego Community College District System. **Admission Plans:** Open Admission **Application Deadline:** Rolling **Application Fee:** $0.00 **H.S. Requirements:** High school diploma or equivalent not required. For applicants under 18: High school diploma required; GED accepted **Scholarships:** Available. **Calendar System:** Semester, Summer session available **Faculty:** Full-time 167, Part-time 636 **Student-Faculty Ratio:** 35:1 **Exams:** ACT essay component used for placement; SAT essay component used for placement. **Final Year or Final Semester Residency Requirement:** Yes **Regional Accreditation:** Western Association of Colleges and Schools **Credit Hours For Degree:** 60 semester hours, Associates **ROTC:** Air Force **Professional Accreditation:** ACEN. **Intercollegiate Athletics:** Baseball M; Basketball M & W; Cross-Country Running M & W; Football M; Golf M & W; Soccer M & W; Softball W; Tennis M & W; Track and Field M & W; Volleyball M & W

SAN DIEGO MESA COLLEGE

7250 Mesa College Dr.
San Diego, CA 92111-4998
Tel: (619)388-2600
Fax: (619)388-2968
E-mail: csawyer@sdccd.edu
Web Site: www.sdmesa.edu
President/CEO: Pres. Pamelar Luster
Admissions: Cheri Sawyer

Type: Two-Year College **Sex:** Coed **Affiliation:** San Diego Community College District System. **Scholarships:** Available. **Calendar System:** Semester, Summer session available **Enrollment:** Full-time 25,464 **Faculty:**

Full-time 199, Part-time 524 **Final Year or Final Semester Residency Requirement:** No **Regional Accreditation:** Western Association of Colleges and Schools **Credit Hours For Degree:** 60 semester units, Associates **Professional Accreditation:** AAMAE, ADA, AHIMA, APTA. **Intercollegiate Athletics:** Baseball M; Basketball M & W; Cross-Country Running M & W; Football M; Soccer M & W; Softball W; Swimming and Diving M & W; Tennis M & W; Track and Field M & W; Volleyball M & W; Water Polo M & W

SAN DIEGO MIRAMAR COLLEGE

10440 Black Mountain Rd.
San Diego, CA 92126-2999
Tel: (619)388-7800
Fax: (619)388-7801
E-mail: dstack@sdccd.edu
Web Site: www.sdmiramar.edu
President/CEO: Patricia Hsieh
Admissions: Dana Stack
Financial Aid: Vincent Ngo

Type: Two-Year College **Sex:** Coed **Affiliation:** San Diego Community College District System. **Admission Plans:** Open Admission **Application Fee:** $0.00 **H.S. Requirements:** High school diploma or equivalent not required **Costs Per Year:** Application fee: $0. State resident tuition: $1380 full-time, $46 per credit hour part-time. Nonresident tuition: $5790 full-time, $193 per credit hour part-time. Mandatory fees: $38 full-time, $19 per term part-time. Tuition guaranteed not to increase for student's term of enrollment. **Scholarships:** Available. **Calendar System:** Semester, Summer session available **Regional Accreditation:** Western Association of Colleges and Schools **Credit Hours For Degree:** 60 credits, Associates **Intercollegiate Athletics:** Basketball M; Water Polo M & W

SAN DIEGO STATE UNIVERSITY

5500 Campanile Dr.
San Diego, CA 92182
Tel: (619)594-5200; Free: 855-594-3983
E-mail: admissions@sdsu.edu
Web Site: www.sdsu.edu
President/CEO: Dr. Elliot Hirshman
Financial Aid: Rose Pasenelli

Type: University **Sex:** Coed **Affiliation:** California State University System. **Scores:** 97% SAT V 400+; 98% SAT M 400+; 32.6% ACT 18-23; 52.4% ACT 24-29 **% Accepted:** 34 **Application Deadline:** November 30 **Application Fee:** $55.00 **H.S. Requirements:** High school diploma required; GED accepted **Costs Per Year:** Application fee: $55. State resident tuition: $5472 full-time. Nonresident tuition: $16,632 full-time. Mandatory fees: $1504 full-time. Full-time tuition and fees vary according to course load, degree level, and location. College room and board: $15,826. Room and board charges vary according to board plan and housing facility. **Scholarships:** Available. **Calendar System:** Semester, Summer session available **Enrollment:** Full-time 26,005, Graduate full-time 2,987, Graduate part-time 2,033, Part-time 3,229 **Faculty:** Full-time 809, Part-time 893 **Student-Faculty Ratio:** 28:1 **Exams:** ACT essay component not used; SAT I or ACT; SAT essay component not used; SAT Reasoning; SAT Subject. **% Receiving Financial Aid:** 56 **% Residing in College-Owned, -Operated, or -Affiliated Housing:** 15 **Final Year or Final Semester Residency Requirement:** No **Regional Accreditation:** Western Association of Colleges and Schools **Credit Hours For Degree:** 120 semester units, Bachelors **ROTC:** Air Force, Army, Navy **Professional Accreditation:** AACN, AACSB, ABET, ACNM, AND, APA, ASHA, CAHME, CEPH, CORE, CSWE, CoA-KT, JRCAT, NASAD, NASPAA, NAST, NCATE, NRPA. **Intercollegiate Athletics:** Baseball M; Basketball M & W; Cross-Country Running W; Football M; Golf M & W; Lacrosse W; Rowing W; Soccer M & W; Softball W; Swimming and Diving W; Tennis M & W; Track and Field W; Volleyball W; Water Polo W

SAN DIEGO STATE UNIVERSITY–IMPERIAL VALLEY CAMPUS

720 Heber Ave.
Calexico, CA 92231
Tel: (760)768-5500
E-mail: transfer@mail.sdsu.edu
Web Site: www.ivcampus.sdsu.edu
President/CEO: David E. Pearson
Admissions: Aracely Bororquez

Type: Comprehensive **Sex:** Coed **Application Fee:** $55.00 **Regional Accreditation:** Western Association of Colleges and Schools

SAN FRANCISCO ART INSTITUTE
800 Chestnut St.
San Francisco, CA 94133
Tel: (415)771-7020; Free: 800-345-SFAI
E-mail: admissions@sfai.edu
Web Site: www.sfai.edu
President/CEO: Rachel Schreiber
Financial Aid: Annita Alldredge

Type: Comprehensive **Sex:** Coed **Scores:** 100% SAT V 400+; 95% SAT M 400+; 25% ACT 18-23; 42% ACT 24-29 **% Accepted:** 65 **Admission Plans:** Deferred Admission **Application Deadline:** Rolling **Application Fee:** $75.00 **H.S. Requirements:** High school diploma required; GED accepted **Costs Per Year:** Application fee: $75. Comprehensive fee: $56,938 includes full-time tuition ($40,402), mandatory fees ($870), and college room and board ($15,666). College room only: $11,500. Full-time tuition and fees vary according to degree level. Room and board charges vary according to housing facility. Part-time tuition: $1770 per unit. Part-time tuition varies according to degree level. **Scholarships:** Available. **Calendar System:** Semester, Summer session available **Enrollment:** Full-time 385, Graduate full-time 170, Graduate part-time 17, Part-time 27 **Faculty:** Full-time 23, Part-time 109 **Student-Faculty Ratio:** 10:1 **Exams:** SAT I or ACT. **% Receiving Financial Aid:** 60 **% Residing in College-Owned, -Operated, or -Affiliated Housing:** 33 **Final Year or Final Semester Residency Requirement:** Yes **Regional Accreditation:** Western Association of Colleges and Schools **Credit Hours For Degree:** 120 units, Bachelors **Professional Accreditation:** NASAD.

SAN FRANCISCO CONSERVATORY OF MUSIC
50 Oak St.
San Francisco, CA 94102
Tel: (415)864-7326
Fax: (415)503-6299
E-mail: admit@sfcm.edu
Web Site: www.sfcm.edu
President/CEO: David Stull
Admissions: Melissa Cocco-Mitten
Financial Aid: Doris Howard

Type: Comprehensive **Sex:** Coed **Costs Per Year:** Comprehensive fee: $56,810 includes full-time tuition ($41,200), mandatory fees ($1010), and college room and board ($14,600). College room only: $11,900. Room and board charges vary according to board plan and housing facility. Part-time tuition: $1816 per credit. Part-time mandatory fees: $1010 per year. Part-time tuition and fees vary according to course load. **Scholarships:** Available. **Calendar System:** Semester, Summer session not available **Enrollment:** Full-time 156, Graduate full-time 219, Graduate part-time 2, Part-time 2 **Faculty:** Full-time 28, Part-time 96 **Student-Faculty Ratio:** 7:1 **Exams:** ACT essay component not used; SAT I or ACT; SAT essay component not used. **% Receiving Financial Aid:** 85 **% Residing in College-Owned, -Operated, or -Affiliated Housing:** 46 **Final Year or Final Semester Residency Requirement:** No **Regional Accreditation:** Western Association of Colleges and Schools **Credit Hours For Degree:** 127 semester hours, depending on program, Bachelors **Professional Accreditation:** AOTA, NASM.

SAN FRANCISCO STATE UNIVERSITY
1600 Holloway Ave.
San Francisco, CA 94132-1722
Tel: (415)338-1100
E-mail: ugadmit@sfsu.edu
Web Site: www.sfsu.edu
President/CEO: Dr. Leslie E. Wong
Financial Aid: Barbara Hubler

Type: University **Sex:** Coed **Affiliation:** California State University System. **Scores:** 87% SAT V 400+; 89% SAT M 400+; 52% ACT 18-23; 23.6% ACT 24-29 **% Accepted:** 68 **Application Deadline:** November 30 **Application Fee:** $55.00 **H.S. Requirements:** High school diploma required; GED accepted **Costs Per Year:** Application fee: $55. State resident tuition: $5472 full-time, $1587 per term part-time. Nonresident tuition: $16,632 full-time, $3819 per term part-time. Mandatory fees: $1004 full-time, $502 per term part-time. Full-time tuition and fees vary according to course load. Part-time tuition and fees vary according to course load. College room and board: $12,234. College room only: $8090. Room and board charges vary according to board plan and housing facility. **Scholarships:** Available. **Calendar System:** Semester, Summer session available **Enrollment:** Full-time

22,206, Graduate full-time 2,067, Graduate part-time 1,283, Part-time 4,700 **Exams:** ACT essay component not used; SAT I or ACT; SAT II; SAT essay component not used; SAT Reasoning. **% Receiving Financial Aid:** 68 **Regional Accreditation:** Western Association of Colleges and Schools **Credit Hours For Degree:** 120 units, Bachelors **ROTC:** Air Force, Army **Professional Accreditation:** AACN, AACSB, AAFCS, ABET, ACA, ACEJMC, AND, APTA, ASHA, CEPH, CORE, CSWE, NAACLS, NASAD, NASM, NASPAA, NAST, NCATE, NRPA. **Intercollegiate Athletics:** Baseball M; Basketball M & W; Cross-Country Running M & W; Soccer M & W; Softball W; Track and Field W; Volleyball W; Wrestling M

SAN JOAQUIN DELTA COLLEGE
5151 Pacific Ave.
Stockton, CA 95207-6370
Tel: (209)954-5151
Fax: (209)954-5600
E-mail: ksea@deltacollege.edu
Web Site: www.deltacollege.edu
President/CEO: Dr. Kathy Hart
Admissions: Karen Sea
Financial Aid: Tina V. Lent

Type: Two-Year College **Sex:** Coed **Affiliation:** California Community College System. **Admission Plans:** Early Admission; Open Admission **Application Deadline:** Rolling **Application Fee:** $0.00 **H.S. Requirements:** High school diploma or equivalent not required. For applicants under 18: High school diploma required; GED accepted **Costs Per Year:** Application fee: $0. State resident tuition: $1380 full-time. Nonresident tuition: $7950 full-time. **Scholarships:** Available. **Calendar System:** Semester, Summer session available **Faculty:** Full-time 222, Part-time 322 **Student-Faculty Ratio:** 27:1 **Regional Accreditation:** Western Association of Colleges and Schools **Credit Hours For Degree:** 60 units, Associates **Professional Accreditation:** ACEN. **Intercollegiate Athletics:** Baseball M; Basketball M & W; Cross-Country Running M & W; Fencing M & W; Football M; Golf M & W; Soccer M & W; Softball W; Swimming and Diving M & W; Tennis M & W; Track and Field M & W; Volleyball W; Water Polo M & W; Wrestling M

SAN JOAQUIN VALLEY COLLEGE (BAKERSFIELD)
201 New Stine Rd.
Bakersfield, CA 93309
Tel: (661)834-0126; Free: 866-544-7898
E-mail: admissions@sjvc.edu
Web Site: www.sjvc.edu/campuses/central-california/bakersfield
President/CEO: Mark Perry

Type: Two-Year College **Sex:** Coed **Affiliation:** San Joaquin Valley College. **Application Deadline:** Rolling **H.S. Requirements:** High school diploma required; GED accepted **Costs Per Year:** Tuition: $16,785 full-time. Tuition guaranteed not to increase for student's term of enrollment. **Calendar System:** Continuous **Enrollment:** Full-time 864 **Faculty:** Full-time 23, Part-time 34 **Student-Faculty Ratio:** 25:1 **Regional Accreditation:** Western Association of Colleges and Schools

SAN JOAQUIN VALLEY COLLEGE (CHULA VISTA)
333 H St.
Ste. 1065
Chula Vista, CA 91910
Tel: (619)426-7582
Web Site: www.sjvc.edu/campuses/southern-california/san-diego
President/CEO: Jean Honny

Type: Two-Year College **Sex:** Coed **Costs Per Year:** Tuition: $28,825 full-time. Tuition guaranteed not to increase for student's term of enrollment. **Calendar System:** Continuous **Enrollment:** Full-time 61 **Faculty:** Full-time 5, Part-time 6 **Student-Faculty Ratio:** 9:1 **Regional Accreditation:** Western Association of Colleges and Schools

SAN JOAQUIN VALLEY COLLEGE (FRESNO)
295 E Sierra Ave.
Fresno, CA 93710-3616
Tel: (209)448-8282
Fax: (209)448-8250
E-mail: admissions@sjvc.edu
Web Site: www.sjvc.edu/campuses/central-california/fresno
President/CEO: Mark Perry

Type: Two-Year College **Sex:** Coed **Affiliation:** San Joaquin Valley College. **Application Deadline:** Rolling **H.S. Requirements:** High school diploma required; GED accepted **Costs Per Year:** Tuition: $15,897 full-time. Full-time tuition varies according to location and program. Tuition guaranteed not to increase for student's term of enrollment. **Calendar System:** Continuous **Enrollment:** Full-time 1,019 **Faculty:** Full-time 19, Part-time 36 **Student-Faculty Ratio:** 33:1 **Regional Accreditation:** Western Association of Colleges and Schools

SAN JOAQUIN VALLEY COLLEGE (HANFORD)
215 W 7th St.
Hanford, CA 93230
Tel: (866)544-7898
Web Site: www.sjvc.edu/campuses/central-california/hanford
Type: Two-Year College **Sex:** Coed **Costs Per Year:** Tuition: $15,603 full-time. Tuition guaranteed not to increase for student's term of enrollment. **Calendar System:** Continuous **Enrollment:** Full-time 275 **Faculty:** Full-time 4, Part-time 2 **Student-Faculty Ratio:** 59:1 **Regional Accreditation:** Western Association of Colleges and Schools

SAN JOAQUIN VALLEY COLLEGE (HESPERIA)
9331 Mariposa Rd.
Hesperia, CA 92344
Tel: (760)948-1947
Web Site: www.sjvc.edu/campuses/southern-california/victor-valley
Type: Two-Year College **Sex:** Coed **Affiliation:** San Joaquin Valley College. **Costs Per Year:** Tuition: $16,952 full-time. Tuition guaranteed not to increase for student's term of enrollment. **Calendar System:** Continuous **Enrollment:** Full-time 804 **Faculty:** Full-time 10, Part-time 30 **Student-Faculty Ratio:** 34:1 **Regional Accreditation:** Western Association of Colleges and Schools

SAN JOAQUIN VALLEY COLLEGE (LANCASTER)
42135 10th St. W
Lancaster, CA 93534
Tel: (661)974-8282
Web Site: www.sjvc.edu/campuses/southern-california/antelope-valley
Type: Two-Year College **Sex:** Coed **Affiliation:** San Joaquin Valley College. **Costs Per Year:** Tuition: $16,684 full-time. Tuition guaranteed not to increase for student's term of enrollment. **Calendar System:** Continuous **Enrollment:** Full-time 328 **Faculty:** Full-time 2, Part-time 16 **Student-Faculty Ratio:** 45:1 **Regional Accreditation:** Western Association of Colleges and Schools

SAN JOAQUIN VALLEY COLLEGE (ONTARIO)
4580 Ontario Mills Pky.
Ontario, CA 91764
Tel: (909)948-7582
E-mail: admissions@sjvc.edu
Web Site: www.sjvc.edu/campuses/southern-california/ontario
President/CEO: Mark Perry
Type: Two-Year College **Sex:** Coed **Affiliation:** San Joaquin Valley College. **Application Deadline:** Rolling **H.S. Requirements:** High school diploma required; GED accepted **Costs Per Year:** Tuition: $17,985 full-time. Full-time tuition varies according to location and program. Tuition guaranteed not to increase for student's term of enrollment. **Calendar System:** Continuous **Enrollment:** Full-time 994 **Faculty:** Full-time 34, Part-time 63 **Student-Faculty Ratio:** 18:1 **Regional Accreditation:** Western Association of Colleges and Schools

SAN JOAQUIN VALLEY COLLEGE (RANCHO CORDOVA)
11050 Olson Dr.
Ste. 210
Rancho Cordova, CA 95670
E-mail: admissions@sjvc.edu
Web Site: www.sjvc.edu/campuses/northern-california/rancho-cordova
President/CEO: Mark Perry
Type: Two-Year College **Sex:** Coed **Affiliation:** San Joaquin Valley College. **Application Deadline:** Rolling **H.S. Requirements:** High school diploma required; GED accepted **Costs Per Year:** Tuition: $24,250 full-time. Full-time tuition varies according to location and program. Tuition guaranteed not to increase for student's term of enrollment. **Calendar System:** Continuous **Enrollment:** Full-time 158 **Faculty:** Full-time 5, Part-time 7 **Student-Faculty Ratio:** 22:1 **Regional Accreditation:** Western Association of Colleges and Schools

SAN JOAQUIN VALLEY COLLEGE (SALIDA)
5380 Pirrone Rd.
Salida, CA 95368
E-mail: admissions@sjvc.edu
Web Site: www.sjvc.edu/campuses/northern-california/modesto
President/CEO: Mark Perry
Type: Two-Year College **Sex:** Coed **Affiliation:** San Joaquin Valley College. **Application Deadline:** Rolling **H.S. Requirements:** High school diploma required; GED accepted **Costs Per Year:** Tuition: $15,478 full-time. Full-time tuition varies according to location and program. Tuition guaranteed not to increase for student's term of enrollment. **Calendar System:** Continuous **Enrollment:** Full-time 465 **Faculty:** Full-time 8, Part-time 21 **Student-Faculty Ratio:** 31:1 **Regional Accreditation:** Western Association of Colleges and Schools

SAN JOAQUIN VALLEY COLLEGE (TEMECULA)
27270 Madison Ave.
Ste. 103
Temecula, CA 92590
Tel: (866)544-7898
E-mail: admissions@sjvc.edu
Web Site: www.sjvc.edu/campuses/southern-california/temecula
President/CEO: Mark Perry
Admissions: Robyn Whiles
Type: Two-Year College **Sex:** Coed **Affiliation:** San Joaquin Valley College. **Costs Per Year:** Tuition: $17,452 full-time. Tuition guaranteed not to increase for student's term of enrollment. **Calendar System:** Continuous **Enrollment:** Full-time 728 **Faculty:** Full-time 13, Part-time 30 **Student-Faculty Ratio:** 32:1 **Regional Accreditation:** Western Association of Colleges and Schools

SAN JOAQUIN VALLEY COLLEGE (VISALIA)
8344 W Mineral King Ave.
Visalia, CA 93291
Tel: (559)651-2500
E-mail: admissions@sjvc.edu
Web Site: www.sjvc.edu/campuses/central-california/visalia
President/CEO: Mark Perry
Admissions: Susie Topjian
Type: Two-Year College **Sex:** Coed **Affiliation:** San Joaquin Valley College. **Application Deadline:** Rolling **H.S. Requirements:** High school diploma required; GED accepted **Costs Per Year:** Tuition: $19,480 full-time. Tuition guaranteed not to increase for student's term of enrollment. **Scholarships:** Available. **Calendar System:** Continuous, Summer session not available **Enrollment:** Full-time 1,294 **Faculty:** Full-time 42, Part-time 59 **Student-Faculty Ratio:** 21:1 **Regional Accreditation:** Western Association of Colleges and Schools **Credit Hours For Degree:** 60 credits, Associates **Professional Accreditation:** ADA, ARCST, CoARC.

SAN JOAQUIN VALLEY COLLEGE–FRESNO AVIATION CAMPUS
4985 E Anderson Ave.
Fresno, CA 93727
E-mail: admissions@sjvc.edu
Web Site: www.sjvc.edu/campuses/central-california/fresno-aviation
Type: Two-Year College **Sex:** Coed **Affiliation:** San Joaquin Valley College. **Application Deadline:** Rolling **H.S. Requirements:** High school diploma required; GED accepted **Costs Per Year:** Tuition: $13,620 full-time. Tuition guaranteed not to increase for student's term of enrollment. **Calendar System:** Semester **Enrollment:** Full-time 130 **Faculty:** Full-time 3, Part-time 5 **Student-Faculty Ratio:** 26:1 **Regional Accreditation:** Western Association of Colleges and Schools

SAN JOAQUIN VALLEY COLLEGE–ONLINE
8344 W Mineral King Ave.
Visalia, CA 93291
Tel: (559)734-7582
Fax: (559)735-0219
E-mail: admissions@sjvc.edu
Web Site: www.sjvc.edu/online-programs
President/CEO: Mark Perry
Type: Two-Year College **Sex:** Coed **Affiliation:** San Joaquin Valley College. **Application Deadline:** Rolling **H.S. Requirements:** High school diploma required; GED accepted **Costs Per Year:** Tuition: $14,645 full-time. Tuition guaranteed not to increase for student's term of enrollment. **Calendar**

System: Continuous **Enrollment:** Full-time 1,005 **Faculty:** Full-time 11, Part-time 39 **Student-Faculty Ratio:** 42:1 **Regional Accreditation:** Western Association of Colleges and Schools

SAN JOSE CITY COLLEGE
2100 Moorpark Ave.
San Jose, CA 95128-2799
Tel: (408)298-2181
Web Site: www.sjcc.edu
President/CEO: Byron Breland
Admissions: Carlo Santos
Type: Two-Year College **Sex:** Coed **Affiliation:** San Jose/Evergreen Community College District System. **Admission Plans:** Deferred Admission; Early Admission; Open Admission; Preferred Admission **Application Deadline:** Rolling **Application Fee:** $0.00 **H.S. Requirements:** High school diploma or equivalent not required. For applicants under 18: High school diploma required; GED accepted **Scholarships:** Available. **Calendar System:** Semester, Summer session available **Regional Accreditation:** Western Association of Colleges and Schools **Credit Hours For Degree:** 60 units, Associates **ROTC:** Air Force, Army **Professional Accreditation:** ADA. **Intercollegiate Athletics:** Baseball M; Basketball M & W; Cross-Country Running M & W; Football M; Golf M; Softball W; Track and Field M & W; Volleyball W

SAN JOSE STATE UNIVERSITY
One Washington Sq.
San Jose, CA 95192-0001
Tel: (408)924-1000
Fax: (408)924-2050
E-mail: admissions@sjsu.edu
Web Site: www.sjsu.edu
President/CEO: Dr. Susan Martin
Financial Aid: Coleetta McElroy
Type: Comprehensive **Sex:** Coed **Affiliation:** California State University System. **Scores:** 92% SAT V 400+ **% Accepted:** 55 **Admission Plans:** Preferred Admission **Application Deadline:** November 30 **Application Fee:** $55.00 **H.S. Requirements:** High school diploma required; GED accepted **Costs Per Year:** Application fee: $55. State resident tuition: $5472 full-time. Nonresident tuition: $14,400 full-time, $372 per unit part-time. Mandatory fees: $1851 full-time. College room and board: $14,217. College room only: $9017. **Scholarships:** Available. **Calendar System:** Semester, Summer session available **Enrollment:** Full-time 21,638, Graduate full-time 3,833, Graduate part-time 2,118, Part-time 5,184 **Faculty:** Full-time 687, Part-time 1,068 **Student-Faculty Ratio:** 28:1 **Exams:** ACT essay component used for placement; SAT I or ACT; SAT essay component used for placement; SAT Reasoning. **% Receiving Financial Aid:** 67 **% Residing in College-Owned, -Operated, or -Affiliated Housing:** 13 **Regional Accreditation:** Western Association of Colleges and Schools **Credit Hours For Degree:** 120 units, Bachelors **ROTC:** Air Force, Army **Professional Accreditation:** AACN, AACSB, ABET, ACEJMC, ACSP, ALA, AND, AOTA, ASHA, ATMAE, CEPH, CSWE, JRCAT, NASAD, NASD, NASM, NASPAA, NAST, NCATE, NRPA. **Intercollegiate Athletics:** Baseball M; Basketball M & W; Cross-Country Running M & W; Football M; Golf M & W; Gymnastics W; Soccer M & W; Softball W; Swimming and Diving W; Table Tennis W; Tennis W; Track and Field W; Volleyball W; Water Polo M & W

SANTA ANA COLLEGE
1530 W 17th St.
Santa Ana, CA 92706-3398
Tel: (714)564-6000
Web Site: www.sac.edu
President/CEO: Erlinda Martinez
Admissions: Christie Steward
Financial Aid: Claudia Cruz
Type: Two-Year College **Sex:** Coed **Affiliation:** California Community College System. **Admission Plans:** Early Admission; Open Admission **Application Deadline:** August 21 **H.S. Requirements:** High school diploma required; GED accepted **Scholarships:** Available. **Calendar System:** Semester, Summer session available **Faculty:** Full-time 249, Part-time 1,047 **Student-Faculty Ratio:** 20:1 **Regional Accreditation:** Western Association of Colleges and Schools **Credit Hours For Degree:** 60 credits, Associates **ROTC:** Air Force **Professional Accreditation:** ACEN, AOTA. **Intercollegiate Athletics:** Baseball M; Basketball M & W; Cross-Country

Running M & W; Football M; Golf M; Soccer M; Softball W; Swimming and Diving M; Tennis M & W; Track and Field M & W; Volleyball W; Water Polo M; Wrestling M

SANTA BARBARA BUSINESS COLLEGE (BAKERSFIELD)
5300 California Ave.
Bakersfield, CA 93309
Tel: (661)835-1100
Web Site: www.sbbcollege.edu
Type: Two-Year College **Sex:** Coed

SANTA BARBARA BUSINESS COLLEGE (SANTA MARIA)
303 E Plz. Dr.
Santa Maria, CA 93454
Tel: (805)922-8256
Web Site: www.sbbcollege.edu
Type: Two-Year College **Sex:** Coed

SANTA BARBARA BUSINESS COLLEGE (VENTURA)
4839 Market St.
Ventura, CA 93003
Tel: (805)339-2999
Web Site: www.sbbcollege.edu
Type: Four-Year College **Sex:** Coed **Professional Accreditation:** ACICS.

SANTA BARBARA CITY COLLEGE
721 Cliff Dr.
Santa Barbara, CA 93109-2394
Tel: (805)965-0581
Fax: (805)963-SBCC
E-mail: admissions@sbcc.edu
Web Site: www.sbcc.edu
President/CEO: Dr. Andreea Serban
Admissions: Allison Curtis
Type: Two-Year College **Sex:** Coed **Affiliation:** California Community College System. **% Accepted:** 100 **Admission Plans:** Early Admission; Open Admission **Application Deadline:** August 19 **Application Fee:** $0.00 **H.S. Requirements:** High school diploma required; GED accepted. For applicants 18 or over: High school diploma or equivalent not required **Scholarships:** Available. **Calendar System:** Semester, Summer session available **Enrollment:** Full-time 7,952, Part-time 10,140 **Faculty:** Full-time 266, Part-time 540 **Student-Faculty Ratio:** 27:1 **Regional Accreditation:** Western Association of Colleges and Schools **Credit Hours For Degree:** 60 units, Associates **ROTC:** Army **Professional Accreditation:** ACEN, ACF, AHIMA, JRCERT. **Intercollegiate Athletics:** Baseball M; Basketball M & W; Cross-Country Running M & W; Football M; Golf M & W; Soccer M & W; Softball W; Tennis M & W; Track and Field M & W; Volleyball M & W

SANTA CLARA UNIVERSITY
500 El Camino Real
Santa Clara, CA 95053
Tel: (408)554-4000
Fax: (408)554-5255
E-mail: admission@scu.edu
Web Site: www.scu.edu
President/CEO: Rev. Michael E. Engh, SJ
Admissions: Eva Blanco
Financial Aid: Nancy Merz
Type: University **Sex:** Coed **Affiliation:** Roman Catholic (Jesuit). **Scores:** 100% SAT V 400+; 100% SAT M 400+; 3% ACT 18-23; 43% ACT 24-29 **% Accepted:** 49 **Admission Plans:** Deferred Admission; Early Action; Early Admission; Early Decision Plan **Application Deadline:** January 7 **Application Fee:** $60.00 **H.S. Requirements:** High school diploma required; GED accepted **Costs Per Year:** Application fee: $60. Comprehensive fee: $58,725 includes full-time tuition ($45,300) and college room and board ($13,425). Room and board charges vary according to board plan, housing facility, location, and student level. Part-time tuition: $1258 per unit. Part-time tuition varies according to course load. **Scholarships:** Available. **Calendar System:** Quarter, Summer session available **Enrollment:** Full-time 5,303, Graduate full-time 1,998, Graduate part-time 1,297, Part-time 82 **Faculty:** Full-time 539, Part-time 395 **Student-Faculty Ratio:** 12:1 **Exams:** ACT essay component not used; SAT I or ACT; SAT essay component not used; SAT Reasoning. **% Receiving Financial Aid:** 38 **% Residing in College-Owned, -Operated, or -Affiliated Housing:** 52 **Final Year or Final**

Semester Residency Requirement: No **Regional Accreditation:** Western Association of Colleges and Schools **Credit Hours For Degree:** 176 units, Bachelors **ROTC:** Air Force, Army **Professional Accreditation:** AACSB, AALS, ABA, ABET, ATS. **Intercollegiate Athletics:** Baseball M; Basketball M & W; Cross-Country Running M & W; Equestrian Sports M & W; Golf M & W; Ice Hockey M; Lacrosse M & W; Rowing M & W; Rugby M & W; Sailing M & W; Soccer M & W; Softball W; Swimming and Diving M & W; Tennis M & W; Track and Field M & W; Triathlon M & W; Ultimate Frisbee M & W; Volleyball M & W; Water Polo M & W

SANTA MONICA COLLEGE

1900 Pico Blvd.
Santa Monica, CA 90405-1628
Tel: (310)434-4000
Web Site: www.smc.edu
President/CEO: Chui L. Tsang
Admissions: Teresita Rodriguez

Type: Two-Year College **Sex:** Coed **Affiliation:** California Community College System. **Admission Plans:** Early Admission; Open Admission **Application Deadline:** August 30 **Application Fee:** $0.00 **H.S. Requirements:** High school diploma required; GED accepted. For international students: High school diploma required; GED not accepted **Scholarships:** Available. **Calendar System:** Miscellaneous, Summer session available **Enrollment:** Full-time 10,722, Part-time 19,278 **Faculty:** Full-time 309, Part-time 994 **Regional Accreditation:** Western Association of Colleges and Schools **Credit Hours For Degree:** 60 units, Associates **ROTC:** Army **Professional Accreditation:** ACEN, CoARC. **Intercollegiate Athletics:** Basketball M & W; Cross-Country Running M & W; Football M; Soccer W; Softball W; Swimming and Diving M & W; Tennis W; Track and Field M & W; Volleyball M & W; Water Polo M & W

SANTA ROSA JUNIOR COLLEGE

1501 Mendocino Ave.
Santa Rosa, CA 95401-4395
Tel: (707)527-4011
E-mail: admininfo@santarosa.edu
Web Site: www.santarosa.edu
President/CEO: Frank Chong, EdD
Admissions: Freyja Pereira
Financial Aid: Lynn McMullin

Type: Two-Year College **Sex:** Coed **Affiliation:** California Community College System. **% Accepted:** 100 **Admission Plans:** Early Admission; Open Admission **Application Deadline:** Rolling **Application Fee:** $0.00 **H.S. Requirements:** High school diploma or equivalent not required. For applicants under 18 and the allied health programs: High school diploma required; GED accepted **Costs Per Year:** Application fee: $0. One-time mandatory fee: $40. State resident tuition: $0 full-time. Nonresident tuition: $5832 full-time, $243 per unit part-time. Mandatory fees: $1104 full-time, $46 per unit part-time, $20 per term part-time. Full-time tuition and fees vary according to course load. Part-time tuition and fees vary according to course load. **Scholarships:** Available. **Calendar System:** Semester, Summer session available **Enrollment:** Full-time 6,830, Part-time 15,178 **Faculty:** Full-time 271, Part-time 1,052 **Student-Faculty Ratio:** 22:1 **Final Year or Final Semester Residency Requirement:** Yes **Regional Accreditation:** Western Association of Colleges and Schools **Credit Hours For Degree:** 60 units, Associates **Professional Accreditation:** ADA, JRCERT. **Intercollegiate Athletics:** Baseball M; Basketball M & W; Cross-Country Running M & W; Football M; Golf M; Ice Hockey M; Rugby M; Soccer M & W; Softball W; Swimming and Diving M & W; Tennis M & W; Track and Field M & W; Volleyball W; Water Polo M & W; Wrestling M

SANTIAGO CANYON COLLEGE

8045 E Chapman Ave.
Orange, CA 92869
Tel: (714)628-4900
Fax: (714)564-4379
Web Site: www.sccollege.edu
President/CEO: John Weispfenning
Admissions: Tuyen Nguyen

Type: Two-Year College **Sex:** Coed **Affiliation:** California Community College System. **Costs Per Year:** State resident tuition: $1326 full-time. Nonresident tuition: $8046 full-time. Full-time tuition varies according to course load. **Calendar System:** Semester, Summer session available **Enrollment:** Full-time 7,987 **Faculty:** Full-time 92, Part-time 325 **Student-**

Faculty Ratio: 23:1 **Final Year or Final Semester Residency Requirement:** No **Regional Accreditation:** Western Association of Colleges and Schools **Credit Hours For Degree:** 60 credits, Associates

SCRIPPS COLLEGE

1030 Columbia Ave.
Claremont, CA 91711-3948
Tel: (909)621-8000; Free: 800-770-1333
Fax: (909)621-8323
E-mail: admission@scrippscollege.edu
Web Site: www.scrippscollege.edu
President/CEO: Amy Marcus-Newhall
Admissions: Laura Stratton
Financial Aid: Patrick Moore

Type: Four-Year College **Sex:** Women **Scores:** 101% SAT V 400+; 101% SAT M 400+; 1% ACT 18-23; 29% ACT 24-29 **% Accepted:** 28 **Admission Plans:** Deferred Admission; Early Action; Early Admission **Application Deadline:** January 1 **Application Fee:** $60.00 **H.S. Requirements:** High school diploma required; GED accepted **Costs Per Year:** Application fee: $60. Comprehensive fee: $64,260 includes full-time tuition ($48,938), mandatory fees ($214), and college room and board ($15,108). College room only: $8232. Full-time tuition and fees vary according to course load and degree level. Room and board charges vary according to board plan. Part-time tuition: $6117 per course. Part-time tuition varies according to course load and degree level. **Scholarships:** Available. **Calendar System:** Semester, Summer session not available **Enrollment:** Full-time 969, Graduate full-time 16, Part-time 4 **Faculty:** Full-time 88, Part-time 34 **Student-Faculty Ratio:** 10:1 **Exams:** ACT essay component not used; SAT I or ACT; SAT essay component not used; SAT Reasoning. **% Receiving Financial Aid:** 39 **% Residing in College-Owned, -Operated, or -Affiliated Housing:** 100 **Final Year or Final Semester Residency Requirement:** No **Regional Accreditation:** Western Association of Colleges and Schools **Credit Hours For Degree:** 32 courses, Bachelors **ROTC:** Air Force, Army **Intercollegiate Athletics:** Basketball W; Cross-Country Running W; Equestrian Sports W; Fencing W; Golf W; Lacrosse W; Rugby W; Skiing (Downhill) W; Soccer W; Softball W; Swimming and Diving W; Tennis W; Track and Field W; Ultimate Frisbee W; Volleyball W; Water Polo W

SHASTA BIBLE COLLEGE

2951 Goodwater Ave.
Redding, CA 96002
Tel: (530)221-4275; Free: 800-800-4SBC
E-mail: registrar@shasta.edu
Web Site: www.shasta.edu
President/CEO: David R. Nicholas
Admissions: Connie Barton
Financial Aid: Linda Iles

Type: Comprehensive **Sex:** Coed **Affiliation:** nondenominational. **% Accepted:** 83 **Admission Plans:** Early Admission; Open Admission **Application Deadline:** Rolling **Application Fee:** $50.00 **H.S. Requirements:** High school diploma required; GED accepted **Scholarships:** Available. **Calendar System:** Semester, Summer session available **Enrollment:** Full-time 29, Graduate full-time 2, Graduate part-time 4, Part-time 15 **Faculty:** Full-time 9, Part-time 28 **Student-Faculty Ratio:** 3:1 **% Receiving Financial Aid:** 61 **% Residing in College-Owned, -Operated, or -Affiliated Housing:** 77 **Final Year or Final Semester Residency Requirement:** No **Credit Hours For Degree:** 64 credit hours, Associates; 128 credit hours, Bachelors **Professional Accreditation:** TRACS.

SHASTA COLLEGE

11555 Old Oregon Trl.
Redding, CA 96049-6006
Tel: (530)242-7500
Web Site: www.shastacollege.edu
President/CEO: Joe Wyse
Admissions: Dr. Kevin O'Rorke
Financial Aid: Lorelei Hartzler

Type: Two-Year College **Sex:** Coed **Affiliation:** California Community College System. **% Accepted:** 100 **Admission Plans:** Early Admission; Open Admission **Application Deadline:** Rolling **Application Fee:** $0.00 **H.S. Requirements:** High school diploma or equivalent not required **Scholarships:** Available. **Calendar System:** Semester, Summer session available **Enrollment:** Full-time 4,336, Part-time 5,904 **Faculty:** Full-time 146, Part-time 345 **Regional Accreditation:** Western Association of Colleges and

Schools **Credit Hours For Degree:** 60 semester hours, Associates **Professional Accreditation:** ADA. **Intercollegiate Athletics:** Baseball M; Basketball M & W; Cross-Country Running M & W; Football M; Golf M & W; Soccer M & W; Softball W; Swimming and Diving M & W; Tennis M & W; Track and Field M & W; Volleyball W

SHEPHERD UNIVERSITY
3200 N San Fernando Rd.
Los Angeles, CA 90065
Tel: (323)550-8888
Web Site: www.shepherduniversity.edu
Type: Comprehensive **Sex:** Coed **Affiliation:** Christian. **Costs Per Year:** One-time mandatory fee: $300. Tuition: $18,976 full-time, $743 per credit part-time. Mandatory fees: $600 full-time, $495 per term part-time. Full-time tuition and fees vary according to course load, degree level, and program. Part-time tuition and fees vary according to course load, degree level, and program. **Professional Accreditation:** ATS.

SIERRA COLLEGE
5000 Rocklin Rd.
Rocklin, CA 95677-3397
Tel: (916)624-3333
E-mail: gmodder@sierracollege.edu
Web Site: www.sierracollege.edu
President/CEO: Dr. Leo Chavez
Admissions: Gail Modder
Financial Aid: Dr. Linda S. Williams
Type: Two-Year College **Sex:** Coed **Affiliation:** California Community College System. **% Accepted:** 100 **Admission Plans:** Early Admission; Open Admission **Application Deadline:** Rolling **Application Fee:** $0.00 **H.S. Requirements:** High school diploma or equivalent not required. For applicants 18 or over: High school diploma required; GED accepted **Costs Per Year:** Application fee: $0. State resident tuition: $1380 full-time, $46 per credit hour part-time. Nonresident tuition: $5790 full-time, $193 per credit hour part-time. Mandatory fees: $46 full-time, $19 per term part-time. Full-time tuition and fees vary according to course load. Part-time tuition and fees vary according to course load. College room and board: $3700. **Scholarships:** Available. **Calendar System:** Semester, Summer session available **Enrollment:** Full-time 4,874, Part-time 13,884 **Faculty:** Full-time 158, Part-time 712 **Student-Faculty Ratio:** 25:1 **% Residing in College-Owned, -Operated, or -Affiliated Housing:** 1 **Regional Accreditation:** Western Association of Colleges and Schools **Credit Hours For Degree:** 60 units, Associates **Intercollegiate Athletics:** Baseball M; Basketball M & W; Football M; Golf M & W; Soccer W; Softball W; Swimming and Diving M & W; Tennis M & W; Volleyball W; Water Polo M & W; Wrestling M

SILICON VALLEY UNIVERSITY
2010 Fortune Dr.
San Jose, CA 95131
Tel: (408)435-8989
Fax: (408)435-8989
E-mail: admission-office@svuca.edu
Web Site: www.svuca.edu
President/CEO: Dr. Jerry Shiao
Admissions: Luna Liu
Type: Comprehensive **Sex:** Coed **% Accepted:** 86 **Admission Plans:** Deferred Admission; Open Admission **Application Deadline:** May 31 **Application Fee:** $75.00 **H.S. Requirements:** High school diploma required; GED accepted **Costs Per Year:** Application fee: $75. Tuition: $7800 full-time, $325 per credit hour part-time. Mandatory fees: $975 full-time, $325 per term part-time. Full-time tuition and fees vary according to course level, course load, and program. Part-time tuition and fees vary according to course level, course load, and program. **Calendar System:** Trimester, Summer session available **Enrollment:** Full-time 206, Graduate full-time 295, Graduate part-time 22 **Faculty:** Full-time 4, Part-time 36 **Student-Faculty Ratio:** 13:1 **Exams:** SAT I and SAT II or ACT. **Final Year or Final Semester Residency Requirement:** No **Credit Hours For Degree:** 128 credit hours, Bachelors **Professional Accreditation:** ACICS.

SIMPSON UNIVERSITY
2211 College View Dr.
Redding, CA 96003-8606
Tel: (530)224-5600; Free: 888-9-SIMPSON
Fax: (530)226-4861

E-mail: admissions@simpsonu.edu
Web Site: www.simpsonu.edu
President/CEO: Dr. Robin K. Dummer
Admissions: Molly McKeever
Financial Aid: Melissa Hudson
Type: Comprehensive **Sex:** Coed **Affiliation:** The Christian and Missionary Alliance. **Scores:** 92% SAT V 400+; 89% SAT M 400+; 46.2% ACT 18-23; 28.2% ACT 24-29 **% Accepted:** 52 **Admission Plans:** Deferred Admission; Early Decision Plan **Application Deadline:** Rolling **Application Fee:** $35.00 **H.S. Requirements:** High school diploma required; GED accepted **Costs Per Year:** Application fee: $35. Comprehensive fee: $33,900 includes full-time tuition ($25,950) and college room and board ($7950). Full-time tuition varies according to course load. Room and board charges vary according to board plan and housing facility. Part-time tuition: $1095 per credit hour. Part-time tuition varies according to course load. **Scholarships:** Available. **Calendar System:** Semester, Summer session available **Enrollment:** Full-time 927, Graduate full-time 84, Graduate part-time 115, Part-time 36 **Faculty:** Full-time 51, Part-time 195 **Student-Faculty Ratio:** 9:1 **Exams:** ACT essay component not used; SAT I or ACT; SAT II; SAT essay component not used. **% Receiving Financial Aid:** 89 **% Residing in College-Owned, -Operated, or -Affiliated Housing:** 39 **Regional Accreditation:** Western Association of Colleges and Schools **Credit Hours For Degree:** 62 credits, Associates; 124 credits, Bachelors **Intercollegiate Athletics:** Baseball M; Basketball M & W; Cross-Country Running M & W; Golf M & W; Soccer M & W; Softball W; Volleyball W; Wrestling M

SKYLINE COLLEGE
3300 College Dr.
San Bruno, CA 94066-1698
Tel: (650)738-4100
E-mail: stats@smccd.net
Web Site: skylinecollege.edu
President/CEO: Dr. Victoria P. Morrow
Admissions: Terry Stats
Financial Aid: Regina Morrison
Type: Two-Year College **Sex:** Coed **Affiliation:** San Mateo County Community College District System. **Admission Plans:** Open Admission **Application Deadline:** Rolling **Application Fee:** $0.00 **H.S. Requirements:** High school diploma or equivalent not required. For applicants under 18, international students: High school diploma required; GED accepted **Scholarships:** Available. **Calendar System:** Semester, Summer session available **Enrollment:** Full-time 2,486, Part-time 5,873 **Faculty:** Full-time 119, Part-time 214 **Student-Faculty Ratio:** 25:1 **Regional Accreditation:** Western Association of Colleges and Schools **Credit Hours For Degree:** 60 credits, Associates **Professional Accreditation:** ACBSP, ARCST, CoARC. **Intercollegiate Athletics:** Baseball M; Basketball M; Cross-Country Running M & W; Soccer M; Softball W; Track and Field M & W; Volleyball W; Wrestling M

SOKA UNIVERSITY OF AMERICA
1 University Dr.
Aliso Viejo, CA 92656
Tel: (949)480-4000; Free: 888-600-SOKA
Fax: (949)480-4001
E-mail: mgrainger@soka.edu
Web Site: www.soka.edu
President/CEO: Danny Habuki
Admissions: Maura Grainger
Financial Aid: Dr. Andrew Woolsey
Type: Comprehensive **Sex:** Coed **Scores:** 97% SAT V 400+; 100% SAT M 400+; 11% ACT 18-23; 56% ACT 24-29 **% Accepted:** 46 **Admission Plans:** Deferred Admission; Early Admission; Early Decision Plan **Application Deadline:** January 15 **Application Fee:** $45.00 **H.S. Requirements:** High school diploma required; GED accepted **Costs Per Year:** Application fee: $45. Comprehensive fee: $42,888 includes full-time tuition ($29,372), mandatory fees ($1704), and college room and board ($11,812). Full-time tuition and fees vary according to class time, course load, and program. Room and board charges vary according to board plan. Part-time tuition: $1224 per credit. Part-time tuition varies according to class time, course load, and program. **Scholarships:** Available. **Calendar System:** Semester, Summer session not available **Enrollment:** Full-time 432, Graduate full-time 12, Part-time 1 **Faculty:** Full-time 46, Part-time 25 **Student-Faculty Ratio:** 8:1 **Exams:** ACT essay component used for admission; ACT essay component used for advising; SAT I or ACT; SAT essay component used for

admission; SAT essay component used for advising; SAT Reasoning. **% Receiving Financial Aid:** 92 **% Residing in College-Owned, -Operated, or -Affiliated Housing:** 99 **Final Year or Final Semester Residency Requirement:** Yes **Regional Accreditation:** Western Association of Colleges and Schools **Credit Hours For Degree:** 120 units, Bachelors **Professional Accreditation:** AALE. **Intercollegiate Athletics:** Cross-Country Running M & W; Golf W; Soccer M & W; Swimming and Diving M & W; Track and Field M & W

SOLANO COMMUNITY COLLEGE
4000 Suisun Valley Rd.
Fairfield, CA 94534
Tel: (707)864-7000
Fax: (707)864-7175
E-mail: barbara.fountain@solano.edu
Web Site: www.solano.edu
President/CEO: Jowel C. Laguerre, PhD
Admissions: Barbara L. Fountain
Type: Two-Year College **Sex:** Coed **Affiliation:** California Community College System. **Admission Plans:** Deferred Admission; Early Admission; Open Admission **Application Deadline:** Rolling **Application Fee:** $0.00 **H.S. Requirements:** High school diploma required; GED accepted **Scholarships:** Available. **Calendar System:** Semester, Summer session available **Faculty:** Full-time 147, Part-time 227 **Student-Faculty Ratio:** 27:1 **Regional Accreditation:** Western Association of Colleges and Schools **Credit Hours For Degree:** 60 credits, Associates **Intercollegiate Athletics:** Baseball M; Basketball M & W; Football M; Softball W; Swimming and Diving M & W; Volleyball W; Water Polo M & W

SONOMA STATE UNIVERSITY
1801 E Cotati Ave.
Rohnert Park, CA 94928-3609
Tel: (707)664-2880
E-mail: natalie.kalogiannis@sonoma.edu
Web Site: www.sonoma.edu
President/CEO: Dr. Ruben Arminana
Admissions: Natalie Kalogiannis
Financial Aid: Susan Gutierrez
Type: Comprehensive **Sex:** Coed **Affiliation:** California State University System. **Scores:** 91% SAT V 400+; 91% SAT M 400+; 56% ACT 18-23; 28% ACT 24-29 **% Accepted:** 77 **Admission Plans:** Early Admission **Application Deadline:** Rolling **Application Fee:** $55.00 **H.S. Requirements:** High school diploma required; GED accepted **Costs Per Year:** Application fee: $55. Area resident tuition: $3174 per year part-time. State resident tuition: $5472 full-time. Nonresident tuition: $16,632 full-time. Mandatory fees: $1858 full-time. Full-time tuition and fees vary according to course load and degree level. Part-time tuition varies according to course load and degree level. College room and board: $12,814. Room and board charges vary according to board plan and housing facility. **Scholarships:** Available. **Calendar System:** Semester, Summer session available **Enrollment:** Full-time 7,382, Graduate full-time 320, Graduate part-time 473, Part-time 1,233 **Faculty:** Full-time 241, Part-time 365 **Student-Faculty Ratio:** 25:1 **Exams:** ACT; ACT essay component not used; SAT I; SAT I and SAT II or ACT; SAT I or ACT; SAT II; SAT essay component not used; SAT Reasoning. **% Receiving Financial Aid:** 55 **% Residing in College-Owned, -Operated, or -Affiliated Housing:** 22 **Regional Accreditation:** Western Association of Colleges and Schools **Credit Hours For Degree:** 120 units, Bachelors **ROTC:** Air Force, Army **Professional Accreditation:** AACSB, ACA, ACEN, NASAD, NASM, NCATE. **Intercollegiate Athletics:** Baseball M; Basketball M & W; Cross-Country Running W; Golf M & W; Soccer M & W; Softball W; Tennis M & W; Track and Field W; Volleyball W; Water Polo W

SOUTH COAST COLLEGE
2011 W Chapman Ave.
Orange, CA 92868
Tel: (714)867-5009; Free: 877-568-6130
Fax: (714)867-5026
Web Site: www.southcoastcollege.com
President/CEO: Jean Gonzalez
Type: Two-Year College **Sex:** Coed **Application Fee:** $99.00 **Professional Accreditation:** ACICS.

SOUTHERN CALIFORNIA INSTITUTE OF ARCHITECTURE
960 E Third St.
Los Angeles, CA 90013
Tel: (213)613-2200
Fax: (213)613-0524
E-mail: admissions@sciarc.edu
Web Site: www.sciarc.edu
President/CEO: Hernan Diaz Alonso
Admissions: Jamie Black
Financial Aid: Marisela De La Torre
Type: Comprehensive **Sex:** Coed **Scores:** 90% SAT V 400+; 100% SAT M 400+; 100% ACT 24-29 **% Accepted:** 73 **Admission Plans:** Deferred Admission **Application Deadline:** January 15 **Application Fee:** $85.00 **H.S. Requirements:** High school diploma required; GED accepted **Costs Per Year:** Application fee: $85. Tuition: $41,800 full-time. Mandatory fees: $1100 full-time. Full-time tuition and fees vary according to course load. **Scholarships:** Available. **Calendar System:** Semester, Summer session available **Enrollment:** Full-time 254; Graduate full-time 237, Graduate part-time 10, Part-time 1 **Faculty:** Full-time 29, Part-time 39 **Student-Faculty Ratio:** 12:1 **Exams:** ACT essay component not used; SAT I or ACT; SAT essay component not used; SAT Reasoning. **% Receiving Financial Aid:** 72 **Final Year or Final Semester Residency Requirement:** No **Regional Accreditation:** Western Association of Colleges and Schools **Credit Hours For Degree:** 63 units, Bachelors **Professional Accreditation:** NAAB.

SOUTHERN CALIFORNIA INSTITUTE OF TECHNOLOGY
525 N Muller St.
Anaheim, CA 92801
Tel: (714)520-5552
E-mail: admissions@scitech.edu
Web Site: www.scitech.edu
President/CEO: Dr. Parviz Shams
Admissions: Sam Rokni
Type: Four-Year College **Sex:** Coed **Scholarships:** Available. **Enrollment:** Full-time 538 **Student-Faculty Ratio:** 21:1 **Exams:** Other. **Final Year or Final Semester Residency Requirement:** No **Credit Hours For Degree:** 124 quarter credit hours, Associates; 180 quarter credit hours, Bachelors **Professional Accreditation:** ACCSC.

SOUTHERN CALIFORNIA SEMINARY
2075 E Madison Ave.
El Cajon, CA 92019
Tel: (619)201-8999; Free: 888-389-7244
Fax: (619)201-8975
E-mail: bill.george@socalsem.edu
Web Site: www.socalsem.edu
President/CEO: Dr. Gary F. Coombs
Admissions: Bill George, III
Type: Comprehensive **Sex:** Coed **Affiliation:** interdenominational. **% Accepted:** 45 **Admission Plans:** Deferred Admission; Early Admission **Application Deadline:** Rolling **Application Fee:** $37.00 **H.S. Requirements:** High school diploma required; GED accepted **Costs Per Year:** Application fee: $37. Tuition: $13,860 full-time, $36 per credit part-time. Mandatory fees: $384 full-time. Full-time tuition and fees vary according to course load, location, program, and reciprocity agreements. Part-time tuition varies according to course load, location, program, and reciprocity agreements. College room only: $6205. **Calendar System:** Trimester, Summer session available **Enrollment:** Full-time 17, Graduate full-time 54, Graduate part-time 121, Part-time 43 **Faculty:** Full-time 11, Part-time 31 **% Residing in College-Owned, -Operated, or -Affiliated Housing:** 7 **Final Year or Final Semester Residency Requirement:** No **Credit Hours For Degree:** 60 units, Associates; 120 units, Bachelors **Professional Accreditation:** TRACS.

SOUTHWESTERN COLLEGE
900 Otay Lakes Rd.
Chula Vista, CA 91910-7299
Tel: (619)421-6700
Web Site: www.swccd.edu
President/CEO: Dr. Raj Chopra
Type: Two-Year College **Sex:** Coed **Affiliation:** California Community College System. **Admission Plans:** Early Admission; Open Admission **Application Deadline:** Rolling **H.S. Requirements:** High school diploma or equivalent not required. For applicants under 18: High school diploma required; GED accepted **Scholarships:** Available. **Calendar System:** Semester, Summer session available **Student-Faculty Ratio:** 22:1 **Regional Accreditation:** Western Association of Colleges and Schools

Credit Hours For Degree: 60 units, Associates **Professional Accreditation:** ACEN, ADA, ARCST. **Intercollegiate Athletics:** Baseball M; Basketball M & W; Cross-Country Running M & W; Football M; Soccer M & W; Softball W; Swimming and Diving M & W; Tennis M & W; Track and Field M & W; Volleyball W; Water Polo M & W

SPARTAN COLLEGE OF AERONAUTICS AND TECHNOLOGY

8911 Aviation Blvd.
Inglewood, CA 90301
Free: 866-451-0818
Fax: (866)451-0818
Web Site: www.spartan.edu
Type: Two-Year College **Sex:** Coed **Admission Plans:** Open Admission **Application Fee:** $100.00 **Calendar System:** Quarter **Student-Faculty Ratio:** 19:1 **Professional Accreditation:** ACCSC, COE.

STANBRIDGE COLLEGE

2041 Business Ctr. Dr.
Irvine, CA 92612
Tel: (949)794-9090
Fax: (949)794-9094
Web Site: www.stanbridge.edu
President/CEO: Yasith Weerasuriya
Type: Two-Year College **Sex:** Coed **% Accepted:** 95 **Professional Accreditation:** ACCSC.

STANFORD UNIVERSITY

Stanford, CA 94305-9991
Tel: (650)723-2300
Fax: (650)725-2846
E-mail: admission@stanford.edu
Web Site: www.stanford.edu
President/CEO: Dr. Marc Tessier-Lavigne
Admissions: Rick Shaw
Type: University **Sex:** Coed **Scores:** 100% SAT V 400+; 100% SAT M 400+; 0.92% ACT 18-23; 11.61% ACT 24-29 **% Accepted:** 5 **Admission Plans:** Deferred Admission; Early Decision Plan **Application Deadline:** January 3 **Application Fee:** $90.00 **H.S. Requirements:** High school diploma required; GED accepted **Costs Per Year:** Application fee: $90. One-time mandatory fee: $609. Comprehensive fee: $61,932 includes full-time tuition ($47,331) and college room and board ($14,601). Room and board charges vary according to board plan. **Scholarships:** Available. **Calendar System:** Quarter, Summer session available **Enrollment:** Full-time 6,999, Graduate full-time 8,779, Graduate part-time 992 **Faculty:** Full-time 1,589, Part-time 26 **Student-Faculty Ratio:** 4:1 **Exams:** ACT essay component not used; SAT I or ACT; SAT II; SAT essay component not used; SAT Reasoning; SAT Subject. **% Receiving Financial Aid:** 49 **% Residing in College-Owned, -Operated, or -Affiliated Housing:** 93 **Final Year or Final Semester Residency Requirement:** No **Regional Accreditation:** Western Association of Colleges and Schools **Credit Hours For Degree:** 180 quarter hours, Bachelors **ROTC:** Air Force, Army, Navy **Professional Accreditation:** AACSB, AALS, ABA, ABET, ACIPE, APA, LCME/AMA, NCATE. **Intercollegiate Athletics:** Archery M & W; Badminton M & W; Baseball M; Basketball M & W; Cheerleading M & W; Crew M & W; Cross-Country Running M & W; Equestrian Sports M & W; Fencing M & W; Field Hockey W; Football M; Golf M & W; Gymnastics M & W; Ice Hockey M; Lacrosse M & W; Racquetball M & W; Rock Climbing M & W; Rowing M & W; Rugby M & W; Sailing M & W; Skiing (Downhill) M & W; Soccer M & W; Softball W; Squash M & W; Swimming and Diving M & W; Tennis M & W; Track and Field M & W; Triathlon M & W; Ultimate Frisbee M & W; Volleyball M & W; Water Polo M & W; Wrestling M

SUM BIBLE COLLEGE & THEOLOGICAL SEMINARY

735 105th Ave.
Oakland, CA 94603
Tel: (510)567-6174; Free: 888-567-6174
Web Site: www.sum.edu
President/CEO: Rev. George Neau
Type: Comprehensive **Sex:** Coed **Affiliation:** interdenominational. **% Accepted:** 59 **Admission Plans:** Deferred Admission **Application Deadline:** Rolling **Application Fee:** $25.00 **H.S. Requirements:** High school diploma required; GED accepted **Calendar System:** Trimester **Enrollment:** Full-time 133, Part-time 6 **Faculty:** Full-time 4, Part-time 18 **Student-Faculty Ratio:** 11:1 **Professional Accreditation:** ABHE.

TAFT COLLEGE

29 Emmons Park Dr.
Taft, CA 93268-2317
Tel: (661)763-7700
Fax: (661)763-7705
E-mail: ncook@taftcollege.edu
Web Site: www.taftcollege.edu
President/CEO: Dr. Dena Maloney
Admissions: Nichole Cook
Financial Aid: Ruthie Welborn
Type: Two-Year College **Sex:** Coed **Affiliation:** California Community College System. **% Accepted:** 100 **Admission Plans:** Open Admission **Application Deadline:** Rolling **Application Fee:** $0.00 **H.S. Requirements:** High school diploma required; GED accepted. For applicants under 18: High school diploma or equivalent not required **Scholarships:** Available. **Calendar System:** Semester, Summer session available **Enrollment:** Full-time 505, Part-time 8,995 **Faculty:** Full-time 37, Part-time 54 **% Residing in College-Owned, -Operated, or -Affiliated Housing:** 6 **Regional Accreditation:** Western Association of Colleges and Schools **Credit Hours For Degree:** 60 units, Associates **Professional Accreditation:** ADA. **Intercollegiate Athletics:** Baseball M; Basketball W; Soccer M; Softball W; Volleyball W

THOMAS AQUINAS COLLEGE

10000 Ojai Rd.
Santa Paula, CA 93060
Tel: (805)525-4417; Free: 800-634-9797
Fax: (805)525-9342
E-mail: admissions@thomasaquinas.edu
Web Site: www.thomasaquinas.edu
President/CEO: Dr. Michael F. McLean
Admissions: Jonathan P. Daly
Financial Aid: Gregory Becher
Type: Four-Year College **Sex:** Coed **Affiliation:** Roman Catholic. **Scores:** 100% SAT V 400+; 100% SAT M 400+; 12% ACT 18-23; 53% ACT 24-29 **% Accepted:** 75 **Application Deadline:** Rolling **Application Fee:** $0.00 **H.S. Requirements:** High school diploma required; GED accepted **Costs Per Year:** Application fee: $0. Comprehensive fee: $32,450 includes full-time tuition ($24,500) and college room and board ($7950). **Scholarships:** Available. **Calendar System:** Semester, Summer session not available **Enrollment:** Full-time 377 **Faculty:** Full-time 32, Part-time 4 **Student-Faculty Ratio:** 11:1 **Exams:** ACT essay component used for admission; SAT I or ACT; SAT essay component used for admission. **% Receiving Financial Aid:** 75 **% Residing in College-Owned, -Operated, or -Affiliated Housing:** 99 **Final Year or Final Semester Residency Requirement:** No **Regional Accreditation:** Western Association of Colleges and Schools **Credit Hours For Degree:** 146 credits, Bachelors **Professional Accreditation:** AALE.

TOURO COLLEGE LOS ANGELES

1317 N Crescent Heights Blvd.
West Hollywood, CA 90046
Tel: (323)822-9700
Web Site: www.touro.edu/losangeles
Type: Four-Year College **Sex:** Coed **Calendar System:** Semester **Regional Accreditation:** Western Association of Colleges and Schools

TOURO UNIVERSITY WORLDWIDE

10601 Calle Lee, Ste. 179
Los Alamitos, CA 90720
Tel: (818)575-6800
Web Site: www.tuw.edu
Type: Comprehensive **Sex:** Coed **Regional Accreditation:** Western Association of Colleges and Schools

TRIDENT UNIVERSITY INTERNATIONAL

5757 Plz. Dr., Ste. 100
Cypress, CA 90630
Tel: (714)816-0366
Fax: (714)816-0367
E-mail: admissions@trident.edu
Web Site: www.trident.edu
President/CEO: Dr. Lucille Sansing
Admissions: Jameela Frierson

Financial Aid: Taisha Azlin
Type: University **Sex:** Coed **Admission Plans:** Open Admission **Application Deadline:** Rolling **H.S. Requirements:** High school diploma required; GED accepted **Costs Per Year:** Tuition: $9000 full-time, $375 per credit hour part-time. **Scholarships:** Available. **Calendar System:** Miscellaneous, Summer session available **Student-Faculty Ratio:** 25:1 **% Receiving Financial Aid:** 7 **Final Year or Final Semester Residency Requirement:** No **Regional Accreditation:** Western Association of Colleges and Schools **Credit Hours For Degree:** 120 credits, Bachelors

UNITED STATES UNIVERSITY

830 Bay Blvd.
Chula Vista, CA 91911
Tel: (619)477-6310; Free: 888-422-3381
Fax: (619)477-7340
Web Site: www.usuniversity.edu
President/CEO: Yoram Neumann, PhD
Type: Comprehensive **Sex:** Coed **Regional Accreditation:** Western Association of Colleges and Schools

UNITEK COLLEGE

4670 Auto Mall Pky.
Fremont, CA 94538
Tel: (510)249-1060
Fax: (510)249-9125
Web Site: www.unitekcollege.edu
President/CEO: Paul Afshar
Type: Two-Year College **Sex:** Coed **Professional Accreditation:** ACCSC.

UNIVERSITY OF ANTELOPE VALLEY

44055 N Sierra Hwy.
Lancaster, CA 93534
Tel: (661)726-1911
Web Site: www.uav.edu
Type: Comprehensive **Sex:** Coed **Professional Accreditation:** ACICS.

UNIVERSITY OF CALIFORNIA, BERKELEY

Berkeley, CA 94720-1500
Tel: (510)642-6000
Fax: (510)642-7333
Web Site: www.berkeley.edu
President/CEO: Dr. Nicholas B. Dirks
Financial Aid: Kathy Bradley
Type: University **Sex:** Coed **Affiliation:** University of California System. **Scores:** 98% SAT V 400+; 101% SAT M 400+; 7% ACT 18-23; 21% ACT 24-29 **% Accepted:** 15 **Admission Plans:** Preferred Admission **Application Fee:** $70.00 **H.S. Requirements:** High school diploma required; GED accepted **Costs Per Year:** Application fee: $70. State resident tuition: $11,220 full-time. Nonresident tuition: $35,928 full-time. Mandatory fees: $2211 full-time. College room and board: $15,422. Room and board charges vary according to board plan and housing facility. **Scholarships:** Available. **Calendar System:** Semester, Summer session available **Enrollment:** Full-time 26,622, Graduate full-time 9,353, Graduate part-time 1,355, Part-time 874 **Faculty:** Full-time 1,623, Part-time 635 **Student-Faculty Ratio:** 17:1 **Exams:** ACT essay component used for admission; ACT essay component used for advising; SAT I or ACT; SAT II; SAT essay component used for admission; SAT essay component used for advising; SAT Reasoning; SAT Subject. **% Receiving Financial Aid:** 49 **% Residing in College-Owned, -Operated, or -Affiliated Housing:** 26 **Regional Accreditation:** Western Association of Colleges and Schools **Credit Hours For Degree:** 120 credits, Bachelors **ROTC:** Air Force, Army, Navy **Professional Accreditation:** AACSB, AALS, ABA, ABET, ACEJMC, ACSP, AND, AOA, APA, ASLA, CAHME, CEPH, CIDA, CSWE, NAAB, SAF. **Intercollegiate Athletics:** Baseball M; Basketball M & W; Crew M & W; Cross-Country Running M & W; Field Hockey W; Football M; Golf M & W; Gymnastics M & W; Lacrosse M & W; Rugby M; Soccer M & W; Softball W; Swimming and Diving M & W; Tennis M & W; Track and Field M & W; Volleyball W; Water Polo M & W

UNIVERSITY OF CALIFORNIA, DAVIS

One Shields Ave.
Davis, CA 95616
Tel: (530)752-1011
Fax: (530)752-6363
E-mail: undergraduateadmissions@ucdavis.edu

Web Site: www.ucdavis.edu
President/CEO: Linda P.B. Katehi
Financial Aid: Deborah G. Agee
Type: University **Sex:** Coed **Affiliation:** University of California System. **Scores:** 98% SAT V 400+; 99% SAT M 400+; 17.55% ACT 18-23; 47.92% ACT 24-29 **% Accepted:** 38 **Admission Plans:** Preferred Admission **Application Deadline:** November 30 **Application Fee:** $70.00 **H.S. Requirements:** High school diploma required; GED accepted **Costs Per Year:** Application fee: $70. State resident tuition: $11,220 full-time. Nonresident tuition: $35,928 full-time. Mandatory fees: $2731 full-time. College room and board: $14,517. Room and board charges vary according to board plan. **Scholarships:** Available. **Calendar System:** Quarter, Summer session available **Enrollment:** Full-time 27,966, Graduate full-time 6,605, Graduate part-time 197, Part-time 418 **Faculty:** Full-time 1,652, Part-time 178 **Student-Faculty Ratio:** 18:1 **Exams:** ACT essay component not used; SAT I or ACT; SAT essay component not used; SAT Reasoning; SAT Subject. **% Receiving Financial Aid:** 61 **% Residing in College-Owned, -Operated, or -Affiliated Housing:** 25 **Regional Accreditation:** Western Association of Colleges and Schools **Credit Hours For Degree:** 180 units, Bachelors **ROTC:** Air Force, Army, Navy **Professional Accreditation:** AACSB, AALS, ABA, ABET, ACIPE, AND, APA, ASLA, AVMA, LCME/AMA, NAACLS. **Intercollegiate Athletics:** Baseball M; Basketball M & W; Cross-Country Running M & W; Field Hockey W; Football M; Golf M & W; Gymnastics W; Lacrosse W; Soccer M & W; Softball W; Swimming and Diving W; Tennis M & W; Track and Field M & W; Volleyball W; Water Polo M & W

UNIVERSITY OF CALIFORNIA, IRVINE

Irvine, CA 92697
Tel: (949)824-5011
E-mail: admissions@uci.edu
Web Site: www.uci.edu
President/CEO: Howard Gillman
Financial Aid: Lindsay Crowell
Type: University **Sex:** Coed **Affiliation:** University of California System. **Scores:** 98% SAT V 400+; 100% SAT M 400+ **% Accepted:** 39 **Application Deadline:** November 30 **Application Fee:** $70.00 **H.S. Requirements:** High school diploma required; GED accepted **Costs Per Year:** Application fee: $70. State resident tuition: $11,220 full-time. Nonresident tuition: $35,928 full-time. Mandatory fees: $3530 full-time. College room and board: $12,947. Room and board charges vary according to board plan and housing facility. **Scholarships:** Available. **Calendar System:** Quarter, Summer session available **Enrollment:** Full-time 24,851, Graduate full-time 5,053, Graduate part-time 527, Part-time 405 **Faculty:** Full-time 1,203, Part-time 307 **Student-Faculty Ratio:** 19:1 **Exams:** ACT essay component used for admission; ACT essay component used for placement; SAT I or ACT; SAT II; SAT essay component used for admission; SAT essay component used for placement; SAT Reasoning; SAT Subject. **% Receiving Financial Aid:** 65 **% Residing in College-Owned, -Operated, or -Affiliated Housing:** 41 **Final Year or Final Semester Residency Requirement:** Yes **Regional Accreditation:** Western Association of Colleges and Schools **Credit Hours For Degree:** 180 units, Bachelors **ROTC:** Air Force, Army **Professional Accreditation:** AACN, AACSB, ABA, ABET, ACSP, APA, LCME/AMA, NAACLS. **Intercollegiate Athletics:** Archery M & W; Badminton M & W; Baseball M; Basketball M & W; Crew M & W; Cross-Country Running M & W; Fencing M & W; Golf M & W; Lacrosse M & W; Rugby M & W; Sailing M & W; Soccer M & W; Table Tennis M & W; Tennis M & W; Track and Field M & W; Ultimate Frisbee M & W; Volleyball M & W; Water Polo M & W; Wrestling M & W

UNIVERSITY OF CALIFORNIA, LOS ANGELES

405 Hilgard Ave.
Los Angeles, CA 90095
Tel: (310)825-4321
E-mail: ugadm@saonet.ucla.edu
Web Site: www.ucla.edu
President/CEO: Dr. Gene D. Block
Admissions: Gary Clark
Financial Aid: Carolyn Turpin
Type: University **Sex:** Coed **Affiliation:** University of California System. **Scores:** 100% SAT V 400+; 100% SAT M 400+; 12.8% ACT 18-23; 29.2% ACT 24-29 **% Accepted:** 17 **Application Deadline:** November 30 **Application Fee:** $70.00 **H.S. Requirements:** High school diploma required; GED accepted **Costs Per Year:** Application fee: $70. State resident tuition: $11,220 full-time. Nonresident tuition: $35,928 full-time. Mandatory fees:

$2031 full-time. College room and board: $13,452. Room and board charges vary according to board plan and housing facility. **Scholarships:** Available. **Calendar System:** Quarter, Summer session available **Enrollment:** Full-time 29,004, Graduate full-time 12,918, Graduate part-time 798, Part-time 581 **Faculty:** Full-time 1,931, Part-time 611 **Student-Faculty Ratio:** 17:1 **Exams:** ACT essay component used for admission; ACT essay component used for placement; SAT I or ACT; SAT essay component used for admission; SAT essay component used for placement; SAT Reasoning; SAT Subject. **% Receiving Financial Aid:** 55 **% Residing in College-Owned, -Operated, or -Affiliated Housing:** 45 **Final Year or Final Semester Residency Requirement:** No **Regional Accreditation:** Western Association of Colleges and Schools **Credit Hours For Degree:** 180 quarter units, Bachelors **ROTC:** Air Force, Army, Navy **Professional Accreditation:** AACN, AACSB, AALS, ABA, ABET, ACSP, ACIPE, ADA, ALA, AND, APA, ASC, CAHME, CEPH, CIDA, CSWE, LCME/AMA, NAAB, NAST. **Intercollegiate Athletics:** Baseball M; Basketball M & W; Crew M; Cross-Country Running M & W; Football M; Golf M & W; Gymnastics W; Soccer M & W; Softball W; Swimming and Diving W; Tennis M & W; Track and Field M & W; Volleyball M & W; Water Polo M & W

UNIVERSITY OF CALIFORNIA, MERCED

5200 N Lake Rd.
Merced, CA 95343
Tel: (209)228-4400
E-mail: admissions@ucmerced.edu
Web Site: www.ucmerced.edu
President/CEO: Dr. Dorothy Leland
Admissions: Ruben Lubers
Financial Aid: Diana M. Ralls

Type: University **Sex:** Coed **Affiliation:** University of California System. **Scores:** 94% SAT V 400+; 96% SAT M 400+ **% Accepted:** 61 **Application Deadline:** November 30 **Application Fee:** $70.00 **H.S. Requirements:** High school diploma required; GED accepted **Costs Per Year:** Application fee: $70. State resident tuition: $11,784 full-time, $2496 per term part-time. Nonresident tuition: $35,808 full-time, $8952 per term part-time. Mandatory fees: $1988 full-time, $1988 per year part-time. Full-time tuition and fees vary according to course load. Part-time tuition and fees vary according to course load. College room and board: $15,646. Room and board charges vary according to board plan. **Scholarships:** Available. **Enrollment:** Full-time 6,164, Graduate full-time 447, Graduate part-time 1, Part-time 73 **Faculty:** Full-time 315, Part-time 58 **Student-Faculty Ratio:** 18:1 **Exams:** ACT essay component used for admission; SAT I or ACT; SAT essay component used for admission; SAT Reasoning; SAT Subject. **% Receiving Financial Aid:** 86 **% Residing in College-Owned, -Operated, or -Affiliated Housing:** 34 **Final Year or Final Semester Residency Requirement:** Yes **Regional Accreditation:** Western Association of Colleges and Schools **Credit Hours For Degree:** 120 units, Bachelors **Intercollegiate Athletics:** Basketball M & W; Cross-Country Running M & W; Golf M & W; Soccer M & W; Volleyball M & W

UNIVERSITY OF CALIFORNIA, RIVERSIDE

900 University Ave.
Riverside, CA 92521-0102
Tel: (951)827-1012
Fax: (951)827-6344
E-mail: discover@ucr.edu
Web Site: www.ucr.edu
President/CEO: Dr. Kim A. Wilcox
Admissions: Emily D. Engelschall
Financial Aid: Jose A. Aguilar

Type: University **Sex:** Coed **Affiliation:** University of California System. **Scores:** 98% SAT V 400+; 98% SAT M 400+; 34% ACT 18-23; 49% ACT 24-29 **% Accepted:** 56 **Application Deadline:** November 30 **Application Fee:** $70.00 **H.S. Requirements:** High school diploma required; GED accepted **Costs Per Year:** Application fee: $70. State resident tuition: $11,220 full-time, $5610 per year part-time. Nonresident tuition: $35,928 full-time, $17,049 per year part-time. Mandatory fees: $2,307 full-time. Full-time tuition and fees vary according to course load. Part-time tuition varies according to course load. College room and board: $15,700. Room and board charges vary according to board plan and housing facility. **Scholarships:** Available. **Calendar System:** Quarter, Summer session available **Enrollment:** Full-time 18,279, Graduate full-time 2,755, Graduate part-time 141, Part-time 329 **Student-Faculty Ratio:** 22:1 **Exams:** ACT essay component used for admission; ACT essay component used for placement; SAT I or ACT; SAT II;

SAT essay component used for admission; SAT essay component used for placement; SAT Reasoning; SAT Subject. **% Receiving Financial Aid:** 78 **% Residing in College-Owned, -Operated, or -Affiliated Housing:** 35 **Final Year or Final Semester Residency Requirement:** Yes **Regional Accreditation:** Western Association of Colleges and Schools **Credit Hours For Degree:** 180 quarter hours, Bachelors **ROTC:** Air Force, Army **Professional Accreditation:** AACSB, ABET. **Intercollegiate Athletics:** Baseball M; Basketball M & W; Cross-Country Running M & W; Golf M; Soccer M & W; Softball W; Tennis M & W; Volleyball W

UNIVERSITY OF CALIFORNIA, SAN DIEGO

9500 Gilman Dr.
La Jolla, CA 92093
Tel: (858)534-2230
E-mail: admissionsreply@ucsd.edu
Web Site: www.ucsd.edu
President/CEO: Dr. Marye Anne Fox
Admissions: Mae Brown
Financial Aid: Vonda Garcia

Type: University **Sex:** Coed **Affiliation:** University of California System. **Scores:** 100% SAT V 400+; 100% SAT M 400+; 11% ACT 18-23; 51% ACT 24-29 **% Accepted:** 38 **Admission Plans:** Preferred Admission **Application Fee:** $60.00 **H.S. Requirements:** High school diploma required; GED accepted **Scholarships:** Available. **Calendar System:** Quarter, Summer session available **Enrollment:** Full-time 22,242, Graduate full-time 5,519, Graduate part-time 99, Part-time 434 **Faculty:** Full-time 1,001, Part-time 212 **Student-Faculty Ratio:** 19:1 **Exams:** ACT essay component used for admission; Other; SAT I or ACT; SAT essay component used for admission; SAT essay component used for placement; SAT Reasoning; SAT Subject. **% Receiving Financial Aid:** 56 **% Residing in College-Owned, -Operated, or -Affiliated Housing:** 43 **Regional Accreditation:** Western Association of Colleges and Schools **Credit Hours For Degree:** 180 credit hours, Bachelors **Professional Accreditation:** AACSB, ABET, ACPE, APA, ASHA, LCME/AMA. **Intercollegiate Athletics:** Baseball M; Basketball M & W; Crew M & W; Cross-Country Running M & W; Fencing M & W; Golf M; Soccer M & W; Softball W; Swimming and Diving M & W; Tennis M & W; Track and Field M & W; Volleyball M & W; Water Polo M & W

UNIVERSITY OF CALIFORNIA, SANTA BARBARA

1210 Cheadle Hall
Santa Barbara, CA 93106-2014
Tel: (805)893-8000
E-mail: admissions@sa.ucsb.edu
Web Site: www.ucsb.edu
President/CEO: Dr. Henry T. Yang
Financial Aid: Mike Miller

Type: University **Sex:** Coed **Affiliation:** University of California System. **Scores:** 100% SAT V 400+; 100% SAT M 400+; 19% ACT 18-23; 45% ACT 24-29 **% Accepted:** 33 **Application Deadline:** November 30 **Application Fee:** $70.00 **H.S. Requirements:** High school diploma required; GED accepted **Costs Per Year:** Application fee: $70. State resident tuition: $11,220 full-time. Nonresident tuition: $36,948 full-time. Mandatory fees: $2748 full-time. College room and board: $14,192. Room and board charges vary according to board plan and housing facility. **Scholarships:** Available. **Calendar System:** Quarter, Summer session available **Enrollment:** Full-time 20,243, Graduate full-time 2,886, Graduate part-time 4, Part-time 364 **Student-Faculty Ratio:** 18:1 **Exams:** ACT essay component used for admission; SAT I or ACT; SAT II; SAT essay component used for admission; SAT Reasoning; SAT Subject. **% Receiving Financial Aid:** 59 **% Residing in College-Owned, -Operated, or -Affiliated Housing:** 39 **Final Year or Final Semester Residency Requirement:** No **Regional Accreditation:** Western Association of Colleges and Schools **Credit Hours For Degree:** 180 quarter units, Bachelors **ROTC:** Air Force, Army **Professional Accreditation:** ABET, APA, NASD. **Intercollegiate Athletics:** Baseball M; Basketball M & W; Bowling M & W; Crew M & W; Cross-Country Running M & W; Equestrian Sports M & W; Fencing M & W; Field Hockey W; Golf M; Gymnastics M & W; Lacrosse M & W; Rugby M; Sailing M & W; Skiing (Downhill) M & W; Soccer M & W; Softball W; Swimming and Diving M & W; Tennis M & W; Track and Field M & W; Ultimate Frisbee M & W; Volleyball M & W; Water Polo M & W

UNIVERSITY OF CALIFORNIA, SANTA CRUZ

1156 High St.
Santa Cruz, CA 95064

Tel: (831)459-0111
Fax: (831)459-4452
E-mail: admissions@ucsc.edu
Web Site: www.ucsc.edu
President/CEO: George Blumenthal
Admissions: Michael McCawley
Financial Aid: John Patrick Register
Type: University **Sex:** Coed **Affiliation:** University of California System. **Scores:** 99% SAT V 400+; 99% SAT M 400+; 25% ACT 18-23; 52% ACT 24-29 **% Accepted:** 51 **Admission Plans:** Preferred Admission **Application Deadline:** November 30 **Application Fee:** $70.00 **H.S. Requirements:** High school diploma required; GED accepted **Costs Per Year:** Application fee: $70. State resident tuition: $12,240 full-time. Nonresident tuition: $36,948 full-time. Mandatory fees: $1241 full-time. College room and board: $15,123. Room and board charges vary according to board plan and housing facility. **Scholarships:** Available. **Calendar System:** Quarter, Summer session available **Enrollment:** Full-time 15,823, Graduate full-time 1,568, Graduate part-time 69, Part-time 408 **Exams:** ACT essay component used for admission; ACT essay component used for advising; ACT essay component used for placement; SAT I or ACT; SAT II; SAT essay component used for admission; SAT essay component used for advising; SAT essay component used for placement; SAT Reasoning. **% Receiving Financial Aid:** 66 **% Residing in College-Owned, -Operated, or -Affiliated Housing:** 98 **Final Year or Final Semester Residency Requirement:** No **Regional Accreditation:** Western Association of Colleges and Schools **Credit Hours For Degree:** 180 credits, Bachelors **ROTC:** Air Force, Army, Navy **Professional Accreditation:** ABET, APA. **Intercollegiate Athletics:** Badminton M & W; Baseball M & W; Basketball M & W; Cheerleading M & W; Cross-Country Running M & W; Equestrian Sports M & W; Fencing M & W; Golf W; Lacrosse M & W; Racquetball M & W; Rowing M & W; Rugby M & W; Sailing M & W; Soccer M & W; Softball W; Swimming and Diving M & W; Table Tennis M & W; Tennis M & W; Track and Field M & W; Triathlon M & W; Ultimate Frisbee M & W; Volleyball M & W; Water Polo M & W

UNIVERSITY OF LA VERNE

1950 Third St.
La Verne, CA 91750-4443
Tel: (909)593-3511; Free: 800-876-4858
Fax: (909)593-0965
E-mail: admissions@ulv.edu
Web Site: www.laverne.edu
President/CEO: Dr. Devorah Lieberman
Admissions: Erasmo Fuentes
Financial Aid: Diane A. Anchundia
Type: University **Sex:** Coed **Scores:** 99% SAT V 400+; 98% SAT M 400+; 58% ACT 18-23; 34% ACT 24-29 **% Accepted:** 47 **Admission Plans:** Deferred Admission **Application Deadline:** February 1 **Application Fee:** $50.00 **H.S. Requirements:** High school diploma required; GED accepted **Costs Per Year:** Application fee: $50. Comprehensive fee: $51,070 includes full-time tuition ($37,100), mandatory fees ($1460), and college room and board ($12,510). College room only: $6580. Full-time tuition and fees vary according to location. Room and board charges vary according to board plan and housing facility. Part-time tuition: $1096 per semester hour. Part-time tuition varies according to location. **Scholarships:** Available. **Calendar System:** 4-1-4, Summer session available **Enrollment:** Full-time 2,775, Graduate full-time 1,192, Graduate part-time 827, Part-time 89 **Faculty:** Full-time 233, Part-time 245 **Student-Faculty Ratio:** 13:1 **Exams:** SAT I or ACT; SAT Reasoning; SAT Subject. **% Receiving Financial Aid:** 83 **% Residing in College-Owned, -Operated, or -Affiliated Housing:** 31 **Final Year or Final Semester Residency Requirement:** Yes **Regional Accreditation:** Western Association of Colleges and Schools **Credit Hours For Degree:** 128 semester hours, Bachelors **ROTC:** Army **Professional Accreditation:** ABA, APA, NASPAA, NCATE. **Intercollegiate Athletics:** Baseball M; Basketball M & W; Cross-Country Running M & W; Football M; Golf M; Soccer M & W; Softball W; Swimming and Diving M & W; Tennis M & W; Track and Field M & W; Volleyball W; Water Polo M & W

UNIVERSITY OF THE PACIFIC

3601 Pacific Ave.
Stockton, CA 95211-0197
Tel: (209)946-2344
Fax: (209)946-2413
E-mail: admissions@pacific.edu
Web Site: www.pacific.edu

President/CEO: Dr. Pamela A. Eibeck
Admissions: Rich Toledo
Financial Aid: Lynn Fox
Type: University **Sex:** Coed **Scores:** 98% SAT V 400+; 98% SAT M 400+; 29.46% ACT 18-23; 44.96% ACT 24-29 **% Accepted:** 65 **Admission Plans:** Early Decision Plan **Application Deadline:** January 15 **Application Fee:** $35.00 **H.S. Requirements:** High school diploma required; GED accepted **Costs Per Year:** Application fee: $35. Comprehensive fee: $55,792 includes full-time tuition ($42,414), mandatory fees ($520), and college room and board ($12,858). Room and board charges vary according to board plan and housing facility. Part-time tuition: $1463 per credit hour. Part-time tuition varies according to course load. **Scholarships:** Available. **Calendar System:** Semester, Summer session available **Enrollment:** Full-time 3,636, Graduate full-time 1,901, Graduate part-time 645, Part-time 99 **Faculty:** Full-time 429, Part-time 339 **Student-Faculty Ratio:** 13:1 **Exams:** SAT I and SAT II or ACT; SAT I or ACT; SAT Reasoning. **% Receiving Financial Aid:** 69 **% Residing in College-Owned, -Operated, or -Affiliated Housing:** 46 **Regional Accreditation:** Western Association of Colleges and Schools **ROTC:** Air Force **Professional Accreditation:** AACSB, AALS, ABA, ABET, ACPE, ADA, APTA, ASHA, NASAD, NASM, NCATE. **Intercollegiate Athletics:** Baseball M; Basketball M & W; Cross-Country Running W; Field Hockey W; Golf M; Soccer W; Softball W; Swimming and Diving M & W; Tennis M & W; Volleyball M & W; Water Polo M & W

UNIVERSITY OF PHOENIX–BAY AREA CAMPUS

3590 N First St.
San Jose, CA 95134-1805
Tel: (925)416-4100; Free: 866-766-0766
Web Site: www.phoenix.edu
President/CEO: Timothy P. Slottow
Admissions: Marc Booker
Type: Comprehensive **Sex:** Coed **Admission Plans:** Deferred Admission; Open Admission **Application Deadline:** Rolling **Application Fee:** $0.00 **H.S. Requirements:** High school diploma required; GED accepted **Scholarships:** Available. **Calendar System:** Continuous, Summer session not available **Enrollment:** Full-time 1,676 **Faculty:** Full-time 29, Part-time 289 **Regional Accreditation:** North Central Association of Colleges and Schools **Credit Hours For Degree:** 60 credits, Associates; 120 credits, Bachelors

UNIVERSITY OF PHOENIX–CENTRAL VALLEY CAMPUS

45 River Park Pl. W
Ste. 101
Fresno, CA 93720-1552
Free: 866-766-0766
Web Site: www.phoenix.edu
President/CEO: Timothy P. Slottow
Admissions: Marc Booker
Type: Comprehensive **Sex:** Coed **Admission Plans:** Deferred Admission; Open Admission **Application Deadline:** Rolling **Application Fee:** $0.00 **H.S. Requirements:** High school diploma required; GED accepted **Scholarships:** Available. **Enrollment:** Full-time 1,928 **Faculty:** Full-time 31, Part-time 241 **Regional Accreditation:** North Central Association of Colleges and Schools **Credit Hours For Degree:** 60 credits, Associates; 120 credits, Bachelors **Professional Accreditation:** ACBSP.

UNIVERSITY OF PHOENIX–SACRAMENTO VALLEY CAMPUS

2860 Gateway Oaks Dr.
Ste. 200
Sacramento, CA 95833-4334
Tel: (916)923-2107; Free: 866-766-0766
Fax: (916)923-3914
Web Site: www.phoenix.edu
President/CEO: Timothy P. Slottow
Admissions: Marc Booker
Type: Comprehensive **Sex:** Coed **Admission Plans:** Deferred Admission; Open Admission **Application Deadline:** Rolling **Application Fee:** $0.00 **H.S. Requirements:** High school diploma required; GED accepted **Scholarships:** Available. **Calendar System:** Continuous, Summer session not available **Enrollment:** Full-time 3,162 **Faculty:** Full-time 49, Part-time 469 **Regional Accreditation:** North Central Association of Colleges and Schools **Credit Hours For Degree:** 60 credits, Associates; 120 credits, Bachelors **Professional Accreditation:** ACBSP.

UNIVERSITY OF PHOENIX–SAN DIEGO CAMPUS

9645 Granite Ridge Dr.
San Diego, CA 92123
Tel: (800)473-4346; Free: 866-766-0766
Fax: (858)576-0032
Web Site: www.phoenix.edu
President/CEO: Timothy P. Slottow
Admissions: Marc Booker

Type: Comprehensive **Sex:** Coed **Admission Plans:** Deferred Admission; Open Admission **Application Deadline:** Rolling **Application Fee:** $0.00 **H.S. Requirements:** High school diploma required; GED accepted **Scholarships:** Available. **Calendar System:** Continuous, Summer session not available **Enrollment:** Full-time 2,500 **Faculty:** Full-time 30, Part-time 369 **Regional Accreditation:** North Central Association of Colleges and Schools **Credit Hours For Degree:** 60 credits, Associates; 120 credits, Bachelors **Professional Accreditation:** ACBSP.

UNIVERSITY OF PHOENIX–SOUTHERN CALIFORNIA CAMPUS

3090 Bristol St.
Costa Mesa, CA 92626
Tel: (800)GO-TO-UOP; Free: 866-766-0766
Web Site: www.phoenix.edu
President/CEO: Timothy P. Slottow
Admissions: Marc Booker

Type: Comprehensive **Sex:** Coed **Admission Plans:** Deferred Admission; Open Admission **Application Deadline:** Rolling **Application Fee:** $0.00 **H.S. Requirements:** High school diploma required; GED accepted **Scholarships:** Available. **Calendar System:** Continuous, Summer session not available **Enrollment:** Full-time 9,196 **Faculty:** Full-time 64, Part-time 1,276 **Regional Accreditation:** North Central Association of Colleges and Schools **Credit Hours For Degree:** 60 credits, Associates; 120 credits, Bachelors **Professional Accreditation:** ACBSP.

UNIVERSITY OF REDLANDS

1200 E Colton Ave.
Redlands, CA 92373-0999
Tel: (909)793-2121; Free: 800-455-5064
Fax: (909)335-4089
E-mail: belinda_sandoval@redlands.edu
Web Site: www.redlands.edu
President/CEO: Dr. Ralph W. Kuncl
Admissions: Belinda Sandoval Zazueta
Financial Aid: Alisha Aguilar

Type: Comprehensive **Sex:** Coed **Scores:** 99% SAT V 400+; 99% SAT M 400+; 41.95% ACT 18-23; 47.94% ACT 24-29 **% Accepted:** 68 **Admission Plans:** Deferred Admission; Early Decision Plan **Application Deadline:** January 15 **Application Fee:** $30.00 **H.S. Requirements:** High school diploma required; GED accepted **Costs Per Year:** Application fee: $30. One-time mandatory fee: $150. Comprehensive fee: $57,990 includes full-time tuition ($44,550), mandatory fees ($350), and college room and board ($13,090). Room and board charges vary according to board plan and housing facility. Part-time tuition: $1393 per credit hour. Part-time mandatory fees: $116 per year. Part-time tuition and fees vary according to course load. **Scholarships:** Available. **Calendar System:** Miscellaneous, Summer session not available **Enrollment:** Full-time 2,709, Graduate full-time 1,470, Graduate part-time 252, Part-time 784 **Exams:** ACT essay component used for placement; SAT I or ACT; SAT essay component used for placement; SAT Reasoning. **Final Year or Final Semester Residency Requirement:** Yes **Regional Accreditation:** Western Association of Colleges and Schools **Credit Hours For Degree:** 132 units, Bachelors **ROTC:** Air Force, Army **Professional Accreditation:** ASHA, NASM. **Intercollegiate Athletics:** Baseball M; Basketball M & W; Cheerleading M & W; Cross-Country Running M & W; Football M; Golf M & W; Lacrosse W; Soccer M & W; Softball W; Swimming and Diving M & W; Tennis M & W; Track and Field M & W; Volleyball W; Water Polo M & W

UNIVERSITY OF SAN DIEGO

5998 Alcala Park
San Diego, CA 92110-2492
Tel: (619)260-4600; Free: 800-248-4873
E-mail: admissions@sandiego.edu
Web Site: www.sandiego.edu
President/CEO: Dr. James T. Harris
Admissions: Minh-Ha Hoang

Financial Aid: Judith Lewis Logue

Type: University **Sex:** Coed **Affiliation:** Roman Catholic. **Scores:** 100% SAT V 400+; 100% SAT M 400+; 10% ACT 18-23; 60% ACT 24-29 **% Accepted:** 52 **Admission Plans:** Deferred Admission **Application Deadline:** December 15 **Application Fee:** $55.00 **H.S. Requirements:** High school diploma required; GED accepted **Costs Per Year:** Application fee: $55. Comprehensive fee: $56,628 includes full-time tuition ($44,000), mandatory fees ($586), and college room and board ($12,042). Room and board charges vary according to board plan and housing facility. Part-time tuition: $1515 per unit. Part-time tuition varies according to course load. **Scholarships:** Available. **Calendar System:** 4-1-4, Summer session available **Enrollment:** Full-time 5,441, Graduate full-time 1,543, Graduate part-time 1,061, Part-time 206 **Faculty:** Full-time 427, Part-time 436 **Student-Faculty Ratio:** 15:1 **Exams:** ACT essay component used for advising; ACT essay component used for placement; SAT I or ACT; SAT essay component used for advising; SAT essay component used for placement; SAT Reasoning. **% Receiving Financial Aid:** 53 **% Residing in College-Owned, -Operated, or -Affiliated Housing:** 45 **Final Year or Final Semester Residency Requirement:** Yes **Regional Accreditation:** Western Association of Colleges and Schools **Credit Hours For Degree:** 124 units, Bachelors **ROTC:** Air Force, Army, Navy **Professional Accreditation:** AACN, AACSB, AALS, AAMFT, ABA, ABET, ACA, APA, NCATE. **Intercollegiate Athletics:** Baseball M; Basketball M & W; Crew M & W; Cross-Country Running M & W; Equestrian Sports M & W; Football M; Golf M; Lacrosse M & W; Rock Climbing M & W; Rugby M; Soccer M & W; Softball W; Swimming and Diving M & W; Tennis M & W; Track and Field W; Ultimate Frisbee M & W; Volleyball M & W

UNIVERSITY OF SAN FRANCISCO

2130 Fulton St.
San Francisco, CA 94117-1080
Tel: (415)422-5555; Free: 800-CALL-USF
Fax: (415)422-2217
E-mail: admissions@usfca.edu
Web Site: www.usfca.edu
President/CEO: Rev. Paul J. Fitzgerald, SJ
Admissions: Michael Hughes
Financial Aid: Susan Murphy

Type: University **Sex:** Coed **Affiliation:** Roman Catholic (Jesuit). **Scores:** 98% SAT V 400+; 100% SAT M 400+; 24% ACT 18-23; 59% ACT 24-29 **% Accepted:** 64 **Admission Plans:** Deferred Admission; Early Action; Early Admission; Early Decision Plan **Application Deadline:** January 15 **Application Fee:** $65.00 **H.S. Requirements:** High school diploma required; GED accepted **Costs Per Year:** Application fee: $65. Comprehensive fee: $58,484 includes full-time tuition ($44,040), mandatory fees ($454), and college room and board ($13,990). College room only: $9400. Full-time tuition and fees vary according to course load, degree level, location, program, and reciprocity agreements. Room and board charges vary according to board plan and housing facility. Part-time tuition: $1565 per credit. Part-time tuition varies according to course load, degree level, location, program, and reciprocity agreements. **Scholarships:** Available. **Calendar System:** 4-1-4, Summer session available **Enrollment:** Full-time 6,448, Graduate full-time 3,316, Graduate part-time 730, Part-time 334 **Faculty:** Full-time 497, Part-time 748 **Student-Faculty Ratio:** 14:1 **Exams:** ACT essay component used for placement; Other; SAT I or ACT; SAT essay component used for placement; SAT Reasoning. **% Receiving Financial Aid:** 54 **% Residing in College-Owned, -Operated, or -Affiliated Housing:** 35 **Final Year or Final Semester Residency Requirement:** No **Regional Accreditation:** Western Association of Colleges and Schools **Credit Hours For Degree:** 128 units, Bachelors **ROTC:** Air Force, Army **Professional Accreditation:** AACN, AACSB, AALS, ABA, NASPAA. **Intercollegiate Athletics:** Baseball M; Basketball M & W; Cross-Country Running M & W; Golf M & W; Soccer M & W; Softball M & W; Tennis M & W; Track and Field M & W; Volleyball M & W

UNIVERSITY OF SOUTHERN CALIFORNIA

University Park Campus
Los Angeles, CA 90089
Tel: (213)740-2311
Fax: (213)740-6364
E-mail: admitusc@usc.edu
Web Site: www.usc.edu
President/CEO: C. L. Max Nikias
Admissions: Timothy Brunold
Financial Aid: Thomas McWhorter

Type: University **Sex:** Coed **Scores:** 100% SAT V 400+; 100% SAT M 400+;

3.5% ACT 18-23; 21.1% ACT 24-29 **% Accepted:** 18 **Admission Plans:** Deferred Admission **Application Deadline:** January 15 **Application Fee:** $80.00 **H.S. Requirements:** High school diploma required; GED not accepted. For Resident Honors Program (students completing both their high school diplomas and freshman years of college concurrently): High school diploma or equivalent not required **Costs Per Year:** Application fee: $80. One-time mandatory fee: $350. Comprehensive fee: $64,065 includes full-time tuition ($49,464), mandatory fees ($746), and college room and board ($13,855). College room only: $8355. Full-time tuition and fees vary according to program. Room and board charges vary according to board plan and housing facility. Part-time tuition: $1666 per unit. Part-time tuition varies according to course load and program. **Scholarships:** Available. **Calendar System:** Semester, Summer session available **Enrollment:** Full-time 18,208, Graduate full-time 16,030, Graduate part-time 8,561, Part-time 602 **Faculty:** Full-time 1,981, Part-time 1,365 **Student-Faculty Ratio:** 9:1 **Exams:** ACT essay component used as validity check; ACT essay component used for admission; ACT essay component used for advising; SAT I or ACT; SAT essay component used as validity check; SAT essay component used for admission; SAT essay component used for advising; SAT Reasoning; SAT Subject. **% Receiving Financial Aid:** 39 **% Residing in College-Owned, -Operated, or -Affiliated Housing:** 33 **Final Year or Final Semester Residency Requirement:** No **Regional Accreditation:** Western Association of Colleges and Schools **Credit Hours For Degree:** 128 units, Bachelors **ROTC:** Air Force, Army, Navy **Professional Accreditation:** AACN, AACSB, AALS, AANA, ABA, ABET, ACEJMC, ACPE, ACSP, ADA, AND, AOTA, APA, APTA, CAHME, CEPH, CSWE, LCME/AMA, NAAB, NASM, NASPAA. **Intercollegiate Athletics:** Archery M & W; Badminton M & W; Baseball M; Basketball M & W; Cheerleading M & W; Crew M & W; Cross-Country Running M & W; Equestrian Sports W; Fencing W; Field Hockey W; Football M; Golf M & W; Gymnastics W; Ice Hockey M & W; Lacrosse M & W; Racquetball M & W; Rock Climbing M & W; Rugby M & W; Sailing W; Skiing (Downhill) M & W; Soccer M & W; Softball W; Squash M & W; Swimming and Diving M & W; Tennis M & W; Track and Field M & W; Ultimate Frisbee M & W; Volleyball M & W; Water Polo M & W

UNIVERSITY OF THE WEST

1409 N Walnut Grove Ave.
Rosemead, CA 91770
Tel: (626)571-8811
Fax: (626)571-1413
E-mail: graceh@uwest.edu
Web Site: www.uwest.edu
President/CEO: Dr. C.S. Wu
Admissions: Grace Hsiao
Financial Aid: Jamie Johnston

Type: Comprehensive **Sex:** Coed **% Accepted:** 85 **Admission Plans:** Deferred Admission **Application Deadline:** June 15 **Application Fee:** $50.00 **H.S. Requirements:** High school diploma required; GED accepted **Scholarships:** Available. **Calendar System:** Semester, Summer session available **Enrollment:** Full-time 127, Graduate full-time 178, Graduate part-time 42, Part-time 15 **Faculty:** Full-time 18, Part-time 41 **Student-Faculty Ratio:** 10:1 **% Receiving Financial Aid:** 25 **% Residing in College-Owned, -Operated, or -Affiliated Housing:** 35 **Final Year or Final Semester Residency Requirement:** Yes **Regional Accreditation:** Western Association of Colleges and Schools **Credit Hours For Degree:** 120 units, Bachelors

VALLEY COLLEGE OF MEDICAL CAREERS

8399 Topanga Canyon Blvd.
Ste. 200
West Hills, CA 91304
Tel: (818)883-9002
Web Site: www.vcmc.edu
Type: Two-Year College **Sex:** Coed **Professional Accreditation:** ABHES.

VANGUARD UNIVERSITY OF SOUTHERN CALIFORNIA

55 Fair Dr.
Costa Mesa, CA 92626-9601
Tel: (714)556-3610; Free: 800-722-6279
Fax: (714)966-5460
E-mail: admissions@vanguard.edu
Web Site: www.vanguard.edu
President/CEO: Dr. Michael Beals, PhD
Admissions: Kristi Pruett

Type: Comprehensive **Sex:** Coed **Affiliation:** Assemblies of God. **Scores:** 87% SAT V 400+; 84% SAT M 400+; 47% ACT 18-23; 21% ACT 24-29 **% Accepted:** 58 **Admission Plans:** Deferred Admission; Early Admission; Early Decision Plan; Preferred Admission **Application Deadline:** August 1 **Application Fee:** $45.00 **H.S. Requirements:** High school diploma required; GED accepted **Costs Per Year:** Application fee: $45. Comprehensive fee: $39,800 includes full-time tuition ($29,980), mandatory fees ($70), and college room and board ($9750). College room only: $5200. Full-time tuition and fees vary according to course load. Room and board charges vary according to board plan and housing facility. Part-time tuition: $1250 per credit hour. Part-time tuition varies according to course load. **Scholarships:** Available. **Calendar System:** Semester, Summer session available **Enrollment:** Full-time 1,482, Graduate full-time 92, Graduate part-time 211, Part-time 399 **Faculty:** Full-time 60, Part-time 183 **Student-Faculty Ratio:** 15:1 **Exams:** ACT; SAT I; SAT I and SAT II or ACT; SAT I or ACT; SAT II; SAT essay component used for advising; SAT Reasoning. **% Receiving Financial Aid:** 85 **% Residing in College-Owned, -Operated, or -Affiliated Housing:** 47 **Final Year or Final Semester Residency Requirement:** Yes **Regional Accreditation:** Western Association of Colleges and Schools **Credit Hours For Degree:** 60 credits, Associates; 124 credits, Bachelors **ROTC:** Air Force **Professional Accreditation:** AACN, JRCAT. **Intercollegiate Athletics:** Baseball M; Basketball M & W; Cross-Country Running M & W; Soccer M & W; Softball W; Track and Field M & W; Volleyball W

VENTURA COLLEGE

4667 Telegraph Rd.
Ventura, CA 93003-3899
Tel: (805)654-6400
Fax: (805)654-6466
E-mail: sbricker@vcccd.net
Web Site: www.venturacollege.edu
President/CEO: Dr. Robin Calote
Admissions: Susan Bricker

Type: Two-Year College **Sex:** Coed **Affiliation:** California Community College System. **Admission Plans:** Open Admission **Application Deadline:** Rolling **Application Fee:** $0.00 **H.S. Requirements:** High school diploma required; GED accepted **Scholarships:** Available. **Calendar System:** Semester, Summer session available **Faculty:** Full-time 136, Part-time 386 **Student-Faculty Ratio:** 26:1 **Regional Accreditation:** Western Association of Colleges and Schools **Credit Hours For Degree:** 60 semester hours, Associates **Intercollegiate Athletics:** Baseball M; Basketball M & W; Cheerleading M & W; Football M; Golf M; Soccer W; Softball W; Swimming and Diving M & W; Tennis M & W; Track and Field M & W; Volleyball W; Water Polo M & W

VICTOR VALLEY COLLEGE

18422 Bear Valley Rd.
Victorville, CA 92395
Tel: (760)245-4271
Fax: (760)245-9745
E-mail: moong@vvc.edu
Web Site: www.vvc.edu
President/CEO: Roger W. Wagner
Admissions: Greta Moon
Financial Aid: Maria Gonzalez

Type: Two-Year College **Sex:** Coed **Affiliation:** California Community College System. **Admission Plans:** Open Admission **Application Deadline:** Rolling **H.S. Requirements:** High school diploma or equivalent not required. For applicants under 18: High school diploma required; GED accepted **Costs Per Year:** State resident tuition: $1104 full-time, $46 per credit part-time. Nonresident tuition: $5904 full-time, $200 per credit part-time. Mandatory fees: $10 full-time. **Scholarships:** Available. **Calendar System:** Semester, Summer session available **Student-Faculty Ratio:** 26:1 **Regional Accreditation:** Western Association of Colleges and Schools **Credit Hours For Degree:** 60 units, Associates **Professional Accreditation:** CoARC. **Intercollegiate Athletics:** Baseball M; Basketball M & W; Cross-Country Running M & W; Football M; Golf M; Soccer M & W; Softball W; Tennis M & W; Track and Field M & W; Volleyball W; Wrestling M

WEST COAST ULTRASOUND INSTITUTE

291 S La Cienega Blvd.
Ste. 500
Beverly Hills, CA 90211

Tel: (310)289-5123
Web Site: wcui.edu
Type: Two-Year College **Sex:** Coed **Calendar System:** Quarter **Professional Accreditation:** ACCSC.

WEST COAST UNIVERSITY (ANAHEIM)
1477 S Manchester Ave.
Anaheim, CA 92802
Tel: (714)782-1700
Web Site: westcoastuniversity.edu
Type: Four-Year College **Sex:** Coed **Costs Per Year:** Tuition: $16,550 full-time. Mandatory fees: $75 full-time. Full-time tuition and fees vary according to course load and program. **Calendar System:** Semester **Regional Accreditation:** Western Association of Colleges and Schools

WEST COAST UNIVERSITY (NORTH HOLLYWOOD)
12215 Victory Blvd.
North Hollywood, CA 91606
Tel: (323)315-5207; Free: 866-508-2684
E-mail: info@katz.wcula.edu
Web Site: www.westcoastuniversity.edu
President/CEO: Barry T. Ryan, PhD
Admissions: Roger A. Miller
Type: Comprehensive **Sex:** Coed **% Accepted:** 83 **Costs Per Year:** Tuition: $16,550 full-time. Mandatory fees: $75 full-time. Full-time tuition and fees vary according to course load and program. **Calendar System:** Miscellaneous **Regional Accreditation:** Western Association of Colleges and Schools **Professional Accreditation:** AACN, ACICS.

WEST COAST UNIVERSITY (ONTARIO)
2855 E Guasti Rd.
Ontario, CA 91761
Tel: (909)467-6100
Web Site: westcoastuniversity.edu
Type: Four-Year College **Sex:** Coed **Costs Per Year:** Tuition: $16,550 full-time. Mandatory fees: $75 full-time, $1836 per credit part-time. Full-time tuition and fees vary according to course load and program. Part-time fees vary according to course load and program. **Calendar System:** Semester **Regional Accreditation:** Western Association of Colleges and Schools

WEST HILLS COMMUNITY COLLEGE
300 Cherry Ln.
Coalinga, CA 93210-1399
Tel: (559)934-2000; Free: 800-266-1114
Fax: (559)934-1511
E-mail: sandradagnino@westhillscollege.com
Web Site: www.westhillscollege.com
President/CEO: Willard Lewallen
Admissions: Sandra Dagnino
Type: Two-Year College **Sex:** Coed **Affiliation:** California Community College System. **Admission Plans:** Early Admission; Open Admission; Preferred Admission **Application Deadline:** Rolling **Application Fee:** $0.00 **H.S. Requirements:** High school diploma or equivalent not required **Scholarships:** Available. **Calendar System:** Semester, Summer session available **Student-Faculty Ratio:** 24:1 **Regional Accreditation:** Western Association of Colleges and Schools **Credit Hours For Degree:** 60 units, Associates **Intercollegiate Athletics:** Baseball M; Basketball M; Equestrian Sports M & W; Football M; Softball W; Tennis W; Volleyball W

WEST HILLS COMMUNITY COLLEGE–LEMOORE
555 College Ave.
Lemoore, CA 93245
Tel: (559)925-3000
Web Site: www.westhillscollege.com
Type: Two-Year College **Sex:** Coed **Regional Accreditation:** Western Association of Colleges and Schools

WEST LOS ANGELES COLLEGE
9000 Overland Ave.
Culver City, CA 90230-3519
Tel: (310)287-4200
Fax: (310)841-0396
Web Site: www.lacolleges.net
President/CEO: Rosemarie Joyce

Admissions: Len Isaksen
Financial Aid: Marsiol Velazquez
Type: Two-Year College **Sex:** Coed **Affiliation:** Los Angeles Community College District System. **Admission Plans:** Early Admission; Open Admission **Application Deadline:** August 16 **H.S. Requirements:** High school diploma or equivalent not required **Scholarships:** Available. **Calendar System:** Semester, Summer session available **Regional Accreditation:** Western Association of Colleges and Schools **Credit Hours For Degree:** 60 units, Associates **ROTC:** Air Force, Army **Professional Accreditation:** ADA. **Intercollegiate Athletics:** Basketball M; Football M; Golf M; Track and Field M & W; Volleyball W

WEST VALLEY COLLEGE
14000 Fruitvale Ave.
Saratoga, CA 95070-5698
Tel: (408)867-2200
Fax: (408)867-5033
E-mail: barbara_ogilvie@westvalley.edu
Web Site: www.westvalley.edu
President/CEO: Dr. Lori Gaskin
Admissions: Barbara Ogilive
Type: Two-Year College **Sex:** Coed **Affiliation:** California Community College System. **Admission Plans:** Early Admission; Open Admission; Preferred Admission **Application Deadline:** Rolling **Application Fee:** $0.00 **H.S. Requirements:** High school diploma or equivalent not required **Scholarships:** Available. **Calendar System:** Semester, Summer session available **Student-Faculty Ratio:** 28:1 **Regional Accreditation:** Western Association of Colleges and Schools **Credit Hours For Degree:** 60 units, Associates **ROTC:** Air Force, Army **Professional Accreditation:** AAMAE, CIDA. **Intercollegiate Athletics:** Basketball M & W; Cross-Country Running M & W; Football M; Golf M; Soccer M; Swimming and Diving M & W; Tennis M & W; Track and Field M; Volleyball M & W; Water Polo M; Wrestling M

WESTMONT COLLEGE
955 La Paz Rd.
Santa Barbara, CA 93108-1099
Tel: (805)565-6000; Free: 800-777-9011
Fax: (805)565-6234
E-mail: admissions@westmont.edu
Web Site: www.westmont.edu
President/CEO: Dr. Gayle Beebe
Admissions: Silvio E. Vazquez
Financial Aid: Sean Smith
Type: Four-Year College **Sex:** Coed **Affiliation:** nondenominational. **Scores:** 100% SAT V 400+; 100% SAT M 400+; 26% ACT 18-23; 51% ACT 24-29 **% Accepted:** 81 **Admission Plans:** Early Decision Plan **Application Deadline:** February 15 **Application Fee:** $50.00 **H.S. Requirements:** High school diploma required; GED accepted **Costs Per Year:** Application fee: $50. One-time mandatory fee: $500. Comprehensive fee: $56,410 includes full-time tuition ($41,850), mandatory fees ($1050), and college room and board ($13,510). College room only: $8400. Room and board charges vary according to board plan. **Scholarships:** Available. **Calendar System:** Semester, Summer session available **Enrollment:** Full-time 1,294, Part-time 10 **Faculty:** Full-time 93, Part-time 54 **Student-Faculty Ratio:** 12:1 **Exams:** ACT essay component used for admission; ACT essay component used for advising; ACT essay component used for placement; SAT I or ACT; SAT essay component used for admission; SAT essay component used for advising; SAT essay component used for placement; SAT Reasoning. **% Receiving Financial Aid:** 66 **% Residing in College-Owned, -Operated, or -Affiliated Housing:** 85 **Final Year or Final Semester Residency Requirement:** Yes **Regional Accreditation:** Western Association of Colleges and Schools **Credit Hours For Degree:** 124 units, Bachelors **ROTC:** Air Force, Army **Professional Accreditation:** NASM. **Intercollegiate Athletics:** Baseball M; Basketball M & W; Cross-Country Running M & W; Equestrian Sports M; Rugby M; Soccer M & W; Tennis M & W; Track and Field M & W; Volleyball M & W

WHITTIER COLLEGE
13406 E Philadelphia St.
Whittier, CA 90608-0634
Tel: (562)907-4200
Fax: (562)907-4870
E-mail: admission@whittier.edu
Web Site: www.whittier.edu

President/CEO: Dr. Sharon D. Herzberger, PhD
Admissions: Kieron Miller
Financial Aid: Julie Aldama
Type: Comprehensive **Sex:** Coed **Scores:** 97% SAT V 400+; 96% SAT M 400+; 53% ACT 18-23; 37% ACT 24-29 **% Accepted:** 63 **Admission Plans:** Deferred Admission; Early Decision Plan **Application Deadline:** Rolling **Application Fee:** $50.00 **H.S. Requirements:** High school diploma required; GED accepted. For transfer students with at least 30 units: High school diploma or equivalent not required **Scholarships:** Available. **Calendar System:** 4-1-4, Summer session available **Enrollment:** Full-time 1,623, Graduate full-time 348, Graduate part-time 191, Part-time 27 **Faculty:** Full-time 116, Part-time 72 **Student-Faculty Ratio:** 12:1 **Exams:** ACT essay component used as validity check; ACT essay component used for admission; ACT essay component used for placement; SAT I or ACT; SAT II; SAT essay component used as validity check; SAT essay component used for admission; SAT essay component used for placement. **% Receiving Financial Aid:** 74 **% Residing in College-Owned, -Operated, or -Affiliated Housing:** 50 **Final Year or Final Semester Residency Requirement:** No **Regional Accreditation:** Western Association of Colleges and Schools **Credit Hours For Degree:** 120 credits, Bachelors **ROTC:** Army **Professional Accreditation:** AALS, ABA, CSWE. **Intercollegiate Athletics:** Baseball M; Basketball M & W; Cross-Country Running M & W; Football M; Golf M & W; Lacrosse M & W; Soccer M & W; Softball W; Swimming and Diving M & W; Tennis M & W; Track and Field M & W; Volleyball W; Water Polo M & W

WILLIAM JESSUP UNIVERSITY

2121 University Ave.
Rocklin, CA 95765
Tel: (916)577-2200
Fax: (916)577-1813
E-mail: admissions@jessup.edu
Web Site: www.jessup.edu
President/CEO: Dr. John Jackson
Type: Comprehensive **Sex:** Coed **Affiliation:** nondenominational. **Scores:** 93% SAT V 400+; 90% SAT M 400+; 50% ACT 18-23; 33% ACT 24-29 **% Accepted:** 76 **Application Deadline:** August 15 **Application Fee:** $45.00 **H.S. Requirements:** High school diploma required; GED accepted **Costs Per Year:** Application fee: $45. Comprehensive fee: $39,350 includes full-time tuition ($28,300), mandatory fees ($400), and college room and board ($10,650). Full-time tuition and fees vary according to course load. Room and board charges vary according to board plan and housing facility. Part-time tuition: $1190 per credit. Part-time tuition varies according to course load. **Scholarships:** Available. **Calendar System:** Semester, Summer session available **Enrollment:** Full-time 906, Graduate full-time 21, Graduate part-time 43, Part-time 191 **Faculty:** Full-time 38, Part-time 162 **Student-Faculty Ratio:** 11:1 **Exams:** SAT I or ACT; SAT Reasoning. **% Receiving Financial Aid:** 82 **% Residing in College-Owned, -Operated, or -Affiliated Housing:** 46 **Final Year or Final Semester Residency Requirement:** Yes **Regional Accreditation:** Western Association of Colleges and Schools **Credit Hours For Degree:** 64 semester hours, Associates; 128 semester hours, Bachelors **ROTC:** Air Force **Intercollegiate Athletics:** Baseball M; Basketball M & W; Cross-Country Running M & W; Golf M; Soccer M & W; Softball W; Track and Field M & W; Volleyball W

WOODBURY UNIVERSITY

7500 Glenoaks Blvd.
Burbank, CA 91504-1099
Tel: (818)767-0888; Free: 800-784-WOOD
Fax: (818)504-9320
E-mail: admissions@woodbury.edu
Web Site: www.woodbury.edu
President/CEO: Dr. David Steele-Figueredo
Financial Aid: Celeastia Williams
Type: Comprehensive **Sex:** Coed **Scores:** 90% SAT V 400+; 90% SAT M 400+; 36.4% ACT 18-23; 18.2% ACT 24-29 **% Accepted:** 58 **Admission Plans:** Deferred Admission **Application Deadline:** Rolling **Application Fee:** $50.00 **H.S. Requirements:** High school diploma required; GED accepted **Costs Per Year:** Application fee: $50. Comprehensive fee: $47,076 includes full-time tuition ($35,808), mandatory fees ($600), and college room and board ($10,668). College room only: $6604. Part-time tuition: $1166 per credit. **Scholarships:** Available. **Calendar System:** Semester, Summer session available **Enrollment:** Full-time 1,088, Graduate full-time 195, Graduate

part-time 19, Part-time 187 **Faculty:** Full-time 86, Part-time 212 **Student-Faculty Ratio:** 8:1 **Exams:** SAT I or ACT. **% Receiving Financial Aid:** 84 **Final Year or Final Semester Residency Requirement:** No **Regional Accreditation:** Western Association of Colleges and Schools **Credit Hours For Degree:** 120 units, Bachelors **Professional Accreditation:** AACSB, ACBSP, CIDA, NAAB, NASAD.

WOODLAND COMMUNITY COLLEGE

2300 E Gibson Rd.
Woodland, CA 95776
Tel: (530)661-5700
Web Site: www.yccd.edu/woodland
President/CEO: Dr. Angela Fairchilds
Type: Two-Year College **Sex:** Coed **Regional Accreditation:** Western Association of Colleges and Schools

WORLD MISSION UNIVERSITY

500 Shatto Pl.
Ste. 600
Los Angeles, CA 90020
Tel: (213)385-2322
Web Site: www.wmu.edu
Type: Four-Year College **Sex:** Coed **Affiliation:** Evangelical Christian Church. **Professional Accreditation:** ABHE, ATS, TRACS.

YESHIVA OHR ELCHONON CHABAD/WEST COAST TALMUDICAL SEMINARY

7215 Waring Ave.
Los Angeles, CA 90046-7660
Tel: (213)937-3763
E-mail: roshyeshiva@yoec.edu
Web Site: www.yoec.edu
President/CEO: Rabbi Ezra Schochet
Admissions: Rabbi Ezra Binyomin Schochet
Financial Aid: Hendy Tauber
Type: Four-Year College **Sex:** Men **Affiliation:** Jewish. **% Accepted:** 100 **Admission Plans:** Deferred Admission; Early Admission; Preferred Admission **Application Deadline:** Rolling **Application Fee:** $0.00 **H.S. Requirements:** High school diploma required; GED accepted **Calendar System:** Semester, Summer session available **Credit Hours For Degree:** 120 credits, Bachelors **Professional Accreditation:** AARTS.

YUBA COLLEGE

2088 N Beale Rd.
Marysville, CA 95901-7699
Tel: (530)741-6700
Fax: (530)741-3541
Web Site: www.yccd.edu
President/CEO: Dr. Kay Adkins
Admissions: Dr. David Farrell
Type: Two-Year College **Sex:** Coed **Affiliation:** California Community College System. **Admission Plans:** Open Admission **Application Deadline:** Rolling **H.S. Requirements:** High school diploma required; GED accepted **Scholarships:** Available. **Calendar System:** Semester, Summer session available **Student-Faculty Ratio:** 29:1 **Regional Accreditation:** Western Association of Colleges and Schools **Credit Hours For Degree:** 60 units, Associates **Professional Accreditation:** JRCERT. **Intercollegiate Athletics:** Baseball M; Basketball M & W; Cross-Country Running M & W; Football M; Soccer M & W; Softball W; Tennis M & W; Track and Field M & W; Volleyball W

ZAYTUNA COLLEGE

2401 Le Conte Ave.
Berkeley, CA 94709
Tel: (510)356-4760
Fax: (510)327-2688
E-mail: admissions@zaytuna.org
Web Site: www.zaytuna.edu
Admissions: Yusuf Samara
Type: Four-Year College **Sex:** Coed **Affiliation:** Muslim faith. **Costs Per Year:** Comprehensive fee: $29,356 includes full-time tuition ($19,000), mandatory fees ($356), and college room and board ($10,000). **Regional Accreditation:** Western Association of Colleges and Schools

ADAMS STATE UNIVERSITY
208 Edgemont Blvd.
Alamosa, CO 81101
Tel: (719)587-7011; Free: 800-824-6494
Fax: (719)587-7522
E-mail: onestop@adams.edu
Web Site: www.adams.edu
President/CEO: Dr. Beverlee J. McClure
Financial Aid: Philip Schroeder
Type: Comprehensive **Sex:** Coed **Scores:** 83% SAT V 400+; 55.1% ACT 18-23; 16.07% ACT 24-29 **% Accepted:** 19 **Admission Plans:** Deferred Admission; Early Admission **Application Deadline:** Rolling **Application Fee:** $30.00 **H.S. Requirements:** High school diploma required; GED accepted **Costs Per Year:** Application fee: $30. State resident tuition: $5448 full-time, $227 per credit hour part-time. Nonresident tuition: $15,960 full-time, $665 per credit hour part-time. Mandatory fees: $3,126 full-time, $126.10 per credit hour part-time. Full-time tuition and fees vary according to course load. Part-time tuition and fees vary according to course load. College room and board: $8500. College room only: $4000. Room and board charges vary according to board plan and housing facility. Tuition guaranteed not to increase for student's term of enrollment. **Scholarships:** Available. **Calendar System:** Semester, Summer session available **Enrollment:** Full-time 1,746, Graduate full-time 342, Graduate part-time 984, Part-time 488 **Faculty:** Full-time 113, Part-time 126 **Student-Faculty Ratio:** 15:1 **Exams:** SAT I or ACT; SAT Reasoning. **% Receiving Financial Aid:** 76 % **Residing in College-Owned, -Operated, or -Affiliated Housing:** 48 **Final Year or Final Semester Residency Requirement:** No **Regional Accreditation:** North Central Association of Colleges and Schools **Credit Hours For Degree:** 60 semester hours, Associates; 120 semester hours, Bachelors **Professional Accreditation:** AACN, ACA, NASM. **Intercollegiate Athletics:** Baseball M; Basketball M & W; Cross-Country Running M & W; Football M; Golf M & W; Lacrosse M & W; Soccer M & W; Softball W; Swimming and Diving M & W; Track and Field M & W; Volleyball W; Wrestling M

AIMS COMMUNITY COLLEGE
Box 69
5401 W 20th St.
Greeley, CO 80632-0069
Tel: (970)330-8008
E-mail: wgreen@chiron.aims.edu
Web Site: www.aims.edu
President/CEO: Dr. Marilynn Liddell
Admissions: Susie Gallardo
Type: Two-Year College **Sex:** Coed **Admission Plans:** Deferred Admission; Early Admission; Open Admission **Application Deadline:** Rolling **H.S. Requirements:** High school diploma or equivalent not required **Scholarships:** Available. **Calendar System:** Semester, Summer session available **Enrollment:** Full-time 1,701, Part-time 2,887 **Faculty:** Full-time 91, Part-time 182 **Student-Faculty Ratio:** 18:1 **Regional Accreditation:** North Central Association of Colleges and Schools **Credit Hours For Degree:** 96 quarter hours, Associates **ROTC:** Air Force **Professional Accreditation:** JRCERT.

AMERICAN SENTINEL UNIVERSITY
2260 S Xanadu Way, Ste. 310
Aurora, CO 80014
Free: 800-729-2427
E-mail: natalie.nixon@AmericanSentinel.edu
Web Site: www.americansentinel.edu
President/CEO: Mary Adams
Admissions: Natalie Nixon
Type: Comprehensive **Sex:** Coed **Professional Accreditation:** AACN, DEAC.

ARAPAHOE COMMUNITY COLLEGE
5900 S Santa Fe Dr.
Littleton, CO 80160-9002
Tel: (303)797-4222
Fax: (303)797-5970
E-mail: darcy.briggs@arapahoe.edu
Web Site: www.arapahoe.edu
President/CEO: Pres. Diana M. Doyle
Admissions: Darcy Briggs
Type: Two-Year College **Sex:** Coed **Affiliation:** Colorado Community College and Occupational Education System. **% Accepted:** 100 **Admission Plans:** Deferred Admission; Early Admission; Open Admission **Application Deadline:** Rolling **Application Fee:** $0.00 **H.S. Requirements:** High school diploma or equivalent not required. For criminal justice, health information technology, law enforcement, medical office and laboratory technology, pharmacy technician, nursing, communications, paralegal, mortuary science, automotive technology programs: High school diploma required; GED accepted **Costs Per Year:** Application fee: $0. State resident tuition: $3915 full-time, $130.50 per credit hour part-time. Nonresident tuition: $16,062 full-time, $535.40 per credit hour part-time. Mandatory fees: $264 full-time. Full-time tuition and fees vary according to program. Part-time tuition varies according to program. **Scholarships:** Available. **Calendar System:** Semester, Summer session available **Enrollment:** Full-time 1,907, Part-time 7,709 **Faculty:** Full-time 105, Part-time 388 **Student-Faculty Ratio:** 19:1 **Exams:** ACT; ACT essay component not used; SAT I or ACT; SAT essay component not used. **Final Year or Final Semester Residency Requirement:** No **Regional Accreditation:** North Central Association of Colleges and Schools **Credit Hours For Degree:** 60 credit hours, Associates **ROTC:** Air Force, Army, Navy **Professional Accreditation:** ABFSE, AHIMA, APTA, NAACLS.

ARGOSY UNIVERSITY, DENVER
7600 E Eastman Ave.
Denver, CO 80231
Tel: (303)923-4110; Free: 866-431-5981
Fax: (303)923-4111
Web Site: www.argosy.edu/locations/denver
President/CEO: Richard Boorom
Type: University **Sex:** Coed **Regional Accreditation:** Western Association of Colleges and Schools

THE ART INSTITUTE OF COLORADO
1200 Lincoln St.
Denver, CO 80203
Tel: (303)837-0825; Free: 800-275-2420
Fax: (303)860-8520
Web Site: www.artinstitutes.edu/denver
President/CEO: Janet Day

Type: Four-Year College **Sex:** Coed **Affiliation:** Education Management Corporation. **Calendar System:** Quarter **Regional Accreditation:** Southern Association of Colleges and Schools **Professional Accreditation:** ACF, ACICS.

ASPEN UNIVERSITY
720 S Colorado Blvd., Ste. 1150N
Denver, CO 80246-1930
Tel: (303)333-4224; Free: 800-441-4746
Fax: (303)336-1144
E-mail: admissions@aspen.edu
Web Site: www.aspen.edu
President/CEO: David Lady
Financial Aid: Jennifer Quinn
Type: Comprehensive **Sex:** Coed **Application Fee:** $50.00 **Costs Per Year:** Application fee: $50. Tuition: $4500 full-time, $150 per credit part-time. Mandatory fees: $150 full-time, $150 per year part-time. **Scholarships:** Available. **Calendar System:** Miscellaneous **Professional Accreditation:** AACN, DEAC.

BEL–REA INSTITUTE OF ANIMAL TECHNOLOGY
1681 S Dayton St.
Denver, CO 80247
Tel: (303)751-8700; Free: 800-950-8001
Fax: (303)751-9969
E-mail: admissions@bel-rea.com
Web Site: www.bel-rea.com
President/CEO: Marc Schapiro
Admissions: Paulette Kaufman
Type: Two-Year College **Sex:** Coed **Application Deadline:** Rolling **H.S. Requirements:** High school diploma required; GED accepted **Scholarships:** Available. **Calendar System:** Quarter, Summer session not available **Credit Hours For Degree:** 125 credits, Associates **Professional Accreditation:** ACCSC.

COLLEGEAMERICA–COLORADO SPRINGS
2020 N Academy Blvd.
Colorado Springs, CO 80909
Tel: (719)227-0170; Free: 800-622-2894
Fax: (719)637-0806
Web Site: www.collegeamerica.edu
President/CEO: Rozann Kunstle
Admissions: Kiersten Murdoch
Type: Two-Year College **Sex:** Coed **Student-Faculty Ratio:** 22:1 **Professional Accreditation:** ACCSC.

COLLEGEAMERICA–DENVER
1385 S Colorado Blvd.
Denver, CO 80222
Tel: (303)534-0226; Free: 800-622-2894
Web Site: www.collegeamerica.edu
President/CEO: Suzanne Scales
Type: Two-Year College **Sex:** Coed **Scholarships:** Available. **Calendar System:** Continuous **Student-Faculty Ratio:** 15:1 **Professional Accreditation:** ACCSC.

COLLEGEAMERICA–FORT COLLINS
4601 S Mason St.
Fort Collins, CO 80525
Tel: (970)221-2769; Free: 800-622-2894
Fax: (970)223-6060
Web Site: www.collegeamerica.edu
President/CEO: Joel V. Scimeca
Admissions: Anna DiTorrice-Mull
Type: Two-Year College **Sex:** Coed **Admission Plans:** Open Admission **Application Fee:** $0.00 **H.S. Requirements:** High school diploma required; GED accepted **Calendar System:** Continuous, Summer session not available **Professional Accreditation:** ACCSC.

COLORADO ACADEMY OF VETERINARY TECHNOLOGY
2766 Janitell Rd.
Colorado Springs, CO 80906
Tel: (719)219-9636
Fax: (719)302-5577

Web Site: www.coloradovettech.com
Type: Two-Year College **Sex:** Coed **Professional Accreditation:** COE.

COLORADO CHRISTIAN UNIVERSITY
8787 W Alameda
Lakewood, CO 80226
Tel: (303)202-0100; Free: 800-44-FAITH
Fax: (303)238-2191
E-mail: jomartin@ccu.edu
Web Site: www.ccu.edu
President/CEO: Bill Armstrong
Admissions: Jo Leda Martin
Financial Aid: Steve Woodburn
Type: Comprehensive **Sex:** Coed **Affiliation:** interdenominational. **Admission Plans:** Deferred Admission **Application Deadline:** August 1 **Application Fee:** $30.00 **H.S. Requirements:** High school diploma required; GED accepted **Costs Per Year:** Application fee: $30. Comprehensive fee: $39,676 includes full-time tuition ($28,860), mandatory fees ($500), and college room and board ($10,316). College room only: $2815. **Scholarships:** Available. **Calendar System:** Semester, Summer session available **Exams:** SAT I or ACT. **% Receiving Financial Aid:** 67 **% Residing in College-Owned, -Operated, or -Affiliated Housing:** 55 **Regional Accreditation:** North Central Association of Colleges and Schools **Credit Hours For Degree:** 64 semester hours, Associates; 128 semester hours, Bachelors **ROTC:** Army **Professional Accreditation:** ACA, NASM. **Intercollegiate Athletics:** Baseball M; Basketball M & W; Cross-Country Running M & W; Golf M & W; Soccer M & W; Softball W; Tennis M & W; Track and Field M & W; Volleyball W

THE COLORADO COLLEGE
14 E Cache La Poudre St.
Colorado Springs, CO 80903-3294
Tel: (719)389-6000; Free: 800-542-7214
Fax: (719)389-6282
E-mail: admission@coloradocollege.edu
Web Site: www.coloradocollege.edu
President/CEO: Dr. Jill Tiefenthaler
Admissions: Carlos Jiminez
Financial Aid: James M. Swanson
Type: Comprehensive **Sex:** Coed **Scores:** 100% SAT V 400+; 100% SAT M 400+; 2.4% ACT 18-23; 39.6% ACT 24-29 **% Accepted:** 17 **Admission Plans:** Deferred Admission; Early Action; Early Decision Plan **Application Deadline:** January 15 **Application Fee:** $60.00 **H.S. Requirements:** High school diploma or equivalent not required **Costs Per Year:** Application fee: $60. One-time mandatory fee: $150. Comprehensive fee: $62,560 includes full-time tuition ($50,472), mandatory fees ($420), and college room and board ($11,668). College room only: $6902. Room and board charges vary according to board plan and housing facility. Part-time tuition: $8482 per course. Part-time tuition varies according to course load. **Scholarships:** Available. **Calendar System:** Miscellaneous, Summer session available **Enrollment:** Full-time 2,096, Graduate full-time 11, Graduate part-time 2, Part-time 22 **Faculty:** Full-time 181, Part-time 31 **Student-Faculty Ratio:** 10:1 **Exams:** ACT essay component not used; SAT I or ACT; SAT II; SAT essay component not used; SAT Reasoning; SAT Subject. **% Receiving Financial Aid:** 35 **% Residing in College-Owned, -Operated, or -Affiliated Housing:** 75 **Final Year or Final Semester Residency Requirement:** No **Regional Accreditation:** North Central Association of Colleges and Schools **Credit Hours For Degree:** 128 credit hours, Bachelors **ROTC:** Army **Intercollegiate Athletics:** Baseball M; Basketball M & W; Cross-Country Running M & W; Equestrian Sports M & W; Ice Hockey M & W; Lacrosse M & W; Rugby M & W; Skiing (Downhill) M & W; Soccer M & W; Softball W; Swimming and Diving M & W; Tennis M & W; Track and Field M & W; Ultimate Frisbee M & W; Volleyball W; Water Polo W

COLORADO HEIGHTS UNIVERSITY
3001 S Federal Blvd.
Denver, CO 80236-2711
Tel: (303)937-4200
E-mail: mnochevnaya@chu.edu
Web Site: www.chu.edu
President/CEO: Bob Rizzuto
Admissions: Marina Nochevnaya
Financial Aid: Amber Bartlett
Type: Comprehensive **Sex:** Coed **Affiliation:** Teikyo University Group.

Admission Plans: Deferred Admission; Open Admission **Application Deadline:** Rolling **Application Fee:** $50.00 **H.S. Requirements:** High school diploma required; GED accepted **Scholarships:** Available. **Enrollment:** Full-time 329, Graduate full-time 20, Graduate part-time 12, Part-time 14 **Faculty:** Full-time 1, Part-time 32 **Student-Faculty Ratio:** 12:1 **% Receiving Financial Aid:** 30 **Final Year or Final Semester Residency Requirement:** No **Credit Hours For Degree:** 120 credit hours, Bachelors **Professional Accreditation:** ACICS.

COLORADO MESA UNIVERSITY

1100 N Ave.
Grand Junction, CO 81501-3122
Tel: (970)248-1020; Free: 800-982-MESA
Fax: (970)248-1973
E-mail: admissions@coloradomeas.edu
Web Site: www.coloradomesa.edu
President/CEO: Timothy Foster
Financial Aid: Curt Martin

Type: Comprehensive **Sex:** Coed **Scores:** 88% SAT V 400+; 87% SAT M 400+; 50% ACT 18-23; 22% ACT 24-29 **% Accepted:** 83 **Admission Plans:** Deferred Admission **Application Deadline:** Rolling **Application Fee:** $30.00 **H.S. Requirements:** High school diploma required; GED accepted **Costs Per Year:** Application fee: $30. State resident tuition: $7185 full-time, $239.50 per credit hour part-time. Nonresident tuition: $18,540 full-time, $618 per credit hour part-time. Mandatory fees: $823 full-time, $27.43 per credit hour part-time. Full-time tuition and fees vary according to course load. Part-time tuition and fees vary according to course load. College room and board: $10,176. College room only: $5750. Room and board charges vary according to board plan and housing facility. **Scholarships:** Available. **Calendar System:** Semester, Summer session available **Enrollment:** Full-time 7,204, Graduate full-time 49, Graduate part-time 100, Part-time 2,095 **Faculty:** Full-time 263, Part-time 279 **Student-Faculty Ratio:** 22:1 **Exams:** SAT I or ACT; SAT Reasoning; SAT Subject. **% Receiving Financial Aid:** 66 **% Residing in College-Owned, -Operated, or -Affiliated Housing:** 25 **Final Year or Final Semester Residency Requirement:** No **Regional Accreditation:** North Central Association of Colleges and Schools **Credit Hours For Degree:** 60 credit hours, Associates; 120 credit hours, Bachelors **Professional Accreditation:** AACN, JRCERT, NASM, NCATE. **Intercollegiate Athletics:** Baseball M; Basketball M & W; Cross-Country Running M & W; Football M; Golf M & W; Lacrosse M & W; Rugby M & W; Skiing (Cross-Country) M & W; Skiing (Downhill) M & W; Soccer M & W; Softball W; Swimming and Diving M & W; Tennis M & W; Track and Field M & W; Volleyball W; Wrestling M

COLORADO MOUNTAIN COLLEGE (GLENWOOD SPRINGS)

1402 Blake Ave.
Glenwood Springs, CO 81601
Tel: (970)945-7486; Free: 800-621-8559
Fax: (970)945-6240
E-mail: vvalentine@coloradomtn.edu
Web Site: www.coloradomtn.edu
President/CEO: Carrie Hauser
Admissions: Vicky Butler
Financial Aid: Thomas S. Valles

Type: Four-Year College **Sex:** Coed **Affiliation:** Colorado Mountain College District System. **% Accepted:** 100 **Admission Plans:** Deferred Admission; Early Admission; Open Admission **Application Deadline:** Rolling **Application Fee:** $0.00 **H.S. Requirements:** High school diploma or equivalent not required **Costs Per Year:** Application fee: $0. Area resident tuition: $62 per credit hour part-time. State resident tuition: $127 per credit hour part-time. Nonresident tuition: $429 per credit hour part-time. **Scholarships:** Available. **Calendar System:** Semester, Summer session available **Enrollment:** Full-time 1,875, Part-time 3,972 **Faculty:** Full-time 109, Part-time 435 **Student-Faculty Ratio:** 13:1 **Exams:** SAT I or ACT. **% Receiving Financial Aid:** 74 **% Residing in College-Owned, -Operated, or -Affiliated Housing:** 44 **Final Year or Final Semester Residency Requirement:** No **Regional Accreditation:** North Central Association of Colleges and Schools **Credit Hours For Degree:** 60 credits, Associates; 120 credits, Bachelors **Intercollegiate Athletics:** Skiing (Downhill) M & W

COLORADO MOUNTAIN COLLEGE (LEADVILLE)

901 S Hwy. 24
Leadville, CO 80461
Tel: (719)486-2015; Free: 800-621-8559

E-mail: joinus@coloradomtn.edu
Web Site: www.coloradomtn.edu
President/CEO: Mike Simon
Admissions: Mary Laing

Type: Four-Year College **Sex:** Coed **Affiliation:** Colorado Mountain College District System. **Admission Plans:** Deferred Admission; Early Admission; Open Admission **Application Deadline:** Rolling **Application Fee:** $0.00 **H.S. Requirements:** High school diploma or equivalent not required **Scholarships:** Available. **Calendar System:** Semester, Summer session available **Faculty:** Full-time 16 **Student-Faculty Ratio:** 12:1 **Exams:** SAT I or ACT. **% Residing in College-Owned, -Operated, or -Affiliated Housing:** 30 **Final Year or Final Semester Residency Requirement:** No **Regional Accreditation:** North Central Association of Colleges and Schools **Credit Hours For Degree:** 60 credits, Associates; 120 credits, Bachelors **Intercollegiate Athletics:** Skiing (Downhill) M & W

COLORADO MOUNTAIN COLLEGE (STEAMBOAT SPRINGS)

1275 Crawford Ave.
Steamboat Springs, CO 80487
Tel: (970)870-4444; Free: 800-621-8559
E-mail: jbrazill@coloradomtn.edu
Web Site: www.coloradomtn.edu
President/CEO: Brian Hoza
Admissions: Jackie Brazill
Financial Aid: Thomas S. Valles

Type: Four-Year College **Sex:** Coed **Affiliation:** Colorado Mountain College District System. **Admission Plans:** Deferred Admission; Early Admission; Open Admission **Application Deadline:** Rolling **Application Fee:** $0.00 **H.S. Requirements:** High school diploma or equivalent not required **Costs Per Year:** Application fee: $0. Area resident tuition: $62 per credit part-time. State resident tuition: $127 per credit part-time. Nonresident tuition: $429 per credit part-time. College room and board: $8572. **Scholarships:** Available. **Calendar System:** Semester, Summer session available **Faculty:** Full-time 25 **Student-Faculty Ratio:** 12:1 **Exams:** SAT I or ACT. **% Residing in College-Owned, -Operated, or -Affiliated Housing:** 44 **Final Year or Final Semester Residency Requirement:** No **Regional Accreditation:** North Central Association of Colleges and Schools **Credit Hours For Degree:** 60 credits, Associates; 120 credits, Bachelors **Intercollegiate Athletics:** Skiing (Downhill) M & W

COLORADO NORTHWESTERN COMMUNITY COLLEGE

500 Kennedy Dr.
Rangely, CO 81648-3598
Tel: (970)675-2261; Free: 800-562-1105
Fax: (970)675-3343
E-mail: kelly.scott@cncc.edu
Web Site: www.cncc.edu
President/CEO: Russell George
Admissions: Kelly Scott
Financial Aid: Merrie Byers

Type: Two-Year College **Sex:** Coed **Affiliation:** Colorado Community College and Occupational Education System. **% Accepted:** 100 **Admission Plans:** Deferred Admission; Early Admission; Open Admission **Application Deadline:** Rolling **Application Fee:** $0.00 **H.S. Requirements:** High school diploma required; GED accepted **Costs Per Year:** Application fee: $0. State resident tuition: $4210 full-time, $205.50 per credit hour part-time. Nonresident tuition: $6999 full-time, $223.45 per credit hour part-time. Mandatory fees: $295 full-time, $7.72 per credit hour part-time, $12.55 per term part-time. Full-time tuition and fees vary according to program. Part-time tuition and fees vary according to program. College room and board: $6654. College room only: $2356. Room and board charges vary according to board plan and housing facility. **Scholarships:** Available. **Calendar System:** Semester, Summer session available **Enrollment:** Full-time 538, Part-time 640 **Faculty:** Full-time 43, Part-time 61 **Student-Faculty Ratio:** 12:1 **Exams:** ACT. **% Residing in College-Owned, -Operated, or -Affiliated Housing:** 24 **Final Year or Final Semester Residency Requirement:** No **Regional Accreditation:** North Central Association of Colleges and Schools **Credit Hours For Degree:** 60 semester hours, Associates **Professional Accreditation:** ADA. **Intercollegiate Athletics:** Baseball M; Basketball M & W; Softball W; Volleyball W

COLORADO SCHOOL OF HEALING ARTS

7655 W Mississippi Ave.
Ste. 100

Lakewood, CO 80226
Tel: (303)988-2320; Free: 800-233-7114
Fax: (303)980-6594
Web Site: www.csha.net
President/CEO: Dennis Simpson
Admissions: Victoria Steere
Type: Two-Year College **Sex:** Coed **Application Fee:** $50.00 **Calendar System:** Quarter **Student-Faculty Ratio:** 16:1 **Professional Accreditation:** ACCSC.

COLORADO SCHOOL OF MINES
1500 Illinois St.
Golden, CO 80401-1887
Tel: (303)273-3000; Free: 800-446-9488
Fax: (303)273-3509
E-mail: admit@mines.edu
Web Site: www.mines.edu
President/CEO: Dr. Paul C. Johnson
Admissions: Marisa Garcia
Financial Aid: Jill Robertson
Type: University **Sex:** Coed **Scores:** 100% SAT V 400+; 100% SAT M 400+; 40% ACT 24-29 **% Accepted:** 38 **Admission Plans:** Deferred Admission **Application Deadline:** April 1 **Application Fee:** $45.00 **H.S. Requirements:** High school diploma required; GED accepted **Costs Per Year:** Application fee: $45. State resident tuition: $15,225 full-time, $508 per credit hour part-time. Nonresident tuition: $32,700 full-time, $1090 per credit hour part-time. Mandatory fees: $2128 full-time. Full-time tuition and fees vary according to course load. College room and board: $11,008. Room and board charges vary according to board plan and housing facility. **Scholarships:** Available. **Calendar System:** Semester, Summer session available **Enrollment:** Full-time 4,386, Graduate full-time 1,132, Graduate part-time 184, Part-time 222 **Faculty:** Full-time 278, Part-time 238 **Student-Faculty Ratio:** 16:1 **Exams:** SAT I or ACT; SAT Reasoning. **% Receiving Financial Aid:** 50 **% Residing in College-Owned, -Operated, or -Affiliated Housing:** 36 **Final Year or Final Semester Residency Requirement:** Yes **Regional Accreditation:** North Central Association of Colleges and Schools **Credit Hours For Degree:** 128.0 - 141.0 semester hours, Bachelors **ROTC:** Air Force, Army **Professional Accreditation:** ABET. **Intercollegiate Athletics:** Baseball M; Basketball M & W; Bowling M & W; Cross-Country Running M & W; Football M; Golf M; Ice Hockey M & W; Lacrosse M & W; Rugby M & W; Soccer M & W; Softball W; Swimming and Diving M & W; Track and Field M & W; Volleyball W; Wrestling M

COLORADO SCHOOL OF TRADES
1575 Hoyt St.
Lakewood, CO 80215-2996
Tel: (303)233-4697; Free: 800-234-4594
Fax: (303)233-4723
E-mail: rm@schooloftrades.edu
Web Site: www.schooloftrades.edu
President/CEO: Robert E. Martin
Admissions: Robert Martin
Financial Aid: Robert E. Martin
Type: Two-Year College **Sex:** Coed **% Accepted:** 87 **Application Fee:** $25.00 **H.S. Requirements:** High school diploma required; GED accepted **Costs Per Year:** Application fee: $25. Tuition: $20,520 full-time. Tuition guaranteed not to increase for student's term of enrollment. **Scholarships:** Available. **Enrollment:** Full-time 134 **Faculty:** Full-time 10 **Student-Faculty Ratio:** 12:1 **Professional Accreditation:** ACCSC.

COLORADO STATE UNIVERSITY
Fort Collins, CO 80523-0015
Tel: (970)491-1101
Fax: (970)491-7799
E-mail: admissions@colostate.edu
Web Site: www.colostate.edu
President/CEO: Dr. Anthony A. Frank
Admissions: Bryan Whish
Type: University **Sex:** Coed **Affiliation:** Colorado State University System. **Scores:** 99% SAT V 400+; 99% SAT M 400+; 35.82% ACT 18-23; 50.69% ACT 24-29 **% Accepted:** 81 **Admission Plans:** Deferred Admission; Early Decision Plan **Application Deadline:** February 1 **Application Fee:** $50.00 **H.S. Requirements:** High school diploma required; GED accepted **Costs Per Year:** Application fee: $50. State resident tuition: $8301 full-time, $377

per credit hour part-time. Nonresident tuition: $25,010 full-time, $1,251 per credit hour part-time. Mandatory fees: $2257 full-time, $51.52 per credit hour part-time, $128.86 per term part-time. Full-time tuition and fees vary according to course level, course load, program, and student level. Part-time tuition and fees vary according to course level, course load, program, and student level. College room and board: $10,794. College room only: $5258. Room and board charges vary according to board plan, housing facility, and location. **Scholarships:** Available. **Calendar System:** Semester, Summer session available **Enrollment:** Full-time 21,764, Graduate full-time 3,228, Graduate part-time 4,282, Part-time 2,669 **Faculty:** Full-time 1,009, Part-time 19 **Student-Faculty Ratio:** 16:1 **Exams:** ACT essay component not used; SAT I or ACT; SAT essay component not used; SAT Reasoning. **% Receiving Financial Aid:** 45 **% Residing in College-Owned, -Operated, or -Affiliated Housing:** 27 **Final Year or Final Semester Residency Requirement:** No **Regional Accreditation:** North Central Association of Colleges and Schools **Credit Hours For Degree:** 120 credits, Bachelors **ROTC:** Air Force, Army **Professional Accreditation:** AACSB, AAFCS, AAMFT, ABET, ACA, ACCE, ACEJMC, AND, AOTA, APA, ASLA, AVMA, CIDA, CSWE, NASM, NRPA, SAF, TEAC. **Intercollegiate Athletics:** Baseball M; Basketball M & W; Crew M & W; Cross-Country Running M & W; Field Hockey M & W; Football M; Golf M & W; Ice Hockey M & W; Lacrosse M & W; Rugby M & W; Skiing (Downhill) M & W; Soccer M & W; Softball W; Swimming and Diving M & W; Tennis W; Track and Field M & W; Triathlon M & W; Ultimate Frisbee M & W; Volleyball M & W; Water Polo M & W; Wrestling M & W

COLORADO STATE UNIVERSITY–GLOBAL CAMPUS
8000 E Maplewood Ave.
Greenwood Village, CO 80111
Tel: (720)279-0159; Free: 800-920-6723
Web Site: csuglobal.edu
Type: Comprehensive **Sex:** Coed **Regional Accreditation:** North Central Association of Colleges and Schools

COLORADO STATE UNIVERSITY–PUEBLO
2200 Bonforte Blvd.
Pueblo, CO 81001-4901
Tel: (719)549-2100
Fax: (719)549-2419
E-mail: tiffany.kingrey@csupueblo.edu
Web Site: www.csupueblo.edu
President/CEO: Dr. Lesley Di Mare
Admissions: Tiffany Kingrey
Financial Aid: Justin Streater
Type: Comprehensive **Sex:** Coed **Affiliation:** Colorado State University System. **Scores:** 81% SAT V 400+; 91% SAT M 400+; 58% ACT 18-23; 21% ACT 24-29 **% Accepted:** 96 **Admission Plans:** Deferred Admission **Application Deadline:** August 1 **Application Fee:** $25.00 **H.S. Requirements:** High school diploma required; GED accepted **Costs Per Year:** Application fee: $25. One-time mandatory fee: $85. State resident tuition: $6159 full-time, $228.58 per credit hour part-time. Nonresident tuition: $17,729 full-time, $687.14 per credit hour part-time. Mandatory fees: $2123 full-time, $70.75 per credit hour part-time. Full-time tuition and fees vary according to course load, degree level, location, program, and reciprocity agreements. Part-time tuition and fees vary according to course load, degree level, location, program, and reciprocity agreements. College room and board: $9230. College room only: $5516. Room and board charges vary according to board plan and housing facility. **Scholarships:** Available. **Calendar System:** Semester, Summer session available **Enrollment:** Full-time 3,398, Graduate full-time 378, Graduate part-time 2,179, Part-time 1,608 **Faculty:** Full-time 172, Part-time 200 **Student-Faculty Ratio:** 16:1 **Exams:** ACT essay component not used; SAT I or ACT; SAT essay component not used; SAT Reasoning. **% Receiving Financial Aid:** 73 **Regional Accreditation:** North Central Association of Colleges and Schools **Credit Hours For Degree:** 120 semester hours, Bachelors **ROTC:** Army **Professional Accreditation:** AACSB, ABET, ACEN, CSWE, NASM, TEAC. **Intercollegiate Athletics:** Baseball M; Basketball M & W; Bowling M & W; Cheerleading M & W; Cross-Country Running M & W; Football M; Golf M & W; Ice Hockey M; Lacrosse M & W; Soccer M & W; Softball W; Swimming and Diving W; Tennis M & W; Track and Field M & W; Volleyball W; Wrestling M

COLORADO TECHNICAL UNIVERSITY COLORADO SPRINGS
4435 N Chestnut St.
Colorado Springs, CO 80907

Tel: (719)598-0200; Free: 866-942-6555
E-mail: bbraaten@coloradotech.edu
Web Site: www.coloradotech.edu
President/CEO: Dr. Wallace K. Pond
Admissions: Beth Braaten
Financial Aid: Jacqueline Harris
Type: University **Sex:** Coed **Affiliation:** Colorado Technical University. **Admission Plans:** Deferred Admission **Application** **Deadline:** Rolling **Application Fee:** $50.00 **H.S. Requirements:** High school diploma required; GED accepted **Scholarships:** Available. **Calendar System:** Quarter, Summer session available **Enrollment:** Full-time 679, Part-time 1,217 **% Receiving Financial Aid:** 69 **Regional Accreditation:** North Central Association of Colleges and Schools **Credit Hours For Degree:** 90 quarter hours, Associates; 178 quarter hours, Bachelors **ROTC:** Army **Professional Accreditation:** ABET, ACBSP.

COLORADO TECHNICAL UNIVERSITY DENVER SOUTH
3151 S Vaughn Way
Aurora, CO 80014
Tel: (303)632-2300; Free: 888-309-6555
E-mail: rgiboney@coloradotech.edu
Web Site: www.coloradotech.edu
President/CEO: Dr. Wallace Pond
Admissions: Rosaland Giboney
Financial Aid: Natalie Dietsch
Type: Comprehensive **Sex:** Coed **Affiliation:** Colorado Technical University. **Admission Plans:** Deferred Admission **Application Deadline:** Rolling **Application Fee:** $50.00 **H.S. Requirements:** High school diploma required; GED accepted **Scholarships:** Available. **Calendar System:** Quarter, Summer session available **Enrollment:** Full-time 229, Part-time 344 **Regional Accreditation:** North Central Association of Colleges and Schools **Credit Hours For Degree:** 90 credit hours, Associates; 178 credit hours, Bachelors

COLORADO TECHNICAL UNIVERSITY ONLINE
4435 N Chestnut St.
Ste. E
Colorado Springs, CO 80907
Tel: (303)362-2900
Fax: (303)362-2945
Web Site: www.coloradotech.edu
President/CEO: Dr. Wallace Pond
Admissions: William Beckley
Type: Comprehensive **Sex:** Coed **Affiliation:** Colorado Technical University. **Admission Plans:** Deferred Admission **Application Deadline:** Rolling **Application Fee:** $50.00 **H.S. Requirements:** High school diploma required; GED accepted **Calendar System:** Quarter **Enrollment:** Full-time 23,094 **Regional Accreditation:** North Central Association of Colleges and Schools

COMMUNITY COLLEGE OF AURORA
16000 E CentreTech Pky.
Aurora, CO 80011-9036
Tel: (303)360-4700
E-mail: kristen.cusack@ccaurora.edu
Web Site: www.ccaurora.edu
President/CEO: Linda S. Bowman
Admissions: Kristen Cusack
Financial Aid: John Young
Type: Two-Year College **Sex:** Coed **Affiliation:** Colorado Community College System. **Costs Per Year:** State resident tuition: $3142 full-time, $130.50 per credit hour part-time. Nonresident tuition: $12,860 full-time, $535.40 per credit hour part-time. Mandatory fees: $396 full-time, $37.08 per credit hour part-time. Full-time tuition and fees vary according to course load, location, program, and reciprocity agreements. Part-time tuition and fees vary according to course load, location, program, and reciprocity agreements. **Scholarships:** Available. **Calendar System:** Semester, Summer session available **Enrollment:** Full-time 1,259, Part-time 5,684 **Student-Faculty Ratio:** 20:1 **Regional Accreditation:** North Central Association of Colleges and Schools **Credit Hours For Degree:** 60 semester hours, Associates **Professional Accreditation:** CoARC.

COMMUNITY COLLEGE OF DENVER
PO Box 173363
Denver, CO 80217-3363
Tel: (303)556-2600

E-mail: enrollment_services@ccd.edu
Web Site: www.ccd.edu
President/CEO: Karen Clos Bleeker
Admissions: Michael Rusk
Financial Aid: Thad Spaulding
Type: Two-Year College **Sex:** Coed **Affiliation:** Colorado Community College System. **Admission Plans:** Deferred Admission; Early Admission; Open Admission **Application Fee:** $0.00 **H.S. Requirements:** High school diploma or equivalent not required **Costs Per Year:** Application fee: $0. State resident tuition: $2998 full-time, $124.90 per credit hour part-time. Nonresident tuition: $12,296 full-time, $512.35 per credit hour part-time. Full-time tuition varies according to course load, location, program, and reciprocity agreements. Part-time tuition varies according to course load, location, program, and reciprocity agreements. **Scholarships:** Available. **Calendar System:** Semester, Summer session available **Enrollment:** Full-time 2,514, Part-time 7,782 **Faculty:** Full-time 123, Part-time 312 **Student-Faculty Ratio:** 25:1 **Exams:** ACT essay component not used; SAT essay component not used. **Regional Accreditation:** North Central Association of Colleges and Schools **Credit Hours For Degree:** 60 credit hours, Associates **ROTC:** Army **Professional Accreditation:** ADA, ARCST, JRCERT.

CONCORDE CAREER COLLEGE
111 N Havana St.
Aurora, CO 80010
Tel: (303)861-1151
Web Site: www.concorde.edu
Type: Two-Year College **Sex:** Coed **Professional Accreditation:** ACCSC.

DENVER SCHOOL OF NURSING
1401 19th St.
Denver, CO 80202
Tel: (303)292-0015; Free: 888-479-5550
Fax: (720)974-0290
Web Site: www.denverschoolofnursing.edu
President/CEO: Marcia Bankirer
Type: Four-Year College **Sex:** Coed **Regional Accreditation:** North Central Association of Colleges and Schools

DEVRY UNIVERSITY (COLORADO SPRINGS)
1175 Kelly Johnson Blvd.
Colorado Springs, CO 80920
Tel: (719)632-3000; Free: 866-338-7941
Web Site: www.devry.edu
Financial Aid: Carol Oppman
Type: Comprehensive **Sex:** Coed **Affiliation:** DeVry University. **Application Deadline:** Rolling **Costs Per Year:** Tuition: $17,052 full-time, $609 per credit hour part-time. Mandatory fees: $80 full-time, $40 per term part-time. **Scholarships:** Available. **Calendar System:** Semester **% Receiving Financial Aid:** 73 **Regional Accreditation:** North Central Association of Colleges and Schools **Professional Accreditation:** ACBSP.

DEVRY UNIVERSITY (WESTMINSTER)
1870 W 122nd Ave.
Westminster, CO 80234-2010
Tel: (303)280-7400; Free: 866-338-7941
Web Site: www.devry.edu
Type: Comprehensive **Sex:** Coed **Application Deadline:** Rolling **Application Fee:** $40.00 **Costs Per Year:** Application fee: $40. Tuition: $17,052 full-time, $609 per credit hour part-time. Mandatory fees: $80 full-time, $40 per term part-time. **Scholarships:** Available. **Calendar System:** Semester **Enrollment:** Full-time 136, Part-time 273 **Faculty:** Full-time 7, Part-time 37 **Student-Faculty Ratio:** 13:1 **Exams:** ACT essay component used for admission; ACT essay component used for placement; SAT essay component used for admission; SAT essay component used for placement. **% Receiving Financial Aid:** 72 **Regional Accreditation:** North Central Association of Colleges and Schools **Professional Accreditation:** ABET.

ECOTECH INSTITUTE
1400 S Abilene St.
Aurora, CO 80012
Tel: (303)586-5290
Web Site: www.ecotechinstitute.com
Type: Two-Year College **Sex:** Coed **Professional Accreditation:** ACICS.

EVEREST COLLEGE (COLORADO SPRINGS)
1815 Jet Wing Dr.
Colorado Springs, CO 80916
Tel: (719)638-6580; Free: 888-741-4270
Fax: (719)638-6818
Web Site: www.everest.edu
President/CEO: Robert Lantzy
Type: Two-Year College **Sex:** Coed **Affiliation:** Zenith Education Group. **Application Deadline:** Rolling **H.S. Requirements:** High school diploma required; GED accepted **Scholarships:** Available. **Calendar System:** Quarter, Summer session not available **Exams:** Other. **Credit Hours For Degree:** 96 credit hours, Associates **Professional Accreditation:** AAMAE, ACICS.

EVEREST COLLEGE (THORNTON)
9065 Grant St.
Thornton, CO 80229
Tel: (303)457-2757; Free: 888-741-4270
Web Site: www.everest.edu
President/CEO: Pat Schlotter
Type: Two-Year College **Sex:** Coed **Affiliation:** Zenith Education Group. **Application Deadline:** Rolling **H.S. Requirements:** High school diploma required; GED accepted **Scholarships:** Available. **Calendar System:** Quarter, Summer session available **Exams:** Other. **Credit Hours For Degree:** 96 credits, Associates **Professional Accreditation:** AAMAE, ACICS.

FORT LEWIS COLLEGE
1000 Rim Dr.
Durango, CO 81301-3999
Tel: (970)247-7010; Free: 877-FLC-COLO
Fax: (970)247-7179
E-mail: admission@fortlewis.edu
Web Site: www.fortlewis.edu
President/CEO: Dr. Dene Thomas
Admissions: Andrew Burns
Financial Aid: Tracey Piccoli
Type: Comprehensive **Sex:** Coed **Scores:** 94% SAT V 400+; 91% SAT M 400+; 56.1% ACT 18-23; 29.63% ACT 24-29 **% Accepted:** 86 **Admission Plans:** Deferred Admission; Early Decision Plan **Application Deadline:** August 1 **Application Fee:** $40.00 **H.S. Requirements:** High school diploma required; GED accepted **Costs Per Year:** Application fee: $40. State resident tuition: $5856 full-time, $244 per credit hour part-time. Nonresident tuition: $16,072 full-time, $670 per credit hour part-time. Mandatory fees: $1745 full-time. Full-time tuition and fees vary according to course load and reciprocity agreements. Part-time tuition varies according to course load and reciprocity agreements. College room and board: $9130. College room only: $4530. Room and board charges vary according to board plan and housing facility. **Scholarships:** Available. **Calendar System:** Semester, Summer session available **Enrollment:** Full-time 3,393, Graduate part-time 13, Part-time 286 **Faculty:** Full-time 174, Part-time 78 **Student-Faculty Ratio:** 17:1 **Exams:** ACT essay component not used; SAT I or ACT; SAT essay component not used; SAT Reasoning; SAT Subject. **% Receiving Financial Aid:** 64 **% Residing in College-Owned, -Operated, or -Affiliated Housing:** 40 **Final Year or Final Semester Residency Requirement:** No **Regional Accreditation:** North Central Association of Colleges and Schools **Credit Hours For Degree:** 120 credits, Bachelors **Professional Accreditation:** AACSB, ABET, JRCAT, NASM. **Intercollegiate Athletics:** Baseball M; Basketball M & W; Cheerleading M & W; Cross-Country Running M & W; Fencing M & W; Football M; Golf M; Ice Hockey M & W; Lacrosse M & W; Rock Climbing M & W; Rugby M & W; Skiing (Cross-Country) M & W; Skiing (Downhill) M & W; Soccer M & W; Softball W; Ultimate Frisbee M & W; Volleyball W; Wrestling M & W

FRONT RANGE COMMUNITY COLLEGE
3645 W 112th Ave.
Westminster, CO 80030
Tel: (303)466-8811
E-mail: miori.gidley@frontrange.edu
Web Site: www.frontrange.edu
President/CEO: Andrew R. Dorsey
Admissions: Miori Gidley
Type: Two-Year College **Sex:** Coed **Affiliation:** Community Colleges of Colorado System. **% Accepted:** 100 **Admission Plans:** Deferred Admis-sion; Early Admission; Open Admission **Application Fee:** $0.00 **H.S. Requirements:** High school diploma or equivalent not required **Costs Per Year:** Application fee: $0. State resident tuition: $3132 full-time, $131 per credit hour part-time. Nonresident tuition: $12,850 full-time, $535 per credit hour part-time. Mandatory fees: $395 full-time, $395 per year part-time. Full-time tuition and fees vary according to program. Part-time tuition and fees vary according to program. **Scholarships:** Available. **Calendar System:** Semester, Summer session available **Enrollment:** Full-time 5,575, Part-time 13,186 **Faculty:** Full-time 245, Part-time 769 **Student-Faculty Ratio:** 20:1 **Final Year or Final Semester Residency Requirement:** No **Regional Accreditation:** North Central Association of Colleges and Schools **Credit Hours For Degree:** 60 credit hours, Associates **ROTC:** Air Force, Army **Professional Accreditation:** ADA, CoARC.

HERITAGE COLLEGE
4704 Harlan St.
Ste. 100
Denver, CO 80212
Tel: (303)477-7240; Free: 888-334-7339
Fax: (303)477-7276
Web Site: www.heritagecollege.edu
President/CEO: Austin Morton
Type: Two-Year College **Sex:** Coed **% Accepted:** 53 **Professional Accreditation:** ACCSC.

IBMC COLLEGE (COLORADO SPRINGS)
6805 Corporate Dr.
Ste. 100
Colorado Springs, CO 80919
Tel: (719)596-7400; Free: 800-748-2282
Fax: (719)596-2464
Web Site: www.ibmc.edu
President/CEO: Todd Matthews
Admissions: Michelle Squibb
Type: Two-Year College **Sex:** Coed **Admission Plans:** Open Admission **Application Deadline:** Rolling **Application Fee:** $0.00 **H.S. Requirements:** High school diploma required; GED accepted **Scholarships:** Available. **Calendar System:** Miscellaneous, Summer session not available **Credit Hours For Degree:** 99 credit hours, Associates **Professional Accreditation:** ABHES.

IBMC COLLEGE (FORT COLLINS)
3842 S Mason St.
Fort Collins, CO 80525
Tel: (970)223-2669; Free: 800-495-2669
E-mail: jshoup@ibmc.edu
Web Site: www.ibmc.edu
President/CEO: Steve Steele
Admissions: Jeremy Shoup
Financial Aid: August Nick Maschka
Type: Two-Year College **Sex:** Coed **% Accepted:** 92 **Admission Plans:** Open Admission **Application Deadline:** Rolling **Application Fee:** $50.00 **H.S. Requirements:** High school diploma required; GED accepted **Costs Per Year:** Application fee: $50. One-time mandatory fee: $100. Tuition: $12,240 full-time. Full-time tuition varies according to course load and program. Tuition guaranteed not to increase for student's term of enrollment. **Scholarships:** Available. **Calendar System:** Continuous, Summer session available **Enrollment:** Full-time 1,020 **Faculty:** Full-time 46, Part-time 69 **Student-Faculty Ratio:** 10:1 **Exams:** Other. **Final Year or Final Semester Residency Requirement:** No **Credit Hours For Degree:** 90 credits, Associates **Professional Accreditation:** ACICS.

INTELLITEC COLLEGE (COLORADO SPRINGS)
2315 E Pikes Peak Ave.
Colorado Springs, CO 80909
Tel: (719)632-7626; Free: 800-748-2282
Fax: (719)632-7451
Web Site: www.intelliteccollege.edu
President/CEO: Raymond Ada
Type: Two-Year College **Sex:** Coed **Affiliation:** Technical Trades Institute, Inc. **Admission Plans:** Open Admission **Application Deadline:** Rolling **Application Fee:** $30.00 **H.S. Requirements:** High school diploma required;

GED accepted **Scholarships:** Available. **Calendar System:** Miscellaneous **Credit Hours For Degree:** 90 credit hours, Associates **Professional Accreditation:** ACCSC.

INTELLITEC COLLEGE (GRAND JUNCTION)

772 Horizon Dr.
Grand Junction, CO 81506
Tel: (970)245-8101; Free: 800-748-2282
Fax: (970)243-8074
Web Site: www.intelliteccollege.edu
President/CEO: Mike Schranz

Type: Two-Year College **Sex:** Coed **Admission Plans:** Open Admission **Application Fee:** $0.00 **H.S. Requirements:** High school diploma required; GED accepted **Costs Per Year:** Application fee: $0. Tuition: $23,151 full-time. Mandatory fees: $480 full-time. Full-time tuition and fees vary according to class time, course load, degree level, location, program, and reciprocity agreements. Tuition guaranteed not to increase for student's term of enrollment. **Scholarships:** Available. **Calendar System:** Continuous **Student-Faculty Ratio:** 22:1 **Credit Hours For Degree:** 90 quarter credits, Associates **Professional Accreditation:** ACCSC.

INTELLITEC COLLEGE (PUEBLO)

3673 Parker Blvd.
Pueblo, CO 81008
Tel: (719)542-3181; Free: 800-748-2282
Fax: (719)543-4196
Web Site: www.intelliteccollege.edu

Type: Two-Year College **Sex:** Coed **Costs Per Year:** Tuition: $23,151 full-time. Full-time tuition varies according to class time, course load, location, and program. Tuition guaranteed not to increase for student's term of enrollment. **Professional Accreditation:** ACCSC.

JOHNSON & WALES UNIVERSITY

7150 Montview Blvd.
Denver, CO 80220
Tel: (303)256-9300; Free: 877-598-3368
Fax: (303)256-9333
E-mail: den@admissions.jwu.edu
Web Site: www.jwu.edu/denver
President/CEO: Bette Matkowski
Admissions: Kim Medina
Financial Aid: Lynn Robinson

Type: Comprehensive **Sex:** Coed **Scores:** 87% SAT M 400+ **% Accepted:** 81 **Admission Plans:** Deferred Admission; Early Admission **Application Fee:** $0.00 **H.S. Requirements:** High school diploma required; GED accepted **Costs Per Year:** Application fee: $0. Tuition: $30,396 full-time. Mandatory fees: $350 full-time. College room only: $8268. **Scholarships:** Available. **Calendar System:** Quarter, Summer session available **Enrollment:** Full-time 1,227, Graduate full-time 30, Graduate part-time 2, Part-time 129 **Faculty:** Full-time 52, Part-time 75 **Student-Faculty Ratio:** 16:1 **Exams:** SAT I or ACT. **% Receiving Financial Aid:** 77 **% Residing in College-Owned, -Operated, or -Affiliated Housing:** 47 **Regional Accreditation:** New England Association of Schools and Colleges **Credit Hours For Degree:** 90 credits, Associates; 180 credits, Bachelors **ROTC:** Army **Intercollegiate Athletics:** Baseball M; Basketball M & W; Cheerleading M & W; Golf M; Soccer M; Tennis M & W

LAMAR COMMUNITY COLLEGE

2401 S Main St.
Lamar, CO 81052-3999
Tel: (719)336-2248; Free: 800-968-6920
Fax: (719)336-2448
E-mail: admissions@lamarcc.edu
Web Site: www.lamarcc.edu
President/CEO: John T. Marrin
Financial Aid: Dorothy Choat

Type: Two-Year College **Sex:** Coed **Affiliation:** Colorado Community College and Occupational Education System. **% Accepted:** 100 **Admission Plans:** Early Admission; Open Admission; Preferred Admission **Application Deadline:** September 16 **Application Fee:** $0.00 **H.S. Requirements:** High school diploma required; GED accepted **Costs Per Year:** Application fee: $0. State resident tuition: $3132 full-time, $131 per credit hour part-time. Nonresident tuition: $5352 full-time, $223 per credit hour part-time. Mandatory fees: $414 full-time. Full-time tuition and fees vary according to course

load, program, and reciprocity agreements. Part-time tuition varies according to course load, program, and reciprocity agreements. College room and board: $6070. College room only: $1950. **Scholarships:** Available. **Calendar System:** Semester, Summer session available **Enrollment:** Full-time 419, Part-time 420 **Faculty:** Full-time 16, Part-time 39 **Student-Faculty Ratio:** 19:1 **% Residing in College-Owned, -Operated, or -Affiliated Housing:** 20 **Final Year or Final Semester Residency Requirement:** No **Regional Accreditation:** North Central Association of Colleges and Schools **Credit Hours For Degree:** 64 semester hours, Associates **Intercollegiate Athletics:** Baseball M; Basketball M & W; Equestrian Sports M & W; Golf M; Soccer M; Softball W; Volleyball W

LINCOLN COLLEGE OF TECHNOLOGY

11194 E 45th Ave.
Denver, CO 80239
Tel: (303)722-5724
Fax: (303)778-8264
Web Site: www.lincolnedu.com/campus/denver-co
President/CEO: Al Short
Admissions: Jennifer Hash

Type: Two-Year College **Sex:** Coed **% Accepted:** 100 **Application Deadline:** Rolling **Application Fee:** $25.00 **H.S. Requirements:** High school diploma required; GED accepted **Scholarships:** Available. **Calendar System:** Miscellaneous, Summer session available **Credit Hours For Degree:** 70 credit hours, Associates **Professional Accreditation:** ACCSC.

METROPOLITAN STATE UNIVERSITY OF DENVER

890 Auraria Pky.
Denver, CO 80204
Tel: (303)556-5740
Web Site: www.msudenver.edu
President/CEO: Stephen Jordan
Admissions: Michelle Brown

Type: Comprehensive **Sex:** Coed **Scores:** 94% SAT V 400+; 94% SAT M 400+; 60.1% ACT 18-23; 19% ACT 24-29 **% Accepted:** 65 **Admission Plans:** Deferred Admission; Open Admission **Application Deadline:** July 1 **Application Fee:** $25.00 **H.S. Requirements:** High school diploma required; GED accepted **Costs Per Year:** Application fee: $25. State resident tuition: $5,693 full-time. Nonresident tuition: $18,859 full-time. Mandatory fees: $1,236 full-time. Full-time tuition and fees vary according to course load and location. **Scholarships:** Available. **Calendar System:** Semester, Summer session available **Enrollment:** Full-time 12,313, Graduate full-time 186, Graduate part-time 304, Part-time 7,873 **Faculty:** Full-time 556, Part-time 862 **Student-Faculty Ratio:** 18:1 **Exams:** ACT; ACT essay component not used; SAT I; SAT I or ACT; SAT essay component not used; SAT Reasoning. **% Receiving Financial Aid:** 62 **Final Year or Final Semester Residency Requirement:** No **Regional Accreditation:** North Central Association of Colleges and Schools **Credit Hours For Degree:** 120 semester hours, Bachelors **ROTC:** Air Force, Army **Professional Accreditation:** ABET, ACEN, APA, CSWE, NASAD, NASM, NCATE, NRPA. **Intercollegiate Athletics:** Baseball M; Basketball M & W; Cross-Country Running M & W; Soccer M & W; Softball W; Tennis M & W; Track and Field M & W; Volleyball W

MORGAN COMMUNITY COLLEGE

920 Barlow Rd.
Fort Morgan, CO 80701-4399
Tel: (970)542-3100; Free: 800-622-0216
E-mail: kim.maxwell@morgancc.edu
Web Site: www.morgancc.edu
President/CEO: Dr. Kerry Hart
Admissions: Kim Maxwell
Financial Aid: Sally Anne Shawcroft

Type: Two-Year College **Sex:** Coed **Affiliation:** Colorado Community College and Occupational Education System. **Admission Plans:** Deferred Admission; Early Admission; Open Admission **Application Deadline:** Rolling **H.S. Requirements:** High school diploma or equivalent not required **Costs Per Year:** State resident tuition: $3132 full-time, $130.50 per credit hour part-time. Nonresident tuition: $12,850 full-time, $535.40 per credit hour part-time. Mandatory fees: $344 full-time, $13.28 per credit hour part-time, $12.85 per term part-time. Full-time tuition and fees vary according to course load, program, and reciprocity agreements. Part-time tuition and fees vary according to course load, program, and reciprocity agreements. **Scholarships:** Available. **Calendar System:** Semester, Summer session available

Enrollment: Full-time 374, Part-time 1,273 **Faculty:** Full-time 33, Part-time 114 **Student-Faculty Ratio:** 15:1 **Regional Accreditation:** North Central Association of Colleges and Schools **Credit Hours For Degree:** 60 credit hours, Associates **Professional Accreditation:** ACEN, APTA.

NAROPA UNIVERSITY

2130 Arapahoe Ave.
Boulder, CO 80302-6697
Tel: (303)444-0202; Free: 800-772-6951
Fax: (303)444-0410
E-mail: kwills@naropa.edu
Web Site: www.naropa.edu
President/CEO: Charles G. Lief
Admissions: Karen Wills
Financial Aid: Nancy Morrell

Type: Comprehensive **Sex:** Coed **% Accepted:** 80 **Admission Plans:** Deferred Admission **Application Deadline:** Rolling **Application Fee:** $50.00 **H.S. Requirements:** High school diploma required; GED accepted **Costs Per Year:** Application fee: $50. Comprehensive fee: $40,045 includes full-time tuition ($30,400), mandatory fees ($180), and college room and board ($9465). Full-time tuition and fees vary according to course load. Part-time tuition: $995 per credit. Part-time mandatory fees: $340 per term. Part-time tuition and fees vary according to course load. **Scholarships:** Available. **Calendar System:** Semester, Summer session available **Enrollment:** Full-time 368, Graduate full-time 371, Graduate part-time 174, Part-time 29 **Faculty:** Full-time 46, Part-time 117 **Student-Faculty Ratio:** 14:1 **% Receiving Financial Aid:** 68 **% Residing in College-Owned, -Operated, or -Affiliated Housing:** 17 **Final Year or Final Semester Residency Requirement:** No **Regional Accreditation:** North Central Association of Colleges and Schools **Credit Hours For Degree:** 120 semester hours, Bachelors

NATIONAL AMERICAN UNIVERSITY (CENTENNIAL)

8242 S University Blvd.
Ste. 100
Centennial, CO 80122
Tel: (303)542-7000; Free: 877-593-0429
Web Site: www.national.edu

Type: Four-Year College **Sex:** Coed **Regional Accreditation:** North Central Association of Colleges and Schools

NATIONAL AMERICAN UNIVERSITY (COLORADO SPRINGS)

1079 Space Ctr. Dr.
Unit 140
Colorado Springs, CO 80915
Tel: (719)208-3800; Free: 877-593-0430
Web Site: www.national.edu

Type: Four-Year College **Sex:** Coed **Regional Accreditation:** North Central Association of Colleges and Schools

NATIONAL AMERICAN UNIVERSITY (COLORADO SPRINGS)

1915 Jamboree Dr., Ste. 185
Colorado Springs, CO 80918
Tel: (719)590-8300
Fax: (719)277-0589
E-mail: csadmissions@national.edu
Web Site: www.national.edu
President/CEO: Dr. Jerry Gallentine

Type: Four-Year College **Sex:** Coed **Admission Plans:** Deferred Admission; Open Admission **Application Deadline:** Rolling **Application Fee:** $25.00 **H.S. Requirements:** High school diploma required; GED accepted **Scholarships:** Available. **Calendar System:** Quarter, Summer session available **Regional Accreditation:** North Central Association of Colleges and Schools **Credit Hours For Degree:** 96 quarter hours, Associates; 193 quarter hours, Bachelors

NATIONAL AMERICAN UNIVERSITY (DENVER)

1325 S Colorado Blvd., Ste. 100
Denver, CO 80222
Tel: (303)758-6700
Fax: (303)758-6810
E-mail: jhaack@national.edu
Web Site: www.national.edu
President/CEO: Dr. Jerry Gallentine

Admissions: Jacklyn Haack
Financial Aid: Cheryl Schunneman

Type: Comprehensive **Sex:** Coed **Admission Plans:** Deferred Admission; Early Admission; Open Admission **Application Deadline:** Rolling **Application Fee:** $25.00 **H.S. Requirements:** High school diploma required; GED accepted **Scholarships:** Available. **Calendar System:** Quarter, Summer session available **Enrollment:** Full-time 54, Part-time 146 **Faculty:** Part-time 35 **Student-Faculty Ratio:** 10:1 **Regional Accreditation:** North Central Association of Colleges and Schools **Credit Hours For Degree:** 97 quarter credits, Associates; 193 quarter credits, Bachelors

NAZARENE BIBLE COLLEGE

1111 Academy Park Loop
Colorado Springs, CO 80910-3704
Tel: (719)884-5000; Free: 800-873-3873
Fax: (719)884-5199
E-mail: semcconnaughey@nbc.edu
Web Site: www.nbc.edu
President/CEO: Dr. Harold B. Graves, Jr.
Admissions: Scott McConnaughey
Financial Aid: Jenny Madsen

Type: Four-Year College **Sex:** Coed **Affiliation:** Church of the Nazarene. **% Accepted:** 18 **Admission Plans:** Deferred Admission; Open Admission **Application Deadline:** Rolling **Application Fee:** $0.00 **H.S. Requirements:** High school diploma required; GED accepted **Costs Per Year:** Application fee: $0. Tuition: $450 per credit hour part-time. Part-time tuition varies according to program. **Scholarships:** Available. **Calendar System:** Trimester, Summer session available **Enrollment:** Full-time 120, Part-time 663 **% Receiving Financial Aid:** 72 **Final Year or Final Semester Residency Requirement:** No **Regional Accreditation:** North Central Association of Colleges and Schools **Credit Hours For Degree:** 64 semester hours, Associates; 120 semester hours, Bachelors **Professional Accreditation:** ABHE.

NORTHEASTERN JUNIOR COLLEGE

100 College Ave.
Sterling, CO 80751-2399
Tel: (970)521-6600; Free: 800-626-4637
Fax: (970)522-4945
E-mail: adam.kunkel@njc.edu
Web Site: www.njc.edu
President/CEO: Dr. Jay Lee
Admissions: Adam Kunkel

Type: Two-Year College **Sex:** Coed **Affiliation:** Colorado Community College and Occupational Education System. **% Accepted:** 100 **Admission Plans:** Deferred Admission; Early Admission; Open Admission; Preferred Admission **Application Deadline:** Rolling **Application Fee:** $0.00 **H.S. Requirements:** High school diploma or equivalent not required **Costs Per Year:** Application fee: $0. State resident tuition: $3708 full-time, $131 per credit hour part-time. Nonresident tuition: $5274 full-time, $196 per credit hour part-time. Mandatory fees: $576 full-time, $22.85 per credit hour part-time, $12.55 per term part-time. Full-time tuition and fees vary according to course load. Part-time tuition and fees vary according to course load. College room and board: $6566. College room only: $2978. Room and board charges vary according to board plan and housing facility. **Scholarships:** Available. **Calendar System:** Semester, Summer session available **Enrollment:** Full-time 981, Part-time 795 **Faculty:** Full-time 49, Part-time 28 **Student-Faculty Ratio:** 21:1 **% Residing in College-Owned, -Operated, or -Affiliated Housing:** 25 **Final Year or Final Semester Residency Requirement:** No **Regional Accreditation:** North Central Association of Colleges and Schools **Credit Hours For Degree:** 60 credit hours, Associates **Intercollegiate Athletics:** Baseball M; Basketball M & W; Equestrian Sports M & W; Golf M & W; Soccer M; Softball W; Volleyball W

OTERO JUNIOR COLLEGE

1802 Colorado Ave.
La Junta, CO 81050-3415
Tel: (719)384-6831
Fax: (719)384-6880
E-mail: lauren.berg@ojc.edu
Web Site: www.ojc.edu
President/CEO: Pres. James T. Rizzuto
Admissions: Lauren Berg

Type: Two-Year College **Sex:** Coed **Affiliation:** Colorado Community College System. **Admission Plans:** Early Admission; Open Admission **Application Deadline:** August 15 **Application Fee:** $0.00 **H.S. Requirements:** High school diploma or equivalent not required **Costs Per Year:** Application fee: $0. State resident tuition: $3132 full-time. Nonresident tuition: $5363 full-time. Mandatory fees: $278 full-time. Full-time tuition and fees vary according to course load. College room and board: $6306. Room and board charges vary according to board plan and housing facility. **Scholarships:** Available. **Calendar System:** Semester, Summer session available **Student-Faculty Ratio:** 19:1 **Final Year or Final Semester Residency Requirement:** No **Regional Accreditation:** North Central Association of Colleges and Schools **Credit Hours For Degree:** 60 semester hours, Associates **Professional Accreditation:** ACEN. **Intercollegiate Athletics:** Baseball M; Basketball M & W; Golf M & W; Soccer M & W; Softball W; Volleyball W; Wrestling M

PIKES PEAK COMMUNITY COLLEGE

5675 S Academy Blvd.
Colorado Springs, CO 80906-5498
Tel: (719)576-7711; Free: 866-411-7722
Fax: (719)540-7614
Web Site: www.ppcc.edu
President/CEO: Dr. Lance Bolton

Type: Two-Year College **Sex:** Coed **Affiliation:** Colorado Community College and Occupational Education System. **Admission Plans:** Open Admission **Application Deadline:** Rolling **H.S. Requirements:** High school diploma or equivalent not required **Scholarships:** Available. **Calendar System:** Semester, Summer session available **Regional Accreditation:** North Central Association of Colleges and Schools **Credit Hours For Degree:** 60 credit hours, Associates **ROTC:** Army **Professional Accreditation:** ACF, ADA.

PIMA MEDICAL INSTITUTE (AURORA)

13750 E Mississippi Ave.
Aurora, CO 80012
Tel: (303)368-7462; Free: 800-477-PIMA
Web Site: www.pmi.edu

Type: Two-Year College **Sex:** Coed **Professional Accreditation:** ABHES.

PIMA MEDICAL INSTITUTE (COLORADO SPRINGS)

3770 Citadel Dr. N
Colorado Springs, CO 80909
Tel: (719)482-7462
E-mail: jalbers@pmi.edu
Web Site: www.pmi.edu
President/CEO: Tara Dailey
Admissions: Joe Albers

Type: Two-Year College **Sex:** Coed **Exams:** Other. **Professional Accreditation:** ABHES.

PIMA MEDICAL INSTITUTE (DENVER)

7475 Dakin St.
Denver, CO 80221
Tel: (303)426-1800; Free: 888-477-PIMA
Fax: (303)412-8752
Web Site: www.pmi.edu
President/CEO: Ryan Minic

Type: Two-Year College **Sex:** Coed **Affiliation:** Vocational Training Institutes, Inc. **Scholarships:** Available. **Calendar System:** Miscellaneous, Summer session not available **Exams:** Other. **Credit Hours For Degree:** 76 credits, Associates **Professional Accreditation:** ABHES, CoARC, JRCERT.

PLATT COLLEGE

3100 S Parker Rd., Ste. 200
Aurora, CO 80014-3141
Tel: (303)369-5151
Web Site: www.plattcolorado.edu
President/CEO: Jerald B. Sirbu
Financial Aid: Margie Rose

Type: Four-Year College **Sex:** Coed **Application Deadline:** Rolling **Application Fee:** $75.00 **H.S. Requirements:** High school diploma required; GED accepted **Scholarships:** Available. **Calendar System:** Continuous **% Receiving Financial Aid:** 87 **Credit Hours For Degree:** 96 quarter hours, Associates; 200 quarter hours, Bachelors **Professional Accreditation:** ACCSC.

PUEBLO COMMUNITY COLLEGE

900 W Orman Ave.
Pueblo, CO 81004-1499
Tel: (719)549-3200; Free: 888-642-6017
Fax: (719)549-3012
E-mail: barbara.benedict@pueblocc.edu
Web Site: www.pueblocc.edu
President/CEO: Patty Erjavec
Admissions: Barbara Benedict

Type: Two-Year College **Sex:** Coed **Affiliation:** Colorado Community College System. **% Accepted:** 100 **Admission Plans:** Deferred Admission; Early Admission; Open Admission **Application Deadline:** Rolling **Application Fee:** $0.00 **H.S. Requirements:** High school diploma or equivalent not required **Costs Per Year:** Application fee: $0. State resident tuition: $4,722 full-time, $157.41 per credit hour part-time. Nonresident tuition: $15,370 full-time, $512.35 per credit hour part-time. Mandatory fees: $1,199 full-time, $19.96 per credit hour part-time, $55.59 per term part-time. Full-time tuition and fees vary according to location, program, and reciprocity agreements. Part-time tuition and fees vary according to location, program, and reciprocity agreements. **Scholarships:** Available. **Calendar System:** Semester, Summer session available **Enrollment:** Full-time 2,281, Part-time 3,922 **Faculty:** Full-time 110, Part-time 317 **Student-Faculty Ratio:** 16:1 **Final Year or Final Semester Residency Requirement:** No **Regional Accreditation:** North Central Association of Colleges and Schools **Credit Hours For Degree:** 60 credits, Associates **Professional Accreditation:** ACEN, ACF, ADA, AOTA, APTA, CoARC, JCAHPO, JRCEMTP.

RED ROCKS COMMUNITY COLLEGE

13300 W 6th Ave.
Lakewood, CO 80228-1255
Tel: (303)914-6600
Fax: (303)914-6666
E-mail: admissions@rrcc.edu
Web Site: www.rrcc.edu
President/CEO: Dr. Michele Haney

Type: Two-Year College **Sex:** Coed **Affiliation:** Colorado Community College and Occupational Education System. **% Accepted:** 100 **Admission Plans:** Early Admission; Open Admission **Application Deadline:** Rolling **Application Fee:** $0.00 **H.S. Requirements:** High school diploma or equivalent not required **Costs Per Year:** Application fee: $0. State resident tuition: $3132 full-time, $130.50 per credit hour part-time. Nonresident tuition: $12,848 full-time, $535.40 per credit hour part-time. Mandatory fees: $438 full-time, $9.58 per credit hour part-time, $103.92 per term part-time. Full-time tuition and fees vary according to program and reciprocity agreements. Part-time tuition and fees vary according to program and reciprocity agreements. **Scholarships:** Available. **Calendar System:** Semester, Summer session available **Enrollment:** Full-time 2,854, Part-time 6,174 **Faculty:** Full-time 93, Part-time 418 **Student-Faculty Ratio:** 23:1 **Exams:** ACT essay component not used; SAT essay component not used. **Regional Accreditation:** North Central Association of Colleges and Schools **Credit Hours For Degree:** 60 credit hours, Associates **ROTC:** Air Force, Army **Professional Accreditation:** AAMAE.

REDSTONE COLLEGE–DENVER

10851 W 120th Ave.
Broomfield, CO 80021
Tel: (303)466-1714; Free: 877-801-1025
Fax: (303)469-3797
Web Site: www.redstone.edu
President/CEO: Glenn Wilson

Type: Two-Year College **Sex:** Coed **H.S. Requirements:** High school diploma required; GED accepted **Scholarships:** Available. **Calendar System:** Continuous **Professional Accreditation:** ACCSC, ACICS.

REGIS UNIVERSITY

3333 Regis Blvd.
Denver, CO 80221-1099
Tel: (303)458-4100; Free: 800-388-2366
Fax: (303)964-5534
E-mail: sengel@regis.edu
Web Site: www.regis.edu
President/CEO: Rev. John Fitzgibbons, SJ
Admissions: Sarah Engel
Financial Aid: Ellie Miller

Type: Comprehensive **Sex:** Coed **Affiliation:** Roman Catholic (Jesuit). **Scores:** 98% SAT V 400+; 97% SAT M 400+; 43.18% ACT 18-23; 44.97% ACT 24-29 **% Accepted:** 66 **Admission Plans:** Deferred Admission **Application Deadline:** April 15 **Application Fee:** $0.00 **H.S. Requirements:** High school diploma required; GED accepted **Costs Per Year:** Application fee: $0. Comprehensive fee: $43,750 includes full-time tuition ($33,110), mandatory fees ($600), and college room and board ($10,040). College room only: $5400. Full-time tuition and fees vary according to class time, course level, course load, degree level, location, program, reciprocity agreements, and student level. Room and board charges vary according to board plan and housing facility. Part-time tuition: $1035 per credit hour. Part-time tuition varies according to class time, course level, course load, degree level, location, program, reciprocity agreements, and student level. **Scholarships:** Available. **Calendar System:** Semester, Summer session available **Enrollment:** Full-time 2,419, Graduate full-time 2,572, Graduate part-time 1,654, Part-time 2,080 **Faculty:** Full-time 274, Part-time 529 **Student-Faculty Ratio:** 14:1 **Exams:** ACT essay component not used; SAT I or ACT; SAT II; SAT essay component not used; SAT Reasoning. **% Receiving Financial Aid:** 67 **Final Year or Final Semester Residency Requirement:** No **Regional Accreditation:** North Central Association of Colleges and Schools **Credit Hours For Degree:** 128 semester hours, Bachelors **ROTC:** Air Force, Army, Navy **Professional Accreditation:** AACN, ABET, ACA, ACPE, AHIMA, APTA, TEAC. **Intercollegiate Athletics:** Baseball M; Basketball M & W; Cross-Country Running M & W; Golf M; Lacrosse W; Soccer M & W; Softball W; Volleyball W

ROCKY MOUNTAIN COLLEGE OF ART + DESIGN

1600 Pierce St.
Lakewood, CO 80214
Tel: (303)753-6046; Free: 800-888-ARTS
Fax: (303)759-4970
E-mail: mabraham@rmcad.edu
Web Site: www.rmcad.edu
President/CEO: Christopher A. Marconi
Admissions: Marc Abraham
Financial Aid: Michael Dulay

Type: Comprehensive **Sex:** Coed **Admission Plans:** Open Admission **Application Deadline:** Rolling **Application Fee:** $50.00 **H.S. Requirements:** High school diploma required; GED accepted **Costs Per Year:** Application fee: $50. Tuition: $15,870 full-time, $594 per credit part-time. Mandatory fees: $525 full-time. Full-time tuition and fees vary according to course load, degree level, and location. Part-time tuition varies according to course load, degree level, and location. **Scholarships:** Available. **Calendar System:** Semester, Summer session available **Enrollment:** Full-time 688, Graduate full-time 14, Graduate part-time 3, Part-time 391 **Faculty:** Full-time 38, Part-time 167 **Student-Faculty Ratio:** 9:1 **Final Year or Final Semester Residency Requirement:** Yes **Regional Accreditation:** North Central Association of Colleges and Schools **Credit Hours For Degree:** 120 credits, Bachelors **Professional Accreditation:** CIDA, NASAD.

TRINIDAD STATE JUNIOR COLLEGE

600 Prospect St.
Trinidad, CO 81082-2396
Tel: (719)846-5011; Free: 800-621-8752
Fax: (719)846-5667
E-mail: bernadine.degarbo@trinidadstate.edu
Web Site: www.trinidadstate.edu
President/CEO: Dr. Carmen M. Simone
Admissions: Bernadine DeGarbo
Financial Aid: Wilma Atencio

Type: Two-Year College **Sex:** Coed **Affiliation:** Colorado Community College and Occupational Education System. **Admission Plans:** Deferred Admission; Open Admission **Application Deadline:** Rolling **Application Fee:** $0.00 **H.S. Requirements:** High school diploma required; GED accepted **Costs Per Year:** Application fee: $0. One-time mandatory fee: $25.20. State resident tuition: $3915 full-time, $131 per credit hour part-time. Nonresident tuition: $6703 full-time, $223 per credit hour part-time. Mandatory fees: $615 full-time, $10.06 per credit hour part-time. Full-time tuition and fees vary according to course load, location, program, and reciprocity agreements. Part-time tuition and fees vary according to course load, location, program, and reciprocity agreements. College room and board: $5884. Room and board charges vary according to board plan. **Scholarships:** Available. **Calendar System:** Semester, Summer session available **Enrollment:** Full-time 882, Part-time 901 **Faculty:** Full-time 50, Part-time 111

Student-Faculty Ratio: 13:1 **% Residing in College-Owned, -Operated, or -Affiliated Housing:** 12 **Regional Accreditation:** North Central Association of Colleges and Schools **Credit Hours For Degree:** 60 semester credit hours, Associates **Professional Accreditation:** ABET. **Intercollegiate Athletics:** Baseball M; Basketball M; Golf M; Soccer M & W; Softball W; Volleyball W

UNITED STATES AIR FORCE ACADEMY

HQ USAFA/A9A
2304 Cadet Dr., Ste. 3800
USAF Academy, CO 80840-5025
Tel: (719)333-1818; Free: 800-443-9266
Fax: (719)333-3012
Web Site: www.usafa.edu
President/CEO: Lt. Gen. Michelle D. Johnson

Type: Four-Year College **Sex:** Coed **Scores:** 100% SAT V 400+; 100% SAT M 400+; 44% ACT 24-29 **% Accepted:** 14 **Application Deadline:** December 31 **Application Fee:** $0.00 **H.S. Requirements:** High school diploma required; GED accepted **Costs Per Year:** Application fee: $0. **Calendar System:** Semester, Summer session available **Enrollment:** Full-time 4,111 **Faculty:** Full-time 501, Part-time 5 **Student-Faculty Ratio:** 8:1 **Exams:** SAT I or ACT; SAT Reasoning. **% Residing in College-Owned, -Operated, or -Affiliated Housing:** 100 **Final Year or Final Semester Residency Requirement:** Yes **Regional Accreditation:** North Central Association of Colleges and Schools **Credit Hours For Degree:** 132 semester hours, Bachelors **Professional Accreditation:** AACSB, ABET. **Intercollegiate Athletics:** Archery M & W; Baseball M; Basketball M & W; Cheerleading M & W; Cross-Country Running M & W; Equestrian Sports M & W; Fencing M & W; Football M; Golf M & W; Gymnastics M & W; Ice Hockey M; Lacrosse M & W; Racquetball M & W; Riflery M & W; Rock Climbing M & W; Skiing (Cross-Country) M & W; Skiing (Downhill) M & W; Soccer M & W; Softball W; Swimming and Diving M & W; Tennis M & W; Track and Field M & W; Ultimate Frisbee M & W; Volleyball M & W; Water Polo M & W; Weight Lifting M & W; Wrestling M

UNIVERSITY OF COLORADO BOULDER

Boulder, CO 80309
Tel: (303)492-1411
Fax: (303)492-7115
E-mail: apply@colorado.edu
Web Site: www.colorado.edu
President/CEO: Philip P. DiStefano
Financial Aid: Gwen E. Pomper

Type: University **Sex:** Coed **Affiliation:** University of Colorado System. **Scores:** 98% SAT V 400+; 100% SAT M 400+; 18% ACT 18-23; 54% ACT 24-29 **% Accepted:** 80 **Admission Plans:** Deferred Admission; Early Decision Plan **Application Deadline:** January 15 **Application Fee:** $50.00 **H.S. Requirements:** High school diploma required; GED accepted **Costs Per Year:** Application fee: $50. One-time mandatory fee: $182. State resident tuition: $9312 full-time. Nonresident tuition: $32,346 full-time. Mandatory fees: $1779 full-time. Full-time tuition and fees vary according to program. College room and board: $13,194. Room and board charges vary according to board plan, housing facility, and location. **Scholarships:** Available. **Calendar System:** Semester, Summer session available **Enrollment:** Full-time 24,906, Graduate full-time 2,412, Graduate part-time 3,353, Part-time 2,104 **Faculty:** Full-time 1,499, Part-time 554 **Student-Faculty Ratio:** 18:1 **Exams:** ACT essay component not used; SAT I or ACT; SAT essay component not used; SAT Reasoning. **% Receiving Financial Aid:** 35 **% Residing in College-Owned, -Operated, or -Affiliated Housing:** 29 **Final Year or Final Semester Residency Requirement:** Yes **Regional Accreditation:** North Central Association of Colleges and Schools **Credit Hours For Degree:** 120 semester hours, Bachelors **ROTC:** Air Force, Army, Navy **Professional Accreditation:** AACSB, AALS, ABA, ABET, ACEJMC, APA, ASHA, NASM, NCATE. **Intercollegiate Athletics:** Baseball M; Basketball M & W; Cheerleading M & W; Crew M & W; Cross-Country Running M & W; Equestrian Sports M & W; Fencing M & W; Field Hockey M & W; Football M; Golf M & W; Ice Hockey M & W; Lacrosse M & W; Racquetball M & W; Rugby M & W; Skiing (Cross-Country) M & W; Skiing (Downhill) M & W; Soccer M & W; Softball W; Swimming and Diving M & W; Tennis M & W; Track and Field M & W; Triathlon M & W; Ultimate Frisbee M & W; Volleyball M & W; Water Polo M & W; Wrestling M

UNIVERSITY OF COLORADO COLORADO SPRINGS

1420 Austin Bluffs Pky.
Colorado Springs, CO 80918

Tel: (719)255-8227; Free: 800-990-8227
E-mail: cbeiswan@uccs.edu
Web Site: www.uccs.edu
President/CEO: Dr. Pamela Shockley-Zalabak
Admissions: Chris Beiswanger
Financial Aid: Jevita Rogers
Type: University **Sex:** Coed **Affiliation:** University of Colorado System. **Scores:** 97% SAT V 400+; 97% SAT M 400+; 49% ACT 18-23; 40% ACT 24-29 **% Accepted:** 91 **Admission Plans:** Deferred Admission **Application Deadline:** Rolling **Application Fee:** $50.00 **H.S. Requirements:** High school diploma required; GED accepted **Costs Per Year:** Application fee: $50. One-time mandatory fee: $140. State resident tuition: $7980 full-time, $266 per credit hour part-time. Nonresident tuition: $20,850 full-time, $695 per credit hour part-time. Mandatory fees: $1448 full-time. Full-time tuition and fees vary according to course load, degree level, location, program, reciprocity agreements, and student level. Part-time tuition varies according to course load, degree level, location, program, reciprocity agreements, and student level. College room and board: $9500. Room and board charges vary according to board plan, housing facility, and student level. **Scholarships:** Available. **Calendar System:** Semester, Summer session available **Enrollment:** Full-time 7,472, Graduate full-time 413, Graduate part-time 1,467, Part-time 2,344 **Faculty:** Full-time 406, Part-time 327 **Student-Faculty Ratio:** 17:1 **Exams:** SAT I or ACT. **% Receiving Financial Aid:** 59 **% Residing in College-Owned, -Operated, or -Affiliated Housing:** 13 **Final Year or Final Semester Residency Requirement:** No **Regional Accreditation:** North Central Association of Colleges and Schools **Credit Hours For Degree:** 120 credit hours, Bachelors **ROTC:** Army **Professional Accreditation:** AACN, AACSB, ABET, ACA, NASPAA, NCATE. **Intercollegiate Athletics:** Baseball M; Basketball M & W; Cross-Country Running M & W; Golf M & W; Lacrosse W; Soccer M & W; Softball W; Track and Field M & W; Volleyball W

UNIVERSITY OF COLORADO DENVER

PO Box 173364
Denver, CO 80217-3364
Tel: (303)556-2400
Fax: (303)556-2398
E-mail: admissions@ucdenver.edu
Web Site: www.ucdenver.edu
President/CEO: Dr. Dorothy Horrell
Admissions: Catherine Wilson
Financial Aid: Justin Jaramillo
Type: University **Sex:** Coed **Affiliation:** University of Colorado System. **Scores:** 97% SAT V 400+; 95% SAT M 400+; 52.78% ACT 18-23; 36.35% ACT 24-29 **% Accepted:** 67 **Admission Plans:** Deferred Admission **Application Deadline:** July 22 **Application Fee:** $50.00 **H.S. Requirements:** High school diploma required; GED accepted **Costs Per Year:** Application fee: $50. State resident tuition: $9090 full-time, $303 per credit hour part-time. Nonresident tuition: $28,020 full-time, $934 per credit hour part-time. Mandatory fees: $1288 full-time, $1288 per year part-time. Full-time tuition and fees vary according to course level, course load, degree level, location, program, reciprocity agreements, and student level. Part-time tuition and fees vary according to course level, course load, degree level, location, program, reciprocity agreements, and student level. **Scholarships:** Available. **Calendar System:** Semester, Summer session available **Enrollment:** Full-time 8,077, Graduate full-time 4,238, Graduate part-time 5,396, Part-time 5,959 **Faculty:** Full-time 3,520, Part-time 588 **Student-Faculty Ratio:** 16:1 **Exams:** ACT essay component not used; SAT I or ACT; SAT essay component not used; SAT Reasoning; SAT Subject. **% Receiving Financial Aid:** 58 **Final Year or Final Semester Residency Requirement:** No **Regional Accreditation:** North Central Association of Colleges and Schools **Credit Hours For Degree:** 120 semester hours, Bachelors **ROTC:** Air Force, Army **Professional Accreditation:** AACN, AACSB, ABET, ACA, ACEN, ACNM, ACPE, ACSP, ADA, APTA, ASLA, CAHME, LCME/AMA, NAAB, NASM, NASPAA, NCATE. **Intercollegiate Athletics:** Basketball M & W; Ice Hockey M; Lacrosse M & W; Soccer M & W; Volleyball M & W

UNIVERSITY OF DENVER

2199 S University Blvd.
Denver, CO 80208
Tel: (303)871-2000; Free: 800-525-9495
Fax: (303)871-3301
E-mail: admission@du.edu
Web Site: www.du.edu

President/CEO: Dr. Rebecca Chopp
Admissions: Todd R. Rinehart
Financial Aid: John Gudvangen
Type: University **Sex:** Coed **Scores:** 99% SAT V 400+; 100% SAT M 400+; 9.8% ACT 18-23; 54.2% ACT 24-29 **% Accepted:** 73 **Admission Plans:** Deferred Admission; Early Decision Plan **Application Deadline:** January 15 **Application Fee:** $65.00 **H.S. Requirements:** High school diploma required; GED accepted **Costs Per Year:** Application fee: $65. Comprehensive fee: $55,676 includes full-time tuition ($43,164), mandatory fees ($1014), and college room and board ($11,498). College room only: $6958. Full-time tuition and fees vary according to course load and program. Room and board charges vary according to board plan and housing facility. Part-time tuition: $1199 per credit hour. Part-time tuition varies according to course load and program. **Scholarships:** Available. **Calendar System:** Quarter, Summer session available **Enrollment:** Full-time 5,448, Graduate full-time 3,184, Graduate part-time 2,855, Part-time 310 **Faculty:** Full-time 701, Part-time 578 **Student-Faculty Ratio:** 11:1 **Exams:** ACT essay component not used; SAT I or ACT; SAT essay component not used; SAT Reasoning. **% Receiving Financial Aid:** 42 **% Residing in College-Owned, -Operated, or -Affiliated Housing:** 44 **Final Year or Final Semester Residency Requirement:** Yes **Regional Accreditation:** North Central Association of Colleges and Schools **Credit Hours For Degree:** 183 quarter hours, Bachelors **ROTC:** Air Force, Army **Professional Accreditation:** AACSB, AALS, ABA, ABET, ALA, APA, CSWE, NASAD, NASM, NCATE. **Intercollegiate Athletics:** Baseball M; Basketball M & W; Cross-Country Running M & W; Equestrian Sports M & W; Golf M & W; Gymnastics W; Ice Hockey M & W; Lacrosse M & W; Racquetball M & W; Skiing (Cross-Country) M & W; Skiing (Downhill) M & W; Soccer M & W; Softball W; Swimming and Diving M & W; Tennis M & W; Volleyball W; Water Polo M & W

UNIVERSITY OF NORTHERN COLORADO

Greeley, CO 80639
Tel: (970)351-1890; Free: 888-700-4UNC
E-mail: admissions@unco.edu
Web Site: www.unco.edu
President/CEO: Kay Norton
Admissions: Sean Broghammer
Financial Aid: Marty Somero
Type: University **Sex:** Coed **Scores:** 92% SAT V 400+; 92% SAT M 400+; 52% ACT 18-23; 31.5% ACT 24-29 **% Accepted:** 89 **Admission Plans:** Deferred Admission **Application Deadline:** August 1 **Application Fee:** $45.00 **H.S. Requirements:** High school diploma required; GED accepted **Costs Per Year:** Application fee: $45. State resident tuition: $6372 full-time, $253 per credit hour part-time. Nonresident tuition: $17,958 full-time, $713.25 per credit hour part-time. Mandatory fees: $1794 full-time, $82.41 per credit hour part-time. Full-time tuition and fees vary according to location and program. Part-time tuition and fees vary according to location and program. College room and board: $10,360. College room only: $5000. Room and board charges vary according to board plan and housing facility. **Scholarships:** Available. **Calendar System:** Semester, Summer session available **Enrollment:** Full-time 8,180, Graduate full-time 968, Graduate part-time 1,574, Part-time 1,214 **Faculty:** Full-time 476, Part-time 236 **Student-Faculty Ratio:** 18:1 **Exams:** ACT essay component not used; SAT I or ACT; SAT essay component not used; SAT Reasoning. **% Receiving Financial Aid:** 70 **% Residing in College-Owned, -Operated, or -Affiliated Housing:** 36 **Final Year or Final Semester Residency Requirement:** Yes **Regional Accreditation:** North Central Association of Colleges and Schools **Credit Hours For Degree:** 120 semester hours, Bachelors **ROTC:** Air Force, Army **Professional Accreditation:** AACN, AACSB, ACA, AND, APA, ASHA, CEPH, CORE, JRCAT, NASM, NCATE. **Intercollegiate Athletics:** Baseball M; Basketball M & W; Cross-Country Running W; Football M; Golf M & W; Ice Hockey M; Lacrosse M; Rugby M & W; Soccer M & W; Softball W; Swimming and Diving W; Tennis M & W; Track and Field M & W; Volleyball W; Wrestling M

UNIVERSITY OF PHOENIX–COLORADO CAMPUS

10004 Park Meadows Dr.
Lone Tree, CO 80124-5453
Tel: (303)694-9093; Free: 866-766-0766
Web Site: www.phoenix.edu
President/CEO: Timothy P. Slottow
Admissions: Marc Booker
Type: Comprehensive **Sex:** Coed **Admission Plans:** Deferred Admission; Open Admission **Application Deadline:** Rolling **Application Fee:** $0.00

H.S. Requirements: High school diploma required; GED accepted **Scholarships:** Available. **Calendar System:** Continuous, Summer session not available **Enrollment:** Full-time 1,289 **Faculty:** Full-time 27, Part-time 275 **Regional Accreditation:** North Central Association of Colleges and Schools **Credit Hours For Degree:** 60 credits, Associates; 120 credits, Bachelors

UNIVERSITY OF PHOENIX–COLORADO SPRINGS DOWNTOWN CAMPUS
2 N Cascade Ave.
Ste. 100
Colorado Springs, CO 80903
Tel: (719)599-5282; Free: 866-766-0766
Web Site: www.phoenix.edu
President/CEO: Timothy P. Slottow
Admissions: Marc Booker

Type: Comprehensive **Sex:** Coed **Admission Plans:** Deferred Admission; Open Admission **Application Deadline:** Rolling **Application Fee:** $0.00 **H.S. Requirements:** High school diploma required; GED accepted **Scholarships:** Available. **Calendar System:** Continuous, Summer session not available **Faculty:** Full-time 9, Part-time 117 **Regional Accreditation:** North Central Association of Colleges and Schools **Credit Hours For Degree:** 60 credits, Associates; 120 credits, Bachelors **Professional Accreditation:** ACBSP.

WESTERN STATE COLORADO UNIVERSITY
600 N Adams St.
Gunnison, CO 81231
Tel: (970)943-0120; Free: 800-876-5309
Fax: (970)943-7069
E-mail: admissions@western.edu
Web Site: www.western.edu
President/CEO: Dr. Greg Salsbury
Admissions: Paul Fitzgerald
Financial Aid: Carrie Shaw

Type: Comprehensive **Sex:** Coed **Scores:** 96% SAT V 400+; 92% SAT M 400+; 54.19% ACT 18-23; 31.03% ACT 24-29 **% Accepted:** 98 **Admission Plans:** Deferred Admission **Application Fee:** $30.00 **H.S. Requirements:** High school diploma required; GED accepted **Costs Per Year:** Application fee: $30. State resident tuition: $5844 full-time, $243 per credit hour part-time. Nonresident tuition: $16,848 full-time, $702 per credit hour part-time. Mandatory fees: $2607 full-time. Full-time tuition and fees vary according to course load and reciprocity agreements. Part-time tuition varies according to course load and reciprocity agreements. College room and board: $9307. College room only: $4923. Room and board charges vary according to board plan and housing facility. **Scholarships:** Available. **Calendar System:** Semester, Summer session available **Enrollment:** Full-time 1,883, Graduate full-time 235, Graduate part-time 72, Part-time 536 **Faculty:** Full-time 117, Part-time 47 **Student-Faculty Ratio:** 16:1 **Exams:** ACT essay component not used; SAT I or ACT; SAT essay component not used. **% Receiving Financial Aid:** 55 **% Residing in College-Owned, -Operated, or -Affiliated Housing:** 45 **Final Year or Final Semester Residency Requirement:** Yes **Regional Accreditation:** North Central Association of Colleges and Schools **Credit Hours For Degree:** 120 credits, Bachelors **Professional Accreditation:** NASM. **Intercollegiate Athletics:** Baseball M; Basketball M & W; Cheerleading M & W; Cross-Country Running M & W; Football M; Ice Hockey M; Lacrosse M & W; Rock Climbing M & W; Rugby M & W; Skiing (Cross-Country) M & W; Skiing (Downhill) M & W; Soccer M & W; Swimming and Diving W; Track and Field M & W; Volleyball M & W; Wrestling M & W

YESHIVA TORAS CHAIM TALMUDICAL SEMINARY
1555 Stuart St.
Denver, CO 80204-1415
Tel: (303)629-8200
Fax: (303)623-5949
President/CEO: Rabbi Isaac Wasserman
Admissions: Rabbi Israel Kagan

Type: Comprehensive **Sex:** Men **Affiliation:** Jewish. **% Accepted:** 100 **Admission Plans:** Early Admission **H.S. Requirements:** High school diploma required; GED accepted **Calendar System:** Trimester **Credit Hours For Degree:** 168 credits, Bachelors **Professional Accreditation:** AARTS.

ALBERTUS MAGNUS COLLEGE

700 Prospect St.
New Haven, CT 06511-1189
Tel: (203)773-8550; Free: 800-578-9160
Fax: (203)785-8652
E-mail: admissions@albertus.edu
Web Site: www.albertus.edu
President/CEO: Dr. Julia M. McNamara
Admissions: Nilvio Perez
Financial Aid: Michelle Cochran

Type: Comprehensive **Sex:** Coed **Affiliation:** Roman Catholic. **Scores:** 84% SAT V 400+; 82% SAT M 400+; 38% ACT 18-23; 48% ACT 24-29 **% Accepted:** 67 **Admission Plans:** Deferred Admission **Application Deadline:** Rolling **Application Fee:** $35.00 **H.S. Requirements:** High school diploma required; GED accepted **Scholarships:** Available. **Calendar System:** Semester, Summer session available **Enrollment:** Full-time 1,146, Graduate full-time 209, Graduate part-time 85, Part-time 110 **Faculty:** Full-time 52, Part-time 82 **Student-Faculty Ratio:** 14:1 **Exams:** SAT I or ACT; SAT II; SAT Reasoning. **% Receiving Financial Aid:** 96 **% Residing in College-Owned, -Operated, or -Affiliated Housing:** 40 **Final Year or Final Semester Residency Requirement:** Yes **Regional Accreditation:** New England Association of Schools and Colleges **Credit Hours For Degree:** 60 credits, Associates; 120 credits, Bachelors **Intercollegiate Athletics:** Baseball M; Basketball M & W; Golf M & W; Lacrosse M & W; Soccer M & W; Softball W; Tennis M & W; Volleyball M & W

ASNUNTUCK COMMUNITY COLLEGE

170 Elm St.
Enfield, CT 06082-3800
Tel: (860)253-3000
Fax: (860)253-9310
E-mail: tstjames@asnuntuck.edu
Web Site: www.asnuntuck.edu
President/CEO: James P. Lombella
Admissions: Timothy St. James
Financial Aid: Donna Jones-Searle

Type: Two-Year College **Sex:** Coed **Affiliation:** Connecticut State Colleges & Universities (CSCU). **% Accepted:** 100 **Admission Plans:** Deferred Admission; Open Admission **Application Deadline:** Rolling **Application Fee:** $20.00 **H.S. Requirements:** High school diploma required; GED accepted **Costs Per Year:** Application fee: $20. State resident tuition: $3600 full-time, $150 per credit hour part-time. Nonresident tuition: $10,800 full-time, $450 per credit hour part-time. Mandatory fees: $432 full-time. **Scholarships:** Available. **Calendar System:** Semester, Summer session available **Enrollment:** Full-time 622, Part-time 949 **Faculty:** Full-time 30, Part-time 98 **Student-Faculty Ratio:** 15:1 **Exams:** Other. **Final Year or Final Semester Residency Requirement:** No **Regional Accreditation:** New England Association of Schools and Colleges **Credit Hours For Degree:** 60 credits, Associates

BAIS BINYOMIN ACADEMY

132 Prospect St.
Stamford, CT 06901-1202
Tel: (203)325-4351
President/CEO: Michoel Bender

Type: Four-Year College **Sex:** Men **Affiliation:** Jewish. **% Accepted:** 100 **H.S. Requirements:** High school diploma required; GED accepted **Calendar System:** Trimester **Student-Faculty Ratio:** 9:1 **Professional Accreditation:** AARTS.

CAPITAL COMMUNITY COLLEGE

950 Main St.
Hartford, CT 06103
Tel: (860)906-5000
E-mail: jphillips@ccc.commnet.edu
Web Site: www.ccc.commnet.edu
President/CEO: Wilfredo Nieves
Admissions: Jackie Phillips

Type: Two-Year College **Sex:** Coed **Affiliation:** Connecticut State Colleges & Universities (CSCU). **Admission Plans:** Open Admission **Application Deadline:** Rolling **Application Fee:** $20.00 **H.S. Requirements:** High school diploma required; GED accepted. For students with baccalaureate degrees: High school diploma or equivalent not required **Scholarships:** Available. **Calendar System:** Semester, Summer session available **Regional Accreditation:** New England Association of Schools and Colleges **Credit Hours For Degree:** 60 credit hours, Associates **Professional Accreditation:** AAMAE, ACEN, APTA, JRCEMTP, JRCERT.

CENTRAL CONNECTICUT STATE UNIVERSITY

1615 Stanley St.
New Britain, CT 06050-4010
Tel: (860)832-2278; Free: 860-733-2278
Fax: (860)832-2522
E-mail: admissions@ccsu.edu
Web Site: www.ccsu.edu
President/CEO: Dr. John W. Miller
Financial Aid: Dennis Williams

Type: Comprehensive **Sex:** Coed **Affiliation:** Connecticut State Colleges & Universities (CSCU). **Scores:** 96% SAT V 400+; 95% SAT M 400+; 47% ACT 18-23; 43% ACT 24-29 **% Accepted:** 59 **Application Deadline:** May 1 **Application Fee:** $50.00 **H.S. Requirements:** High school diploma required; GED accepted **Costs Per Year:** Application fee: $50. State resident tuition: $4968 full-time, $206 per credit hour part-time. Nonresident tuition: $16,078 full-time, $211 per credit hour part-time. Mandatory fees: $4332 full-time, $274 per credit hour part-time. Full-time tuition and fees vary according to course level, course load, and program. Part-time tuition and fees vary according to course level, course load, and program. College room and board: $11,134. College room only: $6404. Room and board charges vary according to board plan and housing facility. **Scholarships:** Available. **Calendar System:** Semester, Summer session available **Enrollment:** Full-time 7,763, Graduate full-time 504, Graduate part-time 1,649, Part-time 2,170 **Faculty:** Full-time 450, Part-time 499 **Student-Faculty Ratio:** 15:1 **Exams:** ACT essay component not used; SAT I or ACT; SAT essay component not used; SAT Reasoning; SAT Subject. **% Receiving Financial Aid:** 69 **% Residing in College-Owned, -Operated, or -Affiliated Housing:** 24 **Regional Accreditation:** New England Association of Schools and Colleges **Credit Hours For Degree:** 120 credit hours, Bachelors **ROTC:** Air Force, Army **Professional Accreditation:** AACN, AAMFT, AANA, ABET, ACA, ACCE, ATMAE, CSWE, JRCAT, NASM, NCATE. **Intercollegiate Athletics:** Baseball M; Basketball M & W; Cross-Country Running M & W;

Football M; Golf M & W; Lacrosse W; Soccer M & W; Softball W; Swimming and Diving W; Track and Field M & W; Volleyball W

CHARTER OAK STATE COLLEGE

55 Paul Manafort Dr.
New Britain, CT 06053-2142
Tel: (860)515-3800
E-mail: lpendleton@charteroak.edu
Web Site: www.charteroak.edu
President/CEO: Ed Klonoski
Admissions: Lori Pendleton
Financial Aid: Ralph Brasure

Type: Four-Year College **Sex:** Coed **Affiliation:** Connecticut State Colleges & Universities (CSCU). **Admission Plans:** Deferred Admission; Open Admission **Application Fee:** $75.00 **H.S. Requirements:** High school diploma or equivalent not required **Costs Per Year:** Application fee: $75. State resident tuition: $8280 full-time, $276 per credit part-time. Nonresident tuition: $10,890 full-time, $363 per credit part-time. Mandatory fees: $735 full-time, $245 per term part-time. Full-time tuition and fees vary according to course load. Part-time tuition and fees vary according to course load. **Scholarships:** Available. **Calendar System:** Semester, Summer session available **Enrollment:** Full-time 329, Part-time 1,406 **Faculty:** Part-time 173 **Student-Faculty Ratio:** 14:1 **% Receiving Financial Aid:** 71 **Final Year or Final Semester Residency Requirement:** No **Regional Accreditation:** New England Association of Schools and Colleges **Credit Hours For Degree:** 60 credits, Associates; 120 credits, Bachelors

CONNECTICUT COLLEGE

270 Mohegan Ave.
New London, CT 06320
Tel: (860)447-1911
Fax: (860)439-4301
E-mail: admission@conncoll.edu
Web Site: www.conncoll.edu
President/CEO: Dr. Katherine Bergeron
Admissions: Andrew Strickler
Financial Aid: Sean Martin

Type: Comprehensive **Sex:** Coed **Scores:** 100% SAT V 400+; 100% SAT M 400+; 1.23% ACT 18-23; 46.91% ACT 24-29 **% Accepted:** 40 **Admission Plans:** Deferred Admission; Early Action **Application Deadline:** January 1 **Application Fee:** $60.00 **H.S. Requirements:** High school diploma required; GED accepted **Costs Per Year:** Application fee: $60. Comprehensive fee: $62,965 includes full-time tuition ($49,030), mandatory fees ($320), and college room and board ($13,615). College room only: $7860. **Scholarships:** Available. **Calendar System:** Semester, Summer session not available **Enrollment:** Full-time 1,857, Graduate full-time 3, Part-time 61 **Faculty:** Full-time 180, Part-time 81 **Student-Faculty Ratio:** 9:1 **Exams:** ACT; ACT essay component used for admission; SAT I; SAT I and SAT II or ACT; SAT I or ACT; SAT II; SAT essay component used for admission; SAT Reasoning; SAT Subject. **% Receiving Financial Aid:** 55 **% Residing in College-Owned, -Operated, or -Affiliated Housing:** 99 **Final Year or Final Semester Residency Requirement:** Yes **Regional Accreditation:** New England Association of Schools and Colleges **Intercollegiate Athletics:** Baseball M; Basketball M & W; Crew M & W; Cross-Country Running M & W; Equestrian Sports M & W; Field Hockey W; Ice Hockey M & W; Lacrosse M & W; Rugby W; Sailing M & W; Skiing (Cross-Country) M & W; Skiing (Downhill) M & W; Soccer M & W; Squash M & W; Swimming and Diving M & W; Tennis M & W; Track and Field M & W; Ultimate Frisbee M & W; Volleyball M & W; Water Polo M & W

EASTERN CONNECTICUT STATE UNIVERSITY

83 Windham St.
Willimantic, CT 06226-2295
Tel: (860)465-5000
E-mail: dorseyc@easternct.edu
Web Site: www.easternct.edu
President/CEO: Dr. Elsa M. Nunez
Admissions: Christopher Dorsey
Financial Aid: Jennifer Horner

Type: Comprehensive **Sex:** Coed **Affiliation:** Connecticut State Colleges & Universities (CSCU). **Scores:** 98% SAT V 400+; 98% SAT M 400+ **% Accepted:** 64 **Admission Plans:** Deferred Admission **Application Deadline:** Rolling **Application Fee:** $50.00 **H.S. Requirements:** High school diploma required; GED accepted **Costs Per Year:** Application fee: $50. State

resident tuition: $4968 full-time, $467 per year part-time. Nonresident tuition: $16,078 full-time, $472 per credit hour part-time. Mandatory fees: $5048 full-time, $80 per year part-time. Part-time tuition and fees vary according to course load. College room and board: $12,108. College room only: $6902. Room and board charges vary according to board plan and housing facility. **Scholarships:** Available. **Calendar System:** Semester, Summer session available **Enrollment:** Full-time 4,267, Graduate full-time 44, Graduate part-time 120, Part-time 830 **Faculty:** Full-time 198, Part-time 301 **Student-Faculty Ratio:** 16:1 **Exams:** ACT essay component used for placement; SAT essay component used for placement. **% Receiving Financial Aid:** 62 **% Residing in College-Owned, -Operated, or -Affiliated Housing:** 53 **Final Year or Final Semester Residency Requirement:** No **Regional Accreditation:** New England Association of Schools and Colleges **Credit Hours For Degree:** 60 credit hours, Associates; 120 credit hours, Bachelors **ROTC:** Air Force, Army **Professional Accreditation:** CSWE, NCATE. **Intercollegiate Athletics:** Baseball M; Basketball M & W; Cheerleading M & W; Cross-Country Running M & W; Fencing M & W; Field Hockey W; Football M & W; Ice Hockey M & W; Lacrosse M & W; Rugby M; Soccer M & W; Softball W; Swimming and Diving W; Track and Field M & W; Volleyball W

FAIRFIELD UNIVERSITY

1073 N Benson Rd.
Fairfield, CT 06824
Tel: (203)254-4000
Fax: (203)254-4199
E-mail: admis@fairfield.edu
Web Site: www.fairfield.edu
President/CEO: Rev. Jeffrey P. von Arx, SJ
Admissions: Alison Hildenbrand
Financial Aid: Diana Draper

Type: Comprehensive **Sex:** Coed **Affiliation:** Roman Catholic (Jesuit). **Scores:** 100% SAT V 400+; 100% SAT M 400+; 9.4% ACT 18-23; 72.8% ACT 24-29 **% Accepted:** 65 **Admission Plans:** Deferred Admission; Early Action; Early Admission; Early Decision Plan **Application Deadline:** January 15 **Application Fee:** $60.00 **H.S. Requirements:** High school diploma required; GED accepted **Costs Per Year:** Application fee: $60. One-time mandatory fee: $280. Comprehensive fee: $59,860 includes full-time tuition ($45,350), mandatory fees ($650), and college room and board ($13,860). College room only: $8490. Full-time tuition and fees vary according to class time, course level, course load, degree level, and program. Room and board charges vary according to board plan and housing facility. Part-time tuition: $725 per credit hour. Part-time mandatory fees: $60 per term. Part-time tuition and fees vary according to class time, course level, course load, degree level, and program. **Scholarships:** Available. **Calendar System:** Semester, Summer session available **Enrollment:** Full-time 3,704, Graduate full-time 513, Graduate part-time 655, Part-time 266 **Faculty:** Full-time 266, Part-time 312 **Student-Faculty Ratio:** 12:1 **Exams:** ACT essay component not used; SAT essay component not used; SAT Reasoning. **% Receiving Financial Aid:** 46 **% Residing in College-Owned, -Operated, or -Affiliated Housing:** 75 **Final Year or Final Semester Residency Requirement:** Yes **Regional Accreditation:** New England Association of Schools and Colleges **Credit Hours For Degree:** 120 credits, Bachelors **ROTC:** Air Force, Army **Professional Accreditation:** AACN, AACSB, AAMFT, AANA, ABET, ACA, NCATE. **Intercollegiate Athletics:** Baseball M; Basketball M & W; Crew M & W; Cross-Country Running M & W; Field Hockey W; Golf M & W; Lacrosse M & W; Soccer M & W; Softball W; Swimming and Diving M & W; Tennis M & W; Volleyball W

GATEWAY COMMUNITY COLLEGE

20 Church St.
New Haven, CT 06510
Tel: (203)285-2000; Free: 800-390-7723
Fax: (203)285-2018
E-mail: jcarberry@gatewayct.edu
Web Site: www.gwcc.commnet.edu
President/CEO: Dr. Dorsey L. Kendrick
Admissions: Joseph Carberry
Financial Aid: Raymond R. Zeek

Type: Two-Year College **Sex:** Coed **Affiliation:** Connecticut Community –Technical College System. **% Accepted:** 97 **Admission Plans:** Deferred Admission; Early Admission; Open Admission **Application Deadline:** September 1 **Application Fee:** $20.00 **H.S. Requirements:** High school diploma required; GED accepted **Scholarships:** Available. **Calendar**

System: Semester, Summer session available **Enrollment:** Full-time 2,590, Part-time 5,611 **Faculty:** Full-time 107, Part-time 474 **Student-Faculty Ratio:** 17:1 **Regional Accreditation:** New England Association of Schools and Colleges **Credit Hours For Degree:** 60 credit hours, Associates **Professional Accreditation:** ABET, ACEN, JRCERT, JRCNMT. **Intercollegiate Athletics:** Baseball M; Basketball M & W; Soccer M; Softball W

GOODWIN COLLEGE

One Riverside Dr.
East Hartford, CT 06118
Tel: (860)528-4111; Free: 800-889-3282
Fax: (860)291-9550
E-mail: nlentino@goodwin.edu
Web Site: www.goodwin.edu
President/CEO: Mark Scheinberg
Admissions: Nicholas Lentino
Financial Aid: William Mangini

Type: Two-Year College **Sex:** Coed **Admission Plans:** Deferred Admission; Early Admission; Open Admission **Application Fee:** $50.00 **H.S. Requirements:** High school diploma required; GED accepted **Costs Per Year:** Application fee: $50. Tuition: $19,500 full-time, $690 per credit hour part-time. Mandatory fees: $900 full-time. Full-time tuition and fees vary according to course load and program. Part-time tuition varies according to course load and program. **Scholarships:** Available. **Calendar System:** Semester, Summer session available **Enrollment:** Full-time 612, Part-time 2,828 **Faculty:** Full-time 90, Part-time 222 **Student-Faculty Ratio:** 10:1 **Exams:** ACT essay component not used; SAT essay component not used. **Final Year or Final Semester Residency Requirement:** No **Regional Accreditation:** New England Association of Schools and Colleges **Credit Hours For Degree:** 62 semester hours, Associates; 120 semester hours, Bachelors **Professional Accreditation:** AAMAE, ACEN, ACICS.

HOLY APOSTLES COLLEGE AND SEMINARY

33 Prospect Hill Rd.
Cromwell, CT 06416-2005
Tel: (860)632-3010
Fax: (860)632-3030
E-mail: pkucer@holyapostles.edu
Web Site: www.holyapostles.edu
President/CEO: Rev. Douglas L. Mosey, CSB
Admissions: Fr. Peter Samuel Kucer

Type: Comprehensive **Sex:** Coed **Affiliation:** Roman Catholic. **% Accepted:** 100 **Admission Plans:** Deferred Admission; Open Admission **Application Deadline:** Rolling **Application Fee:** $50.00 **H.S. Requirements:** High school diploma required; GED accepted **Costs Per Year:** Application fee: $50. One-time mandatory fee: $50. Tuition: $9600 full-time, $960 per course part-time. Mandatory fees: $70 full-time, $35 per term part-time. **Calendar System:** Semester, Summer session available **Enrollment:** Full-time 36, Graduate full-time 87, Graduate part-time 240, Part-time 22 **Faculty:** Full-time 17, Part-time 13 **Student-Faculty Ratio:** 2:1 **Exams:** SAT I. **Regional Accreditation:** New England Association of Schools and Colleges **Credit Hours For Degree:** 60 credit hours, Associates; 120 credit hours, Bachelors

HOUSATONIC COMMUNITY COLLEGE

900 Lafayette Blvd.
Bridgeport, CT 06604-4704
Tel: (203)332-5000
E-mail: egraham@hcc.commnet.edu
Web Site: www.hctc.commnet.edu
President/CEO: Dr. Paul Broadie, II
Admissions: Earl Graham

Type: Two-Year College **Sex:** Coed **Affiliation:** Connecticut State Colleges & Universities (CSCU). **Admission Plans:** Deferred Admission; Open Admission **Application Deadline:** Rolling **Application Fee:** $20.00 **H.S. Requirements:** High school diploma required; GED accepted **Costs Per Year:** Application fee: $20. State resident tuition: $4052 full-time, $150 per semester hour part-time. Nonresident tuition: $12,116 full-time, $450 per semester hour part-time. Mandatory fees: $432 full-time. **Scholarships:** Available. **Calendar System:** Semester, Summer session available **Faculty:** Full-time 73, Part-time 279 **Student-Faculty Ratio:** 13:1 **Regional Accreditation:** New England Association of Schools and Colleges **Credit Hours For Degree:** 60 credits, Associates **ROTC:** Army **Professional Accreditation:** AOTA, APTA, NAACLS.

LINCOLN COLLEGE OF NEW ENGLAND

2279 Mount Vernon Rd.
Southington, CT 06489-1057
Tel: (860)628-4751; Free: 800-825-0087
Fax: (860)628-6444
E-mail: tdquila@lincolncollegene.edu
Web Site: www.lincolncollegene.edu
President/CEO: Denise Lewicki, CPA
Admissions: Tim D' Aquila

Type: Four-Year College **Sex:** Coed **Admission Plans:** Open Admission **Application Deadline:** Rolling **Application Fee:** $25.00 **H.S. Requirements:** High school diploma required; GED accepted **Costs Per Year:** Application fee: $25. Comprehensive fee: $26,050 includes full-time tuition ($18,780), mandatory fees ($1170), and college room and board ($6100). College room only: $4500. Room and board charges vary according to board plan. Part-time tuition: $710 per credit hour. Part-time mandatory fees: $585 per term. Part-time tuition and fees vary according to course load. **Scholarships:** Available. **Calendar System:** Semester, Summer session available **Enrollment:** Full-time 381, Part-time 238 **Faculty:** Full-time 24, Part-time 60 **Student-Faculty Ratio:** 14:1 **Exams:** ACT essay component not used; SAT essay component not used. **Final Year or Final Semester Residency Requirement:** Yes **Regional Accreditation:** New England Association of Schools and Colleges **Credit Hours For Degree:** 60 credit hours, Associates; 120 credit hours, Bachelors **Professional Accreditation:** AAMAE, ABFSE, ADA, AHIMA, AOTA.

MANCHESTER COMMUNITY COLLEGE

PO Box 1046
Manchester, CT 06045-1046
Tel: (860)512-3000
Fax: (860)647-6238
Web Site: www.manchestercc.edu
President/CEO: Gena Glickman
Financial Aid: Ivette Rivera-Dreyer

Type: Two-Year College **Sex:** Coed **Affiliation:** Connecticut State Colleges & Universities (ConnSCU). **% Accepted:** 99 **Admission Plans:** Open Admission **H.S. Requirements:** High school diploma required; GED accepted **Costs Per Year:** State resident tuition: $3600 full-time, $150 per credit hour part-time. Nonresident tuition: $10,800 full-time, $450 per credit hour part-time. Mandatory fees: $452 full-time. **Scholarships:** Available. **Calendar System:** Semester **Enrollment:** Full-time 2,383, Part-time 4,508 **Faculty:** Full-time 108, Part-time 378 **Student-Faculty Ratio:** 16:1 **Exams:** SAT I or ACT. **Regional Accreditation:** New England Association of Schools and Colleges **Credit Hours For Degree:** 60 credit hours, Associates **Professional Accreditation:** ACF, AOTA, APTA, ARCST, CoARC, NAACLS. **Intercollegiate Athletics:** Baseball M; Basketball M & W; Soccer M & W; Softball W

MIDDLESEX COMMUNITY COLLEGE

100 Training Hill Rd.
Middletown, CT 06457-4889
Tel: (860)343-5800
Fax: (860)344-7488
E-mail: mshabazz@mxcc.commnet.edu
Web Site: www.mxcc.commnet.edu
President/CEO: Dr. Jonathan Daube
Admissions: Mensimah Shabazz

Type: Two-Year College **Sex:** Coed **Affiliation:** Connecticut State Colleges & Universities (CSCU). **Admission Plans:** Deferred Admission; Early Admission; Open Admission **Application Deadline:** Rolling **Application Fee:** $20.00 **H.S. Requirements:** High school diploma required; GED accepted **Costs Per Year:** Application fee: $20. State resident tuition: $3600 full-time, $150 per credit part-time. Nonresident tuition: $10,800 full-time, $450 per credit part-time. Mandatory fees: $432 full-time. Full-time tuition and fees vary according to course load, degree level, and program. Part-time tuition varies according to course load, degree level, and program. **Scholarships:** Available. **Calendar System:** Semester, Summer session available **Enrollment:** Full-time 1,186, Part-time 1,766 **Faculty:** Full-time 44, Part-time 103 **Student-Faculty Ratio:** 22:1 **Exams:** Other. **Final Year or Final Semester Residency Requirement:** No **Regional Accreditation:** New England Association of Schools and Colleges **Credit Hours For Degree:** 60 credits, Associates **Professional Accreditation:** COA, JRCERT.

MITCHELL COLLEGE
437 Pequot Ave.
New London, CT 06320-4498
Tel: (860)701-5000; Free: 800-443-2811
Fax: (860)444-1209
E-mail: admissions@mitchell.edu
Web Site: www.mitchell.edu
President/CEO: Janet L. Steinmayer
Admissions: Bob Martin
Financial Aid: Jacklyn Stoltz
Type: Four-Year College **Sex:** Coed **% Accepted:** 74 **Admission Plans:** Deferred Admission; Early Action; Early Admission **Application Deadline:** Rolling **Application Fee:** $30.00 **H.S. Requirements:** High school diploma required; GED accepted **Costs Per Year:** Application fee: $30. Comprehensive fee: $44,280 includes full-time tuition ($29,890), mandatory fees ($1890), and college room and board ($12,500). College room only: $6500. Room and board charges vary according to board plan and housing facility. Part-time tuition: $500 per credit hour. **Scholarships:** Available. **Calendar System:** Semester, Summer session available **Enrollment:** Full-time 615, Part-time 108 **Faculty:** Full-time 23, Part-time 68 **Student-Faculty Ratio:** 14:1 **% Residing in College-Owned, -Operated, or -Affiliated Housing:** 59 **Final Year or Final Semester Residency Requirement:** No **Regional Accreditation:** New England Association of Schools and Colleges **Credit Hours For Degree:** 60 credit hours, Associates; 120 credit hours, Bachelors **Intercollegiate Athletics:** Baseball M; Basketball M & W; Cross-Country Running M & W; Golf M; Lacrosse M; Sailing M & W; Soccer M & W; Softball W; Tennis M & W; Volleyball W

NAUGATUCK VALLEY COMMUNITY COLLEGE
750 Chase Pky.
Waterbury, CT 06708-3000
Tel: (203)575-8040
Fax: (203)596-8766
E-mail: lstango@nvcc.commnet.edu
Web Site: www.nvcc.commnet.edu
President/CEO: Daisy Cocco De Filippis
Admissions: Linda Stango
Type: Two-Year College **Sex:** Coed **Affiliation:** Connecticut State Colleges & Universities (CSCU). **% Accepted:** 85 **Admission Plans:** Deferred Admission; Open Admission **Application Deadline:** Rolling **Application Fee:** $20.00 **H.S. Requirements:** High school diploma required; GED accepted **Costs Per Year:** Application fee: $20. State resident tuition: $4072 full-time, $150 per credit hour part-time. Nonresident tuition: $12,136 full-time, $450 per credit hour part-time. Mandatory fees: $472 full-time. Part-time tuition varies according to course load. **Scholarships:** Available. **Calendar System:** Semester, Summer session available **Enrollment:** Full-time 2,362, Part-time 4,614 **Faculty:** Full-time 104, Part-time 353 **Student-Faculty Ratio:** 17:1 **Exams:** Other. **Regional Accreditation:** New England Association of Schools and Colleges **Credit Hours For Degree:** 60 credits, Associates **Professional Accreditation:** ABET, ACEN, APTA, CoARC, JRCERT.

NORTHWESTERN CONNECTICUT COMMUNITY COLLEGE
Park Pl. E
Winsted, CT 06098-1798
Tel: (860)738-6300
Fax: (860)379-4465
E-mail: admissions@nwcc.commnet.edu
Web Site: www.nwcc.commnet.edu
President/CEO: Dr. Barbara Douglass
Financial Aid: Louis G. Bristol
Type: Two-Year College **Sex:** Coed **Affiliation:** Connecticut State Colleges & Universities (CSCU). **Admission Plans:** Deferred Admission; Open Admission **Application Deadline:** Rolling **Application Fee:** $20.00 **H.S. Requirements:** High school diploma required; GED accepted **Scholarships:** Available. **Calendar System:** Semester, Summer session available **Enrollment:** Full-time 457, Part-time 1,092 **Regional Accreditation:** New England Association of Schools and Colleges **Credit Hours For Degree:** 62 credits, Associates **Professional Accreditation:** AAMAE, APTA.

NORWALK COMMUNITY COLLEGE
188 Richards Ave.
Norwalk, CT 06854-1655
Tel: (203)857-7000
Fax: (203)857-3335

E-mail: admissions@ncc.commnet.edu
Web Site: www.ncc.commnet.edu
President/CEO: Dr. David L. Levinson, PhD
Admissions: Curtis Antrum
Financial Aid: Norma L. McNerney
Type: Two-Year College **Sex:** Coed **Affiliation:** Connecticut State Colleges & Universities (CSCU). **Admission Plans:** Deferred Admission; Open Admission **H.S. Requirements:** High school diploma required; GED accepted **Costs Per Year:** State resident tuition: $3600 full-time, $150 per credit hour part-time. Nonresident tuition: $10,800 full-time, $450 per credit hour part-time. Mandatory fees: $452 full-time. **Scholarships:** Available. **Calendar System:** Semester, Summer session available **Enrollment:** Full-time 2,134, Part-time 3,920 **Faculty:** Full-time 105, Part-time 229 **Student-Faculty Ratio:** 20:1 **Final Year or Final Semester Residency Requirement:** No **Regional Accreditation:** New England Association of Schools and Colleges **Credit Hours For Degree:** 60 credits, Associates **Professional Accreditation:** ACEN, CoARC.

PAIER COLLEGE OF ART, INC.
20 Gorham Ave.
Hamden, CT 06514-3902
Tel: (203)287-3031
E-mail: paier.admission@snet.net
Web Site: www.paiercollegeofart.edu
President/CEO: Jonathan E. Paier
Admissions: Lynn Pascale
Financial Aid: John DeRose
Type: Four-Year College **Sex:** Coed **Scores:** 95% SAT V 400+; 82% SAT M 400+ **Costs Per Year:** Tuition: $15,000 full-time, $500 per credit part-time. Mandatory fees: $450 full-time. Part-time tuition varies according to course load and degree level. **Scholarships:** Available. **Calendar System:** Semester, Summer session not available **Enrollment:** Full-time 93, Part-time 35 **Faculty:** Full-time 8, Part-time 26 **Student-Faculty Ratio:** 4:1 **Exams:** SAT I or ACT; SAT essay component used for advising. **% Receiving Financial Aid:** 88 **Final Year or Final Semester Residency Requirement:** No **Credit Hours For Degree:** 64 semester hours, Associates; 130 semester hours, Bachelors **Professional Accreditation:** ACCSC.

POST UNIVERSITY
800 Country Club Rd.
Waterbury, CT 06723-2540
Tel: (203)596-4500; Free: 800-345-2562
Fax: (203)756-5810
E-mail: admissions@post.edu
Web Site: www.post.edu
President/CEO: Don Mroz, PhD
Admissions: Kathryn Reilly
Financial Aid: Michelle Gambacini
Type: Comprehensive **Sex:** Coed **Scores:** 66% SAT V 400+; 66% SAT M 400+; 30% ACT 18-23; 39% ACT 24-29 **% Accepted:** 47 **Admission Plans:** Deferred Admission **Application Deadline:** Rolling **Application Fee:** $0.00 **H.S. Requirements:** High school diploma required; GED accepted **Costs Per Year:** Application fee: $0. Comprehensive fee: $37,850 includes full-time tuition ($26,250), mandatory fees ($1100), and college room and board ($10,500). Room and board charges vary according to housing facility. Part-time tuition: $875 per credit. Part-time tuition varies according to class time. **Scholarships:** Available. **Calendar System:** Semester, Summer session available **Enrollment:** Full-time 813, Part-time 15 **Faculty:** Full-time 30, Part-time 101 **Student-Faculty Ratio:** 12:1 **Exams:** SAT I or ACT; SAT Reasoning. **% Receiving Financial Aid:** 86 **% Residing in College-Owned, -Operated, or -Affiliated Housing:** 51 **Final Year or Final Semester Residency Requirement:** Yes **Regional Accreditation:** New England Association of Schools and Colleges **Credit Hours For Degree:** 60 credits, Associates; minimum 120 credits, depending on program, Bachelors **Professional Accreditation:** ACBSP. **Intercollegiate Athletics:** Baseball M; Basketball M & W; Cross-Country Running M & W; Equestrian Sports M & W; Football M; Golf M & W; Ice Hockey M & W; Lacrosse M & W; Soccer M & W; Softball W; Tennis M & W; Track and Field M & W; Volleyball W

QUINEBAUG VALLEY COMMUNITY COLLEGE
742 Upper Maple St.
Danielson, CT 06239-1440
Tel: (860)774-1130
Fax: (860)774-7768

E-mail: qu_isd@commnet.edu
Web Site: www.qvcc.commnet.edu
President/CEO: Carlee Drummer
Admissions: Dr. Toni Moumouris
Type: Two-Year College **Sex:** Coed **Affiliation:** Connecticut State Colleges & Universities (CSCU). **% Accepted:** 98 **Admission Plans:** Deferred Admission; Early Admission; Open Admission **Application Deadline:** September 1 **Application Fee:** $20.00 **H.S. Requirements:** High school diploma required; GED accepted **Costs Per Year:** Application fee: $20. State resident tuition: $3600 full-time, $150 per credit hour part-time. Nonresident tuition: $10,800 full-time, $450 per credit hour part-time. Mandatory fees: $432 full-time, $261 per course part-time. Part-time tuition and fees vary according to course load. **Scholarships:** Available. **Calendar System:** Semester, Summer session available **Enrollment:** Full-time 669, Part-time 1,110 **Faculty:** Full-time 29, Part-time 97 **Student-Faculty Ratio:** 18:1 **Regional Accreditation:** New England Association of Schools and Colleges **Credit Hours For Degree:** 60 credit hours, Associates **Professional Accreditation:** AAMAE.

QUINNIPIAC UNIVERSITY

275 Mount Carmel Ave.
Hamden, CT 06518-1940
Tel: (203)582-8200; Free: 800-462-1944
Fax: (203)582-6347
E-mail: admissions@quinnipiac.edu
Web Site: www.quinnipiac.edu
President/CEO: Dr. John L. Lahey
Admissions: Joan Isaac-Mohr
Financial Aid: Dominic Yoia
Type: Comprehensive **Sex:** Coed **Scores:** 100% SAT V 400+; 100% SAT M 400+; 35% ACT 18-23; 55% ACT 24-29 **% Accepted:** 74 **Admission Plans:** Deferred Admission; Early Action **Application Deadline:** February 1 **Application Fee:** $65.00 **H.S. Requirements:** High school diploma required; GED accepted **Costs Per Year:** Application fee: $65. Comprehensive fee: $58,810 includes full-time tuition ($41,990), mandatory fees ($1650), and college room and board ($15,170). Room and board charges vary according to housing facility. Part-time tuition: $995 per credit. Part-time mandatory fees: $38 per credit. Part-time tuition and fees vary according to class time and course load. **Scholarships:** Available. **Calendar System:** Semester, Summer session available **Enrollment:** Full-time 6,703, Graduate full-time 1,359, Graduate part-time 1,313, Part-time 279 **Faculty:** Full-time 399, Part-time 572 **Student-Faculty Ratio:** 12:1 **Exams:** SAT I or ACT; SAT Reasoning. **% Receiving Financial Aid:** 61 **% Residing in College-Owned, -Operated, or -Affiliated Housing:** 77 **Final Year or Final Semester Residency Requirement:** Yes **Regional Accreditation:** New England Association of Schools and Colleges **Credit Hours For Degree:** 120 semester hours, Bachelors **ROTC:** Air Force, Army **Professional Accreditation:** AACSB, AALS, ABA, ABET; ACEN, AOTA, APTA, CoARC, JRCERT, LCME/AMA, NAACLS, NCATE. **Intercollegiate Athletics:** Baseball M; Basketball M & W; Cross-Country Running M & W; Field Hockey W; Golf W; Gymnastics W; Ice Hockey M & W; Lacrosse M & W; Rugby W; Soccer M & W; Softball W; Tennis M & W; Track and Field W; Volleyball W

SACRED HEART UNIVERSITY

5151 Park Ave.
Fairfield, CT 06825
Tel: (203)371-7999
Fax: (203)371-7889
E-mail: enroll@sacredheart.edu
Web Site: www.sacredheart.edu
President/CEO: Dr. John J. Petillo, PhD
Financial Aid: Julie B. Savino
Type: Comprehensive **Sex:** Coed **Affiliation:** Roman Catholic. **Scores:** 99% SAT V 400+; 99% SAT M 400+; 39.23% ACT 18-23; 53.85% ACT 24-29 **% Accepted:** 59 **Admission Plans:** Early Action; Early Admission; Early Decision Plan **Application Fee:** $50.00 **H.S. Requirements:** High school diploma required; GED accepted **Costs Per Year:** Application fee: $50. Comprehensive fee: $51,310 includes full-time tuition ($36,920), mandatory fees ($250), and college room and board ($14,140). College room only: $9900. Room and board charges vary according to board plan and housing facility. Part-time tuition: $600 per credit hour. Part-time tuition varies according to course load. **Scholarships:** Available. **Calendar System:** Semester, Summer session available **Enrollment:** Full-time 4,435, Graduate full-time 1,076, Graduate part-time 1,954, Part-time 770 **Faculty:** Full-time 263, Part-

time 499 **Student-Faculty Ratio:** 15:1 **Exams:** ACT; SAT I; SAT I or ACT; SAT Reasoning. **% Receiving Financial Aid:** 67 **% Residing in College-Owned, -Operated, or -Affiliated Housing:** 50 **Final Year or Final Semester Residency Requirement:** Yes **Regional Accreditation:** New England Association of Schools and Colleges **Credit Hours For Degree:** 60 credits, Associates; 120 credits, Bachelors **ROTC:** Air Force **Professional Accreditation:** AACN, AACSB, AOTA, APTA, CSWE, JRCAT, NCATE. **Intercollegiate Athletics:** Baseball M; Basketball M & W; Bowling W; Cheerleading W; Crew W; Cross-Country Running M & W; Equestrian Sports W; Fencing M & W; Field Hockey W; Football M; Golf M & W; Ice Hockey M & W; Lacrosse M & W; Soccer M & W; Softball W; Swimming and Diving W; Tennis M & W; Track and Field M & W; Volleyball M & W; Wrestling M

ST. VINCENT'S COLLEGE

2800 Main St.
Bridgeport, CT 06606-4292
Tel: (203)576-5235; Free: 800-873-1013
E-mail: jmarrone@stvincentscollege.edu
Web Site: www.stvincentscollege.edu
President/CEO: Dr. Michael Gargano, Jr.
Admissions: Joseph Marrone
Financial Aid: Dorothy Martin-Hatcher
Type: Two-Year College **Sex:** Coed **Affiliation:** Roman Catholic Church. **Scores:** 75% SAT V 400+; 75% SAT M 400+ **Costs Per Year:** Tuition: $14,520 full-time, $605 per credit hour part-time. Mandatory fees: $350 full-time, $350 per year part-time. Full-time tuition and fees vary according to course load. Part-time tuition and fees vary according to course load. **Scholarships:** Available. **Calendar System:** Semester, Summer session available **Enrollment:** Full-time 50, Part-time 625 **Faculty:** Full-time 21, Part-time 53 **Student-Faculty Ratio:** 10:1 **Exams:** SAT I or ACT. **Final Year or Final Semester Residency Requirement:** No **Regional Accreditation:** New England Association of Schools and Colleges **Credit Hours For Degree:** 72 credits, Associates; 120 credits, Bachelors **Professional Accreditation:** AAMAE, ACEN.

SOUTHERN CONNECTICUT STATE UNIVERSITY

501 Crescent St.
New Haven, CT 06515-1355
Tel: (203)392-5200
Fax: (203)392-5727
E-mail: haakonsena1@southernct.edu
Web Site: www.southernct.edu
President/CEO: Dr. Mary A. Papazian
Admissions: Alexis S. Haakonsen
Financial Aid: Gloria Lee
Type: Comprehensive **Sex:** Coed **Affiliation:** Connecticut State Colleges & Universities (CSCU). **Scores:** 88% SAT V 400+; 84% SAT M 400+; 57.34% ACT 18-23; 16.08% ACT 24-29 **% Accepted:** 65 **Admission Plans:** Deferred Admission **Application Deadline:** Rolling **Application Fee:** $50.00 **H.S. Requirements:** High school diploma required; GED accepted **Costs Per Year:** Application fee: $50. State resident tuition: $4968 full-time, $494 per credit hour part-time. Nonresident tuition: $16,078 full-time, $509 per credit hour part-time. Mandatory fees: $4632 full-time, $55 per term part-time. Full-time tuition and fees vary according to course load and reciprocity agreements. Part-time tuition and fees vary according to course load. College room and board: $11,614. College room only: $6402. Room and board charges vary according to board plan and housing facility. **Scholarships:** Available. **Calendar System:** Semester, Summer session available **Enrollment:** Full-time 6,869, Graduate full-time 818, Graduate part-time 1,549, Part-time 1,237 **Faculty:** Full-time 440, Part-time 520 **Student-Faculty Ratio:** 14:1 **Exams:** SAT I or ACT; SAT essay component not used; SAT Reasoning. **% Receiving Financial Aid:** 75 **% Residing in College-Owned, -Operated, or -Affiliated Housing:** 32 **Final Year or Final Semester Residency Requirement:** No **Regional Accreditation:** New England Association of Schools and Colleges **Credit Hours For Degree:** 122 semester hours, Bachelors **ROTC:** Air Force, Army **Professional Accreditation:** AACN, AAMFT, AANA, ABET, ACA, ALA, ASHA, CEPH, CSWE, JRCAT, NCATE. **Intercollegiate Athletics:** Baseball M; Basketball M & W; Cheerleading M & W; Cross-Country Running M & W; Field Hockey W; Football M; Gymnastics W; Lacrosse W; Rugby M & W; Soccer M & W; Softball W; Swimming and Diving M & W; Track and Field M & W; Ultimate Frisbee M & W; Volleyball W

THREE RIVERS COMMUNITY COLLEGE
574 New London Tpke.
Norwich, CT 06360
Tel: (860)215-9000
Fax: (860)886-0691
E-mail: admissions@trcc.commnet.edu
Web Site: www.trcc.commnet.edu
President/CEO: Dr. Mary Ellen Jukoski

Type: Two-Year College **Sex:** Coed **Affiliation:** Connecticut State Colleges & Universities (CSCU). **Admission Plans:** Deferred Admission; Early Admission; Open Admission **Application Deadline:** Rolling **H.S. Requirements:** High school diploma required; GED accepted **Costs Per Year:** State resident tuition: $3600 full-time, $150 per credit hour part-time. Nonresident tuition: $10,800 full-time, $450 per credit hour part-time. Mandatory fees: $472 full-time, $84 per credit hour part-time. Full-time tuition and fees vary according to course load and reciprocity agreements. Part-time tuition and fees vary according to course load and reciprocity agreements. **Scholarships:** Available. **Calendar System:** Semester **Enrollment:** Full-time 1,407, Part-time 2,852 **Faculty:** Full-time 69, Part-time 208 **Student-Faculty Ratio:** 17:1 **Exams:** SAT essay component used for placement. **Final Year or Final Semester Residency Requirement:** No **Regional Accreditation:** New England Association of Schools and Colleges **Credit Hours For Degree:** 60 credits, Associates **Professional Accreditation:** ABET, ACBSP, ACEN, MACTE.

TRINITY COLLEGE
300 Summit St.
Hartford, CT 06106-3100
Tel: (860)297-2000
Fax: (860)297-2287
E-mail: admissions.office@trincoll.edu
Web Site: www.trincoll.edu
President/CEO: Pres. Joanne Berger-Sweeney
Admissions: Dr. Angel B. Perez
Financial Aid: Kelly O'Brien

Type: Comprehensive **Sex:** Coed **Scores:** 100% SAT V 400+; 101% SAT M 400+; 4% ACT 18-23; 59% ACT 24-29 **% Accepted:** 33 **Admission Plans:** Deferred Admission; Early Action; Early Admission **Application Deadline:** January 1 **Application Fee:** $60.00 **H.S. Requirements:** High school diploma required; GED accepted **Costs Per Year:** Application fee: $60. One-time mandatory fee: $25. Comprehensive fee: $63,920 includes full-time tuition ($48,446), mandatory fees ($2330), and college room and board ($13,144). College room only: $8550. Full-time tuition and fees vary according to course load and program. Room and board charges vary according to board plan. Part-time tuition: $5383 per course. Part-time tuition varies according to course load and program. **Scholarships:** Available. **Calendar System:** Semester, Summer session available **Enrollment:** Full-time 2,165, Graduate full-time 1, Graduate part-time 107, Part-time 124 **Faculty:** Full-time 193, Part-time 102 **Student-Faculty Ratio:** 10:1 **Exams:** SAT I or ACT; SAT II; SAT Reasoning; SAT Subject. **% Receiving Financial Aid:** 45 **% Residing in College-Owned, -Operated, or -Affiliated Housing:** 90 **Final Year or Final Semester Residency Requirement:** No **Regional Accreditation:** New England Association of Schools and Colleges **Credit Hours For Degree:** 36 courses, Bachelors **ROTC:** Army **Professional Accreditation:** ABET. **Intercollegiate Athletics:** Baseball M; Basketball M & W; Crew M & W; Cross-Country Running M & W; Equestrian Sports M & W; Fencing M & W; Football M; Golf M; Ice Hockey M & W; Lacrosse M & W; Rugby M & W; Sailing M & W; Skiing (Downhill) M & W; Soccer M & W; Softball W; Squash M & W; Swimming and Diving M & W; Tennis M & W; Track and Field M & W; Ultimate Frisbee M & W; Volleyball W; Water Polo M & W; Wrestling M

TUNXIS COMMUNITY COLLEGE
271 Scott Swamp Rd.
Farmington, CT 06032-3026
Tel: (860)773-1300
E-mail: pmccluskey@tunxis.edu
Web Site: www.tunxis.edu
President/CEO: Dr. Cathryn Addy
Admissions: Tamika Davis

Type: Two-Year College **Sex:** Coed **Affiliation:** Connecticut State Colleges & Universities (CSCU). **Admission Plans:** Deferred Admission; Open Admission **Application Deadline:** Rolling **Application Fee:** $20.00 **H.S. Requirements:** High school diploma required; GED accepted **Costs Per**

Year: Application fee: $20. State resident tuition: $3432 full-time, $143 per semester hour part-time. Nonresident tuition: $10,296 full-time, $429 per semester hour part-time. Mandatory fees: $434 full-time, $124 per term part-time. **Calendar System:** Semester, Summer session available **Enrollment:** Full-time 1,594, Part-time 2,485 **Faculty:** Full-time 67, Part-time 172 **Student-Faculty Ratio:** 17:1 **Final Year or Final Semester Residency Requirement:** No **Regional Accreditation:** New England Association of Schools and Colleges **Credit Hours For Degree:** 60 credits, Associates **Professional Accreditation:** ACBSP, ADA, APTA.

UNITED STATES COAST GUARD ACADEMY
15 Mohegan Ave.
New London, CT 06320-8100
Tel: (860)444-8444; Free: 800-883-8724
Fax: (860)444-8289
E-mail: daniel.v.pinch@uscga.edu
Web Site: www.uscga.edu
President/CEO: Adm. James Rendon
Admissions: Daniel V. Pinch

Type: Four-Year College **Sex:** Coed **Scores:** 100% SAT V 400+; 100% SAT M 400+; 7% ACT 18-23; 60% ACT 24-29 **% Accepted:** 16 **Admission Plans:** Deferred Admission; Early Decision Plan **Application Deadline:** February 1 **Application Fee:** $0.00 **H.S. Requirements:** High school diploma required; GED accepted. For home-schooled applicants: High school diploma or equivalent not required **Calendar System:** Semester, Summer session available **Enrollment:** Full-time 898 **Faculty:** Full-time 115, Part-time 14 **Student-Faculty Ratio:** 8:1 **Exams:** ACT essay component used as validity check; ACT essay component used for admission; ACT essay component used for advising; SAT I or ACT; SAT essay component used as validity check; SAT essay component used for admission; SAT essay component used for advising; SAT Reasoning; SAT Subject. **% Residing in College-Owned, -Operated, or -Affiliated Housing:** 100 **Final Year or Final Semester Residency Requirement:** Yes **Regional Accreditation:** New England Association of Schools and Colleges **Credit Hours For Degree:** 126 credit hours, Bachelors **Professional Accreditation:** AACSB, ABET. **Intercollegiate Athletics:** Baseball M; Basketball M & W; Cheerleading W; Crew M & W; Cross-Country Running M & W; Football M; Ice Hockey M & W; Lacrosse M & W; Riflery M & W; Rugby M & W; Sailing M & W; Soccer M & W; Softball W; Swimming and Diving M & W; Tennis M; Track and Field M & W; Volleyball W; Water Polo M & W; Wrestling M

UNIVERSITY OF BRIDGEPORT
126 Park Ave.
Bridgeport, CT 06604
Tel: (203)576-4000; Free: 800-EXCEL-UB
Fax: (203)576-4941
E-mail: admit@bridgeport.edu
Web Site: www.bridgeport.edu
President/CEO: Dr. Neil Albert Salonen
Admissions: Jessica N. Crowley Goddu
Financial Aid: Christine E. Falzerano

Type: Comprehensive **Sex:** Coed **Scores:** 87% SAT V 400+; 87% SAT M 400+; 59% ACT 18-23; 22% ACT 24-29 **% Accepted:** 52 **Admission Plans:** Deferred Admission; Early Admission **Application Deadline:** Rolling **Application Fee:** $25.00 **H.S. Requirements:** High school diploma required; GED accepted **Costs Per Year:** Application fee: $25. Comprehensive fee: $43,840 includes full-time tuition ($28,800), mandatory fees ($2050), and college room and board ($12,990). Full-time tuition and fees vary according to course load and program. Room and board charges vary according to board plan and housing facility. Part-time tuition: $960 per credit hour. Part-time mandatory fees: $205 per term. Part-time tuition and fees vary according to course load and program. **Scholarships:** Available. **Calendar System:** Semester, Summer session available **Enrollment:** Full-time 2,112, Graduate full-time 1,604, Graduate part-time 932, Part-time 785 **Faculty:** Full-time 127, Part-time 407 **Student-Faculty Ratio:** 16:1 **Exams:** ACT essay component used for admission; ACT essay component used for advising; ACT essay component used for placement; SAT I or ACT; SAT essay component used for admission; SAT essay component used for advising; SAT essay component used for placement. **% Receiving Financial Aid:** 80 **% Residing in College-Owned, -Operated, or -Affiliated Housing:** 42 **Final Year or Final Semester Residency Requirement:** Yes **Regional Accreditation:** New England Association of Schools and Colleges **Credit Hours For Degree:** 60 credits, Associates; 120 credits, Bachelors **Professional Accreditation:** ABET, ACAOM, ACBSP, ADA, CCE, NASAD.

Intercollegiate Athletics: Baseball M; Basketball M & W; Cross-Country Running M & W; Gymnastics W; Lacrosse W; Soccer M & W; Softball W; Swimming and Diving M & W; Volleyball W

UNIVERSITY OF CONNECTICUT

Storrs, CT 06269
Tel: (860)486-2000
Fax: (860)486-1476
E-mail: beahusky@uconn.edu
Web Site: www.uconn.edu
President/CEO: Dr. Susan Herbst
Admissions: Nathan Fuerst
Financial Aid: Mona L. Lucas
Type: University **Sex:** Coed **Scores:** 100% SAT V 400+; 100% SAT M 400+; 8% ACT 18-23; 59% ACT 24-29 **% Accepted:** 50 **Admission Plans:** Deferred Admission **Application Deadline:** January 15 **Application Fee:** $70.00 **H.S. Requirements:** High school diploma required; GED accepted **Costs Per Year:** Application fee: $70. State resident tuition: $10,524 full-time, $439 per credit part-time. Nonresident tuition: $32,066 full-time, $1337 per credit part-time. Mandatory fees: $2842 full-time. Part-time tuition varies according to course load. College room and board: $12,436. College room only: $6660. Room and board charges vary according to board plan and housing facility. **Scholarships:** Available. **Calendar System:** Semester, Summer session available **Enrollment:** Full-time 17,677, Graduate full-time 5,522, Graduate part-time 2,624, Part-time 718 **Faculty:** Full-time 1,223, Part-time 366 **Student-Faculty Ratio:** 16:1 **Exams:** SAT I or ACT; SAT Reasoning. **% Receiving Financial Aid:** 56 **% Residing in College-Owned, -Operated, or -Affiliated Housing:** 71 **Regional Accreditation:** New England Association of Schools and Colleges **Credit Hours For Degree:** 120 credits, Bachelors **ROTC:** Air Force, Army **Professional Accreditation:** AACN, AACSB, AALS, AAMFT, ABA, ABET, ACA, ACEJMC, ACPE, AND, APA, APTA, ASHA, ASLA, CSWE, NAACLS, NASAD, NASM, NASPAA, NAST, NCATE. **Intercollegiate Athletics:** Baseball M; Basketball M & W; Crew W; Cross-Country Running M & W; Field Hockey W; Football M; Golf M; Ice Hockey M & W; Lacrosse W; Soccer M & W; Softball W; Swimming and Diving M & W; Tennis M & W; Track and Field M & W; Volleyball W

UNIVERSITY OF HARTFORD

200 Bloomfield Ave.
West Hartford, CT 06117-1599
Tel: (860)768-4100; Free: 800-947-4303
Fax: (860)768-4961
E-mail: admissions@hartford.edu
Web Site: www.hartford.edu
President/CEO: Dr. Walter Harrison
Admissions: Richard Zeiser
Financial Aid: Victoria Hampton
Type: Comprehensive **Sex:** Coed **Scores:** 97% SAT V 400+; 96% SAT M 400+; 52% ACT 18-23; 33% ACT 24-29 **% Accepted:** 64 **Admission Plans:** Deferred Admission; Early Admission; Early Decision Plan **Application Deadline:** Rolling **Application Fee:** $35.00 **H.S. Requirements:** High school diploma required; GED accepted **Costs Per Year:** Application fee: $35. Comprehensive fee: $49,776 includes full-time tuition ($35,036), mandatory fees ($2754), and college room and board ($11,986). College room only: $7774. Full-time tuition and fees vary according to program. Room and board charges vary according to board plan and housing facility. Part-time tuition: $520 per credit. Part-time tuition varies according to course load and program. **Scholarships:** Available. **Calendar System:** Semester, Summer session available **Enrollment:** Full-time 4,533, Graduate full-time 797, Graduate part-time 869, Part-time 713 **Faculty:** Full-time 354, Part-time 498 **Student-Faculty Ratio:** 9:1 **Exams:** ACT essay component not used; SAT I or ACT; SAT essay component not used. **% Receiving Financial Aid:** 73 **% Residing in College-Owned, -Operated, or -Affiliated Housing:** 62 **Regional Accreditation:** New England Association of Schools and Colleges **Credit Hours For Degree:** 60 credits, Associates; 120 credits, Bachelors **ROTC:** Air Force, Army **Professional Accreditation:** AACN, AACSB, ABET, AOTA, APA, APTA, CoARC, JRCERT, NAACLS, NASAD, NASM, NCATE. **Intercollegiate Athletics:** Badminton M & W; Baseball M; Basketball M & W; Cross-Country Running M & W; Golf M & W; Lacrosse M; Racquetball M & W; Rugby M & W; Soccer M & W; Softball W; Squash M & W; Tennis M & W; Track and Field M & W; Volleyball M & W

UNIVERSITY OF NEW HAVEN

300 Boston Post Rd.
West Haven, CT 06516-1916

Tel: (203)932-7000; Free: 800-342-5864
Fax: (203)937-0756
E-mail: admissions@newhaven.edu
Web Site: www.newhaven.edu
President/CEO: Dr. Steven H. Kaplan, PhD
Admissions: Kevin J. Phillips
Financial Aid: Karen Flynn
Type: Comprehensive **Sex:** Coed **Scores:** 97% SAT V 400+; 97% SAT M 400+; 46.83% ACT 18-23; 41.2% ACT 24-29 **% Accepted:** 82 **Admission Plans:** Early Action; Early Decision Rolling Plan **Application Deadline:** Rolling **Application Fee:** $50.00 **H.S. Requirements:** High school diploma required; GED accepted **Costs Per Year:** Application fee: $50. Comprehensive fee: $50,370 includes full-time tuition ($34,330), mandatory fees ($1320), and college room and board ($14,720). College room only: $9320. Full-time tuition and fees vary according to course load, location, and program. Room and board charges vary according to board plan and housing facility. Part-time tuition: $1145 per credit hour. Part-time mandatory fees: $55 per term. Part-time tuition and fees vary according to class time, course load, location, and program. **Scholarships:** Available. **Calendar System:** 4-1-4, Summer session available **Enrollment:** Full-time 4,611, Graduate full-time 1,145, Graduate part-time 639, Part-time 391 **Faculty:** Full-time 268, Part-time 367 **Student-Faculty Ratio:** 16:1 **Exams:** SAT I or ACT; SAT II; SAT essay component used for placement. **% Receiving Financial Aid:** 75 **% Residing in College-Owned, -Operated, or -Affiliated Housing:** 53 **Final Year or Final Semester Residency Requirement:** No **Regional Accreditation:** New England Association of Schools and Colleges **Credit Hours For Degree:** 60 credit hours, Associates; 120 credit hours, Bachelors **ROTC:** Air Force, Army **Professional Accreditation:** AACSB, ABET, ADA. **Intercollegiate Athletics:** Baseball M; Basketball M & W; Cross-Country Running M & W; Field Hockey W; Football M; Ice Hockey M; Lacrosse M & W; Rugby M; Soccer M & W; Softball W; Tennis W; Track and Field M & W; Ultimate Frisbee M & W; Volleyball M & W; Wrestling M

UNIVERSITY OF SAINT JOSEPH

1678 Asylum Ave.
West Hartford, CT 06117-2700
Tel: (860)232-4571; Free: 866-442-8752
Fax: (860)233-5695
E-mail: admissions@usj.edu
Web Site: www.usj.edu
President/CEO: Dr. Rhona Free
Type: Comprehensive **Sex:** Coed **Affiliation:** Roman Catholic. **Scores:** 82% SAT V 400+; 78% SAT M 400+; 38% ACT 18-23; 24% ACT 24-29 **% Accepted:** 93 **Admission Plans:** Deferred Admission **Application Deadline:** Rolling **Application Fee:** $50.00 **H.S. Requirements:** High school diploma required; GED accepted **Costs Per Year:** Application fee: $50. Comprehensive fee: $50,990 includes full-time tuition ($34,530), mandatory fees ($1610), and college room and board ($14,850). College room only: $6850. Full-time tuition and fees vary according to course load, degree level, location, program, and student level. Room and board charges vary according to board plan and housing facility. Part-time tuition: $780 per credit hour. Part-time mandatory fees: $55 per credit hour. Part-time tuition and fees vary according to course load, degree level, location, program, and student level. **Scholarships:** Available. **Calendar System:** Semester, Summer session available **Enrollment:** Full-time 767, Graduate full-time 574, Graduate part-time 1,019, Part-time 193 **Faculty:** Full-time 131, Part-time 161 **Student-Faculty Ratio:** 11:1 **Exams:** ACT essay component not used; SAT I or ACT; SAT essay component not used. **% Receiving Financial Aid:** 88 **% Residing in College-Owned, -Operated, or -Affiliated Housing:** 29 **Final Year or Final Semester Residency Requirement:** No **Regional Accreditation:** New England Association of Schools and Colleges **Credit Hours For Degree:** 120 credits, Bachelors **Professional Accreditation:** AACN, AAFCS, AAMFT, ACPE, AND, CSWE. **Intercollegiate Athletics:** Basketball W; Cross-Country Running W; Lacrosse W; Soccer W; Softball W; Swimming and Diving W; Tennis W; Volleyball W

WESLEYAN UNIVERSITY

Middletown, CT 06459
Tel: (860)685-2000
Fax: (860)685-3001
E-mail: admission@wesleyan.edu
Web Site: www.wesleyan.edu
President/CEO: Dr. Michael S. Roth
Admissions: Nancy Hargrave Meislahn

Financial Aid: Robert Coughlin

Type: University **Sex:** Coed **Scores:** 100% SAT V 400+; 100% SAT M 400+; 4.64% ACT 18-23; 27.5% ACT 24-29 **% Accepted:** 22 **Admission Plans:** Deferred Admission; Early Action; Early Admission **Application Deadline:** January 1 **Application Fee:** $55.00 **H.S. Requirements:** High school diploma required; GED accepted **Costs Per Year:** Application fee: $55. Comprehensive fee: $64,562 includes full-time tuition ($50,312), mandatory fees ($300), and college room and board ($13,950). Room and board charges vary according to board plan and student level. **Scholarships:** Available. **Calendar System:** Semester, Summer session available **Enrollment:** Full-time 2,820, Graduate full-time 156, Graduate part-time 85, Part-time 77 **Faculty:** Full-time 369, Part-time 76 **Student-Faculty Ratio:** 8:1 **Exams:** ACT essay component not used; SAT I and SAT II or ACT; SAT essay component not used; SAT Reasoning; SAT Subject. **% Receiving Financial Aid: 45 % Residing in College-Owned, -Operated, or -Affiliated Housing: 99 Final Year or Final Semester Residency Requirement:** No **Regional Accreditation:** New England Association of Schools and Colleges **Credit Hours For Degree:** 32 courses, Bachelors **ROTC:** Air Force **Intercollegiate Athletics:** Baseball M; Basketball M & W; Crew M & W; Cross-Country Running M & W; Equestrian Sports M & W; Field Hockey W; Football M; Golf M; Ice Hockey M & W; Lacrosse M & W; Rugby M & W; Sailing M & W; Skiing (Cross-Country) M & W; Skiing (Downhill) M & W; Soccer M & W; Softball W; Squash M & W; Swimming and Diving M & W; Tennis M & W; Track and Field M & W; Volleyball M & W; Water Polo M; Wrestling M

WESTERN CONNECTICUT STATE UNIVERSITY

181 White St.
Danbury, CT 06810-6885
Tel: (203)837-8200; Free: 877-837-WCSU
Fax: (203)837-8320
E-mail: admissions@wcsu.edu
Web Site: www.wcsu.edu
President/CEO: Dr. John B. Clark
Financial Aid: Melissa Stephens

Type: Comprehensive **Sex:** Coed **Affiliation:** Connecticut State Colleges & Universities (CSCU). **Scores:** 95% SAT V 400+; 95% SAT M 400+ **% Accepted:** 57 **Admission Plans:** Deferred Admission; Preferred Admission **Application Deadline:** Rolling **Application Fee:** $50.00 **H.S. Requirements:** High school diploma required; GED accepted **Costs Per Year:** Application fee: $50. State resident tuition: $4968 full-time, $207 per credit hour part-time. Nonresident tuition: $16,078 full-time, $212 per credit hour part-time. Mandatory fees: $4548 full-time, $244 per credit hour part-time. Full-time tuition and fees vary according to course load, program, and reciprocity agreements. College room and board: $11,738. College room only: $6625. Room and board charges vary according to board plan and housing facility. **Scholarships:** Available. **Calendar System:** Semester, Summer session available **Enrollment:** Full-time 4,250, Graduate full-time 78, Graduate part-time 450, Part-time 1,048 **Faculty:** Full-time 205, Part-time 409 **Student-**

Faculty Ratio: 14:1 **Exams:** ACT essay component used for placement; SAT I or ACT; SAT essay component used for placement. **% Receiving Financial Aid:** 65 **% Residing in College-Owned, -Operated, or -Affiliated Housing:** 33 **Final Year or Final Semester Residency Requirement:** Yes **Regional Accreditation:** New England Association of Schools and Colleges **Credit Hours For Degree:** 60 semester hours, Associates; 120 semester hours, Bachelors **ROTC:** Air Force, Army **Professional Accreditation:** AACN, ACA, CSWE, NASM, NCATE. **Intercollegiate Athletics:** Baseball M; Basketball M & W; Cheerleading W; Field Hockey W; Football M; Lacrosse M & W; Soccer M & W; Softball W; Swimming and Diving W; Tennis M & W; Volleyball W

YALE UNIVERSITY

New Haven, CT 06520
Tel: (203)432-4771
Fax: (203)432-9392
E-mail: student.questions@yale.edu
Web Site: www.yale.edu
President/CEO: Peter Salovey, PhD
Financial Aid: Caesar T. Storlazzi

Type: University **Sex:** Coed **Scores:** 100% SAT V 400+ **Admission Plans:** Deferred Admission; Early Admission; Early Decision Plan **Application Deadline:** January 1 **Application Fee:** $80.00 **H.S. Requirements:** High school diploma required; GED accepted **Costs Per Year:** Application fee: $80. Comprehensive fee: $64,650 includes full-time tuition ($49,480) and college room and board ($15,170). College room only: $8520. Room and board charges vary according to board plan. **Scholarships:** Available. **Calendar System:** Semester, Summer session available **Enrollment:** Full-time 5,509, Graduate full-time 6,741, Graduate part-time 112, Part-time 23 **Faculty:** Full-time 1,159, Part-time 476 **Student-Faculty Ratio:** 6:1 **Exams:** ACT essay component used as validity check; ACT essay component used for admission; SAT I or ACT; SAT II; SAT essay component used as validity check; SAT essay component used for admission; SAT Reasoning; SAT Subject. **% Receiving Financial Aid:** 50 **% Residing in College-Owned, -Operated, or -Affiliated Housing:** 84 **Final Year or Final Semester Residency Requirement:** No **Regional Accreditation:** New England Association of Schools and Colleges **Credit Hours For Degree:** 36 semester courses, Bachelors **ROTC:** Air Force, Army, Navy **Professional Accreditation:** AACN, AACSB, AALS, ABA, ABET, ACNM, ACIPE, AND, APA, ATS, CAHME, CEPH, LCME/AMA, NAAB, NASM, SAF. **Intercollegiate Athletics:** Archery M & W; Badminton M & W; Baseball M; Basketball M & W; Cheerleading M & W; Crew M & W; Cross-Country Running M & W; Equestrian Sports M & W; Fencing M & W; Field Hockey W; Football M; Golf M & W; Gymnastics W; Ice Hockey M & W; Lacrosse M & W; Riflery M & W; Rock Climbing M & W; Rugby M & W; Sailing M & W; Skiing (Cross-Country) M & W; Skiing (Downhill) M & W; Soccer M & W; Softball W; Squash M & W; Swimming and Diving M & W; Table Tennis M & W; Tennis M & W; Track and Field M & W; Ultimate Frisbee M & W; Volleyball M & W; Water Polo M & W; Wrestling M & W

DELAWARE COLLEGE OF ART AND DESIGN

600 N Market St.
Wilmington, DE 19801
Tel: (302)622-8000
Fax: (302)622-8870
E-mail: agullo@dcad.edu
Web Site: www.dcad.edu
President/CEO: James P. Lecky
Admissions: Allison Gullo
Type: Two-Year College **Sex:** Coed **Affiliation:** Corcoran College of Art and Design. **% Accepted:** 58 **Admission Plans:** Deferred Admission **Application Deadline:** Rolling **Application Fee:** $25.00 **H.S. Requirements:** High school diploma required; GED accepted **Calendar System:** Semester, Summer session available **Enrollment:** Full-time 192, Part-time 18 **Faculty:** Full-time 7, Part-time 20 **Student-Faculty Ratio:** 8:1 **% Residing in College-Owned, -Operated, or -Affiliated Housing:** 50 **Regional Accreditation:** Middle States Association of Colleges and Schools **Credit Hours For Degree:** 68 semester hours, Associates **Professional Accreditation:** NASAD.

DELAWARE STATE UNIVERSITY

1200 N DuPont Hwy.
Dover, DE 19901-2277
Tel: (302)857-6290; Free: 800-845-2544
Fax: (302)857-6352
E-mail: ehill@desu.edu
Web Site: www.desu.edu
President/CEO: Dr. Harry L. Williams
Admissions: Erin Hill
Financial Aid: Stephen J. Ampersand
Type: University **Sex:** Coed **Affiliation:** Delaware Higher Education Commission. **Scores:** 83% SAT V 400+; 81% SAT M 400+; 53% ACT 18-23; 5% ACT 24-29 **% Accepted:** 44 **Admission Plans:** Early Admission; Early Decision Plan; Preferred Admission **Application Fee:** $35.00 **H.S. Requirements:** High school diploma required; GED accepted **Costs Per Year:** Application fee: $35. State resident tuition: $7523 full-time, $280 per credit hour part-time. Nonresident tuition: $16,138 full-time, $638 per credit hour part-time. Mandatory fees: $300 per term part-time. Full-time tuition varies according to course load and reciprocity agreements. Part-time tuition and fees vary according to course load and reciprocity agreements. College room and board: $10,820. College room only: $6976. Room and board charges vary according to board plan and housing facility. **Scholarships:** Available. **Calendar System:** Semester, Summer session available **Enrollment:** Full-time 3,596, Graduate full-time 305, Graduate part-time 40, Part-time 347 **Faculty:** Full-time 221, Part-time 129 **Student-Faculty Ratio:** 15:1 **Exams:** SAT I or ACT. **% Receiving Financial Aid:** 81 **% Residing in College-Owned, -Operated, or -Affiliated Housing:** 59 **Regional Accreditation:** Middle States Association of Colleges and Schools **Credit Hours For Degree:** 121 credit hours, Bachelors **ROTC:** Air Force, Army **Professional Accreditation:** AACN, AACSB, ACEN, CSWE, NCATE. **Intercollegiate Athletics:** Baseball M; Basketball M & W; Bowling W; Cheerleading M & W; Cross-Country Running M & W; Equestrian Sports W; Football M; Soccer W; Softball W; Tennis W; Track and Field M & W; Volleyball W

DELAWARE TECHNICAL & COMMUNITY COLLEGE, JACK F. OWENS CAMPUS

PO Box 610
Georgetown, DE 19947
Tel: (302)856-5400
Fax: (302)856-9461
Web Site: www.dtcc.edu
President/CEO: Dr. Orlando George
Admissions: Claire McDonald
Type: Two-Year College **Sex:** Coed **Affiliation:** Delaware Technical and Community College System. **% Accepted:** 100 **Admission Plans:** Deferred Admission; Early Admission; Open Admission; Preferred Admission **Application Fee:** $10.00 **H.S. Requirements:** High school diploma required; GED accepted **Scholarships:** Available. **Calendar System:** Semester **Enrollment:** Full-time 1,981, Part-time 2,448 **Regional Accreditation:** Middle States Association of Colleges and Schools **Professional Accreditation:** ABET, ACBSP, ACEN, AOTA, APTA, CoARC, JRCERT, NAACLS. **Intercollegiate Athletics:** Baseball M; Golf M; Softball W

DELAWARE TECHNICAL & COMMUNITY COLLEGE, STANTON/WILMINGTON CAMPUS

400 Stanton-Christiana Rd.
Newark, DE 19713
Tel: (302)454-3900
Fax: (302)577-2548
Web Site: www.dtcc.edu
President/CEO: Dr. Orlando George
Admissions: Rebecca Bailey
Type: Two-Year College **Sex:** Coed **Affiliation:** Delaware Technical and Community College System. **% Accepted:** 100 **Admission Plans:** Deferred Admission; Early Admission; Open Admission **Application Deadline:** Rolling **Application Fee:** $10.00 **H.S. Requirements:** High school diploma required; GED accepted **Scholarships:** Available. **Calendar System:** Semester **Enrollment:** Full-time 2,616, Part-time 4,419 **Final Year or Final Semester Residency Requirement:** No **Regional Accreditation:** Middle States Association of Colleges and Schools **Professional Accreditation:** AAMAE, ABET, ACBSP, ACEN, ACF, ADA, AOTA, APTA, CoARC, JRCEDMS, JRCERT, JRCNMT, NAACLS. **Intercollegiate Athletics:** Basketball M & W; Soccer M; Softball W

DELAWARE TECHNICAL & COMMUNITY COLLEGE, TERRY CAMPUS

100 Campus Dr.
Dover, DE 19901
Tel: (302)857-1000
Fax: (302)857-1296
E-mail: terry-info@dtcc.edu
Web Site: www.dtcc.edu
President/CEO: Dr. Orlando George
Admissions: Maria Harris
Type: Two-Year College **Sex:** Coed **Affiliation:** Delaware Technical and Community College System. **% Accepted:** 100 **Admission Plans:** Deferred Admission; Early Admission; Open Admission; Preferred Admission **Application Fee:** $10.00 **H.S. Requirements:** High school diploma required; GED accepted **Scholarships:** Available. **Calendar System:** Semester **Enroll-

ment: Full-time 1,285, Part-time 1,670 **Regional Accreditation:** Middle States Association of Colleges and Schools **Professional Accreditation:** ACBSP, ACEN, JRCEMTP. **Intercollegiate Athletics:** Lacrosse M; Soccer M & W; Softball W

GOLDEY-BEACOM COLLEGE

4701 Limestone Rd.
Wilmington, DE 19808-1999
Tel: (302)998-8814; Free: 800-833-4877
Fax: (302)996-5408
E-mail: admissions@gbc.edu
Web Site: www.gbc.edu
President/CEO: Dr. Mohammad Ilyas
Admissions: Larry Eby
Financial Aid: Jane H. Lysle

Type: Comprehensive **Sex:** Coed **Scholarships:** Available. **Calendar System:** Semester, Summer session available **Enrollment:** Full-time 462, Graduate full-time 77, Graduate part-time 650, Part-time 163 **Faculty:** Full-time 18, Part-time 38 **Student-Faculty Ratio:** 26:1 **Exams:** ACT essay component used for admission; SAT I or ACT; SAT essay component used for admission. **% Residing in College-Owned, -Operated, or -Affiliated Housing:** 32 **Final Year or Final Semester Residency Requirement:** No **Regional Accreditation:** Middle States Association of Colleges and Schools **Credit Hours For Degree:** 66 credits, Associates; 131 credits, Bachelors **Professional Accreditation:** ACBSP. **Intercollegiate Athletics:** Basketball M & W; Cross-Country Running M & W; Golf M & W; Soccer M & W; Softball W; Tennis W; Volleyball W

STRAYER UNIVERSITY–CHRISTIANA CAMPUS

240 Continental Dr.
Ste. 108
Newark, DE 19713
Tel: (302)292-6100
Fax: (302)292-6130
Web Site: www.strayer.edu/delaware/christiana
President/CEO: Brian W. Jones

Type: Comprehensive **Sex:** Coed **Regional Accreditation:** Middle States Association of Colleges and Schools

UNIVERSITY OF DELAWARE

Newark, DE 19716
Tel: (302)831-2000
Fax: (302)831-6905
E-mail: admissions@udel.edu
Web Site: www.udel.edu
President/CEO: Dr. Patrick T. Harker
Admissions: Dr. Jose Aviles
Financial Aid: James Holloway

Type: University **Sex:** Coed **Scores:** 100% SAT V 400+; 100% SAT M 400+; 15% ACT 18-23; 64% ACT 24-29 **% Accepted:** 63 **Admission Plans:** Deferred Admission; Early Admission; Preferred Admission **Application Fee:** $75.00 **H.S. Requirements:** High school diploma required; GED accepted **Costs Per Year:** Application fee: $75. State resident tuition: $11,230 full-time, $468 per credit hour part-time. Nonresident tuition: $30,130 full-time, $1255 per credit hour part-time. Mandatory fees: $1290 full-time. College room and board: $11,830. College room only: $7172. Room and board charges vary according to board plan, housing facility, and student level. **Scholarships:** Available. **Calendar System:** 4-1-4, Summer session available **Enrollment:** Full-time 16,812, Graduate full-time 3,006, Graduate part-time 746, Part-time 1,510 **Faculty:** Full-time 1,181, Part-time 474 **Student-Faculty Ratio:** 13:1 **Exams:** ACT essay component used as validity check; ACT essay component used for admission; ACT essay component used for placement; SAT I or ACT; SAT II; SAT essay component used as validity check; SAT essay component used for admission; SAT essay component

used for placement; SAT Reasoning; SAT Subject. **% Receiving Financial Aid:** 48 **% Residing in College-Owned, -Operated, or -Affiliated Housing:** 43 **Regional Accreditation:** Middle States Association of Colleges and Schools **Credit Hours For Degree:** 60 credit hours, Associates; 120 credit hours, Bachelors **ROTC:** Air Force, Army **Professional Accreditation:** AACN, AACSB, ABET, ACEN, AND, APA, APTA, JRCAT, NAACLS, NASM, NASPAA, NCATE. **Intercollegiate Athletics:** Baseball M; Basketball M & W; Bowling M & W; Cheerleading M & W; Crew M & W; Cross-Country Running M & W; Equestrian Sports M & W; Field Hockey W; Football M; Golf M & W; Ice Hockey M & W; Lacrosse M & W; Rugby M & W; Sailing M & W; Soccer M & W; Softball W; Swimming and Diving M & W; Tennis M & W; Track and Field M & W; Volleyball W; Wrestling M

WESLEY COLLEGE

120 N State St.
Dover, DE 19901-3875
Tel: (302)736-2300; Free: 800-937-5398
Fax: (302)736-2301
E-mail: christopher.jester@wesley.edu
Web Site: www.wesley.edu
President/CEO: Dr. William N. Johnston
Admissions: Christopher Jester
Financial Aid: Michael Hall

Type: Comprehensive **Sex:** Coed **Affiliation:** United Methodist. **Scores:** 62% SAT V 400+; 67% SAT M 400+ **% Accepted:** 63 **Application Deadline:** Rolling **Application Fee:** $25.00 **H.S. Requirements:** High school diploma required; GED accepted **Scholarships:** Available. **Calendar System:** Semester, Summer session available **Enrollment:** Full-time 1,345, Graduate full-time 80, Graduate part-time 29, Part-time 316 **Faculty:** Full-time 70, Part-time 100 **Exams:** Other; SAT I. **% Receiving Financial Aid:** 73 **% Residing in College-Owned, -Operated, or -Affiliated Housing:** 66 **Regional Accreditation:** Middle States Association of Colleges and Schools **Credit Hours For Degree:** 64 credit hours, Associates; 124 credit hours, Bachelors **ROTC:** Army **Professional Accreditation:** ACEN, NCATE. **Intercollegiate Athletics:** Baseball M; Basketball M & W; Field Hockey W; Football M; Golf M & W; Lacrosse M & W; Soccer M & W; Softball W; Tennis M & W

WILMINGTON UNIVERSITY

320 N DuPont Hwy.
New Castle, DE 19720-6491
Tel: (302)328-9401; Free: 877-967-5464
Fax: (302)328-5902
E-mail: undergradadmissions@wilmu.edu
Web Site: www.wilmu.edu
President/CEO: Dr. Jack P. Varsalona
Admissions: Laura Morris
Financial Aid: J. Lynn Iocono

Type: University **Sex:** Coed **% Accepted:** 100 **Admission Plans:** Deferred Admission; Early Admission; Open Admission **Application Deadline:** Rolling **Application Fee:** $25.00 **H.S. Requirements:** High school diploma required; GED accepted **Costs Per Year:** Application fee: $25. Tuition: $8304 full-time, $346 per credit part-time. Mandatory fees: $50 full-time, $25 per term part-time. Full-time tuition and fees vary according to location. Part-time tuition and fees vary according to location. **Scholarships:** Available. **Calendar System:** Semester, Summer session available **Enrollment:** Full-time 3,986, Graduate full-time 2,541, Graduate part-time 3,611, Part-time 5,690 **Faculty:** Full-time 124, Part-time 2,047 **Student-Faculty Ratio:** 17:1 **% Receiving Financial Aid:** 40 **Regional Accreditation:** Middle States Association of Colleges and Schools **Credit Hours For Degree:** 60 credit hours, Associates; 120 credit hours, Bachelors **ROTC:** Air Force, Army **Professional Accreditation:** AACN, ACA, NCATE. **Intercollegiate Athletics:** Baseball M; Basketball M & W; Cross-Country Running M & W; Softball W; Volleyball W

AMERICAN UNIVERSITY
4400 Massachusetts Ave., NW
Washington, DC 20016-8001
Tel: (202)885-1000
Fax: (202)885-6014
E-mail: admissions@american.edu
Web Site: www.american.edu
President/CEO: Dr. Cornelius M. Kerwin
Admissions: Greg Grauman
Financial Aid: Brian Lee Sang
Type: University **Sex:** Coed **Affiliation:** Methodist. **Scores:** 100% SAT V 400+; 100% SAT M 400+; 9.95% ACT 18-23; 57.46% ACT 24-29 **% Accepted:** 35 **Admission Plans:** Deferred Admission; Early Action **Application Deadline:** January 10 **Application Fee:** $70.00 **H.S. Requirements:** High school diploma required; GED accepted **Costs Per Year:** Application fee: $70. Comprehensive fee: $59,119 includes full-time tuition ($44,046), mandatory fees ($547), and college room and board ($14,526). College room only: $9800. Full-time tuition and fees vary according to course load. Room and board charges vary according to board plan, housing facility, and location. Part-time tuition: $1467 per credit hour. Part-time mandatory fees: $85 per term. **Scholarships:** Available. **Calendar System:** Semester, Summer session available **Enrollment:** Full-time 7,540, Graduate full-time 2,922, Graduate part-time 2,369, Part-time 369 **Faculty:** Full-time 785, Part-time 624 **Student-Faculty Ratio:** 12:1 **Exams:** ACT essay component not used; SAT essay component not used; SAT Reasoning; SAT Subject. **% Receiving Financial Aid:** 53 **Final Year or Final Semester Residency Requirement:** Yes **Regional Accreditation:** Middle States Association of Colleges and Schools **Credit Hours For Degree:** 60 credits, Associates; 120 credits, Bachelors **ROTC:** Air Force, Army **Professional Accreditation:** AACSB, AALS, ABA, ACEJMC, APA, NASM, NASPAA, NCATE. **Intercollegiate Athletics:** Basketball M & W; Cross-Country Running M & W; Field Hockey W; Lacrosse W; Soccer M & W; Swimming and Diving M & W; Track and Field M & W; Volleyball W; Wrestling M

THE CATHOLIC UNIVERSITY OF AMERICA
Cardinal Station
Washington, DC 20064
Tel: (202)319-5000; Free: 800-673-2772
Fax: (202)319-6533
E-mail: cua-admissions@cua.edu
Web Site: www.cua.edu
President/CEO: Dr. John H. Garvey
Admissions: Dr. Christopher Lydon
Financial Aid: Joseph Dobrota
Type: University **Sex:** Coed **Affiliation:** Roman Catholic Church. **Scores:** 99% SAT V 400+; 99% SAT M 400+; 33% ACT 18-23; 50% ACT 24-29 **Costs Per Year:** One-time mandatory fee: $425. Comprehensive fee: $54,288 includes full-time tuition ($40,400), mandatory fees ($532), and college room and board ($13,356). Full-time tuition and fees vary according to program. Room and board charges vary according to board plan and housing facility. Part-time tuition: $1600 per credit hour. Part-time mandatory fees: $306 per year. Part-time tuition and fees vary according to course load and program. **Scholarships:** Available. **Calendar System:** Semester, Summer session available **Enrollment:** Full-time 3,331, Graduate full-time 1,164, Graduate part-time 1,877, Part-time 149 **Faculty:** Full-time 399, Part-time 367 **Student-Faculty Ratio:** 7:1 **Exams:** ACT essay component used for advising; SAT essay component used for advising. **% Receiving Financial Aid:** 56 **% Residing in College-Owned, -Operated, or -Affiliated Housing:** 57 **Regional Accreditation:** Middle States Association of Colleges and Schools **Credit Hours For Degree:** 120 credits, Bachelors **ROTC:** Air Force, Army, Navy **Professional Accreditation:** AACN, AALS, ABA, ABET, ALA, APA, ATS, CSWE, NAAB, NASM, NCATE. **Intercollegiate Athletics:** Baseball M; Basketball M & W; Cross-Country Running M & W; Field Hockey W; Football M; Lacrosse M & W; Soccer M & W; Softball W; Swimming and Diving M & W; Tennis M & W; Track and Field M & W; Volleyball W

GALLAUDET UNIVERSITY
800 Florida Ave., NE
Washington, DC 20002-3625
Tel: (202)651-5000; Free: 800-995-0550
Fax: (202)651-5774
E-mail: Beth.Benedict@gallaudet.edu
Web Site: www.gallaudet.edu
President/CEO: Roberta Cordano
Admissions: Dr. Beth Benedict
Financial Aid: Shondra Dickson
Type: University **Sex:** Coed **Scores:** 30% SAT V 400+; 70% SAT M 400+; 38% ACT 18-23; 15% ACT 24-29 **% Accepted:** 62 **Admission Plans:** Deferred Admission **Application Deadline:** Rolling **Application Fee:** $50.00 **H.S. Requirements:** High school diploma required; GED accepted **Costs Per Year:** Application fee: $50. Tuition: $15,552 full-time, $648 per credit part-time. Mandatory fees: $526 full-time. Full-time tuition and fees vary according to course load. Part-time tuition varies according to course load. **Scholarships:** Available. **Calendar System:** Semester, Summer session available **Enrollment:** Full-time 959, Graduate full-time 295, Graduate part-time 171, Part-time 52 **Faculty:** Full-time 181, Part-time 117 **Student-Faculty Ratio:** 6:1 **Exams:** ACT; ACT essay component used for placement; SAT I or ACT. **% Receiving Financial Aid:** 75 **% Residing in College-Owned, -Operated, or -Affiliated Housing:** 72 **Final Year or Final Semester Residency Requirement:** Yes **Regional Accreditation:** Middle States Association of Colleges and Schools **Credit Hours For Degree:** 120 credit hours, Bachelors **Professional Accreditation:** ACA, ACBSP, APA, ASHA, CSWE, NCATE, NRPA. **Intercollegiate Athletics:** Baseball M; Basketball M & W; Cheerleading M & W; Cross-Country Running M & W; Football M; Soccer M & W; Softball W; Swimming and Diving M & W; Track and Field M & W; Volleyball W

THE GEORGE WASHINGTON UNIVERSITY
2121 I St., NW
Washington, DC 20052
Tel: (202)994-1000
E-mail: gwadm@gwis2.circ.gwu.edu
Web Site: www.gwu.edu
President/CEO: Steven Knapp
Admissions: Karen Felton
Financial Aid: Dan Small
Type: University **Sex:** Coed **Scores:** 100% SAT V 400+; 100% SAT M 400+; 4% ACT 18-23; 46% ACT 24-29 **% Accepted:** 46 **Admission Plans:** Deferred Admission; Early Action; Early Admission **Application Deadline:** January 1 **Application Fee:** $75.00 **H.S. Requirements:** High school diploma required; GED accepted **Costs Per Year:** Application fee: $75.

Comprehensive fee: $65,042 includes full-time tuition ($49,772), mandatory fees ($65), and college room and board ($15,205). College room only: $11,305. Full-time tuition and fees vary according to student level. Room and board charges vary according to housing facility. Part-time tuition: $1475 per credit hour. Part-time tuition varies according to course load. Tuition guaranteed not to increase for student's term of enrollment. **Scholarships:** Available. **Calendar System:** Semester, Summer session available **Enrollment:** Full-time 10,163, Graduate full-time 7,526, Graduate part-time 7,529, Part-time 994 **Faculty:** Full-time 1,095, Part-time 1,392 **Student-Faculty Ratio:** 13:1 **Exams:** SAT I and SAT II or ACT; SAT I or ACT; SAT Reasoning; SAT Subject. **% Receiving Financial Aid:** 46 **% Residing in College-Owned, -Operated, or -Affiliated Housing:** 62 **Regional Accreditation:** Middle States Association of Colleges and Schools **Credit Hours For Degree:** 60 semester hours, Associates; 120 semester hours, Bachelors **ROTC:** Air Force, Army, Navy **Professional Accreditation:** AABB, AACN, AACSB, AALS, ABA, ABET, ACA, APA, APTA, ASHA, CAHME, CEPH, CIDA, CORE, JRCAT, JRCEDMS, LCME/AMA, NAACLS, NASAD, NASM, NASPAA, NCATE. **Intercollegiate Athletics:** Baseball M; Basketball M & W; Crew M & W; Cross-Country Running M & W; Golf M; Gymnastics W; Soccer M & W; Swimming and Diving M & W; Tennis M & W; Volleyball W; Water Polo M

GEORGETOWN UNIVERSITY

37th and O Sts., NW
Washington, DC 20057
Tel: (202)687-0100
Fax: (202)687-6660
Web Site: www.georgetown.edu
President/CEO: Dr. John J. Degioia
Admissions: Dean Charles A. Deacon
Financial Aid: Patricia A. McWade

Type: University **Sex:** Coed **Affiliation:** Roman Catholic (Jesuit). **Scores:** 100% SAT V 400+; 100% SAT M 400+; 2.86% ACT 18-23; 19.73% ACT 24-29 **% Accepted:** 17 **Admission Plans:** Deferred Admission; Early Decision Plan **Application Deadline:** January 10 **Application Fee:** $75.00 **H.S. Requirements:** High school diploma required; GED accepted **Costs Per Year:** Application fee: $75. Comprehensive fee: $66,115 includes full-time tuition ($49,968), mandatory fees ($579), and college room and board ($15,568). College room only: $10,726. Full-time tuition and fees vary according to course load and program. Room and board charges vary according to board plan and housing facility. Part-time tuition: $2082 per credit hour. Part-time tuition varies according to course load and program. **Scholarships:** Available. **Calendar System:** Semester, Summer session available **Enrollment:** Full-time 7,175, Graduate full-time 7,548, Graduate part-time 3,349, Part-time 387 **Faculty:** Full-time 1,004, Part-time 1,037 **Student-Faculty Ratio:** 11:1 **Exams:** SAT I or ACT; SAT II; SAT Reasoning; SAT Subject. **% Receiving Financial Aid:** 38 **% Residing in College-Owned, -Operated, or -Affiliated Housing:** 65 **Regional Accreditation:** Middle States Association of Colleges and Schools **Credit Hours For Degree:** 120 credit hours, Bachelors **ROTC:** Air Force, Army, Navy **Professional Accreditation:** AACN, AACSB, AALS, AANA, ABA, ACNM, ACIPE, LCME/AMA. **Intercollegiate Athletics:** Baseball M; Basketball M & W; Crew M & W; Cross-Country Running M & W; Field Hockey W; Football M; Golf M & W; Ice Hockey M; Lacrosse M & W; Rugby M & W; Sailing M & W; Soccer M & W; Softball W; Swimming and Diving M & W; Tennis M & W; Track and Field M & W; Ultimate Frisbee M & W; Volleyball M & W; Water Polo M

GRADUATE SCHOOL USA

600 Maryland Ave., SW
Washington, DC 20024
Tel: (202)314-3300
Web Site: www.graduateschool.edu

Type: Two-Year College **Sex:** Coed **Regional Accreditation:** Middle States Association of Colleges and Schools

HOWARD UNIVERSITY

2400 Sixth St., NW
Washington, DC 20059-0002
Tel: (202)806-6100; Free: 800-822-6363
E-mail: admission@howard.edu
Web Site: www.howard.edu
President/CEO: Dr. Wayne Frederick
Admissions: Tammy McCants
Financial Aid: Derek Kindle

Type: University **Sex:** Coed **Scores:** 100% SAT V 400+; 99% SAT M 400+; 50.8% ACT 18-23; 38.6% ACT 24-29 **% Accepted:** 49 **Admission Plans:** Deferred Admission; Early Admission; Early Decision Plan **Application Deadline:** February 15 **Application Fee:** $45.00 **H.S. Requirements:** High school diploma required; GED accepted **Costs Per Year:** Application fee: $45. Comprehensive fee: $37,616 includes full-time tuition ($22,737), mandatory fees ($1233), and college room and board ($13,646). College room only: $9506. Full-time tuition and fees vary according to course load. Room and board charges vary according to board plan and housing facility. Part-time tuition: $980 per credit hour. Part-time mandatory fees: $1233 per term. Part-time tuition and fees vary according to course load. **Scholarships:** Available. **Calendar System:** Semester, Summer session available **Enrollment:** Full-time 6,412, Graduate full-time 2,614, Graduate part-time 505, Part-time 471 **Faculty:** Full-time 1,149, Part-time 371 **Student-Faculty Ratio:** 10:1 **Exams:** ACT essay component used for admission; ACT essay component used for placement; SAT I and SAT II or ACT; SAT I or ACT; SAT essay component used for admission; SAT essay component used for placement. **% Receiving Financial Aid:** 82 **% Residing in College-Owned, -Operated, or -Affiliated Housing:** 56 **Final Year or Final Semester Residency Requirement:** Yes **Regional Accreditation:** Middle States Association of Colleges and Schools **Credit Hours For Degree:** 120 credit hours, Bachelors **ROTC:** Air Force, Army **Professional Accreditation:** AACN, AACSB, AALS, ABA, ABET, ACEJMC, ACPE, ACIPE, ADA, AND, AOTA, APA, APTA, ASHA, ATS, CSWE, JRCERT, LCME/AMA, NAAB, NASAD, NASM, NASPAA, NAST, NCATE. **Intercollegiate Athletics:** Basketball M & W; Bowling W; Cross-Country Running M & W; Football M; Lacrosse W; Soccer M & W; Softball W; Swimming and Diving M & W; Tennis M & W; Track and Field M & W; Volleyball W

RADIANS COLLEGE

1025 Vermont Ave., NW, Ste. 200
Washington, DC 20005
Tel: (202)291-9020
Web Site: www.radianscollege.edu

Type: Two-Year College **Sex:** Coed **Professional Accreditation:** ACICS.

STRAYER UNIVERSITY–TAKOMA PARK CAMPUS

6830 Laurel St., NW
Washington, DC 20012
Tel: (202)722-8100
Web Site: www.strayer.edu/district-columbia/takoma-park
President/CEO: Brian W. Jones

Type: Comprehensive **Sex:** Coed **Regional Accreditation:** Middle States Association of Colleges and Schools

STRAYER UNIVERSITY–WASHINGTON CAMPUS

1133 15th St., NW
Washington, DC 20005
Tel: (202)408-2400
Fax: (202)419-1425
Web Site: www.strayer.edu/district-columbia/washington
President/CEO: Brian W. Jones

Type: Comprehensive **Sex:** Coed **Regional Accreditation:** Middle States Association of Colleges and Schools

TRINITY WASHINGTON UNIVERSITY

125 Michigan Ave., NE
Washington, DC 20017-1094
Tel: (202)884-9000; Free: 800-IWANTTC
Fax: (202)884-9229
E-mail: admissions@trinitydc.edu
Web Site: www.trinitydc.edu
President/CEO: Patricia A. McGuire
Financial Aid: Catherine H. Geier

Type: Comprehensive **Sex:** Women **Affiliation:** Roman Catholic. **Admission Plans:** Deferred Admission; Early Decision Plan **Application Deadline:** March 1 **Application Fee:** $40.00 **H.S. Requirements:** High school diploma required; GED accepted **Scholarships:** Available. **Calendar System:** Semester, Summer session available **Exams:** SAT I or ACT. **% Receiving Financial Aid:** 87 **Regional Accreditation:** Middle States Association of Colleges and Schools **Credit Hours For Degree:** 128 credit hours, Bachelors **ROTC:** Army **Professional Accreditation:** AACN, NCATE. **Intercollegiate Athletics:** Basketball W; Field Hockey W; Lacrosse W; Soccer W; Softball W; Swimming and Diving W; Tennis W; Volleyball W

UNIVERSITY OF THE DISTRICT OF COLUMBIA

4200 Connecticut Ave., NW

Washington, DC 20008-1175

Tel: (202)274-5000

E-mail: nicole.daniels@udc.edu

Web Site: www.udc.edu

President/CEO: Dr. James E. Lyons

Admissions: Nicole L. Daniels

Financial Aid: Nailah Williams

Type: Comprehensive **Sex:** Coed **Admission Plans:** Deferred Admission; Open Admission; Preferred Admission **Application Deadline:** August 1 **Application Fee:** $35.00 **H.S. Requirements:** High school diploma required; GED accepted **Costs Per Year:** Application fee: $35. District resident tuition: $6801 full-time, $283.38 per credit hour part-time. Nonresident tuition: $14,263 full-time, $594.30 per credit hour part-time. Mandatory fees: $620 full-time, $30 per credit hour part-time. Full-time tuition and fees vary according to course load and location. Part-time tuition and fees vary according to course load. College room and board: $15,027. College room only: $12,495. **Scholarships:** Available. **Calendar System:** Semester, Summer session available **Enrollment:** Full-time 1,902, Graduate full-time 212, Graduate part-time 100, Part-time 2,589 **Faculty:** Full-time 260, Part-time 316 **Student-Faculty Ratio:** 11:1 **Exams:** SAT I. **% Receiving Financial Aid:** 64 **Regional Accreditation:** Middle States Association of Colleges and Schools **Credit Hours For Degree:** 60 semester hours, Associates; 120 semester hours, Bachelors **ROTC:** Air Force, Army **Professional Accreditation:** ABA, ABET, ABFSE, ACA, ACBSP, ACEN, ASHA, CSWE, CoARC, JRCERT, NAAB, NCATE. **Intercollegiate Athletics:** Basketball M & W; Cross-Country Running W; Lacrosse M & W; Soccer M; Tennis M & W; Track and Field W

UNIVERSITY OF PHOENIX–WASHINGTON D.C. CAMPUS

25 Massachusetts Ave. NW, Ste. 150

Washington, DC 20001

Free: 866-766-0766

Web Site: www.phoenix.edu

President/CEO: Timothy P. Slottow

Admissions: Marc Booker

Type: Comprehensive **Sex:** Coed **Admission Plans:** Deferred Admission; Open Admission **Application Fee:** $0.00 **H.S. Requirements:** High school diploma required; GED accepted **Enrollment:** Full-time 14 **Faculty:** Full-time 3, Part-time 22 **Regional Accreditation:** North Central Association of Colleges and Schools

UNIVERSITY OF THE POTOMAC

1401 H St., NW

Washington, DC 20005

Tel: (202)686-0876; Free: 888-686-0876

Fax: (202)686-0818

E-mail: admissions@potomac.edu

Web Site: www.potomac.edu

Admissions: Niambi Green

Financial Aid: Phyllis Crews

Type: Comprehensive **Sex:** Coed **Admission Plans:** Open Admission **Application Deadline:** Rolling **Application Fee:** $0.00 **H.S. Requirements:** High school diploma required; GED accepted **Costs Per Year:** Application fee: $0. Tuition: $12,984 full-time, $541 per credit hour part-time. Mandatory fees: $900 full-time, $450 per term part-time. Tuition guaranteed not to increase for student's term of enrollment. **Scholarships:** Available. **Calendar System:** Miscellaneous, Summer session not available **Enrollment:** Full-time 210, Graduate full-time 133, Part-time 19 **Faculty:** Full-time 5, Part-time 50 **Student-Faculty Ratio:** 10:1 **Final Year or Final Semester Residency Requirement:** Yes **Regional Accreditation:** Middle States Association of Colleges and Schools **Credit Hours For Degree:** 60 semester credits, Associates; 120 semester credits, Bachelors

ACADEMY FOR NURSING AND HEALTH OCCUPATIONS

5154 Okeechobee Blvd.
Ste. 201
West Palm Beach, FL 33417
Tel: (561)683-1400
Web Site: www.apnho.com
Type: Two-Year College **Sex:** Coed **Professional Accreditation:** COE.

ADVANCE SCIENCE INSTITUTE

3750 W 12 Ave.
Hialeah, FL 33012
Tel: (305)827-5452
Web Site: www.asimedschool.com
Type: Two-Year College **Sex:** Coed **Professional Accreditation:** ACCSC.

ADVENTIST UNIVERSITY OF HEALTH SCIENCES

671 Winyah Dr.
Orlando, FL 32803
Tel: (407)303-7747; Free: 800-500-7747
E-mail: katie.shaw@adu.edu
Web Site: www.adu.edu
President/CEO: David E. Greenlaw
Admissions: Katie Shaw
Financial Aid: Rebecca Valencia
Type: Comprehensive **Sex:** Coed **Scores:** 92% SAT V 400+; 76% SAT M 400+; 66% ACT 18-23; 11% ACT 24-29 **% Accepted:** 60 **Admission Plans:** Early Admission; Early Decision Plan; Open Admission **Application Deadline:** July 1 **Application Fee:** $20.00 **H.S. Requirements:** High school diploma required; GED accepted **Costs Per Year:** Application fee: $20. Tuition: $12,900 full-time, $430 per credit hour part-time. Mandatory fees: $580 full-time, $290 per term part-time. Full-time tuition and fees vary according to course load, degree level, and program. Part-time tuition and fees vary according to course load, degree level, and program. College room only: $4200. **Scholarships:** Available. **Calendar System:** Trimester, Summer session available **Enrollment:** Full-time 639, Graduate full-time 133, Graduate part-time 45, Part-time 1,167 **Faculty:** Full-time 87, Part-time 179 **Student-Faculty Ratio:** 8:1 **Exams:** ACT essay component not used; SAT I or ACT; SAT essay component not used; SAT Reasoning; SAT Subject. **Final Year or Final Semester Residency Requirement:** No **Regional Accreditation:** Southern Association of Colleges and Schools **Credit Hours For Degree:** 64 credits, Associates; 120 credits, Bachelors **Professional Accreditation:** AANA, ACEN, AOTA, JRCEDMS, JRCERT, JRCNMT.

AMERICAN COLLEGE FOR MEDICAL CAREERS

5959 Lake Ellenor Dr.
Orlando, FL 32809
Tel: (407)738-4488; Free: 888-599-7887
Fax: (407)386-7522
Web Site: www.acmc.edu
Type: Four-Year College **Sex:** Coed **Professional Accreditation:** ACICS.

AMERICAN MEDICAL ACADEMY

12215 SW 112 St.
Miami, FL 33186-4830
Web Site: www.ama.edu
Type: Two-Year College **Sex:** Coed **Professional Accreditation:** ABHES.

ARGOSY UNIVERSITY, SARASOTA

5250 17th St.
Sarasota, FL 34235
Tel: (941)379-0404; Free: 800-331-5995
Fax: (941)379-9464
Web Site: www.argosy.edu/locations/sarasota
President/CEO: Sandra Wise
Type: University **Sex:** Coed **Affiliation:** Education Management Corporation. **Calendar System:** Semester **Regional Accreditation:** Western Association of Colleges and Schools **Professional Accreditation:** ACBSP.

ARGOSY UNIVERSITY, TAMPA

1403 N Howard Ave.
Tampa, FL 33607
Tel: (813)393-5290; Free: 800-850-6488
Fax: (813)246-4045
Web Site: www.argosy.edu/locations/tampa
President/CEO: Daniel Richins
Type: University **Sex:** Coed **Affiliation:** Education Management Corporation. **Calendar System:** Semester **Regional Accreditation:** Western Association of Colleges and Schools **Professional Accreditation:** ACBSP, APA.

THE ART INSTITUTE OF FORT LAUDERDALE

1799 SE 17th St.
Fort Lauderdale, FL 33316
Tel: (954)463-3000; Free: 800-275-7603
Fax: (954)728-8637
Web Site: www.artinstitutes.edu/fortlauderdale
President/CEO: Carol Menck
Type: Four-Year College **Sex:** Coed **Affiliation:** Education Management Corporation. **Calendar System:** Quarter **Professional Accreditation:** ACF, ACICS.

THE ART INSTITUTE OF TAMPA, A BRANCH OF MIAMI INTERNATIONAL UNIVERSITY OF ART & DESIGN

Parkside at Tampa Bay Park
4401 N Himes Ave., Ste. 150
Tampa, FL 33614
Tel: (813)873-2112; Free: 866-703-3277
Fax: (813)873-2171
Web Site: www.artinstitutes.edu/tampa
Type: Four-Year College **Sex:** Coed **Affiliation:** Education Management Corporation. **Calendar System:** Quarter **Regional Accreditation:** Southern Association of Colleges and Schools **Professional Accreditation:** ACF.

ATA CAREER EDUCATION

7351 Spring Hill Dr.
Ste. 11
Spring Hill, FL 34606
Tel: (352)684-3007
Web Site: www.atafl.edu
Type: Two-Year College **Sex:** Coed **Professional Accreditation:** ABHES.

AVE MARIA UNIVERSITY

5050 Ave. Maria Blvd.
Ave Maria, FL 34142
Tel: (239)280-2556; Free: 877-283-8648
Fax: (239)352-2392
E-mail: brett.ormandy@avemaria.edu
Web Site: www.avemaria.edu
President/CEO: James Towey, Jr.
Admissions: Billee Silva
Financial Aid: Anne Hart

Type: Comprehensive **Sex:** Coed **Affiliation:** Roman Catholic. **Scores:** 100% SAT V 400+; 96% SAT M 400+; 44% ACT 18-23; 27% ACT 24-29 **% Accepted:** 43 **Admission Plans:** Deferred Admission **Application Deadline:** Rolling **Application Fee:** $0.00 **H.S. Requirements:** High school diploma required; GED accepted **Costs Per Year:** Application fee: $0. Comprehensive fee: $29,681 includes full-time tuition ($18,675), mandatory fees ($773), and college room and board ($10,233). College room only: $5956. **Scholarships:** Available. **Calendar System:** Semester, Summer session available **Enrollment:** Full-time 1,046, Graduate full-time 36, Graduate part-time 4, Part-time 22 **Faculty:** Full-time 67, Part-time 26 **Student-Faculty Ratio:** 14:1 **Exams:** ACT essay component not used; SAT I or ACT; SAT essay component not used; SAT Reasoning. **% Receiving Financial Aid:** 63 **% Residing in College-Owned, -Operated, or -Affiliated Housing:** 90 **Final Year or Final Semester Residency Requirement:** No **Regional Accreditation:** Southern Association of Colleges and Schools **Credit Hours For Degree:** 128 credit hours, Bachelors **Professional Accreditation:** AALE. **Intercollegiate Athletics:** Baseball M; Basketball M & W; Cheerleading W; Cross-Country Running M & W; Football M; Golf M & W; Lacrosse W; Soccer M & W; Softball W; Tennis M & W; Volleyball W

AVIATOR COLLEGE OF AERONAUTICAL SCIENCE & TECHNOLOGY

3800 St. Lucie Blvd.
Fort Pierce, FL 34946
Tel: (772)466-4822
Web Site: aviator.edu/FlightSchool
Type: Two-Year College **Sex:** Coed **Professional Accreditation:** ACCSC.

THE BAPTIST COLLEGE OF FLORIDA

5400 College Dr.
Graceville, FL 32440-1898
Tel: (850)263-3261; Free: 800-328-2660
Fax: (850)263-7506
E-mail: skrichards@baptistcollege.edu
Web Site: www.baptistcollege.edu
President/CEO: Dr. Thomas A. Kinchen
Admissions: Sandra Richards
Financial Aid: Stephanie E. Powell

Type: Comprehensive **Sex:** Coed **Affiliation:** Southern Baptist. **% Accepted:** 52 **Admission Plans:** Deferred Admission; Open Admission; Preferred Admission **Application Deadline:** August 11 **Application Fee:** $25.00 **H.S. Requirements:** High school diploma required; GED accepted **Costs Per Year:** Application fee: $25. Comprehensive fee: $13,722 includes full-time tuition ($9600), mandatory fees ($400), and college room and board ($3722). Full-time tuition and fees vary according to location and program. Room and board charges vary according to board plan and housing facility. Part-time tuition: $320 per credit. Part-time mandatory fees: $150 per term. Part-time tuition and fees vary according to location and program. **Scholarships:** Available. **Calendar System:** Semester, Summer session available **Enrollment:** Full-time 333, Graduate full-time 18, Part-time 127 **Faculty:** Full-time 25, Part-time 45 **Student-Faculty Ratio:** 8:1 **Exams:** ACT essay component not used; SAT I or ACT; SAT essay component not used. **% Receiving Financial Aid:** 58 **% Residing in College-Owned, -Operated, or -Affiliated Housing:** 39 **Final Year or Final Semester Residency Requirement:** No **Regional Accreditation:** Southern Association of Colleges and Schools **Credit Hours For Degree:** 63 credit hours, Associates; 120 semester hours, Bachelors **Professional Accreditation:** AACN, NASM.

BARRY UNIVERSITY

11300 NE Second Ave.
Miami Shores, FL 33161-6695
Tel: (305)899-3000; Free: 800-695-2279
Fax: (305)899-2971

E-mail: admissions@mail.barry.edu
Web Site: www.barry.edu
President/CEO: Señor Linda M. Bevilacqua, OP, PhD
Admissions: Sarah Riley
Financial Aid: Dart Humeston

Type: University **Sex:** Coed **Affiliation:** Roman Catholic. **Scores:** 91% SAT V 400+; 85% SAT M 400+; 64% ACT 18-23; 10% ACT 24-29 **% Accepted:** 55 **Admission Plans:** Deferred Admission; Early Admission **Application Deadline:** Rolling **Application Fee:** $30.00 **H.S. Requirements:** High school diploma required; GED accepted **Costs Per Year:** Application fee: $30. Comprehensive fee: $39,222 includes full-time tuition ($28,800), mandatory fees ($22), and college room and board ($10,400). Room and board charges vary according to board plan. Part-time tuition: $865 per credit. Part-time tuition varies according to course load. **Scholarships:** Available. **Calendar System:** Semester, Summer session available **Enrollment:** Full-time 3,178, Graduate full-time 2,306, Graduate part-time 1,889, Part-time 598 **Exams:** SAT I or ACT. **% Receiving Financial Aid:** 77 **Regional Accreditation:** Southern Association of Colleges and Schools **Credit Hours For Degree:** 120 credits, Bachelors **ROTC:** Air Force, Army **Professional Accreditation:** AACN, AACSB, AANA, ABA, ACA, ACPeE, AOTA, APMA, ATS, CSWE, JRCAT, MACTE. **Intercollegiate Athletics:** Baseball M; Basketball M & W; Crew W; Golf M & W; Soccer M & W; Softball W; Tennis M & W; Volleyball W

BEACON COLLEGE

105 E Main St.
Leesburg, FL 34748
Tel: (352)787-7660
Fax: (352)787-0721
E-mail: dherold@beaconcollege.edu
Web Site: www.beaconcollege.edu
President/CEO: Dr. George J. Hagerty
Admissions: Dale Herold
Financial Aid: Shawna L. Wells-Booth

Type: Four-Year College **Sex:** Coed **% Accepted:** 57 **Admission Plans:** Deferred Admission; Early Admission **Application Deadline:** Rolling **Application Fee:** $50.00 **H.S. Requirements:** High school diploma required; GED accepted **Costs Per Year:** Application fee: $50. Comprehensive fee: $46,862 includes full-time tuition ($36,172) and college room and board ($10,690). College room only: $6794. Room and board charges vary according to housing facility. Part-time tuition: $1210 per credit. Part-time tuition varies according to course load. **Scholarships:** Available. **Calendar System:** Semester, Summer session available **Enrollment:** Full-time 265, Part-time 9 **Faculty:** Full-time 21, Part-time 10 **Exams:** SAT I or ACT. **% Receiving Financial Aid:** 45 **% Residing in College-Owned, -Operated, or -Affiliated Housing:** 77 **Final Year or Final Semester Residency Requirement:** Yes **Regional Accreditation:** Southern Association of Colleges and Schools **Credit Hours For Degree:** 61 credits, Associates; 120 credits, Bachelors

BELHAVEN UNIVERSITY

5200 Vineland Rd.
Ste. 100
Orlando, FL 32811
Tel: (407)804-1424; Free: 877-804-1424
Fax: (407)661-1732
E-mail: orlando@belhaven.edu
Web Site: orlando.belhaven.edu
President/CEO: Dr. Roger Parrott
Admissions: Jeremy Couch

Type: Comprehensive **Sex:** Coed **Affiliation:** Presbyterian. **Application Fee:** $25.00 **Calendar System:** Semester **Regional Accreditation:** Southern Association of Colleges and Schools

BETHUNE-COOKMAN UNIVERSITY

640 Dr. Mary McLeod Bethune Blvd.
Daytona Beach, FL 32114-3099
Tel: (386)481-2000; Free: 800-448-0228
Fax: (386)481-2010
E-mail: mccallj@cookman.edu
Web Site: www.cookman.edu
President/CEO: Dr. Edison Ovanda Jackson, EdD
Admissions: Junell McCall
Financial Aid: Salina Hamilton

Type: Comprehensive **Sex:** Coed **Affiliation:** Methodist. **Scores:** 29% ACT 18-23; 2% ACT 24-29 **% Accepted:** 54 **Admission Plans:** Deferred Admission; Early Admission **Application Deadline:** June 30 **Application Fee:** $25.00 **H.S. Requirements:** High school diploma required; GED accepted **Costs Per Year:** Application fee: $25. Comprehensive fee: $23,120 includes full-time tuition ($13,440), mandatory fees ($970), and college room and board ($8710). College room only: $6710. Full-time tuition and fees vary according to course load and degree level. Room and board charges vary according to housing facility. Part-time tuition: $50 per credit hour. Part-time tuition varies according to course load and degree level. **Scholarships:** Available. **Calendar System:** Semester, Summer session available **Enrollment:** Full-time 3,497, Graduate full-time 108, Graduate part-time 44, Part-time 182 **Faculty:** Full-time 197, Part-time 95 **Student-Faculty Ratio:** 16:1 **Exams:** ACT essay component used for admission; SAT I or ACT; SAT essay component used for admission; SAT Reasoning. **% Receiving Financial Aid:** 97 **% Residing in College-Owned, -Operated, or -Affiliated Housing:** 54 **Final Year or Final Semester Residency Requirement:** No **Regional Accreditation:** Southern Association of Colleges and Schools **Credit Hours For Degree:** 124 credit hours, Bachelors **ROTC:** Air Force, Army **Professional Accreditation:** ACBSP, ACEN, NCATE. **Intercollegiate Athletics:** Baseball M; Basketball M & W; Bowling W; Cheerleading W; Cross-Country Running M & W; Football M; Golf M & W; Softball W; Tennis M & W; Track and Field M & W; Volleyball W

BROWARD COLLEGE
111 E Las Olas Blvd.
Fort Lauderdale, FL 33301-2298
Tel: (954)201-7350
E-mail: walexand@broward.edu
Web Site: www.broward.edu
President/CEO: J. David Armstrong, Jr.
Admissions: Willie J. Alexander
Type: Two-Year College **Sex:** Coed **Affiliation:** Florida College System. **Admission Plans:** Deferred Admission; Early Admission; Open Admission; Preferred Admission **Application Fee:** $35.00 **H.S. Requirements:** High school diploma required; GED accepted **Scholarships:** Available. **Calendar System:** Trimester, Summer session available **Enrollment:** Full-time 13,327, Part-time 30,388 **Student-Faculty Ratio:** 30:1 **Final Year or Final Semester Residency Requirement:** No **Regional Accreditation:** Southern Association of Colleges and Schools **Credit Hours For Degree:** 60 semester hours, Associates; 120 semester hours, Bachelors **ROTC:** Army **Professional Accreditation:** ACEN, ADA, AHIMA, APTA, CoARC, JRCEDMS, JRCEMTP, JRCNMT, NASM. **Intercollegiate Athletics:** Baseball M; Basketball M & W; Softball W; Tennis W; Volleyball W

BURNETT INTERNATIONAL COLLEGE
1903 S Congress Ave.
Boynton Beach, FL 33426-6591
Tel: (561)736-3998
Web Site: www.burnett.edu
Type: Two-Year College **Sex:** Coed **Professional Accreditation:** COE.

CAMBRIDGE INSTITUTE OF ALLIED HEALTH AND TECHNOLOGY
5150 Linton Blvd.
Ste. 340
Delray Beach, FL 33484
Tel: (561)381-4990
Web Site: www.cambridgehealth.edu
Type: Two-Year College **Sex:** Coed **Professional Accreditation:** ABHES.

CARLOS ALBIZU UNIVERSITY, MIAMI CAMPUS
2173 NW 99th Ave.
Miami, FL 33172-2209
Tel: (305)593-1223; Free: 800-GO-TO-CAU
Fax: (305)592-7930
E-mail: matorres@albizu.edu
Web Site: www.albizu.edu
President/CEO: Sylvia Lopez-Jorge
Admissions: Maria Elena Torres
Financial Aid: Suset Menendez
Type: Comprehensive **Sex:** Coed **Affiliation:** Carlos Albizu University. **% Accepted:** 72 **Application Deadline:** Rolling **Application Fee:** $25.00 **H.S. Requirements:** High school diploma required; GED accepted **Costs Per Year:** Application fee: $25. Tuition: $11,628 full-time, $323 per credit part-

time. Mandatory fees: $756 full-time, $252 per term part-time. Full-time tuition and fees vary according to course load, degree level, and program. Part-time tuition and fees vary according to course load, degree level, and program. **Scholarships:** Available. **Calendar System:** Trimester, Summer session available **Enrollment:** Full-time 234, Graduate full-time 519, Graduate part-time 171, Part-time 122 **Faculty:** Full-time 8, Part-time 48 **Student-Faculty Ratio:** 11:1 **Regional Accreditation:** Middle States Association of Colleges and Schools **Credit Hours For Degree:** 120 credits, Bachelors **Professional Accreditation:** ACBSP, APA.

CHAMBERLAIN COLLEGE OF NURSING (JACKSONVILLE)
5200 Belfort Rd.
Jacksonville, FL 32256
Tel: (904)251-8110; Free: 877-751-5783
Fax: (904)251-8390
Web Site: www.chamberlain.edu
President/CEO: Katherine Walls
Type: Four-Year College **Sex:** Coed **Costs Per Year:** Tuition: $17,560 full-time, $665 per credit hour part-time. Mandatory fees: $600 full-time, $300 per term part-time. Full-time tuition and fees vary according to course load. Part-time tuition and fees vary according to course load. **Calendar System:** Semester **Enrollment:** Full-time 183, Part-time 173 **Faculty:** Full-time 9, Part-time 44 **Student-Faculty Ratio:** 10:1 **Exams:** ACT essay component used for admission; SAT I or ACT; SAT essay component used for admission. **Regional Accreditation:** North Central Association of Colleges and Schools

CHAMBERLAIN COLLEGE OF NURSING (MIRAMAR)
2300 SW 145th Ave.
Miramar, FL 33027
Tel: (954)885-3510; Free: 877-751-5783
Fax: (954)885-3601
Web Site: www.chamberlain.edu
Type: Four-Year College **Sex:** Coed **Application Fee:** $95.00 **H.S. Requirements:** High school diploma required; GED accepted **Costs Per Year:** Application fee: $95. Tuition: $17,560 full-time, $665 per credit hour part-time. Mandatory fees: $600 full-time, $300 per term part-time. Full-time tuition and fees vary according to course load. Part-time tuition and fees vary according to course load. **Enrollment:** Full-time 247, Part-time 250 **Faculty:** Full-time 10, Part-time 64 **Student-Faculty Ratio:** 11:1 **Exams:** ACT essay component used for admission; SAT I or ACT; SAT essay component used for admission. **Regional Accreditation:** North Central Association of Colleges and Schools

CHIPOLA COLLEGE
3094 Indian Cir.
Marianna, FL 32446-3065
Tel: (850)526-2761
Fax: (850)718-2388
E-mail: rehbergk@chipola.edu
Web Site: www.chipola.edu
President/CEO: Dr. Jason Hurst
Admissions: Kathy L. Rehberg
Type: Two-Year College **Sex:** Coed **Scores:** 76% SAT V 400+; 72% SAT M 400+; 56% ACT 18-23; 22% ACT 24-29 **Admission Plans:** Early Admission; Open Admission **Application Deadline:** Rolling **Application Fee:** $0.00 **H.S. Requirements:** High school diploma required; GED accepted **Costs Per Year:** Application fee: $0. State resident tuition: $3060 full-time, $102 per semester hour part-time. Nonresident tuition: $8,890 full-time, $296.35 per semester hour part-time. Mandatory fees: $40 full-time. Full-time tuition and fees vary according to degree level. Part-time tuition varies according to degree level. **Scholarships:** Available. **Calendar System:** Semester, Summer session available **Enrollment:** Full-time 863, Part-time 1,284 **Faculty:** Full-time 39, Part-time 88 **Student-Faculty Ratio:** 24:1 **Final Year or Final Semester Residency Requirement:** No **Regional Accreditation:** Southern Association of Colleges and Schools **Credit Hours For Degree:** 60 semester hours, Associates; 120 semester hours, Bachelors **Intercollegiate Athletics:** Baseball M; Basketball M & W; Softball W

CITY COLLEGE (ALTAMONTE SPRINGS)
177 Montgomery Rd.
Altamonte Springs, FL 32714
Tel: (407)831-9816
Fax: (407)831-1147

E-mail: kbowden@citycollege.edu
Web Site: www.citycollege.edu
President/CEO: Steve Schwab
Admissions: Kimberly Bowden
Type: Two-Year College **Sex:** Coed **Application Fee:** $25.00 **H.S. Require-ments:** High school diploma required; GED accepted **Calendar System:** Semester **Enrollment:** Full-time 217 **Faculty:** Full-time 2, Part-time 35 **Student-Faculty Ratio:** 17:1 **Exams:** Other. **Professional Accreditation:** ACICS.

CITY COLLEGE (FORT LAUDERDALE)

2000 W Commercial Blvd.
Ste. 200
Fort Lauderdale, FL 33309
Tel: (954)492-5353; Free: 866-314-5681
Fax: (954)491-1965
E-mail: tcarpenter@citycollege.edu
Web Site: www.citycollege.edu
President/CEO: R. Ester Fike
Admissions: Thomas Carpenter
Financial Aid: Ginger Ruback
Type: Two-Year College **Sex:** Coed **% Accepted:** 91 **Application Fee:** $40.00 **Scholarships:** Available. **Calendar System:** Semester **Student-Faculty Ratio:** 20:1 **Exams:** Other. **Professional Accreditation:** ACICS.

CITY COLLEGE (GAINESVILLE)

7001 NW 4th Blvd.
Gainesville, FL 32607
Tel: (352)335-4000
Fax: (352)335-4303
Web Site: www.citycollege.edu
President/CEO: R. Ester Fike
Type: Two-Year College **Sex:** Coed **% Accepted:** 98 **Application Fee:** $40.00 **Calendar System:** Semester **Student-Faculty Ratio:** 15:1 **Exams:** Other. **Professional Accreditation:** ACICS.

CITY COLLEGE (HOLLYWOOD)

6565 Taft St.
Hollywood, FL 33024
Tel: (954)744-1777; Free: 866-314-5681
Fax: (954)983-0118
Web Site: www.citycollege.edu
Type: Four-Year College **Sex:** Coed **Professional Accreditation:** ACICS.

CITY COLLEGE (MIAMI)

9300 S Dadeland Blvd.
Ste. 200
Miami, FL 33156
Tel: (305)666-9242
Fax: (305)666-9243
Web Site: www.citycollege.edu
President/CEO: R. Ester Fike
Type: Two-Year College **Sex:** Coed **% Accepted:** 62 **Application Fee:** $40.00 **Calendar System:** Semester **Student-Faculty Ratio:** 22:1 **Exams:** Other. **Professional Accreditation:** ACICS.

COLLEGE OF BUSINESS AND TECHNOLOGY–CUTLER BAY CAMPUS

19151 S Dixie Hwy.
Cutler Bay, FL 33157
Tel: (305)273-4499
E-mail: armando.alvarez@cbt.edu
Web Site: www.cbt.edu
President/CEO: Monica Llerena
Admissions: Armando Alvarez
Type: Two-Year College **Sex:** Coed **Admission Plans:** Open Admission **Application Fee:** $25.00 **H.S. Requirements:** High school diploma required; GED accepted **Costs Per Year:** Application fee: $25. Tuition: $11,952 full-time. Mandatory fees: $1400 full-time. **Calendar System:** Semester **Enrollment:** Full-time 112 **Faculty:** Full-time 4, Part-time 14 **Student-Faculty Ratio:** 13:1 **Final Year or Final Semester Residency Requirement:** No **Credit Hours For Degree:** 60 to 72 credits depending on the program, Associates **Professional Accreditation:** ACICS.

COLLEGE OF BUSINESS AND TECHNOLOGY–FLAGLER CAMPUS

8230 W Flagler St.
Miami, FL 33144
Tel: (305)273-4499
E-mail: armando.alvarez@cbt.edu
Web Site: www.cbt.edu
President/CEO: Monica Llerena
Admissions: Armando Alvarez
Type: Two-Year College **Sex:** Coed **Admission Plans:** Open Admission **Application Fee:** $25.00 **H.S. Requirements:** High school diploma required; GED accepted **Costs Per Year:** Application fee: $25. Tuition: $11,952 full-time. Mandatory fees: $1400 full-time. **Calendar System:** Semester **Enrollment:** Full-time 304 **Faculty:** Full-time 11, Part-time 21 **Student-Faculty Ratio:** 17:1 **Final Year or Final Semester Residency Requirement:** No **Credit Hours For Degree:** 60 or 68 credits depending on the program, Associates **Professional Accreditation:** ACICS.

COLLEGE OF BUSINESS AND TECHNOLOGY–HIALEAH CAMPUS

935 W 49 St.
Hialeah, FL 33012
Tel: (305)273-4499
E-mail: armando.alvarez@cbt.edu
Web Site: www.cbt.edu
President/CEO: Monica Llerena
Admissions: Armando Alvarez
Type: Two-Year College **Sex:** Coed **Admission Plans:** Open Admission **Application Fee:** $25.00 **H.S. Requirements:** High school diploma required; GED accepted **Costs Per Year:** Application fee: $25. Tuition: $11,952 full-time. Mandatory fees: $1400 full-time. **Calendar System:** Semester **Enrollment:** Full-time 211 **Faculty:** Full-time 8, Part-time 20 **Student-Faculty Ratio:** 14:1 **Final Year or Final Semester Residency Requirement:** No **Credit Hours For Degree:** 30 credits, Associates **Professional Accreditation:** ACICS.

COLLEGE OF BUSINESS AND TECHNOLOGY–MAIN CAMPUS

8700 W Flagler St., Ste. 420
Miami, FL 33174
Tel: (305)273-4499
Fax: (305)273-5216
E-mail: armando.alvarez@cbt.edu
Web Site: www.cbt.edu
President/CEO: Monica Llerena
Admissions: Armando Alvarez
Type: Two-Year College **Sex:** Coed **Admission Plans:** Open Admission **Application Fee:** $25.00 **H.S. Requirements:** High school diploma required; GED accepted **Costs Per Year:** Application fee: $25. Tuition: $11,952 full-time. Mandatory fees: $1400 full-time. **Calendar System:** Semester **Enrollment:** Full-time 9 **Faculty:** Full-time 1, Part-time 2 **Student-Faculty Ratio:** 5:1 **Final Year or Final Semester Residency Requirement:** No **Credit Hours For Degree:** 60 to 68 credits depending on the program, Associates; 120 credits, Bachelors **Professional Accreditation:** ACICS, COE.

COLLEGE OF BUSINESS AND TECHNOLOGY–MIAMI GARDENS

5190 NW 167 St.
Miami Gardens, FL 33014
Tel: (305)273-4499
E-mail: armando.alvarez@cbt.edu
Web Site: www.cbt.edu
President/CEO: Monica Llerena
Admissions: Armando Alavarez
Type: Two-Year College **Sex:** Coed **Admission Plans:** Open Admission **Application Fee:** $25.00 **H.S. Requirements:** High school diploma required; GED accepted **Costs Per Year:** Application fee: $25. Tuition: $11,952 full-time. Mandatory fees: $1400 full-time. **Calendar System:** Semester **Enrollment:** Full-time 90 **Faculty:** Full-time 2, Part-time 12 **Student-Faculty Ratio:** 15:1 **Final Year or Final Semester Residency Requirement:** No **Credit Hours For Degree:** 60 to 68 credits depending on the program, Associates; 120 credits, Bachelors **Professional Accreditation:** ACICS.

COLLEGE OF CENTRAL FLORIDA

3001 SW College Rd.
Ocala, FL 34474
Tel: (352)854-2322
Fax: (352)237-3747

E-mail: sewelld@cf.edu
Web Site: www.cf.edu
President/CEO: Dr. James D. Henningsen
Admissions: Devona Sewell
Type: Two-Year College **Sex:** Coed **Affiliation:** Florida Community College System. **% Accepted:** 55 **Admission Plans:** Early Admission; Open Admission **Application Deadline:** Rolling **Application Fee:** $30.00 **H.S. Requirements:** High school diploma required; GED accepted **Costs Per Year:** Application fee: $30. State resident tuition: $3213 full-time, $107 per credit hour part-time. Nonresident tuition: $12,656 full-time, $422 per credit hour part-time. Full-time tuition varies according to course level, degree level, program, and student level. Part-time tuition varies according to course level, degree level, program, and student level. **Scholarships:** Available. **Calendar System:** Semester, Summer session available **Enrollment:** Full-time 3,036, Part-time 4,895 **Faculty:** Full-time 138, Part-time 236 **Exams:** ACT; ACT essay component not used; SAT I; SAT I and SAT II or ACT; SAT I or ACT; SAT II; SAT essay component not used. **Final Year or Final Semester Residency Requirement:** No **Regional Accreditation:** Southern Association of Colleges and Schools **Credit Hours For Degree:** 60 credit hours, Associates; 120 credits hours, acceptance into the bachelor's degree programs requires an earned associate degree. (2+2), Bachelors **Professional Accreditation:** ACEN, APTA, JRCEMTP. **Intercollegiate Athletics:** Baseball M; Basketball M & W; Softball W; Volleyball W

CONCORDE CAREER INSTITUTE (JACKSONVILLE)
7259 Salisbury Rd.
Jacksonville, FL 32256
Tel: (904)725-0525
Fax: (904)721-9944
Web Site: www.concorde.edu
Type: Two-Year College **Sex:** Coed **Professional Accreditation:** ACCSC.

CONCORDE CAREER INSTITUTE (MIRAMAR)
10933 Marks Way
Miramar, FL 33025
Tel: (954)731-8880
Web Site: www.concorde.edu
Type: Two-Year College **Sex:** Coed **Professional Accreditation:** ACCSC.

CONCORDE CAREER INSTITUTE (ORLANDO)
3444 McCrory Pl.
Orlando, FL 32803
Tel: (407)812-3060
Web Site: www.concorde.edu
Type: Two-Year College **Sex:** Coed **Professional Accreditation:** ACCSC.

CONCORDE CAREER INSTITUTE (TAMPA)
4202 W Spruce St.
Tampa, FL 33607
Tel: (813)874-0094
Fax: (813)872-6884
Web Site: www.concorde.edu
Type: Two-Year College **Sex:** Coed **Professional Accreditation:** ACCSC.

DAYTONA COLLEGE
469 S Nova Rd.
Ormond Beach, FL 32174-8445
Tel: (386)267-0565
Web Site: www.daytonacollege.edu
Type: Two-Year College **Sex:** Coed **Professional Accreditation:** ACCSC.

DAYTONA STATE COLLEGE
1200 W International Speedway Blvd.
Daytona Beach, FL 32114
Tel: (386)506-3000
E-mail: sanderk@daytonastate.edu
Web Site: www.daytonastate.edu
President/CEO: Dr. Tom LoBasso
Admissions: Dr. Karen Sanders
Financial Aid: Kevin McCrary
Type: Two-Year College **Sex:** Coed **Affiliation:** Florida Community College System. **Scores:** 91% SAT V 400+; 87% SAT M 400+; 50% ACT 18-23; 10% ACT 24-29 **% Accepted:** 43 **Admission Plans:** Deferred Admission; Early Admission; Open Admission **Application Deadline:** Rolling **H.S. Require-**

ments: High school diploma required; GED accepted. For some vocational programs: High school diploma required; GED not accepted **Costs Per Year:** State resident tuition: $1,901 full-time, $79.22 per credit hour part-time. Nonresident tuition: $7,621 full-time, $317.53 per credit hour part-time. Mandatory fees: $543 full-time, $23.16 per credit hour part-time. Full-time tuition and fees vary according to course load and degree level. Part-time tuition and fees vary according to course load and degree level. **Scholarships:** Available. **Calendar System:** Semester, Summer session available **Enrollment:** Full-time 5,544, Part-time 8,054 **Faculty:** Full-time 302, Part-time 574 **Student-Faculty Ratio:** 17:1 **Regional Accreditation:** Southern Association of Colleges and Schools **Credit Hours For Degree:** 60 semester hours, Associates; 120 semester hours, Bachelors **ROTC:** Air Force, Army **Professional Accreditation:** ACEN, ADA, AHIMA, AOTA, APTA, CoARC, JRCEMTP. **Intercollegiate Athletics:** Baseball M; Basketball M & W; Golf W; Softball W; Volleyball W

DEVRY UNIVERSITY (JACKSONVILLE)
5200 Belfort Rd., Ste. 175
Jacksonville, FL 32256-6040
Web Site: www.devry.edu
Type: Comprehensive **Sex:** Coed **Application Deadline:** Rolling **Costs Per Year:** Tuition: $17,052 full-time, $609 per credit hour part-time. Mandatory fees: $80 full-time, $40 per term part-time. **Regional Accreditation:** North Central Association of Colleges and Schools **Professional Accreditation:** ACBSP.

DEVRY UNIVERSITY (MIRAMAR)
2300 SW 145th Ave.
Miramar, FL 33027-4150
Tel: (954)499-9775; Free: 866-338-7941
Web Site: www.devry.edu
Type: Comprehensive **Sex:** Coed **Affiliation:** DeVry University. **Application Fee:** $40.00 **H.S. Requirements:** High school diploma required; GED accepted **Costs Per Year:** Application fee: $40. Tuition: $17,052 full-time, $609 per credit hour part-time. Mandatory fees: $80 full-time, $40 per term part-time. **Scholarships:** Available. **Calendar System:** Semester **Enrollment:** Full-time 206, Graduate full-time 33, Graduate part-time 112, Part-time 297 **Faculty:** Full-time 13, Part-time 63 **Student-Faculty Ratio:** 11:1 **Exams:** ACT essay component used for admission; ACT essay component used for placement; SAT essay component used for admission; SAT essay component used for placement. **% Receiving Financial Aid:** 68 **Regional Accreditation:** North Central Association of Colleges and Schools **Credit Hours For Degree:** 66 credit hours, Associates; 122 credit hours, Bachelors **Professional Accreditation:** ABET.

DEVRY UNIVERSITY (ORLANDO)
4000 Millenia Blvd.
Orlando, FL 32839
Tel: (407)345-2800; Free: 866-338-7941
Web Site: www.devry.edu
Financial Aid: Estrella Velazquez-Domenech
Type: Comprehensive **Sex:** Coed **Affiliation:** DeVry University. **Application Fee:** $40.00 **H.S. Requirements:** High school diploma required; GED accepted **Costs Per Year:** Application fee: $40. Tuition: $17,052 full-time, $609 per credit hour part-time. Mandatory fees: $80 full-time, $40 per term part-time. **Scholarships:** Available. **Calendar System:** Semester **Enrollment:** Full-time 411, Graduate full-time 64, Graduate part-time 227, Part-time 503 **Faculty:** Full-time 17, Part-time 31 **Student-Faculty Ratio:** 26:1 **Exams:** ACT essay component used for admission; ACT essay component used for placement; SAT essay component used for admission; SAT essay component used for placement. **% Receiving Financial Aid:** 73 **Regional Accreditation:** North Central Association of Colleges and Schools **Credit Hours For Degree:** 67 credit hours, Associates; 122 credit hours, Bachelors **Professional Accreditation:** ABET.

DIGITAL MEDIA ARTS COLLEGE
5400 Broken Sound Blvd. NW No.100
Boca Raton, FL 33487
Free: 866-255-DMAC
Web Site: www.dmac.edu
Type: Comprehensive **Sex:** Coed **Professional Accreditation:** ACICS.

EASTERN FLORIDA STATE COLLEGE
1519 Clearlake Rd.
Cocoa, FL 32922-6597

Tel: (321)632-1111
Fax: (321)633-4565
E-mail: cocoaadmissions@brevardcc.edu
Web Site: www.easternflorida.edu
President/CEO: Dr. James H. Richey
Admissions: Stephanie Burnette

Type: Two-Year College **Sex:** Coed **Affiliation:** Florida Community College System. **% Accepted:** 100 **Admission Plans:** Early Admission; Open Admission **Application Deadline:** Rolling **Application Fee:** $30.00 **H.S. Requirements:** High school diploma required; GED accepted **Scholarships:** Available. **Calendar System:** Semester, Summer session available **Enrollment:** Full-time 5,929, Part-time 10,782 **Faculty:** Full-time 239, Part-time 769 **Student-Faculty Ratio:** 23:1 **Regional Accreditation:** Southern Association of Colleges and Schools **Credit Hours For Degree:** 60 credit hours, Associates **ROTC:** Air Force, Army **Professional Accreditation:** ADA, CoARC, JRCEMTP, JRCERT, MACTE, NAACLS. **Intercollegiate Athletics:** Baseball M; Basketball M & W; Golf M; Softball W; Volleyball W

ECKERD COLLEGE

4200 54th Ave. S
Saint Petersburg, FL 33711
Tel: (727)867-1166; Free: 800-456-9009
Fax: (727)866-2304
E-mail: admissions@eckerd.edu
Web Site: www.eckerd.edu
President/CEO: Dr. Donald R. Eastman, III
Admissions: Lucille Lopez
Financial Aid: Dr. Pat Garrett Watkins

Type: Four-Year College **Sex:** Coed **Affiliation:** Presbyterian. **Scores:** 98% SAT V 400+; 98% SAT M 400+; 28% ACT 18-23; 54% ACT 24-29 **% Accepted:** 73 **Admission Plans:** Deferred Admission; Early Decision Plan **Application Deadline:** Rolling **Application Fee:** $40.00 **H.S. Requirements:** High school diploma required; GED accepted **Costs Per Year:** Application fee: $40. Comprehensive fee: $50,940 includes full-time tuition ($39,684), mandatory fees ($336), and college room and board ($10,920). College room only: $5496. Room and board charges vary according to board plan and housing facility. Part-time tuition: $4617 per course. **Scholarships:** Available. **Calendar System:** 4-1-4, Summer session available **Enrollment:** Full-time 1,748, Part-time 41 **Faculty:** Full-time 115, Part-time 53 **Student-Faculty Ratio:** 13:1 **Exams:** ACT essay component not used; SAT I or ACT; SAT II; SAT essay component not used; SAT Reasoning; SAT Subject. **% Receiving Financial Aid:** 57 **% Residing in College-Owned, -Operated, or -Affiliated Housing:** 87 **Final Year or Final Semester Residency Requirement:** Yes **Regional Accreditation:** Southern Association of Colleges and Schools **ROTC:** Air Force, Army **Intercollegiate Athletics:** Baseball M; Basketball M & W; Golf M & W; Sailing M & W; Soccer M & W; Softball W; Tennis M & W; Volleyball W

ECPI UNIVERSITY

660 Century Point
Ste. 1050
Lake Mary, FL 32746
Tel: (800)416-3195
Web Site: www.ecpi.edu

Type: Four-Year College **Sex:** Coed **Regional Accreditation:** Southern Association of Colleges and Schools

EDWARD WATERS COLLEGE

1658 Kings Rd.
Jacksonville, FL 32209-6199
Tel: (904)470-8000; Free: 888-898-3191
Fax: (904)470-8039
E-mail: edward.alexander@ewc.edu
Web Site: www.ewc.edu
President/CEO: Nathaniel Glover
Admissions: Edward Alexander
Financial Aid: Gabriel Mbomeh

Type: Four-Year College **Sex:** Coed **Affiliation:** African Methodist Episcopal. **% Accepted:** 23 **Admission Plans:** Open Admission **Application Deadline:** Rolling **Application Fee:** $25.00 **H.S. Requirements:** High school diploma required; GED accepted **Costs Per Year:** Application fee: $25. Comprehensive fee: $19,807 includes full-time tuition ($12,325), mandatory fees ($200), and college room and board ($7282). **Scholarships:** Available. **Calendar System:** Semester, Summer session available **Enroll-**

ment: Full-time 739, Part-time 12 **Faculty:** Full-time 36, Part-time 45 **Student-Faculty Ratio:** 9:1 **Exams:** SAT I or ACT. **% Receiving Financial Aid:** 91 **Regional Accreditation:** Southern Association of Colleges and Schools **Credit Hours For Degree:** 120 semester hours, Bachelors **ROTC:** Army **Intercollegiate Athletics:** Basketball M & W; Tennis M & W; Track and Field M & W

EMBRY-RIDDLE AERONAUTICAL UNIVERSITY–DAYTONA

600 S Clyde Morris Blvd.
Daytona Beach, FL 32114-3900
Tel: (386)226-6000; Free: 800-862-2416
Fax: (386)226-7070
E-mail: dbadmit@erau.edu
Web Site: www.embryriddle.edu
President/CEO: Dr. John R. Watret
Financial Aid: Barbara Dryden

Type: University **Sex:** Coed **Scores:** 97% SAT V 400+; 99% SAT M 400+; 30.96% ACT 18-23; 50.68% ACT 24-29 **% Accepted:** 69 **Admission Plans:** Deferred Admission **Application Deadline:** Rolling **Application Fee:** $50.00 **H.S. Requirements:** High school diploma required; GED accepted **Costs Per Year:** Application fee: $50. Comprehensive fee: $44,712 includes full-time tuition ($32,592), mandatory fees ($1294), and college room and board ($10,826). College room only: $6500. Room and board charges vary according to board plan, housing facility, and location. Part-time tuition: $1358 per credit hour. Part-time mandatory fees: $647 per term. **Scholarships:** Available. **Calendar System:** Semester, Summer session available **Enrollment:** Full-time 4,876, Graduate full-time 425, Graduate part-time 103, Part-time 402 **Exams:** SAT I or ACT. **% Receiving Financial Aid:** 62 **% Residing in College-Owned, -Operated, or -Affiliated Housing:** 37 **Final Year or Final Semester Residency Requirement:** Yes **Regional Accreditation:** Southern Association of Colleges and Schools **Credit Hours For Degree:** 63 credit hours, Associates; 120 credit hours, Bachelors **ROTC:** Air Force, Army, Navy **Professional Accreditation:** AABI, ABET, ACBSP. **Intercollegiate Athletics:** Baseball M; Basketball M & W; Cheerleading M & W; Cross-Country Running M & W; Golf M & W; Lacrosse M & W; Rowing M & W; Soccer M & W; Softball W; Tennis M & W; Track and Field M & W; Volleyball W

EMBRY-RIDDLE AERONAUTICAL UNIVERSITY–WORLDWIDE

600 S Clyde Morris Blvd.
Daytona Beach, FL 32114-3900
Tel: (386)226-6910; Free: 800-522-6787
Fax: (386)226-6984
E-mail: worldwide@erau.edu
Web Site: www.embryriddle.edu
President/CEO: Dr. John R. Watret
Financial Aid: Dagmar Bowen

Type: Comprehensive **Sex:** Coed **% Accepted:** 67 **Admission Plans:** Deferred Admission **Application Deadline:** Rolling **Application Fee:** $50.00 **H.S. Requirements:** High school diploma required; GED accepted **Costs Per Year:** Application fee: $50. Tuition: $8760 full-time, $365 per credit hour part-time. Mandatory fees: $76 full-time. Full-time tuition and fees vary according to course load. Part-time tuition varies according to course load. **Scholarships:** Available. **Calendar System:** Miscellaneous, Summer session available **Enrollment:** Full-time 3,046, Graduate full-time 2,047, Graduate part-time 2,110, Part-time 7,498 **Exams:** ACT essay component not used; SAT I and SAT II or ACT; SAT I or ACT; SAT essay component not used. **% Receiving Financial Aid:** 26 **Final Year or Final Semester Residency Requirement:** No **Regional Accreditation:** Southern Association of Colleges and Schools **Credit Hours For Degree:** 60 credit hours, Associates; 120 credit hours, Bachelors **Professional Accreditation:** ACBSP.

EVEREST UNIVERSITY (LARGO)

1199 E Bay Dr.
Largo, FL 33770
Tel: (727)725-2688; Free: 888-741-4270
Fax: (727)796-3722
E-mail: kbuskirk@cci.edu
Web Site: www.everest.edu
President/CEO: Tina Barnes
Admissions: Ted Wilkins
Financial Aid: Will Scott

Type: Comprehensive **Sex:** Coed **Affiliation:** Zenith Education Group.

Admission Plans: Deferred Admission; Early Admission **Application Deadline:** Rolling **Application Fee:** $25.00 **H.S. Requirements:** High school diploma required; GED accepted **Scholarships:** Available. **Calendar System:** Quarter, Summer session available **Exams:** Other; SAT I or ACT. **% Receiving Financial Aid:** 98 **Credit Hours For Degree:** 96 quarter hours, Associates; 192 quarter hours, Bachelors **Professional Accreditation:** AAMAE, ACICS.

EVEREST UNIVERSITY (ORANGE PARK)

805 Wells Rd.
Orange Park, FL 32073
Tel: (904)264-9122
Fax: (904)264-9952
Web Site: www.everest.edu
President/CEO: Scot Haynes
Type: Two-Year College **Sex:** Coed **Affiliation:** Zenith Education Group. **% Accepted:** 65 **Calendar System:** Quarter **Student-Faculty Ratio:** 14:1 **Professional Accreditation:** ACICS.

EVEREST UNIVERSITY (ORLANDO)

9200 S Park Ctr. Loop
Orlando, FL 32819
Tel: (407)851-2525; Free: 888-471-4270
Fax: (407)851-1477
Web Site: www.everest.edu
President/CEO: Thomas Scheer
Admissions: Annette Cloin
Financial Aid: Sherri Williams
Type: Comprehensive **Sex:** Coed **Affiliation:** Zenith Education Group. **Application Deadline:** Rolling **H.S. Requirements:** High school diploma required; GED accepted **Scholarships:** Available. **Calendar System:** Quarter, Summer session not available **Credit Hours For Degree:** 96 quarter hours, Associates; 192 quarter hours, Bachelors **Professional Accreditation:** AAMAE, ACICS.

EVEREST UNIVERSITY (TAMPA)

3319 W Hillsborough Ave.
Tampa, FL 33614
Tel: (813)879-6000
Fax: (813)871-2483
Web Site: www.everest.edu
President/CEO: Thomas Barlow
Admissions: Donnie Broughton
Financial Aid: Rod Kirkwood
Type: Comprehensive **Sex:** Coed **Affiliation:** Zenith Education Group. **% Accepted:** 74 **Admission Plans:** Deferred Admission **Application Deadline:** Rolling **Application Fee:** $25.00 **H.S. Requirements:** High school diploma required; GED accepted **Scholarships:** Available. **Calendar System:** Quarter, Summer session available **Enrollment:** Full-time 2,750, Graduate full-time 44, Part-time 636 **Faculty:** Full-time 13, Part-time 48 **Student-Faculty Ratio:** 20:1 **Exams:** ACT; Other; SAT I. **% Receiving Financial Aid:** 85 **Credit Hours For Degree:** 96 quarter hours, Associates; 192 quarter hours, Bachelors **Professional Accreditation:** AAMAE, ACICS.

EVERGLADES UNIVERSITY (BOCA RATON)

5002 T-Rex Ave., Ste. 100
Boca Raton, FL 33431
Tel: (561)912-1211; Free: 888-772-6077
Fax: (561)912-1191
E-mail: admissions-boca@evergladesuniversity.edu
Web Site: www.evergladesuniversity.edu
President/CEO: Kristi Mollis
Admissions: Debra Veloso Rodrigues
Financial Aid: Seeta Singh Moonilall
Type: Comprehensive **Sex:** Coed **% Accepted:** 84 **Admission Plans:** Open Admission **Application Deadline:** Rolling **Application Fee:** $50.00 **H.S. Requirements:** High school diploma required; GED accepted **Costs Per Year:** Application fee: $50. One-time mandatory fee: $145. Tuition: $15,048 full-time, $627 per credit part-time. Mandatory fees: $1600 full-time, $100 per term part-time. **Scholarships:** Available. **Calendar System:** Semester, Summer session available **Enrollment:** Full-time 1,284, Graduate full-time 61, Graduate part-time 77, Part-time 29 **Faculty:** Full-time 91, Part-time 138 **Student-Faculty Ratio:** 10:1 **Exams:** SAT I or ACT. **% Receiving Financial Aid:** 84 **Final Year or Final Semester Residency Requirement:** No

Regional Accreditation: Southern Association of Colleges and Schools **Credit Hours For Degree:** 123 credits, Bachelors **Professional Accreditation:** ACCSC.

EVERGLADES UNIVERSITY (MAITLAND)

850 Trafalgar Ct., Ste. 100
Maitland, FL 32751
Tel: (407)277-0311; Free: 866-289-1078
Fax: (407)482-9801
E-mail: admissions-orl@evergladesuniversity.edu
Web Site: www.evergladesuniversity.edu
President/CEO: Kristi Mollis
Admissions: Mariluz Contreras
Financial Aid: Seeta Singh Moonilall
Type: Comprehensive **Sex:** Coed **% Accepted:** 84 **Admission Plans:** Open Admission **Application Deadline:** Rolling **Application Fee:** $50.00 **H.S. Requirements:** High school diploma required; GED accepted **Costs Per Year:** Application fee: $50. One-time mandatory fee: $145. Tuition: $15,048 full-time, $627 per credit hour part-time. Mandatory fees: $1600 full-time, $100 per term part-time. **Scholarships:** Available. **Calendar System:** Semester, Summer session available **Enrollment:** Full-time 1,284, Graduate full-time 61, Graduate part-time 77, Part-time 29 **Faculty:** Full-time 91, Part-time 138 **Student-Faculty Ratio:** 10:1 **% Receiving Financial Aid:** 88 **Final Year or Final Semester Residency Requirement:** No **Credit Hours For Degree:** 123 credits, Bachelors **Professional Accreditation:** ACCSC.

EVERGLADES UNIVERSITY (SARASOTA)

6001 Lake Osprey Dr. No.110
Sarasota, FL 34240
Tel: (561)912-1211; Free: 888-854-8308
Fax: (941)907-6634
E-mail: bbeasley@evergladesuniversity.edu
Web Site: www.evergladesuniversity.edu
President/CEO: Kristi Mollis
Admissions: Barbara Beasley
Financial Aid: Seeta Singh Moonilall
Type: Comprehensive **Sex:** Coed **% Accepted:** 84 **Admission Plans:** Open Admission **Application Deadline:** Rolling **Application Fee:** $50.00 **H.S. Requirements:** High school diploma required; GED accepted **Costs Per Year:** Application fee: $50. One-time mandatory fee: $145. Tuition: $15,048 full-time, $627 per credit hour part-time. Mandatory fees: $1600 full-time, $100 per term part-time. **Scholarships:** Available. **Calendar System:** Semester, Summer session available **Enrollment:** Full-time 1,284, Graduate full-time 61, Graduate part-time 77, Part-time 29 **Faculty:** Full-time 91, Part-time 138 **Student-Faculty Ratio:** 10:1 **% Receiving Financial Aid:** 89 **Final Year or Final Semester Residency Requirement:** No **Credit Hours For Degree:** 123 credit hours, Bachelors **Professional Accreditation:** ACCSC.

FLAGLER COLLEGE

74 King St.
Saint Augustine, FL 32085-1027
Tel: (904)829-6481; Free: 800-304-4208
Fax: (904)826-0094
E-mail: rbranch@flagler.edu
Web Site: www.flagler.edu
President/CEO: Dr. William T. Abare, Jr.
Admissions: Rachel Branch
Type: Four-Year College **Sex:** Coed **Scores:** 99% SAT V 400+; 99% SAT M 400+; 47.6% ACT 18-23; 44.86% ACT 24-29 **% Accepted:** 50 **Admission Plans:** Early Action; Early Admission **Application Deadline:** March 1 **Application Fee:** $50.00 **H.S. Requirements:** High school diploma required; GED accepted **Costs Per Year:** Application fee: $50. Comprehensive fee: $27,615 includes full-time tuition ($17,500), mandatory fees ($100), and college room and board ($10,015). College room only: $4910. Full-time tuition and fees vary according to location. Room and board charges vary according to board plan and housing facility. Part-time tuition: $585 per credit hour. Part-time tuition varies according to location. **Scholarships:** Available. **Calendar System:** Semester, Summer session available **Enrollment:** Full-time 2,602, Part-time 100 **Faculty:** Full-time 112, Part-time 125 **Student-Faculty Ratio:** 16:1 **Exams:** ACT essay component used for admission; ACT essay component used for advising; ACT essay component used for placement; SAT I or ACT; SAT essay component used for admission; SAT essay component used for advising; SAT essay component used for placement; SAT Reasoning. **% Receiving Financial Aid:** 61 **% Residing in**

College-Owned, -Operated, or -Affiliated Housing: 35 Final Year or Final Semester Residency Requirement: No Regional Accreditation: Southern Association of Colleges and Schools Credit Hours For Degree: 120 credit hours, Bachelors Intercollegiate Athletics: Baseball M; Basketball M & W; Cheerleading M & W; Cross-Country Running M & W; Golf M & W; Soccer M & W; Softball W; Tennis M & W; Volleyball W

FLAGLER COLLEGE–TALLAHASSEE
444 Appleyard Dr.
Tallahassee, FL 32304
Tel: (850)201-8070
Web Site: www.flagler.edu
Type: Four-Year College Sex: Coed Regional Accreditation: Southern Association of Colleges and Schools

FLORIDA AGRICULTURAL AND MECHANICAL UNIVERSITY
Tallahassee, FL 32307-3200
Tel: (850)599-3000; Free: 866-642-1198
Fax: (850)561-2428
E-mail: ugrdadmissions@famu.edu
Web Site: www.famu.edu
President/CEO: Dr. Elmira Mangum
Admissions: Barbara R. Cox
Financial Aid: Lisa A. Stewart
Type: University Sex: Coed Affiliation: State University System of Florida. Scores: 87% SAT V 400+; 86% SAT M 400+; 60.83% ACT 18-23; 19.1% ACT 24-29 % Accepted: 51 Admission Plans: Early Admission; Preferred Admission Application Deadline: May 15 Application Fee: $30.00 H.S. Requirements: High school diploma required; GED accepted Costs Per Year: Application fee: $30. One-time mandatory fee: $35. State resident tuition: $5645 full-time, $188.16 per credit hour part-time. Nonresident tuition: $17,585 full-time, $586.16 per credit hour part-time. Mandatory fees: $140 full-time. College room and board: $10,100. College room only: $5780. Room and board charges vary according to board plan and housing facility. Scholarships: Available. Calendar System: Semester, Summer session available Enrollment: Full-time 6,967, Graduate full-time 1,523, Graduate part-time 277, Part-time 1,161 Faculty: Full-time 545, Part-time 183 Student-Faculty Ratio: 15:1 Exams: SAT I or ACT; SAT Reasoning. % Receiving Financial Aid: 84 % Residing in College-Owned, -Operated, or -Affiliated Housing: 28 Final Year or Final Semester Residency Requirement: No Regional Accreditation: Southern Association of Colleges and Schools Credit Hours For Degree: 60 semester hours, Associates; 120 semester hours, Bachelors ROTC: Air Force, Army, Navy Professional Accreditation: ABA, ABET, ACBSP, ACEJMC, ACEN, ACPE, AHIMA, AOTA, APTA, CEPH, CSWE, CoARC, NAAB, NCATE. Intercollegiate Athletics: Baseball M; Basketball M & W; Bowling W; Cheerleading M & W; Cross-Country Running M & W; Football M; Golf M & W; Softball W; Swimming and Diving M & W; Tennis M & W; Track and Field M & W; Volleyball W

FLORIDA ATLANTIC UNIVERSITY
777 Glades Rd.
Boca Raton, FL 33431-0991
Tel: (561)297-3000
E-mail: recruitment@fau.edu
Web Site: www.fau.edu
President/CEO: Dr. John Kelly
Admissions: Mary Edmunds
Financial Aid: Tracy Boulukos
Type: University Sex: Coed Affiliation: State University System of Florida. Scores: 100% SAT V 400+; 100% SAT M 400+; 62% ACT 18-23; 33% ACT 24-29 % Accepted: 66 Admission Plans: Deferred Admission; Early Admission Application Deadline: May 1 Application Fee: $30.00 H.S. Requirements: High school diploma required; GED accepted Costs Per Year: Application fee: $30. State resident tuition: $6039 full-time, $105.07 per credit hour part-time. Nonresident tuition: $21,595 full-time, $598.93 per credit hour part-time. Mandatory fees: $96.29 per credit hour part-time. Full-time tuition varies according to course load. Part-time tuition and fees vary according to course load. College room and board: $11,748. Room and board charges vary according to board plan and housing facility. Scholarships: Available. Calendar System: Semester, Summer session available Enrollment: Full-time 15,524, Graduate full-time 2,035, Graduate part-time 3,120, Part-time 9,685 Faculty: Full-time 762, Part-time 486 Student-Faculty Ratio: 24:1 Exams: SAT I or ACT; SAT Reasoning. % Receiving Financial Aid: 62 % Residing in College-Owned, -Operated, or

-Affiliated Housing: 6 Final Year or Final Semester Residency Requirement: Yes Regional Accreditation: Southern Association of Colleges and Schools Credit Hours For Degree: 60 semester hours, Associates; 120 semester hours, Bachelors ROTC: Air Force, Army Professional Accreditation: AACN, AACSB, ABET, ACA, ACEN, ACSP, ASHA, CSWE, NASM, NASPAA, NCATE, TEAC. Intercollegiate Athletics: Baseball M; Basketball M & W; Cheerleading M & W; Cross-Country Running M & W; Football M; Golf M & W; Soccer M & W; Softball W; Swimming and Diving M & W; Tennis M & W; Track and Field W; Volleyball W

FLORIDA CAREER COLLEGE
1321 SW 107 Ave.
Ste. 201B
Miami, FL 33174
Tel: (305)553-6065; Free: 888-852-7272
Fax: (305)225-0128
Web Site: www.careercollege.edu
President/CEO: Fardad Fateri
Admissions: David Knobel
Type: Two-Year College Sex: Coed Admission Plans: Deferred Admission; Open Admission Application Deadline: Rolling Application Fee: $100.00 H.S. Requirements: High school diploma required; GED accepted Scholarships: Available. Calendar System: Quarter, Summer session available Credit Hours For Degree: 90 credits, Associates Professional Accreditation: ACICS.

FLORIDA COLLEGE
119 N Glen Arven Ave.
Temple Terrace, FL 33617
Tel: (813)988-5131
Fax: (813)899-6772
E-mail: admissions@floridacollege.edu
Web Site: www.floridacollege.edu
President/CEO: Dr. Harry E. Payne, IHM
Admissions: Colleen Engel
Financial Aid: Stephen Blaylock
Type: Four-Year College Sex: Coed % Accepted: 71 Application Deadline: August 1 Application Fee: $40.00 H.S. Requirements: High school diploma required; GED accepted Costs Per Year: Application fee: $40. Comprehensive fee: $24,164 includes full-time tuition ($15,214), mandatory fees ($860), and college room and board ($8090). College room only: $4100. Room and board charges vary according to board plan and housing facility. Part-time tuition: $600 per credit. Part-time tuition varies according to course load. Scholarships: Available. Calendar System: Semester, Summer session available Enrollment: Full-time 537, Part-time 13 Faculty: Full-time 35, Part-time 21 Student-Faculty Ratio: 13:1 Exams: ACT essay component not used; SAT I or ACT; SAT essay component not used; SAT Reasoning. % Receiving Financial Aid: 70 % Residing in College-Owned, -Operated, or -Affiliated Housing: 81 Final Year or Final Semester Residency Requirement: No Regional Accreditation: Southern Association of Colleges and Schools Credit Hours For Degree: 64 semester hours, Associates; 124 semester hours, Bachelors ROTC: Air Force, Army Professional Accreditation: NASM. Intercollegiate Athletics: Basketball M & W; Cheerleading W; Cross-Country Running M & W; Soccer M & W; Volleyball W

FLORIDA COLLEGE OF NATURAL HEALTH (MAITLAND)
2600 Lake Lucien Dr.
Ste. 140
Maitland, FL 32751
Tel: (407)261-0319; Free: 800-393-7337
Fax: (407)261-0342
Web Site: www.fcnh.com
President/CEO: Stephen Lazarus
Type: Two-Year College Sex: Coed Student-Faculty Ratio: 25:1 Professional Accreditation: ACCSC.

FLORIDA COLLEGE OF NATURAL HEALTH (MIAMI)
7925 NW 12th St.
Ste. 201
Miami, FL 33126
Tel: (305)597-9599; Free: 800-599-9599
Fax: (305)597-9110
Web Site: www.fcnh.com

President/CEO: Stephen Lazarus
Type: Two-Year College **Sex:** Coed **Student-Faculty Ratio:** 25:1 **Professional Accreditation:** ACCSC.

FLORIDA COLLEGE OF NATURAL HEALTH (POMPANO BEACH)

2001 W Sample Rd.
Ste. 100
Pompano Beach, FL 33064
Tel: (954)975-6400; Free: 800-541-9299
Fax: (954)975-9633
Web Site: www.fcnh.com
President/CEO: Stephen Lazarus
Type: Two-Year College **Sex:** Coed **Student-Faculty Ratio:** 25:1 **Professional Accreditation:** ACCSC.

FLORIDA GATEWAY COLLEGE

149 SE College Pl.
Lake City, FL 32025
Tel: (386)752-1822
Fax: (386)755-1521
E-mail: admissions@fgc.edu
Web Site: www.fgc.edu
President/CEO: Dr. Lawrence Barrett
Financial Aid: Bobbie Starling
Type: Two-Year College **Sex:** Coed **Affiliation:** Florida Community College System. **Admission Plans:** Open Admission **Application Deadline:** August 6 **Application Fee:** $0.00 **H.S. Requirements:** High school diploma required; GED accepted. For high school diploma/GED not required for Cosmetology, Heating and Air Conditioning, Patient Care Assistant, Phlebotomy and Welding: High school diploma or equivalent not required **Costs Per Year:** Application fee: $0. State resident tuition: $2,368 full-time, $103.32 per credit hour part-time. Nonresident tuition: $11,747 full-time, $391.57 per credit hour part-time. Mandatory fees: $731 full-time. Full-time tuition and fees vary according to course level, course load, degree level, program, reciprocity agreements, and student level. Part-time tuition varies according to course level, course load, degree level, program, reciprocity agreements, and student level. **Scholarships:** Available. **Calendar System:** Semester, Summer session available **Enrollment:** Full-time 831, Part-time 2,081 **Faculty:** Full-time 65, Part-time 123 **Student-Faculty Ratio:** 14:1 **Exams:** ACT essay component not used; SAT essay component not used. **Regional Accreditation:** Southern Association of Colleges and Schools **Credit Hours For Degree:** 60 semester hours, Associates; 120 semester hours, Bachelors **Professional Accreditation:** ACEN, APTA, JRCEMTP, NAACLS.

FLORIDA GULF COAST UNIVERSITY

10501 FGCU Blvd. S
Fort Myers, FL 33965-6565
Tel: (239)590-1000; Free: 888-889-1095
Fax: (239)590-7894
Web Site: www.fgcu.edu
President/CEO: Wilson Bradshaw
Admissions: Marc Laviolette
Financial Aid: Jorge Lopez-Rosado
Type: Comprehensive **Sex:** Coed **Affiliation:** State University System of Florida. **Scores:** 100% SAT V 400+; 100% SAT M 400+; 53% ACT 18-23; 44% ACT 24-29 **Admission Plans:** Deferred Admission **Application Deadline:** May 1 **Application Fee:** $30.00 **H.S. Requirements:** High school diploma required; GED accepted **Costs Per Year:** Application fee: $30. **Scholarships:** Available. **Calendar System:** Semester, Summer session available **Enrollment:** Full-time 10,796, Graduate full-time 388, Graduate part-time 755, Part-time 2,921 **Faculty:** Full-time 456, Part-time 343 **Student-Faculty Ratio:** 22:1 **Exams:** ACT essay component used for admission; SAT I or ACT; SAT essay component used for admission. **% Receiving Financial Aid:** 49 **% Residing in College-Owned, -Operated, or -Affiliated Housing:** 36 **Regional Accreditation:** Southern Association of Colleges and Schools **Credit Hours For Degree:** 60 credits, Associates; 120 credits, Bachelors **Professional Accreditation:** AACN, AACSB, AANA, ABET, ACA, AOTA, APTA, CSWE, NAACLS, NASPAA. **Intercollegiate Athletics:** Baseball M; Basketball M & W; Cheerleading W; Cross-Country Running M & W; Golf M & W; Soccer M & W; Softball W; Swimming and Diving W; Tennis M & W; Volleyball W

FLORIDA INSTITUTE OF TECHNOLOGY

150 W University Blvd.
Melbourne, FL 32901-6975
Tel: (321)674-8000; Free: 800-888-4348
Fax: (321)723-9468
E-mail: admission@fit.edu
Web Site: www.fit.edu
President/CEO: Dr. Anthony J. Catanese
Admissions: Michael J. Perry
Financial Aid: John W. Duncan
Type: University **Sex:** Coed **Scores:** 100% SAT V 400+; 100% SAT M 400+; 20% ACT 18-23; 60% ACT 24-29 **% Accepted:** 57 **Admission Plans:** Deferred Admission **Application Deadline:** Rolling **H.S. Requirements:** High school diploma required; GED accepted **Costs Per Year:** Comprehensive fee: $54,056 includes full-time tuition ($39,696), mandatory fees ($750), and college room and board ($13,610). College room only: $7730. Full-time tuition and fees vary according to course load and program. Room and board charges vary according to board plan and housing facility. Part-time tuition: $1148 per credit hour. **Scholarships:** Available. **Calendar System:** Semester, Summer session available **Enrollment:** Full-time 3,253, Graduate full-time 1,515, Graduate part-time 1,530, Part-time 333 **Faculty:** Full-time 321, Part-time 241 **Student-Faculty Ratio:** 8:1 **Exams:** ACT essay component not used; SAT I or ACT; SAT essay component not used; SAT Reasoning. **% Receiving Financial Aid:** 50 **% Residing in College-Owned, -Operated, or -Affiliated Housing:** 42 **Final Year or Final Semester Residency Requirement:** No **Regional Accreditation:** Southern Association of Colleges and Schools **Credit Hours For Degree:** 120 credits, Bachelors **ROTC:** Army **Professional Accreditation:** AABI, ABET, APA. **Intercollegiate Athletics:** Baseball M; Basketball M & W; Crew M & W; Cross-Country Running M & W; Football M; Golf M & W; Lacrosse M & W; Soccer M & W; Softball W; Swimming and Diving M & W; Tennis M & W; Track and Field M & W; Volleyball W; Water Polo M & W

FLORIDA INTERNATIONAL UNIVERSITY

11200 SW 8th St.
Miami, FL 33199
Tel: (305)348-2000
Fax: (305)348-3648
E-mail: admiss@fiu.edu
Web Site: www.fiu.edu
President/CEO: Dr. Mark Rosenberg
Admissions: Luisa Havens
Financial Aid: Francisco Valines
Type: University **Sex:** Coed **Affiliation:** State University System of Florida. **Scores:** 100% SAT V 400+; 100% SAT M 400+; 38% ACT 18-23; 55% ACT 24-29 **% Accepted:** 50 **Application Deadline:** November 1 **Application Fee:** $30.00 **H.S. Requirements:** High school diploma required; GED accepted **Costs Per Year:** Application fee: $30. State resident tuition: $6167 full-time, $205.57 per credit hour part-time. Nonresident tuition: $18,566 full-time, $618.87 per credit hour part-time. Mandatory fees: $389 full-time. College room and board: $10,870. College room only: $6964. Room and board charges vary according to board plan and housing facility. **Scholarships:** Available. **Calendar System:** Semester, Summer session available **Enrollment:** Full-time 25,655, Graduate full-time 6,083, Graduate part-time 2,771, Part-time 15,383 **Faculty:** Full-time 1,232, Part-time 1,115 **Student-Faculty Ratio:** 25:1 **Exams:** Other; SAT I or ACT; SAT Reasoning; SAT Subject. **% Receiving Financial Aid:** 69 **% Residing in College-Owned, -Operated, or -Affiliated Housing:** 8 **Final Year or Final Semester Residency Requirement:** No **Regional Accreditation:** Southern Association of Colleges and Schools **Credit Hours For Degree:** 120 credit hours, Bachelors **ROTC:** Air Force, Army **Professional Accreditation:** AACN, AACSB, AANA, ABA, ABET, ACA, ACCE, ACEJMC, AHIMA, AND, AOTA, APTA, ASHA, ASLA, CAHME, CEPH, CIDA, CSWE, LCME/AMA, NASAD, NASM, NASPAA, NAST, NCATE, NRPA. **Intercollegiate Athletics:** Baseball M; Basketball M & W; Cross-Country Running M & W; Football M; Golf W; Soccer M & W; Softball W; Swimming and Diving W; Tennis W; Track and Field M & W; Volleyball W

FLORIDA KEYS COMMUNITY COLLEGE

5901 College Rd.
Key West, FL 33040-4397
Tel: (305)296-9081
Web Site: www.fkcc.edu
President/CEO: Jonathan Gueverra

Admissions: Cheryl A. Malsheimer
Type: Two-Year College **Sex:** Coed **Affiliation:** Florida Community College System. **Admission Plans:** Deferred Admission; Early Admission; Open Admission **Application Deadline:** Rolling **Application Fee:** $20.00 **H.S. Requirements:** High school diploma required; GED accepted **Costs Per Year:** Application fee: $20. State resident tuition: $2483 full-time, $109 per credit hour part-time. Nonresident tuition: $9933 full-time, $439 per credit hour part-time. Mandatory fees: $793 full-time. Full-time tuition and fees vary according to course load. Part-time tuition varies according to course load. College room and board: $11,650. College room only: $9620. **Scholarships:** Available. **Calendar System:** Trimester, Summer session available **Regional Accreditation:** Southern Association of Colleges and Schools **Credit Hours For Degree:** 60 credits, Associates

FLORIDA MEMORIAL UNIVERSITY
15800 NW 42nd Ave.
Miami Gardens, FL 33054
Tel: (305)626-3600; Free: 800-822-1362
Web Site: www.fmuniv.edu
President/CEO: Dr. Karl S. Wright
Admissions: Peggy Murray Martin
Financial Aid: Brian Phillip
Type: Comprehensive **Sex:** Coed **Affiliation:** Baptist Church. **% Accepted:** 39 **Admission Plans:** Open Admission **Application Deadline:** July 1 **Application Fee:** $15.00 **H.S. Requirements:** High school diploma required; GED accepted **Costs Per Year:** Application fee: $15. Comprehensive fee: $21,702 includes full-time tuition ($12,384), mandatory fees ($2896), and college room and board ($6422). College room only: $3260. Room and board charges vary according to housing facility. Part-time tuition: $516 per credit hour. **Scholarships:** Available. **Calendar System:** Semester, Summer session available **Enrollment:** Full-time 1,516, Part-time 153 **Faculty:** Full-time 105, Part-time 68 **Student-Faculty Ratio:** 12:1 **Exams:** SAT I or ACT. **% Receiving Financial Aid:** 82 **Regional Accreditation:** Southern Association of Colleges and Schools **Credit Hours For Degree:** 124 credit hours, Bachelors **ROTC:** Air Force, Army **Professional Accreditation:** ABET, ACBSP, NASM. **Intercollegiate Athletics:** Baseball M; Basketball M & W; Cross-Country Running M & W; Track and Field M & W; Volleyball M & W

FLORIDA NATIONAL UNIVERSITY
4425 W 20th Ave.
Hialeah, FL 33012
Tel: (305)821-3333
Fax: (305)362-0595
E-mail: rlopez@fnu.edu
Web Site: www.fnu.edu
President/CEO: Dr. Maria Cristina Regueiro, EdD
Admissions: Robert Lopez
Financial Aid: Omar Sanchez
Type: Comprehensive **Sex:** Coed **% Accepted:** 97 **Admission Plans:** Deferred Admission **Application Deadline:** Rolling **Application Fee:** $0.00 **H.S. Requirements:** High school diploma required; GED accepted **Costs Per Year:** Application fee: $0. Tuition: $12,600 full-time, $525 per credit part-time. Mandatory fees: $650 full-time. Tuition guaranteed not to increase for student's term of enrollment. **Scholarships:** Available. **Calendar System:** Semester, Summer session available **Enrollment:** Full-time 2,191, Graduate full-time 34, Graduate part-time 2, Part-time 265 **Faculty:** Full-time 75, Part-time 48 **Student-Faculty Ratio:** 24:1 **Exams:** ACT essay component used for admission; ACT essay component used for advising; ACT essay component used for placement; SAT I or ACT; SAT essay component used for admission; SAT essay component used for advising; SAT essay component used for placement. **% Receiving Financial Aid:** 93 **Regional Accreditation:** Southern Association of Colleges and Schools **Credit Hours For Degree:** 60 credits, Associates; 120 credits, Bachelors **Intercollegiate Athletics:** Basketball M; Soccer M; Volleyball W

THE FLORIDA SCHOOL OF TRADITIONAL MIDWIFERY
810 E University Ave., 2nd Fl.
Gainseville, FL 32601
Tel: (352)338-0766
Fax: (352)338-2013
E-mail: info@midwiferyschool.org
Web Site: www.midwiferyschool.org
President/CEO: Diane Garrison

Type: Two-Year College **Sex:** Women **Costs Per Year:** Tuition: $33,124 full-time. Mandatory fees: $11,640 full-time. Full-time tuition and fees vary according to class time, course level, course load, degree level, location, program, reciprocity agreements, and student level. **Calendar System:** Quarter **Professional Accreditation:** MEAC.

FLORIDA SOUTHERN COLLEGE
111 Lake Hollingsworth Dr.
Lakeland, FL 33801-5698
Tel: (863)680-4111; Free: 800-274-4131
Fax: (863)680-4120
E-mail: amitchell@flsouthern.edu
Web Site: www.flsouthern.edu
President/CEO: Dr. Anne B. Kerr
Admissions: Arden Mitchell
Financial Aid: William L. Healy
Type: Comprehensive **Sex:** Coed **Affiliation:** United Methodist Church. **Scores:** 100% SAT V 400+; 100% SAT M 400+; 31% ACT 18-23; 61% ACT 24-29 **% Accepted:** 45 **Admission Plans:** Deferred Admission; Early Action; Early Admission **Application Deadline:** March 1 **Application Fee:** $30.00 **H.S. Requirements:** High school diploma required; GED accepted **Costs Per Year:** Application fee: $30. Comprehensive fee: $41,670 includes full-time tuition ($30,810), mandatory fees ($650), and college room and board ($10,210). College room only: $6030. Room and board charges vary according to board plan and housing facility. Part-time tuition: $900 per credit hour. Part-time tuition varies according to class time and course load. **Scholarships:** Available. **Calendar System:** Semester, Summer session available **Enrollment:** Full-time 2,260, Graduate full-time 190, Graduate part-time 120, Part-time 59 **Faculty:** Full-time 132, Part-time 124 **Student-Faculty Ratio:** 13:1 **Exams:** ACT essay component used for advising; SAT I or ACT; SAT essay component used for advising. **% Receiving Financial Aid:** 68 % Residing in College-Owned, -Operated, or -Affiliated Housing: 86 **Final Year or Final Semester Residency Requirement:** Yes **Regional Accreditation:** Southern Association of Colleges and Schools **Credit Hours For Degree:** 124 semester hours, Bachelors **ROTC:** Air Force, Army **Professional Accreditation:** AACN, JRCAT. **Intercollegiate Athletics:** Baseball M; Basketball M & W; Cheerleading W; Cross-Country Running M & W; Equestrian Sports W; Golf M & W; Lacrosse M & W; Soccer M & W; Softball W; Swimming and Diving M & W; Tennis M & W; Track and Field M & W; Volleyball W

FLORIDA SOUTHWESTERN STATE COLLEGE
8099 College Pky.
Fort Myers, FL 33919
Tel: (239)489-9300
Fax: (239)489-9399
E-mail: admissions@fsw.edu
Web Site: www.fsw.edu
President/CEO: Dr. Jeffery S. Allbritten
Type: Two-Year College **Sex:** Coed **Affiliation:** Florida College System. **Scores:** 85% SAT V 400+; 83% SAT M 400+ **% Accepted:** 81 **Admission Plans:** Deferred Admission; Early Admission; Open Admission **Application Deadline:** August 17 **Application Fee:** $30.00 **H.S. Requirements:** High school diploma required; GED accepted **Costs Per Year:** Application fee: $30. State resident tuition: $2436 full-time, $81.21 per credit hour part-time. Nonresident tuition: $9750 full-time, $325 per credit hour part-time. Mandatory fees: $965 full-time, $32.15 per credit hour part-time. Full-time tuition and fees vary according to degree level. Part-time tuition and fees vary according to degree level. College room and board: $9000. College room only: $6000. **Scholarships:** Available. **Calendar System:** Semester, Summer session available **Enrollment:** Full-time 5,389, Part-time 10,353 **Faculty:** Full-time 183, Part-time 418 **Student-Faculty Ratio:** 27:1 **% Residing in College-Owned, -Operated, or -Affiliated Housing:** 2 **Regional Accreditation:** Southern Association of Colleges and Schools **Credit Hours For Degree:** 60 credits, Associates; 120 credits, Bachelors **Professional Accreditation:** ACEN, ADA, CoARC, JRCECT, JRCEMTP, JRCERT. **Intercollegiate Athletics:** Baseball M; Softball W

FLORIDA STATE COLLEGE AT JACKSONVILLE
501 W State St.
Jacksonville, FL 32202-4030
Tel: (904)632-3000; Free: 888-873-1145
Fax: (904)632-3393
E-mail: pbiegel@fscj.edu

Web Site: www.fscj.edu
President/CEO: Dr. Cynthia A. Bioteau
Admissions: Dr. Peter Biegel
Type: Two-Year College **Sex:** Coed **Affiliation:** Florida College System. **Admission Plans:** Deferred Admission; Early Admission; Open Admission **Application Deadline:** Rolling **Application Fee:** $25.00 **H.S. Requirements:** High school diploma required; GED accepted **Costs Per Year:** Application fee: $25. State resident tuition: $2518 full-time, $105 per credit hour part-time. Nonresident tuition: $9632 full-time, $402 per credit hour part-time. Mandatory fees: $360 full-time. Full-time tuition and fees vary according to degree level and program. Part-time tuition varies according to degree level and program. **Calendar System:** Semester, Summer session available **Enrollment:** Full-time 7,819, Part-time 17,695 **Faculty:** Full-time 401, Part-time 779 **Student-Faculty Ratio:** 21:1 **Final Year or Final Semester Residency Requirement:** No **Regional Accreditation:** Southern Association of Colleges and Schools **Credit Hours For Degree:** 60 semester hours, Associates; 120 semester hours, Bachelors **ROTC:** Navy **Professional Accreditation:** ABFSE, ACBSP, ACEN, ACF, ADA, AHIMA, APTA, CoARC, JRCEMTP, NAACLS. **Intercollegiate Athletics:** Baseball M; Basketball M & W; Softball W; Tennis W; Volleyball W

FLORIDA STATE UNIVERSITY

Tallahassee, FL 32306
Tel: (850)644-2525
Fax: (850)644-0197
E-mail: admissions@admin.fsu.edu
Web Site: www.fsu.edu
President/CEO: John Thrasher
Admissions: Hege Ferguson
Financial Aid: Darryl Marshall
Type: University **Sex:** Coed **Affiliation:** State University System of Florida. **Scores:** 100% SAT V 400+; 100% SAT M 400+; 18.7% ACT 18-23; 69.4% ACT 24-29 **% Accepted:** 56 **Admission Plans:** Deferred Admission; Early Admission **Application Deadline:** January 13 **Application Fee:** $30.00 **H.S. Requirements:** High school diploma required; GED accepted **Scholarships:** Available. **Calendar System:** Semester, Summer session available **Enrollment:** Full-time 29,072, Graduate full-time 5,958, Graduate part-time 2,322, Part-time 3,568 **Faculty:** Full-time 1,382, Part-time 376 **Exams:** ACT essay component used for admission; SAT I or ACT; SAT essay component used for admission; SAT Reasoning. **% Receiving Financial Aid:** 52 **% Residing in College-Owned, -Operated, or -Affiliated Housing:** 19 **Regional Accreditation:** Southern Association of Colleges and Schools **Credit Hours For Degree:** 60 semester hours, Associates; 120 semester hours, Bachelors **ROTC:** Air Force, Army, Navy **Professional Accreditation:** AACN, AACSB, AAFCS, AALS, AAMFT, ABA, ABET, ACA, ACSP, ALA, AND, APA, ASHA, CIDA, CORE, CSWE, LCME/AMA, NASAD, NASD, NASM, NASPAA, NAST, NCATE, NRPA. **Intercollegiate Athletics:** Baseball M; Basketball M & W; Bowling M & W; Cheerleading M & W; Cross-Country Running M & W; Football M; Golf M & W; Rugby M & W; Soccer M & W; Softball W; Swimming and Diving M & W; Table Tennis M & W; Tennis M & W; Track and Field M & W; Volleyball M & W; Wrestling M & W

FLORIDA TECHNICAL COLLEGE (DELAND)

1199 S Woodland Blvd., 3rd Fl.
DeLand, FL 32720
Tel: (904)734-3303
Fax: (904)734-5150
Web Site: www.ftccollege.edu
Admissions: Bill Atkinson
Type: Two-Year College **Sex:** Coed **Application Fee:** $25.00 **Calendar System:** Quarter **Enrollment:** Full-time 260 **Faculty:** Full-time 11, Part-time 2 **Student-Faculty Ratio:** 22:1 **Professional Accreditation:** ACICS.

FLORIDA TECHNICAL COLLEGE (ORLANDO)

12900 Challenger Pky.
Orlando, FL 32826
Tel: (407)447-7300; Free: 888-574-2082
Web Site: www.ftccollege.edu
President/CEO: Gabe Garces
Admissions: Jeanette E. Muschlitz
Type: Two-Year College **Sex:** Coed **Affiliation:** Fore Front Education, Inc. **Application Fee:** $25.00 **H.S. Requirements:** High school diploma required; GED accepted **Scholarships:** Available. **Calendar System:**

Quarter, Summer session not available **Credit Hours For Degree:** 90 quarter hours, Associates **Professional Accreditation:** ACICS.

FORTIS COLLEGE (CUTLER BAY)

19600 S Dixie Hwy.
Ste. B
Cutler Bay, FL 33157
Tel: (786)345-5300; Free: 855-4-FORTIS
Web Site: www.fortis.edu
Type: Two-Year College **Sex:** Coed **Professional Accreditation:** ACCSC.

FORTIS COLLEGE (LARGO)

6565 Ulmerton Rd.
Largo, FL 33771
Tel: (727)531-5900; Free: 855-4-FORTIS
Web Site: www.fortis.edu
Type: Two-Year College **Sex:** Coed **Professional Accreditation:** ACCSC.

FORTIS COLLEGE (ORANGE PARK)

700 Blanding Blvd.
Ste. 16
Orange Park, FL 32065
Tel: (904)269-7086; Free: 855-4-FORTIS
Fax: (904)269-6664
Web Site: www.fortis.edu
Type: Two-Year College **Sex:** Coed **Application Fee:** $75.00 **Professional Accreditation:** ACICS.

FORTIS COLLEGE (WINTER PARK)

1573 W Fairbanks Ave.
Ste. 100
Winter Park, FL 32789
Tel: (407)843-3984; Free: 855-4-FORTIS
Fax: (407)843-9828
Web Site: www.fortis.edu
President/CEO: Richard J. Zaiden, Jr.
Type: Two-Year College **Sex:** Coed **Application Fee:** $50.00 **Student-Faculty Ratio:** 12:1 **Professional Accreditation:** ACCSC.

FORTIS INSTITUTE (FORT LAUDERDALE)

4850 W Oakland Park Blvd.
Ste. 200
Fort Lauderdale, FL 33313
Free: 855-4-FORTIS
Web Site: www.fortis.edu
Type: Two-Year College **Sex:** Coed **Professional Accreditation:** ABHES.

FORTIS INSTITUTE (PALM SPRINGS)

1630 S Congress Ave.
Palm Springs, FL 33461
Tel: (561)304-3466; Free: 855-4-FORTIS
Fax: (561)304-3471
Web Site: www.fortis.edu
President/CEO: Fabian Fernandez
Type: Two-Year College **Sex:** Coed **Application Fee:** $25.00 **Calendar System:** Quarter **Professional Accreditation:** ABHES, COE.

FORTIS INSTITUTE (PENSACOLA)

4081 E Olive Rd., Ste. B
Pensacola, FL 32514
Tel: (850)476-7607; Free: 855-4-FORTIS
Web Site: www.fortis.edu
Type: Two-Year College **Sex:** Coed **Professional Accreditation:** ABHES.

FORTIS INSTITUTE (PORT SAINT LUCIE)

9022 S US Hwy. 1
Port Saint Lucie, FL 34952
Tel: (772)221-9799; Free: 855-4-FORTIS
Web Site: www.fortis.edu
Type: Two-Year College **Sex:** Coed **Professional Accreditation:** ABHES.

FULL SAIL UNIVERSITY
3300 University Blvd.
Winter Park, FL 32792-7437
Tel: (407)679-6333; Free: 800-226-7625
Fax: (407)678-0070
E-mail: admissions@fullsail.com
Web Site: www.fullsail.edu
President/CEO: Garry Jones
Admissions: Mary Beth Plank

Type: Comprehensive **Sex:** Coed **Admission Plans:** Open Admission **Application Deadline:** Rolling **Application Fee:** $150.00 **H.S. Requirements:** High school diploma required; GED accepted **Scholarships:** Available. **Calendar System:** Miscellaneous, Summer session available **Student-Faculty Ratio:** 8:1 **% Receiving Financial Aid:** 56 **Professional Accreditation:** ACCSC.

GOLF ACADEMY OF AMERICA
510 S Hunt Club Blvd.
Apopka, FL 32703
Tel: (407)699-1990
Web Site: www.golfacademy.edu

Type: Two-Year College **Sex:** Coed **Calendar System:** Semester **Professional Accreditation:** ACICS.

GULF COAST STATE COLLEGE
5230 W Hwy. 98
Panama City, FL 32401-1058
Tel: (850)769-1551
Fax: (850)913-3308
E-mail: dnewell@gulfcoast.edu
Web Site: www.gulfcoast.edu
President/CEO: Dr. John Holdnak
Admissions: Donna Newell

Type: Two-Year College **Sex:** Coed **Affiliation:** Florida College System. **Admission Plans:** Deferred Admission; Early Admission; Open Admission **Application Deadline:** Rolling **Application Fee:** $20.00 **H.S. Requirements:** High school diploma required; GED accepted **Costs Per Year:** Application fee: $20. State resident tuition: $2370 full-time, $98.75 per credit hour part-time. Nonresident tuition: $8635 full-time, $359.71 per credit hour part-time. Mandatory fees: $620 full-time, $25.83 per credit hour part-time. Full-time tuition and fees vary according to degree level. Part-time tuition and fees vary according to degree level. **Scholarships:** Available. **Calendar System:** Semester, Summer session available **Enrollment:** Full-time 2,216, Part-time 3,642 **Faculty:** Full-time 107, Part-time 186 **Student-Faculty Ratio:** 19:1 **Final Year or Final Semester Residency Requirement:** No **Regional Accreditation:** Southern Association of Colleges and Schools **Credit Hours For Degree:** 60 credit hours, Associates; 120 credit hours, Bachelors **Professional Accreditation:** ACEN, ACF, ADA, APTA, CoARC, JRCEMTP, JRCERT. **Intercollegiate Athletics:** Baseball M; Basketball M & W; Softball W; Volleyball W

HERITAGE INSTITUTE (FORT MYERS)
6630 Orion Dr.
Fort Myers, FL 33912
Tel: (239)936-5822
Web Site: www.heritage-education.com
Type: Two-Year College **Sex:** Coed **Professional Accreditation:** ABHES.

HERITAGE INSTITUTE (JACKSONVILLE)
4130 Salisbury Rd.
Ste. 1100
Jacksonville, FL 32216
Web Site: www.heritage-education.com
Type: Two-Year College **Sex:** Coed **Professional Accreditation:** ABHES.

HERZING UNIVERSITY
1865 SR 436
Winter Park, FL 32792
Tel: (407)641-5227; Free: 800-596-0724
Fax: (407)478-0501
Web Site: www.herzing.edu/orlando
President/CEO: Heather Antonacci
Type: Four-Year College **Sex:** Coed **Scholarships:** Available. **Calendar**

System: Semester **Regional Accreditation:** North Central Association of Colleges and Schools **Professional Accreditation:** ACICS.

HILLSBOROUGH COMMUNITY COLLEGE
PO Box 31127
Tampa, FL 33631-3127
Tel: (813)253-7000
Fax: (813)253-7196
E-mail: jyoung92@hccfl.edu
Web Site: www.hccfl.edu
President/CEO: Dr. Kenneth H. Atwater, PhD
Admissions: Jennifer Young

Type: Two-Year College **Sex:** Coed **Affiliation:** Florida College System. **Admission Plans:** Early Admission; Open Admission **Application Deadline:** Rolling **Application Fee:** $0.00 **H.S. Requirements:** High school diploma required; GED accepted **Costs Per Year:** Application fee: $0. State resident tuition: $2505 full-time, $104.39 per credit hour part-time. Nonresident tuition: $9111 full-time, $379.61 per credit hour part-time. **Scholarships:** Available. **Calendar System:** Semester, Summer session available **Enrollment:** Full-time 10,566, Part-time 16,005 **Faculty:** Full-time 310, Part-time 1,142 **Student-Faculty Ratio:** 23:1 **Exams:** Other. **Final Year or Final Semester Residency Requirement:** No **Regional Accreditation:** Southern Association of Colleges and Schools **Credit Hours For Degree:** 60 credit hours, Associates **ROTC:** Air Force, Army **Professional Accreditation:** ACEN, ACF, ADA, COA, CoARC, JRCEDMS, JRCEMTP, JRCERT, JRCNMT, NASM. **Intercollegiate Athletics:** Baseball M; Basketball M & W; Softball W; Tennis W; Volleyball W

HOBE SOUND BIBLE COLLEGE
PO Box 1065
Hobe Sound, FL 33475-1065
Tel: (772)546-5534
Fax: (561)545-1422
E-mail: pamdavis@hsbc.edu
Web Site: www.hsbc.edu
President/CEO: Daniel Stetler
Admissions: Pamela S. Davis

Type: Four-Year College **Sex:** Coed **Affiliation:** nondenominational. **Admission Plans:** Early Admission; Open Admission; Preferred Admission **Application Deadline:** Rolling **Application Fee:** $25.00 **H.S. Requirements:** High school diploma required; GED accepted **Costs Per Year:** Application fee: $25. Comprehensive fee: $11,760 includes full-time tuition ($5200), mandatory fees ($720), and college room and board ($5840). College room only: $2240. Part-time tuition: $275 per credit hour. Part-time mandatory fees: $720 per year. Part-time tuition and fees vary according to course load. **Scholarships:** Available. **Calendar System:** Semester, Summer session available **Exams:** ACT essay component used for advising; ACT essay component used for placement; SAT I or ACT; SAT essay component used for advising; SAT essay component used for placement. **Credit Hours For Degree:** 70 semester hours, Associates; 128 semester hours, Bachelors **Professional Accreditation:** ABHE.

HODGES UNIVERSITY
2655 Northbrooke Dr.
Naples, FL 34119
Tel: (239)513-1122; Free: 800-466-8017
Fax: (239)513-9071
E-mail: bpassey@hodges.edu
Web Site: www.hodges.edu
President/CEO: Dr. David Borofsky
Admissions: Brent Passey
Financial Aid: Joe Gilchrist

Type: Comprehensive **Sex:** Coed **Admission Plans:** Deferred Admission **Application Deadline:** Rolling **Application Fee:** $20.00 **H.S. Requirements:** High school diploma required; GED accepted **Costs Per Year:** Application fee: $20. Tuition: $12,720 full-time, $530 per credit hour part-time. Mandatory fees: $500 full-time. **Scholarships:** Available. **Calendar System:** Trimester, Summer session available **Enrollment:** Full-time 991, Graduate full-time 47, Graduate part-time 190, Part-time 496 **Faculty:** Full-time 59, Part-time 60 **Student-Faculty Ratio:** 15:1 **Exams:** Other. **% Receiving Financial Aid:** 95 **Final Year or Final Semester Residency Requirement:** Yes **Regional Accreditation:** Southern Association of Colleges and Schools

Credit Hours For Degree: 60 semester hour credits, Associates; 122 semester hour credits, Bachelors **Professional Accreditation:** AAMAE, AHIMA.

INDIAN RIVER STATE COLLEGE

3209 Virginia Ave.
Fort Pierce, FL 34981-5596
Tel: (772)462-4700; Free: 866-792-4772
Fax: (772)462-4796
E-mail: estrock@irsc.edu
Web Site: www.irsc.edu
President/CEO: Dr. Edwin R. Massey
Admissions: Eileen Storck
Financial Aid: Mary Lewis
Type: Four-Year College **Sex:** Coed **Affiliation:** Florida Community College System. **% Accepted:** 100 **Admission Plans:** Deferred Admission; Early Admission; Open Admission **Application Deadline:** Rolling **Application Fee:** $0.00 **H.S. Requirements:** High school diploma required; GED accepted **Costs Per Year:** Application fee: $0. State resident tuition: $2,492 full-time, $103.83 per credit hour part-time. Nonresident tuition: $9,372 full-time, $390.49 per credit hour part-time. Full-time tuition varies according to course load and degree level. Part-time tuition varies according to course load and degree level. College room and board: $5700. College room only: $3150. **Scholarships:** Available. **Calendar System:** Semester, Summer session available **Enrollment:** Full-time 5,950, Part-time 11,715 **Faculty:** Full-time 239, Part-time 620 **Student-Faculty Ratio:** 22:1 **Final Year or Final Semester Residency Requirement:** No **Regional Accreditation:** Southern Association of Colleges and Schools **Credit Hours For Degree:** 60 semester hours, Associates; 120 semester hours, Bachelors **Professional Accreditation:** AAMAE, ACEN, ADA, AHIMA, APTA, CoARC, JRCEMTP, JRCERT, NAACLS. **Intercollegiate Athletics:** Baseball M; Basketball M & W; Softball W; Swimming and Diving M & W; Volleyball W

JACKSONVILLE UNIVERSITY

2800 University Blvd. N
Jacksonville, FL 32211
Tel: (904)256-8000; Free: 800-225-2027
Fax: (904)256-7086
E-mail: admissions@ju.edu
Web Site: www.ju.edu
President/CEO: Tim Cost
Admissions: Allana Forte
Financial Aid: Karen Laverdiere
Type: Comprehensive **Sex:** Coed **Scores:** 92% SAT V 400+; 96% SAT M 400+; 52.99% ACT 18-23; 34.19% ACT 24-29 **% Accepted:** 54 **Admission Plans:** Deferred Admission; Early Admission **Application Deadline:** Rolling **Application Fee:** $30.00 **H.S. Requirements:** High school diploma required; GED accepted **Costs Per Year:** Application fee: $30. Comprehensive fee: $45,940 includes full-time tuition ($32,620) and college room and board ($13,320). College room only: $8800. Full-time tuition varies according to course level, course load, degree level, and program. Room and board charges vary according to board plan and housing facility. Part-time tuition: $1085 per credit hour. Part-time mandatory fees: $540 per credit hour. Part-time tuition and fees vary according to course level, course load, degree level, and program. **Scholarships:** Available. **Calendar System:** Semester, Summer session available **Enrollment:** Full-time 2,065, Graduate full-time 300, Graduate part-time 716, Part-time 967 **Faculty:** Full-time 201, Part-time 139 **Student-Faculty Ratio:** 11:1 **Exams:** ACT essay component used for admission; ACT essay component used for advising; ACT essay component used for placement; SAT I and SAT II or ACT; SAT I or ACT; SAT essay component used for admission; SAT essay component used for advising; SAT essay component used for placement; SAT Reasoning; SAT Subject. **% Receiving Financial Aid:** 86 **% Residing in College-Owned, -Operated, or -Affiliated Housing:** 30 **Final Year or Final Semester Residency Requirement:** No **Regional Accreditation:** Southern Association of Colleges and Schools **Credit Hours For Degree:** 128 credit hours, Bachelors **ROTC:** Army, Navy **Professional Accreditation:** AACN, AACSB, NASD, NASM. **Intercollegiate Athletics:** Baseball M; Basketball M & W; Crew M & W; Cross-Country Running M & W; Football M; Golf M & W; Lacrosse M & W; Soccer M & W; Softball W; Track and Field W; Volleyball W

JOHNSON UNIVERSITY FLORIDA

1011 Bill Beck Blvd.
Kissimmee, FL 34744-5301

Tel: (407)847-8966; Free: 888-GO-TO-FCC
Fax: (407)847-3925
E-mail: admissionsforms@fcc.edu
Web Site: www.johnsonu.edu
President/CEO: Dr. David L. Eubanks
Financial Aid: Sandra Peppard
Type: Four-Year College **Sex:** Coed **Affiliation:** Christian Churches and Churches of Christ. **% Accepted:** 35 **Admission Plans:** Deferred Admission; Early Admission **Application Deadline:** July 15 **Application Fee:** $35.00 **H.S. Requirements:** High school diploma required; GED accepted **Scholarships:** Available. **Calendar System:** Semester, Summer session available **Enrollment:** Full-time 281, Part-time 99 **Faculty:** Full-time 12, Part-time 17 **Student-Faculty Ratio:** 18:1 **Exams:** ACT essay component not used; SAT I or ACT; SAT essay component not used; SAT Reasoning; SAT Subject. **% Receiving Financial Aid:** 100 **% Residing in College-Owned, -Operated, or -Affiliated Housing:** 62 **Final Year or Final Semester Residency Requirement:** No **Regional Accreditation:** Southern Association of Colleges and Schools **Credit Hours For Degree:** 65 credits, Associates; 135 credits, Bachelors **Professional Accreditation:** ABHE. **Intercollegiate Athletics:** Baseball M; Basketball M; Cross-Country Running M & W; Soccer W; Volleyball W

JOHNSON & WALES UNIVERSITY

1701 NE 127th St.
North Miami, FL 33181
Tel: (305)892-7000; Free: 866-598-3567
Fax: (305)892-7030
E-mail: mia@admissions.jwu.edu
Web Site: www.jwu.edu/northmiami
President/CEO: Donald G. McGregor, JD
Admissions: Jeff Greenip
Financial Aid: Lynn Robinson
Type: Four-Year College **Sex:** Coed **Scores:** 72% SAT V 400+; 57% SAT M 400+ **% Accepted:** 76 **Admission Plans:** Deferred Admission; Early Admission **Application Deadline:** Rolling **Application Fee:** $0.00 **H.S. Requirements:** High school diploma required; GED accepted **Costs Per Year:** Application fee: $0. Comprehensive fee: $39,014 includes full-time tuition ($30,396), mandatory fees ($350), and college room and board ($8268). **Scholarships:** Available. **Calendar System:** Quarter, Summer session available **Enrollment:** Full-time 1,576, Part-time 176 **Faculty:** Full-time 57, Part-time 22 **Student-Faculty Ratio:** 25:1 **Exams:** SAT I or ACT. **% Receiving Financial Aid:** 78 **% Residing in College-Owned, -Operated, or -Affiliated Housing:** 55 **Regional Accreditation:** New England Association of Schools and Colleges **Credit Hours For Degree:** 90 quarter credit hours, Associates; 180 quarter credit hours, Bachelors

JONES COLLEGE

1195 Edgewood Ave. S
Jacksonville, FL 32205
Tel: (904)743-1122; Free: 800-331-0176
Web Site: www.jones.edu
President/CEO: Dr. Mayra Nunez
Financial Aid: Becky Davis
Type: Four-Year College **Sex:** Coed **Admission Plans:** Open Admission **Application Deadline:** Rolling **Application Fee:** $0.00 **H.S. Requirements:** High school diploma required; GED accepted **Costs Per Year:** Application fee: $0. Tuition: $7560 full-time, $315 per credit hour part-time. Mandatory fees: $90 full-time, $45 per term part-time. Full-time tuition and fees vary according to course load. Part-time tuition and fees vary according to course load. **Scholarships:** Available. **Calendar System:** Trimester, Summer session available **Exams:** Other. **Final Year or Final Semester Residency Requirement:** No **Credit Hours For Degree:** 60 credit hours, Associates; 120 credit hours, Bachelors **Professional Accreditation:** ACICS.

JOSE MARIA VARGAS UNIVERSITY

10131 Pines Blvd.
Pembroke Pines, FL 33026
Tel: (954)322-4446
Web Site: www.jmvu.edu
Type: Comprehensive **Sex:** Coed **Professional Accreditation:** ACICS.

KEISER UNIVERSITY

1500 NW 49th St.
Fort Lauderdale, FL 33309

Tel: (954)776-4456; Free: 888-534-7379
E-mail: bwoods@keiseruniversity.edu
Web Site: www.keiseruniversity.edu
President/CEO: Dr. Arthur Keiser
Admissions: Brian J. Woods
Financial Aid: Fred Pfeffer
Type: University **Sex:** Coed **Application Deadline:** Rolling **Application Fee:** $50.00 **H.S. Requirements:** High school diploma required; GED accepted **Scholarships:** Available. **Calendar System:** Miscellaneous, Summer session available **Enrollment:** Full-time 12,007, Graduate full-time 257, Graduate part-time 833, Part-time 4,032 **Faculty:** Full-time 982, Part-time 615 **Student-Faculty Ratio:** 12:1 **Exams:** Other. **% Receiving Financial Aid:** 93 **Regional Accreditation:** Southern Association of Colleges and Schools **Credit Hours For Degree:** 60 semester hours, Associates; 120 semester hours, Bachelors **Professional Accreditation:** ABHES, ACBSP, ACEN, AOTA, APTA, JRCEDMS, JRCERT, NAACLS.

KEY COLLEGE
225 E Dania Beach Blvd.
Dania Beach, FL 33004
Tel: (954)246-4529; Free: 877-421-6149
Fax: (954)923-9226
Web Site: www.keycollege.edu
President/CEO: Ronald Dooley
Admissions: Ronald H. Dooley
Type: Two-Year College **Sex:** Coed **% Accepted:** 100 **Admission Plans:** Deferred Admission **Application Deadline:** Rolling **Application Fee:** $35.00 **H.S. Requirements:** High school diploma required; GED accepted **Scholarships:** Available. **Calendar System:** Quarter, Summer session not available **Exams:** Other. **Credit Hours For Degree:** 90 credits, Associates **Professional Accreditation:** ACICS.

LAKE-SUMTER STATE COLLEGE
9501 US Hwy. 441
Leesburg, FL 34788-8751
Tel: (352)787-3747
E-mail: admissinquiry@lscc.edu
Web Site: www.lssc.edu
President/CEO: Dr. Charles R. Mojock
Admissions: Bonnie Yanick
Type: Two-Year College **Sex:** Coed **Affiliation:** Florida College System. **% Accepted:** 100 **Admission Plans:** Open Admission **Application Deadline:** Rolling **Application Fee:** $25.00 **H.S. Requirements:** High school diploma required; GED accepted **Scholarships:** Available. **Calendar System:** Semester, Summer session available **Enrollment:** Full-time 1,641, Part-time 3,288 **Faculty:** Full-time 84, Part-time 344 **Student-Faculty Ratio:** 17:1 **Regional Accreditation:** Southern Association of Colleges and Schools **Credit Hours For Degree:** 60 semester hours, Associates **Professional Accreditation:** ACEN, AHIMA. **Intercollegiate Athletics:** Baseball M; Softball W; Volleyball W

LINCOLN COLLEGE OF TECHNOLOGY
2410 Metrocentre Blvd.
West Palm Beach, FL 33407
Tel: (561)842-8324
Fax: (561)842-9503
Web Site: www.lincolnedu.com
President/CEO: Helen Carver
Admissions: Kevin Cassidy
Type: Two-Year College **Sex:** Coed **Admission Plans:** Early Admission; Open Admission **Application Deadline:** Rolling **Application Fee:** $25.00 **H.S. Requirements:** High school diploma required; GED accepted **Scholarships:** Available. **Calendar System:** Quarter, Summer session not available **Credit Hours For Degree:** 90 quarter hours, Associates **Professional Accreditation:** AAMAE, ACICS, COE.

LINCOLN CULINARY INSTITUTE
2410 Metrocentre Blvd.
West Palm Beach, FL 33407
Tel: (561)842-8324
E-mail: info@floridaculinary.com
Web Site: www.lincolnedu.com/campus/west-palm-beach-culinary-fl
Admissions: David Conway

Type: Four-Year College **Sex:** Coed **Affiliation:** Lincoln Educational Services. **Scholarships:** Available. **Enrollment:** Full-time 600 **Professional Accreditation:** ACF, COE.

LINCOLN TECHNICAL INSTITUTE
7275 Estapona Cir.
Fern Park, FL 32730
Tel: (407)673-7406
Web Site: www.lincolnedu.com
Type: Two-Year College **Sex:** Coed **Professional Accreditation:** ABHES.

LYNN UNIVERSITY
3601 N Military Trl.
Boca Raton, FL 33431-5598
Tel: (561)237-7000; Free: 800-888-5966
Fax: (561)241-3552
E-mail: spapaleo@lynn.edu
Web Site: www.lynn.edu
President/CEO: Dr. Kevin M. Ross
Admissions: Stefano Papaleo
Financial Aid: John Chambers
Type: Comprehensive **Sex:** Coed **Scores:** 96% SAT V 400+; 90% SAT M 400+; 59% ACT 18-23; 28% ACT 24-29 **% Accepted:** 76 **Admission Plans:** Deferred Admission; Early Admission; Early Decision Plan **Application Deadline:** August 1 **Application Fee:** $45.00 **H.S. Requirements:** High school diploma required; GED accepted **Costs Per Year:** Application fee: $45. Comprehensive fee: $47,790 includes full-time tuition ($34,400), mandatory fees ($1750), and college room and board ($11,640). Full-time tuition and fees vary according to class time, degree level, and program. Room and board charges vary according to board plan and housing facility. Part-time tuition: $995 per credit hour. Part-time tuition varies according to class time, course load, and program. **Scholarships:** Available. **Calendar System:** Semester, Summer session available **Enrollment:** Full-time 1,867, Graduate full-time 581, Graduate part-time 109, Part-time 136 **Student-Faculty Ratio:** 19:1 **Exams:** ACT essay component not used; SAT I or ACT; SAT essay component not used; SAT Reasoning. **% Receiving Financial Aid:** 45 **% Residing in College-Owned, -Operated, or -Affiliated Housing:** 51 **Final Year or Final Semester Residency Requirement:** No **Regional Accreditation:** Southern Association of Colleges and Schools **Credit Hours For Degree:** 120 credit hours, Bachelors **ROTC:** Air Force **Professional Accreditation:** NASM. **Intercollegiate Athletics:** Baseball M; Basketball M & W; Cross-Country Running W; Golf M & W; Lacrosse M; Soccer M & W; Softball W; Swimming and Diving W; Tennis M & W; Volleyball W

MANAGEMENT RESOURCES COLLEGE
10 NW LeJeune Rd.
Miami, FL 33126
Tel: (305)442-9223
Web Site: www.mrc.edu
Type: Two-Year College **Sex:** Coed **Professional Accreditation:** COE.

MARCONI INTERNATIONAL UNIVERSITY
1806 Flamingo Rd., Ste. 120
Pembroke Pines, FL 33028
Tel: (954)374-4701
E-mail: info@marconiinternational.org
Web Site: www.marconiinternationaluniversity.edu
Type: Comprehensive **Sex:** Coed **Professional Accreditation:** ACICS.

MEDTECH COLLEGE
1900 N Alafaya Trl.
Orlando, FL 32826-4906
Web Site: www.medtech.edu
Type: Two-Year College **Sex:** Coed **Professional Accreditation:** ACICS.

MERIDIAN COLLEGE
7020 Professional Pky. E
Sarasota, FL 34240
Tel: (941)377-4880
Web Site: www.meridian.edu
Type: Two-Year College **Sex:** Coed **Professional Accreditation:** ACCSC.

MIAMI DADE COLLEGE

300 NE Second Ave.
Miami, FL 33132
Tel: (305)237-8888
Fax: (305)237-3761
E-mail: fcreary@mdc.edu
Web Site: www.mdc.edu
President/CEO: Dr. Eduardo J. Padron
Admissions: Ferne Creary

Type: Two-Year College **Sex:** Coed **Affiliation:** Florida College System. **% Accepted:** 100 **Admission Plans:** Early Admission; Open Admission **Application Deadline:** Rolling **Application Fee:** $30.00 **H.S. Requirements:** High school diploma required; GED accepted **Costs Per Year:** Application fee: $30. One-time mandatory fee: $30. State resident tuition: $1,987 full-time, $82.78 per credit hour part-time. Nonresident tuition: $7,947 full-time, $331.11 per credit hour part-time. Mandatory fees: $851 full-time, $35.44 per credit hour part-time. Full-time tuition and fees vary according to course load, degree level, and program. Part-time tuition and fees vary according to course load, degree level, and program. **Scholarships:** Available. **Calendar System:** Miscellaneous, Summer session available **Enrollment:** Full-time 24,716, Part-time 37,616 **Faculty:** Full-time 736, Part-time 1,872 **Student-Faculty Ratio:** 27:1 **Final Year or Final Semester Residency Requirement:** No **Regional Accreditation:** Southern Association of Colleges and Schools **Credit Hours For Degree:** 60 credit hours, Associates; 120 credit hours, Bachelors **ROTC:** Air Force, Army **Professional Accreditation:** ABFSE, ACEN, ADA, AHIMA, APTA, COA, CoARC, JRCEDMS, JRCEMTP, JRCERT, MEAC, NAACLS. **Intercollegiate Athletics:** Baseball M; Basketball M & W; Softball W; Volleyball W

MIAMI INTERNATIONAL UNIVERSITY OF ART & DESIGN

1501 Biscayne Blvd., Ste. 100
Miami, FL 33132-1418
Tel: (305)428-5700; Free: 800-225-9023
Fax: (305)374-7946
Web Site: www.artinstitutes.edu/miami
President/CEO: Erika Fleming
Financial Aid: Mitzie Forrest

Type: Comprehensive **Sex:** Coed **Affiliation:** Education Management Corporation. **Calendar System:** Quarter **Regional Accreditation:** Southern Association of Colleges and Schools

MILLENNIA ATLANTIC UNIVERSITY

3801 NW 97th Ave.
Doral, FL 33178
Tel: (786)331-1000
Web Site: www.maufl.edu
Financial Aid: Karen S. Terry

Type: Comprehensive **Sex:** Coed **Scholarships:** Available. **Calendar System:** Semester **Professional Accreditation:** ACICS.

NEW COLLEGE OF FLORIDA

5800 Bay Shore Rd.
Sarasota, FL 34243
Tel: (941)359-4269
Fax: (941)359-4435
E-mail: admissions@ncf.edu
Web Site: www.ncf.edu
President/CEO: Dr. Donal O'Shea
Financial Aid: Tara Karas

Type: Comprehensive **Sex:** Coed **Affiliation:** State University System of Florida. **Scores:** 99% SAT V 400+; 100% SAT M 400+; 4% ACT 18-23; 51% ACT 24-29 **% Accepted:** 61 **Admission Plans:** Deferred Admission; Early Admission **Application Deadline:** April 15 **Application Fee:** $30.00 **H.S. Requirements:** High school diploma required; GED accepted **Costs Per Year:** Application fee: $30. State resident tuition: $6916 full-time. Nonresident tuition: $29,944 full-time. Full-time tuition varies according to course load. College room and board: $9060. College room only: $6348. Room and board charges vary according to board plan and housing facility. **Scholarships:** Available. **Calendar System:** 4-1-4, Summer session available **Enrollment:** Full-time 861 **Faculty:** Full-time 77, Part-time 26 **Student-Faculty Ratio:** 10:1 **Exams:** ACT; SAT I; SAT I and SAT II or ACT; SAT I or ACT; SAT II; SAT Reasoning. **% Receiving Financial Aid:** 51 **% Residing in College-Owned, -Operated, or -Affiliated Housing:** 76 **Final Year or Final Semester Residency Requirement:** Yes **Regional Accreditation:**

Southern Association of Colleges and Schools **Credit Hours For Degree:** 7 academic contracts and 3 independent study projects, Bachelors **Intercollegiate Athletics:** Sailing M & W

NEW WORLD SCHOOL OF THE ARTS

300 NE 2nd Ave.
Miami, FL 33132
Tel: (305)237-3135
Fax: (305)237-3794
E-mail: nwsaadm@mdc.edu
Web Site: www.mdc.edu/nwsa
President/CEO: Mercedes Quiroga

Type: Four-Year College **Sex:** Coed **Affiliation:** Miami Dade County Public Schools, Miami Dade College and the University of Florida. **% Accepted:** 52 **Admission Plans:** Early Action **Application Deadline:** Rolling **Application Fee:** $0.00 **H.S. Requirements:** High school diploma required; GED accepted **Calendar System:** Semester, Summer session available **Enrollment:** Full-time 335 **Faculty:** Full-time 22, Part-time 55 **Student-Faculty Ratio:** 5:1 **Exams:** SAT I or ACT. **Final Year or Final Semester Residency Requirement:** Yes **Credit Hours For Degree:** 72 credit hours, Associates; 136 credit hours, Bachelors **Professional Accreditation:** NASAD, NASD, NASM, NAST.

NORTH FLORIDA COMMUNITY COLLEGE

325 NW Turner Davis Dr.
Madison, FL 32340
Tel: (850)973-2288; Free: 866-937-6322
Fax: (850)973-1696
Web Site: www.nfcc.edu
President/CEO: John Grosskopf
Admissions: Bobby Scott

Type: Two-Year College **Sex:** Coed **Admission Plans:** Early Admission; Open Admission **Application Deadline:** Rolling **Application Fee:** $20.00 **H.S. Requirements:** High school diploma required; GED accepted **Scholarships:** Available. **Calendar System:** Semester, Summer session available **Enrollment:** Full-time 593, Part-time 704 **Faculty:** Full-time 25, Part-time 19 **Student-Faculty Ratio:** 18:1 **Regional Accreditation:** Southern Association of Colleges and Schools **Credit Hours For Degree:** 60 semester hours, Associates

NORTHWEST FLORIDA STATE COLLEGE

100 College Blvd.
Niceville, FL 32578-1295
Tel: (850)678-5111
E-mail: cooperk@nwfsc.edu
Web Site: www.nwfsc.edu
President/CEO: Dr. Ty Julian Handy
Admissions: Karen Cooper
Financial Aid: Wanda Morgan

Type: Two-Year College **Sex:** Coed **Affiliation:** Florida College System. **Admission Plans:** Open Admission; Preferred Admission **Application Deadline:** Rolling **Application Fee:** $0.00 **H.S. Requirements:** High school diploma required; GED accepted. For limited access programs: High school diploma or equivalent not required **Scholarships:** Available. **Calendar System:** Semester, Summer session available **Enrollment:** Full-time 2,758, Part-time 4,180 **Faculty:** Full-time 102, Part-time 164 **Student-Faculty Ratio:** 26:1 **Final Year or Final Semester Residency Requirement:** No **Regional Accreditation:** Southern Association of Colleges and Schools **Credit Hours For Degree:** 60 semester hours, Associates; 120 semester hours, Bachelors **ROTC:** Army **Professional Accreditation:** AACN, ADA. **Intercollegiate Athletics:** Baseball M; Basketball M & W; Cheerleading M & W; Softball W

NOVA SOUTHEASTERN UNIVERSITY

3301 College Ave.
Fort Lauderdale, FL 33314-7796
Tel: (954)262-7300; Free: 800-541-NOVA
Fax: (954)262-3967
E-mail: nsuinfo@nova.edu
Web Site: www.nova.edu
President/CEO: Dr. George L. Hanbury, II
Admissions: Mensima Biney
Financial Aid: Dr. Stephanie G. Brown

Type: University **Sex:** Coed **Scores:** 98% SAT V 400+; 98% SAT M 400+;

39.24% ACT 18-23; 40.05% ACT 24-29 **% Accepted:** 59 **Admission Plans:** Deferred Admission **Application Deadline:** Rolling **Application Fee:** $50.00 **H.S. Requirements:** High school diploma required; GED accepted **Costs Per Year:** Application fee: $50. Tuition: $26,910 full-time, $897 per credit hour part-time. Full-time tuition varies according to class time and program. Part-time tuition varies according to class time, course load, and program. **Scholarships:** Available. **Calendar System:** Trimester, Summer session available **Enrollment:** Full-time 3,194, Graduate full-time 9,892, Graduate part-time 8,703, Part-time 1,447 **Faculty:** Full-time 857, Part-time 842 **Student-Faculty Ratio:** 16:1 **Exams:** ACT essay component not used; SAT I or ACT; SAT essay component not used; SAT Reasoning. **% Receiving Financial Aid:** 74 **% Residing in College-Owned, -Operated, or -Affiliated Housing:** 23 **Regional Accreditation:** Southern Association of Colleges and Schools **Credit Hours For Degree:** 60 credits, Associates; 120 credits, Bachelors **Professional Accreditation:** AACN, AALS, AAMFT, ABA, ACPE, ADA, AOA, AOTA, AOsA, APA, APTA, ASHA, CEPH, NCATE. **Intercollegiate Athletics:** Baseball M; Basketball M & W; Cheerleading W; Crew W; Cross-Country Running M & W; Golf M & W; Soccer M & W; Softball W; Swimming and Diving M & W; Tennis W; Track and Field M & W; Volleyball W

ORION COLLEGE
51 N State Rd. 7
Plantation, FL 33317
Free: 888-331-9957
Fax: (877)493-7416
Web Site: www.orioncollege.org
Type: Two-Year College **Sex:** Coed **Professional Accreditation:** ABHES.

PALM BEACH ATLANTIC UNIVERSITY
901 S Flagler Dr.
West Palm Beach, FL 33416-4708
Tel: (561)803-2000; Free: 888-GO-TO-PBA
E-mail: joe_sharp@pba.edu
Web Site: www.pba.edu
President/CEO: William M.B. Fleming, Jr.
Admissions: Joe Sharp
Financial Aid: Joseph Bryan
Type: Comprehensive **Sex:** Coed **Affiliation:** nondenominational. **Scores:** 98% SAT V 400+; 92% SAT M 400+; 50% ACT 18-23; 38% ACT 24-29 **% Accepted:** 93 **Admission Plans:** Deferred Admission; Early Admission; Early Decision Plan **Application Deadline:** Rolling **Application Fee:** $50.00 **H.S. Requirements:** High school diploma required; GED accepted **Costs Per Year:** Application fee: $50. Comprehensive fee: $36,004 includes full-time tuition ($26,750), mandatory fees ($400), and college room and board ($8854). College room only: $4560. Full-time tuition and fees vary according to course load, location, and program. Room and board charges vary according to board plan and housing facility. Part-time tuition: $645 per credit hour. Part-time mandatory fees: $130 per term. Part-time tuition and fees vary according to course load, location, and program. **Scholarships:** Available. **Calendar System:** Semester, Summer session available **Enrollment:** Full-time 2,418, Graduate full-time 790, Graduate part-time 89, Part-time 621 **Faculty:** Full-time 174, Part-time 191 **Student-Faculty Ratio:** 13:1 **Exams:** ACT essay component used for advising; ACT essay component used for placement; SAT I or ACT; SAT essay component used for advising; SAT essay component used for placement; SAT Reasoning. **% Receiving Financial Aid:** 72 **% Residing in College-Owned, -Operated, or -Affiliated Housing:** 48 **Final Year or Final Semester Residency Requirement:** No **Regional Accreditation:** Southern Association of Colleges and Schools **Credit Hours For Degree:** 66 credit hours, Associates; 120 credit hours, Bachelors **ROTC:** Army **Professional Accreditation:** AACN, ACPE, NASM. **Intercollegiate Athletics:** Baseball M; Basketball M & W; Cheerleading M & W; Crew M & W; Cross-Country Running W; Golf M & W; Lacrosse M & W; Soccer M & W; Softball W; Tennis M & W; Volleyball W

PALM BEACH STATE COLLEGE
4200 Congress Ave.
Lake Worth, FL 33461-4796
Tel: (561)967-7222
E-mail: enrollmt@palmbeachstate.edu
Web Site: www.palmbeachstate.edu
President/CEO: Ava L. Parker
Admissions: Anne Guiler
Type: Four-Year College **Sex:** Coed **Affiliation:** Florida College System. **%**

Accepted: 100 **Admission Plans:** Deferred Admission; Early Admission; Open Admission; Preferred Admission **Application Deadline:** August 20 **Application Fee:** $30.00 **H.S. Requirements:** High school diploma required; GED accepted **Costs Per Year:** Application fee: $30. State resident tuition: $2424 full-time, $101 per credit part-time. Nonresident tuition: $8712 full-time, $363 per credit hour part-time. Mandatory fees: $20 full-time, $20 per year part-time, $10 per term part-time. Full-time tuition and fees vary according to degree level. Part-time tuition and fees vary according to degree level. **Scholarships:** Available. **Calendar System:** Semester, Summer session available **Enrollment:** Full-time 9,410, Part-time 19,764 **Faculty:** Full-time 282, Part-time 903 **Student-Faculty Ratio:** 49:1 **Exams:** SAT I and SAT II or ACT. **Regional Accreditation:** Southern Association of Colleges and Schools **Credit Hours For Degree:** 60 semester hours, Associates; 120 semester hours, Bachelors **Professional Accreditation:** ACEN, ADA, CoARC, JRCEMTP, JRCERT, MACTE. **Intercollegiate Athletics:** Baseball M; Basketball M & W; Softball W; Volleyball W

PASCO-HERNANDO STATE COLLEGE
10230 Ridge Rd.
New Port Richey, FL 34654-5199
Tel: (727)847-2727; Free: 877-TRY-PHSC
Fax: (727)816-3450
E-mail: carrioe@phsc.edu
Web Site: www.phsc.edu
President/CEO: Dr. Timothy Beard, PhD
Admissions: Estela Carrion
Type: Two-Year College **Sex:** Coed **Affiliation:** Florida College System. **Admission Plans:** Open Admission **Application Deadline:** Rolling **Application Fee:** $25.00 **H.S. Requirements:** High school diploma required; GED accepted **Scholarships:** Available. **Calendar System:** Semester, Summer session available **Enrollment:** Full-time 4,004, Part-time 6,202 **Faculty:** Full-time 125, Part-time 252 **Student-Faculty Ratio:** 26:1 **Exams:** Other; SAT I and SAT II or ACT. **Final Year or Final Semester Residency Requirement:** No **Regional Accreditation:** Southern Association of Colleges and Schools **Credit Hours For Degree:** 60 semester hours, Associates; 120 semester hours, Bachelors **ROTC:** Army **Professional Accreditation:** ACEN, ADA, JRCEMTP. **Intercollegiate Athletics:** Baseball M; Basketball M; Cross-Country Running W; Softball W; Volleyball W

PENSACOLA STATE COLLEGE
1000 College Blvd.
Pensacola, FL 32504-8998
Tel: (850)484-1000
Fax: (850)484-1826
E-mail: kdutremble@pensacolastate.edu
Web Site: www.pensacolastate.edu
President/CEO: Dr. C. Edward Meadows
Admissions: Susan Desbrow
Type: Two-Year College **Sex:** Coed **Affiliation:** Florida College System. **Admission Plans:** Early Admission; Open Admission **Application Deadline:** August 30 **Application Fee:** $30.00 **H.S. Requirements:** High school diploma required; GED accepted. For certificate program applicants who have not graduated from high school but are at least 16 years of age and legally withdrawn from high school: High school diploma or equivalent not required **Costs Per Year:** Application fee: $30. Area resident tuition: $104.58 per credit hour part-time. State resident tuition: $2510 full-time, $104.59 per credit hour part-time. Nonresident tuition: $10,075 full-time, $419.76 per credit hour part-time. Full-time tuition varies according to degree level. Part-time tuition varies according to degree level. **Scholarships:** Available. **Calendar System:** Semester, Summer session available **Enrollment:** Full-time 3,592, Part-time 6,248 **Faculty:** Full-time 180, Part-time 419 **Student-Faculty Ratio:** 21:1 **Exams:** ACT essay component not used; SAT essay component not used. **Final Year or Final Semester Residency Requirement:** No **Regional Accreditation:** Southern Association of Colleges and Schools **Credit Hours For Degree:** 60 semester hours, Associates; 120 semester hours, Bachelors **ROTC:** Army **Professional Accreditation:** ACEN, ACF, ADA, AHIMA, APTA, CoARC, JRCEMTP, JRCERT. **Intercollegiate Athletics:** Baseball M; Basketball M & W; Softball W; Volleyball W

POLK STATE COLLEGE
999 Ave. H, NE
Winter Haven, FL 33881-4299
Tel: (863)297-1000

Fax: (863)297-1060
E-mail: kbucklew@polk.edu
Web Site: www.polk.edu
President/CEO: Eileen Holden, EdD
Admissions: Kathy Bucklew
Financial Aid: Lenora Burnett
Type: Four-Year College **Sex:** Coed **Affiliation:** Florida College System. **Scores:** 100% SAT V 400+; 75% SAT M 400+; 77% ACT 18-23; 10% ACT 24-29 **Admission Plans:** Deferred Admission; Early Admission; Open Admission **Application Deadline:** Rolling **Application Fee:** $0.00 **H.S. Requirements:** High school diploma required; GED accepted **Costs Per Year:** Application fee: $0. State resident tuition: $3367 full-time, $112.22 per credit hour part-time. Nonresident tuition: $12,272 full-time, $409.06 per credit hour part-time. Full-time tuition varies according to course level, course load, and degree level. Part-time tuition varies according to course level, course load, and degree level. **Scholarships:** Available. **Calendar System:** Semester, Summer session available **Enrollment:** Full-time 3,269, Part-time 7,388 **Faculty:** Full-time 158, Part-time 209 **Student-Faculty Ratio:** 25:1 **Final Year or Final Semester Residency Requirement:** No **Regional Accreditation:** Southern Association of Colleges and Schools **Credit Hours For Degree:** 60 credit hours, Associates; 120 credit hours, Bachelors **ROTC:** Army **Professional Accreditation:** ACEN, AHIMA, AOTA, APTA, JRCEMTP, JRCERT. **Intercollegiate Athletics:** Baseball M; Basketball M; Cheerleading W; Soccer W; Softball W; Volleyball W

POLYTECHNIC UNIVERSITY OF PUERTO RICO, MIAMI CAMPUS
8180 NW 36th St.
Ste. 401
Miami, FL 33166
Tel: (305)592-7659; Free: 888-729-7659
Web Site: www.pupr.edu/miami
President/CEO: Ernesto Vazquez-Barquet
Financial Aid: Maria Victoria Shehadeh
Type: Comprehensive **Sex:** Coed **Application Fee:** $30.00 **Scholarships:** Available. **Student-Faculty Ratio:** 10:1 **Regional Accreditation:** Middle States Association of Colleges and Schools

POLYTECHNIC UNIVERSITY OF PUERTO RICO, ORLANDO CAMPUS
550 N Econlockhatchee Trl.
Orlando, FL 32825
Tel: (407)677-7000; Free: 888-577-POLY
Fax: (407)677-5082
Web Site: www.pupr.edu/orlando
President/CEO: Ernest Vazquez-Barquet
Admissions: Teresa Cardona
Financial Aid: Ileana Diaz
Type: Comprehensive **Sex:** Coed **% Accepted:** 89 **Application Fee:** $30.00 **Scholarships:** Available. **Student-Faculty Ratio:** 8:1 **% Receiving Financial Aid:** 92 **Regional Accreditation:** Middle States Association of Colleges and Schools

PRAXIS INSTITUTE
1850 SW 8th St.
4th Fl.
Miami, FL 33135
Tel: (305)642-4104
Web Site: the-praxisinstitute.com
Type: Two-Year College **Sex:** Coed **Professional Accreditation:** COE.

PROFESSIONAL HANDS INSTITUTE
10 NW 42 Ave., Ste. 200
Miami, FL 33126
Tel: (305)442-6011
Web Site: prohands.edu
Type: Two-Year College **Sex:** Coed **Professional Accreditation:** COE.

RASMUSSEN COLLEGE FORT MYERS
9160 Forum Corporate Pky.
Ste. 100
Fort Myers, FL 33905
Tel: (239)477-2100; Free: 888-549-6755
Fax: (239)477-2101
E-mail: susan.hammerstrom@rasmussen.edu

Web Site: www.rasmussen.edu
President/CEO: Kristi Waite
Admissions: Susan Hammerstrom
Type: Four-Year College **Sex:** Coed **Affiliation:** Rasmussen College System. **Admission Plans:** Deferred Admission; Early Admission **Application Deadline:** Rolling **Application Fee:** $0.00 **H.S. Requirements:** High school diploma required; GED accepted **Costs Per Year:** Application fee: $0. Tuition: $13,455 full-time. Mandatory fees: $1800 full-time. Full-time tuition and fees vary according to course level, course load, degree level, location, and program. Tuition guaranteed not to increase for student's term of enrollment. **Calendar System:** Quarter, Summer session available **Enrollment:** Full-time 294, Part-time 504 **Faculty:** Full-time 10, Part-time 49 **Student-Faculty Ratio:** 22:1 **Exams:** ACT essay component not used; Other; SAT essay component not used. **Final Year or Final Semester Residency Requirement:** No **Regional Accreditation:** North Central Association of Colleges and Schools **Credit Hours For Degree:** 90 credits, Associates; 180 credits, Bachelors **Professional Accreditation:** ACBSP.

RASMUSSEN COLLEGE LAND O' LAKES
18600 Fernview St.
Land O' Lakes, FL 34638
Tel: (813)435-3601; Free: 888-549-6755
E-mail: susan.hammerstrom@rasmussen.edu
Web Site: www.rasmussen.edu
President/CEO: Kristi Waite
Admissions: Susan Hammerstrom
Type: Four-Year College **Sex:** Coed **Affiliation:** Rasmussen College System. **Admission Plans:** Deferred Admission; Early Admission **Application Deadline:** Rolling **Application Fee:** $0.00 **H.S. Requirements:** High school diploma required; GED accepted **Costs Per Year:** Application fee: $0. Tuition: $13,455 full-time. Mandatory fees: $1800 full-time. Full-time tuition and fees vary according to course level, course load, degree level, location, and program. Tuition guaranteed not to increase for student's term of enrollment. **Calendar System:** Quarter, Summer session available **Enrollment:** Full-time 108, Part-time 206 **Faculty:** Full-time 4, Part-time 29 **Student-Faculty Ratio:** 22:1 **Exams:** ACT essay component not used; Other; SAT essay component not used. **Final Year or Final Semester Residency Requirement:** No **Regional Accreditation:** North Central Association of Colleges and Schools **Credit Hours For Degree:** 90 credits, Associates; 180 credits, Bachelors

RASMUSSEN COLLEGE NEW PORT RICHEY
8661 Citizens Dr.
New Port Richey, FL 34654
Tel: (727)942-0069; Free: 888-549-6755
Fax: (727)938-5709
E-mail: susan.hammerstrom@rasmussen.edu
Web Site: www.rasmussen.edu
President/CEO: Kristi Waite
Admissions: Susan Hammerstrom
Type: Four-Year College **Sex:** Coed **Affiliation:** Rasmussen College System. **Admission Plans:** Deferred Admission; Early Admission **Application Deadline:** Rolling **H.S. Requirements:** High school diploma required; GED accepted **Costs Per Year:** Tuition: $13,455 full-time. Mandatory fees: $1800 full-time. Full-time tuition and fees vary according to course level, course load, degree level, location, and program. Tuition guaranteed not to increase for student's term of enrollment. **Scholarships:** Available. **Calendar System:** Quarter, Summer session available **Enrollment:** Full-time 251, Part-time 528 **Faculty:** Full-time 17, Part-time 19 **Student-Faculty Ratio:** 22:1 **Exams:** ACT essay component not used; Other; SAT essay component not used. **Final Year or Final Semester Residency Requirement:** No **Credit Hours For Degree:** 90 credits, Associates; 180 credits, Bachelors **Professional Accreditation:** ACICS.

RASMUSSEN COLLEGE OCALA
4755 SW 46th Ct.
Ocala, FL 34471
Tel: (352)629-1941; Free: 888-549-6755
Fax: (352)629-0926
E-mail: susan.hammerstrom@rasmussen.edu
Web Site: www.rasmussen.edu
President/CEO: Kristi Waite
Admissions: Susan Hammerstrom
Type: Four-Year College **Sex:** Coed **Affiliation:** Rasmussen College

System. **Admission Plans:** Deferred Admission; Early Admission; Open Admission **Application Deadline:** Rolling **H.S. Requirements:** High school diploma required; GED accepted **Costs Per Year:** Tuition: $13,455 full-time, $299 per credit hour part-time. Mandatory fees: $1800 full-time. Full-time tuition and fees vary according to course level, course load, degree level, location, and program. Part-time tuition varies according to course level, course load, degree level, location, and program. Tuition guaranteed not to increase for student's term of enrollment. **Scholarships:** Available. **Calendar System:** Quarter, Summer session available **Enrollment:** Full-time 390, Part-time 632 **Student-Faculty Ratio:** 22:1 **Exams:** ACT essay component not used; Other; SAT essay component not used. **Final Year or Final Semester Residency Requirement:** No **Regional Accreditation:** North Central Association of Colleges and Schools **Credit Hours For Degree:** 90 credits, Associates; 180 credits, Bachelors **Professional Accreditation:** ACBSP, ACICS.

RASMUSSEN COLLEGE OCALA SCHOOL OF NURSING
2100 SW 22nd Pl.
Ocala, FL 34471
Tel: (352)291-8560; Free: 888-549-6755
E-mail: susan.hammerstrom@rasmussen.edu
Web Site: www.rasmussen.edu
President/CEO: Kristi Waite
Admissions: Susan Hammerstrom

Type: Four-Year College **Sex:** Coed **Affiliation:** Rasmussen College System. **Admission Plans:** Deferred Admission; Early Admission **Application Deadline:** Rolling **Application Fee:** $0.00 **H.S. Requirements:** High school diploma required; GED accepted **Costs Per Year:** Application fee: $0. Tuition: $17,775 full-time, $395 per credit hour part-time. Mandatory fees: $1800 full-time. Full-time tuition and fees vary according to course level, course load, degree level, location, and program. Part-time tuition varies according to course level, course load, degree level, location, and program. Tuition guaranteed not to increase for student's term of enrollment. **Calendar System:** Quarter, Summer session available **Enrollment:** Full-time 233, Part-time 332 **Faculty:** Full-time 17, Part-time 26 **Student-Faculty Ratio:** 22:1 **Exams:** ACT essay component not used; Other; SAT essay component not used. **Final Year or Final Semester Residency Requirement:** No **Regional Accreditation:** North Central Association of Colleges and Schools **Credit Hours For Degree:** 90 credits, Associates; 180 credits, Bachelors

RASMUSSEN COLLEGE TAMPA/BRANDON
4042 Park Oaks Blvd.
Tampa, FL 33610
Tel: (813)246-7600; Free: 888-549-6755
E-mail: susan.hammerstrom@rasmussen.edu
Web Site: www.rasmussen.edu
President/CEO: Kristi Waite
Admissions: Susan Hammerstrom

Type: Four-Year College **Sex:** Coed **Affiliation:** Rasmussen College System. **Admission Plans:** Deferred Admission; Early Admission **Application Deadline:** Rolling **Application Fee:** $0.00 **H.S. Requirements:** High school diploma required; GED accepted **Costs Per Year:** Application fee: $0. Tuition: $13,455 full-time. Mandatory fees: $1800 full-time. Full-time tuition and fees vary according to course level, course load, degree level, location, and program. Tuition guaranteed not to increase for student's term of enrollment. **Calendar System:** Quarter, Summer session available **Enrollment:** Full-time 211, Part-time 488 **Faculty:** Full-time 9, Part-time 53 **Student-Faculty Ratio:** 22:1 **Exams:** ACT essay component not used; Other; SAT essay component not used. **Final Year or Final Semester Residency Requirement:** No **Credit Hours For Degree:** 90 credits, Associates; 180 credits, Bachelors **Professional Accreditation:** ACBSP.

REMINGTON COLLEGE–HEATHROW CAMPUS
500 International Pky.
Heathrow, FL 32746
Free: 800-560-6192
Web Site: www.remingtoncollege.edu
Type: Two-Year College **Sex:** Coed **Professional Accreditation:** ACCSC.

RINGLING COLLEGE OF ART AND DESIGN
2700 N Tamiami Trl.
Sarasota, FL 34234-5895
Tel: (941)351-5100; Free: 800-255-7695

Fax: (941)359-7517
E-mail: admissions@ringling.edu
Web Site: www.ringling.edu
President/CEO: Dr. Larry R. Thompson
Financial Aid: Lee Harrell

Type: Four-Year College **Sex:** Coed **% Accepted:** 77 **Admission Plans:** Deferred Admission **Application Deadline:** Rolling **Application Fee:** $70.00 **H.S. Requirements:** High school diploma required; GED accepted **Costs Per Year:** Application fee: $70. Comprehensive fee: $55,870 includes full-time tuition ($38,710), mandatory fees ($3310), and college room and board ($13,850). College room only: $7450. Full-time tuition and fees vary according to course load, program, and student level. Room and board charges vary according to board plan and housing facility. Part-time tuition: $1780 per credit hour. Part-time tuition varies according to program and student level. **Scholarships:** Available. **Calendar System:** Semester, Summer session not available **Enrollment:** Full-time 1,181, Part-time 81 **Faculty:** Full-time 96, Part-time 58 **Student-Faculty Ratio:** 11:1 **% Receiving Financial Aid:** 64 **% Residing in College-Owned, -Operated, or -Affiliated Housing:** 69 **Final Year or Final Semester Residency Requirement:** Yes **Regional Accreditation:** Southern Association of Colleges and Schools **Credit Hours For Degree:** 120 semester hours, Bachelors **Professional Accreditation:** CIDA, NASAD.

ROLLINS COLLEGE
1000 Holt Ave.
Winter Park, FL 32789-4499
Tel: (407)646-2000
Fax: (407)646-2600
E-mail: admission@rollins.edu
Web Site: www.rollins.edu
President/CEO: Dr. Grant Cornwell
Admissions: Holly Pohlig
Financial Aid: Steve Booker

Type: Comprehensive **Sex:** Coed **Scores:** 100% SAT V 400+; 100% SAT M 400+; 11.69% ACT 18-23; 64.8% ACT 24-29 **% Accepted:** 60 **Admission Plans:** Deferred Admission; Early Action; Early Admission **Application Deadline:** February 15 **Application Fee:** $40.00 **H.S. Requirements:** High school diploma required; GED accepted **Costs Per Year:** Application fee: $40. Comprehensive fee: $58,670 includes full-time tuition ($44,760) and college room and board ($13,910). College room only: $8230. Room and board charges vary according to housing facility. **Scholarships:** Available. **Calendar System:** Semester, Summer session available **Enrollment:** Full-time 1,948, Graduate full-time 285, Graduate part-time 288 **Faculty:** Full-time 233 **Student-Faculty Ratio:** 10:1 **Exams:** ACT essay component not used; SAT I or ACT; SAT essay component not used; SAT Reasoning; SAT Subject. **% Receiving Financial Aid:** 50 **% Residing in College-Owned, -Operated, or -Affiliated Housing:** 60 **Final Year or Final Semester Residency Requirement:** Yes **Regional Accreditation:** Southern Association of Colleges and Schools **Credit Hours For Degree:** 35 courses/140 credit hours, Bachelors **Professional Accreditation:** AACSB, ACA, NASM. **Intercollegiate Athletics:** Baseball M; Basketball M & W; Crew M & W; Cross-Country Running M & W; Golf M & W; Lacrosse M & W; Sailing M & W; Skiing (Downhill) M & W; Soccer M & W; Softball W; Swimming and Diving M & W; Tennis M & W; Volleyball W

SABER COLLEGE
3990 W Flagler St.
Ste. 103
Miami, FL 33134
Tel: (305)443-9170
Web Site: www.sabercollege.com
Type: Two-Year College **Sex:** Coed **Professional Accreditation:** COE.

ST. JOHN VIANNEY COLLEGE SEMINARY
2900 SW 87th Ave.
Miami, FL 33165-3244
Tel: (305)223-4561
Web Site: www.sjvcs.edu
President/CEO: Roberto Garza
Admissions: Bro. Edward Van Merrienboer
Financial Aid: Bonnie DeAngulo

Type: Four-Year College **Sex:** Coed **Affiliation:** Roman Catholic. **% Accepted:** 100 **Admission Plans:** Preferred Admission **Application Deadline:** Rolling **Application Fee:** $0.00 **H.S. Requirements:** High school diploma required; GED accepted **Scholarships:** Available. **Calendar System:** Semester, Summer session not available **Exams:** SAT I or ACT. **Regional Accreditation:** Southern Association of Colleges and Schools **Credit Hours For Degree:** 128 semester hours, Bachelors **Professional Accreditation:** ATS.

ST. JOHNS RIVER STATE COLLEGE
5001 Saint Johns Ave.
Palatka, FL 32177-3897
Tel: (386)312-4200
Fax: (386)312-4292
Web Site: www.sjrstate.edu
President/CEO: Dr. R. L. McLendon, Jr.
Type: Two-Year College **Sex:** Coed **Admission Plans:** Early Admission; Open Admission **Application Deadline:** Rolling **Application Fee:** $30.00 **H.S. Requirements:** High school diploma required; GED accepted **Scholarships:** Available. **Calendar System:** Semester, Summer session available **Faculty:** Full-time 111, Part-time 154 **Student-Faculty Ratio:** 24:1 **Regional Accreditation:** Southern Association of Colleges and Schools **Credit Hours For Degree:** 60 credit hours, Associates **Intercollegiate Athletics:** Baseball M; Basketball M; Softball W; Volleyball W

SAINT LEO UNIVERSITY
PO Box 6665
Saint Leo, FL 33574-6665
Tel: (352)588-8200; Free: 800-334-5532
Fax: (352)588-8257
E-mail: admissions@saintleo.edu
Web Site: www.saintleo.edu
President/CEO: Dr. William Lennox
Admissions: Peter Littlefield
Financial Aid: Melinda Clark
Type: Comprehensive **Sex:** Coed **Affiliation:** Roman Catholic. **Scores:** 99% SAT V 400+; 94% SAT M 400+; 61% ACT 18-23; 34% ACT 24-29 **% Accepted:** 73 **Admission Plans:** Deferred Admission; Early Admission **Application Deadline:** Rolling **Application Fee:** $40.00 **H.S. Requirements:** High school diploma required; GED accepted **Costs Per Year:** Application fee: $40. Comprehensive fee: $31,340 includes full-time tuition ($20,760), mandatory fees ($370), and college room and board ($10,210). College room only: $5430. Room and board charges vary according to board plan and housing facility. **Scholarships:** Available. **Calendar System:** Semester, Summer session available **Enrollment:** Full-time 2,275, Graduate full-time 206, Graduate part-time 3,562, Part-time 95 **Faculty:** Full-time 125, Part-time 87 **Student-Faculty Ratio:** 15:1 **Exams:** ACT essay component used for advising; ACT essay component used for placement; SAT I or ACT; SAT essay component used for advising; SAT essay component used for placement; SAT Reasoning. **% Receiving Financial Aid:** 70 **% Residing in College-Owned, -Operated, or -Affiliated Housing:** 64 **Final Year or Final Semester Residency Requirement:** No **Regional Accreditation:** Southern Association of Colleges and Schools **Credit Hours For Degree:** 60 semester hours, Associates; 120 semester hours, Bachelors **ROTC:** Air Force, Army **Professional Accreditation:** ACBSP, CSWE. **Intercollegiate Athletics:** Baseball M; Basketball M & W; Cross-Country Running M & W; Golf M & W; Lacrosse M & W; Soccer M & W; Softball W; Swimming and Diving M & W; Tennis M & W; Track and Field M & W; Volleyball W

ST. PETERSBURG COLLEGE
PO Box 13489
Saint Petersburg, FL 33733-3489
Tel: (727)341-3600
Fax: (727)341-3150
E-mail: information@spcollege.edu
Web Site: www.spcollege.edu
President/CEO: Dr. Bill Law
Admissions: Susan Fell
Type: Four-Year College **Sex:** Coed **% Accepted:** 25 **Admission Plans:** Early Admission; Open Admission **Application Deadline:** Rolling **Application Fee:** $30.00 **H.S. Requirements:** High school diploma required; GED accepted **Scholarships:** Available. **Calendar System:** Semester, Summer session available **Enrollment:** Full-time 9,301, Part-time 22,466 **Faculty:** Full-time 381, Part-time 1,399 **Student-Faculty Ratio:** 22:1 **Final Year or Final Semester Residency Requirement:** No **Regional Accreditation:** Southern Association of Colleges and Schools **Credit Hours For Degree:** 60 credit hours, Associates; 120 credit hours, Bachelors **ROTC:** Army

Professional Accreditation: AACN, ABFSE, ACBSP, ACEN, ADA, AHIMA, APTA, CoARC, JRCEMTP, NAACLS. **Intercollegiate Athletics:** Baseball M; Basketball M & W; Softball W; Tennis W; Volleyball W

ST. THOMAS UNIVERSITY
16401 NW 37th Ave.
Miami Gardens, FL 33054-6459
Tel: (305)625-6000; Free: 800-367-9010
Fax: (305)628-6591
E-mail: cjalvarez@stu.edu
Web Site: www.stu.edu
President/CEO: Rev. Franklyn Casale
Admissions: Celso Alvarez
Financial Aid: Luis Betancourt
Type: Comprehensive **Sex:** Coed **Affiliation:** Roman Catholic. **Scores:** 81% SAT M 400+; 56.3% ACT 18-23; 12.6% ACT 24-29 **Costs Per Year:** Comprehensive fee: $39,280 includes full-time tuition ($27,960) and college room and board ($11,320). College room only: $7200. Full-time tuition varies according to course load. Room and board charges vary according to board plan and housing facility. Part-time tuition: $559 per credit hour. Part-time tuition varies according to course load. **Scholarships:** Available. **Calendar System:** Semester, Summer session available **Enrollment:** Full-time 849, Graduate full-time 1,334, Graduate part-time 419, Part-time 2,333 **Faculty:** Full-time 103, Part-time 180 **Student-Faculty Ratio:** 11:1 **Exams:** ACT essay component not used; SAT I or ACT; SAT essay component not used. **% Residing in College-Owned, -Operated, or -Affiliated Housing:** 39 **Final Year or Final Semester Residency Requirement:** No **Regional Accreditation:** Southern Association of Colleges and Schools **Credit Hours For Degree:** 120 credits, Bachelors **Professional Accreditation:** AALS, ABA, ATS. **Intercollegiate Athletics:** Baseball M; Basketball M & W; Cheerleading W; Cross-Country Running M & W; Golf M & W; Soccer M & W; Softball W; Tennis M & W; Volleyball W

SANTA FE COLLEGE
3000 NW 83rd St.
Gainesville, FL 32606
Tel: (352)395-5000
Fax: (352)395-5581
E-mail: michael.hutley@sfcollege.edu
Web Site: www.sfcollege.edu
President/CEO: Dr. Jackson N. Sasser, PhD
Admissions: Mike Hutley
Type: Four-Year College **Sex:** Coed **Affiliation:** Florida College System. **Admission Plans:** Early Admission; Open Admission **Application Deadline:** Rolling **Application Fee:** $0.00 **H.S. Requirements:** High school diploma required; GED accepted **Scholarships:** Available. **Calendar System:** Semester, Summer session available **Enrollment:** Full-time 6,777, Part-time 8,968 **Faculty:** Full-time 245, Part-time 584 **Student-Faculty Ratio:** 25:1 **Final Year or Final Semester Residency Requirement:** No **Regional Accreditation:** Southern Association of Colleges and Schools **Credit Hours For Degree:** 60 semester hours, Associates **ROTC:** Air Force, Army **Professional Accreditation:** ACCE, ACEN, ADA, AHIMA, CoARC, JRCEMTP, JRCERT, JRCNMT. **Intercollegiate Athletics:** Baseball M; Basketball M & W; Softball W; Volleyball W

SCHILLER INTERNATIONAL UNIVERSITY
8560 Ulmerton Rd.
Largo, FL 33771
Tel: (727)736-5082; Free: 800-261-9751
Fax: (727)734-0359
E-mail: admissions@schiller.edu
Web Site: www.schiller.edu
President/CEO: Dr. Manuel Alonso
Type: Comprehensive **Sex:** Coed **Affiliation:** Schiller International University. **Admission Plans:** Deferred Admission **Application Deadline:** Rolling **Application Fee:** $20.00 **H.S. Requirements:** High school diploma required; GED accepted **Calendar System:** Semester, Summer session available **Enrollment:** Full-time 153, Part-time 38 **Faculty:** Full-time 2, Part-time 64 **Student-Faculty Ratio:** 16:1 **% Residing in College-Owned, -Operated, or -Affiliated Housing:** 85 **Final Year or Final Semester Residency Requirement:** No **Credit Hours For Degree:** 60 semester credit hours, Associates; 120 semester credit hours, Bachelors **Professional Accreditation:** ACICS.

SEMINOLE STATE COLLEGE OF FLORIDA
100 Weldon Blvd.
Sanford, FL 32773-6199
Tel: (407)708-4722
Fax: (407)328-2395
E-mail: admissions@scc-fl.edu
Web Site: www.seminolestate.edu
President/CEO: Dr. E. Ann McGee
Admissions: Pamela Mennechey

Type: Two-Year College **Sex:** Coed **% Accepted:** 64 **Admission Plans:** Deferred Admission; Early Admission; Open Admission **Application Deadline:** Rolling **Application Fee:** $0.00 **H.S. Requirements:** High school diploma required; GED accepted **Costs Per Year:** Application fee: $0. State resident tuition: $3131 full-time, $104.38 per credit hour part-time. Nonresident tuition: $11,456 full-time, $381.87 per credit hour part-time. Full-time tuition varies according to course level, course load, degree level, and program. Part-time tuition varies according to course level, course load, degree level, and program. **Scholarships:** Available. **Calendar System:** Semester, Summer session available **Enrollment:** Full-time 5,995, Part-time 11,746 **Faculty:** Full-time 209, Part-time 589 **Student-Faculty Ratio:** 26:1 **Exams:** ACT; Other; SAT I; SAT I and SAT II or ACT; SAT I or ACT; SAT II. **Final Year or Final Semester Residency Requirement:** No **Regional Accreditation:** Southern Association of Colleges and Schools **Credit Hours For Degree:** 60 credit hours, Associates **ROTC:** Army **Professional Accreditation:** ACEN, APTA, CoARC, JRCEMTP. **Intercollegiate Athletics:** Baseball M; Golf W; Softball W

SOUTH FLORIDA BIBLE COLLEGE AND THEOLOGICAL SEMINARY
1100 S Federal Hwy.
Deerfield Beach, FL 33441
Tel: (954)428-8980
Web Site: www.sfbc.edu
Type: Comprehensive **Sex:** Coed **Professional Accreditation:** ABHE.

SOUTH FLORIDA STATE COLLEGE
600 W College Dr.
Avon Park, FL 33825-9356
Tel: (863)453-6661
Fax: (863)453-0165
Web Site: www.southflorida.edu
President/CEO: Dr. Thomas C. Leitzel
Admissions: Mary Puckorius

Type: Two-Year College **Sex:** Coed **Affiliation:** Florida State College System. **% Accepted:** 54 **Admission Plans:** Deferred Admission; Early Admission; Open Admission **Application Deadline:** Rolling **Application Fee:** $15.00 **H.S. Requirements:** High school diploma required; GED accepted **Costs Per Year:** Application fee: $15. One-time mandatory fee: $15. State resident tuition: $104.52 per credit hour part-time. Nonresident tuition: $394.31 per credit hour part-time. Part-time tuition varies according to course level, course load, degree level, and program. College room and board: $5920. College room only: $2000. **Scholarships:** Available. **Calendar System:** Semester, Summer session available **Enrollment:** Full-time 900, Part-time 1,759 **Faculty:** Full-time 65, Part-time 80 **Student-Faculty Ratio:** 16:1 **Exams:** ACT essay component not used; SAT essay component not used. **Final Year or Final Semester Residency Requirement:** No **Regional Accreditation:** Southern Association of Colleges and Schools **Credit Hours For Degree:** 60 semester hours, Associates; 120 semester hours, Bachelors **Professional Accreditation:** ADA. **Intercollegiate Athletics:** Baseball M; Cross-Country Running W; Softball W; Volleyball W

SOUTH UNIVERSITY (ROYAL PALM BEACH)
University Centre
9801 Belvedere Rd.
Royal Palm Beach, FL 33411
Tel: (561)697-9200; Free: 866-629-2902
Fax: (561)697-9944
Web Site: www.southuniversity.edu/west-palm-beach
President/CEO: David McGuire

Type: Comprehensive **Sex:** Coed **Affiliation:** Education Management Corporation. **Calendar System:** Quarter **Regional Accreditation:** Southern Association of Colleges and Schools **Professional Accreditation:** AAMAE, ACBSP, APTA.

SOUTH UNIVERSITY (TAMPA)
4401 N Himes Ave.
Ste. 175
Tampa, FL 33614
Tel: (813)393-3800; Free: 800-846-1472
Web Site: www.southuniversity.edu/tampa
President/CEO: Dan Coble

Type: Comprehensive **Sex:** Coed **Affiliation:** Education Management Corporation. **Regional Accreditation:** Southern Association of Colleges and Schools **Professional Accreditation:** ACBSP.

SOUTHEASTERN COLLEGE–JACKSONVILLE
6700 Southpoint Pky.
Ste. 400
Jacksonville, FL 32216
Tel: (904)448-9499
Web Site: www.sec.edu
Financial Aid: Fred Pfeffer

Type: Two-Year College **Sex:** Coed **Application Fee:** $55.00 **Costs Per Year:** Application fee: $55. Tuition: $16,784 full-time. Mandatory fees: $1600 full-time. **Scholarships:** Available. **Calendar System:** Quarter **Enrollment:** Full-time 67, Part-time 58 **Professional Accreditation:** ACCSC.

SOUTHEASTERN COLLEGE–WEST PALM BEACH
2081 Vista Pky.
West Palm Beach, FL 33411
Tel: (561)433-2330
Web Site: www.sec.edu
President/CEO: John Huston

Type: Two-Year College **Sex:** Coed **Application Fee:** $55.00 **Costs Per Year:** Application fee: $55. Tuition: $16,784 full-time, $699 per credit hour part-time. Mandatory fees: $1600 full-time. Full-time tuition and fees vary according to course load and program. Part-time tuition varies according to course load and program. **Enrollment:** Full-time 292, Part-time 386 **Professional Accreditation:** ACCSC.

SOUTHEASTERN UNIVERSITY
1000 Longfellow Blvd.
Lakeland, FL 33801-6099
Tel: (863)667-5000; Free: 800-500-8760
Fax: (863)667-5200
E-mail: admission@seu.edu
Web Site: www.seu.edu
President/CEO: Dr. Kent Ingle
Admissions: Roy Rowland, III
Financial Aid: Carol B. Bradley

Type: Comprehensive **Sex:** Coed **Affiliation:** Assemblies of God. **Scores:** 87% SAT V 400+; 80% SAT M 400+; 51.09% ACT 18-23; 21.87% ACT 24-29 **% Accepted:** 46 **Admission Plans:** Deferred Admission; Early Admission; Open Admission **Application Deadline:** May 1 **Application Fee:** $40.00 **H.S. Requirements:** High school diploma required; GED accepted **Costs Per Year:** Application fee: $40. Comprehensive fee: $31,988 includes full-time tuition ($21,840), mandatory fees ($1000), and college room and board ($9148). Full-time tuition and fees vary according to class time, degree level, location, and reciprocity agreements. Room and board charges vary according to board plan and housing facility. Part-time tuition: $910 per hour. Part-time mandatory fees: $200 per term. Part-time tuition and fees vary according to class time, course load, degree level, location, and reciprocity agreements. **Scholarships:** Available. **Calendar System:** Semester, Summer session available **Enrollment:** Full-time 3,185, Graduate full-time 243, Graduate part-time 299, Part-time 811 **Faculty:** Full-time 128, Part-time 213 **Student-Faculty Ratio:** 20:1 **Exams:** ACT essay component used for placement; SAT I or ACT; SAT essay component used for placement. **% Receiving Financial Aid:** 78 **% Residing in College-Owned, -Operated, or -Affiliated Housing:** 57 **Final Year or Final Semester Residency Requirement:** No **Regional Accreditation:** Southern Association of Colleges and Schools **Credit Hours For Degree:** 120 credits, Bachelors **ROTC:** Army **Intercollegiate Athletics:** Baseball M; Basketball M & W; Cheerleading M & W; Cross-Country Running M & W; Football M; Golf M & W; Soccer M & W; Softball W; Tennis M & W; Volleyball W; Wrestling M

SOUTHERN TECHNICAL COLLEGE (FORT MYERS)
1685 Medical Ln.
Fort Myers, FL 33907

Tel: (239)939-4766; Free: 877-347-5492
Fax: (239)936-4040
E-mail: tquinlan@southerntech.edu
Web Site: www.southerntech.edu/locations/ft-myers
President/CEO: Pedro De Guzman
Admissions: Tiffany Quinlan
Type: Four-Year College **Sex:** Coed **Admission Plans:** Open Admission **Application Deadline:** Rolling **Application Fee:** $0.00 **H.S. Requirements:** High school diploma required; GED accepted **Scholarships:** Available. **Calendar System:** Quarter, Summer session available **Enrollment:** Full-time 883, Part-time 376 **Faculty:** Full-time 16, Part-time 144 **Student-Faculty Ratio:** 16:1 **Final Year or Final Semester Residency Requirement:** No **Credit Hours For Degree:** 90 to 115 quarter hours depending on the program, Associates; 180 to 192 quarter hours dependin8 on the program, Bachelors **Professional Accreditation:** ACICS.

SOUTHERN TECHNICAL COLLEGE (ORLANDO)
1485 Florida Mall Ave.
Orlando, FL 32809
Tel: (407)438-6000
E-mail: relie@southerntech.edu
Web Site: www.southerntech.edu
President/CEO: Pedro De Guzman
Admissions: Robinson Elie
Type: Two-Year College **Sex:** Coed **Admission Plans:** Open Admission **Application Deadline:** Rolling **Application Fee:** $0.00 **H.S. Requirements:** High school diploma required; GED accepted **Calendar System:** Quarter, Summer session available **Enrollment:** Full-time 1,445 **Faculty:** Full-time 57 **Student-Faculty Ratio:** 25:1 **Final Year or Final Semester Residency Requirement:** No **Credit Hours For Degree:** 91.5 credits, Associates **Professional Accreditation:** ACICS.

SOUTHERN TECHNICAL COLLEGE (TAMPA)
3910 Riga Blvd.
Tampa, FL 33619
Tel: (813)630-4401; Free: 877-347-5492
Web Site: www.southerntech.edu/locations/tampa
Type: Two-Year College **Sex:** Coed **Calendar System:** Quarter **Professional Accreditation:** ACICS.

STATE COLLEGE OF FLORIDA MANATEE-SARASOTA
5840 26th St. W
Bradenton, FL 34206-7046
Tel: (941)752-5000
Fax: (941)727-6177
E-mail: lewym@scf.edu
Web Site: www.scf.edu
President/CEO: Dr. Carol Probstfeld
Admissions: MariLynn Lewy
Type: Four-Year College **Sex:** Coed **Affiliation:** Florida Community College System. **Scores:** 100% SAT V 400+; 76% SAT M 400+; 41% ACT 18-23; 12.9% ACT 24-29 **% Accepted:** 100 **Admission Plans:** Early Admission; Open Admission **Application Deadline:** August 20 **Application Fee:** $0.00 **H.S. Requirements:** High school diploma required; GED accepted **Costs Per Year:** Application fee: $0. One-time mandatory fee: $40. State resident tuition: $3074 full-time, $102.48 per credit part-time. Nonresident tuition: $11,596 full-time, $386.52 per credit part-time. Full-time tuition varies according to degree level. Part-time tuition varies according to degree level. **Scholarships:** Available. **Calendar System:** Semester, Summer session available **Enrollment:** Full-time 4,173, Part-time 6,141 **Faculty:** Full-time 149, Part-time 293 **Regional Accreditation:** Southern Association of Colleges and Schools **Credit Hours For Degree:** 60 credit hours, Associates; 120 credit hours, Bachelors **Professional Accreditation:** ACEN, ADA, AOTA, APTA, CoARC, JRCERT. **Intercollegiate Athletics:** Baseball M; Basketball M; Softball W; Volleyball W

STETSON UNIVERSITY
421 N Woodland Blvd.
DeLand, FL 32723
Tel: (386)822-7000; Free: 800-688-0101
Fax: (386)822-8832
E-mail: admissions@stetson.edu
Web Site: www.stetson.edu
President/CEO: Dr. Wendy B. Libby

Financial Aid: Susan Merchant
Type: Comprehensive **Sex:** Coed **Scores:** 99% SAT V 400+; 100% SAT M 400+; 24.7% ACT 18-23; 58% ACT 24-29 **% Accepted:** 63 **Admission Plans:** Deferred Admission **Application Deadline:** Rolling **Application Fee:** $50.00 **H.S. Requirements:** High school diploma required; GED accepted **Costs Per Year:** Application fee: $50. Comprehensive fee: $55,566 includes full-time tuition ($42,890), mandatory fees ($350), and college room and board ($12,326). College room only: $7094. Room and board charges vary according to board plan and housing facility. Part-time tuition: $4445 per course. Part-time tuition varies according to course load. **Scholarships:** Available. **Calendar System:** Semester, Summer session available **Enrollment:** Full-time 3,037, Graduate full-time 1,044, Graduate part-time 202, Part-time 47 **Faculty:** Full-time 265, Part-time 160 **Student-Faculty Ratio:** 13:1 **Exams:** SAT I or ACT; SAT Reasoning. **% Receiving Financial Aid:** 73 **% Residing in College-Owned, -Operated, or -Affiliated Housing:** 65 **Final Year or Final Semester Residency Requirement:** Yes **Regional Accreditation:** Southern Association of Colleges and Schools **Credit Hours For Degree:** 128 hours, Bachelors **ROTC:** Army **Professional Accreditation:** AACSB, AALS, ABA, ACA, JRCAT, NASM, NCATE. **Intercollegiate Athletics:** Baseball M; Basketball M & W; Crew M & W; Cross-Country Running M & W; Football M; Golf M & W; Lacrosse W; Soccer M & W; Softball W; Tennis M & W; Volleyball W

STRAYER UNIVERSITY–BAYMEADOWS CAMPUS
8375 Dix Ellis Trl.
Ste. 200
Jacksonville, FL 32256
Tel: (904)538-1000
Fax: (904)538-1030
Web Site: www.strayer.edu/florida/baymeadows
President/CEO: Brian W. Jones
Type: Comprehensive **Sex:** Coed **Regional Accreditation:** Middle States Association of Colleges and Schools

STRAYER UNIVERSITY–BRICKELL CAMPUS
1201 Brickell Ave.
Ste. 700
Miami, FL 33131
Tel: (305)507-5800
Fax: (305)416-2970
Web Site: www.strayer.edu/florida/brickell
President/CEO: Brian W. Jones
Type: Comprehensive **Sex:** Coed **Regional Accreditation:** Middle States Association of Colleges and Schools

STRAYER UNIVERSITY–CORAL SPRINGS CAMPUS
5830 Coral Ridge Dr.
Ste. 300
Pompano Beach, FL 33076
Tel: (954)369-0700
Fax: (954)369-0730
Web Site: www.strayer.edu/florida/coral-springs
President/CEO: Brian W. Jones
Type: Comprehensive **Sex:** Coed **Regional Accreditation:** Middle States Association of Colleges and Schools

STRAYER UNIVERSITY–DORAL CAMPUS
11430 NW 20th St.
Ste. 150
Miami, FL 33172
Tel: (305)507-5700
Fax: (305)470-3988
Web Site: www.strayer.edu/florida/doral
President/CEO: Brian W. Jones
Type: Comprehensive **Sex:** Coed **Regional Accreditation:** Middle States Association of Colleges and Schools

STRAYER UNIVERSITY–FORT LAUDERDALE CAMPUS
2307 W Broward Blvd.
Ste. 100
Fort Lauderdale, FL 33312
Tel: (954)745-6960
Fax: (954)745-6930
Web Site: www.strayer.edu/florida/fort-lauderdale

President/CEO: Brian W. Jones
Type: Comprehensive **Sex:** Coed **Regional Accreditation:** Middle States Association of Colleges and Schools

STRAYER UNIVERSITY–MAITLAND CAMPUS

850 Trafalgar Ct.
Ste. 360
Maitland, FL 32751
Tel: (407)618-5900
Fax: (407)618-5930
Web Site: www.strayer.edu/florida/maitland
President/CEO: Brian W. Jones
Type: Comprehensive **Sex:** Coed **Regional Accreditation:** Middle States Association of Colleges and Schools

STRAYER UNIVERSITY–MIRAMAR CAMPUS

15620 SW 29th St.
Miramar, FL 33027
Tel: (954)378-2400
Fax: (305)207-3042
Web Site: www.strayer.edu/florida/miramar
President/CEO: Brian W. Jones
Type: Comprehensive **Sex:** Coed **Regional Accreditation:** Middle States Association of Colleges and Schools

STRAYER UNIVERSITY–ORLANDO EAST CAMPUS

2200 N Alafaya Trl.
Ste. 500
Orlando, FL 32826
Tel: (407)926-2000
Fax: (407)926-2030
Web Site: www.strayer.edu/florida/orlando-east
President/CEO: Brian W. Jones
Type: Comprehensive **Sex:** Coed **Regional Accreditation:** Middle States Association of Colleges and Schools

STRAYER UNIVERSITY–PALM BEACH GARDENS CAMPUS

11025 RCA Ctr. Dr.
Ste. 200
West Palm Beach, FL 33410
Tel: (561)904-3000
Fax: (561)904-3030
Web Site: www.strayer.edu/florida/palm-beach-gardens
President/CEO: Brian W. Jones
Type: Comprehensive **Sex:** Coed **Regional Accreditation:** Middle States Association of Colleges and Schools

STRAYER UNIVERSITY–SAND LAKE CAMPUS

8541 S Park Cir.
Bldg. 900
Orlando, FL 32819
Tel: (407)264-9400
Fax: (407)264-9430
Web Site: www.strayer.edu/florida/sand-lake
President/CEO: Brian W. Jones
Type: Comprehensive **Sex:** Coed **Regional Accreditation:** Middle States Association of Colleges and Schools

STRAYER UNIVERSITY–TAMPA EAST CAMPUS

5650 Breckenridge Park Dr.
Ste. 300
Tampa, FL 33610
Tel: (813)663-0100
Fax: (813)626-2245
Web Site: www.strayer.edu/florida/tampa-east
President/CEO: Brian W. Jones
Type: Comprehensive **Sex:** Coed **Regional Accreditation:** Middle States Association of Colleges and Schools

STRAYER UNIVERSITY–TAMPA WESTSHORE CAMPUS

4902 Eisenhower Blvd., Ste. 100
Tampa, FL 33634
Tel: (813)882-0100
Fax: (813)249-2483

Web Site: www.strayer.edu/florida/tampa-westshore
President/CEO: Brian W. Jones
Type: Comprehensive **Sex:** Coed **Regional Accreditation:** Middle States Association of Colleges and Schools

SULLIVAN AND COGLIANO TRAINING CENTER

4760 NW 167th St.
Miami Gardens, FL 33014
Tel: (305)624-3035
Web Site: www.sctrain.edu
Type: Two-Year College **Sex:** Coed **Professional Accreditation:** COE.

TALLAHASSEE COMMUNITY COLLEGE

444 Appleyard Dr.
Tallahassee, FL 32304-2895
Tel: (850)201-6200
E-mail: admissions@tcc.fl.edu
Web Site: www.tcc.fl.edu
President/CEO: Dr. Jim Murdaugh
Type: Two-Year College **Sex:** Coed **Affiliation:** Florida College System. **% Accepted:** 51 **Admission Plans:** Deferred Admission; Early Admission; Open Admission **Application Deadline:** August 1 **Application Fee:** $0.00 **H.S. Requirements:** High school diploma required; GED accepted **Costs Per Year:** Application fee: $0. State resident tuition: $3025 full-time, $100.83 per credit hour part-time. Nonresident tuition: $11,288 full-time, $387.27 per credit hour part-time. Full-time tuition varies according to course load. Part-time tuition varies according to course load. **Scholarships:** Available. **Calendar System:** Semester, Summer session available **Enrollment:** Full-time 5,740, Part-time 6,705 **Faculty:** Full-time 190, Part-time 378 **Student-Faculty Ratio:** 22:1 **Final Year or Final Semester Residency Requirement:** No **Regional Accreditation:** Southern Association of Colleges and Schools **Credit Hours For Degree:** 60 semester hours, Associates **ROTC:** Air Force, Army, Navy **Professional Accreditation:** ADA, CoARC, JRCEMTP. **Intercollegiate Athletics:** Baseball M; Basketball M & W; Softball W

TALMUDIC UNIVERSITY

4000 Alton Rd.
Miami Beach, FL 33140
Tel: (305)534-7050
Fax: (305)534-8444
E-mail: yandtg@gmail.com
Web Site: www.talmudicu.edu
President/CEO: Rabbi Yitzchak Zweig
Admissions: Rabbi Yeshaya Greenberg
Financial Aid: Rabbi Ira Hill
Type: Comprehensive **Sex:** Men **Affiliation:** Jewish. **% Accepted:** 80 **Admission Plans:** Deferred Admission; Early Admission **Application Deadline:** Rolling **Application Fee:** $250.00 **H.S. Requirements:** High school diploma required; GED accepted **Scholarships:** Available. **Calendar System:** Semester, Summer session available **Enrollment:** Full-time 30 **Faculty:** Full-time 6 **Student-Faculty Ratio:** 5:1 **% Receiving Financial Aid:** 70 **% Residing in College-Owned, -Operated, or -Affiliated Housing:** 99 **Credit Hours For Degree:** 120 credits, Bachelors **Professional Accreditation:** AARTS.

TRINITY BAPTIST COLLEGE

800 Hammond Blvd.
Jacksonville, FL 32221
Tel: (904)596-2400; Free: 800-786-2206
Fax: (904)596-2531
E-mail: trinity@tbc.edu
Web Site: www.tbc.edu
President/CEO: Mac Heavener, Jr.
Financial Aid: Mark Elkins
Type: Comprehensive **Sex:** Coed **Affiliation:** Baptist. **Application Deadline:** Rolling **Application Fee:** $30.00 **H.S. Requirements:** High school diploma required; GED accepted **Costs Per Year:** Application fee: $30. Comprehensive fee: $12,315 includes full-time tuition ($4995), mandatory fees ($1050), and college room and board ($6270). Full-time tuition and fees vary according to course load. Room and board charges vary according to board plan. Part-time tuition: $420 per credit hour. Part-time tuition varies according to course load. **Scholarships:** Available. **Calendar System:** Semester, Summer session available **Student-Faculty Ratio:** 9:1 **Exams:**

SAT I or ACT; SAT essay component not used. **Final Year or Final Semester Residency Requirement:** Yes **Credit Hours For Degree:** 64 semester hours, Associates; 128 semester hours, Bachelors **Professional Accreditation:** TRACS. **Intercollegiate Athletics:** Basketball M & W; Cheerleading W; Soccer M; Volleyball W

TRINITY COLLEGE OF FLORIDA

2430 Welbilt Blvd.
Trinity, FL 34655
Tel: (727)376-6911; Free: 800-388-0869
Fax: (727)376-0781
E-mail: ashady@trinitycollege.edu
Web Site: www.trinitycollege.edu
President/CEO: Mark T. O'Farrell
Admissions: Alton Shady
Financial Aid: Sue Wayne
Type: Four-Year College **Sex:** Coed **Affiliation:** nondenominational. **Scores:** 90% SAT V 400+; 65% SAT M 400+; 30% ACT 18-23; 10% ACT 24-29 **% Accepted:** 74 **Admission Plans:** Deferred Admission **Application Deadline:** July 31 **Application Fee:** $35.00 **H.S. Requirements:** High school diploma required; GED accepted **Costs Per Year:** Application fee: $35. Comprehensive fee: $22,140 includes full-time tuition ($14,850), mandatory fees ($840), and college room and board ($6450). Full-time tuition and fees vary according to program. Part-time tuition: $495 per credit hour. Part-time mandatory fees: $420 per term. Part-time tuition and fees vary according to program. **Scholarships:** Available. **Calendar System:** Semester, Summer session available **Enrollment:** Full-time 164, Part-time 40 **Faculty:** Full-time 7, Part-time 21 **Student-Faculty Ratio:** 8:1 **Exams:** SAT I or ACT; SAT Reasoning; SAT Subject. **% Receiving Financial Aid:** 84 **% Residing in College-Owned, -Operated, or -Affiliated Housing:** 29 **Final Year or Final Semester Residency Requirement:** Yes **Credit Hours For Degree:** 61 credit hours, Associates; 123 credit hours, Bachelors **Professional Accreditation:** ABHE. **Intercollegiate Athletics:** Basketball M & W; Soccer M; Volleyball W

ULTIMATE MEDICAL ACADEMY CLEARWATER

1255 Cleveland St.
Clearwater, FL 33756
Tel: (727)298-8685; Free: 888-205-8685
Web Site: www.ultimatemedical.edu
President/CEO: Steve Kemler
Type: Two-Year College **Sex:** Coed **H.S. Requirements:** High school diploma required; GED accepted **Calendar System:** Continuous **Professional Accreditation:** ABHES.

ULTIMATE MEDICAL ACADEMY ONLINE

1255 Cleveland St.
Clearwater, FL 33756
Tel: (727)298-8685; Free: 888-205-2510
E-mail: onlineadmissions@ultimatemedical.edu
Web Site: www.ultimatemedical.edu
Type: Two-Year College **Sex:** Coed **Calendar System:** Continuous **Professional Accreditation:** ABHES.

ULTIMATE MEDICAL ACADEMY TAMPA

9309 N Florida Ave.
Ste. 100
Tampa, FL 33612
Tel: (813)386-6350; Free: 888-205-2510
Web Site: www.ultimatemedical.edu
Type: Two-Year College **Sex:** Coed **H.S. Requirements:** High school diploma required; GED accepted **Calendar System:** Continuous **Professional Accreditation:** ABHES.

UNIVERSAL CAREER SCHOOL

10720 W Flagler St.
Ste. 21
Sweetwater, FL 33174
Tel: (305)485-7700
Web Site: www.ucs.edu
Type: Two-Year College **Sex:** Coed **Professional Accreditation:** COE.

UNIVERSITY OF CENTRAL FLORIDA

4000 Central Florida Blvd.
Orlando, FL 32816
Tel: (407)823-2000
Fax: (407)823-3419
E-mail: admission@ucf.edu
Web Site: www.ucf.edu
President/CEO: Dr. John Hitt
Admissions: Dr. Gordon Chavis, Jr.
Financial Aid: Inez Ford
Type: University **Sex:** Coed **Affiliation:** State University System of Florida. **Scores:** 100% SAT V 400+; 100% SAT M 400+; 20.8% ACT 18-23; 63% ACT 24-29 **% Accepted:** 49 **Admission Plans:** Early Admission; Preferred Admission **Application Deadline:** May 1 **Application Fee:** $30.00 **H.S. Requirements:** High school diploma required; GED accepted **Costs Per Year:** Application fee: $30. State resident tuition: $6368 full-time, $212.28 per credit hour part-time. Nonresident tuition: $22,467 full-time, $748.89 per credit hour part-time. Full-time tuition varies according to course load. Part-time tuition varies according to course load. College room and board: $9300. College room only: $5400. Room and board charges vary according to board plan and housing facility. **Scholarships:** Available. **Calendar System:** Semester, Summer session available **Enrollment:** Full-time 37,596, Graduate full-time 4,332, Graduate part-time 4,157, Part-time 16,917 **Faculty:** Full-time 1,434, Part-time 504 **Student-Faculty Ratio:** 30:1 **Exams:** ACT essay component used for admission; SAT I or ACT; SAT essay component used for admission; SAT Reasoning. **% Receiving Financial Aid:** 62 **% Residing in College-Owned, -Operated, or -Affiliated Housing:** 17 **Final Year or Final Semester Residency Requirement:** Yes **Regional Accreditation:** Southern Association of Colleges and Schools **Credit Hours For Degree:** 60 semester hours, Associates; 120 semester hours, Bachelors **ROTC:** Air Force, Army **Professional Accreditation:** AACN, AACSB, ABET, ACA, AHIMA, APA, APTA, ASHA, CAHME, CSWE, CoARC, JRCERT, LCME/AMA, NAACLS, NASM, NASPAA, NCATE. **Intercollegiate Athletics:** Baseball M; Basketball M & W; Crew W; Cross-Country Running W; Football M; Golf M & W; Soccer M & W; Softball W; Tennis M & W; Track and Field W; Volleyball W

UNIVERSITY OF FLORIDA

Gainesville, FL 32611
Tel: (352)392-3261
Web Site: www.ufl.edu
President/CEO: Dr. W. Kent Fuchs
Financial Aid: Richard D. Wilder
Type: University **Sex:** Coed **Scores:** 100% SAT V 400+; 100% SAT M 400+; 8% ACT 18-23; 51% ACT 24-29 **% Accepted:** 48 **Admission Plans:** Early Admission **Application Deadline:** November 1 **Application Fee:** $30.00 **H.S. Requirements:** High school diploma required; GED accepted **Costs Per Year:** Application fee: $30. State resident tuition: $4477 full-time, $149.24 per credit hour part-time. Nonresident tuition: $26,755 full-time, $856.45 per credit hour part-time. Mandatory fees: $1912 full-time. College room and board: $9910. College room only: $5440. **Scholarships:** Available. **Calendar System:** Semester, Summer session available **Enrollment:** Full-time 30,907, Graduate full-time 12,479, Graduate part-time 4,764, Part-time 4,136 **Faculty:** Full-time 3,543, Part-time 372 **Exams:** ACT essay component used for admission; SAT I or ACT; SAT II; SAT essay component used for admission; SAT Reasoning; SAT Subject. **% Receiving Financial Aid:** 51 **% Residing in College-Owned, -Operated, or -Affiliated Housing:** 24 **Final Year or Final Semester Residency Requirement:** Yes **Regional Accreditation:** Southern Association of Colleges and Schools **Credit Hours For Degree:** 60 semester hours, Associates; 120 semester hours, Bachelors **ROTC:** Air Force, Army, Navy **Professional Accreditation:** AACN, AACSB, AAFCS, AALS, ABA, ABET, ACA, ACCE, ACEJMC, ACNM, ACPE, ACSP, ADA, AND, AOTA, APA, APTA, ASHA, ASLA, AVMA, CAHME, CIDA, CORE, JRCAT, LCME/AMA, NAAB, NASAD, NASD, NASM, NAST, NCATE, NRPA, SAF. **Intercollegiate Athletics:** Baseball M; Basketball M & W; Bowling M & W; Cheerleading M & W; Cross-Country Running M & W; Football M; Golf M & W; Gymnastics W; Lacrosse W; Racquetball M & W; Soccer M & W; Softball W; Swimming and Diving M & W; Table Tennis M & W; Tennis M & W; Track and Field M & W; Ultimate Frisbee M & W; Volleyball M & W

UNIVERSITY OF FORT LAUDERDALE

4093 NW 16th St.
Lauderhill, FL 33313

Tel: (954)486-7728
Web Site: uftl.edu
Type: Comprehensive **Sex:** Coed **Affiliation:** Christian. **Calendar System:** Semester **Professional Accreditation:** TRACS.

UNIVERSITY OF MIAMI

PO Box 248025
Coral Gables, FL 33124
Tel: (305)284-2211
Fax: (305)284-2507
E-mail: admission@miami.edu
Web Site: www.miami.edu
President/CEO: Dr. Donna E. Shalala
Admissions: Deanna Lynn Voss
Financial Aid: Raymond Nault-Hix
Type: University **Sex:** Coed **Scores:** 101% SAT V 400+; 100% SAT M 400+; 2% ACT 18-23; 38% ACT 24-29 **% Accepted:** 38 **Admission Plans:** Deferred Admission; Early Action; Early Admission; Early Decision Plan **Application Deadline:** January 1 **Application Fee:** $70.00 **H.S. Requirements:** High school diploma required; GED accepted **Costs Per Year:** Application fee: $70. Comprehensive fee: $60,314 includes full-time tuition ($45,600), mandatory fees ($1404), and college room and board ($13,310). College room only: $7720. Full-time tuition and fees vary according to course load. Room and board charges vary according to board plan and housing facility. Part-time tuition: $1900 per credit hour. Part-time tuition varies according to course load and program. **Scholarships:** Available. **Calendar System:** Semester, Summer session available **Enrollment:** Full-time 10,482, Graduate full-time 4,932, Graduate part-time 793, Part-time 641 **Faculty:** Full-time 1,131, Part-time 418 **Student-Faculty Ratio:** 12:1 **Exams:** ACT essay component used for placement; SAT I and SAT II or ACT; SAT I or ACT; SAT essay component used for placement; SAT Reasoning; SAT Subject. **% Receiving Financial Aid:** 19 **% Residing in College-Owned, -Operated, or -Affiliated Housing:** 37 **Final Year or Final Semester Residency Requirement:** Yes **Regional Accreditation:** Southern Association of Colleges and Schools **Credit Hours For Degree:** 120 credits, Bachelors **ROTC:** Air Force, Army **Professional Accreditation:** AACN, AACSB, AALS, AANA, ABA, ABET, ACEJMC, ACNM, APA, APTA, CAHME, CEPH, LCME/AMA, NAAB, NASM, NCATE, TEAC. **Intercollegiate Athletics:** Baseball M; Basketball M & W; Cheerleading M & W; Crew W; Cross-Country Running M & W; Football M; Golf W; Soccer W; Swimming and Diving M & W; Tennis M & W; Track and Field M & W; Volleyball W

UNIVERSITY OF NORTH FLORIDA

1 UNF Dr.
Jacksonville, FL 32224
Tel: (904)620-1000
Fax: (904)620-1040
E-mail: admissions@unf.edu
Web Site: www.unf.edu
President/CEO: John A. Delaney
Admissions: Karen Lucas
Financial Aid: Anissa Agne
Type: Comprehensive **Sex:** Coed **Affiliation:** State University System of Florida. **Scores:** 100% SAT V 400+; 100% SAT M 400+; 42% ACT 18-23; 48% ACT 24-29 **% Accepted:** 57 **Admission Plans:** Deferred Admission **Application Deadline:** Rolling **Application Fee:** $30.00 **H.S. Requirements:** High school diploma required; GED accepted **Costs Per Year:** Application fee: $30. State resident tuition: $4281 full-time, $142.70 per credit hour part-time. Nonresident tuition: $17,999 full-time, $599.97 per credit hour part-time. Mandatory fees: $2113 full-time, $70.43 per credit hour part-time. Full-time tuition and fees vary according to course load. Part-time tuition and fees vary according to course load. College room and board: $9664. Room and board charges vary according to board plan and housing facility. **Scholarships:** Available. **Calendar System:** Semester, Summer session available **Enrollment:** Full-time 9,562, Graduate full-time 824, Graduate part-time 1,034, Part-time 4,255 **Faculty:** Full-time 543, Part-time 357 **Student-Faculty Ratio:** 18:1 **Exams:** ACT essay component used for admission; SAT I or ACT; SAT essay component used for admission; SAT Reasoning. **% Receiving Financial Aid:** 51 **% Residing in College-Owned, -Operated, or -Affiliated Housing:** 21 **Final Year or Final Semester Residency Requirement:** No **Regional Accreditation:** Southern Association of Colleges and Schools **Credit Hours For Degree:** 60 semester hours, Associates; 120 semester hours, Bachelors **ROTC:** Army, Navy **Professional Accreditation:** AACN, AACSB, AANA, ABET, ACA,

ACCE, AND, APTA, CORE, JRCAT, NASM, NASPAA, NCATE. **Intercollegiate Athletics:** Baseball M; Basketball M & W; Cross-Country Running M & W; Golf M & W; Soccer M & W; Softball W; Swimming and Diving W; Tennis M & W; Track and Field M & W; Volleyball W

UNIVERSITY OF PHOENIX–CENTRAL FLORIDA CAMPUS

8325 S Park Cir.
Orlando, FL 32819
Tel: (407)667-0555; Free: 866-766-0766
Web Site: www.phoenix.edu
President/CEO: Timothy P. Slottow
Admissions: Marc Booker
Type: Comprehensive **Sex:** Coed **Admission Plans:** Deferred Admission; Open Admission **Application Deadline:** Rolling **Application Fee:** $0.00 **H.S. Requirements:** High school diploma required; GED accepted **Scholarships:** Available. **Calendar System:** Continuous, Summer session not available **Enrollment:** Full-time 1,174 **Faculty:** Full-time 33, Part-time 182 **Regional Accreditation:** North Central Association of Colleges and Schools **Credit Hours For Degree:** 60 credits, Associates; 120 credits, Bachelors

UNIVERSITY OF PHOENIX–NORTH FLORIDA CAMPUS

4500 Salisbury Rd.
Jacksonville, FL 32216-0959
Tel: (904)636-6645; Free: 866-766-0766
Web Site: www.phoenix.edu
President/CEO: Timothy P. Slottow
Admissions: Marc Booker
Type: Comprehensive **Sex:** Coed **Admission Plans:** Deferred Admission; Open Admission **Application Deadline:** Rolling **Application Fee:** $0.00 **H.S. Requirements:** High school diploma required; GED accepted **Scholarships:** Available. **Calendar System:** Continuous, Summer session not available **Enrollment:** Full-time 1,019 **Faculty:** Full-time 24, Part-time 186 **Regional Accreditation:** North Central Association of Colleges and Schools **Credit Hours For Degree:** 60 credits, Associates; 120 credits, Bachelors **Professional Accreditation:** ACBSP.

UNIVERSITY OF PHOENIX–SOUTH FLORIDA CAMPUS

2400 SW 145th Ave.
Miramar, FL 33027-4145
Tel: (954)382-5303; Free: 866-766-0766
Web Site: www.phoenix.edu
President/CEO: Timothy P. Slottow
Admissions: Marc Booker
Type: Comprehensive **Sex:** Coed **Admission Plans:** Deferred Admission; Open Admission **Application Deadline:** Rolling **Application Fee:** $0.00 **H.S. Requirements:** High school diploma required; GED accepted **Scholarships:** Available. **Calendar System:** Continuous, Summer session not available **Enrollment:** Full-time 1,961 **Faculty:** Full-time 22, Part-time 211 **Regional Accreditation:** North Central Association of Colleges and Schools **Credit Hours For Degree:** 60 credits, Associates; 120 credits, Bachelors **Professional Accreditation:** ACBSP.

UNIVERSITY OF SOUTH FLORIDA

4202 E Fowler Ave.
Tampa, FL 33620-9951
Tel: (813)974-2011
Fax: (813)974-9689
E-mail: admissions@usf.edu
Web Site: www.usf.edu
President/CEO: Dr. Judy Genshaft, PhD
Financial Aid: Billie Jo Hamilton
Type: University **Sex:** Coed **Affiliation:** State University System of Florida. **Scores:** 100% SAT V 400+; 100% SAT M 400+; 18.21% ACT 18-23; 65.62% ACT 24-29 **% Accepted:** 45 **Admission Plans:** Deferred Admission; Early Admission **Application Deadline:** March 1 **Application Fee:** $30.00 **H.S. Requirements:** High school diploma required; GED accepted **Costs Per Year:** Application fee: $30. State resident tuition: $4559 full-time, $211 per credit hour part-time. Nonresident tuition: $15,474 full-time, $575 per credit hour part-time. Mandatory fees: $1851 full-time. Full-time tuition and fees vary according to course level, course load, and location. Part-time tuition varies according to course level, course load, and location. College room and board: $9400. College room only: $5750. Room and board charges vary according to board plan, housing facility, and location. **Scholarships:** Available. **Calendar System:** Semester, Summer session available **Enrollment:**

Full-time 24,088, Graduate full-time 6,214, Graduate part-time 4,742, Part-time 7,023 **Faculty:** Full-time 1,208, Part-time 526 **Student-Faculty Ratio:** 24:1 **Exams:** ACT essay component used for admission; SAT I and SAT II or ACT; SAT I or ACT; SAT II; SAT essay component used for admission; SAT Reasoning. **% Receiving Financial Aid:** 66 **% Residing in College-Owned, -Operated, or -Affiliated Housing:** 21 **Final Year or Final Semester Residency Requirement:** Yes **Regional Accreditation:** Southern Association of Colleges and Schools **Credit Hours For Degree:** 60 semester hours, Associates; 120 semester hours, Bachelors **ROTC:** Air Force, Army, Navy **Professional Accreditation:** AACN, AACSB, AANA, ABET, ACA, ACEJMC, ACPE, ALA, APA, APTA, ASHA, CAHME, CEPH, CORE, CSWE, LCME/AMA, NAAB, NASAD, NASM, NASPAA, NAST, NCATE. **Intercollegiate Athletics:** Badminton M & W; Baseball M; Basketball W; Bowling M & W; Crew M & W; Cross-Country Running M & W; Fencing M & W; Football M; Golf M & W; Gymnastics M & W; Rugby M & W; Soccer M & W; Softball W; Tennis M & W; Track and Field M & W; Volleyball M & W

UNIVERSITY OF SOUTH FLORIDA, ST. PETERSBURG

140 Seventh Ave. S
Saint Petersburg, FL 33701
Tel: (727)873-7748
E-mail: admissions@usfsp.edu
Web Site: www.stpt.usf.edu
President/CEO: Sophia T. Wisniewska, PhD
Admissions: Holly Kickliter

Type: Comprehensive **Sex:** Coed **Affiliation:** University of South Florida System. **Scores:** 100% SAT V 400+; 100% SAT M 400+; 47% ACT 18-23; 47% ACT 24-29 **Costs Per Year:** State resident tuition: $5820 full-time, $193.70 per credit hour part-time. Nonresident tuition: $16,736 full-time, $557.52 per credit hour part-time. Mandatory fees: $10 full-time. College room and board: $9250. Room and board charges vary according to board plan and housing facility. **Calendar System:** Semester, Summer session available **Enrollment:** Full-time 2,653, Graduate full-time 144, Graduate part-time 427, Part-time 1,526 **Faculty:** Full-time 133, Part-time 145 **Student-Faculty Ratio:** 17:1 **Exams:** ACT essay component not used; SAT I or ACT; SAT essay component not used. **% Residing in College-Owned, -Operated, or -Affiliated Housing:** 16 **Final Year or Final Semester Residency Requirement:** No **Regional Accreditation:** Southern Association of Colleges and Schools **Credit Hours For Degree:** 60 credits, Associates; 120 credits, Bachelors **ROTC:** Army **Professional Accreditation:** AACSB, NCATE. **Intercollegiate Athletics:** Baseball M; Sailing W

UNIVERSITY OF SOUTH FLORIDA SARASOTA-MANATEE

8350 N Tamiami Trl.
Sarasota, FL 34243
Tel: (941)359-4200
E-mail: atelatovich@sar.usf.edu
Web Site: www.usfsm.edu
President/CEO: Dr. Sandra S. Stone
Admissions: Andy Telatovich

Type: Comprehensive **Sex:** Coed **Affiliation:** University of South Florida System. **Scores:** 100% SAT V 400+; 100% SAT M 400+; 39% ACT 18-23; 52% ACT 24-29 **Costs Per Year:** State resident tuition: $4206 full-time, $186 per credit hour part-time. Nonresident tuition: $15,120 full-time, $549 per credit hour part-time. Mandatory fees: $1381 full-time, $5 per term part-time. Full-time tuition and fees vary according to course load and program. Part-time tuition and fees vary according to course load and program. **Calendar System:** Semester, Summer session available **Enrollment:** Full-time 980, Graduate full-time 41, Graduate part-time 155, Part-time 865 **Faculty:** Full-time 80, Part-time 59 **Student-Faculty Ratio:** 14:1 **Exams:** ACT essay component not used; SAT I or ACT; SAT II; SAT essay component not used. **Final Year or Final Semester Residency Requirement:** No **Regional Accreditation:** Southern Association of Colleges and Schools **Credit Hours For Degree:** 60 credit hours, Associates; 120 credit hours, Bachelors **ROTC:** Air Force, Army, Navy **Professional Accreditation:** AACSB.

THE UNIVERSITY OF TAMPA

401 W Kennedy Blvd.
Tampa, FL 33606-1490
Tel: (813)253-3333; Free: 888-MINARET
Fax: (813)254-4955
E-mail: admissions@ut.edu
Web Site: www.ut.edu

President/CEO: Dr. Ronald L. Vaughn
Admissions: Dennis Nostrand
Financial Aid: Jacqueline M. LaTorella

Type: Comprehensive **Sex:** Coed **Scores:** 99% SAT V 400+; 99% SAT M 400+; 43.31% ACT 18-23; 49.01% ACT 24-29 **% Accepted:** 51 **Admission Plans:** Deferred Admission; Early Admission; Early Decision Plan **Application Deadline:** Rolling **Application Fee:** $40.00 **H.S. Requirements:** High school diploma required; GED accepted **Costs Per Year:** Application fee: $40. One-time mandatory fee: $85. Comprehensive fee: $36,944 includes full-time tuition ($25,202), mandatory fees ($1842), and college room and board ($9900). College room only: $5240. Full-time tuition and fees vary according to class time, course load, and program. Room and board charges vary according to board plan and housing facility. Part-time tuition: $536 per credit hour. Part-time mandatory fees: $40 per term. Part-time tuition and fees vary according to class time, course load, and program. **Scholarships:** Available. **Calendar System:** Semester, Summer session available **Enrollment:** Full-time 6,820, Graduate full-time 386, Graduate part-time 494, Part-time 259 **Faculty:** Full-time 295, Part-time 360 **Student-Faculty Ratio:** 17:1 **Exams:** ACT essay component used for advising; ACT essay component used for placement; SAT I or ACT; SAT essay component used for advising; SAT essay component used for placement; SAT Reasoning; SAT Subject. **% Receiving Financial Aid:** 58 **% Residing in College-Owned, -Operated, or -Affiliated Housing:** 58 **Final Year or Final Semester Residency Requirement:** Yes **Regional Accreditation:** Southern Association of Colleges and Schools **Credit Hours For Degree:** 124 semester hours, Bachelors **ROTC:** Air Force, Army, Navy **Professional Accreditation:** AACSB, ABET, ACEN, NASM. **Intercollegiate Athletics:** Baseball M; Basketball M & W; Crew W; Cross-Country Running M & W; Golf M & W; Lacrosse M; Soccer M & W; Softball W; Swimming and Diving M & W; Tennis W; Volleyball W

UNIVERSITY OF WEST FLORIDA

11000 University Pky.
Pensacola, FL 32514-5750
Tel: (850)474-2000; Free: 800-263-1074
Fax: (850)474-2096
E-mail: admissions@uwf.edu
Web Site: www.uwf.edu
President/CEO: Dr. Judy A. Bense
Admissions: Katie Condon
Financial Aid: Shana Gore

Type: Comprehensive **Sex:** Coed **Affiliation:** State University System of Florida. **Scores:** 97% SAT V 400+; 97% SAT M 400+; 50% ACT 18-23; 42% ACT 24-29 **% Accepted:** 42 **Admission Plans:** Deferred Admission; Early Admission; Preferred Admission **Application Deadline:** June 1 **Application Fee:** $30.00 **H.S. Requirements:** High school diploma required; GED accepted **Costs Per Year:** Application fee: $30. State resident tuition: $6360 full-time, $212 per semester hour part-time. Nonresident tuition: $19,241 full-time, $641 per semester hour part-time. Mandatory fees: $2041 full-time. Full-time tuition and fees vary according to location and reciprocity agreements. Part-time tuition varies according to location and reciprocity agreements. College room and board: $9912. Room and board charges vary according to board plan, housing facility, and student level. **Scholarships:** Available. **Calendar System:** Semester, Summer session available **Enrollment:** Full-time 7,164, Graduate full-time 559, Graduate part-time 2,039, Part-time 3,036 **Faculty:** Full-time 338, Part-time 268 **Student-Faculty Ratio:** 21:1 **Exams:** ACT essay component used for admission; ACT essay component used for advising; ACT essay component used for placement; SAT I and SAT II or ACT; SAT I or ACT; SAT essay component used for admission; SAT essay component used for advising; SAT essay component used for placement; SAT Reasoning; SAT Subject. **% Receiving Financial Aid:** 65 **% Residing in College-Owned, -Operated, or -Affiliated Housing:** 18 **Final Year or Final Semester Residency Requirement:** No **Regional Accreditation:** Southern Association of Colleges and Schools **Credit Hours For Degree:** 60 semester hours, Associates; 120 semester hours, Bachelors **ROTC:** Air Force, Army **Professional Accreditation:** AACN, AACSB, ABET, CSWE, NAACLS, NASM, NASPAA, NCATE. **Intercollegiate Athletics:** Baseball M; Basketball M & W; Cross-Country Running M & W; Golf M & W; Soccer M & W; Softball W; Swimming and Diving W; Tennis M & W; Volleyball W

VALENCIA COLLEGE

PO Box 3028
Orlando, FL 32802-3028

Tel: (407)299-5000
E-mail: lherlocker@valenciacollege.edu
Web Site: valenciacollege.edu
President/CEO: Dr. Sanford C. Shugart
Admissions: Dr. Linda K. Herlocker

Type: Four-Year College **Sex:** Coed **Affiliation:** Florida College System. **% Accepted:** 98 **Admission Plans:** Deferred Admission; Early Admission; Open Admission **Application Deadline:** Rolling **H.S. Requirements:** High school diploma required; GED accepted **Costs Per Year:** State resident tuition: $2474 full-time, $103.06 per credit hour part-time. Nonresident tuition: $9383 full-time, $390.96 per credit hour part-time. Full-time tuition varies according to degree level. Part-time tuition varies according to degree level. **Scholarships:** Available. **Calendar System:** Semester, Summer session available **Enrollment:** Full-time 16,339, Part-time 27,711 **Faculty:** Full-time 535, Part-time 1,182 **Student-Faculty Ratio:** 28:1 **% Receiving Financial Aid:** 31 **Final Year or Final Semester Residency Requirement:** No **Regional Accreditation:** Southern Association of Colleges and Schools **Credit Hours For Degree:** 60 semester hours, Associates; 128 credit hours, Bachelors **ROTC:** Army, Navy **Professional Accreditation:** ACEN, ADA, CoARC, JRCEDMS, JRCEMTP, JRCERT.

VIRGINIA COLLEGE IN FORT PIERCE
2810 S Federal Hwy.
Fort Pierce, FL 34982-6331
Tel: (772)448-2000
Web Site: www.vc.edu
Type: Two-Year College **Sex:** Coed **Professional Accreditation:** ACICS.

VIRGINIA COLLEGE IN JACKSONVILLE
5940 Beach Blvd.
Jacksonville, FL 32207
Tel: (904)520-7400
Web Site: www.vc.edu
Type: Two-Year College **Sex:** Coed **Professional Accreditation:** ACICS.

VIRGINIA COLLEGE IN PENSACOLA
312 E Nine Mile Rd.
Ste. 34
Pensacola, FL 32514
Tel: (850)436-8444
Fax: (850)436-8470
Web Site: www.vc.edu
Type: Two-Year College **Sex:** Coed **Professional Accreditation:** ACICS.

WARNER UNIVERSITY
13895 US Hwy. 27
Lake Wales, FL 33859
Tel: (863)638-1426; Free: 800-309-9563
E-mail: admissions@warner.edu
Web Site: www.warner.edu
President/CEO: Gregory V. Hall
Admissions: Jason Roe
Type: Comprehensive **Sex:** Coed **Affiliation:** Church of God. **Scores:** 76% SAT V 400+; 75% SAT M 400+; 48% ACT 18-23; 6% ACT 24-29 **% Accepted:** 58 **Admission Plans:** Deferred Admission **Application Deadline:** Rolling **Application Fee:** $20.00 **H.S. Requirements:** High school diploma required; GED accepted **Costs Per Year:** Application fee: $20. One-time mandatory fee: $50. Comprehensive fee: $27,678 includes full-time tuition ($19,154), mandatory fees ($600), and college room and board ($7924). College room only: $4020. Full-time tuition and fees vary according to class time, degree level, and program. Room and board charges vary according to board plan. Part-time tuition: $375 per credit hour. Part-time tuition varies according to class time, degree level, and program. **Scholarships:** Available. **Calendar System:** Semester, Summer session available **Enrollment:** Full-time 778, Part-time 143 **Faculty:** Full-time 35, Part-time 64 **Student-**

Faculty Ratio: 16:1 **Exams:** SAT I or ACT. **% Receiving Financial Aid:** 66 **% Residing in College-Owned, -Operated, or -Affiliated Housing:** 41 **Regional Accreditation:** Southern Association of Colleges and Schools **Credit Hours For Degree:** 64 credit hours, Associates; 128 credit hours, Bachelors **Intercollegiate Athletics:** Baseball M; Basketball M & W; Cheerleading M & W; Cross-Country Running M & W; Golf M & W; Soccer M & W; Softball W; Tennis M & W; Track and Field M & W; Volleyball W

WEBBER INTERNATIONAL UNIVERSITY
1201 N Scenic Hwy.
Babson Park, FL 33827-0096
Tel: (863)638-1431; Free: 800-741-1844
Fax: (863)638-2823
E-mail: admissions@webber.edu
Web Site: www.webber.edu
President/CEO: Dr. Keith Wade
Financial Aid: Kathleen Wilson
Type: Comprehensive **Sex:** Coed **Scores:** 77% SAT V 400+; 82% SAT M 400+; 66% ACT 18-23; 7% ACT 24-29 **% Accepted:** 53 **Application Fee:** $35.00 **H.S. Requirements:** High school diploma required; GED accepted **Costs Per Year:** Application fee: $35. Comprehensive fee: $33,504 includes full-time tuition ($22,326), mandatory fees ($2466), and college room and board ($8712). College room only: $5592. Full-time tuition and fees vary according to class time, course load, and program. Room and board charges vary according to board plan, gender, and housing facility. Part-time tuition: $325 per semester hour. Part-time tuition varies according to class time, course load, and program. **Scholarships:** Available. **Calendar System:** Semester, Summer session available **Enrollment:** Full-time 649, Graduate full-time 37, Graduate part-time 8, Part-time 39 **Faculty:** Full-time 21, Part-time 26 **Student-Faculty Ratio:** 24:1 **Exams:** ACT essay component not used; ACT essay component used as validity check; ACT essay component used for admission; ACT essay component used in place of application essay; SAT I or ACT; SAT essay component not used; SAT essay component used as validity check; SAT essay component used for admission; SAT essay component used in place of application essay; SAT Reasoning. **% Receiving Financial Aid:** 68 **Final Year or Final Semester Residency Requirement:** No **Regional Accreditation:** Southern Association of Colleges and Schools **Credit Hours For Degree:** 60 credit hours, Associates; 120 credit hours, Bachelors **Intercollegiate Athletics:** Baseball M; Basketball M & W; Bowling M & W; Cheerleading M & W; Cross-Country Running M & W; Football M; Golf M & W; Soccer M & W; Softball W; Tennis M & W; Track and Field M & W; Volleyball W

WEST COAST UNIVERSITY
9250 NW 36th St.
Doral, FL 33178
Tel: (786)501-7070
Web Site: westcoastuniversity.edu
Type: Four-Year College **Sex:** Coed **Regional Accreditation:** Western Association of Colleges and Schools

WYOTECH DAYTONA
470 Destination Daytona Ln.
Ormond Beach, FL 32174
Tel: (904)255-0295; Free: 800-881-2AMI
Fax: (904)252-3523
Web Site: www.wyotech.edu
Type: Two-Year College **Sex:** Coed **Affiliation:** Zenith Education Group. **Professional Accreditation:** ACCSC.

YESHIVA GEDOLAH RABBINICAL COLLEGE
1140 Alton Rd.
Miami Beach, FL 33139
Tel: (305)673-5664
Fax: (305)532-9820
President/CEO: Rabbi Abraham Korf
Type: Comprehensive **Sex:** Men **Affiliation:** Jewish. **Admission Plans:** Open Admission **Professional Accreditation:** AARTS.

ABRAHAM BALDWIN AGRICULTURAL COLLEGE

2802 Moore Hwy.
Tifton, GA 31793
Tel: (229)391-5001; Free: 800-733-3653
Fax: (229)386-7006
E-mail: dwebb@abac.edu
Web Site: www.abac.edu
President/CEO: Dr. David C. Bridges
Admissions: Donna Webb
Financial Aid: Michael Wright
Type: Four-Year College **Sex:** Coed **Affiliation:** University System of Georgia. **% Accepted:** 79 **Admission Plans:** Deferred Admission; Early Admission **Application Fee:** $20.00 **H.S. Requirements:** High school diploma required; GED accepted **Costs Per Year:** Application fee: $20. State resident tuition: $3064 full-time, $102.13 per semester hour part-time. Nonresident tuition: $11,322 full-time, $377.40 per semester hour part-time. Mandatory fees: $1002 full-time, $374 per term part-time. College room and board: $9105. College room only: $6155. **Scholarships:** Available. **Calendar System:** Semester, Summer session available **Enrollment:** Full-time 2,475, Part-time 852 **Faculty:** Full-time 94, Part-time 68 **Student-Faculty Ratio:** 24:1 **Exams:** ACT essay component not used; SAT I or ACT; SAT essay component not used. **% Residing in College-Owned, -Operated, or -Affiliated Housing:** 32 **Final Year or Final Semester Residency Requirement:** No **Regional Accreditation:** Southern Association of Colleges and Schools **Credit Hours For Degree:** 60 hours, Associates; 120 hours, Bachelors **Professional Accreditation:** ACEN. **Intercollegiate Athletics:** Baseball M; Golf M; Soccer W; Softball W; Tennis M & W

AGNES SCOTT COLLEGE

141 E College Ave.
Decatur, GA 30030-3797
Tel: (404)471-6000; Free: 800-868-8602
Fax: (404)471-6414
E-mail: admission@agnesscott.edu
Web Site: www.agnesscott.edu
President/CEO: Dr. Elizabeth Kiss
Admissions: Alexa Gaeta
Financial Aid: Patrick Bonones
Type: Four-Year College **Sex:** Women **Affiliation:** Presbyterian Church (U.S.A.). **Scores:** 99% SAT V 400+; 99% SAT M 400+; 23.1% ACT 18-23; 52.7% ACT 24-29 **% Accepted:** 62 **Admission Plans:** Deferred Admission; Early Action; Early Admission; Early Decision Plan **Application Deadline:** March 15 **H.S. Requirements:** High school diploma required; GED accepted **Costs Per Year:** Comprehensive fee: $49,992 includes full-time tuition ($38,232), mandatory fees ($240), and college room and board ($11,520). Room and board charges vary according to board plan and housing facility. Part-time tuition: $1593 per credit. Part-time tuition varies according to course load. **Scholarships:** Available. **Calendar System:** Semester, Summer session available **Enrollment:** Full-time 876, Part-time 26 **Faculty:** Full-time 78, Part-time 39 **Student-Faculty Ratio:** 10:1 **Exams:** ACT essay component used for admission; SAT I and SAT II or ACT; SAT I or ACT; SAT essay component used for admission; SAT Subject. **% Receiving Financial Aid:** 78 **% Residing in College-Owned, -Operated, or -Affiliated Housing:** 87 **Final Year or Final Semester Residency Requirement:** Yes **Regional Accreditation:** Southern Association of Colleges and Schools **Credit Hours For Degree:** 128 semester hours, Bachelors **ROTC:** Air Force, Army **Intercollegiate Athletics:** Basketball W; Cross-Country Running W; Soccer W; Softball W; Tennis W; Volleyball W

ALBANY STATE UNIVERSITY

504 College Dr.
Albany, GA 31705-2717
Tel: (229)430-4600; Free: 800-822-7267
Fax: (229)430-3936
E-mail: enrollmentservices@asurams.edu
Web Site: www.asurams.edu
President/CEO: Dr. Arthur Dunning
Financial Aid: Thomas A. Harris
Type: Comprehensive **Sex:** Coed **Affiliation:** University System of Georgia. **Scores:** 87% SAT V 400+; 85% SAT M 400+; 53% ACT 18-23; 2% ACT 24-29 **% Accepted:** 47 **Admission Plans:** Deferred Admission; Early Admission **Application Deadline:** June 1 **Application Fee:** $25.00 **H.S. Requirements:** High school diploma required; GED accepted **Costs Per Year:** Application fee: $25. State resident tuition: $3886 full-time, $161.93 per credit hour part-time. Nonresident tuition: $14,142 full-time, $589.27 per credit hour part-time. Mandatory fees: $1602 full-time. Full-time tuition and fees vary according to course load and degree level. Part-time tuition varies according to course load and degree level. College room and board: $7788. College room only: $4940. Room and board charges vary according to board plan and housing facility. **Scholarships:** Available. **Calendar System:** Semester, Summer session available **Enrollment:** Full-time 2,780, Graduate full-time 208, Graduate part-time 386, Part-time 536 **Faculty:** Full-time 196, Part-time 24 **Student-Faculty Ratio:** 16:1 **Exams:** ACT essay component not used; SAT I or ACT; SAT essay component not used; SAT Reasoning. **% Receiving Financial Aid:** 94 **Final Year or Final Semester Residency Requirement:** No **Regional Accreditation:** Southern Association of Colleges and Schools **Credit Hours For Degree:** 120 credits, Bachelors **ROTC:** Army **Professional Accreditation:** ACBSP, ACEN, CSWE, NASPAA, NCATE. **Intercollegiate Athletics:** Baseball M; Basketball M & W; Cheerleading M & W; Cross-Country Running M & W; Football M; Softball W; Tennis W; Track and Field M & W; Volleyball W

ALBANY TECHNICAL COLLEGE

1704 S Slappey Blvd.
Albany, GA 31701
Tel: (229)430-3500; Free: 877-261-3113
Fax: (229)430-5155
E-mail: ldejesus@albanytech.edu
Web Site: www.albanytech.edu
President/CEO: Anthony O. Parker
Type: Two-Year College **Sex:** Coed **Affiliation:** Technical College System of Georgia. **Admission Plans:** Early Admission; Open Admission **Application Fee:** $23.00 **H.S. Requirements:** High school diploma required; GED accepted **Costs Per Year:** Application fee: $23. State resident tuition: $89 per credit hour part-time. Nonresident tuition: $178 per credit hour part-time. **Calendar System:** Quarter **Enrollment:** Full-time 1,537, Part-time 1,794 **Regional Accreditation:** Southern Association of Colleges and Schools **Professional Accreditation:** ADA, COE, JRCERT.

AMERICAN INTERCONTINENTAL UNIVERSITY ATLANTA

6600 Peachtree-Dunwoody Rd.
500 Embassy Row

Atlanta, GA 30328
Tel: (404)965-6500; Free: 800-353-1744
Fax: (404)965-6501
Web Site: www.aiuniv.edu
President/CEO: Stephen J. Tober
Admissions: Harold Saulsby
Type: Comprehensive **Sex:** Coed **Affiliation:** American InterContinental University. **Admission Plans:** Deferred Admission **Application Deadline:** Rolling **Application Fee:** $50.00 **H.S. Requirements:** High school diploma required; GED accepted **Calendar System:** Quarter **Enrollment:** Full-time 315, Part-time 119 **Regional Accreditation:** North Central Association of Colleges and Schools **Professional Accreditation:** ACBSP.

ANDREW COLLEGE

501 College St.
Cuthbert, GA 39840
Tel: (229)732-2171; Free: 800-664-9250
Fax: (229)732-2176
E-mail: admissions@andrewcollege.edu
Web Site: www.andrewcollege.edu
President/CEO: Dr. David Seyle
Admissions: Bridget Kurkowski
Type: Two-Year College **Sex:** Coed **Affiliation:** United Methodist. **Admission Plans:** Deferred Admission; Early Admission **Application Deadline:** August 15 **Application Fee:** $20.00 **H.S. Requirements:** High school diploma required; GED accepted **Scholarships:** Available. **Calendar System:** Semester, Summer session available **Faculty:** Full-time 17, Part-time 5 **Student-Faculty Ratio:** 12:1 **Exams:** SAT I or ACT. **Regional Accreditation:** Southern Association of Colleges and Schools **Credit Hours For Degree:** 64 credit hours, Associates **Intercollegiate Athletics:** Baseball M; Basketball W; Cross-Country Running M & W; Golf M & W; Soccer M & W; Softball W

ARGOSY UNIVERSITY, ATLANTA

980 Hammond Dr.
Ste. 100
Atlanta, GA 30328
Tel: (770)671-1200; Free: 888-671-4777
Fax: (770)671-0476
Web Site: www.argosy.edu/locations/atlanta
President/CEO: Dr. Steven Yoho
Type: University **Sex:** Coed **Affiliation:** Education Management Corporation. **Calendar System:** Semester **Regional Accreditation:** Western Association of Colleges and Schools **Professional Accreditation:** APA.

ARMSTRONG STATE UNIVERSITY

11935 Abercorn St.
Savannah, GA 31419-1997
Tel: (912)344-2576; Free: 800-633-2349
Fax: (912)921-5462
E-mail: admissions.info@armstrong.edu
Web Site: www.armstrong.edu
President/CEO: Dr. Linda M. Bleicken
Admissions: Dr. Georj Lewis
Type: Comprehensive **Sex:** Coed **Affiliation:** University System of Georgia. **Scores:** 98% SAT V 400+; 97% SAT M 400+; 70.2% ACT 18-23; 19.9% ACT 24-29 **Costs Per Year:** State resident tuition: $4858 full-time, $161.93 per credit hour part-time. Nonresident tuition: $17,678 full-time, $589.27 per credit hour part-time. Mandatory fees: $1474 full-time, $612 per term part-time. Full-time tuition and fees vary according to course load, location, and program. Part-time tuition and fees vary according to course load, location, and program. College room and board: $10,498. College room only: $6400. Room and board charges vary according to board plan and housing facility. **Scholarships:** Available. **Calendar System:** Semester, Summer session available **Enrollment:** Full-time 4,650, Graduate full-time 330, Graduate part-time 442, Part-time 1,681 **Faculty:** Full-time 265, Part-time 179 **Student-Faculty Ratio:** 18:1 **Exams:** ACT essay component used for advising; SAT I or ACT; SAT II; SAT essay component used for advising. **% Receiving Financial Aid:** 69 **% Residing in College-Owned, -Operated, or -Affiliated Housing:** 20 **Final Year or Final Semester Residency Requirement:** No **Regional Accreditation:** Southern Association of Colleges and Schools **Credit Hours For Degree:** 64 semester hours, Associates; 124 semester hours, Bachelors **ROTC:** Army, Navy **Professional Accreditation:** AACN, ABET, ADA, APTA, CAHME, CEPH, CoARC, JRCERT,

NAACLS, NASM, NCATE. **Intercollegiate Athletics:** Baseball M; Basketball M & W; Cross-Country Running M; Golf M & W; Soccer W; Softball W; Tennis M & W; Volleyball W

THE ART INSTITUTE OF ATLANTA

6600 Peachtree Dunwoody Rd., NE
100 Embassy Row
Atlanta, GA 30328
Tel: (770)394-8300; Free: 800-275-4242
Fax: (770)394-0008
Web Site: www.artinstitutes.edu/atlanta
President/CEO: Newton Myvett
Type: Four-Year College **Sex:** Coed **Affiliation:** Education Management Corporation. **Calendar System:** Quarter **Regional Accreditation:** Southern Association of Colleges and Schools **Professional Accreditation:** ACF, CIDA, NASAD.

ASHWORTH COLLEGE

6625 The Corners Pky.
Ste. 500
Norcross, GA 30092
Tel: (770)729-8400; Free: 800-957-5412
Fax: (770)729-9296
Web Site: www.ashworthcollege.edu
President/CEO: Gary Keisling
Admissions: Eric Ryall
Type: Comprehensive **Sex:** Coed **Affiliation:** Professional Career Development, LLC. **Admission Plans:** Open Admission **Application Fee:** $0.00 **H.S. Requirements:** High school diploma required; GED accepted **Calendar System:** Semester, Summer session available **Final Year or Final Semester Residency Requirement:** No **Credit Hours For Degree:** 20 courses, Associates; 40 courses, Bachelors **Professional Accreditation:** DEAC.

ATHENS TECHNICAL COLLEGE

800 US Hwy. 29 N
Athens, GA 30601-1500
Tel: (706)355-5000
Fax: (706)369-5753
E-mail: lreid@athenstech.edu
Web Site: www.athenstech.edu
President/CEO: Flora W. Tydings, EdD
Type: Two-Year College **Sex:** Coed **Affiliation:** Technical College System of Georgia. **Admission Plans:** Early Admission; Open Admission **Application Fee:** $20.00 **H.S. Requirements:** High school diploma required; GED accepted **Costs Per Year:** Application fee: $20. State resident tuition: $89 per credit hour part-time. Nonresident tuition: $178 per credit hour part-time. **Scholarships:** Available. **Calendar System:** Quarter **Enrollment:** Full-time 970, Part-time 3,229 **Regional Accreditation:** Southern Association of Colleges and Schools **Professional Accreditation:** ACBSP, ACEN, ADA, APTA, CoARC, JRCERT.

ATLANTA METROPOLITAN STATE COLLEGE

1630 Metropolitan Pky., SW
Atlanta, GA 30310-4498
Tel: (404)756-4000
E-mail: admissions@atlm.edu
Web Site: www.atlm.edu
President/CEO: Gary A. McGaha, PhD
Admissions: Audrey Reid
Type: Two-Year College **Sex:** Coed **Affiliation:** University System of Georgia. **Application Deadline:** July 15 **Application Fee:** $20.00 **H.S. Requirements:** High school diploma required; GED accepted **Scholarships:** Available. **Calendar System:** Semester, Summer session available **Student-Faculty Ratio:** 23:1 **Regional Accreditation:** Southern Association of Colleges and Schools **Credit Hours For Degree:** 60 credit hours, Associates **Professional Accreditation:** ACBSP. **Intercollegiate Athletics:** Basketball M & W

ATLANTA TECHNICAL COLLEGE

1560 Metropolitan Pky., SW
Atlanta, GA 30310
Tel: (404)225-4400
Fax: (404)752-0809

E-mail: vbillups@atlantatech.edu
Web Site: www.atlantatech.edu
President/CEO: Alvetta P. Thomas, EdD
Type: Two-Year College **Sex:** Coed **Affiliation:** Technical College System of Georgia. **Admission Plans:** Early Admission; Open Admission **Application Fee:** $25.00 **H.S. Requirements:** High school diploma required; GED accepted **Costs Per Year:** Application fee: $25. State resident tuition: $89 per credit hour part-time. Nonresident tuition: $178 per credit hour part-time. **Calendar System:** Quarter **Enrollment:** Full-time 1,413, Part-time 2,376 **Regional Accreditation:** Southern Association of Colleges and Schools **Professional Accreditation:** ADA, COE.

AUGUSTA TECHNICAL COLLEGE

3200 Augusta Tech Dr.
Augusta, GA 30906
Tel: (706)771-4000
Fax: (706)771-4016
E-mail: dwendt@augustatech.edu
Web Site: www.augustatech.edu
President/CEO: Terry Elam
Type: Two-Year College **Sex:** Coed **Affiliation:** Technical College System of Georgia. **Admission Plans:** Early Admission; Open Admission **Application Fee:** $25.00 **H.S. Requirements:** High school diploma required; GED accepted **Costs Per Year:** Application fee: $25. State resident tuition: $89 per credit hour part-time. Nonresident tuition: $176 per credit hour part-time. **Scholarships:** Available. **Calendar System:** Quarter **Enrollment:** Full-time 1,631, Part-time 2,859 **Regional Accreditation:** Southern Association of Colleges and Schools **Professional Accreditation:** ABET, ADA, AOTA, ARCST, CoARC, JRCECT.

AUGUSTA UNIVERSITY

1120 15th St.
Augusta, GA 30912
Tel: (706)721-0211; Free: 800-519-3388
Fax: (706)721-3461
E-mail: ksweeney@gru.edu
Web Site: www.gru.edu
President/CEO: Dr. Ricardo Azziz
Admissions: Scott Argo
Financial Aid: Brenda Burney
Type: Comprehensive **Sex:** Coed **Affiliation:** University System of Georgia. **Application Fee:** $50.00 **H.S. Requirements:** High school diploma required; GED accepted **Costs Per Year:** Application fee: $50. State resident tuition: $6592 full-time. Nonresident tuition: $21,300 full-time. Mandatory fees: $1690 full-time. Full-time tuition and fees vary according to course load, location, program, and reciprocity agreements. College room and board: $13,200. Room and board charges vary according to housing facility and location. **Scholarships:** Available. **Calendar System:** Semester, Summer session available **Enrollment:** Full-time 4,077, Graduate full-time 2,272, Graduate part-time 461, Part-time 1,147 **Faculty:** Full-time 960, Part-time 522 **% Receiving Financial Aid:** 58 **Final Year or Final Semester Residency Requirement:** No **Regional Accreditation:** Southern Association of Colleges and Schools **Credit Hours For Degree:** 61-62 for AASCJ and 63 for AACC and ASCC, Associates; 120 credits (exclusive of credit earned in lower division Physical Education courses), Bachelors **ROTC:** Army **Professional Accreditation:** AACN, AACSB, AANA, ACA, ADA, AHIMA, AOTA, APA, APTA, ARCMI, CoARC, JRCEDMS, JRCERT, JRCNMT, LCME/AMA, NAACLS, NCATE. **Intercollegiate Athletics:** Baseball M; Basketball M & W; Cross-Country Running M & W; Golf M & W; Softball W; Tennis M & W; Track and Field M & W

BAINBRIDGE STATE COLLEGE

2500 E Shotwell St.
Bainbridge, GA 39819
Tel: (229)248-2500; Free: 888-825-1715
Fax: (229)248-2525
E-mail: melanie.cleveland@bainbridge.edu
Web Site: www.bainbridge.edu
President/CEO: Shawn McGee
Admissions: Melanie Cleveland
Type: Two-Year College **Sex:** Coed **Affiliation:** University System of Georgia. **Admission Plans:** Early Admission **Application Deadline:** Rolling **Application Fee:** $0.00 **H.S. Requirements:** High school diploma required; GED accepted **Costs Per Year:** Application fee: $0. State resident tuition:

$2,181 full-time, $90.87 per credit hour part-time. Nonresident tuition: $8256 full-time, $344 per credit hour part-time. Mandatory fees: $1046 full-time, $523 per term part-time. Full-time tuition and fees vary according to course load and program. Part-time tuition and fees vary according to course load and program. **Scholarships:** Available. **Calendar System:** Semester, Summer session available **Enrollment:** Full-time 818, Part-time 1,583 **Faculty:** Full-time 62, Part-time 76 **Exams:** Other; SAT I or ACT. **Final Year or Final Semester Residency Requirement:** No **Regional Accreditation:** Southern Association of Colleges and Schools **Credit Hours For Degree:** 60 semester hours, Associates **Professional Accreditation:** ACEN.

BERRY COLLEGE

PO Box 490159
Mount Berry, GA 30149-0159
Tel: (706)232-5374; Free: 800-237-7942
Fax: (706)236-2248
E-mail: admissions@berry.edu
Web Site: www.berry.edu
President/CEO: Dr. Stephen R. Briggs
Admissions: Timothy Tarpley
Financial Aid: Donna Childres
Type: Comprehensive **Sex:** Coed **Affiliation:** interdenominational. **Scores:** 100% SAT V 400+; 100% SAT M 400+; 25% ACT 18-23; 58% ACT 24-29 **% Accepted:** 55 **Application Deadline:** July 22 **Application Fee:** $0.00 **H.S. Requirements:** High school diploma required; GED accepted **Costs Per Year:** Application fee: $0. Comprehensive fee: $43,186 includes full-time tuition ($31,770), mandatory fees ($226), and college room and board ($11,190). College room only: $6320. Room and board charges vary according to board plan and housing facility. Part-time tuition: $1059 per credit hour. **Scholarships:** Available. **Calendar System:** Semester, Summer session available **Enrollment:** Full-time 2,078, Graduate full-time 50, Graduate part-time 72, Part-time 45 **Faculty:** Full-time 167, Part-time 60 **Student-Faculty Ratio:** 12:1 **Exams:** SAT I or ACT; SAT Reasoning. **% Receiving Financial Aid:** 70 **% Residing in College-Owned, -Operated, or -Affiliated Housing:** 87 **Final Year or Final Semester Residency Requirement:** Yes **Regional Accreditation:** Southern Association of Colleges and Schools **Credit Hours For Degree:** 124 semester hours, Bachelors **Professional Accreditation:** AACSB, AAFCS, NASM, NCATE. **Intercollegiate Athletics:** Baseball M; Basketball M & W; Cross-Country Running M & W; Equestrian Sports W; Football M; Golf M & W; Lacrosse M & W; Soccer M & W; Softball W; Swimming and Diving M & W; Tennis M & W; Track and Field M & W; Volleyball W

BEULAH HEIGHTS UNIVERSITY

892 Berne St., SE
Atlanta, GA 30316
Tel: (404)627-2681; Free: 888-777-BHBC
Fax: (404)627-0702
E-mail: arthur.breland@beulah.edu
Web Site: www.beulah.org
President/CEO: Dr. Benson Karanja
Admissions: Willie Marcellin
Financial Aid: Patricia Banks
Type: Comprehensive **Sex:** Coed **Affiliation:** Pentecostal. **Admission Plans:** Early Admission; Open Admission **Application Deadline:** Rolling **Application Fee:** $30.00 **H.S. Requirements:** High school diploma required; GED accepted **Costs Per Year:** Application fee: $30. Tuition: $9090 full-time, $303 per credit hour part-time. Mandatory fees: $300 full-time. Full-time tuition and fees vary according to course load. College room only: $6000. Room charges vary according to housing facility. **Scholarships:** Available. **Calendar System:** Semester, Summer session available **Enrollment:** Full-time 170, Graduate full-time 77, Graduate part-time 120, Part-time 284 **Faculty:** Full-time 17, Part-time 65 **Student-Faculty Ratio:** 8:1 **Exams:** Other; SAT I or ACT. **% Receiving Financial Aid:** 32 **% Residing in College-Owned, -Operated, or -Affiliated Housing:** 10 **Final Year or Final Semester Residency Requirement:** No **Credit Hours For Degree:** 66 semester hours, Associates; 129 semester hours, Bachelors **Professional Accreditation:** ABHE, TRACS.

BRENAU UNIVERSITY

500 Washington St., SE
Gainesville, GA 30501
Tel: (770)534-6299; Free: 800-252-5119
Fax: (770)534-6114

E-mail: admissions@brenau.edu
Web Site: www.brenau.edu
President/CEO: Dr. Ed Schrader
Admissions: Ray Tatum
Financial Aid: Pam Barrett

Type: Comprehensive **Sex:** Women **Scores:** 90% SAT V 400+ **% Accepted:** 76 **Admission Plans:** Deferred Admission **Application Deadline:** Rolling **Application Fee:** $35.00 **H.S. Requirements:** High school diploma required; GED accepted **Costs Per Year:** Application fee: $35. Comprehensive fee: $37,876 includes full-time tuition ($25,478), mandatory fees ($400), and college room and board ($11,998). Part-time tuition and fees vary according to course load, location, and program. Part-time tuition: $849 per credit hour. Part-time mandatory fees: $200 per term. Part-time tuition and fees vary according to course load, location, and program. **Scholarships:** Available. **Calendar System:** Semester, Summer session available **Enrollment:** Full-time 1,000, Graduate full-time 645, Graduate part-time 548, Part-time 596 **Faculty:** Full-time 112, Part-time 214 **Student-Faculty Ratio:** 11:1 **Exams:** ACT essay component not used; SAT I or ACT; SAT essay component not used; SAT Reasoning. **% Receiving Financial Aid:** 80 **Final Year or Final Semester Residency Requirement:** No **Regional Accreditation:** Southern Association of Colleges and Schools **Professional Accreditation:** AACN, ACBSP, ACEN, AOTA, CIDA, NASD, NCATE. **Intercollegiate Athletics:** Basketball W; Cheerleading W; Crew W; Cross-Country Running W; Soccer W; Softball W; Swimming and Diving W; Tennis W; Volleyball W

BREWTON-PARKER COLLEGE
201 David-Eliza Fountain Cir.
Mount Vernon, GA 30445
Tel: (912)583-2241; Free: 800-342-1087
Fax: (912)583-4498
E-mail: admissions@bpc.edu
Web Site: www.bpc.edu
President/CEO: Dr. Mike Simoneaux
Financial Aid: Shannon Mullins

Type: Four-Year College **Sex:** Coed **Affiliation:** Southern Baptist. **Scores:** 81% SAT V 400+; 80% SAT M 400+; 46.4% ACT 18-23; 3.6% ACT 24-29 **Application Deadline:** August 1 **Application Fee:** $35.00 **H.S. Requirements:** High school diploma required; GED accepted **Costs Per Year:** Application fee: $35. One-time mandatory fee: $200. Comprehensive fee: $23,490 includes full-time tuition ($14,940), mandatory fees ($1200), and college room and board ($7350). College room only: $3150. Full-time tuition and fees vary according to course load, location, and program. Room and board charges vary according to board plan and housing facility. Part-time tuition: $415 per credit hour. Part-time mandatory fees: $640 per year. Part-time tuition and fees vary according to course load, location, and program. **Scholarships:** Available. **Calendar System:** Semester, Summer session available **Enrollment:** Full-time 468, Part-time 161 **Faculty:** Full-time 31, Part-time 54 **Student-Faculty Ratio:** 11:1 **Exams:** SAT I or ACT. **% Receiving Financial Aid:** 80 **% Residing in College-Owned, -Operated, or -Affiliated Housing:** 55 **Final Year or Final Semester Residency Requirement:** No **Regional Accreditation:** Southern Association of Colleges and Schools **Credit Hours For Degree:** 61 credit hours, Associates; 121 credit hours, Bachelors **Professional Accreditation:** NCATE. **Intercollegiate Athletics:** Baseball M; Basketball M & W; Cheerleading M & W; Cross-Country Running M & W; Soccer M & W; Softball W; Volleyball W; Wrestling M

BROWN COLLEGE OF COURT REPORTING
1900 Emery St. NW
Ste. 200
Atlanta, GA 30318
Tel: (404)876-1227
Fax: (404)876-4415
Web Site: www.bccr.edu
Type: Two-Year College **Sex:** Coed **Professional Accreditation:** COE.

CARVER COLLEGE
3870 Cascade Rd. SW
Atlanta, GA 30331
Tel: (404)527-4520
Fax: (404)527-4526
E-mail: info@carver.edu
Web Site: www.carver.edu

President/CEO: Pres. Robert W. Crummie
Admissions: Bertha Mack

Type: Four-Year College **Sex:** Coed **Affiliation:** nondenominational. **% Accepted:** 100 **Admission Plans:** Open Admission **Application Deadline:** August 1 **Application Fee:** $35.00 **H.S. Requirements:** High school diploma required; GED accepted **Costs Per Year:** Application fee: $35. Comprehensive fee: $16,460 includes full-time tuition ($9360), mandatory fees ($500), and college room and board ($6600). College room only: $4800. Full-time tuition and fees vary according to course load, location, and reciprocity agreements. Room and board charges vary according to board plan. Part-time tuition: $390 per credit hour. Part-time mandatory fees: $250 per term. Part-time tuition and fees vary according to course load, location, and reciprocity agreements. **Calendar System:** Semester, Summer session available **Enrollment:** Full-time 62, Part-time 42 **Faculty:** Full-time 2, Part-time 17 **Student-Faculty Ratio:** 6:1 **Exams:** SAT Reasoning; SAT Subject. **% Residing in College-Owned, -Operated, or -Affiliated Housing:** 35 **Final Year or Final Semester Residency Requirement:** No **Credit Hours For Degree:** 60 hours, Associates; 120 hours, Bachelors **Professional Accreditation:** ABHE. **Intercollegiate Athletics:** Basketball M & W

CENTRAL GEORGIA TECHNICAL COLLEGE
80 Cohen Walker Dr.
Warner Robins, GA 31088
Tel: (478)988-6800; Free: 866-430-0135
E-mail: tcarter@centralgatech.edu
Web Site: www.centralgatech.edu
Type: Two-Year College **Sex:** Coed **Affiliation:** Technical College System of Georgia. **Admission Plans:** Early Admission; Open Admission **Application Fee:** $25.00 **H.S. Requirements:** High school diploma required; GED accepted **Costs Per Year:** Application fee: $25. State resident tuition: $89 per credit hour part-time. Nonresident tuition: $178 per credit hour part-time. **Scholarships:** Available. **Calendar System:** Quarter **Enrollment:** Full-time 2,649, Part-time 5,183 **Regional Accreditation:** Southern Association of Colleges and Schools **Professional Accreditation:** ADA, COE, NAACLS.

CHAMBERLAIN COLLEGE OF NURSING
5775 Peachtree Dunwoody Rd. NE
Ste. A-100
Atlanta, GA 30342
Tel: (404)250-8500; Free: 877-751-5783
Fax: (404)250-8599
Web Site: www.chamberlain.edu
Type: Four-Year College **Sex:** Coed **Application Fee:** $95.00 **H.S. Requirements:** High school diploma required; GED accepted **Costs Per Year:** Application fee: $95. Tuition: $17,560 full-time, $665 per credit hour part-time. Mandatory fees: $600 full-time, $300 per term part-time. **Enrollment:** Full-time 457, Part-time 422 **Faculty:** Full-time 29, Part-time 73 **Student-Faculty Ratio:** 11:1 **Exams:** ACT essay component used for admission; SAT I or ACT; SAT essay component used for admission. **Regional Accreditation:** North Central Association of Colleges and Schools

CHATTAHOOCHEE TECHNICAL COLLEGE
980 S Cobb Dr., SE
Marietta, GA 30060
Tel: (770)528-4545
Fax: (770)528-4578
E-mail: mcusack@chattahoocheetech.edu
Web Site: www.chattahoocheetech.edu
President/CEO: Ron Newcomb
Type: Two-Year College **Sex:** Coed **Affiliation:** Technical College System of Georgia. **Admission Plans:** Early Admission; Open Admission **Application Fee:** $20.00 **H.S. Requirements:** High school diploma required; GED accepted **Costs Per Year:** Application fee: $20. State resident tuition: $89 per credit hour part-time. Nonresident tuition: $178 per credit hour part-time. **Scholarships:** Available. **Calendar System:** Quarter **Enrollment:** Full-time 2,902, Part-time 6,915 **Regional Accreditation:** Southern Association of Colleges and Schools **Professional Accreditation:** ABET, ACF.

CLARK ATLANTA UNIVERSITY
223 James P. Brawley Dr., SW
Atlanta, GA 30314
Tel: (404)880-8000; Free: 800-688-3228
Fax: (404)880-6174
E-mail: cauadmissions@cau.edu

Web Site: www.cau.edu
President/CEO: Dr. Ronald A. Johnson
Admissions: Lorri Rice
Type: University **Sex:** Coed **Affiliation:** United Methodist. **Scores:** 67% SAT V 400+; 60% SAT M 400+; 48% ACT 18-23; 8% ACT 24-29 **% Accepted:** 52 **Admission Plans:** Deferred Admission; Early Admission **Application Deadline:** June 1 **Application Fee:** $35.00 **H.S. Requirements:** High school diploma required; GED accepted **Costs Per Year:** Application fee: $35. Comprehensive fee: $32,423 includes full-time tuition ($19,880), mandatory fees ($2065), and college room and board ($10,478). Room and board charges vary according to board plan and housing facility. Part-time tuition: $828 per credit. Part-time mandatory fees: $948 per term. **Scholarships:** Available. **Calendar System:** Semester, Summer session available **Enrollment:** Full-time 2,629, Graduate full-time 657, Graduate part-time 263, Part-time 112 **Faculty:** Full-time 173, Part-time 119 **Student-Faculty Ratio:** 17:1 **Exams:** SAT I or ACT; SAT Reasoning. **% Receiving Financial Aid:** 91 **% Residing in College-Owned, -Operated, or -Affiliated Housing:** 64 **Final Year or Final Semester Residency Requirement:** Yes **Regional Accreditation:** Southern Association of Colleges and Schools **Credit Hours For Degree:** 122 credits, Bachelors **ROTC:** Army, Navy **Professional Accreditation:** AACSB, ACA, AHIMA, ALA, CSWE, NASPAA, NCATE. **Intercollegiate Athletics:** Baseball M; Basketball M & W; Cross-Country Running M & W; Football M; Softball W; Tennis W; Track and Field M & W; Volleyball W

CLAYTON STATE UNIVERSITY

2000 Clayton State Blvd.
Morrow, GA 30260-0285
Tel: (678)466-4000
E-mail: csc-info@clayton.edu
Web Site: www.clayton.edu
President/CEO: Dr. Thomas J. Hynes, Jr.
Admissions: Theadora Riley
Financial Aid: Patricia Barton
Type: Comprehensive **Sex:** Coed **Affiliation:** University System of Georgia. **Scores:** 96% SAT V 400+; 93% SAT M 400+; 70.2% ACT 18-23; 10.3% ACT 24-29 **% Accepted:** 39 **Admission Plans:** Deferred Admission; Early Admission **Application Deadline:** July 17 **Application Fee:** $40.00 **H.S. Requirements:** High school diploma required; GED accepted **Costs Per Year:** Application fee: $40. State resident tuition: $4740 full-time. Nonresident tuition: $17,246 full-time. Mandatory fees: $1454 full-time. Full-time tuition and fees vary according to course load. College room and board: $9926. Room and board charges vary according to board plan and housing facility. **Scholarships:** Available. **Calendar System:** Semester, Summer session available **Enrollment:** Full-time 3,626, Graduate full-time 135, Graduate part-time 290, Part-time 2,961 **Faculty:** Full-time 249, Part-time 146 **Student-Faculty Ratio:** 16:1 **Exams:** SAT I or ACT; SAT Reasoning. **% Receiving Financial Aid:** 87 **% Residing in College-Owned, -Operated, or -Affiliated Housing:** 14 **Final Year or Final Semester Residency Requirement:** No **Regional Accreditation:** Southern Association of Colleges and Schools **Credit Hours For Degree:** 60 credit hours, Associates; 120 credit hours, Bachelors **ROTC:** Air Force, Army, Navy **Professional Accreditation:** AACN, AACSB, ADA, NASM, NCATE. **Intercollegiate Athletics:** Basketball M & W; Cheerleading W; Cross-Country Running M & W; Golf M; Soccer M & W; Tennis W; Track and Field M & W

COASTAL PINES TECHNICAL COLLEGE

1701 Carswell Ave.
Waycross, GA 31503
Tel: (912)287-6584; Free: 877-ED-AT-OTC
Fax: (912)287-4865
E-mail: nmurphy@okefenokeetech.edu
Web Site: www.coastalpines.edu
Type: Two-Year College **Sex:** Coed **Affiliation:** Technical College System of Georgia. **Admission Plans:** Early Admission; Open Admission **Application Fee:** $20.00 **H.S. Requirements:** High school diploma required; GED accepted **Costs Per Year:** Application fee: $20. State resident tuition: $89 per credit hour part-time. Nonresident tuition: $178 per credit hour part-time. **Calendar System:** Quarter **Enrollment:** Full-time 599, Part-time 1,846 **Regional Accreditation:** Southern Association of Colleges and Schools **Professional Accreditation:** COE, NAACLS.

COLLEGE OF COASTAL GEORGIA

One College Dr.
Brunswick, GA 31520

Tel: (912)279-5700; Free: 800-675-7235
Fax: (912)262-3072
E-mail: admiss@ccga.edu
Web Site: www.ccga.edu
President/CEO: Dr. Gregory F. Aloia
Admissions: Clayton Daniels
Type: Four-Year College **Sex:** Coed **Affiliation:** University System of Georgia. **Scores:** 88% SAT V 400+; 79% SAT M 400+; 51% ACT 18-23; 14% ACT 24-29 **% Accepted:** 72 **Admission Plans:** Deferred Admission; Early Admission **Application Deadline:** August 24 **Application Fee:** $25.00 **H.S. Requirements:** High school diploma required; GED accepted **Costs Per Year:** Application fee: $25. State resident tuition: $3064 full-time. Nonresident tuition: $11,322 full-time. Mandatory fees: $1370 full-time. Full-time tuition and fees vary according to course load and location. College room and board: $8458. College room only: $5008. Room and board charges vary according to board plan, housing facility, and location. **Scholarships:** Available. **Calendar System:** Semester, Summer session available **Enrollment:** Full-time 1,966, Part-time 1,165 **Faculty:** Full-time 88, Part-time 102 **Student-Faculty Ratio:** 19:1 **Exams:** ACT essay component not used; SAT I or ACT; SAT essay component not used; SAT Reasoning; SAT Subject. **% Residing in College-Owned, -Operated, or -Affiliated Housing:** 15 **Final Year or Final Semester Residency Requirement:** No **Regional Accreditation:** Southern Association of Colleges and Schools **Credit Hours For Degree:** 62 semester hours, Associates; 120 semester hours, Bachelors **Professional Accreditation:** ACEN, ACF, JRCERT, NAACLS. **Intercollegiate Athletics:** Basketball M & W; Golf M & W; Softball W; Tennis M & W; Volleyball W

COLUMBUS STATE UNIVERSITY

4225 University Ave.
Columbus, GA 31907-5645
Tel: (706)568-2001; Free: 866-264-2035
Fax: (706)568-2123
E-mail: alexander_viola@columbusstate.edu
Web Site: www.columbusstate.edu
President/CEO: Dr. Chris Markwood
Admissions: Viola Alexander
Financial Aid: Patricia Garrett
Type: Comprehensive **Sex:** Coed **Affiliation:** University System of Georgia. **Scores:** 92% SAT V 400+; 89% SAT M 400+; 60.74% ACT 18-23; 16.48% ACT 24-29 **% Accepted:** 56 **Admission Plans:** Deferred Admission; Early Admission **Application Deadline:** June 30 **Application Fee:** $40.00 **H.S. Requirements:** High school diploma required; GED not accepted **Costs Per Year:** Application fee: $40. State resident tuition: $5226 full-time, $174.20 per credit hour part-time. Nonresident tuition: $18,444 full-time, $614.80 per credit hour part-time. Mandatory fees: $1830 full-time, $915 per term part-time. Full-time tuition and fees vary according to course load, degree level, and program. Part-time tuition and fees vary according to course load, degree level, and program. College room and board: $8780. College room only: $4820. Room and board charges vary according to board plan and housing facility. **Scholarships:** Available. **Calendar System:** Semester, Summer session available **Enrollment:** Full-time 4,937, Graduate full-time 507, Graduate part-time 996, Part-time 2,000 **Faculty:** Full-time 287, Part-time 238 **Student-Faculty Ratio:** 18:1 **Exams:** SAT I or ACT; SAT Reasoning. **% Receiving Financial Aid:** 72 **% Residing in College-Owned, -Operated, or -Affiliated Housing:** 20 **Final Year or Final Semester Residency Requirement:** No **Regional Accreditation:** Southern Association of Colleges and Schools **Credit Hours For Degree:** 63 credits, Associates; 123 credits, Bachelors **ROTC:** Army **Professional Accreditation:** AACN, AACSB, ACA, ACEN, NASAD, NASM, NAST, NCATE. **Intercollegiate Athletics:** Baseball M; Basketball M & W; Cheerleading M & W; Cross-Country Running M & W; Golf M & W; Riflery M & W; Soccer W; Softball W; Tennis M & W; Volleyball W

COLUMBUS TECHNICAL COLLEGE

928 Manchester Expy.
Columbus, GA 31904-6572
Tel: (706)649-1800
Fax: (706)649-1937
E-mail: taskew@columbustech.edu
Web Site: www.columbustech.edu
President/CEO: Lorette M. Hoover
Type: Two-Year College **Sex:** Coed **Affiliation:** Technical College System of Georgia. **Admission Plans:** Early Admission; Open Admission **Application**

Fee: $20.00 **H.S. Requirements:** High school diploma required; GED accepted **Costs Per Year:** Application fee: $20. State resident tuition: $89 per credit hour part-time. Nonresident tuition: $178 per credit hour part-time. **Scholarships:** Available. **Calendar System:** Quarter **Enrollment:** Full-time 981, Part-time 2,819 **Regional Accreditation:** Southern Association of Colleges and Schools **Professional Accreditation:** ACEN, ADA, ARCST.

COVENANT COLLEGE

14049 Scenic Hwy.
Lookout Mountain, GA 30750
Tel: (706)820-1560; Free: 888-451-2683
E-mail: admissions@covenant.edu
Web Site: www.covenant.edu
President/CEO: Dr. Neil B. Nielson
Admissions: Philip Howlett
Financial Aid: Margaret Stewart
Type: Comprehensive **Sex:** Coed **Affiliation:** Presbyterian Church in America. **Scores:** 99% SAT V 400+; 100% SAT M 400+; 18% ACT 18-23; 62.5% ACT 24-29 **% Accepted:** 94 **Admission Plans:** Deferred Admission; Early Admission **Application Fee:** $35.00 **H.S. Requirements:** High school diploma required; GED accepted **Costs Per Year:** Application fee: $35. Comprehensive fee: $40,490 includes full-time tuition ($30,440), mandatory fees ($880), and college room and board ($9170). Full-time tuition and fees vary according to course load. Room and board charges vary according to board plan and housing facility. Part-time tuition: $1295 per credit hour. Part-time tuition varies according to course load. **Scholarships:** Available. **Calendar System:** Semester, Summer session available **Enrollment:** Full-time 999, Graduate full-time 47, Graduate part-time 11, Part-time 45 **Faculty:** Full-time 65, Part-time 34 **Student-Faculty Ratio:** 13:1 **Exams:** ACT essay component used as validity check; SAT I or ACT; SAT essay component used as validity check; SAT Reasoning. **% Receiving Financial Aid:** 63 **% Residing in College-Owned, -Operated, or -Affiliated Housing:** 81 **Regional Accreditation:** Southern Association of Colleges and Schools **Credit Hours For Degree:** 62 units, Associates; 126 units, Bachelors **ROTC:** Army **Intercollegiate Athletics:** Baseball M; Basketball M & W; Cross-Country Running M & W; Golf M & W; Soccer M & W; Softball W; Tennis M & W; Volleyball W

DALTON STATE COLLEGE

650 College Dr.
Dalton, GA 30720
Tel: (706)272-4436; Free: 800-829-4436
Fax: (706)272-2530
Web Site: www.daltonstate.edu
President/CEO: Dr. John O. Schwenn
Admissions: Dr. Angela Harris
Financial Aid: Holly Woods
Type: Four-Year College **Sex:** Coed **Affiliation:** University System of Georgia. **Scores:** 78% SAT V 400+; 73% SAT M 400+; 55.27% ACT 18-23; 10.35% ACT 24-29 **% Accepted:** 36 **Admission Plans:** Deferred Admission; Open Admission **Application Deadline:** July 1 **Application Fee:** $30.00 **H.S. Requirements:** High school diploma required; GED accepted **Costs Per Year:** Application fee: $30. State resident tuition: $3156 full-time, $105.20 per credit hour part-time. Nonresident tuition: $11,662 full-time, $388.72 per credit hour part-time. Mandatory fees: $1082 full-time. College room and board: $8446. College room only: $5290. **Scholarships:** Available. **Calendar System:** Semester, Summer session available **Enrollment:** Full-time 3,248, Part-time 1,792 **Faculty:** Full-time 167, Part-time 77 **Exams:** ACT essay component not used; SAT I or ACT; SAT essay component not used; SAT Reasoning; SAT Subject. **% Receiving Financial Aid:** 52 **% Residing in College-Owned, -Operated, or -Affiliated Housing:** 5 **Regional Accreditation:** Southern Association of Colleges and Schools **Credit Hours For Degree:** 60 semester hours, Associates; 120 semester hours, Bachelors **Professional Accreditation:** AACSB, AAMAE, ACEN, NAACLS, NCATE. **Intercollegiate Athletics:** Basketball M & W; Golf W; Softball M & W; Table Tennis M & W; Tennis M & W; Volleyball M & W

DARTON STATE COLLEGE

2400 Gillionville Rd.
Albany, GA 31707-3098
Tel: (229)317-6000; Free: 866-775-1214
Fax: (229)430-2926
E-mail: info@darton.edu
Web Site: www.darton.edu

President/CEO: Dr. Paul Jones
Admissions: Susan Bowen
Type: Two-Year College **Sex:** Coed **Affiliation:** University System of Georgia. **Scores:** 72% SAT V 400+; 74% SAT M 400+; 32% ACT 18-23; 9% ACT 24-29 **% Accepted:** 48 **Admission Plans:** Deferred Admission; Open Admission **Application Deadline:** August 1 **Application Fee:** $20.00 **H.S. Requirements:** High school diploma required; GED accepted **Scholarships:** Available. **Calendar System:** Semester, Summer session available **Enrollment:** Full-time 2,577, Part-time 3,043 **Faculty:** Full-time 133, Part-time 132 **Student-Faculty Ratio:** 25:1 **Exams:** Other; SAT I or ACT; SAT II. **Final Year or Final Semester Residency Requirement:** No **Regional Accreditation:** Southern Association of Colleges and Schools **Credit Hours For Degree:** 60 semester hours, Associates; 121 semester hours, Bachelors **ROTC:** Army **Professional Accreditation:** ACEN, ADA, AHIMA, AOTA, APTA, CoARC, NAACLS. **Intercollegiate Athletics:** Baseball M; Basketball W; Cross-Country Running M & W; Golf M; Soccer M & W; Softball W; Swimming and Diving M & W; Wrestling M

DEVRY UNIVERSITY (ALPHARETTA)

2555 Northwinds Pky.
Alpharetta, GA 30009
Tel: (770)521-4900; Free: 866-338-7941
Web Site: www.devry.edu
Financial Aid: David Pickett
Type: Comprehensive **Sex:** Coed **Affiliation:** DeVry University. **Application Deadline:** Rolling **Costs Per Year:** Tuition: $17,052 full-time, $609 per credit hour part-time. Mandatory fees: $80 full-time, $40 per term part-time. **Scholarships:** Available. **Calendar System:** Semester **% Receiving Financial Aid:** 74 **Regional Accreditation:** North Central Association of Colleges and Schools **Professional Accreditation:** ABET, ACBSP.

DEVRY UNIVERSITY (ATLANTA)

100 Galleria Pky. SE, Ste. 100
Atlanta, GA 30339
Tel: (678)424-5630
Fax: (678)424-5631
Web Site: www.devry.edu/universities/us-locations/georgia/cobb-galleria-center.html
Type: Comprehensive **Sex:** Coed **Costs Per Year:** Tuition: $17,052 full-time, $609 per credit hour part-time. Mandatory fees: $80 full-time, $40 per term part-time. **Regional Accreditation:** North Central Association of Colleges and Schools

DEVRY UNIVERSITY (DECATUR)

1 W Ct. Sq.
Ste. 100
Decatur, GA 30030-2556
Tel: (404)292-7900; Free: 866-338-7941
Fax: (404)292-2321
Web Site: www.devry.edu
Type: Comprehensive **Sex:** Coed **Affiliation:** DeVry University. **Application Fee:** $40.00 **H.S. Requirements:** High school diploma required; GED accepted **Costs Per Year:** Application fee: $40. Tuition: $17,052 full-time, $609 per credit hour part-time. Mandatory fees: $80 full-time, $40 per term part-time. **Scholarships:** Available. **Calendar System:** Semester **Enrollment:** Full-time 598, Graduate full-time 32, Graduate part-time 205, Part-time 1,086 **Faculty:** Full-time 28, Part-time 120 **Student-Faculty Ratio:** 16:1 **Exams:** ACT essay component used for admission; ACT essay component used for placement; SAT essay component used for admission; SAT essay component used for placement. **Regional Accreditation:** North Central Association of Colleges and Schools **Credit Hours For Degree:** 66 credit hours, Associates; 122 credit hours, Bachelors **Professional Accreditation:** ABET, ACBSP.

DEVRY UNIVERSITY (DULUTH)

3505 Koger Blvd., Ste. 170
Duluth, GA 30096-7671
Tel: (678)380-9780; Free: 866-338-7941
Fax: (678)924-0958
Web Site: www.devry.edu
Type: Comprehensive **Sex:** Coed **Application Deadline:** Rolling **Costs Per Year:** Tuition: $17,052 full-time, $609 per credit hour part-time. Mandatory

fees: $80 full-time, $40 per term part-time. **Calendar System:** Semester **Regional Accreditation:** North Central Association of Colleges and Schools **Professional Accreditation:** ACBSP.

EAST GEORGIA STATE COLLEGE
131 College Cir.
Swainsboro, GA 30401-2699
Tel: (478)289-2000
Fax: (478)289-2038
E-mail: kjones@ega.edu
Web Site: www.ega.edu
President/CEO: Dr. John Black
Admissions: Karen S. Jones
Type: Two-Year College **Sex:** Coed **Affiliation:** University System of Georgia. **Admission Plans:** Deferred Admission; Early Admission **Application Deadline:** Rolling **Application Fee:** $20.00 **H.S. Requirements:** High school diploma required; GED accepted **Costs Per Year:** Application fee: $20. State resident tuition: $2726 full-time, $90.87 per credit hour part-time. Nonresident tuition: $10,320 full-time, $344 per credit hour part-time. Mandatory fees: $1329 full-time, $443 per term part-time. Full-time tuition and fees vary according to course load and location. Part-time tuition and fees vary according to course load and location. College room and board: $3853. College room only: $2812. **Scholarships:** Available. **Calendar System:** Semester, Summer session available **Student-Faculty Ratio:** 26:1 **Regional Accreditation:** Southern Association of Colleges and Schools **Credit Hours For Degree:** 64 semester hours, Associates

EMMANUEL COLLEGE
181 Springs St.
Franklin Springs, GA 30639-0129
Tel: (706)245-7226; Free: 800-860-8800
E-mail: admissions@ec.edu
Web Site: www.ec.edu
President/CEO: Dr. Ronald G. White
Admissions: Kay Clifton
Financial Aid: Niki Stinson
Type: Four-Year College **Sex:** Coed **Affiliation:** Pentecostal Holiness Church. **% Accepted:** 35 **Admission Plans:** Deferred Admission; Early Admission **Application Deadline:** August 1 **Application Fee:** $25.00 **H.S. Requirements:** High school diploma required; GED accepted **Costs Per Year:** Application fee: $25. Comprehensive fee: $26,070 includes full-time tuition ($18,540), mandatory fees ($330), and college room and board ($7200). Room and board charges vary according to housing facility. Part-time tuition: $775 per credit hour. **Scholarships:** Available. **Calendar System:** Semester, Summer session available **Enrollment:** Full-time 758, Part-time 126 **Faculty:** Full-time 48, Part-time 41 **Student-Faculty Ratio:** 13:1 **Exams:** SAT I or ACT; SAT Reasoning. **% Receiving Financial Aid:** 79 **% Residing in College-Owned, -Operated, or -Affiliated Housing:** 59 **Final Year or Final Semester Residency Requirement:** No **Regional Accreditation:** Southern Association of Colleges and Schools **Credit Hours For Degree:** 60 semester hours, Associates; 124 semester hours, Bachelors **Intercollegiate Athletics:** Archery M & W; Baseball M; Basketball M & W; Bowling M & W; Cross-Country Running M & W; Golf M & W; Lacrosse M & W; Riflery M & W; Soccer M & W; Softball W; Swimming and Diving M & W; Tennis M & W; Track and Field M & W; Volleyball M & W; Wrestling M & W

EMORY UNIVERSITY
201 Dowman Dr.
Atlanta, GA 30322-1100
Tel: (404)727-6123; Free: 800-727-6036
E-mail: admiss@emory.edu
Web Site: www.emory.edu
President/CEO: Dr. James W. Wagner
Admissions: Dr. John Latting
Financial Aid: John Leach
Type: University **Sex:** Coed **Affiliation:** Methodist. **Scores:** 100% SAT V 400+; 100% SAT M 400+; 1.9% ACT 18-23; 28.8% ACT 24-29 **% Accepted:** 24 **Admission Plans:** Deferred Admission; Early Action; Early Admission **Application Deadline:** January 1 **Application Fee:** $75.00 **H.S. Requirements:** High school diploma required; GED not accepted. For transfer students with a full year of college credit: High school diploma or equivalent not required **Costs Per Year:** Application fee: $75. Comprehensive fee: $61,440 includes full-time tuition ($47,300), mandatory fees ($654), and college room and board ($13,486). College room only: $7914. Full-time tuition

and fees vary according to degree level and location. Room and board charges vary according to board plan, housing facility, location, and student level. Part-time tuition: $1971 per credit hour. **Scholarships:** Available. **Calendar System:** Semester, Summer session available **Enrollment:** Full-time 6,751, Graduate full-time 5,632, Graduate part-time 1,289, Part-time 116 **Faculty:** Full-time 1,023, Part-time 154 **Student-Faculty Ratio:** 8:1 **Exams:** ACT essay component used for admission; SAT I or ACT; SAT essay component used for admission; SAT Reasoning; SAT Subject. **% Receiving Financial Aid:** 43 **% Residing in College-Owned, -Operated, or -Affiliated Housing:** 64 **Final Year or Final Semester Residency Requirement:** No **Regional Accreditation:** Southern Association of Colleges and Schools **Credit Hours For Degree:** 127 semester hours, Bachelors **ROTC:** Air Force, Army, Navy **Professional Accreditation:** AACN, AACSB, AALS, ABA, ACNM, ACIPE, AND, APA, APTA, ARCEAA, ATS, CEPH, JCAHPO, JRCERT, LCME/AMA, NCATE, NPWH. **Intercollegiate Athletics:** Badminton M & W; Baseball M; Basketball M & W; Crew M & W; Cross-Country Running M & W; Equestrian Sports M & W; Fencing M & W; Field Hockey M & W; Golf M & W; Gymnastics W; Lacrosse M & W; Rock Climbing M & W; Rugby M; Sailing M & W; Soccer M & W; Softball W; Squash M & W; Swimming and Diving M & W; Tennis M & W; Track and Field M & W; Ultimate Frisbee M & W; Volleyball M & W; Water Polo M & W; Weight Lifting M & W

EMORY UNIVERSITY, OXFORD COLLEGE
100 Hamill St.
Oxford, GA 30054
Tel: (770)784-8888; Free: 800-723-8328
Fax: (770)784-8359
E-mail: oxadmission@emory.edu
Web Site: oxford.emory.edu
President/CEO: Dr. Stephen Bowen
Admissions: Jennifer B. Taylor
Type: Two-Year College **Sex:** Coed **Affiliation:** Methodist; Emory University. **Scores:** 100% SAT V 400+; 100% SAT M 400+; 2.1% ACT 18-23; 45.7% ACT 24-29 **% Accepted:** 39 **Admission Plans:** Deferred Admission; Early Action; Early Admission **Application Deadline:** January 1 **Application Fee:** $75.00 **H.S. Requirements:** High school diploma required; GED not accepted **Costs Per Year:** Application fee: $75. Comprehensive fee: $55,260 includes full-time tuition ($42,600), mandatory fees ($654), and college room and board ($12,006). College room only: $7788. Part-time tuition: $1775 per credit hour. **Scholarships:** Available. **Calendar System:** Semester, Summer session available **Enrollment:** Full-time 932, Part-time 4 **Student-Faculty Ratio:** 12:1 **Exams:** ACT essay component used for admission; SAT I or ACT; SAT essay component used for admission; SAT Reasoning; SAT Subject. **% Residing in College-Owned, -Operated, or -Affiliated Housing:** 99 **Final Year or Final Semester Residency Requirement:** No **Regional Accreditation:** Southern Association of Colleges and Schools **Credit Hours For Degree:** 67 semester hours, Associates **ROTC:** Air Force, Army, Navy **Intercollegiate Athletics:** Basketball M; Soccer W; Tennis M & W

EVEREST INSTITUTE
1750 Beaver Ruin Rd.
Ste. 500
Norcross, GA 30093
Tel: (770)921-1085
Web Site: www.everest.edu
Type: Two-Year College **Sex:** Coed **Affiliation:** Zenith Education Group. **Professional Accreditation:** ACCSC.

FORT VALLEY STATE UNIVERSITY
1005 State University Dr.
Fort Valley, GA 31030
Tel: (478)825-6211; Free: 877-462-3878
Fax: (478)825-6394
E-mail: admissap@fvsu.edu
Web Site: www.fvsu.edu
President/CEO: Ivelaw Griffith
Admissions: Donald Moore
Financial Aid: James Stotts
Type: Comprehensive **Sex:** Coed **Affiliation:** University System of Georgia. **Scores:** 86% SAT V 400+; 83% SAT M 400+; 57.03% ACT 18-23; 3.13% ACT 24-29 **% Accepted:** 24 **Admission Plans:** Deferred Admission; Early Admission **Application Fee:** $20.00 **H.S. Requirements:** High school

diploma required; GED accepted **Scholarships:** Available. **Calendar System:** Semester, Summer session available **Enrollment:** Full-time 1,947, Graduate full-time 149, Graduate part-time 216, Part-time 282 **Faculty:** Full-time 129, Part-time 13 **Student-Faculty Ratio:** 16:1 **Exams:** SAT I or ACT. **% Receiving Financial Aid:** 100 **% Residing in College-Owned, -Operated, or -Affiliated Housing:** 40 **Regional Accreditation:** Southern Association of Colleges and Schools **Credit Hours For Degree:** 60 hours, Associates; 120 hours, Bachelors **ROTC:** Army **Professional Accreditation:** AAFCS, ABET, ACA, CORE, MACTE, NCATE. **Intercollegiate Athletics:** Basketball M & W; Football M; Golf M; Tennis M & W; Track and Field M & W; Volleyball W

FORTIS COLLEGE

2108 Cobb Pky.
Smyrna, GA 30080
Tel: (770)980-0002; Free: 855-4-FORTIS
Fax: (770)980-0811
Web Site: www.fortis.edu
Type: Two-Year College **Sex:** Coed **Professional Accreditation:** ABHES.

GEORGIA CHRISTIAN UNIVERSITY

6789 Peachtree Industrial Blvd.
Atlanta, GA 30360
Tel: (770)279-0507
Fax: (770)279-0308
Web Site: www.gcuniv.edu
Type: Comprehensive **Sex:** Coed **Affiliation:** Christian. **Professional Accreditation:** ATS, TRACS.

GEORGIA COLLEGE & STATE UNIVERSITY

231 W Hancock St.
Milledgeville, GA 31061
Tel: (478)445-5004; Free: 800-342-0471
Fax: (478)445-6795
E-mail: admissions@gcsu.edu
Web Site: www.gcsu.edu
President/CEO: Dr. Steve Michael Dorman
Admissions: Ramon Blakley
Financial Aid: Cathy Crawley
Type: Comprehensive **Sex:** Coed **Affiliation:** University System of Georgia. **Scores:** 100% SAT V 400+; 100% SAT M 400+; 36% ACT 18-23; 58% ACT 24-29 **% Accepted:** 76 **Admission Plans:** Deferred Admission; Early Admission; Early Decision Plan **Application Deadline:** April 1 **Application Fee:** $40.00 **H.S. Requirements:** High school diploma required; GED accepted **Costs Per Year:** Application fee: $40. State resident tuition: $7180 full-time. Nonresident tuition: $25,528 full-time. Mandatory fees: $1990 full-time. Full-time tuition and fees vary according to course load, location, and program. College room and board: $11,612. College room only: $6124. Room and board charges vary according to board plan and housing facility. **Scholarships:** Available. **Calendar System:** Semester, Summer session available **Enrollment:** Full-time 5,586, Graduate full-time 313, Graduate part-time 540, Part-time 450 **Faculty:** Full-time 337, Part-time 99 **Student-Faculty Ratio:** 17:1 **Exams:** SAT I or ACT; SAT II; SAT Reasoning. **% Receiving Financial Aid:** 49 **% Residing in College-Owned, -Operated, or -Affiliated Housing:** 38 **Final Year or Final Semester Residency Requirement:** No **Regional Accreditation:** Southern Association of Colleges and Schools **Credit Hours For Degree:** 120 semester hours, Bachelors **ROTC:** Army **Professional Accreditation:** AACSB, ACEN, NASM, NASPAA, NCATE. **Intercollegiate Athletics:** Baseball M; Basketball M & W; Cheerleading M & W; Cross-Country Running M & W; Golf M; Soccer W; Softball W; Tennis M & W; Volleyball W

GEORGIA GWINNETT COLLEGE

1000 University Ctr. Ln.
Lawrenceville, GA 30043
Tel: (678)407-5000; Free: 877-704-4422
E-mail: ggcadmissions@ggc.edu
Web Site: www.ggc.edu
President/CEO: Dr. Stanley C. Preczewski
Type: Four-Year College **Sex:** Coed **Affiliation:** University System of Georgia. **Scores:** 78% SAT V 400+; 79% SAT M 400+; 46.68% ACT 18-23; 12.13% ACT 24-29 **% Accepted:** 84 **Admission Plans:** Deferred Admission; Open Admission **Application Deadline:** June 1 **Application Fee:** $20.00 **H.S. Requirements:** High school diploma required; GED accepted

Costs Per Year: Application fee: $20. State resident tuition: $3844 full-time, $128.13 per credit hour part-time. Nonresident tuition: $14,348 full-time, $478.27 per credit hour part-time. Mandatory fees: $1804 full-time, $882 per term part-time. Full-time tuition and fees vary according to reciprocity agreements. Part-time tuition and fees vary according to reciprocity agreements. College room and board: $12,300. College room only: $8476. Room and board charges vary according to housing facility. **Calendar System:** Semester, Summer session available **Enrollment:** Full-time 7,794, Part-time 3,674 **Faculty:** Full-time 419, Part-time 231 **Student-Faculty Ratio:** 18:1 **Exams:** ACT essay component not used; SAT I or ACT; SAT essay component not used; SAT Reasoning; SAT Subject. **% Residing in College-Owned, -Operated, or -Affiliated Housing:** 7 **Final Year or Final Semester Residency Requirement:** No **Regional Accreditation:** Southern Association of Colleges and Schools **Credit Hours For Degree:** 123 credit hours, Bachelors **ROTC:** Army **Intercollegiate Athletics:** Baseball M; Soccer M & W; Softball W; Tennis M & W

GEORGIA HIGHLANDS COLLEGE

3175 Cedartown Hwy.
Rome, GA 30161
Tel: (706)802-5000; Free: 800-332-2406
Fax: (706)295-6610
E-mail: sdavis@highlands.edu
Web Site: www.highlands.edu
President/CEO: Dr. Donald Green
Admissions: Sandie Davis
Type: Two-Year College **Sex:** Coed **Affiliation:** University System of Georgia. **Scores:** 83% SAT V 400+; 80% SAT M 400+; 59% ACT 18-23; 9% ACT 24-29 **% Accepted:** 81 **Admission Plans:** Deferred Admission **Application Deadline:** Rolling **Application Fee:** $30.00 **H.S. Requirements:** High school diploma required; GED accepted **Costs Per Year:** Application fee: $30. State resident tuition: $3,115 full-time, $90.87 per credit hour part-time. Nonresident tuition: $9190 full-time, $344 per credit hour part-time. Mandatory fees: $934 full-time, $347 per term part-time. Full-time tuition and fees vary according to course load and location. Part-time tuition and fees vary according to course load and location. **Scholarships:** Available. **Calendar System:** Semester, Summer session available **Enrollment:** Full-time 2,681, Part-time 3,067 **Faculty:** Full-time 123, Part-time 154 **Student-Faculty Ratio:** 21:1 **Exams:** ACT essay component not used; Other; SAT I and SAT II or ACT; SAT I or ACT; SAT essay component not used. **Final Year or Final Semester Residency Requirement:** No **Regional Accreditation:** Southern Association of Colleges and Schools **Credit Hours For Degree:** 60 semester hours, Associates; 127 semester hours, Bachelors **Professional Accreditation:** ACEN, ADA. **Intercollegiate Athletics:** Baseball M & W; Basketball M & W; Softball M & W

GEORGIA INSTITUTE OF TECHNOLOGY

225 N Ave., NW
Atlanta, GA 30332-0001
Tel: (404)894-2000
Fax: (404)853-9163
E-mail: admission@gatech.edu
Web Site: www.gatech.edu
President/CEO: Dr. G.P. 'Bud' Peterson
Admissions: Rick A. Clark, Jr.
Financial Aid: Marie Mons
Type: University **Sex:** Coed **Affiliation:** University System of Georgia. **Scores:** 100% SAT V 400+; 100% SAT M 400+; 1.06% ACT 18-23; 17.89% ACT 24-29 **% Accepted:** 32 **Admission Plans:** Deferred Admission; Early Admission; Early Decision Plan; Preferred Admission **Application Deadline:** January 10 **Application Fee:** $75.00 **H.S. Requirements:** High school diploma required; GED not accepted **Costs Per Year:** Application fee: $75. State resident tuition: $9812 full-time, $2916 per term part-time. Nonresident tuition: $30,004 full-time, $8903 per term part-time. Mandatory fees: $2392 full-time, $1196 per term part-time. Part-time tuition and fees vary according to course load. College room and board: $13,194. College room only: $8740. Room and board charges vary according to board plan and housing facility. **Scholarships:** Available. **Calendar System:** Semester, Summer session available **Enrollment:** Full-time 13,668, Graduate full-time 5,873, Graduate part-time 3,511, Part-time 1,216 **Faculty:** Full-time 1,076, Part-time 99 **Student-Faculty Ratio:** 19:1 **Exams:** ACT essay component used for admission; SAT I or ACT; SAT essay component used for admission; SAT Reasoning. **% Receiving Financial Aid:** 42 **% Residing in College-Owned, -Operated, or -Affiliated Housing:** 53 **Final Year or Final**

Semester Residency Requirement: No **Regional Accreditation:** Southern Association of Colleges and Schools **Credit Hours For Degree:** 122 semester hours (minimum-varies by program), Bachelors **ROTC:** Air Force, Army, Navy **Professional Accreditation:** AACSB, ABET, ACCE, ACSP, NAAB, NASAD. **Intercollegiate Athletics:** Baseball M; Basketball M & W; Cross-Country Running M & W; Football M; Golf M; Softball W; Swimming and Diving M & W; Tennis M & W; Track and Field M & W; Volleyball W

GEORGIA MILITARY COLLEGE

201 E Greene St.
Old Capitol Bldg.
Milledgeville, GA 31061-3398
Tel: (478)387-4900; Free: 800-342-0413
Fax: (478)445-2688
E-mail: rknight@gmc.edu
Web Site: www.gmc.edu
President/CEO: Gen. William B. Caldwell, IV
Admissions: Robin Knight
Financial Aid: Alisa W. Stephens
Type: Two-Year College **Sex:** Coed **Admission Plans:** Deferred Admission; Early Admission; Open Admission **Application Deadline:** Rolling **Application Fee:** $35.00 **H.S. Requirements:** High school diploma required; GED accepted **Costs Per Year:** Application fee: $35. State resident tuition: $5445 full-time, $121 per quarter hour part-time. Nonresident tuition: $5445 full-time, $121 per quarter hour part-time. Mandatory fees: $683 full-time, $13.75 per quarter hour part-time, $13.75. Full-time tuition and fees vary according to location. Part-time tuition and fees vary according to location. College room and board: $7500. College room only: $3150. Room and board charges vary according to location. **Scholarships:** Available. **Calendar System:** Quarter, Summer session available **Enrollment:** Full-time 4,754, Part-time 3,122 **Faculty:** Full-time 120, Part-time 261 **Student-Faculty Ratio:** 23:1 **% Residing in College-Owned, -Operated, or -Affiliated Housing:** 3 **Final Year or Final Semester Residency Requirement:** No **Regional Accreditation:** Southern Association of Colleges and Schools **Credit Hours For Degree:** 90 quarter hours, Associates; 180 quarter hours (BAS only), Bachelors **ROTC:** Army **Intercollegiate Athletics:** Cross-Country Running M & W; Football M; Golf M & W; Riflery M & W; Soccer M & W; Softball W

GEORGIA NORTHWESTERN TECHNICAL COLLEGE

One Maurice Culberson Dr.
Rome, GA 30161
Tel: (706)295-6963; Free: 866-983-GNTC
Fax: (706)295-6944
E-mail: dmcburnett@gntc.edu
Web Site: www.gntc.edu
President/CEO: Pete McDonald
Type: Two-Year College **Sex:** Coed **Affiliation:** Technical College System of Georgia. **Admission Plans:** Early Admission; Open Admission **Application Fee:** $15.00 **H.S. Requirements:** High school diploma required; GED accepted **Costs Per Year:** Application fee: $15. State resident tuition: $89 per credit hour part-time. Nonresident tuition: $178 per credit hour part-time. **Scholarships:** Available. **Calendar System:** Quarter **Enrollment:** Full-time 1,803, Part-time 4,071 **Regional Accreditation:** Southern Association of Colleges and Schools **Professional Accreditation:** ACEN, COE.

GEORGIA PIEDMONT TECHNICAL COLLEGE

495 N Indian Creek Dr.
Clarkston, GA 30021-2397
Tel: (404)297-9522
Fax: (404)294-4234
E-mail: richardt@dekalbtech.edu
Web Site: www.gptc.edu
President/CEO: Jabari Simama
Financial Aid: Genevieve Randall
Type: Two-Year College **Sex:** Coed **Affiliation:** Technical College System of Georgia. **Admission Plans:** Early Admission; Open Admission **Application Fee:** $20.00 **H.S. Requirements:** High school diploma required; GED accepted **Costs Per Year:** Application fee: $20. State resident tuition: $89 per credit hour part-time. Nonresident tuition: $178 per credit hour part-time. **Scholarships:** Available. **Calendar System:** Quarter **Enrollment:** Full-time 927, Part-time 2,981 **Regional Accreditation:** Southern Association of Colleges and Schools **Professional Accreditation:** ABET, COA, NAACLS.

GEORGIA SOUTHERN UNIVERSITY

1332 Southern Dr.
Statesboro, GA 30458
Tel: (912)478-4636
Fax: (912)681-5635
E-mail: admissions@georgiasouthern.edu
Web Site: www.georgiasouthern.edu
President/CEO: Dr. Jean Bartels
Admissions: Amy Smith
Financial Aid: Elise Boyett
Type: University **Sex:** Coed **Affiliation:** University System of Georgia (USG) - http://www.usg.edu/. **Scores:** 99% SAT V 400+; 100% SAT M 400+; 59% ACT 18-23; 37% ACT 24-29 **% Accepted:** 60 **Admission Plans:** Deferred Admission; Early Admission **Application Deadline:** May 1 **Application Fee:** $30.00 **H.S. Requirements:** High school diploma required; GED not accepted. For applicants out of high school at least 5 years: High school diploma or equivalent not required **Costs Per Year:** Application fee: $30. State resident tuition: $5226 full-time, $174.20 per credit hour part-time. Nonresident tuition: $18,444 full-time, $614.80 per credit hour part-time. Mandatory fees: $2092 full-time, $1046 per term part-time. Full-time tuition and fees vary according to course load, degree level, location, and program. Part-time tuition and fees vary according to course load, degree level, location, and program. College room and board: $9800. College room only: $6050. Room and board charges vary according to board plan and housing facility. **Scholarships:** Available. **Calendar System:** Semester, Summer session available **Enrollment:** Full-time 15,872, Graduate full-time 1,032, Graduate part-time 1,464, Part-time 2,091 **Faculty:** Full-time 794, Part-time 90 **Student-Faculty Ratio:** 21:1 **Exams:** ACT essay component not used; ACT essay component used as validity check; SAT I or ACT; SAT essay component not used; SAT essay component used as validity check; SAT Reasoning; SAT Subject. **% Receiving Financial Aid:** 67 **% Residing in College-Owned, -Operated, or -Affiliated Housing:** 27 **Final Year or Final Semester Residency Requirement:** Yes **Regional Accreditation:** Southern Association of Colleges and Schools **Credit Hours For Degree:** 126 semester hours, Bachelors **ROTC:** Army **Professional Accreditation:** AACN, AACSB, AAFCS, ABET, ACA, ACCE, ATMAE, CIDA, JRCAT, NASAD, NASM, NASPAA, NCATE, NRPA. **Intercollegiate Athletics:** Baseball M; Basketball M & W; Cheerleading M & W; Cross-Country Running W; Football M; Golf M; Riflery M & W; Soccer M & W; Softball W; Swimming and Diving W; Tennis M & W; Track and Field W; Volleyball W

GEORGIA SOUTHWESTERN STATE UNIVERSITY

800 Georgia Southwestern State University Dr.
Americus, GA 31709-4693
Tel: (229)928-1273; Free: 800-338-0082
Fax: (229)931-2983
E-mail: admissions@gsw.edu
Web Site: www.gsw.edu
President/CEO: Dr. Charles Patterson
Admissions: David Jenkins
Financial Aid: Angela Bryant
Type: Comprehensive **Sex:** Coed **Affiliation:** University System of Georgia. **Scores:** 97% SAT V 400+; 94% SAT M 400+; 58% ACT 18-23; 24% ACT 24-29 **% Accepted:** 72 **Admission Plans:** Deferred Admission; Early Admission **Application Deadline:** July 21 **Application Fee:** $25.00 **H.S. Requirements:** High school diploma required; GED not accepted **Costs Per Year:** Application fee: $25. State resident tuition: $4858 full-time, $161.93 per credit hour part-time. Nonresident tuition: $17,678 full-time, $589.27 per credit hour part-time. Mandatory fees: $1340 full-time, $670 per term part-time. Full-time tuition and fees vary according to course load and location. Part-time tuition and fees vary according to course load and location. College room and board: $8640. College room only: $4980. Room and board charges vary according to board plan and housing facility. **Scholarships:** Available. **Calendar System:** Semester, Summer session available **Enrollment:** Full-time 1,641, Graduate full-time 234, Graduate part-time 86, Part-time 794 **Faculty:** Full-time 108, Part-time 45 **Student-Faculty Ratio:** 18:1 **Exams:** SAT I or ACT; SAT Reasoning; SAT Subject. **% Receiving Financial Aid:** 74 **% Residing in College-Owned, -Operated, or -Affiliated Housing:** 32 **Final Year or Final Semester Residency Requirement:** Yes **Regional Accreditation:** Southern Association of Colleges and Schools **Professional Accreditation:** AACSB, ACEN, NCATE. **Intercollegiate Athletics:** Baseball M; Basketball M & W; Cross-Country Running W; Golf M; Soccer M & W; Softball W; Tennis M & W

GEORGIA STATE UNIVERSITY

33 Gilmer St.
Atlanta, GA 30302-3083
Tel: (404)651-2000
E-mail: onestopshop@gsu.edu
Web Site: www.gsu.edu
President/CEO: Dr. Mark P. Becker
Admissions: Scott Burke
Financial Aid: Louis Scott

Type: University **Sex:** Coed **Affiliation:** University System of Georgia. **Scores:** 99% SAT V 400+; 99% SAT M 400+; 57.86% ACT 18-23; 32.27% ACT 24-29 **% Accepted:** 58 **Admission Plans:** Deferred Admission; Early Admission; Early Decision Plan **Application Deadline:** March 1 **Application Fee:** $60.00 **H.S. Requirements:** High school diploma required; GED not accepted **Costs Per Year:** Application fee: $60. State resident tuition: $8558 full-time, $285.27 per credit hour part-time. Nonresident tuition: $26,768 full-time, $892.27 per credit hour part-time. Mandatory fees: $2128 full-time, $1064 per term part-time. Part-time tuition and fees vary according to course load. College room and board: $13,646. College room only: $9850. Room and board charges vary according to board plan and housing facility. **Scholarships:** Available. **Calendar System:** Semester, Summer session available **Enrollment:** Full-time 18,964, Graduate full-time 5,077, Graduate part-time 1,843, Part-time 6,196 **Faculty:** Full-time 1,219, Part-time 488 **Student-Faculty Ratio:** 22:1 **Exams:** SAT I or ACT; SAT Reasoning. **% Receiving Financial Aid:** 78 **% Residing in College-Owned, -Operated, or -Affiliated Housing:** 18 **Final Year or Final Semester Residency Requirement:** No **Regional Accreditation:** Southern Association of Colleges and Schools **Credit Hours For Degree:** 120 semester hours, Bachelors **ROTC:** Air Force, Army, Navy **Professional Accreditation:** AACN, AACSB, AALS, ABA, ACA, AND, APA, APTA, ASHA, CAHME, CORE, CSWE, CoARC, NASAD, NASM, NASPAA, NCATE. **Intercollegiate Athletics:** Baseball M; Basketball M & W; Crew M & W; Cross-Country Running W; Equestrian Sports M & W; Football M; Golf M & W; Ice Hockey M; Lacrosse M; Rugby M; Soccer M & W; Softball W; Squash M & W; Swimming and Diving M & W; Table Tennis M & W; Tennis M & W; Track and Field W; Ultimate Frisbee M & W; Volleyball W

GORDON STATE COLLEGE

419 College Dr.
Barnesville, GA 30204-1762
Tel: (678)359-5555; Free: 800-282-6504
E-mail: benf@gordonstate.edu
Web Site: www.gordonstate.edu
President/CEO: Max Burns, PhD
Admissions: Bennett Ferguson

Type: Two-Year College **Sex:** Coed **Affiliation:** University System of Georgia. **% Accepted:** 43 **Admission Plans:** Deferred Admission; Early Admission; Open Admission **Application Deadline:** Rolling **Application Fee:** $30.00 **H.S. Requirements:** High school diploma required; GED accepted **Costs Per Year:** Application fee: $30. State resident tuition: $2451 full-time. Nonresident tuition: $9058 full-time. Mandatory fees: $1100 full-time. College room and board: $8101. College room only: $5290. Room and board charges vary according to board plan and housing facility. **Scholarships:** Available. **Calendar System:** Semester, Summer session available **Faculty:** Full-time 119, Part-time 83 **Student-Faculty Ratio:** 21:1 **Exams:** SAT I and SAT II or ACT. **Final Year or Final Semester Residency Requirement:** No **Regional Accreditation:** Southern Association of Colleges and Schools **Credit Hours For Degree:** 64 semester hours, Associates; 120 credit hours, Bachelors **Professional Accreditation:** ACEN. **Intercollegiate Athletics:** Baseball M; Basketball M; Soccer M & W; Softball W

GUPTON-JONES COLLEGE OF FUNERAL SERVICE

5141 Snapfinger Woods Dr.
Decatur, GA 30035-4022
Tel: (770)593-2257; Free: 800-848-5352
Fax: (770)593-1891
Web Site: www.gupton-jones.edu
President/CEO: Walter Crox
Admissions: Felicia Smith

Type: Two-Year College **Sex:** Coed **Affiliation:** Pierce Mortuary Colleges, Inc. **Admission Plans:** Open Admission **Application Deadline:** Rolling **Application Fee:** $50.00 **H.S. Requirements:** High school diploma required; GED accepted **Scholarships:** Available. **Calendar System:** Quarter, Sum-

mer session available **Credit Hours For Degree:** 109 quarter hours, Associates **Professional Accreditation:** ABFSE.

GWINNETT COLLEGE

4230 Hwy. 29
Ste. 11
Lilburn, GA 30047
Tel: (770)381-7200
Web Site: www.gwinnettcollege.edu

Type: Two-Year College **Sex:** Coed **Professional Accreditation:** ACF, ACICS.

GWINNETT TECHNICAL COLLEGE

5150 Sugarloaf Pky.
Lawrenceville, GA 30043-5702
Tel: (770)962-7580
E-mail: fhalloran@gwinnetttech.edu
Web Site: www.gwinnetttech.edu
President/CEO: D. Glen Cannon

Type: Two-Year College **Sex:** Coed **Affiliation:** Technical College System of Georgia. **Admission Plans:** Early Admission; Open Admission **Application Fee:** $20.00 **H.S. Requirements:** High school diploma required; GED accepted **Costs Per Year:** Application fee: $20. State resident tuition: $89 per credit hour part-time. Nonresident tuition: $178 per credit hour part-time. **Scholarships:** Available. **Calendar System:** Semester, Summer session available **Enrollment:** Full-time 1,659, Part-time 5,300 **Faculty:** Full-time 102, Part-time 302 **Student-Faculty Ratio:** 25:1 **Final Year or Final Semester Residency Requirement:** No **Regional Accreditation:** Southern Association of Colleges and Schools **Professional Accreditation:** ADA, APTA, CoARC, JRCERT.

HERZING UNIVERSITY

3393 Peachtree Rd.
Ste. 1003
Atlanta, GA 30326
Tel: (404)816-4533; Free: 800-596-0724
Fax: (404)816-5576
Web Site: www.herzing.edu/atlanta
President/CEO: Theo Anderson

Type: Four-Year College **Sex:** Coed **H.S. Requirements:** High school diploma required; GED accepted **Scholarships:** Available. **Calendar System:** Semester **Final Year or Final Semester Residency Requirement:** No **Regional Accreditation:** North Central Association of Colleges and Schools **Credit Hours For Degree:** 63 credit hours, Associates; 124 credit hours, Bachelors **Professional Accreditation:** ACICS.

INTERACTIVE COLLEGE OF TECHNOLOGY (CHAMBLEE)

5303 New Peachtree Rd.
Chamblee, GA 30341
Tel: (770)216-2960; Free: 800-447-2011
Fax: (770)216-2989
Web Site: ict.edu
President/CEO: Elmer R. Smith

Type: Two-Year College **Sex:** Coed **Affiliation:** Interactive Learning Systems. **Admission Plans:** Open Admission **Application Deadline:** Rolling **Application Fee:** $50.00 **H.S. Requirements:** High school diploma required; GED accepted **Calendar System:** Semester **Student-Faculty Ratio:** 25:1 **Professional Accreditation:** COE.

INTERACTIVE COLLEGE OF TECHNOLOGY (GAINESVILLE)

2323-C Browns Bridge Rd.
Gainesville, GA 30504
Tel: (678)450-0550
Web Site: ict.edu

Type: Two-Year College **Sex:** Coed **Calendar System:** Semester **Professional Accreditation:** COE.

INTERACTIVE COLLEGE OF TECHNOLOGY (MORROW)

1580 Southlake Pky.
Ste. C
Morrow, GA 30260
Tel: (770)960-1298
Web Site: ict.edu

Type: Two-Year College **Sex:** Coed **Calendar System:** Semester

KENNESAW STATE UNIVERSITY

1000 Chastain Rd.
Kennesaw, GA 30144
Tel: (470)578-6000
Fax: (770)423-6541
E-mail: ksuadmit@kennesaw.edu
Web Site: www.kennesaw.edu
President/CEO: Dr. Daniel Papp
Financial Aid: Ron H. Day

Type: Comprehensive **Sex:** Coed **Affiliation:** University System of Georgia. **Scores:** 99% SAT V 400+; 99% SAT M 400+; 59% ACT 18-23; 35% ACT 24-29 **% Accepted:** 59 **Admission Plans:** Deferred Admission; Early Admission **Application Deadline:** May 6 **Application Fee:** $40.00 **H.S. Requirements:** High school diploma required; GED not accepted **Costs Per Year:** Application fee: $40. State resident tuition: $5320 full-time, $177 per credit hour part-time. Nonresident tuition: $18,776 full-time, $626 per credit hour part-time. Mandatory fees: $2006 full-time, $1003 per term part-time. Part-time tuition and fees vary according to course load. College room and board: $9497. Room and board charges vary according to board plan, housing facility, and student level. **Scholarships:** Available. **Calendar System:** Semester, Summer session available **Enrollment:** Full-time 22,974, Graduate full-time 929, Graduate part-time 1,843, Part-time 7,506 **Faculty:** Full-time 1,019, Part-time 736 **Student-Faculty Ratio:** 21:1 **Exams:** SAT I or ACT; SAT II; SAT Reasoning; SAT Subject. **% Receiving Financial Aid:** 71 **% Residing in College-Owned, -Operated, or -Affiliated Housing:** 18 **Final Year or Final Semester Residency Requirement:** Yes **Regional Accreditation:** Southern Association of Colleges and Schools **Credit Hours For Degree:** 123 semester hours, Bachelors **ROTC:** Air Force, Army **Professional Accreditation:** AACN, AACSB, ABET, CSWE, NASAD, NASM, NASPAA, NAST, NCATE. **Intercollegiate Athletics:** Baseball M; Basketball M & W; Cross-Country Running M & W; Football M; Golf M & W; Lacrosse W; Soccer W; Softball W; Tennis M & W; Track and Field M & W; Volleyball W

LAGRANGE COLLEGE

601 Broad St.
LaGrange, GA 30240-2999
Tel: (706)880-8000; Free: 800-593-2885
Fax: (706)880-8040
E-mail: dmcgreal@lagrange.edu
Web Site: www.lagrange.edu
President/CEO: Dr. Dan McAlexander
Admissions: David McGreal
Financial Aid: Michelle Reeves

Type: Comprehensive **Sex:** Coed **Affiliation:** United Methodist. **Scores:** 100% SAT V 400+; 98% SAT M 400+; 67.3% ACT 18-23; 25.6% ACT 24-29 **% Accepted:** 57 **Admission Plans:** Deferred Admission **Application Deadline:** Rolling **Application Fee:** $0.00 **H.S. Requirements:** High school diploma required; GED accepted **Costs Per Year:** Application fee: $0. One-time mandatory fee: $150. Comprehensive fee: $38,590 includes full-time tuition ($27,210), mandatory fees ($330), and college room and board ($11,050). College room only: $6310. Full-time tuition and fees vary according to class time, course load, and program. Room and board charges vary according to board plan and housing facility. Part-time tuition: $1120 per credit hour. Part-time tuition varies according to class time, course load, and program. **Scholarships:** Available. **Calendar System:** 4-1-4, Summer session available **Enrollment:** Full-time 856, Graduate full-time 89, Graduate part-time 27, Part-time 56 **Faculty:** Full-time 71, Part-time 36 **Student-Faculty Ratio:** 12:1 **Exams:** ACT; ACT essay component used as validity check; ACT essay component used for advising; ACT essay component used in place of application essay; SAT I; SAT I or ACT; SAT essay component used as validity check; SAT essay component used for advising; SAT essay component used in place of application essay; SAT Reasoning. **% Residing in College-Owned, -Operated, or -Affiliated Housing:** 65 **Final Year or Final Semester Residency Requirement:** Yes **Regional Accreditation:** Southern Association of Colleges and Schools **Credit Hours For Degree:** 120 semester hours, Bachelors **Professional Accreditation:** ACBSP, ACEN. **Intercollegiate Athletics:** Baseball M; Basketball M & W; Cheerleading W; Cross-Country Running M & W; Football M; Golf M; Lacrosse W; Soccer M & W; Softball W; Swimming and Diving M & W; Tennis M & W; Volleyball W

LANIER TECHNICAL COLLEGE

2990 Landrum Education Dr.
Oakwood, GA 30566
Tel: (770)531-6300
Fax: (770)531-6328
E-mail: mike@laniertech.edu
Web Site: www.laniertech.edu
President/CEO: Dr. Ray Perren

Type: Two-Year College **Sex:** Coed **Affiliation:** Technical College System of Georgia. **Admission Plans:** Early Admission; Open Admission **Application Fee:** $15.00 **H.S. Requirements:** High school diploma required; GED accepted **Costs Per Year:** Application fee: $15. State resident tuition: $89 per credit hour part-time. Nonresident tuition: $178 per credit hour part-time. **Calendar System:** Quarter **Enrollment:** Full-time 984, Part-time 2,662 **Regional Accreditation:** Southern Association of Colleges and Schools **Professional Accreditation:** ADA, COE, NAACLS.

LIFE UNIVERSITY

1269 Barclay Cir.
Marietta, GA 30060-2903
Tel: (770)426-2600; Free: 800-543-3202
E-mail: admissions@life.edu
Web Site: www.life.edu
President/CEO: Dr. Guy Rieckeman
Admissions: Stephanie Buchanan
Financial Aid: Melissa Waters

Type: Comprehensive **Sex:** Coed **Scores:** 72% SAT V 400+; 70% SAT M 400+ **% Accepted:** 59 **Application Deadline:** September 1 **Application Fee:** $50.00 **H.S. Requirements:** High school diploma required; GED accepted **Costs Per Year:** Application fee: $50. Comprehensive fee: $23,310 includes full-time tuition ($9810), mandatory fees ($1050), and college room and board ($12,450). College room only: $6300. Full-time tuition and fees vary according to course load, degree level, and student level. Room and board charges vary according to housing facility. Part-time tuition: $218 per credit hour. Part-time tuition varies according to degree level and student level. **Scholarships:** Available. **Calendar System:** Quarter, Summer session available **Enrollment:** Full-time 524, Graduate full-time 1,786, Graduate part-time 204, Part-time 194 **Faculty:** Full-time 130, Part-time 54 **Student-Faculty Ratio:** 17:1 **Exams:** SAT I or ACT. **% Receiving Financial Aid:** 72 **% Residing in College-Owned, -Operated, or -Affiliated Housing:** 10 **Final Year or Final Semester Residency Requirement:** No **Regional Accreditation:** Southern Association of Colleges and Schools **Credit Hours For Degree:** 95-98 quarter hours, Associates; 185-190 quarter hours, Bachelors **Professional Accreditation:** AND, CCE. **Intercollegiate Athletics:** Cross-Country Running W; Ice Hockey M; Rugby M & W; Swimming and Diving W; Track and Field W; Wrestling M & W

LINCOLN COLLEGE OF TECHNOLOGY

2359 Windy Hill Rd., SE
Ste. 280
Marietta, GA 30067-8645
Web Site: www.lincolnedu.com/campus/marietta-ga

Type: Two-Year College **Sex:** Coed **Professional Accreditation:** ACICS.

LUTHER RICE COLLEGE & SEMINARY

3038 Evans Mill Rd.
Lithonia, GA 30038-2454
Tel: (770)484-1204; Free: 800-442-1577
E-mail: admissions@lru.edu
Web Site: www.lutherrice.edu
President/CEO: James Flanagan
Admissions: Steve Pray
Financial Aid: Casey Kuffrey

Type: Comprehensive **Sex:** Coed **Affiliation:** Baptist. **% Accepted:** 81 **Admission Plans:** Early Admission; Open Admission **Application Deadline:** Rolling **Application Fee:** $50.00 **H.S. Requirements:** High school diploma required; GED accepted **Scholarships:** Available. **Calendar System:** Semester **Exams:** Other. **Credit Hours For Degree:** 126 semester hours, Bachelors **Professional Accreditation:** ABHE, TRACS.

MEDTECH COLLEGE

4501 Cir. 75 Pky.
Ste. C-3180
Atlanta, GA 30339
Tel: (770)859-9779
Web Site: www.medtech-atlanta.com/atlanta-marietta-ga

Type: Two-Year College **Sex:** Coed **Professional Accreditation:** COE.

MERCER UNIVERSITY
1501 Mercer University Dr.
Macon, GA 31207
Tel: (478)301-2700; Free: 800-MERCER-U
Fax: (478)301-2828
E-mail: holloway_kl@mercer.edu
Web Site: www.mercer.edu
President/CEO: William D. Underwood
Admissions: Kelly L. Holloway
Financial Aid: Maria Hammett
Type: University **Sex:** Coed **Affiliation:** Baptist. **Scores:** 100% SAT V 400+; 100% SAT M 400+; 14.2% ACT 18-23; 60.4% ACT 24-29 **% Accepted:** 67 **Admission Plans:** Deferred Admission; Early Admission; Early Decision Plan **Application Deadline:** April 1 **Application Fee:** $50.00 **H.S. Requirements:** High school diploma required; GED accepted **Costs Per Year:** Application fee: $50. Comprehensive fee: $45,910 includes full-time tuition ($34,150), mandatory fees ($300), and college room and board ($11,460). College room only: $5542. Full-time tuition and fees vary according to location. Room and board charges vary according to board plan, housing facility, location, and student level. Part-time tuition: $1,139 per credit hour. Part-time mandatory fees: $10 per credit hour. Part-time tuition and fees vary according to course load and location. **Scholarships:** Available. **Calendar System:** Semester, Summer session available **Enrollment:** Full-time 2,837, Graduate full-time 2,818, Graduate part-time 1,115, Part-time 62 **Faculty:** Full-time 391, Part-time 324 **Student-Faculty Ratio:** 13:1 **Exams:** SAT I or ACT; SAT Reasoning. **% Receiving Financial Aid:** 71 **% Residing in College-Owned, -Operated, or -Affiliated Housing:** 69 **Final Year or Final Semester Residency Requirement:** Yes **Regional Accreditation:** Southern Association of Colleges and Schools **Credit Hours For Degree:** 120 semester hours, Bachelors **ROTC:** Army **Professional Accreditation:** AACN, AACSB, AALS, AAMFT, ABA, ABET, ACPE, ATS, LCME/AMA, NASM, NCATE. **Intercollegiate Athletics:** Baseball M; Basketball M & W; Cross-Country Running M & W; Football M; Golf M & W; Lacrosse M & W; Soccer M & W; Softball W; Tennis M & W; Track and Field W; Volleyball W

MIDDLE GEORGIA STATE UNIVERSITY
100 University Pky.
Macon, GA 31206
Tel: (478)471-2700; Free: 800-272-7619
Fax: (478)471-2846
E-mail: admissions@mga.edu
Web Site: www.mga.edu
President/CEO: Dr. Christopher Blake
Admissions: Margo Woodham
Type: Comprehensive **Sex:** Coed **Affiliation:** University System of Georgia. **Scores:** 85% SAT V 400+; 85% SAT M 400+; 51.6% ACT 18-23; 11.1% ACT 24-29 **% Accepted:** 62 **Admission Plans:** Early Admission **Application Deadline:** Rolling **Application Fee:** $30.00 **H.S. Requirements:** High school diploma required; GED accepted **Costs Per Year:** Application fee: $30. State resident tuition: $3260 full-time, $108.67 per hour part-time. Nonresident tuition: $12,046 full-time, $401.53 per hour part-time. Mandatory fees: $1282 full-time. College room and board: $7870. Room and board charges vary according to board plan, housing facility, and location. **Scholarships:** Available. **Calendar System:** Semester, Summer session available **Enrollment:** Full-time 4,864, Part-time 2,812 **Faculty:** Full-time 245, Part-time 115 **Student-Faculty Ratio:** 21:1 **Exams:** SAT I or ACT; SAT Reasoning; SAT Subject. **% Receiving Financial Aid:** 65 **% Residing in College-Owned, -Operated, or -Affiliated Housing:** 20 **Final Year or Final Semester Residency Requirement:** No **Regional Accreditation:** Southern Association of Colleges and Schools **Credit Hours For Degree:** 60 semester hours, Associates; 120 semester hours, Bachelors **ROTC:** Army **Professional Accreditation:** ABET, ACEN, AHIMA, CoARC, NCATE. **Intercollegiate Athletics:** Baseball M; Basketball M & W; Cross-Country Running W; Soccer M & W; Softball W; Tennis M & W

MILLER-MOTTE TECHNICAL COLLEGE (AUGUSTA)
621 NW Frontage Rd.
Augusta, GA 30907
Tel: (706)396-8000; Free: 866-297-0267
Web Site: www.miller-motte.edu
Type: Two-Year College **Sex:** Coed **Professional Accreditation:** ACICS.

MILLER-MOTTE TECHNICAL COLLEGE (COLUMBUS)
1800 Box Rd.
Columbus, GA 31907

Tel: (706)225-5002
Web Site: www.miller-motte.edu
Type: Two-Year College **Sex:** Coed **Professional Accreditation:** ACICS.

MILLER-MOTTE TECHNICAL COLLEGE (MACON)
175 Tom Hill Sr. Blvd.
Macon, GA 31210
Tel: (478)803-4800; Free: 866-297-0267
Web Site: www.miller-motte.edu
Type: Two-Year College **Sex:** Coed **Professional Accreditation:** ACICS.

MOREHOUSE COLLEGE
830 Westview Dr., SW
Atlanta, GA 30314
Tel: (404)681-2800; Free: 800-851-1254
Fax: (404)659-6536
E-mail: Darryl.Isom@morehouse.edu
Web Site: www.morehouse.edu
President/CEO: Dr. John S. Wilson, Jr.
Admissions: Darryl D. Isom
Financial Aid: Sheryl T. Spivey
Type: Four-Year College **Sex:** Men **Scores:** 92% SAT V 400+; 87% SAT M 400+; 58% ACT 18-23; 18% ACT 24-29 **% Accepted:** 76 **Admission Plans:** Deferred Admission; Early Action; Early Admission; Early Decision Plan **Application Deadline:** February 1 **Application Fee:** $50.00 **H.S. Requirements:** High school diploma required; GED accepted **Costs Per Year:** Application fee: $50. Comprehensive fee: $40,064 includes full-time tuition ($24,565), mandatory fees ($2177), and college room and board ($13,322). College room only: $7510. Full-time tuition and fees vary according to course load. Room and board charges vary according to board plan. Part-time tuition: $1013 per hour. Part-time tuition varies according to course load. **Scholarships:** Available. **Calendar System:** Semester, Summer session available **Enrollment:** Full-time 2,069, Part-time 98 **Faculty:** Full-time 158, Part-time 54 **Student-Faculty Ratio:** 12:1 **Exams:** ACT essay component used for admission; SAT I and SAT II or ACT; SAT I or ACT; SAT essay component used for admission; SAT Reasoning; SAT Subject. **% Receiving Financial Aid:** 79 **% Residing in College-Owned, -Operated, or -Affiliated Housing:** 68 **Regional Accreditation:** Southern Association of Colleges and Schools **Credit Hours For Degree:** 120 semester hours, Bachelors **ROTC:** Air Force, Army, Navy **Professional Accreditation:** AACSB, NASM. **Intercollegiate Athletics:** Baseball M; Basketball M; Cross-Country Running M; Football M; Golf M; Tennis M; Track and Field M

NORTH GEORGIA TECHNICAL COLLEGE
1500 Georgia Hwy. 197, N
Clarkesville, GA 30523
Tel: (706)754-7700
Fax: (706)754-7777
E-mail: amitchell@northgatech.edu
Web Site: www.northgatech.edu
President/CEO: Gail Thaxton
Type: Two-Year College **Sex:** Coed **Affiliation:** Technical College System of Georgia. **Admission Plans:** Early Admission; Open Admission **Application Fee:** $20.00 **H.S. Requirements:** High school diploma required; GED accepted **Costs Per Year:** Application fee: $20. State resident tuition: $89 per credit hour part-time. Nonresident tuition: $178 per credit hour part-time. **Calendar System:** Quarter **Enrollment:** Full-time 970, Part-time 1,695 **Regional Accreditation:** Southern Association of Colleges and Schools **Professional Accreditation:** COE, NAACLS.

OCONEE FALL LINE TECHNICAL COLLEGE
1189 Deepstep Rd.
Sandersville, GA 31082
Tel: (478)553-2050; Free: 877-399-8324
Fax: (478)553-2118
Web Site: www.oftc.edu
President/CEO: Lloyd Horadan
Type: Two-Year College **Sex:** Coed **Affiliation:** Technical College System of Georgia. **Admission Plans:** Early Admission; Open Admission **Application Fee:** $20.00 **H.S. Requirements:** High school diploma required; GED accepted **Costs Per Year:** Application fee: $20. State resident tuition: $89 per credit hour part-time. Nonresident tuition: $178 per credit hour part-time.

Calendar System: Quarter **Enrollment:** Full-time 434, Part-time 1,135 **Regional Accreditation:** Southern Association of Colleges and Schools **Professional Accreditation:** COE.

OGEECHEE TECHNICAL COLLEGE

One Joe Kennedy Blvd.
Statesboro, GA 30458
Tel: (912)681-5500; Free: 800-646-1316
E-mail: lsaunders@ogeecheetech.edu
Web Site: www.ogeecheetech.edu
President/CEO: Dr. Dawn Cartee

Type: Two-Year College **Sex:** Coed **Affiliation:** Technical College System of Georgia. **Admission Plans:** Early Admission; Open Admission **Application Fee:** $20.00 **H.S. Requirements:** High school diploma required; GED accepted **Costs Per Year:** Application fee: $20. State resident tuition: $89 per credit hour part-time. Nonresident tuition: $178 per credit hour part-time. **Calendar System:** Quarter **Enrollment:** Full-time 759, Part-time 1,309 **Regional Accreditation:** Southern Association of Colleges and Schools **Professional Accreditation:** ABFSE, ADA, COA, COE.

OGLETHORPE UNIVERSITY

4484 Peachtree Rd., NE
Atlanta, GA 30319-2797
Tel: (404)261-1441; Free: 800-428-4484
Fax: (404)364-8500
E-mail: admission@oglethorpe.edu
Web Site: www.oglethorpe.edu
President/CEO: Dr. Lawrence Miller Schall
Admissions: Lucy Leusch
Financial Aid: Chris Summers

Type: Four-Year College **Sex:** Coed **Scores:** 99% SAT V 400+; 99% SAT M 400+; 35.4% ACT 18-23; 52.5% ACT 24-29 **% Accepted:** 78 **Admission Plans:** Deferred Admission; Early Admission; Early Decision Plan **Application Deadline:** Rolling **Application Fee:** $50.00 **H.S. Requirements:** High school diploma required; GED accepted **Costs Per Year:** Application fee: $50. Comprehensive fee: $48,135 includes full-time tuition ($35,000), mandatory fees ($425), and college room and board ($12,710). College room only: $4050. Full-time tuition and fees vary according to degree level. Room and board charges vary according to housing facility and location. Part-time tuition: $1467 per credit hour. Part-time tuition varies according to class time, course load, and degree level. **Scholarships:** Available. **Calendar System:** Semester, Summer session available **Enrollment:** Full-time 1,068, Part-time 79 **Faculty:** Full-time 59, Part-time 39 **Student-Faculty Ratio:** 15:1 **Exams:** SAT I or ACT; SAT Reasoning; SAT Subject. **% Receiving Financial Aid:** 70 **% Residing in College-Owned, -Operated, or -Affiliated Housing:** 57 **Final Year or Final Semester Residency Requirement:** Yes **Regional Accreditation:** Southern Association of Colleges and Schools **Credit Hours For Degree:** 120 semester hours, Bachelors **ROTC:** Air Force, Army, Navy **Intercollegiate Athletics:** Baseball M; Basketball M & W; Cross-Country Running M & W; Golf M & W; Lacrosse M & W; Soccer M & W; Tennis M & W; Track and Field M & W; Volleyball W

PAINE COLLEGE

1235 15th St.
Augusta, GA 30901-3182
Tel: (706)821-8200; Free: 800-476-7703
Fax: (706)821-8293
E-mail: rbeaty@paine.edu
Web Site: www.paine.edu
President/CEO: Dr. George C. Bradley
Admissions: Reginald Beaty
Financial Aid: Gerri Bogan

Type: Four-Year College **Sex:** Coed **Affiliation:** Methodist. **Scores:** 44% SAT V 400+; 44% SAT M 400+; 26% ACT 18-23; 2% ACT 24-29 **% Accepted:** 44 **Admission Plans:** Deferred Admission; Early Admission **Application Deadline:** July 1 **Application Fee:** $35.00 **H.S. Requirements:** High school diploma required; GED accepted **Scholarships:** Available. **Calendar System:** Semester, Summer session available **Enrollment:** Full-time 838, Part-time 52 **Faculty:** Full-time 86, Part-time 25 **Student-Faculty Ratio:** 14:1 **Exams:** SAT I or ACT; SAT Reasoning; SAT Subject. **% Residing in College-Owned, -Operated, or -Affiliated Housing:** 53 **Final Year or Final Semester Residency Requirement:** No **Regional Accreditation:** Southern Association of Colleges and Schools **Credit Hours For Degree:** 124 semester hours, Bachelors **ROTC:** Army **Professional Accreditation:**

ACBSP, NCATE. **Intercollegiate Athletics:** Baseball M; Basketball M & W; Cross-Country Running M & W; Golf M; Softball W; Track and Field M & W; Volleyball W

PIEDMONT COLLEGE

1021 Central Ave.
Demorest, GA 30535
Tel: (706)778-3000; Free: 800-277-7020
Fax: (706)776-6635
E-mail: bboonstra@piedmont.edu
Web Site: www.piedmont.edu
President/CEO: Dr. James F. Mellichamp
Admissions: Brenda Boonstra
Financial Aid: David Richmond McMillion

Type: Comprehensive **Sex:** Coed **Affiliation:** United Church of Christ. **Scores:** 90% SAT V 400+; 90% SAT M 400+; 61% ACT 18-23; 25% ACT 24-29 **% Accepted:** 57 **Admission Plans:** Deferred Admission; Early Admission **Application Deadline:** July 1 **Application Fee:** $0.00 **H.S. Requirements:** High school diploma required; GED accepted. For Home-schooled students can submit a portfolio: High school diploma or equivalent not required **Costs Per Year:** Application fee: $0. Comprehensive fee: $31,040 includes full-time tuition ($21,990) and college room and board ($9050). College room only: $5032. Full-time tuition varies according to course load, degree level, location, and program. Room and board charges vary according to board plan. Part-time tuition: $917 per credit hour. Part-time tuition varies according to course load, degree level, location, and program. **Scholarships:** Available. **Calendar System:** Semester, Summer session available **Enrollment:** Full-time 1,133, Graduate full-time 206, Graduate part-time 774, Part-time 151 **Faculty:** Full-time 128, Part-time 110 **Student-Faculty Ratio:** 11:1 **Exams:** SAT I or ACT. **% Receiving Financial Aid:** 82 **% Residing in College-Owned, -Operated, or -Affiliated Housing:** 45 **Regional Accreditation:** Southern Association of Colleges and Schools **Credit Hours For Degree:** 120 semester hours, Bachelors **Professional Accreditation:** ACBSP, ACEN. **Intercollegiate Athletics:** Baseball M; Basketball M & W; Cross-Country Running M & W; Golf M & W; Lacrosse M & W; Soccer M & W; Softball W; Tennis M & W; Track and Field M & W; Volleyball W

POINT UNIVERSITY

507 W 10th St.
West Point, GA 31833
Tel: (706)385-1000; Free: 855-37-POINT
E-mail: admissions@point.edu
Web Site: point.edu
President/CEO: Dean Collins
Admissions: Rusty Hassell
Financial Aid: Blair Walker

Type: Four-Year College **Sex:** Coed **Affiliation:** Christian. **Scores:** 77% SAT V 400+; 82% SAT M 400+; 59.7% ACT 18-23; 6.9% ACT 24-29 **% Accepted:** 49 **Admission Plans:** Deferred Admission **Application Deadline:** August 1 **Application Fee:** $0.00 **H.S. Requirements:** High school diploma required; GED accepted **Costs Per Year:** Application fee: $0. Comprehensive fee: $25,100 includes full-time tuition ($17,400), mandatory fees ($1100), and college room and board ($6600). College room only: $4000. Full-time tuition and fees vary according to course load. **Scholarships:** Available. **Calendar System:** Semester, Summer session available **Enrollment:** Full-time 1,191, Part-time 391 **Faculty:** Full-time 35, Part-time 117 **Student-Faculty Ratio:** 18:1 **Exams:** ACT essay component not used; SAT I or ACT; SAT essay component not used; SAT Reasoning; SAT Subject. **% Residing in College-Owned, -Operated, or -Affiliated Housing:** 30 **Final Year or Final Semester Residency Requirement:** No **Regional Accreditation:** Southern Association of Colleges and Schools **Credit Hours For Degree:** 60 semester hours, Associates; 120 semester hours, Bachelors **Professional Accreditation:** NCATE. **Intercollegiate Athletics:** Baseball M; Basketball M & W; Cheerleading W; Cross-Country Running M & W; Football M; Golf M & W; Lacrosse M & W; Soccer M & W; Softball W; Swimming and Diving M & W; Tennis M & W; Volleyball W

REINHARDT UNIVERSITY

7300 Reinhardt Cir.
Waleska, GA 30183-2981
Tel: (770)720-5600
Fax: (770)720-5602
E-mail: admissions@mail.reinhardt.edu

Web Site: www.reinhardt.edu
President/CEO: J. Thomas Isherwood
Admissions: Julie Fleming
Financial Aid: Angela D. Harlow
Type: Comprehensive **Sex:** Coed **Affiliation:** United Methodist Church. **Scores:** 95% SAT V 400+; 90% SAT M 400+; 72% ACT 18-23; 14% ACT 24-29 **% Accepted:** 90 **Admission Plans:** Deferred Admission; Early Admission **H.S. Requirements:** High school diploma required; GED accepted **Costs Per Year:** Comprehensive fee: $27,834 includes full-time tuition ($19,946), mandatory fees ($320), and college room and board ($7568). Part-time tuition: $665 per credit hour. **Scholarships:** Available. **Calendar System:** Semester, Summer session available **Enrollment:** Full-time 1,231, Graduate full-time 55, Graduate part-time 33, Part-time 103 **Faculty:** Full-time 68, Part-time 104 **Student-Faculty Ratio:** 12:1 **Exams:** ACT essay component not used; SAT I or ACT; SAT essay component not used. **% Receiving Financial Aid:** 77 **% Residing in College-Owned, -Operated, or -Affiliated Housing:** 43 **Final Year or Final Semester Residency Requirement:** No **Regional Accreditation:** Southern Association of Colleges and Schools **Credit Hours For Degree:** 60 credit hours, Associates; 120 credit hours, Bachelors **Professional Accreditation:** NASM. **Intercollegiate Athletics:** Baseball M; Basketball M & W; Cross-Country Running M & W; Football M; Golf M; Lacrosse M & W; Soccer M & W; Softball W; Tennis M & W; Volleyball W

SAE INSTITUTE ATLANTA

215 Peachtree St.
Ste. 300
Atlanta, GA 30303
Tel: (404)526-9366
Fax: (404)526-9367
Web Site: www.sae.edu
Type: Two-Year College **Sex:** Coed **Professional Accreditation:** ACICS.

SAVANNAH COLLEGE OF ART AND DESIGN

342 Bull St.
Savannah, GA 31402-3146
Tel: (912)525-5000; Free: 800-869-7223
Fax: (912)238-2436
E-mail: admission@scad.edu
Web Site: www.scad.edu
President/CEO: Paula Wallace
Admissions: Emilio Reyes Le Blanc
Financial Aid: Kim Beveridge
Type: Comprehensive **Sex:** Coed **Scores:** 95% SAT V 400+; 92% SAT M 400+; 40% ACT 18-23; 43% ACT 24-29 **% Accepted:** 69 **Admission Plans:** Deferred Admission; Early Admission **Application Deadline:** Rolling **Application Fee:** $70.00 **H.S. Requirements:** High school diploma required; GED accepted **Scholarships:** Available. **Calendar System:** Quarter, Summer session available **Enrollment:** Full-time 8,372, Graduate full-time 1,576, Graduate part-time 694, Part-time 1,813 **Faculty:** Full-time 526, Part-time 169 **Student-Faculty Ratio:** 19:1 **Exams:** ACT essay component not used; SAT I or ACT; SAT essay component not used. **% Receiving Financial Aid:** 51 **% Residing in College-Owned, -Operated, or -Affiliated Housing:** 42 **Final Year or Final Semester Residency Requirement:** Yes **Regional Accreditation:** Southern Association of Colleges and Schools **Credit Hours For Degree:** 180 quarter credit hours, Bachelors **Professional Accreditation:** NAAB. **Intercollegiate Athletics:** Cross-Country Running M & W; Equestrian Sports M & W; Golf M & W; Lacrosse M & W; Soccer M & W; Swimming and Diving M & W; Tennis M & W; Track and Field M & W

SAVANNAH STATE UNIVERSITY

3219 College St.
Savannah, GA 31404
Tel: (912)358-4778; Free: 800-788-0478
E-mail: potierd@savannahstate.edu
Web Site: www.savannahstate.edu
President/CEO: Dr. Cheryl D. Dozier
Admissions: Descatur Potier
Financial Aid: Kenneth Wilson
Type: Comprehensive **Sex:** Coed **Affiliation:** University System of Georgia. **Scores:** 72% SAT V 400+; 68% SAT M 400+; 42.3% ACT 18-23; 3.4% ACT 24-29 **% Accepted:** 83 **Admission Plans:** Deferred Admission; Early Admission **Application Deadline:** July 15 **Application Fee:** $0.00 **H.S. Requirements:** High school diploma required; GED accepted **Costs Per**

Year: Application fee: $0. State resident tuition: $4858 full-time, $161.93 per credit hour part-time. Nonresident tuition: $17,678 full-time, $589.27 per credit hour part-time. Mandatory fees: $1758 full-time, $879 per term part-time. Full-time tuition and fees vary according to course load, program, and reciprocity agreements. Part-time tuition and fees vary according to course load, program, and reciprocity agreements. College room and board: $7520. College room only: $3488. Room and board charges vary according to board plan and housing facility. **Scholarships:** Available. **Calendar System:** Semester, Summer session available **Enrollment:** Full-time 4,062, Graduate full-time 104, Graduate part-time 51, Part-time 583 **Faculty:** Full-time 191, Part-time 29 **Student-Faculty Ratio:** 21:1 **Exams:** ACT essay component not used; SAT I; SAT I or ACT; SAT II; SAT essay component not used; SAT Reasoning. **Final Year or Final Semester Residency Requirement:** No **Regional Accreditation:** Southern Association of Colleges and Schools **Credit Hours For Degree:** 66 semester hours, Associates; 125 semester hours, Bachelors **ROTC:** Army, Navy **Professional Accreditation:** AACSB, ABET, CSWE, NASPAA. **Intercollegiate Athletics:** Baseball M; Basketball M & W; Cheerleading M & W; Cross-Country Running M & W; Football M; Golf M & W; Softball W; Tennis W; Track and Field M & W; Volleyball W

SAVANNAH TECHNICAL COLLEGE

5717 White Bluff Rd.
Savannah, GA 31405
Tel: (912)443-5700; Free: 800-769-6362
Fax: (912)352-4362
E-mail: gmoore@savannahtech.edu
Web Site: www.savannahtech.edu
President/CEO: Dr. Kathy Love
Type: Two-Year College **Sex:** Coed **Affiliation:** Technical College System of Georgia. **Admission Plans:** Early Admission; Open Admission **Application Fee:** $20.00 **H.S. Requirements:** High school diploma required; GED accepted **Costs Per Year:** Application fee: $20. State resident tuition: $89 per credit hour part-time. Nonresident tuition: $178 per credit hour part-time. **Scholarships:** Available. **Calendar System:** Quarter **Enrollment:** Full-time 1,390, Part-time 2,806 **Regional Accreditation:** Southern Association of Colleges and Schools **Professional Accreditation:** ABET, ACEN, ACF, ADA.

SHORTER UNIVERSITY

315 Shorter Ave.
Rome, GA 30165
Tel: (706)291-2121; Free: 800-868-6980
Fax: (706)236-1515
E-mail: admissions@shorter.edu
Web Site: www.shorter.edu
President/CEO: Dr. Donald V. Dowless
Admissions: Emily Messer
Financial Aid: Tara Jones
Type: Comprehensive **Sex:** Coed **Affiliation:** Baptist. **Scores:** 82% SAT V 400+; 88% SAT M 400+; 54.71% ACT 18-23; 24.12% ACT 24-29 **% Accepted:** 63 **Admission Plans:** Deferred Admission; Early Admission **Application Deadline:** August 25 **Application Fee:** $25.00 **H.S. Requirements:** High school diploma required; GED accepted **Costs Per Year:** Application fee: $25. Comprehensive fee: $30,246 includes full-time tuition ($20,476), mandatory fees ($370), and college room and board ($9400). College room only: $5000. Full-time tuition and fees vary according to course load, location, and program. Room and board charges vary according to board plan and housing facility. Part-time tuition: $550 per credit hour. Part-time tuition varies according to location and program. **Scholarships:** Available. **Calendar System:** Semester, Summer session available **Enrollment:** Full-time 1,205, Graduate full-time 36, Graduate part-time 59, Part-time 172 **Faculty:** Full-time 98, Part-time 47 **Student-Faculty Ratio:** 12:1 **Exams:** ACT essay component used for admission; ACT essay component used for advising; ACT essay component used for placement; SAT I or ACT; SAT essay component used for admission; SAT essay component used for advising; SAT essay component used for placement; SAT Reasoning. **% Receiving Financial Aid:** 82 **% Residing in College-Owned, -Operated, or -Affiliated Housing:** 54 **Regional Accreditation:** Southern Association of Colleges and Schools **Credit Hours For Degree:** 60 semester hours, Associates; 120 semester hours, Bachelors **Professional Accreditation:** NASM. **Intercollegiate Athletics:** Baseball M; Basketball M & W; Cheerleading M & W; Cross-Country Running M & W; Football M; Golf M & W; Soccer M & W; Softball W; Tennis M & W; Track and Field M & W; Volleyball W

SOUTH GEORGIA STATE COLLEGE

100 W College Park Dr.
Douglas, GA 31533-5098
Tel: (912)260-4200; Free: 800-342-6364
Fax: (912)389-4392
E-mail: angie.evans@sgsc.edu
Web Site: www.sgc.edu
President/CEO: Dr. Virginia McSwain Carson
Admissions: Angie Evans

Type: Two-Year College **Sex:** Coed **Affiliation:** University System of Georgia. **Admission Plans:** Deferred Admission; Early Admission **Application Deadline:** Rolling **Application Fee:** $20.00 **H.S. Requirements:** High school diploma required; GED accepted **Costs Per Year:** Application fee: $20. State resident tuition: $2726 full-time, $90.87 per credit hour part-time. Nonresident tuition: $10,320 full-time, $344 per credit hour part-time. Mandatory fees: $1030 full-time, $515 per term part-time. Full-time tuition and fees vary according to course load and location. Part-time tuition and fees vary according to course load and location. College room and board: $8250. College room only: $4740. Room and board charges vary according to board plan and location. **Scholarships:** Available. **Calendar System:** Semester, Summer session available **Enrollment:** Full-time 1,877, Part-time 702 **Faculty:** Full-time 61, Part-time 54 **Student-Faculty Ratio:** 27:1 **% Residing in College-Owned, -Operated, or -Affiliated Housing:** 13 **Final Year or Final Semester Residency Requirement:** No **Regional Accreditation:** Southern Association of Colleges and Schools **Credit Hours For Degree:** 64 semester hours, Associates **Professional Accreditation:** ACEN. **Intercollegiate Athletics:** Baseball M; Basketball M; Cross-Country Running M & W; Soccer W; Softball W; Swimming and Diving M & W

SOUTH GEORGIA TECHNICAL COLLEGE

900 S Georgia Tech Pky.
Americus, GA 31709
Tel: (229)931-2394
Fax: (229)931-2459
E-mail: wcrisp@southgatech.edu
Web Site: www.southgatech.edu
President/CEO: Sparky Reeves

Type: Two-Year College **Sex:** Coed **Affiliation:** Technical College System of Georgia. **Admission Plans:** Early Admission; Open Admission **Application Fee:** $25.00 **H.S. Requirements:** High school diploma required; GED accepted **Costs Per Year:** Application fee: $25. State resident tuition: $89 per credit hour part-time. Nonresident tuition: $178 per credit hour part-time. **Calendar System:** Quarter **Enrollment:** Full-time 833, Part-time 835 **Regional Accreditation:** Southern Association of Colleges and Schools **Professional Accreditation:** COE.

SOUTH UNIVERSITY

709 Mall Blvd.
Savannah, GA 31406
Tel: (912)201-8000; Free: 866-629-2901
Fax: (912)201-8070
Web Site: www.southuniversity.edu/savannah
President/CEO: Todd Cellini

Type: Comprehensive **Sex:** Coed **Affiliation:** Education Management Corporation. **Calendar System:** Quarter **Regional Accreditation:** Southern Association of Colleges and Schools **Professional Accreditation:** AACN, AAMAE, ACBSP, ACPE, APTA.

SOUTHEASTERN TECHNICAL COLLEGE

3001 E First St.
Vidalia, GA 30474
Tel: (912)538-3100
Fax: (912)538-3156
E-mail: brhart@southeasterntech.edu
Web Site: www.southeasterntech.edu
President/CEO: Cathryn T. Mitchell

Type: Two-Year College **Sex:** Coed **Affiliation:** Technical College System of Georgia. **Admission Plans:** Early Admission; Open Admission **Application Fee:** $20.00 **H.S. Requirements:** High school diploma required; GED accepted **Costs Per Year:** Application fee: $20. State resident tuition: $89 per credit hour part-time. Nonresident tuition: $178 per credit hour part-time. **Calendar System:** Quarter **Enrollment:** Full-time 429, Part-time 1,238 **Regional Accreditation:** Southern Association of Colleges and Schools **Professional Accreditation:** COE.

SOUTHERN CRESCENT TECHNICAL COLLEGE

501 Varsity Rd.
Griffin, GA 30223
Tel: (770)228-7348
Fax: (770)229-3227
E-mail: tkinard@sctech.edu
Web Site: www.sctech.edu
President/CEO: Dr. Randall Peters

Type: Two-Year College **Sex:** Coed **Affiliation:** Technical College System of Georgia. **Admission Plans:** Early Admission; Open Admission **Application Fee:** $20.00 **H.S. Requirements:** High school diploma required; GED accepted **Costs Per Year:** Application fee: $20. State resident tuition: $89 per credit hour part-time. Nonresident tuition: $178 per credit hour part-time. **Scholarships:** Available. **Calendar System:** Quarter **Enrollment:** Full-time 1,764, Part-time 3,103 **Regional Accreditation:** Southern Association of Colleges and Schools **Professional Accreditation:** ARCST, COE.

SOUTHERN REGIONAL TECHNICAL COLLEGE

15689 US 19 N
Thomasville, GA 31792
Tel: (229)225-4096
Fax: (229)225-4330
E-mail: whancock@southwestgatech.edu
Web Site: www.southwestgatech.edu
President/CEO: Craig Wentworth

Type: Two-Year College **Sex:** Coed **Affiliation:** Technical College System of Georgia. **Admission Plans:** Early Admission; Open Admission **Application Fee:** $25.00 **H.S. Requirements:** High school diploma required; GED accepted **Costs Per Year:** Application fee: $25. State resident tuition: $89 per credit hour part-time. Nonresident tuition: $178 per credit hour part-time. **Scholarships:** Available. **Calendar System:** Quarter **Enrollment:** Full-time 1,122, Part-time 2,368 **Regional Accreditation:** Southern Association of Colleges and Schools **Professional Accreditation:** ACEN, APTA, COE, CoARC, NAACLS.

SPELMAN COLLEGE

350 Spelman Ln., SW
Atlanta, GA 30314-4399
Tel: (404)681-3643; Free: 800-982-2411
Fax: (404)215-7788
E-mail: admiss@spelman.edu
Web Site: www.spelman.edu
President/CEO: Dr. Mary Schmidt Campbell
Admissions: Tiffany Nelson
Financial Aid: Lenora Jackson

Type: Four-Year College **Sex:** Women **Scores:** 98% SAT V 400+; 95% SAT M 400+; 58% ACT 18-23; 32% ACT 24-29 **% Accepted:** 48 **Admission Plans:** Deferred Admission; Early Action; Early Admission; Early Decision Plan **Application Deadline:** February 1 **Application Fee:** $35.00 **H.S. Requirements:** High school diploma required; GED accepted **Costs Per Year:** Application fee: $35. Comprehensive fee: $39,001 includes full-time tuition ($22,827), mandatory fees ($3811), and college room and board ($12,363). Full-time tuition and fees vary according to course load. Room and board charges vary according to board plan and housing facility. Part-time mandatory fees: $950 per credit hour. Part-time fees vary according to course load. **Scholarships:** Available. **Calendar System:** Semester **Enrollment:** Full-time 2,090, Part-time 54 **Faculty:** Full-time 180, Part-time 70 **Student-Faculty Ratio:** 10:1 **Exams:** ACT essay component not used; SAT I or ACT; SAT essay component not used; SAT Reasoning. **% Receiving Financial Aid:** 82 **% Residing in College-Owned, -Operated, or -Affiliated Housing:** 68 **Final Year or Final Semester Residency Requirement:** No **Regional Accreditation:** Southern Association of Colleges and Schools **Credit Hours For Degree:** 120 credits, Bachelors **ROTC:** Air Force, Army, Navy **Professional Accreditation:** NASM, NCATE.

STRAYER UNIVERSITY–AUGUSTA CAMPUS

1330 Augusta W Pky.
Augusta, GA 30909
Tel: (706)855-8233
Fax: (706)855-8234
Web Site: www.strayer.edu/georgia/augusta
President/CEO: Brian W. Jones

Type: Comprehensive **Sex:** Coed **Regional Accreditation:** Middle States Association of Colleges and Schools

STRAYER UNIVERSITY–CHAMBLEE CAMPUS
3355 NE Expy.
Ste. 100
Atlanta, GA 30341
Tel: (770)454-9270
Fax: (770)457-6958
Web Site: www.strayer.edu/georgia/chamblee
President/CEO: Brian W. Jones
Type: Comprehensive **Sex:** Coed **Regional Accreditation:** Middle States
Association of Colleges and Schools

STRAYER UNIVERSITY–COBB COUNTY CAMPUS
3101 Towercreek Pky., SE
Ste. 700
Atlanta, GA 30339-3256
Tel: (770)612-2170
Fax: (770)956-7241
Web Site: www.strayer.edu/georgia/cobb-county
President/CEO: Brian W. Jones
Type: Comprehensive **Sex:** Coed **Regional Accreditation:** Middle States
Association of Colleges and Schools

STRAYER UNIVERSITY–COLUMBUS CAMPUS
6003 Veterans Pky.
Ste. 100
Columbus, GA 31909
Tel: (706)225-5300
Web Site: www.strayer.edu/georgia/columbus
President/CEO: Brian W. Jones
Type: Comprehensive **Sex:** Coed **Regional Accreditation:** Middle States
Association of Colleges and Schools

STRAYER UNIVERSITY–DOUGLASVILLE CAMPUS
4655 Timber Ridge Dr.
Douglasville, GA 30135
Tel: (678)715-2200
Fax: (678)715-2230
Web Site: www.strayer.edu/georgia/douglasville
President/CEO: Brian W. Jones
Type: Comprehensive **Sex:** Coed **Regional Accreditation:** Middle States
Association of Colleges and Schools

STRAYER UNIVERSITY–LITHONIA CAMPUS
3120 Stonecrest Blvd.
Ste. 200
Lithonia, GA 30038
Tel: (678)323-7700
Fax: (678)323-7730
Web Site: www.strayer.edu/georgia/lithonia
President/CEO: Brian W. Jones
Type: Comprehensive **Sex:** Coed **Regional Accreditation:** Middle States
Association of Colleges and Schools

STRAYER UNIVERSITY–MORROW CAMPUS
3000 Corporate Ctr. Dr., Ste. 100
Morrow, GA 30260
Tel: (678)422-4100
Fax: (678)422-4130
Web Site: www.strayer.edu/georgia/morrow
President/CEO: Brian W. Jones
Type: Comprehensive **Sex:** Coed **Regional Accreditation:** Middle States
Association of Colleges and Schools

STRAYER UNIVERSITY–ROSWELL CAMPUS
100 Mansell Ct. E, Ste. 100
Roswell, GA 30076
Tel: (770)650-3000
Fax: (770)650-3030
Web Site: www.strayer.edu/georgia/roswell
President/CEO: Brian W. Jones
Type: Comprehensive **Sex:** Coed **Regional Accreditation:** Middle States
Association of Colleges and Schools

STRAYER UNIVERSITY–SAVANNAH CAMPUS
20 Martin Ct.
Savannah, GA 31419
Tel: (912)921-2900
Fax: (912)291-2930
Web Site: www.strayer.edu/georgia/savannah
President/CEO: Brian W. Jones
Type: Comprehensive **Sex:** Coed **Regional Accreditation:** Middle States
Association of Colleges and Schools

THOMAS UNIVERSITY
1501 Millpond Rd.
Thomasville, GA 31792-7499
Tel: (229)226-1621; Free: 800-538-9784
E-mail: kknight@thomasu.edu
Web Site: www.thomasu.edu
President/CEO: Gary Bonvillian
Admissions: Kerri Knight
Financial Aid: Christina J. Gass
Type: Comprehensive **Sex:** Coed **Admission Plans:** Deferred Admission;
Early Admission; Open Admission **Application Deadline:** Rolling **Application Fee:** $25.00 **H.S. Requirements:** High school diploma required; GED
accepted **Scholarships:** Available. **Calendar System:** Semester, Summer
session available **Enrollment:** Full-time 519, Graduate full-time 94, Graduate part-time 148, Part-time 363 **Faculty:** Full-time 51, Part-time 2 **Student-Faculty Ratio:** 6:1 **Exams:** SAT I; SAT I and SAT II or ACT. **% Residing in
College-Owned, -Operated, or -Affiliated Housing:** 9 **Regional Accreditation:** Southern Association of Colleges and Schools **Credit Hours
For Degree:** 60 semester hours, Associates; 120 semester hours, Bachelors
Professional Accreditation: ACEN, CORE. **Intercollegiate Athletics:**
Baseball M; Golf M & W; Soccer M & W; Softball W

TOCCOA FALLS COLLEGE
107 Kincaid Dr.
Toccoa Falls, GA 30598
Tel: (706)886-6831; Free: 888-785-5624
Fax: (706)282-6012
E-mail: zwhitt@tfc.edu
Web Site: www.tfc.edu
President/CEO: Dr. Robert Myers
Admissions: Zack Whitt
Financial Aid: Stuart E. Spires
Type: Four-Year College **Sex:** Coed **Affiliation:** interdenominational.
Scores: 89% SAT V 400+; 86% SAT M 400+; 41% ACT 18-23; 31% ACT
24-29 **% Accepted:** 45 **Admission Plans:** Deferred Admission; Early
Admission **Application Deadline:** Rolling **Application Fee:** $25.00 **H.S.
Requirements:** High school diploma required; GED accepted **Costs Per
Year:** Application fee: $25. Comprehensive fee: $28,949 includes full-time
tuition ($20,714), mandatory fees ($600), and college room and board
($7635). Full-time tuition and fees vary according to location. Room and
board charges vary according to board plan. Part-time tuition: $863 per
credit hour. Part-time mandatory fees: $600 per year. Part-time tuition and
fees vary according to location. **Scholarships:** Available. **Calendar
System:** 4-1-4, Summer session available **Enrollment:** Full-time 732, Part-time 205 **Faculty:** Full-time 40, Part-time 59 **Student-Faculty Ratio:** 13:1
Exams: SAT I or ACT. **% Receiving Financial Aid:** 87 **% Residing in
College-Owned, -Operated, or -Affiliated Housing:** 62 **Final Year or Final
Semester Residency Requirement:** Yes **Regional Accreditation:**
Southern Association of Colleges and Schools **Credit Hours For Degree:**
60 credit hours, Associates; 126 credit hours, Bachelors **Professional Accreditation:** NASM. **Intercollegiate Athletics:** Baseball M; Basketball M &
W; Cross-Country Running M & W; Soccer M & W; Volleyball W

TRUETT-MCCONNELL COLLEGE
100 Alumni Dr.
Cleveland, GA 30528
Tel: (706)865-2134; Free: 800-226-8621
Fax: (706)219-3339
E-mail: agailey@truett.edu
Web Site: www.truett.edu
President/CEO: Dr. Emir Caner
Admissions: Andrew Gailey
Financial Aid: Katie Collis
Type: Comprehensive **Sex:** Coed **Affiliation:** Baptist. **Scores:** 85% SAT V

400+; 84% SAT M 400+; 57% ACT 18-23; 12% ACT 24-29 **% Accepted:** 91 **Admission Plans:** Deferred Admission; Early Admission **Application Deadline:** August 1 **Application Fee:** $0.00 **H.S. Requirements:** High school diploma required; GED accepted **Costs Per Year:** Application fee: $0. Comprehensive fee: $25,320 includes full-time tuition ($17,250), mandatory fees ($650), and college room and board ($7420). Full-time tuition and fees vary according to course load, degree level, location, and program. Room and board charges vary according to housing facility. Part-time tuition: $575 per credit hour. Part-time tuition varies according to course load, degree level, location, and program. **Scholarships:** Available. **Calendar System:** Semester, Summer session available **Enrollment:** Full-time 733, Graduate full-time 17, Graduate part-time 3, Part-time 1,264 **Faculty:** Full-time 50, Part-time 65 **Student-Faculty Ratio:** 17:1 **Exams:** SAT I or ACT. **% Receiving Financial Aid:** 86 **Final Year or Final Semester Residency Requirement:** Yes **Regional Accreditation:** Southern Association of Colleges and Schools **Credit Hours For Degree:** 122 semester hours, Bachelors **Professional Accreditation:** NASM. **Intercollegiate Athletics:** Baseball M; Basketball M & W; Cross-Country Running M & W; Golf M & W; Lacrosse W; Soccer M & W; Softball W; Volleyball W; Wrestling M

UNIVERSITY OF GEORGIA
Athens, GA 30602
Tel: (706)542-3000
E-mail: admproc@uga.edu
Web Site: www.uga.edu
President/CEO: Jere W. Morehead
Admissions: Charles Carabello
Financial Aid: Bonnie C. Joerschke

Type: Comprehensive **Sex:** Coed **Affiliation:** University System of Georgia. **Scores:** 100% SAT V 400+; 100% SAT M 400+; 8.09% ACT 18-23; 58.33% ACT 24-29 **% Accepted:** 53 **Admission Plans:** Deferred Admission; Early Admission; Early Decision Plan **Application Deadline:** January 15 **Application Fee:** $60.00 **H.S. Requirements:** High school diploma required; GED accepted **Costs Per Year:** Application fee: $60. State resident tuition: $9364 full-time. Nonresident tuition: $27,574 full-time. Mandatory fees: $2258 full-time. Full-time tuition and fees vary according to course load, location, and program. College room and board: $9450. College room only: $5494. Room and board charges vary according to board plan and housing facility. **Scholarships:** Available. **Calendar System:** Semester, Summer session available **Enrollment:** Full-time 25,906, Graduate full-time 6,640, Graduate part-time 1,943, Part-time 1,641 **Faculty:** Full-time 1,776 **Exams:** ACT essay component used as validity check; ACT essay component used for admission; SAT I or ACT; SAT essay component used as validity check; SAT essay component used for admission; SAT Reasoning; SAT Subject. **% Receiving Financial Aid:** 43 **% Residing in College-Owned, -Operated, or -Affiliated Housing:** 36 **Final Year or Final Semester Residency Requirement:** No **Regional Accreditation:** Southern Association of Colleges and Schools **Credit Hours For Degree:** 120 semester hours, Bachelors **ROTC:** Air Force, Army **Professional Accreditation:** AACSB, AAFCS, AALS, AAMFT, ABA, ABET, ACA, ACEJMC, ACPE, AND, APA, ASHA, ASLA, AVMA, CIDA, CSWE, JRCAT, NASAD, NASD, NASM, NASPAA, NAST, NCATE, NRPA, SAF. **Intercollegiate Athletics:** Badminton M & W; Baseball M; Basketball M & W; Cheerleading M & W; Crew M & W; Cross-Country Running M & W; Equestrian Sports W; Fencing M & W; Football M; Golf M & W; Gymnastics W; Ice Hockey M; Lacrosse M & W; Racquetball M & W; Rugby M & W; Sailing M & W; Soccer W; Softball W; Swimming and Diving M & W; Tennis M & W; Track and Field M & W; Ultimate Frisbee M & W; Volleyball W; Water Polo M & W; Wrestling M

UNIVERSITY OF NORTH GEORGIA
82 College Cir.
Dahlonega, GA 30597
Tel: (706)864-1400; Free: 800-498-9581
Fax: (706)864-1478
E-mail: molly.potts@ung.edu
Web Site: www.ung.edu
President/CEO: Dr. Bonita Jacobs
Admissions: Molly Potts
Financial Aid: Jill Rayner

Type: Comprehensive **Sex:** Coed **Affiliation:** University System of Georgia. **Scores:** 100% SAT V 400+; 100% SAT M 400+; 46.9% ACT 18-23; 48.89% ACT 24-29 **% Accepted:** 64 **Admission Plans:** Early Admission **Application Deadline:** July 1 **Application Fee:** $30.00 **H.S. Requirements:** High school diploma required; GED accepted **Costs Per Year:** Application fee:

$30. State resident tuition: $5352 full-time, $178.40 per credit hour part-time. Nonresident tuition: $18,894 full-time, $629.80 per credit hour part-time. Mandatory fees: $1826 full-time. Full-time tuition and fees vary according to course load, degree level, and location. Part-time tuition varies according to course load, degree level, and location. College room and board: $9494. College room only: $5242. Room and board charges vary according to board plan and housing facility. **Scholarships:** Available. **Calendar System:** Semester, Summer session available **Enrollment:** Full-time 11,756, Graduate full-time 141, Graduate part-time 419, Part-time 4,973 **Faculty:** Full-time 507, Part-time 272 **Student-Faculty Ratio:** 21:1 **Exams:** ACT essay component not used; SAT I or ACT; SAT essay component not used; SAT Reasoning; SAT Subject. **% Receiving Financial Aid:** 60 **% Residing in College-Owned, -Operated, or -Affiliated Housing:** 14 **Final Year or Final Semester Residency Requirement:** Yes **Regional Accreditation:** Southern Association of Colleges and Schools **Credit Hours For Degree:** 60 semester hours, Associates; 120 semester hours, Bachelors **ROTC:** Army **Professional Accreditation:** AACSB, ACA, ACEN, APTA, NCATE. **Intercollegiate Athletics:** Baseball M; Basketball M & W; Cheerleading M & W; Cross-Country Running M & W; Equestrian Sports W; Golf M & W; Lacrosse M & W; Riflery M & W; Soccer M & W; Softball W; Tennis M & W; Wrestling M

UNIVERSITY OF PHOENIX–ATLANTA CAMPUS
8200 Roberts Dr.
Sandy Springs, GA 30350-4147
Tel: (678)731-0555; Free: 866-766-0766
Fax: (770)821-5399
Web Site: www.phoenix.edu
President/CEO: Timothy P. Slottow
Admissions: Marc Booker

Type: Comprehensive **Sex:** Coed **Admission Plans:** Deferred Admission; Open Admission **Application Deadline:** Rolling **Application Fee:** $0.00 **H.S. Requirements:** High school diploma required; GED accepted **Scholarships:** Available. **Calendar System:** Continuous, Summer session not available **Enrollment:** Full-time 1,196 **Faculty:** Full-time 17, Part-time 203 **Regional Accreditation:** North Central Association of Colleges and Schools **Credit Hours For Degree:** 60 credits, Associates; 120 credits, Bachelors

UNIVERSITY OF PHOENIX–AUGUSTA CAMPUS
3150 Perimeter Pky.
Augusta, GA 30909-4583
Tel: (706)868-2000; Free: 866-766-0766
Web Site: www.phoenix.edu
President/CEO: Timothy P. Slottow

Type: Comprehensive **Sex:** Coed **Regional Accreditation:** North Central Association of Colleges and Schools **Professional Accreditation:** ACBSP.

UNIVERSITY OF PHOENIX–COLUMBUS GEORGIA CAMPUS
7200 N Lake Dr.
Columbus, GA 31909
Tel: (706)320-1266; Free: 866-766-0766
Web Site: www.phoenix.edu
President/CEO: Timothy P. Slottow
Admissions: Marc Booker

Type: Comprehensive **Sex:** Coed **Admission Plans:** Deferred Admission; Open Admission **Application Deadline:** Rolling **Application Fee:** $0.00 **H.S. Requirements:** High school diploma required; GED accepted **Scholarships:** Available. **Calendar System:** Continuous, Summer session not available **Enrollment:** Full-time 704 **Faculty:** Full-time 12, Part-time 95 **Regional Accreditation:** North Central Association of Colleges and Schools **Credit Hours For Degree:** 60 credits, Associates; 120 credits, Bachelors **Professional Accreditation:** ACBSP.

UNIVERSITY OF WEST GEORGIA
1601 Maple St.
Carrollton, GA 30118
Tel: (678)839-5000
E-mail: admiss@westga.edu
Web Site: www.westga.edu
President/CEO: Dr. Kyle Marrero
Admissions: Ketty Ballard
Financial Aid: Dr. Philip Hawkins

Type: Comprehensive **Sex:** Coed **Affiliation:** University System of Georgia. **Scores:** 95% SAT V 400+; 94% SAT M 400+; 70.8% ACT 18-23; 13% ACT

24-29 **% Accepted:** 57 **Admission Plans:** Deferred Admission; Early Admission **Application Deadline:** Rolling **Application Fee:** $40.00 **H.S. Requirements:** High school diploma required; GED accepted **Costs Per Year:** Application fee: $40. State resident tuition: $5226 full-time, $174.20 per semester hour part-time. Nonresident tuition: $18,444 full-time, $614.80 per semester hour part-time. Mandatory fees: $1962 full-time, $90.80 per semester hour part-time, $529 per term part-time. Full-time tuition and fees vary according to course load, degree level, location, and program. Part-time tuition and fees vary according to course load, degree level, location, and program. College room and board: $8998. College room only: $5100. Room and board charges vary according to board plan and housing facility. **Scholarships:** Available. **Calendar System:** Semester, Summer session available **Enrollment:** Full-time 8,816, Graduate full-time 625, Graduate part-time 1,456, Part-time 1,937 **Faculty:** Full-time 423, Part-time 271 **Student-Faculty Ratio:** 20:1 **Exams:** ACT essay component used for placement; SAT I or ACT; SAT essay component used for placement; SAT Reasoning. **% Receiving Financial Aid:** 74 **% Residing in College-Owned, -Operated, or -Affiliated Housing:** 29 **Final Year or Final Semester Residency Requirement:** Yes **Regional Accreditation:** Southern Association of Colleges and Schools **Credit Hours For Degree:** 120 semester hours, Bachelors **ROTC:** Air Force **Professional Accreditation:** AACN, AACSB, ABET, ACA, NASAD, NASM, NASPAA, NAST, NCATE. **Intercollegiate Athletics:** Baseball M; Basketball M & W; Cheerleading W; Cross-Country Running M & W; Football M; Golf M & W; Soccer W; Softball W; Tennis W; Track and Field W; Volleyball W

VALDOSTA STATE UNIVERSITY
1500 N Patterson St.
Valdosta, GA 31698
Tel: (229)333-5800; Free: 800-618-1878
Fax: (229)333-5482
E-mail: admissions@valdosta.edu
Web Site: www.valdosta.edu
President/CEO: Dr. Cecil P. Staton
Admissions: Ryan M. Hogan
Financial Aid: Douglas R. Tanner
Type: University **Sex:** Coed **Affiliation:** University System of Georgia. **Scores:** 98% SAT V 400+; 97% SAT M 400+; 77% ACT 18-23; 16% ACT 24-29 **% Accepted:** 50 **Admission Plans:** Deferred Admission **Application Deadline:** June 15 **Application Fee:** $40.00 **H.S. Requirements:** High school diploma required; GED accepted **Costs Per Year:** Application fee: $40. State resident tuition: $4,182 full-time, $174.20 per credit hour part-time. Nonresident tuition: $14,755 full-time, $614.80 per credit hour part-time. Mandatory fees: $2116 full-time, $1058 per term part-time. Full-time tuition and fees vary according to course load, location, program, and reciprocity agreements. Part-time tuition and fees vary according to course load, location, program, and reciprocity agreements. College room and board: $7912. College room only: $4072. Room and board charges vary according to board plan and housing facility. **Scholarships:** Available. **Calendar System:** Semester, Summer session available **Enrollment:** Full-time 7,256, Graduate full-time 814, Graduate part-time 1,692, Part-time 1,540 **Faculty:** Full-time 467, Part-time 139 **Student-Faculty Ratio:** 19:1 **Exams:** ACT essay component not used; SAT I or ACT; SAT essay component not used; SAT Reasoning. **% Receiving Financial Aid:** 73 **% Residing in College-Owned, -Operated, or -Affiliated Housing:** 27 **Final Year or Final Semester Residency Requirement:** No **Regional Accreditation:** Southern Association of Colleges and Schools **Credit Hours For Degree:** 60 credit hours, Associates; 120 credit hours, Bachelors **ROTC:** Air Force **Professional Accreditation:** AACN, AACSB, AAMFT, ADA, ALA, ASHA, CSWE, JRCAT, NASAD, NASM, NASPAA, NAST, NCATE. **Intercollegiate Athletics:** Baseball M; Basketball M & W; Cheerleading M & W; Cross-Country Running M & W; Football M; Golf M; Soccer W; Softball W; Tennis M & W; Volleyball W

VIRGINIA COLLEGE IN AUGUSTA
2807 Wylds Rd. Ext.
Ste. B
Augusta, GA 30909
Tel: (706)288-2500
Web Site: www.vc.edu
Type: Two-Year College **Sex:** Coed **Professional Accreditation:** ACICS.

VIRGINIA COLLEGE IN COLUMBUS
5601 Veterans Pky.
Columbus, GA 31904

Tel: (762)207-1600
Web Site: www.vc.edu
Type: Two-Year College **Sex:** Coed **Professional Accreditation:** ACICS.

VIRGINIA COLLEGE IN MACON
1901 Paul Walsh Dr.
Macon, GA 31206
Tel: (478)803-4802
Web Site: www.vc.edu
Type: Two-Year College **Sex:** Coed **Calendar System:** Quarter **Professional Accreditation:** ACICS.

VIRGINIA COLLEGE IN SAVANNAH
14045 Abercorn St.
Ste. 1503
Savannah, GA 31419
Tel: (912)721-5600
Web Site: www.vc.edu
Type: Two-Year College **Sex:** Coed **Professional Accreditation:** ACICS.

WESLEYAN COLLEGE
4760 Forsyth Rd.
Macon, GA 31210-4462
Tel: (478)477-1110; Free: 800-447-6610
Fax: (478)757-4030
E-mail: admissions@wesleyancollege.edu
Web Site: www.wesleyancollege.edu
President/CEO: Ruth A. Knox
Admissions: Stephen Farr
Financial Aid: Danielle Lodge
Type: Comprehensive **Affiliation:** United Methodist. **Scores:** 86% SAT V 400+; 88% SAT M 400+; 58% ACT 18-23; 23% ACT 24-29 **% Accepted:** 45 **Admission Plans:** Deferred Admission; Early Action; Early Admission; Early Decision Plan **Application Deadline:** February 15 **Application Fee:** $30.00 **H.S. Requirements:** High school diploma required; GED accepted **Costs Per Year:** Application fee: $30. One-time mandatory fee: $250. Comprehensive fee: $29,310 includes full-time tuition ($20,140), mandatory fees ($150), and college room and board ($9020). Full-time tuition and fees vary according to course load, degree level, program, and reciprocity agreements. Room and board charges vary according to board plan and housing facility. Part-time tuition: $480 per credit hour. Part-time tuition and fees vary according to course load, degree level, program, and reciprocity agreements. **Scholarships:** Available. **Calendar System:** Semester, Summer session available **Enrollment:** Full-time 489, Graduate full-time 50, Part-time 176 **Faculty:** Full-time 51, Part-time 1 **Student-Faculty Ratio:** 13:1 **Exams:** ACT essay component used for placement; SAT I or ACT; SAT essay component used for placement; SAT Reasoning. **% Receiving Financial Aid:** 69 **% Residing in College-Owned, -Operated, or -Affiliated Housing:** 82 **Final Year or Final Semester Residency Requirement:** No **Regional Accreditation:** Southern Association of Colleges and Schools **Credit Hours For Degree:** 120 semester hours, Bachelors **ROTC:** Army **Professional Accreditation:** NASM. **Intercollegiate Athletics:** Basketball W; Cross-Country Running W; Equestrian Sports W; Soccer W; Softball W; Tennis W; Volleyball W

WEST GEORGIA TECHNICAL COLLEGE
176 Murphy Campus Blvd.
Waco, GA 30182
Tel: (770)537-6000
E-mail: mary.aderhold@westgatech.edu
Web Site: www.westgatech.edu
President/CEO: Steve Daniel
Type: Two-Year College **Sex:** Coed **Affiliation:** Technical College System of Georgia. **Admission Plans:** Early Admission; Open Admission **Application Fee:** $24.00 **H.S. Requirements:** High school diploma required; GED accepted **Costs Per Year:** Application fee: $24. State resident tuition: $89 per credit hour part-time. Nonresident tuition: $178 per credit hour part-time. **Scholarships:** Available. **Calendar System:** Quarter **Enrollment:** Full-time 1,881, Part-time 4,550 **Regional Accreditation:** Southern Association of Colleges and Schools **Professional Accreditation:** ACBSP, ACEN, COE.

WIREGRASS GEORGIA TECHNICAL COLLEGE
4089 Val Tech Rd.
Valdosta, GA 31602

Tel: (229)333-2100
Fax: (229)333-2129
E-mail: teresa.spires@wiregrass.edu
Web Site: www.wiregrass.edu
President/CEO: Tina Anderson
Type: Two-Year College **Sex:** Coed **Affiliation:** Technical College System of Georgia. **Admission Plans:** Early Admission; Open Admission **Application Fee:** $25.00 **H.S. Requirements:** High school diploma required; GED accepted **Costs Per Year:** Application fee: $25. State resident tuition: $89 per credit hour part-time. Nonresident tuition: $178 per credit hour part-time. **Calendar System:** Quarter **Enrollment:** Full-time 871, Part-time 2,837 **Regional Accreditation:** Southern Association of Colleges and Schools **Professional Accreditation:** ADA, COE, JRCERT, NAACLS.

YOUNG HARRIS COLLEGE
1 College St.
Young Harris, GA 30582
Tel: (706)379-3111
Fax: (706)379-4306
E-mail: admissions@yhc.edu
Web Site: www.yhc.edu
President/CEO: Cathy Cox
Admissions: Clinton G. Hobbs

Financial Aid: Linda Adams
Type: Four-Year College **Sex:** Coed **Affiliation:** United Methodist. **Scores:** 92% SAT V 400+; 91% SAT M 400+; 60% ACT 18-23; 20% ACT 24-29 **% Accepted:** 48 **Application Deadline:** Rolling **Application Fee:** $0.00 **H.S. Requirements:** High school diploma required; GED accepted **Costs Per Year:** Application fee: $0. Comprehensive fee: $39,272 includes full-time tuition ($27,012), mandatory fees ($1185), and college room and board ($11,075). Full-time tuition and fees vary according to course load. Room and board charges vary according to board plan and housing facility. Part-time tuition: $900 per credit hour. Part-time tuition varies according to course load. **Scholarships:** Available. **Calendar System:** Semester, Summer session available **Enrollment:** Full-time 999, Part-time 35 **Faculty:** Full-time 77, Part-time 28 **Student-Faculty Ratio:** 12:1 **Exams:** ACT essay component not used; SAT I or ACT; SAT essay component not used. **% Receiving Financial Aid:** 72 **% Residing in College-Owned, -Operated, or -Affiliated Housing:** 87 **Final Year or Final Semester Residency Requirement:** Yes **Regional Accreditation:** Southern Association of Colleges and Schools **Credit Hours For Degree:** 62 semester hours, Associates; 120 semester hours, Bachelors **Professional Accreditation:** NASM. **Intercollegiate Athletics:** Baseball M; Basketball M & W; Cheerleading M & W; Cross-Country Running M & W; Golf M & W; Lacrosse M & W; Soccer M & W; Softball W; Tennis M & W

ARGOSY UNIVERSITY, HAWAI'I

1001 Bishop St., Ste. 400
Honolulu, HI 96813
Tel: (808)536-5555; Free: 888-323-2777
Fax: (808)536-5505
Web Site: www.argosy.edu/locations/hawaii
President/CEO: Warren Evans
Type: University **Sex:** Coed **Affiliation:** Education Management Corporation. **Calendar System:** Semester **Regional Accreditation:** Western Association of Colleges and Schools **Professional Accreditation:** ACBSP, APA.

BRIGHAM YOUNG UNIVERSITY–HAWAII

55-220 Kulanui St.
Laie, HI 96762-1294
Tel: (808)293-3211
E-mail: admissions@byuh.edu
Web Site: www.byuh.edu
President/CEO: Dr. Steven C. Wheelwright
Admissions: Arapata P. Meha
Financial Aid: Wes Duke
Type: Four-Year College **Sex:** Coed **Affiliation:** Latter-day Saints; Brigham Young University. **Scores:** 89% SAT V 400+; 98% SAT M 400+; 43% ACT 18-23; 48% ACT 24-29 **% Accepted:** 58 **Admission Plans:** Deferred Admission; Early Admission; Preferred Admission **Application Deadline:** February 15 **Application Fee:** $30.00 **H.S. Requirements:** High school diploma required; GED not accepted **Scholarships:** Available. **Calendar System:** Semester, Summer session available **Enrollment:** Full-time 2,380, Part-time 175 **Faculty:** Full-time 121, Part-time 107 **Student-Faculty Ratio:** 15:1 **Exams:** ACT; SAT I or ACT. **% Receiving Financial Aid:** 89 **% Residing in College-Owned, -Operated, or -Affiliated Housing:** 57 **Regional Accreditation:** Western Association of Colleges and Schools **Credit Hours For Degree:** 60 credits, Associates; 120 credits, Bachelors **ROTC:** Air Force, Army, Navy **Professional Accreditation:** CSWE. **Intercollegiate Athletics:** Basketball M & W; Cross-Country Running M & W; Golf M; Soccer M & W; Softball W; Tennis M & W; Volleyball W

CHAMINADE UNIVERSITY OF HONOLULU

3140 Waialae Ave.
Honolulu, HI 96816-1578
Tel: (808)735-4711; Free: 800-735-3733
Fax: (808)739-4647
E-mail: admissions@chaminade.edu
Web Site: www.chaminade.edu
President/CEO: Dr. Bernard Ploeger
Financial Aid: Amy Takiguchi
Type: Comprehensive **Sex:** Coed **Affiliation:** Roman Catholic. **Scores:** 93% SAT V 400+; 96% SAT M 400+; 78.22% ACT 18-23; 10.89% ACT 24-29 **% Accepted:** 82 **Admission Plans:** Deferred Admission **Application Deadline:** Rolling **Application Fee:** $50.00 **H.S. Requirements:** High school diploma required; GED accepted **Costs Per Year:** Application fee: $50. One-time mandatory fee: $180. Comprehensive fee: $34,070 includes full-time tuition ($21,650), mandatory fees ($130), and college room and board ($12,290). Full-time tuition and fees vary according to course load, location, and program. Room and board charges vary according to board

plan and housing facility. Part-time tuition: $722 per credit. Part-time tuition varies according to course load, location, and program. **Scholarships:** Available. **Calendar System:** Semester, Summer session available **Enrollment:** Full-time 1,200, Graduate full-time 422, Graduate part-time 217, Part-time 26 **Faculty:** Full-time 99, Part-time 50 **Student-Faculty Ratio:** 10:1 **Exams:** ACT essay component not used; Other; SAT I or ACT; SAT essay component not used. **% Receiving Financial Aid:** 71 **% Residing in College-Owned, -Operated, or -Affiliated Housing:** 25 **Final Year or Final Semester Residency Requirement:** Yes **Regional Accreditation:** Western Association of Colleges and Schools **Credit Hours For Degree:** 60 credit hours, Associates; 120 credit hours, Bachelors **ROTC:** Air Force, Army **Professional Accreditation:** MACTE, NCATE. **Intercollegiate Athletics:** Basketball M & W; Cross-Country Running M & W; Golf M; Soccer M & W; Softball W; Tennis W; Volleyball W

HAWAII COMMUNITY COLLEGE

200 W Kawili St.
Hilo, HI 96720-4091
Tel: (808)974-7611
Fax: (808)974-7692
Web Site: www.hawcc.hawaii.edu
President/CEO: Noreen Yamane
Admissions: Tammy M. Tanaka
Type: Two-Year College **Sex:** Coed **Affiliation:** University of Hawaii System. **Admission Plans:** Early Admission; Open Admission **Application Deadline:** August 1 **Application Fee:** $25.00 **H.S. Requirements:** High school diploma or equivalent not required. For nursing program: High school diploma required; GED accepted **Calendar System:** Semester, Summer session available **Regional Accreditation:** Western Association of Colleges and Schools **Credit Hours For Degree:** 60 credit hours, Associates **Professional Accreditation:** ACEN, ACF.

HAWAI'I PACIFIC UNIVERSITY

1164 Bishop St.
Honolulu, HI 96813
Tel: (808)544-0200; Free: 866-225-5478
Fax: (808)544-1136
E-mail: mbratton@hpu.edu
Web Site: www.hpu.edu
President/CEO: Dr. Geoffrey Bannister
Admissions: Marissa Bratton
Financial Aid: James M. Oshiro
Type: Comprehensive **Sex:** Coed **Scores:** 87% SAT V 400+; 86% SAT M 400+; 54% ACT 18-23; 29% ACT 24-29 **% Accepted:** 91 **Admission Plans:** Deferred Admission **Application Deadline:** Rolling **Application Fee:** $50.00 **H.S. Requirements:** High school diploma required; GED accepted **Costs Per Year:** Application fee: $50. Comprehensive fee: $37,359 includes full-time tuition ($23,160), mandatory fees ($300), and college room and board ($13,899). Full-time tuition and fees vary according to course level, course load, degree level, location, program, and student level. Room and board charges vary according to housing facility. Part-time tuition: $775 per credit. Part-time mandatory fees: $25 per term. Part-time tuition and fees vary according to course level, course load, degree level, location, program, and student level. **Scholarships:** Available. **Calendar System:** Semester, Summer session available **Enrollment:** Full-time 2,826, Graduate full-time 510,

Graduate part-time 278, Part-time 1,167 **Faculty:** Full-time 243, Part-time 267 **Student-Faculty Ratio:** 13:1 **Exams:** Other; SAT I or ACT; SAT Reasoning; SAT Subject. **Final Year or Final Semester Residency Requirement:** Yes **Regional Accreditation:** Western Association of Colleges and Schools **Credit Hours For Degree:** 60 credits, Associates; 124 credits, Bachelors **ROTC:** Air Force, Army **Professional Accreditation:** AACN, ACEN, CSWE, TEAC. **Intercollegiate Athletics:** Baseball M; Basketball M & W; Cross-Country Running M & W; Golf M & W; Gymnastics W; Soccer M & W; Softball W; Tennis M & W; Volleyball W

HAWAII TOKAI INTERNATIONAL COLLEGE

91-971 Farrington Hwy.
Kapolei, HI 96707
Tel: (808)983-4100
Fax: (808)983-4107
E-mail: admissions@tokai.edu
Web Site: www.hawaiitokai.edu
President/CEO: Prof. Takuya Yoshimura
Admissions: Darrell Kicker

Type: Two-Year College **Sex:** Coed **Affiliation:** Tokai University Educational System. **% Accepted:** 88 **Admission Plans:** Deferred Admission **Application Deadline:** Rolling **Application Fee:** $50.00 **H.S. Requirements:** High school diploma required; GED accepted **Costs Per Year:** Application fee: $50. One-time mandatory fee: $20. Comprehensive fee: $20,925 includes full-time tuition ($11,550), mandatory fees ($675), and college room and board ($8700). Room and board charges vary according to board plan and housing facility. Part-time tuition: $475 per credit hour. Part-time tuition varies according to course load. **Scholarships:** Available. **Calendar System:** Quarter, Summer session available **Enrollment:** Full-time 79 **Faculty:** Full-time 6, Part-time 11 **Student-Faculty Ratio:** 5:1 **Exams:** Other. **% Residing in College-Owned, -Operated, or -Affiliated Housing:** 90 **Final Year or Final Semester Residency Requirement:** No **Regional Accreditation:** Western Association of Colleges and Schools **Credit Hours For Degree:** 60 credits, Associates

HONOLULU COMMUNITY COLLEGE

874 Dillingham Blvd.
Honolulu, HI 96817-4598
Tel: (808)845-9211
E-mail: honcc@hawaii.edu
Web Site: www.honolulu.hawaii.edu
President/CEO: Erika Lacro
Financial Aid: Jannine Oyama

Type: Two-Year College **Sex:** Coed **Affiliation:** University of Hawaii System. **Admission Plans:** Early Admission; Open Admission **Application Deadline:** August 15 **Application Fee:** $0.00 **H.S. Requirements:** High school diploma or equivalent not required. For cosmetology program: High school diploma required; GED accepted **Scholarships:** Available. **Calendar System:** Semester, Summer session available **Enrollment:** Full-time 1,632, Part-time 2,736 **Faculty:** Full-time 131, Part-time 85 **Student-Faculty Ratio:** 16:1 **Exams:** Other. **Final Year or Final Semester Residency Requirement:** No **Regional Accreditation:** Western Association of Colleges and Schools **Credit Hours For Degree:** 60 semester hours, Associates **ROTC:** Air Force, Army

KAPIOLANI COMMUNITY COLLEGE

4303 Diamond Head Rd.
Honolulu, HI 96816-4421
Tel: (808)734-9111
E-mail: kapinfo@hawaii.edu
Web Site: www.kapiolani.hawaii.edu
President/CEO: Leon Richards

Type: Two-Year College **Sex:** Coed **Affiliation:** University of Hawaii System. **Admission Plans:** Early Admission; Open Admission; Preferred Admission **Application Deadline:** July 15 **Application Fee:** $25.00 **H.S. Requirements:** High school diploma or equivalent not required. For nursing, health sciences, paralegal programs: High school diploma required; GED accepted **Scholarships:** Available. **Calendar System:** Semester, Summer session available **Student-Faculty Ratio:** 21:1 **Regional Accreditation:** Western Association of Colleges and Schools **Credit Hours For Degree:** 60 credits, Associates **ROTC:** Air Force, Army **Professional Accreditation:** AAMAE, ACEN, ACF, AOTA, APTA, CoARC, JRCERT, NAACLS.

KAUAI COMMUNITY COLLEGE

3-1901 Kaumualii Hwy.
Lihue, HI 96766
Tel: (808)245-8311
Fax: (808)245-8297
E-mail: arkauai@hawaii.edu
Web Site: kauai.hawaii.edu
President/CEO: Helen Cox
Admissions: Leighton Oride

Type: Two-Year College **Sex:** Coed **Affiliation:** University of Hawaii System. **Admission Plans:** Early Admission; Open Admission; Preferred Admission **Application Deadline:** August 1 **Application Fee:** $0.00 **H.S. Requirements:** High school diploma or equivalent not required. For nursing program: High school diploma required; GED accepted **Scholarships:** Available. **Calendar System:** Semester, Summer session available **Regional Accreditation:** Western Association of Colleges and Schools **Credit Hours For Degree:** 60 credits, Associates **Professional Accreditation:** ACEN, ACF.

LEEWARD COMMUNITY COLLEGE

96-045 Ala Ike
Pearl City, HI 96782-3393
Tel: (808)455-0011
Fax: (808)455-0471
Web Site: www.leeward.hawaii.edu
President/CEO: Manuel J. Cabral
Admissions: Sheryl Higa
Financial Aid: Aileen Lum-Akana

Type: Two-Year College **Sex:** Coed **Affiliation:** University of Hawaii System. **% Accepted:** 100 **Admission Plans:** Early Admission; Open Admission; Preferred Admission **Application Deadline:** July 15 **Application Fee:** $25.00 **H.S. Requirements:** High school diploma required; GED accepted. For applicants 18 or over: High school diploma or equivalent not required **Costs Per Year:** Application fee: $25. State resident tuition: $2880 full-time, $120 per credit hour part-time. Nonresident tuition: $7872 full-time, $328 per credit hour part-time. Mandatory fees: $55 full-time, $27.50 per term part-time. Full-time tuition and fees vary according to course level and course load. Part-time tuition and fees vary according to course level and course load. **Scholarships:** Available. **Calendar System:** Semester, Summer session available **Enrollment:** Full-time 3,296, Part-time 4,646 **Faculty:** Full-time 178, Part-time 105 **Student-Faculty Ratio:** 23:1 **Final Year or Final Semester Residency Requirement:** No **Regional Accreditation:** Western Association of Colleges and Schools **Credit Hours For Degree:** 60 credits, Associates **ROTC:** Air Force **Professional Accreditation:** ACF.

PACIFIC RIM CHRISTIAN UNIVERSITY

290 Sand Island Access Rd.
Honolulu, HI 96819
Tel: (808)518-4791
Fax: (808)670-3957
Web Site: hawaii.newhope.edu

Type: Comprehensive **Sex:** Coed **Affiliation:** Christian. **Professional Accreditation:** ABHE.

REMINGTON COLLEGE–HONOLULU CAMPUS

1111 Bishop St.
Ste. 400
Honolulu, HI 96813
Tel: (808)942-1000
Fax: (808)533-3064
E-mail: louis.lamair@remingtoncollege.edu
Web Site: www.remingtoncollege.edu
President/CEO: Kenneth Heinemann
Admissions: Louis LaMair

Type: Two-Year College **Sex:** Coed **Professional Accreditation:** ACCSC, ACICS.

UNIVERSITY OF HAWAII AT HILO

200 W Kawili St.
Hilo, HI 96720-4091
Tel: (808)932-7446; Free: 800-897-4456
Fax: (808)933-0861
E-mail: uhhadm@hawaii.edu
Web Site: hilo.hawaii.edu

President/CEO: Dr. Donald O. Straney
Type: Comprehensive **Sex:** Coed **Affiliation:** University of Hawaii System.
Scores: 81% SAT V 400+; 87% SAT M 400+ **% Accepted:** 71 **Admission Plans:** Deferred Admission **Application Deadline:** July 1 **Application Fee:** $50.00 **H.S. Requirements:** High school diploma required; GED accepted **Costs Per Year:** Application fee: $50. State resident tuition: $7128 full-time, $297 per credit hour part-time. Nonresident tuition: $19,368 full-time, $807 per credit hour part-time. Mandatory fees: $420 full-time. Full-time tuition and fees vary according to program and reciprocity agreements. Part-time tuition varies according to course load and program. College room and board: $9970. Room and board charges vary according to board plan, housing facility, and location. **Scholarships:** Available. **Calendar System:** Semester, Summer session available **Enrollment:** Full-time 2,726, Graduate full-time 433, Graduate part-time 129, Part-time 636 **Faculty:** Full-time 241, Part-time 97 **Student-Faculty Ratio:** 13:1 **Exams:** ACT essay component used for placement; SAT I or ACT; SAT essay component used for placement; SAT Reasoning. **% Receiving Financial Aid:** 65 **Final Year or Final Semester Residency Requirement:** No **Regional Accreditation:** Western Association of Colleges and Schools **Credit Hours For Degree:** 120 semester hours, Bachelors **ROTC:** Army **Professional Accreditation:** AACSB, ACEN, ACPE, NCATE, TEAC. **Intercollegiate Athletics:** Baseball M; Basketball M & W; Cross-Country Running M & W; Golf M & W; Soccer M & W; Softball W; Tennis M & W; Volleyball W

UNIVERSITY OF HAWAII AT MANOA

2500 Campus Rd.
Honolulu, HI 96822
Tel: (808)956-8111; Free: 800-823-9771
E-mail: uhmanoa.admissions@hawaii.edu
Web Site: manoa.hawaii.edu
President/CEO: Dr. Robert Bley-Vroman
Admissions: Lisa Buto
Financial Aid: Jodie Kuba
Type: University **Sex:** Coed **Affiliation:** University of Hawaii System.
Scores: 97% SAT V 400+; 98% SAT M 400+; 55% ACT 18-23; 34% ACT 24-29 **% Accepted:** 79 **Admission Plans:** Preferred Admission **Application Deadline:** March 1 **Application Fee:** $70.00 **H.S. Requirements:** High school diploma required; GED accepted **Costs Per Year:** Application fee: $70. State resident tuition: $10,872 full-time, $453 per credit hour part-time. Nonresident tuition: $32,904 full-time, $1371 per credit hour part-time. Mandatory fees: $820 full-time, $405 per term part-time. Full-time tuition and fees vary according to class time, course level, course load, degree level, program, reciprocity agreements, and student level. Part-time tuition and fees vary according to class time, course level, course load, degree level, program, reciprocity agreements, and student level. College room and board: $11,529. College room only: $6253. Room and board charges vary according to board plan and housing facility. **Scholarships:** Available. **Calendar System:** Semester, Summer session available **Enrollment:** Full-time 11,413, Graduate full-time 2,780, Graduate part-time 2,396, Part-time 2,276 **Faculty:** Full-time 1,201, Part-time 258 **Student-Faculty Ratio:** 13:1 **Exams:** ACT; ACT essay component used for admission; SAT I; SAT I and SAT II or ACT; SAT I or ACT; SAT II; SAT essay component used for admission; SAT Reasoning. **% Receiving Financial Aid:** 55 **% Residing in College-Owned, -Operated, or -Affiliated Housing:** 25 **Final Year or Final Semester Residency Requirement:** No **Regional Accreditation:** Western Association of Colleges and Schools **Credit Hours For Degree:** 124 semester hours, Bachelors **ROTC:** Air Force, Army **Professional Accreditation:** AACN, AACSB, AALS, ABA, ABET, ACA, ACEJMC, ACSP, ADA, ALA, APA, ASHA, CEPH, CORE, CSWE, LCME/AMA, NAAB, NAACLS, NASM, NCATE. **Intercollegiate Athletics:** Baseball M; Basketball M & W; Cheerleading M & W; Cross-Country Running W; Football M; Golf M & W; Sailing M & W; Soccer W; Softball W; Swimming and Diving M & W; Tennis M & W; Track and Field W; Volleyball M & W; Water Polo W

UNIVERSITY OF HAWAII MAUI COLLEGE

310 Kaahumanu Ave.
Kahului, HI 96732
Tel: (808)984-3500; Free: 800-479-6692
Fax: (808)242-9618
E-mail: skameda@hawaii.edu

Web Site: maui.hawaii.edu
President/CEO: Clyde Sakamoto
Admissions: Stephen Kameda
Type: Two-Year College **Sex:** Coed **Affiliation:** University of Hawaii System.
Admission Plans: Early Admission; Open Admission **Application Deadline:** Rolling **Application Fee:** $25.00 **H.S. Requirements:** High school diploma or equivalent not required **Scholarships:** Available. **Calendar System:** Semester, Summer session available **Enrollment:** Full-time 1,446, Part-time 2,625 **Faculty:** Full-time 116, Part-time 1 **% Residing in College-Owned, -Operated, or -Affiliated Housing:** 1 **Regional Accreditation:** Western Association of Colleges and Schools **Credit Hours For Degree:** 60 credits, Associates **Professional Accreditation:** ACEN, ACF, ADA.

UNIVERSITY OF HAWAII–WEST OAHU

91-1001 Farrington Hwy.
Kapolei, HI 96707
Tel: (808)689-2800; Free: 866-299-8656
E-mail: uhwoadm@hawaii.edu
Web Site: www.uhwo.hawaii.edu
President/CEO: Dr. Doris Ching
Admissions: Craig Morimoto
Financial Aid: Lester Ishimoto
Type: Four-Year College **Sex:** Coed **Affiliation:** University of Hawaii System. **Scores:** 74% SAT V 400+; 77% SAT M 400+; 45% ACT 18-23; 14% ACT 24-29 **% Accepted:** 70 **Admission Plans:** Deferred Admission; Preferred Admission **Application Deadline:** August 1 **Application Fee:** $50.00 **H.S. Requirements:** High school diploma required; GED accepted **Costs Per Year:** Application fee: $50. State resident tuition: $7200 full-time, $300 per credit part-time. Nonresident tuition: $20,160 full-time, $840 per credit part-time. Mandatory fees: $252 full-time, $252 per term part-time. **Scholarships:** Available. **Calendar System:** Semester **Enrollment:** Full-time 1,438, Part-time 1,254 **Faculty:** Full-time 77 **Student-Faculty Ratio:** 24:1 **Exams:** ACT; SAT I; SAT I or ACT; SAT Reasoning; SAT Subject. **% Receiving Financial Aid:** 100 **Regional Accreditation:** Western Association of Colleges and Schools **Credit Hours For Degree:** 120 credits, Bachelors **ROTC:** Air Force, Army

UNIVERSITY OF PHOENIX–HAWAII CAMPUS

745 Fort St.
Honolulu, HI 96813-3800
Tel: (808)536-2686; Free: 866-766-0766
Web Site: www.phoenix.edu
President/CEO: Timothy P. Slottow
Admissions: Marc Booker
Type: Comprehensive **Sex:** Coed **Admission Plans:** Deferred Admission; Open Admission **Application Deadline:** Rolling **Application Fee:** $0.00 **H.S. Requirements:** High school diploma required; GED accepted **Scholarships:** Available. **Calendar System:** Continuous, Summer session not available **Enrollment:** Full-time 743 **Faculty:** Full-time 20, Part-time 158 **Regional Accreditation:** North Central Association of Colleges and Schools **Credit Hours For Degree:** 60 credits, Associates; 120 credits, Bachelors **Professional Accreditation:** ACBSP.

WINDWARD COMMUNITY COLLEGE

45-720 Keaahala Rd.
Kaneohe, HI 96744-3528
Tel: (808)235-7400
E-mail: gerii@hawaii.edu
Web Site: www.windward.hawaii.edu
President/CEO: Douglas Dykstra
Admissions: Geri Imai
Type: Two-Year College **Sex:** Coed **Affiliation:** University of Hawaii System.
Admission Plans: Early Admission; Open Admission; Preferred Admission **Application Deadline:** Rolling **Application Fee:** $25.00 **H.S. Requirements:** High school diploma or equivalent not required **Scholarships:** Available. **Calendar System:** Semester, Summer session available **Student-Faculty Ratio:** 15:1 **Regional Accreditation:** Western Association of Colleges and Schools **Credit Hours For Degree:** 60 credits, Associates **ROTC:** Air Force, Army

BOISE BIBLE COLLEGE

8695 W Marigold St.
Boise, ID 83714-1220
Tel: (208)376-7731; Free: 800-893-7755
Fax: (208)376-7743
E-mail: rgrove@boisebible.edu
Web Site: www.boisebible.edu
President/CEO: Terry E. Stine
Admissions: Russell Grove
Financial Aid: Beth Turner
Type: Four-Year College **Sex:** Coed **Affiliation:** nondenominational. **% Accepted:** 100 **Admission Plans:** Deferred Admission **Application Deadline:** August 1 **Application Fee:** $25.00 **H.S. Requirements:** High school diploma required; GED accepted **Scholarships:** Available. **Calendar System:** Semester, Summer session not available **Student-Faculty Ratio:** 15:1 **Exams:** SAT I or ACT. **% Receiving Financial Aid:** 81 **Credit Hours For Degree:** 64 semester hours, Associates; 128 semester hours, Bachelors **Professional Accreditation:** ABHE.

BOISE STATE UNIVERSITY

1910 University Dr.
Boise, ID 83725-0399
Tel: (208)426-1011; Free: 800-824-7017
E-mail: bsuinfo@boisestate.edu
Web Site: www.boisestate.edu
President/CEO: Dr. Robert Kustra
Admissions: Kelly Talbert
Type: University **Sex:** Coed **Affiliation:** Idaho System of Higher Education. **Scores:** 92% SAT V 400+; 92% SAT M 400+; 44.4% ACT 18-23; 38.4% ACT 24-29 **% Accepted:** 80 **Application Fee:** $50.00 **H.S. Requirements:** High school diploma required; GED accepted **Costs Per Year:** Application fee: $50. One-time mandatory fee: $175. State resident tuition: $4768 full-time, $177 per credit hour part-time. Nonresident tuition: $18,818 full-time, $427 per credit hour part-time. Mandatory fees: $2108 full-time, $96. Full-time tuition and fees vary according to course load and reciprocity agreements. Part-time tuition and fees vary according to course load. College room and board: $6429. College room only: $3159. Room and board charges vary according to board plan and housing facility. **Scholarships:** Available. **Calendar System:** Semester, Summer session available **Enrollment:** Full-time 12,034, Graduate full-time 903, Graduate part-time 2,088, Part-time 7,088 **Faculty:** Full-time 713, Part-time 589 **Student-Faculty Ratio:** 18:1 **Exams:** ACT essay component not used; SAT I or ACT; SAT essay component not used; SAT Reasoning; SAT Subject. **% Receiving Financial Aid:** 61 **% Residing in College-Owned, -Operated, or -Affiliated Housing:** 14 **Credit Hours For Degree:** 64 semester hours, Associates; 128 semester hours, Bachelors **ROTC:** Army **Professional Accreditation:** AACSB, ABET, ACA, ACCE, ACEN, ACF, ADA, AHIMA, CSWE, CoARC, JRCAT, JRCEDMS, JRCERT, NASAD, NASM, NASPAA, NAST, NCATE, NCCU. **Intercollegiate Athletics:** Basketball M & W; Cross-Country Running M & W; Football M; Golf M & W; Gymnastics W; Soccer W; Softball W; Swimming and Diving W; Tennis M & W; Track and Field M & W; Volleyball W; Wrestling M

BRIGHAM YOUNG UNIVERSITY–IDAHO

Rexburg, ID 83460
Tel: (208)496-2011

Fax: (208)496-1220
E-mail: williamst@byui.edu
Web Site: www.byui.edu
President/CEO: Kim Clark
Admissions: Tyler Williams
Type: Four-Year College **Sex:** Coed **Affiliation:** The Church of Jesus Christ of Latter-day Saints. **% Accepted:** 97 **Admission Plans:** Preferred Admission **Application Deadline:** February 15 **Application Fee:** $35.00 **H.S. Requirements:** High school diploma required; GED accepted **Scholarships:** Available. **Calendar System:** Semester, Summer session available **Student-Faculty Ratio:** 23:1 **Exams:** SAT I or ACT. **Credit Hours For Degree:** 64 semester hours, Associates **ROTC:** Army **Professional Accreditation:** ABET, ACEN, CIDA, NASM, NCCU.

BROADVIEW UNIVERSITY–BOISE

2750 E Gala Ct.
Meridian, ID 83642
Tel: (208)577-2900; Free: 877-572-5757
Fax: (208)577-2901
Web Site: www.broadviewuniversity.edu
President/CEO: Michael McAllister
Type: Four-Year College **Sex:** Coed **Affiliation:** Globe Education Network (GEN). **Admission Plans:** Open Admission **Application Deadline:** Rolling **Application Fee:** $50.00 **H.S. Requirements:** High school diploma required; GED accepted **Scholarships:** Available. **Enrollment:** Full-time 107, Part-time 35 **Faculty:** Full-time 6, Part-time 17 **Exams:** Other. **Final Year or Final Semester Residency Requirement:** No **Credit Hours For Degree:** 90 quarter credits, Associates; 180 quarter credits, Bachelors **Professional Accreditation:** ACICS.

CARRINGTON COLLEGE–BOISE

1122 N Liberty St.
Boise, ID 83704
Tel: (208)377-8080
Web Site: carrington.edu
President/CEO: Danielle Horras
Type: Two-Year College **Sex:** Coed **Affiliation:** Carrington Colleges Group, Inc. **H.S. Requirements:** High school diploma required; GED accepted **Costs Per Year:** Tuition: $58,183 per degree program. Part-time tuition varies according to program. **Scholarships:** Available. **Calendar System:** Semester, Summer session not available **Enrollment:** Full-time 380, Part-time 40 **Faculty:** Full-time 20, Part-time 36 **Student-Faculty Ratio:** 12:1 **Professional Accreditation:** ABHES, ADA.

THE COLLEGE OF IDAHO

2112 Cleveland Blvd.
Caldwell, ID 83605
Tel: (208)459-5011; Free: 800-244-3246
Fax: (208)454-2077
E-mail: admission@collegeofidaho.edu
Web Site: www.collegeofidaho.edu
President/CEO: Dr. Charlotte Borst
Admissions: Lorna Hunter
Type: Comprehensive **Sex:** Coed **Scores:** 97% SAT V 400+; 97% SAT M 400+; 53% ACT 18-23; 37% ACT 24-29 **% Accepted:** 90 **Admission Plans:**

Deferred Admission; Early Admission; Early Decision Plan **Application Deadline:** August 1 **Application Fee:** $0.00 **H.S. Requirements:** High school diploma required; GED accepted **Costs Per Year:** Application fee: $0. Comprehensive fee: $35,815 includes full-time tuition ($26,070), mandatory fees ($755), and college room and board ($8990). Part-time tuition: $1060 per credit. **Scholarships:** Available. **Calendar System:** Miscellaneous, Summer session available **Enrollment:** Full-time 1,007, Graduate full-time 20, Graduate part-time 11, Part-time 32 **Faculty:** Full-time 84, Part-time 56 **Student-Faculty Ratio:** 10:1 **Exams:** ACT essay component not used; SAT I or ACT; SAT essay component not used; SAT Reasoning. **% Receiving Financial Aid:** 70 **% Residing in College-Owned, -Operated, or -Affiliated Housing:** 59 **Final Year or Final Semester Residency Requirement:** Yes **Credit Hours For Degree:** 124 credits, Bachelors **ROTC:** Army **Professional Accreditation:** NCCU. **Intercollegiate Athletics:** Baseball M; Basketball M & W; Cross-Country Running M & W; Golf M & W; Lacrosse M; Skiing (Downhill) M & W; Soccer M & W; Softball W; Swimming and Diving M & W; Tennis W; Track and Field M & W; Volleyball W

COLLEGE OF SOUTHERN IDAHO

PO Box 1238
Twin Falls, ID 83303-1238
Tel: (208)733-9554; Free: 800-680-0274
Fax: (208)736-3014
Web Site: www.csi.edu
President/CEO: Dr. Gerald Beck
Financial Aid: Jennifer Zimmers

Type: Two-Year College **Sex:** Coed **Admission Plans:** Open Admission **Application Fee:** $10.00 **H.S. Requirements:** High school diploma required; GED accepted **Costs Per Year:** Application fee: $10. Area resident tuition: $2880 full-time, $120 per credit hour part-time. State resident tuition: $3880 full-time, $170 per credit hour part-time. Nonresident tuition: $6720 full-time, $280 per credit hour part-time. Full-time tuition varies according to course load. Part-time tuition varies according to course load. College room and board: $5540. College room only: $2500. Room and board charges vary according to board plan. **Scholarships:** Available. **Calendar System:** Semester, Summer session available **Enrollment:** Full-time 2,402, Part-time 6,071 **Faculty:** Full-time 155, Part-time 177 **Student-Faculty Ratio:** 21:1 **Exams:** ACT essay component used for advising; SAT essay component used for advising. **% Residing in College-Owned, -Operated, or -Affiliated Housing:** 4 **Credit Hours For Degree:** 64 credits, Associates **Professional Accreditation:** AAMAE, ACEN, NCCU. **Intercollegiate Athletics:** Baseball M; Basketball M & W; Cheerleading M & W; Equestrian Sports M & W; Softball W; Volleyball M & W

COLLEGE OF WESTERN IDAHO

6056 Birch Ln.
Nampa, ID 83687
Tel: (208)562-3000
Web Site: cwidaho.cc
Financial Aid: Nicole McMillin

Type: Two-Year College **Sex:** Coed **Admission Plans:** Open Admission **Application Deadline:** Rolling **Application Fee:** $25.00 **H.S. Requirements:** High school diploma required; GED accepted **Scholarships:** Available. **Calendar System:** Semester, Summer session available **Faculty:** Full-time 125, Part-time 283 **Student-Faculty Ratio:** 22:1 **Exams:** ACT essay component not used; Other; SAT I or ACT; SAT essay component not used. **Final Year or Final Semester Residency Requirement:** No **Credit Hours For Degree:** 64 credits, Associates **Professional Accreditation:** NCCU.

EASTERN IDAHO TECHNICAL COLLEGE

1600 S 25th E
Idaho Falls, ID 83404-5788
Tel: (208)524-3000; Free: 800-662-0261
Fax: (208)524-3007
E-mail: hailey.mack@my.eitc.edu
Web Site: www.eitc.edu
President/CEO: Dr. Rick Aman
Admissions: Hailey Mack

Type: Two-Year College **Sex:** Coed **Admission Plans:** Deferred Admission; Open Admission **Application Deadline:** Rolling **Application Fee:** $10.00 **H.S. Requirements:** High school diploma required; GED accepted **Costs Per Year:** Application fee: $10. State resident tuition: $2234 full-time, $102.50 per credit part-time. Nonresident tuition: $8550 full-time, $205 per

credit part-time. Mandatory fees: $1645 full-time, $15 per term part-time. Full-time tuition and fees vary according to course load and program. Part-time tuition and fees vary according to course load and program. **Scholarships:** Available. **Calendar System:** Semester, Summer session available **Student-Faculty Ratio:** 8:1 **Exams:** ACT essay component used for admission; Other; SAT I and SAT II or ACT; SAT I or ACT; SAT essay component used for admission. **Final Year or Final Semester Residency Requirement:** No **Credit Hours For Degree:** 60 credits, Associates **Professional Accreditation:** AAMAE, ARCST, NCCU.

IDAHO STATE UNIVERSITY

921 S 8th Ave.
Pocatello, ID 83209
Tel: (208)282-0211
E-mail: admiss@isu.edu
Web Site: www.isu.edu
President/CEO: Dr. Arthur C. Vailas
Financial Aid: James R. Martin

Type: University **Sex:** Coed **Scores:** 82% SAT V 400+; 82% SAT M 400+; 48.4% ACT 18-23; 28.6% ACT 24-29 **% Accepted:** 99 **Admission Plans:** Deferred Admission; Early Admission **Application Deadline:** Rolling **Application Fee:** $50.00 **H.S. Requirements:** High school diploma required; GED accepted **Costs Per Year:** Application fee: $50. State resident tuition: $5106 full-time, $339 per credit hour part-time. Nonresident tuition: $18,504 full-time, $556 per credit hour part-time. Mandatory fees: $1678 full-time. Full-time tuition and fees vary according to course load, program, and reciprocity agreements. Part-time tuition varies according to course load. College room and board: $6338. College room only: $2660. Room and board charges vary according to board plan, housing facility, and location. **Scholarships:** Available. **Calendar System:** Semester, Summer session available **Enrollment:** Full-time 6,951, Graduate full-time 1,203, Graduate part-time 687, Part-time 4,292 **Faculty:** Full-time 585, Part-time 149 **Student-Faculty Ratio:** 15:1 **Exams:** ACT; ACT essay component not used; SAT I or ACT; SAT essay component not used. **% Receiving Financial Aid:** 64 **% Residing in College-Owned, -Operated, or -Affiliated Housing:** 11 **Final Year or Final Semester Residency Requirement:** No **Credit Hours For Degree:** 64 credits, Associates; 128 credits, Bachelors **ROTC:** Army **Professional Accreditation:** AACN, AACSB, AAMAE, ABET, ACA, ACEN, ACF, ACPE, ADA, AHIMA, AND, AOTA, APA, APTA, ASHA, CEPH, CSWE, NAACLS, NASM, NAST, NCATE, NCCU. **Intercollegiate Athletics:** Basketball M & W; Cross-Country Running M & W; Football M; Golf W; Soccer W; Softball W; Tennis M & W; Track and Field M & W; Volleyball W

LEWIS-CLARK STATE COLLEGE

500 Eighth Ave.
Lewiston, ID 83501-2698
Tel: (208)792-5272; Free: 800-933-5272
Fax: (208)799-2063
E-mail: admissions@lcsc.edu
Web Site: www.lcsc.edu
President/CEO: J. Anthony Fernandez
Admissions: Soo Lee Bruce-Smith
Financial Aid: Laura Hughes

Type: Four-Year College **Sex:** Coed **Scores:** 82% SAT V 400+; 79% SAT M 400+; 59.2% ACT 18-23; 19% ACT 24-29 **% Accepted:** 99 **Admission Plans:** Deferred Admission **Application Fee:** $0.00 **H.S. Requirements:** High school diploma required; GED accepted **Scholarships:** Available. **Calendar System:** Semester **Enrollment:** Full-time 2,274, Part-time 1,359 **Faculty:** Full-time 173, Part-time 80 **Student-Faculty Ratio:** 14:1 **Exams:** ACT essay component not used; SAT I or ACT; SAT essay component not used. **% Receiving Financial Aid:** 74 **% Residing in College-Owned, -Operated, or -Affiliated Housing:** 14 **Credit Hours For Degree:** 64 credit hours, Associates; 128 credit hours, Bachelors **ROTC:** Air Force, Army, Navy **Professional Accreditation:** AACN, CSWE, NCCU. **Intercollegiate Athletics:** Baseball M; Basketball M & W; Cross-Country Running M & W; Golf M & W; Tennis M & W; Volleyball W

NEW SAINT ANDREWS COLLEGE

405 S Main St.
Moscow, ID 83843
Tel: (208)882-1566
Fax: (208)882-4293
E-mail: info@nsa.edu
Web Site: www.nsa.edu

President/CEO: Dr. Ben Merkle
Admissions: John Sawyer
Financial Aid: Brenda Schlect
Type: Comprehensive **Sex:** Coed **Affiliation:** Christian. **Scores:** 99% SAT V 400+; 91% SAT M 400+; 18% ACT 18-23; 45% ACT 24-29 **% Accepted:** 93 **Admission Plans:** Deferred Admission **Application Deadline:** February 15 **Application Fee:** $40.00 **H.S. Requirements:** High school diploma required; GED accepted **Costs Per Year:** Application fee: $40. Tuition: $12,100 full-time, $950 per course part-time. Full-time tuition varies according to program. Part-time tuition varies according to program. Tuition guaranteed not to increase for student's term of enrollment. **Scholarships:** Available. **Calendar System:** Miscellaneous, Summer session available **Enrollment:** Full-time 128, Graduate full-time 7, Graduate part-time 11, Part-time 12 **Faculty:** Full-time 6, Part-time 12 **Student-Faculty Ratio:** 12:1 **Exams:** ACT essay component not used; SAT I or ACT; SAT essay component not used; SAT Reasoning. **Final Year or Final Semester Residency Requirement:** Yes **Credit Hours For Degree:** 62 credits, Associates; 122 credits, Bachelors **Professional Accreditation:** TRACS.

NORTH IDAHO COLLEGE

1000 W Garden Ave.
Coeur d'Alene, ID 83814-2199
Tel: (208)769-3300; Free: 877-404-4536
Fax: (208)769-3273
E-mail: admit@nic.edu
Web Site: www.nic.edu
President/CEO: Dr. Priscilla Bell
Type: Two-Year College **Sex:** Coed **% Accepted:** 58 **Admission Plans:** Deferred Admission; Early Admission **Application Deadline:** August 20 **Application Fee:** $25.00 **H.S. Requirements:** High school diploma or equivalent not required **Scholarships:** Available. **Calendar System:** Semester, Summer session available **Enrollment:** Full-time 3,437, Part-time 2,286 **Faculty:** Full-time 160, Part-time 287 **Student-Faculty Ratio:** 17:1 **Credit Hours For Degree:** 64 credit hours, Associates **ROTC:** Army **Professional Accreditation:** ACEN, NCCU. **Intercollegiate Athletics:** Basketball M & W; Cheerleading M & W; Soccer M & W; Softball W; Volleyball W; Wrestling M

NORTHWEST NAZARENE UNIVERSITY

623 S University Blvd.
Nampa, ID 83686-5897
Tel: (208)467-8011; Free: 877-668-4968
Fax: (208)467-8645
E-mail: sablenker@nnu.edu
Web Site: www.nnu.edu
President/CEO: Dr. David Alexander
Admissions: Shawn Blenker
Financial Aid: Ann Crabb
Type: Comprehensive **Sex:** Coed **Affiliation:** Church of the Nazarene. **Scores:** 94% SAT V 400+; 91% SAT M 400+; 45.1% ACT 18-23; 37.3% ACT 24-29 **% Accepted:** 55 **Admission Plans:** Deferred Admission; Early Decision Plan **Application Deadline:** August 15 **Application Fee:** $40.00 **H.S. Requirements:** High school diploma required; GED accepted **Costs Per Year:** Application fee: $40. Comprehensive fee: $35,150 includes full-time tuition ($27,750), mandatory fees ($400), and college room and board ($7000). College room only: $3000. Full-time tuition and fees vary according to class time, course load, degree level, location, program, and reciprocity agreements. Room and board charges vary according to board plan. Part-time tuition: $1199 per credit hour. Part-time tuition varies according to class time, location, and program. **Scholarships:** Available. **Calendar System:** Semester, Summer session available **Enrollment:** Full-time 1,170, Graduate full-time 551, Graduate part-time 161, Part-time 347 **Student-Faculty Ratio:** 15:1 **Exams:** ACT essay component not used; SAT I or ACT; SAT essay component not used; SAT Reasoning; SAT Subject. **% Receiving Financial Aid:** 80 **% Residing in College-Owned, -Operated, or -Affiliated Housing:** 70 **Credit Hours For Degree:** 124 semester credits, Bachelors **ROTC:** Army **Professional Accreditation:** AACN, ACA, ACBSP, CSWE, NASM, NCATE, NCCU. **Intercollegiate Athletics:** Baseball M; Basketball M & W; Cheerleading W; Cross-Country Running M & W; Golf M & W; Soccer M & W; Softball W; Track and Field M & W; Volleyball W

STEVENS-HENAGER COLLEGE (BOISE)

1444 S Entertainment Ave.
Boise, ID 83709
Tel: (208)336-7671; Free: 800-622-2640
Web Site: www.stevenshenager.edu
Admissions: David Breck
Financial Aid: Jaime L. Davis
Type: Four-Year College **Sex:** Coed **Scholarships:** Available. **% Receiving Financial Aid:** 85 **Professional Accreditation:** ACCSC.

STEVENS-HENAGER COLLEGE (IDAHO FALLS)

901 Pier View Dr.
Ste. 105
Idaho Falls, ID 83402
Tel: (208)522-0887; Free: 800-622-2640
Web Site: www.stevenshenager.edu
Type: Four-Year College **Sex:** Coed **Professional Accreditation:** ACCSC.

UNIVERSITY OF IDAHO

875 Perimeter Dr.
Moscow, ID 83844-2282
Tel: (208)885-6111; Free: 888-884-3246
Fax: (208)885-6911
E-mail: admissions@uidaho.edu
Web Site: www.uidaho.edu
Admissions: Melissa Goodwin
Financial Aid: Dan D. Davenport
Type: University **Sex:** Coed **Scores:** 95% SAT V 400+; 94% SAT M 400+; 42% ACT 18-23; 38% ACT 24-29 **% Accepted:** 72 **Admission Plans:** Deferred Admission **Application Deadline:** August 1 **Application Fee:** $60.00 **H.S. Requirements:** High school diploma required; GED accepted **Costs Per Year:** Application fee: $60. State resident tuition: $5003 full-time, $293 per credit hour part-time. Nonresident tuition: $19,007 full-time, $293 per credit hour part-time. Mandatory fees: $2017 full-time. Full-time tuition and fees vary according to course load, program, and reciprocity agreements. Part-time tuition varies according to program and reciprocity agreements. College room and board: $8328. Room and board charges vary according to board plan. **Scholarships:** Available. **Calendar System:** Semester, Summer session available **Enrollment:** Full-time 7,400, Graduate full-time 1,291, Graduate part-time 965, Part-time 1,716 **Faculty:** Full-time 558, Part-time 145 **Student-Faculty Ratio:** 16:1 **Exams:** ACT essay component not used; SAT I or ACT; SAT essay component not used. **% Receiving Financial Aid:** 67 **% Residing in College-Owned, -Operated, or -Affiliated Housing:** 42 **Final Year or Final Semester Residency Requirement:** No **Credit Hours For Degree:** 120 credits, Bachelors **ROTC:** Air Force, Army, Navy **Professional Accreditation:** AACSB, AAFCS, AALS, ABA, ABET, ACA, AND, ASLA, CORE, NAAB, NASAD, NASM, NCATE, NCCU, NRPA, SAF. **Intercollegiate Athletics:** Basketball M & W; Cross-Country Running M & W; Football M; Golf M & W; Soccer W; Swimming and Diving W; Tennis M & W; Track and Field M & W; Volleyball W

AMBRIA COLLEGE OF NURSING

5210 Trillium Blvd.
Hoffman Estates, IL 60192
Tel: (847)397-0300
Web Site: www.ambria.edu
Type: Two-Year College **Sex:** Coed **Professional Accreditation:** ACICS.

AMERICAN ACADEMY OF ART

332 S Michigan Ave.
Chicago, IL 60604-4302
Tel: (312)461-0600; Free: 888-461-0600
E-mail: srosenbloom@aaart.edu
Web Site: www.aaart.edu
President/CEO: Richard H. Otto
Admissions: Stuart Rosenbloom
Financial Aid: Ione Fitzgerald
Type: Four-Year College **Sex:** Coed **Application Deadline:** Rolling **Application Fee:** $25.00 **H.S. Requirements:** High school diploma required; GED accepted **Costs Per Year:** Application fee: $25. Tuition: $15,400 full-time, $7700 per term part-time. Mandatory fees: $500 full-time. Full-time tuition and fees vary according to course load. Part-time tuition varies according to course load. **Scholarships:** Available. **Calendar System:** Semester, Summer session available **Enrollment:** Full-time 225, Part-time 92 **Faculty:** Full-time 25 **Student-Faculty Ratio:** 10:1 **Final Year or Final Semester Residency Requirement:** No **Regional Accreditation:** North Central Association of Colleges and Schools **Credit Hours For Degree:** 122 semester hours, Bachelors **Professional Accreditation:** ACCSC.

AMERICAN INTERCONTINENTAL UNIVERSITY ONLINE

231 N Martingale Rd.
6th Fl.
Schaumburg, IL 60173
Tel: (847)851-5000; Free: 877-701-3800
Fax: (847)851-6002
E-mail: jziegenmier@aiuonline.edu
Web Site: www.aiuniv.edu
President/CEO: Steve Tober
Admissions: Jennifer Ziegenmier
Type: Comprehensive **Sex:** Coed **Affiliation:** American InterContinental University. **Admission Plans:** Deferred Admission **Application Deadline:** Rolling **Application Fee:** $50.00 **H.S. Requirements:** High school diploma required; GED accepted **Calendar System:** Miscellaneous **Enrollment:** Full-time 20,341 **Regional Accreditation:** North Central Association of Colleges and Schools **Professional Accreditation:** ACBSP, TEAC.

ARGOSY UNIVERSITY, CHICAGO

225 N Michigan Ave., Ste. 1300
Chicago, IL 60601
Tel: (312)777-7600; Free: 800-626-4123
Fax: (312)201-1907
Web Site: www.argosy.edu/chicago-illinois/default.aspx
President/CEO: Ron Kimberling
Type: University **Sex:** Coed **H.S. Requirements:** High school diploma required; GED accepted **Calendar System:** Semester **Regional Accreditation:** Western Association of Colleges and Schools **Professional Accreditation:** ACA, ACBSP, APA.

ARGOSY UNIVERSITY, SCHAUMBURG

999 N Plz. Dr., Ste. 111
Schaumburg, IL 60173-5403
Tel: (847)969-4900; Free: 866-290-2777
Fax: (847)598-6191
Web Site: www.argosy.edu/locations/chicago-schaumburg
President/CEO: Leon Kelley
Type: University **Sex:** Coed **Calendar System:** Semester **Regional Accreditation:** Western Association of Colleges and Schools **Professional Accreditation:** ACA, ACBSP, APA.

AUGUSTANA COLLEGE

639 38th St.
Rock Island, IL 61201-2296
Tel: (309)794-7000; Free: 800-798-8100
Fax: (309)794-7431
E-mail: admissions@augustana.edu
Web Site: www.augustana.edu
President/CEO: Steven C. Bahls
Admissions: W. Kent Barnds
Financial Aid: Sue Standley
Type: Four-Year College **Sex:** Coed **Affiliation:** Evangelical Lutheran Church in America. **Scores:** 94% SAT V 400+; 100% SAT M 400+; 29.17% ACT 18-23; 54.01% ACT 24-29 **% Accepted:** 49 **Admission Plans:** Deferred Admission; Early Action; Early Admission; Early Decision Plan **Application Deadline:** Rolling **Application Fee:** $0.00 **H.S. Requirements:** High school diploma required; GED accepted **Costs Per Year:** Application fee: $0. Comprehensive fee: $49,658 includes full-time tuition ($39,621) and college room and board ($10,037). College room only: $5079. Room and board charges vary according to board plan and housing facility. Part-time tuition: $1700 per credit. Part-time tuition varies according to course load. **Scholarships:** Available. **Calendar System:** Quarter, Summer session available **Enrollment:** Full-time 2,460, Part-time 18 **Faculty:** Full-time 190 **Student-Faculty Ratio:** 12:1 **Exams:** ACT essay component not used; SAT I or ACT; SAT essay component not used. **% Receiving Financial Aid:** 77 % **Residing in College-Owned, -Operated, or -Affiliated Housing:** 70 **Final Year or Final Semester Residency Requirement:** Yes **Regional Accreditation:** North Central Association of Colleges and Schools **Credit Hours For Degree:** 123 credits, Bachelors **Professional Accreditation:** NASM, NCATE. **Intercollegiate Athletics:** Baseball M; Basketball M & W; Cheerleading M & W; Crew M & W; Cross-Country Running M & W; Equestrian Sports M & W; Fencing M & W; Football M; Golf M & W; Ice Hockey M; Lacrosse M & W; Soccer M & W; Softball W; Swimming and Diving M & W; Tennis M & W; Track and Field M & W; Ultimate Frisbee M & W; Volleyball M & W; Water Polo M & W; Wrestling M

AURORA UNIVERSITY

347 S Gladstone Ave.
Aurora, IL 60506-4892
Tel: (630)892-6431; Free: 800-742-5281
Fax: (630)844-5535

E-mail: admission@aurora.edu
Web Site: www.aurora.edu
President/CEO: Dr. Rebecca L. Sherrick
Admissions: James Lancaster
Financial Aid: Heather Granart
Type: Comprehensive **Sex:** Coed **Scores:** 94% SAT V 400+; 98% SAT M 400+; 70.9% ACT 18-23; 21.1% ACT 24-29 **% Accepted:** 77 **Admission Plans:** Deferred Admission **Application Deadline:** Rolling **Application Fee:** $0.00 **H.S. Requirements:** High school diploma required; GED accepted **Costs Per Year:** Application fee: $0. Comprehensive fee: $32,830 includes full-time tuition ($22,580), mandatory fees ($250), and college room and board ($10,000). Full-time tuition and fees vary according to course load, location, and program. Room and board charges vary according to board plan, housing facility, and location. **Scholarships:** Available. **Calendar System:** Semester, Summer session available **Enrollment:** Full-time 3,132, Graduate full-time 569, Graduate part-time 1,274, Part-time 448 **Faculty:** Full-time 159, Part-time 342 **Student-Faculty Ratio:** 16:1 **Exams:** ACT essay component not used; SAT I or ACT; SAT essay component not used. **% Receiving Financial Aid:** 80 **% Residing in College-Owned, -Operated, or -Affiliated Housing:** 21 **Final Year or Final Semester Residency Requirement:** Yes **Regional Accreditation:** North Central Association of Colleges and Schools **ROTC:** Army **Professional Accreditation:** AACN, CSWE, NCATE, NRPA. **Intercollegiate Athletics:** Baseball M; Basketball M & W; Bowling W; Cross-Country Running M & W; Football M; Golf M & W; Ice Hockey M & W; Lacrosse M & W; Soccer M & W; Softball W; Tennis M & W; Track and Field M & W; Volleyball W

BENEDICTINE UNIVERSITY
5700 College Rd.
Lisle, IL 60532
Tel: (630)829-6000; Free: 888-829-6363
Fax: (630)960-1126
E-mail: admissions@ben.edu
Web Site: www.ben.edu
President/CEO: Dr. William J. Carroll
Admissions: Kari Gibbons
Financial Aid: Diane Battistella
Type: Comprehensive **Sex:** Coed **Affiliation:** Roman Catholic. **Scores:** 54% ACT 18-23; 27% ACT 24-29 **% Accepted:** 79 **Admission Plans:** Deferred Admission **Application Fee:** $40.00 **H.S. Requirements:** High school diploma required; GED accepted **Costs Per Year:** Application fee: $40. Comprehensive fee: $41,370 includes full-time tuition ($30,780), mandatory fees ($1390), and college room and board ($9200). College room only: $6300. Full-time tuition and fees vary according to course load, degree level, and location. Room and board charges vary according to board plan, housing facility, and location. Part-time tuition: $1030 per hour. Part-time tuition varies according to course load, degree level, and location. **Scholarships:** Available. **Calendar System:** Semester, Summer session available **Enrollment:** Full-time 2,756, Graduate full-time 500, Graduate part-time 2,107, Part-time 591 **Faculty:** Full-time 161, Part-time 502 **Student-Faculty Ratio:** 12:1 **Exams:** ACT essay component used for admission; SAT I or ACT. **% Receiving Financial Aid:** 76 **% Residing in College-Owned, -Operated, or -Affiliated Housing:** 23 **Regional Accreditation:** North Central Association of Colleges and Schools **Credit Hours For Degree:** 60 semester hours, Associates; 120 semester hours, Bachelors **ROTC:** Army **Professional Accreditation:** AACN, AND. **Intercollegiate Athletics:** Baseball M; Basketball M & W; Cross-Country Running M & W; Football M; Golf M & W; Lacrosse M & W; Soccer M & W; Softball W; Tennis W; Track and Field M & W; Volleyball W

BLACK HAWK COLLEGE
6600 34th Ave.
Moline, IL 61265-5899
Tel: (309)796-5000; Free: 800-334-1311
E-mail: ghurtado@bhc.edu
Web Site: www.bhc.edu
President/CEO: Dr. Thomas Baynum
Admissions: Gabriella Hurtado
Financial Aid: Joanna Dye
Type: Two-Year College **Sex:** Coed **Affiliation:** Black Hawk College District System. **Scores:** 40% ACT 18-23; 13% ACT 24-29 **Costs Per Year:** Area resident tuition: $4050 full-time. State resident tuition: $7500 full-time. Nonresident tuition: $7650 full-time. **Scholarships:** Available. **Calendar System:** Semester, Summer session available **Enrollment:** Full-time 2,581,

Part-time 3,993 **Faculty:** Full-time 133, Part-time 188 **Student-Faculty Ratio:** 20:1 **Exams:** ACT essay component not used; SAT essay component not used. **Final Year or Final Semester Residency Requirement:** No **Regional Accreditation:** North Central Association of Colleges and Schools **Credit Hours For Degree:** 60 semester hours, Associates **Professional Accreditation:** ACEN, APTA. **Intercollegiate Athletics:** Baseball M; Basketball M & W; Golf M; Softball W; Volleyball W

BLACKBURN COLLEGE
700 College Ave.
Carlinville, IL 62626-1498
Tel: (217)854-3231; Free: 800-233-3550
Fax: (217)854-3713
E-mail: alisha.kapp@blackburn.edu
Web Site: www.blackburn.edu
President/CEO: Dr. John Comerford
Admissions: Alisha Kapp
Financial Aid: Jane Kelsey
Type: Four-Year College **Sex:** Coed **Affiliation:** Presbyterian. **Scores:** 38% SAT V 400+; 88% SAT M 400+; 57% ACT 18-23; 23% ACT 24-29 **% Accepted:** 55 **Admission Plans:** Deferred Admission **Application Deadline:** Rolling **Application Fee:** $20.00 **H.S. Requirements:** High school diploma required; GED accepted **Costs Per Year:** Application fee: $20. Comprehensive fee: $28,526 includes full-time tuition ($20,752), mandatory fees ($410), and college room and board ($7364). College room only: $4276. Full-time tuition and fees vary according to student level. Room and board charges vary according to board plan. Part-time tuition: $680 per credit hour. Part-time tuition varies according to student level. **Scholarships:** Available. **Calendar System:** Semester, Summer session available **Enrollment:** Full-time 561, Part-time 24 **Faculty:** Full-time 37, Part-time 21 **Student-Faculty Ratio:** 13:1 **Exams:** SAT I or ACT. **% Receiving Financial Aid:** 83 **% Residing in College-Owned, -Operated, or -Affiliated Housing:** 68 **Final Year or Final Semester Residency Requirement:** Yes **Regional Accreditation:** North Central Association of Colleges and Schools **Credit Hours For Degree:** 122 credit hours, Bachelors **Intercollegiate Athletics:** Baseball M; Basketball M & W; Cross-Country Running M & W; Golf M; Soccer M & W; Softball W; Tennis W; Volleyball W

BLESSING-RIEMAN COLLEGE OF NURSING
Broadway at 11th St.
Quincy, IL 62305-7005
Tel: (217)228-5520; Free: 800-877-9140
Fax: (217)223-6400
E-mail: admissions@brcn.edu
Web Site: www.brcn.edu
President/CEO: Dr. Pamela S. Brown
Admissions: Heather Mutter
Financial Aid: Kevin Turnbull
Type: Comprehensive **Sex:** Coed **Scores:** 51% ACT 18-23; 49% ACT 24-29 **% Accepted:** 66 **Admission Plans:** Deferred Admission **Application Deadline:** Rolling **Application Fee:** $0.00 **H.S. Requirements:** High school diploma required; GED accepted **Costs Per Year:** Application fee: $0. Tuition: $21,810 full-time, $727 per credit hour part-time. Full-time tuition varies according to course load, degree level, and student level. Part-time tuition varies according to course load, degree level, and student level. **Scholarships:** Available. **Calendar System:** Semester, Summer session available **Enrollment:** Full-time 192, Graduate part-time 18, Part-time 41 **Faculty:** Full-time 18 **Student-Faculty Ratio:** 12:1 **Exams:** SAT I or ACT. **% Receiving Financial Aid:** 100 **% Residing in College-Owned, -Operated, or -Affiliated Housing:** 82 **Regional Accreditation:** North Central Association of Colleges and Schools **Credit Hours For Degree:** 124 semester hours, Bachelors **Professional Accreditation:** AACN. **Intercollegiate Athletics:** Baseball M & W; Basketball M & W; Football M; Soccer M & W; Volleyball M & W

BRADLEY UNIVERSITY
1501 W Bradley Ave.
Peoria, IL 61625-0002
Tel: (309)676-7611; Free: 800-447-6460
E-mail: admissions@bradley.edu
Web Site: www.bradley.edu
President/CEO: Gary R. Roberts
Admissions: Dr. Justin Ball
Financial Aid: Debora Jackson

Type: Comprehensive **Sex:** Coed **Scores:** 99% SAT V 400+; 98% SAT M 400+; 34.69% ACT 18-23; 51.41% ACT 24-29 **% Accepted:** 66 **Admission Plans:** Deferred Admission; Early Admission **Application Deadline:** Rolling **Application Fee:** $35.00 **H.S. Requirements:** High school diploma required; GED accepted **Costs Per Year:** Application fee: $35. One-time mandatory fee: $200. Comprehensive fee: $41,180 includes full-time tuition ($31,110), mandatory fees ($370), and college room and board ($9700). College room only: $5620. Full-time tuition and fees vary according to course load and program. Room and board charges vary according to board plan. Part-time tuition: $830 per credit hour. Part-time mandatory fees: $370 per year. Part-time tuition and fees vary according to course load and program. **Scholarships:** Available. **Calendar System:** Semester, Summer session available **Enrollment:** Full-time 4,222, Graduate full-time 477, Graduate part-time 422, Part-time 217 **Faculty:** Full-time 343, Part-time 210 **Student-Faculty Ratio:** 12:1 **Exams:** ACT essay component not used; SAT I or ACT; SAT essay component not used; SAT Reasoning. **% Receiving Financial Aid:** 67 **% Residing in College-Owned, -Operated, or -Affiliated Housing:** 51 **Final Year or Final Semester Residency Requirement:** Yes **Regional Accreditation:** North Central Association of Colleges and Schools **Credit Hours For Degree:** 124 credits, Bachelors **ROTC:** Army **Professional Accreditation:** AACSB, AAFCS, AANA, ABET, ACA, ACCE, ACEN, APTA, CSWE, NASAD, NASM, NAST, NCATE. **Intercollegiate Athletics:** Baseball M; Basketball M & W; Cheerleading M & W; Cross-Country Running M & W; Golf M & W; Soccer M; Softball W; Tennis W; Track and Field M & W; Volleyball W

CARL SANDBURG COLLEGE

2400 Tom L. Wilson Blvd.
Galesburg, IL 61401-9576
Tel: (309)344-2518
Fax: (309)344-1395
Web Site: www.sandburg.edu
President/CEO: Lori L. Sundberg
Admissions: Carol Kreider
Financial Aid: Lisa Hanson
Type: Two-Year College **Sex:** Coed **Affiliation:** Illinois Community College Board. **Admission Plans:** Deferred Admission; Early Admission; Open Admission **Application Deadline:** Rolling **Application Fee:** $0.00 **H.S. Requirements:** High school diploma or equivalent not required. For allied health programs: High school diploma required; GED accepted **Scholarships:** Available. **Calendar System:** Semester, Summer session available **Regional Accreditation:** North Central Association of Colleges and Schools **Credit Hours For Degree:** 64 semester hours, Associates **ROTC:** Army **Professional Accreditation:** ABFSE, ACEN, ADA, JRCERT. **Intercollegiate Athletics:** Baseball M; Basketball M & W; Volleyball W

CHAMBERLAIN COLLEGE OF NURSING (ADDISON)

1221 N Swift Rd.
Addison, IL 60101
Tel: (630)953-3660; Free: 877-751-5783
Fax: (630)628-1154
Web Site: www.chamberlain.edu
President/CEO: Janet Snow
Type: Four-Year College **Sex:** Coed **Costs Per Year:** Tuition: $17,560 full-time, $665 per credit hour part-time. Mandatory fees: $600 full-time, $300 per term part-time. Full-time tuition and fees vary according to course load. Part-time tuition and fees vary according to course load. **Calendar System:** Semester **Enrollment:** Full-time 2,128, Graduate full-time 286, Graduate part-time 5,100, Part-time 9,860 **Faculty:** Full-time 71, Part-time 317 **Student-Faculty Ratio:** 42:1 **Exams:** ACT essay component used for admission; SAT I or ACT; SAT essay component used for admission. **Regional Accreditation:** North Central Association of Colleges and Schools

CHAMBERLAIN COLLEGE OF NURSING (CHICAGO)

3300 N Campbell Ave.
Chicago, IL 60618
Tel: (773)961-3000; Free: 877-751-5783
Fax: (773)961-3190
Web Site: www.chamberlain.edu
Type: Four-Year College **Sex:** Coed **Costs Per Year:** Tuition: $17,560 full-time, $665 per credit hour part-time. Mandatory fees: $600 full-time, $300 per term part-time. Full-time tuition and fees vary according to course load. Part-time tuition and fees vary according to course load. **Calendar System:** Semester **Enrollment:** Full-time 442, Part-time 450 **Faculty:** Full-time 16,

Part-time 86 **Student-Faculty Ratio:** 13:1 **Exams:** ACT essay component used for admission; SAT I or ACT; SAT essay component used for admission. **Regional Accreditation:** North Central Association of Colleges and Schools

CHAMBERLAIN COLLEGE OF NURSING (TINLEY PARK)

18624 W Creek Dr.
Tinley Park, IL 60477
Tel: (708)560-2000; Free: 877-751-5783
Fax: (708)560-2099
Web Site: www.chamberlain.edu
Type: Four-Year College **Sex:** Coed **Application Fee:** $95.00 **H.S. Requirements:** High school diploma required; GED accepted **Costs Per Year:** Application fee: $95. Tuition: $17,560 full-time, $665 per credit hour part-time. Mandatory fees: $600 full-time, $300 per term part-time. **Enrollment:** Full-time 280, Part-time 119 **Faculty:** Full-time 7, Part-time 31 **Student-Faculty Ratio:** 18:1 **Exams:** ACT essay component used for admission; SAT I or ACT; SAT essay component used for admission. **Regional Accreditation:** North Central Association of Colleges and Schools

CHICAGO STATE UNIVERSITY

9501 S King Dr.
Chicago, IL 60628
Tel: (773)995-2000
E-mail: jmarti21@csu.edu
Web Site: www.csu.edu
President/CEO: Dr. Wayne Watson
Admissions: John Martinez
Financial Aid: Cathy Davis
Type: Comprehensive **Sex:** Coed **Scores:** 57.5% ACT 18-23; 7.7% ACT 24-29 **% Accepted:** 30 **Application Fee:** $25.00 **H.S. Requirements:** High school diploma required; GED accepted **Costs Per Year:** Application fee: $25. State resident tuition: $7056 full-time, $294 per credit hour part-time. Nonresident tuition: $14,016 full-time, $584 per credit hour part-time. Mandatory fees: $2790 full-time, $460 per term part-time. Full-time tuition and fees vary according to course load, degree level, location, program, reciprocity agreements, and student level. Part-time tuition and fees vary according to course load, degree level, location, program, reciprocity agreements, and student level. College room and board: $8724. Room and board charges vary according to housing facility. Tuition guaranteed not to increase for student's term of enrollment. **Scholarships:** Available. **Calendar System:** Semester, Summer session available **Enrollment:** Full-time 2,498, Graduate full-time 736, Graduate part-time 563, Part-time 1,414 **Faculty:** Full-time 269, Part-time 97 **Student-Faculty Ratio:** 13:1 **Exams:** SAT I or ACT. **% Receiving Financial Aid:** 95 **Regional Accreditation:** North Central Association of Colleges and Schools **Credit Hours For Degree:** 120 credit hours, Bachelors **ROTC:** Air Force, Army, Navy **Professional Accreditation:** ACA, ACBSP, ACEN, ACPE, AHIMA, AOTA, CSWE, NASM, NCATE. **Intercollegiate Athletics:** Baseball M; Basketball M & W; Cross-Country Running M & W; Golf M & W; Tennis M & W; Track and Field M & W; Volleyball W

CHRISTIAN LIFE COLLEGE

400 E Gregory St.
Mount Prospect, IL 60056
Tel: (847)259-1840
E-mail: mbell@christianlifecollege.edu
Web Site: www.christianlifecollege.edu
President/CEO: Harry Schmidt
Admissions: Michael W. Bell
Financial Aid: Christina Bell
Type: Four-Year College **Sex:** Coed **Affiliation:** Christian. **Admission Plans:** Deferred Admission; Early Admission **Application Deadline:** Rolling **Application Fee:** $40.00 **H.S. Requirements:** High school diploma required; GED accepted **Scholarships:** Available. **Calendar System:** Semester, Summer session not available **Enrollment:** Full-time 33, Part-time 7 **Faculty:** Full-time 1, Part-time 6 **Student-Faculty Ratio:** 4:1 **Exams:** SAT I or ACT; SAT Reasoning; SAT Subject. **% Receiving Financial Aid:** 48 **Final Year or Final Semester Residency Requirement:** No **Credit Hours For Degree:** 64 units, Associates; 128 units, Bachelors **Professional Accreditation:** TRACS.

CITY COLLEGES OF CHICAGO, HAROLD WASHINGTON COLLEGE

30 E Lake St.
Chicago, IL 60601-2449

Tel: (312)553-5600
Fax: (312)553-6077
Web Site: hwashington.ccc.edu
President/CEO: John H. Metoyer
Type: Two-Year College **Sex:** Coed **Affiliation:** City Colleges of Chicago. **Admission Plans:** Deferred Admission; Early Admission; Open Admission **Application Deadline:** Rolling **Application Fee:** $0.00 **H.S. Requirements:** High school diploma required; GED accepted **Scholarships:** Available. **Calendar System:** Semester, Summer session available **Student-Faculty Ratio:** 33:1 **Regional Accreditation:** North Central Association of Colleges and Schools **Credit Hours For Degree:** 60 credit hours, Associates **Professional Accreditation:** ACBSP.

CITY COLLEGES OF CHICAGO, HARRY S. TRUMAN COLLEGE
1145 W Wilson Ave.
Chicago, IL 60640-5616
Tel: (773)907-4000
Fax: (773)907-4464
E-mail: mlatuszek@ccc.edu
Web Site: www.trumancollege.edu
President/CEO: Lynn M. Walker
Admissions: Mark J. Latuszek
Type: Two-Year College **Sex:** Coed **Affiliation:** City Colleges of Chicago. **Admission Plans:** Deferred Admission; Early Admission; Open Admission **Application Deadline:** Rolling **Application Fee:** $0.00 **H.S. Requirements:** High school diploma required; GED accepted **Scholarships:** Available. **Calendar System:** Semester, Summer session available **Student-Faculty Ratio:** 34:1 **Regional Accreditation:** North Central Association of Colleges and Schools **Credit Hours For Degree:** 60 semester hours, Associates **Professional Accreditation:** ACEN. **Intercollegiate Athletics:** Basketball M

CITY COLLEGES OF CHICAGO, KENNEDY-KING COLLEGE
6301 S Halstead St.
Chicago, IL 60621
Tel: (773)602-5000
Web Site: kennedyking.ccc.edu
President/CEO: John Dozier
Type: Two-Year College **Sex:** Coed **Affiliation:** City Colleges of Chicago. **Admission Plans:** Open Admission; Preferred Admission **Application Deadline:** Rolling **Application Fee:** $0.00 **H.S. Requirements:** High school diploma or equivalent not required **Scholarships:** Available. **Calendar System:** Semester, Summer session available **Student-Faculty Ratio:** 30:1 **Regional Accreditation:** North Central Association of Colleges and Schools **Credit Hours For Degree:** 90 quarter credits, Associates **Professional Accreditation:** ADA. **Intercollegiate Athletics:** Basketball M & W; Soccer M; Wrestling M

CITY COLLEGES OF CHICAGO, MALCOLM X COLLEGE
1900 W Van Buren St.
Chicago, IL 60612-3145
Tel: (312)850-7000
Fax: (312)850-7092
E-mail: khollingsworth@ccc.edu
Web Site: malcolmx.ccc.edu
President/CEO: Ghingo Brooks
Admissions: Kimberly Hollingsworth
Type: Two-Year College **Sex:** Coed **Affiliation:** City Colleges of Chicago. **Admission Plans:** Open Admission; Preferred Admission **Application Deadline:** Rolling **Application Fee:** $0.00 **H.S. Requirements:** High school diploma required; GED accepted **Scholarships:** Available. **Calendar System:** Semester, Summer session available **Enrollment:** Full-time 2,522, Part-time 3,509 **Faculty:** Full-time 75, Part-time 165 **Student-Faculty Ratio:** 25:1 **Final Year or Final Semester Residency Requirement:** Yes **Regional Accreditation:** North Central Association of Colleges and Schools **Credit Hours For Degree:** 60 credit hours, Associates **Professional Accreditation:** ABFSE, ARCST, JRCERT. **Intercollegiate Athletics:** Basketball M & W; Cross-Country Running M

CITY COLLEGES OF CHICAGO, OLIVE-HARVEY COLLEGE
10001 S Woodlawn Ave.
Chicago, IL 60628-1645
Tel: (773)291-6100
Fax: (773)291-6304

E-mail: dthomas236@ccc.edu
Web Site: oliveharvey.ccc.edu
President/CEO: Angelia Millender
Admissions: Dorian Thomas
Type: Two-Year College **Sex:** Coed **Affiliation:** City Colleges of Chicago. **Admission Plans:** Deferred Admission; Early Admission; Open Admission; Preferred Admission **Application Deadline:** Rolling **Application Fee:** $0.00 **H.S. Requirements:** High school diploma required; GED accepted **Costs Per Year:** Application fee: $0. Area resident tuition: $3506 full-time, $137 per credit hour part-time. State resident tuition: $8126 full-time, $436 per credit hour part-time. Nonresident tuition: $11,906 full-time, $554 per credit hour part-time. Full-time tuition varies according to course load. Part-time tuition varies according to course load. **Scholarships:** Available. **Calendar System:** Semester, Summer session available **Enrollment:** Full-time 1,322, Part-time 2,143 **Faculty:** Full-time 53, Part-time 104 **Student-Faculty Ratio:** 23:1 **Final Year or Final Semester Residency Requirement:** No **Regional Accreditation:** North Central Association of Colleges and Schools **Credit Hours For Degree:** 60 credit hours, Associates **Intercollegiate Athletics:** Baseball M; Basketball M & W; Volleyball W

CITY COLLEGES OF CHICAGO, RICHARD J. DALEY COLLEGE
7500 S Pulaski Rd.
Chicago, IL 60652-1242
Tel: (773)838-7500
Fax: (773)838-7524
E-mail: mwright@ccc.edu
Web Site: daley.ccc.edu
President/CEO: Dr. Jose Aybar
Admissions: Milton Wright
Type: Two-Year College **Sex:** Coed **Affiliation:** City Colleges of Chicago. **% Accepted:** 100 **Admission Plans:** Deferred Admission; Early Admission; Open Admission; Preferred Admission **Application Deadline:** Rolling **Application Fee:** $0.00 **H.S. Requirements:** High school diploma required; GED accepted **Scholarships:** Available. **Calendar System:** Semester, Summer session available **Enrollment:** Full-time 3,507, Part-time 6,204 **Faculty:** Full-time 56, Part-time 106 **Exams:** ACT essay component used for placement. **Regional Accreditation:** North Central Association of Colleges and Schools **Credit Hours For Degree:** 60 credit hours, Associates **ROTC:** Air Force **Professional Accreditation:** ACEN. **Intercollegiate Athletics:** Basketball M & W; Soccer M & W

CITY COLLEGES OF CHICAGO, WILBUR WRIGHT COLLEGE
4300 N Narragansett Ave.
Chicago, IL 60634-1591
Tel: (773)777-7900
E-mail: aaiello@ccc.edu
Web Site: wright.ccc.edu
President/CEO: Dr. Phoebe Wood
Admissions: Amy Aiello
Type: Two-Year College **Sex:** Coed **Affiliation:** City Colleges of Chicago. **% Accepted:** 100 **Admission Plans:** Deferred Admission; Early Admission; Open Admission; Preferred Admission **Application Deadline:** Rolling **Application Fee:** $0.00 **H.S. Requirements:** High school diploma required; GED accepted. For applicants 18 or over: High school diploma or equivalent not required **Scholarships:** Available. **Calendar System:** Semester, Summer session available **Enrollment:** Full-time 2,214, Part-time 4,612 **Faculty:** Full-time 112, Part-time 150 **Student-Faculty Ratio:** 23:1 **Regional Accreditation:** North Central Association of Colleges and Schools **Credit Hours For Degree:** 64 credit hours, Associates **Professional Accreditation:** ACBSP, AOTA, JRCERT. **Intercollegiate Athletics:** Basketball M & W; Wrestling M

COLLEGE OF DUPAGE
425 Fawell Blvd.
Glen Ellyn, IL 60137-6599
Tel: (630)942-2800
Fax: (630)790-2686
E-mail: admissions@cod.edu
Web Site: www.cod.edu
President/CEO: Dr. Robert Breuder
Type: Two-Year College **Sex:** Coed **% Accepted:** 87 **Admission Plans:** Deferred Admission; Early Admission; Open Admission **Application Deadline:** Rolling **Application Fee:** $20.00 **H.S. Requirements:** High school diploma or equivalent not required **Scholarships:** Available.

Calendar System: Semester, Summer session available **Enrollment:** Full-time 9,464, Part-time 16,745 **Faculty:** Full-time 273, Part-time 861 **Student-Faculty Ratio:** 21:1 **Exams:** ACT. **Final Year or Final Semester Residency Requirement:** No **Regional Accreditation:** North Central Association of Colleges and Schools **Credit Hours For Degree:** 60 semester hours, Associates **Professional Accreditation:** ACF, ADA, AHIMA, APTA, CoARC, JRCERT, NASAD. **Intercollegiate Athletics:** Baseball M; Basketball M & W; Golf M; Soccer M & W; Softball M & W

COLLEGE OF LAKE COUNTY
19351 W Washington St.
Grayslake, IL 60030-1198
Tel: (847)543-2000
Fax: (847)223-1017
Web Site: www.clcillinois.edu
President/CEO: Dr. Girard Weber
Type: Two-Year College **Sex:** Coed **Affiliation:** Illinois Community College Board. **Admission Plans:** Deferred Admission; Early Admission; Open Admission; Preferred Admission **Application Deadline:** Rolling **Application Fee:** $0.00 **H.S. Requirements:** High school diploma or equivalent not required. For health programs: High school diploma required; GED accepted **Scholarships:** Available. **Calendar System:** Semester, Summer session available **Enrollment:** Full-time 4,945, Part-time 12,632 **Faculty:** Full-time 210, Part-time 822 **Student-Faculty Ratio:** 17:1 **Regional Accreditation:** North Central Association of Colleges and Schools **Credit Hours For Degree:** 60 credits, Associates **Professional Accreditation:** ACEN, ADA, AHIMA, JRCERT. **Intercollegiate Athletics:** Baseball M; Basketball M & W; Cross-Country Running M & W; Golf M; Soccer M & W; Softball W; Tennis M & W; Volleyball W

COLUMBIA COLLEGE CHICAGO
600 S Michigan Ave.
Chicago, IL 60605-1996
Tel: (312)663-1600
E-mail: admissions@colum.edu
Web Site: www.colum.edu
President/CEO: Dr. Kwang-wu Kim
Admissions: Katherine Lelek
Financial Aid: Jennifer Waters
Type: Comprehensive **Sex:** Coed **Scores:** 47% ACT 18-23; 35% ACT 24-29 **% Accepted:** 88 **Admission Plans:** Deferred Admission **Application Fee:** $35.00 **H.S. Requirements:** High school diploma required; GED accepted **Costs Per Year:** Application fee: $35. Comprehensive fee: $39,096 includes full-time tuition ($25,798) and college room and board ($13,298). Full-time tuition varies according to course load. Room and board charges vary according to housing facility. **Scholarships:** Available. **Calendar System:** Semester, Summer session available **Enrollment:** Full-time 7,806, Graduate full-time 256, Graduate part-time 97, Part-time 802 **Faculty:** Full-time 324, Part-time 809 **Student-Faculty Ratio:** 14:1 **Exams:** ACT essay component not used; SAT I or ACT; SAT essay component not used. **% Receiving Financial Aid:** 59 **% Residing in College-Owned, -Operated, or -Affiliated Housing:** 27 **Final Year or Final Semester Residency Requirement:** Yes **Regional Accreditation:** North Central Association of Colleges and Schools **Credit Hours For Degree:** 120 credits, Bachelors **Intercollegiate Athletics:** Baseball M; Basketball M; Lacrosse M

CONCORDIA UNIVERSITY CHICAGO
7400 Augusta St.
River Forest, IL 60305-1499
Tel: (708)771-8300; Free: 800-285-2668
Fax: (708)209-3176
E-mail: gwen.kanelos@cuchicago.edu
Web Site: www.cuchicago.edu
President/CEO: Dr. John F. Johnson
Admissions: Gwen Kanelos
Financial Aid: Aida Asencio-Pinto
Type: Comprehensive **Sex:** Coed **Affiliation:** Lutheran Church–Missouri Synod; Concordia University System. **Scores:** 88% SAT V 400+; 92% SAT M 400+; 57% ACT 18-23; 31% ACT 24-29 **% Accepted:** 50 **Admission Plans:** Deferred Admission; Early Admission **Application Deadline:** Rolling **Application Fee:** $0.00 **H.S. Requirements:** High school diploma required; GED accepted **Costs Per Year:** Application fee: $0. Comprehensive fee: $39,812 includes full-time tuition ($29,760), mandatory fees ($880), and college room and board ($9172). College room only: $4414. Full-time tuition

and fees vary according to course load, degree level, and reciprocity agreements. Room and board charges vary according to board plan and housing facility. Part-time tuition: $899 per credit hour. Part-time tuition varies according to course load, degree level, and reciprocity agreements. **Scholarships:** Available. **Calendar System:** Semester **Enrollment:** Full-time 1,348, Graduate full-time 190, Graduate part-time 3,539, Part-time 161 **Faculty:** Full-time 265, Part-time 164 **Student-Faculty Ratio:** 15:1 **Exams:** Other; SAT I or ACT. **% Receiving Financial Aid:** 86 **% Residing in College-Owned, -Operated, or -Affiliated Housing:** 36 **Regional Accreditation:** North Central Association of Colleges and Schools **Credit Hours For Degree:** 128 semester hours, Bachelors **Professional Accreditation:** ACA, NASM, NCATE. **Intercollegiate Athletics:** Baseball M; Basketball M & W; Cheerleading M & W; Cross-Country Running M & W; Football M; Golf M; Soccer M & W; Softball W; Tennis M & W; Track and Field M & W; Volleyball W

COYNE COLLEGE
330 N Green St.
Chicago, IL 60607
Tel: (773)577-8100; Free: 800-707-1922
E-mail: csilverman@coynecollege.edu
Web Site: www.coynecollege.edu
President/CEO: Russell T. Freeman
Admissions: Claudia M. Macias-Silverman
Type: Two-Year College **Sex:** Coed **Calendar System:** Continuous **Enrollment:** Full-time 522 **Exams:** ACT essay component not used; Other; SAT I or ACT; SAT essay component not used. **Final Year or Final Semester Residency Requirement:** No **Credit Hours For Degree:** 91 quarter credit hours, Associates **Professional Accreditation:** ACCSC.

DANVILLE AREA COMMUNITY COLLEGE
2000 E Main St.
Danville, IL 61832-5199
Tel: (217)443-3222
Fax: (217)443-8560
E-mail: ncatlett@dacc.edu
Web Site: www.dacc.edu
President/CEO: Dr. Alice Marie Jacobs
Admissions: Nick Catlett
Financial Aid: Janet M. Ingargiola
Type: Two-Year College **Sex:** Coed **Affiliation:** Illinois Community College Board. **Admission Plans:** Deferred Admission; Early Admission; Open Admission **Application Deadline:** Rolling **Application Fee:** $0.00 **H.S. Requirements:** High school diploma required; GED accepted **Costs Per Year:** Application fee: $0. Area resident tuition: $3600 full-time, $130 per credit hour part-time. State resident tuition: $6000 full-time, $200 per credit hour part-time. Nonresident tuition: $6000 full-time, $200 per credit hour part-time. Mandatory fees: $600 full-time, $20 per credit hour part-time. Full-time tuition and fees vary according to program. Part-time tuition and fees vary according to program. **Scholarships:** Available. **Calendar System:** Semester, Summer session available **Enrollment:** Full-time 1,070, Part-time 1,622 **Faculty:** Full-time 69, Part-time 98 **Student-Faculty Ratio:** 17:1 **Regional Accreditation:** North Central Association of Colleges and Schools **Credit Hours For Degree:** 60 semester hours, Associates **Intercollegiate Athletics:** Baseball M; Basketball M & W; Cheerleading W; Cross-Country Running M & W; Softball W

DEPAUL UNIVERSITY
1 E Jackson Blvd.
Chicago, IL 60604-2287
Tel: (312)362-8000; Free: 800-4DE-PAUL
Fax: (312)362-3322
E-mail: admission@depaul.edu
Web Site: www.depaul.edu
President/CEO: Rev. Dennis H. Holtschneider, CM
Admissions: Carlene Klaas-Kennelly
Financial Aid: DePaul Central
Type: University **Sex:** Coed **Affiliation:** Roman Catholic. **Scores:** 98% SAT V 400+; 97% SAT M 400+; 31.69% ACT 18-23; 51.77% ACT 24-29 **% Accepted:** 72 **Admission Plans:** Deferred Admission; Early Decision Plan **Application Deadline:** February 1 **H.S. Requirements:** High school diploma required; GED accepted **Costs Per Year:** Comprehensive fee: $49,234 includes full-time tuition ($35,680), mandatory fees ($681), and college room and board ($12,873). College room only: $9261. Full-time tuition and fees

vary according to course load and program. Room and board charges vary according to board plan, housing facility, and location. Part-time tuition: $585 per credit hour. Part-time tuition varies according to course load and program. **Scholarships:** Available. **Calendar System:** Quarter, Summer session available **Enrollment:** Full-time 13,664, Graduate full-time 5,104, Graduate part-time 2,474, Part-time 2,297 **Faculty:** Full-time 914, Part-time 971 **Student-Faculty Ratio:** 16:1 **Exams:** SAT I or ACT; SAT Reasoning. **% Receiving Financial Aid:** 67 % **Residing in College-Owned, -Operated, or -Affiliated Housing:** 17 **Final Year or Final Semester Residency Requirement:** Yes **Regional Accreditation:** North Central Association of Colleges and Schools **Credit Hours For Degree:** 192 quarter hours, Bachelors **ROTC:** Army **Professional Accreditation:** AACN, AACSB, AALS, AANA, ABA, APA, CSWE, NASM, NASPAA, NCATE. **Intercollegiate Athletics:** Basketball M & W; Cross-Country Running M & W; Golf M; Soccer M & W; Softball W; Tennis M & W; Track and Field M & W; Volleyball W

DEVRY UNIVERSITY (ADDISON)

1221 N Swift Rd.
Addison, IL 60101-6106
Tel: (630)953-1300; Free: 866-338-7941
Fax: (630)953-1236
Web Site: www.devry.edu
Financial Aid: Sejal Amin

Type: Four-Year College **Sex:** Coed **Affiliation:** DeVry University. **Application Deadline:** Rolling **Costs Per Year:** Tuition: $17,052 full-time, $609 per credit hour part-time. Mandatory fees: $80 full-time, $40 per term part-time. **Scholarships:** Available. **Calendar System:** Semester **% Receiving Financial Aid:** 70 **Regional Accreditation:** North Central Association of Colleges and Schools **Professional Accreditation:** ABET.

DEVRY UNIVERSITY (CHICAGO)

3300 N Campbell Ave.
Chicago, IL 60618-5994
Tel: (773)929-8500; Free: 866-338-7941
Web Site: www.devry.edu
Financial Aid: Milena Dobrina

Type: Comprehensive **Sex:** Coed **Affiliation:** DeVry University. **Application Fee:** $40.00. **H.S. Requirements:** High school diploma required; GED accepted **Costs Per Year:** Application fee: $40. Tuition: $17,052 full-time, $609 per credit hour part-time. Mandatory fees: $80 full-time, $40 per term part-time. **Scholarships:** Available. **Calendar System:** Semester **Enrollment:** Full-time 738, Graduate full-time 50, Graduate part-time 95, Part-time 411 **Faculty:** Full-time 28, Part-time 136 **Student-Faculty Ratio:** 13:1 **Exams:** ACT essay component used for admission; ACT essay component used for placement; SAT essay component used for admission; SAT essay component used for placement. **% Receiving Financial Aid:** 72 **Regional Accreditation:** North Central Association of Colleges and Schools **Credit Hours For Degree:** 67 credit hours, Associates; 122 credit hours, Bachelors **Professional Accreditation:** ABET, ACBSP.

DEVRY UNIVERSITY (DOWNERS GROVE)

3005 Highland Pky., Ste. 100
Downers Grove, IL 60515
Tel: (630)515-3000; Free: 866-338-7941
Web Site: www.devry.edu
President/CEO: Rob Paul

Type: Comprehensive **Sex:** Coed **Application Deadline:** Rolling **Costs Per Year:** Tuition: $17,052 full-time, $609 per credit hour part-time. Mandatory fees: $80 full-time, $40 per term part-time. **Calendar System:** Semester **Regional Accreditation:** North Central Association of Colleges and Schools **Professional Accreditation:** ABET, ACBSP.

DEVRY UNIVERSITY (ELGIN)

Randall Point
2250 Point Blvd., Ste. 250
Elgin, IL 60123
Tel: (847)649-3980; Free: 866-338-7941
Web Site: www.devry.edu

Type: Comprehensive **Sex:** Coed **Application Deadline:** Rolling **Costs Per Year:** Tuition: $17,052 full-time, $609 per credit hour part-time. Mandatory fees: $80 full-time, $40 per term part-time. **Calendar System:** Semester **Regional Accreditation:** North Central Association of Colleges and Schools **Professional Accreditation:** ACBSP.

DEVRY UNIVERSITY (GURNEE)

1075 Tri-State Pky., Ste. 800
Gurnee, IL 60031-9126
Tel: (847)855-2649; Free: 866-338-7941
Fax: (847)855-5932
Web Site: www.devry.edu

Type: Comprehensive **Sex:** Coed **Application Deadline:** Rolling **Costs Per Year:** Tuition: $17,052 full-time, $609 per credit hour part-time. Mandatory fees: $80 full-time, $40 per term part-time. **Calendar System:** Semester **Regional Accreditation:** North Central Association of Colleges and Schools **Professional Accreditation:** ACBSP.

DEVRY UNIVERSITY (NAPERVILLE)

2056 Westings Ave., Ste. 40
Naperville, IL 60563-2361
Tel: (630)428-9086; Free: 866-338-7941
Fax: (630)428-4721
Web Site: www.devry.edu

Type: Comprehensive **Sex:** Coed **Application Deadline:** Rolling **Costs Per Year:** Tuition: $17,052 full-time, $609 per credit hour part-time. Mandatory fees: $80 full-time, $40 per term part-time. **Calendar System:** Semester **Regional Accreditation:** North Central Association of Colleges and Schools **Professional Accreditation:** ACBSP.

DEVRY UNIVERSITY (TINLEY PARK)

18624 W Creek Dr.
Tinley Park, IL 60477
Tel: (708)342-3300; Free: 866-338-7941
Web Site: www.devry.edu

Type: Comprehensive **Sex:** Coed **Affiliation:** DeVry University. **Application Deadline:** Rolling **Scholarships:** Available. **Calendar System:** Semester **% Receiving Financial Aid:** 83 **Regional Accreditation:** North Central Association of Colleges and Schools **Credit Hours For Degree:** 67 credit hours, Associates; 122 credit hours, Bachelors **Professional Accreditation:** ACBSP.

DEVRY UNIVERSITY ONLINE

1221 N Swift Rd.
Addison, IL 60101-6106
Free: 866-338-7941
Web Site: www.devry.edu

Type: Comprehensive **Sex:** Coed **Application Deadline:** Rolling **Application Fee:** $40.00. **H.S. Requirements:** High school diploma required; GED accepted **Costs Per Year:** Application fee: $40. Tuition: $17,052 full-time, $609 per credit hour part-time. Mandatory fees: $80 full-time, $40 per term part-time. **Scholarships:** Available. **Calendar System:** Semester **Enrollment:** Full-time 4,535, Graduate full-time 739, Graduate part-time 3,898, Part-time 11,260 **Faculty:** Full-time 106, Part-time 2,394 **Student-Faculty Ratio:** 11:1 **Exams:** ACT essay component used for admission; ACT essay component used for placement; SAT essay component used for admission; SAT essay component used for placement. **% Receiving Financial Aid:** 52 **Regional Accreditation:** North Central Association of Colleges and Schools **Professional Accreditation:** ABET.

DOMINICAN UNIVERSITY

7900 W Division St.
River Forest, IL 60305-1099
Tel: (708)366-2490; Free: 800-828-8475
Fax: (708)366-5360
E-mail: domadmis@dom.edu
Web Site: www.dom.edu
President/CEO: Dr. Donna M. Carroll
Admissions: Glenn Hamilton
Financial Aid: Victoria Lamick

Type: Comprehensive **Sex:** Coed **Affiliation:** Roman Catholic. **Scores:** 92% SAT V 400+; 100% SAT M 400+; 25% ACT 18-23; 67% ACT 24-29 **% Accepted:** 63 **Admission Plans:** Deferred Admission **Application Deadline:** Rolling **Application Fee:** $25.00 **H.S. Requirements:** High school diploma required; GED accepted **Costs Per Year:** Application fee: $25. One-time mandatory fee: $150. Comprehensive fee: $40,050 includes full-time tuition ($30,300), mandatory fees ($370), and college room and board ($9380). Full-time tuition and fees vary according to course load, program, and reciprocity agreements. Room and board charges vary according to board plan and housing facility. Part-time tuition: $1010 per credit hour.

Part-time mandatory fees: $90 per term. Part-time tuition and fees vary according to course load, program, and reciprocity agreements. **Scholarships:** Available. **Calendar System:** Semester, Summer session available **Enrollment:** Full-time 2,076, Graduate full-time 359, Graduate part-time 1,065, Part-time 196 **Faculty:** Full-time 167, Part-time 295 **Student-Faculty Ratio:** 12:1 **Exams:** ACT essay component not used; SAT I or ACT; SAT essay component not used; SAT Reasoning; SAT Subject. **% Receiving Financial Aid:** 83 **% Residing in College-Owned, -Operated, or -Affiliated Housing:** 26 **Final Year or Final Semester Residency Requirement:** Yes **Regional Accreditation:** North Central Association of Colleges and Schools **Credit Hours For Degree:** 120 credit hours, Bachelors **Professional Accreditation:** AACSB, ACBSP, ALA, CSWE, NCATE. **Intercollegiate Athletics:** Baseball M; Basketball M & W; Cross-Country Running M & W; Golf M; Soccer M & W; Softball W; Tennis M & W; Volleyball M & W

EAST-WEST UNIVERSITY
816 S Michigan Ave.
Chicago, IL 60605-2103
Tel: (312)939-0111
Fax: (312)939-0083
Web Site: www.eastwest.edu
President/CEO: Dr. M. Wasiullah Khan
Admissions: Bryan Lambert
Financial Aid: Cesar Campos
Type: Four-Year College **Sex:** Coed **Scores:** 35% ACT 18-23; 4% ACT 24-29 **% Accepted:** 89 **Admission Plans:** Early Action **Application Deadline:** Rolling **Application Fee:** $40.00 **H.S. Requirements:** High school diploma required; GED accepted **Scholarships:** Available. **Calendar System:** Quarter, Summer session available **Enrollment:** Full-time 737, Part-time 18 **Faculty:** Full-time 18, Part-time 49 **Student-Faculty Ratio:** 15:1 **Exams:** ACT. **Final Year or Final Semester Residency Requirement:** No **Regional Accreditation:** North Central Association of Colleges and Schools **Credit Hours For Degree:** 92 quarter hours, Associates; 180 quarter hours, Bachelors **Intercollegiate Athletics:** Basketball M

EASTERN ILLINOIS UNIVERSITY
600 Lincoln Ave.
Charleston, IL 61920
Tel: (217)581-5000; Free: 877-581-2348
Fax: (217)581-7060
E-mail: dalee@eiu.edu
Web Site: www.eiu.edu
President/CEO: Dr. David Glassman
Admissions: Denise Lee
Financial Aid: Mandi Starwalt
Type: Comprehensive **Sex:** Coed **Scores:** 60% ACT 18-23; 24% ACT 24-29 **% Accepted:** 50 **Admission Plans:** Deferred Admission **Application Deadline:** Rolling **Application Fee:** $30.00 **H.S. Requirements:** High school diploma required; GED accepted **Costs Per Year:** Application fee: $30. State resident tuition: $8550 full-time, $285 per credit hour part-time. Nonresident tuition: $10,680 full-time, $356 per credit hour part-time. Mandatory fees: $2762 full-time, $102 per credit hour part-time. Full-time tuition and fees vary according to course load and student level. Part-time tuition and fees vary according to course load and student level. College room and board: $9546. Room and board charges vary according to board plan and housing facility. Tuition guaranteed not to increase for student's term of enrollment. **Scholarships:** Available. **Calendar System:** Semester, Summer session available **Enrollment:** Full-time 6,255, Graduate full-time 656, Graduate part-time 662, Part-time 947 **Faculty:** Full-time 468, Part-time 129 **Student-Faculty Ratio:** 15:1 **Exams:** SAT I or ACT; SAT Reasoning. **% Receiving Financial Aid:** 68 **% Residing in College-Owned, -Operated, or -Affiliated Housing:** 39 **Final Year or Final Semester Residency Requirement:** Yes **Regional Accreditation:** North Central Association of Colleges and Schools **Credit Hours For Degree:** 120 semester hours, Bachelors **ROTC:** Army **Professional Accreditation:** AACN, AACSB, AAFCS, ACA, ACEJMC, AND, ASHA, ATMAE, JRCAT, NASAD, NASM, NCATE, NRPA. **Intercollegiate Athletics:** Badminton M & W; Baseball M; Basketball M & W; Cross-Country Running M & W; Equestrian Sports M & W; Football M; Golf M & W; Ice Hockey M; Soccer M & W; Softball W; Swimming and Diving M & W; Tennis M & W; Track and Field M & W; Ultimate Frisbee M & W; Volleyball W; Water Polo M & W; Wrestling M & W

ELGIN COMMUNITY COLLEGE
1700 Spartan Dr.
Elgin, IL 60123-7193

Tel: (847)697-1000
E-mail: admissions@elgin.edu
Web Site: www.elgin.edu
President/CEO: Dr. David Sam
Type: Two-Year College **Sex:** Coed **Affiliation:** Illinois Community College Board. **Admission Plans:** Open Admission **Application Deadline:** Rolling **Application Fee:** $0.00 **H.S. Requirements:** High school diploma or equivalent not required. For nursing, selected health programs: High school diploma required; GED accepted **Costs Per Year:** Application fee: $0. Area resident tuition: $3570 full-time, $119 per credit hour part-time. State resident tuition: $13,035 full-time, $434.49 per credit hour part-time. Nonresident tuition: $14,934 full-time, $497.79 per credit hour part-time. Mandatory fees: $10 full-time, $5 per term part-time. **Calendar System:** Semester, Summer session available **Enrollment:** Full-time 3,780, Part-time 7,505 **Final Year or Final Semester Residency Requirement:** No **Regional Accreditation:** North Central Association of Colleges and Schools **Credit Hours For Degree:** 60 credit hours, Associates **Professional Accreditation:** ACEN, ADA, NAACLS. **Intercollegiate Athletics:** Baseball M; Basketball M & W; Cross-Country Running M & W; Golf M; Soccer M & W; Softball W; Tennis M & W; Volleyball W

ELLIS UNIVERSITY
2 Mid America Plz.
Ste. 824AB
Oakbrook Terrace, IL 60181
Free: 877-355-4762
E-mail: admissions@ellis.edu
Web Site: www.ellis.edu
President/CEO: Roger Widmer
Type: Comprehensive **Sex:** Coed **Application Fee:** $75.00 **Calendar System:** Trimester **Enrollment:** Full-time 9, Graduate full-time 5, Graduate part-time 8, Part-time 6 **Student-Faculty Ratio:** 8:1 **Professional Accreditation:** DEAC.

ELMHURST COLLEGE
190 Prospect Ave.
Elmhurst, IL 60126-3296
Tel: (630)617-3500; Free: 800-697-1871
Fax: (630)617-5501
E-mail: admit@elmhurst.edu
Web Site: www.elmhurst.edu
President/CEO: Dr. Larry Braskamp
Admissions: Stephanie Levenson
Financial Aid: Ruth A. Pusich
Type: Comprehensive **Sex:** Coed **Affiliation:** United Church of Christ. **Scores:** 97% SAT V 400+; 97% SAT M 400+; 44.47% ACT 18-23; 41.43% ACT 24-29 **% Accepted:** 55 **Admission Plans:** Deferred Admission **Application Deadline:** Rolling **Application Fee:** $0.00 **H.S. Requirements:** High school diploma required; GED accepted **Costs Per Year:** Application fee: $0. Comprehensive fee: $45,578 includes full-time tuition ($35,250), mandatory fees ($250), and college room and board ($10,078). College room only: $6152. Room and board charges vary according to board plan and housing facility. Part-time tuition: $997 per semester hour. Part-time tuition varies according to course load. **Scholarships:** Available. **Calendar System:** 4-1-4, Summer session available **Enrollment:** Full-time 2,677, Graduate full-time 83, Graduate part-time 375, Part-time 163 **Faculty:** Full-time 141, Part-time 210 **Student-Faculty Ratio:** 14:1 **Exams:** SAT I or ACT. **% Receiving Financial Aid:** 75 **% Residing in College-Owned, -Operated, or -Affiliated Housing:** 32 **Regional Accreditation:** North Central Association of Colleges and Schools **Credit Hours For Degree:** 32 courses, Bachelors **ROTC:** Air Force, Army **Professional Accreditation:** AACN. **Intercollegiate Athletics:** Baseball M; Basketball M & W; Bowling W; Cross-Country Running M & W; Football M; Golf M & W; Lacrosse M & W; Soccer M & W; Softball W; Tennis M & W; Track and Field M & W; Volleyball W; Wrestling M

EUREKA COLLEGE
300 E College Ave.
Eureka, IL 61530
Tel: (309)467-3721; Free: 888-4-EUREKA
Fax: (309)467-6576
E-mail: mmurtagh@eureka.edu
Web Site: www.eureka.edu
President/CEO: Dr. J. David Arnold

Admissions: Mike Murtagh

Financial Aid: Erin Bline

Type: Four-Year College **Sex:** Coed **Affiliation:** Christian Church (Disciples of Christ). **Scores:** 100% SAT V 400+; 100% SAT M 400+; 51% ACT 18-23; 30% ACT 24-29 **% Accepted:** 65 **Application Deadline:** August 1 **Application Fee:** $0.00 **H.S. Requirements:** High school diploma required; GED accepted **Costs Per Year:** Application fee: $0. Comprehensive fee: $27,130 includes full-time tuition ($20,880), mandatory fees ($240), and college room and board ($6010). Full-time tuition and fees vary according to course load and program. Room and board charges vary according to board plan and housing facility. Part-time tuition: $595 per semester hour. Part-time tuition varies according to course load and program. **Scholarships:** Available. **Calendar System:** Semester, Summer session available **Enrollment:** Full-time 657, Part-time 38 **Faculty:** Full-time 44, Part-time 23 **Student-Faculty Ratio:** 10:1 **Exams:** ACT essay component not used; SAT I or ACT; SAT essay component not used; SAT Reasoning. **% Receiving Financial Aid:** 75 **% Residing in College-Owned, -Operated, or -Affiliated Housing:** 66 **Final Year or Final Semester Residency Requirement:** Yes **Regional Accreditation:** North Central Association of Colleges and Schools **Credit Hours For Degree:** 124 semester hours, Bachelors **Intercollegiate Athletics:** Baseball M; Basketball M & W; Cross-Country Running M & W; Football M; Golf M; Soccer M & W; Softball W; Swimming and Diving M & W; Track and Field M & W; Volleyball W

FOX COLLEGE

6640 S Cicero

Bedford Park, IL 60638

Tel: (708)636-7700

Fax: (708)636-8078

Web Site: www.foxcollege.edu

President/CEO: Carey Cranston

Type: Two-Year College **Sex:** Coed **% Accepted:** 68 **Calendar System:** Semester **Regional Accreditation:** North Central Association of Colleges and Schools **Professional Accreditation:** ACICS.

GOVERNORS STATE UNIVERSITY

One University Pky.

University Park, IL 60484

Tel: (708)534-5000; Free: 800-478-8478

Fax: (708)534-1640

E-mail: ydaniels@govst.edu

Web Site: www.govst.edu

President/CEO: Dr. Elaine Maimon

Admissions: Yakeea Daniels

Financial Aid: John Perry

Type: University **Sex:** Coed **Scores:** 75% SAT V 400+; 80% SAT M 400+; 61.8% ACT 18-23; 8.9% ACT 24-29 **% Accepted:** 39 **Admission Plans:** Deferred Admission; Early Action; Early Admission; Early Decision Plan **Application Fee:** $25.00 **H.S. Requirements:** High school diploma required; GED accepted **Costs Per Year:** Application fee: $25. State resident tuition: $10,246 full-time, $272 per credit hour part-time. Nonresident tuition: $18,406 full-time, $544 per credit hour part-time. Mandatory fees: $2086 full-time, $67 per credit hour part-time, $38 per term part-time. Full-time tuition and fees vary according to course load, degree level, reciprocity agreements, and student level. Part-time tuition and fees vary according to course load, degree level, reciprocity agreements, and student level. College room and board: $9638. College room only: $7638. Room and board charges vary according to board plan and housing facility. Tuition guaranteed not to increase for student's term of enrollment. **Scholarships:** Available. **Calendar System:** Semester, Summer session available **Enrollment:** Full-time 1,869, Graduate full-time 978, Graduate part-time 1,390, Part-time 1,701 **Faculty:** Full-time 222, Part-time 265 **Student-Faculty Ratio:** 12:1 **Exams:** ACT essay component not used; SAT I and SAT II or ACT; SAT essay component not used; SAT Reasoning; SAT Subject. **% Residing in College-Owned, -Operated, or -Affiliated Housing:** 5 **Final Year or Final Semester Residency Requirement:** No **Regional Accreditation:** North Central Association of Colleges and Schools **Credit Hours For Degree:** 120 credit hours, Bachelors **Professional Accreditation:** ACA, ACBSP, ACEN, AOTA, APTA, ASHA, CAHME, CSWE, NASPAA, NCATE. **Intercollegiate Athletics:** Basketball M & W; Cross-Country Running M & W; Golf M & W; Volleyball W

GREENVILLE COLLEGE

315 E College Ave.

Greenville, IL 62246-0159

Tel: (618)664-2800; Free: 800-345-4440

Fax: (618)664-9841

E-mail: admissions@greenville.edu

Web Site: www.greenville.edu

President/CEO: Dr. Ivan L. Filby

Admissions: Karl Hatton

Financial Aid: Marilae Latham

Type: Comprehensive **Sex:** Coed **Affiliation:** Free Methodist. **Scores:** 92% SAT V 400+; 92% SAT M 400+; 52% ACT 18-23; 32% ACT 24-29 **% Accepted:** 72 **Admission Plans:** Deferred Admission; Early Admission **Application Deadline:** Rolling **H.S. Requirements:** High school diploma required; GED accepted **Costs Per Year:** Comprehensive fee: $33,376 includes full-time tuition ($24,864), mandatory fees ($224), and college room and board ($8288). College room only: $4012. Full-time tuition and fees vary according to degree level. Room and board charges vary according to housing facility. Part-time tuition: $526 per credit. Part-time tuition varies according to course load and degree level. **Scholarships:** Available. **Calendar System:** 4-1-4, Summer session available **Enrollment:** Full-time 1,030, Graduate full-time 31, Graduate part-time 213, Part-time 47 **Faculty:** Full-time 60, Part-time 120 **Student-Faculty Ratio:** 13:1 **Exams:** SAT I or ACT; SAT Reasoning; SAT Subject. **% Receiving Financial Aid:** 87 **% Residing in College-Owned, -Operated, or -Affiliated Housing:** 73 **Regional Accreditation:** North Central Association of Colleges and Schools **Credit Hours For Degree:** 126 credits, Bachelors **Intercollegiate Athletics:** Baseball M; Basketball M & W; Cross-Country Running M & W; Football M; Soccer M & W; Softball W; Tennis M & W; Track and Field M & W; Volleyball M & W

HARPER COLLEGE

1200 W Algonquin Rd.

Palatine, IL 60067-7398

Tel: (847)925-6000

Fax: (847)925-6044

E-mail: admissions@harpercollege.edu

Web Site: goforward.harpercollege.edu

President/CEO: Dr. Kenneth L. Ender

Type: Two-Year College **Sex:** Coed **Affiliation:** Illinois Community College Board. **Scores:** 47.1% ACT 18-23; 25.3% ACT 24-29 **% Accepted:** 92 **Admission Plans:** Deferred Admission; Early Admission; Open Admission; Preferred Admission **Application Deadline:** Rolling **Application Fee:** $25.00 **H.S. Requirements:** High school diploma required; GED accepted **Costs Per Year:** Application fee: $25. Area resident tuition: $3413 full-time, $113.75 per credit hour part-time. State resident tuition: $11,123 full-time, $370.75 per credit hour part-time. Nonresident tuition: $13,388 full-time, $446.25 per credit hour part-time. Mandatory fees: $619 full-time, $16 per credit hour part-time. Full-time tuition and fees vary according to course load and program. Part-time tuition and fees vary according to course load and program. Tuition guaranteed not to increase for student's term of enrollment. **Scholarships:** Available. **Calendar System:** Semester, Summer session available **Faculty:** Full-time 210, Part-time 575 **Student-Faculty Ratio:** 8:1 **Final Year or Final Semester Residency Requirement:** No **Regional Accreditation:** North Central Association of Colleges and Schools **Credit Hours For Degree:** 60 semester hours, Associates **Professional Accreditation:** AAMAE, ACBSP, ACEN, ADA, NASM. **Intercollegiate Athletics:** Baseball M; Basketball M & W; Cross-Country Running M & W; Soccer M & W; Softball W; Track and Field M & W; Volleyball W; Wrestling M

HEARTLAND COMMUNITY COLLEGE

1500 W Raab Rd.

Normal, IL 61761

Tel: (309)268-8000

Fax: (309)268-7999

E-mail: candace.brownlee@heartland.edu

Web Site: www.heartland.edu

President/CEO: Dr. Jonathan M. Astroth

Admissions: Candace Brownlee

Financial Aid: Todd Burns

Type: Two-Year College **Sex:** Coed **Affiliation:** Illinois Community College Board. **Admission Plans:** Open Admission **Application Deadline:** Rolling **Application Fee:** $0.00 **H.S. Requirements:** High school diploma required; GED accepted **Scholarships:** Available. **Calendar System:** Semester, Summer session available **Faculty:** Full-time 70, Part-time 183 **Student-Faculty Ratio:** 19:1 **Regional Accreditation:** North Central Association of Colleges and Schools **Credit Hours For Degree:** 60 semester hours, Associates **ROTC:** Army **Professional Accreditation:** ACEN. **Intercollegiate Athletics:** Baseball M; Soccer M & W; Softball W

HEBREW THEOLOGICAL COLLEGE

7135 N Carpenter Rd.
Skokie, IL 60077-3263
Tel: (847)982-2500
Web Site: www.htc.edu
President/CEO: Rabbi Shmuel Schuman
Admissions: Rabbi Berish Cardash
Financial Aid: Rhoda Morris

Type: Four-Year College **Affiliation:** Jewish. **Application Deadline:** August 15 **Application Fee:** $75.00 **H.S. Requirements:** High school diploma required; GED accepted **Calendar System:** Semester, Summer session available **Exams:** SAT I or ACT. **Regional Accreditation:** North Central Association of Colleges and Schools **Credit Hours For Degree:** 120 credit hours, Bachelors

HIGHLAND COMMUNITY COLLEGE

2998 W Pearl City Rd.
Freeport, IL 61032-9341
Tel: (815)235-6121
Fax: (815)235-6130
E-mail: jeremy.bradt@highland.edu
Web Site: www.highland.edu
President/CEO: Tim Hood
Admissions: Jeremy Bradt
Financial Aid: Kathy Bangasser

Type: Two-Year College **Sex:** Coed **Affiliation:** Illinois Community College Board. **% Accepted:** 100 **Admission Plans:** Deferred Admission; Early Admission; Open Admission; Preferred Admission **Application Deadline:** Rolling **Application Fee:** $0.00 **H.S. Requirements:** High school diploma required; GED accepted **Costs Per Year:** Application fee: $0. Area resident tuition: $3690 full-time, $123 per credit hour part-time. State resident tuition: $5910 full-time, $197 per credit hour part-time. Nonresident tuition: $6180 full-time, $206 per credit hour part-time. Mandatory fees: $600 full-time, $19 per credit hour part-time, $15 per term part-time. Full-time tuition and fees vary according to program and reciprocity agreements. Part-time tuition and fees vary according to program and reciprocity agreements. **Scholarships:** Available. **Calendar System:** Semester, Summer session available **Enrollment:** Full-time 924, Part-time 880 **Faculty:** Full-time 48, Part-time 72 **Student-Faculty Ratio:** 17:1 **Final Year or Final Semester Residency Requirement:** No **Regional Accreditation:** North Central Association of Colleges and Schools **Credit Hours For Degree:** 62 credit hours, Associates **Intercollegiate Athletics:** Baseball M; Basketball M & W; Bowling M & W; Golf M & W; Softball W; Volleyball W

ILLINOIS CENTRAL COLLEGE

1 College Dr.
East Peoria, IL 61635-0001
Tel: (309)694-5011
Fax: (309)694-5450
Web Site: www.icc.edu
President/CEO: Bruce Budde
Admissions: Angela Dreessen

Type: Two-Year College **Sex:** Coed **Affiliation:** Illinois Community College Board. **Scores:** 48% ACT 18-23; 12.8% ACT 24-29 **% Accepted:** 41 **Admission Plans:** Early Admission; Open Admission **Application Deadline:** Rolling **Application Fee:** $0.00 **H.S. Requirements:** High school diploma or equivalent not required **Costs Per Year:** Application fee: $0. Area resident tuition: $3240 full-time, $135 per credit hour part-time. State resident tuition: $6960 full-time, $290 per credit hour part-time. Nonresident tuition: $8040 full-time, $335 per credit hour part-time. Full-time tuition varies according to course load. Part-time tuition varies according to course load. **Scholarships:** Available. **Calendar System:** Semester, Summer session available **Enrollment:** Full-time 3,475, Part-time 6,229 **Faculty:** Full-time 178, Part-time 370 **Student-Faculty Ratio:** 18:1 **Final Year or Final Semester Residency Requirement:** Yes **Regional Accreditation:** North Central Association of Colleges and Schools **Credit Hours For Degree:** 64 semester hours, Associates **Professional Accreditation:** ACEN, ADA, AOTA, APTA, CoARC, JRCERT, NAACLS, NASM. **Intercollegiate Athletics:** Baseball M; Basketball M & W; Cross-Country Running M & W; Golf M; Soccer M & W; Softball W; Volleyball W; Weight Lifting M & W

ILLINOIS COLLEGE

1101 W College Ave.
Jacksonville, IL 62650-2299
Tel: (217)245-3000; Free: 866-464-5265
Fax: (217)245-3034
E-mail: admissions@ic.edu
Web Site: www.ic.edu
President/CEO: Dr. Axel D. Steuer
Admissions: Rick Bystry
Financial Aid: Kate Taylor

Type: Comprehensive **Sex:** Coed **Affiliation:** interdenominational. **Scores:** 90% SAT V 400+; 84% SAT M 400+; 43.3% ACT 18-23; 31.4% ACT 24-29 **% Accepted:** 61 **Admission Plans:** Deferred Admission; Early Admission; Early Decision Plan **Application Fee:** $0.00 **H.S. Requirements:** High school diploma required; GED accepted **Costs Per Year:** Application fee: $0. Comprehensive fee: $40,850 includes full-time tuition ($31,110), mandatory fees ($550), and college room and board ($9190). College room only: $4890. Room and board charges vary according to board plan and housing facility. Part-time tuition: $890 per credit hour. Part-time mandatory fees: $137.50 per term. Part-time tuition and fees vary according to course load. **Scholarships:** Available. **Calendar System:** Semester **Enrollment:** Full-time 948, Graduate part-time 3, Part-time 4 **Faculty:** Full-time 84, Part-time 20 **Student-Faculty Ratio:** 11:1 **Exams:** SAT I or ACT. **% Receiving Financial Aid:** 84 **% Residing in College-Owned, -Operated, or -Affiliated Housing:** 84 **Regional Accreditation:** North Central Association of Colleges and Schools **Credit Hours For Degree:** 120 credits, Bachelors **Intercollegiate Athletics:** Baseball M; Cheerleading W; Cross-Country Running M & W; Football M; Golf M & W; Soccer M & W; Softball W; Swimming and Diving M & W; Tennis M & W; Track and Field M & W; Volleyball W

ILLINOIS EASTERN COMMUNITY COLLEGES, FRONTIER COMMUNITY COLLEGE

2 Frontier Dr.
Fairfield, IL 62837
Tel: (618)842-3711; Free: 877-464-3687
Fax: (618)842-4425
E-mail: johnstonm@iecc.edu
Web Site: www.iecc.edu/fcc
President/CEO: Dr. Gerald Edgren
Admissions: Mary Johnston
Financial Aid: Lori Noe

Type: Two-Year College **Sex:** Coed **Affiliation:** Illinois Eastern Community Colleges System. **Admission Plans:** Deferred Admission; Early Admission; Open Admission; Preferred Admission **Application Deadline:** Rolling **H.S. Requirements:** High school diploma required; GED accepted **Costs Per Year:** Area resident tuition: $2656 full-time, $83 per semester hour part-time. State resident tuition: $8589 full-time, $268.41 per semester hour part-time. Nonresident tuition: $10,580 full-time, $330.61 per semester hour part-time. Mandatory fees: $490 full-time, $15 per semester hour part-time, $5 per term part-time. **Scholarships:** Available. **Calendar System:** Semester, Summer session available **Faculty:** Full-time 6, Part-time 89 **Student-Faculty Ratio:** 23:1 **Regional Accreditation:** North Central Association of Colleges and Schools **Credit Hours For Degree:** 64 credit hours, Associates **Intercollegiate Athletics:** Golf M & W; Squash W; Volleyball W

ILLINOIS EASTERN COMMUNITY COLLEGES, LINCOLN TRAIL COLLEGE

11220 State Hwy. 1
Robinson, IL 62454
Tel: (618)544-8657; Free: 866-582-4322
Fax: (618)544-4705
E-mail: scottm@iecc.edu
Web Site: www.iecc.edu/ltc
President/CEO: Kathy Harris
Admissions: Megan Scott
Financial Aid: Aaron White

Type: Two-Year College **Sex:** Coed **Affiliation:** Illinois Eastern Community Colleges System. **Admission Plans:** Deferred Admission; Early Admission; Open Admission; Preferred Admission **Application Deadline:** Rolling **H.S. Requirements:** High school diploma required; GED accepted **Costs Per Year:** Area resident tuition: $2656 full-time, $83 per semester hour part-time. State resident tuition: $8589 full-time, $268.41 per semester hour part-time. Nonresident tuition: $10,580 full-time, $330.61 per semester hour part-time. Mandatory fees: $490 full-time, $15 per semester hour part-time, $5 per term part-time. **Scholarships:** Available. **Calendar System:** Semester, Summer session available **Enrollment:** Full-time 427, Part-time 583 **Faculty:** Full-time 16, Part-time 48 **Student-Faculty Ratio:** 17:1 **Regional Accreditation:** North Central Association of Colleges and Schools **Credit Hours For Degree:** 64 credit hours, Associates **Intercollegiate Athletics:** Baseball M; Basketball M & W; Softball W

ILLINOIS EASTERN COMMUNITY COLLEGES, OLNEY CENTRAL COLLEGE

305 NW St.
Olney, IL 62450
Tel: (618)395-7777; Free: 866-622-4322
Fax: (618)395-1261
E-mail: greathousea@iecc.edu
Web Site: www.iecc.edu/occ
President/CEO: Rodney Ranes
Admissions: Adam Greathouse
Financial Aid: Veralee Harris

Type: Two-Year College **Sex:** Coed **Affiliation:** Illinois Eastern Community Colleges System. **Admission Plans:** Deferred Admission; Early Admission; Open Admission; Preferred Admission **Application Deadline:** Rolling **H.S. Requirements:** High school diploma required; GED accepted **Costs Per Year:** Area resident tuition: $2656 full-time, $83 per semester hour part-time. State resident tuition: $8589 full-time, $268.41 per semester hour part-time. Nonresident tuition: $10,580 full-time, $330.61 per semester hour part-time. Mandatory fees: $490 full-time, $15 per semester hour part-time, $5 per term part-time. **Scholarships:** Available. **Calendar System:** Semester, Summer session available **Enrollment:** Full-time 612, Part-time 683 **Faculty:** Full-time 43, Part-time 54 **Student-Faculty Ratio:** 14:1 **Regional Accreditation:** North Central Association of Colleges and Schools **Credit Hours For Degree:** 64 credit hours, Associates **Professional Accreditation:** ACEN, JRCERT. **Intercollegiate Athletics:** Baseball M; Basketball M & W; Softball W

ILLINOIS EASTERN COMMUNITY COLLEGES, WABASH VALLEY COLLEGE

2200 College Dr.
Mount Carmel, IL 62863
Tel: (618)262-8641; Free: 866-982-4322
Fax: (618)262-8841
E-mail: cowgert@iecc.edu
Web Site: www.iecc.edu/wvc
President/CEO: Matt Fowler
Admissions: Tiffany Cowger
Financial Aid: Mary Johnson

Type: Two-Year College **Sex:** Coed **Affiliation:** Illinois Eastern Community Colleges System. **Admission Plans:** Deferred Admission; Early Admission; Open Admission; Preferred Admission **Application Deadline:** Rolling **H.S. Requirements:** High school diploma required; GED accepted **Costs Per Year:** Area resident tuition: $2656 full-time, $83 per semester hour part-time. State resident tuition: $8589 full-time, $268.41 per semester hour part-time. Nonresident tuition: $10,580 full-time, $330.61 per semester hour part-time. Mandatory fees: $490 full-time. **Scholarships:** Available. **Calendar System:** Semester, Summer session available **Enrollment:** Full-time 530, Part-time 3,744 **Faculty:** Full-time 35, Part-time 45 **Student-Faculty Ratio:** 34:1 **Regional Accreditation:** North Central Association of Colleges and Schools **Credit Hours For Degree:** 64 credit hours, Associates **Intercollegiate Athletics:** Baseball M; Basketball M & W; Softball W

THE ILLINOIS INSTITUTE OF ART–CHICAGO

350 N Orleans St.
Chicago, IL 60654
Tel: (312)280-3500; Free: 800-351-3450
Fax: (312)280-3528
Web Site: www.artinstitutes.edu/chicago
President/CEO: David Ray

Type: Four-Year College **Sex:** Coed **Affiliation:** Education Management Corporation. **Calendar System:** Quarter **Regional Accreditation:** North Central Association of Colleges and Schools **Professional Accreditation:** ACCSC, ACF, CIDA.

THE ILLINOIS INSTITUTE OF ART–SCHAUMBURG

1000 N Plz. Dr., Ste. 100
Schaumburg, IL 60173

Tel: (847)619-3450; Free: 800-314-3450
Fax: (847)619-3064
Web Site: www.artinstitutes.edu/schaumburg
President/CEO: John Jenkins

Type: Four-Year College **Sex:** Coed **Affiliation:** Education Management Corporation. **Calendar System:** Quarter **Regional Accreditation:** North Central Association of Colleges and Schools **Professional Accreditation:** CIDA.

ILLINOIS INSTITUTE OF TECHNOLOGY

3300 S Federal St.
Chicago, IL 60616-3793
Tel: (312)567-3000; Free: 800-448-2329
Fax: (312)567-6939
E-mail: admission@iit.edu
Web Site: www.iit.edu
President/CEO: Dr. Alan Cramb
Admissions: Toni Riley
Financial Aid: Abby McGrath

Type: University **Sex:** Coed **Scores:** 97% SAT V 400+; 100% SAT M 400+; 8.69% ACT 18-23; 58.82% ACT 24-29 **% Accepted:** 53 **Admission Plans:** Deferred Admission; Early Admission **Application Deadline:** August 1 **Application Fee:** $0.00 **H.S. Requirements:** High school diploma required; GED accepted **Costs Per Year:** Application fee: $0. One-time mandatory fee: $330. Comprehensive fee: $57,702 includes full-time tuition ($43,500), mandatory fees ($1384), and college room and board ($12,818). College room only: $6062. Full-time tuition and fees vary according to student level. Room and board charges vary according to board plan and housing facility. Part-time tuition: $1359 per credit hour. Part-time tuition varies according to course load and student level. **Scholarships:** Available. **Calendar System:** Semester, Summer session available **Enrollment:** Full-time 2,790, Graduate full-time 3,789, Graduate part-time 1,012, Part-time 201 **Faculty:** Full-time 423, Part-time 377 **Student-Faculty Ratio:** 13:1 **Exams:** ACT essay component used as validity check; ACT essay component used for advising; ACT essay component used for placement; SAT I or ACT; SAT II; SAT essay component used as validity check; SAT essay component used for advising; SAT essay component used for placement; SAT Reasoning; SAT Subject. **% Receiving Financial Aid:** 55 **% Residing in College-Owned, -Operated, or -Affiliated Housing:** 64 **Final Year or Final Semester Residency Requirement:** Yes **Regional Accreditation:** North Central Association of Colleges and Schools **Credit Hours For Degree:** 126 semester hours, Bachelors **ROTC:** Air Force, Army, Navy **Professional Accreditation:** AACSB, AALS, ABA, ABET, APA, ASLA, CORE, NAAB. **Intercollegiate Athletics:** Badminton M & W; Baseball M; Basketball M & W; Bowling M & W; Cross-Country Running M & W; Lacrosse M & W; Rugby M & W; Soccer M & W; Swimming and Diving M & W; Track and Field M & W; Ultimate Frisbee M & W; Volleyball M & W

ILLINOIS STATE UNIVERSITY

Normal, IL 61790-2200
Tel: (309)438-2111; Free: 800-366-2478
Fax: (309)438-3932
E-mail: admissions@ilstu.edu
Web Site: www.illinoisstate.edu
President/CEO: Dr. Larry Dietz
Admissions: Jeff Mavros
Financial Aid: David Krueger

Type: University **Sex:** Coed **Scores:** 52.75% ACT 18-23; 41.18% ACT 24-29 **% Accepted:** 80 **Admission Plans:** Deferred Admission **Application Deadline:** April 1 **Application Fee:** $50.00 **H.S. Requirements:** High school diploma required; GED accepted **Costs Per Year:** Application fee: $50. State resident tuition: $10,784 full-time, $359.47 per credit hour part-time. Nonresident tuition: $18,600 full-time, $620 per credit hour part-time. Mandatory fees: $2,882 full-time, $79.46 per credit hour part-time. Full-time tuition and fees vary according to degree level. Part-time tuition and fees vary according to degree level. College room and board: $9850. College room only: $5282. Room and board charges vary according to board plan and housing facility. Tuition guaranteed not to increase for student's term of enrollment. **Scholarships:** Available. **Calendar System:** Semester, Summer session available **Enrollment:** Full-time 17,151, Graduate full-time 312, Graduate part-time 2,022, Part-time 1,275 **Faculty:** Full-time 877, Part-time 387 **Student-Faculty Ratio:** 17:1 **Exams:** ACT essay component used for advising; SAT I or ACT; SAT essay component used for advising; SAT Reasoning; SAT Subject. **% Receiving Financial Aid:** 60 **% Residing in**

College-Owned, -Operated, or -Affiliated Housing: 32 **Final Year or Final Semester Residency Requirement:** No **Regional Accreditation:** North Central Association of Colleges and Schools **Credit Hours For Degree:** 120 credits, Bachelors **ROTC:** Army **Professional Accreditation:** AACN, AACSB, AAFCS, ABET, ACA, AHIMA, AND, APA, ASHA, ATMAE, CIDA, CSWE, JRCAT, NAACLS, NASAD, NASM, NAST, NCATE, NRPA. **Intercollegiate Athletics:** Baseball M; Basketball M & W; Cross-Country Running M & W; Football M; Golf M & W; Gymnastics W; Soccer W; Softball W; Swimming and Diving W; Tennis M & W; Track and Field M & W; Volleyball W

ILLINOIS VALLEY COMMUNITY COLLEGE
815 N Orlando Smith Rd.
Oglesby, IL 61348-9692
Tel: (815)224-2720
Fax: (815)224-3033
E-mail: mark_grzybowski@ivcc.edu
Web Site: www.ivcc.edu
President/CEO: Dr. Jerome Corcoran
Admissions: Mark Grzybowski

Type: Two-Year College **Sex:** Coed **Affiliation:** Illinois Community College Board. **Admission Plans:** Deferred Admission; Early Admission; Open Admission **Application Deadline:** Rolling **H.S. Requirements:** High school diploma or equivalent not required **Costs Per Year:** One-time mandatory fee: $10. Area resident tuition: $3818 full-time, $111.60 per credit hour part-time. State resident tuition: $10,359 full-time, $323.72 per credit hour part-time. Nonresident tuition: $11,221 full-time, $350.65 per credit hour part-time. Mandatory fees: $234 full-time, $7.40 per credit hour part-time, $5 per term part-time. Full-time tuition and fees vary according to course load and reciprocity agreements. Part-time tuition and fees vary according to course load and reciprocity agreements. **Scholarships:** Available. **Calendar System:** Semester, Summer session available **Enrollment:** Full-time 1,881, Part-time 2,474 **Faculty:** Full-time 91, Part-time 179 **Student-Faculty Ratio:** 18:1 **Exams:** ACT. **Final Year or Final Semester Residency Requirement:** No **Regional Accreditation:** North Central Association of Colleges and Schools **Credit Hours For Degree:** 64 semester hours, Associates **Professional Accreditation:** ACEN, ADA. **Intercollegiate Athletics:** Baseball M; Basketball M & W; Golf M; Softball W; Tennis M & W

ILLINOIS WESLEYAN UNIVERSITY
PO Box 2900
Bloomington, IL 61702-2900
Tel: (309)556-1000; Free: 800-332-2498
Fax: (309)556-3411
E-mail: iwuadmit@iwu.edu
Web Site: www.iwu.edu
President/CEO: Dr. Eric R. Jensen
Admissions: Bob Geraty
Financial Aid: Scott Seibring

Type: Four-Year College **Sex:** Coed **Scores:** 15% ACT 18-23; 58.6% ACT 24-29 **% Accepted:** 62 **Admission Plans:** Deferred Admission; Early Admission; Early Decision Plan **Application Fee:** $0.00 **H.S. Requirements:** High school diploma required; GED accepted **Costs Per Year:** Application fee: $0. Comprehensive fee: $52,286 includes full-time tuition ($42,290), mandatory fees ($200), and college room and board ($9796). College room only: $6134. Room and board charges vary according to housing facility. Part-time tuition: $1322 per credit hour. **Scholarships:** Available. **Calendar System:** Miscellaneous **Enrollment:** Full-time 1,828, Part-time 14 **Faculty:** Full-time 150, Part-time 63 **Student-Faculty Ratio:** 11:1 **Exams:** ACT essay component not used; SAT I or ACT; SAT essay component not used; SAT Reasoning; SAT Subject. **% Receiving Financial Aid:** 65 **% Residing in College-Owned, -Operated, or -Affiliated Housing:** 70 **Regional Accreditation:** North Central Association of Colleges and Schools **Credit Hours For Degree:** 32 courses, Bachelors **ROTC:** Army **Professional Accreditation:** AACN, NASM. **Intercollegiate Athletics:** Baseball M; Basketball M & W; Cheerleading M & W; Cross-Country Running M & W; Football M; Golf M & W; Lacrosse M & W; Soccer M & W; Softball W; Swimming and Diving M & W; Tennis M & W; Track and Field M & W; Ultimate Frisbee M & W; Volleyball M & W; Water Polo M

JOHN A. LOGAN COLLEGE
700 Logan College Rd.
Carterville, IL 62918-9900
Tel: (618)985-3741
Fax: (618)985-2248

E-mail: terrycrain@jalc.edu
Web Site: www.jalc.edu
President/CEO: Dr. Robert Mees
Admissions: Terry Crain

Type: Two-Year College **Sex:** Coed **Affiliation:** Illinois Community College Board. **Admission Plans:** Early Admission; Open Admission **Application Deadline:** August 25 **Application Fee:** $0.00 **H.S. Requirements:** High school diploma required; GED accepted **Scholarships:** Available. **Calendar System:** Semester, Summer session available **Enrollment:** Full-time 2,368, Part-time 5,191 **Faculty:** Full-time 103, Part-time 210 **Student-Faculty Ratio:** 24:1 **Regional Accreditation:** North Central Association of Colleges and Schools **Credit Hours For Degree:** 62 semester hours, Associates **ROTC:** Air Force, Army **Professional Accreditation:** ACCE, ADA, AHIMA, AOTA, NAACLS. **Intercollegiate Athletics:** Baseball M; Basketball M & W; Golf M & W; Softball W; Volleyball W

JOHN WOOD COMMUNITY COLLEGE
1301 S 48th St.
Quincy, IL 62301-9147
Tel: (217)224-6500
Fax: (217)224-4208
E-mail: admissions@jwcc.edu
Web Site: www.jwcc.edu
President/CEO: Dr. John Letts
Admissions: Lee Wibbell
Financial Aid: Melanie Lechtenberg

Type: Two-Year College **Sex:** Coed **Affiliation:** Illinois Community College Board. **Scores:** 50% ACT 18-23; 16% ACT 24-29 **Admission Plans:** Early Admission; Open Admission; Preferred Admission **Application Deadline:** Rolling **Application Fee:** $0.00 **H.S. Requirements:** High school diploma required; GED accepted **Costs Per Year:** Application fee: $0. Area resident tuition: $4020 full-time, $134 per credit hour part-time. State resident tuition: $7170 full-time, $244 per credit hour part-time. Nonresident tuition: $7170 full-time, $244 per credit hour part-time. Mandatory fees: $390 full-time, $13 per credit hour part-time. Full-time tuition and fees vary according to program and reciprocity agreements. Part-time tuition and fees vary according to program and reciprocity agreements. **Scholarships:** Available. **Calendar System:** Semester, Summer session available **Enrollment:** Full-time 1,178, Part-time 1,212 **Faculty:** Full-time 56, Part-time 202 **Student-Faculty Ratio:** 13:1 **Exams:** ACT; ACT essay component not used; SAT essay component not used. **Final Year or Final Semester Residency Requirement:** No **Regional Accreditation:** North Central Association of Colleges and Schools **Credit Hours For Degree:** 64 credit hours, Associates **Intercollegiate Athletics:** Baseball M; Basketball M & W; Softball W

JOLIET JUNIOR COLLEGE
1215 Houbolt Rd.
Joliet, IL 60431-8938
Tel: (815)729-9020
E-mail: admission@jjc.edu
Web Site: www.jjc.edu
President/CEO: Gena Proulx, PhD
Admissions: Jennifer Kloberdanz

Type: Two-Year College **Sex:** Coed **Affiliation:** Illinois Community College Board. **Admission Plans:** Deferred Admission; Early Admission; Open Admission; Preferred Admission **Application Deadline:** Rolling **Application Fee:** $0.00 **H.S. Requirements:** High school diploma or equivalent not required. For nursing and veterinary technician programs: High school diploma required; GED accepted **Scholarships:** Available. **Calendar System:** Semester, Summer session available **Student-Faculty Ratio:** 25:1 **Regional Accreditation:** North Central Association of Colleges and Schools **Credit Hours For Degree:** 64 credits, Associates **Professional Accreditation:** ACBSP, ACEN, ACF, NASM. **Intercollegiate Athletics:** Baseball M; Basketball M & W; Football M; Soccer M & W; Softball W; Track and Field M & W; Volleyball W

JUDSON UNIVERSITY
1151 N State St.
Elgin, IL 60123-1498
Tel: (847)628-2500; Free: 800-879-5376
Fax: (847)695-0712
E-mail: nbinger@judsonu.edu
Web Site: www.judsonu.edu
President/CEO: Dr. Gene C. Crume, Jr.

Admissions: Nancy Binger

Financial Aid: Roberto Santizo

Type: Comprehensive **Sex:** Coed **Affiliation:** Baptist. **Scores:** 96% SAT V 400+; 100% SAT M 400+; 46% ACT 18-23; 41% ACT 24-29 **% Accepted:** 71 **Application Deadline:** Rolling **Application Fee:** $50.00 **H.S. Requirements:** High school diploma required; GED accepted **Costs Per Year:** Application fee: $50. One-time mandatory fee: $100. Comprehensive fee: $38,350 includes full-time tuition ($27,820), mandatory fees ($880), and college room and board ($9650). Full-time tuition and fees vary according to course load and program. Room and board charges vary according to board plan. Part-time tuition: $1165 per credit. Part-time tuition varies according to course load and program. **Scholarships:** Available. **Calendar System:** Semester, Summer session available **Enrollment:** Full-time 739, Graduate full-time 85, Graduate part-time 79, Part-time 371 **Faculty:** Full-time 66, Part-time 93 **Student-Faculty Ratio:** 10:1 **Exams:** SAT I or ACT; SAT Reasoning; SAT Subject. **% Receiving Financial Aid:** 82 **% Residing in College-Owned, -Operated, or -Affiliated Housing:** 65 **Final Year or Final Semester Residency Requirement:** Yes **Regional Accreditation:** North Central Association of Colleges and Schools **Credit Hours For Degree:** 60 semester hours, Associates; 120 semester hours, Bachelors **ROTC:** Army **Intercollegiate Athletics:** Baseball M; Basketball M & W; Bowling M & W; Cheerleading W; Cross-Country Running M & W; Golf M & W; Lacrosse M; Soccer M & W; Softball W; Tennis M & W; Track and Field M & W; Volleyball W

KANKAKEE COMMUNITY COLLEGE

100 College Dr.

Kankakee, IL 60901

Tel: (815)802-8100

Fax: (815)933-0217

E-mail: kharpin@kcc.edu

Web Site: www.kcc.edu

President/CEO: Dr. John Avendano

Admissions: Kim Harpin

Type: Two-Year College **Sex:** Coed **Affiliation:** Illinois Community College Board. **Scores:** 52.5% ACT 18-23; 12.7% ACT 24-29 **% Accepted:** 100 **Admission Plans:** Early Admission; Open Admission; Preferred Admission **Application Deadline:** Rolling **Application Fee:** $0.00 **H.S. Requirements:** High school diploma required; GED accepted **Costs Per Year:** Application fee: $0. Area resident tuition: $3660 full-time, $122 per credit hour part-time. State resident tuition: $8700 full-time, $290 per credit hour part-time. Nonresident tuition: $17,340 full-time, $578 per credit hour part-time. Mandatory fees: $420 full-time. **Scholarships:** Available. **Calendar System:** Semester, Summer session available **Enrollment:** Full-time 1,222, Part-time 2,084 **Faculty:** Full-time 59, Part-time 186 **Student-Faculty Ratio:** 14:1 **Exams:** ACT essay component used for advising. **Final Year or Final Semester Residency Requirement:** Yes **Regional Accreditation:** North Central Association of Colleges and Schools **Credit Hours For Degree:** 61 semester hours, Associates **ROTC:** Army **Professional Accreditation:** CoARC, NAACLS. **Intercollegiate Athletics:** Baseball M; Basketball M & W; Soccer M; Softball W; Volleyball W

KASKASKIA COLLEGE

27210 College Rd.

Centralia, IL 62801-7878

Tel: (618)545-3000; Free: 800-642-0859

Fax: (618)532-1135

E-mail: jripperda@kaskaskia.edu

Web Site: www.kaskaskia.edu

President/CEO: Dr. Penny Quinn

Admissions: Jan Ripperda

Financial Aid: Carrie Hancock

Type: Two-Year College **Sex:** Coed **Affiliation:** Illinois Community College Board. **% Accepted:** 100 **Admission Plans:** Deferred Admission; Early Admission; Open Admission; Preferred Admission **Application Deadline:** Rolling **Application Fee:** $0.00 **H.S. Requirements:** High school diploma required; GED accepted **Costs Per Year:** Application fee: $0. Area resident tuition: $3680 full-time, $115 per credit hour part-time. State resident tuition: $6944 full-time, $217 per credit hour part-time. Nonresident tuition: $12,640 full-time, $395 per credit hour part-time. Mandatory fees: $480 full-time, $16 per credit hour part-time. Full-time tuition and fees vary according to program. Part-time tuition and fees vary according to program. **Scholarships:** Available. **Calendar System:** Semester, Summer session available **Enrollment:** Full-time 1,458, Part-time 3,014 **Faculty:** Full-time 76, Part-

time 130 **Student-Faculty Ratio:** 21:1 **Exams:** ACT; ACT essay component not used; SAT essay component not used. **Regional Accreditation:** North Central Association of Colleges and Schools **Credit Hours For Degree:** 64 semester hours, Associates **ROTC:** Army **Professional Accreditation:** ACEN, ADA, APTA, CoARC, JRCERT. **Intercollegiate Athletics:** Baseball M; Basketball M & W; Cheerleading M & W; Cross-Country Running M & W; Golf M & W; Soccer W; Softball W; Tennis M; Volleyball W

KENDALL COLLEGE

900 N N Branch St.

Chicago, IL 60201-2899

Tel: (312)752-2000; Free: 888-90-KENDALL

E-mail: info@kendall.edu

Web Site: www.kendall.edu

President/CEO: Kimberly Shambrook

Admissions: Geni Burke

Financial Aid: Chris Miller

Type: Four-Year College **Sex:** Coed **Affiliation:** United Methodist; Laureate International Universities. **Scores:** 38% ACT 18-23; 19% ACT 24-29 **% Accepted:** 74 **Admission Plans:** Deferred Admission **Application Deadline:** Rolling **Application Fee:** $50.00 **H.S. Requirements:** High school diploma required; GED accepted **Costs Per Year:** Application fee: $50. Comprehensive fee: $29,809 includes full-time tuition ($18,446), mandatory fees ($1013), and college room and board ($10,350). **Scholarships:** Available. **Calendar System:** Quarter, Summer session available **Enrollment:** Full-time 772, Part-time 503 **Faculty:** Full-time 45, Part-time 164 **Student-Faculty Ratio:** 13:1 **Exams:** ACT essay component not used; SAT I or ACT; SAT essay component not used. **% Receiving Financial Aid:** 65 **Final Year or Final Semester Residency Requirement:** No **Regional Accreditation:** North Central Association of Colleges and Schools **Credit Hours For Degree:** 90 quarter hours, Associates; 180 quarter hours, Bachelors **Professional Accreditation:** ACF.

KISHWAUKEE COLLEGE

21193 Malta Rd.

Malta, IL 60150

Tel: (815)825-2086

Fax: (815)825-2306

E-mail: bryce.law@kishwaukeecollege.edu

Web Site: www.kishwaukeecollege.edu

President/CEO: Dr. Thomas Choice

Admissions: Bryce Law

Financial Aid: Cynthia J. Stonesifer

Type: Two-Year College **Sex:** Coed **Affiliation:** Illinois Community College Board. **Admission Plans:** Deferred Admission; Early Admission; Open Admission **Application Deadline:** Rolling **Application Fee:** $0.00 **H.S. Requirements:** High school diploma or equivalent not required **Costs Per Year:** Application fee: $0. Area resident tuition: $3570 full-time, $119 per credit hour part-time. State resident tuition: $9330 full-time, $311 per credit hour part-time. Nonresident tuition: $15,030 full-time, $501 per credit hour part-time. Mandatory fees: $420 full-time, $12 per credit hour part-time. Full-time tuition and fees vary according to program and reciprocity agreements. Part-time tuition and fees vary according to program and reciprocity agreements. **Scholarships:** Available. **Calendar System:** Semester, Summer session available **Enrollment:** Full-time 2,030, Part-time 2,445 **Faculty:** Full-time 81, Part-time 162 **Exams:** ACT essay component not used; SAT essay component not used. **Final Year or Final Semester Residency Requirement:** No **Regional Accreditation:** North Central Association of Colleges and Schools **Credit Hours For Degree:** 64 semester hours, Associates **Professional Accreditation:** JRCERT. **Intercollegiate Athletics:** Baseball M; Basketball M & W; Softball W; Volleyball W

KNOX COLLEGE

2 E S St.

Galesburg, IL 61401

Tel: (309)341-7000; Free: 800-678-KNOX

Fax: (309)341-7070

E-mail: admission@knox.edu

Web Site: www.knox.edu

President/CEO: Dr. Teresa Amott

Admissions: Paul Steenis

Financial Aid: Ann M. Brill

Type: Four-Year College **Sex:** Coed **Scores:** 100% SAT V 400+; 26% ACT 18-23; 49% ACT 24-29 **% Accepted:** 64 **Admission Plans:** Deferred Admission; Early Admission; Early Decision Plan **Application Deadline:** January 15 **Application Fee:** $50.00 **H.S. Requirements:** High school diploma required; GED accepted **Costs Per Year:** Application fee: $50. Comprehensive fee: $50,859 includes full-time tuition ($41,094), mandatory fees ($753), and college room and board ($9012). College room only: $4512. Full-time tuition and fees vary according to course load. Room and board charges vary according to housing facility. Part-time tuition: $4566 per credit. Part-time tuition varies according to course load. **Scholarships:** Available. **Calendar System:** Trimester, Summer session not available **Enrollment:** Full-time 1,368, Part-time 29 **Faculty:** Full-time 115, Part-time 27 **Student-Faculty Ratio:** 11:1 **Exams:** SAT I or ACT; SAT Reasoning. **% Receiving Financial Aid:** 78 **% Residing in College-Owned, -Operated, or -Affiliated Housing:** 87 **Final Year or Final Semester Residency Requirement:** Yes **Regional Accreditation:** North Central Association of Colleges and Schools **Credit Hours For Degree:** 35.8 course credits, Bachelors **Intercollegiate Athletics:** Baseball M; Basketball M & W; Cross-Country Running M & W; Football M; Golf M & W; Soccer M & W; Softball W; Swimming and Diving M & W; Tennis M & W; Track and Field M & W; Volleyball W

LAKE FOREST COLLEGE

555 N Sheridan Rd.
Lake Forest, IL 60045
Tel: (847)234-3100; Free: 800-828-4751
Fax: (847)735-6271
E-mail: admissions@lakeforest.edu
Web Site: www.lakeforest.edu
President/CEO: Stephen D. Schutt
Admissions: Christopher Ellertson
Financial Aid: Jerry Cebrzynski

Type: Comprehensive **Sex:** Coed **Scores:** 35% ACT 18-23; 50% ACT 24-29 **% Accepted:** 55 **Admission Plans:** Deferred Admission; Early Action; Early Decision Plan **Application Deadline:** February 15 **Application Fee:** $0.00 **H.S. Requirements:** High school diploma required; GED accepted **Costs Per Year:** Application fee: $0. Comprehensive fee: $54,650 includes full-time tuition ($44,116), mandatory fees ($724), and college room and board ($9810). College room only: $4684. Room and board charges vary according to board plan and housing facility. **Scholarships:** Available. **Calendar System:** Semester, Summer session available **Enrollment:** Full-time 1,553, Graduate full-time 11, Graduate part-time 14, Part-time 19 **Faculty:** Full-time 98, Part-time 98 **Student-Faculty Ratio:** 12:1 **Exams:** ACT essay component used for advising; SAT I or ACT; SAT essay component used for advising. **% Residing in College-Owned, -Operated, or -Affiliated Housing:** 74 **Final Year or Final Semester Residency Requirement:** No **Regional Accreditation:** North Central Association of Colleges and Schools **Credit Hours For Degree:** 32 courses, Bachelors **Intercollegiate Athletics:** Archery M & W; Baseball M; Basketball M & W; Cheerleading M & W; Cross-Country Running M & W; Equestrian Sports M & W; Fencing M & W; Football M; Golf M & W; Ice Hockey M & W; Lacrosse M & W; Rugby M & W; Sailing M & W; Soccer M & W; Softball W; Swimming and Diving M & W; Tennis M & W; Track and Field M & W; Ultimate Frisbee M & W; Volleyball M & W; Water Polo M & W

LAKE LAND COLLEGE

5001 Lake Land Blvd.
Mattoon, IL 61938-9366
Tel: (217)234-5253
E-mail: admissions@lakeland.cc.il.us
Web Site: www.lakelandcollege.edu
President/CEO: Dr. Josh Bullock
Admissions: Jon VanDyke

Type: Two-Year College **Sex:** Coed **Affiliation:** Illinois Community College Board. **Admission Plans:** Early Admission; Open Admission **Application Deadline:** Rolling **Application Fee:** $0.00 **H.S. Requirements:** High school diploma or equivalent not required **Costs Per Year:** Application fee: $0. Area resident tuition: $2775 full-time, $92.50 per credit hour part-time. State resident tuition: $6599 full-time, $219.96 per credit hour part-time. Nonresident tuition: $12,400 full-time, $413.36 per credit hour part-time. Mandatory fees: $684 full-time, $22.80 per credit hour part-time. **Scholarships:** Available. **Calendar System:** Semester, Summer session available **Enrollment:** Full-time 2,809, Part-time 3,542 **Faculty:** Full-time 116, Part-time 75 **Student-Faculty Ratio:** 21:1 **Exams:** ACT. **Regional Accreditation:** North Central Association of Colleges and Schools **Credit Hours For Degree:** 64 semester hours, Associates **Professional Accreditation:**

ACEN, ADA, APTA. **Intercollegiate Athletics:** Baseball M; Basketball M & W; Cheerleading W; Softball W; Tennis M & W; Volleyball W

LAKEVIEW COLLEGE OF NURSING

903 N Logan Ave.
Danville, IL 61832
Tel: (217)709-0920
E-mail: admission@lakeviewcol.edu
Web Site: www.lakeviewcol.edu
President/CEO: Sheila Mingee
Financial Aid: Tammy Garza

Type: Two-Year Upper Division **Sex:** Coed **Admission Plans:** Early Action; Early Admission **Application Fee:** $100.00 **H.S. Requirements:** High school diploma required; GED accepted **Costs Per Year:** Application fee: $100. Tuition: $13,760 full-time. Mandatory fees: $2080 full-time. Full-time tuition and fees vary according to course level, course load, and location. **Scholarships:** Available. **Calendar System:** Semester, Summer session available **Enrollment:** Full-time 258, Part-time 44 **Faculty:** Full-time 16, Part-time 10 **Student-Faculty Ratio:** 10:1 **Exams:** Other. **% Receiving Financial Aid:** 86 **Final Year or Final Semester Residency Requirement:** Yes **Regional Accreditation:** North Central Association of Colleges and Schools **Credit Hours For Degree:** 124 credit hours, Bachelors **ROTC:** Air Force, Army **Professional Accreditation:** AACN, ACEN.

LEWIS AND CLARK COMMUNITY COLLEGE

5800 Godfrey Rd.
Godfrey, IL 62035-2466
Tel: (618)466-7000; Free: 800-YES-LCCC
Fax: (618)466-2798
Web Site: www.lc.edu
President/CEO: Dale T. Chapman
Admissions: Peggy Hudson
Financial Aid: Angela Weaver

Type: Two-Year College **Sex:** Coed **Affiliation:** Illinois Community College Board. **Admission Plans:** Deferred Admission; Early Admission; Open Admission **Application Deadline:** Rolling **Application Fee:** $0.00 **H.S. Requirements:** High school diploma or equivalent not required. For nursing, dental assisting, dental hygiene, occupational therapy programs: High school diploma required; GED accepted **Scholarships:** Available. **Calendar System:** Semester, Summer session available **Regional Accreditation:** North Central Association of Colleges and Schools **Credit Hours For Degree:** 60 credit hours, Associates **ROTC:** Army **Professional Accreditation:** ACEN, ADA, AOTA. **Intercollegiate Athletics:** Baseball M; Basketball M & W; Golf M; Soccer M & W; Softball W; Tennis M & W; Volleyball W

LEWIS UNIVERSITY

One University Pky.
Romeoville, IL 60446
Tel: (815)838-0500; Free: 800-897-9000
Fax: (815)838-9456
E-mail: cockerry@lewisu.edu
Web Site: www.lewisu.edu
President/CEO: Bro. James Gaffney, FSC
Admissions: Ryan Cockerill
Financial Aid: Janeen Decharinte

Type: Comprehensive **Sex:** Coed **Affiliation:** Roman Catholic Church. **Scores:** 99% SAT V 400+; 92% SAT M 400+; 57% ACT 18-23; 36% ACT 24-29 **% Accepted:** 62 **Admission Plans:** Deferred Admission **Application Deadline:** August 1 **Application Fee:** $40.00 **H.S. Requirements:** High school diploma required; GED accepted **Costs Per Year:** Application fee: $40. Comprehensive fee: $40,370 includes full-time tuition ($29,950), mandatory fees ($100), and college room and board ($10,320). College room only: $6560. Full-time tuition and fees vary according to course load, location, and program. Room and board charges vary according to board plan and housing facility. Part-time tuition: $880 per credit. Part-time mandatory fees: $50 per term. Part-time tuition and fees vary according to course load, location, and program. **Scholarships:** Available. **Calendar System:** Semester, Summer session available **Enrollment:** Full-time 3,809, Graduate full-time 379, Graduate part-time 1,648, Part-time 843 **Faculty:** Full-time 232, Part-time 443 **Student-Faculty Ratio:** 13:1 **Exams:** ACT essay component not used; SAT I or ACT; SAT essay component not used; SAT Reasoning. **% Receiving Financial Aid:** 76 **% Residing in College-Owned, -Operated, or -Affiliated Housing:** 26 **Final Year or Final Semester Residency Requirement:** Yes **Regional Accreditation:** North

Central Association of Colleges and Schools **Credit Hours For Degree:** 75 credit hours, Associates; 128 credit hours, Bachelors **ROTC:** Air Force, Army **Professional Accreditation:** AACN, ACBSP, NCATE. **Intercollegiate Athletics:** Baseball M; Basketball M & W; Cheerleading W; Cross-Country Running M & W; Golf M & W; Ice Hockey M; Lacrosse M & W; Rugby M; Skiing (Downhill) M & W; Soccer M & W; Softball W; Swimming and Diving M & W; Tennis M & W; Track and Field M & W; Ultimate Frisbee M & W; Volleyball M & W; Water Polo M & W

LINCOLN CHRISTIAN UNIVERSITY

100 Campus View Dr.
Lincoln, IL 62656-2167
Tel: (217)732-3168; Free: 888-522-5228
Fax: (217)732-5914
E-mail: enroll@lincolnchristian.edu
Web Site: www.lincolnchristian.edu
President/CEO: Dr. Don L. Green
Admissions: Mary K. Davis
Financial Aid: Nancy Siddens

Type: Comprehensive **Sex:** Coed **Affiliation:** Christian Churches and Churches of Christ. **Scores:** 89% SAT V 400+; 78% SAT M 400+; 51% ACT 18-23; 31% ACT 24-29 **% Accepted:** 60 **Admission Plans:** Deferred Admission; Preferred Admission **Application Deadline:** Rolling **Application Fee:** $25.00 **H.S. Requirements:** High school diploma required; GED accepted **Costs Per Year:** Application fee: $25. Comprehensive fee: $20,584 includes full-time tuition ($13,020) and college room and board ($7564). College room only: $3600. Part-time tuition: $434 per credit hour. **Scholarships:** Available. **Calendar System:** Semester, Summer session available **Enrollment:** Full-time 417, Graduate full-time 95, Graduate part-time 263, Part-time 111 **Faculty:** Full-time 39, Part-time 63 **Student-Faculty Ratio:** 15:1 **Exams:** ACT essay component not used; SAT I or ACT; SAT essay component not used; SAT Reasoning. **% Receiving Financial Aid:** 89 **% Residing in College-Owned, -Operated, or -Affiliated Housing:** 51 **Final Year or Final Semester Residency Requirement:** No **Regional Accreditation:** North Central Association of Colleges and Schools **Credit Hours For Degree:** 60 semester hours, Associates; 120 semester hours, Bachelors **Professional Accreditation:** ABHE, ATS. **Intercollegiate Athletics:** Baseball M; Basketball M & W; Soccer M & W; Volleyball W

LINCOLN COLLEGE

300 Keokuk St.
Lincoln, IL 62656-1699
Tel: (217)732-3155; Free: 800-569-0558
Fax: (217)732-8859
E-mail: gbree@lincolncollege.edu
Web Site: www.lincolncollege.edu
President/CEO: Jonathan Astroth
Admissions: Gretchen Bree

Type: Two-Year College **Sex:** Coed **% Accepted:** 68 **Admission Plans:** Deferred Admission; Early Admission **Application Deadline:** Rolling **Application Fee:** $25.00 **H.S. Requirements:** High school diploma required; GED accepted **Scholarships:** Available. **Calendar System:** Semester, Summer session available **Student-Faculty Ratio:** 15:1 **Exams:** SAT I or ACT. **Regional Accreditation:** North Central Association of Colleges and Schools **Credit Hours For Degree:** 64 semester hours, Associates

LINCOLN COLLEGE OF TECHNOLOGY

8317 W N Ave.
Melrose Park, IL 60160
Tel: (312)625-1535
Web Site: www.lincolnedu.com

Type: Two-Year College **Sex:** Coed **Costs Per Year:** Tuition: $28,000 full-time. Mandatory fees: $620 full-time. Full-time tuition and fees vary according to program.

LINCOLN COLLEGE–NORMAL

715 W Raab Rd.
Normal, IL 61761
Tel: (309)452-0500; Free: 800-569-0558
Fax: (309)454-5652
E-mail: spuck@lincolncollege.edu
Web Site: www.lincolncollege.edu/normal
President/CEO: John Hutchinson
Admissions: Steve Puck

Type: Four-Year College **Sex:** Coed **Scores:** 28% ACT 18-23; 3% ACT 24-29 **% Accepted:** 72 **Admission Plans:** Deferred Admission **Application Deadline:** September 1 **Application Fee:** $25.00 **H.S. Requirements:** High school diploma required; GED accepted **Scholarships:** Available. **Calendar System:** Miscellaneous, Summer session available **Enrollment:** Full-time 290, Part-time 237 **Faculty:** Full-time 9, Part-time 49 **Student-Faculty Ratio:** 14:1 **Exams:** ACT essay component not used; SAT I or ACT; SAT essay component not used; SAT Reasoning. **% Receiving Financial Aid:** 92 **% Residing in College-Owned, -Operated, or -Affiliated Housing:** 35 **Regional Accreditation:** North Central Association of Colleges and Schools **Credit Hours For Degree:** 63 credit hours, Associates; 123 credit hours, Bachelors

LINCOLN LAND COMMUNITY COLLEGE

5250 Shepherd Rd.
Springfield, IL 62794-9256
Tel: (217)786-2200; Free: 800-727-4161
Fax: (217)786-2492
E-mail: ron.gregoire@llcc.edu
Web Site: www.llcc.edu
President/CEO: Dr. Charlotte Warren
Admissions: Ron Gregoire

Type: Two-Year College **Sex:** Coed **Affiliation:** Illinois Community College Board. **Scores:** 49% ACT 18-23; 7% ACT 24-29 **Admission Plans:** Deferred Admission; Early Admission; Open Admission **Application Deadline:** Rolling **Application Fee:** $0.00 **H.S. Requirements:** High school diploma or equivalent not required. For allied health programs: High school diploma required; GED accepted **Scholarships:** Available. **Calendar System:** Semester, Summer session available **Enrollment:** Full-time 2,985, Part-time 4,035 **Faculty:** Full-time 129, Part-time 242 **Student-Faculty Ratio:** 21:1 **Final Year or Final Semester Residency Requirement:** No **Regional Accreditation:** North Central Association of Colleges and Schools **Credit Hours For Degree:** 60 credit hours, Associates **Professional Accreditation:** ACEN, AOTA, CoARC, JRCERT. **Intercollegiate Athletics:** Baseball M; Basketball M & W; Soccer M; Softball W; Volleyball W

LOYOLA UNIVERSITY CHICAGO

1032 W Sheridan Rd.
Chicago, IL 60660
Tel: (773)274-3000; Free: 800-262-2373
Fax: (773)915-6414
E-mail: admission@luc.edu
Web Site: www.luc.edu
President/CEO: Dr. John Pelissero
Admissions: Erin Moriarty
Financial Aid: Tobyn Friar

Type: University **Sex:** Coed **Affiliation:** Roman Catholic (Jesuit). **Scores:** 98% SAT V 400+; 99% SAT M 400+; 22.2% ACT 18-23; 57.7% ACT 24-29 **% Accepted:** 71 **Application Fee:** $0.00 **H.S. Requirements:** High school diploma required; GED accepted **Costs Per Year:** Application fee: $0. Comprehensive fee: $55,154 includes full-time tuition ($40,052), mandatory fees ($1332), and college room and board ($13,770). College room only: $8590. Full-time tuition and fees vary according to location, program, and student level. Room and board charges vary according to board plan, housing facility, and location. Part-time tuition: $751 per credit. Part-time tuition varies according to course load. **Scholarships:** Available. **Calendar System:** Semester, Summer session available **Enrollment:** Full-time 9,774, Graduate full-time 3,959, Graduate part-time 1,399, Part-time 1,305 **Faculty:** Full-time 767, Part-time 865 **Student-Faculty Ratio:** 14:1 **Exams:** ACT essay component not used; SAT I or ACT; SAT essay component not used; SAT Reasoning. **% Receiving Financial Aid:** 67 **% Residing in College-Owned, -Operated, or -Affiliated Housing:** 41 **Final Year or Final Semester Residency Requirement:** No **Regional Accreditation:** North Central Association of Colleges and Schools **Credit Hours For Degree:** 120 semester hours, Bachelors **ROTC:** Air Force, Army, Navy **Professional Accreditation:** AACN, AACSB, AALS, ABA, ACEN, ACIPE, AND, APA, CSWE, LCME/AMA, NAST, NCATE. **Intercollegiate Athletics:** Basketball M & W; Cross-Country Running M & W; Golf M & W; Soccer M & W; Softball W; Track and Field M & W; Volleyball M & W

MACCORMAC COLLEGE

506 S Wabash Ave.
Chicago, IL 60605-1667
Tel: (312)922-1884

Fax: (312)922-3196
Web Site: www.maccormac.edu
President/CEO: Leo Loughead
Admissions: David Grassi
Type: Two-Year College **Sex:** Coed **Admission Plans:** Deferred Admission **Application Deadline:** Rolling **Application Fee:** $20.00 **H.S. Requirements:** High school diploma required; GED accepted **Scholarships:** Available. **Calendar System:** Semester, Summer session available **Enrollment:** Full-time 159, Part-time 218 **Faculty:** Full-time 4, Part-time 30 **Student-Faculty Ratio:** 9:1 **Exams:** ACT; SAT I. **Regional Accreditation:** North Central Association of Colleges and Schools **Credit Hours For Degree:** 96 quarter hours, Associates

MACMURRAY COLLEGE

447 E College Ave.
Jacksonville, IL 62650
Tel: (217)479-7000; Free: 800-252-7485
Fax: (217)245-0405
E-mail: tressman.goode@mac.edu
Web Site: www.mac.edu
President/CEO: Dr. Mark Tierno
Admissions: Tressman L. Goode
Financial Aid: Laci N. Engelbrecht
Type: Four-Year College **Sex:** Coed **Affiliation:** United Methodist. **% Accepted:** 84 **Admission Plans:** Early Admission **Application Deadline:** Rolling **Application Fee:** $0.00 **H.S. Requirements:** High school diploma required; GED accepted **Costs Per Year:** Application fee: $0. Comprehensive fee: $33,620 includes full-time tuition ($24,390), mandatory fees ($720), and college room and board ($8510). Full-time tuition and fees vary according to course load and location. Room and board charges vary according to housing facility. Part-time tuition: $750 per credit hour. Part-time mandatory fees: $30 per credit hour, $5 per term. Part-time tuition and fees vary according to course load and location. **Scholarships:** Available. **Calendar System:** 4-1-4, Summer session available **Enrollment:** Full-time 435, Part-time 93 **Faculty:** Full-time 33, Part-time 22 **Student-Faculty Ratio:** 14:1 **Exams:** SAT I or ACT. **% Receiving Financial Aid:** 88 **% Residing in College-Owned, -Operated, or -Affiliated Housing:** 51 **Final Year or Final Semester Residency Requirement:** Yes **Regional Accreditation:** North Central Association of Colleges and Schools **Credit Hours For Degree:** 60 semester hours, Associates; 120 semester hours, Bachelors **Professional Accreditation:** AACN, CSWE. **Intercollegiate Athletics:** Baseball M; Basketball M & W; Football M; Golf M & W; Soccer M & W; Softball W; Volleyball W; Wrestling M & W

MCHENRY COUNTY COLLEGE

8900 US Hwy. 14
Crystal Lake, IL 60012-2761
Tel: (815)455-3700
E-mail: admissions@mchenry.edu
Web Site: www.mchenry.edu
President/CEO: Dr. Clinton Gabbard
Admissions: Kellie Carper-Sowiak
Type: Two-Year College **Sex:** Coed **Affiliation:** Illinois Community College Board. **Scores:** 60% ACT 18-23; 20% ACT 24-29 **% Accepted:** 100 **Admission Plans:** Deferred Admission; Early Admission; Open Admission **Application Deadline:** Rolling **Application Fee:** $15.00 **H.S. Requirements:** High school diploma or equivalent not required **Costs Per Year:** Application fee: $15. Area resident tuition: $3030 full-time, $101 per credit hour part-time. State resident tuition: $10,416 full-time, $347.21 per credit hour part-time. Nonresident tuition: $12,958 full-time, $431.93 per credit hour part-time. Mandatory fees: $284 full-time, $9 per credit hour part-time, $7 per term part-time. Full-time tuition and fees vary according to course load. Part-time tuition and fees vary according to course load. **Scholarships:** Available. **Calendar System:** Semester, Summer session available **Enrollment:** Full-time 2,460, Part-time 4,107 **Faculty:** Full-time 97, Part-time 263 **Student-Faculty Ratio:** 20:1 **Regional Accreditation:** North Central Association of Colleges and Schools **Credit Hours For Degree:** 60 credit hours, Associates **Intercollegiate Athletics:** Baseball M; Basketball M & W; Soccer M; Softball W; Tennis M & W; Volleyball W

MCKENDREE UNIVERSITY

701 College Rd.
Lebanon, IL 62254-1299
Tel: (618)537-4481; Free: 800-232-7228

Fax: (618)537-6259
E-mail: jlblasdel@mckendree.edu
Web Site: www.mckendree.edu
President/CEO: Dr. James M. Dennis
Admissions: Josie Blasdel
Financial Aid: Elizabeth L. Juehne
Type: Comprehensive **Sex:** Coed **Affiliation:** United Methodist Church. **Scores:** 85% SAT V 400+; 95% SAT M 400+ **% Accepted:** 63 **Admission Plans:** Deferred Admission **Application Deadline:** Rolling **H.S. Requirements:** High school diploma required; GED accepted **Costs Per Year:** Comprehensive fee: $37,940 includes full-time tuition ($27,740), mandatory fees ($1000), and college room and board ($9200). College room only: $4920. Full-time tuition and fees vary according to course load, degree level, and location. Room and board charges vary according to board plan and housing facility. Part-time tuition: $910 per credit hour. Part-time tuition varies according to course load, degree level, and location. **Scholarships:** Available. **Calendar System:** Semester, Summer session available **Enrollment:** Full-time 1,820, Graduate full-time 162, Graduate part-time 497, Part-time 522 **Student-Faculty Ratio:** 14:1 **Exams:** ACT essay component not used; SAT I or ACT; SAT essay component not used; SAT Reasoning. **% Receiving Financial Aid:** 78 **% Residing in College-Owned, -Operated, or -Affiliated Housing:** 73 **Final Year or Final Semester Residency Requirement:** Yes **Regional Accreditation:** North Central Association of Colleges and Schools **Credit Hours For Degree:** 68 credit hours, Associates; 120 credit hours, Bachelors **ROTC:** Air Force, Army **Professional Accreditation:** AACN, NCATE. **Intercollegiate Athletics:** Baseball M; Basketball M & W; Bowling M & W; Cheerleading M & W; Cross-Country Running M & W; Fencing M & W; Football M; Golf M & W; Ice Hockey M & W; Lacrosse W; Soccer M & W; Softball W; Swimming and Diving M & W; Tennis M & W; Track and Field M & W; Volleyball M & W; Water Polo M & W; Weight Lifting M & W; Wrestling M & W

METHODIST COLLEGE

415 St. Mark Ct.
Peoria, IL 61603
Tel: (309)672-5513
Fax: (309)671-8303
Web Site: www.methodistcol.edu
Type: Four-Year College **Sex:** Coed **Regional Accreditation:** North Central Association of Colleges and Schools

MIDSTATE COLLEGE

411 W Northmoor Rd.
Peoria, IL 61614
Tel: (309)692-4092; Free: 800-251-4299
Fax: (309)692-3893
E-mail: jhancock2@midstate.edu
Web Site: www.midstate.edu
President/CEO: Meredith Bunch
Admissions: Jessica Hancock
Type: Four-Year College **Sex:** Coed **Admission Plans:** Deferred Admission; Early Admission **Application Deadline:** Rolling **Application Fee:** $25.00 **H.S. Requirements:** High school diploma required; GED accepted **Scholarships:** Available. **Calendar System:** Quarter, Summer session available **Exams:** Other. **Regional Accreditation:** North Central Association of Colleges and Schools **Credit Hours For Degree:** 92 quarter hours, Associates **Professional Accreditation:** AAMAE, ACBSP.

MIDWESTERN CAREER COLLEGE

20 N Wacker Dr. No.3800
Chicago, IL 60606
Tel: (312)236-9000
Web Site: www.mccollege.edu
Type: Two-Year College **Sex:** Coed **Professional Accreditation:** COE.

MILLIKIN UNIVERSITY

1184 W Main St.
Decatur, IL 62522-2084
Tel: (217)424-6211; Free: 800-373-7733
Fax: (217)425-4669
E-mail: admis@millikin.edu
Web Site: www.millikin.edu
President/CEO: Dr. Patrick E. White
Admissions: Kevin McIntyre

Financial Aid: Cheryl Howerton

Type: Comprehensive **Sex:** Coed **Affiliation:** Presbyterian Church (U.S.A.). **Scores:** 97% SAT V 400+; 97% SAT M 400+; 51% ACT 18-23; 33% ACT 24-29 **% Accepted:** 60 **Admission Plans:** Deferred Admission **Application Deadline:** Rolling **Application Fee:** $0.00 **H.S. Requirements:** High school diploma required; GED accepted **Costs Per Year:** Application fee: $0. Comprehensive fee: $40,546 includes full-time tuition ($29,838), mandatory fees ($792), and college room and board ($9916). College room only: $7726. Room and board charges vary according to board plan and housing facility. Part-time tuition: $499 per credit hour. Part-time mandatory fees: $22 per credit hour. **Scholarships:** Available. **Calendar System:** Semester, Summer session available **Enrollment:** Full-time 1,984, Graduate full-time 73, Graduate part-time 18, Part-time 79 **Faculty:** Full-time 141, Part-time 131 **Student-Faculty Ratio:** 11:1 **Exams:** SAT I or ACT; SAT Reasoning. **% Receiving Financial Aid:** 84 **% Residing in College-Owned, -Operated, or -Affiliated Housing:** 61 **Final Year or Final Semester Residency Requirement:** No **Regional Accreditation:** North Central Association of Colleges and Schools **Credit Hours For Degree:** 124 credits, Bachelors **Professional Accreditation:** AACN, AANA, ACBSP, NASM, NCATE. **Intercollegiate Athletics:** Baseball M; Basketball M & W; Cheerleading M & W; Cross-Country Running M & W; Football M; Golf M & W; Soccer M & W; Softball W; Swimming and Diving M & W; Tennis W; Track and Field M & W; Volleyball W; Wrestling M

MONMOUTH COLLEGE

700 E Broadway
Monmouth, IL 61462-1998
Tel: (309)457-2311; Free: 800-747-2687
Fax: (309)457-2141
E-mail: admissions@monmouthcollege.edu
Web Site: www.monmouthcollege.edu
President/CEO: Dr. Clarence Wyatt
Admissions: Nick Spaeth
Financial Aid: Jayne A. Schreck

Type: Four-Year College **Sex:** Coed **Affiliation:** Presbyterian Church. **Scores:** 55% ACT 18-23; 33% ACT 24-29 **% Accepted:** 62 **Admission Plans:** Deferred Admission **Application Deadline:** Rolling **Application Fee:** $0.00 **H.S. Requirements:** High school diploma required; GED accepted **Costs Per Year:** Application fee: $0. Comprehensive fee: $43,600 includes full-time tuition ($35,300) and college room and board ($8300). College room only: $4696. Full-time tuition varies according to course load. Room and board charges vary according to housing facility. Part-time tuition: $4412 per course. **Scholarships:** Available. **Calendar System:** Semester, Summer session not available **Enrollment:** Full-time 1,179, Part-time 19 **Faculty:** Full-time 92, Part-time 41 **Student-Faculty Ratio:** 11:1 **Exams:** ACT essay component used for advising; SAT I or ACT; SAT essay component used for advising; SAT Reasoning; SAT Subject. **% Receiving Financial Aid:** 85 **% Residing in College-Owned, -Operated, or -Affiliated Housing:** 92 **Final Year or Final Semester Residency Requirement:** Yes **Regional Accreditation:** North Central Association of Colleges and Schools **Credit Hours For Degree:** 128 semester hours, Bachelors **ROTC:** Army **Intercollegiate Athletics:** Baseball M; Basketball M & W; Cross-Country Running M & W; Football M; Golf M & W; Lacrosse M & W; Soccer M & W; Softball W; Swimming and Diving M & W; Tennis M & W; Track and Field M & W; Volleyball W; Water Polo M & W

MOODY BIBLE INSTITUTE

820 N LaSalle Blvd.
Chicago, IL 60610-3284
Tel: (312)329-4000; Free: 800-967-4MBI
Fax: (312)329-8987
E-mail: admissions@moody.edu
Web Site: www.moody.edu
President/CEO: Dr. J. Paul Nyquist
Admissions: Jacqueline Holman

Type: Comprehensive **Sex:** Coed **Affiliation:** nondenominational. **% Accepted:** 89 **Admission Plans:** Early Action; Early Admission **Application Deadline:** March 1 **H.S. Requirements:** High school diploma required; GED accepted **Scholarships:** Available. **Calendar System:** Semester, Summer session available **Enrollment:** Full-time 2,275, Graduate full-time 122, Graduate part-time 299, Part-time 653 **Faculty:** Full-time 90, Part-time 121 **Student-Faculty Ratio:** 20:1 **Exams:** ACT essay component not used; SAT I and SAT II or ACT; SAT essay component not used; SAT Reasoning; SAT Subject. **Final Year or Final Semester Residency Requirement:** No

Regional Accreditation: North Central Association of Colleges and Schools **Credit Hours For Degree:** 60 semester hours, Associates; 130 semester hours, Bachelors **Professional Accreditation:** ABHE, ATS, NASM. **Intercollegiate Athletics:** Basketball M & W; Soccer M; Volleyball M & W

MORAINE VALLEY COMMUNITY COLLEGE

9000 W College Pky.
Palos Hills, IL 60465
Tel: (708)974-4300
Fax: (708)974-0681
E-mail: saratataa@morainevalley.edu
Web Site: www.morainevalley.edu
President/CEO: Dr. Sylvia M. Jenkins, PhD
Admissions: Andrew Sarata
Financial Aid: Laurie Anema

Type: Two-Year College **Sex:** Coed **Affiliation:** Illinois Community College Board. **Scores:** 47.2% ACT 18-23; 14.2% ACT 24-29 **Admission Plans:** Deferred Admission; Early Admission; Open Admission; Preferred Admission **Application Deadline:** Rolling **Application Fee:** $0.00 **H.S. Requirements:** High school diploma required; GED accepted **Costs Per Year:** Application fee: $0. Area resident tuition: $3996 full-time, $116 per credit hour part-time. State resident tuition: $8916 full-time, $280 per credit hour part-time. Nonresident tuition: $10,326 full-time, $327 per credit hour part-time. Mandatory fees: $516 full-time, $17 per credit hour part-time, $3 per term part-time. **Scholarships:** Available. **Calendar System:** Semester, Summer session available **Enrollment:** Full-time 6,393, Part-time 8,623 **Faculty:** Full-time 196, Part-time 763 **Student-Faculty Ratio:** 21:1 **Exams:** ACT essay component not used; SAT essay component not used. **Regional Accreditation:** North Central Association of Colleges and Schools **Credit Hours For Degree:** 62 semester hours, Associates **Professional Accreditation:** ACEN, AHIMA, CoARC, JRCERT. **Intercollegiate Athletics:** Baseball M; Basketball M & W; Cross-Country Running M & W; Golf M; Soccer M & W; Softball W; Tennis M & W; Volleyball W

MORRISON INSTITUTE OF TECHNOLOGY

701 Portland Ave.
Morrison, IL 61270-0410
Tel: (815)772-7218
Fax: (815)772-7584
E-mail: admissions@morrison.tec.il.us
Web Site: www.morrisontech.edu
President/CEO: Christopher Scott
Admissions: Tammy Pruis
Financial Aid: Julie Damhoff

Type: Two-Year College **Sex:** Coed **% Accepted:** 100 **Admission Plans:** Deferred Admission; Open Admission **Application Deadline:** Rolling **Application Fee:** $100.00 **H.S. Requirements:** High school diploma required; GED accepted **Scholarships:** Available. **Calendar System:** Semester, Summer session not available **Enrollment:** Full-time 142, Part-time 2 **Faculty:** Full-time 10, Part-time 1 **Student-Faculty Ratio:** 13:1 **Exams:** SAT I or ACT. **% Residing in College-Owned, -Operated, or -Affiliated Housing:** 55 **Credit Hours For Degree:** 67 semester hours, Associates **Professional Accreditation:** ABET, COE.

MORTHLAND COLLEGE

202 E Oak St.
West Frankfort, IL 62896
Tel: (618)937-2127
Web Site: www.morthland.edu

Type: Four-Year College **Sex:** Coed **Affiliation:** interdenominational. **Professional Accreditation:** TRACS.

MORTON COLLEGE

3801 S Central Ave.
Cicero, IL 60804-4398
Tel: (708)656-8000
Fax: (708)656-9592
Web Site: www.morton.edu
President/CEO: Dr. Leslie Navarro
Admissions: Victor Sanchez

Type: Two-Year College **Sex:** Coed **Affiliation:** Illinois Community College Board. **% Accepted:** 100 **Admission Plans:** Open Admission; Preferred Admission **Application Deadline:** Rolling **Application Fee:** $10.00 **H.S. Requirements:** High school diploma required; GED accepted **Costs Per**

Year: Application fee: $10. Area resident tuition: $2816 full-time, $88 per credit hour part-time. State resident tuition: $6912 full-time, $216 per credit hour part-time. Nonresident tuition: $8960 full-time, $280 per credit hour part-time. Mandatory fees: $852 full-time, $26 per credit hour part-time, $10 per term part-time. **Scholarships:** Available. **Calendar System:** Semester, Summer session available **Faculty:** Full-time 52, Part-time 218 **Student-Faculty Ratio:** 23:1 **Final Year or Final Semester Residency Requirement:** No **Regional Accreditation:** North Central Association of Colleges and Schools **Credit Hours For Degree:** 62 semester hours, Associates **Professional Accreditation:** APTA. **Intercollegiate Athletics:** Baseball M; Basketball M & W; Cross-Country Running M & W; Soccer M & W; Softball W; Volleyball W

NATIONAL LOUIS UNIVERSITY

122 S Michigan Ave.
Chicago, IL 60603
Tel: (312)621-9650; Free: 888-658-8632
Fax: (312)261-3057
Web Site: www.nl.edu
President/CEO: Dr. Nivine Megahed
Financial Aid: Janet Jazwiec

Type: University **Sex:** Coed **% Accepted:** 81 **Admission Plans:** Deferred Admission **Application Deadline:** Rolling **Application Fee:** $0.00 **H.S. Requirements:** High school diploma required; GED accepted **Scholarships:** Available. **Calendar System:** Quarter, Summer session available **Enrollment:** Full-time 615, Graduate full-time 1,263, Graduate part-time 1,815, Part-time 691 **Faculty:** Full-time 129, Part-time 308 **Student-Faculty Ratio:** 12:1 **Exams:** ACT essay component not used; SAT I or ACT; SAT essay component not used. **% Receiving Financial Aid:** 84 **Final Year or Final Semester Residency Requirement:** No **Regional Accreditation:** North Central Association of Colleges and Schools **Credit Hours For Degree:** 180 quarter hours, Bachelors **Professional Accreditation:** CoARC, JRCERT, NCATE.

NORTH CENTRAL COLLEGE

30 N Brainard St.
Naperville, IL 60566-7063
Tel: (630)637-5100; Free: 800-411-1861
E-mail: admissions@noctrl.edu
Web Site: www.northcentralcollege.edu
President/CEO: Dr. Troy D. Hammond
Admissions: Martha Stolze
Financial Aid: Martin R. Sauer

Type: Comprehensive **Sex:** Coed **Affiliation:** United Methodist. **Scores:** 42.1% ACT 18-23; 48.1% ACT 24-29 **% Accepted:** 57 **Admission Plans:** Deferred Admission **Application Deadline:** Rolling **Application Fee:** $25.00 **H.S. Requirements:** High school diploma required; GED accepted **Costs Per Year:** Application fee: $25. Comprehensive fee: $45,510 includes full-time tuition ($35,241), mandatory fees ($180), and college room and board ($10,089). College room only: $6999. Room and board charges vary according to housing facility. Part-time tuition: $979 per credit hour. Part-time mandatory fees: $20 per term. Part-time tuition and fees vary according to course load. **Scholarships:** Available. **Calendar System:** Quarter, Summer session available **Enrollment:** Full-time 2,590, Graduate full-time 85, Graduate part-time 144, Part-time 143 **Faculty:** Full-time 142, Part-time 132 **Student-Faculty Ratio:** 15:1 **Exams:** ACT; SAT I or ACT; SAT Reasoning; SAT Subject. **% Receiving Financial Aid:** 77 **% Residing in College-Owned, -Operated, or -Affiliated Housing:** 56 **Final Year or Final Semester Residency Requirement:** Yes **Regional Accreditation:** North Central Association of Colleges and Schools **Credit Hours For Degree:** 120 semester hours, Bachelors **ROTC:** Air Force, Army **Intercollegiate Athletics:** Baseball M; Basketball M & W; Cheerleading W; Cross-Country Running M & W; Football M; Golf M & W; Lacrosse M & W; Soccer M & W; Softball W; Swimming and Diving M & W; Tennis M & W; Track and Field M & W; Triathlon W; Volleyball M & W; Wrestling M

NORTH PARK UNIVERSITY

3225 W Foster Ave.
Chicago, IL 60625-4895
Tel: (773)244-6200; Free: 800-888-NPC8
Fax: (773)583-0858
E-mail: afao@northpark.edu
Web Site: www.northpark.edu
President/CEO: Daivd L. Parkyn

Financial Aid: Dr. Lucy Shaker
Type: Comprehensive **Sex:** Coed **Affiliation:** Evangelical Covenant Church. **Scores:** 94% SAT V 400+; 96% SAT M 400+; 52% ACT 18-23; 30% ACT 24-29 **% Accepted:** 52 **Admission Plans:** Early Admission **Application Deadline:** Rolling **Application Fee:** $40.00 **H.S. Requirements:** High school diploma required; GED accepted **Costs Per Year:** Application fee: $40. Comprehensive fee: $34,320 includes full-time tuition ($25,740), mandatory fees ($120), and college room and board ($8460). College room only: $4560. Room and board charges vary according to board plan and housing facility. Part-time tuition: $850 per credit hour. **Scholarships:** Available. **Calendar System:** Semester, Summer session available **Enrollment:** Full-time 1,824, Graduate full-time 109, Graduate part-time 824, Part-time 381 **Faculty:** Full-time 118, Part-time 187 **Student-Faculty Ratio:** 13:1 **Exams:** ACT essay component used for admission; ACT essay component used for advising; ACT essay component used for placement; SAT I or ACT; SAT essay component used for admission; SAT essay component used for advising; SAT essay component used for placement. **% Residing in College-Owned, -Operated, or -Affiliated Housing:** 47 **Final Year or Final Semester Residency Requirement:** Yes **Regional Accreditation:** North Central Association of Colleges and Schools **Credit Hours For Degree:** 120 semester hours, Bachelors **ROTC:** Army **Professional Accreditation:** AACN, NASM. **Intercollegiate Athletics:** Baseball M; Basketball M & W; Crew M & W; Cross-Country Running M & W; Football M; Golf M & W; Soccer M & W; Softball W; Tennis W; Track and Field M & W; Ultimate Frisbee M & W; Volleyball W

NORTHEASTERN ILLINOIS UNIVERSITY

5500 N St. Louis Ave.
Chicago, IL 60625-4699
Tel: (773)583-4050
Fax: (773)794-6243
E-mail: admrec@neiu.edu
Web Site: www.neiu.edu
President/CEO: Dr. Sharon K. Hahs
Admissions: Zarrin Kerwell
Financial Aid: Maureen T. Amos

Type: Comprehensive **Sex:** Coed **Scores:** 43.2% ACT 18-23; 8.2% ACT 24-29 **% Accepted:** 67 **Admission Plans:** Deferred Admission **Application Deadline:** July 1 **Application Fee:** $30.00 **H.S. Requirements:** High school diploma required; GED accepted **Costs Per Year:** Application fee: $30. State resident tuition: $7728 full-time, $322 per credit hour part-time. Nonresident tuition: $15,456 full-time, $644 per credit hour part-time. Mandatory fees: $3322 full-time, $56.70 per credit hour part-time. Full-time tuition and fees vary according to course load and degree level. Part-time tuition and fees vary according to course load and degree level. College room and board: $11,100. College room only: $8100. Tuition guaranteed not to increase for student's term of enrollment. **Scholarships:** Available. **Calendar System:** Semester, Summer session available **Enrollment:** Full-time 4,502, Graduate full-time 374, Graduate part-time 1,422, Part-time 3,593 **Faculty:** Full-time 374, Part-time 251 **Student-Faculty Ratio:** 14:1 **Exams:** SAT I or ACT; SAT Reasoning. **% Receiving Financial Aid:** 65 **Regional Accreditation:** North Central Association of Colleges and Schools **Credit Hours For Degree:** 120 credit hours, Bachelors **ROTC:** Air Force, Army **Professional Accreditation:** ACA, CSWE, NASAD, NASM, NCATE.

NORTHERN ILLINOIS UNIVERSITY

De Kalb, IL 60115-2854
Tel: (815)753-1000; Free: 800-892-3050
E-mail: admissions@niu.edu
Web Site: www.niu.edu
President/CEO: Dr. Douglas D. Baker
Admissions: Dr. Dani Rollins
Financial Aid: Rebecca A. Babel

Type: University **Sex:** Coed **Scores:** 52% ACT 18-23; 31% ACT 24-29 **% Accepted:** 50 **Application Deadline:** August 1 **Application Fee:** $40.00 **H.S. Requirements:** High school diploma required; GED accepted **Costs Per Year:** Application fee: $40. State resident tuition: $9466 full-time. Nonresident tuition: $18,506 full-time. Mandatory fees: $2736 full-time. College room and board: $9670. Room and board charges vary according to board plan and housing facility. **Scholarships:** Available. **Calendar System:** Semester, Summer session available **Enrollment:** Full-time 13,224, Graduate full-time 2,321, Graduate part-time 2,782, Part-time 1,803 **Faculty:** Full-time 847, Part-time 252 **Student-Faculty Ratio:** 15:1 **Exams:** SAT I or ACT. **% Receiving Financial Aid:** 73 **% Residing in College-Owned, -Operated, or -Affiliated Housing: 28 Regional Accreditation: North Central Association of Colleges and Schools Credit Hours For Degree: 124 credit hours, Bachelors ROTC: Air Force, Army Professional Accreditation: AACN, AACSB, AAFCS, AALS, AAMFT, ABA, ABET, ACA, AND, APA, APTA, ASHA, ATMAE, CEPH, CORE, JRCAT, NAACLS, NASAD, NASM, NASPAA, NAST, NCATE. Intercollegiate Athletics: Baseball M; Basketball M & W; Cross-Country Running W; Football M; Golf M & W; Gymnastics W; Soccer M & W; Softball W; Swimming and Diving M & W; Tennis M & W; Volleyball W; Wrestling M

NORTHWESTERN COLLEGE–BRIDGEVIEW CAMPUS

7725 S Harlem Ave.
Bridgeview, IL 60455
Tel: (708)237-5000; Free: 888-205-2283
Web Site: www.nc.edu/locations/bridgeview-campus
Type: Two-Year College Sex: Coed % Accepted: 98 Application Fee: $25.00 Calendar System: Quarter Regional Accreditation: North Central Association of Colleges and Schools

NORTHWESTERN COLLEGE–CHICAGO CAMPUS

4829 N Lipps Ave.
Chicago, IL 60630
Tel: (847)233-7700; Free: 888-205-2283
Web Site: www.nc.edu/locations/chicago-campus
President/CEO: Lawrence Schumacher
Admissions: Shahed Kasem
Type: Two-Year College Sex: Coed % Accepted: 95 Application Deadline: Rolling Application Fee: $25.00 H.S. Requirements: High school diploma required; GED accepted Costs Per Year: Application fee: $25. Tuition: $20,925 full-time, $465 per quarter hour part-time. Mandatory fees: $370 full-time. Scholarships: Available. Calendar System: Quarter, Summer session available Enrollment: Full-time 472, Part-time 610 Faculty: Full-time 35, Part-time 57 Exams: SAT I or ACT. Regional Accreditation: North Central Association of Colleges and Schools Credit Hours For Degree: 90 quarter hours, Associates Professional Accreditation: AAMAE, ACBSP, AHIMA.

NORTHWESTERN UNIVERSITY

Evanston, IL 60208
Tel: (847)491-3741
E-mail: ug-admission@northwestern.edu
Web Site: www.northwestern.edu
President/CEO: Morton Shapiro
Admissions: Christopher Watson
Type: University Sex: Coed Scores: 100% SAT V 400+; 100% SAT M 400+; 0.67% ACT 18-23; 24.33% ACT 24-29 % Accepted: 13 Admission Plans: Deferred Admission; Early Action; Early Admission Application Deadline: January 1 Application Fee: $75.00 H.S. Requirements: High school diploma required; GED accepted Costs Per Year: Application fee: $75. Comprehensive fee: $63,983 includes full-time tuition ($48,624), mandatory fees ($423), and college room and board ($14,936). Room and board charges vary according to board plan and housing facility. Scholarships: Available. Calendar System: Quarter, Summer session available Enrollment: Full-time 8,255, Graduate full-time 8,928, Graduate part-time 3,713, Part-time 746 Faculty: Full-time 1,446, Part-time 247 Student-Faculty Ratio: 7:1 Exams: SAT I or ACT; SAT II; SAT Reasoning; SAT Subject. % Receiving Financial Aid: 44 % Residing in College-Owned, -Operated, or -Affiliated Housing: 99 Regional Accreditation: North Central Association of Colleges and Schools Credit Hours For Degree: 45 courses, Bachelors ROTC: Air Force, Army, Navy Professional Accreditation: AACSB, AALS, AAMFT, ABA, ABET, ACEJMC, APA, APTA, ASHA, CAHME, CEPH, LCME/AMA, NASM, NAST.

OAKTON COMMUNITY COLLEGE

1600 E Golf Rd.
Des Plaines, IL 60016-1268
Tel: (847)635-1600
Fax: (847)635-1706
E-mail: ncisarik@oakton.edu
Web Site: www.oakton.edu
President/CEO: Margaret B. Lee
Admissions: Nicci Cisarik
Type: Two-Year College Sex: Coed Affiliation: Illinois Community College Board. Admission Plans: Open Admission Application Deadline: Rolling

Application Fee: $25.00 H.S. Requirements: High school diploma required; GED accepted Costs Per Year: Application fee: $25. Area resident tuition: $2845 full-time. State resident tuition: $7639 full-time. Nonresident tuition: $9673 full-time. Full-time tuition varies according to course load. Scholarships: Available. Calendar System: Semester, Summer session available Regional Accreditation: North Central Association of Colleges and Schools Credit Hours For Degree: 60 semester hours, Associates Professional Accreditation: ACEN, AHIMA, APTA, NAACLS. Intercollegiate Athletics: Baseball M; Basketball M & W; Cross-Country Running M & W; Soccer M & W; Softball W; Tennis M & W; Track and Field M & W; Volleyball W

OLIVET NAZARENE UNIVERSITY

One University Ave.
Bourbonnais, IL 60914
Tel: (815)939-5011; Free: 800-648-1463
Web Site: www.olivet.edu
President/CEO: John C. Bowling
Admissions: Jordan Gerstenberger
Financial Aid: Greg Bruner
Type: Comprehensive Sex: Coed Affiliation: Church of the Nazarene. % Accepted: 77 Admission Plans: Deferred Admission Application Deadline: Rolling Application Fee: $25.00 H.S. Requirements: High school diploma required; GED accepted Costs Per Year: Application fee: $25. Comprehensive fee: $40,690 includes full-time tuition ($31,950), mandatory fees ($840), and college room and board ($7900). Full-time tuition and fees vary according to course load. Room and board charges vary according to board plan. Part-time tuition: $1332 per semester hour. Part-time tuition varies according to course load. Scholarships: Available. Calendar System: Semester, Summer session available Enrollment: Full-time 3,043, Graduate full-time 616, Graduate part-time 873, Part-time 360 Faculty: Full-time 136, Part-time 306 Student-Faculty Ratio: 17:1 Exams: SAT I or ACT. % Receiving Financial Aid: 81 % Residing in College-Owned, -Operated, or -Affiliated Housing: 70 Final Year or Final Semester Residency Requirement: Yes Regional Accreditation: North Central Association of Colleges and Schools Credit Hours For Degree: 64 semester hours, Associates; 128 semester hours, Bachelors ROTC: Army Professional Accreditation: AACN, AAFCS, ABET, CSWE, NASM, NCATE. Intercollegiate Athletics: Baseball M; Basketball M & W; Cheerleading M & W; Cross-Country Running M & W; Football M; Golf M; Soccer M & W; Softball W; Tennis M & W; Track and Field M & W; Volleyball W

PARKLAND COLLEGE

2400 W Bradley Ave.
Champaign, IL 61821-1899
Tel: (217)351-2200; Free: 800-346-8089
Fax: (217)351-7640
E-mail: admissions@parkland.edu
Web Site: www.parkland.edu
President/CEO: Thomas Ramage
Admissions: Tim Wendt
Financial Aid: Tim Wendt
Type: Two-Year College Sex: Coed Affiliation: Illinois Community College Board. Scores: 45% ACT 18-23; 15% ACT 24-29 % Accepted: 100 Admission Plans: Deferred Admission; Open Admission Application Deadline: Rolling Application Fee: $0.00 H.S. Requirements: High school diploma required; GED accepted Costs Per Year: Application fee: $0. Area resident tuition: $4215 full-time, $125 per credit hour part-time. State resident tuition: $10,095 full-time, $321 per credit hour part-time. Nonresident tuition: $14,985 full-time, $484 per credit hour part-time. Mandatory fees: $15.50 per credit hour part-time. Scholarships: Available. Calendar System: Semester, Summer session available Student-Faculty Ratio: 15:1 Exams: ACT. Regional Accreditation: North Central Association of Colleges and Schools Credit Hours For Degree: 60 semester hours, Associates ROTC: Air Force, Army, Navy Professional Accreditation: ACEN, ADA, AOTA, ARCST, CoARC, JRCERT. Intercollegiate Athletics: Baseball M; Basketball M & W; Golf M; Soccer M & W; Softball W; Volleyball W

PRAIRIE STATE COLLEGE

202 S Halsted St.
Chicago Heights, IL 60411-8226
Tel: (708)709-3500
E-mail: jmmiller@prairiestate.edu

Web Site: www.prairiestate.edu
President/CEO: Dr. Eric Radtke
Admissions: Jaime Miller

Type: Two-Year College **Sex:** Coed **Affiliation:** Illinois Community College Board. **Admission Plans:** Deferred Admission; Open Admission **Application Deadline:** Rolling **H.S. Requirements:** High school diploma or equivalent not required. For transfer associate programs: High school diploma required; GED accepted **Scholarships:** Available. **Calendar System:** Semester, Summer session available **Student-Faculty Ratio:** 17:1 **Regional Accreditation:** North Central Association of Colleges and Schools **Credit Hours For Degree:** 62 credit hours, Associates **Professional Accreditation:** ACEN, ADA. **Intercollegiate Athletics:** Baseball M; Basketball M & W; Golf M; Soccer M; Softball W; Track and Field M & W; Volleyball W

PRINCIPIA COLLEGE

One Maybeck Pl.
Elsah, IL 62028-9799
Tel: (618)374-2131; Free: 800-277-4648
Fax: (618)374-4000
Web Site: www.principiacollege.edu
President/CEO: Dr. Jonathan Palmer
Admissions: Tami Gavaletz
Financial Aid: Katie Schiele

Type: Four-Year College **Sex:** Coed **Affiliation:** Christian Science. **Scores:** 96% SAT V 400+; 92% SAT M 400+; 34% ACT 18-23; 56% ACT 24-29 **% Accepted:** 75 **Admission Plans:** Deferred Admission **Application Deadline:** Rolling **Application Fee:** $0.00 **H.S. Requirements:** High school diploma required; GED accepted **Costs Per Year:** Application fee: $0. Comprehensive fee: $39,010 includes full-time tuition ($27,480), mandatory fees ($500), and college room and board ($11,030). College room only: $5230. Full-time tuition and fees vary according to course load. Room and board charges vary according to board plan. **Scholarships:** Available. **Calendar System:** Semester, Summer session available **Enrollment:** Full-time 450, Part-time 14 **Faculty:** Full-time 60 **Student-Faculty Ratio:** 7:1 **Exams:** SAT I or ACT; SAT II; SAT Reasoning; SAT Subject. **% Receiving Financial Aid:** 70 **% Residing in College-Owned, -Operated, or -Affiliated Housing:** 100 **Final Year or Final Semester Residency Requirement:** Yes **Regional Accreditation:** North Central Association of Colleges and Schools **Credit Hours For Degree:** 120 semester hours, Bachelors **Intercollegiate Athletics:** Baseball M; Basketball M & W; Cross-Country Running M & W; Lacrosse W; Rugby M; Soccer M & W; Softball W; Swimming and Diving M & W; Tennis M & W; Track and Field M & W; Volleyball W

QUINCY UNIVERSITY

1800 College Ave.
Quincy, IL 62301-2699
Tel: (217)222-8020; Free: 800-688-4295
Fax: (217)228-5479
E-mail: admissions@quincy.edu
Web Site: www.quincy.edu
President/CEO: Dr. Robert A. Gervasi
Admissions: Abby Wayman
Financial Aid: Lisa Flack

Type: Comprehensive **Sex:** Coed **Affiliation:** Roman Catholic. **Scores:** 100% SAT V 400+; 89% SAT M 400+; 53% ACT 18-23; 30% ACT 24-29 **% Accepted:** 63 **Admission Plans:** Deferred Admission **Application Deadline:** Rolling **Application Fee:** $25.00 **H.S. Requirements:** High school diploma required; GED accepted **Costs Per Year:** Application fee: $25. Comprehensive fee: $37,128 includes full-time tuition ($25,998), mandatory fees ($1130), and college room and board ($10,000). College room only: $5500. Room and board charges vary according to board plan, housing facility, and student level. Part-time tuition: $700 per semester hour. Part-time mandatory fees: $30 per semester hour. Part-time tuition and fees vary according to course load. **Scholarships:** Available. **Calendar System:** Semester, Summer session available **Enrollment:** Full-time 1,024, Graduate full-time 19, Graduate part-time 134, Part-time 116 **Faculty:** Full-time 52, Part-time 62 **Student-Faculty Ratio:** 14:1 **Exams:** ACT essay component not used; SAT I or ACT; SAT essay component not used; SAT Reasoning. **% Receiving Financial Aid:** 79 **% Residing in College-Owned, -Operated, or -Affiliated Housing:** 54 **Final Year or Final Semester Residency Requirement:** No **Regional Accreditation:** North Central Association of Colleges and Schools **Credit Hours For Degree:** 64 credit hours, Associates; 124 credit hours, Bachelors **Intercollegiate Athletics:** Baseball M;

Basketball M & W; Cheerleading M & W; Cross-Country Running M & W; Football M; Golf M & W; Soccer M & W; Softball W; Swimming and Diving W; Tennis M & W; Volleyball M & W

RASMUSSEN COLLEGE AURORA

2363 Sequoia Dr.
Aurora, IL 60506
Tel: (630)888-3500; Free: 888-549-6755
Fax: (630)888-3501
E-mail: susan.hammerstrom@rasmussen.edu
Web Site: www.rasmussen.edu
President/CEO: Kristi Waite
Admissions: Susan Hammerstrom

Type: Four-Year College **Sex:** Coed **Affiliation:** Rasmussen College System. **Admission Plans:** Deferred Admission; Early Admission **Application Deadline:** Rolling **Application Fee:** $0.00 **H.S. Requirements:** High school diploma required; GED accepted **Costs Per Year:** Application fee: $0. Tuition: $13,455 full-time. Mandatory fees: $1800 full-time. Full-time tuition and fees vary according to course level, course load, degree level, location, and program. Tuition guaranteed not to increase for student's term of enrollment. **Calendar System:** Quarter, Summer session available **Enrollment:** Full-time 165, Part-time 289 **Faculty:** Full-time 3, Part-time 12 **Student-Faculty Ratio:** 22:1 **Exams:** ACT essay component not used; Other; SAT essay component not used. **Final Year or Final Semester Residency Requirement:** No **Regional Accreditation:** North Central Association of Colleges and Schools **Credit Hours For Degree:** 90 credits, Associates; 180 credits, Bachelors **Professional Accreditation:** ACBSP.

RASMUSSEN COLLEGE MOKENA/TINLEY PARK

8650 W Spring Lake Rd.
Mokena, IL 60448
Tel: (815)534-3300; Free: 888-549-6755
Web Site: www.rasmussen.edu
President/CEO: Kristi Waite
Admissions: Susan Hammerstrom

Type: Four-Year College **Sex:** Coed **Affiliation:** Rasmussen College System. **Admission Plans:** Deferred Admission; Early Admission **Application Deadline:** Rolling **Application Fee:** $0.00 **H.S. Requirements:** High school diploma required; GED accepted **Costs Per Year:** Application fee: $0. Tuition: $13,455 full-time. Mandatory fees: $1800 full-time. Full-time tuition and fees vary according to course level, course load, degree level, location, and program. Tuition guaranteed not to increase for student's term of enrollment. **Calendar System:** Quarter, Summer session available **Enrollment:** Full-time 150, Part-time 356 **Faculty:** Full-time 1, Part-time 24 **Student-Faculty Ratio:** 22:1 **Exams:** ACT essay component not used; Other; SAT essay component not used. **Final Year or Final Semester Residency Requirement:** No **Credit Hours For Degree:** 90 credits, Associates; 180 credits, Bachelors **Professional Accreditation:** ACBSP.

RASMUSSEN COLLEGE ROCKFORD

6000 E State St., Fourth Fl.
Rockford, IL 61108-2513
Tel: (815)316-4800; Free: 888-549-6755
Fax: (815)316-4801
E-mail: susan.hammerstrom@rasmussen.edu
Web Site: www.rasmussen.edu
President/CEO: Kristi Waite
Admissions: Susan Hammerstrom

Type: Four-Year College **Sex:** Coed **Affiliation:** Rasmussen College System. **Admission Plans:** Deferred Admission; Early Admission **Application Deadline:** Rolling **Application Fee:** $0.00 **H.S. Requirements:** High school diploma required; GED accepted **Costs Per Year:** Application fee: $0. Tuition: $13,455 full-time. Mandatory fees: $1800 full-time. Full-time tuition and fees vary according to course level, course load, degree level, location, and program. Tuition guaranteed not to increase for student's term of enrollment. **Calendar System:** Quarter, Summer session available **Enrollment:** Full-time 249, Part-time 510 **Faculty:** Full-time 12, Part-time 42 **Student-Faculty Ratio:** 22:1 **Exams:** ACT essay component not used; Other; SAT essay component not used. **Final Year or Final Semester Residency Requirement:** No **Regional Accreditation:** North Central Association of Colleges and Schools **Credit Hours For Degree:** 90 credits, Associates; 180 credits, Bachelors **Professional Accreditation:** ACBSP.

RASMUSSEN COLLEGE ROMEOVILLE/JOLIET

1400 W Normantown Rd.
Romeoville, IL 60446
Tel: (815)306-2600; Free: 888-549-6755
E-mail: susan.hammerstrom@rasmussen.edu
Web Site: www.rasmussen.edu
President/CEO: Kristi Waite
Admissions: Susan Hammerstrom

Type: Four-Year College **Sex:** Coed **Affiliation:** Rasmussen College System. **Admission Plans:** Deferred Admission; Early Admission **Application Deadline:** Rolling **Application Fee:** $0.00 **H.S. Requirements:** High school diploma required; GED accepted **Costs Per Year:** Application fee: $0. Tuition: $13,455 full-time. Mandatory fees: $1800 full-time. Full-time tuition and fees vary according to course level, course load, degree level, location, and program. Tuition guaranteed not to increase for student's term of enrollment. **Calendar System:** Quarter, Summer session available **Enrollment:** Full-time 242, Part-time 587 **Faculty:** Full-time 13, Part-time 45 **Student-Faculty Ratio:** 22:1 **Exams:** ACT essay component not used; Other; SAT essay component not used. **Final Year or Final Semester Residency Requirement:** No **Credit Hours For Degree:** 90 credits, Associates; 180 credits, Bachelors **Professional Accreditation:** ACBSP.

REND LAKE COLLEGE

468 N Ken Gray Pky.
Ina, IL 62846-9801
Tel: (618)437-5321; Free: 800-369-5321
Fax: (618)437-5677
E-mail: swannj@rlc.edu
Web Site: www.rlc.edu
President/CEO: Terry Wilkerson
Admissions: Jason Swann

Type: Two-Year College **Sex:** Coed **Affiliation:** Illinois Community College Board. **Admission Plans:** Deferred Admission; Open Admission **Application Deadline:** August 18 **Application Fee:** $0.00 **H.S. Requirements:** High school diploma required; GED accepted **Costs Per Year:** Application fee: $0. Area resident tuition: $3300 full-time, $110 per credit hour part-time. State resident tuition: $5250 full-time, $175 per credit hour part-time. Nonresident tuition: $6000 full-time, $200 per credit hour part-time. Mandatory fees: $450 full-time, $15 per credit hour part-time. Full-time tuition and fees vary according to course level, course load, program, and reciprocity agreements. Part-time tuition and fees vary according to course level, course load, program, and reciprocity agreements. **Scholarships:** Available. **Calendar System:** Semester, Summer session available **Enrollment:** Full-time 1,198, Part-time 991 **Faculty:** Full-time 66, Part-time 149 **Student-Faculty Ratio:** 15:1 **Exams:** Other; SAT I or ACT. **Final Year or Final Semester Residency Requirement:** No **Regional Accreditation:** North Central Association of Colleges and Schools **Credit Hours For Degree:** 64 semester hours, Associates **Professional Accreditation:** AHIMA, AOTA, NAACLS. **Intercollegiate Athletics:** Baseball M; Basketball M & W; Golf M & W; Softball W; Tennis W; Volleyball W

RESURRECTION UNIVERSITY

1431 N Claremont Ave.
Chicago, IL 60622
Tel: (708)763-6530
Fax: (708)763-1531
Web Site: www.resu.edu
President/CEO: Dr. Beth Brooks
Financial Aid: Shirley Howell

Type: Two-Year Upper Division **Sex:** Coed **Admission Plans:** Deferred Admission **Application Fee:** $50.00 **H.S. Requirements:** High school diploma required; GED accepted **Scholarships:** Available. **Calendar System:** Semester, Summer session available **Enrollment:** Full-time 219, Graduate full-time 109, Graduate part-time 28, Part-time 120 **Faculty:** Full-time 26, Part-time 33 **Student-Faculty Ratio:** 10:1 **Exams:** Other. **% Receiving Financial Aid:** 98 **Final Year or Final Semester Residency Requirement:** No **Regional Accreditation:** North Central Association of Colleges and Schools **Credit Hours For Degree:** 120 semester hours, Bachelors **Professional Accreditation:** AACN.

RICHLAND COMMUNITY COLLEGE

One College Park
Decatur, IL 62521-8513
Tel: (217)875-7200

Fax: (217)875-6991
E-mail: csebok@richland.edu
Web Site: www.richland.edu
President/CEO: Dr. Gayle Saunders
Admissions: Catherine Sebok

Type: Two-Year College **Sex:** Coed **Affiliation:** Illinois Community College Board. **% Accepted:** 66 **Admission Plans:** Early Admission; Open Admission **Application Deadline:** Rolling **Application Fee:** $0.00 **H.S. Requirements:** High school diploma required; GED accepted **Costs Per Year:** Application fee: $0. Area resident tuition: $3744 full-time, $119 per credit hour part-time. State resident tuition: $5445 full-time, $200.50 per credit hour part-time. Nonresident tuition: $462 per credit part-time. Mandatory fees: $324 full-time, $2 per credit part-time. Full-time tuition and fees vary according to program and reciprocity agreements. Part-time tuition and fees vary according to program and reciprocity agreements. **Scholarships:** Available. **Calendar System:** Semester, Summer session available **Enrollment:** Full-time 951, Part-time 2,054 **Faculty:** Full-time 75, Part-time 128 **Student-Faculty Ratio:** 15:1 **Exams:** ACT; ACT essay component used for advising; ACT essay component used for placement. **Regional Accreditation:** North Central Association of Colleges and Schools **Credit Hours For Degree:** 60 semester hours, Associates **Professional Accreditation:** ACEN, ARCST.

ROBERT MORRIS UNIVERSITY ILLINOIS

401 S State St.
Chicago, IL 60605
Tel: (312)935-6800; Free: 800-762-5960
Fax: (312)836-4599
E-mail: enroll@robertmorris.edu
Web Site: www.robertmorris.edu
President/CEO: Mablene Krueger
Financial Aid: Leigh Brinson

Type: Comprehensive **Sex:** Coed **Scores:** 38% ACT 18-23; 14% ACT 24-29 **% Accepted:** 24 **Admission Plans:** Deferred Admission **Application Deadline:** Rolling **Application Fee:** $20.00 **H.S. Requirements:** High school diploma required; GED accepted **Costs Per Year:** Application fee: $20. Comprehensive fee: $38,550 includes full-time tuition ($25,800), mandatory fees ($150), and college room and board ($12,600). Part-time tuition: $717 per quarter hour. Part-time tuition varies according to course load. **Scholarships:** Available. **Calendar System:** Miscellaneous, Summer session available **Enrollment:** Full-time 2,553, Graduate full-time 36, Graduate part-time 334, Part-time 133 **Faculty:** Full-time 71, Part-time 151 **Student-Faculty Ratio:** 23:1 **Exams:** Other; SAT I or ACT. **% Receiving Financial Aid:** 85 **% Residing in College-Owned, -Operated, or -Affiliated Housing:** 9 **Final Year or Final Semester Residency Requirement:** Yes **Regional Accreditation:** North Central Association of Colleges and Schools **Credit Hours For Degree:** 92 quarter hours, Associates; 188 quarter hours, Bachelors **ROTC:** Army **Professional Accreditation:** AAMAE, ACEN. **Intercollegiate Athletics:** Baseball M; Basketball M & W; Bowling M & W; Cheerleading M & W; Cross-Country Running M & W; Football M; Golf M & W; Ice Hockey M & W; Lacrosse M & W; Soccer M & W; Softball W; Tennis M & W; Track and Field M & W; Volleyball M & W

ROCK VALLEY COLLEGE

3301 N Mulford Rd.
Rockford, IL 61114-5699
Tel: (815)921-7821; Free: 800-973-7821
Fax: (815)654-5568
E-mail: p.peyer@rockvalleycollege.edu
Web Site: www.rockvalleycollege.edu
President/CEO: Dr. Jack Becherer
Admissions: Patrick Peyer

Type: Two-Year College **Sex:** Coed **Affiliation:** Illinois Community College Board. **Admission Plans:** Open Admission **Application Fee:** $0.00 **H.S. Requirements:** High school diploma or equivalent not required. For nursing, respiratory therapy programs: High school diploma required; GED accepted **Costs Per Year:** Application fee: $0. Area resident tuition: $2730 full-time, $91 per credit hour part-time. State resident tuition: $7620 full-time, $254 per credit hour part-time. Nonresident tuition: $14,460 full-time, $482 per credit hour part-time. Mandatory fees: $314 full-time. Full-time tuition and fees vary according to course load. Part-time tuition varies according to course load. **Scholarships:** Available. **Calendar System:** Semester, Summer session available **Enrollment:** Full-time 3,138, Part-time 3,799 **Faculty:** Full-time 157, Part-time 304 **Exams:** ACT essay component not used; SAT essay component not used. **Regional Accreditation:** North Central Association of

Colleges and Schools **Credit Hours For Degree:** 64 semester hours, Associates **Professional Accreditation:** ADA, CoARC. **Intercollegiate Athletics:** Baseball M; Basketball M & W; Golf M; Soccer M & W; Softball W; Squash W; Tennis M & W; Volleyball W

ROCKFORD CAREER COLLEGE
1130 S Alpine Rd.
Ste. 100
Rockford, IL 61108
Tel: (815)965-8616
Fax: (815)965-0360
Web Site: www.rockfordcareercollege.edu
President/CEO: Richard Denhart
Admissions: Barbara Holliman

Type: Two-Year College **Sex:** Coed **Admission Plans:** Early Admission; Open Admission **Application Deadline:** September 4 **Application Fee:** $50.00 **H.S. Requirements:** High school diploma required; GED accepted **Scholarships:** Available. **Calendar System:** Quarter, Summer session available **Enrollment:** Full-time 243, Part-time 185 **Faculty:** Full-time 8, Part-time 18 **Student-Faculty Ratio:** 15:1 **Credit Hours For Degree:** 100 credits, Associates **Professional Accreditation:** AAMAE, ACCSC, ACICS.

ROCKFORD UNIVERSITY
5050 E State St.
Rockford, IL 61108-2393
Tel: (815)226-4000; Free: 800-892-2984
Fax: (815)226-4119
E-mail: admissions@rockford.edu
Web Site: www.rockford.edu
President/CEO: Dr. Robert Head, PhD
Admissions: Jennifer Nordstrom
Financial Aid: Todd M. Fischer-Free

Type: Comprehensive **Sex:** Coed **Scores:** 90% SAT V 400+; 90% SAT M 400+; 63% ACT 18-23; 27% ACT 24-29 **Costs Per Year:** Comprehensive fee: $37,320 includes full-time tuition ($29,050), mandatory fees ($130), and college room and board ($8140). College room only: $4400. Full-time tuition and fees vary according to course load. Room and board charges vary according to board plan and housing facility. Part-time tuition: $765 per credit hour. Part-time tuition varies according to course load. **Scholarships:** Available. **Calendar System:** Semester, Summer session available **Enrollment:** Full-time 925, Graduate full-time 66, Graduate part-time 154, Part-time 136 **Faculty:** Full-time 76, Part-time 89 **Student-Faculty Ratio:** 10:1 **Exams:** ACT essay component not used; SAT I or ACT; SAT essay component not used. **% Receiving Financial Aid:** 90 **% Residing in College-Owned, -Operated, or -Affiliated Housing:** 36 **Final Year or Final Semester Residency Requirement:** No **Regional Accreditation:** North Central Association of Colleges and Schools **Credit Hours For Degree:** 124 credits, Bachelors **Professional Accreditation:** ACEN. **Intercollegiate Athletics:** Baseball M; Basketball M & W; Cross-Country Running M & W; Football M; Golf M; Soccer M & W; Softball W; Track and Field M & W; Volleyball W

ROOSEVELT UNIVERSITY
430 S Michigan Ave.
Chicago, IL 60605
Tel: (312)341-3500; Free: 877-APPLYRU
E-mail: admission@roosevelt.edu
Web Site: www.roosevelt.edu
President/CEO: Dr. Ali Malekzadeh

Type: Comprehensive **Sex:** Coed **Scores:** 95% SAT V 400+; 95% SAT M 400+; 56.4% ACT 18-23; 34.1% ACT 24-29 **% Accepted:** 72 **Admission Plans:** Deferred Admission **Application Deadline:** August 15 **Application Fee:** $25.00 **H.S. Requirements:** High school diploma required; GED accepted **Costs Per Year:** Application fee: $25. Comprehensive fee: $40,919 includes full-time tuition ($28,119) and college room and board ($12,800). Full-time tuition varies according to program. Part-time tuition: $759 per credit. Part-time tuition varies according to program. **Scholarships:** Available. **Calendar System:** Semester, Summer session available **Enrollment:** Full-time 2,569, Graduate full-time 1,072, Graduate part-time 1,041, Part-time 670 **Faculty:** Full-time 242, Part-time 394 **Student-Faculty Ratio:** 11:1 **Exams:** ACT essay component not used; ACT essay component used for advising; SAT I or ACT; SAT essay component not used; SAT essay component used for advising; SAT Reasoning; SAT Subject. **% Receiving Financial Aid:** 80 **% Residing in College-Owned, -Operated, or -Affiliated Housing:** 23 **Final Year or Final Semester Residency Require-**

ment: Yes **Regional Accreditation:** North Central Association of Colleges and Schools **Credit Hours For Degree:** 120 semester hours, Bachelors **Professional Accreditation:** ACA, ACBSP, ACPE, APA, NASM, NCATE. **Intercollegiate Athletics:** Baseball M; Basketball M & W; Cross-Country Running M & W; Golf M; Soccer M & W; Softball W; Tennis M & W; Volleyball W

RUSH UNIVERSITY
600 S Paulina
Chicago, IL 60612-3832
Tel: (312)942-5000
Fax: (312)942-2100
E-mail: hicela_castruita@rush.edu
Web Site: www.rushu.rush.edu
President/CEO: Dr. Larry J. Goodman
Admissions: Hicela Castruita Woods
Financial Aid: Mike Frechette

Type: Two-Year Upper Division **Sex:** Coed **% Accepted:** 37 **Admission Plans:** Preferred Admission **Application Fee:** $40.00 **Scholarships:** Available. **Calendar System:** Quarter, Summer session not available **Enrollment:** Full-time 159, Part-time 7 **Faculty:** Full-time 796 **Student-Faculty Ratio:** 8:1 **% Receiving Financial Aid:** 92 **% Residing in College-Owned, -Operated, or -Affiliated Housing:** 10 **Regional Accreditation:** North Central Association of Colleges and Schools **Credit Hours For Degree:** 180 quarter hours, Bachelors **Professional Accreditation:** AACN, AANA, ACEN, ACPeE, ACIPE, AND, AOTA, ASHA, CAHME, LCME/AMA, NAACLS.

SAE INSTITUTE CHICAGO
820 N Orleans St.
Chicago, IL 60610-3132
Tel: (312)300-5685
Web Site: www.sae.edu

Type: Two-Year College **Sex:** Coed **Professional Accreditation:** ACCSC.

SAINT ANTHONY COLLEGE OF NURSING
5658 E State St.
Rockford, IL 61108-2468
Tel: (815)395-5091
E-mail: admissions@sacn.edu
Web Site: www.sacn.edu
President/CEO: Dr. Terese Burch
Admissions: April Lipnitzky
Financial Aid: Serrita Woods

Type: Two-Year Upper Division **Sex:** Coed **Affiliation:** Roman Catholic. **Application Fee:** $50.00 **H.S. Requirements:** High school diploma or equivalent not required **Scholarships:** Available. **Calendar System:** Semester, Summer session available **Enrollment:** Full-time 152, Graduate full-time 1, Graduate part-time 74, Part-time 83 **Faculty:** Full-time 20, Part-time 23 **Student-Faculty Ratio:** 7:1 **% Receiving Financial Aid:** 89 **Final Year or Final Semester Residency Requirement:** No **Regional Accreditation:** North Central Association of Colleges and Schools **Credit Hours For Degree:** 128 credits, Bachelors **Professional Accreditation:** AACN.

ST. AUGUSTINE COLLEGE
1333-1345 W Argyle
Chicago, IL 60640-3501
Tel: (773)878-8756
E-mail: info@staugustine.edu
Web Site: www.staugustine.edu
President/CEO: Andrew C. Sund
Admissions: Gloria Quiroz
Financial Aid: Maria Zambonino

Type: Four-Year College **Sex:** Coed **Admission Plans:** Open Admission **Application Deadline:** Rolling **Application Fee:** $0.00 **H.S. Requirements:** High school diploma required; GED accepted. For international students: High school diploma or equivalent not required **Costs Per Year:** Application fee: $0. Tuition: $9840 full-time, $410 per semester hour part-time. **Scholarships:** Available. **Calendar System:** Semester, Summer session available **Enrollment:** Full-time 1,218, Part-time 212 **Faculty:** Full-time 20, Part-time 134 **Student-Faculty Ratio:** 20:1 **% Receiving Financial Aid:** 83 **Regional Accreditation:** North Central Association of Colleges and Schools **Credit Hours For Degree:** 60 semester hours, Associates; 128 semester hours, Bachelors **Professional Accreditation:** CoARC.

SAINT FRANCIS MEDICAL CENTER COLLEGE OF NURSING

511 NE Greenleaf St.
Peoria, IL 61603-3783
Tel: (309)655-2201
E-mail: janice.farquharson@osfhealthcare.org
Web Site: www.sfmccon.edu
President/CEO: Pres. Patricia A. Stockert, PhD
Admissions: Janice Farquharson
Financial Aid: Nancy Perryman

Type: Two-Year Upper Division **Sex:** Coed **Affiliation:** Roman Catholic. **% Accepted:** 59 **Admission Plans:** Deferred Admission **Application Fee:** $50.00 **H.S. Requirements:** High school diploma required; GED accepted **Costs Per Year:** Application fee: $50. Tuition: $18,850 full-time. Mandatory fees: $840 full-time. Full-time tuition and fees vary according to course load, degree level, program, and student level. College room only: $3500. **Scholarships:** Available. **Calendar System:** Semester, Summer session available **Enrollment:** Full-time 287, Graduate full-time 13, Graduate part-time 257, Part-time 121 **Faculty:** Full-time 36, Part-time 19 **Student-Faculty Ratio:** 10:1 **% Receiving Financial Aid:** 64 **% Residing in College-Owned, -Operated, or -Affiliated Housing:** 18 **Final Year or Final Semester Residency Requirement:** No **Regional Accreditation:** North Central Association of Colleges and Schools **Credit Hours For Degree:** 124 semester hours, Bachelors **Professional Accreditation:** ACEN.

ST. JOHN'S COLLEGE

729 E Carpenter St.
Springfield, IL 62702
Tel: (217)525-5628
E-mail: college@st-johns.org
Web Site: www.stjohnscollegespringfield.edu
President/CEO: Dr. Brenda Recchia Jeffers
Financial Aid: Mary M. Deatherage

Type: Two-Year Upper Division **Sex:** Coed **Affiliation:** Roman Catholic. **% Accepted:** 68 **Application Fee:** $60.00 **H.S. Requirements:** High school diploma required; GED accepted **Costs Per Year:** Application fee: $60. Tuition: $18,072 full-time, $753 per credit hour part-time. Mandatory fees: $1165 full-time. Full-time tuition and fees vary according to course load, program, and student level. Part-time tuition varies according to course load, program, and student level. Tuition guaranteed not to increase for student's term of enrollment. **Scholarships:** Available. **Calendar System:** Semester, Summer session not available **Enrollment:** Full-time 113, Part-time 9 **Student-Faculty Ratio:** 6:1 **Exams:** Other. **% Receiving Financial Aid:** 72 **Regional Accreditation:** North Central Association of Colleges and Schools **Credit Hours For Degree:** 125 semester hours, Bachelors **Professional Accreditation:** ACEN.

SAINT XAVIER UNIVERSITY

3700 W 103rd St.
Chicago, IL 60655-3105
Tel: (773)298-3000; Free: 800-462-9288
Fax: (773)298-3076
E-mail: carlson@sxu.edu
Web Site: www.sxu.edu
President/CEO: Christine M. Wiseman, JD
Admissions: Dr. Kathleen Carlson
Financial Aid: Susan Swisher

Type: Comprehensive **Sex:** Coed **Affiliation:** Roman Catholic. **Scores:** 95% SAT V 400+; 95% SAT M 400+; 58% ACT 18-23; 33% ACT 24-29 **% Accepted:** 83 **Admission Plans:** Deferred Admission **Application Deadline:** Rolling **Application Fee:** $25.00 **H.S. Requirements:** High school diploma required; GED accepted **Scholarships:** Available. **Calendar System:** Semester, Summer session available **Enrollment:** Full-time 2,537, Graduate full-time 275, Graduate part-time 1,441, Part-time 456 **Faculty:** Full-time 173, Part-time 258 **Student-Faculty Ratio:** 14:1 **Exams:** ACT essay component used for placement; SAT I or ACT. **% Receiving Financial Aid:** 89 **% Residing in College-Owned, -Operated, or -Affiliated Housing:** 29 **Final Year or Final Semester Residency Requirement:** No **Regional Accreditation:** North Central Association of Colleges and Schools **Credit Hours For Degree:** 120 semester hours, Bachelors **ROTC:** Air Force **Professional Accreditation:** AACN, AACSB, ACBSP, ASHA, NASM, NCATE. **Intercollegiate Athletics:** Baseball M; Basketball M & W; Cross-Country Running W; Football M; Golf M; Soccer M & W; Softball W; Volleyball W

SAUK VALLEY COMMUNITY COLLEGE

173 Illinois Rte. 2
Dixon, IL 61021
Tel: (815)288-5511
E-mail: pamela.s.medema@svcc.edu
Web Site: www.svcc.edu
President/CEO: Dr. George J. Mihel
Admissions: Pamela Medema
Financial Aid: Jennifer Ann Schultz

Type: Two-Year College **Sex:** Coed **Affiliation:** Illinois Community College Board. **% Accepted:** 100 **Admission Plans:** Deferred Admission; Early Admission; Open Admission **Application Deadline:** Rolling **Application Fee:** $0.00 **H.S. Requirements:** High school diploma or equivalent not required **Costs Per Year:** Application fee: $0. Area resident tuition: $3108 full-time, $111 per credit hour part-time. State resident tuition: $8960 full-time, $320 per credit hour part-time. Nonresident tuition: $9566 full-time, $347 per credit hour part-time. Mandatory fees: $300 full-time, $5 per credit hour part-time. Full-time tuition and fees vary according to course load and program. Part-time tuition and fees vary according to course load and program. **Scholarships:** Available. **Calendar System:** Semester, Summer session available **Enrollment:** Full-time 998, Part-time 1,222 **Faculty:** Full-time 44, Part-time 101 **Student-Faculty Ratio:** 21:1 **Exams:** ACT. **Regional Accreditation:** North Central Association of Colleges and Schools **Credit Hours For Degree:** 64 semester hours, Associates **Professional Accreditation:** JRCERT. **Intercollegiate Athletics:** Baseball M; Basketball M & W; Cross-Country Running M & W; Softball W; Tennis M & W

SCHOOL OF THE ART INSTITUTE OF CHICAGO

37 S Wabash
Chicago, IL 60603-3103
Tel: (312)899-5100; Free: 800-232-SAIC
Fax: (312)263-0141
E-mail: ugadmiss@saic.edu
Web Site: www.saic.edu
President/CEO: Walter Massey
Admissions: Asia Mitchell
Financial Aid: Patrick James

Type: Comprehensive **Sex:** Coed **Admission Plans:** Deferred Admission; Early Decision Plan **Application Deadline:** June 1 **Application Fee:** $65.00 **H.S. Requirements:** High school diploma required; GED accepted **Costs Per Year:** Application fee: $65. Comprehensive fee: $56,810 includes full-time tuition ($43,140), mandatory fees ($820), and college room and board ($12,850). College room only: $11,300. Full-time tuition and fees vary according to course load, degree level, and program. Room and board charges vary according to board plan. Part-time tuition: $1438 per credit hour. Part-time mandatory fees: $275 per term. Part-time tuition and fees vary according to course load, degree level, and program. **Scholarships:** Available. **Calendar System:** Semester, Summer session available **Enrollment:** Full-time 2,623, Graduate full-time 688, Graduate part-time 60, Part-time 220 **Faculty:** Full-time 168, Part-time 596 **Student-Faculty Ratio:** 11:1 **Exams:** SAT I or ACT. **% Receiving Financial Aid:** 50 **% Residing in College-Owned, -Operated, or -Affiliated Housing:** 17 **Regional Accreditation:** North Central Association of Colleges and Schools **Credit Hours For Degree:** 126 credits, Bachelors **Professional Accreditation:** NASAD.

SHAWNEE COMMUNITY COLLEGE

8364 Shawnee College Rd.
Ullin, IL 62992
Tel: (618)634-3200
Fax: (618)634-3300
E-mail: erink@shawneecc.edu
Web Site: www.shawneecc.edu
President/CEO: Dr. Tim Bellamey
Admissions: Erin King

Type: Two-Year College **Sex:** Coed **Affiliation:** Illinois Community College Board. **% Accepted:** 100 **Admission Plans:** Deferred Admission; Early Admission; Open Admission; Preferred Admission **Application Deadline:** Rolling **Application Fee:** $0.00 **H.S. Requirements:** High school diploma required; GED accepted **Costs Per Year:** Application fee: $0. Area resident tuition: $2376 full-time, $99 per hour part-time. State resident tuition: $3936 full-time, $164 per hour part-time. Nonresident tuition: $3984 full-time, $166 per hour part-time. **Scholarships:** Available. **Calendar System:** Semester, Summer session available **Enrollment:** Full-time 801, Part-time 1,018 **Faculty:** Full-time 40, Part-time 129 **Student-Faculty Ratio:** 13:1 **Exams:**

ACT; ACT essay component not used. **Final Year or Final Semester Residency Requirement:** No **Regional Accreditation:** North Central Association of Colleges and Schools **Credit Hours For Degree:** 64 semester hours, Associates **Professional Accreditation:** AHIMA, AOTA, NAACLS. **Intercollegiate Athletics:** Baseball M; Basketball M & W; Softball W

SHIMER COLLEGE

3424 S State St.
Chicago, IL 60616
Tel: (312)235-3500; Free: 800-215-7173
Fax: (312)235-3501
E-mail: admission@shimer.edu
Web Site: www.shimer.edu
President/CEO: Ed Noonan
Admissions: Amy Pritts
Financial Aid: Janet Henthorn
Type: Four-Year College **Sex:** Coed **Scores:** 100% SAT V 400+; 100% SAT M 400+ **% Accepted:** 84 **Application Fee:** $25.00 **H.S. Requirements:** High school diploma required; GED accepted **Costs Per Year:** Application fee: $25. Comprehensive fee: $45,004 includes full-time tuition ($29,876), mandatory fees ($4128), and college room and board ($11,000). Room and board charges vary according to board plan and housing facility. Part-time tuition: $1086 per credit hour. Part-time mandatory fees: $2625 per year. **Scholarships:** Available. **Calendar System:** Semester, Summer session available **Enrollment:** Full-time 67, Part-time 10 **Faculty:** Full-time 9, Part-time 3 **Student-Faculty Ratio:** 7:1 **Exams:** ACT essay component not used; SAT I and SAT II or ACT; SAT essay component not used; SAT Reasoning; SAT Subject. **% Receiving Financial Aid:** 76 **% Residing in College-Owned, -Operated, or -Affiliated Housing:** 10 **Regional Accreditation:** North Central Association of Colleges and Schools **Credit Hours For Degree:** 125 credit hours, Bachelors

SOLEX COLLEGE

350 E Dundee Rd.
Wheeling, IL 60090
Tel: (847)229-9595
Web Site: www.solex.edu
President/CEO: Leon E. Linton
Type: Two-Year College **Sex:** Coed **Affiliation:** The School of Massage Therapy at SOLEX. **Application Fee:** $150.00 **H.S. Requirements:** High school diploma required; GED accepted **Exams:** ACT essay component used for admission; ACT essay component used for placement; SAT I or ACT; SAT essay component used for admission; SAT essay component used for placement. **Final Year or Final Semester Residency Requirement:** No **Credit Hours For Degree:** 60 credit hours, Associates **Professional Accreditation:** ACICS.

SOUTH SUBURBAN COLLEGE

15800 S State St.
South Holland, IL 60473-1270
Tel: (708)596-2000
E-mail: admissionsquestions@ssc.edu
Web Site: www.ssc.edu
President/CEO: Don Manning
Admissions: Tiffane Jones
Financial Aid: John William Semple
Type: Two-Year College **Sex:** Coed **Affiliation:** Illinois Community College Board. **Admission Plans:** Deferred Admission; Early Admission; Open Admission; Preferred Admission **Application Deadline:** Rolling **H.S. Requirements:** High school diploma required; GED accepted **Costs Per Year:** Area resident tuition: $4050 full-time. State resident tuition: $9990 full-time. Nonresident tuition: $11,640 full-time. Mandatory fees: $533 full-time. Full-time tuition and fees vary according to course load and reciprocity agreements. **Scholarships:** Available. **Calendar System:** Semester, Summer session available **Enrollment:** Full-time 1,614, Part-time 2,787 **Faculty:** Full-time 126, Part-time 318 **Student-Faculty Ratio:** 14:1 **Regional Accreditation:** North Central Association of Colleges and Schools **Credit Hours For Degree:** 60 semester hours, Associates **Professional Accreditation:** ACEN, AOTA, JRCERT, NASM. **Intercollegiate Athletics:** Baseball M; Basketball M & W; Soccer M & W; Softball W; Volleyball W

SOUTHEASTERN ILLINOIS COLLEGE

3575 College Rd.
Harrisburg, IL 62946-4925

Tel: (618)252-5400; Free: 866-338-2742
Web Site: www.sic.edu
President/CEO: Dr. Jonah Rice
Admissions: Dr. David Nudo
Financial Aid: Emily Kaye Henson
Type: Two-Year College **Sex:** Coed **Affiliation:** Illinois Community College Board. **Admission Plans:** Deferred Admission; Early Admission; Open Admission; Preferred Admission **Application Deadline:** September 1 **Application Fee:** $0.00 **H.S. Requirements:** High school diploma required; GED accepted **Scholarships:** Available. **Calendar System:** Semester, Summer session available **Regional Accreditation:** North Central Association of Colleges and Schools **Credit Hours For Degree:** 62 semester hours, Associates **Professional Accreditation:** AHIMA, AOTA, NAACLS. **Intercollegiate Athletics:** Baseball M; Basketball M & W; Softball W

SOUTHERN ILLINOIS UNIVERSITY CARBONDALE

Carbondale, IL 62901-4701
Tel: (618)453-2121
Fax: (618)453-3250
E-mail: regstrar@siu.edu
Web Site: www.siuc.edu
President/CEO: Pres. Randy Dunn
Admissions: Tamora Workman
Financial Aid: Terri R. Harfst
Type: University **Sex:** Coed **Affiliation:** Southern Illinois University. **Scores:** 89% SAT V 400+; 98% SAT M 400+; 50% ACT 18-23; 29% ACT 24-29 **% Accepted:** 81 **Admission Plans:** Deferred Admission **Application Deadline:** Rolling **Application Fee:** $40.00 **H.S. Requirements:** High school diploma required; GED accepted **Costs Per Year:** Application fee: $40. State resident tuition: $8835 full-time, $295 per credit hour part-time. Nonresident tuition: $22,088 full-time, $736 per credit hour part-time. Mandatory fees: $4302 full-time, $189 per credit hour part-time. Full-time tuition and fees vary according to course load, location, program, reciprocity agreements, and student level. Part-time tuition and fees vary according to course load, location, program, reciprocity agreements, and student level. College room and board: $9996. Room and board charges vary according to board plan and housing facility. Tuition guaranteed not to increase for student's term of enrollment. **Scholarships:** Available. **Calendar System:** Semester, Summer session available **Enrollment:** Full-time 11,371, Graduate full-time 2,589, Graduate part-time 1,672, Part-time 1,660 **Faculty:** Full-time 812, Part-time 88 **Student-Faculty Ratio:** 15:1 **Exams:** ACT essay component used for placement; SAT I or ACT; SAT essay component not used; SAT Reasoning; SAT Subject. **% Receiving Financial Aid:** 70 **% Residing in College-Owned, -Operated, or -Affiliated Housing:** 30 **Final Year or Final Semester Residency Requirement:** No **Regional Accreditation:** North Central Association of Colleges and Schools **Credit Hours For Degree:** 60 semester hours, Associates; 120 semester hours, Bachelors **ROTC:** Air Force, Army **Professional Accreditation:** AACSB, AALS, ABA, ABET, ABFSE, ACA, ACEJMC, ADA, AND, APA, APTA, ASHA, ATMAE, CIDA, CORE, CSWE, CoARC, JRCAT, LCME/AMA, NAACLS, NASAD, NASM, NASPAA, NAST, NCATE, NRPA, SAF. **Intercollegiate Athletics:** Baseball M; Basketball M & W; Cheerleading M & W; Cross-Country Running M & W; Football M; Golf M & W; Softball W; Swimming and Diving M & W; Tennis M & W; Track and Field M & W; Volleyball W

SOUTHERN ILLINOIS UNIVERSITY EDWARDSVILLE

Edwardsville, IL 62026-0001
Tel: (618)650-2000; Free: 800-447-SIUE
Fax: (618)692-2081
E-mail: admissions@siue.edu
Web Site: www.siue.edu
President/CEO: Dr. Stephen Hansen
Admissions: Todd Burrell
Financial Aid: Sally Mullen
Type: Comprehensive **Sex:** Coed **Affiliation:** Southern Illinois University. **Scores:** 52% ACT 18-23; 37% ACT 24-29 **% Accepted:** 88 **Admission Plans:** Deferred Admission **Application Deadline:** May 1 **Application Fee:** $30.00 **H.S. Requirements:** High school diploma required; GED accepted **Costs Per Year:** Application fee: $30. State resident tuition: $8199 full-time, $273.28 per credit hour part-time. Nonresident tuition: $20,498 full-time, $638.50 per credit hour part-time. Mandatory fees: $2656 full-time, $898 per term part-time. Full-time tuition and fees vary according to course load. Part-time tuition and fees vary according to course load. College room and board: $9211. College room only: $5851. Room and board charges vary according

to board plan and housing facility. Tuition guaranteed not to increase for student's term of enrollment. **Scholarships:** Available. **Calendar System:** Semester, Summer session available **Enrollment:** Full-time 9,953, Graduate full-time 1,245, Graduate part-time 1,239, Part-time 1,828 **Faculty:** Full-time 605, Part-time 240 **Student-Faculty Ratio:** 20:1 **Exams:** ACT essay component not used; SAT I or ACT; SAT essay component not used; SAT Reasoning. **% Receiving Financial Aid:** 63 **% Residing in College-Owned, -Operated, or -Affiliated Housing:** 30 **Final Year or Final Semester Residency Requirement:** No **Regional Accreditation:** North Central Association of Colleges and Schools **Credit Hours For Degree:** 124 semester hours, Bachelors **ROTC:** Air Force, Army **Professional Accreditation:** AACN, AACSB, AANA, ABET, ACCE, ACPE, ADA, ASHA, CSWE, NAACLS, NASM, NASPAA, NCATE. **Intercollegiate Athletics:** Baseball M; Basketball M & W; Cheerleading M & W; Cross-Country Running M & W; Golf M & W; Soccer M & W; Softball W; Tennis M & W; Track and Field M & W; Volleyball W; Wrestling M

SOUTHWESTERN ILLINOIS COLLEGE

2500 Carlyle Ave.
Belleville, IL 62221-5899
Tel: (618)235-2700
Fax: (618)235-1578
E-mail: michelle.birk@swic.edu
Web Site: www.swic.edu
President/CEO: Dr. Georgia Costello, PhD
Admissions: Michelle Birk

Type: Two-Year College **Sex:** Coed **Affiliation:** Illinois Community College Board. **% Accepted:** 100 **Admission Plans:** Deferred Admission; Early Admission; Open Admission **Application Deadline:** Rolling **H.S. Requirements:** High school diploma required; GED accepted **Costs Per Year:** Area resident tuition: $3270 full-time, $109 per credit hour part-time. State resident tuition: $11,970 full-time, $399 per credit hour part-time. Nonresident tuition: $15,600 full-time, $520 per credit hour part-time. Mandatory fees: $150 full-time, $5 per credit hour part-time. Full-time tuition and fees vary according to program and reciprocity agreements. Part-time tuition and fees vary according to program and reciprocity agreements. **Scholarships:** Available. **Calendar System:** Semester, Summer session available **Enrollment:** Full-time 4,591, Part-time 5,954 **Faculty:** Full-time 156, Part-time 818 **Student-Faculty Ratio:** 15:1 **Exams:** ACT; Other. **Regional Accreditation:** North Central Association of Colleges and Schools **Credit Hours For Degree:** 64 credit hours, Associates **ROTC:** Air Force, Army **Professional Accreditation:** AAMAE, ACEN, ACF, AHIMA, APTA, CoARC, JRCERT, NAACLS. **Intercollegiate Athletics:** Baseball M; Basketball M & W; Soccer M & W; Softball W; Volleyball W

SPOON RIVER COLLEGE

23235 N County 22
Canton, IL 61520-9801
Tel: (309)647-4645; Free: 800-334-7337
Fax: (309)649-6235
E-mail: info@spoonrivercollege.edu
Web Site: www.src.edu
President/CEO: Curt Oldfield, EdD
Admissions: Missy Wilkinson

Type: Two-Year College **Sex:** Coed **Affiliation:** Illinois Community College Board. **Scores:** 49% ACT 18-23; 16% ACT 24-29 **Admission Plans:** Deferred Admission; Early Admission; Open Admission **Application Deadline:** Rolling **Application Fee:** $0.00 **H.S. Requirements:** High school diploma required; GED accepted **Costs Per Year:** Application fee: $0. Area resident tuition: $4200 full-time, $140 per credit hour part-time. State resident tuition: $9240 full-time, $308 per credit hour part-time. Nonresident tuition: $10,020 full-time, $334 per credit hour part-time. Mandatory fees: $600 full-time, $20 per credit hour part-time. Full-time tuition and fees vary according to course load and location. Part-time tuition and fees vary according to course load and location. **Scholarships:** Available. **Calendar System:** Semester, Summer session available **Enrollment:** Full-time 739, Part-time 926 **Faculty:** Full-time 37, Part-time 85 **Student-Faculty Ratio:** 14:1 **Final Year or Final Semester Residency Requirement:** No **Regional Accreditation:** North Central Association of Colleges and Schools **Credit Hours For Degree:** 64 semester hours, Associates **ROTC:** Army **Intercollegiate Athletics:** Baseball M; Cross-Country Running M & W; Softball W; Track and Field M & W

TAYLOR BUSINESS INSTITUTE

318 W Adams
Chicago, IL 60606

Tel: (312)658-5100
Fax: (312)658-0867
Web Site: www.tbiil.edu
President/CEO: Janice C. Parker

Type: Two-Year College **Sex:** Coed **% Accepted:** 78 **Application Fee:** $25.00 **Regional Accreditation:** North Central Association of Colleges and Schools **Professional Accreditation:** ACICS.

TELSHE YESHIVA–CHICAGO

3535 W Foster Ave.
Chicago, IL 60625-5598
Tel: (773)463-7738
President/CEO: Rabbi Avrohom C. Levin

Type: Comprehensive **Sex:** Men **Affiliation:** Jewish. **% Accepted:** 100 **Application Fee:** $100.00 **H.S. Requirements:** High school diploma required; GED not accepted **Calendar System:** Semester, Summer session available **Credit Hours For Degree:** 150 credits, Bachelors **Professional Accreditation:** AARTS.

TRIBECA FLASHPOINT COLLEGE

28 N Clark St.
Chicago, IL 60602
Tel: (312)332-0707
Web Site: www.tribecaflashpoint.edu

Type: Two-Year College **Sex:** Coed **Costs Per Year:** Tuition: $24,990 full-time, $833 per credit hour part-time. Mandatory fees: $1000 full-time, $700 per year part-time, $300 per year part-time. **Professional Accreditation:** ACICS.

TRINITY CHRISTIAN COLLEGE

6601 W College Dr.
Palos Heights, IL 60463-0929
Tel: (708)597-3000; Free: 866-TRIN-4-ME
Fax: (708)239-3995
E-mail: admissions@trnty.edu
Web Site: www.trnty.edu
President/CEO: Kurt D. Dykstra
Admissions: Jeremy Klyn
Financial Aid: Ryan P. Zantingh

Type: Comprehensive **Sex:** Coed **Affiliation:** Christian Reformed. **Scores:** 89% SAT V 400+; 95% SAT M 400+; 52% ACT 18-23; 38% ACT 24-29 **% Accepted:** 88 **Admission Plans:** Deferred Admission **Application Deadline:** Rolling **Application Fee:** $30.00 **H.S. Requirements:** High school diploma required; GED accepted **Costs Per Year:** Application fee: $30. One-time mandatory fee: $225. Comprehensive fee: $35,830 includes full-time tuition ($26,190), mandatory fees ($250), and college room and board ($9390). College room only: $4960. Full-time tuition and fees vary according to course load and degree level. Room and board charges vary according to board plan. Part-time tuition: $874 per credit hour. Part-time tuition varies according to course load and degree level. **Scholarships:** Available. **Calendar System:** Semester, Summer session available **Enrollment:** Full-time 1,032, Graduate full-time 82, Graduate part-time 1, Part-time 205 **Faculty:** Full-time 75, Part-time 71 **Student-Faculty Ratio:** 11:1 **Exams:** ACT essay component not used; SAT I or ACT; SAT essay component not used; SAT Reasoning; SAT Subject. **% Receiving Financial Aid:** 65 **% Residing in College-Owned, -Operated, or -Affiliated Housing:** 50 **Final Year or Final Semester Residency Requirement:** No **Regional Accreditation:** North Central Association of Colleges and Schools **Credit Hours For Degree:** 120 credit hours, Bachelors **Professional Accreditation:** AACN, ACBSP. **Intercollegiate Athletics:** Baseball M; Basketball M & W; Cross-Country Running M & W; Golf M & W; Soccer M & W; Softball W; Track and Field M & W; Volleyball M & W

TRINITY COLLEGE OF NURSING AND HEALTH SCIENCES

2122 25th Ave.
Rock Island, IL 61201
Tel: (309)779-7700
Fax: (309)779-7796
E-mail: perezlj@ihs.org
Web Site: www.trinitycollegeqc.edu
President/CEO: Dr. Susan C. Wajert, PhD
Admissions: Lori Perez
Financial Aid: Christine Carol Christopherson

Type: Four-Year College **Sex:** Coed **Affiliation:** Trinity Medical Center.

Scores: 58% ACT 18-23; 23% ACT 24-29 **% Accepted:** 50 **Admission Plans:** Early Action; Early Admission **Application Deadline:** Rolling **Application Fee:** $50.00 **H.S. Requirements:** High school diploma required; GED accepted **Scholarships:** Available. **Calendar System:** Semester, Summer session available **Enrollment:** Full-time 119, Part-time 113 **Faculty:** Full-time 16, Part-time 10 **Student-Faculty Ratio:** 9:1 **Exams:** ACT essay component not used; SAT I or ACT; SAT essay component not used. **% Receiving Financial Aid:** 97 **Final Year or Final Semester Residency Requirement:** No **Regional Accreditation:** North Central Association of Colleges and Schools **Credit Hours For Degree:** 68 credits, Associates; 121 credits, Bachelors **Professional Accreditation:** AACN, ACEN.

TRINITY INTERNATIONAL UNIVERSITY

2065 Half Day Rd.
Deerfield, IL 60015-1284
Tel: (847)945-8800; Free: 800-822-3225
Fax: (847)317-7081
E-mail: tcadmissions@tiu.edu
Web Site: www.tiu.edu
President/CEO: Dr. Jeanette Hsieh
Admissions: Aaron Mahl
Financial Aid: Pat Coles

Type: University **Sex:** Coed **Affiliation:** Evangelical Free Church of America; Evangelical Free Church of America. **Scores:** 89% SAT V 400+; 93% SAT M 400+; 50% ACT 18-23; 29% ACT 24-29 **% Accepted:** 63 **Admission Plans:** Deferred Admission **Application Deadline:** Rolling **Application Fee:** $25.00 **H.S. Requirements:** High school diploma required; GED accepted **Scholarships:** Available. **Calendar System:** Semester, Summer session not available **Enrollment:** Full-time 841, Part-time 127 **Faculty:** Full-time 43, Part-time 39 **Student-Faculty Ratio:** 12:1 **Exams:** SAT I or ACT. **% Receiving Financial Aid:** 77 **% Residing in College-Owned, -Operated, or -Affiliated Housing:** 70 **Regional Accreditation:** North Central Association of Colleges and Schools **Credit Hours For Degree:** 126 hours, Bachelors **Professional Accreditation:** ATS. **Intercollegiate Athletics:** Baseball M; Basketball M & W; Football M; Soccer M & W; Softball W; Track and Field M & W; Volleyball W

TRITON COLLEGE

2000 5th Ave.
River Grove, IL 60171
Tel: (708)456-0300
Fax: (708)583-3121
E-mail: mpatrice@triton.edu
Web Site: www.triton.edu
President/CEO: Dr. Patricia Granados
Admissions: Mary-Rita Moore

Type: Two-Year College **Sex:** Coed **Affiliation:** Illinois Community College Board. **Admission Plans:** Deferred Admission; Open Admission; Preferred Admission **Application Deadline:** Rolling **Application Fee:** $10.00 **H.S. Requirements:** High school diploma required; GED accepted **Scholarships:** Available. **Calendar System:** Semester, Summer session available **Enrollment:** Full-time 3,893, Part-time 11,765 **Faculty:** Full-time 123, Part-time 521 **Student-Faculty Ratio:** 24:1 **Regional Accreditation:** North Central Association of Colleges and Schools **Credit Hours For Degree:** 64 credit hours, Associates **Professional Accreditation:** ACEN, CoARC, JCAHPO, JRCEDMS, JRCERT, JRCNMT. **Intercollegiate Athletics:** Baseball M; Basketball M & W; Soccer M; Softball W; Volleyball W; Wrestling M

UNIVERSITY OF CHICAGO

5801 S Ellis Ave.
Chicago, IL 60637-1513
Tel: (773)702-1234
Fax: (773)702-4199
E-mail: collegeadmissions@uchicago.edu
Web Site: www.uchicago.edu
President/CEO: Robert Zimmer
Admissions: James G. Nondorf

Type: University **Sex:** Coed **Scores:** 100% SAT V 400+; 100% SAT M 400+; 0.12% ACT 18-23; 4.89% ACT 24-29 **% Accepted:** 8 **Admission Plans:** Deferred Admission; Early Admission; Early Decision Plan **Application Deadline:** January 1 **Application Fee:** $75.00 **H.S. Requirements:** High school diploma required; GED accepted **Costs Per Year:** Application fee:

$75. One-time mandatory fee: $1158. Comprehensive fee: $64,965 includes full-time tuition ($49,026), mandatory fees ($1167), and college room and board ($14,772). Full-time tuition and fees vary according to course load. Room and board charges vary according to board plan and housing facility. **Scholarships:** Available. **Calendar System:** Quarter, Summer session available **Enrollment:** Full-time 5,795, Graduate full-time 4,015, Graduate part-time 3,103, Part-time 49 **Faculty:** Full-time 1,305, Part-time 445 **Student-Faculty Ratio:** 5:1 **Exams:** ACT essay component not used; SAT I or ACT; SAT essay component not used. **% Receiving Financial Aid:** 44 **% Residing in College-Owned, -Operated, or -Affiliated Housing:** 52 **Final Year or Final Semester Residency Requirement:** No **Regional Accreditation:** North Central Association of Colleges and Schools **Credit Hours For Degree:** 140 credits, Bachelors **ROTC:** Air Force, Army **Professional Accreditation:** AACSB, AALS, ABA, ACIPE, APA, ATS, CSWE, LCME/AMA. **Intercollegiate Athletics:** Baseball M; Basketball M & W; Cross-Country Running M & W; Football M; Soccer M & W; Softball W; Swimming and Diving M & W; Tennis M & W; Track and Field M & W; Volleyball W; Wrestling M

UNIVERSITY OF ILLINOIS AT CHICAGO

601 S Morgan St.
Chicago, IL 60607-7128
Tel: (312)996-7000
E-mail: uic.admit@uic.edu
Web Site: www.uic.edu
President/CEO: Dr. Michael Amiridis
Admissions: Maureen Woods
Financial Aid: Deidre Rush

Type: University **Sex:** Coed **Affiliation:** University of Illinois System. **Scores:** 95% SAT V 400+; 99% SAT M 400+; 48.06% ACT 18-23; 41.95% ACT 24-29 **% Accepted:** 77 **Admission Plans:** Early Admission; Early Decision Plan **Application Deadline:** January 15 **Application Fee:** $50.00 **H.S. Requirements:** High school diploma required; GED accepted **Costs Per Year:** Application fee: $50. State resident tuition: $10,584 full-time. Nonresident tuition: $23,440 full-time. Mandatory fees: $3080 full-time. Full-time tuition and fees vary according to degree level and program. College room and board: $10,882. College room only: $7891. Room and board charges vary according to board plan and housing facility. Tuition guaranteed not to increase for student's term of enrollment. **Scholarships:** Available. **Calendar System:** Semester, Summer session available **Enrollment:** Full-time 16,176, Graduate full-time 8,107, Graduate part-time 3,366, Part-time 1,399 **Faculty:** Full-time 1,141, Part-time 431 **Student-Faculty Ratio:** 18:1 **Exams:** ACT essay component not used; SAT I or ACT; SAT essay component not used; SAT Reasoning; SAT Subject. **% Receiving Financial Aid:** 74 **% Residing in College-Owned, -Operated, or -Affiliated Housing:** 16 **Final Year or Final Semester Residency Requirement:** No **Regional Accreditation:** North Central Association of Colleges and Schools **Credit Hours For Degree:** 120 semester hours, Bachelors **ROTC:** Air Force, Army, Navy **Professional Accreditation:** AABB, AACN, AACSB, ABET, ACNM, ACPE, ACSP, ADA, AHIMA, AND, AOTA, APA, APTA, ARCMI, CEPH, CSWE, LCME/AMA, NAAB, NASAD, NASPAA. **Intercollegiate Athletics:** Baseball M; Basketball M & W; Cross-Country Running M & W; Gymnastics M & W; Soccer M; Softball W; Swimming and Diving M & W; Tennis M & W; Track and Field M & W; Volleyball W

UNIVERSITY OF ILLINOIS AT SPRINGFIELD

One University Plz.
Springfield, IL 62703-5407
Tel: (217)206-6600; Free: 888-977-4847
Fax: (217)206-7279
E-mail: admissions@uis.edu
Web Site: www.uis.edu
President/CEO: Dr. Susan J. Koch
Admissions: Fernando Planas
Financial Aid: Carolyn Schloemann

Type: Comprehensive **Sex:** Coed **Affiliation:** University of Illinois System. **Scores:** 93% SAT V 400+; 99% SAT M 400+; 53% ACT 18-23; 36% ACT 24-29 **% Accepted:** 63 **Admission Plans:** Deferred Admission **Application Deadline:** Rolling **Application Fee:** $50.00 **H.S. Requirements:** High school diploma required; GED accepted **Costs Per Year:** Application fee: $50. State resident tuition: $9405 full-time, $313.50 per credit hour part-time. Nonresident tuition: $18,930 full-time, $631 per credit hour part-time. Mandatory fees: $2998 full-time, $18.40 per credit hour part-time, $1,090 per term part-time. Full-time tuition and fees vary according to course load. Part-time tuition and fees vary according to course load. College room and board: $11,600. College room only: $7400. Room and board charges vary according to board plan and housing facility. Tuition guaranteed not to increase for student's term of enrollment. **Scholarships:** Available. **Calendar System:** Semester, Summer session available **Enrollment:** Full-time 1,899, Graduate full-time 1,054, Graduate part-time 1,411, Part-time 1,038 **Faculty:** Full-time 223, Part-time 157 **Student-Faculty Ratio:** 14:1 **Exams:** ACT essay component not used; SAT I and SAT II or ACT; SAT I or ACT; SAT II; SAT essay component not used. **% Receiving Financial Aid:** 69 **% Residing in College-Owned, -Operated, or -Affiliated Housing:** 31 **Final Year or Final Semester Residency Requirement:** No **Regional Accreditation:** North Central Association of Colleges and Schools **Credit Hours For Degree:** 120 semester hours, Bachelors **Professional Accreditation:** AACSB, ACA, CSWE, NAACLS, NASPAA. **Intercollegiate Athletics:** Baseball M; Basketball M & W; Cheerleading M & W; Cross-Country Running M & W; Golf M & W; Soccer M & W; Softball W; Tennis M & W; Track and Field W; Volleyball W

UNIVERSITY OF ILLINOIS AT URBANA–CHAMPAIGN

601 E John St.
Champaign, IL 61820
Tel: (217)333-1000
Fax: (217)244-7278
E-mail: ugradadmissions@uiuc.edu
Web Site: www.illinois.edu
President/CEO: Dr. Phyllis M. Wise
Admissions: Stacey Kostell
Financial Aid: Daniel Mann

Type: University **Sex:** Coed **Affiliation:** University of Illinois System. **Scores:** 100% SAT V 400+; 100% SAT M 400+; 8.97% ACT 18-23; 46.19% ACT 24-29 **% Accepted:** 62 **Admission Plans:** Deferred Admission; Early Admission **Application Deadline:** January 2 **Application Fee:** $50.00 **H.S. Requirements:** High school diploma required; GED accepted **Costs Per Year:** Application fee: $50. State resident tuition: $12,036 full-time. Nonresident tuition: $27,196 full-time. Mandatory fees: $3590 full-time. Full-time tuition and fees vary according to program and student level. College room and board: $11,000. Room and board charges vary according to board plan, housing facility, and location. Tuition guaranteed not to increase for student's term of enrollment. **Scholarships:** Available. **Calendar System:** Semester, Summer session available **Enrollment:** Full-time 31,516, Graduate full-time 9,602, Graduate part-time 2,645, Part-time 1,179 **Student-Faculty Ratio:** 18:1 **Exams:** ACT essay component not used; SAT I or ACT; SAT essay component not used; SAT Reasoning. **% Receiving Financial Aid:** 44 **% Residing in College-Owned, -Operated, or -Affiliated Housing:** 50 **Final Year or Final Semester Residency Requirement:** No **Regional Accreditation:** North Central Association of Colleges and Schools **Credit Hours For Degree:** 120 semester hours, Bachelors **ROTC:** Air Force, Army, Navy **Professional Accreditation:** AACSB, AALS, ABA, ABET, ACEJMC, ACSP, ALA, AND, APA, ASHA, ASLA, AVMA, CORE, CSWE, JRCAT, NAAB, NASAD, NASD, NASM, NAST, NRPA, SAF. **Intercollegiate Athletics:** Baseball M; Basketball M & W; Cheerleading M & W; Cross-Country Running M & W; Football M; Golf M & W; Gymnastics M & W; Soccer W; Softball W; Swimming and Diving W; Tennis M & W; Track and Field M & W; Volleyball W; Wrestling M

UNIVERSITY OF ST. FRANCIS

500 Wilcox St.
Joliet, IL 60435-6169
Tel: (815)740-3400; Free: 800-735-7500
Fax: (815)740-4285
E-mail: clambert@stfrancis.edu
Web Site: www.stfrancis.edu
President/CEO: Dr. Arvid C. Johnson, PhD
Admissions: Cynthia Lambert
Financial Aid: Bruce A. Foote

Type: Comprehensive **Sex:** Coed **Affiliation:** Roman Catholic. **Scores:** 100% SAT V 400+; 100% SAT M 400+; 57% ACT 18-23; 38% ACT 24-29 **% Accepted:** 51 **Admission Plans:** Deferred Admission **Application Deadline:** August 1 **Application Fee:** $0.00 **H.S. Requirements:** High school diploma required; GED accepted **Costs Per Year:** Application fee: $0. Comprehensive fee: $39,034 includes full-time tuition ($29,630), mandatory fees ($320), and college room and board ($9084). Full-time tuition and fees vary according to degree level, location, and program. Room and board charges vary according to housing facility. Part-time tuition: $825 per credit

hour. Part-time mandatory fees: $75 per term. Part-time tuition and fees vary according to degree level and program. **Scholarships:** Available. **Calendar System:** Semester, Summer session available **Enrollment:** Full-time 1,273, Graduate full-time 196, Graduate part-time 1,010, Part-time 76 **Faculty:** Full-time 100, Part-time 204 **Student-Faculty Ratio:** 11:1 **Exams:** SAT I or ACT. **% Receiving Financial Aid:** 88 **% Residing in College-Owned, -Operated, or -Affiliated Housing:** 26 **Final Year or Final Semester Residency Requirement:** Yes **Regional Accreditation:** North Central Association of Colleges and Schools **Credit Hours For Degree:** 128 credits, Bachelors **ROTC:** Army **Professional Accreditation:** AACN, ACBSP, CSWE, NASAD, NCATE, NRPA. **Intercollegiate Athletics:** Baseball M; Basketball M & W; Bowling M & W; Cheerleading M & W; Cross-Country Running M & W; Football M; Golf M & W; Soccer M & W; Softball W; Tennis M & W; Track and Field M & W; Volleyball W

VANDERCOOK COLLEGE OF MUSIC

3140 S Federal St.
Chicago, IL 60616-3731
Tel: (312)225-6288
Fax: (312)225-5211
E-mail: lmeyer@vandercook.edu
Web Site: www.vandercook.edu
President/CEO: Dr. Charles T. Menghini
Admissions: LeeAnn L. Meyer
Financial Aid: Sirena Covington

Type: Comprehensive **Sex:** Coed **Scores:** 75% SAT V 400+; 100% SAT M 400+; 29% ACT 18-23; 35% ACT 24-29 **Costs Per Year:** Comprehensive fee: $37,816 includes full-time tuition ($24,700), mandatory fees ($1600), and college room and board ($11,516). College room only: $5884. Full-time tuition and fees vary according to course level, course load, and program. Room and board charges vary according to board plan and housing facility. Part-time tuition: $1020 per semester hour. Part-time mandatory fees: $1250 per year. Part-time tuition and fees vary according to course level, course load, and program. **Scholarships:** Available. **Calendar System:** Semester, Summer session not available **Enrollment:** Full-time 97, Graduate full-time 7, Graduate part-time 136, Part-time 58 **Faculty:** Full-time 9, Part-time 24 **Student-Faculty Ratio:** 6:1 **Exams:** ACT essay component used for admission; ACT essay component used for advising; ACT essay component used for placement; SAT I or ACT; SAT essay component used for admission; SAT essay component used for advising; SAT essay component used for placement. **% Receiving Financial Aid:** 89 **% Residing in College-Owned, -Operated, or -Affiliated Housing:** 18 **Final Year or Final Semester Residency Requirement:** No **Regional Accreditation:** North Central Association of Colleges and Schools **Credit Hours For Degree:** 137.5 semester hours, Bachelors **Professional Accreditation:** NASM.

VATTEROTT COLLEGE (FAIRVIEW HEIGHTS)

110 Commerce Ln.
Fairview Heights, IL 62208
Tel: (618)489-2400; Free: 888-202-2636
Web Site: www.vatterott.edu
Type: Two-Year College **Sex:** Coed **Professional Accreditation:** ACCSC.

VATTEROTT COLLEGE (QUINCY)

3609 N Marx Dr.
Quincy, IL 62305
Web Site: www.vatterott.edu
Type: Two-Year College **Sex:** Coed

VET TECH INSTITUTE AT FOX COLLEGE

18020 S Oak Park Ave.
Tinley Park, IL 60477
Tel: (708)444-4500; Free: 888-884-3694
Web Site: chicago.vettechinstitute.edu
Type: Two-Year College **Sex:** Coed **% Accepted:** 65 **H.S. Requirements:** High school diploma required; GED accepted **Calendar System:** Semester **Professional Accreditation:** AVMA.

WAUBONSEE COMMUNITY COLLEGE

Rte. 47 at Waubonsee Dr.
Sugar Grove, IL 60554-9799
Tel: (630)466-7900
Fax: (630)466-4964
E-mail: admissions@waubonsee.edu

Web Site: www.waubonsee.edu
President/CEO: Dr. Christine J. Sobek
Admissions: Joy Sanders
Type: Two-Year College **Sex:** Coed **Affiliation:** Illinois Community College Board. **% Accepted:** 100 **Admission Plans:** Open Admission; Preferred Admission **Application Deadline:** Rolling **Application Fee:** $0.00 **H.S. Requirements:** High school diploma or equivalent not required **Scholarships:** Available. **Calendar System:** Semester, Summer session available **Enrollment:** Full-time 3,469, Part-time 7,252 **Exams:** ACT essay component used for placement. **Regional Accreditation:** North Central Association of Colleges and Schools **Credit Hours For Degree:** 60 semester hours, Associates **ROTC:** Army **Intercollegiate Athletics:** Baseball M; Basketball M & W; Cheerleading M & W; Cross-Country Running M & W; Golf M; Soccer M & W; Softball W; Tennis M & W; Volleyball W; Wrestling M

WESTERN ILLINOIS UNIVERSITY

1 University Cir.
Macomb, IL 61455-1390
Tel: (309)298-1414; Free: 877-742-5948
Fax: (309)298-3111
E-mail: aj-borst@wiu.edu
Web Site: www.wiu.edu
President/CEO: Dr. Jack Thomas
Admissions: Dr. Andrew Borst
Type: Comprehensive **Sex:** Coed **Scores:** 60.3% ACT 18-23; 17.6% ACT 24-29 **% Accepted:** 60 **Admission Plans:** Deferred Admission **Application Deadline:** May 15 **Application Fee:** $30.00 **H.S. Requirements:** High school diploma required; GED accepted **Costs Per Year:** Application fee: $30. State resident tuition: $8805 full-time, $293.50 per credit hour part-time. Nonresident tuition: $13,207 full-time, $440.25 per credit hour part-time. Mandatory fees: $2704 full-time, $90.12 per credit hour part-time. Full-time tuition and fees vary according to course load, location, and student level. Part-time tuition and fees vary according to course load, location, and student level. College room and board: $9580. College room only: $5880. Room and board charges vary according to board plan, housing facility, and student level. Tuition guaranteed not to increase for student's term of enrollment. **Scholarships:** Available. **Calendar System:** Semester, Summer session available **Enrollment:** Full-time 8,106, Graduate full-time 882, Graduate part-time 1,071, Part-time 1,035 **Faculty:** Full-time 632, Part-time 47 **Student-Faculty Ratio:** 14:1 **Exams:** SAT I or ACT; SAT Reasoning. **% Receiving Financial Aid:** 73 **% Residing in College-Owned, -Operated, or -Affiliated Housing:** 44 **Final Year or Final Semester Residency Requirement:** Yes **Regional Accreditation:** North Central Association of Colleges and Schools **Credit Hours For Degree:** 120 credit hours, Bachelors **ROTC:** Army **Professional Accreditation:** AACN, AACSB, AAFCS, ACA, ASHA, CSWE, JRCAT, NASAD, NASM, NAST, NCATE, NRPA. **Intercollegiate Athletics:** Baseball M; Basketball M & W; Cross-Country Running M & W; Football M; Golf M & W; Soccer M & W; Softball W; Swimming and Diving M & W; Tennis M & W; Track and Field M & W; Volleyball W

WHEATON COLLEGE

501 College Ave.
Wheaton, IL 60187-5593
Tel: (630)752-5000; Free: 800-222-2419
Fax: (630)752-5285
E-mail: admissions@wheaton.edu
Web Site: www.wheaton.edu
President/CEO: Dr. Philip Graham Ryken
Admissions: Shawn Leftwich
Financial Aid: Karen Belling
Type: Comprehensive **Sex:** Coed **Affiliation:** nondenominational. **Scores:** 100% SAT V 400+; 100% SAT M 400+; 8.2% ACT 18-23; 40% ACT 24-29 **% Accepted:** 71 **Admission Plans:** Deferred Admission; Early Decision Plan; Preferred Admission **Application Deadline:** January 10 **Application Fee:** $50.00 **H.S. Requirements:** High school diploma required; GED accepted **Costs Per Year:** Application fee: $50. Comprehensive fee: $42,150 includes full-time tuition ($32,950) and college room and board ($9200). College room only: $5410. Full-time tuition varies according to program. Room and board charges vary according to board plan and housing facility. Part-time tuition: $1373 per credit hour. Part-time tuition varies according to course load and program. **Scholarships:** Available. **Calendar System:** Semester, Summer session available **Enrollment:** Full-time 2,410, Graduate full-time 249, Graduate part-time 217, Part-time 53 **Faculty:** Full-time 204, Part-time 101 **Student-Faculty Ratio:** 12:1 **Exams:** ACT essay component used as validity check; ACT essay component used for placement; SAT I or ACT; SAT essay component used as validity check; SAT essay component used for placement; SAT Reasoning. **% Receiving Financial Aid:** 54 **% Residing in College-Owned, -Operated, or -Affiliated Housing:** 87 **Final Year or Final Semester Residency Requirement:** Yes **Regional Accreditation:** North Central Association of Colleges and Schools **Credit Hours For Degree:** 124 hours, Bachelors **ROTC:** Air Force, Army **Professional Accreditation:** APA, NASM, NCATE. **Intercollegiate Athletics:** Baseball M; Basketball M & W; Cheerleading W; Crew M & W; Cross-Country Running M & W; Football M; Golf M & W; Ice Hockey M; Lacrosse M & W; Soccer M & W; Softball W; Swimming and Diving M & W; Tennis M & W; Track and Field M & W; Volleyball M & W; Wrestling M

WORSHAM COLLEGE OF MORTUARY SCIENCE

495 Northgate Pky.
Wheeling, IL 60090-2646
Tel: (847)808-8444
Fax: (847)808-8493
Web Site: www.worshamcollege.com
President/CEO: Karl Kann
Type: Two-Year College **Sex:** Coed **Application Fee:** $30.00 **Scholarships:** Available. **Calendar System:** Quarter **Student-Faculty Ratio:** 21:1 **Professional Accreditation:** ABFSE.

ANCILLA COLLEGE

9601 S Union Rd.
Donaldson, IN 46513
Tel: (574)936-8898; Free: 866-ANCILLA
Fax: (574)935-1773
E-mail: admissions@ancilla.edu
Web Site: www.ancilla.edu
President/CEO: Dr. Ken Zirkle
Admissions: Eric Wignall
Financial Aid: Marcella M. Hopple

Type: Two-Year College **Sex:** Coed **Affiliation:** Roman Catholic. **Scores:** 61% SAT V 400+; 62% SAT M 400+; 43% ACT 18-23; 10% ACT 24-29 **% Accepted:** 62 **Admission Plans:** Open Admission **Application Deadline:** Rolling **Application Fee:** $0.00 **H.S. Requirements:** High school diploma required; GED accepted **Costs Per Year:** Application fee: $0. Comprehensive fee: $23,830 includes full-time tuition ($14,700), mandatory fees ($230), and college room and board ($8900). Full-time tuition and fees vary according to course load and program. Part-time tuition: $490 per credit hour. Part-time mandatory fees: $55 per term. Part-time tuition and fees vary according to course load and program. **Scholarships:** Available. **Calendar System:** Semester, Summer session available **Enrollment:** Full-time 382, Part-time 122 **Faculty:** Full-time 16, Part-time 33 **Student-Faculty Ratio:** 16:1 **Exams:** ACT essay component not used; SAT I or ACT; SAT essay component not used. **% Residing in College-Owned, -Operated, or -Affiliated Housing:** 24 **Final Year or Final Semester Residency Requirement:** No **Regional Accreditation:** North Central Association of Colleges and Schools **Credit Hours For Degree:** 60 Credit Hours, Associates **Intercollegiate Athletics:** Baseball M; Basketball M & W; Bowling M & W; Cheerleading M & W; Cross-Country Running M & W; Golf M & W; Lacrosse M; Soccer M & W; Softball W; Tennis M & W; Volleyball W; Wrestling M

ANDERSON UNIVERSITY

1100 E Fifth St.
Anderson, IN 46012-3495
Tel: (765)649-9071; Free: 800-428-6414
Fax: (765)641-3851
E-mail: info@anderson.edu
Web Site: www.anderson.edu
President/CEO: Dr. John S. Pistole
Admissions: Kynan Simison
Financial Aid: Kenneth Nieman

Type: Comprehensive **Sex:** Coed **Affiliation:** Church of God. **Scores:** 95% SAT V 400+; 94% SAT M 400+; 48% ACT 18-23; 37% ACT 24-29 **% Accepted:** 60 **Admission Plans:** Deferred Admission **Application Deadline:** July 1 **Application Fee:** $25.00 **H.S. Requirements:** High school diploma required; GED accepted **Costs Per Year:** Application fee: $25. Comprehensive fee: $38,200 includes full-time tuition ($28,500), mandatory fees ($150), and college room and board ($9550). College room only: $6050. Room and board charges vary according to board plan and housing facility. Part-time tuition: $1188 per semester hour. Part-time tuition varies according to course load. **Scholarships:** Available. **Calendar System:** Semester, Summer session available **Enrollment:** Full-time 1,610, Graduate full-time 47, Graduate part-time 371, Part-time 297 **Faculty:** Full-time 129, Part-time 148 **Student-Faculty Ratio:** 11:1 **Exams:** ACT essay component used for advising; ACT essay component used for placement; SAT I or ACT; SAT essay component used for advising; SAT essay component used for placement; SAT Reason-

ing. **% Receiving Financial Aid:** 84 **% Residing in College-Owned, -Operated, or -Affiliated Housing:** 77 **Final Year or Final Semester Residency Requirement:** Yes **Regional Accreditation:** North Central Association of Colleges and Schools **Credit Hours For Degree:** 60 semester hours, Associates; 120 semester hours, Bachelors **Professional Accreditation:** AACN, ACBSP, ACIPE, ATS, CSWE, JRCAT, NASM, NCATE. **Intercollegiate Athletics:** Baseball M; Basketball M & W; Cross-Country Running M & W; Football M; Golf M & W; Soccer M & W; Softball W; Tennis M & W; Track and Field M & W; Volleyball W

THE ART INSTITUTE OF INDIANAPOLIS

3500 Depauw Blvd.
Ste. 1010
Indianapolis, IN 46268
Tel: (317)613-4800; Free: 866-441-9031
Web Site: www.artinstitutes.edu/indianapolis
President/CEO: Mike Morphew

Type: Four-Year College **Sex:** Coed **Affiliation:** Education Management Corporation. **Regional Accreditation:** Southern Association of Colleges and Schools **Professional Accreditation:** ACICS.

BALL STATE UNIVERSITY

2000 W University Ave.
Muncie, IN 47306
Tel: (765)289-1241; Free: 800-482-4BSU
Fax: (765)285-1632
E-mail: cmunchel@bsu.edu
Web Site: www.bsu.edu
President/CEO: Dr. Terry S. King
Admissions: Christopher Munchel
Financial Aid: Dr. John McPherson

Type: University **Sex:** Coed **Scores:** 100% SAT V 400+; 100% SAT M 400+; 70% ACT 18-23; 26% ACT 24-29 **Costs Per Year:** State resident tuition: $8836 full-time, $290 per credit hour part-time. Nonresident tuition: $24,354 full-time, $963 per credit hour part-time. Mandatory fees: $662 full-time. Full-time tuition and fees vary according to program and reciprocity agreements. Part-time tuition varies according to course load, program, and reciprocity agreements. College room and board: $9656. Room and board charges vary according to board plan and housing facility. **Scholarships:** Available. **Calendar System:** Semester, Summer session available **Enrollment:** Full-time 14,716, Graduate full-time 1,395, Graduate part-time 3,199, Part-time 1,886 **Faculty:** Full-time 1,017, Part-time 228 **Student-Faculty Ratio:** 14:1 **Exams:** ACT essay component not used; SAT I and SAT II or ACT; SAT I or ACT; SAT II; SAT essay component not used. **% Receiving Financial Aid:** 67 **% Residing in College-Owned, -Operated, or -Affiliated Housing:** 41 **Regional Accreditation:** North Central Association of Colleges and Schools **Credit Hours For Degree:** 60 credit hours, Associates; 120 credit hours, Bachelors **ROTC:** Army **Professional Accreditation:** AACN, AACSB, AAFCS, ABET, ACA, ACEJMC, ACSP, AND, APA, ASHA, ASLA, CORE, CSWE, JRCAT, JRCERT, NAAB, NASAD, NASD, NASM, NAST, NCATE. **Intercollegiate Athletics:** Baseball M & W; Basketball M & W; Bowling M & W; Cheerleading M & W; Cross-Country Running W; Equestrian Sports M & W; Fencing M & W; Field Hockey W; Football M; Golf M & W; Gymnastics W; Lacrosse M & W; Racquetball M & W; Rock Climbing M & W; Rugby M & W;

Soccer M & W; Softball W; Swimming and Diving M & W; Tennis M & W; Track and Field W; Triathlon M & W; Ultimate Frisbee M & W; Volleyball M & W; Water Polo M & W; Wrestling M

BETHEL COLLEGE
1001 Bethel Cir.
Mishawaka, IN 46545-5591
Tel: (574)259-8511; Free: 800-422-4101
Fax: (574)257-3326
E-mail: admissions@bethelcollege.edu
Web Site: www.bethelcollege.edu
President/CEO: Dr. Gregg A. Chenoweth
Admissions: Andrea Helmuth
Financial Aid: Jody Walker

Type: Comprehensive **Sex:** Coed **Affiliation:** Missionary Church. **Scores:** 91% SAT V 400+; 87% SAT M 400+; 45% ACT 18-23; 36% ACT 24-29 **% Accepted:** 66 **Admission Plans:** Deferred Admission; Early Admission **Application Deadline:** August 15 **Application Fee:** $0.00 **H.S. Requirements:** High school diploma required; GED accepted **Costs Per Year:** Application fee: $0. Comprehensive fee: $35,860 includes full-time tuition ($27,040), mandatory fees ($350), and college room and board ($8470). College room only: $4040. Full-time tuition and fees vary according to program. Room and board charges vary according to board plan and housing facility. Part-time tuition: $860 per credit. Part-time mandatory fees: $150 per year. Part-time tuition and fees vary according to course load and program. **Scholarships:** Available. **Calendar System:** Semester, Summer session available **Enrollment:** Full-time 1,168, Graduate full-time 45, Graduate part-time 185, Part-time 321 **Faculty:** Full-time 75, Part-time 130 **Student-Faculty Ratio:** 12:1 **Exams:** ACT essay component not used; SAT I or ACT; SAT essay component not used; SAT Reasoning; SAT Subject. **% Residing in College-Owned, -Operated, or -Affiliated Housing:** 51 **Final Year or Final Semester Residency Requirement:** Yes **Regional Accreditation:** North Central Association of Colleges and Schools **Credit Hours For Degree:** 62 semester hours, Associates; 120 semester hours, Bachelors **ROTC:** Air Force, Army **Professional Accreditation:** ACEN, NASM, NCATE, TEAC. **Intercollegiate Athletics:** Baseball M; Basketball M & W; Cheerleading M & W; Cross-Country Running M & W; Golf M & W; Lacrosse W; Rugby M; Soccer M & W; Softball W; Tennis M & W; Track and Field M & W; Volleyball W

BRIGHTWOOD COLLEGE, HAMMOND CAMPUS
7833 Indianapolis Blvd.
Hammond, IN 46324
Tel: (219)844-0100; Free: 800-935-1857
Web Site: www.brightwood.edu
President/CEO: Johnny Craig

Type: Two-Year College **Sex:** Coed **H.S. Requirements:** High school diploma required; GED accepted **Scholarships:** Available. **Calendar System:** Quarter **Professional Accreditation:** ACICS.

BRIGHTWOOD COLLEGE, INDIANAPOLIS CAMPUS
4200 SE St.
Indianapolis, IN 46227
Tel: (317)782-0315
Web Site: www.brightwood.edu
President/CEO: Carey Cseszko

Type: Two-Year College **Sex:** Coed **Professional Accreditation:** ACICS.

BUTLER UNIVERSITY
4600 Sunset Ave.
Indianapolis, IN 46208-3485
Tel: (317)940-8000; Free: 888-940-8100
Fax: (317)940-8150
E-mail: admission@butler.edu
Web Site: www.butler.edu
President/CEO: James Danko
Admissions: Aimee Rust-Scheuermann
Financial Aid: Leslie Middleton

Type: Comprehensive **Sex:** Coed **Scores:** 100% SAT V 400+; 100% SAT M 400+; 15.3% ACT 18-23; 57.3% ACT 24-29 **% Accepted:** 70 **Admission Plans:** Deferred Admission; Early Decision Plan **Application Deadline:** Rolling **Application Fee:** $0.00 **H.S. Requirements:** High school diploma required; GED accepted **Costs Per Year:** Application fee: $0. Comprehensive fee: $49,065 includes full-time tuition ($36,050), mandatory fees ($960),

and college room and board ($12,055). Full-time tuition and fees vary according to course load, degree level, and program. Room and board charges vary according to housing facility. Part-time tuition: $1502 per credit hour. Part-time tuition varies according to course load, degree level, and program. **Scholarships:** Available. **Calendar System:** Semester, Summer session available **Enrollment:** Full-time 3,978, Graduate full-time 393, Graduate part-time 377, Part-time 50 **Faculty:** Full-time 363, Part-time 199 **Student-Faculty Ratio:** 11:1 **Exams:** ACT essay component used as validity check; ACT essay component used for admission; SAT I or ACT; SAT essay component used as validity check; SAT essay component used for admission; SAT Reasoning. **% Receiving Financial Aid:** 61 **% Residing in College-Owned, -Operated, or -Affiliated Housing:** 66 **Final Year or Final Semester Residency Requirement:** No **Regional Accreditation:** North Central Association of Colleges and Schools **Credit Hours For Degree:** 60 semester hours, Associates; 120 semester hours, Bachelors **ROTC:** Air Force, Army **Professional Accreditation:** AACSB, ACA, ACPE, APA, NASD, NASM, NAST, NCATE. **Intercollegiate Athletics:** Baseball M; Basketball M & W; Crew M & W; Cross-Country Running M & W; Equestrian Sports W; Football M; Golf M & W; Ice Hockey M; Lacrosse M & W; Rugby M; Soccer M & W; Softball W; Swimming and Diving M & W; Tennis M & W; Track and Field M & W; Ultimate Frisbee M & W; Volleyball M & W

CALUMET COLLEGE OF SAINT JOSEPH
2400 New York Ave.
Whiting, IN 46394-2195
Tel: (219)473-7770; Free: 877-700-9100
Fax: (219)473-4259
E-mail: admissions@ccsj.edu
Web Site: www.ccsj.edu
President/CEO: Dr. Dan Lowery
Admissions: Carl Cuttone
Financial Aid: Gina Pirtle

Type: Comprehensive **Sex:** Coed **Affiliation:** Roman Catholic. **Scores:** 74% SAT V 400+; 36% ACT 18-23; 17% ACT 24-29 **% Accepted:** 35 **Admission Plans:** Deferred Admission; Open Admission **Application Deadline:** Rolling **Application Fee:** $0.00 **H.S. Requirements:** High school diploma required; GED accepted **Costs Per Year:** Application fee: $0. Tuition: $17,300 full-time, $550 per credit hour part-time. Mandatory fees: $270 full-time, $135 per term part-time. Full-time tuition and fees vary according to course load and program. Part-time tuition and fees vary according to course load and program. Tuition guaranteed not to increase for student's term of enrollment. **Scholarships:** Available. **Calendar System:** Semester, Summer session available **Enrollment:** Full-time 532, Graduate full-time 65, Graduate part-time 154, Part-time 349 **Faculty:** Full-time 30, Part-time 106 **Student-Faculty Ratio:** 10:1 **Exams:** ACT essay component not used; Other; SAT I or ACT; SAT essay component not used; SAT Reasoning. **% Receiving Financial Aid:** 80 **Final Year or Final Semester Residency Requirement:** No **Regional Accreditation:** North Central Association of Colleges and Schools **Credit Hours For Degree:** 60 credit hours, Associates; 124 credit hours, Bachelors **Intercollegiate Athletics:** Baseball M; Basketball M & W; Bowling M & W; Cross-Country Running M & W; Golf M & W; Soccer M & W; Softball W; Tennis M & W; Track and Field M & W; Volleyball M & W; Wrestling M

CHAMBERLAIN COLLEGE OF NURSING
9100 Keystone Crossing
Ste. 600
Indianapolis, IN 46240
Tel: (317)816-7335; Free: 877-751-5783
Fax: (317)815-3066
Web Site: www.chamberlain.edu

Type: Four-Year College **Sex:** Coed **Application Fee:** $95.00 **H.S. Requirements:** High school diploma required; GED accepted **Costs Per Year:** Application fee: $95. Tuition: $17,560 full-time, $665 per credit hour part-time. Mandatory fees: $600 full-time, $300 per term part-time. **Enrollment:** Full-time 131, Part-time 88 **Faculty:** Full-time 8, Part-time 5 **Student-Faculty Ratio:** 17:1 **Exams:** ACT essay component used for admission; SAT I or ACT; SAT essay component used for admission. **Regional Accreditation:** North Central Association of Colleges and Schools

COLLEGE OF COURT REPORTING
111 W Tenth St.
Ste. 111
Hobart, IN 46342

Tel: (219)942-1459; Free: 866-294-3974
Fax: (219)942-1631
E-mail: nrodriquez@ccr.edu
Web Site: www.ccr.edu
President/CEO: Jeff Moody
Admissions: Nicky Rodriquez
Type: Two-Year College **Sex:** Coed **Application Fee:** $50.00 **Student-Faculty Ratio:** 17:1 **Professional Accreditation:** ACICS.

CROSSROADS BIBLE COLLEGE
601 N Shortridge Rd.
Indianapolis, IN 46219
Tel: (317)352-8736; Free: 800-822-3119
Fax: (317)352-9145
E-mail: admissions@crossroads.edu
Web Site: www.crossroads.edu
President/CEO: Dr. A. Charles Ware
Admissions: Michael Garrison
Financial Aid: Phyllis Dodson
Type: Four-Year College **Sex:** Coed **Affiliation:** Baptist. **% Accepted:** 95 **Admission Plans:** Deferred Admission; Open Admission **Application Deadline:** August 8 **Application Fee:** $10.00 **H.S. Requirements:** High school diploma required; GED accepted **Scholarships:** Available. **Calendar System:** Semester, Summer session available **Enrollment:** Full-time 127, Part-time 105 **Faculty:** Full-time 6, Part-time 29 **Student-Faculty Ratio:** 7:1 **Exams:** ACT essay component used as validity check; ACT essay component used for admission; ACT essay component used for advising; ACT essay component used for placement; SAT essay component not used; SAT essay component used as validity check; SAT essay component used for admission; SAT essay component used for advising; SAT essay component used for placement. **% Receiving Financial Aid:** 97 **% Residing in College-Owned, -Operated, or -Affiliated Housing:** 5 **Final Year or Final Semester Residency Requirement:** No **Credit Hours For Degree:** 69 credit hours, Associates; 129 credit hours, Bachelors **Professional Accreditation:** ABHE.

DEPAUW UNIVERSITY
313 S Locust St.
Greencastle, IN 46135
Tel: (765)658-4800; Free: 800-447-2495
Fax: (765)658-4007
E-mail: emacam@depauw.edu
Web Site: www.depauw.edu
President/CEO: Brian W. Casey
Admissions: Earl Macam
Financial Aid: Craig Slaughter
Type: Four-Year College **Sex:** Coed **Affiliation:** United Methodist Church. **Scores:** 100% SAT V 400+; 99% SAT M 400+; 14.6% ACT 18-23; 64.8% ACT 24-29 **% Accepted:** 65 **Admission Plans:** Deferred Admission; Early Action; Early Admission; Early Decision Plan **H.S. Requirements:** High school diploma required; GED accepted **Costs Per Year:** Comprehensive fee: $56,378 includes full-time tuition ($43,950), mandatory fees ($728), and college room and board ($11,700). Room and board charges vary according to board plan. Part-time tuition: $1374 per credit hour. **Scholarships:** Available. **Calendar System:** 4-1-4 **Enrollment:** Full-time 2,229, Part-time 36 **Faculty:** Full-time 227, Part-time 39 **Student-Faculty Ratio:** 9:1 **Exams:** ACT essay component used as validity check; SAT I and SAT II or ACT; SAT I or ACT; SAT essay component used as validity check; SAT Reasoning. **% Receiving Financial Aid:** 56 **% Residing in College-Owned, -Operated, or -Affiliated Housing:** 97 **Regional Accreditation:** North Central Association of Colleges and Schools **Credit Hours For Degree:** 31 courses, Bachelors **ROTC:** Air Force, Army **Professional Accreditation:** JRCAT, NASM, NCATE. **Intercollegiate Athletics:** Baseball M; Basketball M & W; Cheerleading M & W; Crew M & W; Cross-Country Running M & W; Field Hockey W; Football M; Golf M & W; Rugby M; Soccer M & W; Softball W; Swimming and Diving M & W; Tennis M & W; Track and Field M & W; Volleyball W

DEVRY UNIVERSITY
100 E 80th Pl., Ste. 222 Mall
Merrillville, IN 46410-5673
Tel: (219)736-7440; Free: 866-338-7941
Fax: (219)736-7874
Web Site: www.devry.edu

Type: Comprehensive **Sex:** Coed **Application Deadline:** Rolling **Costs Per Year:** Tuition: $17,052 full-time, $609 per credit hour part-time. Mandatory fees: $80 full-time, $40 per term part-time. **Calendar System:** Semester **Regional Accreditation:** North Central Association of Colleges and Schools **Professional Accreditation:** ACBSP.

EARLHAM COLLEGE
801 National Rd. W
Richmond, IN 47374-4095
Tel: (765)983-1200; Free: 800-327-5426
Fax: (765)983-1560
E-mail: admission@earlham.edu
Web Site: www.earlham.edu
President/CEO: David Dawson
Admissions: Shenita Piper
Financial Aid: Kathy Gottschalk
Type: Comprehensive **Sex:** Coed **Affiliation:** Society of Friends. **Scores:** 99% SAT V 400+; 99% SAT M 400+; 15% ACT 18-23; 48% ACT 24-29 **% Accepted:** 62 **Admission Plans:** Deferred Admission; Early Action; Early Admission; Early Decision Plan; Preferred Admission **Application Deadline:** February 15 **Application Fee:** $0.00 **H.S. Requirements:** High school diploma required; GED accepted. For home-schooled students: High school diploma or equivalent not required **Costs Per Year:** Application fee: $0. Comprehensive fee: $53,510 includes full-time tuition ($43,500), mandatory fees ($890), and college room and board ($9120). College room only: $4620. Part-time tuition: $1450 per credit hour. **Scholarships:** Available. **Calendar System:** Semester, Summer session not available **Enrollment:** Full-time 980, Part-time 8 **Faculty:** Full-time 111, Part-time 11 **Student-Faculty Ratio:** 9:1 **Exams:** ACT essay component used for admission; SAT I or ACT; SAT essay component used for admission; SAT Reasoning. **% Receiving Financial Aid:** 82 **% Residing in College-Owned, -Operated, or -Affiliated Housing:** 96 **Final Year or Final Semester Residency Requirement:** Yes **Regional Accreditation:** North Central Association of Colleges and Schools **Credit Hours For Degree:** 122 semester hours, Bachelors **Intercollegiate Athletics:** Baseball M; Basketball M & W; Cheerleading W; Cross-Country Running M & W; Equestrian Sports W; Field Hockey W; Football M; Golf M & W; Lacrosse M & W; Rugby M & W; Soccer M & W; Tennis M & W; Track and Field M & W; Ultimate Frisbee M & W; Volleyball M & W

FORTIS COLLEGE
9001 N Wesleyan Rd., Ste. 101
Indianapolis, IN 46268
Tel: (317)808-4800; Free: 855-4-FORTIS
E-mail: kbennett@edaff.com
Web Site: www.fortis.edu
Admissions: Alex Teitelbaum
Type: Two-Year College **Sex:** Coed **Professional Accreditation:** ACCSC.

FRANKLIN COLLEGE
101 Branigin Blvd.
Franklin, IN 46131
Tel: (317)738-8000; Free: 800-852-0232
Fax: (317)738-8274
E-mail: admissions@franklincollege.edu
Web Site: www.franklincollege.edu
President/CEO: Dr. James Moseley
Admissions: Jennifer Bostrom
Financial Aid: Elizabeth Sappenfield
Type: Comprehensive **Sex:** Coed **Affiliation:** American Baptist Churches in the U.S.A. **Scores:** 94% SAT V 400+; 95% SAT M 400+; 62% ACT 18-23; 24% ACT 24-29 **% Accepted:** 60 **Admission Plans:** Deferred Admission **Application Deadline:** Rolling **Application Fee:** $0.00 **H.S. Requirements:** High school diploma required; GED accepted **Costs Per Year:** Application fee: $0. Comprehensive fee: $37,675 includes full-time tuition ($28,840), mandatory fees ($185), and college room and board ($8650). College room only: $5150. Room and board charges vary according to board plan. **Scholarships:** Available. **Calendar System:** 4-1-4, Summer session available **Enrollment:** Full-time 1,008, Part-time 67 **Faculty:** Full-time 77, Part-time 32 **Student-Faculty Ratio:** 12:1 **Exams:** ACT essay component used for admission; ACT essay component used for advising; ACT essay component used for placement; ACT essay component used in place of application essay; SAT I or ACT; SAT essay component used for admission; SAT essay component used for advising; SAT essay component used for

placement; SAT essay component used in place of application essay. **%
Receiving Financial Aid:** 83 **% Residing in College-Owned, -Operated,
or -Affiliated Housing:** 76 **Final Year or Final Semester Residency
Requirement:** No **Regional Accreditation:** North Central Association of
Colleges and Schools **Credit Hours For Degree:** 120 credit hours,
Bachelors **ROTC:** Army **Professional Accreditation:** NCATE. **Intercol-
legiate Athletics:** Baseball M; Basketball M & W; Cheerleading W; Cross-
Country Running M & W; Football M; Golf M & W; Lacrosse W; Soccer M &
W; Softball W; Swimming and Diving M & W; Tennis M & W; Track and Field
M & W; Volleyball W

GOSHEN COLLEGE

1700 S Main St.
Goshen, IN 46526-4794
Tel: (574)535-7000; Free: 800-348-7422
Fax: (574)535-7060
E-mail: ahufford@goshen.edu
Web Site: www.goshen.edu
President/CEO: Dr. James E. Brenneman
Admissions: Adela Hufford
Financial Aid: Joel D. Short

Type: Comprehensive **Sex:** Coed **Affiliation:** Mennonite. **Scores:** 87% SAT
V 400+; 92% SAT M 400+ **% Accepted:** 66 **Admission Plans:** Deferred
Admission **Application Deadline:** August 15 **Application Fee:** $25.00 **H.S.
Requirements:** High school diploma required; GED accepted **Costs Per
Year:** Application fee: $25. Comprehensive fee: $42,500 includes full-time
tuition ($32,200) and college room and board ($10,300). College room only:
$5560. Full-time tuition varies according to degree level and program. Room
and board charges vary according to board plan and housing facility. Part-
time tuition: $1340 per credit hour. Part-time tuition varies according to
course load, degree level, and program. **Scholarships:** Available. **Calendar
System:** Semester, Summer session available **Enrollment:** Full-time 713,
Graduate full-time 60, Graduate part-time 6, Part-time 60 **Faculty:** Full-time
67, Part-time 39 **Student-Faculty Ratio:** 9:1 **Exams:** ACT essay component
not used; SAT I or ACT; SAT essay component not used; SAT Reasoning. **%
Receiving Financial Aid:** 73 **% Residing in College-Owned, -Operated,
or -Affiliated Housing:** 64 **Final Year or Final Semester Residency
Requirement:** No **Regional Accreditation:** North Central Association of
Colleges and Schools **Credit Hours For Degree:** 120 credit hours,
Bachelors **Professional Accreditation:** AACN, CSWE, NCATE. **Intercol-
legiate Athletics:** Baseball M; Basketball M & W; Cross-Country Running M
& W; Soccer M & W; Softball W; Tennis M & W; Track and Field M & W;
Volleyball W

GRACE COLLEGE

200 Seminary Dr.
Winona Lake, IN 46590-1294
Tel: (574)372-5100; Free: 800-54-GRACE
Fax: (574)372-5139
E-mail: enroll@grace.edu
Web Site: www.grace.edu
President/CEO: Dr. William J. Katip
Admissions: Nikki Sproul
Financial Aid: Charlette Sauders

Type: Comprehensive **Sex:** Coed **Affiliation:** Fellowship of Grace Brethren
Churches; Grace Theological Seminary. **Scores:** 94% SAT V 400+; 92%
SAT M 400+; 34% ACT 18-23; 49% ACT 24-29 **% Accepted:** 78 **Admission
Plans:** Deferred Admission; Early Admission; Early Decision Plan **Applica-
tion Deadline:** August 1 **Application Fee:** $30.00 **H.S. Requirements:**
High school diploma required; GED accepted **Scholarships:** Available.
Calendar System: Semester, Summer session available **Enrollment:** Full-
time 1,484, Graduate full-time 153, Graduate part-time 228, Part-time 438
Faculty: Full-time 49, Part-time 150 **Student-Faculty Ratio:** 20:1 **Exams:**
ACT essay component not used; SAT I or ACT; SAT essay component not
used. **% Receiving Financial Aid:** 98 **% Residing in College-Owned,
-Operated, or -Affiliated Housing:** 51 **Final Year or Final Semester
Residency Requirement:** No **Regional Accreditation:** North Central As-
sociation of Colleges and Schools **Credit Hours For Degree:** 73 semester
hours, Associates; 124 semester hours, Bachelors **Professional Accredita-
tion:** ACA, ATS, CSWE, NCATE. **Intercollegiate Athletics:** Baseball M;
Basketball M & W; Cheerleading M & W; Cross-Country Running M & W;
Golf M & W; Soccer M & W; Softball W; Tennis M & W; Track and Field M &
W; Volleyball W

HANOVER COLLEGE

PO Box 108
Hanover, IN 47243-0108
Tel: (812)866-7000; Free: 800-213-2178
Fax: (812)866-7098
E-mail: admission@hanover.edu
Web Site: www.hanover.edu
President/CEO: Dr. Lake Lambert
Admissions: Harrison Campbell
Financial Aid: Richard A. Nash

Type: Four-Year College **Sex:** Coed **Affiliation:** Presbyterian. **Scores:** 99%
SAT V 400+; 98% SAT M 400+; 42% ACT 18-23; 46% ACT 24-29 **% Ac-
cepted:** 61 **Admission Plans:** Deferred Admission; Early Admission; Early
Decision Plan **Application Deadline:** March 1 **Application Fee:** $0.00 **H.S.
Requirements:** High school diploma required; GED not accepted **Costs Per
Year:** Application fee: $0. One-time mandatory fee: $300. Comprehensive
fee: $44,966 includes full-time tuition ($33,744), mandatory fees ($770), and
college room and board ($10,452). College room only: $5200. Full-time
tuition and fees vary according to reciprocity agreements. Room and board
charges vary according to housing facility. Part-time tuition: $3750 per unit.
Part-time tuition varies according to course load and reciprocity agreements.
Scholarships: Available. **Calendar System:** Miscellaneous, Summer session not available **Enrollment:** Full-time 1,127, Part-time 6 **Faculty:** Full-
time 97, Part-time 4 **Student-Faculty Ratio:** 11:1 **Exams:** SAT I or ACT;
SAT Reasoning. **% Receiving Financial Aid:** 76 **% Residing in College-
Owned, -Operated, or -Affiliated Housing:** 92 **Final Year or Final
Semester Residency Requirement:** Yes **Regional Accreditation:** North
Central Association of Colleges and Schools **Credit Hours For Degree:** 36
units, Bachelors **Professional Accreditation:** NCATE. **Intercollegiate
Athletics:** Baseball M; Basketball M & W; Cross-Country Running M & W;
Football M; Golf M & W; Lacrosse M & W; Soccer M & W; Softball W; Tennis
M & W; Track and Field M & W; Volleyball W

HARRISON COLLEGE

550 E Washington St.
Indianapolis, IN 46204
Tel: (317)447-6200; Free: 888-544-4422
E-mail: admissions@harrison.edu
Web Site: www.harrison.edu
President/CEO: Jason Konesco
Admissions: Jason Howanec

Type: Four-Year College **Sex:** Coed **% Accepted:** 100 **Application
Deadline:** Rolling **Application Fee:** $0.00 **H.S. Requirements:** High school
diploma required; GED accepted **Scholarships:** Available. **Calendar
System:** Quarter, Summer session available **Enrollment:** Full-time 2,401,
Part-time 1,355 **Faculty:** Full-time 54, Part-time 236 **Student-Faculty Ratio:**
13:1 **Exams:** Other. **Final Year or Final Semester Residency Requirement:** No **Regional Accreditation:** North Central Association of Colleges
and Schools **Professional Accreditation:** ACF, ACICS.

HOLY CROSS COLLEGE

54515 State Rd. 933 N
Notre Dame, IN 46556-0308
Tel: (574)239-8400
Fax: (574)239-8323
E-mail: admissions@hcc-nd.edu
Web Site: www.hcc-nd.edu
President/CEO: Bro. John R. Paige, CSC
Admissions: Adam DeBeck
Financial Aid: Robert Benjamin

Type: Four-Year College **Sex:** Coed **Affiliation:** Roman Catholic. **Scores:**
89% SAT V 400+; 87% SAT M 400+ **% Accepted:** 91 **Admission Plans:**
Deferred Admission **Application Deadline:** Rolling **Application Fee:** $0.00
H.S. Requirements: High school diploma required; GED accepted **Costs
Per Year:** Application fee: $0. Comprehensive fee: $39,360 includes full-time
tuition ($27,810), mandatory fees ($1050), and college room and board
($10,500). Full-time tuition and fees vary according to course load. Part-time
tuition: $927 per credit. Part-time tuition varies according to course load.
Scholarships: Available. **Calendar System:** Semester, Summer session
available **Enrollment:** Full-time 541, Part-time 60 **Faculty:** Full-time 26,
Part-time 40 **Student-Faculty Ratio:** 14:1 **Exams:** ACT essay component
used for advising; ACT essay component used for placement; SAT I or ACT;
SAT essay component used for advising; SAT essay component used for
placement; SAT Reasoning; SAT Subject. **Final Year or Final Semester**

Residency Requirement: No **Regional Accreditation:** North Central Association of Colleges and Schools **Credit Hours For Degree:** 61 semester hours, Associates; 120 semester hours, Bachelors **ROTC:** Air Force, Army **Intercollegiate Athletics:** Basketball M & W; Golf M & W; Ice Hockey M; Lacrosse M; Soccer M & W

HUNTINGTON UNIVERSITY

2303 College Ave.
Huntington, IN 46750-1299
Tel: (260)356-6000; Free: 800-642-6493
Fax: (260)356-9448
E-mail: admissions@huntington.edu
Web Site: www.huntington.edu
President/CEO: Dr. Sherilyn Emberton
Admissions: Jeff Berggren
Financial Aid: Jerry W. Davis

Type: Comprehensive **Sex:** Coed **Affiliation:** Church of the United Brethren in Christ; Church of the United Brethren in Christ. **Scores:** 91% SAT V 400+; 91% SAT M 400+; 41.5% ACT 18-23; 43.5% ACT 24-29 **% Accepted:** 97 **Admission Plans:** Deferred Admission **Application Deadline:** August 1 **Application Fee:** $20.00 **H.S. Requirements:** High school diploma required; GED accepted **Scholarships:** Available. **Calendar System:** 4-1-4, Summer session available **Enrollment:** Full-time 961, Graduate full-time 55, Graduate part-time 26, Part-time 92 **Faculty:** Full-time 55, Part-time 51 **Student-Faculty Ratio:** 13:1 **Exams:** ACT essay component not used; SAT I or ACT; SAT essay component not used; SAT Reasoning. **% Receiving Financial Aid:** 76 **% Residing in College-Owned, -Operated, or -Affiliated Housing:** 76 **Regional Accreditation:** North Central Association of Colleges and Schools **Credit Hours For Degree:** 64 semester hours, Associates; 128 semester hours, Bachelors **Professional Accreditation:** NCATE. **Intercollegiate Athletics:** Baseball M; Basketball M & W; Bowling M & W; Cheerleading M & W; Cross-Country Running M & W; Golf M; Soccer M & W; Softball W; Tennis M & W; Track and Field M & W; Ultimate Frisbee M; Volleyball W

INDIANA STATE UNIVERSITY

210 N Seventh St.
Terre Haute, IN 47809
Tel: (812)237-6311; Free: 800-468-6478
Fax: (812)237-8023
E-mail: admissions@indstate.edu
Web Site: www.indstate.edu
President/CEO: Dr. Daniel J. Bradley
Admissions: Richard Toomey
Financial Aid: Crystal Baker

Type: University **Sex:** Coed **Scores:** 78% SAT V 400+; 76% SAT M 400+; 42.98% ACT 18-23; 16.06% ACT 24-29 **% Accepted:** 85 **Admission Plans:** Deferred Admission **Application Deadline:** August 15 **Application Fee:** $25.00 **H.S. Requirements:** High school diploma required; GED accepted **Costs Per Year:** Application fee: $25. State resident tuition: $8380 full-time, $304 per credit hour part-time. Nonresident tuition: $18,508 full-time, $656 per credit hour part-time. Mandatory fees: $200 full-time, $100 per term part-time. Full-time tuition and fees vary according to reciprocity agreements. Part-time tuition and fees vary according to course load and reciprocity agreements. College room and board: $9028. Room and board charges vary according to board plan, housing facility, and student level. **Scholarships:** Available. **Calendar System:** Semester, Summer session available **Enrollment:** Full-time 9,659, Graduate full-time 991, Graduate part-time 1,336, Part-time 1,598 **Faculty:** Full-time 505, Part-time 188 **Student-Faculty Ratio:** 20:1 **Exams:** ACT essay component not used; SAT I or ACT; SAT essay component not used; SAT Reasoning; SAT Subject. **% Receiving Financial Aid:** 71 **% Residing in College-Owned, -Operated, or -Affiliated Housing:** 40 **Final Year or Final Semester Residency Requirement:** No **Regional Accreditation:** North Central Association of Colleges and Schools **Credit Hours For Degree:** 120 credit hours, Bachelors **ROTC:** Air Force, Army **Professional Accreditation:** AACSB, AAFCS, AAMFT, ABET, ACA, ACCE, ACEN, AND, APA, ASHA, ATMAE, CSWE, JRCAT, NASAD, NASM, NCATE, NRPA. **Intercollegiate Athletics:** Baseball M; Basketball M & W; Cross-Country Running M & W; Football M; Golf W; Soccer W; Softball W; Swimming and Diving W; Track and Field M & W; Volleyball W

INDIANA TECH

1600 E Washington Blvd.
Fort Wayne, IN 46803-1297

Tel: (260)422-5561; Free: 800-937-2448
Fax: (260)422-7696
E-mail: admissions@indianatech.edu
Web Site: www.indianatech.edu
President/CEO: Dr. Arthur E. Snyder
Admissions: Monica L. Chamberlain
Financial Aid: Lisa Claudette Green

Type: Comprehensive **Sex:** Coed **Scores:** 73% SAT V 400+; 51% ACT 18-23; 18% ACT 24-29 **% Accepted:** 72 **Application Deadline:** August 15 **Application Fee:** $50.00 **H.S. Requirements:** High school diploma required; GED accepted **Scholarships:** Available. **Calendar System:** Semester, Summer session available **Enrollment:** Full-time 3,727, Graduate full-time 138, Graduate part-time 479, Part-time 2,011 **Faculty:** Full-time 59, Part-time 451 **Student-Faculty Ratio:** 19:1 **Exams:** ACT essay component used for advising; ACT essay component used for placement; SAT I or ACT; SAT essay component used for advising; SAT essay component used for placement; SAT Reasoning. **% Receiving Financial Aid:** 87 **% Residing in College-Owned, -Operated, or -Affiliated Housing:** 55 **Final Year or Final Semester Residency Requirement:** No **Regional Accreditation:** North Central Association of Colleges and Schools **Credit Hours For Degree:** 60 credit hours, Associates; 123 credit hours, Bachelors **ROTC:** Army **Professional Accreditation:** ABET. **Intercollegiate Athletics:** Baseball M; Basketball M & W; Bowling M & W; Cheerleading M & W; Cross-Country Running M & W; Golf M & W; Lacrosse M & W; Soccer M & W; Softball W; Tennis M & W; Track and Field M & W; Volleyball W; Wrestling M

INDIANA UNIVERSITY BLOOMINGTON

107 S Indiana Ave.
Bloomington, IN 47405-7000
Tel: (812)855-4848
Fax: (812)855-1871
E-mail: iuadmit@indiana.edu
Web Site: www.iub.edu
President/CEO: Dr. Michael A. McRobbie
Admissions: Sacha Thieme
Financial Aid: Jackie Kennedy-Fletcher

Type: University **Sex:** Coed **Affiliation:** Indiana University System. **Scores:** 99% SAT V 400+; 99% SAT M 400+; 18.1% ACT 18-23; 50.8% ACT 24-29 **% Accepted:** 78 **Admission Plans:** Deferred Admission; Preferred Admission **Application Deadline:** Rolling **Application Fee:** $60.00 **H.S. Requirements:** High school diploma required; GED accepted **Costs Per Year:** Application fee: $60. State resident tuition: $9,087 full-time, $283.92 per credit hour part-time. Nonresident tuition: $32,945 full-time, $1,029.54 per credit hour part-time. Mandatory fees: $1,301 full-time. Full-time tuition and fees vary according to location and program. Part-time tuition varies according to course load, location, and program. **Scholarships:** Available. **Calendar System:** Semester, Summer session available **Enrollment:** Full-time 31,728, Graduate full-time 6,275, Graduate part-time 3,875, Part-time 6,636 **Faculty:** Full-time 2,059, Part-time 320 **Student-Faculty Ratio:** 17:1 **Exams:** SAT I or ACT; SAT II; SAT essay component used for placement; SAT Reasoning; SAT Subject. **% Receiving Financial Aid:** 40 **% Residing in College-Owned, -Operated, or -Affiliated Housing:** 35 **Final Year or Final Semester Residency Requirement:** No **Regional Accreditation:** North Central Association of Colleges and Schools **Credit Hours For Degree:** 60 credit hours, Associates; 120 credit hours, Bachelors **ROTC:** Air Force, Army **Professional Accreditation:** AACSB, ABA, ACA, ACEJMC, ALA, AOA, APA, ASHA, CEPH, CIDA, COA, CSWE, JRCAT, NASAD, NASM, NASPAA, NAST, NCATE, NRPA. **Intercollegiate Athletics:** Baseball M; Basketball M & W; Crew W; Cross-Country Running M & W; Field Hockey W; Football M; Golf M & W; Soccer M & W; Softball W; Swimming and Diving M & W; Tennis M & W; Track and Field M & W; Volleyball W; Water Polo W; Wrestling M

INDIANA UNIVERSITY EAST

2325 Chester Blvd.
Richmond, IN 47374-1289
Tel: (765)973-8200; Free: 800-959-EAST
Fax: (765)973-8288
E-mail: applynow@iue.edu
Web Site: www.iue.edu
President/CEO: Kathryn Cruz-Uribe
Admissions: Molly Vanderpool
Financial Aid: Sarah Soper

Type: Comprehensive **Sex:** Coed **Affiliation:** Indiana University System.

Scores: 86% SAT V 400+; 86% SAT M 400+; 56.7% ACT 18-23; 19.1% ACT 24-29 **% Accepted:** 62 **Admission Plans:** Deferred Admission; Early Admission **Application Deadline:** Rolling **Application Fee:** $35.00 **H.S. Requirements:** High school diploma required; GED accepted **Costs Per Year:** Application fee: $35. State resident tuition: $6,478 full-time, $215.92 per credit hour part-time. Nonresident tuition: $18,088 full-time, $602.93 per credit hour part-time. Mandatory fees: $595 full-time. Full-time tuition and fees vary according to course load, location, program, and reciprocity agreements. Part-time tuition varies according to course load, location, program, and reciprocity agreements. **Scholarships:** Available. **Calendar System:** Semester, Summer session available **Enrollment:** Full-time 1,964, Graduate full-time 36, Graduate part-time 118, Part-time 2,598 **Faculty:** Full-time 107, Part-time 189 **Student-Faculty Ratio:** 15:1 **Exams:** SAT I or ACT. **% Receiving Financial Aid:** 78 **Regional Accreditation:** North Central Association of Colleges and Schools **Credit Hours For Degree:** 60 credit hours, Associates; 120 credit hours, Bachelors **Professional Accreditation:** ACBSP, ACEN, CSWE, NCATE. **Intercollegiate Athletics:** Basketball M & W; Cross-Country Running M & W; Golf M & W; Tennis M & W; Track and Field M & W; Volleyball W

INDIANA UNIVERSITY KOKOMO

2300 S Washington St.
Kokomo, IN 46904-9003
Tel: (765)453-2000; Free: 888-875-4485
Fax: (765)455-9537
E-mail: iuadmis@iuk.edu
Web Site: www.iuk.edu
President/CEO: Susan Sciame-Giesecke
Admissions: Angie Siders
Financial Aid: Karen Shaw

Type: Comprehensive **Sex:** Coed **Affiliation:** Indiana University System. **Scores:** 84% SAT V 400+; 88% SAT M 400+; 58% ACT 18-23; 20% ACT 24-29 **% Accepted:** 71 **Admission Plans:** Deferred Admission **Application Deadline:** Rolling **Application Fee:** $35.00 **H.S. Requirements:** High school diploma required; GED accepted **Costs Per Year:** Application fee: $35. State resident tuition: $6,478 full-time, $215.92 per credit hour part-time. Nonresident tuition: $18,088 full-time, $602.93 per credit hour part-time. Mandatory fees: $595 full-time. Full-time tuition and fees vary according to course load, location, and program. Part-time tuition varies according to course load, location, and program. **Scholarships:** Available. **Calendar System:** Semester, Summer session available **Enrollment:** Full-time 2,160, Graduate full-time 46, Graduate part-time 100, Part-time 1,784 **Faculty:** Full-time 117, Part-time 116 **Student-Faculty Ratio:** 16:1 **Exams:** ACT essay component used for placement; SAT I or ACT; SAT essay component used for placement; SAT Reasoning; SAT Subject. **% Receiving Financial Aid:** 72 **Final Year or Final Semester Residency Requirement:** No **Regional Accreditation:** North Central Association of Colleges and Schools **Credit Hours For Degree:** 60 credit hours, Associates; 120 credit hours, Bachelors **ROTC:** Army **Professional Accreditation:** AACN, AACSB, NCATE. **Intercollegiate Athletics:** Basketball M & W; Cross-Country Running M & W; Golf M & W; Volleyball W

INDIANA UNIVERSITY NORTHWEST

3400 Broadway
Gary, IN 46408-1197
Tel: (219)980-6500; Free: 800-968-7486
Fax: (219)981-4219
E-mail: admit@iun.edu
Web Site: www.iun.edu
President/CEO: Dr. William J. Lowe
Financial Aid: Harold Burtley

Type: Comprehensive **Sex:** Coed **Affiliation:** Indiana University System. **Scores:** 80% SAT V 400+; 77% SAT M 400+; 53% ACT 18-23; 20% ACT 24-29 **% Accepted:** 79 **Admission Plans:** Deferred Admission **Application Deadline:** Rolling **Application Fee:** $35.00 **H.S. Requirements:** High school diploma required; GED accepted **Costs Per Year:** Application fee: $35. State resident tuition: $6,478 full-time, $215.92 per credit hour part-time. Nonresident tuition: $18,088 full-time, $602.93 per credit hour part-time. Mandatory fees: $595 full-time. Full-time tuition and fees vary according to course load, location, and program. Part-time tuition varies according to course load, location, and program. **Scholarships:** Available. **Calendar System:** Semester, Summer session available **Enrollment:** Full-time 2,957, Graduate full-time 94, Graduate part-time 268, Part-time 2,529 **Faculty:** Full-time 167, Part-time 197 **Student-Faculty Ratio:** 15:1 **Exams:** ACT essay

component not used; SAT I or ACT; SAT essay component not used. **% Receiving Financial Aid:** 66 **Regional Accreditation:** North Central Association of Colleges and Schools **Credit Hours For Degree:** 60 credits, Associates; 120 credits, Bachelors **ROTC:** Army **Professional Accreditation:** AACN, AACSB, ACEN, ADA, AHIMA, CSWE, CoARC, JRCERT, NAACLS, NASPAA, NCATE. **Intercollegiate Athletics:** Basketball M & W; Cross-Country Running M & W; Golf M & W; Volleyball W

INDIANA UNIVERSITY SOUTH BEND

1700 Mishawaka Ave.
South Bend, IN 46634-7111
Tel: (574)520-4872; Free: 877-GO-2-IUSB
Fax: (574)520-4834
E-mail: admissions@iusb.edu
Web Site: www.iusb.edu
President/CEO: Terry Allison
Admissions: Connie Peterson-Miller
Financial Aid: Cathy Buckman

Type: Comprehensive **Sex:** Coed **Affiliation:** Indiana University System. **Scores:** 88% SAT V 400+; 86% SAT M 400+; 56.5% ACT 18-23; 21.2% ACT 24-29 **% Accepted:** 76 **Admission Plans:** Deferred Admission **Application Deadline:** Rolling **Application Fee:** $35.00 **H.S. Requirements:** High school diploma required; GED accepted **Costs Per Year:** Application fee: $35. State resident tuition: $6,478 full-time, $215.92 per credit hour part-time. Nonresident tuition: $18,088 full-time, $602.93 per credit hour part-time. Mandatory fees: $595 full-time. Full-time tuition and fees vary according to course load, location, and program. Part-time tuition varies according to course load, location, and program. **Scholarships:** Available. **Calendar System:** Semester, Summer session available **Enrollment:** Full-time 3,851, Graduate full-time 104, Graduate part-time 454, Part-time 3,165 **Faculty:** Full-time 268, Part-time 208 **Student-Faculty Ratio:** 13:1 **Exams:** SAT I or ACT. **% Receiving Financial Aid:** 74 **% Residing in College-Owned, -Operated, or -Affiliated Housing:** 7 **Regional Accreditation:** North Central Association of Colleges and Schools **Credit Hours For Degree:** 60 credit hours, Associates; 120 credit hours, Bachelors **ROTC:** Air Force, Army, Navy **Professional Accreditation:** AACN, AACSB, ACA, ADA, CSWE, JRCERT, MACTE, NASPAA, NCATE. **Intercollegiate Athletics:** Baseball M; Basketball M & W; Cross-Country Running M & W; Golf M; Volleyball W

INDIANA UNIVERSITY SOUTHEAST

4201 Grant Line Rd.
New Albany, IN 47150-6405
Tel: (812)941-2000; Free: 800-852-8835
E-mail: admissions@ius.edu
Web Site: www.ius.edu
President/CEO: Ray Wallace
Admissions: Chris Crews
Financial Aid: Traci Armes

Type: Comprehensive **Sex:** Coed **Affiliation:** Indiana University System. **Scores:** 84% SAT V 400+; 82% SAT M 400+; 57.4% ACT 18-23; 19.3% ACT 24-29 **% Accepted:** 85 **Admission Plans:** Deferred Admission; Early Admission **Application Deadline:** Rolling **Application Fee:** $35.00 **H.S. Requirements:** High school diploma required; GED accepted **Costs Per Year:** Application fee: $35. State resident tuition: $6,478 full-time, $215.92 per credit hour part-time. Nonresident tuition: $18,088 full-time, $602.93 per credit hour part-time. Mandatory fees: $595 full-time. Full-time tuition and fees vary according to course load, location, program, and reciprocity agreements. Part-time tuition varies according to course load, location, program, and reciprocity agreements. **Scholarships:** Available. **Calendar System:** Semester, Summer session available **Enrollment:** Full-time 3,452, Graduate full-time 25, Graduate part-time 394, Part-time 2,302 **Faculty:** Full-time 211, Part-time 272 **Student-Faculty Ratio:** 14:1 **Exams:** ACT essay component used for admission; SAT I or ACT; SAT essay component used for admission; SAT Reasoning. **% Receiving Financial Aid:** 67 **% Residing in College-Owned, -Operated, or -Affiliated Housing:** 7 **Regional Accreditation:** North Central Association of Colleges and Schools **Credit Hours For Degree:** 60 credit hours, Associates; 120 credit hours, Bachelors **ROTC:** Air Force, Army **Professional Accreditation:** AACN, AACSB, NCATE. **Intercollegiate Athletics:** Baseball M; Basketball M & W; Softball W; Tennis M & W; Volleyball W

INDIANA UNIVERSITY–PURDUE UNIVERSITY FORT WAYNE

2101 E Coliseum Blvd.
Fort Wayne, IN 46805-1499

Tel: (260)481-6100; Free: 800-324-4739
E-mail: morrena@ipfw.edu
Web Site: www.ipfw.edu
President/CEO: Dr. Vicky L. Carwein
Admissions: Angela Morren
Financial Aid: David Peterson
Type: Comprehensive Sex: Coed Affiliation: Indiana University System and Purdue University System. Scores: 93% SAT V 400+; 93% SAT M 400+; 53% ACT 18-23; 27% ACT 24-29 % Accepted: 91 Admission Plans: Deferred Admission Application Deadline: August 1 Application Fee: $50.00 H.S. Requirements: High school diploma required; GED accepted Costs Per Year: Application fee: $50. State resident tuition: $7,052 full-time, $235.05 per credit hour part-time. Nonresident tuition: $18,380 full-time, $612.65 per credit hour part-time. Mandatory fees: $1,028 full-time, $34.25 per credit hour part-time. Full-time tuition and fees vary according to course load. Part-time tuition and fees vary according to course load. College room only: $6844. Room charges vary according to housing facility. Scholarships: Available. Calendar System: Semester, Summer session available Enrollment: Full-time 6,971, Graduate full-time 135, Graduate part-time 405, Part-time 5,703 Faculty: Full-time 403, Part-time 398 Student-Faculty Ratio: 17:1 Exams: ACT essay component used for placement; SAT I or ACT; SAT essay component used for placement; SAT Reasoning. % Receiving Financial Aid: 69 % Residing in College-Owned, -Operated, or -Affiliated Housing: 8 Final Year or Final Semester Residency Requirement: No Regional Accreditation: North Central Association of Colleges and Schools Credit Hours For Degree: 60 semester hours, Associates; 120 semester hours, Bachelors ROTC: Army Professional Accreditation: AACSB, ABET, ACEN, ADA, AHIMA, NASM, NASPAA, NCATE. Intercollegiate Athletics: Baseball M; Basketball M & W; Cross-Country Running M & W; Golf M & W; Soccer M & W; Softball W; Tennis M & W; Track and Field W; Volleyball M & W

INDIANA UNIVERSITY–PURDUE UNIVERSITY INDIANAPOLIS

420 University Blvd.
Indianapolis, IN 46202
Tel: (317)274-5555
Fax: (317)278-1862
E-mail: apply@iupui.edu
Web Site: www.iupui.edu
President/CEO: Dr. Nasser H. Paydar
Financial Aid: Marvin Smith
Type: University Sex: Coed Affiliation: Indiana University System. Scores: 92% SAT V 400+; 92% SAT M 400+; 48.6% ACT 18-23; 31.4% ACT 24-29 % Accepted: 70 Admission Plans: Deferred Admission Application Deadline: May 1 Application Fee: $55.00 H.S. Requirements: High school diploma required; GED accepted Costs Per Year: Application fee: $55. State resident tuition: $8,141 full-time, $271.37 per credit hour part-time. Nonresident tuition: $28,727 full-time, $957.58 per credit hour part-time. Mandatory fees: $1,064 full-time. Full-time tuition and fees vary according to course load, location, and program. Part-time tuition varies according to course load, location, and program. Scholarships: Available. Calendar System: Semester, Summer session available Enrollment: Full-time 17,051, Graduate full-time 4,575, Graduate part-time 3,545, Part-time 4,934 Faculty: Full-time 2,269, Part-time 1,058 Student-Faculty Ratio: 19:1 Exams: SAT I or ACT; SAT essay component used for admission; SAT essay component used for advising; SAT essay component used for placement; SAT Reasoning. % Receiving Financial Aid: 67 % Residing in College-Owned, -Operated, or -Affiliated Housing: 9 Regional Accreditation: North Central Association of Colleges and Schools Credit Hours For Degree: 60 credit hours, Associates; 120 credit hours, Bachelors ROTC: Air Force, Army Professional Accreditation: AACN, AACSB, ABA, ABET, ACEN, ACIPE, ADA, AHIMA, AND, AOTA, APA, APTA, ASC, CAHME, CEPH, CSWE, CoARC, JRCERT, JRCNMT, LCME/AMA, NAACLS, NASAD, NASM, NASPAA. Intercollegiate Athletics: Basketball M & W; Cross-Country Running M & W; Golf M & W; Soccer M & W; Softball W; Swimming and Diving M & W; Tennis M & W; Track and Field M & W; Volleyball W

INDIANA WESLEYAN UNIVERSITY

4201 S Washington St.
Marion, IN 46953-4974
Tel: (765)674-6901; Free: 866-468-6498
Fax: (765)677-2333
E-mail: admissions@indwes.edu
Web Site: www.indwes.edu

President/CEO: Dr. David Wright
Admissions: Adam Farmer
Financial Aid: Lisa Montany
Type: Comprehensive Sex: Coed Affiliation: Wesleyan. Scores: 96% SAT V 400+; 95% SAT M 400+; 38% ACT 18-23; 47% ACT 24-29 % Accepted: 96 Admission Plans: Deferred Admission H.S. Requirements: High school diploma required; GED accepted Costs Per Year: Comprehensive fee: $32,716 includes full-time tuition ($24,728) and college room and board ($7988). College room only: $3994. Full-time tuition varies according to course load and degree level. Room and board charges vary according to board plan. Part-time tuition: $1050 per credit hour. Part-time tuition varies according to course load and degree level. Scholarships: Available. Calendar System: Semester, Summer session available Enrollment: Full-time 2,688, Graduate full-time 117, Graduate part-time 136, Part-time 245 Faculty: Full-time 160, Part-time 107 Student-Faculty Ratio: 14:1 Exams: Other; SAT I or ACT; SAT Reasoning. % Receiving Financial Aid: 59 % Residing in College-Owned, -Operated, or -Affiliated Housing: 82 Final Year or Final Semester Residency Requirement: No Regional Accreditation: North Central Association of Colleges and Schools Credit Hours For Degree: 62 credit hours, Associates; 124 credit hours, Bachelors ROTC: Army Professional Accreditation: AACN, ACA, ATS, CSWE, NASM, NCATE. Intercollegiate Athletics: Baseball M; Basketball M & W; Cheerleading M & W; Cross-Country Running M & W; Golf M & W; Soccer M & W; Softball W; Swimming and Diving W; Tennis M & W; Track and Field M & W; Volleyball W

INTERNATIONAL BUSINESS COLLEGE (FORT WAYNE)

5699 Coventry Ln.
Fort Wayne, IN 46804
Tel: (260)459-4500; Free: 800-589-6363
Fax: (260)436-1896
Web Site: www.ibcfortwayne.edu
President/CEO: Steve Kinzer
Type: Four-Year College Sex: Coed % Accepted: 75 H.S. Requirements: High school diploma required; GED accepted Scholarships: Available. Calendar System: Semester Professional Accreditation: AAMAE, ACICS.

INTERNATIONAL BUSINESS COLLEGE (INDIANAPOLIS)

7205 Shadeland Station
Indianapolis, IN 46256
Tel: (317)813-2300; Free: 800-589-6500
Fax: (317)841-6419
Web Site: www.ibcindianapolis.edu
President/CEO: Kathy Chiudioni
Financial Aid: Carrie Mengerink
Type: Two-Year College Sex: Coed % Accepted: 71 H.S. Requirements: High school diploma required; GED accepted Scholarships: Available. Calendar System: Semester Professional Accreditation: ACICS.

IVY TECH COMMUNITY COLLEGE–BLOOMINGTON

200 Daniels Way
Bloomington, IN 47404
Tel: (812)332-1559; Free: 888-IVY-LINE
Fax: (812)332-8147
E-mail: nfrederi@ivytech.edu
Web Site: www.ivytech.edu
Admissions: Neil Frederick
Type: Two-Year College Sex: Coed Affiliation: Ivy Tech Community College System. % Accepted: 100 Admission Plans: Deferred Admission; Open Admission; Preferred Admission Application Deadline: Rolling Application Fee: $0.00 Costs Per Year: Application fee: $0. State resident tuition: $3995 full-time, $133.15 per credit hour part-time. Nonresident tuition: $7872 full-time, $262.40 per credit hour part-time. Mandatory fees: $120 full-time, $60 per term part-time. Scholarships: Available. Calendar System: Semester, Summer session available Enrollment: Full-time 2,017, Part-time 4,090 Faculty: Full-time 84, Part-time 325 Student-Faculty Ratio: 20:1 Regional Accreditation: North Central Association of Colleges and Schools Credit Hours For Degree: 60 credits, Associates Professional Accreditation: ACBSP.

IVY TECH COMMUNITY COLLEGE–CENTRAL INDIANA

50 W Fall Creek Pky. N Dr.
Indianapolis, IN 46206-1763
Tel: (317)921-4800; Free: 888-IVYLINE

E-mail: tfunk@ivytech.edu
Web Site: www.ivytech.edu
Admissions: Tracy Funk
Type: Two-Year College **Sex:** Coed **Affiliation:** Ivy Tech Community College System. **Admission Plans:** Deferred Admission; Early Admission; Open Admission; Preferred Admission **Application Deadline:** Rolling **Application Fee:** $0.00 **H.S. Requirements:** High school diploma or equivalent not required. For allied health programs: High school diploma required; GED accepted **Costs Per Year:** Application fee: $0. State resident tuition: $3995 full-time, $131.15 per credit hour part-time. Nonresident tuition: $7872 full-time, $262.40 per credit hour part-time. Mandatory fees: $120 full-time, $60 per term part-time. **Scholarships:** Available. **Calendar System:** Semester, Summer session available **Enrollment:** Full-time 5,270, Part-time 13,834 **Faculty:** Full-time 187, Part-time 759 **Student-Faculty Ratio:** 23:1 **Regional Accreditation:** North Central Association of Colleges and Schools **Credit Hours For Degree:** 60 credits, Associates **Professional Accreditation:** AAMAE, ACBSP, ACEN, ACF, ARCST, ATMAE, CoARC, JRCERT.

IVY TECH COMMUNITY COLLEGE–COLUMBUS
4475 Central Ave.
Columbus, IN 47203-1868
Tel: (812)372-9925; Free: 888-IVY-LINE
Fax: (812)372-0311
E-mail: adeck@ivytech.edu
Web Site: www.ivytech.edu
Admissions: Alisa Deck
Type: Two-Year College **Sex:** Coed **Affiliation:** Ivy Tech Community College System. **Admission Plans:** Deferred Admission; Early Admission; Open Admission; Preferred Admission **Application Deadline:** Rolling **Application Fee:** $0.00 **H.S. Requirements:** High school diploma or equivalent not required. For allied health programs: High school diploma required; GED accepted **Costs Per Year:** Application fee: $0. State resident tuition: $3995 full-time, $133.15 per credit hour part-time. Nonresident tuition: $7872 full-time, $262.40 per credit hour part-time. Mandatory fees: $120 full-time, $60 per term part-time. **Scholarships:** Available. **Calendar System:** Semester, Summer session available **Enrollment:** Full-time 781, Part-time 2,084 **Faculty:** Full-time 53, Part-time 230 **Student-Faculty Ratio:** 18:1 **Regional Accreditation:** North Central Association of Colleges and Schools **Credit Hours For Degree:** 60 credits, Associates **Professional Accreditation:** AAMAE, ACBSP, ADA, ARCST, NASAD.

IVY TECH COMMUNITY COLLEGE–EAST CENTRAL
4301 S Cowan Rd.
Muncie, IN 47302-9448
Tel: (765)289-2291; Free: 888-IVY-LINE
E-mail: mlewelle@ivytech.edu
Web Site: www.ivytech.edu
Admissions: Mary Lewellen
Type: Two-Year College **Sex:** Coed **Affiliation:** Ivy Tech Community College System. **Admission Plans:** Deferred Admission; Early Admission; Open Admission; Preferred Admission **Application Deadline:** Rolling **Application Fee:** $0.00 **H.S. Requirements:** High school diploma or equivalent not required. For allied health programs: High school diploma required; GED accepted **Costs Per Year:** Application fee: $0. State resident tuition: $3995 full-time, $133.15 per credit hour part-time. Nonresident tuition: $7872 full-time, $262.40 per credit hour part-time. Mandatory fees: $120 full-time, $60 per term part-time. **Scholarships:** Available. **Calendar System:** Semester, Summer session not available **Enrollment:** Full-time 2,571, Part-time 3,372 **Faculty:** Full-time 111, Part-time 455 **Student-Faculty Ratio:** 18:1 **Regional Accreditation:** North Central Association of Colleges and Schools **Credit Hours For Degree:** 60 credits, Associates **Professional Accreditation:** AAMAE, ACBSP, ACF, APTA, ARCST.

IVY TECH COMMUNITY COLLEGE–KOKOMO
1815 E Morgan St.
Kokomo, IN 46903-1373
Tel: (765)459-0561; Free: 888-IVY-LINE
E-mail: mfedersp@ivytech.edu
Web Site: www.ivytech.edu
Admissions: Mike Federspill
Type: Two-Year College **Sex:** Coed **Affiliation:** Ivy Tech Community College System. **Admission Plans:** Early Admission; Open Admission; Preferred Admission **Application Deadline:** Rolling **Application Fee:** $0.00 **H.S. Requirements:** High school diploma or equivalent not required. For allied

health programs: High school diploma required; GED accepted **Costs Per Year:** Application fee: $0. State resident tuition: $3995 full-time, $133.15 per credit hour part-time. Nonresident tuition: $7872 full-time, $262.40 per credit hour part-time. Mandatory fees: $120 full-time. **Scholarships:** Available. **Calendar System:** Semester, Summer session available **Enrollment:** Full-time 1,046, Part-time 1,801 **Faculty:** Full-time 76, Part-time 253 **Student-Faculty Ratio:** 15:1 **Regional Accreditation:** North Central Association of Colleges and Schools **Credit Hours For Degree:** 60 credits, Associates **Professional Accreditation:** AAMAE, ACBSP.

IVY TECH COMMUNITY COLLEGE–LAFAYETTE
3101 S Creasy Ln.
Lafayette, IN 47905-5266
Tel: (765)772-9100; Free: 888-IVY-LINE
E-mail: ihernand@ivytech.edu
Web Site: www.ivytech.edu
Admissions: Ivan Hernanadez
Type: Two-Year College **Sex:** Coed **Affiliation:** Ivy Tech Community College System. **Admission Plans:** Open Admission; Preferred Admission **Application Deadline:** Rolling **Application Fee:** $0.00 **H.S. Requirements:** High school diploma or equivalent not required. For allied health programs: High school diploma required; GED accepted **Costs Per Year:** Application fee: $0. State resident tuition: $3995 full-time, $133.15 per credit hour part-time. Nonresident tuition: $7872 full-time, $262.40 per credit hour part-time. Mandatory fees: $120 full-time. **Scholarships:** Available. **Calendar System:** Semester, Summer session available **Enrollment:** Full-time 2,144, Part-time 2,916 **Faculty:** Full-time 98, Part-time 341 **Student-Faculty Ratio:** 15:1 **Regional Accreditation:** North Central Association of Colleges and Schools **Credit Hours For Degree:** 60 credits, Associates **Professional Accreditation:** AAMAE, ACBSP, ADA, ARCST, ATMAE, CoARC.

IVY TECH COMMUNITY COLLEGE–NORTH CENTRAL
220 Dean Johnson Blvd.
South Bend, IN 46601
Tel: (574)289-7001; Free: 888-IVY-LINE
Fax: (574)236-7181
E-mail: jaustin@ivytech.edu
Web Site: www.ivytech.edu
Admissions: Janice Austin
Type: Two-Year College **Sex:** Coed **Affiliation:** Ivy Tech Community College System. **Admission Plans:** Deferred Admission; Early Admission; Open Admission; Preferred Admission **Application Deadline:** Rolling **Application Fee:** $0.00 **H.S. Requirements:** High school diploma or equivalent not required. For allied health programs: High school diploma required; GED accepted **Costs Per Year:** Application fee: $0. State resident tuition: $3995 full-time, $133.15 per credit hour part-time. Nonresident tuition: $7872 full-time, $262.40 per credit hour part-time. Mandatory fees: $120 full-time. **Scholarships:** Available. **Calendar System:** Semester, Summer session available **Enrollment:** Full-time 1,635, Part-time 3,618 **Faculty:** Full-time 108, Part-time 307 **Student-Faculty Ratio:** 14:1 **Regional Accreditation:** North Central Association of Colleges and Schools **Credit Hours For Degree:** 60 credits, Associates **Professional Accreditation:** AAMAE, ACBSP, ACF, NAACLS, NASAD.

IVY TECH COMMUNITY COLLEGE–NORTHEAST
3800 N Anthony Blvd.
Fort Wayne, IN 46805-1430
Tel: (260)482-9171; Free: 888-IVY-LINE
Fax: (260)480-4177
E-mail: rboss1@ivytech.edu
Web Site: www.ivytech.edu
Admissions: Robyn Boss
Type: Two-Year College **Sex:** Coed **Affiliation:** Ivy Tech Community College System. **Admission Plans:** Early Admission; Open Admission; Preferred Admission **Application Deadline:** Rolling **Application Fee:** $0.00 **H.S. Requirements:** High school diploma or equivalent not required. For allied health programs: High school diploma required; GED accepted **Costs Per Year:** Application fee: $0. State resident tuition: $3995 full-time, $133.15 per credit hour part-time. Nonresident tuition: $7872 full-time, $262.40 per credit hour part-time. Mandatory fees: $120 full-time. **Scholarships:** Available. **Calendar System:** Semester, Summer session available **Enrollment:** Full-time 2,409, Part-time 5,251 **Faculty:** Full-time 133, Part-time 408 **Student-Faculty Ratio:** 15:1 **Regional Accreditation:** North Central Association of

Colleges and Schools **Credit Hours For Degree:** 60 credits, Associates **Professional Accreditation:** AAMAE, ACBSP, ACF, ATMAE, CoARC.

IVY TECH COMMUNITY COLLEGE–NORTHWEST
1440 E 35th Ave.
Gary, IN 46409-1499
Tel: (219)981-1111; Free: 888-IVY-LINE
E-mail: tlewis@ivytech.edu
Web Site: www.ivytech.edu
Admissions: Twilla Lewis

Type: Two-Year College **Sex:** Coed **Affiliation:** Ivy Tech Community College System. **Admission Plans:** Deferred Admission; Open Admission; Preferred Admission **Application Deadline:** Rolling **Application Fee:** $0.00 **H.S. Requirements:** High school diploma or equivalent not required. For allied health programs: High school diploma required; GED accepted **Costs Per Year:** Application fee: $0. State resident tuition: $3995 full-time, $133.15 per credit hour part-time. Nonresident tuition: $7872 full-time, $262.40 per credit hour part-time. Mandatory fees: $120 full-time. **Scholarships:** Available. **Calendar System:** Semester, Summer session available **Enrollment:** Full-time 2,673, Part-time 5,493 **Faculty:** Full-time 126, Part-time 410 **Student-Faculty Ratio:** 17:1 **Regional Accreditation:** North Central Association of Colleges and Schools **Credit Hours For Degree:** 60 credits, Associates **Professional Accreditation:** AAMAE, ACBSP, ACF, APTA, ARCST, CoARC.

IVY TECH COMMUNITY COLLEGE–RICHMOND
2357 Chester Blvd.
Richmond, IN 47374-1220
Tel: (765)966-2656; Free: 888-IVY-LINE
E-mail: crethlake@ivytech.edu
Web Site: www.ivytech.edu
Admissions: Christine Seger

Type: Two-Year College **Sex:** Coed **Affiliation:** Ivy Tech Community College System. **Admission Plans:** Early Admission; Open Admission; Preferred Admission **Application Deadline:** Rolling **Application Fee:** $0.00 **H.S. Requirements:** High school diploma or equivalent not required. For allied health programs: High school diploma required; GED accepted **Costs Per Year:** Application fee: $0. State resident tuition: $3995 full-time, $133.15 per credit hour part-time. Nonresident tuition: $7872 full-time, $262.40 per credit hour part-time. Mandatory fees: $120 full-time. **Scholarships:** Available. **Calendar System:** Semester, Summer session available **Enrollment:** Full-time 639, Part-time 1,543 **Faculty:** Full-time 40, Part-time 158 **Student-Faculty Ratio:** 19:1 **Regional Accreditation:** North Central Association of Colleges and Schools **Credit Hours For Degree:** 60 credits, Associates **Professional Accreditation:** AAMAE, ACBSP, ATMAE.

IVY TECH COMMUNITY COLLEGE–SOUTHEAST
590 Ivy Tech Dr.
Madison, IN 47250-1883
Tel: (812)265-4028; Free: 888-IVY-LINE
E-mail: chutcher@ivytech.edu
Web Site: www.ivytech.edu
Admissions: Cindy Hutcherson

Type: Two-Year College **Sex:** Coed **Affiliation:** Ivy Tech Community College System. **Admission Plans:** Open Admission; Preferred Admission **Application Deadline:** Rolling **Application Fee:** $0.00 **H.S. Requirements:** High school diploma or equivalent not required. For allied health programs: High school diploma required; GED accepted **Costs Per Year:** Application fee: $0. State resident tuition: $3995 full-time, $133.15 per credit hour part-time. Nonresident tuition: $7872 full-time, $262.40 per credit hour part-time. Mandatory fees: $120 full-time, $60 per term part-time. **Scholarships:** Available. **Calendar System:** Semester, Summer session available **Enrollment:** Full-time 739, Part-time 1,575 **Faculty:** Full-time 49, Part-time 177 **Student-Faculty Ratio:** 15:1 **Regional Accreditation:** North Central Association of Colleges and Schools **Credit Hours For Degree:** 60 credits, Associates **Professional Accreditation:** ACBSP.

IVY TECH COMMUNITY COLLEGE–SOUTHERN INDIANA
8204 Hwy. 311
Sellersburg, IN 47172-1829
Tel: (812)246-3301; Free: 888-IVY-LINE
E-mail: bharris88@ivytech.edu
Web Site: www.ivytech.edu
Admissions: Ben Harris

Type: Two-Year College **Sex:** Coed **Affiliation:** Ivy Tech Community College

System. **Admission Plans:** Deferred Admission; Early Admission; Open Admission; Preferred Admission **Application Deadline:** Rolling **Application Fee:** $0.00 **H.S. Requirements:** High school diploma or equivalent not required. For allied health programs: High school diploma required; GED accepted **Costs Per Year:** Application fee: $0. State resident tuition: $3995 full-time, $133.15 per credit hour part-time. Nonresident tuition: $7872 full-time, $262.40 per credit hour part-time. Mandatory fees: $120 full-time, $60 per term part-time. **Scholarships:** Available. **Calendar System:** Semester, Summer session available **Enrollment:** Full-time 972, Part-time 3,778 **Faculty:** Full-time 58, Part-time 217 **Student-Faculty Ratio:** 19:1 **Regional Accreditation:** North Central Association of Colleges and Schools **Credit Hours For Degree:** 60 credits, Associates **Professional Accreditation:** AAMAE, ACBSP, ATMAE.

IVY TECH COMMUNITY COLLEGE–SOUTHWEST
3501 First Ave.
Evansville, IN 47710-3398
Tel: (812)426-2865; Free: 888-IVY-LINE
E-mail: ajohnson@ivytech.edu
Web Site: www.ivytech.edu
Admissions: Denise Johnson-Kincade

Type: Two-Year College **Sex:** Coed **Affiliation:** Ivy Tech Community College System. **Admission Plans:** Deferred Admission; Early Admission; Open Admission; Preferred Admission **Application Deadline:** Rolling **Application Fee:** $0.00 **H.S. Requirements:** High school diploma or equivalent not required. For allied health programs: High school diploma required; GED accepted **Costs Per Year:** Application fee: $0. State resident tuition: $3995 full-time, $133.15 per credit hour part-time. Nonresident tuition: $7872 full-time, $262.40 per credit hour part-time. Mandatory fees: $120 full-time, $60 per term part-time. **Scholarships:** Available. **Calendar System:** Semester, Summer session available **Enrollment:** Full-time 1,280, Part-time 3,862 **Faculty:** Full-time 85, Part-time 259 **Student-Faculty Ratio:** 18:1 **Regional Accreditation:** North Central Association of Colleges and Schools **Credit Hours For Degree:** 60 credits, Associates **Professional Accreditation:** AAMAE, ACBSP, ARCST, ATMAE, JRCEMTP.

IVY TECH COMMUNITY COLLEGE–WABASH VALLEY
8000 S Education Dr.
Terre Haute, IN 47802
Tel: (812)299-1121; Free: 888-IVY-LINE
E-mail: mfisher@ivytech.edu
Web Site: www.ivytech.edu
Admissions: Michael Fisher

Type: Two-Year College **Sex:** Coed **Affiliation:** Ivy Tech Community College System. **Admission Plans:** Deferred Admission; Early Admission; Open Admission; Preferred Admission **Application Deadline:** Rolling **Application Fee:** $0.00 **H.S. Requirements:** High school diploma or equivalent not required. For allied health programs: High school diploma required; GED accepted **Costs Per Year:** Application fee: $0. State resident tuition: $3995 full-time, $133.15 per credit hour part-time. Nonresident tuition: $7872 full-time, $262.40 per credit hour part-time. Mandatory fees: $120 full-time. **Scholarships:** Available. **Calendar System:** Semester, Summer session available **Enrollment:** Full-time 1,441, Part-time 2,923 **Faculty:** Full-time 98, Part-time 189 **Student-Faculty Ratio:** 19:1 **Regional Accreditation:** North Central Association of Colleges and Schools **Credit Hours For Degree:** 60 credits, Associates **Professional Accreditation:** AAMAE, ACBSP, ARCST, ATMAE, JRCERT, NAACLS.

LINCOLN COLLEGE OF TECHNOLOGY
7225 Winton Dr.
Bldg. 128
Indianapolis, IN 46268
Tel: (317)632-5553
Web Site: www.lincolnedu.com
President/CEO: Todd Clark
Admissions: Cindy Ryan

Type: Two-Year College **Sex:** Coed **Affiliation:** Lincoln Technical Institute, Inc. **Application Deadline:** Rolling **H.S. Requirements:** High school diploma required; GED accepted **Scholarships:** Available. **Calendar System:** Miscellaneous, Summer session available **Credit Hours For Degree:** 59 credits, Associates **Professional Accreditation:** ACCSC.

MANCHESTER UNIVERSITY
604 E College Ave.
North Manchester, IN 46962-1225

Tel: (260)982-5000; Free: 800-852-3648
Fax: (260)982-5043
E-mail: arhohman@manchester.edu
Web Site: www.manchester.edu
President/CEO: Dr. Dave McFadden
Admissions: Adam Hohman
Financial Aid: Sherri Shockey

Type: Comprehensive **Sex:** Coed **Affiliation:** Church of the Brethren. **Scores:** 88% SAT V 400+; 90% SAT M 400+; 41.52% ACT 18-23; 38.6% ACT 24-29 **% Accepted:** 74 **Admission Plans:** Deferred Admission **Application Deadline:** Rolling **Application Fee:** $25.00 **H.S. Requirements:** High school diploma required; GED accepted **Costs Per Year:** Application fee: $25. One-time mandatory fee: $250. Comprehensive fee: $40,422 includes full-time tuition ($29,650), mandatory fees ($1152), and college room and board ($9620). College room only: $5700. Room and board charges vary according to board plan and housing facility. Part-time tuition: $700 per credit hour. Part-time mandatory fees: $30 per credit hour. Part-time tuition and fees vary according to course load. **Scholarships:** Available. **Calendar System:** 4-1-4, Summer session available **Enrollment:** Full-time 1,235, Graduate full-time 284, Graduate part-time 6, Part-time 11 **Faculty:** Full-time 81, Part-time 17 **Student-Faculty Ratio:** 14:1 **Exams:** ACT essay component used for placement; SAT I or ACT; SAT essay component used for placement; SAT Reasoning. **% Receiving Financial Aid:** 85 **% Residing in College-Owned, -Operated, or -Affiliated Housing:** 75 **Final Year or Final Semester Residency Requirement:** No **Regional Accreditation:** North Central Association of Colleges and Schools **Credit Hours For Degree:** 64 semester hours, Associates; 128 semester hours, Bachelors **Professional Accreditation:** CSWE, JRCAT, NCATE. **Intercollegiate Athletics:** Baseball M; Basketball M & W; Cheerleading W; Cross-Country Running M & W; Equestrian Sports W; Football M; Golf M & W; Soccer M & W; Softball W; Swimming and Diving M & W; Tennis M & W; Track and Field M & W; Volleyball W; Wrestling M

MARIAN UNIVERSITY
3200 Cold Spring Rd.
Indianapolis, IN 46222-1997
Tel: (317)955-6000
E-mail: admissions@marian.edu
Web Site: www.marian.edu
President/CEO: Daniel Elsener
Admissions: Luann Brames
Financial Aid: John E. Shelton

Type: Comprehensive **Sex:** Coed **Affiliation:** Roman Catholic. **Scores:** 98% SAT V 400+; 100% SAT M 400+; 49% ACT 18-23; 36% ACT 24-29 **% Accepted:** 55 **Admission Plans:** Deferred Admission **Application Deadline:** August 1 **Application Fee:** $0.00 **H.S. Requirements:** High school diploma required; GED accepted **Costs Per Year:** Application fee: $0. Comprehensive fee: $39,936 includes full-time tuition ($30,500) and college room and board ($9436). Room and board charges vary according to housing facility. Part-time tuition: $1350 per credit hour. **Scholarships:** Available. **Calendar System:** Semester, Summer session available **Enrollment:** Full-time 1,686, Graduate full-time 502, Graduate part-time 299, Part-time 413 **Faculty:** Full-time 148, Part-time 135 **Student-Faculty Ratio:** 12:1 **Exams:** ACT essay component used for admission; ACT essay component used for advising; ACT essay component used for placement; SAT I or ACT; SAT essay component used for admission; SAT essay component used for advising; SAT essay component used for placement; SAT Reasoning. **% Receiving Financial Aid:** 81 **% Residing in College-Owned, -Operated, or -Affiliated Housing:** 38 **Final Year or Final Semester Residency Requirement:** Yes **Regional Accreditation:** North Central Association of Colleges and Schools **Credit Hours For Degree:** 64 credit hours, Associates; 128 credit hours, Bachelors **ROTC:** Army **Professional Accreditation:** AACN, AOsA, NCATE. **Intercollegiate Athletics:** Baseball M; Basketball M & W; Bowling M & W; Cheerleading M & W; Cross-Country Running M & W; Football M; Golf M & W; Lacrosse W; Soccer M & W; Softball W; Tennis M & W; Track and Field M & W; Volleyball W

MARTIN UNIVERSITY
2171 Avondale Pl.
Indianapolis, IN 46218-3867
Tel: (317)543-3235
Fax: (317)543-3257
Web Site: www.martin.edu
President/CEO: Dr. Algeania Freeman

Admissions: Brenda Shaheed
Financial Aid: Berdia Marshall

Type: Comprehensive **Sex:** Coed **% Accepted:** 96 **Admission Plans:** Deferred Admission; Early Admission; Open Admission **Application Deadline:** Rolling **Application Fee:** $25.00 **H.S. Requirements:** High school diploma required; GED accepted **Scholarships:** Available. **Calendar System:** Semester, Summer session available **Enrollment:** Full-time 336, Part-time 738 **Faculty:** Full-time 26, Part-time 17 **Student-Faculty Ratio:** 21:1 **% Receiving Financial Aid:** 89 **Regional Accreditation:** North Central Association of Colleges and Schools **Credit Hours For Degree:** 134 credits, Bachelors

MEDTECH COLLEGE (FORT WAYNE)
7230 Engle Rd.
Fort Wayne, IN 46804
Tel: (260)436-3272
Web Site: www.medtech.edu
Type: Two-Year College **Sex:** Coed **Professional Accreditation:** ACICS.

MEDTECH COLLEGE (GREENWOOD)
1500 American Way
Greenwood, IN 46143
Tel: (317)534-0322
Web Site: www.medtech.edu
Type: Two-Year College **Sex:** Coed **Professional Accreditation:** ACICS.

MEDTECH COLLEGE (INDIANAPOLIS)
6612 E 75th St.
Ste. 300
Indianapolis, IN 46250-2865
Web Site: www.medtech.edu
Type: Two-Year College **Sex:** Coed **Professional Accreditation:** ACICS.

MID-AMERICA COLLEGE OF FUNERAL SERVICE
3111 Hamburg Pke.
Jeffersonville, IN 47130-9630
Tel: (812)288-8878; Free: 800-221-6158
Fax: (812)288-5942
E-mail: macfs@mindspring.com
Web Site: www.mid-america.edu
President/CEO: Lauren Budrow Budrow
Admissions: Richard Nelson

Type: Two-Year College **Sex:** Coed **Admission Plans:** Deferred Admission; Open Admission **Application Deadline:** Rolling **Application Fee:** $25.00 **H.S. Requirements:** High school diploma required; GED accepted **Scholarships:** Available. **Calendar System:** Quarter, Summer session not available **Enrollment:** Full-time 120 **Faculty:** Full-time 6, Part-time 1 **Student-Faculty Ratio:** 13:1 **Credit Hours For Degree:** 133 quarter hours, Associates **Professional Accreditation:** ABFSE. **Intercollegiate Athletics:** Softball M & W

OAKLAND CITY UNIVERSITY
138 N Lucretia St.
Oakland City, IN 47660-1099
Tel: (812)749-4781; Free: 800-737-5125
Fax: (812)749-1233
E-mail: mmcdaniel@oak.edu
Web Site: www.oak.edu
President/CEO: Dr. Ray Barber
Admissions: Mariah McDaniel
Financial Aid: Nicole Sharp

Type: Comprehensive **Sex:** Coed **Affiliation:** General Baptist. **Scores:** 82% SAT V 400+; 85% SAT M 400+; 44% ACT 18-23; 23% ACT 24-29 **% Accepted:** 55 **Admission Plans:** Deferred Admission; Early Admission **Application Fee:** $35.00 **H.S. Requirements:** High school diploma required; GED accepted **Costs Per Year:** Application fee: $35. Comprehensive fee: $32,580 includes full-time tuition ($23,400) and college room and board ($9180). College room only: $3200. Full-time tuition varies according to degree level. Room and board charges vary according to board plan and housing facility. Part-time tuition: $780 per credit hour. **Scholarships:** Available. **Calendar System:** Semester, Summer session available **Enrollment:** Full-time 431, Graduate full-time 5, Graduate part-time 210, Part-time 804 **Faculty:** Full-time 82, Part-time 15 **Student-Faculty Ratio:** 12:1 **Exams:** ACT essay component not used; SAT I or ACT; SAT essay component not used; SAT Reasoning. **% Receiving Financial Aid:** 15 **% Residing in College-Owned, -Operated, or -Affiliated Housing:** 50 **Regional Accreditation:** North Central Association of Colleges and Schools **Credit Hours For Degree:** 60 semester hours, Associates; 120 semester hours, Bachelors **Professional Accreditation:** ATS, NCATE. **Intercollegiate Athletics:** Baseball M; Basketball M & W; Cheerleading W; Cross-Country Running M & W; Golf M & W; Soccer M & W; Softball W; Tennis M & W; Volleyball W

PURDUE UNIVERSITY

West Lafayette, IN 47907
Tel: (765)494-4600
Fax: (765)494-0544
E-mail: admissions@purdue.edu
Web Site: www.purdue.edu
President/CEO: Pres. Mitchell E. Daniels, Jr.
Admissions: Pamela T. Horne
Financial Aid: Theodore E. Malone

Type: University **Sex:** Coed **Affiliation:** Purdue University System. **Scores:** 100% SAT V 400+; 100% SAT M 400+; 15.92% ACT 18-23; 47.45% ACT 24-29 **% Accepted:** 59 **Admission Plans:** Deferred Admission; Early Admission; Early Decision Plan **Application Deadline:** Rolling **Application Fee:** $60.00 **H.S. Requirements:** High school diploma required; GED accepted **Costs Per Year:** Application fee: $60. State resident tuition: $9208 full-time, $330 per credit hour part-time. Nonresident tuition: $28,010 full-time, $930 per credit hour part-time. Mandatory fees: $794 full-time, $18 per credit hour part-time, $18. Full-time tuition and fees vary according to course load and program. Part-time tuition and fees vary according to course load. College room and board: $10,030. Room and board charges vary according to board plan and housing facility. **Scholarships:** Available. **Calendar System:** Semester, Summer session available **Enrollment:** Full-time 28,131, Graduate full-time 6,348, Graduate part-time 3,564, Part-time 1,366 **Faculty:** Full-time 2,256, Part-time 337 **Student-Faculty Ratio:** 12:1 **Exams:** ACT essay component used for admission; SAT I or ACT; SAT essay component used for admission; SAT Reasoning. **% Receiving Financial Aid:** 43 **% Residing in College-Owned, -Operated, or -Affiliated Housing:** 39 **Final Year or Final Semester Residency Requirement:** No **Regional Accreditation:** North Central Association of Colleges and Schools **Credit Hours For Degree:** 60 credit hours, Associates; 120 credit hours, Bachelors **ROTC:** Air Force, Army, Navy **Professional Accreditation:** AABI, AACN, AACSB, AAFCS, AAMFT, ABET, ACA, ACCE, ACPE, AND, APA, ASHA, ASLA, ATMAE, AVMA, CIDA, JRCAT, NASAD, NAST, NCATE, SAF. **Intercollegiate Athletics:** Baseball M; Basketball M & W; Cross-Country Running M & W; Football M; Golf M & W; Soccer W; Softball W; Swimming and Diving M & W; Tennis M & W; Track and Field M & W; Volleyball W; Wrestling M

PURDUE UNIVERSITY NORTHWEST (HAMMOND)

2200 169th St.
Hammond, IN 46323-2094
Tel: (219)989-2400; Free: 800-447-8738
Fax: (219)989-2775
E-mail: giannini@purduecal.edu
Web Site: www.pnw.edu
President/CEO: Dr. Thomas L. Keon
Admissions: Susan K. Giannini
Financial Aid: Mary Ann Bishel

Type: Comprehensive **Sex:** Coed **Affiliation:** Purdue University System. **Scores:** 88% SAT V 400+; 85% SAT M 400+ **% Accepted:** 65 **Application Deadline:** August 1 **Application Fee:** $25.00 **H.S. Requirements:** High school diploma required; GED accepted **Scholarships:** Available. **Calendar System:** Semester, Summer session available **Enrollment:** Full-time 4,862, Graduate full-time 320, Graduate part-time 562, Part-time 3,557 **Faculty:** Full-time 270, Part-time 236 **Student-Faculty Ratio:** 19:1 **Exams:** ACT essay component used for advising; SAT I or ACT; SAT essay component used for advising; SAT Reasoning; SAT Subject. **% Receiving Financial Aid:** 64 **% Residing in College-Owned, -Operated, or -Affiliated Housing:** 8 **Final Year or Final Semester Residency Requirement:** Yes **Regional Accreditation:** North Central Association of Colleges and Schools **Credit Hours For Degree:** 61 credit hours, Associates; 120 credit hours, Bachelors **ROTC:** Army **Professional Accreditation:** AACN, AAMFT, ABET, ACEN, NCATE. **Intercollegiate Athletics:** Baseball M; Basketball M & W; Cross-Country Running M & W; Golf M; Soccer M & W; Softball W; Tennis M & W; Volleyball W

PURDUE UNIVERSITY NORTHWEST (WESTVILLE)

1401 S US Hwy. 421
Westville, IN 46391-9542
Tel: (219)785-5200
Fax: (219)785-5538
E-mail: jwhisler@pnc.edu
Web Site: www.pnw.edu
President/CEO: Dr. James B. Dworkin
Admissions: Janice Whisler
Financial Aid: Brad Remmenga

Type: Comprehensive **Sex:** Coed **Affiliation:** Purdue University System. **Scores:** 78% SAT V 400+; 87% SAT M 400+; 53.09% ACT 18-23; 22.84% ACT 24-29 **% Accepted:** 74 **Admission Plans:** Deferred Admission **Application Fee:** $0.00 **H.S. Requirements:** High school diploma required; GED accepted **Scholarships:** Available. **Calendar System:** Semester, Summer session available **Enrollment:** Full-time 2,566, Graduate part-time 35, Part-time 3,576 **Faculty:** Full-time 128, Part-time 161 **Student-Faculty Ratio:** 15:1 **Exams:** SAT I or ACT. **% Receiving Financial Aid:** 70 **Regional Accreditation:** North Central Association of Colleges and Schools **Credit Hours For Degree:** 60 credit hours, Associates; 120 credit hours, Bachelors **Professional Accreditation:** ABET, ACBSP, ACEN, NCATE. **Intercollegiate Athletics:** Cheerleading M & W

ROSE-HULMAN INSTITUTE OF TECHNOLOGY

5500 Wabash Ave.
Terre Haute, IN 47803-3999
Tel: (812)877-1511; Free: 800-248-7448
Fax: (812)877-8941
E-mail: admissions@rose-hulman.edu
Web Site: www.rose-hulman.edu
President/CEO: Dr. James Conwell
Admissions: Lisa Norton
Financial Aid: Melinda L. Middleton

Type: Comprehensive **Sex:** Coed **Scores:** 100% SAT V 400+; 100% SAT M 400+; 2.2% ACT 18-23; 42.8% ACT 24-29 **% Accepted:** 58 **Admission Plans:** Deferred Admission; Early Decision Plan **Application Deadline:** March 1 **Application Fee:** $40.00 **H.S. Requirements:** High school diploma required; GED not accepted **Costs Per Year:** Application fee: $40. One-time mandatory fee: $2400. Comprehensive fee: $55,401 includes full-time tuition ($41,865), mandatory fees ($876), and college room and board ($12,660). College room only: $7761. Full-time tuition and fees vary according to course load. Room and board charges vary according to board plan. Part-time tuition: $1222 per credit hour. Part-time tuition varies according to course load. **Scholarships:** Available. **Calendar System:** Quarter, Summer session available **Enrollment:** Full-time 2,241, Graduate full-time 52, Graduate part-time 34, Part-time 29 **Faculty:** Full-time 181, Part-time 12 **Student-Faculty Ratio:** 13:1 **Exams:** ACT essay component not used; SAT I or ACT; SAT essay component not used. **% Receiving Financial Aid:** 62 **% Residing in College-Owned, -Operated, or -Affiliated Housing:** 57 **Final Year or Final Semester Residency Requirement:** Yes **Regional Accreditation:** North Central Association of Colleges and Schools **Credit Hours For Degree:** 188 quarter hours, Bachelors **ROTC:** Air Force, Army **Professional Accreditation:** ABET. **Intercollegiate Athletics:** Baseball M; Basketball M & W; Cross-Country Running M & W; Football M; Golf M & W; Riflery M & W; Soccer M & W; Softball W; Swimming and Diving M & W; Tennis M & W; Track and Field M & W; Volleyball W

SAINT JOSEPH'S COLLEGE

1498 S College Ave.
Rensselaer, IN 47978
Tel: (219)866-6000; Free: 800-447-8781
Fax: (219)866-6122
E-mail: admissions@saintjoe.edu
Web Site: www.saintjoe.edu
President/CEO: Dr. Robert Pastoor
Admissions: Michael Ramian
Financial Aid: Debra Sizemore

Type: Comprehensive **Sex:** Coed **Affiliation:** Roman Catholic. **Scores:** 97% SAT V 400+; 92% SAT M 400+; 63% ACT 18-23; 21% ACT 24-29 **% Accepted:** 66 **Admission Plans:** Deferred Admission **Application Deadline:** Rolling **Application Fee:** $25.00 **H.S. Requirements:** High school diploma required; GED accepted **Costs Per Year:** Application fee: $25. Comprehensive fee: $36,720 includes full-time tuition ($27,630), mandatory fees ($190), and college room and board ($8900). College room only: $4300. Full-time tuition and fees vary according to reciprocity agreements and student level. Room and board charges vary according to board plan and housing facility. Part-time tuition: $925 per credit. Part-time tuition varies according to course load and reciprocity agreements. Tuition guaranteed not to increase for student's term of enrollment. **Scholarships:** Available. **Calendar System:** Semester, Summer session available **Enrollment:** Full-time 1,012, Graduate full-time 8, Graduate part-time 16, Part-time 130 **Faculty:** Full-time 79, Part-time 46 **Student-Faculty Ratio:** 11:1 **Exams:** ACT essay component not used; SAT I or ACT; SAT essay component not used; SAT Reasoning. **% Receiving Financial Aid:** 87 **% Residing in College-Owned, -Operated, or -Affiliated Housing:** 68 **Final Year or Final Semester Residency Requirement:** Yes **Regional Accreditation:** North Central Association of Colleges and Schools **Credit Hours For Degree:** 60 credits, Associates; 120 credits, Bachelors **Professional Accreditation:** NCATE. **Intercollegiate Athletics:** Baseball M; Basketball M & W; Cheerleading M & W; Cross-Country Running M & W; Football M; Golf M & W; Soccer M & W; Softball W; Tennis M & W; Track and Field M & W; Volleyball W

SAINT MARY-OF-THE-WOODS COLLEGE

Saint Mary of the Woods, IN 47876
Tel: (812)535-5151; Free: 800-926-SMWC
Fax: (812)535-5215
E-mail: rmcdonald@smwc.edu
Web Site: www.smwc.edu
President/CEO: Dr. Dottie King, PhD
Admissions: Ryan McDonald
Financial Aid: Darla Hopper

Type: Comprehensive **Sex:** Coed **Affiliation:** Roman Catholic. **% Accepted:** 100 **Admission Plans:** Deferred Admission; Early Admission; Open Admission **Application Fee:** $0.00 **H.S. Requirements:** High school diploma required; GED accepted **Costs Per Year:** Application fee: $0. Comprehensive fee: $39,432 includes full-time tuition ($28,932) and college room and board ($10,500). College room only: $4126. Full-time tuition varies according to student level. Room and board charges vary according to housing facility. Part-time tuition: $496 per credit hour. Part-time tuition varies according to course load and student level. Tuition guaranteed not to increase for student's term of enrollment. **Scholarships:** Available. **Calendar System:** Semester, Summer session available **Enrollment:** Full-time 407, Graduate full-time 172, Graduate part-time 12, Part-time 339 **Faculty:** Full-time 47, Part-time 120 **Student-Faculty Ratio:** 8:1 **Exams:** ACT essay component used for admission; SAT I or ACT; SAT essay component used for admission. **% Receiving Financial Aid:** 95 **Final Year or Final Semester Residency Requirement:** Yes **Regional Accreditation:** North Central Association of Colleges and Schools **Credit Hours For Degree:** 62 credit hours, Associates; 125 credit hours, Bachelors **Professional Accreditation:** NASM, NCATE. **Intercollegiate Athletics:** Basketball W; Cross-Country Running W; Equestrian Sports W; Golf W; Soccer W; Softball W

SAINT MARY'S COLLEGE

Notre Dame, IN 46556
Tel: (574)284-4000; Free: 800-551-7621
Fax: (574)284-4713
E-mail: sdvorak@saintmarys.edu
Web Site: www.saintmarys.edu
President/CEO: Dr. Carol Ann Mooney
Admissions: Sarah Dvorak
Financial Aid: Kathleen M. Brown

Type: Comprehensive **Sex:** Women **Affiliation:** Roman Catholic. **Scores:** 99% SAT V 400+; 95% SAT M 400+; 35.9% ACT 18-23; 49.4% ACT 24-29 **% Accepted:** 80 **Admission Plans:** Deferred Admission; Early Action; Early Admission **Application Deadline:** February 15 **Application Fee:** $0.00 **H.S. Requirements:** High school diploma required; GED accepted **Costs Per Year:** Application fee: $0. Comprehensive fee: $48,720 includes full-time tuition ($36,620), mandatory fees ($780), and college room and board ($11,320). College room only: $7000. Room and board charges vary according to board plan and housing facility. Part-time tuition: $1440 per credit hour. **Scholarships:** Available. **Calendar System:** Semester, Summer session available **Enrollment:** Full-time 1,558, Graduate full-time 29, Graduate part-time 9, Part-time 61 **Faculty:** Full-time 133, Part-time 73 **Student-Faculty Ratio:** 10:1 **Exams:** SAT I or ACT; SAT Reasoning. **% Receiving Financial Aid:** 66 **% Residing in College-Owned, -Operated, or -Affiliated Housing:** 86 **Final Year or Final Semester Residency Requirement:** No

Regional Accreditation: North Central Association of Colleges and Schools **Credit Hours For Degree:** 128 semester hours, Bachelors **ROTC:** Air Force, Army, Navy **Professional Accreditation:** ACEN, CSWE, NASAD, NASM, NCATE. **Intercollegiate Athletics:** Basketball W; Cross-Country Running W; Golf W; Lacrosse W; Soccer W; Softball W; Tennis W; Volleyball W

TAYLOR UNIVERSITY

236 W Reade Ave.
Upland, IN 46989-1001
Tel: (765)998-2751; Free: 800-882-3456
Fax: (765)998-4925
E-mail: admissions@taylor.edu
Web Site: www.taylor.edu
President/CEO: Dr. Eugene Habecker
Admissions: Jonny Rupp
Financial Aid: Timothy A. Nace

Type: Comprehensive **Sex:** Coed **Affiliation:** interdenominational. **Scores:** 96% SAT V 400+; 95% SAT M 400+; 21% ACT 18-23; 45% ACT 24-29 **% Accepted:** 81 **Admission Plans:** Deferred Admission; Preferred Admission **Application Deadline:** Rolling **Application Fee:** $25.00 **H.S. Requirements:** High school diploma required; GED accepted **Costs Per Year:** Application fee: $25. Comprehensive fee: $38,767 includes full-time tuition ($30,030), mandatory fees ($240), and college room and board ($8497). College room only: $4462. Full-time tuition and fees vary according to course load. Room and board charges vary according to board plan and housing facility. Part-time tuition: $1058 per credit hour. Part-time tuition and fees vary according to course load. **Scholarships:** Available. **Calendar System:** 4-1-4, Summer session available **Enrollment:** Full-time 1,854, Graduate full-time 41, Part-time 273 **Faculty:** Full-time 129, Part-time 86 **Student-Faculty Ratio:** 13:1 **Exams:** SAT I or ACT; SAT Reasoning. **% Receiving Financial Aid:** 62 **% Residing in College-Owned, -Operated, or -Affiliated Housing:** 88 **Final Year or Final Semester Residency Requirement:** No **Regional Accreditation:** North Central Association of Colleges and Schools **Credit Hours For Degree:** 64 credit hours, Associates; 128 credit hours, Bachelors **Professional Accreditation:** ABET, CSWE, NASM, NCATE. **Intercollegiate Athletics:** Baseball M; Basketball M & W; Cross-Country Running M & W; Football M; Golf M & W; Soccer M & W; Softball W; Tennis M & W; Track and Field M & W; Volleyball W

TRINE UNIVERSITY

1 University Ave.
Angola, IN 46703-1764
Tel: (260)665-4100; Free: 800-347-4878
Fax: (260)665-4292
E-mail: admit@trine.edu
Web Site: www.trine.edu
President/CEO: Dr. Earl D. Brooks, II
Admissions: Travis Foster
Financial Aid: Kim Bennett

Type: Comprehensive **Sex:** Coed **Scores:** 96% SAT V 400+; 99% SAT M 400+; 39% ACT 18-23; 45.17% ACT 24-29 **% Accepted:** 78 **Admission Plans:** Deferred Admission **Application Deadline:** August 1 **Application Fee:** $0.00 **H.S. Requirements:** High school diploma required; GED accepted **Costs Per Year:** Application fee: $0. Tuition: $30,500 full-time, $950 per credit hour part-time. Mandatory fees: $460 full-time. Full-time tuition and fees vary according to degree level, location, and program. Part-time tuition varies according to degree level, location, and program. **Scholarships:** Available. **Calendar System:** Semester, Summer session available **Enrollment:** Full-time 1,719, Graduate full-time 258, Graduate part-time 7, Part-time 1,436 **Faculty:** Full-time 89, Part-time 123 **Student-Faculty Ratio:** 13:1 **Exams:** ACT essay component not used; SAT I or ACT; SAT essay component not used; SAT Reasoning. **% Receiving Financial Aid:** 80 **% Residing in College-Owned, -Operated, or -Affiliated Housing:** 69 **Final Year or Final Semester Residency Requirement:** Yes **Regional Accreditation:** North Central Association of Colleges and Schools **Credit Hours For Degree:** 61 semester hours, Associates; 120 semester hours, Bachelors **ROTC:** Air Force **Professional Accreditation:** ABET, ACBSP, NCATE. **Intercollegiate Athletics:** Baseball M; Basketball M & W; Cross-Country Running M & W; Field Hockey W; Football M; Golf M & W; Lacrosse M & W; Soccer M & W; Softball W; Tennis M & W; Track and Field M & W; Volleyball W; Wrestling M

UNIVERSITY OF EVANSVILLE

1800 Lincoln Ave.
Evansville, IN 47722

Tel: (812)488-2000; Free: 800-423-8633

Fax: (812)474-4076

E-mail: admission@evansville.edu

Web Site: www.evansville.edu

President/CEO: Dr. Thomas A. Kazee

Admissions: Scott Henne

Financial Aid: Cathleen Wright

Type: Comprehensive **Sex:** Coed **Affiliation:** United Methodist Church. **Scores:** 97% SAT V 400+; 98% SAT M 400+; 27% ACT 18-23; 49% ACT 24-29 **% Accepted:** 70 **Admission Plans:** Deferred Admission; Early Admission; Early Decision Plan **Application Deadline:** August 15 **Application Fee:** $0.00 **H.S. Requirements:** High school diploma required; GED accepted **Costs Per Year:** Application fee: $0. Comprehensive fee: $44,186 includes full-time tuition ($31,900), mandatory fees ($1046), and college room and board ($11,240). College room only: $5920. Room and board charges vary according to board plan and housing facility. Part-time tuition: $890 per credit hour. Part-time mandatory fees: $135 per term. Part-time tuition and fees vary according to course load. **Scholarships:** Available. **Calendar System:** Semester, Summer session available **Enrollment:** Full-time 2,082, Graduate full-time 161, Graduate part-time 3, Part-time 152 **Faculty:** Full-time 169, Part-time 65 **Student-Faculty Ratio:** 13:1 **Exams:** ACT essay component used as validity check; ACT essay component used for advising; ACT essay component used for placement; SAT I or ACT; SAT essay component used as validity check; SAT essay component used for advising; SAT essay component used for placement. **% Receiving Financial Aid:** 69 **% Residing in College-Owned, -Operated, or -Affiliated Housing:** 63 **Final Year or Final Semester Residency Requirement:** Yes **Regional Accreditation:** North Central Association of Colleges and Schools **Credit Hours For Degree:** 71 semester hours, Associates; 120 semester hours, Bachelors **ROTC:** Army **Professional Accreditation:** AACSB, ABET, ACEN, APTA, NASM, NCATE. **Intercollegiate Athletics:** Baseball M; Basketball M & W; Cross-Country Running M & W; Golf M & W; Soccer M & W; Softball W; Swimming and Diving M & W; Tennis W; Volleyball W

UNIVERSITY OF INDIANAPOLIS

1400 E Hanna Ave.

Indianapolis, IN 46227-3697

Tel: (317)788-3368; Free: 800-232-8634

Fax: (317)788-3300

E-mail: admissions@uindy.edu

Web Site: www.uindy.edu

President/CEO: Dr. Robert Manuel

Admissions: Ronald Wilks

Financial Aid: Linda B. Handy

Type: Comprehensive **Sex:** Coed **Affiliation:** United Methodist Church. **Scores:** 92% SAT V 400+; 93% SAT M 400+; 51% ACT 18-23; 32% ACT 24-29 **% Accepted:** 66 **Admission Plans:** Deferred Admission **Application Deadline:** Rolling **Application Fee:** $25.00 **H.S. Requirements:** High school diploma required; GED accepted **Costs Per Year:** Application fee: $25. Comprehensive fee: $35,494 includes full-time tuition ($25,910), mandatory fees ($260), and college room and board ($9324). College room only: $5340. Full-time tuition and fees vary according to class time. Room and board charges vary according to board plan and housing facility. Part-time tuition: $1080 per credit hour. Part-time tuition varies according to class time and course load. **Scholarships:** Available. **Calendar System:** Semester, Summer session available **Enrollment:** Full-time 3,364, Graduate full-time 420, Graduate part-time 853, Part-time 805 **Faculty:** Full-time 243, Part-time 299 **Student-Faculty Ratio:** 11:1 **Exams:** ACT essay component used for admission; ACT essay component used for placement; SAT I or ACT; SAT essay component used for admission; SAT essay component used for placement; SAT Reasoning. **% Receiving Financial Aid:** 71 **% Residing in College-Owned, -Operated, or -Affiliated Housing:** 36 **Final Year or Final Semester Residency Requirement:** No **Regional Accreditation:** North Central Association of Colleges and Schools **Credit Hours For Degree:** 62 credit hours, Associates; 124 credit hours, Bachelors **ROTC:** Army **Professional Accreditation:** AACN, ACBSP, ACEN, ACNM, AOTA, APA, APTA, CSWE, JRCAT, NASAD, NASM, NCATE. **Intercollegiate Athletics:** Baseball M; Basketball M & W; Cross-Country Running M & W; Football M; Golf M & W; Lacrosse M & W; Soccer M & W; Softball W; Swimming and Diving M & W; Tennis M & W; Track and Field M & W; Volleyball W; Wrestling M

UNIVERSITY OF NOTRE DAME

Notre Dame, IN 46556

Tel: (574)631-5000

Fax: (574)631-8865

E-mail: admissions@nd.edu

Web Site: www.nd.edu

President/CEO: Rev. John I. Jenkins, CSC

Financial Aid: Mary Nucciarone

Type: University **Sex:** Coed **Affiliation:** Roman Catholic. **Scores:** 100% SAT V 400+; 100% SAT M 400+; 1% ACT 18-23; 8% ACT 24-29 **% Accepted:** 21 **Admission Plans:** Deferred Admission; Early Decision Plan **Application Deadline:** January 1 **Application Fee:** $75.00 **H.S. Requirements:** High school diploma required; GED not accepted **Costs Per Year:** Application fee: $75. Comprehensive fee: $61,775 includes full-time tuition ($47,422), mandatory fees ($507), and college room and board ($13,846). Part-time tuition: $1976 per credit hour. **Scholarships:** Available. **Calendar System:** Semester, Summer session available **Enrollment:** Full-time 8,430, Graduate full-time 3,562, Graduate part-time 169, Part-time 18 **Faculty:** Full-time 1,119, Part-time 190 **Student-Faculty Ratio:** 10:1 **Exams:** ACT essay component used for advising; SAT I or ACT; SAT II; SAT essay component used for advising; SAT Reasoning; SAT Subject. **% Receiving Financial Aid:** 44 **% Residing in College-Owned, -Operated, or -Affiliated Housing:** 80 **Final Year or Final Semester Residency Requirement:** Yes **Regional Accreditation:** North Central Association of Colleges and Schools **Credit Hours For Degree:** 120 credit hours, Bachelors **ROTC:** Air Force, Army, Navy **Professional Accreditation:** AACSB, AALS, ABA, ABET, ACIPE, APA, ATS, NAAB, NASAD. **Intercollegiate Athletics:** Baseball M; Basketball M & W; Crew W; Cross-Country Running M & W; Fencing M & W; Football M; Golf M & W; Ice Hockey M; Lacrosse M & W; Soccer M & W; Softball W; Swimming and Diving M & W; Tennis M & W; Track and Field M & W; Volleyball W

UNIVERSITY OF SAINT FRANCIS

2701 Spring St.

Fort Wayne, IN 46808-3994

Tel: (260)399-7700; Free: 800-729-4732

E-mail: admis@sf.edu

Web Site: www.sf.edu

President/CEO: Señor M. Elise Kriss

Admissions: Maria Gerber

Type: Comprehensive **Sex:** Coed **Affiliation:** Roman Catholic. **Scores:** 87% SAT V 400+; 90% SAT M 400+; 52% ACT 18-23; 30% ACT 24-29 **% Accepted:** 95 **Admission Plans:** Deferred Admission **Application Deadline:** Rolling **H.S. Requirements:** High school diploma required; GED accepted **Costs Per Year:** One-time mandatory fee: $100. Comprehensive fee: $37,400 includes full-time tuition ($27,300), mandatory fees ($1010), and college room and board ($9090). Full-time tuition and fees vary according to course load. Room and board charges vary according to board plan and housing facility. Part-time tuition: $865 per credit hour. Part-time mandatory fees: $25 per credit hour, $140 per term. Part-time tuition and fees vary according to course load. **Scholarships:** Available. **Calendar System:** Semester, Summer session available **Enrollment:** Full-time 1,502, Graduate full-time 215, Graduate part-time 221, Part-time 302 **Faculty:** Full-time 125, Part-time 145 **Student-Faculty Ratio:** 11:1 **Exams:** SAT I and SAT II or ACT; SAT I or ACT; SAT Reasoning; SAT Subject. **% Receiving Financial Aid:** 87 **% Residing in College-Owned, -Operated, or -Affiliated Housing:** 22 **Final Year or Final Semester Residency Requirement:** No **Regional Accreditation:** North Central Association of Colleges and Schools **Credit Hours For Degree:** minimum 60 credit hours, depending on program, Associates; minimum of 120 credit hours, Bachelors **Professional Accreditation:** AACN, ACBSP, ACEN, AOTA, APTA, ARCST, CSWE, JRCERT, NASAD, NCATE. **Intercollegiate Athletics:** Baseball M; Basketball M & W; Cheerleading W; Cross-Country Running M & W; Football M; Golf M & W; Soccer M & W; Softball W; Tennis M & W; Track and Field M & W; Volleyball W

UNIVERSITY OF SOUTHERN INDIANA

8600 University Blvd.

Evansville, IN 47712-3590

Tel: (812)464-8600; Free: 800-467-1965

Fax: (812)465-7154

E-mail: enroll@usi.edu

Web Site: www.usi.edu

President/CEO: Dr. Linda L.M. Bennett

Admissions: Mark Rusk
Financial Aid: Mary Harper
Type: Comprehensive **Sex:** Coed **Affiliation:** Indiana Commission for Higher Education. **Scores:** 94% SAT V 400+; 93% SAT M 400+; 56.86% ACT 18-23; 24.68% ACT 24-29 **% Accepted:** 69 **Application Deadline:** August 15 **Application Fee:** $40.00 **H.S. Requirements:** High school diploma required; GED accepted **Costs Per Year:** Application fee: $40. One-time mandatory fee: $150. State resident tuition: $7,045 full-time, $234.82 per credit hour part-time. Nonresident tuition: $17,287 full-time, $576.22 per credit hour part-time. Mandatory fees: $340 full-time, $22.75 per term part-time. Full-time tuition and fees vary according to course load, program, and reciprocity agreements. Part-time tuition and fees vary according to course load, program, and reciprocity agreements. College room and board: $8532. College room only: $4492. Room and board charges vary according to board plan and housing facility. **Scholarships:** Available. **Calendar System:** Semester, Summer session available **Enrollment:** Full-time 6,869, Graduate full-time 156, Graduate part-time 743, Part-time 1,261 **Faculty:** Full-time 347, Part-time 330 **Student-Faculty Ratio:** 17:1 **Exams:** ACT essay component used for advising; SAT I or ACT; SAT essay component used for advising. **% Receiving Financial Aid:** 61 **% Residing in College-Owned, -Operated, or -Affiliated Housing:** 33 **Final Year or Final Semester Residency Requirement:** No **Regional Accreditation:** North Central Association of Colleges and Schools **Credit Hours For Degree:** 60 semester hours, Associates; 120 semester hours, Bachelors **ROTC:** Army **Professional Accreditation:** AACN, AACSB, ABET, ADA, AOTA, CSWE, CoARC, JRCERT, NCATE. **Intercollegiate Athletics:** Baseball M; Basketball M & W; Cross-Country Running M & W; Golf M & W; Rugby M & W; Soccer M & W; Softball W; Tennis M & W; Track and Field M & W; Ultimate Frisbee M & W; Volleyball W

VALPARAISO UNIVERSITY

1700 Chapel Dr.
Valparaiso, IN 46383
Tel: (219)464-5000; Free: 888-GO-VALPO
Fax: (219)464-6898
E-mail: undergrad.admission@valpo.edu
Web Site: www.valpo.edu
President/CEO: Dr. Mark Heckler
Admissions: Bart Harvey
Financial Aid: Karen Klimczyk
Type: University **Sex:** Coed **Affiliation:** Lutheran Church. **Scores:** 98% SAT V 400+; 99% SAT M 400+; 24.8% ACT 18-23; 52.9% ACT 24-29 **% Accepted:** 82 **Admission Plans:** Deferred Admission **Application Deadline:** Rolling **H.S. Requirements:** High school diploma required; GED accepted **Costs Per Year:** Comprehensive fee: $46,680 includes full-time tuition ($35,030), mandatory fees ($1130), and college room and board ($10,520). College room only: $6400. Full-time tuition and fees vary according to course load and program. Room and board charges vary according to housing facility and student level. Part-time tuition: $1565 per credit hour. Part-time mandatory fees: $102 per term. Part-time tuition and fees vary according to course load and program. **Scholarships:** Available. **Calendar System:** Semester, Summer session available **Enrollment:** Full-time 3,098, Graduate full-time 954, Graduate part-time 407, Part-time 81 **Faculty:** Full-time 312, Part-time 102 **Student-Faculty Ratio:** 12:1 **Exams:** SAT I or ACT. **% Receiving Financial Aid:** 74 **% Residing in College-Owned, -Operated, or -Affiliated Housing:** 66 **Final Year or Final Semester Residency Requirement:** Yes **Regional Accreditation:** North Central Association of Colleges and Schools **Credit Hours For Degree:** 60 credits, Associates; 124 credits, Bachelors **ROTC:** Air Force, Army **Professional Accreditation:** AACN, AACSB, AALS, ABA, ABET, ACA, CSWE, NASM, NCATE. **Intercollegiate Athletics:** Baseball M; Basketball M & W; Bowling W; Cross-Country Running M & W; Football M; Golf M & W; Soccer M & W; Softball W; Swimming and Diving M & W; Tennis M & W; Track and Field M & W; Volleyball W

VET TECH INSTITUTE AT INTERNATIONAL BUSINESS COLLEGE (FORT WAYNE)

5699 Coventry Ln.
Fort Wayne, IN 46804
Tel: (260)459-4500; Free: 800-589-6363
Web Site: ftwayne.vettechinstitute.edu
Type: Two-Year College **Sex:** Coed **% Accepted:** 54 **Calendar System:** Semester **Professional Accreditation:** AVMA.

VET TECH INSTITUTE AT INTERNATIONAL BUSINESS COLLEGE (INDIANAPOLIS)

7205 Shadeland Station
Indianapolis, IN 46256
Tel: (317)813-2300; Free: 800-589-6500
Fax: (317)841-6419
Web Site: indianapolis.vettechinstitute.edu
Type: Two-Year College **Sex:** Coed **% Accepted:** 51 **H.S. Requirements:** High school diploma required; GED accepted **Calendar System:** Semester **Professional Accreditation:** AVMA.

VINCENNES UNIVERSITY

1002 N First St.
Vincennes, IN 47591-5202
Tel: (812)888-8888; Free: 800-742-9198
Fax: (812)888-5868
Web Site: www.vinu.edu
President/CEO: Dr. Charles R. Johnson
Admissions: Heidi M. Whitehead
Type: Two-Year College **Sex:** Coed **Admission Plans:** Deferred Admission; Early Admission; Open Admission **Application Deadline:** Rolling **Application Fee:** $20.00 **H.S. Requirements:** High school diploma required; GED accepted **Costs Per Year:** Application fee: $20. State resident tuition: $5374 full-time, $2294 per year part-time. Nonresident tuition: $12,710 full-time, $5227 per year part-time. Full-time tuition varies according to course level, course load, location, program, reciprocity agreements, and student level. Part-time tuition varies according to course level, course load, location, program, reciprocity agreements, and student level. College room and board: $8732. Room and board charges vary according to board plan, gender, and housing facility. **Scholarships:** Available. **Calendar System:** Semester, Summer session available **Enrollment:** Full-time 5,773, Part-time 12,938 **% Residing in College-Owned, -Operated, or -Affiliated Housing:** 45 **Final Year or Final Semester Residency Requirement:** No **Regional Accreditation:** North Central Association of Colleges and Schools **Credit Hours For Degree:** 60 hours, Associates; 120 hours, Bachelors **ROTC:** Air Force, Army **Professional Accreditation:** ABFSE, ACBSP, ACEN, AHIMA, APTA, ARCST, CoARC, NASAD, NAST. **Intercollegiate Athletics:** Baseball M; Basketball M & W; Bowling M; Cross-Country Running M & W; Golf M; Track and Field M & W; Volleyball W

WABASH COLLEGE

PO Box 352
Crawfordsville, IN 47933-0352
Tel: (765)361-6100; Free: 800-345-5385
Fax: (765)361-6437
E-mail: admissions@wabash.edu
Web Site: www.wabash.edu
President/CEO: Dr. Gregory D. Hess
Admissions: Charles Timmons
Financial Aid: Heidi Carl
Type: Four-Year College **Sex:** Men **Scores:** 99% SAT V 400+; 100% SAT M 400+; 33.8% ACT 18-23; 48.1% ACT 24-29 **% Accepted:** 61 **Admission Plans:** Deferred Admission; Early Action; Early Admission; Early Decision Plan **Application Deadline:** Rolling **Application Fee:** $40.00 **H.S. Requirements:** High school diploma required; GED accepted **Costs Per Year:** Application fee: $40. Comprehensive fee: $50,650 includes full-time tuition ($40,400), mandatory fees ($650), and college room and board ($9600). College room only: $5000. Room and board charges vary according to board plan and housing facility. **Scholarships:** Available. **Calendar System:** Semester, Summer session not available **Enrollment:** Full-time 867, Part-time 1 **Faculty:** Full-time 80, Part-time 25 **Student-Faculty Ratio:** 10:1 **Exams:** ACT essay component used for admission; ACT essay component used for advising; ACT essay component used for placement; SAT I or ACT; SAT essay component used for admission; SAT essay component used for advising; SAT essay component used for placement. **% Receiving Financial Aid:** 74 **% Residing in College-Owned, -Operated, or -Affiliated Housing:** 91 **Final Year or Final Semester Residency Requirement:** No **Regional Accreditation:** North Central Association of Colleges and Schools **Credit Hours For Degree:** 34 credits, Bachelors **Professional Accreditation:** NCATE. **Intercollegiate Athletics:** Baseball M; Basketball M; Cross-Country Running M; Football M; Golf M; Lacrosse M; Rugby M; Soccer M; Swimming and Diving M; Tennis M; Track and Field M; Ultimate Frisbee M; Wrestling M

ALLEN COLLEGE
1825 Logan Ave.
Waterloo, IA 50703
Tel: (319)226-2000
Fax: (319)226-2020
E-mail: admissions@allencollege.edu
Web Site: www.allencollege.edu
President/CEO: Dr. Jerry Durham
Admissions: Adriane McKernan
Financial Aid: Kathie S. Aswegan
Type: Comprehensive **Sex:** Coed **% Accepted:** 100 **Application Deadline:** February 1 **Application Fee:** $50.00 **H.S. Requirements:** High school diploma required; GED accepted **Costs Per Year:** Application fee: $50. Comprehensive fee: $25,957 includes full-time tuition ($16,464), mandatory fees ($2212), and college room and board ($7281). College room only: $3641. Full-time tuition and fees vary according to course load, degree level, and program. Part-time tuition: $588 per credit hour. Part-time mandatory fees: $79 per credit hour. Part-time tuition and fees vary according to course load, degree level, and program. **Scholarships:** Available. **Calendar System:** Semester, Summer session not available **Enrollment:** Full-time 251, Graduate full-time 63, Graduate part-time 178, Part-time 119 **Student-Faculty Ratio:** 17:1 **Exams:** ACT essay component not used; Other; SAT I or ACT; SAT essay component not used. **% Receiving Financial Aid:** 89 % **Residing in College-Owned, -Operated, or -Affiliated Housing:** 3 **Final Year or Final Semester Residency Requirement:** No **Regional Accreditation:** North Central Association of Colleges and Schools **Credit Hours For Degree:** 73 credit hours, Associates; 124 credit hours, Bachelors **ROTC:** Army **Professional Accreditation:** AACN, ACEN, JRCERT.

BRIAR CLIFF UNIVERSITY
3303 Rebecca St.
Sioux City, IA 51104-0100
Tel: (712)279-5321; Free: 800-662-3303
Fax: (712)279-5410
E-mail: admissions@briarcliff.edu
Web Site: www.briarcliff.edu
President/CEO: Beverly A. Wharton
Admissions: Brian Eben
Financial Aid: Brian K. Eben
Type: Comprehensive **Sex:** Coed **Affiliation:** Roman Catholic. **Scores:** 92% SAT V 400+; 92% SAT M 400+; 66% ACT 18-23; 20% ACT 24-29 **% Accepted:** 53 **Admission Plans:** Deferred Admission; Early Admission **Application Fee:** $20.00 **H.S. Requirements:** High school diploma required; GED accepted **Costs Per Year:** Application fee: $20. Comprehensive fee: $37,570 includes full-time tuition ($27,684), mandatory fees ($1104), and college room and board ($8782). College room only: $4158. Full-time tuition and fees vary according to class time, course load, degree level, and program. Room and board charges vary according to board plan and housing facility. Part-time tuition: $945 per credit hour. Part-time tuition varies according to class time, course load, degree level, and program. **Scholarships:** Available. **Calendar System:** Miscellaneous, Summer session available **Enrollment:** Full-time 792, Graduate full-time 54, Graduate part-time 73, Part-time 230 **Faculty:** Full-time 61, Part-time 33 **Student-Faculty Ratio:** 14:1 **Exams:** ACT essay component not used; SAT I or ACT; SAT essay component not used; SAT Reasoning. **% Receiving Financial Aid:** 84 % **Residing in College-Owned, -Operated, or -Affiliated Housing:** 47

Final Year or Final Semester Residency Requirement: Yes **Regional Accreditation:** North Central Association of Colleges and Schools **Credit Hours For Degree:** 60 credit hours, Associates; 124 credit hours, Bachelors **Professional Accreditation:** AACN, ACEN, CSWE. **Intercollegiate Athletics:** Baseball M; Basketball M & W; Cheerleading W; Cross-Country Running M & W; Football M; Golf M & W; Soccer M & W; Softball W; Tennis M & W; Track and Field M & W; Volleyball W; Wrestling M

BROWN MACKIE COLLEGE–QUAD CITIES
2119 E Kimberly Rd.
Bettendorf, IA 52722
Tel: (563)344-1500; Free: 888-420-1652
Web Site: www.brownmackie.edu/quad-cities
President/CEO: Jennifer Opp-Jackson
Type: Two-Year College **Sex:** Coed **Affiliation:** Education Management Corporation. **Professional Accreditation:** ACICS.

BUENA VISTA UNIVERSITY
610 W Fourth St.
Storm Lake, IA 50588
Tel: (712)749-2351; Free: 800-383-9600
Fax: (712)749-2037
E-mail: admissions@bvu.edu
Web Site: www.bvu.edu
President/CEO: Dr. Frederick V. Moore
Admissions: Michael Fox
Financial Aid: Leanne Valentine
Type: Comprehensive **Sex:** Coed **Affiliation:** Presbyterian Church (U.S.A.). **Scores:** 59% ACT 18-23; 26% ACT 24-29 **% Accepted:** 68 **Admission Plans:** Deferred Admission **H.S. Requirements:** High school diploma required; GED accepted **Costs Per Year:** Comprehensive fee: $40,364 includes full-time tuition ($31,318) and college room and board ($9046). Full-time tuition varies according to location. Room and board charges vary according to board plan. Part-time tuition: $1053 per credit hour. Part-time tuition varies according to location. **Scholarships:** Available. **Calendar System:** 4-1-4, Summer session available **Enrollment:** Full-time 872, Graduate part-time 109, Part-time 9 **Faculty:** Full-time 76, Part-time 30 **Student-Faculty Ratio:** 10:1 **Exams:** ACT; SAT I; SAT I and SAT II or ACT; SAT I or ACT; SAT II. **% Receiving Financial Aid:** 79 % **Residing in College-Owned, -Operated, or -Affiliated Housing:** 90 **Regional Accreditation:** North Central Association of Colleges and Schools **Credit Hours For Degree:** 128 semester hours, Bachelors **ROTC:** Army **Professional Accreditation:** CSWE. **Intercollegiate Athletics:** Baseball M; Basketball M & W; Cross-Country Running M & W; Football M; Golf M & W; Soccer M & W; Softball W; Tennis M & W; Track and Field M & W; Volleyball W; Wrestling M

CENTRAL COLLEGE
812 University St.
Pella, IA 50219
Tel: (641)628-9000; Free: 877-462-3687
Fax: (641)628-5316
E-mail: freiburgerc@central.edu
Web Site: www.central.edu
President/CEO: Dr. Mark Putnam, EdD

Admissions: Chevy Freiburger

Financial Aid: Wayne Dille

Type: Four-Year College **Sex:** Coed **Affiliation:** Reformed Church in America. **Scores:** 80% SAT V 400+; 100% SAT M 400+; 47% ACT 18-23; 37% ACT 24-29 **% Accepted:** 64 **Admission Plans:** Deferred Admission **Application Deadline:** August 15 **Application Fee:** $25.00 **H.S. Requirements:** High school diploma required; GED accepted **Costs Per Year:** Application fee: $25. Comprehensive fee: $44,592 includes full-time tuition ($34,612) and college room and board ($9980). College room only: $4892. Room and board charges vary according to board plan. Part-time tuition: $1442 per credit hour. Part-time tuition varies according to course load. **Scholarships:** Available. **Calendar System:** Semester, Summer session available **Enrollment:** Full-time 1,230, Part-time 44 **Faculty:** Full-time 100, Part-time 5 **Student-Faculty Ratio:** 12:1 **Exams:** ACT essay component not used; SAT I or ACT; SAT essay component not used; SAT Reasoning; SAT Subject. **% Receiving Financial Aid:** 82 **% Residing in College-Owned, -Operated, or -Affiliated Housing:** 91 **Final Year or Final Semester Residency Requirement:** Yes **Regional Accreditation:** North Central Association of Colleges and Schools **Credit Hours For Degree:** 120 semester hours, Bachelors **Professional Accreditation:** NASM. **Intercollegiate Athletics:** Baseball M; Basketball M & W; Cross-Country Running M & W; Football M; Golf M & W; Soccer M & W; Softball W; Tennis M & W; Track and Field M & W; Volleyball W; Wrestling M

CLARKE UNIVERSITY

1550 Clarke Dr.

Dubuque, IA 52001-3198

Tel: (563)588-6300; Free: 800-383-2345

Fax: (563)588-6789

E-mail: admissions@clarke.edu

Web Site: www.clarke.edu

President/CEO: Señor Joanne Burrows, SC

Admissions: Alicia Schmitt

Financial Aid: Amy Norton

Type: Comprehensive **Sex:** Coed **Affiliation:** Roman Catholic. **Scores:** 100% SAT V 400+; 100% SAT M 400+; 56% ACT 18-23; 37% ACT 24-29 **% Accepted:** 72 **Admission Plans:** Deferred Admission **Application Deadline:** Rolling **Application Fee:** $25.00 **H.S. Requirements:** High school diploma required; GED accepted **Costs Per Year:** Application fee: $25. Comprehensive fee: $38,940 includes full-time tuition ($29,000), mandatory fees ($940), and college room and board ($9000). College room only: $4300. Room and board charges vary according to board plan. Part-time tuition: $690 per credit. **Scholarships:** Available. **Calendar System:** Semester, Summer session available **Enrollment:** Full-time 792, Graduate full-time 148, Graduate part-time 59, Part-time 76 **Faculty:** Full-time 89, Part-time 53 **Student-Faculty Ratio:** 10:1 **Exams:** ACT essay component not used; SAT I or ACT; SAT essay component not used. **% Receiving Financial Aid:** 87 **% Residing in College-Owned, -Operated, or -Affiliated Housing:** 48 **Final Year or Final Semester Residency Requirement:** No **Regional Accreditation:** North Central Association of Colleges and Schools **Credit Hours For Degree:** 62 credits, Associates; 124 credits, Bachelors **ROTC:** Army **Professional Accreditation:** AACN, APTA, CSWE, NASM. **Intercollegiate Athletics:** Baseball M; Basketball M & W; Bowling M & W; Cheerleading W; Cross-Country Running M & W; Golf M & W; Lacrosse M & W; Soccer M & W; Softball W; Track and Field M & W; Volleyball M & W

CLINTON COMMUNITY COLLEGE

1000 Lincoln Blvd.

Clinton, IA 52732-6299

Tel: (563)244-7001; Free: 800-462-3255

Fax: (563)244-7107

E-mail: gmohr@eicc.edu

Web Site: www.eicc.edu/ccc

President/CEO: Dean Karen Vickers

Admissions: Gary Mohr

Financial Aid: Teresa Thiede

Type: Two-Year College **Sex:** Coed **Affiliation:** Eastern Iowa Community College District. **% Accepted:** 100 **Admission Plans:** Deferred Admission; Early Admission; Open Admission **Application Deadline:** Rolling **Application Fee:** $0.00 **H.S. Requirements:** High school diploma or equivalent not required **Scholarships:** Available. **Calendar System:** Semester, Summer session available **Enrollment:** Full-time 571, Part-time 669 **Faculty:** Full-time 30, Part-time 13 **Student-Faculty Ratio:** 23:1 **Regional Accreditation:**

North Central Association of Colleges and Schools **Credit Hours For Degree:** 62 semester hours, Associates **Intercollegiate Athletics:** Basketball M; Cheerleading M & W; Soccer M & W; Softball W; Volleyball W

COE COLLEGE

1220 1st Ave., NE

Cedar Rapids, IA 52402-5092

Tel: (319)399-8000; Free: 877-225-5263

Fax: (319)399-8816

E-mail: admission@coe.edu

Web Site: www.coe.edu

President/CEO: Dr. David McInally

Admissions: Julie Staker

Financial Aid: Barbara Hoffman

Type: Four-Year College **Sex:** Coed **Affiliation:** Presbyterian Church. **Scores:** 100% SAT V 400+; 97% SAT M 400+; 36.8% ACT 18-23; 49.1% ACT 24-29 **% Accepted:** 63 **Admission Plans:** Deferred Admission; Early Admission; Early Decision Plan **Application Deadline:** March 1 **Application Fee:** $30.00 **H.S. Requirements:** High school diploma required; GED accepted **Costs Per Year:** Application fee: $30. Comprehensive fee: $47,590 includes full-time tuition ($38,750), mandatory fees ($330), and college room and board ($8510). College room only: $3860. Room and board charges vary according to board plan and housing facility. Part-time tuition: $4840 per course. Part-time tuition varies according to course load. **Scholarships:** Available. **Calendar System:** Miscellaneous, Summer session available **Enrollment:** Full-time 1,357, Part-time 59 **Faculty:** Full-time 96, Part-time 81 **Student-Faculty Ratio:** 11:1 **Exams:** ACT essay component not used; SAT I or ACT; SAT essay component not used; SAT Reasoning; SAT Subject. **% Receiving Financial Aid:** 83 **% Residing in College-Owned, -Operated, or -Affiliated Housing:** 89 **Final Year or Final Semester Residency Requirement:** No **Regional Accreditation:** North Central Association of Colleges and Schools **Credit Hours For Degree:** 32 credits, Bachelors **ROTC:** Air Force, Army **Professional Accreditation:** AACN, NASM. **Intercollegiate Athletics:** Baseball M; Basketball M & W; Cross-Country Running M & W; Football M; Golf M & W; Soccer M & W; Softball W; Swimming and Diving M & W; Tennis M & W; Track and Field M & W; Volleyball W; Wrestling M

CORNELL COLLEGE

600 First St. SW

Mount Vernon, IA 52314-1098

Tel: (319)895-4000; Free: 800-747-1112

Fax: (319)895-4492

E-mail: admission@cornellcollege.edu

Web Site: www.cornellcollege.edu

President/CEO: Jonathan Brand, JD

Admissions: Marie Schofer

Financial Aid: Shannon Amundson

Type: Four-Year College **Sex:** Coed **Affiliation:** Methodist. **Scores:** 100% SAT V 400+; 98% SAT M 400+; 27% ACT 18-23; 47% ACT 24-29 **% Accepted:** 74 **Admission Plans:** Deferred Admission; Early Action; Early Admission; Early Decision Plan **Application Deadline:** February 1 **Application Fee:** $30.00 **H.S. Requirements:** High school diploma required; GED accepted **Costs Per Year:** Application fee: $30. Comprehensive fee: $46,225 includes full-time tuition ($37,500), mandatory fees ($225), and college room and board ($8500). College room only: $3800. Room and board charges vary according to board plan and housing facility. Part-time tuition: $1520 per credit. Part-time tuition varies according to course load. **Scholarships:** Available. **Calendar System:** Miscellaneous, Summer session not available **Enrollment:** Full-time 1,070, Part-time 5 **Student-Faculty Ratio:** 11:1 **Exams:** ACT essay component not used; SAT I or ACT; SAT essay component not used; SAT Reasoning. **% Receiving Financial Aid:** 75 **% Residing in College-Owned, -Operated, or -Affiliated Housing:** 92 **Final Year or Final Semester Residency Requirement:** Yes **Regional Accreditation:** North Central Association of Colleges and Schools **Credit Hours For Degree:** 31 courses, Bachelors **Intercollegiate Athletics:** Baseball M; Basketball M & W; Cross-Country Running M & W; Football M; Lacrosse M & W; Soccer M & W; Softball W; Tennis M & W; Track and Field M & W; Ultimate Frisbee M & W; Volleyball M & W; Wrestling M

DES MOINES AREA COMMUNITY COLLEGE

2006 S Ankeny Blvd.

Ankeny, IA 50021-8995

Tel: (515)964-6200; Free: 800-362-2127
E-mail: mjleutsch@dmacc.edu
Web Site: www.dmacc.edu
President/CEO: Dr. Robert J. Denson
Admissions: Michael Lentsch
Type: Two-Year College **Sex:** Coed **Affiliation:** Iowa Area Community Colleges System. **Admission Plans:** Deferred Admission; Early Admission; Open Admission **Application Deadline:** Rolling **Application Fee:** $0.00 **H.S. Requirements:** High school diploma or equivalent not required. For health programs: High school diploma required; GED accepted **Costs Per Year:** Application fee: $0. State resident tuition: $3913 full-time, $143 per credit hour part-time. Nonresident tuition: $7826 full-time, $286 per credit hour part-time. Full-time tuition varies according to course load and reciprocity agreements. Part-time tuition varies according to course load and reciprocity agreements. College room only: $4400. Room charges vary according to location. **Scholarships:** Available. **Calendar System:** Semester, Summer session available **Enrollment:** Full-time 8,947, Part-time 13,377 **Faculty:** Full-time 322, Part-time 4 **Student-Faculty Ratio:** 33:1 **Exams:** Other; SAT I or ACT. **Regional Accreditation:** North Central Association of Colleges and Schools **Credit Hours For Degree:** 64 semester hours, Associates **Professional Accreditation:** ACBSP, ACEN, ACF, ADA, CoARC, NAACLS. **Intercollegiate Athletics:** Baseball M; Basketball M & W; Cross-Country Running W; Golf M & W; Volleyball W

DIVINE WORD COLLEGE
102 Jacoby Dr. SW
Epworth, IA 52045-0380
Tel: (563)876-3353; Free: 800-553-3321
Fax: (563)876-3407
E-mail: luhal@dwci.edu
Web Site: www.dwci.edu
President/CEO: Rev. Michael Hutchins, SVD
Admissions: Len Uhal
Type: Four-Year College **Sex:** Coed **Affiliation:** Roman Catholic. **Admission Plans:** Early Admission **Application Deadline:** July 15 **Application Fee:** $25.00 **H.S. Requirements:** High school diploma required; GED accepted **Calendar System:** Semester, Summer session not available **Enrollment:** Full-time 121, Part-time 12 **Exams:** SAT I or ACT. **Final Year or Final Semester Residency Requirement:** No **Regional Accreditation:** North Central Association of Colleges and Schools **Credit Hours For Degree:** 60 semester hours, Associates; 125 semester hours, Bachelors

DORDT COLLEGE
498 4th Ave., NE
Sioux Center, IA 51250-1697
Tel: (712)722-6000; Free: 800-343-6738
Fax: (712)722-1967
E-mail: admissions@dordt.edu
Web Site: www.dordt.edu
President/CEO: Dr. Erik Hoekstra
Admissions: Howard Wislon
Financial Aid: Harlan Harmelink
Type: Comprehensive **Sex:** Coed **Affiliation:** Christian Reformed. **Scores:** 90% SAT V 400+; 96% SAT M 400+; 39% ACT 18-23; 45% ACT 24-29 **% Accepted:** 75 **Admission Plans:** Deferred Admission **Application Deadline:** August 1 **Application Fee:** $0.00 **H.S. Requirements:** High school diploma required; GED accepted **Scholarships:** Available. **Calendar System:** Semester, Summer session not available **Enrollment:** Full-time 1,345, Graduate full-time 6, Graduate part-time 23, Part-time 31 **Faculty:** Full-time 80, Part-time 25 **Student-Faculty Ratio:** 15:1 **Exams:** SAT I or ACT. **% Receiving Financial Aid:** 68 **% Residing in College-Owned, -Operated, or -Affiliated Housing:** 90 **Regional Accreditation:** North Central Association of Colleges and Schools **Credit Hours For Degree:** 63 credits, Associates; 126 credits, Bachelors **Professional Accreditation:** AACN, ABET, CSWE. **Intercollegiate Athletics:** Baseball M; Basketball M & W; Cross-Country Running M & W; Football M; Golf M & W; Ice Hockey M; Lacrosse M; Soccer M & W; Softball W; Track and Field M & W; Volleyball W

DRAKE UNIVERSITY
2507 University Ave.
Des Moines, IA 50311-4516
Tel: (515)271-2011; Free: 800-44-DRAKE
Fax: (515)271-2831
E-mail: admission@drake.edu

Web Site: www.drake.edu
President/CEO: Earl Martin
Admissions: Laura Linn
Type: University **Sex:** Coed **Scores:** 100% SAT V 400+; 100% SAT M 400+; 18% ACT 18-23; 56% ACT 24-29 **% Accepted:** 67 **Admission Plans:** Deferred Admission; Early Admission **Application Deadline:** March 1 **Application Fee:** $25.00 **H.S. Requirements:** High school diploma required; GED accepted **Costs Per Year:** Application fee: $25. Comprehensive fee: $45,056 includes full-time tuition ($35,060), mandatory fees ($146), and college room and board ($9850). College room only: $5300. Full-time tuition and fees vary according to course load, degree level, program, and student level. Room and board charges vary according to board plan. Part-time tuition: $695 per credit. Part-time tuition varies according to class time, degree level, and program. **Scholarships:** Available. **Calendar System:** Semester, Summer session available **Enrollment:** Full-time 3,167, Graduate full-time 856, Graduate part-time 797, Part-time 171 **Faculty:** Full-time 289, Part-time 167 **Student-Faculty Ratio:** 13:1 **Exams:** ACT essay component not used; SAT I or ACT; SAT essay component not used; SAT Reasoning. **% Receiving Financial Aid:** 59 **% Residing in College-Owned, -Operated, or -Affiliated Housing:** 70 **Regional Accreditation:** North Central Association of Colleges and Schools **Credit Hours For Degree:** 124 semester hours, Bachelors **ROTC:** Air Force, Army **Professional Accreditation:** AACSB, AALS, ABA, ACEJMC, ACEN, ACPE, CORE, NASAD, NASM. **Intercollegiate Athletics:** Basketball M & W; Cheerleading M & W; Crew W; Cross-Country Running M & W; Football M; Golf M & W; Soccer M & W; Softball W; Tennis M & W; Track and Field M & W; Volleyball W

ELLSWORTH COMMUNITY COLLEGE
1100 College Ave.
Iowa Falls, IA 50126-1199
Tel: (641)648-4611; Free: 800-ECC-9235
Fax: (641)648-3128
Web Site: www.iavalley.cc.ia.us/ecc
President/CEO: Christopher Duree
Admissions: Nancy Walters
Type: Two-Year College **Sex:** Coed **Affiliation:** Iowa Valley Community College District System. **Admission Plans:** Deferred Admission; Early Admission; Open Admission **Application Deadline:** Rolling **H.S. Requirements:** High school diploma required; GED accepted **Scholarships:** Available. **Calendar System:** Semester, Summer session available **Regional Accreditation:** North Central Association of Colleges and Schools **Credit Hours For Degree:** 64 semester hours, Associates **Intercollegiate Athletics:** Baseball M; Basketball M & W; Football M; Golf M & W; Softball W; Track and Field M & W; Volleyball W; Wrestling M

EMMAUS BIBLE COLLEGE
2570 Asbury Rd.
Dubuque, IA 52001-3097
Tel: (319)588-8000; Free: 800-397-2425
Fax: (319)588-1216
E-mail: sjohnson@emmaus.edu
Web Site: www.emmaus.edu
President/CEO: Pres. Phillip Boom
Admissions: Stefan Johnson
Financial Aid: Steve Seeman
Type: Four-Year College **Sex:** Coed **Affiliation:** nondenominational. **Scores:** 93% SAT V 400+; 77% SAT M 400+; 38% ACT 18-23; 45% ACT 24-29 **% Accepted:** 95 **Admission Plans:** Deferred Admission; Open Admission **Application Deadline:** June 1 **Application Fee:** $25.00 **H.S. Requirements:** High school diploma required; GED accepted **Scholarships:** Available. **Calendar System:** Semester, Summer session available **Student-Faculty Ratio:** 9:1 **Exams:** SAT I or ACT. **Regional Accreditation:** North Central Association of Colleges and Schools **Credit Hours For Degree:** 63 semester hours, Associates; 128 semester hours, Bachelors **Professional Accreditation:** ABHE. **Intercollegiate Athletics:** Basketball M & W; Soccer M; Volleyball W

FAITH BAPTIST BIBLE COLLEGE AND THEOLOGICAL SEMINARY
1900 NW 4th St.
Ankeny, IA 50023
Tel: (515)964-0601; Free: 888-FAITH 4U
Fax: (515)964-1638
E-mail: admissions@faith.edu
Web Site: www.faith.edu

President/CEO: Rev. James Tillotson
Admissions: Stacy Lansdown
Financial Aid: Breck Appell
Type: Comprehensive **Sex:** Coed **Affiliation:** General Association of Regular Baptist Churches. **Scores:** 100% SAT V 400+; 67% SAT M 400+; 52% ACT 18-23; 31% ACT 24-29 **% Accepted:** 64 **Admission Plans:** Deferred Admission **Application Deadline:** August 1 **Application Fee:** $45.00 **H.S. Requirements:** High school diploma required; GED accepted **Scholarships:** Available. **Calendar System:** Semester, Summer session available **Enrollment:** Full-time 211, Graduate full-time 12, Graduate part-time 27, Part-time 29 **Faculty:** Full-time 16, Part-time 14 **Student-Faculty Ratio:** 11:1 **Exams:** ACT essay component not used; SAT I or ACT; SAT essay component not used; SAT Reasoning; SAT Subject. **% Receiving Financial Aid:** 91 **% Residing in College-Owned, -Operated, or -Affiliated Housing:** 99 **Final Year or Final Semester Residency Requirement:** No **Regional Accreditation:** North Central Association of Colleges and Schools **Credit Hours For Degree:** 64 semester hours, Associates; 126 semester hours, Bachelors **Professional Accreditation:** ABHE. **Intercollegiate Athletics:** Basketball M & W; Cross-Country Running M & W; Soccer M & W; Track and Field M & W; Volleyball W

GRACELAND UNIVERSITY

1 University Pl.
Lamoni, IA 50140
Tel: (641)784-5000; Free: 866-GRACELAND
Fax: (641)784-5480
E-mail: admissions@graceland.edu
Web Site: www.graceland.edu
President/CEO: Dr. John Sellars
Admissions: Kevin Brown
Financial Aid: Talia Brown
Type: Comprehensive **Sex:** Coed **Affiliation:** Community of Christ. **Scores:** 61% SAT V 400+; 80% SAT M 400+; 39.73% ACT 18-23; 17.81% ACT 24-29 **% Accepted:** 48 **Application Deadline:** Rolling **Application Fee:** $0.00 **H.S. Requirements:** High school diploma required; GED accepted **Costs Per Year:** Application fee: $0. Comprehensive fee: $35,290 includes full-time tuition ($26,440), mandatory fees ($570), and college room and board ($8280). College room only: $3230. Full-time tuition and fees vary according to course load, location, and program. Room and board charges vary according to board plan, housing facility, and location. Part-time tuition: $800 per credit hour. Part-time tuition varies according to course load, location, and program. **Scholarships:** Available. **Calendar System:** 4-1-4, Summer session available **Enrollment:** Full-time 1,243, Graduate full-time 380, Graduate part-time 356, Part-time 313 **Faculty:** Full-time 88, Part-time 77 **Student-Faculty Ratio:** 15:1 **Exams:** ACT essay component not used; Other; SAT I or ACT; SAT essay component not used. **% Receiving Financial Aid:** 78 **% Residing in College-Owned, -Operated, or -Affiliated Housing:** 70 **Final Year or Final Semester Residency Requirement:** Yes **Regional Accreditation:** North Central Association of Colleges and Schools **Credit Hours For Degree:** 124 credits, Bachelors **Professional Accreditation:** NCATE. **Intercollegiate Athletics:** Baseball M; Basketball M & W; Bowling M & W; Cheerleading M & W; Cross-Country Running M & W; Football M; Golf M & W; Soccer M & W; Softball W; Tennis M & W; Track and Field M & W; Volleyball M & W; Wrestling M

GRAND VIEW UNIVERSITY

1200 Grandview Ave.
Des Moines, IA 50316-1599
Tel: (515)263-2800; Free: 800-444-6083
Fax: (515)263-2974
E-mail: admissions@grandview.edu
Web Site: www.grandview.edu
President/CEO: Kent Henning
Admissions: Ryan Thompson
Financial Aid: Michele Dunne
Type: Comprehensive **Sex:** Coed **Affiliation:** Evangelical Lutheran Church in America. **Scores:** 72% SAT V 400+; 86% SAT M 400+; 67% ACT 18-23; 19% ACT 24-29 **% Accepted:** 98 **Application Deadline:** August 15 **Application Fee:** $0.00 **H.S. Requirements:** High school diploma required; GED accepted **Costs Per Year:** Application fee: $0. Comprehensive fee: $33,646 includes full-time tuition ($24,794), mandatory fees ($680), and college room and board ($8172). Full-time tuition and fees vary according to class time and course load. Room and board charges vary according to board plan and housing facility. Part-time tuition: $616 per credit hour. Part-

time tuition varies according to class time and course load. **Scholarships:** Available. **Calendar System:** Semester, Summer session available **Enrollment:** Full-time 1,634, Graduate full-time 10, Graduate part-time 57, Part-time 287 **Faculty:** Full-time 97, Part-time 119 **Student-Faculty Ratio:** 13:1 **Exams:** ACT essay component used for admission; ACT essay component used for advising; ACT essay component used for placement; SAT I or ACT; SAT essay component used for admission; SAT essay component used for advising; SAT essay component used for placement. **% Receiving Financial Aid:** 83 **% Residing in College-Owned, -Operated, or -Affiliated Housing:** 43 **Final Year or Final Semester Residency Requirement:** Yes **Regional Accreditation:** North Central Association of Colleges and Schools **Credit Hours For Degree:** 62 semester hours, Associates; 124 semester hours, Bachelors **ROTC:** Air Force, Army **Professional Accreditation:** AACN. **Intercollegiate Athletics:** Baseball M; Basketball M & W; Bowling M & W; Cheerleading W; Cross-Country Running M & W; Football M; Golf M & W; Soccer M & W; Softball W; Tennis M & W; Track and Field M & W; Volleyball M & W; Wrestling M

GRINNELL COLLEGE

1103 Park St.
Grinnell, IA 50112-1690
Tel: (641)269-4000; Free: 800-247-0113
Fax: (641)269-3408
E-mail: askgrin@grinnell.edu
Web Site: www.grinnell.edu
President/CEO: Dr. Raynard S. Kington
Admissions: Gregory Sneed
Financial Aid: Brad Lindberg
Type: Four-Year College **Sex:** Coed **Scores:** 100% SAT V 400+; 100% SAT M 400+; 4% ACT 18-23; 20% ACT 24-29 **% Accepted:** 25 **Admission Plans:** Deferred Admission; Early Action; Early Admission **Application Deadline:** January 15 **Application Fee:** $0.00 **H.S. Requirements:** High school diploma required; GED accepted **Costs Per Year:** Application fee: $0. Comprehensive fee: $60,738 includes full-time tuition ($48,322), mandatory fees ($436), and college room and board ($11,980). College room only: $5658. Room and board charges vary according to board plan and housing facility. **Scholarships:** Available. **Calendar System:** Semester, Summer session not available **Enrollment:** Full-time 1,665, Part-time 40 **Faculty:** Full-time 171, Part-time 38 **Student-Faculty Ratio:** 9:1 **Exams:** ACT essay component not used; SAT I or ACT; SAT essay component not used; SAT Reasoning. **% Receiving Financial Aid:** 68 **% Residing in College-Owned, -Operated, or -Affiliated Housing:** 82 **Final Year or Final Semester Residency Requirement:** No **Regional Accreditation:** North Central Association of Colleges and Schools **Credit Hours For Degree:** 124 credits, Bachelors **Intercollegiate Athletics:** Baseball M; Basketball M & W; Cross-Country Running M & W; Football M; Golf M & W; Soccer M & W; Softball W; Swimming and Diving M & W; Tennis M & W; Track and Field M & W; Volleyball W

HAMILTON TECHNICAL COLLEGE

1011 E 53rd St.
Davenport, IA 52807-2653
Tel: (563)386-3570; Free: 866-966-4825
Fax: (563)386-6756
E-mail: servin@hamiltontechcollege.com
Web Site: www.hamiltontechcollege.edu
President/CEO: Maryanne Hamilton
Admissions: Scott Ervin
Financial Aid: Lisa Boyd
Type: Four-Year College **Sex:** Coed **Admission Plans:** Deferred Admission; Open Admission **Application Deadline:** Rolling **Application Fee:** $25.00 **H.S. Requirements:** High school diploma required; GED accepted **Scholarships:** Available. **Calendar System:** Continuous, Summer session not available **Faculty:** Full-time 11, Part-time 1 **Student-Faculty Ratio:** 20:1 **Credit Hours For Degree:** 75 credit hours, Associates; 120 credit hours, Bachelors **Professional Accreditation:** ACCSC.

HAWKEYE COMMUNITY COLLEGE

PO Box 8015
Waterloo, IA 50704-8015
Tel: (319)296-2320; Free: 800-670-4769
Fax: (319)296-2874
E-mail: holly.grimm-see@hawkeyecollege.edu
Web Site: www.hawkeyecollege.edu

President/CEO: Linda Allen

Admissions: Holly Grimm-See

Type: Two-Year College **Sex:** Coed **Scores:** 33% ACT 18-23; 13% ACT 24-29 **% Accepted:** 69 **Admission Plans:** Deferred Admission; Open Admission **Application Deadline:** Rolling **Application Fee:** $0.00 **H.S. Requirements:** High school diploma required; GED accepted **Costs Per Year:** Application fee: $0. State resident tuition: $4256 full-time, $152 per credit hour part-time. Nonresident tuition: $4956 full-time, $177 per credit hour part-time. Mandatory fees: $210 full-time, $7.50 per credit hour part-time. **Scholarships:** Available. **Calendar System:** Semester, Summer session available **Enrollment:** Full-time 2,566, Part-time 2,804 **Faculty:** Full-time 118, Part-time 224 **Student-Faculty Ratio:** 18:1 **Exams:** ACT; ACT essay component not used; Other; SAT essay component not used. **Final Year or Final Semester Residency Requirement:** Yes **Regional Accreditation:** North Central Association of Colleges and Schools **Credit Hours For Degree:** 62 credits, Associates **ROTC:** Army **Professional Accreditation:** ADA, CoARC, NAACLS.

INDIAN HILLS COMMUNITY COLLEGE

525 Grandview Ave., Bldg. No.1

Ottumwa, IA 52501-1398

Tel: (641)683-5111; Free: 800-726-2585

Web Site: www.ihcc.cc.ia.us

President/CEO: Marlene Sprouse

Admissions: Jane Sapp

Financial Aid: Kim A. Thornbrugh

Type: Two-Year College **Sex:** Coed **Affiliation:** Iowa Area Community Colleges System. **Admission Plans:** Early Admission; Open Admission **Application Deadline:** Rolling **Application Fee:** $0.00 **H.S. Requirements:** High school diploma required; GED accepted **Scholarships:** Available. **Calendar System:** Quarter, Summer session available **Regional Accreditation:** North Central Association of Colleges and Schools **Credit Hours For Degree:** 61 credit hours, Associates **Professional Accreditation:** ACF, AHIMA, APTA, JRCERT. **Intercollegiate Athletics:** Baseball M; Basketball M; Golf M; Softball W; Volleyball W

INSTE BIBLE COLLEGE

2302 SW 3rd St.

Ankeny, IA 50023

Tel: (515)289-9200

Fax: (515)289-9201

E-mail: inste@inste.edu

Web Site: www.inste.edu

President/CEO: Nicholas Venditti

Type: Four-Year College **Sex:** Coed **Professional Accreditation:** DEAC.

IOWA CENTRAL COMMUNITY COLLEGE

One Triton Cir.

Fort Dodge, IA 50501

Tel: (515)576-7201; Free: 800-362-2793

Fax: (515)576-7724

E-mail: flattery@iowacentral.com

Web Site: www.iccc.cc.ia.us

President/CEO: Dr. Dan Kinney

Admissions: Sue Flattery

Type: Two-Year College **Sex:** Coed **Admission Plans:** Deferred Admission; Early Admission; Open Admission **Application Deadline:** Rolling **Application Fee:** $0.00 **H.S. Requirements:** High school diploma required; GED accepted **Costs Per Year:** Application fee: $0. State resident tuition: $4564 full-time, $163 per credit hour part-time. Nonresident tuition: $6650 full-time, $237.50 per credit hour part-time. Mandatory fees: $420 per term part-time. Full-time tuition varies according to course load and program. Part-time tuition and fees vary according to course load and program. College room and board: $6350. College room only: $4098. **Scholarships:** Available. **Calendar System:** Semester, Summer session available **Enrollment:** Full-time 2,956, Part-time 2,678 **Faculty:** Full-time 87, Part-time 329 **Student-Faculty Ratio:** 19:1 **% Residing in College-Owned, -Operated, or -Affiliated Housing:** 18 **Final Year or Final Semester Residency Requirement:** No **Regional Accreditation:** North Central Association of Colleges and Schools **Credit Hours For Degree:** 60 credits, Associates **Professional Accreditation:** JRCERT, NAACLS. **Intercollegiate Athletics:** Baseball M; Basketball M & W; Bowling M & W; Cheerleading M & W; Cross-Country Running M & W; Football M; Golf M & W; Rugby M; Soccer M & W; Softball W; Swimming and Diving M & W; Tennis M & W; Volleyball W; Wrestling M

IOWA LAKES COMMUNITY COLLEGE

19 S 7th St.

Estherville, IA 51334-2295

Tel: (712)362-2604; Free: 800-521-5054

E-mail: info@iowalakes.edu

Web Site: www.iowalakes.edu

President/CEO: Valerie Newhouse

Financial Aid: Steve Pelzer

Type: Two-Year College **Sex:** Coed **Affiliation:** Iowa Community College System. **% Accepted:** 92 **Admission Plans:** Open Admission **Application Deadline:** Rolling **Application Fee:** $0.00 **H.S. Requirements:** High school diploma required; GED accepted **Costs Per Year:** Application fee: $0. State resident tuition: $5676 full-time, $160 per credit hour part-time. Nonresident tuition: $6028 full-time, $171 per credit hour part-time. Mandatory fees: $16.75 per credit hour part-time. Full-time tuition varies according to program and reciprocity agreements. Part-time tuition and fees vary according to program and reciprocity agreements. **Scholarships:** Available. **Calendar System:** Semester, Summer session available **Enrollment:** Full-time 1,090, Part-time 1,250 **Faculty:** Full-time 91, Part-time 86 **Student-Faculty Ratio:** 18:1 **% Residing in College-Owned, -Operated, or -Affiliated Housing:** 37 **Final Year or Final Semester Residency Requirement:** No **Regional Accreditation:** North Central Association of Colleges and Schools **Credit Hours For Degree:** 64 credit hours, Associates **Professional Accreditation:** AAMAE. **Intercollegiate Athletics:** Baseball M; Basketball M & W; Cheerleading W; Cross-Country Running M & W; Golf M & W; Soccer M & W; Softball W; Swimming and Diving M & W; Volleyball W; Wrestling M

IOWA STATE UNIVERSITY OF SCIENCE AND TECHNOLOGY

Ames, IA 50011

Tel: (515)294-4111; Free: 800-262-3810

Fax: (515)294-2592

E-mail: admissions@iastate.edu

Web Site: www.iastate.edu

President/CEO: Dr. Steven Leath

Admissions: Phillip B. Caffrey

Financial Aid: Roberta Johnson

Type: University **Sex:** Coed **Scores:** 94% SAT V 400+; 97% SAT M 400+; 34% ACT 18-23; 50% ACT 24-29 **% Accepted:** 87 **Admission Plans:** Deferred Admission; Early Admission **Application Deadline:** Rolling **Application Fee:** $40.00 **H.S. Requirements:** High school diploma required; GED accepted **Costs Per Year:** Application fee: $40. State resident tuition: $6848 full-time, $286 per semester hour part-time. Nonresident tuition: $20,362 full-time, $849 per semester hour part-time. Mandatory fees: $1121 full-time. Full-time tuition and fees vary according to class time, degree level, and program. Part-time tuition varies according to class time, course load, degree level, and program. College room and board: $8070. College room only: $4279. Room and board charges vary according to board plan and housing facility. **Scholarships:** Available. **Calendar System:** Semester, Summer session available **Enrollment:** Full-time 28,202, Graduate full-time 3,499, Graduate part-time 2,181, Part-time 1,832 **Faculty:** Full-time 1,603, Part-time 281 **Student-Faculty Ratio:** 19:1 **Exams:** ACT essay component not used; SAT I or ACT; SAT essay component not used; SAT Reasoning; SAT Subject. **% Receiving Financial Aid:** 51 **% Residing in College-Owned, -Operated, or -Affiliated Housing:** 41 **Regional Accreditation:** North Central Association of Colleges and Schools **Credit Hours For Degree:** 120 semester hours, depending on program, Bachelors **ROTC:** Air Force, Army, Navy **Professional Accreditation:** AACSB, AAFCS, AAMFT, ABET, ACEJMC, ACSP, AND, APA, ASLA, ATMAE, AVMA, CIDA, JRCAT, NAAB, NASAD, NASM, SAF. **Intercollegiate Athletics:** Basketball M & W; Cross-Country Running M & W; Football M; Golf M & W; Gymnastics W; Soccer W; Softball W; Swimming and Diving M & W; Tennis W; Track and Field M & W; Volleyball W; Wrestling M

IOWA WESLEYAN UNIVERSITY

601 N Main St.

Mount Pleasant, IA 52641-1398

Tel: (319)385-8021; Free: 800-582-2383

Fax: (319)385-6296

E-mail: scott.briell@iwc.edu

Web Site: www.iwc.edu

President/CEO: Dr. Steven E. Titus

Admissions: Scott A. Briell

Financial Aid: Julie Duplessis

Type: Four-Year College **Sex:** Coed **Affiliation:** United Methodist. **Scores:** 80% SAT V 400+; 100% SAT M 400+; 60% ACT 18-23; 27.15% ACT 24-29 **% Accepted:** 41 **Admission Plans:** Deferred Admission; Early Admission **Application Deadline:** August 15 **Application Fee:** $20.00 **H.S. Requirements:** High school diploma required; GED accepted **Costs Per Year:** Application fee: $20. Comprehensive fee: $36,862 includes full-time tuition ($26,806), mandatory fees ($480), and college room and board ($9576). College room only: $3644. Room and board charges vary according to housing facility. Part-time tuition: $675 per credit hour. Part-time mandatory fees: $20 per credit hour. Part-time tuition and fees vary according to class time, course load, and location. **Scholarships:** Available. **Calendar System:** Semester, Summer session available **Enrollment:** Full-time 386, Part-time 87 **Faculty:** Full-time 36, Part-time 48 **Student-Faculty Ratio:** 10:1 **Exams:** ACT essay component used for advising; SAT I or ACT; SAT essay component used for advising; SAT Reasoning; SAT Subject. **% Receiving Financial Aid:** 82 **% Residing in College-Owned, -Operated, or -Affiliated Housing:** 68 **Final Year or Final Semester Residency Requirement:** No **Regional Accreditation:** North Central Association of Colleges and Schools **Credit Hours For Degree:** 124 credit hours, Bachelors **Professional Accreditation:** ACEN. **Intercollegiate Athletics:** Baseball M; Basketball M & W; Football M; Golf M & W; Soccer M & W; Softball W; Volleyball W

IOWA WESTERN COMMUNITY COLLEGE

2700 College Rd., Box 4-C
Council Bluffs, IA 51502
Tel: (712)325-3200; Free: 800-432-5852
Fax: (712)325-3720
E-mail: admissions@iwcc.edu
Web Site: www.iwcc.edu
President/CEO: Dan Kinney
Admissions: Tori Christie

Type: Two-Year College **Sex:** Coed **Affiliation:** Iowa Department of Education Division of Community Colleges. **Admission Plans:** Deferred Admission; Early Admission; Open Admission **Application Deadline:** Rolling **H.S. Requirements:** High school diploma required; GED accepted **Scholarships:** Available. **Calendar System:** Semester, Summer session available **Regional Accreditation:** North Central Association of Colleges and Schools **Credit Hours For Degree:** 64 credit hours, Associates **ROTC:** Air Force, Army **Professional Accreditation:** ABET, ACF, ADA. **Intercollegiate Athletics:** Baseball M; Basketball M & W; Golf M & W; Softball W; Track and Field M & W; Volleyball W

KAPLAN UNIVERSITY, CEDAR FALLS

7009 Nordic Dr.
Cedar Falls, IA 50613
Tel: (319)277-0220; Free: 800-527-5268
Web Site: www.kaplanuniversity.edu
President/CEO: Gwen Bramlet-Hecker

Type: Two-Year College **Sex:** Coed **Application Deadline:** Rolling **H.S. Requirements:** High school diploma required; GED accepted **Calendar System:** Quarter **Regional Accreditation:** North Central Association of Colleges and Schools

KAPLAN UNIVERSITY, CEDAR RAPIDS

3165 Edgewood Pky., SW
Cedar Rapids, IA 52404
Tel: (319)363-0481; Free: 800-527-5268
Fax: (319)363-3812
Web Site: www.kaplanuniversity.edu
President/CEO: Susan Spivey

Type: Two-Year College **Sex:** Coed **Affiliation:** Kaplan University - Davenport Campus. **H.S. Requirements:** High school diploma required; GED accepted **Scholarships:** Available. **Calendar System:** Quarter **Regional Accreditation:** North Central Association of Colleges and Schools **Credit Hours For Degree:** 92 credit hours, Associates **Professional Accreditation:** AAMAE.

KAPLAN UNIVERSITY, DAVENPORT CAMPUS

1801 E Kimberly Rd.
Ste. 1
Davenport, IA 52807-2095
Tel: (563)355-3500; Free: 800-527-5268
Web Site: www.kaplanuniversity.edu

President/CEO: Wade Dyke

Type: Comprehensive **Sex:** Coed **H.S. Requirements:** High school diploma required; GED accepted **Scholarships:** Available. **Calendar System:** Quarter **Regional Accreditation:** North Central Association of Colleges and Schools **Professional Accreditation:** AAMAE, ACBSP.

KAPLAN UNIVERSITY, DES MOINES

4655 121st St.
Urbandale, IA 50323
Tel: (515)727-2100; Free: 800-527-5268
Web Site: www.kaplanuniversity.edu
President/CEO: Kacy Webster

Type: Two-Year College **Sex:** Coed **H.S. Requirements:** High school diploma required; GED accepted **Regional Accreditation:** North Central Association of Colleges and Schools

KAPLAN UNIVERSITY, MASON CITY CAMPUS

2570 4th St., SW
Mason City, IA 50401
Tel: (641)423-2530; Free: 800-527-5268
Web Site: www.kaplanuniversity.edu
President/CEO: Julie Valencia

Type: Four-Year College **Sex:** Coed **H.S. Requirements:** High school diploma required; GED accepted **Regional Accreditation:** North Central Association of Colleges and Schools

KIRKWOOD COMMUNITY COLLEGE

PO Box 2068
Cedar Rapids, IA 52406-2068
Tel: (319)398-5411; Free: 800-332-2055
Fax: (319)398-1244
E-mail: dbannon@kirkwood.cc.ia.us
Web Site: www.kirkwood.edu
President/CEO: Dr. Mick Starcevich
Admissions: Doug Bannon

Type: Two-Year College **Sex:** Coed **Affiliation:** Iowa Department of Education Division of Community Colleges. **Admission Plans:** Early Admission; Open Admission **Application Deadline:** Rolling **Application Fee:** $0.00 **H.S. Requirements:** High school diploma or equivalent not required **Scholarships:** Available. **Calendar System:** Semester, Summer session available **Enrollment:** Full-time 9,715, Part-time 8,126 **Faculty:** Full-time 288, Part-time 680 **Student-Faculty Ratio:** 24:1 **Regional Accreditation:** North Central Association of Colleges and Schools **Credit Hours For Degree:** 62 semester hours, Associates **Professional Accreditation:** AAMAE, ACBSP, ACF, ADA, AHIMA, AOTA, APTA, ARCST, CoARC, JRCEND. **Intercollegiate Athletics:** Baseball M; Basketball M & W; Golf M; Soccer M & W; Softball W; Volleyball W

LORAS COLLEGE

1450 Alta Vista
Dubuque, IA 52004-0178
Tel: (563)588-7100; Free: 800-245-6727
Fax: (563)588-7964
E-mail: admissions@loras.edu
Web Site: www.loras.edu
President/CEO: James E. Collins
Financial Aid: Julie A. Dunn

Type: Comprehensive **Sex:** Coed **Affiliation:** Roman Catholic. **Scores:** 88% SAT V 400+; 89% SAT M 400+; 45.6% ACT 18-23; 45.6% ACT 24-29 **% Accepted:** 95 **Admission Plans:** Deferred Admission **Application Deadline:** Rolling **Application Fee:** $0.00 **H.S. Requirements:** High school diploma required; GED accepted **Costs Per Year:** Application fee: $0. Comprehensive fee: $39,225 includes full-time tuition ($30,065), mandatory fees ($1460), and college room and board ($7700). College room only: $4000. Full-time tuition and fees vary according to course load and degree level. Room and board charges vary according to board plan and housing facility. Part-time tuition: $610 per credit. Part-time mandatory fees: $29 per credit. **Scholarships:** Available. **Calendar System:** Semester, Summer session available **Enrollment:** Full-time 1,418, Graduate full-time 53, Graduate part-time 13, Part-time 44 **Faculty:** Full-time 103, Part-time 52 **Student-Faculty Ratio:** 12:1 **Exams:** SAT I and SAT II or ACT; SAT I or ACT; SAT II; SAT Reasoning; SAT Subject. **% Receiving Financial Aid:** 74 **% Residing in College-Owned, -Operated, or -Affiliated Housing:** 68 **Final Year or Final Semester Residency Requirement:** Yes **Regional Accreditation:**

North Central Association of Colleges and Schools **Credit Hours For Degree:** 60 credits, Associates; 120 credits, Bachelors **ROTC:** Army **Professional Accreditation:** CSWE. **Intercollegiate Athletics:** Baseball M; Basketball M & W; Cheerleading M & W; Cross-Country Running M & W; Football M; Golf M & W; Ice Hockey M & W; Lacrosse W; Rugby M & W; Soccer M & W; Softball W; Swimming and Diving M & W; Tennis M & W; Track and Field M & W; Ultimate Frisbee M & W; Volleyball M & W; Wrestling M

LUTHER COLLEGE

700 College Dr.
Decorah, IA 52101
Tel: (563)387-2000; Free: 800-458-8437
Fax: (563)387-2159
E-mail: neubauki@luther.edu
Web Site: www.luther.edu
President/CEO: Dr. Paula J. Carlson, PhD
Admissions: Kirk Neubauer
Financial Aid: Janice Cordell

Type: Four-Year College **Sex:** Coed **Affiliation:** Evangelical Lutheran Church in America. **Scores:** 95% SAT V 400+; 93% SAT M 400+; 29.3% ACT 18-23; 51.5% ACT 24-29 **% Accepted:** 67 **Admission Plans:** Deferred Admission **H.S. Requirements:** High school diploma required; GED accepted **Costs Per Year:** Comprehensive fee: $48,540 includes full-time tuition ($39,760), mandatory fees ($280), and college room and board ($8500). College room only: $3930. Full-time tuition and fees vary according to course load. Room and board charges vary according to board plan and housing facility. Part-time tuition: $1420 per credit hour. Part-time tuition varies according to course load. **Scholarships:** Available. **Calendar System:** 4-1-4, Summer session available **Enrollment:** Full-time 2,303, Part-time 34 **Faculty:** Full-time 177, Part-time 57 **Student-Faculty Ratio:** 12:1 **Exams:** SAT I or ACT. **% Receiving Financial Aid:** 69 **% Residing in College-Owned, -Operated, or -Affiliated Housing:** 90 **Regional Accreditation:** North Central Association of Colleges and Schools **Credit Hours For Degree:** 128 semester hours, Bachelors **Professional Accreditation:** AACN, CSWE, NASM, NCATE. **Intercollegiate Athletics:** Baseball M; Basketball M & W; Cross-Country Running M & W; Football M; Golf M & W; Soccer M & W; Softball W; Swimming and Diving M & W; Tennis M & W; Track and Field M & W; Ultimate Frisbee M & W; Volleyball W; Wrestling M

MAHARISHI UNIVERSITY OF MANAGEMENT

1000 N 4th St.
Fairfield, IA 52557
Tel: (641)472-7000; Free: 800-369-6480
Fax: (641)472-1189
E-mail: admissions@mum.edu
Web Site: www.mum.edu
President/CEO: Dr. Bevan Morris
Financial Aid: Bill Christensen

Type: University **Sex:** Coed **% Accepted:** 37 **Admission Plans:** Deferred Admission; Early Admission; Preferred Admission **Application Fee:** $25.00 **H.S. Requirements:** High school diploma required; GED accepted **Costs Per Year:** Application fee: $25. Comprehensive fee: $33,930 includes full-time tuition ($26,000), mandatory fees ($530), and college room and board ($7400). **Scholarships:** Available. **Calendar System:** Semester **Enrollment:** Full-time 224, Graduate full-time 802, Graduate part-time 375, Part-time 129 **Student-Faculty Ratio:** 9:1 **Exams:** ACT essay component used for admission; SAT I or ACT; SAT essay component used for admission. **% Receiving Financial Aid:** 92 **% Residing in College-Owned, -Operated, or -Affiliated Housing:** 49 **Regional Accreditation:** North Central Association of Colleges and Schools **Credit Hours For Degree:** 166 units, Bachelors **Intercollegiate Athletics:** Soccer M & W; Ultimate Frisbee M & W; Volleyball M & W

MARSHALLTOWN COMMUNITY COLLEGE

3700 S Ctr. St.
Marshalltown, IA 50158-4760
Tel: (641)752-7106; Free: 866-622-4748
Fax: (641)752-8149
Web Site: www.marshalltowncommunitycollege.com
President/CEO: Christopher Duree
Admissions: Deana Inman

Type: Two-Year College **Sex:** Coed **Affiliation:** Iowa Valley Community College District System. **Admission Plans:** Early Admission; Open Admission

Application Deadline: Rolling **Application Fee:** $0.00 **H.S. Requirements:** High school diploma required; GED accepted **Scholarships:** Available. **Calendar System:** Semester, Summer session available **Exams:** ACT; Other. **Regional Accreditation:** North Central Association of Colleges and Schools **Credit Hours For Degree:** 64 credits, Associates **ROTC:** Air Force **Professional Accreditation:** ADA. **Intercollegiate Athletics:** Baseball M; Basketball M & W; Cheerleading M & W; Golf M & W; Soccer M & W; Softball W; Volleyball W

MERCY COLLEGE OF HEALTH SCIENCES

928 Sixth Ave.
Des Moines, IA 50309-1239
Tel: (515)643-3180; Free: 800-637-2994
Fax: (515)643-6698
E-mail: mtingle-williams@mercydesmoines.org
Web Site: www.mchs.edu
President/CEO: Barbara Q. Decker, JD
Admissions: Melinda Tingle-Williams
Financial Aid: Lisa Croat

Type: Four-Year College **Sex:** Coed **Affiliation:** Roman Catholic Church; Catholic Health Initiatives, Mercy Medial Center. **Costs Per Year:** Tuition: $16,268 full-time, $563 per credit hour part-time. Full-time tuition varies according to program. Part-time tuition varies according to course load. **Scholarships:** Available. **Calendar System:** Semester, Summer session available **Enrollment:** Full-time 440, Part-time 349 **Faculty:** Full-time 43, Part-time 39 **Student-Faculty Ratio:** 9:1 **Exams:** ACT; ACT essay component not used. **Final Year or Final Semester Residency Requirement:** Yes **Regional Accreditation:** North Central Association of Colleges and Schools **Professional Accreditation:** AACN, ACEN, ARCST, JRCEDMS.

MORNINGSIDE COLLEGE

1501 Morningside Ave.
Sioux City, IA 51106
Tel: (712)274-5000; Free: 800-831-0806
E-mail: mscadm@morningside.edu
Web Site: www.morningside.edu
President/CEO: John Reynders
Admissions: Stephanie Peters
Financial Aid: Karen Gagnon

Type: Comprehensive **Sex:** Coed **Affiliation:** United Methodist Church. **Scores:** 52% ACT 18-23; 30% ACT 24-29 **% Accepted:** 56 **Admission Plans:** Deferred Admission **Application Deadline:** Rolling **Application Fee:** $0.00 **H.S. Requirements:** High school diploma required; GED accepted. For home-schooled students (must provide transcript/record of courses and grades): High school diploma or equivalent not required **Costs Per Year:** Application fee: $0. Comprehensive fee: $36,865 includes full-time tuition ($26,680), mandatory fees ($1475), and college room and board ($8710). College room only: $4600. Full-time tuition and fees vary according to program. Room and board charges vary according to housing facility. Part-time tuition: $850 per credit hour. Part-time tuition varies according to course load and program. **Scholarships:** Available. **Calendar System:** Semester, Summer session available **Enrollment:** Full-time 1,310, Graduate full-time 23, Graduate part-time 1,467, Part-time 30 **Faculty:** Full-time 85, Part-time 162 **Student-Faculty Ratio:** 13:1 **Exams:** ACT essay component not used; SAT I or ACT; SAT essay component not used; SAT Reasoning. **% Receiving Financial Aid:** 83 **% Residing in College-Owned, -Operated, or -Affiliated Housing:** 60 **Final Year or Final Semester Residency Requirement:** Yes **Regional Accreditation:** North Central Association of Colleges and Schools **Credit Hours For Degree:** 124 semester hours, Bachelors **ROTC:** Army **Professional Accreditation:** AACN, NASM. **Intercollegiate Athletics:** Baseball M; Basketball M & W; Bowling M & W; Cross-Country Running M & W; Football M; Golf M & W; Soccer M & W; Softball W; Swimming and Diving M & W; Tennis M & W; Track and Field M & W; Volleyball W; Wrestling M

MOUNT MERCY UNIVERSITY

1330 Elmhurst Dr., NE
Cedar Rapids, IA 52402-4797
Tel: (319)363-8213; Free: 800-248-4504
Fax: (319)368-6492
E-mail: lgarcia@mtmercy.edu
Web Site: www.mtmercy.edu
President/CEO: Laurie M. Hamen, JD

Admissions: Lauren Garcia

Financial Aid: Bethany Rinderknecht

Type: Comprehensive **Sex:** Coed **Affiliation:** Roman Catholic. **Scores:** 65.6% ACT 18-23; 21% ACT 24-29 **% Accepted:** 61 **Admission Plans:** Deferred Admission **Application Deadline:** August 15 **Application Fee:** $0.00 **H.S. Requirements:** High school diploma required; GED accepted **Costs Per Year:** Application fee: $0. Comprehensive fee: $36,826 includes full-time tuition ($28,226) and college room and board ($8600). Full-time tuition varies according to course load. Room and board charges vary according to board plan and housing facility. Part-time tuition: $768 per credit. Part-time tuition varies according to course load. **Scholarships:** Available. **Calendar System:** 4-1-4, Summer session available **Enrollment:** Full-time 957, Graduate full-time 147, Graduate part-time 187, Part-time 586 **Faculty:** Full-time 81, Part-time 70 **Student-Faculty Ratio:** 14:1 **Exams:** ACT essay component not used; SAT I or ACT; SAT essay component not used. **% Receiving Financial Aid:** 71 **% Residing in College-Owned, -Operated, or -Affiliated Housing:** 45 **Final Year or Final Semester Residency Requirement:** Yes **Regional Accreditation:** North Central Association of Colleges and Schools **Credit Hours For Degree:** 123 credit hours, Bachelors **Professional Accreditation:** AACN, AAMFT, CSWE. **Intercollegiate Athletics:** Baseball M; Basketball M & W; Bowling M & W; Cross-Country Running M & W; Golf M & W; Soccer M & W; Softball W; Track and Field M & W; Volleyball W

MUSCATINE COMMUNITY COLLEGE

152 Colorado St.

Muscatine, IA 52761-5396

Tel: (563)288-6001; Free: 800-351-4669

Fax: (563)288-6074

E-mail: gmohr@eicc.edu

Web Site: www.eicc.edu/general/muscatine

President/CEO: Dr. Jeffrey Armstrong, PhD

Admissions: Gary Mohr

Financial Aid: Robin Jennings

Type: Two-Year College **Sex:** Coed **Affiliation:** Eastern Iowa Community College District. **Scores:** 56% ACT 18-23; 23% ACT 24-29 **% Accepted:** 100 **Admission Plans:** Open Admission **Application Deadline:** Rolling **H.S. Requirements:** High school diploma or equivalent not required **Scholarships:** Available. **Calendar System:** Semester, Summer session available **Enrollment:** Full-time 608, Part-time 1,016 **Faculty:** Full-time 32, Part-time 59 **% Residing in College-Owned, -Operated, or -Affiliated Housing:** 4 **Regional Accreditation:** North Central Association of Colleges and Schools **Credit Hours For Degree:** 62 credits, Associates **Intercollegiate Athletics:** Baseball M; Softball W

NORTH IOWA AREA COMMUNITY COLLEGE

500 College Dr.

Mason City, IA 50401-7299

Tel: (641)423-1264; Free: 888-GO NIACC

Fax: (641)423-1711

E-mail: request@niacc.edu

Web Site: www.niacc.edu

President/CEO: Dr. Steven Schulz

Admissions: Rachel McGuire

Type: Two-Year College **Sex:** Coed **Affiliation:** Iowa Community College System. **Scores:** 58% SAT V 400+; 46% SAT M 400+ **Admission Plans:** Open Admission **Application Deadline:** Rolling **H.S. Requirements:** High school diploma required; GED accepted **Costs Per Year:** State resident tuition: $4013 full-time, $133 per semester hour part-time. Nonresident tuition: $6019 full-time, $200 per semester hour part-time. Mandatory fees: $780 full-time, $26 per semester hour part-time. Full-time tuition and fees vary according to course load. Part-time tuition and fees vary according to course load. College room and board: $6518. Room and board charges vary according to housing facility. **Scholarships:** Available. **Calendar System:** Semester, Summer session available **Enrollment:** Full-time 1,420, Part-time 1,530 **Faculty:** Full-time 80, Part-time 133 **Student-Faculty Ratio:** 13:1 **Final Year or Final Semester Residency Requirement:** No **Regional Accreditation:** North Central Association of Colleges and Schools **Credit Hours For Degree:** 60 Credits, Associates **Professional Accreditation:** ACEN, APTA. **Intercollegiate Athletics:** Baseball M; Basketball M & W; Cross-Country Running M & W; Golf M & W; Soccer M; Softball W; Track and Field M & W; Volleyball W; Wrestling M

NORTHEAST IOWA COMMUNITY COLLEGE

Box 400

Calmar, IA 52132-0480

Tel: (563)562-3263; Free: 800-728-CALMAR

Fax: (563)562-3719

E-mail: mcconnellb@nicc.edu

Web Site: www.nicc.edu

President/CEO: Dr. Penelope Wills

Admissions: Brynn McConnell

Financial Aid: Kim Baumler

Type: Two-Year College **Sex:** Coed **Affiliation:** Iowa Area Community Colleges System. **% Accepted:** 79 **Admission Plans:** Open Admission **Application Fee:** $0.00 **H.S. Requirements:** High school diploma or equivalent not required **Costs Per Year:** Application fee: $0. State resident tuition: $4312 full-time, $154 per credit hour part-time. Nonresident tuition: $4312 full-time, $154 per credit hour part-time. Mandatory fees: $364 full-time, $13 per credit hour part-time. Full-time tuition and fees vary according to course load and program. Part-time tuition and fees vary according to course load and program. **Scholarships:** Available. **Calendar System:** Semester, Summer session available **Enrollment:** Full-time 1,485, Part-time 3,380 **Faculty:** Full-time 116, Part-time 238 **Student-Faculty Ratio:** 14:1 **Exams:** ACT. **Final Year or Final Semester Residency Requirement:** No **Regional Accreditation:** North Central Association of Colleges and Schools **Credit Hours For Degree:** 64 credit hours, Associates **Professional Accreditation:** AHIMA, CoARC.

NORTHWEST IOWA COMMUNITY COLLEGE

603 W Park St.

Sheldon, IA 51201-1046

Tel: (712)324-5061; Free: 800-352-4907

Fax: (712)324-4136

E-mail: lstory@nwicc.edu

Web Site: www.nwicc.edu

President/CEO: Dr. William G. Giddings

Admissions: Lisa Story

Type: Two-Year College **Sex:** Coed **Affiliation:** Iowa Department of Education Division of Community Colleges. **Admission Plans:** Open Admission **Application Deadline:** Rolling **Application Fee:** $10.00 **H.S. Requirements:** High school diploma required; GED accepted **Scholarships:** Available. **Calendar System:** Semester **Faculty:** Full-time 40, Part-time 99 **Student-Faculty Ratio:** 11:1 **Exams:** Other. **Regional Accreditation:** North Central Association of Colleges and Schools **Credit Hours For Degree:** 60 credit hours, Associates **Professional Accreditation:** AHIMA.

NORTHWESTERN COLLEGE

101 Seventh St., SW

Orange City, IA 51041-1996

Tel: (712)707-7000; Free: 800-747-4757

Fax: (712)707-7247

E-mail: admissions@nwciowa.edu

Web Site: www.nwciowa.edu

President/CEO: Greg Christy

Admissions: Jackie Davis

Financial Aid: Eric Anderson

Type: Comprehensive **Sex:** Coed **Affiliation:** Reformed Church in America. **Scores:** 97% SAT V 400+; 94% SAT M 400+; 38% ACT 18-23; 45% ACT 24-29 **% Accepted:** 72 **Admission Plans:** Deferred Admission; Early Admission **Application Deadline:** Rolling **Application Fee:** $0.00 **H.S. Requirements:** High school diploma required; GED accepted **Costs Per Year:** Application fee: $0. Comprehensive fee: $38,500 includes full-time tuition ($29,300), mandatory fees ($300), and college room and board ($8900). Room and board charges vary according to board plan and housing facility. **Scholarships:** Available. **Calendar System:** Semester, Summer session available **Enrollment:** Full-time 1,061, Graduate full-time 1, Graduate part-time 89, Part-time 59 **Faculty:** Full-time 82, Part-time 63 **Student-Faculty Ratio:** 11:1 **Exams:** ACT essay component not used; SAT I or ACT; SAT essay component not used; SAT Reasoning; SAT Subject. **% Receiving Financial Aid:** 73 **% Residing in College-Owned, -Operated, or -Affiliated Housing:** 90 **Final Year or Final Semester Residency Requirement:** No **Regional Accreditation:** North Central Association of Colleges and Schools **Credit Hours For Degree:** 124 credit hours, Bachelors **Professional Accreditation:** AACN, CSWE, NCATE. **Intercollegiate Athletics:** Baseball M; Basketball M & W; Cheerleading M & W; Cross-Country Running M & W; Football M; Golf M & W; Soccer M & W; Softball W; Tennis W; Track and Field M & W; Volleyball W; Wrestling M

PALMER COLLEGE OF CHIROPRACTIC
1000 Brady St.
Davenport, IA 52803-5287
Tel: (563)884-5000; Free: 800-722-3648
Fax: (563)884-5897
E-mail: lisa.gisel@palmer.edu
Web Site: www.palmer.edu
President/CEO: Dr. Dennis Marchiori, DC
Admissions: Lisa Gisel

Type: Comprehensive **Sex:** Coed **% Accepted:** 83 **Admission Plans:** Deferred Admission; Open Admission **Application Deadline:** Rolling **Application Fee:** $50.00 **H.S. Requirements:** High school diploma required; GED accepted **Calendar System:** Trimester, Summer session available **Enrollment:** Full-time 39, Graduate full-time 2,246, Graduate part-time 15, Part-time 10 **Faculty:** Full-time 2, Part-time 13 **Student-Faculty Ratio:** 3:1 **Regional Accreditation:** North Central Association of Colleges and Schools **Credit Hours For Degree:** 60 credit hours, Associates; 120 credit hours, Bachelors **Professional Accreditation:** CCE. **Intercollegiate Athletics:** Rugby M & W

ST. AMBROSE UNIVERSITY
518 W Locust St.
Davenport, IA 52803-2898
Tel: (563)333-6000; Free: 800-383-2627
Fax: (563)383-8791
E-mail: conklinallisonj@sau.edu
Web Site: www.sau.edu
President/CEO: Señor Joan Lescinski, CSJ
Admissions: Allison Conklin
Financial Aid: Julie Haack

Type: Comprehensive **Sex:** Coed **Affiliation:** Roman Catholic. **Scores:** 58% ACT 18-23; 34% ACT 24-29 **% Accepted:** 73 **Admission Plans:** Deferred Admission **Application Deadline:** Rolling **H.S. Requirements:** High school diploma required; GED accepted **Costs Per Year:** Comprehensive fee: $39,019 includes full-time tuition ($28,870), mandatory fees ($280), and college room and board ($9869). College room only: $6250. Full-time tuition and fees vary according to course load and location. Room and board charges vary according to board plan and housing facility. Part-time tuition: $890 per credit hour. Part-time mandatory fees: $140 per term. Part-time tuition and fees vary according to course load and location. **Scholarships:** Available. **Calendar System:** 4-1-4, Summer session available **Enrollment:** Full-time 2,259, Graduate full-time 424, Graduate part-time 359, Part-time 269 **Faculty:** Full-time 219, Part-time 75 **Student-Faculty Ratio:** 12:1 **Exams:** ACT; ACT essay component not used; SAT I or ACT; SAT essay component not used. **% Receiving Financial Aid:** 76 **% Residing in College-Owned, -Operated, or -Affiliated Housing:** 60 **Regional Accreditation:** North Central Association of Colleges and Schools **Credit Hours For Degree:** 120 credit hours, Bachelors **Professional Accreditation:** AACN, ABET, ACBSP, AOTA, APTA, CSWE, TEAC. **Intercollegiate Athletics:** Baseball M; Basketball M & W; Bowling M & W; Cheerleading M & W; Cross-Country Running M & W; Football M; Golf M & W; Lacrosse M; Soccer M & W; Softball W; Tennis M & W; Track and Field M & W; Volleyball M & W

ST. LUKE'S COLLEGE
2800 Pierce St.
Sioux City, IA 51104
Tel: (712)279-3149; Free: 800-352-4660
Fax: (712)233-8017
E-mail: sherry.mccarthy@stlukescollege.edu
Web Site: stlukescollege.edu
President/CEO: Michael D. Stiles
Admissions: Sherry McCarthy
Financial Aid: Danelle D. Johannsen

Type: Two-Year College **Sex:** Coed **Affiliation:** UnityPoint Health. **Scores:** 100% SAT V 400+; 100% SAT M 400+; 49% ACT 18-23; 34% ACT 24-29 **% Accepted:** 80 **Application Deadline:** August 1 **Application Fee:** $50.00 **H.S. Requirements:** High school diploma required; GED accepted **Costs Per Year:** Application fee: $50. Tuition: $18,900 full-time, $525 per credit part-time. Mandatory fees: $1560 full-time. Full-time tuition and fees vary according to course load, degree level, and program. Part-time tuition varies according to course load, degree level, and program. **Scholarships:** Available. **Calendar System:** Semester, Summer session available **Enrollment:** Full-time 128, Part-time 113 **Faculty:** Full-time 24, Part-time 23 **Student-**

Faculty Ratio: 7:1 **Exams:** ACT essay component not used; SAT I or ACT; SAT essay component not used; SAT Reasoning; SAT Subject. **Final Year or Final Semester Residency Requirement:** No **Regional Accreditation:** North Central Association of Colleges and Schools **Credit Hours For Degree:** 71 credit hours, Associates; 120 credit hours, Bachelors **Professional Accreditation:** ACEN.

SCOTT COMMUNITY COLLEGE
500 Belmont Rd.
Bettendorf, IA 52722-6804
Tel: (563)441-4001; Free: 800-895-0811
Fax: (563)441-4066
E-mail: gmohr@eicc.edu
Web Site: www.eicc.edu/scc
President/CEO: Dr. Thomas Coley
Admissions: Gary Mohr
Financial Aid: Jeannine Ingelson

Type: Two-Year College **Sex:** Coed **Affiliation:** Eastern Iowa Community College District. **% Accepted:** 100 **Admission Plans:** Open Admission **Application Deadline:** Rolling **H.S. Requirements:** High school diploma or equivalent not required **Scholarships:** Available. **Calendar System:** Semester, Summer session available **Enrollment:** Full-time 2,059, Part-time 2,052 **Faculty:** Full-time 86, Part-time 164 **Student-Faculty Ratio:** 20:1 **Regional Accreditation:** North Central Association of Colleges and Schools **Credit Hours For Degree:** 62 credits, Associates **Professional Accreditation:** ADA, JRCEND, JRCERT. **Intercollegiate Athletics:** Golf M & W; Soccer M & W

SHILOH UNIVERSITY
100 Shiloh Dr.
Kalona, IA 52247
Tel: (319)656-2447
E-mail: admissions@shilohuniversity.edu
Web Site: www.shilohuniversity.edu
President/CEO: Christopher J. Reeves
Admissions: Andrew R. Thompson

Type: Comprehensive **Sex:** Coed **% Accepted:** 100 **Admission Plans:** Deferred Admission; Early Admission **Application Deadline:** July 6 **Application Fee:** $0.00 **H.S. Requirements:** High school diploma required; GED accepted **Costs Per Year:** Application fee: $0. Tuition: $3600 full-time, $150 per credit part-time. Mandatory fees: $10 full-time, $10 per year part-time. Full-time tuition and fees vary according to course load. Part-time tuition and fees vary according to course load. **Enrollment:** Full-time 1, Graduate full-time 1, Graduate part-time 19, Part-time 16 **Faculty:** Full-time 3, Part-time 37 **Student-Faculty Ratio:** 1:1 **Exams:** SAT I and SAT II or ACT. **Final Year or Final Semester Residency Requirement:** No **Credit Hours For Degree:** 61 credit hours, Associates; 120 credit hours, Bachelors **Professional Accreditation:** DEAC.

SIMPSON COLLEGE
701 N C St.
Indianola, IA 50125-1297
Tel: (515)961-6251; Free: 800-362-2454
Fax: (515)961-1498
E-mail: admiss@simpson.edu
Web Site: www.simpson.edu
President/CEO: Jay K. Simmons
Admissions: Deborah Tierney
Financial Aid: Tracie Lynn Pavon

Type: Comprehensive **Sex:** Coed **Affiliation:** United Methodist. **Scores:** 46% ACT 18-23; 42% ACT 24-29 **% Accepted:** 89 **Admission Plans:** Deferred Admission **Application Deadline:** August 15 **Application Fee:** $0.00 **H.S. Requirements:** High school diploma required; GED accepted **Costs Per Year:** Application fee: $0. One-time mandatory fee: $200. Comprehensive fee: $43,839 includes full-time tuition ($35,209), mandatory fees ($667), and college room and board ($7963). College room only: $3860. Full-time tuition and fees vary according to class time, course load, degree level, and program. Room and board charges vary according to board plan and housing facility. Part-time tuition: $397 per credit hour. Part-time mandatory fees: $6 per credit hour. Part-time tuition and fees vary according to class time, course load, degree level, and program. **Scholarships:** Available. **Calendar System:** Miscellaneous, Summer session available **Enrollment:** Full-time 1,426, Graduate full-time 11, Graduate part-time 56, Part-time 197 **Faculty:** Full-time 95, Part-time 103 **Student-Faculty**

Ratio: 12:1 **Exams:** ACT essay component not used; SAT I or ACT; SAT essay component not used; SAT Reasoning; SAT Subject. **% Receiving Financial Aid:** 81 **% Residing in College-Owned, -Operated, or -Affiliated Housing:** 85 **Final Year or Final Semester Residency Requirement:** Yes **Regional Accreditation:** North Central Association of Colleges and Schools **Credit Hours For Degree:** 128-132 credit hours, depending on program, Bachelors **Professional Accreditation:** NASM. **Intercollegiate Athletics:** Baseball M; Basketball M & W; Cheerleading M & W; Cross-Country Running M & W; Football M; Golf M & W; Soccer M & W; Softball W; Swimming and Diving M & W; Tennis M & W; Track and Field M & W; Volleyball W; Wrestling M

SOUTHEASTERN COMMUNITY COLLEGE

1500 W Agency Rd.
West Burlington, IA 52655-0180
Tel: (319)752-2731; Free: 866-722-4692
Fax: (319)752-4957
E-mail: admoff@scciowa.edu
Web Site: www.scciowa.edu
President/CEO: Dr. Beverly Simone
Admissions: Stacy White
Financial Aid: Ean Freels

Type: Two-Year College **Sex:** Coed **Affiliation:** Iowa Department of Education Division of Community Colleges. **Scores:** 55.2% ACT 18-23; 18.4% ACT 24-29 **% Accepted:** 84 **Admission Plans:** Deferred Admission; Early Admission; Open Admission **Application Fee:** $0.00 **H.S. Requirements:** High school diploma or equivalent not required **Costs Per Year:** Application fee: $0. State resident tuition: $4740 full-time, $158 per credit hour part-time. Nonresident tuition: $4890 full-time, $163 per credit hour part-time. Mandatory fees: $50 full-time. Full-time tuition and fees vary according to course load, program, and reciprocity agreements. Part-time tuition varies according to course load, program, and reciprocity agreements. College room and board: $6216. Room and board charges vary according to board plan and housing facility. **Scholarships:** Available. **Calendar System:** Semester **Enrollment:** Full-time 1,280, Part-time 1,588 **Faculty:** Full-time 60, Part-time 69 **Student-Faculty Ratio:** 16:1 **Exams:** ACT; ACT essay component not used; SAT I; SAT essay component not used. **% Residing in College-Owned, -Operated, or -Affiliated Housing:** 4 **Regional Accreditation:** North Central Association of Colleges and Schools **Credit Hours For Degree:** 62 credit hours, Associates **Professional Accreditation:** AAMAE. **Intercollegiate Athletics:** Baseball M; Basketball M; Softball W; Volleyball W

SOUTHWESTERN COMMUNITY COLLEGE

1501 W Townline St.
Creston, IA 50801
Tel: (641)782-7081; Free: 800-247-4023
Fax: (641)782-3312
E-mail: carstens@swcciowa.edu
Web Site: www.swcciowa.edu
President/CEO: Dr. Barb Crittenden
Admissions: Lisa Carstens

Type: Two-Year College **Sex:** Coed **Affiliation:** Iowa Department of Education Division of Community Colleges. **Admission Plans:** Early Admission; Open Admission **Application Deadline:** September 5 **H.S. Requirements:** High school diploma required; GED accepted **Scholarships:** Available. **Calendar System:** Semester, Summer session available **Enrollment:** Full-time 839, Part-time 841 **Faculty:** Full-time 43, Part-time 80 **Student-Faculty Ratio:** 13:1 **Exams:** Other; SAT I or ACT. **% Residing in College-Owned, -Operated, or -Affiliated Housing:** 3 **Final Year or Final Semester Residency Requirement:** No **Regional Accreditation:** North Central Association of Colleges and Schools **Credit Hours For Degree:** 64 credit hours, Associates **Intercollegiate Athletics:** Baseball M; Basketball M & W

UNIVERSITY OF DUBUQUE

2000 University Ave.
Dubuque, IA 52001-5099
Tel: (563)589-3000; Free: 800-722-5583
Fax: (563)589-3690
E-mail: admissns@dbq.edu
Web Site: www.dbq.edu
President/CEO: Rev. Jeffrey F. Bullock
Admissions: Bob Broshous
Financial Aid: Timothy Kremer

Type: Comprehensive **Sex:** Coed **Affiliation:** Presbyterian. **Scores:** 81% SAT V 400+; 75% SAT M 400+; 51% ACT 18-23; 19% ACT 24-29 **% Accepted:** 78 **Application Deadline:** Rolling **Application Fee:** $25.00 **H.S. Requirements:** High school diploma required; GED accepted **Costs Per Year:** Application fee: $25. Comprehensive fee: $36,965 includes full-time tuition ($26,630), mandatory fees ($1265), and college room and board ($9070). College room only: $4380. Room and board charges vary according to board plan and housing facility. Part-time mandatory fees: $710 per credit hour. **Scholarships:** Available. **Calendar System:** Semester, Summer session available **Enrollment:** Full-time 1,590, Graduate full-time 241, Graduate part-time 113, Part-time 174 **Faculty:** Full-time 86, Part-time 130 **Student-Faculty Ratio:** 13:1 **Exams:** ACT essay component not used; SAT I or ACT; SAT essay component not used; SAT Reasoning; SAT Subject. **% Receiving Financial Aid:** 88 **% Residing in College-Owned, -Operated, or -Affiliated Housing:** 42 **Regional Accreditation:** North Central Association of Colleges and Schools **Credit Hours For Degree:** 120 semester hours, Bachelors **ROTC:** Army **Professional Accreditation:** ACIPE, ATS. **Intercollegiate Athletics:** Baseball M; Basketball M & W; Cross-Country Running M & W; Football M; Golf M & W; Soccer M & W; Softball W; Tennis M & W; Track and Field M & W; Volleyball W; Wrestling M

THE UNIVERSITY OF IOWA

Iowa City, IA 52242-1316
Tel: (319)335-3500; Free: 800-553-4692
Fax: (319)335-1535
E-mail: admissions@uiowa.edu
Web Site: www.uiowa.edu
President/CEO: Dr. Sally Mason
Admissions: Debra Miller
Financial Aid: Mark Warner

Type: University **Sex:** Coed **Scores:** 91% SAT V 400+; 99% SAT M 400+; 32% ACT 18-23; 51% ACT 24-29 **% Accepted:** 81 **Admission Plans:** Deferred Admission; Early Admission **Application Deadline:** April 1 **Application Fee:** $40.00 **H.S. Requirements:** High school diploma required; GED accepted **Costs Per Year:** Application fee: $40. State resident tuition: $6678 full-time, $279 per credit hour part-time. Nonresident tuition: $26,464 full-time, $1103 per credit hour part-time. Mandatory fees: $1426 full-time, $297 per term part-time. Full-time tuition and fees vary according to course level, course load, degree level, program, and student level. Part-time tuition and fees vary according to course level, course load, degree level, program, and student level. College room and board: $9728. College room only: $6345. Room and board charges vary according to board plan and housing facility. **Scholarships:** Available. **Calendar System:** Semester, Summer session available **Enrollment:** Full-time 19,546, Graduate full-time 5,623, Graduate part-time 3,410, Part-time 2,808 **Faculty:** Full-time 1,484, Part-time 132 **Student-Faculty Ratio:** 16:1 **Exams:** ACT essay component not used; SAT I or ACT; SAT essay component not used; SAT Reasoning; SAT Subject. **% Receiving Financial Aid:** 48 **% Residing in College-Owned, -Operated, or -Affiliated Housing:** 26 **Final Year or Final Semester Residency Requirement:** No **Regional Accreditation:** North Central Association of Colleges and Schools **Credit Hours For Degree:** 120 semester hours, Bachelors **ROTC:** Air Force, Army **Professional Accreditation:** AACN, AACSB, AALS, AANA, ABA, ABET, ACA, ACEJMC, ACPE, ACSP, ACIPE, ADA, ALA, AND, APA, APTA, ASHA, CAHME, CEPH, CORE, CSWE, JRCAT, JRCNMT, LCME/AMA, NAACLS, NASD, NASM, NAST, NRPA. **Intercollegiate Athletics:** Baseball M; Basketball M & W; Cheerleading M & W; Crew M & W; Cross-Country Running M & W; Field Hockey W; Football M; Golf M & W; Gymnastics M & W; Ice Hockey M & W; Lacrosse M & W; Rugby M & W; Sailing M & W; Soccer M & W; Softball W; Swimming and Diving M & W; Table Tennis M & W; Tennis M & W; Track and Field M & W; Ultimate Frisbee M & W; Volleyball M & W; Wrestling M

UNIVERSITY OF NORTHERN IOWA

1227 W 27th St.
Cedar Falls, IA 50614
Tel: (319)273-2311; Free: 800-772-2037
Fax: (319)273-2885
E-mail: admissions@uni.edu
Web Site: www.uni.edu
President/CEO: Dr. William N. Ruud
Admissions: Amy Schipper
Financial Aid: Heather Soesbe

Type: Comprehensive **Sex:** Coed **Affiliation:** Board of Regents, State of Iowa. **Scores:** 53.81% ACT 18-23; 35.12% ACT 24-29 **% Accepted:** 80

Admission Plans: Deferred Admission **Application Deadline:** August 15 **Application Fee:** $40.00 **H.S. Requirements:** High school diploma required; GED accepted **Costs Per Year:** Application fee: $40. State resident tuition: $6648 full-time, $277 per credit hour part-time. Nonresident tuition: $16,836 full-time, $701 per credit hour part-time. Mandatory fees: $1169 full-time. Full-time tuition and fees vary according to course load and program. Part-time tuition varies according to course load and program. College room and board: $8320. College room only: $4176. Room and board charges vary according to board plan and housing facility. **Scholarships:** Available. **Calendar System:** Semester, Summer session available **Enrollment:** Full-time 9,127, Graduate full-time 562, Graduate part-time 1,250, Part-time 1,042 **Faculty:** Full-time 556, Part-time 184 **Student-Faculty Ratio:** 17:1 **Exams:** ACT; ACT essay component not used; SAT I; SAT I or ACT; SAT essay component not used; SAT Reasoning; SAT Subject. **% Receiving Financial Aid:** 58 **% Residing in College-Owned, -Operated, or -Affiliated Housing:** 40 **Final Year or Final Semester Residency Requirement:** Yes **Regional Accreditation:** North Central Association of Colleges and Schools **Credit Hours For Degree:** 120 semester hours, Bachelors **ROTC:** Army **Professional Accreditation:** AACSB, AAFCS, ABET, ACA, ASHA, ATMAE, CSWE, JRCAT, NASAD, NASM, NRPA. **Intercollegiate Athletics:** Basketball M & W; Cross-Country Running M & W; Football M; Golf M & W; Soccer W; Softball W; Swimming and Diving W; Tennis W; Track and Field M & W; Volleyball W; Wrestling M

UPPER IOWA UNIVERSITY

605 Washington St., Box 1857
Fayette, IA 52142-1857
Tel: (563)425-5200; Free: 800-553-4150
Fax: (563)425-5277
E-mail: schmitts@uiu.edu
Web Site: www.uiu.edu
President/CEO: Dr. William R. Duffy, PhD
Admissions: Storm M. Schmitt
Financial Aid: Emily Sillcocks
Type: Comprehensive **Sex:** Coed **Scores:** 48% ACT 18-23; 41% ACT 24-29 **% Accepted:** 70 **Application Deadline:** Rolling **H.S. Requirements:** High school diploma required; GED accepted **Costs Per Year:** Comprehensive fee: $35,983 includes full-time tuition ($27,323), mandatory fees ($750), and college room and board ($7910). College room only: $3213. Full-time tuition and fees vary according to degree level, location, and program. Room and board charges vary according to board plan, housing facility, and location. **Scholarships:** Available. **Calendar System:** Miscellaneous, Summer session available **Enrollment:** Full-time 2,684, Graduate full-time 720, Graduate part-time 3, Part-time 1,755 **Faculty:** Full-time 71, Part-time 588 **Student-Faculty Ratio:** 18:1 **Exams:** SAT I or ACT; SAT Reasoning; SAT Subject. **% Receiving Financial Aid:** 100 **% Residing in College-Owned, -Operated, or -Affiliated Housing:** 96 **Final Year or Final Semester Residency Requirement:** Yes **Regional Accreditation:** North Central Association of Colleges and Schools **Credit Hours For Degree:** 60 semester hours, Associates; 120 semester hours, Bachelors **Professional Accreditation:** AACN. **Intercollegiate Athletics:** Baseball M; Basketball M & W; Cross-Country Running W; Football M; Golf M & W; Soccer M & W; Softball W; Tennis W; Track and Field W; Volleyball W; Wrestling M

VATTEROTT COLLEGE

7000 Fleur Dr.
Ste. 290
Des Moines, IA 50321
Tel: (515)309-9000; Free: 888-553-6627
Fax: (515)309-0366
Web Site: www.vatterott.edu
President/CEO: Sarah Bouma
Admissions: Dana Smith
Type: Two-Year College **Sex:** Coed **Calendar System:** Miscellaneous **Faculty:** Full-time 8, Part-time 6 **Student-Faculty Ratio:** 15:1 **Professional Accreditation:** ACCSC.

WALDORF COLLEGE

106 S 6th St.
Forest City, IA 50436-1713
Tel: (641)585-2450; Free: 800-292-1903
Fax: (641)585-8194
E-mail: admissions@waldorf.edu
Web Site: www.waldorf.edu

President/CEO: Dr. Robert Alsop
Admissions: Scott Pitcher
Financial Aid: Duane Polsdofer
Type: Comprehensive **Sex:** Coed **Affiliation:** Lutheran; Columbia Southern Education Group. **Scores:** 81% SAT V 400+; 70% SAT M 400+; 55% ACT 18-23; 15% ACT 24-29 **% Accepted:** 69 **Application Deadline:** Rolling **Application Fee:** $0.00 **H.S. Requirements:** High school diploma required; GED accepted **Costs Per Year:** Application fee: $0. Comprehensive fee: $27,878 includes full-time tuition ($19,804), mandatory fees ($1080), and college room and board ($6994). Full-time tuition and fees vary according to class time, course load, and program. Room and board charges vary according to board plan and housing facility. **Scholarships:** Available. **Calendar System:** Semester, Summer session available **Enrollment:** Full-time 1,119, Graduate full-time 32, Part-time 306 **Faculty:** Full-time 42, Part-time 4 **Student-Faculty Ratio:** 12:1 **Exams:** ACT essay component not used; SAT I or ACT; SAT essay component not used; SAT Reasoning; SAT Subject. **% Receiving Financial Aid:** 73 **% Residing in College-Owned, -Operated, or -Affiliated Housing:** 70 **Final Year or Final Semester Residency Requirement:** No **Regional Accreditation:** North Central Association of Colleges and Schools **Credit Hours For Degree:** 64 semester hours residential, 60 term hours online, Associates; 124 semester hours residential / 120 term hours online, Bachelors **Intercollegiate Athletics:** Baseball M; Basketball M & W; Bowling M & W; Cheerleading W; Cross-Country Running M & W; Football M; Golf M & W; Ice Hockey M; Soccer M & W; Softball W; Volleyball W; Wrestling M & W

WARTBURG COLLEGE

100 Wartburg Blvd.
Waverly, IA 50677-0903
Tel: (319)352-8200; Free: 800-772-2085
Fax: (319)352-8279
E-mail: admissions@wartburg.edu
Web Site: www.wartburg.edu
President/CEO: Dr. Darrel D. Colson
Admissions: Todd Coleman
Financial Aid: Jennifer Sassman
Type: Four-Year College **Sex:** Coed **Affiliation:** Lutheran. **Scores:** 90% SAT V 400+; 97% SAT M 400+; 45.4% ACT 18-23; 40.36% ACT 24-29 **% Accepted:** 74 **Admission Plans:** Deferred Admission; Early Decision Plan **Application Deadline:** Rolling **Application Fee:** $0.00 **H.S. Requirements:** High school diploma required; GED accepted **Costs Per Year:** Application fee: $0. Comprehensive fee: $47,840 includes full-time tuition ($37,400), mandatory fees ($980), and college room and board ($9460). College room only: $4685. Room and board charges vary according to board plan and housing facility. **Scholarships:** Available. **Calendar System:** Miscellaneous, Summer session available **Enrollment:** Full-time 1,474, Part-time 63 **Faculty:** Full-time 105, Part-time 72 **Student-Faculty Ratio:** 11:1 **Exams:** ACT; SAT I; SAT I and SAT II or ACT; SAT I or ACT; SAT II. **% Receiving Financial Aid:** 73 **% Residing in College-Owned, -Operated, or -Affiliated Housing:** 82 **Regional Accreditation:** North Central Association of Colleges and Schools **Credit Hours For Degree:** 126 semester hours, Bachelors **Professional Accreditation:** CSWE, NASM, NCATE. **Intercollegiate Athletics:** Baseball M; Basketball M & W; Cheerleading W; Cross-Country Running M & W; Football M; Golf M & W; Lacrosse W; Soccer M & W; Softball W; Tennis M & W; Track and Field M & W; Volleyball W; Wrestling M

WESTERN IOWA TECH COMMUNITY COLLEGE

4647 Stone Ave.
Sioux City, IA 51102-5199
Tel: (712)274-6400; Free: 800-352-4649
Fax: (712)274-6412
E-mail: lora.vanderzwaag@witcc.edu
Web Site: www.witcc.edu
President/CEO: Terry Murrell, PhD
Admissions: Lora Vander Zwaag
Type: Two-Year College **Sex:** Coed **Affiliation:** Iowa Department of Education Division of Community Colleges. **Scores:** 62% ACT 18-23; 11% ACT 24-29 **Admission Plans:** Deferred Admission; Early Admission; Open Admission **Application Deadline:** Rolling **Application Fee:** $0.00 **H.S. Requirements:** High school diploma required; GED accepted **Costs Per Year:** Application fee: $0. State resident tuition: $4100 full-time, $139 per credit hour part-time. Nonresident tuition: $4130 full-time, $140 per credit hour part-time. Mandatory fees: $944 full-time, $32 per credit hour part-time.

College room and board: $5355. College room only: $3069. **Scholarships:** Available. **Calendar System:** Semester, Summer session available **Enrollment:** Full-time 2,292, Part-time 3,860 **Faculty:** Full-time 80, Part-time 438 **Student-Faculty Ratio:** 16:1 **Exams:** ACT; SAT I or ACT. **% Residing in College-Owned, -Operated, or -Affiliated Housing: 5 Final Year or Final Semester Residency Requirement:** Yes **Regional Accreditation:** North Central Association of Colleges and Schools **Credit Hours For Degree:** 64 credits, Associates **Professional Accreditation:** ADA, APTA.

WILLIAM PENN UNIVERSITY
201 Trueblood Ave.
Oskaloosa, IA 52577-1799
Tel: (641)673-1001
Fax: (641)673-1396
E-mail: admissions@wmpenn.edu
Web Site: www.wmpenn.edu
President/CEO: Dr. John EE Ottosson
Admissions: Kerra Strong
Financial Aid: Cyndi Peiffer
Type: Comprehensive **Sex:** Coed **Affiliation:** Society of Friends. **Scores:** 52% ACT 18-23; 8% ACT 24-29 **% Accepted:** 27 **Admission Plans:** Deferred Admission **Application Fee:** $0.00 **H.S. Requirements:** High school diploma required; GED accepted **Costs Per Year:** Application fee: $0. Comprehensive fee: $28,248 includes full-time tuition ($23,780), mandatory fees ($730), and college room and board ($3738). College room only: $2914. Full-time tuition and fees vary according to class time, course load, degree level, location, and program. Room and board charges vary according to housing facility. Part-time tuition: $450 per credit hour. Part-time tuition varies according to class time, course load, degree level, location, and program. **Scholarships:** Available. **Calendar System:** Semester, Summer session available **Enrollment:** Full-time 1,415, Graduate full-time 82, Part-time 138 **Student-Faculty Ratio:** 15:1 **Exams:** ACT essay component not used; SAT I or ACT; SAT essay component not used; SAT Reasoning; SAT Subject. **% Receiving Financial Aid:** 94 **% Residing in College-Owned, -Operated, or -Affiliated Housing:** 40 **Final Year or Final Semester Residency Requirement:** Yes **Regional Accreditation:** North Central Association of Colleges and Schools **Credit Hours For Degree:** 64 credit hours, Associates; 124 credit hours, Bachelors **Intercollegiate Athletics:** Baseball M; Basketball M & W; Bowling M & W; Cheerleading M & W; Cross-Country Running M & W; Football M; Golf M & W; Soccer M & W; Softball W; Track and Field M & W; Volleyball W; Wrestling M

Tel: (502)852-5555; Free: 800-334-8635
Fax: (502)852-4776
E-mail: admitme@louisville.edu
Web Site: www.louisville.edu
President/CEO: Dr. James R. Ramsey
Admissions: Jenny L. Sawyer
Financial Aid: Patricia O. Arauz
Type: University **Sex:** Coed **Scores:** 97% SAT V 400+; 98% SAT M 400+; 34.3% ACT 18-23; 45.22% ACT 24-29 **% Accepted:** 72 **Admission Plans:** Deferred Admission **Application Deadline:** February 15 **Application Fee:** $50.00 **H.S. Requirements:** High school diploma required; GED accepted **Costs Per Year:** Application fee: $50. State resident tuition: $10,542 full-time, $440 per credit hour part-time. Nonresident tuition: $24,848 full-time, $1036 per credit hour part-time. Full-time tuition varies according to reciprocity agreements. Part-time tuition varies according to reciprocity agreements. College room and board: $7942. College room only: $4932. Room and board charges vary according to board plan and housing facility. **Scholarships:** Available. **Calendar System:** Semester, Summer session available **Enrollment:** Full-time 12,336, Graduate full-time 3,889, Graduate part-time 1,637, Part-time 3,433 **Faculty:** Full-time 824, Part-time 439 **Student-Faculty Ratio:** 16:1 **Exams:** Other; SAT I and SAT II or ACT; SAT I or ACT; SAT II. **% Receiving Financial Aid:** 58 **% Residing in College-Owned, -Operated, or -Affiliated Housing:** 33 **Final Year or Final Semester Residency Requirement:** No **Regional Accreditation:** Southern Association of Colleges and Schools **Credit Hours For Degree:** 63 credit hours, Associates; 121 credit hours, Bachelors **ROTC:** Air Force, Army **Professional Accreditation:** AACN, AACSB, AALS, AAMFT, ABA, ABET, ACSP, ACIPE, ADA, APA, APTA, ASHA, CIDA, CSWE, JRCERT, LCME/AMA, NASM, NASPAA, NAST, NCATE. **Intercollegiate Athletics:** Baseball M; Basketball M & W; Cheerleading M & W; Crew W; Cross-Country Running M & W; Field Hockey W; Football M; Golf M & W; Lacrosse W; Soccer M & W; Softball W; Swimming and Diving M & W; Tennis M & W; Track and Field M & W; Volleyball W

UNIVERSITY OF PIKEVILLE

147 Sycamore St.
Pikeville, KY 41501
Tel: (606)218-5250; Free: 866-232-7700
Fax: (606)218-5269
E-mail: wewantyou@pc.edu
Web Site: www.upike.edu
President/CEO: Dr. Burton Webb
Admissions: Teresa Lockhart
Financial Aid: Judy Vance Bradley
Type: Comprehensive **Sex:** Coed **Affiliation:** Presbyterian Church (U.S.A.). **Scores:** 94% SAT V 400+; 77% SAT M 400+; 56% ACT 18-23; 21% ACT 24-29 **% Accepted:** 100 **Admission Plans:** Deferred Admission; Open Admission **Application Deadline:** August 15 **Application Fee:** $0.00 **H.S. Requirements:** High school diploma required; GED accepted **Costs Per Year:** Application fee: $0. Comprehensive fee: $27,976 includes full-time tuition ($19,600) and college room and board ($8376). Full-time tuition varies according to course load. Room and board charges vary according to housing facility. Part-time tuition: $817 per semester hour. Part-time tuition varies according to course load. **Scholarships:** Available. **Calendar System:** Semester, Summer session available **Enrollment:** Full-time 1,220, Graduate full-time 624, Graduate part-time 3, Part-time 686 **Faculty:** Full-time 69, Part-time 82 **Student-Faculty Ratio:** 15:1 **Exams:** ACT essay component not used; SAT I or ACT; SAT essay component not used; SAT Reasoning. **% Receiving Financial Aid:** 98 **% Residing in College-Owned, -Operated, or -Affiliated Housing:** 58 **Final Year or Final Semester Residency Requirement:** No **Regional Accreditation:** Southern Association of Col-

leges and Schools **Credit Hours For Degree:** 64 semester hours, Associates; 120 semester hours, Bachelors **Professional Accreditation:** AOsA, NAACLS. **Intercollegiate Athletics:** Baseball M; Basketball M & W; Bowling M & W; Cheerleading M & W; Cross-Country Running M & W; Football M; Golf M & W; Lacrosse W; Soccer M & W; Softball W; Tennis M & W; Track and Field M & W; Volleyball W

WEST KENTUCKY COMMUNITY AND TECHNICAL COLLEGE

4810 Alben Barkley Dr.
Paducah, KY 42001
Tel: (270)554-9200
Fax: (270)554-6217
E-mail: debbie.smith@kctcs.edu
Web Site: www.westkentucky.kctcs.edu
President/CEO: Dr. Barbara Veazey
Admissions: Debbie Smith
Type: Two-Year College **Sex:** Coed **Affiliation:** Kentucky Community and Technical College System. **Admission Plans:** Early Admission; Open Admission **Application Deadline:** Rolling **H.S. Requirements:** High school diploma required; GED accepted **Scholarships:** Available. **Calendar System:** Semester, Summer session not available **Enrollment:** Full-time 2,364, Part-time 2,304 **Exams:** ACT; SAT I or ACT. **Regional Accreditation:** Southern Association of Colleges and Schools **Credit Hours For Degree:** 60 credit hours, Associates **Professional Accreditation:** ACBSP, ACEN, ACF, ADA, APTA, COE.

WESTERN KENTUCKY UNIVERSITY

1906 College Heights Blvd.
Bowling Green, KY 42101
Tel: (270)745-0111; Free: 800-495-8463
Fax: (270)745-6133
E-mail: jace.lux@wku.edu
Web Site: www.wku.edu
President/CEO: Gary A. Ransdell
Admissions: Dr. Jace Thomas Lux
Financial Aid: Cindy Burnette
Type: Comprehensive **Sex:** Coed **Scores:** 87% SAT V 400+; 87% SAT M 400+; 44.4% ACT 18-23; 31.9% ACT 24-29 **% Accepted:** 93 **Application Deadline:** August 1 **Application Fee:** $45.00 **H.S. Requirements:** High school diploma required; GED accepted **Costs Per Year:** Application fee: $45. State resident tuition: $9482 full-time, $395 per credit hour part-time. Nonresident tuition: $24,132 full-time, $1006 per credit hour part-time. Full-time tuition varies according to program and reciprocity agreements. Part-time tuition varies according to course load, program, and reciprocity agreements. College room and board: $7368. College room only: $4268. Room and board charges vary according to board plan and housing facility. **Scholarships:** Available. **Calendar System:** Semester, Summer session available **Enrollment:** Full-time 13,152, Graduate full-time 1,028, Graduate part-time 1,725, Part-time 4,158 **Faculty:** Full-time 776, Part-time 409 **Student-Faculty Ratio:** 18:1 **Exams:** ACT essay component not used; SAT I or ACT; SAT essay component not used; SAT Reasoning; SAT Subject. **% Receiving Financial Aid:** 63 **% Residing in College-Owned, -Operated, or -Affiliated Housing:** 32 **Final Year or Final Semester Residency Requirement:** No **Regional Accreditation:** Southern Association of Colleges and Schools **Credit Hours For Degree:** 60 hours, Associates; 120 hours, Bachelors **ROTC:** Air Force, Army **Professional Accreditation:** AACN, AACSB, AAFCS, ABET, ACA, ACEJMC, ACEN, ADA, AHIMA, AOTA, ASHA, ATMAE, CEPH, CSWE, NASAD, NASD, NASM, NASPAA, NCATE, NRPA. **Intercollegiate Athletics:** Baseball M; Basketball M & W; Cross-Country Running M & W; Football M; Golf M & W; Soccer W; Softball W; Tennis M & W; Track and Field M & W; Volleyball W

BATON ROUGE COMMUNITY COLLEGE
201 Community College Dr.
Baton Rouge, LA 70806
Tel: (225)216-8000; Free: 800-601-4558
Fax: (225)216-8100
Web Site: www.mybrcc.edu
President/CEO: Andrea Lewis Miller
Admissions: Nancy Clay
Type: Two-Year College **Sex:** Coed **Admission Plans:** Open Admission **Application Fee:** $7.00 **Calendar System:** Semester **Regional Accreditation:** Southern Association of Colleges and Schools **Professional Accreditation:** ACBSP. **Intercollegiate Athletics:** Baseball M

BATON ROUGE SCHOOL OF COMPUTERS
10425 Plz. Americana
Baton Rouge, LA 70816
Tel: (504)923-2525; Free: 888-920-BRSC
Fax: (504)923-2979
E-mail: admissions@brsc.net
Web Site: www.brsc.edu
President/CEO: Betty D. Truxillo
Type: Two-Year College **Sex:** Coed **Student-Faculty Ratio:** 25:1 **Exams:** Other. **Professional Accreditation:** ACCSC.

BLUE CLIFF COLLEGE–SHREVEPORT
8731 Park Plz. Dr.
Shreveport, LA 71105
Tel: (318)798-6868; Free: 800-516-6597
Web Site: www.bluecliffcollege.edu
President/CEO: Simon Lumley
Type: Two-Year College **Sex:** Coed **Application Fee:** $0.00 **H.S. Requirements:** High school diploma required; GED accepted **Faculty:** Full-time 19, Part-time 2 **Student-Faculty Ratio:** 12:1 **Final Year or Final Semester Residency Requirement:** No **Professional Accreditation:** ACCSC.

BOSSIER PARISH COMMUNITY COLLEGE
6220 E Texas St.
Bossier City, LA 71111
Tel: (318)678-6000
Web Site: www.bpcc.edu
President/CEO: James B. Henderson
Admissions: Richard Cockerham
Financial Aid: Vicki Temple
Type: Two-Year College **Sex:** Coed **Affiliation:** Louisiana Community and Technical College System. **Scores:** 50% SAT V 400+; 80% SAT M 400+; 41.8% ACT 18-23; 4.1% ACT 24-29 **% Accepted:** 91 **Admission Plans:** Early Admission; Open Admission **Application Fee:** $15.00 **H.S. Requirements:** High school diploma required; GED accepted **Costs Per Year:** Application fee: $15. State resident tuition: $139 per credit hour part-time. Nonresident tuition: $334 per credit hour part-time. Mandatory fees: $24 per credit hour part-time, $30 per term part-time. Part-time tuition and fees vary according to course load, location, and program. **Scholarships:** Available. **Calendar System:** Semester, Summer session available **Enrollment:** Full-time 3,741, Part-time 2,882 **Faculty:** Full-time 134, Part-time 152 **Student-Faculty Ratio:** 23:1 **Regional Accreditation:** Southern Association of Col-

leges and Schools **Credit Hours For Degree:** 66 semester hours, Associates **Professional Accreditation:** AAMAE, ACF, APTA, CoARC. **Intercollegiate Athletics:** Baseball M; Basketball M; Soccer W; Softball W

CAMERON COLLEGE
2740 Canal St.
New Orleans, LA 70119
Tel: (504)821-5881
Web Site: www.cameroncollege.com
President/CEO: Eleanor Cameron
Type: Two-Year College **Sex:** Coed **Admission Plans:** Open Admission **Application Fee:** $100.00 **Professional Accreditation:** COE.

CENTENARY COLLEGE OF LOUISIANA
2911 Centenary Blvd.
Shreveport, LA 71104
Tel: (318)869-5011; Free: 800-234-4448
Fax: (318)869-5005
E-mail: pcolbert@centenary.edu
Web Site: www.centenary.edu
President/CEO: Dr. B. David Rowe
Admissions: Peter Colbert
Financial Aid: Lynette Viskozki
Type: Comprehensive **Sex:** Coed **Affiliation:** United Methodist. **Scores:** 100% SAT V 400+; 100% SAT M 400+; 41.5% ACT 18-23; 48.5% ACT 24-29 **% Accepted:** 67 **Admission Plans:** Deferred Admission; Early Admission; Early Decision Plan **Application Deadline:** Rolling **Application Fee:** $0.00 **H.S. Requirements:** High school diploma required; GED accepted **Costs Per Year:** Application fee: $0. One-time mandatory fee: $250. Comprehensive fee: $46,250 includes full-time tuition ($33,900) and college room and board ($12,350). Full-time tuition varies according to course load, degree level, and student level. Room and board charges vary according to board plan, housing facility, and student level. **Scholarships:** Available. **Calendar System:** Miscellaneous, Summer session available **Enrollment:** Full-time 513, Graduate full-time 8, Graduate part-time 57, Part-time 10 **Faculty:** Full-time 57, Part-time 32 **Student-Faculty Ratio:** 8:1 **Exams:** ACT essay component not used; SAT I or ACT; SAT essay component not used. **% Receiving Financial Aid:** 78 **% Residing in College-Owned, -Operated, or -Affiliated Housing:** 77 **Final Year or Final Semester Residency Requirement:** Yes **Regional Accreditation:** Southern Association of Colleges and Schools **Credit Hours For Degree:** 124 semester credit hours, Bachelors **Professional Accreditation:** NASM, NCATE, TEAC. **Intercollegiate Athletics:** Baseball M; Basketball M & W; Cross-Country Running M & W; Golf M & W; Gymnastics W; Lacrosse M; Soccer M & W; Softball W; Swimming and Diving M & W; Tennis M & W; Volleyball W

CENTRAL LOUISIANA TECHNICAL COMMUNITY COLLEGE
4311 S MacArthur Dr.
Alexandria, LA 71302
Tel: (318)487-5439
Web Site: www.cltcc.edu
Admissions: Janice Bolden
Financial Aid: Kelly G. Caruso
Type: Two-Year College **Sex:** Coed **% Accepted:** 100 **Application Fee:** $5.00 **Scholarships:** Available. **Calendar System:** Semester **Enrollment:**

Full-time 8,416, Part-time 7,065 **Faculty:** Full-time 707, Part-time 379 **Student-Faculty Ratio:** 14:1 **Professional Accreditation:** COE.

DELGADO COMMUNITY COLLEGE

615 City Park Ave.
New Orleans, LA 70119
Tel: (504)671-5000
Fax: (504)483-1986
E-mail: enroll@dcc.edu
Web Site: www.dcc.edu
President/CEO: Joan Davis, JD
Admissions: Gwen Boute

Type: Two-Year College **Sex:** Coed **Affiliation:** Louisiana Community and Technical College System. **Admission Plans:** Open Admission **Application Deadline:** Rolling **Application Fee:** $25.00 **H.S. Requirements:** High school diploma required; GED accepted **Scholarships:** Available. **Calendar System:** Semester, Summer session available **Enrollment:** Full-time 7,906, Part-time 10,792 **Faculty:** Full-time 380, Part-time 220 **Student-Faculty Ratio:** 42:1 **Final Year or Final Semester Residency Requirement:** No **Regional Accreditation:** Southern Association of Colleges and Schools **Credit Hours For Degree:** 60 semester hours, Associates **ROTC:** Air Force, Army **Professional Accreditation:** ABET, ABFSE, ACBSP, ACEN, ACF, AHIMA, AOTA, APTA, ATMAE, CoARC, JRCEMTP, JRCERT, NAACLS. **Intercollegiate Athletics:** Baseball M; Basketball M & W; Track and Field W

DELTA SCHOOL OF BUSINESS AND TECHNOLOGY

517 Broad St.
Lake Charles, LA 70601
Tel: (337)439-5765
Fax: (337)436-5151
Web Site: www.deltatech.edu
President/CEO: Jeffrey Edwards
Admissions: Jeffery Tibodeaux

Type: Two-Year College **Sex:** Coed **Scholarships:** Available. **Calendar System:** Quarter **Student-Faculty Ratio:** 12:1 **Professional Accreditation:** ACICS.

DILLARD UNIVERSITY

2601 Gentilly Blvd.
New Orleans, LA 70122-3097
Tel: (504)283-8822; Free: 800-216-8094
Fax: (504)286-4895
E-mail: acyprian@dillard.edu
Web Site: www.dillard.edu
President/CEO: Dr. Walter Kimbrough
Admissions: Monica White
Financial Aid: Theodis Wright

Type: Four-Year College **Sex:** Coed **Affiliation:** interdenominational. **Scores:** 75% SAT V 400+; 72% SAT M 400+; 61% ACT 18-23; 8% ACT 24-29 **% Accepted:** 48 **Admission Plans:** Early Admission **Application Deadline:** Rolling **Application Fee:** $35.00 **H.S. Requirements:** High school diploma required; GED accepted **Costs Per Year:** Application fee: $35. Tuition: $15,038 full-time, $627 per credit hour part-time. Mandatory fees: $1214 full-time. **Scholarships:** Available. **Calendar System:** Semester, Summer session available **Enrollment:** Full-time 1,133, Part-time 52 **Faculty:** Full-time 72, Part-time 67 **Student-Faculty Ratio:** 12:1 **Exams:** ACT essay component not used; Other; SAT I or ACT; SAT essay component not used; SAT Reasoning; SAT Subject. **% Receiving Financial Aid:** 94 **% Residing in College-Owned, -Operated, or -Affiliated Housing:** 40 **Final Year or Final Semester Residency Requirement:** Yes **Regional Accreditation:** Southern Association of Colleges and Schools **Credit Hours For Degree:** 124 credit hours, Bachelors **ROTC:** Air Force, Army, Navy **Professional Accreditation:** ACEN. **Intercollegiate Athletics:** Basketball M & W; Cross-Country Running M & W; Track and Field M & W; Volleyball W

FLETCHER TECHNICAL COMMUNITY COLLEGE

1407 Hwy. 311
Schriever, LA 70395
Tel: (985)448-7900
Fax: (985)446-3308
Web Site: www.fletcher.edu
President/CEO: Earl Meador

Type: Two-Year College **Sex:** Coed **Application Fee:** $5.00 **Scholarships:**

Available. **Calendar System:** Semester **Faculty:** Full-time 26, Part-time 35 **Regional Accreditation:** Southern Association of Colleges and Schools **Professional Accreditation:** COE.

FORTIS COLLEGE

9255 Interline Ave.
Baton Rouge, LA 70809
Tel: (225)248-1015; Free: 855-4-FORTIS
Fax: (225)248-9571
Web Site: www.fortis.edu
President/CEO: Vaughn Hartunian
Admissions: Sheri Kirley

Type: Two-Year College **Sex:** Coed **Application Deadline:** Rolling **Application Fee:** $25.00 **H.S. Requirements:** High school diploma required; GED accepted **Scholarships:** Available. **Calendar System:** Quarter, Summer session not available **Exams:** Other. **Credit Hours For Degree:** 96 quarter hours, Associates **Professional Accreditation:** COE, NAACLS.

GRAMBLING STATE UNIVERSITY

403 Main St.
Grambling, LA 71245
Tel: (318)247-3811; Free: 800-569-4714
Fax: (318)274-6172
E-mail: flemingl@gram.edu
Web Site: www.gram.edu
President/CEO: Dr. Willie D. Larkin
Admissions: Latari Fleming
Financial Aid: Gavin Hamms

Type: University **Sex:** Coed **Affiliation:** University of Louisiana System. **Scores:** 62% SAT V 400+; 84% SAT M 400+; 51% ACT 18-23; 3% ACT 24-29 **% Accepted:** 38 **Admission Plans:** Early Admission **Application Deadline:** August 15 **Application Fee:** $20.00 **H.S. Requirements:** High school diploma required; GED not accepted **Costs Per Year:** Application fee: $20. State resident tuition: $5140 full-time, $215 per credit hour part-time. Nonresident tuition: $14,163 full-time, $591 per credit hour part-time. Full-time tuition varies according to course load, degree level, and student level. Part-time tuition varies according to course load, degree level, and student level. College room and board: $8638. College room only: $5320. Room and board charges vary according to housing facility. **Scholarships:** Available. **Calendar System:** Semester, Summer session available **Enrollment:** Full-time 3,308, Graduate full-time 339, Graduate part-time 631, Part-time 275 **Faculty:** Full-time 184, Part-time 15 **Student-Faculty Ratio:** 20:1 **Exams:** ACT essay component not used; SAT I or ACT; SAT essay component not used; SAT Reasoning. **% Receiving Financial Aid:** 82 **% Residing in College-Owned, -Operated, or -Affiliated Housing:** 49 **Final Year or Final Semester Residency Requirement:** No **Regional Accreditation:** Southern Association of Colleges and Schools **Credit Hours For Degree:** 60 credit hours, Associates; 125 credit hours, Bachelors **ROTC:** Air Force, Army **Professional Accreditation:** AACSB, ABET, ACEJMC, ACEN, CSWE, NASM, NASPAA, NAST, NCATE, NRPA. **Intercollegiate Athletics:** Baseball M; Basketball M & W; Bowling W; Cross-Country Running M & W; Football M; Soccer W; Softball W; Tennis W; Track and Field M & W; Volleyball W

HERZING UNIVERSITY

2500 Williams Blvd.
Kenner, LA 70062
Tel: (504)733-0074; Free: 800-596-0724
Fax: (504)733-0020
Web Site: www.herzing.edu/new-orleans
President/CEO: Mark Aspiazu

Type: Four-Year College **Sex:** Coed **Calendar System:** Semester **Regional Accreditation:** North Central Association of Colleges and Schools **Professional Accreditation:** ACICS.

ITI TECHNICAL COLLEGE

13944 Airline Hwy.
Baton Rouge, LA 70817
Tel: (225)752-4233; Free: 888-211-7165
Fax: (225)756-0903
E-mail: snorris@iticollege.edu
Web Site: www.iticollege.edu
President/CEO: Joe Martin
Admissions: Shawn Norris

Type: Two-Year College **Sex:** Coed **Calendar System:** Quarter **Final Year or Final Semester Residency Requirement:** No **Professional Accreditation:** ACCSC.

LOUISIANA COLLEGE
1140 College Dr.
Pineville, LA 71359-0001
Tel: (318)487-7011; Free: 800-487-1906
Fax: (318)487-7550
E-mail: admissions@lacollege.edu
Web Site: www.lacollege.edu
President/CEO: Dr. Rick Brewer
Admissions: Dr. Brandon Bannon
Financial Aid: David Barnard
Type: Comprehensive **Sex:** Coed **Affiliation:** Southern Baptist. **Scores:** 100% SAT V 400+; 60% SAT M 400+; 61% ACT 18-23; 19% ACT 24-29 **% Accepted:** 69 **Admission Plans:** Early Admission **Application Deadline:** August 22 **Application Fee:** $25.00 **H.S. Requirements:** High school diploma required; GED accepted **Costs Per Year:** Application fee: $25. Comprehensive fee: $20,202 includes full-time tuition ($13,200), mandatory fees ($1870), and college room and board ($5132). Full-time tuition and fees vary according to course load. Room and board charges vary according to board plan and housing facility. Part-time tuition: $440 per credit hour. Part-time mandatory fees: $364 per term. Part-time tuition and fees vary according to course load. **Scholarships:** Available. **Calendar System:** Semester, Summer session available **Enrollment:** Full-time 859, Graduate full-time 133, Graduate part-time 52, Part-time 48 **Faculty:** Full-time 74, Part-time 34 **Student-Faculty Ratio:** 11:1 **Exams:** SAT I or ACT. **% Residing in College-Owned, -Operated, or -Affiliated Housing:** 55 **Final Year or Final Semester Residency Requirement:** Yes **Regional Accreditation:** Southern Association of Colleges and Schools **Credit Hours For Degree:** 127 credit hours, Bachelors **ROTC:** Army **Professional Accreditation:** AACN, ACBSP, CSWE, NCATE. **Intercollegiate Athletics:** Baseball M; Basketball M & W; Cheerleading M & W; Cross-Country Running M & W; Football M; Golf M & W; Soccer M & W; Softball W; Tennis M & W

LOUISIANA CULINARY INSTITUTE
10550 Airline Hwy.
Baton Rouge, LA 70816
Tel: (225)769-8820; Free: 877-533-3198
Fax: (225)769-8792
Web Site: www.lci.edu
Type: Two-Year College **Sex:** Coed **Calendar System:** Quarter **Professional Accreditation:** COE.

LOUISIANA DELTA COMMUNITY COLLEGE
7500 Millhaven Rd.
Monroe, LA 71203
Tel: (318)345-9000; Free: 866-500-LDCC
Web Site: www.ladelta.edu
President/CEO: Dr. Barbara M. Hanson, EdD
Admissions: Kathy Gardner
Type: Two-Year College **Sex:** Coed **Affiliation:** Louisiana Community and Technical College System. **Calendar System:** Semester, Summer session available **Enrollment:** Full-time 2,259, Part-time 2,674 **Faculty:** Full-time 91, Part-time 106 **Student-Faculty Ratio:** 19:1 **Exams:** Other; SAT I or ACT. **Final Year or Final Semester Residency Requirement:** No **Regional Accreditation:** Southern Association of Colleges and Schools **Credit Hours For Degree:** 60 credit hours, Associates

LOUISIANA STATE UNIVERSITY AND AGRICULTURAL & MECHANICAL COLLEGE
Baton Rouge, LA 70803
Tel: (225)578-3202
Fax: (225)578-4433
E-mail: glamadrid@lsu.edu
Web Site: www.lsu.edu
President/CEO: Dr. F. King Alexander
Admissions: Guadalupe Lamadrid
Financial Aid: Amy Marix
Type: University **Sex:** Coed **Affiliation:** Louisiana State University System. **Scores:** 98% SAT V 400+; 99% SAT M 400+; 30.27% ACT 18-23; 54.26% ACT 24-29 **% Accepted:** 76 **Admission Plans:** Deferred Admission; Early Admission **Application Deadline:** April 15 **Application Fee:** $40.00 **H.S.**

Requirements: High school diploma required; GED accepted **Costs Per Year:** Application fee: $40. State resident tuition: $7552 full-time. Nonresident tuition: $24,715 full-time. Mandatory fees: $2290 full-time. College room and board: $11,200. College room only: $7230. Room and board charges vary according to board plan and housing facility. **Scholarships:** Available. **Calendar System:** Semester, Summer session available **Enrollment:** Full-time 23,602, Graduate full-time 4,236, Graduate part-time 1,132, Part-time 2,554 **Faculty:** Full-time 1,278, Part-time 172 **Student-Faculty Ratio:** 22:1 **Exams:** ACT essay component used in place of application essay; SAT I or ACT; SAT II; SAT essay component used in place of application essay; SAT Reasoning. **% Receiving Financial Aid:** 43 **% Residing in College-Owned, -Operated, or -Affiliated Housing:** 24 **Final Year or Final Semester Residency Requirement:** No **Regional Accreditation:** Southern Association of Colleges and Schools **Credit Hours For Degree:** 120 semester hours, Bachelors **ROTC:** Air Force, Army, Navy **Professional Accreditation:** AACSB, AAFCS, AALS, ABA, ABET, ACA, ACCE, ACEJMC, ALA, AND, APA, ASHA, ASLA, AVMA, CIDA, CSWE, NAAB, NASAD, NASM, NASPAA, NAST, NCATE, SAF. **Intercollegiate Athletics:** Baseball M; Basketball M & W; Cheerleading M & W; Cross-Country Running M & W; Football M; Golf M & W; Gymnastics W; Soccer W; Softball W; Swimming and Diving M & W; Tennis M & W; Track and Field M & W; Volleyball W

LOUISIANA STATE UNIVERSITY AT ALEXANDRIA
8100 Hwy. 71 S
Alexandria, LA 71302-9121
Tel: (318)445-3672; Free: 888-473-6417
Fax: (318)473-6418
E-mail: admissions@lsua.edu
Web Site: www.lsua.edu
President/CEO: Dr. Dan Howard
Admissions: Shelly Kieffer
Type: Four-Year College **Sex:** Coed **Affiliation:** Louisiana State University System. **Scores:** 94% SAT V 400+; 65.74% ACT 18-23; 17.99% ACT 24-29 **% Accepted:** 62 **Admission Plans:** Early Admission; Open Admission **Application Deadline:** Rolling **Application Fee:** $20.00 **H.S. Requirements:** High school diploma required; GED not accepted. For students 25 years and older: High school diploma or equivalent not required **Costs Per Year:** Application fee: $20. State resident tuition: $4170 full-time, $197 per credit hour part-time. Nonresident tuition: $11,703 full-time, $489 per credit hour part-time. Mandatory fees: $1413 full-time. College room and board: $9750. **Scholarships:** Available. **Calendar System:** Semester, Summer session available **Enrollment:** Full-time 1,741, Part-time 1,363 **Faculty:** Full-time 81, Part-time 89 **Student-Faculty Ratio:** 20:1 **Exams:** ACT essay component not used; SAT I or ACT; SAT essay component not used; SAT Reasoning; SAT Subject. **% Residing in College-Owned, -Operated, or -Affiliated Housing:** 9 **Final Year or Final Semester Residency Requirement:** No **Regional Accreditation:** Southern Association of Colleges and Schools **Credit Hours For Degree:** 60 credits, Associates; 120 credits, Bachelors **ROTC:** Army **Professional Accreditation:** ACEN, NAACLS, NCATE. **Intercollegiate Athletics:** Baseball M; Basketball M & W; Golf M & W; Rugby M; Soccer M & W; Softball W; Tennis W

LOUISIANA STATE UNIVERSITY AT EUNICE
PO Box 1129
Eunice, LA 70535-1129
Tel: (337)457-7311
Fax: (337)457-7311
Web Site: www.lsue.edu
President/CEO: William Nunez
Admissions: Gracie Guillory
Type: Two-Year College **Sex:** Coed **Affiliation:** Louisiana State University System. **Scores:** 54% ACT 18-23; 20% ACT 24-29 **% Accepted:** 99 **Admission Plans:** Early Admission; Open Admission **Application Deadline:** August 7 **Application Fee:** $25.00 **H.S. Requirements:** High school diploma required; GED accepted **Scholarships:** Available. **Calendar System:** Semester, Summer session available **Regional Accreditation:** Southern Association of Colleges and Schools **Credit Hours For Degree:** 66 credit hours, Associates **Professional Accreditation:** ACEN, CoARC, JRCERT. **Intercollegiate Athletics:** Baseball M; Basketball W

LOUISIANA STATE UNIVERSITY HEALTH SCIENCES CENTER
433 Bolivar St.
New Orleans, LA 70112-2223
Tel: (504)568-4808

Web Site: www.lsuhsc.edu
President/CEO: Dr. Larry Hollier, MD
Admissions: William Bryant Faust, IV
Financial Aid: Patrick Gorman

Type: University **Sex:** Coed **Affiliation:** Louisiana State University System. **Application Fee:** $50.00 **H.S. Requirements:** High school diploma required; GED accepted **Costs Per Year:** Application fee: $50. State resident tuition: $5101 full-time, $325 per semester hour part-time. Nonresident tuition: $9920 full-time, $677 per semester hour part-time. Mandatory fees: $992 full-time, $56 per semester hour part-time. Full-time tuition and fees vary according to degree level, program, and reciprocity agreements. Part-time tuition and fees vary according to course load, degree level, program, and reciprocity agreements. College room only: $4797. Room charges vary according to housing facility. **Scholarships:** Available. **Calendar System:** Miscellaneous, Summer session available **Enrollment:** Full-time 589, Graduate full-time 732, Graduate part-time 118, Part-time 288 **Faculty:** Full-time 726, Part-time 167 **% Residing in College-Owned, -Operated, or -Affiliated Housing:** 10 **Final Year or Final Semester Residency Requirement:** Yes **Regional Accreditation:** Southern Association of Colleges and Schools **Credit Hours For Degree:** 60 credits, Associates; 120 credits, Bachelors **ROTC:** Air Force, Army, Navy **Professional Accreditation:** AACN, AANA, ABET, ADA, AOTA, APA, APTA, ASHA, CEPH, CORE, CoARC, JCAHPO, LCME/AMA, NAACLS.

LOUISIANA STATE UNIVERSITY IN SHREVEPORT

1 University Pl.
Shreveport, LA 71115-2399
Tel: (318)797-5000; Free: 800-229-5957
Fax: (318)797-5286
E-mail: admissions@lsus.edu
Web Site: www.lsus.edu
President/CEO: Larry Clark
Admissions: Darlenna Atkins

Type: Comprehensive **Sex:** Coed **Affiliation:** Louisiana State University System. **Scores:** 100% SAT V 400+; 60.12% ACT 18-23; 31.67% ACT 24-29 **% Accepted:** 81 **Application Deadline:** Rolling **Application Fee:** $20.00 **H.S. Requirements:** High school diploma required; GED accepted **Costs Per Year:** Application fee: $20. State resident tuition: $5,630 full-time, $218.24 per credit hour part-time. Nonresident tuition: $18,784 full-time, $766.33 per credit hour part-time. Mandatory fees: $1,273 full-time, $51.28 per credit hour part-time. Full-time tuition and fees vary according to course load. Part-time tuition and fees vary according to course load. **Scholarships:** Available. **Calendar System:** Semester, Summer session available **Enrollment:** Full-time 1,826, Graduate full-time 375, Graduate part-time 1,277, Part-time 950 **Faculty:** Full-time 117, Part-time 61 **Student-Faculty Ratio:** 21:1 **Exams:** ACT essay component not used; SAT I or ACT; SAT essay component not used. **% Receiving Financial Aid:** 88 **Final Year or Final Semester Residency Requirement:** Yes **Regional Accreditation:** Southern Association of Colleges and Schools **Credit Hours For Degree:** 120 semester hours, Bachelors **ROTC:** Army **Professional Accreditation:** AACSB, ABET, APTA, LCME/AMA, NCATE. **Intercollegiate Athletics:** Baseball M; Basketball M & W; Cross-Country Running M & W; Soccer W; Tennis W

LOUISIANA TECH UNIVERSITY

PO Box 3168
Ruston, LA 71272
Tel: (318)257-0211; Free: 800-528-3241
E-mail: bulldog@latech.edu
Web Site: www.latech.edu
President/CEO: Dr. Daniel D. Reneau
Admissions: Jan B. Albritton
Financial Aid: Aimee D. Baxter

Type: University **Sex:** Coed **Affiliation:** University of Louisiana System. **Scores:** 42% ACT 18-23; 43% ACT 24-29 **% Accepted:** 64 **Admission Plans:** Early Admission **Application Fee:** $20.00 **H.S. Requirements:** High school diploma required; GED not accepted **Costs Per Year:** Application fee: $20. State resident tuition: $6400 full-time, $369 per credit hour part-time. Nonresident tuition: $23,398 full-time, $1077 per credit hour part-time. Mandatory fees: $2454 full-time. Full-time tuition and fees vary according to course load, location, and program. Part-time tuition varies according to course load, location, and program. College room and board: $5670. Room and board charges vary according to board plan and housing facility. **Scholarships:** Available. **Calendar System:** Quarter, Summer session

available **Enrollment:** Full-time 7,386, Graduate full-time 946, Graduate part-time 743, Part-time 3,296 **Faculty:** Full-time 353, Part-time 84 **Student-Faculty Ratio:** 22:1 **Exams:** ACT; SAT I and SAT II or ACT; SAT I or ACT; SAT Reasoning. **% Receiving Financial Aid:** 55 **% Residing in College-Owned, -Operated, or -Affiliated Housing:** 15 **Regional Accreditation:** Southern Association of Colleges and Schools **Credit Hours For Degree:** 60 credit hours, Associates; 126 credit hours, Bachelors **ROTC:** Air Force, Army **Professional Accreditation:** AABI, AACSB, AAFCS, ABET, ACEN, AHIMA, AND, APA, ASHA, CIDA, NAAB, NASAD, NASM, NCATE, SAF. **Intercollegiate Athletics:** Baseball M; Basketball M & W; Cross-Country Running M & W; Football M; Golf M; Softball W; Tennis W; Track and Field M & W; Volleyball W; Weight Lifting M & W

LOYOLA UNIVERSITY NEW ORLEANS

6363 Saint Charles Ave.
New Orleans, LA 70118-6195
Tel: (504)865-2011; Free: 800-4-LOYOLA
Fax: (504)865-3383
E-mail: rekaskel@loyno.edu
Web Site: www.loyno.edu
President/CEO: Rev. Kevin Wildes, SJ
Admissions: Roberta E. Kaskel
Financial Aid: Carrie E. Glass

Type: Comprehensive **Sex:** Coed **Affiliation:** Roman Catholic (Jesuit). **Scores:** 99% SAT V 400+; 96% SAT M 400+; 37.26% ACT 18-23; 47.58% ACT 24-29 **% Accepted:** 90 **Admission Plans:** Early Admission **Application Deadline:** Rolling **H.S. Requirements:** High school diploma required; GED accepted **Costs Per Year:** One-time mandatory fee: $250. Comprehensive fee: $51,468 includes full-time tuition ($36,938), mandatory fees ($1566), and college room and board ($12,964). College room only: $7430. Full-time tuition and fees vary according to class time, course load, and degree level. Room and board charges vary according to board plan and housing facility. Part-time tuition: $1052 per credit. Part-time tuition varies according to class time and degree level. **Scholarships:** Available. **Calendar System:** Semester, Summer session available **Enrollment:** Full-time 2,510, Graduate full-time 587, Graduate part-time 809, Part-time 181 **Faculty:** Full-time 257, Part-time 173 **Student-Faculty Ratio:** 12:1 **Exams:** ACT essay component used for advising; ACT essay component used for placement; SAT I or ACT; SAT essay component used for advising; SAT essay component used for placement; SAT Reasoning. **% Receiving Financial Aid:** 71 **% Residing in College-Owned, -Operated, or -Affiliated Housing:** 49 **Final Year or Final Semester Residency Requirement:** Yes **Regional Accreditation:** Southern Association of Colleges and Schools **Credit Hours For Degree:** 120 credit hours, Bachelors **ROTC:** Air Force, Army, Navy **Professional Accreditation:** AACSB, AALS, ABA, ACA, ACEN, NASM. **Intercollegiate Athletics:** Baseball M; Basketball M & W; Cheerleading M & W; Cross-Country Running M & W; Golf M & W; Swimming and Diving M & W; Table Tennis M & W; Tennis M & W; Track and Field M & W; Volleyball W

MCCANN SCHOOL OF BUSINESS & TECHNOLOGY (MONROE)

2319 Louisville Ave.
Monroe, LA 71201
Tel: (318)323-2889; Free: 800-923-1947
Fax: (318)324-9883
E-mail: susan.boudreaux@careertc.edu
Web Site: www.mccann.edu
President/CEO: Cheryl Powers Lokey
Admissions: Susan Boudreaux

Type: Two-Year College **Sex:** Coed **Affiliation:** Delta Career Education Corporation. **Admission Plans:** Deferred Admission **Application Deadline:** Rolling **Application Fee:** $40.00 **H.S. Requirements:** High school diploma required; GED accepted **Calendar System:** Quarter **Enrollment:** Full-time 450, Part-time 126 **Faculty:** Full-time 19, Part-time 16 **Student-Faculty Ratio:** 20:1 **Exams:** Other. **Final Year or Final Semester Residency Requirement:** No **Credit Hours For Degree:** 96 credits, Associates **Professional Accreditation:** ACICS, ARCST, COE.

MCCANN SCHOOL OF BUSINESS & TECHNOLOGY (SHREVEPORT)

1227 Shreveport-Barksdale Hwy.
Shreveport, LA 71105
Web Site: www.mccann.edu

Type: Two-Year College **Sex:** Coed **Professional Accreditation:** ACICS.

MCNEESE STATE UNIVERSITY

4205 Ryan St.
Lake Charles, LA 70609
Tel: (337)475-5000; Free: 800-622-3352
E-mail: ksmith2@mcneese.edu
Web Site: www.mcneese.edu
President/CEO: Dr. Philip C. Williams
Admissions: Kara Smith
Financial Aid: Taina J. Savoit
Type: Comprehensive **Sex:** Coed **Affiliation:** University of Louisiana System. **% Accepted:** 48 **Admission Plans:** Deferred Admission; Early Admission **Application Deadline:** Rolling **Application Fee:** $20.00 **H.S. Requirements:** High school diploma required; GED accepted **Costs Per Year:** Application fee: $20. Area resident tuition: $642.75 per credit hour part-time. State resident tuition: $5148 full-time. Nonresident tuition: $16,222 full-time. Mandatory fees: $2,142 full-time. Full-time tuition and fees vary according to course load. Part-time tuition varies according to course load. College room and board: $6814. College room only: $3900. Room and board charges vary according to board plan and housing facility. **Scholarships:** Available. **Calendar System:** Semester, Summer session available **Enrollment:** Full-time 5,721, Graduate full-time 316, Graduate part-time 381, Part-time 1,744 **Faculty:** Full-time 256, Part-time 147 **Student-Faculty Ratio:** 21:1 **Exams:** ACT essay component not used; SAT I or ACT; SAT essay component not used. **% Receiving Financial Aid:** 61 **Regional Accreditation:** Southern Association of Colleges and Schools **Credit Hours For Degree:** 60 semester hours, Associates; 120 semester hours, Bachelors **Professional Accreditation:** AACN, AACSB, AAFCS, ABET, ACEN, AND, JRCERT, NAACLS, NASAD, NASM, NCATE. **Intercollegiate Athletics:** Baseball M; Basketball M & W; Cross-Country Running M & W; Football M; Golf M & W; Soccer W; Softball W; Tennis W; Track and Field M & W; Volleyball W

NEW ORLEANS BAPTIST THEOLOGICAL SEMINARY

3939 Gentilly Blvd.
New Orleans, LA 70126-4858
Tel: (504)282-4455; Free: 800-662-8701
Web Site: www.nobts.edu
President/CEO: Charles S. Kelley, Jr.
Admissions: Dr. Paul E. Gregoire, Jr.
Financial Aid: Owen Nease
Type: Comprehensive **Sex:** Coed **Affiliation:** Southern Baptist. **Admission Plans:** Deferred Admission; Open Admission **Application Deadline:** August 9 **Application Fee:** $25.00 **H.S. Requirements:** High school diploma required; GED accepted **Scholarships:** Available. **Calendar System:** Semester, Summer session available **% Receiving Financial Aid:** 17 **Regional Accreditation:** Southern Association of Colleges and Schools **Credit Hours For Degree:** 69 hours, Associates; 126 hours, Bachelors **Professional Accreditation:** ACIPE, ATS, NASM.

NICHOLLS STATE UNIVERSITY

906 E First St.
Thibodaux, LA 70310
Tel: (985)446-8111; Free: 877-NICHOLLS
Fax: (985)448-4929
E-mail: nicholls@nicholls.edu
Web Site: www.nicholls.edu
President/CEO: Dr. Bruce Murphy
Admissions: Becky L. Durocher
Financial Aid: Casie Triche
Type: Comprehensive **Sex:** Coed **Affiliation:** University of Louisiana System. **Scores:** 96% SAT V 400+; 66% ACT 18-23; 27% ACT 24-29 **% Accepted:** 88 **Admission Plans:** Deferred Admission; Early Admission **Application Deadline:** Rolling **Application Fee:** $20.00 **H.S. Requirements:** High school diploma required; GED accepted **Costs Per Year:** Application fee: $20. State resident tuition: $4,922 full-time. Nonresident tuition: $15,854 full-time. Mandatory fees: $2,426 full-time. Full-time tuition and fees vary according to program. College room and board: $9676. Room and board charges vary according to board plan, housing facility, and location. **Scholarships:** Available. **Calendar System:** Semester, Summer session available **Enrollment:** Full-time 4,769, Graduate full-time 170, Graduate part-time 433, Part-time 926 **Faculty:** Full-time 257, Part-time 54 **Student-Faculty Ratio:** 20:1 **Exams:** SAT I or ACT; SAT Reasoning; SAT Subject. **% Receiving Financial Aid:** 63 **% Residing in College-Owned, -Operated, or -Affiliated Housing:** 18 **Regional Accreditation:** Southern Association

of Colleges and Schools **Credit Hours For Degree:** 60 semester hours, Associates; 120 semester hours, Bachelors **Professional Accreditation:** AACN, AACSB, AAFCS, ABET, ACEJMC, ACEN, AND, ASC, CoARC, JRCEMTP, NASAD, NASM, NCATE. **Intercollegiate Athletics:** Baseball M; Basketball M & W; Cross-Country Running M & W; Football M; Golf M; Soccer W; Softball W; Tennis M & W; Track and Field W; Volleyball W

NORTHSHORE TECHNICAL COMMUNITY COLLEGE

1710 Sullivan Dr.
Bogalusa, LA 70427
Tel: (504)732-6640
Web Site: www.northshorecollege.edu
Type: Two-Year College **Sex:** Coed **Application Fee:** $5.00 **Scholarships:** Available. **Calendar System:** Semester **Faculty:** Full-time 41, Part-time 39 **Professional Accreditation:** COE.

NORTHWEST LOUISIANA TECHNICAL COLLEGE

9500 Industrial Dr.
Minden, LA 71055
Tel: (318)371-3035
Web Site: www.nwltc.edu
Admissions: Helen Deville
Type: Two-Year College **Sex:** Coed **Application Fee:** $5.00 **Scholarships:** Available. **Calendar System:** Semester **Faculty:** Full-time 34, Part-time 48 **Professional Accreditation:** COE.

NORTHWESTERN STATE UNIVERSITY OF LOUISIANA

715 University Pky.
Natchitoches, LA 71497
Tel: (318)357-6361; Free: 800-327-1903
E-mail: recruiting@nsula.edu
Web Site: www.nsula.edu
President/CEO: Dr. Randall Webb
Admissions: Jana Lucky
Financial Aid: Lauren Jackson
Type: Comprehensive **Sex:** Coed **Affiliation:** University of Louisiana System. **Scores:** 86% SAT V 400+; 89% SAT M 400+; 61% ACT 18-23; 26% ACT 24-29 **% Accepted:** 58 **Admission Plans:** Deferred Admission **Application Deadline:** July 6 **Application Fee:** $20.00 **H.S. Requirements:** High school diploma required; GED accepted **Costs Per Year:** Application fee: $20. State resident tuition: $5180 full-time. Nonresident tuition: $15,968 full-time. Mandatory fees: $1826 full-time. Full-time tuition and fees vary according to course load and location. College room and board: $8584. College room only: $5356. Room and board charges vary according to board plan, housing facility, and location. **Scholarships:** Available. **Calendar System:** Semester, Summer session available **Enrollment:** Full-time 5,013, Graduate full-time 236, Graduate part-time 872, Part-time 2,823 **Faculty:** Full-time 264, Part-time 228 **Student-Faculty Ratio:** 19:1 **Exams:** ACT essay component not used; SAT I or ACT; SAT essay component not used; SAT Reasoning. **% Receiving Financial Aid:** 72 **% Residing in College-Owned, -Operated, or -Affiliated Housing:** 19 **Final Year or Final Semester Residency Requirement:** Yes **Regional Accreditation:** Southern Association of Colleges and Schools **Credit Hours For Degree:** 63 credit hours, Associates; 120 credit hours, Bachelors **ROTC:** Air Force, Army **Professional Accreditation:** AACN, AACSB, AAFCS, ABET, ACA, ACEJMC, ACEN, CSWE, JRCERT, NASAD, NASM, NAST, NCATE. **Intercollegiate Athletics:** Baseball M; Basketball M & W; Cross-Country Running M & W; Football M; Soccer W; Softball W; Tennis W; Track and Field M & W; Volleyball W

NUNEZ COMMUNITY COLLEGE

3710 Paris Rd.
Chalmette, LA 70043
Tel: (504)278-6200
Fax: (504)680-2243
E-mail: bmaillet@nunez.edu
Web Site: www.nunez.edu
President/CEO: Dr. Thomas R. Warner
Admissions: Becky Maillet
Type: Two-Year College **Sex:** Coed **Affiliation:** Louisiana Community and Technical College System. **Admission Plans:** Deferred Admission; Early Admission; Open Admission **Application Deadline:** Rolling **Application Fee:** $20.00 **H.S. Requirements:** High school diploma or equivalent not required. For practical nursing, EMT programs: High school diploma

required; GED accepted **Costs Per Year:** Application fee: $20. State resident tuition: $3335 full-time. Nonresident tuition: $6834 full-time. Mandatory fees: $689 full-time. Full-time tuition and fees vary according to course load and location. **Scholarships:** Available. **Calendar System:** Semester, Summer session available **Enrollment:** Full-time 878, Part-time 1,751 **Faculty:** Full-time 47, Part-time 52 **Student-Faculty Ratio:** 23:1 **Exams:** ACT. **Regional Accreditation:** Southern Association of Colleges and Schools **Credit Hours For Degree:** 60 semester hours, Associates **Professional Accreditation:** ATMAE.

OUR LADY OF THE LAKE COLLEGE
5414 Brittany Dr.
Baton Rouge, LA 70808
Tel: (225)768-1700
Fax: (225)768-1726
E-mail: admissions@ololcollege.edu
Web Site: www.ololcollege.edu
President/CEO: Dr. Tina Holland
Financial Aid: Tiffany D. Magee

Type: Comprehensive **Sex:** Coed **Affiliation:** Roman Catholic. **Scores:** 78.3% ACT 18-23; 16.04% ACT 24-29 **% Accepted:** 53 **Admission Plans:** Deferred Admission; Early Admission **Application Deadline:** August 15 **Application Fee:** $35.00 **H.S. Requirements:** High school diploma required; GED accepted **Costs Per Year:** Application fee: $35. Tuition: $10,387 full-time, $432.81 per credit hour part-time. Mandatory fees: $1052 full-time. **Scholarships:** Available. **Calendar System:** Semester, Summer session available **Enrollment:** Full-time 662, Graduate full-time 121, Graduate part-time 35, Part-time 823 **Exams:** Other; SAT I or ACT; SAT Reasoning; SAT Subject. **% Receiving Financial Aid:** 66 **Regional Accreditation:** Southern Association of Colleges and Schools **Credit Hours For Degree:** 63 credit hours, Associates; 129 credit hours, Bachelors **ROTC:** Air Force, Army **Professional Accreditation:** AANA, ACEN, APTA, ARCST, JRCERT, NAACLS.

REMINGTON COLLEGE–BATON ROUGE CAMPUS
10551 Coursey Blvd.
Baton Rouge, LA 70816
Tel: (225)922-3990
Fax: (225)922-6569
E-mail: monica.johnson@remingtoncollege.edu
Web Site: www.remingtoncollege.edu
President/CEO: Mike Smith
Admissions: Monica Butler-Johnson

Type: Two-Year College **Sex:** Coed **Calendar System:** Continuous **Professional Accreditation:** ACCSC, ACICS.

REMINGTON COLLEGE–LAFAYETTE CAMPUS
303 Rue Louis XIV
Lafayette, LA 70508
Tel: (337)981-4010; Free: 800-560-6192
Fax: (337)983-7130
E-mail: shannon.williams@remingtoncollege.edu
Web Site: www.remingtoncollege.edu
President/CEO: Jo Ann Boudreaux
Admissions: Shannon Lee Williams

Type: Two-Year College **Sex:** Coed **H.S. Requirements:** High school diploma required; GED accepted **Scholarships:** Available. **Calendar System:** Continuous, Summer session not available **Professional Accreditation:** ACCSC, ACICS.

REMINGTON COLLEGE–SHREVEPORT
2106 Bert Kouns Industrial Loop
Shreveport, LA 71118
E-mail: marc.wright@remingtoncollege.edu
Web Site: www.remingtoncollege.edu
President/CEO: Jerry Driskill
Admissions: Marc Wright

Type: Two-Year College **Sex:** Coed **Professional Accreditation:** ACCSC.

RIVER PARISHES COMMUNITY COLLEGE
925 W Edenborne Pky.
Gonzales, LA 70737
Tel: (225)675-8270
Fax: (225)675- 5478

E-mail: adauzat@rpcc.cc.la.us
Web Site: www.rpcc.edu
President/CEO: Dr. Dale Doty
Admissions: Allison Dauzat
Financial Aid: Terry Martin

Type: Two-Year College **Sex:** Coed **Application Fee:** $10.00 **Calendar System:** Semester **Regional Accreditation:** Southern Association of Colleges and Schools **Credit Hours For Degree:** 61 credits, Associates

SAINT JOSEPH SEMINARY COLLEGE
Saint Benedict, LA 70457
Tel: (985)867-2299
E-mail: registrar@sjasc.edu
Web Site: www.sjasc.edu
President/CEO: Rev. Gregory Boquet, OSB
Financial Aid: Katie F. Plude

Type: Four-Year College **Sex:** Men **Affiliation:** Roman Catholic. **Scores:** 33% ACT 18-23; 22% ACT 24-29 **Admission Plans:** Deferred Admission; Early Admission; Preferred Admission **Application Deadline:** Rolling **Application Fee:** $0.00 **H.S. Requirements:** High school diploma required; GED accepted **Scholarships:** Available. **Calendar System:** Semester, Summer session not available **Enrollment:** Full-time 104, Part-time 3 **Faculty:** Full-time 10, Part-time 12 **Student-Faculty Ratio:** 3:1 **Exams:** ACT; ACT essay component not used. **% Residing in College-Owned, -Operated, or -Affiliated Housing:** 100 **Final Year or Final Semester Residency Requirement:** Yes **Regional Accreditation:** Southern Association of Colleges and Schools **Credit Hours For Degree:** 124 semester hours, Bachelors

SOUTH CENTRAL LOUISIANA TECHNICAL COLLEGE
900 Youngs Rd.
Morgan City, LA 70380
Tel: (985)380-2957
Web Site: www.scl.edu
President/CEO: Earl W. Meador, DJ
Admissions: Melanie Henry

Type: Two-Year College **Sex:** Coed **Application Fee:** $5.00 **Scholarships:** Available. **Calendar System:** Semester **Faculty:** Full-time 39, Part-time 24 **Professional Accreditation:** COE.

SOUTH LOUISIANA COMMUNITY COLLEGE
1101 Bertrand Dr.
Lafayette, LA 70506
Tel: (337)521-9000
E-mail: admissions@solacc.edu
Web Site: www.solacc.edu
President/CEO: Dr. Natalie Harder

Type: Two-Year College **Sex:** Coed **Affiliation:** Louisiana Community and Technical College System. **Admission Plans:** Open Admission **Application Fee:** $0.00 **H.S. Requirements:** High school diploma required; GED accepted **Costs Per Year:** Application fee: $0. State resident tuition: $3,335 full-time, $138.96 per credit hour part-time. Nonresident tuition: $6,940 full-time, $289.16 per credit hour part-time. Mandatory fees: $639 full-time, $28 per credit hour part-time, $15 per term part-time. Full-time tuition and fees vary according to course load and program. Part-time tuition and fees vary according to course load and program. **Calendar System:** Semester, Summer session available **Enrollment:** Full-time 3,436, Part-time 2,896 **Faculty:** Full-time 133, Part-time 124 **Student-Faculty Ratio:** 25:1 **Final Year or Final Semester Residency Requirement:** No **Regional Accreditation:** Southern Association of Colleges and Schools **Credit Hours For Degree:** 60 semester credit hours, Associates

SOUTHEASTERN LOUISIANA UNIVERSITY
548 Ned McGehee Dr.
Hammond, LA 70402
Tel: (985)549-2000; Free: 800-222-7358
Fax: (985)549-5095
E-mail: admissions@selu.edu
Web Site: www.selu.edu
President/CEO: Dr. John Crain
Admissions: Mike Rivault
Financial Aid: Charles Cambre

Type: Comprehensive **Sex:** Coed **Affiliation:** University of Louisiana System. **Scores:** 64.6% ACT 18-23; 27.6% ACT 24-29 **% Accepted:** 87

Admission Plans: Deferred Admission; Early Admission **Application Deadline:** August 1 **Application Fee:** $20.00 **H.S. Requirements:** High school diploma required; GED accepted **Costs Per Year:** Application fee: $20. State resident tuition: $5278 full-time, $303 per credit hour part-time. Nonresident tuition: $17,756 full-time, $823 per credit hour part-time. Mandatory fees: $2002 full-time. Full-time tuition and fees vary according to course load. Part-time tuition varies according to course load. College room and board: $7370. College room only: $4660. Room and board charges vary according to board plan and housing facility. **Scholarships:** Available. **Calendar System:** Semester, Summer session available **Enrollment:** Full-time 9,580, Graduate full-time 369, Graduate part-time 658, Part-time 3,987 **Faculty:** Full-time 482, Part-time 113 **Student-Faculty Ratio:** 21:1 **Exams:** ACT essay component not used; SAT I or ACT; SAT essay component not used; SAT Reasoning. **% Receiving Financial Aid:** 62 **% Residing in College-Owned, -Operated, or -Affiliated Housing:** 21 **Final Year or Final Semester Residency Requirement:** Yes **Regional Accreditation:** Southern Association of Colleges and Schools **Credit Hours For Degree:** 60 semester hours, Associates; 120 semester hours, Bachelors **ROTC:** Army **Professional Accreditation:** AACN, AACSB, ABET, ACA, ASHA, ATMAE, CSWE, NASAD, NASM, NCATE. **Intercollegiate Athletics:** Baseball M; Basketball M & W; Cross-Country Running M & W; Football M; Golf M; Soccer W; Softball W; Tennis W; Track and Field M & W; Volleyball W

SOUTHERN UNIVERSITY AND AGRICULTURAL AND MECHANICAL COLLEGE

Baton Rouge, LA 70813
Tel: (225)771-4500
E-mail: velva_thomas@subr.edu
Web Site: www.subr.edu
President/CEO: Dr. Kofi Lomotey
Admissions: Velva Thomas
Financial Aid: Phillip Rodgers, Sr.

Type: University **Sex:** Coed **Affiliation:** Southern University System. **Scores:** 72% SAT M 400+; 53.7% ACT 18-23; 10% ACT 24-29 **% Accepted:** 57 **Admission Plans:** Early Admission **Application Deadline:** July 1 **Application Fee:** $20.00 **H.S. Requirements:** High school diploma required; GED accepted **Scholarships:** Available. **Calendar System:** Semester, Summer session available **Enrollment:** Full-time 5,763, Part-time 696 **Faculty:** Full-time 405, Part-time 141 **Student-Faculty Ratio:** 16:1 **Exams:** SAT I or ACT. **% Receiving Financial Aid:** 85 **% Residing in College-Owned, -Operated, or -Affiliated Housing:** 31 **Regional Accreditation:** Southern Association of Colleges and Schools **Credit Hours For Degree:** 65 credits, Associates; 124 credits, Bachelors **ROTC:** Air Force, Army, Navy **Professional Accreditation:** AACN, AACSB, AAFCS, ABA, ABET, ACA, ACEJMC, ACEN, AND, ASHA, CORE, CSWE, NASAD, NASM, NASPAA, NCATE. **Intercollegiate Athletics:** Baseball M; Basketball M & W; Bowling W; Cross-Country Running M; Football M; Golf M & W; Softball W; Tennis M & W; Track and Field M & W; Volleyball W

SOUTHERN UNIVERSITY AT NEW ORLEANS

6400 Press Dr.
New Orleans, LA 70126-1009
Tel: (504)286-5000
E-mail: llatimor@suno.edu
Web Site: www.suno.edu
President/CEO: Dr. Victor Ukpolo
Admissions: Leatrice D. Latimore
Financial Aid: La'Charlotte C. Garrett

Type: Comprehensive **Sex:** Coed **Affiliation:** Southern University System. **% Accepted:** 79 **Admission Plans:** Deferred Admission; Early Action; Early Admission; Early Decision Plan **Application Deadline:** July 1 **Application Fee:** $20.00 **H.S. Requirements:** High school diploma required; GED accepted **Scholarships:** Available. **Calendar System:** Semester, Summer session available **Enrollment:** Full-time 2,048, Graduate full-time 228, Graduate part-time 323, Part-time 542 **Faculty:** Full-time 100, Part-time 2 **Exams:** ACT; ACT essay component not used; ACT essay component used for admission; ACT essay component used for advising; ACT essay component used for placement; SAT I or ACT. **Regional Accreditation:** Southern Association of Colleges and Schools **Credit Hours For Degree:** 62 semester hours, Associates; 124 semester hours, Bachelors **ROTC:** Air Force, Army **Professional Accreditation:** CSWE, NCATE. **Intercollegiate Athletics:** Basketball M & W; Cross-Country Running M & W; Track and Field M & W; Ultimate Frisbee M & W; Volleyball M & W

SOUTHERN UNIVERSITY AT SHREVEPORT

3050 Martin Luther King, Jr. Dr.
Shreveport, LA 71107
Tel: (318)670-6000; Free: 800-458-1472
Fax: (318)674-3489
E-mail: danderson@susla.edu
Web Site: www.susla.edu
Admissions: Danielle Anderson

Type: Two-Year College **Sex:** Coed **Affiliation:** Southern University System. **Scores:** 7.7% ACT 18-23 **Scholarships:** Available. **Calendar System:** Semester, Summer session available **Enrollment:** Full-time 1,922, Part-time 1,252 **Faculty:** Full-time 68, Part-time 55 **Student-Faculty Ratio:** 27:1 **Exams:** ACT; ACT essay component not used; SAT I or ACT; SAT essay component not used. **% Residing in College-Owned, -Operated, or -Affiliated Housing:** 7 **Final Year or Final Semester Residency Requirement:** No **Regional Accreditation:** Southern Association of Colleges and Schools **Credit Hours For Degree:** 68 credits, Associates **ROTC:** Army **Professional Accreditation:** ACEN, ADA, AHIMA, ARCST, ATMAE, CoARC, JRCERT, NAACLS. **Intercollegiate Athletics:** Basketball M & W

SOUTHWEST UNIVERSITY

2200 Veterans Memorial Blvd.
Kenner, LA 70062
Tel: (504)468-2900; Free: 800-433-5923
E-mail: admissions@southwest.edu
Web Site: www.southwest.edu
President/CEO: Grayce Lee

Type: Comprehensive **Sex:** Coed **Application Fee:** $75.00 **H.S. Requirements:** High school diploma required; GED accepted **Costs Per Year:** Application fee: $75. Tuition: $825 per course part-time. **Credit Hours For Degree:** 60 semester hours, Associates; 120 semester hours, Bachelors **Professional Accreditation:** DEAC.

SOWELA TECHNICAL COMMUNITY COLLEGE

3820 Senator J. Bennett Johnston Ave.
Lake Charles, LA 70615
Tel: (337)421-6565; Free: 800-256-0483
Web Site: www.sowela.edu
President/CEO: Dr. Neil Aspinwall

Type: Two-Year College **Sex:** Coed **Affiliation:** Louisiana Community and Technical College System. **% Accepted:** 100 **Admission Plans:** Early Admission; Open Admission **Application Deadline:** Rolling **Application Fee:** $0.00 **H.S. Requirements:** High school diploma required; GED accepted. For diploma program students: High school diploma or equivalent not required **Costs Per Year:** Application fee: $0. State resident tuition: $3,335 full-time, $138.96 per credit hour part-time. Nonresident tuition: $6762 full-time, $281.75 per credit hour part-time. Mandatory fees: $742 full-time, $35 per credit hour part-time, $5 per term part-time. Full-time tuition and fees vary according to course load, program, and reciprocity agreements. Part-time tuition and fees vary according to course load, program, and reciprocity agreements. **Scholarships:** Available. **Calendar System:** Semester, Summer session available **Enrollment:** Full-time 1,796, Part-time 1,926 **Faculty:** Full-time 92, Part-time 73 **Student-Faculty Ratio:** 22:1 **Exams:** ACT essay component not used; SAT essay component not used; SAT Reasoning; SAT Subject. **Final Year or Final Semester Residency Requirement:** No **Regional Accreditation:** Southern Association of Colleges and Schools **Credit Hours For Degree:** minimum 60 credit hours, Associates **Professional Accreditation:** COE.

TULANE UNIVERSITY

6823 St. Charles Ave.
New Orleans, LA 70118-5669
Tel: (504)865-5000; Free: 800-873-9283
Fax: (504)862-8715
E-mail: undergrad.admission@tulane.edu
Web Site: www.tulane.edu
President/CEO: Michael A. Fitts
Admissions: Earl Retif
Financial Aid: Michael T. Goodman

Type: University **Sex:** Coed **Scores:** 100% SAT V 400+; 100% SAT M 400+; 2.68% ACT 18-23; 31.45% ACT 24-29 **% Accepted:** 30 **Admission Plans:** Deferred Admission; Early Decision Plan **Application Deadline:** January 15 **Application Fee:** $0.00 **H.S. Requirements:** High school diploma required; GED accepted **Costs Per Year:** Application fee: $0. Comprehensive fee:

$63,396 includes full-time tuition ($45,758), mandatory fees ($3880), and college room and board ($13,758). College room only: $8140. Room and board charges vary according to board plan, housing facility, and student level. **Scholarships:** Available. **Calendar System:** Semester, Summer session available **Enrollment:** Full-time 6,752, Graduate full-time 4,385, Graduate part-time 725, Part-time 1,587 **Faculty:** Full-time 704, Part-time 500 **Student-Faculty Ratio:** 9:1 **Exams:** ACT essay component not used; SAT I or ACT; SAT essay component not used; SAT Reasoning; SAT Subject. **% Receiving Financial Aid:** 36 **% Residing in College-Owned, -Operated, or -Affiliated Housing:** 45 **Regional Accreditation:** Southern Association of Colleges and Schools **Credit Hours For Degree:** 120 credit hours, Bachelors **ROTC:** Air Force, Army, Navy **Professional Accreditation:** AACSB, AALS, ABA, ABET, AND, APA, CAHME, CEPH, CSWE, LCME/AMA, NAAB, TEAC. **Intercollegiate Athletics:** Baseball M; Basketball M & W; Crew M & W; Cross-Country Running M & W; Football M; Golf W; Gymnastics M & W; Ice Hockey M & W; Lacrosse M & W; Rugby M; Sailing M & W; Soccer M & W; Swimming and Diving M & W; Tennis M & W; Track and Field M & W; Volleyball M & W; Water Polo M & W

UNIVERSITY OF HOLY CROSS

4123 Woodland Dr.
New Orleans, LA 70131-7399
Tel: (504)394-7744; Free: 800-259-7744
Fax: (504)391-2421
E-mail: dkennedy@olhcc.edu
Web Site: www.olhcc.edu
President/CEO: Dr. David Landry
Admissions: Donna Kennedy
Financial Aid: Hayden Wagar
Type: Comprehensive **Sex:** Coed **Affiliation:** Roman Catholic. **Admission Plans:** Deferred Admission; Open Admission **Application Deadline:** July 20 **Application Fee:** $15.00 **H.S. Requirements:** High school diploma required; GED accepted **Costs Per Year:** Application fee: $15. Tuition: $9792 full-time, $408 per credit hour part-time. Mandatory fees: $1120 full-time, $502.50 per term part-time. Full-time tuition and fees vary according to course load and degree level. Part-time tuition and fees vary according to course load and degree level. **Scholarships:** Available. **Calendar System:** Semester, Summer session available **% Receiving Financial Aid:** 87 **Regional Accreditation:** Southern Association of Colleges and Schools **Credit Hours For Degree:** 60 semester hours, Associates; 125 semester hours, Bachelors **ROTC:** Air Force, Army **Professional Accreditation:** ACA, ACEN, CoARC, NCATE.

UNIVERSITY OF LOUISIANA AT LAFAYETTE

104 University Cir.
PO Drawer 41008
Lafayette, LA 70504
Tel: (337)482-1000; Free: 800-752-6553
Fax: (337)482-6195
E-mail: admissions@louisiana.edu
Web Site: www.louisiana.edu
President/CEO: Dr. Joseph Savoie
Admissions: Andy Benoit, Jr.
Financial Aid: Cindy S. Perez
Type: University **Sex:** Coed **Affiliation:** University of Louisiana System. **Scores:** 94% SAT M 400+; 56% ACT 18-23; 38% ACT 24-29 **% Accepted:** 55 **Admission Plans:** Deferred Admission; Early Admission **Application Deadline:** Rolling **Application Fee:** $25.00 **H.S. Requirements:** High school diploma required; GED accepted. For applicants 21 or over: High school diploma or equivalent not required **Costs Per Year:** Application fee: $25. State resident tuition: $5407 full-time, $344 per credit hour part-time. Nonresident tuition: $19,135 full-time, $916 per credit hour part-time. Mandatory fees: $2849 full-time. College room and board: $8952. College room only: $5756. **Scholarships:** Available. **Calendar System:** Semester, Summer session available **Enrollment:** Full-time 12,867, Graduate full-time 987, Graduate part-time 651, Part-time 3,003 **Faculty:** Full-time 601, Part-time 192 **Student-Faculty Ratio:** 23:1 **Exams:** SAT I or ACT. **% Receiving Financial Aid:** 56 **% Residing in College-Owned, -Operated, or -Affiliated Housing:** 20 **Regional Accreditation:** Southern Association of Colleges and Schools **Credit Hours For Degree:** 124 semester hours, Bachelors **ROTC:** Army **Professional Accreditation:** AACN, AACSB, AAFCS, ABET, ACEJMC, AHIMA, AND, ASHA, ATMAE, CIDA, NAAB, NASAD, NASM, NCATE. **Intercollegiate Athletics:** Baseball M; Basketball M & W; Cross-Country Running M & W; Football M; Golf M; Soccer W; Softball W; Tennis M & W; Track and Field M & W; Volleyball W

UNIVERSITY OF LOUISIANA AT MONROE

700 University Ave.
Monroe, LA 71209-0001
Tel: (318)342-1000; Free: 800-372-5127
Fax: (318)342-1049
E-mail: peterson@ulm.edu
Web Site: www.ulm.edu
President/CEO: Dr. Nick Bruno
Admissions: Mary Peterson
Financial Aid: Teresa Smith
Type: University **Sex:** Coed **Affiliation:** University of Louisiana System. **Scores:** 97% SAT M 400+; 62.01% ACT 18-23; 29.54% ACT 24-29 **% Accepted:** 94 **Admission Plans:** Early Admission **Application Deadline:** Rolling **Application Fee:** $20.00 **H.S. Requirements:** High school diploma required; GED accepted **Costs Per Year:** Application fee: $20. State resident tuition: $5,483 full-time, $345 per credit hour part-time. Nonresident tuition: $17,584 full-time, $345 per credit hour part-time. Mandatory fees: $2,174 full-time, $268.40 per credit hour part-time. Full-time tuition and fees vary according to course load, degree level, and program. Part-time tuition and fees vary according to course load, degree level, and program. College room and board: $7048. College room only: $4158. Room and board charges vary according to board plan and housing facility. **Scholarships:** Available. **Calendar System:** Semester, Summer session available **Enrollment:** Full-time 4,894, Graduate full-time 845, Graduate part-time 524, Part-time 2,382 **Faculty:** Full-time 288, Part-time 127 **Student-Faculty Ratio:** 19:1 **Exams:** SAT I or ACT. **% Residing in College-Owned, -Operated, or -Affiliated Housing:** 24 **Final Year or Final Semester Residency Requirement:** No **Regional Accreditation:** Southern Association of Colleges and Schools **Credit Hours For Degree:** 60 credit hours, Associates; 120 credit hours, Bachelors **ROTC:** Army **Professional Accreditation:** AACN, AACSB, AAFCS, AAMFT, ABET, ACA, ACCE, ACEJMC, ACPE, ADA, AOTA, ASHA, CSWE, JRCERT, NASM, NCATE. **Intercollegiate Athletics:** Baseball M; Basketball M & W; Cross-Country Running M & W; Football M; Golf M & W; Soccer W; Softball W; Tennis W; Track and Field M & W; Volleyball W

UNIVERSITY OF NEW ORLEANS

2000 Lakeshore Dr.
New Orleans, LA 70148
Tel: (504)280-6000; Free: 888-514-4275
Fax: (504)280-5522
E-mail: cagooden@uno.edu
Web Site: www.uno.edu
President/CEO: Dr. John W. Nicklow
Admissions: Carlos Gooden
Financial Aid: Ann Lockridge
Type: University **Sex:** Coed **Affiliation:** University of Louisiana System. **Scores:** 93% SAT V 400+; 94% SAT M 400+; 62.57% ACT 18-23; 28.51% ACT 24-29 **% Accepted:** 58 **Admission Plans:** Deferred Admission; Early Admission **Application Deadline:** July 25 **Application Fee:** $20.00 **H.S. Requirements:** High school diploma required; GED accepted **Costs Per Year:** Application fee: $20. State resident tuition: $6090 full-time. Nonresident tuition: $19,907 full-time. Mandatory fees: $2004 full-time. Full-time tuition and fees vary according to course load. College room and board: $9515. Room and board charges vary according to board plan and housing facility. **Scholarships:** Available. **Calendar System:** Semester, Summer session available **Enrollment:** Full-time 4,847, Graduate full-time 983, Graduate part-time 839, Part-time 1,754 **Faculty:** Full-time 270, Part-time 132 **Student-Faculty Ratio:** 20:1 **Exams:** ACT essay component not used; SAT I or ACT; SAT essay component not used; SAT Reasoning. **% Receiving Financial Aid:** 67 **% Residing in College-Owned, -Operated, or -Affiliated Housing:** 10 **Final Year or Final Semester Residency Requirement:** No **Regional Accreditation:** Southern Association of Colleges and Schools **Credit Hours For Degree:** 120 semester hours, Bachelors **ROTC:** Air Force, Army, Navy **Professional Accreditation:** AACSB, ABET, ACA, ACSP, NASAD, NASM, NASPAA, NAST, NCATE. **Intercollegiate Athletics:** Baseball M; Basketball M & W; Cross-Country Running M & W; Golf M; Tennis M & W; Track and Field M & W; Volleyball W

VIRGINIA COLLEGE IN BATON ROUGE

9501 Cortana Pl.
Baton Rouge, LA 70815

Tel: (225)236-3900
Web Site: www.vc.edu
Type: Two-Year College **Sex:** Coed **Calendar System:** Quarter **Professional Accreditation:** ACICS.

VIRGINIA COLLEGE IN SHREVEPORT/BOSSIER CITY
2950 E Texas St.
Ste. C
Bossier City, LA 71111
Tel: (318)741-8020
Web Site: www.vc.edu
Type: Two-Year College **Sex:** Coed **Professional Accreditation:** ACICS.

XAVIER UNIVERSITY OF LOUISIANA
1 Drexel Dr.
New Orleans, LA 70125-1098
Tel: (504)486-7411; Free: 877-XAVIERU
E-mail: apply@xula.edu
Web Site: www.xula.edu
President/CEO: Dr. Norman C. Francis
Admissions: Winston Brown
Financial Aid: Emily Jones

Type: Comprehensive **Sex:** Coed **Affiliation:** Roman Catholic. **Scores:** 94% SAT V 400+; 84% SAT M 400+; 50% ACT 18-23; 37% ACT 24-29 **% Accepted:** 66 **Application Fee:** $0.00 **H.S. Requirements:** High school diploma required; GED accepted **Costs Per Year:** Application fee: $0. Comprehensive fee: $31,149 includes full-time tuition ($19,800), mandatory fees ($2549), and college room and board ($8800). Room and board charges vary according to housing facility. Part-time tuition: $825 per credit hour. Part-time mandatory fees: $240 per term. Part-time tuition and fees vary according to course load. **Scholarships:** Available. **Calendar System:** Semester, Summer session available **Enrollment:** Full-time 2,242, Graduate full-time 558, Graduate part-time 45, Part-time 124 **Faculty:** Full-time 220, Part-time 28 **Student-Faculty Ratio:** 14:1 **Exams:** ACT essay component used for advising; ACT essay component used for placement; SAT I and SAT II or ACT; SAT I or ACT; SAT II; SAT essay component used for advising; SAT essay component used for placement; SAT Reasoning; SAT Subject. **% Residing in College-Owned, -Operated, or -Affiliated Housing:** 46 **Regional Accreditation:** Southern Association of Colleges and Schools **Credit Hours For Degree:** 128 semester hours, Bachelors **ROTC:** Air Force, Army, Navy **Professional Accreditation:** AANA, ACBSP, ACPE, NASM, NCATE. **Intercollegiate Athletics:** Basketball M & W; Cross-Country Running M & W; Tennis M & W

BATES COLLEGE
2 Andrews Rd.
Lewiston, ME 04240-6028
Tel: (207)786-6255; Free: 855-228-3755
Fax: (207)786-6025
E-mail: admission@bates.edu
Web Site: www.bates.edu
President/CEO: A. Clayton Spencer
Admissions: Leigh Weisenburger
Financial Aid: Wendy G. Glass
Type: Four-Year College **Sex:** Coed **Scores:** 100% SAT V 400+; 101% SAT M 400+; 1% ACT 18-23; 41% ACT 24-29 **% Accepted:** 22 **Admission Plans:** Deferred Admission; Early Action; Early Admission **Application Fee:** $60.00 **H.S. Requirements:** High school diploma required; GED not accepted **Costs Per Year:** Application fee: $60. Comprehensive fee: $62,540 includes full-time tuition ($48,435) and college room and board ($14,105). **Scholarships:** Available. **Calendar System:** Miscellaneous, Summer session not available **Enrollment:** Full-time 1,792 **Faculty:** Full-time 170, Part-time 14 **Student-Faculty Ratio:** 10:1 **Exams:** ACT essay component used for admission; SAT essay component used for admission; SAT Reasoning; SAT Subject. **% Receiving Financial Aid:** 43 **% Residing in College-Owned, -Operated, or -Affiliated Housing:** 91 **Regional Accreditation:** New England Association of Schools and Colleges **Credit Hours For Degree:** 34 course credits, Bachelors **Intercollegiate Athletics:** Baseball M; Basketball M & W; Crew M & W; Cross-Country Running M & W; Equestrian Sports M & W; Fencing M & W; Field Hockey W; Football M; Golf M & W; Ice Hockey M & W; Lacrosse M & W; Rugby M & W; Sailing M & W; Skiing (Cross-Country) M & W; Skiing (Downhill) M & W; Soccer M & W; Softball W; Squash M & W; Swimming and Diving M & W; Tennis M & W; Track and Field M & W; Ultimate Frisbee M & W; Volleyball M & W; Water Polo M & W

BEAL COLLEGE
99 Farm Rd.
Bangor, ME 04401
Tel: (207)947-4591; Free: 800-660-7351
E-mail: admissions@bealcollege.edu
Web Site: www.bealcollege.edu
President/CEO: Sheryl DeWalt
Admissions: Sierra Kennedy
Type: Two-Year College **Sex:** Coed **Admission Plans:** Deferred Admission; Open Admission **Application Deadline:** Rolling **Application Fee:** $30.00 **H.S. Requirements:** High school diploma required; GED accepted **Scholarships:** Available. **Calendar System:** Miscellaneous, Summer session available **Enrollment:** Full-time 363, Part-time 101 **Faculty:** Full-time 8, Part-time 32 **Student-Faculty Ratio:** 30:1 **Final Year or Final Semester Residency Requirement:** No **Credit Hours For Degree:** 62 credit hours, Associates **Professional Accreditation:** AAMAE, ACICS.

BOWDOIN COLLEGE
255 Maine St.
Brunswick, ME 04011
Tel: (207)725-3000
Fax: (207)725-3003
E-mail: admissions@bowdoin.edu

Web Site: www.bowdoin.edu
President/CEO: Clayton Rose
Admissions: Jacob Daly
Financial Aid: Michael D. Bartini
Type: Four-Year College **Sex:** Coed **Scores:** 100% SAT V 400+; 100% SAT M 400+; 11% ACT 24-29 **% Accepted:** 15 **Admission Plans:** Deferred Admission; Early Action; Early Admission **Application Deadline:** January 1 **Application Fee:** $60.00 **H.S. Requirements:** High school diploma required; GED not accepted **Costs Per Year:** Application fee: $60. Comprehensive fee: $61,354 includes full-time tuition ($47,744), mandatory fees ($468), and college room and board ($13,142). College room only: $6142. Room and board charges vary according to board plan. Part-time tuition: $933 per credit hour. **Scholarships:** Available. **Calendar System:** Semester, Summer session not available **Enrollment:** Full-time 1,794, Part-time 5 **Faculty:** Full-time 190, Part-time 50 **Student-Faculty Ratio:** 9:1 **Exams:** ACT essay component used for admission; ACT essay component used for advising; SAT I and SAT II or ACT; SAT I or ACT; SAT II; SAT essay component used for admission; SAT essay component used for advising; SAT Reasoning; SAT Subject. **% Receiving Financial Aid:** 45 **% Residing in College-Owned, -Operated, or -Affiliated Housing:** 91 **Final Year or Final Semester Residency Requirement:** No **Regional Accreditation:** New England Association of Schools and Colleges **Credit Hours For Degree:** 32 courses, Bachelors **Intercollegiate Athletics:** Baseball M; Basketball M & W; Crew M & W; Cross-Country Running M & W; Equestrian Sports M & W; Fencing M & W; Field Hockey W; Football M; Golf M & W; Ice Hockey M & W; Lacrosse M & W; Rugby M & W; Sailing M & W; Skiing (Cross-Country) M & W; Soccer M & W; Softball W; Squash M & W; Swimming and Diving M & W; Tennis M & W; Track and Field M & W; Ultimate Frisbee M & W; Volleyball M & W; Water Polo M & W

CENTRAL MAINE COMMUNITY COLLEGE
1250 Turner St.
Auburn, ME 04210-6498
Tel: (207)755-5100; Free: 800-891-2002
Fax: (207)755-5491
E-mail: enroll@cmcc.edu
Web Site: www.cmcc.edu
President/CEO: Dr. Scott E. Knapp
Admissions: Joan Nichols
Type: Two-Year College **Sex:** Coed **Affiliation:** Maine Community College System. **% Accepted:** 29 **Admission Plans:** Deferred Admission **Application Deadline:** Rolling **Application Fee:** $20.00 **H.S. Requirements:** High school diploma required; GED accepted **Costs Per Year:** Application fee: $20. State resident tuition: $2700 full-time, $1350 per year part-time. Nonresident tuition: $5400 full-time, $2700 per year part-time. Mandatory fees: $1050 full-time, $35 per credit hour part-time. Full-time tuition and fees vary according to course load and program. Part-time tuition and fees vary according to course load and program. College room and board: $8916. College room only: $4150. Room and board charges vary according to housing facility. **Scholarships:** Available. **Calendar System:** Semester, Summer session available **Enrollment:** Full-time 1,263, Part-time 1,721 **Faculty:** Full-time 55, Part-time 154 **Student-Faculty Ratio:** 17:1 **Exams:** SAT I; SAT I and SAT II or ACT; SAT II; SAT essay component not used. **% Residing in College-Owned, -Operated, or -Affiliated Housing:** 8 **Final Year or Final Semester Residency Requirement:** No **Regional Accreditation:** New England Association of Schools and Colleges **Credit Hours For Degree:** 60

credits, Associates **Professional Accreditation:** ABET, ACEN, NAACLS. **Intercollegiate Athletics:** Baseball M; Basketball M & W; Golf M & W; Soccer M & W; Softball W

COLBY COLLEGE

4000 Mayflower Hill
Waterville, ME 04901-8840
Tel: (207)859-4000; Free: 800-723-3032
Fax: (207)872-3474
E-mail: admissions@colby.edu
Web Site: www.colby.edu
President/CEO: David A. Greene
Admissions: Denise Walden
Financial Aid: Elreo Campbell

Type: Four-Year College **Sex:** Coed **Scores:** 101% SAT V 400+; 100% SAT M 400+; 2% ACT 18-23; 36% ACT 24-29 **% Accepted:** 23 **Admission Plans:** Deferred Admission; Early Action; Early Admission **Application Deadline:** January 1 **Application Fee:** $0.00 **H.S. Requirements:** High school diploma or equivalent not required **Costs Per Year:** Application fee: $0. Comprehensive fee: $61,730 includes full-time tuition ($47,060), mandatory fees ($2060), and college room and board ($12,610). Room and board charges vary according to housing facility. **Scholarships:** Available. **Calendar System:** 4-1-4, Summer session not available **Enrollment:** Full-time 1,857 **Faculty:** Full-time 191, Part-time 20 **Student-Faculty Ratio:** 9:1 **Exams:** ACT; Other; SAT I; SAT I and SAT II or ACT; SAT I or ACT; SAT II; SAT Reasoning; SAT Subject. **% Receiving Financial Aid:** 37 **% Residing in College-Owned, -Operated, or -Affiliated Housing:** 94 **Final Year or Final Semester Residency Requirement:** Yes **Regional Accreditation:** New England Association of Schools and Colleges **Credit Hours For Degree:** 128 credit hours earned in at least seven semesters of full-time college-level study, Bachelors **ROTC:** Army **Intercollegiate Athletics:** Baseball M; Basketball M & W; Crew M & W; Cross-Country Running M & W; Fencing M & W; Field Hockey W; Football M; Golf M & W; Ice Hockey M & W; Lacrosse M & W; Rugby M & W; Sailing M & W; Skiing (Cross-Country) M & W; Skiing (Downhill) M & W; Soccer M & W; Softball W; Squash M & W; Swimming and Diving M & W; Tennis M & W; Track and Field M & W; Ultimate Frisbee M & W; Volleyball M & W; Water Polo M & W

COLLEGE OF THE ATLANTIC

105 Eden St.
Bar Harbor, ME 04609-1198
Tel: (207)288-5015; Free: 800-528-0025
Fax: (207)288-4126
E-mail: inquiry@coa.edu
Web Site: www.coa.edu
President/CEO: Darron A. Collins, PhD
Admissions: Heather Albert-Knopp
Financial Aid: Bruce Hazam

Type: Comprehensive **Sex:** Coed **Scores:** 100% SAT V 400+; 100% SAT M 400+; 19% ACT 18-23; 57% ACT 24-29 **% Accepted:** 76 **Admission Plans:** Deferred Admission; Early Action; Early Admission **Application Deadline:** February 15 **Application Fee:** $50.00 **H.S. Requirements:** High school diploma required; GED accepted **Costs Per Year:** Application fee: $50. Comprehensive fee: $53,289 includes full-time tuition ($42,993), mandatory fees ($549), and college room and board ($9747). College room only: $6210. Full-time tuition and fees vary according to course load and degree level. Room and board charges vary according to board plan. Part-time tuition: $4777 per credit. Part-time mandatory fees: $183 per term. Part-time tuition and fees vary according to course load and degree level. **Scholarships:** Available. **Calendar System:** Trimester, Summer session available **Enrollment:** Full-time 328, Graduate full-time 9, Graduate part-time 1, Part-time 10 **Faculty:** Full-time 27, Part-time 19 **Student-Faculty Ratio:** 10:1 **Exams:** SAT I or ACT; SAT II. **% Receiving Financial Aid:** 85 **% Residing in College-Owned, -Operated, or -Affiliated Housing:** 47 **Final Year or Final Semester Residency Requirement:** No **Regional Accreditation:** New England Association of Schools and Colleges **Credit Hours For Degree:** 36 credits, Bachelors

EASTERN MAINE COMMUNITY COLLEGE

354 Hogan Rd.
Bangor, ME 04401-4206
Tel: (207)974-4600
Fax: (207)974-4683
E-mail: admissions@emcc.edu

Web Site: www.emcc.edu
President/CEO: Lawrence Barrett
Admissions: W. Gregory Swett

Type: Two-Year College **Sex:** Coed **Affiliation:** Maine Community College System. **Admission Plans:** Deferred Admission; Preferred Admission **Application Deadline:** Rolling **Application Fee:** $20.00 **H.S. Requirements:** High school diploma required; GED accepted **Costs Per Year:** Application fee: $20. State resident tuition: $2700 full-time, $90 per credit hour part-time. Nonresident tuition: $5400 full-time, $180 per credit hour part-time. Mandatory fees: $705 full-time, $23.50 per credit hour part-time. Full-time tuition and fees vary according to course load and program. Part-time tuition and fees vary according to course load and program. College room and board: $8002. College room only: $4100. Room and board charges vary according to board plan and housing facility. **Scholarships:** Available. **Calendar System:** Semester, Summer session available **Exams:** Other; SAT I. **Regional Accreditation:** New England Association of Schools and Colleges **Credit Hours For Degree:** 62 credit hours, Associates **Professional Accreditation:** ACEN, JRCERT. **Intercollegiate Athletics:** Basketball M & W; Golf M

HUSSON UNIVERSITY

1 College Cir.
Bangor, ME 04401-2999
Tel: (207)941-7000; Free: 800-4-HUSSON
Fax: (207)941-7935
E-mail: beanc@husson.edu
Web Site: www.husson.edu
President/CEO: Dr. Robert Clark
Admissions: John Champoli
Financial Aid: Anne Tabor

Type: Comprehensive **Sex:** Coed **Scores:** 88% SAT V 400+; 90% SAT M 400+; 63% ACT 18-23; 21% ACT 24-29 **% Accepted:** 78 **Admission Plans:** Deferred Admission **Application Deadline:** August 15 **Application Fee:** $40.00 **H.S. Requirements:** High school diploma required; GED accepted **Costs Per Year:** Application fee: $40. One-time mandatory fee: $100. Comprehensive fee: $24,982 includes full-time tuition ($15,660), mandatory fees ($400), and college room and board ($8922). Full-time tuition and fees vary according to class time and location. Room and board charges vary according to board plan and housing facility. Part-time tuition: $522 per credit. Part-time tuition varies according to class time, course load, and location. **Scholarships:** Available. **Calendar System:** Semester, Summer session available **Enrollment:** Full-time 2,217, Graduate full-time 563, Graduate part-time 164, Part-time 474 **Faculty:** Full-time 152, Part-time 197 **Student-Faculty Ratio:** 15:1 **Exams:** ACT essay component used as validity check; ACT essay component used for admission; SAT I or ACT; SAT essay component used as validity check; SAT essay component used for admission; SAT Reasoning; SAT Subject. **% Receiving Financial Aid:** 82 **% Residing in College-Owned, -Operated, or -Affiliated Housing:** 39 **Final Year or Final Semester Residency Requirement:** Yes **Regional Accreditation:** New England Association of Schools and Colleges **Credit Hours For Degree:** 60 semester hours, Associates; 120 semester hours, Bachelors **ROTC:** Army, Navy **Professional Accreditation:** AACN, ACPE, AOTA, APTA. **Intercollegiate Athletics:** Baseball M; Basketball M & W; Cross-Country Running M & W; Field Hockey W; Football M; Golf M & W; Lacrosse M & W; Soccer M & W; Softball W; Swimming and Diving M & W; Tennis M; Track and Field M & W; Volleyball W

KAPLAN UNIVERSITY, AUGUSTA

14 Marketplace Dr.
Augusta, ME 04330
Tel: (207)213-2500; Free: 888-561-4343
Fax: (207)774-1715
Web Site: www.kaplanuniversity.edu
Type: Comprehensive **Sex:** Coed **Regional Accreditation:** North Central Association of Colleges and Schools

KAPLAN UNIVERSITY, LEWISTON

475 Lisbon St.
Lewiston, ME 04240
Tel: (207)333-3300; Free: 800-527-5268
Web Site: www.kaplanuniversity.edu
Type: Two-Year College **Sex:** Coed **H.S. Requirements:** High school diploma required; GED accepted **Regional Accreditation:** North Central Association of Colleges and Schools

KAPLAN UNIVERSITY, SOUTH PORTLAND

265 Western Ave.
South Portland, ME 04106
Tel: (207)774-6126; Free: 800-527-5268
Fax: (207)774-1715
Web Site: www.kaplanuniversity.edu
President/CEO: Dr. Christopher Quinn
Type: Two-Year College **Sex:** Coed **H.S. Requirements:** High school diploma required; GED accepted **Scholarships:** Available. **Calendar System:** Miscellaneous **Regional Accreditation:** North Central Association of Colleges and Schools

KENNEBEC VALLEY COMMUNITY COLLEGE

92 Western Ave.
Fairfield, ME 04937-1367
Tel: (207)453-5000; Free: 800-528-5882
E-mail: admissions@kvcc.me.edu
Web Site: www.kvcc.me.edu
President/CEO: Dr. Richard Hopper
Admissions: Crichton McKenna
Financial Aid: Bobbi-Jo Seamans
Type: Two-Year College **Sex:** Coed **Affiliation:** Maine Community College System. **Admission Plans:** Deferred Admission; Open Admission **Application Deadline:** Rolling **Application Fee:** $20.00 **H.S. Requirements:** High school diploma required; GED accepted **Costs Per Year:** Application fee: $20. One-time mandatory fee: $30. State resident tuition: $2700 full-time, $90 per credit hour part-time. Nonresident tuition: $5400 full-time, $180 per credit hour part-time. Mandatory fees: $610 full-time, $3 per credit hour part-time. **Scholarships:** Available. **Calendar System:** Semester, Summer session available **Enrollment:** Full-time 724, Part-time 1,727 **Faculty:** Full-time 41, Part-time 2 **Exams:** Other; SAT I or ACT. **Final Year or Final Semester Residency Requirement:** No **Regional Accreditation:** New England Association of Schools and Colleges **Credit Hours For Degree:** 61 credits, Associates **Professional Accreditation:** ACBSP, ACEN, AHIMA, AOTA, APTA, CoARC. **Intercollegiate Athletics:** Ice Hockey M & W

THE LANDING SCHOOL

286 River Rd.
Arundel, ME 04046
Tel: (207)985-7976
Fax: (207)985-7942
E-mail: info@landingschool.edu
Web Site: www.landingschool.edu
President/CEO: Dr. Richard Schuhmann
Admissions: Kristin Potter
Type: Two-Year College **Sex:** Coed **% Accepted:** 68 **Admission Plans:** Deferred Admission; Early Admission; Open Admission **Application Deadline:** Rolling **Application Fee:** $0.00 **H.S. Requirements:** High school diploma required; GED accepted **Costs Per Year:** Application fee: $0. Tuition: $20,107 full-time. Mandatory fees: $1000 full-time. Full-time tuition and fees vary according to program. **Calendar System:** Continuous **Enrollment:** Full-time 81 **Faculty:** Full-time 10 **Student-Faculty Ratio:** 9:1 **Final Year or Final Semester Residency Requirement:** No **Credit Hours For Degree:** Two ten month programs plus 15 credit-hours of general education, Associates **Professional Accreditation:** ACCSC.

MAINE COLLEGE OF ART

522 Congress St.
Portland, ME 04101
Tel: (207)775-3052; Free: 800-699-1509
Fax: (207)772-5069
E-mail: scote@meca.edu
Web Site: www.meca.edu
President/CEO: Donald Tuski
Admissions: Shannon Cote
Financial Aid: Adrienne J. Amari
Type: Comprehensive **Sex:** Coed **Scholarships:** Available. **Calendar System:** Semester, Summer session not available **Enrollment:** Full-time 353, Graduate full-time 36, Part-time 16 **% Residing in College-Owned, -Operated, or -Affiliated Housing:** 44 **Final Year or Final Semester Residency Requirement:** No **Regional Accreditation:** New England Association of Schools and Colleges **Credit Hours For Degree:** 120 credits, Bachelors **Professional Accreditation:** NASAD.

MAINE COLLEGE OF HEALTH PROFESSIONS

70 Middle St.
Lewiston, ME 04240-0305
Tel: (207)795-2840
Fax: (207)795-2849
E-mail: watsoner@cmhc.org
Web Site: www.mchp.edu
President/CEO: J. Otis Vance, CPA
Admissions: Erica Watson
Financial Aid: Keith R. Bourgault
Type: Two-Year College **Sex:** Coed **Scores:** 100% SAT V 400+; 67% SAT M 400+ **% Accepted:** 25 **Application Deadline:** January 15 **Application Fee:** $50.00 **H.S. Requirements:** High school diploma required; GED accepted **Costs Per Year:** Application fee: $50. Tuition: $9310 full-time. Mandatory fees: $1590 full-time. College room only: $2350. **Scholarships:** Available. **Calendar System:** Semester, Summer session available **Enrollment:** Full-time 60, Part-time 139 **Faculty:** Full-time 18, Part-time 7 **Student-Faculty Ratio:** 10:1 **Exams:** ACT essay component not used; Other; SAT I or ACT; SAT essay component not used; SAT Reasoning. **% Residing in College-Owned, -Operated, or -Affiliated Housing:** 3 **Final Year or Final Semester Residency Requirement:** No **Regional Accreditation:** New England Association of Schools and Colleges **Credit Hours For Degree:** 70 credits, Associates **Professional Accreditation:** ACEN.

MAINE MARITIME ACADEMY

Castine, ME 04420
Tel: (207)326-4311; Free: 800-227-8465
Fax: (207)326-2515
E-mail: jeff.wright@mma.edu
Web Site: www.mainemaritime.edu
President/CEO: Dr. William Brennan, PhD
Admissions: Jeffrey C. Wright
Financial Aid: Kathy S. Heath
Type: Comprehensive **Sex:** Coed **Scores:** 93% SAT V 400+; 97% SAT M 400+; 60% ACT 18-23; 32% ACT 24-29 **% Accepted:** 79 **Admission Plans:** Deferred Admission; Early Admission; Early Decision Plan **Application Deadline:** Rolling **Application Fee:** $0.00 **H.S. Requirements:** High school diploma required; GED accepted **Scholarships:** Available. **Calendar System:** Semester, Summer session not available **Enrollment:** Full-time 1,024, Graduate full-time 15, Graduate part-time 14, Part-time 13 **Faculty:** Full-time 65, Part-time 28 **Student-Faculty Ratio:** 13:1 **Exams:** SAT I or ACT; SAT Reasoning. **% Receiving Financial Aid:** 85 **% Residing in College-Owned, -Operated, or -Affiliated Housing:** 78 **Regional Accreditation:** New England Association of Schools and Colleges **Credit Hours For Degree:** 78 credit hours, Associates; 140 credit hours, Bachelors **ROTC:** Army, Navy **Professional Accreditation:** ABET. **Intercollegiate Athletics:** Basketball M & W; Cross-Country Running M & W; Football M; Lacrosse M; Sailing M & W; Soccer M & W; Softball W; Volleyball W

NORTHERN MAINE COMMUNITY COLLEGE

33 Edgemont Dr.
Presque Isle, ME 04769-2016
Tel: (207)768-2700; Free: 800-535-6682
Fax: (207)768-2831
E-mail: ngagnon@nmcc.edu
Web Site: www.nmcc.edu
President/CEO: Timothy Crowley
Admissions: Nancy Gagnon
Financial Aid: Norma Smith
Type: Two-Year College **Sex:** Coed **Affiliation:** Maine Community College System. **% Accepted:** 53 **Admission Plans:** Deferred Admission; Early Admission; Open Admission **Application Deadline:** Rolling **Application Fee:** $20.00 **H.S. Requirements:** High school diploma required; GED accepted **Scholarships:** Available. **Calendar System:** Semester, Summer session available **Faculty:** Full-time 45, Part-time 32 **Student-Faculty Ratio:** 18:1 **Exams:** Other. **% Residing in College-Owned, -Operated, or -Affiliated Housing:** 63 **Regional Accreditation:** New England Association of Schools and Colleges **Credit Hours For Degree:** 64 credit hours, Associates **Professional Accreditation:** ACBSP, ACEN. **Intercollegiate Athletics:** Golf M & W; Soccer M & W

SAINT JOSEPH'S COLLEGE OF MAINE

278 Whites Bridge Rd.
Standish, ME 04084

Tel: (207)892-6766; Free: 800-338-7057
Fax: (207)893-7862
E-mail: admission@sjcme.edu
Web Site: www.sjcme.edu
President/CEO: Kenneth Lemanski
Admissions: Kathleen Davis
Type: Comprehensive Sex: Coed Affiliation: Roman Catholic Church. Scores: 89% SAT V 400+; 86% SAT M 400+; 25% ACT 18-23; 25% ACT 24-29 % Accepted: 88 Admission Plans: Deferred Admission; Early Decision Plan Application Deadline: Rolling Application Fee: $0.00 H.S. Requirements: High school diploma required; GED accepted Scholarships: Available. Calendar System: Semester, Summer session available Enrollment: Full-time 1,728, Graduate part-time 971, Part-time 656 Faculty: Full-time 68, Part-time 58 Student-Faculty Ratio: 14:1 Exams: ACT essay component not used; SAT I or ACT; SAT essay component not used. % Residing in College-Owned, -Operated, or -Affiliated Housing: 74 Final Year or Final Semester Residency Requirement: No Regional Accreditation: New England Association of Schools and Colleges Credit Hours For Degree: 128 credit hours, Bachelors ROTC: Army Professional Accreditation: AACN. Intercollegiate Athletics: Baseball M; Basketball M & W; Cheerleading M & W; Cross-Country Running M & W; Field Hockey W; Golf M; Ice Hockey M & W; Lacrosse M & W; Soccer M & W; Softball W; Swimming and Diving M & W; Volleyball W

SOUTHERN MAINE COMMUNITY COLLEGE

2 Fort Rd.
South Portland, ME 04106
Tel: (207)741-5500; Free: 877-282-2182
Fax: (207)741-5751
E-mail: alee@smccme.edu
Web Site: www.smccme.edu
President/CEO: Dr. Ronald G. Cantor
Admissions: Amy Lee
Type: Two-Year College Sex: Coed Affiliation: Maine Community College System. Admission Plans: Open Admission Application Deadline: Rolling Application Fee: $20.00 H.S. Requirements: High school diploma required; GED accepted Costs Per Year: Application fee: $20. State resident tuition: $2700 full-time, $90 per credit part-time. Nonresident tuition: $5400 full-time, $180 per credit part-time. Mandatory fees: $950 full-time, $30 per credit hour part-time, $25 per term part-time. College room and board: $8788. Scholarships: Available. Calendar System: Semester, Summer session available Enrollment: Full-time 2,618, Part-time 3,427 Faculty: Full-time 106, Part-time 321 Student-Faculty Ratio: 18:1 Exams: SAT I or ACT. % Residing in College-Owned, -Operated, or -Affiliated Housing: 5 Final Year or Final Semester Residency Requirement: No Regional Accreditation: New England Association of Schools and Colleges Credit Hours For Degree: 60 credit hours, Associates Professional Accreditation: ACEN, ACF, CoARC, JRCERT. Intercollegiate Athletics: Baseball M; Basketball M & W; Golf M & W; Soccer M & W; Softball W

THOMAS COLLEGE

180 W River Rd.
Waterville, ME 04901-5097
Tel: (207)859-1111; Free: 800-339-7001
Fax: (207)859-1114
E-mail: admiss@thomas.edu
Web Site: www.thomas.edu
President/CEO: Laurie G. Lachance
Admissions: Angela Stinchfield
Financial Aid: Jeannine Bosse
Type: Comprehensive Sex: Coed Costs Per Year: Comprehensive fee: $35,950 includes full-time tuition ($24,468), mandatory fees ($1254), and college room and board ($10,228). College room only: $4990. Room and board charges vary according to board plan and housing facility. Part-time tuition: $3059 per course. Part-time tuition varies according to class time. Scholarships: Available. Calendar System: Semester, Summer session available Enrollment: Full-time 808, Graduate full-time 60, Graduate part-time 95, Part-time 404 Faculty: Full-time 33, Part-time 54 Student-Faculty Ratio: 19:1 Exams: SAT I or ACT. % Receiving Financial Aid: 87 % Residing in College-Owned, -Operated, or -Affiliated Housing: 64 Final Year or Final Semester Residency Requirement: Yes Regional Accreditation: New England Association of Schools and Colleges Credit Hours For Degree: 60 credits, Associates; 120 credits, Bachelors Intercollegiate Athletics: Baseball M; Basketball M & W; Cross-Country Running M & W;

Field Hockey W; Golf M; Ice Hockey M; Lacrosse M & W; Soccer M & W; Softball W; Tennis M & W; Track and Field M & W

UNITY COLLEGE

90 Quaker Hill Rd.
Unity, ME 04988
Tel: (207)509-7100
Fax: (207)948-6277
E-mail: jsalty@unity.edu
Web Site: www.unity.edu
President/CEO: Dr. Melik Peter Khoury
Admissions: Joe Saltalamachia
Financial Aid: Rand E. Newell
Type: Comprehensive Sex: Coed Scores: 93% SAT V 400+; 91% SAT M 400+; 74% ACT 18-23; 3% ACT 24-29 % Accepted: 91 Admission Plans: Deferred Admission; Early Decision Plan Application Deadline: February 15 Application Fee: $0.00 H.S. Requirements: High school diploma required; GED accepted Costs Per Year: Application fee: $0. Comprehensive fee: $37,670 includes full-time tuition ($26,370), mandatory fees ($1200), and college room and board ($10,100). Room and board charges vary according to board plan and housing facility. Part-time tuition: $950 per credit. Scholarships: Available. Calendar System: Semester, Summer session available Enrollment: Full-time 638, Part-time 5 Faculty: Full-time 42, Part-time 31 Student-Faculty Ratio: 12:1 Exams: SAT I or ACT. % Receiving Financial Aid: 84 % Residing in College-Owned, -Operated, or -Affiliated Housing: 72 Final Year or Final Semester Residency Requirement: No Regional Accreditation: New England Association of Schools and Colleges Credit Hours For Degree: 60 semester hours, Associates; 120 semester hours, Bachelors Intercollegiate Athletics: Basketball M & W; Cross-Country Running M & W; Soccer M & W; Volleyball W

UNIVERSITY OF MAINE

Orono, ME 04469
Tel: (207)581-1865; Free: 877-486-2364
Fax: (207)581-1213
E-mail: um-admit@maine.edu
Web Site: www.umaine.edu
President/CEO: Dr. Susan J. Hunter
Financial Aid: Sarah Doheny
Type: University Sex: Coed Affiliation: University of Maine System. Scores: 98% SAT V 400+; 97% SAT M 400+; 35% ACT 18-23; 51% ACT 24-29 % Accepted: 91 Admission Plans: Deferred Admission; Early Admission; Early Decision Plan Application Deadline: Rolling Application Fee: $40.00 H.S. Requirements: High school diploma required; GED accepted Costs Per Year: Application fee: $40. State resident tuition: $8370 full-time, $279 per credit hour part-time. Nonresident tuition: $26,640 full-time, $888 per credit hour part-time. Mandatory fees: $2240 full-time. Full-time tuition and fees vary according to course load. Part-time tuition varies according to course load. College room and board: $9576. College room only: $5004. Room and board charges vary according to board plan and housing facility. Scholarships: Available. Calendar System: Semester, Summer session available Enrollment: Full-time 8,120, Graduate full-time 785, Graduate part-time 840, Part-time 1,177 Faculty: Full-time 493, Part-time 352 Student-Faculty Ratio: 16:1 Exams: ACT essay component not used for admission; SAT I or ACT; SAT essay component used for admission; SAT Reasoning. % Receiving Financial Aid: 69 % Residing in College-Owned, -Operated, or -Affiliated Housing: 39 Final Year or Final Semester Residency Requirement: No Regional Accreditation: New England Association of Schools and Colleges Credit Hours For Degree: 120 credit hours, Bachelors ROTC: Army, Navy Professional Accreditation: AACN, AACSB, AALS, ABET, AHIMA, AND, APA, ASHA, CSWE, NASAD, NASM, NASPAA, NCATE, SAF. Intercollegiate Athletics: Baseball M; Basketball M & W; Cheerleading M & W; Cross-Country Running M & W; Field Hockey W; Football M; Ice Hockey M & W; Soccer W; Softball W; Swimming and Diving M & W; Track and Field M & W

UNIVERSITY OF MAINE AT AUGUSTA

46 University Dr.
Augusta, ME 04330-9410
Tel: (207)621-3000; Free: 877-862-1234
Fax: (207)621-3116
E-mail: umaadm@maine.edu
Web Site: www.uma.maine.edu
President/CEO: Dr. James F. Conneely

Admissions: Pamela Proulx-Curry
Type: Four-Year College **Sex:** Coed **Affiliation:** University of Maine System. **% Accepted:** 98 **Admission Plans:** Deferred Admission; Early Admission **Application Fee:** $40.00 **H.S. Requirements:** High school diploma required; GED accepted **Costs Per Year:** Application fee: $40. State resident tuition: $6510 full-time, $217 per credit hour part-time. Nonresident tuition: $15,750 full-time, $525 per credit hour part-time. Mandatory fees: $938 full-time, $31.25 per credit hour part-time. Full-time tuition and fees vary according to course load, location, program, and reciprocity agreements. Part-time tuition and fees vary according to course load, location, program, and reciprocity agreements. **Scholarships:** Available. **Calendar System:** Semester, Summer session available **Enrollment:** Full-time 1,663, Part-time 3,020 **Faculty:** Full-time 87, Part-time 173 **Student-Faculty Ratio:** 16:1 **% Receiving Financial Aid:** 85 **Final Year or Final Semester Residency Requirement:** No **Regional Accreditation:** New England Association of Schools and Colleges **Credit Hours For Degree:** 60 credits, Associates; 120 credits, Bachelors **ROTC:** Army **Professional Accreditation:** ACEN, ADA, NAACLS. **Intercollegiate Athletics:** Basketball M & W; Bowling M & W; Cross-Country Running M & W; Golf M & W

UNIVERSITY OF MAINE AT FARMINGTON

224 Main St.
Farmington, ME 04938-1990
Tel: (207)778-7000
Fax: (207)778-8182
E-mail: ellrich@maine.edu
Web Site: www.umf.maine.edu
President/CEO: Kathryn Foster
Admissions: Lisa Ellrich
Financial Aid: Ronald P. Milliken
Type: Comprehensive **Sex:** Coed **Affiliation:** University of Maine System. **Scores:** 89% SAT V 400+; 86% SAT M 400+ **Costs Per Year:** State resident tuition: $8352 full-time, $261 per credit hour part-time. Nonresident tuition: $17,440 full-time, $545 per credit hour part-time. Mandatory fees: $865 full-time. Full-time tuition and fees vary according to course load and reciprocity agreements. Part-time tuition varies according to course load and reciprocity agreements. College room and board: $8970. College room only: $4750. Room and board charges vary according to board plan and housing facility. **Scholarships:** Available. **Calendar System:** Semester, Summer session available **Enrollment:** Full-time 1,688, Graduate part-time 221, Part-time 107 **Faculty:** Full-time 113, Part-time 60 **Student-Faculty Ratio:** 14:1 **% Receiving Financial Aid:** 81 **% Residing in College-Owned, -Operated, or -Affiliated Housing:** 53 **Final Year or Final Semester Residency Requirement:** No **Regional Accreditation:** New England Association of Schools and Colleges **Credit Hours For Degree:** 128 credit hours, Bachelors **Professional Accreditation:** NCATE. **Intercollegiate Athletics:** Baseball M; Basketball M & W; Cross-Country Running M & W; Field Hockey W; Golf M; Lacrosse M & W; Skiing (Cross-Country) M & W; Skiing (Downhill) M & W; Soccer M & W; Softball W; Tennis M & W; Track and Field M & W

UNIVERSITY OF MAINE AT FORT KENT

23 University Dr.
Fort Kent, ME 04743-1292
Tel: (207)834-7500; Free: 888-TRY-UMFK
Fax: (207)834-7609
E-mail: jillb@maine.edu
Web Site: www.umfk.maine.edu
President/CEO: Dr. John Short
Admissions: Jill Cairns
Financial Aid: Lisa Lipe
Type: Four-Year College **Sex:** Coed **Affiliation:** University of Maine System. **Scores:** 76% SAT V 400+; 43% ACT 18-23 **% Accepted:** 89 **Admission Plans:** Deferred Admission **Application Deadline:** Rolling **Application Fee:** $40.00 **H.S. Requirements:** High school diploma required; GED accepted **Costs Per Year:** Application fee: $40. State resident tuition: $6600 full-time, $220 per credit part-time. Nonresident tuition: $9900 full-time, $330 per credit part-time. Mandatory fees: $975 full-time, $32.50 per credit part-time. Full-time tuition and fees vary according to program. Part-time tuition and fees vary according to program. College room and board: $7590. College room only: $4100. Room and board charges vary according to board plan and housing facility. **Scholarships:** Available. **Calendar System:** Semester, Summer session available **Enrollment:** Full-time 583, Part-time 976 **Faculty:** Full-time 33, Part-time 54 **Student-Faculty Ratio:** 15:1 **Exams:**

ACT essay component used for advising; ACT essay component used for placement; SAT I; SAT I and SAT II or ACT; SAT essay component used for advising; SAT essay component used for placement. **% Receiving Financial Aid:** 74 **% Residing in College-Owned, -Operated, or -Affiliated Housing:** 29 **Regional Accreditation:** New England Association of Schools and Colleges **Credit Hours For Degree:** 60 credit hours, Associates; 120 credit hours, Bachelors **Professional Accreditation:** AACN. **Intercollegiate Athletics:** Basketball M & W; Soccer M & W; Volleyball W

UNIVERSITY OF MAINE AT MACHIAS

116 O'Brien Ave.
Machias, ME 04654
Tel: (207)255-1200; Free: 888-468-6866
Fax: (207)255-1363
E-mail: ummadmissions@maine.edu
Web Site: www.machias.edu
President/CEO: Cynthia E. Huggins
Financial Aid: Stephanie Larrabee
Type: Four-Year College **Sex:** Coed **Affiliation:** University of Maine System. **Scores:** 74% SAT V 400+; 73% SAT M 400+; 50% ACT 18-23; 25% ACT 24-29 **% Accepted:** 87 **Admission Plans:** Deferred Admission; Early Admission; Early Decision Plan **Application Fee:** $40.00 **H.S. Requirements:** High school diploma required; GED accepted **Costs Per Year:** Application fee: $40. State resident tuition: $6660 full-time, $222 per semester hour part-time. Nonresident tuition: $18,480 full-time, $616 per semester hour part-time. Mandatory fees: $820 full-time. College room and board: $8466. **Scholarships:** Available. **Calendar System:** Semester, Summer session available **Enrollment:** Full-time 409, Part-time 377 **Faculty:** Full-time 30, Part-time 41 **Student-Faculty Ratio:** 12:1 **Exams:** SAT I or ACT; SAT essay component used for advising; SAT essay component used for placement; SAT Reasoning. **% Receiving Financial Aid:** 88 **% Residing in College-Owned, -Operated, or -Affiliated Housing:** 41 **Regional Accreditation:** New England Association of Schools and Colleges **Credit Hours For Degree:** 60 credits, Associates; 120 credits, Bachelors **Professional Accreditation:** NRPA. **Intercollegiate Athletics:** Basketball M & W; Cross-Country Running M & W; Lacrosse M & W; Soccer M & W; Volleyball W

UNIVERSITY OF MAINE AT PRESQUE ISLE

181 Main St.
Presque Isle, ME 04769-2888
Tel: (207)768-9400
Fax: (207)768-9608
E-mail: erin.benson@maine.edu
Web Site: www.umpi.edu
President/CEO: Linda K. Schott
Admissions: Erin V. Benson
Financial Aid: Christopher A.R. Bell
Type: Four-Year College **Sex:** Coed **Affiliation:** University of Maine System. **Scores:** 78% SAT V 400+; 80% SAT M 400+; 73% ACT 18-23; 9% ACT 24-29 **% Accepted:** 77 **Admission Plans:** Deferred Admission; Early Admission **Application Deadline:** Rolling **H.S. Requirements:** High school diploma required; GED accepted **Costs Per Year:** State resident tuition: $6600 full-time, $220 per credit hour part-time. Nonresident tuition: $9900 full-time, $330 per credit hour part-time. Mandatory fees: $700 full-time. College room and board: $8044. College room only: $4488. Room and board charges vary according to board plan. **Scholarships:** Available. **Calendar System:** Semester, Summer session available **Enrollment:** Full-time 675, Part-time 614 **Faculty:** Full-time 42, Part-time 60 **Student-Faculty Ratio:** 15:1 **Exams:** ACT; ACT essay component not used; SAT I; SAT I and SAT II or ACT; SAT I or ACT; SAT II; SAT essay component not used. **% Receiving Financial Aid:** 77 **% Residing in College-Owned, -Operated, or -Affiliated Housing:** 29 **Final Year or Final Semester Residency Requirement:** No **Regional Accreditation:** New England Association of Schools and Colleges **Credit Hours For Degree:** 61 credit hours, Associates; 120 credit hours, Bachelors **Professional Accreditation:** CSWE, NAACLS, NRPA. **Intercollegiate Athletics:** Baseball M; Basketball M & W; Cross-Country Running M & W; Golf M; Skiing (Cross-Country) M & W; Soccer M & W; Softball W; Volleyball W

UNIVERSITY OF NEW ENGLAND

11 Hills Beach Rd.
Biddeford, ME 04005-9526
Tel: (207)283-0171; Free: 800-477-4UNE

E-mail: admissions@une.edu
Web Site: www.une.edu
President/CEO: Dr. Danielle N. Ripich
Admissions: Peter Heeley
Financial Aid: Paul Henderson
Type: Comprehensive **Sex:** Coed **Scores:** 97% SAT V 400+; 98% SAT M 400+ **% Accepted:** 85 **Admission Plans:** Deferred Admission; Early Admission; Early Decision Plan **Application Deadline:** February 15 **Application Fee:** $40.00 **H.S. Requirements:** High school diploma required; GED accepted **Costs Per Year:** Application fee: $40. Comprehensive fee: $47,680 includes full-time tuition ($33,540), mandatory fees ($1220), and college room and board ($12,920). Full-time tuition and fees vary according to course load and program. Room and board charges vary according to board plan and housing facility. Part-time tuition: $1180 per credit hour. Part-time tuition varies according to course load and program. **Scholarships:** Available. **Calendar System:** Semester, Summer session available **Enrollment:** Full-time 2,268, Graduate full-time 3,413, Graduate part-time 581, Part-time 1,533 **Faculty:** Full-time 269, Part-time 276 **Student-Faculty Ratio:** 13:1 **Exams:** ACT essay component not used; SAT I or ACT; SAT essay component not used; SAT Reasoning. **Final Year or Final Semester Residency Requirement:** No **Regional Accreditation:** New England Association of Schools and Colleges **Credit Hours For Degree:** 120 credits, Bachelors **ROTC:** Army **Professional Accreditation:** AANA, ACBSP, ACEN, ACPE, ADA, AOTA, AOsA, APTA, CSWE. **Intercollegiate Athletics:** Basketball M & W; Cross-Country Running M & W; Field Hockey W; Golf M; Ice Hockey M & W; Lacrosse M & W; Rugby W; Soccer M & W; Softball W; Swimming and Diving W; Volleyball W

UNIVERSITY OF SOUTHERN MAINE

96 Falmouth St.
Portland, ME 04104-9300
Tel: (207)780-4141; Free: 800-800-4USM
Fax: (207)780-5640
E-mail: usmadm@usm.maine.edu
Web Site: www.usm.maine.edu
President/CEO: Dr. Theo Kalikow
Admissions: Rachel Morales
Financial Aid: Keith P. Dubois
Type: Comprehensive **Sex:** Coed **Affiliation:** University of Maine System. **Scores:** 89% SAT V 400+; 89% SAT M 400+; 50.88% ACT 18-23; 29.82% ACT 24-29 **% Accepted:** 88 **Admission Plans:** Deferred Admission; Early Admission **Application Fee:** $40.00 **H.S. Requirements:** High school diploma required; GED accepted **Costs Per Year:** Application fee: $40. State resident tuition: $7590 full-time, $253 per credit hour part-time. Nonresident tuition: $19,950 full-time, $665 per credit hour part-time. Mandatory fees: $1330 full-time, $1330 per year part-time. Full-time tuition and fees vary according to course load, degree level, and reciprocity agreements. Part-time tuition and fees vary according to course load, degree level, and reciprocity agreements. College room and board: $9400. College room only: $4900. Room and board charges vary according to board plan and housing facility. **Scholarships:** Available. **Calendar System:** Semester, Summer session available **Enrollment:** Full-time 3,730, Graduate full-time 713, Graduate part-time 900, Part-time 2,396 **Faculty:** Full-time 248, Part-time 293 **Student-Faculty Ratio:** 16:1 **Exams:** SAT I or ACT; SAT Reasoning. **% Receiving Financial Aid:** 75 **% Residing in College-Owned, -Operated, or -Affiliated Housing:** 20 **Final Year or Final Semester Residency**

Requirement: No **Regional Accreditation:** New England Association of Schools and Colleges **Credit Hours For Degree:** 120 credit hours, Bachelors **ROTC:** Air Force, Army **Professional Accreditation:** AACN, AACSB, ABA, ABET, ACA, ACSP, AOTA, ATMAE, CAHME, CORE, CSWE, JRCAT, NASAD, NASM, NASPAA, NCATE, TEAC. **Intercollegiate Athletics:** Baseball M; Basketball M & W; Cross-Country Running M & W; Fencing M & W; Field Hockey W; Golf M & W; Ice Hockey M & W; Lacrosse M & W; Sailing M & W; Soccer M & W; Softball W; Tennis M & W; Track and Field M & W; Volleyball W; Wrestling M

WASHINGTON COUNTY COMMUNITY COLLEGE

One College Dr.
Calais, ME 04619
Tel: (207)454-1000
Fax: (207)454-1026
Web Site: www.wccc.me.edu
President/CEO: Joseph Cassidy
Admissions: Diana St. Pierre
Financial Aid: William P. O'Shea
Type: Two-Year College **Sex:** Coed **Affiliation:** Maine Community College System. **Admission Plans:** Deferred Admission; Open Admission **Application Deadline:** Rolling **Application Fee:** $20.00 **H.S. Requirements:** High school diploma required; GED accepted **Costs Per Year:** Application fee: $20. Area resident tuition: $135 per credit hour part-time. State resident tuition: $2700 full-time, $90 per credit hour part-time. Nonresident tuition: $5400 full-time, $180 per credit hour part-time. Mandatory fees: $830 full-time. Full-time tuition and fees vary according to course load and program. Part-time tuition varies according to course load and program. College room and board: $5340. College room only: $3770. **Scholarships:** Available. **Calendar System:** Semester **Student-Faculty Ratio:** 11:1 **Regional Accreditation:** New England Association of Schools and Colleges **Credit Hours For Degree:** 64 credits, Associates

YORK COUNTY COMMUNITY COLLEGE

112 College Dr.
Wells, ME 04090
Tel: (207)646-9282; Free: 800-580-3820
Fax: (207)641-0837
Web Site: www.yccc.edu
President/CEO: Dr. Barbara Finkelstein
Admissions: Fred Quistgard
Type: Two-Year College **Sex:** Coed **Affiliation:** Maine Community College System. **% Accepted:** 58 **Admission Plans:** Open Admission **Application Deadline:** Rolling **Application Fee:** $0.00 **H.S. Requirements:** High school diploma required; GED accepted **Costs Per Year:** Application fee: $0. State resident tuition: $2700 full-time, $90 per credit part-time. Nonresident tuition: $5400 full-time, $180 per credit part-time. Mandatory fees: $780 full-time. Full-time tuition and fees vary according to course level and course load. Part-time tuition varies according to course level and course load. **Scholarships:** Available. **Calendar System:** Semester, Summer session available **Enrollment:** Full-time 466, Part-time 1,292 **Faculty:** Full-time 25, Part-time 127 **Student-Faculty Ratio:** 13:1 **Final Year or Final Semester Residency Requirement:** No **Regional Accreditation:** New England Association of Schools and Colleges **Credit Hours For Degree:** 60 credit hours, Associates

ALLEGANY COLLEGE OF MARYLAND

12401 Willowbrook Rd., SE

Cumberland, MD 21502-2596

Tel: (301)784-5000

Fax: (301)784-5024

E-mail: cnolan@allegany.edu

Web Site: www.allegany.edu

President/CEO: Gary Durr

Admissions: Cathy Nolan

Financial Aid: Deborah D. Yonker

Type: Two-Year College **Sex:** Coed **Affiliation:** Maryland State Community Colleges System. **Admission Plans:** Early Admission; Open Admission **Application Deadline:** Rolling **Application Fee:** $0.00 **H.S. Requirements:** High school diploma required; GED accepted. For Dislocated Workers Program: High school diploma required; GED not accepted **Scholarships:** Available. **Calendar System:** Semester, Summer session available **Faculty:** Full-time 114, Part-time 118 **Student-Faculty Ratio:** 16:1 **Exams:** ACT. **% Residing in College-Owned, -Operated, or -Affiliated Housing:** 7 **Regional Accreditation:** Middle States Association of Colleges and Schools **Credit Hours For Degree:** 60 credits, Associates **ROTC:** Army **Professional Accreditation:** ACEN, ADA, AOTA, APTA, CoARC, JRCERT, NAACLS. **Intercollegiate Athletics:** Baseball M; Basketball M & W; Soccer M & W; Softball W; Tennis M & W; Volleyball W

ANNE ARUNDEL COMMUNITY COLLEGE

101 College Pky.

Arnold, MD 21012-1895

Tel: (410)647-7100

Fax: (410)541-2245

E-mail: 4info@aacc.edu

Web Site: www.aacc.edu

President/CEO: Dr. Dawn Lindsay

Admissions: Thomas McGinn

Financial Aid: Richard C. Heath

Type: Two-Year College **Sex:** Coed **Scores:** 85% SAT V 400+; 91% SAT M 400+; 44% ACT 18-23; 18% ACT 24-29 **Admission Plans:** Deferred Admission; Early Admission; Open Admission **Application Deadline:** Rolling **Application Fee:** $0.00 **H.S. Requirements:** High school diploma or equivalent not required. For certain allied health programs: High school diploma required; GED accepted **Costs Per Year:** Application fee: $0. Area resident tuition: $3150 full-time, $105 per credit hour part-time. State resident tuition: $6060 full-time, $202 per credit hour part-time. Nonresident tuition: $10,710 full-time, $357 per credit hour part-time. Mandatory fees: $770 full-time, $26. Full-time tuition and fees vary according to program. Part-time tuition and fees vary according to program. **Scholarships:** Available. **Calendar System:** Semester, Summer session available **Enrollment:** Full-time 4,257, Part-time 10,432 **Faculty:** Full-time 262, Part-time 1,004 **Student-Faculty Ratio:** 13:1 **Regional Accreditation:** Middle States Association of Colleges and Schools **Credit Hours For Degree:** 60 credit hours, Associates **ROTC:** Air Force, Army **Professional Accreditation:** ACEN, ACF, APTA, JRCERT. **Intercollegiate Athletics:** Baseball M; Basketball M & W; Cross-Country Running W; Golf M; Lacrosse M & W; Soccer M & W; Softball W; Volleyball W

BAIS HAMEDRASH AND MESIVTA OF BALTIMORE

6823 Old Pimlico Rd.

Baltimore, MD 21209

Tel: (410)486-0006

Type: Four-Year College **Sex:** Coed **Affiliation:** Jewish. **Professional Accreditation:** AARTS.

BALTIMORE CITY COMMUNITY COLLEGE

2901 Liberty Heights Ave.

Baltimore, MD 21215-7893

Tel: (410)462-8300

Fax: (410)462-7677

E-mail: dedangerfield@bccc.edu

Web Site: www.bccc.edu

President/CEO: Dr. Carolane Williams

Admissions: Deneen Dangerfield

Type: Two-Year College **Sex:** Coed **Admission Plans:** Deferred Admission; Early Admission; Open Admission **Application Deadline:** August 9 **Application Fee:** $10.00 **H.S. Requirements:** High school diploma required; GED accepted **Costs Per Year:** Application fee: $10. One-time mandatory fee: $10. State resident tuition: $2304 full-time, $864 per term part-time. Nonresident tuition: $5980 full-time, $2205 per term part-time. Mandatory fees: $494 full-time, $18 per credit hour part-time, $193. Full-time tuition and fees vary according to course load. Part-time tuition and fees vary according to course load. **Scholarships:** Available. **Calendar System:** Semester, Summer session available **Student-Faculty Ratio:** 18:1 **Exams:** Other. **Regional Accreditation:** Middle States Association of Colleges and Schools **Credit Hours For Degree:** 62 credits, Associates **Professional Accreditation:** ACBSP, ACEN, ADA, AHIMA, APTA, ARCST, CoARC. **Intercollegiate Athletics:** Baseball M; Basketball M & W; Volleyball W

BOWIE STATE UNIVERSITY

14000 Jericho Park Rd.

Bowie, MD 20715-9465

Tel: (301)860-4000; Free: 877-772-6943

Fax: (301)860-3510

E-mail: sholt@bowiestate.edu

Web Site: www.bowiestate.edu

President/CEO: Dr. Mickey L. Burnim

Admissions: Shirley Holt

Financial Aid: Linda Gayton

Type: Comprehensive **Sex:** Coed **Affiliation:** University System of Maryland. **Scores:** 94% SAT V 400+; 90% SAT M 400+ **% Accepted:** 57 **Admission Plans:** Preferred Admission **Application Deadline:** April 1 **Application Fee:** $40.00 **H.S. Requirements:** High school diploma required; GED accepted **Costs Per Year:** Application fee: $40. State resident tuition: $5217 full-time, $230 per credit hour part-time. Nonresident tuition: $15,700 full-time, $660 per credit hour part-time. Mandatory fees: $2,440 full-time, $110.03 per credit hour part-time. Part-time tuition and fees vary according to course load. College room and board: $10,850. College room only: $6970. Room and board charges vary according to board plan and housing facility. **Scholarships:** Available. **Calendar System:** Semester, Summer session available **Enrollment:** Full-time 3,533, Graduate full-time 474, Graduate part-time 641, Part-time 782 **Faculty:** Full-time 216, Part-time 192 **Student-Faculty Ratio:** 16:1 **Exams:** SAT I or ACT. **% Receiving Financial Aid:** 84 **% Residing in College-Owned, -Operated, or -Affiliated Housing:** 35 **Final Year or Final Semester Residency Requirement:** No **Regional Accreditation:** Middle States Association of Colleges and Schools **Credit

Hours For Degree: 120 credits, Bachelors ROTC: Army Professional Accreditation: ABET, ACBSP, ACEN, CSWE, NASPAA, NCATE. Intercollegiate Athletics: Basketball M & W; Bowling W; Cross-Country Running M & W; Football M; Softball W; Tennis W; Track and Field M & W; Volleyball W

BRIGHTWOOD COLLEGE, BALTIMORE CAMPUS

1520 S Caton Ave.
Baltimore, MD 21227
Tel: (410)644-6400; Free: 800-935-1857
Fax: (410)644-6481
Web Site: www.brightwood.edu
President/CEO: Johnny Craig

Type: Two-Year College Sex: Coed H.S. Requirements: High school diploma required; GED accepted Calendar System: Quarter Professional Accreditation: ACCSC, ACICS.

BRIGHTWOOD COLLEGE, BELTSVILLE CAMPUS

4600 Powder Mill Rd.
Beltsville, MD 20705
Tel: (301)937-8448; Free: 800-935-1857
Fax: (301)937-5327
Web Site: www.brightwood.edu
President/CEO: Kevin Beaver

Type: Two-Year College Sex: Coed Application Fee: $20.00 H.S. Requirements: High school diploma required; GED accepted Calendar System: Quarter Professional Accreditation: ACCSC, ACICS.

BRIGHTWOOD COLLEGE, TOWSON CAMPUS

803 Glen Eagles Ct.
Towson, MD 21286
Tel: (410)296-5350; Free: 800-935-1857
Fax: (410)296-5356
Web Site: www.brightwood.edu
President/CEO: Susan Sherwood

Type: Two-Year College Sex: Coed H.S. Requirements: High school diploma required; GED accepted Calendar System: Quarter Professional Accreditation: ACCSC, ACICS.

CAPITOL TECHNOLOGY UNIVERSITY

11301 Springfield Rd.
Laurel, MD 20708-9759
Tel: (301)369-2800; Free: 800-950-1992
E-mail: ghwalls@captechu.edu
Web Site: www.captechu.edu
President/CEO: Michael T. Wood, PhD
Admissions: George Walls
Financial Aid: Suzanne Thompson

Type: Comprehensive Sex: Coed Admission Plans: Deferred Admission Application Deadline: Rolling Application Fee: $25.00 H.S. Requirements: High school diploma required; GED accepted Costs Per Year: Application fee: $25. Tuition: $22,788 full-time, $750 per credit part-time. Scholarships: Available. Calendar System: Semester, Summer session available Student-Faculty Ratio: 12:1 Exams: SAT I or ACT. % Receiving Financial Aid: 71 Regional Accreditation: Middle States Association of Colleges and Schools Credit Hours For Degree: 62 semester hours, Associates; 122 semester hours, Bachelors ROTC: Army Professional Accreditation: ABET.

CARROLL COMMUNITY COLLEGE

1601 Washington Rd.
Westminster, MD 21157
Tel: (410)386-8000; Free: 888-221-9748
Fax: (410)876-8855
E-mail: cedwards@carrollcc.edu
Web Site: www.carrollcc.edu
President/CEO: Dr. James Ball
Admissions: Candace Edwards
Financial Aid: John Gay

Type: Two-Year College Sex: Coed Affiliation: Maryland Higher Education Commission. % Accepted: 100 Admission Plans: Open Admission Application Deadline: Rolling Application Fee: $0.00 H.S. Requirements: High school diploma or equivalent not required Costs Per Year: Application fee: $0. Area resident tuition: $4524 full-time, $150.80 per credit hour part-time. State resident tuition: $6576 full-time, $219.20 per credit hour part-

time. Nonresident tuition: $9168 full-time, $305.60 per credit hour part-time. Scholarships: Available. Calendar System: Semester, Summer session available Enrollment: Full-time 1,297, Part-time 2,252 Faculty: Full-time 79, Part-time 184 Student-Faculty Ratio: 14:1 Regional Accreditation: Middle States Association of Colleges and Schools Credit Hours For Degree: 60 credits, Associates Professional Accreditation: APTA.

CECIL COLLEGE

One Seahawk Dr.
North East, MD 21901-1999
Tel: (410)287-6060
Fax: (410)287-1026
E-mail: dlane@cecil.edu
Web Site: www.cecil.edu
President/CEO: Dr. Mary Bolt
Admissions: Dr. Diane Lane
Financial Aid: Amanda Solecki

Type: Two-Year College Sex: Coed % Accepted: 100 Admission Plans: Deferred Admission; Early Admission; Open Admission Application Deadline: Rolling H.S. Requirements: High school diploma required; GED accepted Costs Per Year: Area resident tuition: $3000 full-time, $100 per credit hour part-time. State resident tuition: $5700 full-time, $190 per credit hour part-time. Nonresident tuition: $7050 full-time, $235 per credit hour part-time. Mandatory fees: $362 full-time. Scholarships: Available. Calendar System: Semester, Summer session available Enrollment: Full-time 1,003, Part-time 1,588 Faculty: Full-time 49, Part-time 262 Student-Faculty Ratio: 13:1 Regional Accreditation: Middle States Association of Colleges and Schools Credit Hours For Degree: 60 credits, Associates Professional Accreditation: ACEN. Intercollegiate Athletics: Baseball M; Basketball M & W; Cheerleading W; Lacrosse M; Soccer M & W; Softball W; Tennis W; Volleyball W

CHESAPEAKE COLLEGE

PO Box 8
Wye Mills, MD 21679-0008
Tel: (410)822-5400
Fax: (410)827-9466
E-mail: mleach@chesapeake.edu
Web Site: www.chesapeake.edu
President/CEO: Dr. Barbara Viniar
Admissions: Marci Leach

Type: Two-Year College Sex: Coed Admission Plans: Deferred Admission; Early Admission; Open Admission Application Deadline: Rolling Application Fee: $0.00 H.S. Requirements: High school diploma required; GED accepted Costs Per Year: Application fee: $0. Area resident tuition: $3450 full-time, $115 per credit hour part-time. State resident tuition: $5490 full-time, $183 per credit hour part-time. Nonresident tuition: $7800 full-time, $260 per credit hour part-time. Mandatory fees: $1045 full-time, $34 per credit hour part-time, $25 per term part-time. Scholarships: Available. Calendar System: Semester, Summer session available Enrollment: Full-time 773, Part-time 1,296 Faculty: Full-time 54, Part-time 73 Student-Faculty Ratio: 17:1 Final Year or Final Semester Residency Requirement: No Regional Accreditation: Middle States Association of Colleges and Schools Credit Hours For Degree: 60 credit hours, Associates Professional Accreditation: ACEN, APTA, JRCERT. Intercollegiate Athletics: Baseball M; Basketball M & W; Soccer M; Softball W; Volleyball W

COLLEGE OF SOUTHERN MARYLAND

8730 Mitchell Rd.
La Plata, MD 20646-0910
Tel: (301)934-2251; Free: 800-933-9177
Fax: (301)934-5255
E-mail: askme@csmd.edu
Web Site: www.csmd.edu
President/CEO: Dr. Bradley Gottfried

Type: Two-Year College Sex: Coed Admission Plans: Deferred Admission; Early Admission; Open Admission Application Deadline: Rolling Application Fee: $0.00 H.S. Requirements: High school diploma or equivalent not required. For nursing program: High school diploma required; GED accepted Scholarships: Available. Calendar System: Semester, Summer session available Enrollment: Full-time 3,087, Part-time 5,324 Faculty: Full-time 125, Part-time 388 Student-Faculty Ratio: 19:1 Final Year or Final Semester Residency Requirement: No Regional Accreditation: Middle States Association of Colleges and Schools Professional Accreditation:

ACBSP, ACEN, APTA. **Intercollegiate Athletics:** Baseball M; Basketball M & W; Golf M & W; Lacrosse M & W; Soccer M & W; Softball W; Volleyball W

COMMUNITY COLLEGE OF BALTIMORE COUNTY

7201 Rossville Blvd.
Baltimore, MD 21237-3899
Tel: (443)840-2222
E-mail: ddrake@ccbcmd.edu
Web Site: www.ccbcmd.edu
President/CEO: Dr. Sandra Kurtinitis, PhD
Admissions: Diane Drake

Type: Two-Year College **Sex:** Coed **Application Deadline:** Rolling **H.S. Requirements:** High school diploma required; GED accepted **Costs Per Year:** Area resident tuition: $3390 full-time, $113 per credit part-time. State resident tuition: $6480 full-time, $216 per credit part-time. Nonresident tuition: $9720 full-time, $324 per credit part-time. Mandatory fees: $862 full-time. Full-time tuition and fees vary according to course load. Part-time tuition varies according to course load. **Calendar System:** Semester, Summer session available **Enrollment:** Full-time 6,454, Part-time 15,945 **Faculty:** Full-time 438, Part-time 844 **Exams:** SAT I or ACT. **Regional Accreditation:** Middle States Association of Colleges and Schools **Professional Accreditation:** ABFSE, ACBSP, ACEN, AOTA, CoARC, JRCERT, NASM, NAST. **Intercollegiate Athletics:** Baseball M; Basketball M & W; Cross-Country Running W; Lacrosse M & W; Soccer M & W; Softball W; Track and Field W; Volleyball W

COPPIN STATE UNIVERSITY

2500 W N Ave.
Baltimore, MD 21216-3698
Tel: (410)951-3000; Free: 800-635-3674
Fax: (410)523-7238
E-mail: mgross@coppin.edu
Web Site: www.coppin.edu
President/CEO: Dr. Reginald S. Avery
Admissions: Michelle Gross
Financial Aid: Thelma Ross

Type: Comprehensive **Sex:** Coed **Affiliation:** University System of Maryland. **Scores:** 76% SAT V 400+; 72% SAT M 400+ **% Accepted:** 54 **Admission Plans:** Deferred Admission; Early Admission **Application Deadline:** July 15 **Application Fee:** $35.00 **H.S. Requirements:** High school diploma required; GED accepted **Scholarships:** Available. **Calendar System:** Semester, Summer session available **Enrollment:** Full-time 2,599, Graduate full-time 134, Graduate part-time 368, Part-time 699 **Faculty:** Full-time 157, Part-time 155 **Student-Faculty Ratio:** 15:1 **Exams:** SAT I or ACT. **% Receiving Financial Aid:** 91 **Regional Accreditation:** Middle States Association of Colleges and Schools **Credit Hours For Degree:** 120 credit hours, Bachelors **ROTC:** Army **Professional Accreditation:** AACN, ACEN, CORE, CSWE, NCATE. **Intercollegiate Athletics:** Baseball M; Basketball M & W; Bowling W; Cross-Country Running M & W; Rugby M; Softball W; Tennis M & W; Track and Field M & W; Volleyball W

FAITH THEOLOGICAL SEMINARY

529 Walker Ave.
Baltimore, MD 21212
Tel: (410)323-6211
Fax: (410)323-6331
E-mail: sjwood@faiththeological.org
Web Site: www.faiththeological.org
President/CEO: Dr. Norman J. Manohar
Admissions: Susan J. Wood

Type: Comprehensive **Sex:** Coed **Affiliation:** Christian non-denominational. **Application Fee:** $50.00 **H.S. Requirements:** High school diploma required; GED accepted **Professional Accreditation:** TRACS.

FORTIS COLLEGE

4351 Garden City Dr.
Landover, MD 20785
Tel: (301)459-3650; Free: 855-4-FORTIS
Web Site: www.fortis.edu

Type: Two-Year College **Sex:** Coed **Professional Accreditation:** ACICS.

FREDERICK COMMUNITY COLLEGE

7932 Opossumtown Pke.
Frederick, MD 21702-2097
Tel: (301)846-2400
E-mail: admissions@frederick.edu
Web Site: www.frederick.edu
President/CEO: Elizabeth Burmaster
Admissions: Lisa A. Freel

Type: Two-Year College **Sex:** Coed **Admission Plans:** Open Admission **Application Deadline:** Rolling **Application Fee:** $0.00 **H.S. Requirements:** High school diploma or equivalent not required **Costs Per Year:** Application fee: $0. Area resident tuition: $4166 full-time, $116 per credit hour part-time. State resident tuition: $8246 full-time, $252 per credit hour part-time. Nonresident tuition: $10,946 full-time, $342 per credit hour part-time. Mandatory fees: $19.79 per credit hour part-time, $57. **Scholarships:** Available. **Calendar System:** Semester, Summer session available **Enrollment:** Full-time 2,057, Part-time 4,140 **Faculty:** Full-time 102, Part-time 429 **Student-Faculty Ratio:** 11:1 **Exams:** SAT Reasoning; SAT Subject. **Final Year or Final Semester Residency Requirement:** No **Regional Accreditation:** Middle States Association of Colleges and Schools **Credit Hours For Degree:** 60 credit hours, Associates **Professional Accreditation:** ACEN, ARCST, CoARC. **Intercollegiate Athletics:** Baseball M; Basketball M & W; Golf M & W; Lacrosse M & W; Soccer M & W; Softball W; Volleyball W

FROSTBURG STATE UNIVERSITY

101 Braddock Rd.
Frostburg, MD 21532-1099
Tel: (301)687-4000
Fax: (301)687-7074
E-mail: fsuadmissions@frostburg.edu
Web Site: www.frostburg.edu
President/CEO: Dr. Jonathan Gibralter
Admissions: Patricia Gregory
Financial Aid: Angela Hovatter

Type: Comprehensive **Sex:** Coed **Affiliation:** University System of Maryland. **Scores:** 93% SAT V 400+; 93% SAT M 400+; 61% ACT 18-23; 12% ACT 24-29 **% Accepted:** 59 **Admission Plans:** Early Admission **Application Deadline:** February 15 **Application Fee:** $30.00 **H.S. Requirements:** High school diploma required; GED accepted **Costs Per Year:** Application fee: $30. State resident tuition: $6214 full-time, $257 per credit part-time. Nonresident tuition: $18,314 full-time, $514 per credit part-time. Mandatory fees: $2274 full-time, $106 per credit part-time, $25 per term part-time. Full-time tuition and fees vary according to location. Part-time tuition and fees vary according to course load and location. College room and board: $8574. College room only: $4110. Room and board charges vary according to board plan and housing facility. **Scholarships:** Available. **Calendar System:** Semester, Summer session available **Enrollment:** Full-time 4,228, Graduate full-time 209, Graduate part-time 521, Part-time 687 **Faculty:** Full-time 254, Part-time 132 **Student-Faculty Ratio:** 16:1 **Exams:** SAT I or ACT. **% Receiving Financial Aid:** 65 **% Residing in College-Owned, -Operated, or -Affiliated Housing:** 32 **Regional Accreditation:** Middle States Association of Colleges and Schools **Credit Hours For Degree:** 120 credit hours, Bachelors **Professional Accreditation:** AACSB, CSWE, NCATE, NRPA. **Intercollegiate Athletics:** Baseball M; Basketball M & W; Cross-Country Running M & W; Field Hockey W; Football M; Lacrosse M & W; Soccer M & W; Softball W; Swimming and Diving M & W; Tennis M & W; Track and Field M & W; Volleyball W

GARRETT COLLEGE

687 Mosser Rd.
McHenry, MD 21541
Tel: (301)387-3000; Free: 866-55-GARRETT
Fax: (301)387-3055
E-mail: admissions@garrettcollege.edu
Web Site: www.garrettcollege.edu
President/CEO: Dr. Richard L. MacLennan
Admissions: Rachelle Davis
Financial Aid: Andrew Harvey

Type: Two-Year College **Sex:** Coed **Scores:** 69% SAT M 400+; 50% ACT 18-23; 25% ACT 24-29 **% Accepted:** 71 **Admission Plans:** Deferred Admission; Early Admission; Open Admission **Application Deadline:** Rolling **Application Fee:** $0.00 **H.S. Requirements:** High school diploma required; GED accepted **Costs Per Year:** Application fee: $0. Area resident tuition: $2884 full-time, $103 per credit hour part-time. State resident tuition: $6300 full-time, $225 per credit hour part-time. Nonresident tuition: $7420 full-time, $265 per credit hour part-time. Mandatory fees: $896 full-time, $32 per credit hour part-time, $25 per term part-time. Full-time tuition and fees vary according to program and reciprocity agreements. Part-time tuition and fees vary according to program and reciprocity agreements. College room and board: $7400. College room only: $5400. Room and board charges vary according to board plan and housing facility. **Scholarships:** Available. **Calendar System:** Semester, Summer session available **Enrollment:** Full-time 549, Part-time 162 **Faculty:** Full-time 24, Part-time 60 **Student-Faculty Ratio:** 13:1 **Exams:** ACT essay component not used; SAT I or ACT; SAT essay component not used. **% Residing in College-Owned, -Operated, or -Affiliated Housing:** 24 **Final Year or Final Semester Residency Requirement:** No **Regional Accreditation:** Middle States Association of Colleges and Schools **Credit Hours For Degree:** 60 credit hours, Associates **Intercollegiate Athletics:** Baseball M; Basketball M & W; Golf M; Softball W; Volleyball W

GOUCHER COLLEGE

1021 Dulaney Valley Rd.
Baltimore, MD 21204-2794
Tel: (410)337-6000; Free: 800-468-2437
Fax: (410)337-6236
E-mail: admissions@goucher.edu
Web Site: www.goucher.edu
President/CEO: Dr. Jose Antonio Bowen
Admissions: Carlton E. Surbeck
Financial Aid: Stephanie Bender

Type: Comprehensive **Sex:** Coed **Scores:** 97% SAT V 400+; 95% SAT M 400+; 27.56% ACT 18-23; 54.33% ACT 24-29 **% Accepted:** 78 **Admission Plans:** Deferred Admission; Early Action; Early Admission; Early Decision Plan **Application Deadline:** February 1 **Application Fee:** $55.00 **H.S. Requirements:** High school diploma required; GED accepted **Costs Per Year:** Application fee: $55. Comprehensive fee: $54,122 includes full-time tuition ($41,400), mandatory fees ($780), and college room and board ($11,942). Room and board charges vary according to board plan and housing facility. Part-time tuition: $1380 per credit hour. **Scholarships:** Available. **Calendar System:** Semester, Summer session available **Enrollment:** Full-time 1,452, Graduate full-time 131, Graduate part-time 539, Part-time 26 **Faculty:** Full-time 138, Part-time 48 **Student-Faculty Ratio:** 11:1 **Exams:** ACT essay component not used; SAT I or ACT; SAT essay component not used; SAT Reasoning. **% Receiving Financial Aid:** 64 **% Residing in College-Owned, -Operated, or -Affiliated Housing:** 82 **Final Year or Final Semester Residency Requirement:** No **Regional Accreditation:** Middle States Association of Colleges and Schools **Credit Hours For Degree:** 120 semester hours, Bachelors **ROTC:** Air Force, Army **Intercollegiate Athletics:** Basketball M & W; Cross-Country Running M & W; Equestrian Sports M & W; Field Hockey W; Lacrosse M & W; Soccer M & W; Swimming and Diving M & W; Tennis M & W; Track and Field M & W; Volleyball W

HAGERSTOWN COMMUNITY COLLEGE

11400 Robinwood Dr.
Hagerstown, MD 21742
Tel: (240)500-2000
Fax: (301)739-0737
E-mail: klcrawford@hagerstowncc.edu
Web Site: www.hagerstowncc.edu
President/CEO: Dr. Guy Altieri
Admissions: Kevin L. Crawford
Financial Aid: Carolyn Cox

Type: Two-Year College **Sex:** Coed **Admission Plans:** Deferred Admission; Early Admission; Open Admission **Application Deadline:** Rolling **Application Fee:** $0.00 **H.S. Requirements:** High school diploma or equivalent not required. For students receiving financial aid: High school diploma required; GED accepted **Costs Per Year:** Application fee: $0. Area resident tuition: $3042 full-time, $117 per credit hour part-time. State resident tuition: $4758 full-time, $183 per credit hour part-time. Nonresident tuition: $6266 full-time, $241 per credit hour part-time. Mandatory fees: $522 full-time, $12 per credit hour part-time, $30 per term part-time. Full-time tuition and fees vary according to course load, program, and reciprocity agreements. Part-time tuition and fees vary according to course load, program, and reciprocity agreements. **Scholarships:** Available. **Calendar System:** Semester, Summer session available **Enrollment:** Full-time 1,090, Part-time 3,186 **Faculty:** Full-time 80, Part-time 152 **Student-Faculty Ratio:** 16:1 **Regional Accreditation:** Middle States Association of Colleges and Schools **Credit Hours For Degree:** 60 credit hours, Associates **Professional Accreditation:** JRCERT. **Intercollegiate Athletics:** Baseball M; Basketball M & W; Cross-Country Running M & W; Golf M & W; Soccer M & W; Softball W; Track and Field M & W; Volleyball W

HARFORD COMMUNITY COLLEGE

401 Thomas Run Rd.
Bel Air, MD 21015-1698
Tel: (443)412-2000
E-mail: jestarkey@harford.edu
Web Site: www.harford.edu
President/CEO: Dr. Dennis Golladay
Admissions: Jennifer Starkey
Financial Aid: Lynn Lee

Type: Two-Year College **Sex:** Coed **Scores:** 96% SAT V 400+; 96% SAT M 400+ **Admission Plans:** Open Admission **Application Deadline:** Rolling **Application Fee:** $0.00 **H.S. Requirements:** High school diploma or equivalent not required **Costs Per Year:** Application fee: $0. Area resident tuition: $3480 full-time, $116 per credit hour part-time. State resident tuition: $6090 full-time, $203 per credit hour part-time. Nonresident tuition: $8700 full-time, $290 per credit hour part-time. Mandatory fees: $696 full-time, $23.20 per credit hour part-time. **Scholarships:** Available. **Calendar System:** Semester, Summer session available **Enrollment:** Full-time 2,395, Part-time 4,125 **Faculty:** Full-time 101, Part-time 243 **Student-Faculty Ratio:** 21:1 **Exams:** ACT essay component used for advising; SAT essay component used for advising. **Final Year or Final Semester Residency Requirement:** No **Regional Accreditation:** Middle States Association of Colleges and Schools **Credit Hours For Degree:** 60 credit hours, Associates **Professional Accreditation:** ACEN, NAACLS. **Intercollegiate Athletics:** Baseball M; Basketball M & W; Cross-Country Running M & W; Golf M; Lacrosse M & W; Soccer M & W; Softball W; Tennis M & W; Volleyball W

HOOD COLLEGE

401 Rosemont Ave.
Frederick, MD 21701-8575
Tel: (301)663-3131; Free: 800-922-1599
E-mail: admission@hood.edu
Web Site: www.hood.edu
President/CEO: Dr. Andrea E. Chapdelaine
Admissions: Jennifer Decker
Financial Aid: Brenda DiSorbo

Type: Comprehensive **Sex:** Coed **Scores:** 95% SAT V 400+; 97% SAT M 400+; 44% ACT 18-23; 36% ACT 24-29 **% Accepted:** 79 **Application Deadline:** Rolling **H.S. Requirements:** High school diploma required; GED accepted **Costs Per Year:** Comprehensive fee: $46,990 includes full-time tuition ($34,630), mandatory fees ($520), and college room and board ($11,840). College room only: $6200. Room and board charges vary according to board plan and housing facility. Part-time tuition: $1005 per credit. Part-time mandatory fees: $260 per term. **Scholarships:** Available. **Calendar System:** Semester, Summer session available **Enrollment:** Full-time 1,179, Graduate full-time 164, Graduate part-time 847, Part-time 98 **Faculty:** Full-time 100, Part-time 164 **Student-Faculty Ratio:** 11:1 **Exams:** SAT essay component used for advising; SAT essay component used for placement. **% Receiving Financial Aid:** 78 **% Residing in College-Owned, -Operated, or -Affiliated Housing:** 55 **Final Year or Final Semester Residency Requirement:** Yes **Regional Accreditation:** Middle States Association of Colleges and Schools **Credit Hours For Degree:** 124 credits, Bachelors **ROTC:** Army **Professional Accreditation:** ACBSP, CSWE, NCATE. **Intercollegiate Athletics:** Baseball M; Basketball M & W; Cross-Country Running M & W; Equestrian Sports M & W; Field Hockey W; Golf M & W; Lacrosse M & W; Soccer M & W; Softball W; Swimming and Diving M & W; Tennis M & W; Track and Field M & W; Volleyball W

HOWARD COMMUNITY COLLEGE

10901 Little Patuxent Pky.
Columbia, MD 21044-3197
Tel: (443)518-1200
E-mail: admissions@howardcc.edu
Web Site: www.howardcc.edu
President/CEO: Dr. Kate Hetherington
Admissions: Christine Palmer

Type: Two-Year College **Sex:** Coed **% Accepted:** 98 **Admission Plans:** Deferred Admission; Early Admission; Open Admission **Application Deadline:** Rolling **Application Fee:** $25.00 **H.S. Requirements:** High school diploma or equivalent not required **Scholarships:** Available. **Calendar System:** Semester, Summer session available **Enrollment:** Full-time 3,729, Part-time 6,191 **Faculty:** Full-time 193, Part-time 612 **Student-Faculty Ratio:** 15:1 **Exams:** ACT essay component not used; SAT I or ACT; SAT II; SAT essay component not used. **Final Year or Final Semester**

Residency Requirement: No **Regional Accreditation:** Middle States Association of Colleges and Schools **Credit Hours For Degree:** 60 credit hours, Associates **Professional Accreditation:** ACEN, NASM. **Intercollegiate Athletics:** Basketball M & W; Cross-Country Running M & W; Lacrosse M & W; Soccer M & W; Track and Field M & W; Volleyball W

JOHNS HOPKINS UNIVERSITY

3400 N Charles St.
Baltimore, MD 21218
Tel: (410)516-8000
Fax: (410)516-6025
E-mail: gotojhu@jhu.edu
Web Site: www.jhu.edu
President/CEO: Ronald J. Daniels
Admissions: Kate Estes
Financial Aid: Tom McDermott

Type: University **Sex:** Coed **Scores:** 100% SAT V 400+; 100% SAT M 400+; 0.36% ACT 18-23; 3.13% ACT 24-29 **% Accepted:** 13 **Admission Plans:** Deferred Admission; Early Action; Early Decision Plan **Application Deadline:** January 1 **Application Fee:** $70.00 **H.S. Requirements:** High school diploma or equivalent not required **Costs Per Year:** Application fee: $70. Comprehensive fee: $65,386 includes full-time tuition ($50,410) and college room and board ($14,976). College room only: $8652. Part-time tuition: $1680 per credit hour. **Scholarships:** Available. **Calendar System:** 4-1-4, Summer session available **Enrollment:** Full-time 5,339, Graduate full-time 1,900, Graduate part-time 88, Part-time 47 **Faculty:** Full-time 707, Part-time 44 **Student-Faculty Ratio:** 10:1 **Exams:** Other; SAT I and SAT II or ACT; SAT I or ACT; SAT Reasoning. **% Receiving Financial Aid:** 48 **% Residing in College-Owned, -Operated, or -Affiliated Housing:** 52 **Final Year or Final Semester Residency Requirement:** Yes **Regional Accreditation:** Middle States Association of Colleges and Schools **Credit Hours For Degree:** 120 credits, Bachelors **ROTC:** Air Force, Army **Professional Accreditation:** AACN, ABET, ACA, ACEN, ACIPE, AND, APA, ARCMI, CAHME, CEPH, LCME/AMA, NASM, NCATE. **Intercollegiate Athletics:** Baseball M; Basketball M & W; Cross-Country Running M & W; Fencing M & W; Field Hockey W; Football M; Lacrosse M & W; Soccer M & W; Swimming and Diving M & W; Tennis M & W; Track and Field M & W; Volleyball W; Water Polo M; Wrestling M

KAPLAN UNIVERSITY, HAGERSTOWN CAMPUS

18618 Crestwood Dr.
Hagerstown, MD 21742-2797
Tel: (301)739-2670; Free: 800-527-5268
Fax: (301)791-7661
Web Site: www.kaplanuniversity.edu
President/CEO: W. Christopher Motz

Type: Two-Year College **Sex:** Coed **Affiliation:** Kaplan Higher Education. **H.S. Requirements:** High school diploma required; GED accepted **Scholarships:** Available. **Calendar System:** Quarter **% Residing in College-Owned, -Operated, or -Affiliated Housing:** 3 **Regional Accreditation:** North Central Association of Colleges and Schools **Professional Accreditation:** ACICS, AHIMA.

LINCOLN COLLEGE OF TECHNOLOGY

9325 Snowden River Pky.
Columbia, MD 21046
Tel: (410)290-7100
Web Site: www.lincolnedu.com

Type: Two-Year College **Sex:** Coed **Professional Accreditation:** ACCSC.

LOYOLA UNIVERSITY MARYLAND

4501 N Charles St.
Baltimore, MD 21210-2699
Tel: (410)617-2000; Free: 800-221-9107
Fax: (410)323-2768
Web Site: www.loyola.edu
President/CEO: Fr. Brian Linnane
Admissions: Elena Hicks

Type: University **Sex:** Coed **Affiliation:** Roman Catholic (Jesuit). **Scores:** 100% SAT V 400+; 100% SAT M 400+; 12% ACT 18-23; 73% ACT 24-29 **% Accepted:** 58 **Admission Plans:** Deferred Admission; Early Action; Early Admission; Early Decision Plan **Application Deadline:** January 15 **Application Fee:** $50.00 **H.S. Requirements:** High school diploma required; GED accepted **Costs Per Year:** Application fee: $50. Comprehensive fee:

$58,675 includes full-time tuition ($43,800), mandatory fees ($1565), and college room and board ($13,310). Full-time tuition and fees vary according to course load. Room and board charges vary according to board plan and housing facility. Part-time tuition: $710 per credit. Part-time tuition varies according to course load. **Scholarships:** Available. **Calendar System:** Semester, Summer session available **Enrollment:** Full-time 3,951, Graduate full-time 634, Graduate part-time 1,339, Part-time 53 **Faculty:** Full-time 354, Part-time 223 **Student-Faculty Ratio:** 12:1 **Exams:** ACT essay component not used; SAT essay component not used. **% Receiving Financial Aid:** 57 **% Residing in College-Owned, -Operated, or -Affiliated Housing:** 83 **Final Year or Final Semester Residency Requirement:** No **Regional Accreditation:** Middle States Association of Colleges and Schools **Credit Hours For Degree:** 120 credits, Bachelors **ROTC:** Air Force, Army **Professional Accreditation:** AACSB, ABET, ACA, APA, ASHA, NCATE. **Intercollegiate Athletics:** Basketball M & W; Crew M & W; Cross-Country Running M & W; Golf M; Lacrosse M & W; Soccer M & W; Swimming and Diving M & W; Tennis M & W; Track and Field W; Volleyball W

MAPLE SPRINGS BAPTIST BIBLE COLLEGE AND SEMINARY

4130 Belt Rd.
Capitol Heights, MD 20743
Tel: (301)736-3631
Fax: (301)735-6507
Web Site: www.msbbcs.edu
President/CEO: Larry W. Jordan
Admissions: Jeannie Bowman
Financial Aid: Fannie G. Thompson

Type: Comprehensive **Sex:** Coed **Affiliation:** Baptist. **% Accepted:** 100 **Admission Plans:** Deferred Admission; Open Admission **Application Deadline:** Rolling **Application Fee:** $50.00 **H.S. Requirements:** High school diploma required; GED accepted **Scholarships:** Available. **Calendar System:** Semester **Enrollment:** Full-time 3, Graduate full-time 3, Graduate part-time 22, Part-time 71 **Faculty:** Full-time 3, Part-time 20 **Credit Hours For Degree:** 66 credit hours, Associates; 132 credit hours, Bachelors **Professional Accreditation:** TRACS.

MARYLAND INSTITUTE COLLEGE OF ART

1300 Mount Royal Ave.
Baltimore, MD 21217
Tel: (410)669-9200
Fax: (410)225-2337
E-mail: cgyland@mica.edu
Web Site: www.mica.edu
President/CEO: Fred Lazarus, IV
Admissions: Christine Seese
Financial Aid: Diane Prengaman

Type: Comprehensive **Sex:** Coed **Scores:** 99% SAT V 400+; 99% SAT M 400+ **% Accepted:** 58 **Admission Plans:** Deferred Admission; Early Action; Early Admission **Application Deadline:** February 1 **Application Fee:** $60.00 **H.S. Requirements:** High school diploma required; GED accepted **Costs Per Year:** Application fee: $60. One-time mandatory fee: $175. Comprehensive fee: $55,900 includes full-time tuition ($42,280), mandatory fees ($1590), and college room and board ($12,030). College room only: $9030. Room and board charges vary according to board plan and housing facility. Part-time tuition: $1760 per credit hour. Part-time mandatory fees: $795 per term. **Scholarships:** Available. **Calendar System:** Semester, Summer session available **Enrollment:** Full-time 1,759, Graduate full-time 261, Graduate part-time 116, Part-time 19 **Faculty:** Full-time 152, Part-time 190 **Student-Faculty Ratio:** 10:1 **Exams:** SAT I or ACT; SAT essay component used for admission. **% Residing in College-Owned, -Operated, or -Affiliated Housing:** 42 **Final Year or Final Semester Residency Requirement:** Yes **Regional Accreditation:** Middle States Association of Colleges and Schools **Credit Hours For Degree:** 126 credits, Bachelors **ROTC:** Army **Professional Accreditation:** NASAD.

MCDANIEL COLLEGE

2 College Hill
Westminster, MD 21157-4390
Tel: (410)848-7000; Free: 800-638-5005
Fax: (410)857-2729
E-mail: admissions@mcdaniel.edu
Web Site: www.mcdaniel.edu
President/CEO: Dr. Roger Casey
Admissions: Florence Hines

Type: Comprehensive **Sex:** Coed **Scores:** 98% SAT V 400+; 98% SAT M 400+; 46.79% ACT 18-23; 31.19% ACT 24-29 **% Accepted:** 80 **Admission Plans:** Deferred Admission; Early Action; Early Admission; Early Decision Plan **Application Deadline:** February 15 **Application Fee:** $50.00 **H.S. Requirements:** High school diploma required; GED accepted **Costs Per Year:** Application fee: $50. Comprehensive fee: $51,380 includes full-time tuition ($40,580) and college room and board ($10,800). College room only: $5000. Full-time tuition varies according to course load. Room and board charges vary according to board plan and housing facility. **Scholarships:** Available. **Calendar System:** 4-1-4, Summer session available **Enrollment:** Full-time 1,613, Graduate full-time 131, Graduate part-time 1,332, Part-time 50 **Faculty:** Full-time 141, Part-time 445 **Student-Faculty Ratio:** 11:1 **Exams:** ACT essay component not used; SAT I or ACT; SAT II; SAT essay component not used; SAT Reasoning. **% Receiving Financial Aid:** 76 **% Residing in College-Owned, -Operated, or -Affiliated Housing:** 80 **Final Year or Final Semester Residency Requirement:** Yes **Regional Accreditation:** Middle States Association of Colleges and Schools **Credit Hours For Degree:** 128 semester hours, Bachelors **ROTC:** Army **Professional Accreditation:** CSWE, NCATE. **Intercollegiate Athletics:** Baseball M; Basketball M & W; Cross-Country Running M & W; Field Hockey W; Football M; Golf M & W; Lacrosse M & W; Soccer M & W; Softball W; Swimming and Diving M & W; Tennis M & W; Track and Field M & W; Volleyball W; Wrestling M

MONTGOMERY COLLEGE

51 Mannakee St.
Rockville, MD 20850
Tel: (240)567-5000
E-mail: melissa.gregory@montgomerycollege.edu
Web Site: www.montgomerycollege.edu
President/CEO: DeRionne P. Pollard, PhD
Admissions: Melissa F. Gregory

Type: Two-Year College **Sex:** Coed **% Accepted:** 100 **Admission Plans:** Deferred Admission; Early Admission; Open Admission **Application Deadline:** Rolling **Application Fee:** $25.00 **H.S. Requirements:** High school diploma or equivalent not required **Costs Per Year:** Application fee: $25. Area resident tuition: $3304 full-time, $118 per credit hour part-time. State resident tuition: $6748 full-time, $241 per credit hour part-time. Nonresident tuition: $9296 full-time, $332 per credit hour part-time. Mandatory fees: $1,109 full-time, $39.60 per credit hour part-time. Full-time tuition and fees vary according to course load. Part-time tuition and fees vary according to course load. **Scholarships:** Available. **Calendar System:** Semester, Summer session available **Enrollment:** Full-time 8,890, Part-time 16,430 **Faculty:** Full-time 504, Part-time 948 **Student-Faculty Ratio:** 18:1 **Exams:** ACT essay component not used; SAT essay component not used. **Regional Accreditation:** Middle States Association of Colleges and Schools **Credit Hours For Degree:** 60 credits, Associates **ROTC:** Air Force **Professional Accreditation:** ACEN, AHIMA, APTA, ARCST, NASM. **Intercollegiate Athletics:** Baseball M; Basketball M & W; Soccer M & W; Softball W; Tennis M & W; Track and Field M & W; Volleyball W

MORGAN STATE UNIVERSITY

1700 E Cold Spring Ln.
Baltimore, MD 21251
Tel: (443)885-3333; Free: 800-332-6674
E-mail: shantell.saunders@morgan.edu
Web Site: www.morgan.edu
President/CEO: Dr. Earl Richardson
Admissions: Shonda Gray
Financial Aid: Tanya Wilkerson

Type: University **Sex:** Coed **% Accepted:** 43 **Admission Plans:** Deferred Admission; Early Admission; Preferred Admission **Application Deadline:** April 15 **Application Fee:** $35.00 **H.S. Requirements:** High school diploma required; GED accepted **Scholarships:** Available. **Calendar System:** Semester, Summer session available **Enrollment:** Full-time 5,472, Part-time 642 **Faculty:** Full-time 436, Part-time 122 **Student-Faculty Ratio:** 13:1 **Exams:** SAT I or ACT; SAT II. **% Receiving Financial Aid:** 82 **% Residing in College-Owned, -Operated, or -Affiliated Housing:** 46 **Regional Accreditation:** Middle States Association of Colleges and Schools **Credit Hours For Degree:** 120 semester hours, Bachelors **ROTC:** Army **Professional Accreditation:** AACSB, ABET, ACSP, ASLA, CEPH, CSWE, NAAB, NAACLS, NASM, NCATE. **Intercollegiate Athletics:** Basketball M & W; Bowling W; Cheerleading W; Cross-Country Running M & W; Football M; Softball W; Tennis M & W; Track and Field M & W; Volleyball W

MOUNT ST. MARY'S UNIVERSITY

16300 Old Emmitsburg Rd.
Emmitsburg, MD 21727-7799
Tel: (301)447-6122; Free: 800-448-4347
E-mail: admissions@msmary.edu
Web Site: www.msmary.edu
President/CEO: Simon Newman
Admissions: Michael Post
Financial Aid: David C. Reeder

Type: Comprehensive **Sex:** Coed **Affiliation:** Roman Catholic. **Scores:** 96% SAT V 400+; 93% SAT M 400+; 57% ACT 18-23; 23% ACT 24-29 **% Accepted:** 67 **Admission Plans:** Deferred Admission; Early Decision Plan **Application Deadline:** March 1 **Application Fee:** $45.00 **H.S. Requirements:** High school diploma required; GED accepted **Costs Per Year:** Application fee: $45. Comprehensive fee: $49,900 includes full-time tuition ($36,250), mandatory fees ($1250), and college room and board ($12,400). College room only: $6070. Full-time tuition and fees vary according to location and program. Room and board charges vary according to housing facility. Part-time tuition: $1210 per credit. Part-time tuition varies according to location and program. **Scholarships:** Available. **Calendar System:** Semester, Summer session available **Enrollment:** Full-time 1,689, Graduate full-time 200, Graduate part-time 262, Part-time 106 **Faculty:** Full-time 126, Part-time 94 **Student-Faculty Ratio:** 12:1 **Exams:** SAT I or ACT; SAT Reasoning. **% Receiving Financial Aid:** 70 **% Residing in College-Owned, -Operated, or -Affiliated Housing:** 81 **Final Year or Final Semester Residency Requirement:** Yes **Regional Accreditation:** Middle States Association of Colleges and Schools **Credit Hours For Degree:** 120 credits, Bachelors **ROTC:** Army **Professional Accreditation:** ATS, NCATE. **Intercollegiate Athletics:** Baseball M; Basketball M & W; Cheerleading W; Cross-Country Running M & W; Equestrian Sports M & W; Ice Hockey M & W; Lacrosse M & W; Rugby M & W; Soccer W; Softball W; Swimming and Diving W; Tennis M & W; Track and Field M & W

NER ISRAEL RABBINICAL COLLEGE

400 Mount Wilson Ln.
Baltimore, MD 21208
Tel: (410)484-7200
Fax: (410)484-3060
President/CEO: Sheftel Neuberger
Financial Aid: Moshe Pelberg

Type: Comprehensive **Sex:** Men **Affiliation:** Jewish. **Admission Plans:** Deferred Admission; Early Admission **Application Deadline:** Rolling **Application Fee:** $50.00 **H.S. Requirements:** High school diploma required; GED accepted **Calendar System:** Semester, Summer session available **Credit Hours For Degree:** 120 credits, Bachelors **Professional Accreditation:** AARTS.

NOTRE DAME OF MARYLAND UNIVERSITY

4701 N Charles St.
Baltimore, MD 21210-2476
Tel: (410)435-0100; Free: 800-435-0200
Fax: (410)532-6287
E-mail: abaumler@ndm.edu
Web Site: www.ndm.edu
President/CEO: Dr. Marylou Yam
Admissions: Angela Baumler
Financial Aid: Audrey Brooks

Type: Comprehensive **Sex:** Coed **Affiliation:** Roman Catholic. **Scores:** 100% SAT V 400+; 99% SAT M 400+; 47% ACT 18-23; 47% ACT 24-29 **% Accepted:** 49 **Admission Plans:** Deferred Admission; Early Admission; Early Decision Plan **Application Deadline:** Rolling **Application Fee:** $45.00 **H.S. Requirements:** High school diploma required; GED accepted **Costs Per Year:** Application fee: $45. Comprehensive fee: $44,600 includes full-time tuition ($32,548), mandatory fees ($1122), and college room and board ($10,930). Part-time tuition: $485 per credit. Part-time mandatory fees: $130 per term. Part-time tuition and fees vary according to course load and reciprocity agreements. **Scholarships:** Available. **Calendar System:** 4-1-4, Summer session available **Enrollment:** Full-time 538, Graduate full-time 356, Graduate part-time 1,239, Part-time 631 **Faculty:** Full-time 126, Part-time 10 **Student-Faculty Ratio:** 11:1 **Exams:** ACT essay component used for advising; ACT essay component used in place of application essay; SAT I or ACT; SAT essay component used for advising; SAT essay component used in place of application essay; SAT Reasoning. **% Receiving Financial Aid:** 84 **Final Year or Final Semester Residency Requirement:** Yes

Regional Accreditation: Middle States Association of Colleges and Schools **Credit Hours For Degree:** 120 credits, Bachelors **ROTC:** Army **Professional Accreditation:** ACEN, NCATE. **Intercollegiate Athletics:** Basketball W; Field Hockey W; Lacrosse W; Soccer W; Softball W; Swimming and Diving W; Tennis W; Volleyball W

PEABODY CONSERVATORY OF THE JOHNS HOPKINS UNIVERSITY
1 E Mount Vernon Pl.
Baltimore, MD 21202-2397
Tel: (410)659-8150; Free: 800-368-2521
Web Site: www.peabody.jhu.edu
President/CEO: Dr. Fred Bronstein
Admissions: David Lane
Financial Aid: Rebecca Polgar

Type: Comprehensive **Sex:** Coed **Affiliation:** Johns Hopkins University. **% Accepted:** 52 **Application Deadline:** December 1 **Application Fee:** $100.00 **H.S. Requirements:** High school diploma required; GED accepted **Costs Per Year:** Application fee: $100. One-time mandatory fee: $700. Comprehensive fee: $57,550 includes full-time tuition ($42,630), mandatory fees ($720), and college room and board ($14,200). Full-time tuition and fees vary according to program. Room and board charges vary according to board plan. Part-time tuition: $1215 per semester hour. Part-time tuition varies according to course load. **Scholarships:** Available. **Calendar System:** Semester, Summer session not available **Enrollment:** Full-time 262, Graduate full-time 277, Graduate part-time 21, Part-time 7 **Faculty:** Full-time 82, Part-time 96 **Student-Faculty Ratio:** 6:1 **Exams:** SAT I or ACT. **% Receiving Financial Aid:** 56 **% Residing in College-Owned, -Operated, or -Affiliated Housing:** 40 **Regional Accreditation:** Middle States Association of Colleges and Schools **Credit Hours For Degree:** 149 semester hours, Bachelors **Professional Accreditation:** NASM.

PRINCE GEORGE'S COMMUNITY COLLEGE
301 Largo Rd.
Largo, MD 20774-2199
Tel: (301)336-6000
E-mail: enrollmentservices@pgcc.edu
Web Site: www.pgcc.edu
President/CEO: Dr. Charlene Dukes
Admissions: Vera Bagley

Type: Two-Year College **Sex:** Coed **% Accepted:** 100 **Admission Plans:** Early Admission; Open Admission **Application Deadline:** Rolling **Application Fee:** $25.00 **H.S. Requirements:** High school diploma or equivalent not required. For nursing, allied health programs: High school diploma required; GED accepted **Scholarships:** Available. **Calendar System:** Semester, Summer session available **Enrollment:** Full-time 3,007, Part-time 8,854 **Faculty:** Full-time 244, Part-time 451 **Student-Faculty Ratio:** 15:1 **Regional Accreditation:** Middle States Association of Colleges and Schools **Credit Hours For Degree:** 62 credits, Associates **ROTC:** Army **Professional Accreditation:** ABET, ACEN, AHIMA, CoARC, JRCERT, JRCNMT. **Intercollegiate Athletics:** Baseball M; Basketball M & W; Bowling M & W; Golf M; Soccer M & W; Softball W; Tennis M & W; Volleyball W

ST. JOHN'S COLLEGE
60 College Ave.
Annapolis, MD 21401
Tel: (410)263-2371; Free: 800-727-9238
E-mail: annapolis.admissions@sjc.edu
Web Site: www.stjohnscollege.edu
President/CEO: Christopher B. Nelson
Admissions: Benjamin Baum
Financial Aid: Dana Kennedy

Type: Comprehensive **Sex:** Coed **Scores:** 100% SAT V 400+; 100% SAT M 400+; 16% ACT 18-23; 42% ACT 24-29 **% Accepted:** 78 **Admission Plans:** Deferred Admission; Early Admission; Early Decision Plan **Application Deadline:** Rolling **Application Fee:** $0.00 **H.S. Requirements:** High school diploma required; GED accepted **Costs Per Year:** Application fee: $0. Comprehensive fee: $60,592 includes full-time tuition ($48,544), mandatory fees ($450), and college room and board ($11,598). Room and board charges vary according to board plan and housing facility. **Scholarships:** Available. **Calendar System:** Semester, Summer session not available **Enrollment:** Full-time 406, Graduate full-time 34, Graduate part-time 11 **Faculty:** Full-time 75, Part-time 6 **Student-Faculty Ratio:** 6:1 **Exams:** Other; SAT I or ACT. **% Receiving Financial Aid:** 72 **% Residing in College-Owned, -Operated, or -Affiliated Housing:** 80 **Final Year or Final**

Semester Residency Requirement: Yes **Regional Accreditation:** Middle States Association of Colleges and Schools **Credit Hours For Degree:** 136 credits, Bachelors **Intercollegiate Athletics:** Crew M & W; Fencing M & W; Sailing M & W

ST. MARY'S COLLEGE OF MARYLAND
18952 E Fisher Rd.
Saint Mary's City, MD 20686-3001
Tel: (240)895-2000; Free: 800-492-7181
Fax: (240)895-5001
E-mail: admissions@smcm.edu
Web Site: www.smcm.edu
President/CEO: Dr. Tuajuanda C. Jordan
Admissions: Gary Sherman
Financial Aid: Nadine Hutton

Type: Comprehensive **Sex:** Coed **Scores:** 99% SAT V 400+; 98% SAT M 400+; 36.84% ACT 18-23; 41.23% ACT 24-29 **% Accepted:** 79 **Admission Plans:** Deferred Admission; Early Admission **Application Deadline:** February 15 **Application Fee:** $50.00 **H.S. Requirements:** High school diploma required; GED accepted **Costs Per Year:** Application fee: $50. State resident tuition: $11,195 full-time, $195 per credit hour part-time. Nonresident tuition: $26,045 full-time, $195 per credit hour part-time. Mandatory fees: $2700 full-time. Full-time tuition and fees vary according to course load. Part-time tuition varies according to course load. College room and board: $12,080. College room only: $6975. Room and board charges vary according to board plan and housing facility. **Scholarships:** Available. **Calendar System:** Semester, Summer session available **Enrollment:** Full-time 1,683, Graduate full-time 27, Part-time 63 **Faculty:** Full-time 141, Part-time 49 **Student-Faculty Ratio:** 11:1 **Exams:** ACT essay component not used; SAT I or ACT; SAT essay component not used; SAT Reasoning. **% Receiving Financial Aid:** 47 **% Residing in College-Owned, -Operated, or -Affiliated Housing:** 84 **Final Year or Final Semester Residency Requirement:** Yes **Regional Accreditation:** Middle States Association of Colleges and Schools **Credit Hours For Degree:** 128 credits, Bachelors **Intercollegiate Athletics:** Badminton M & W; Baseball M; Basketball M & W; Cheerleading M & W; Crew M & W; Cross-Country Running M & W; Equestrian Sports M & W; Fencing M & W; Field Hockey W; Lacrosse M & W; Rock Climbing M & W; Rugby M & W; Sailing M & W; Soccer M & W; Swimming and Diving M & W; Tennis M & W; Ultimate Frisbee M & W; Volleyball W

SALISBURY UNIVERSITY
1101 Camden Ave.
Salisbury, MD 21801-6837
Tel: (410)543-6000; Free: 888-543-0148
Fax: (410)548-2587
E-mail: admissions@salisbury.edu
Web Site: www.salisbury.edu
President/CEO: Dr. Janet Dudley-Eshbach
Admissions: Elizabeth Skoglund
Financial Aid: Elizabeth Zimmerman

Type: Comprehensive **Sex:** Coed **Affiliation:** University System of Maryland. **Scores:** 100% SAT V 400+; 100% SAT M 400+; 53.3% ACT 18-23; 40.2% ACT 24-29 **% Accepted:** 61 **Admission Plans:** Deferred Admission; Early Action; Early Admission; Early Decision Plan **Application Deadline:** January 15 **Application Fee:** $50.00 **H.S. Requirements:** High school diploma required; GED accepted **Costs Per Year:** Application fee: $50. State resident tuition: $6712 full-time, $276 per credit hour part-time. Nonresident tuition: $15,058 full-time, $623 per credit hour part-time. Mandatory fees: $2374 full-time, $78 per credit hour part-time. College room and board: $11,010. College room only: $6360. Room and board charges vary according to board plan and housing facility. **Scholarships:** Available. **Calendar System:** 4-1-4, Summer session available **Enrollment:** Full-time 7,148, Graduate full-time 403, Graduate part-time 419, Part-time 701 **Faculty:** Full-time 415, Part-time 241 **Student-Faculty Ratio:** 16:1 **Exams:** ACT essay component used for admission; SAT I or ACT; SAT essay component used for admission; SAT Reasoning; SAT Subject. **% Receiving Financial Aid:** 52 **% Residing in College-Owned, -Operated, or -Affiliated Housing:** 42 **Final Year or Final Semester Residency Requirement:** No **Regional Accreditation:** Middle States Association of Colleges and Schools **Credit Hours For Degree:** 120 semester hours, Bachelors **ROTC:** Air Force, Army **Professional Accreditation:** AACN, AACSB, CSWE, CoARC, JRCAT, NAACLS, NASM, NCATE. **Intercollegiate Athletics:** Baseball M; Basketball M & W; Cross-Country Running M & W; Field

Hockey W; Football M; Lacrosse M & W; Soccer M & W; Softball W; Swimming and Diving M & W; Tennis M & W; Track and Field M & W; Volleyball W

STEVENSON UNIVERSITY

1525 Greenspring Valley Rd.
Stevenson, MD 21153
Tel: (410)486-7000; Free: 877-468-3852
E-mail: admissions@stevenson.edu
Web Site: www.stevenson.edu
President/CEO: Dr. Kevin J. Manning, PhD
Admissions: Mark Hergan
Financial Aid: Barbara L. Miller

Type: Comprehensive **Sex:** Coed **Scores:** 96% SAT V 400+; 94% SAT M 400+; 56.07% ACT 18-23; 26.59% ACT 24-29 **% Accepted:** 60 **Admission Plans:** Deferred Admission **Application Deadline:** Rolling **Application Fee:** $40.00 **H.S. Requirements:** High school diploma required; GED accepted **Costs Per Year:** Application fee: $40. Comprehensive fee: $43,488 includes full-time tuition ($28,864), mandatory fees ($2134), and college room and board ($12,490). College room only: $8284. Full-time tuition and fees vary according to degree level. Room and board charges vary according to board plan and housing facility. Part-time tuition: $730 per credit. Part-time tuition and fees vary according to course load and degree level. **Scholarships:** Available. **Calendar System:** Semester, Summer session available **Enrollment:** Full-time 3,122, Graduate full-time 77, Graduate part-time 408, Part-time 578 **Faculty:** Full-time 144, Part-time 330 **Student-Faculty Ratio:** 15:1 **Exams:** ACT essay component not used; SAT I or ACT; SAT essay component not used; SAT essay component used for admission; SAT Reasoning. **% Receiving Financial Aid:** 78 **% Residing in College-Owned, -Operated, or -Affiliated Housing:** 48 **Regional Accreditation:** Middle States Association of Colleges and Schools **Credit Hours For Degree:** 120 credits, Bachelors **ROTC:** Air Force, Army **Professional Accreditation:** AACN, ACEN, NAACLS, NCATE. **Intercollegiate Athletics:** Baseball M; Basketball M & W; Cheerleading M & W; Cross-Country Running M & W; Field Hockey W; Football M; Golf M & W; Ice Hockey W; Lacrosse M & W; Soccer M & W; Softball W; Tennis M & W; Track and Field M & W; Volleyball M & W

STRATFORD UNIVERSITY

210 S Central Ave.
Baltimore, MD 21202-3230
Tel: (410)752-4710; Free: 800-624-9926
Fax: (410)752-3730
E-mail: baadmissions@stratford.edu
Web Site: www.stratford.edu
President/CEO: Dr. Richard Shurtz
Financial Aid: Lesley Otterbein

Type: Comprehensive **Sex:** Coed **Admission Plans:** Open Admission **Application Deadline:** Rolling **Application Fee:** $50.00 **H.S. Requirements:** High school diploma required; GED accepted **Costs Per Year:** Application fee: $50. Tuition: $14,985 full-time, $1665 per course part-time. Full-time tuition varies according to course level, degree level, and program. Part-time tuition varies according to course level, degree level, and program. **Scholarships:** Available. **Calendar System:** Quarter, Summer session available **Enrollment:** Full-time 48, Graduate part-time 9, Part-time 418 **Faculty:** Full-time 18, Part-time 30 **Final Year or Final Semester Residency Requirement:** No **Credit Hours For Degree:** 90 credits, Associates; 180 credits, Bachelors **Professional Accreditation:** ACF, ACICS.

STRAYER UNIVERSITY–ANNE ARUNDEL CAMPUS

1520 Jabez Run
Millersville, MD 21108
Tel: (410)923-4500
Fax: (410)923-4570
Web Site: www.strayer.edu/maryland/anne-arundel
President/CEO: Brian W. Jones

Type: Comprehensive **Sex:** Coed **Regional Accreditation:** Middle States Association of Colleges and Schools

STRAYER UNIVERSITY–OWINGS MILLS CAMPUS

500 Redland Ct., Ste. 100
Owings Mills, MD 21117
Tel: (443)394-3339
Fax: (443)394-3394
Web Site: www.strayer.edu/maryland/owings-mills

President/CEO: Brian W. Jones

Type: Comprehensive **Sex:** Coed **Regional Accreditation:** Middle States Association of Colleges and Schools

STRAYER UNIVERSITY–PRINCE GEORGE'S CAMPUS

4710 Auth Pl.
First Fl.
Suitland, MD 20746
Tel: (301)423-3600
Fax: (301)423-3999
Web Site: www.strayer.edu/maryland/prince-georges
President/CEO: Brian W. Jones

Type: Comprehensive **Sex:** Coed **Regional Accreditation:** Middle States Association of Colleges and Schools

STRAYER UNIVERSITY–ROCKVILLE CAMPUS

4 Research Pl., Ste. 100
Rockville, MD 20850
Tel: (301)548-5500
Fax: (301)548-5530
Web Site: www.strayer.edu/maryland/rockville
President/CEO: Brian W. Jones

Type: Comprehensive **Sex:** Coed **Regional Accreditation:** Middle States Association of Colleges and Schools

STRAYER UNIVERSITY–WHITE MARSH CAMPUS

9920 Franklin Sq. Dr.
Ste. 200
Nottingham, MD 21236
Tel: (410)238-9000
Fax: (410)238-9099
Web Site: www.strayer.edu/maryland/white-marsh
President/CEO: Brian W. Jones

Type: Comprehensive **Sex:** Coed **Regional Accreditation:** Middle States Association of Colleges and Schools

TOWSON UNIVERSITY

8000 York Rd.
Towson, MD 21252-0001
Tel: (410)704-2000
Fax: (410)704-3030
E-mail: admissions@towson.edu
Web Site: www.towson.edu
President/CEO: Dr. Kim E. Schatzel, PhD
Admissions: Dr. David Fedorchak
Financial Aid: David Horne

Type: University **Sex:** Coed **Affiliation:** University System of Maryland. **Scores:** 99% SAT V 400+; 99% SAT M 400+; 55% ACT 18-23; 40% ACT 24-29 **% Accepted:** 73 **Admission Plans:** Deferred Admission; Early Admission **Application Deadline:** January 15 **Application Fee:** $45.00 **H.S. Requirements:** High school diploma required; GED accepted **Costs Per Year:** Application fee: $45. State resident tuition: $6430 full-time, $278 per credit hour part-time. Nonresident tuition: $18,036 full-time, $756 per credit hour part-time. Mandatory fees: $2752 full-time, $118 per credit hour part-time. Full-time tuition and fees vary according to course load and location. Part-time tuition and fees vary according to course load and location. College room and board: $11,638. College room only: $6488. Room and board charges vary according to board plan and housing facility. **Scholarships:** Available. **Calendar System:** Semester, Summer session available **Enrollment:** Full-time 16,768, Graduate full-time 1,078, Graduate part-time 2,157, Part-time 2,281 **Faculty:** Full-time 899, Part-time 779 **Student-Faculty Ratio:** 17:1 **Exams:** ACT essay component used for admission; ACT essay component used for placement; SAT I or ACT; SAT essay component used for admission; SAT essay component used for placement; SAT Reasoning. **% Receiving Financial Aid:** 53 **% Residing in College-Owned, -Operated, or -Affiliated Housing:** 26 **Final Year or Final Semester Residency Requirement:** No **Regional Accreditation:** Middle States Association of Colleges and Schools **Credit Hours For Degree:** 120 credit hours, Bachelors **ROTC:** Air Force, Army **Professional Accreditation:** AACN, AACSB, ABET, AOTA, APA, ASHA, JRCAT, NASD, NASM, NAST, NCATE. **Intercollegiate Athletics:** Baseball M; Basketball M & W; Cross-Country Running W; Field Hockey W; Football M; Golf M & W; Gymnastics W; Lacrosse M & W; Soccer W; Softball W; Swimming and Diving M & W; Tennis W; Track and Field W; Ultimate Frisbee M & W; Volleyball M & W

UNITED STATES NAVAL ACADEMY

121 Blake Rd.
Annapolis, MD 21402-5000
Tel: (410)293-1000; Free: 888-249-7707
Fax: (410)293-4348
E-mail: webmail@usna.edu
Web Site: www.usna.edu
President/CEO: Vice Adm. Walter E. Carter, Jr.
Admissions: Capt. Ann Kubera
Type: Four-Year College **Sex:** Coed **Scores:** 100% SAT V 400+; 100% SAT M 400+ **% Accepted:** 9 **Admission Plans:** Early Decision Plan **Application Deadline:** January 31 **Application Fee:** $0.00 **H.S. Requirements:** High school diploma or equivalent not required **Costs Per Year:** Application fee: $0. **Calendar System:** Semester, Summer session available **Enrollment:** Full-time 4,525 **Faculty:** Full-time 554, Part-time 38 **Student-Faculty Ratio:** 8:1 **Exams:** ACT essay component not used; SAT I or ACT; SAT essay component not used; SAT Reasoning. **% Residing in College-Owned, -Operated, or -Affiliated Housing:** 100 **Final Year or Final Semester Residency Requirement:** Yes **Regional Accreditation:** Middle States Association of Colleges and Schools **Credit Hours For Degree:** 137 semester hours, Bachelors **Professional Accreditation:** ABET. **Intercollegiate Athletics:** Baseball M; Basketball M & W; Cheerleading M & W; Crew M & W; Cross-Country Running M & W; Fencing M & W; Field Hockey W; Football M; Golf M & W; Gymnastics M & W; Ice Hockey M & W; Lacrosse M & W; Riflery M & W; Rugby M & W; Sailing M & W; Skiing (Downhill) M & W; Soccer M & W; Softball W; Squash M; Swimming and Diving M & W; Tennis M & W; Track and Field M & W; Volleyball M & W; Water Polo M; Weight Lifting M & W; Wrestling M

UNIVERSITY OF BALTIMORE

1420 N Charles St.
Baltimore, MD 21201-5779
Tel: (410)837-4200
Fax: (410)837-4793
E-mail: admission@ubalt.edu
Web Site: www.ubalt.edu
President/CEO: Robert Bologomny
Admissions: David Waggoner
Type: Comprehensive **Sex:** Coed **Affiliation:** University System of Maryland. **Scores:** 86% SAT V 400+; 80% SAT M 400+; 56.2% ACT 18-23 **% Accepted:** 60 **Admission Plans:** Deferred Admission **Application Deadline:** Rolling **Application Fee:** $30.00 **H.S. Requirements:** High school diploma required; GED accepted **Scholarships:** Available. **Calendar System:** Semester, Summer session available **Enrollment:** Graduate full-time 1,495, Graduate part-time 1,780 **Faculty:** Full-time 199, Part-time 206 **Student-Faculty Ratio:** 19:1 **Exams:** SAT I or ACT; SAT Reasoning. **Regional Accreditation:** Middle States Association of Colleges and Schools **Credit Hours For Degree:** 120 semester hours, Bachelors **ROTC:** Air Force, Army **Professional Accreditation:** AACSB, AALS, ABA, NASPAA.

UNIVERSITY OF MARYLAND, BALTIMORE COUNTY

1000 Hilltop Cir.
Baltimore, MD 21250
Tel: (410)455-1000; Free: 800-862-2402
Fax: (410)455-1210
E-mail: admissions@umbc.edu
Web Site: www.umbc.edu
President/CEO: Dr. Freeman Hrabowski
Admissions: Dale Bittinger
Financial Aid: Jane Hickey
Type: University **Sex:** Coed **Affiliation:** University System of Maryland. **Scores:** 99% SAT V 400+; 100% SAT M 400+; 17% ACT 18-23; 56% ACT 24-29 **% Accepted:** 59 **Admission Plans:** Deferred Admission; Early Admission; Early Decision Plan **Application Deadline:** February 1 **Application Fee:** $50.00 **H.S. Requirements:** High school diploma required; GED accepted **Costs Per Year:** Application fee: $50. One-time mandatory fee: $125. State resident tuition: $8044 full-time, $335 per credit hour part-time. Nonresident tuition: $20,808 full-time, $864 per credit hour part-time. Mandatory fees: $2962 full-time. Full-time tuition and fees vary according to location and program. Part-time tuition varies according to location and program. College room and board: $10,868. College room only: $6566. Room and board charges vary according to board plan and housing facility. **Scholarships:** Available. **Calendar System:** 4-1-4, Summer session available **Enrollment:** Full-time 9,592, Graduate full-time 1,160, Graduate part-time

1,436, Part-time 1,651 **Faculty:** Full-time 527, Part-time 298 **Student-Faculty Ratio:** 19:1 **Exams:** ACT; ACT essay component used for admission; SAT I; SAT I and SAT II or ACT; SAT I or ACT; SAT I; SAT essay component used for admission; SAT Reasoning. **% Receiving Financial Aid:** 50 **% Residing in College-Owned, -Operated, or -Affiliated Housing:** 34 **Final Year or Final Semester Residency Requirement:** Yes **Regional Accreditation:** Middle States Association of Colleges and Schools **Credit Hours For Degree:** 120 credit hours, Bachelors **ROTC:** Air Force, Army **Professional Accreditation:** ABET, APA, CSWE, JRCEMTP, NASPAA, NCATE. **Intercollegiate Athletics:** Badminton M & W; Baseball M; Basketball M & W; Bowling M & W; Crew M & W; Cross-Country Running M & W; Fencing M & W; Field Hockey W; Ice Hockey M; Lacrosse M & W; Rugby M & W; Sailing M & W; Skiing (Downhill) M & W; Soccer M & W; Softball W; Swimming and Diving M & W; Tennis M & W; Track and Field M & W; Ultimate Frisbee M & W; Volleyball M & W; Wrestling M

UNIVERSITY OF MARYLAND, COLLEGE PARK

College Park, MD 20742
Tel: (301)405-1000; Free: 800-422-5867
Fax: (301)314-9693
Web Site: www.maryland.edu
President/CEO: Dr. Wallace D. Loh, Jr.
Admissions: Barbara Gill
Financial Aid: Monique Boyd
Type: University **Sex:** Coed **Affiliation:** University System of Maryland. **Scores:** 100% SAT V 400+ **% Accepted:** 45 **Admission Plans:** Deferred Admission; Early Admission; Early Decision Plan; Preferred Admission **Application Deadline:** January 20 **Application Fee:** $65.00 **H.S. Requirements:** High school diploma required; GED accepted **Costs Per Year:** Application fee: $65. State resident tuition: $8152 full-time, $340 per credit hour part-time. Nonresident tuition: $29,300 full-time, $1221 per credit hour part-time. Mandatory fees: $1844 full-time, $427.11 per term part-time. Full-time tuition and fees vary according to location, program, and student level. Part-time tuition and fees vary according to course load, location, program, and student level. College room and board: $10,972. College room only: $6678. Room and board charges vary according to board plan and housing facility. **Scholarships:** Available. **Calendar System:** Semester, Summer session available **Faculty:** Full-time 1,813, Part-time 675 **Student-Faculty Ratio:** 16:1 **Exams:** SAT I or ACT; SAT essay component not used; SAT Reasoning. **% Receiving Financial Aid:** 43 **% Residing in College-Owned, -Operated, or -Affiliated Housing:** 44 **Final Year or Final Semester Residency Requirement:** No **Regional Accreditation:** Middle States Association of Colleges and Schools **Credit Hours For Degree:** 120 semester hours, depending on program, Bachelors **ROTC:** Air Force, Army, Navy **Professional Accreditation:** AACSB, AAMFT, ABET, ACA, ACEJMC, ACSP, ALA, AND, APA, ASHA, ASLA, AVMA, CEPH, CORE, NAAB, NASM, NASPAA, NAST, NCATE. **Intercollegiate Athletics:** Baseball M; Basketball M & W; Cross-Country Running W; Field Hockey W; Football M; Golf M & W; Gymnastics W; Lacrosse M & W; Soccer M & W; Softball W; Swimming and Diving M & W; Tennis M & W; Track and Field M & W; Volleyball W; Water Polo W; Wrestling M

UNIVERSITY OF MARYLAND EASTERN SHORE

Princess Anne, MD 21853-1299
Tel: (410)651-2200
Fax: (410)651-7922
Web Site: www.umes.edu
President/CEO: Dr. Mortimer Neufville
Admissions: Tyrone Young
Financial Aid: Vera Miles-Heath
Type: University **Sex:** Coed **Affiliation:** University System of Maryland. **Scores:** 72% SAT V 400+; 73% SAT M 400+; 34.6% ACT 18-23; 5.2% ACT 24-29 **% Accepted:** 57 **Admission Plans:** Deferred Admission **Application Deadline:** July 15 **Application Fee:** $25.00 **H.S. Requirements:** High school diploma required; GED accepted **Scholarships:** Available. **Calendar System:** Semester **Enrollment:** Full-time 3,449, Graduate full-time 441, Graduate part-time 255, Part-time 309 **Faculty:** Full-time 217, Part-time 128 **Student-Faculty Ratio:** 16:1 **Exams:** ACT essay component not used; SAT I or ACT; SAT essay component not used; SAT Reasoning. **% Receiving Financial Aid:** 81 **% Residing in College-Owned, -Operated, or -Affiliated Housing:** 60 **Final Year or Final Semester Residency Requirement:** No **Regional Accreditation:** Middle States Association of Colleges and Schools **Credit Hours For Degree:** 127 credits, Bachelors **ROTC:** Army **Professional Accreditation:** AACSB, AAFCS, ACCE, AND, APTA, CORE,

NCATE, NCCU. **Intercollegiate Athletics:** Baseball M; Basketball M & W; Cheerleading M & W; Cross-Country Running M & W; Softball W; Tennis M & W; Track and Field M & W; Volleyball W; Wrestling M

UNIVERSITY OF MARYLAND UNIVERSITY COLLEGE

3501 University Blvd. E
Adelphi, MD 20783
Tel: (301)985-7000; Free: 800-888-8682
Fax: (301)985-7678
E-mail: enroll@umuc.edu
Web Site: www.umuc.edu
President/CEO: Javier Miyares
Financial Aid: Cheryl Storie
Type: Comprehensive **Sex:** Coed **Affiliation:** University System of Maryland. **% Accepted:** 100 **Admission Plans:** Deferred Admission; Open Admission **Application Deadline:** Rolling **Application Fee:** $50.00 **H.S. Requirements:** High school diploma required; GED accepted **Costs Per Year:** Application fee: $50. State resident tuition: $6696 full-time, $279 per credit hour part-time. Nonresident tuition: $11,976 full-time, $499 per credit hour part-time. Mandatory fees: $360 full-time. **Scholarships:** Available. **Calendar System:** Semester, Summer session available **Enrollment:** Full-time 8,578, Graduate full-time 108, Graduate part-time 12,785, Part-time 28,776 **Faculty:** Full-time 145, Part-time 2,666 **Student-Faculty Ratio:** 22:1 **% Receiving Financial Aid:** 43 **Final Year or Final Semester Residency Requirement:** No **Regional Accreditation:** Middle States Association of Colleges and Schools **Credit Hours For Degree:** 60 semester hours, Associates; 120 semester hours, Bachelors **Professional Accreditation:** AACSB, NCATE.

WASHINGTON ADVENTIST UNIVERSITY

7600 Flower Ave.
Takoma Park, MD 20912
Tel: (301)891-4000; Free: 800-835-4212
Fax: (301)891-4230
E-mail: enroll@cuc.edu
Web Site: www.wau.edu
President/CEO: Dr. Weymouth Spence
Admissions: Elaine Oliver
Financial Aid: Sharon Conway
Type: Comprehensive **Sex:** Coed **Affiliation:** Seventh-day Adventist. **Admission Plans:** Deferred Admission; Early Admission **Application Deadline:** August 1 **Application Fee:** $25.00 **H.S. Requirements:** High school diploma required; GED accepted **Scholarships:** Available. **Calendar System:** Semester **Enrollment:** Full-time 1,058, Graduate full-time 38, Graduate part-time 128, Part-time 269 **Faculty:** Full-time 52, Part-time 82 **Student-Faculty Ratio:** 14:1 **Exams:** ACT essay component used for admission; ACT essay component used for placement; SAT I or ACT; SAT essay component used for admission; SAT essay component used for placement; SAT Subject. **% Receiving Financial Aid:** 95 **Regional Accreditation:** Middle States Association of Colleges and Schools **Credit Hours For Degree:** 64 semester hours, Associates; 128 semester hours, Bachelors **Professional Accreditation:** ACEN, CoARC. **Intercollegiate Athletics:** Baseball M; Basketball M & W; Cross-Country Running M & W; Soccer M & W; Softball W; Track and Field M & W

WASHINGTON COLLEGE

300 Washington Ave.
Chestertown, MD 21620-1197
Tel: (410)778-2800; Free: 800-422-1782
Fax: (410)778-7287

E-mail: wc_admissions@washcoll.edu
Web Site: www.washcoll.edu
President/CEO: Sheila C. Bair
Admissions: Bradly Booke
Financial Aid: Cailean D. Leith
Type: Four-Year College **Sex:** Coed **Scores:** 100% SAT V 400+; 100% SAT M 400+; 14% ACT 18-23; 67% ACT 24-29 **% Accepted:** 54 **Admission Plans:** Deferred Admission; Early Action; Early Admission; Early Decision Plan **Application Deadline:** February 15 **Application Fee:** $50.00 **H.S. Requirements:** High school diploma required; GED accepted **Costs Per Year:** Application fee: $50. Comprehensive fee: $54,462 includes full-time tuition ($42,844), mandatory fees ($1006), and college room and board ($10,612). College room only: $5390. Room and board charges vary according to board plan, housing facility, and location. Part-time tuition: $1785 per credit hour. Part-time tuition varies according to course load. **Scholarships:** Available. **Calendar System:** Semester, Summer session available **Enrollment:** Full-time 1,400, Graduate part-time 4, Part-time 100, Part-time 71 **Faculty:** Full-time 100, Part-time 71 **Student-Faculty Ratio:** 11:1 **Exams:** ACT essay component not used; SAT I or ACT; SAT essay component not used; SAT Reasoning. **% Receiving Financial Aid:** 60 **% Residing in College-Owned, -Operated, or -Affiliated Housing:** 85 **Final Year or Final Semester Residency Requirement:** Yes **Regional Accreditation:** Middle States Association of Colleges and Schools **Credit Hours For Degree:** 128 credits, Bachelors **Intercollegiate Athletics:** Baseball M; Basketball M & W; Cheerleading W; Crew M & W; Equestrian Sports M & W; Field Hockey W; Ice Hockey M; Lacrosse M & W; Rugby M & W; Sailing M & W; Soccer M & W; Softball W; Swimming and Diving M & W; Tennis M & W; Volleyball W; Water Polo M & W

WOR-WIC COMMUNITY COLLEGE

32000 Campus Dr.
Salisbury, MD 21804
Tel: (410)334-2800
E-mail: admissions@worwic.edu
Web Site: www.worwic.edu
President/CEO: Dr. Ray Hoy
Admissions: Richard Webster
Type: Two-Year College **Sex:** Coed **% Accepted:** 100 **Admission Plans:** Early Admission; Open Admission **Application Deadline:** Rolling **Application Fee:** $0.00 **H.S. Requirements:** High school diploma or equivalent not required **Costs Per Year:** Application fee: $0. Area resident tuition: $3090 full-time, $103 per credit part-time. State resident tuition: $6930 full-time, $231 per credit part-time. Nonresident tuition: $8520 full-time, $284 per credit part-time. Mandatory fees: $510 full-time, $17 per credit part-time. **Calendar System:** Semester, Summer session available **Enrollment:** Full-time 864, Part-time 2,273 **Faculty:** Full-time 69, Part-time 99 **Student-Faculty Ratio:** 16:1 **Regional Accreditation:** Middle States Association of Colleges and Schools **Credit Hours For Degree:** 60 credit hours, Associates **Professional Accreditation:** JRCERT.

YESHIVA COLLEGE OF THE NATION'S CAPITAL

1216 Arcola Ave.
Silver Spring, MD 20902
Tel: (301)593-2534
Fax: (301)949-7040
Web Site: www.yeshiva.edu
President/CEO: Rabbi Yitzchok Merkin
Type: Four-Year College **Sex:** Men **Affiliation:** Jewish; Yeshiva of Greater Washington. **Admission Plans:** Open Admission **Application Fee:** $50.00 **Enrollment:** Full-time 45 **Professional Accreditation:** AARTS.

AMERICAN INTERNATIONAL COLLEGE

1000 State St.
Springfield, MA 01109-3189
Tel: (413)737-7000; Free: 800-242-3142
Fax: (413)737-2803
E-mail: jonathan.scully@aic.edu
Web Site: www.aic.edu
President/CEO: Dr. Vincent Maniaci
Admissions: Jonathan Scully
Financial Aid: Sage Stachowiak

Type: Comprehensive **Sex:** Coed **Scores:** 71% SAT V 400+; 78% SAT M 400+; 46% ACT 18-23; 20% ACT 24-29 **% Accepted:** 64 **Admission Plans:** Deferred Admission **Application Deadline:** Rolling **Application Fee:** $0.00 **H.S. Requirements:** High school diploma required; GED accepted **Costs Per Year:** Application fee: $0. Comprehensive fee: $46,620 includes full-time tuition ($33,140), mandatory fees ($60), and college room and board ($13,420). Full-time tuition and fees vary according to course load and program. Room and board charges vary according to board plan and housing facility. Part-time tuition: $685 per credit. Part-time mandatory fees: $30 per term. Part-time tuition and fees vary according to course load. **Scholarships:** Available. **Calendar System:** Semester, Summer session available **Enrollment:** Full-time 1,392, Graduate full-time 1,868, Graduate part-time 188, Part-time 94 **Faculty:** Full-time 74, Part-time 366 **Student-Faculty Ratio:** 14:1 **Exams:** ACT essay component used for admission; ACT essay component used for advising; ACT essay component used for placement; SAT I and SAT II or ACT; SAT I or ACT; SAT II; SAT essay component used for admission; SAT essay component used for advising; SAT essay component used for placement; SAT Reasoning. **% Receiving Financial Aid:** 88 **% Residing in College-Owned, -Operated, or -Affiliated Housing:** 50 **Final Year or Final Semester Residency Requirement:** No **Regional Accreditation:** New England Association of Schools and Colleges **Credit Hours For Degree:** 60 credits, Associates; 120 credits, Bachelors **ROTC:** Air Force, Army **Professional Accreditation:** AACN, AOTA, APTA. **Intercollegiate Athletics:** Baseball M; Basketball M & W; Cross-Country Running M & W; Field Hockey W; Football M; Golf M & W; Ice Hockey M; Lacrosse M & W; Rugby M & W; Soccer M & W; Softball W; Tennis M & W; Track and Field M & W; Volleyball W; Wrestling M

AMHERST COLLEGE

PO Box 5000
Amherst, MA 01002-5000
Tel: (413)542-2000
Fax: (413)542-2040
E-mail: admission@amherst.edu
Web Site: www.amherst.edu
President/CEO: Caroline Martin, PhD
Admissions: Katharine L. Fretwell
Financial Aid: Gail W. Holt

Type: Four-Year College **Sex:** Coed **Scores:** 100% SAT V 400+; 100% SAT M 400+; 0.43% ACT 18-23; 11.07% ACT 24-29 **% Accepted:** 14 **Admission Plans:** Deferred Admission; Early Action; Early Admission **Application Deadline:** January 1 **Application Fee:** $60.00 **H.S. Requirements:** High school diploma or equivalent not required **Costs Per Year:** Application fee: $60. Comprehensive fee: $63,772 includes full-time tuition ($49,730), mandatory fees ($832), and college room and board ($13,210). College room only: $7160. **Scholarships:** Available. **Calendar System:** Semester,

Summer session not available **Enrollment:** Full-time 1,795 **Faculty:** Full-time 211, Part-time 74 **Student-Faculty Ratio:** 8:1 **Exams:** SAT I and SAT II or ACT; SAT Reasoning; SAT Subject. **% Receiving Financial Aid:** 58 **% Residing in College-Owned, -Operated, or -Affiliated Housing:** 98 **Regional Accreditation:** New England Association of Schools and Colleges **Credit Hours For Degree:** 32 courses, Bachelors **ROTC:** Air Force, Army **Intercollegiate Athletics:** Baseball M; Basketball M & W; Cheerleading W; Crew M & W; Cross-Country Running M & W; Equestrian Sports M & W; Fencing M & W; Field Hockey W; Football M; Golf M & W; Ice Hockey M & W; Lacrosse M & W; Rugby M & W; Sailing M & W; Skiing (Downhill) M & W; Soccer M & W; Softball W; Squash M & W; Swimming and Diving M & W; Tennis M & W; Track and Field M & W; Ultimate Frisbee M & W; Volleyball M & W; Water Polo M & W; Wrestling M & W

ANNA MARIA COLLEGE

50 Sunset Ln.
Paxton, MA 01612
Tel: (508)849-3300
E-mail: admissions@annamaria.edu
Web Site: www.annamaria.edu
President/CEO: Mary Lou Retelle
Admissions: Peter Miller
Financial Aid: Sandra J. Pereira

Type: Comprehensive **Sex:** Coed **Affiliation:** Roman Catholic. **% Accepted:** 80 **Admission Plans:** Deferred Admission **Application Deadline:** Rolling **Application Fee:** $25.00 **H.S. Requirements:** High school diploma required; GED accepted **Costs Per Year:** Application fee: $25. Comprehensive fee: $48,186 includes full-time tuition ($32,880), mandatory fees ($2194), and college room and board ($13,112). Full-time tuition and fees vary according to course load, degree level, and program. Room and board charges vary according to board plan and housing facility. Part-time tuition: $1200 per course. Part-time tuition varies according to course load, degree level, and program. **Scholarships:** Available. **Calendar System:** Semester, Summer session available **Enrollment:** Full-time 811, Graduate full-time 227, Graduate part-time 113, Part-time 317 **Faculty:** Full-time 38 **Student-Faculty Ratio:** 11:1 **Exams:** ACT essay component not used; SAT I or ACT; SAT essay component not used. **% Receiving Financial Aid:** 88 **% Residing in College-Owned, -Operated, or -Affiliated Housing:** 60 **Final Year or Final Semester Residency Requirement:** No **Regional Accreditation:** New England Association of Schools and Colleges **Credit Hours For Degree:** 60 credit hours, Associates; 120 credit hours, Bachelors **ROTC:** Air Force, Army **Professional Accreditation:** ACEN, CSWE, NASM. **Intercollegiate Athletics:** Baseball M; Basketball M & W; Cross-Country Running M & W; Field Hockey W; Football M; Golf M; Lacrosse M & W; Soccer M & W; Softball W; Tennis M & W; Volleyball W

ASSUMPTION COLLEGE

500 Salisbury St.
Worcester, MA 01609-1296
Tel: (508)767-7000; Free: 866-477-7776
Fax: (508)799-4412
E-mail: admiss@assumption.edu
Web Site: www.assumption.edu
President/CEO: Dr. Francesco C. Cesareo
Admissions: Kathleen Murphy

Financial Aid: William C. Smith

Type: Comprehensive **Sex:** Coed **Affiliation:** Roman Catholic. **Scores:** 98% SAT V 400+; 98% SAT M 400+; 20.69% ACT 18-23; 72.41% ACT 24-29 **% Accepted:** 76 **Admission Plans:** Deferred Admission; Early Decision Plan **Application Deadline:** February 15 **Application Fee:** $50.00 **H.S. Requirements:** High school diploma required; GED accepted **Costs Per Year:** Application fee: $50. Comprehensive fee: $47,424 includes full-time tuition ($35,510), mandatory fees ($650), and college room and board ($11,264). College room only: $7106. Full-time tuition and fees vary according to course load and reciprocity agreements. Room and board charges vary according to housing facility. Part-time tuition: $1,183.67 per credit hour. Part-time tuition varies according to course load. Tuition guaranteed not to increase for student's term of enrollment. **Scholarships:** Available. **Calendar System:** Semester, Summer session available **Enrollment:** Full-time 1,975, Graduate full-time 163, Graduate part-time 283, Part-time 12 **Faculty:** Full-time 144, Part-time 80 **Student-Faculty Ratio:** 12:1 **Exams:** SAT I or ACT; SAT Reasoning. **% Receiving Financial Aid:** 75 **% Residing in College-Owned, -Operated, or -Affiliated Housing:** 87 **Final Year or Final Semester Residency Requirement:** No **Regional Accreditation:** New England Association of Schools and Colleges **Credit Hours For Degree:** 120 credits, Bachelors **ROTC:** Air Force, Army **Professional Accreditation:** CORE. **Intercollegiate Athletics:** Baseball M; Basketball M & W; Cheerleading M & W; Cross-Country Running M & W; Field Hockey W; Football M; Golf M; Ice Hockey M; Lacrosse M & W; Rowing W; Soccer M & W; Softball W; Swimming and Diving W; Tennis M & W; Track and Field M & W; Volleyball M & W

BABSON COLLEGE

Babson Park, MA 02457-0310
Tel: (781)235-1200; Free: 800-488-3696
Fax: (781)239-5614
E-mail: ugradadmission@babson.edu
Web Site: www.babson.edu
President/CEO: Kerry Healey
Admissions: Adrienne Ramsey
Financial Aid: Melissa Shaak

Type: Comprehensive **Sex:** Coed **Scores:** 100% SAT V 400+; 100% SAT M 400+; 3% ACT 18-23; 59% ACT 24-29 **% Accepted:** 26 **Admission Plans:** Deferred Admission; Early Action; Early Decision Plan **Application Deadline:** January 3 **Application Fee:** $75.00 **H.S. Requirements:** High school diploma required; GED accepted **Costs Per Year:** Application fee: $75. Comprehensive fee: $61,712 includes full-time tuition ($46,784) and college room and board ($14,928). College room only: $9634. Room and board charges vary according to board plan and housing facility. **Scholarships:** Available. **Calendar System:** Semester, Summer session available **Enrollment:** Full-time 2,141, Graduate full-time 427, Graduate part-time 489 **Faculty:** Full-time 194, Part-time 66 **Student-Faculty Ratio:** 14:1 **Exams:** Other; SAT I or ACT; SAT Reasoning. **% Receiving Financial Aid:** 44 **% Residing in College-Owned, -Operated, or -Affiliated Housing:** 78 **Final Year or Final Semester Residency Requirement:** No **Regional Accreditation:** New England Association of Schools and Colleges **Credit Hours For Degree:** 128 credit hours, Bachelors **ROTC:** Air Force, Army, Navy **Professional Accreditation:** AACSB. **Intercollegiate Athletics:** Baseball M; Basketball M & W; Cheerleading W; Cross-Country Running M & W; Field Hockey W; Golf M; Ice Hockey M & W; Lacrosse M & W; Rugby M & W; Skiing (Downhill) M & W; Soccer M & W; Softball W; Swimming and Diving M & W; Tennis M & W; Track and Field M & W; Volleyball W

BARD COLLEGE AT SIMON'S ROCK

84 Alford Rd.
Great Barrington, MA 01230-9702
Tel: (413)644-4400; Free: 800-235-7186
Fax: (413)528-7334
E-mail: admit@simons-rock.edu
Web Site: www.simons-rock.edu
President/CEO: Dr. Ian Bickford
Admissions: Chandra Joos deKoven
Financial Aid: Ann Murtagh Gitto

Type: Four-Year College **Sex:** Coed **Affiliation:** Bard College. **Scores:** 100% SAT V 400+; 100% SAT M 400+; 75% ACT 24-29 **% Accepted:** 89 **Application Deadline:** May 1 **Application Fee:** $50.00 **H.S. Requirements:** High school diploma or equivalent not required **Costs Per Year:** Application fee: $50. Comprehensive fee: $63,869 includes full-time tuition ($49,102), mandatory fees ($1107), and college room and board ($13,660).

Full-time tuition and fees vary according to course load. Part-time tuition: $2050 per credit hour. Part-time tuition varies according to course load. **Scholarships:** Available. **Calendar System:** Semester, Summer session not available **Enrollment:** Full-time 323, Part-time 6 **Faculty:** Full-time 46, Part-time 24 **Student-Faculty Ratio:** 6:1 **Exams:** SAT Reasoning; SAT Subject. **% Receiving Financial Aid:** 71 **% Residing in College-Owned, -Operated, or -Affiliated Housing:** 92 **Final Year or Final Semester Residency Requirement:** Yes **Regional Accreditation:** New England Association of Schools and Colleges **Credit Hours For Degree:** 60 credit hours, Associates; 120 credit hours, Bachelors **Intercollegiate Athletics:** Basketball M & W; Racquetball M & W; Soccer M & W; Swimming and Diving M & W

BAY PATH UNIVERSITY

588 Longmeadow St.
Longmeadow, MA 01106-2292
Tel: (413)565-1000; Free: 800-782-7284
Fax: (413)567-0501
E-mail: admiss@baypath.edu
Web Site: www.baypath.edu
President/CEO: Dr. Carol A. Leary
Admissions: Dawn Bryden
Financial Aid: Stephanie King

Type: Comprehensive **% Accepted:** 78 **Admission Plans:** Deferred Admission; Early Decision Plan **Application Deadline:** August 1 **Application Fee:** $25.00 **H.S. Requirements:** High school diploma required; GED accepted **Costs Per Year:** Application fee: $25. Comprehensive fee: $45,349 includes full-time tuition ($32,739) and college room and board ($12,610). Room and board charges vary according to board plan. Part-time tuition: $500 per credit hour. Part-time tuition varies according to course load. **Scholarships:** Available. **Calendar System:** Semester, Summer session available **Enrollment:** Full-time 1,471, Graduate full-time 569, Graduate part-time 682, Part-time 385 **Faculty:** Full-time 56, Part-time 337 **Student-Faculty Ratio:** 12:1 **Exams:** ACT essay component used for advising; ACT essay component used for placement; SAT essay component used for advising; SAT essay component used for placement. **% Receiving Financial Aid:** 92 **% Residing in College-Owned, -Operated, or -Affiliated Housing:** 45 **Final Year or Final Semester Residency Requirement:** No **Regional Accreditation:** New England Association of Schools and Colleges **Credit Hours For Degree:** 60 credits, Associates; 120 credits, Bachelors **ROTC:** Air Force, Army **Professional Accreditation:** AOTA. **Intercollegiate Athletics:** Basketball W; Cross-Country Running W; Field Hockey W; Lacrosse W; Soccer W; Softball W; Tennis W; Volleyball W

BAY STATE COLLEGE

122 Commonwealth Ave.
Boston, MA 02116-2975
Tel: (617)217-9000; Free: 800-81-LEARN
Fax: (617)536-1735
E-mail: admissions@baystate.edu
Web Site: www.baystate.edu
President/CEO: Craig F. Pfannenstiehl
Admissions: Kimberly Odusami

Type: Two-Year College **Sex:** Coed **% Accepted:** 53 **Admission Plans:** Early Admission **Application Deadline:** Rolling **Application Fee:** $0.00 **H.S. Requirements:** High school diploma required; GED accepted **Scholarships:** Available. **Calendar System:** Semester, Summer session available **Student-Faculty Ratio:** 20:1 **Exams:** SAT I or ACT. **% Residing in College-Owned, -Operated, or -Affiliated Housing:** 26 **Final Year or Final Semester Residency Requirement:** No **Regional Accreditation:** New England Association of Schools and Colleges **Credit Hours For Degree:** 60 credits, Associates; 120 credits, Bachelors **Professional Accreditation:** ABHES, APTA.

BECKER COLLEGE

61 Sever St.
Worcester, MA 01609
Tel: (508)791-9241; Free: 877-5BECKER
Fax: (508)831-7505
E-mail: admissions@becker.edu
Web Site: www.becker.edu
President/CEO: Dr. Robert E. Johnson
Admissions: Michael Perron
Financial Aid: Heather Ruland

Type: Comprehensive **Sex:** Coed **Scores:** 93% SAT V 400+; 91% SAT M 400+; 46.48% ACT 18-23; 33.8% ACT 24-29 **% Accepted:** 67 **Admission Plans:** Deferred Admission; Early Action; Early Admission; Early Decision Plan **Application Deadline:** Rolling **H.S. Requirements:** High school diploma required; GED accepted **Costs Per Year:** Comprehensive fee: $45,210 includes full-time tuition ($31,230), mandatory fees ($1580), and college room and board ($12,400). College room only: $6050. Full-time tuition and fees vary according to class time, course load, program, and student level. Room and board charges vary according to board plan and housing facility. Part-time tuition: $1301 per credit. Part-time tuition varies according to class time, course load, program, and student level. **Scholarships:** Available. **Calendar System:** Semester, Summer session not available **Enrollment:** Full-time 1,581, Graduate full-time 5, Part-time 567 **Faculty:** Full-time 43, Part-time 187 **Exams:** SAT I or ACT; SAT Reasoning. **% Receiving Financial Aid:** 84 **% Residing in College-Owned, -Operated, or -Affiliated Housing:** 50 **Final Year or Final Semester Residency Requirement:** No **Regional Accreditation:** New England Association of Schools and Colleges **Credit Hours For Degree:** 60 credits, Associates; 120 credits, Bachelors **ROTC:** Air Force, Army **Professional Accreditation:** ACEN, APTA. **Intercollegiate Athletics:** Baseball M; Basketball M & W; Cheerleading M & W; Equestrian Sports M & W; Field Hockey W; Football M; Golf M; Ice Hockey M & W; Lacrosse M & W; Soccer M & W; Softball W; Tennis M & W; Volleyball W

BENJAMIN FRANKLIN INSTITUTE OF TECHNOLOGY

41 Berkeley St.
Boston, MA 02116-6296
Tel: (617)423-4630; Free: 877-400-BFIT
Fax: (617)482-3706
E-mail: bjohnson@bfit.edu
Web Site: www.bfit.edu
President/CEO: Michael Taylor
Admissions: Brittainy Johnson

Type: Two-Year College **Sex:** Coed **Scores:** 52% SAT V 400+; 77% SAT M 400+ **% Accepted:** 64 **Admission Plans:** Deferred Admission; Open Admission **Application Fee:** $25.00 **H.S. Requirements:** High school diploma required; GED accepted **Costs Per Year:** Application fee: $25. Comprehensive fee: $32,815 includes full-time tuition ($16,950), mandatory fees ($1265), and college room and board ($14,600). Full-time tuition and fees vary according to course load, degree level, and program. Room and board charges vary according to housing facility. Part-time tuition: $707 per credit hour. Part-time tuition varies according to course load, degree level, and program. **Calendar System:** Semester, Summer session available **Enrollment:** Full-time 428, Part-time 65 **Exams:** ACT essay component not used; SAT I or ACT; SAT essay component not used. **Regional Accreditation:** New England Association of Schools and Colleges **Credit Hours For Degree:** 70 credits, Associates; 134 credits, Bachelors **Professional Accreditation:** ABET. **Intercollegiate Athletics:** Soccer M

BENTLEY UNIVERSITY

175 Forest St.
Waltham, MA 02452-4705
Tel: (781)891-2000; Free: 800-523-2354
Fax: (781)891-3414
E-mail: ugadmission@bentley.edu
Web Site: www.bentley.edu
President/CEO: Gloria Cordes Larson, JD
Financial Aid: Donna Kendall

Type: Comprehensive **Sex:** Coed **Scores:** 100% SAT V 400+; 100% SAT M 400+; 9.9% ACT 18-23; 60.7% ACT 24-29 **% Accepted:** 42 **Admission Plans:** Deferred Admission; Early Action; Early Admission **Application Deadline:** January 7 **Application Fee:** $50.00 **H.S. Requirements:** High school diploma required; GED accepted **Costs Per Year:** Application fee: $50. Comprehensive fee: $58,605 includes full-time tuition ($42,550), mandatory fees ($1535), and college room and board ($14,520). College room only: $8800. Room and board charges vary according to board plan and housing facility. Part-time tuition: $2160 per course. Part-time mandatory fees: $25 per term. Part-time tuition and fees vary according to class time and course load. **Scholarships:** Available. **Calendar System:** Semester, Summer session available **Enrollment:** Full-time 4,137, Graduate full-time 765, Graduate part-time 584, Part-time 66 **Faculty:** Full-time 289, Part-time 195 **Student-Faculty Ratio:** 12:1 **Exams:** ACT essay component not used; Other; SAT I or ACT; SAT essay component used for admission; SAT Reasoning. **% Receiving Financial Aid:** 44 **% Residing in College-**

Owned, -Operated, or -Affiliated Housing: 79 **Regional Accreditation:** New England Association of Schools and Colleges **Credit Hours For Degree:** 122 credits, Bachelors **ROTC:** Air Force, Army **Professional Accreditation:** AACSB. **Intercollegiate Athletics:** Baseball M; Basketball M & W; Cross-Country Running M & W; Field Hockey W; Football M; Golf M; Ice Hockey M; Lacrosse M & W; Soccer M & W; Softball W; Swimming and Diving M & W; Tennis M & W; Track and Field M & W; Volleyball W

BERKLEE COLLEGE OF MUSIC

1140 Boylston St.
Boston, MA 02215-3693
Tel: (617)266-1400; Free: 800-BERKLEE
Fax: (617)747-2047
E-mail: admissions@berklee.edu
Web Site: www.berklee.edu
President/CEO: Roger H. Brown
Admissions: Damien Bracken

Type: Comprehensive **Sex:** Coed **% Accepted:** 26 **Admission Plans:** Deferred Admission; Early Decision Plan **Application Deadline:** January 15 **Application Fee:** $150.00 **H.S. Requirements:** High school diploma required; GED accepted **Costs Per Year:** Application fee: $150. Comprehensive fee: $59,398 includes full-time tuition ($40,220), mandatory fees ($1178), and college room and board ($18,000). Part-time tuition: $1461 per credit. **Scholarships:** Available. **Calendar System:** Semester **Enrollment:** Full-time 4,291, Graduate full-time 160, Part-time 821 **Faculty:** Full-time 266, Part-time 426 **Student-Faculty Ratio:** 11:1 **Exams:** ACT essay component not used; SAT essay component not used. **% Receiving Financial Aid:** 21 **% Residing in College-Owned, -Operated, or -Affiliated Housing:** 27 **Regional Accreditation:** New England Association of Schools and Colleges **Credit Hours For Degree:** 120 credit hours, Bachelors

BERKSHIRE COMMUNITY COLLEGE

1350 W St.
Pittsfield, MA 01201-5786
Tel: (413)499-4660
Fax: (606)224-7744
E-mail: tschetti@berkshirecc.edu
Web Site: www.berkshirecc.edu
President/CEO: Dr. Ellen L. Kennedy
Admissions: Tina Schettini
Financial Aid: Natalia Eddy

Type: Two-Year College **Sex:** Coed **Affiliation:** Massachusetts Public Higher Education System. **% Accepted:** 100 **Admission Plans:** Deferred Admission; Open Admission **Application Deadline:** Rolling **Application Fee:** $0.00 **H.S. Requirements:** High school diploma required; GED accepted **Costs Per Year:** Application fee: $0. State resident tuition: $1248 full-time. Nonresident tuition: $12,480 full-time. Mandatory fees: $8484 full-time. **Scholarships:** Available. **Calendar System:** Semester, Summer session available **Enrollment:** Full-time 721, Part-time 1,390 **Faculty:** Full-time 56, Part-time 120 **Student-Faculty Ratio:** 15:1 **Final Year or Final Semester Residency Requirement:** No **Regional Accreditation:** New England Association of Schools and Colleges **Credit Hours For Degree:** 60 credits, Associates **Professional Accreditation:** ACEN, APTA, CoARC.

BOSTON ARCHITECTURAL COLLEGE

320 Newbury St.
Boston, MA 02115-2795
Tel: (617)262-5000
Fax: (617)585-0111
E-mail: admissions@the-bac.edu
Web Site: www.the-bac.edu
President/CEO: Glen LeRoy
Financial Aid: Janice Wilkos-Greenberg

Type: Comprehensive **Sex:** Coed **% Accepted:** 16 **Admission Plans:** Open Admission **H.S. Requirements:** High school diploma required; GED accepted **Costs Per Year:** Tuition: $20,016 full-time, $1688 per credit hour part-time. Mandatory fees: $650 full-time, $175 per term part-time. Full-time tuition and fees vary according to course load, degree level, and program. Part-time tuition and fees vary according to course load, degree level, and program. **Scholarships:** Available. **Calendar System:** Semester, Summer session available **Enrollment:** Full-time 354, Graduate full-time 399, Graduate part-time 7, Part-time 118 **Faculty:** Full-time 22, Part-time 349 **Student-Faculty Ratio:** 2:1 **% Receiving Financial Aid:** 63 **Regional Accredita-**

tion: New England Association of Schools and Colleges **Credit Hours For Degree:** 120 credit hours, Bachelors **Professional Accreditation:** CIDA, NAAB.

BOSTON BAPTIST COLLEGE

950 Metropolitan Ave.
Boston, MA 02136
Tel: (617)364-3510; Free: 888-235-2014
Fax: (617)364-0723
E-mail: kmelton@boston.edu
Web Site: www.boston.edu
President/CEO: Rev. David V. Melton
Admissions: Kim Melton

Type: Four-Year College **Sex:** Coed **Affiliation:** Baptist. **Admission Plans:** Deferred Admission **Application Deadline:** Rolling **Application Fee:** $50.00 **H.S. Requirements:** High school diploma required; GED accepted **Scholarships:** Available. **Calendar System:** Semester, Summer session available **Enrollment:** Full-time 73, Part-time 23 **Exams:** ACT essay component used for placement; SAT I or ACT; SAT essay component used for placement. **% Residing in College-Owned, -Operated, or -Affiliated Housing:** 65 **Final Year or Final Semester Residency Requirement:** Yes **Credit Hours For Degree:** 64 credit hours, Associates; 128 credit hours, Bachelors **Professional Accreditation:** TRACS. **Intercollegiate Athletics:** Basketball M

BOSTON COLLEGE

140 Commonwealth Ave.
Chestnut Hill, MA 02467-3800
Tel: (617)552-8000; Free: 800-360-2522
Fax: (617)552-0798
Web Site: www.bc.edu
President/CEO: Fr. William P. Leahy

Type: University **Sex:** Coed **Affiliation:** Roman Catholic (Jesuit). **Scores:** 100% SAT V 400+; 100% SAT M 400+; 2.18% ACT 18-23; 16.4% ACT 24-29 **% Accepted:** 29 **Admission Plans:** Deferred Admission; Early Admission; Early Decision Plan **Application Deadline:** January 1 **Application Fee:** $75.00 **H.S. Requirements:** High school diploma required; GED accepted **Costs Per Year:** Application fee: $75. One-time mandatory fee: $482. Comprehensive fee: $62,820 includes full-time tuition ($48,540), mandatory fees ($784), and college room and board ($13,496). College room only: $8390. Room and board charges vary according to housing facility. **Scholarships:** Available. **Calendar System:** Semester, Summer session available **Enrollment:** Full-time 9,192, Graduate full-time 3,491, Graduate part-time 1,022 **Faculty:** Full-time 786, Part-time 744 **Student-Faculty Ratio:** 12:1 **Exams:** ACT essay component used as validity check; ACT essay component used for admission; SAT I or ACT; SAT essay component used as validity check; SAT essay component used for admission; SAT Reasoning; SAT Subject. **% Receiving Financial Aid:** 41 **% Residing in College-Owned, -Operated, or -Affiliated Housing:** 85 **Final Year or Final Semester Residency Requirement:** No **Regional Accreditation:** New England Association of Schools and Colleges **Credit Hours For Degree:** 38 courses, Bachelors **ROTC:** Air Force, Army, Navy **Professional Accreditation:** AACN, AACSB, AALS, AANA, ABA, APA, ATS, CSWE, NCATE, TEAC. **Intercollegiate Athletics:** Baseball M; Basketball M & W; Cheerleading M & W; Crew W; Cross-Country Running M & W; Fencing M & W; Field Hockey W; Football M; Golf M & W; Ice Hockey M & W; Lacrosse W; Sailing M & W; Skiing (Downhill) M & W; Soccer M & W; Softball W; Swimming and Diving M & W; Tennis M & W; Track and Field M & W; Volleyball W

BOSTON UNIVERSITY

Boston, MA 02215
Tel: (617)353-2000
Fax: (617)353-9695
E-mail: admissions@bu.edu
Web Site: www.bu.edu
President/CEO: Dr. Robert A. Brown
Admissions: Kelly A. Walter
Financial Aid: Julie Wickstrom

Type: University **Sex:** Coed **Scores:** 100% SAT V 400+; 100% SAT M 400+; 2% ACT 18-23; 48% ACT 24-29 **% Accepted:** 33 **Admission Plans:** Deferred Admission; Early Action; Early Admission **Application Deadline:** January 3 **Application Fee:** $80.00 **H.S. Requirements:** High school diploma required; GED accepted **Costs Per Year:** Application fee: $80. Comprehensive fee: $62,956 includes full-time tuition ($47,422), mandatory fees ($1014), and college room and board ($14,520). College room only:

$9570. Full-time tuition and fees vary according to class time. Room and board charges vary according to board plan, housing facility, and location. Part-time tuition: $1482 per credit hour. Part-time mandatory fees: $60 per term. Part-time tuition and fees vary according to class time and course load. **Scholarships:** Available. **Calendar System:** Semester, Summer session available **Enrollment:** Full-time 16,585, Graduate full-time 9,414, Graduate part-time 4,812, Part-time 1,347 **Faculty:** Full-time 1,699, Part-time 957 **Student-Faculty Ratio:** 13:1 **Exams:** ACT essay component used for admission; SAT I or ACT; SAT II; SAT essay component used for admission; SAT Reasoning; SAT Subject. **% Receiving Financial Aid:** 36 **% Residing in College-Owned, -Operated, or -Affiliated Housing:** 75 **Final Year or Final Semester Residency Requirement:** No **Regional Accreditation:** New England Association of Schools and Colleges **Credit Hours For Degree:** 128 credits, Bachelors **ROTC:** Air Force, Army, Navy **Professional Accreditation:** AACSB, AALS, ABA, ABET, ACNM, ACIPE, ADA, AND, AOTA, APA, APTA, ASHA, ATS, CAHME, CEPH, CORE, CSWE, JRCAT, LCME/AMA, NASM. **Intercollegiate Athletics:** Badminton M & W; Baseball M; Basketball M & W; Cheerleading M & W; Crew M & W; Cross-Country Running M & W; Equestrian Sports M & W; Fencing M & W; Field Hockey W; Golf M & W; Gymnastics M & W; Ice Hockey M & W; Lacrosse M & W; Rugby M & W; Sailing M & W; Skiing (Downhill) M & W; Soccer M & W; Softball W; Squash M & W; Swimming and Diving M & W; Table Tennis M & W; Tennis M & W; Track and Field M & W; Ultimate Frisbee M & W; Volleyball M & W; Water Polo M & W

BRANDEIS UNIVERSITY

415 S St.
Waltham, MA 02454-9110
Tel: (781)736-2000; Free: 800-622-0622
Fax: (781)736-3536
E-mail: admissions@brandeis.edu
Web Site: www.brandeis.edu
President/CEO: Lisa M. Lynch
Admissions: Jennifer Walker
Financial Aid: Tim Brown

Type: University **Sex:** Coed **Scores:** 100% SAT V 400+; 100% SAT M 400+; 2.47% ACT 18-23; 26.34% ACT 24-29 **% Accepted:** 34 **Admission Plans:** Deferred Admission; Early Action; Early Admission **Application Deadline:** January 1 **Application Fee:** $75.00 **H.S. Requirements:** High school diploma required; GED accepted **Costs Per Year:** Application fee: $75. Comprehensive fee: $63,304 includes full-time tuition ($47,702), mandatory fees ($1896), and college room and board ($13,706). College room only: $7750. Full-time tuition and fees vary according to student level. Room and board charges vary according to board plan and housing facility. Part-time tuition: $5963 per course. Part-time mandatory fees: $798 per term. Part-time tuition and fees vary according to course load. **Scholarships:** Available. **Calendar System:** Semester, Summer session available **Enrollment:** Full-time 3,602, Graduate full-time 1,600, Graduate part-time 531, Part-time 19 **Faculty:** Full-time 358, Part-time 162 **Student-Faculty Ratio:** 10:1 **Exams:** SAT I or ACT; SAT Reasoning; SAT Subject. **% Receiving Financial Aid:** 53 **% Residing in College-Owned, -Operated, or -Affiliated Housing:** 79 **Final Year or Final Semester Residency Requirement:** Yes **Regional Accreditation:** New England Association of Schools and Colleges **Credit Hours For Degree:** 32 courses, Bachelors **ROTC:** Air Force, Army **Professional Accreditation:** AACSB. **Intercollegiate Athletics:** Baseball M; Basketball M & W; Cross-Country Running M & W; Fencing M & W; Soccer M & W; Softball W; Swimming and Diving M & W; Tennis M & W; Track and Field M & W; Volleyball W

BRIDGEWATER STATE UNIVERSITY

Bridgewater, MA 02325-0001
Tel: (508)531-1000
Fax: (508)531-1707
E-mail: admission@bridgew.edu
Web Site: www.bridgew.edu
President/CEO: Frederick Clark
Admissions: Gregg Meyer

Type: Comprehensive **Sex:** Coed **Affiliation:** Massachusetts Department of Higher Education. **Scores:** 91% SAT V 400+; 92% SAT M 400+; 67.8% ACT 18-23; 25.3% ACT 24-29 **% Accepted:** 81 **Admission Plans:** Deferred Admission; Early Decision Plan **Application Deadline:** February 15 **Application Fee:** $50.00 **H.S. Requirements:** High school diploma required; GED accepted **Costs Per Year:** Application fee: $50. State resident tuition: $910 full-time, $38 per credit hour part-time. Nonresident tuition: $7050 full-time, $294 per credit hour part-time. Mandatory fees: $7993 full-time, $327.63 per credit hour part-time. Full-time tuition and fees vary according to course load. College room and board: $11,700. College room only: $7700. Room and board charges vary according to board plan and housing facility. **Scholarships:** Available. **Calendar System:** Semester, Summer session available **Enrollment:** Full-time 7,933, Graduate full-time 457, Graduate part-time 1,024, Part-time 1,675 **Faculty:** Full-time 335, Part-time 475 **Student-Faculty Ratio:** 19:1 **Exams:** ACT essay component not used; SAT I or ACT; SAT essay component not used. **% Receiving Financial Aid:** 71 % **Residing in College-Owned, -Operated, or -Affiliated Housing:** 41 **Final Year or Final Semester Residency Requirement:** No **Regional Accreditation:** New England Association of Schools and Colleges **Credit Hours For Degree:** 120 semester hours, Bachelors **ROTC:** Air Force, Army **Professional Accreditation:** ACA, CSWE, JRCAT, NASM, NASPAA, NCATE. **Intercollegiate Athletics:** Baseball M; Basketball M & W; Cross-Country Running M & W; Field Hockey W; Football M; Lacrosse W; Soccer M & W; Softball W; Swimming and Diving M & W; Tennis M & W; Track and Field M & W; Volleyball W; Wrestling M

BRISTOL COMMUNITY COLLEGE
777 Elsbree St.
Fall River, MA 02720-7395
Tel: (508)678-2811
Fax: (508)674-8838
E-mail: shilo.henriques@bristolcc.edu
Web Site: www.bristolcc.edu
President/CEO: John J. Sbrega, PhD
Admissions: Shilo Henriques
Type: Two-Year College **Sex:** Coed **Affiliation:** Massachusetts Community College System. **Admission Plans:** Deferred Admission; Open Admission **Application Fee:** $10.00 **H.S. Requirements:** High school diploma required; GED accepted **Costs Per Year:** Application fee: $10. State resident tuition: $576 full-time, $24 per credit part-time. Nonresident tuition: $5520 full-time, $230 per credit part-time. Mandatory fees: $3720 full-time, $155 per credit part-time. Full-time tuition and fees vary according to course load. Part-time tuition and fees vary according to course load. **Scholarships:** Available. **Calendar System:** Semester, Summer session available **Enrollment:** Full-time 4,429, Part-time 4,906 **Faculty:** Full-time 131, Part-time 555 **Student-Faculty Ratio:** 19:1 **Regional Accreditation:** New England Association of Schools and Colleges **Credit Hours For Degree:** 60 credits, Associates **Professional Accreditation:** ACEN, ADA, AHIMA, AOTA, NAACLS.

BUNKER HILL COMMUNITY COLLEGE
250 New Rutherford Ave.
Boston, MA 02129
Tel: (617)228-2000
Fax: (617)228-2120
E-mail: admissions@bhcc.mass.edu
Web Site: www.bhcc.mass.edu
President/CEO: Pam Y. Eddinger, PhD
Admissions: Vanessa Whaley Rowley
Financial Aid: Melissa Holster
Type: Two-Year College **Sex:** Coed **% Accepted:** 77 **Admission Plans:** Open Admission **Application Deadline:** Rolling **H.S. Requirements:** High school diploma required; GED accepted. For non-degree seeking students: High school diploma or equivalent not required **Costs Per Year:** State resident tuition: $576 full-time, $24 per credit hour part-time. Nonresident tuition: $5520 full-time, $230 per credit hour part-time. Mandatory fees: $3312 full-time, $138 per credit hour part-time. Full-time tuition and fees vary according to course load, program, and reciprocity agreements. Part-time tuition and fees vary according to course load, program, and reciprocity agreements. **Scholarships:** Available. **Calendar System:** Semester, Summer session available **Enrollment:** Full-time 4,191, Part-time 9,856 **Faculty:** Full-time 156, Part-time 612 **Student-Faculty Ratio:** 17:1 **Final Year or Final Semester Residency Requirement:** No **Regional Accreditation:** New England Association of Schools and Colleges **Credit Hours For Degree:** 60 credits, Associates **Professional Accreditation:** ACEN, ARCST, JRCEDMS, JRCERT. **Intercollegiate Athletics:** Baseball M; Basketball M & W; Soccer M & W; Volleyball W

CAMBRIDGE COLLEGE
1000 Massachusetts Ave.
Cambridge, MA 02138-5304

Tel: (617)868-1000; Free: 800-877-4723
Fax: (617)349-3545
E-mail: denise.haile@cambridgecollege.edu
Web Site: www.cambridgecollege.edu
President/CEO: Deborah Jackson
Admissions: Denise Haile
Financial Aid: Dr. Frank Lauder
Type: Comprehensive **Sex:** Coed **% Accepted:** 64 **Admission Plans:** Deferred Admission; Open Admission **Application Deadline:** Rolling **Application Fee:** $30.00 **H.S. Requirements:** High school diploma required; GED accepted **Scholarships:** Available. **Calendar System:** Trimester, Summer session available **Enrollment:** Full-time 270, Graduate full-time 1,003, Graduate part-time 1,664, Part-time 820 **Faculty:** Full-time 19, Part-time 434 **Student-Faculty Ratio:** 13:1 **% Receiving Financial Aid:** 63 **Regional Accreditation:** New England Association of Schools and Colleges **Credit Hours For Degree:** 120 credit hours, Bachelors **Professional Accreditation:** TEAC.

CAPE COD COMMUNITY COLLEGE
2240 Iyannough Rd.
West Barnstable, MA 02668-1599
Tel: (508)362-2131; Free: 877-846-3672
E-mail: admiss@capecod.edu
Web Site: www.capecod.edu
President/CEO: Kathleen Schatzberg
Type: Two-Year College **Sex:** Coed **Affiliation:** Massachusetts Public Higher Education System. **Admission Plans:** Deferred Admission; Open Admission; Preferred Admission **Application Deadline:** August 10 **H.S. Requirements:** High school diploma required; GED accepted **Costs Per Year:** State resident tuition: $176 per credit hour part-time. Nonresident tuition: $382 per credit hour part-time. **Scholarships:** Available. **Calendar System:** Semester, Summer session available **Student-Faculty Ratio:** 18:1 **Regional Accreditation:** New England Association of Schools and Colleges **Credit Hours For Degree:** 60 credit hours, Associates **Professional Accreditation:** ACEN, ADA.

CLARK UNIVERSITY
950 Main St.
Worcester, MA 01610-1477
Tel: (508)793-7711; Free: 800-GO-CLARK
Fax: (508)793-8821
E-mail: admissions@clarku.edu
Web Site: www.clarku.edu
President/CEO: Pres. David Angel
Admissions: Donald Honeman
Financial Aid: Mary Ellen Severance
Type: University **Sex:** Coed **Scores:** 100% SAT V 400+; 100% SAT M 400+; 12% ACT 18-23; 55% ACT 24-29 **% Accepted:** 55 **Admission Plans:** Deferred Admission; Early Action; Early Admission; Early Decision Plan **Application Deadline:** January 15 **Application Fee:** $60.00 **H.S. Requirements:** High school diploma required; GED accepted **Costs Per Year:** Application fee: $60. Comprehensive fee: $51,600 includes full-time tuition ($42,800), mandatory fees ($350), and college room and board ($8450). College room only: $4900. Room and board charges vary according to board plan and housing facility. Part-time tuition: $1,338 per credit. **Scholarships:** Available. **Calendar System:** Semester, Summer session available **Enrollment:** Full-time 2,320, Graduate full-time 843, Graduate part-time 245, Part-time 77 **Faculty:** Full-time 203, Part-time 109 **Student-Faculty Ratio:** 10:1 **Exams:** ACT essay component not used; SAT essay component not used. **% Receiving Financial Aid:** 58 % **Residing in College-Owned, -Operated, or -Affiliated Housing:** 70 **Final Year or Final Semester Residency Requirement:** Yes **Regional Accreditation:** New England Association of Schools and Colleges **Credit Hours For Degree:** 32 courses, Bachelors **ROTC:** Air Force, Army **Professional Accreditation:** AACSB, APA. **Intercollegiate Athletics:** Baseball M; Basketball M & W; Crew M & W; Cross-Country Running M & W; Field Hockey W; Lacrosse M; Soccer M & W; Softball W; Swimming and Diving M & W; Tennis M & W; Volleyball W

COLLEGE OF THE HOLY CROSS
1 College St.
Worcester, MA 01610-2395
Tel: (508)793-2011; Free: 800-442-2421
Fax: (508)793-3888
E-mail: admissions@holycross.edu

Web Site: www.holycross.edu
President/CEO: Rev. Philip L. Boroughs, SJ
Admissions: Ann McDermott
Financial Aid: Lynne Myers

Type: Four-Year College **Sex:** Coed **Affiliation:** Roman Catholic (Jesuit). **Scores:** 100% SAT V 400+; 100% SAT M 400+; 2% ACT 18-23; 43% ACT 24-29 **% Accepted:** 37 **Admission Plans:** Deferred Admission; Early Action; Early Admission **Application Deadline:** January 15 **Application Fee:** $60.00 **H.S. Requirements:** High school diploma required; GED accepted **Costs Per Year:** Application fee: $60. Comprehensive fee: $62,165 includes full-time tuition ($48,295), mandatory fees ($645), and college room and board ($13,225). College room only: $7135. Room and board charges vary according to housing facility. **Scholarships:** Available. **Calendar System:** Semester, Summer session not available **Enrollment:** Full-time 2,885, Part-time 31 **Faculty:** Full-time 296, Part-time 38 **Student-Faculty Ratio:** 9:1 **Exams:** ACT essay component not used; SAT I and SAT II or ACT; SAT I or ACT; SAT essay component not used; SAT Reasoning; SAT Subject. **% Receiving Financial Aid:** 52 **% Residing in College-Owned, -Operated, or -Affiliated Housing:** 91 **Final Year or Final Semester Residency Requirement:** Yes **Regional Accreditation:** New England Association of Schools and Colleges **Credit Hours For Degree:** 32 courses, Bachelors **Professional Accreditation:** NAST. **Intercollegiate Athletics:** Baseball M; Basketball M & W; Crew M & W; Cross-Country Running M & W; Field Hockey W; Football M; Golf M & W; Ice Hockey M & W; Lacrosse M & W; Soccer M & W; Softball W; Swimming and Diving M & W; Tennis M & W; Track and Field M & W; Volleyball W

CURRY COLLEGE

1071 Blue Hill Ave.
Milton, MA 02186-9984
Tel: (617)333-0500; Free: 800-669-0686
Fax: (617)333-6860
E-mail: curryadm@curry.edu
Web Site: www.curry.edu
President/CEO: Kenneth Quigley, Jr.
Admissions: Jane P. Fidler
Financial Aid: Linda Brennan

Type: Comprehensive **Sex:** Coed **Scores:** 85% SAT V 400+; 84% SAT M 400+; 64% ACT 18-23; 11% ACT 24-29 **% Accepted:** 88 **Admission Plans:** Deferred Admission; Early Admission; Early Decision Plan **Application Deadline:** April 1 **Application Fee:** $50.00 **H.S. Requirements:** High school diploma required; GED accepted **Costs Per Year:** Application fee: $50. One-time mandatory fee: $330. Comprehensive fee: $52,475 includes full-time tuition ($35,740), mandatory fees ($1765), and college room and board ($14,970). College room only: $8030. Full-time tuition and fees vary according to class time, course load, location, and program. Room and board charges vary according to board plan and housing facility. Part-time tuition: $1192 per credit. Part-time tuition varies according to class time, course load, location, and program. **Scholarships:** Available. **Calendar System:** Semester, Summer session available **Enrollment:** Full-time 2,012, Graduate full-time 195, Graduate part-time 27, Part-time 716 **Faculty:** Full-time 125, Part-time 365 **Student-Faculty Ratio:** 10:1 **Exams:** Other; SAT I or ACT; SAT essay component used for advising; SAT essay component used for placement; SAT Reasoning. **% Receiving Financial Aid:** 75 **% Residing in College-Owned, -Operated, or -Affiliated Housing:** 88 **Final Year or Final Semester Residency Requirement:** No **Regional Accreditation:** New England Association of Schools and Colleges **Credit Hours For Degree:** 120 credit hours, Bachelors **ROTC:** Army **Professional Accreditation:** AACN. **Intercollegiate Athletics:** Baseball M; Basketball M & W; Cross-Country Running W; Equestrian Sports M & W; Football M; Ice Hockey M & W; Lacrosse M & W; Rugby M; Soccer M & W; Softball W; Tennis M & W; Volleyball W

DEAN COLLEGE

99 Main St.
Franklin, MA 02038-1994
Tel: (508)541-1900; Free: 877-TRY-DEAN
Fax: (508)541-8726
E-mail: igodes@dean.edu
Web Site: www.dean.edu
President/CEO: Dr. Paula M. Rooney
Admissions: Iris P. Godes

Type: Two-Year College **Sex:** Coed **Scores:** 69% SAT V 400+; 63% SAT M 400+ **% Accepted:** 68 **Admission Plans:** Deferred Admission; Early Admis-

sion; Early Decision Plan **Application Deadline:** Rolling **Application Fee:** $0.00 **H.S. Requirements:** High school diploma required; GED accepted **Costs Per Year:** Application fee: $0. Comprehensive fee: $50,920 includes full-time tuition ($35,420), mandatory fees ($300), and college room and board ($15,200). College room only: $9600. Full-time tuition and fees vary according to class time, course load, and program. Room and board charges vary according to housing facility. Part-time tuition: $313 per credit. Part-time mandatory fees: $25 per term. Part-time tuition and fees vary according to class time, course load, and program. **Scholarships:** Available. **Calendar System:** Semester, Summer session available **Enrollment:** Full-time 1,069, Part-time 223 **Faculty:** Full-time 31, Part-time 120 **Student-Faculty Ratio:** 16:1 **Exams:** ACT essay component used for admission; ACT essay component used for placement; SAT I or ACT; SAT essay component used for admission; SAT essay component used for placement; SAT Reasoning. **% Residing in College-Owned, -Operated, or -Affiliated Housing:** 89 **Final Year or Final Semester Residency Requirement:** No **Regional Accreditation:** New England Association of Schools and Colleges **Credit Hours For Degree:** 60 credits, Associates; 120 credits, Bachelors **Intercollegiate Athletics:** Baseball M; Basketball M & W; Football M; Golf M; Lacrosse M & W; Soccer M & W; Softball W; Volleyball W

EASTERN NAZARENE COLLEGE

23 E Elm Ave.
Quincy, MA 02170
Tel: (617)745-3000; Free: 800-88-ENC88
Fax: (617)745-3907
E-mail: andrew.wright@enc.edu
Web Site: www.enc.edu
President/CEO: Dr. Corlis A. McGee
Admissions: Andrew R. Wright
Financial Aid: Lisa Seals

Type: Comprehensive **Sex:** Coed **Affiliation:** Church of the Nazarene. **Scores:** 80% SAT V 400+; 85% SAT M 400+; 52% ACT 18-23; 24% ACT 24-29 **% Accepted:** 63 **Admission Plans:** Deferred Admission; Early Admission **Application Deadline:** Rolling **H.S. Requirements:** High school diploma required; GED accepted **Scholarships:** Available. **Calendar System:** Semester, Summer session available **Enrollment:** Full-time 850, Graduate full-time 124, Graduate part-time 50, Part-time 12 **Faculty:** Full-time 48, Part-time 74 **Student-Faculty Ratio:** 17:1 **Exams:** ACT essay component used as validity check; ACT essay component used for admission; ACT essay component used for advising; ACT essay component used for placement; ACT essay component used in place of application essay; SAT I and SAT II or ACT; SAT I or ACT; SAT II; SAT essay component used as validity check; SAT essay component used for admission; SAT essay component used for advising; SAT essay component used for placement; SAT essay component used in place of application essay; SAT Reasoning; SAT Subject. **% Receiving Financial Aid:** 44 **% Residing in College-Owned, -Operated, or -Affiliated Housing:** 52 **Final Year or Final Semester Residency Requirement:** No **Regional Accreditation:** New England Association of Schools and Colleges **Credit Hours For Degree:** 65 hours, Associates; 130 hours, Bachelors **ROTC:** Air Force, Army, Navy **Professional Accreditation:** CSWE. **Intercollegiate Athletics:** Baseball M; Basketball M & W; Cross-Country Running M & W; Golf M & W; Skiing (Downhill) M; Soccer M & W; Softball W; Tennis M & W; Volleyball M & W

ELMS COLLEGE

291 Springfield St.
Chicopee, MA 01013-2839
Tel: (413)594-2761; Free: 800-255-ELMS
Fax: (413)594-2781
E-mail: admissions@elms.edu
Web Site: www.elms.edu
President/CEO: Señor Mary Reap
Admissions: Joseph Wagner

Type: Comprehensive **Sex:** Coed **Affiliation:** Roman Catholic. **Scores:** 88% SAT V 400+; 86% SAT M 400+; 50% ACT 18-23; 35.71% ACT 24-29 **% Accepted:** 75 **Admission Plans:** Deferred Admission; Early Admission **Application Deadline:** Rolling **Application Fee:** $30.00 **H.S. Requirements:** High school diploma required; GED accepted **Costs Per Year:** Application fee: $30. Comprehensive fee: $43,988 includes full-time tuition ($30,768), mandatory fees ($1512), and college room and board ($11,708). Room and board charges vary according to board plan. Part-time tuition: $624 per credit hour. Part-time tuition varies according to location and program. **Scholarships:** Available. **Calendar System:** Semester, Summer session available **Enrollment:** Full-time 969, Graduate full-time 61, Graduate part-time 340, Part-time 342 **Faculty:** Full-time 60, Part-time 117 **Student-Faculty Ratio:** 13:1 **Exams:** ACT essay component used for admission; SAT I or ACT; SAT essay component used for admission; SAT Reasoning. **% Receiving Financial Aid:** 90 **Regional Accreditation:** New England Association of Schools and Colleges **Credit Hours For Degree:** 120 credits, Bachelors **ROTC:** Air Force, Army **Professional Accreditation:** AACN, CSWE. **Intercollegiate Athletics:** Baseball M; Basketball M & W; Cross-Country Running M & W; Field Hockey W; Golf M; Lacrosse W; Soccer M & W; Softball W; Swimming and Diving M & W; Volleyball M & W

EMERSON COLLEGE

120 Boylston St.
Boston, MA 02116-4624
Tel: (617)824-8500
Fax: (617)824-8609
E-mail: admission@emerson.edu
Web Site: www.emerson.edu
President/CEO: Dr. Lee Pelton
Admissions: Michael Lynch
Financial Aid: Angela Grant

Type: Comprehensive **Sex:** Coed **Scores:** 100% SAT V 400+; 100% SAT M 400+; 9% ACT 18-23; 66% ACT 24-29 **% Accepted:** 49 **Admission Plans:** Deferred Admission; Early Admission; Early Decision Plan **Application Deadline:** January 15 **Application Fee:** $65.00 **H.S. Requirements:** High school diploma required; GED accepted **Costs Per Year:** Application fee: $65. Comprehensive fee: $56,752 includes full-time tuition ($40,320), mandatory fees ($732), and college room and board ($15,700). Full-time tuition and fees vary according to student level. Room and board charges vary according to board plan. Part-time tuition: $1260 per credit. Part-time tuition varies according to student level. **Scholarships:** Available. **Calendar System:** Semester, Summer session available **Enrollment:** Full-time 3,734, Graduate full-time 598, Graduate part-time 80, Part-time 55 **Faculty:** Full-time 202, Part-time 277 **Student-Faculty Ratio:** 13:1 **Exams:** ACT essay component not used; SAT I or ACT; SAT II; SAT essay component not used; SAT Reasoning. **% Receiving Financial Aid:** 52 **% Residing in College-Owned, -Operated, or -Affiliated Housing:** 57 **Final Year or Final Semester Residency Requirement:** No **Regional Accreditation:** New England Association of Schools and Colleges **Credit Hours For Degree:** 128 credits, Bachelors **Professional Accreditation:** ASHA. **Intercollegiate Athletics:** Baseball M; Basketball M & W; Cross-Country Running M & W; Golf M & W; Lacrosse M & W; Soccer M & W; Softball W; Tennis M & W; Track and Field W; Volleyball M & W

EMMANUEL COLLEGE

400 The Fenway
Boston, MA 02115
Tel: (617)277-9340
Fax: (617)735-9801
E-mail: enroll@emmanuel.edu
Web Site: www.emmanuel.edu
President/CEO: Señor Janet Eisner, SND
Admissions: Sandra Robbins
Financial Aid: Jennifer Porter

Type: Comprehensive **Sex:** Coed **Affiliation:** Roman Catholic. **Scores:** 100% SAT V 400+; 100% SAT M 400+; 32.88% ACT 18-23; 57.53% ACT 24-29 **% Accepted:** 78 **Admission Plans:** Deferred Admission; Early Admission; Early Decision Plan **Application Deadline:** February 15 **Application Fee:** $60.00 **H.S. Requirements:** High school diploma required; GED accepted **Costs Per Year:** Application fee: $60. One-time mandatory fee: $280. Comprehensive fee: $50,424 includes full-time tuition ($36,284), mandatory fees ($220), and college room and board ($13,920). Room and board charges vary according to housing facility. Part-time tuition: $1134 per credit hour. **Scholarships:** Available. **Calendar System:** Semester, Summer session available **Enrollment:** Full-time 1,775, Graduate full-time 14, Graduate part-time 201, Part-time 211 **Faculty:** Full-time 94, Part-time 107 **Student-Faculty Ratio:** 13:1 **Exams:** SAT I or ACT; SAT Reasoning; SAT Subject. **% Receiving Financial Aid:** 81 **% Residing in College-Owned, -Operated, or -Affiliated Housing:** 73 **Final Year or Final Semester Residency Requirement:** Yes **Regional Accreditation:** New England Association of Schools and Colleges **Credit Hours For Degree:** 128 credits, Bachelors **ROTC:** Air Force, Army **Professional Accreditation:** AACN. **Intercollegiate Athletics:** Basketball M & W; Cross-Country Running M & W; Golf M; Lacrosse M & W; Soccer M & W; Softball W; Track and Field M & W; Volleyball M & W

ENDICOTT COLLEGE

376 Hale St.
Beverly, MA 01915-2096
Tel: (978)927-0585; Free: 800-325-1114
Fax: (978)927-0084
E-mail: admissio@endicott.edu
Web Site: www.endicott.edu
President/CEO: Richard E. Wylie
Admissions: Thomas J. Redman
Financial Aid: Marcia Toomey

Type: Comprehensive **Sex:** Coed **Scores:** 98% SAT V 400+; 97% SAT M 400+; 44% ACT 18-23; 49% ACT 24-29 **% Accepted:** 73 **Application Deadline:** February 15 **Application Fee:** $50.00 **H.S. Requirements:** High school diploma required; GED accepted **Costs Per Year:** Application fee: $50. Comprehensive fee: $44,604 includes full-time tuition ($29,792), mandatory fees ($700), and college room and board ($14,112). College room only: $9728. Full-time tuition and fees vary according to location and program. Room and board charges vary according to housing facility. Part-time tuition: $914 per credit hour. Part-time tuition varies according to location and program. **Scholarships:** Available. **Calendar System:** Semester, Summer session available **Enrollment:** Full-time 2,809, Graduate full-time 471, Graduate part-time 1,147, Part-time 452 **Faculty:** Full-time 98, Part-time 371 **Student-Faculty Ratio:** 14:1 **Exams:** ACT essay component used for admission; SAT I or ACT; SAT essay component used for admission; SAT Reasoning; SAT Subject. **% Receiving Financial Aid:** 64 **% Residing in College-Owned, -Operated, or -Affiliated Housing:** 92 **Final Year or Final Semester Residency Requirement:** No **Regional Accreditation:** New England Association of Schools and Colleges **Credit Hours For Degree:** 67 credits, Associates; 124 credits, Bachelors **ROTC:** Army **Professional Accreditation:** ACEN, CIDA, JRCAT, NASAD. **Intercollegiate Athletics:** Baseball M; Basketball M & W; Cheerleading W; Crew M & W; Cross-Country Running M & W; Equestrian Sports M & W; Field Hockey W; Football M; Golf M; Ice Hockey M & W; Lacrosse M & W; Rowing M & W; Rugby M & W; Sailing M & W; Soccer M & W; Softball W; Tennis M & W; Volleyball M & W

FINE MORTUARY COLLEGE, LLC

150 Kerry Pl.
Norwood, MA 02062
Tel: (781)762-1211
Fax: (781)762-7177
E-mail: mwise@fine-ne.com
Web Site: www.fine-ne.com
President/CEO: Dr. Louis Misantone, PhD
Admissions: Dean Marsha Wise

Type: Two-Year College **Sex:** Coed **Application Fee:** $55.00 **H.S. Requirements:** High school diploma required; GED accepted **Calendar System:** Continuous, Summer session available **Faculty:** Full-time 2, Part-time 15 **Student-Faculty Ratio:** 5:1 **Exams:** Other. **Credit Hours For Degree:** 64 credits, Associates **Professional Accreditation:** ABFSE.

FISHER COLLEGE

118 Beacon St.
Boston, MA 02116-1500
Tel: (617)236-8800
Fax: (617)236-8858
E-mail: admissions@fisher.edu
Web Site: www.fisher.edu
President/CEO: Dr. Thomas McGovern
Admissions: Robert Melaragni
Financial Aid: Pamela Walker

Type: Comprehensive **Sex:** Coed **Scores:** 55% SAT V 400+; 47% SAT M 400+; 59% ACT 18-23; 12% ACT 24-29 **Costs Per Year:** Comprehensive fee: $45,099 includes full-time tuition ($28,645), mandatory fees ($995), and college room and board ($15,459). Room and board charges vary according to housing facility. Part-time tuition: $359 per credit. Part-time tuition varies according to course load. **Scholarships:** Available. **Calendar System:** Semester, Summer session available **Enrollment:** Full-time 1,232, Graduate full-time 7, Graduate part-time 14, Part-time 706 **Student-Faculty Ratio:** 18:1 **Exams:** ACT essay component not used; SAT I or ACT; SAT essay component not used. **% Receiving Financial Aid:** 64 **% Residing in College-Owned, -Operated, or -Affiliated Housing:** 16 **Final Year or Final Semester Residency Requirement:** No **Regional Accreditation:** New England Association of Schools and Colleges **Credit Hours For Degree:** 60

credits, Associates; 120 credits, Bachelors **ROTC:** Army **Professional Accreditation:** AHIMA. **Intercollegiate Athletics:** Baseball M; Basketball M & W; Soccer M & W; Softball W

FITCHBURG STATE UNIVERSITY

160 Pearl St.
Fitchburg, MA 01420-2697
Tel: (978)345-2151; Free: 800-705-9692
Fax: (978)665-4540
E-mail: admissions@fitchburgstate.edu
Web Site: www.fitchburgstate.edu
President/CEO: Robert V. Antonucci
Admissions: Sean Ganas

Type: Comprehensive **Sex:** Coed **Affiliation:** Massachusetts Public Higher Education System. **Scores:** 93% SAT V 400+; 94% SAT M 400+; 60.5% ACT 18-23; 20% ACT 24-29 **% Accepted:** 72 **Admission Plans:** Deferred Admission **Application Deadline:** Rolling **Application Fee:** $25.00 **H.S. Requirements:** High school diploma required; GED accepted **Scholarships:** Available. **Calendar System:** Semester, Summer session available **Enrollment:** Full-time 3,419, Graduate full-time 194, Graduate part-time 2,412, Part-time 793 **Faculty:** Full-time 193, Part-time 111 **Student-Faculty Ratio:** 16:1 **Exams:** SAT I or ACT; SAT Reasoning. **% Receiving Financial Aid:** 65 % **Residing in College-Owned, -Operated, or -Affiliated Housing:** 41 **Final Year or Final Semester Residency Requirement:** No **Regional Accreditation:** New England Association of Schools and Colleges **Credit Hours For Degree:** 120 credit hours, Bachelors **ROTC:** Army **Professional Accreditation:** AACN, ABET, NAACLS, NCATE. **Intercollegiate Athletics:** Baseball M; Basketball M & W; Cross-Country Running M & W; Field Hockey W; Football M; Ice Hockey M; Lacrosse W; Soccer M & W; Softball W; Track and Field M & W

FRAMINGHAM STATE UNIVERSITY

100 State St.
Framingham, MA 01701-9101
Tel: (508)620-1220
Fax: (508)626-4017
E-mail: admissions@framingham.edu
Web Site: www.framingham.edu
President/CEO: Dr. Javier Cevallos, PhD
Admissions: Shayna Eddy

Type: Comprehensive **Sex:** Coed **Affiliation:** Massachusetts Public Higher Education System. **Scores:** 92% SAT V 400+; 92% SAT M 400+; 55% ACT 18-23; 27% ACT 24-29 **% Accepted:** 71 **Admission Plans:** Deferred Admission; Early Admission; Preferred Admission **Application Deadline:** February 15 **Application Fee:** $50.00 **H.S. Requirements:** High school diploma required; GED accepted **Costs Per Year:** Application fee: $50. State resident tuition: $970 full-time, $162 per course part-time. Nonresident tuition: $7050 full-time, $1175 per course part-time. Mandatory fees: $7730 full-time, $1,353 per course part-time. Full-time tuition and fees vary according to class time and degree level. Part-time tuition and fees vary according to class time, course load, and degree level. College room and board: $10,840. College room only: $7280. Room and board charges vary according to board plan and housing facility. **Scholarships:** Available. **Calendar System:** Semester, Summer session available **Enrollment:** Full-time 3,826, Graduate full-time 75, Graduate part-time 1,845, Part-time 652 **Faculty:** Full-time 194, Part-time 143 **Student-Faculty Ratio:** 15:1 **Exams:** ACT essay component not used; SAT I or ACT; SAT essay component not used; SAT Reasoning. **% Receiving Financial Aid:** 66 % **Residing in College-Owned, -Operated, or -Affiliated Housing:** 50 **Final Year or Final Semester Residency Requirement:** No **Regional Accreditation:** New England Association of Schools and Colleges **Credit Hours For Degree:** 128 semester hours, Bachelors **Professional Accreditation:** AACN, AAFCS, ACEN, AND. **Intercollegiate Athletics:** Baseball M; Basketball M & W; Cross-Country Running M & W; Field Hockey W; Football M; Ice Hockey M; Lacrosse W; Soccer M & W; Softball W; Volleyball W

FRANKLIN W. OLIN COLLEGE OF ENGINEERING

1000 Olin Way
Needham, MA 02492-1200
Tel: (781)292-2300
E-mail: info@olin.edu
Web Site: www.olin.edu
President/CEO: Dr. Richard K. Miller, PhD
Financial Aid: Jean Ricker

Type: Four-Year College **Sex:** Coed **Scores:** 100% SAT V 400+; 100% SAT M 400+; 7% ACT 24-29 **% Accepted:** 11 **Admission Plans:** Deferred Admission **Application Deadline:** January 1 **Application Fee:** $80.00 **H.S. Requirements:** High school diploma required; GED accepted **Costs Per Year:** Application fee: $80. One-time mandatory fee: $2656. Comprehensive fee: $63,130 includes full-time tuition ($46,800), mandatory fees ($530), and college room and board ($15,800). College room only: $9500. **Scholarships:** Available. **Calendar System:** Semester, Summer session not available **Enrollment:** Full-time 342, Part-time 28 **Faculty:** Full-time 37, Part-time 18 **Student-Faculty Ratio:** 8:1 **Exams:** ACT essay component used for admission; SAT I or ACT; SAT II; SAT essay component used for admission; SAT Reasoning; SAT Subject. **% Receiving Financial Aid:** 45 % **Residing in College-Owned, -Operated, or -Affiliated Housing:** 100 **Final Year or Final Semester Residency Requirement:** No **Regional Accreditation:** New England Association of Schools and Colleges **Credit Hours For Degree:** 120 credits, Bachelors **Professional Accreditation:** ABET. **Intercollegiate Athletics:** Soccer M & W; Ultimate Frisbee M & W

GORDON COLLEGE

255 Grapevine Rd.
Wenham, MA 01984-1899
Tel: (978)927-2300; Free: 866-464-6736
Fax: (978)524-3704
E-mail: admissions@gordon.edu
Web Site: www.gordon.edu
President/CEO: Dr. D. Michael Lindsay, PhD
Admissions: June Bodoni
Financial Aid: Daniel O'Connell

Type: Comprehensive **Sex:** Coed **Affiliation:** nondenominational. **Scores:** 98% SAT V 400+; 98% SAT M 400+; 26% ACT 18-23; 50% ACT 24-29 **% Accepted:** 93 **Admission Plans:** Deferred Admission; Early Action; Early Admission; Early Decision Plan **Application Deadline:** August 1 **Application Fee:** $50.00 **H.S. Requirements:** High school diploma required; GED accepted **Costs Per Year:** Application fee: $50. Comprehensive fee: $46,472 includes full-time tuition ($34,528), mandatory fees ($1532), and college room and board ($10,412). College room only: $6878. Full-time tuition and fees vary according to course load and program. Room and board charges vary according to board plan and housing facility. Part-time tuition: $863 per credit. Part-time tuition varies according to course load and program. **Scholarships:** Available. **Calendar System:** Semester, Summer session available **Enrollment:** Full-time 1,644, Graduate full-time 92, Graduate part-time 259, Part-time 50 **Faculty:** Full-time 101, Part-time 93 **Student-Faculty Ratio:** 13:1 **Exams:** ACT essay component not used; SAT I or ACT; SAT essay component not used; SAT Reasoning; SAT Subject. **% Receiving Financial Aid:** 67 % **Residing in College-Owned, -Operated, or -Affiliated Housing:** 87 **Final Year or Final Semester Residency Requirement:** No **Regional Accreditation:** New England Association of Schools and Colleges **Credit Hours For Degree:** 124 semester hours, Bachelors **ROTC:** Army **Professional Accreditation:** CSWE, NASM. **Intercollegiate Athletics:** Baseball M; Basketball M & W; Cross-Country Running M & W; Field Hockey W; Lacrosse M & W; Soccer M & W; Softball W; Swimming and Diving M & W; Tennis M & W; Track and Field M & W; Volleyball W

GREENFIELD COMMUNITY COLLEGE

1 College Dr.
Greenfield, MA 01301-9739
Tel: (413)775-1000
Fax: (413)773-5129
E-mail: admission@gcc.mass.edu
Web Site: www.gcc.mass.edu
President/CEO: Dr. Robert L. Pura
Admissions: Colleen Kucinski

Type: Two-Year College **Sex:** Coed **Affiliation:** Commonwealth of Massachusetts Department of Higher Education. **Admission Plans:** Open Admission; Preferred Admission **Application Deadline:** Rolling **Application Fee:** $0.00 **H.S. Requirements:** High school diploma required; GED accepted **Costs Per Year:** Application fee: $0. State resident tuition: $624 full-time. Nonresident tuition: $6744 full-time. Mandatory fees: $4334 full-time. Full-time tuition and fees vary according to class time, course load, and program. **Scholarships:** Available. **Calendar System:** Semester, Summer session available **Enrollment:** Full-time 758, Part-time 1,369 **Student-Faculty Ratio:** 13:1 **Exams:** Other. **Regional Accreditation:** New England

Association of Schools and Colleges **Credit Hours For Degree:** 60 credits, Associates **Professional Accreditation:** ACEN.

HAMPSHIRE COLLEGE

893 W St.
Amherst, MA 01002
Tel: (413)549-4600; Free: 877-937-4267
Fax: (413)582-5631
E-mail: admissions@hampshire.edu
Web Site: www.hampshire.edu
President/CEO: Jonathan Lash
Financial Aid: Jennifer Garratt Lawton

Type: Four-Year College **Sex:** Coed **% Accepted:** 70 **Admission Plans:** Deferred Admission; Early Action; Early Admission; Early Decision Plan **Application Deadline:** January 15 **Application Fee:** $0.00 **H.S. Requirements:** High school diploma required; GED accepted **Costs Per Year:** Application fee: $0. Comprehensive fee: $62,084 includes full-time tuition ($48,810) and college room and board ($13,274). College room only: $8312. Room and board charges vary according to board plan. **Scholarships:** Available. **Calendar System:** 4-1-4, Summer session not available **Enrollment:** Full-time 1,410 **Faculty:** Full-time 119, Part-time 46 **Student-Faculty Ratio:** 10:1 **Exams:** ACT; ACT essay component not used; SAT I; SAT I and SAT II or ACT; SAT I or ACT; SAT II; SAT essay component not used; SAT Subject. **% Receiving Financial Aid:** 64 **% Residing in College-Owned, -Operated, or -Affiliated Housing:** 82 **Final Year or Final Semester Residency Requirement:** Yes **Regional Accreditation:** New England Association of Schools and Colleges **ROTC:** Army **Intercollegiate Athletics:** Basketball M & W; Cross-Country Running M & W; Equestrian Sports M & W; Fencing M & W; Soccer M & W; Ultimate Frisbee M & W

HARVARD UNIVERSITY

Cambridge, MA 02138
Tel: (617)495-1000
E-mail: college@harvard.edu
Web Site: www.harvard.edu
President/CEO: Drew Gilpin Faust
Admissions: Dr. William R. Fitzsimmons

Type: University **Sex:** Coed **Scores:** 100% SAT V 400+; 100% SAT M 400+; 0.31% ACT 18-23; 9.72% ACT 24-29 **% Accepted:** 6 **Admission Plans:** Deferred Admission; Early Decision Plan **Application Deadline:** January 1 **Application Fee:** $75.00 **H.S. Requirements:** High school diploma or equivalent not required **Costs Per Year:** Application fee: $75. Comprehensive fee: $60,659 includes full-time tuition ($41,632), mandatory fees ($3646), and college room and board ($15,381). College room only: $9523. **Scholarships:** Available. **Calendar System:** Semester, Summer session available **Enrollment:** Full-time 6,698, Graduate full-time 4,140, Graduate part-time 18, Part-time 1 **Faculty:** Full-time 965, Part-time 187 **Student-Faculty Ratio:** 7:1 **Exams:** ACT essay component used for admission; ACT essay component used for advising; ACT essay component used for placement; SAT I or ACT; SAT II; SAT essay component used for admission; SAT essay component used for advising; SAT essay component used for placement; SAT Reasoning; SAT Subject. **% Receiving Financial Aid:** 57 **% Residing in College-Owned, -Operated, or -Affiliated Housing:** 98 **Regional Accreditation:** New England Association of Schools and Colleges **Credit Hours For Degree:** 16 courses, Bachelors **ROTC:** Air Force, Army, Navy **Professional Accreditation:** AACSB, AALS, ABA, ABET, ACSP, ACIPE, ADA, AND, APA, ASLA, ATS, CEPH, LCME/AMA, NAAB. **Intercollegiate Athletics:** Baseball M; Basketball M & W; Crew M & W; Cross-Country Running M & W; Fencing M & W; Field Hockey W; Football M; Golf M & W; Ice Hockey M & W; Lacrosse M & W; Rugby W; Sailing M & W; Skiing (Cross-Country) M & W; Skiing (Downhill) M & W; Soccer M & W; Softball W; Squash M & W; Swimming and Diving M & W; Tennis M & W; Track and Field M & W; Volleyball M & W; Water Polo M & W; Wrestling M

HELLENIC COLLEGE

50 Goddard Ave.
Brookline, MA 02445-7496
Tel: (617)731-3500; Free: 866-424-2338
Fax: (617)232-7819
E-mail: admissions@hchc.edu
Web Site: www.hchc.edu
President/CEO: Rev. Christopher T. Metropulos
Admissions: Gregory Floor
Financial Aid: Michael Kirchmaier

Type: Comprehensive **Sex:** Coed **Affiliation:** Greek Orthodox. **% Accepted:** 65 **Admission Plans:** Deferred Admission; Early Decision Plan **Application Deadline:** Rolling **Application Fee:** $50.00 **H.S. Requirements:** High school diploma required; GED accepted **Costs Per Year:** Application fee: $50. Tuition: $21,940 full-time, $950 per credit hour part-time. Mandatory fees: $550 full-time, $450 per year part-time. **Scholarships:** Available. **Calendar System:** Semester, Summer session available **Enrollment:** Full-time 91, Graduate full-time 91, Graduate part-time 10, Part-time 1 **Faculty:** Full-time 20, Part-time 30 **Student-Faculty Ratio:** 9:1 **Exams:** ACT essay component not used; Other; SAT I or ACT; SAT essay component not used; SAT Reasoning. **% Residing in College-Owned, -Operated, or -Affiliated Housing:** 71 **Regional Accreditation:** New England Association of Schools and Colleges

HOLYOKE COMMUNITY COLLEGE

303 Homestead Ave.
Holyoke, MA 01040-1099
Tel: (413)538-7000
E-mail: admissions@hcc.edu
Web Site: www.hcc.edu
President/CEO: Dr. William F. Messner
Admissions: Renee Tastad

Type: Two-Year College **Sex:** Coed **Affiliation:** Massachusetts Public Higher Education System. **Admission Plans:** Deferred Admission; Early Admission; Open Admission **Application Deadline:** Rolling **Application Fee:** $0.00 **H.S. Requirements:** High school diploma or equivalent not required **Costs Per Year:** Application fee: $0. One-time mandatory fee: $65. State resident tuition: $576 full-time, $168 per credit hour part-time. Nonresident tuition: $5520 full-time, $370 per credit hour part-time. Mandatory fees: $3590 full-time, $95 per term part-time. Full-time tuition and fees vary according to course load. Part-time tuition and fees vary according to course load. **Scholarships:** Available. **Calendar System:** Semester, Summer session available **Enrollment:** Full-time 2,956, Part-time 3,329 **Faculty:** Full-time 131, Part-time 355 **Student-Faculty Ratio:** 16:1 **Regional Accreditation:** New England Association of Schools and Colleges **Credit Hours For Degree:** 60 credits, Associates **ROTC:** Air Force, Army **Professional Accreditation:** ACEN, COA, JRCERT, NASM. **Intercollegiate Athletics:** Baseball M; Basketball M & W; Cross-Country Running M & W; Golf M & W; Soccer M & W; Softball W; Track and Field M & W; Volleyball W

HULT INTERNATIONAL BUSINESS SCHOOL

1 Education St.
Cambridge, MA 02141
Tel: (617)746-1990
Fax: (617)746-1991
Web Site: www.hult.edu

Type: Comprehensive **Sex:** Coed **Calendar System:** Trimester **Regional Accreditation:** New England Association of Schools and Colleges

LABOURÉ COLLEGE

2120 Dorchester Ave.
Boston, MA 02124-5698
Tel: (617)296-8300
Web Site: www.laboure.edu
President/CEO: Maureen A. Smith
Admissions: Gina M. Morrissette

Type: Two-Year College **Sex:** Coed **Affiliation:** Roman Catholic. **Admission Plans:** Deferred Admission **Application Deadline:** Rolling **Application Fee:** $25.00 **H.S. Requirements:** High school diploma required; GED accepted **Scholarships:** Available. **Calendar System:** Semester, Summer session available **Regional Accreditation:** New England Association of Schools and Colleges **Credit Hours For Degree:** 60 credits, Associates **Professional Accreditation:** ACEN, AHIMA, JRCEND, JRCERT.

LASELL COLLEGE

1844 Commonwealth Ave.
Newton, MA 02466-2709
Tel: (617)243-2000; Free: 888-LASELL-4
Fax: (617)796-4343
E-mail: info@lasell.edu
Web Site: www.lasell.edu
President/CEO: Michael Alexander
Admissions: Dean James Tweed
Financial Aid: Michele R. Kosboth

Type: Comprehensive **Sex:** Coed **Scores:** 89% SAT V 400+; 87% SAT M 400+; 55% ACT 18-23; 26% ACT 24-29 **% Accepted:** 78 **Admission Plans:** Deferred Admission; Early Decision Plan **Application Deadline:** September 1 **Application Fee:** $40.00 **H.S. Requirements:** High school diploma required; GED accepted **Costs Per Year:** Application fee: $40. Comprehensive fee: $47,500 includes full-time tuition ($32,300), mandatory fees ($1300), and college room and board ($13,900). Room and board charges vary according to board plan and housing facility. Part-time tuition: $1015 per credit hour. Part-time mandatory fees: $310 per term. Part-time tuition and fees vary according to course load. **Scholarships:** Available. **Calendar System:** Semester, Summer session available **Enrollment:** Full-time 1,788, Graduate full-time 143, Graduate part-time 251, Part-time 27 **Faculty:** Full-time 87, Part-time 176 **Student-Faculty Ratio:** 14:1 **Exams:** ACT essay component used for placement; SAT I or ACT; SAT essay component used for placement; SAT Reasoning; SAT Subject. **% Receiving Financial Aid:** 82 **% Residing in College-Owned, -Operated, or -Affiliated Housing:** 74 **Final Year or Final Semester Residency Requirement:** Yes **Regional Accreditation:** New England Association of Schools and Colleges **Credit Hours For Degree:** 120 credits, Bachelors **Professional Accreditation:** ACBSP, JRCAT. **Intercollegiate Athletics:** Baseball M; Basketball M & W; Cross-Country Running M & W; Field Hockey W; Lacrosse M & W; Soccer M & W; Softball W; Track and Field M & W; Volleyball M & W

LESLEY UNIVERSITY

29 Everett St.
Cambridge, MA 02138-2790
Tel: (617)868-9600; Free: 800-999-1959
Fax: (617)349-8150
E-mail: lcadmissions@lesley.edu
Web Site: www.lesley.edu
President/CEO: Joseph B. Moore
Admissions: Deborah Kocar
Financial Aid: Scott A. Jewell

Type: Comprehensive **Sex:** Coed **Scores:** 97% SAT V 400+; 98% SAT M 400+; 36% ACT 18-23; 54% ACT 24-29 **% Accepted:** 69 **Admission Plans:** Deferred Admission; Early Decision Plan **Application Deadline:** Rolling **H.S. Requirements:** High school diploma required; GED accepted **Costs Per Year:** Comprehensive fee: $41,550 includes full-time tuition ($25,500), mandatory fees ($750), and college room and board ($15,300). College room only: $9300. Full-time tuition and fees vary according to class time, course level, course load, degree level, location, program, and reciprocity agreements. Room and board charges vary according to housing facility. Part-time tuition: $850 per credit hour. **Scholarships:** Available. **Calendar System:** Semester, Summer session available **Enrollment:** Full-time 1,365, Graduate full-time 850, Graduate part-time 2,235, Part-time 156 **Faculty:** Full-time 80, Part-time 163 **Student-Faculty Ratio:** 9:1 **Exams:** ACT essay component used as validity check; ACT essay component used for admission; ACT essay component used for placement; SAT I or ACT; SAT essay component used as validity check; SAT essay component used for admission; SAT essay component used for placement; SAT Reasoning. **% Receiving Financial Aid:** 70 **% Residing in College-Owned, -Operated, or -Affiliated Housing:** 60 **Regional Accreditation:** New England Association of Schools and Colleges **Professional Accreditation:** TEAC. **Intercollegiate Athletics:** Baseball M; Basketball M & W; Cross-Country Running M & W; Soccer M & W; Softball W; Volleyball M & W

MASSACHUSETTS BAY COMMUNITY COLLEGE

50 Oakland St.
Wellesley Hills, MA 02481
Tel: (781)239-3000
Fax: (781)239-1047
E-mail: lslavin@massbay.edu
Web Site: www.massbay.edu
President/CEO: Dr. Yves Salomon-Fernandez
Admissions: Lisa Slavin
Financial Aid: Paula Ogden

Type: Two-Year College **Sex:** Coed **% Accepted:** 100 **Admission Plans:** Deferred Admission; Open Admission **Application Deadline:** Rolling **Application Fee:** $0.00 **H.S. Requirements:** High school diploma required; GED accepted **Costs Per Year:** Application fee: $0. State resident tuition: $576 full-time, $24 per credit part-time. Nonresident tuition: $5520 full-time, $230 per credit part-time. Mandatory fees: $3920 full-time, $160 per credit part-time, $40 per term part-time. Full-time tuition and fees vary according to class time, program, and reciprocity agreements. Part-time tuition and fees vary according to class time, program, and reciprocity agreements. **Scholarships:** Available. **Calendar System:** Semester, Summer session available **Enrollment:** Full-time 1,648, Part-time 3,211 **Faculty:** Full-time 75, Part-time 241 **Student-Faculty Ratio:** 18:1 **Regional Accreditation:** New England Association of Schools and Colleges **Credit Hours For Degree:** 62 credits, Associates **Professional Accreditation:** ACEN, APTA, CoARC, JRCERT. **Intercollegiate Athletics:** Baseball M; Basketball M & W; Cross-Country Running M & W; Golf M & W; Soccer M & W; Softball W; Tennis M & W; Volleyball W

MASSACHUSETTS COLLEGE OF ART AND DESIGN

621 Huntington Ave.
Boston, MA 02115-5882
Tel: (617)879-7000
Fax: (617)879-7250
E-mail: admissions@massart.edu
Web Site: www.massart.edu
President/CEO: Ken Strickland
Admissions: Lauren Wilshusen
Financial Aid: Auelio Ramirez

Type: Comprehensive **Sex:** Coed **Affiliation:** Massachusetts Public Higher Education System. **Scores:** 96% SAT V 400+; 96% SAT M 400+ **% Accepted:** 71 **Admission Plans:** Deferred Admission; Early Decision Plan; Preferred Admission **Application Deadline:** February 1 **Application Fee:** $50.00 **H.S. Requirements:** High school diploma required; GED accepted **Costs Per Year:** Application fee: $50. State resident tuition: $11,725 full-time. Nonresident tuition: $31,225 full-time. College room and board: $13,175. Room and board charges vary according to board plan and housing facility. **Scholarships:** Available. **Calendar System:** Semester, Summer session available **Enrollment:** Full-time 1,547, Graduate full-time 91, Graduate part-time 32, Part-time 320 **Faculty:** Full-time 115, Part-time 152 **Student-Faculty Ratio:** 10:1 **Exams:** SAT I or ACT. **% Receiving Financial Aid:** 52 **% Residing in College-Owned, -Operated, or -Affiliated Housing:** 38 **Regional Accreditation:** New England Association of Schools and Colleges **Credit Hours For Degree:** 120 credits, Bachelors **Professional Accreditation:** NASAD.

MASSACHUSETTS COLLEGE OF LIBERAL ARTS

375 Church St.
North Adams, MA 01247-4100
Tel: (413)662-5000; Free: 800-989-MCLA
Fax: (413)662-5179
E-mail: g.puc@mcla.edu
Web Site: www.mcla.edu
President/CEO: Dr. James Clemmer
Admissions: Gina Puc
Financial Aid: Elizabeth M. Petri

Type: Comprehensive **Sex:** Coed **Affiliation:** Massachusetts State University System. **Scores:** 92% SAT V 400+; 91% SAT M 400+; 40% ACT 18-23; 50% ACT 24-29 **% Accepted:** 73 **Admission Plans:** Deferred Admission; Early Admission; Early Decision Plan **Application Deadline:** Rolling **Application Fee:** $40.00 **H.S. Requirements:** High school diploma required; GED accepted **Costs Per Year:** Application fee: $40. State resident tuition: $1030 full-time, $42.92 per credit part-time. Nonresident tuition: $9975 full-time, $415.63 per credit part-time. Mandatory fees: $8445 full-time, $285.09 per credit part-time. Full-time tuition and fees vary according to reciprocity agreements. Part-time tuition and fees vary according to course load and reciprocity agreements. College room and board: $9828. Room and board charges vary according to board plan and housing facility. **Scholarships:** Available. **Calendar System:** Semester, Summer session available **Enrollment:** Full-time 1,280, Graduate full-time 14, Graduate part-time 170, Part-time 177 **Faculty:** Full-time 90, Part-time 78 **Student-Faculty Ratio:** 12:1 **Exams:** SAT I or ACT; SAT Reasoning. **% Receiving Financial Aid:** 77 **% Residing in College-Owned, -Operated, or -Affiliated Housing:** 59 **Final Year or Final Semester Residency Requirement:** No **Regional Accreditation:** New England Association of Schools and Colleges **Credit Hours For Degree:** 120 credits, Bachelors **Intercollegiate Athletics:** Baseball M; Basketball M & W; Cross-Country Running M & W; Golf M; Lacrosse W; Soccer M & W; Softball W; Tennis M & W; Volleyball W

MASSACHUSETTS INSTITUTE OF TECHNOLOGY

77 Massachusetts Ave.
Cambridge, MA 02139-4307
Tel: (617)253-1000

Fax: (617)258-8304
E-mail: admissions@mit.edu
Web Site: web.mit.edu
President/CEO: Dr. L. Rafael Reif
Financial Aid: Stuart Schmill

Type: University **Sex:** Coed **Scores:** 100% SAT V 400+; 100% SAT M 400+; 3.3% ACT 24-29 **% Accepted:** 8 **Admission Plans:** Deferred Admission; Early Decision Plan **Application Deadline:** January 1 **Application Fee:** $75.00 **H.S. Requirements:** High school diploma or equivalent not required **Costs Per Year:** Application fee: $75. Comprehensive fee: $60,434 includes full-time tuition ($46,400), mandatory fees ($304), and college room and board ($13,730). College room only: $8710. Room and board charges vary according to board plan and housing facility. Part-time tuition: $725 per unit. Part-time tuition varies according to course load. **Scholarships:** Available. **Calendar System:** 4-1-4 **Enrollment:** Full-time 4,492, Graduate full-time 6,689, Graduate part-time 115, Part-time 35 **Faculty:** Full-time 1,246, Part-time 298 **Student-Faculty Ratio:** 3:1 **Exams:** ACT essay component used for admission; SAT I or ACT; SAT II; SAT essay component used for admission; SAT Reasoning; SAT Subject. **% Receiving Financial Aid:** 57 % **Residing in College-Owned, -Operated, or -Affiliated Housing:** 94 **Final Year or Final Semester Residency Requirement:** Yes **Regional Accreditation:** New England Association of Schools and Colleges **ROTC:** Air Force, Army, Navy **Professional Accreditation:** AACSB, ABET, ACSP, NAAB. **Intercollegiate Athletics:** Baseball M; Basketball M & W; Crew M & W; Cross-Country Running M & W; Fencing M & W; Field Hockey W; Football M; Lacrosse M & W; Riflery M & W; Rowing M & W; Sailing M & W; Soccer M & W; Softball W; Squash M; Swimming and Diving M & W; Tennis M & W; Track and Field M & W; Volleyball M & W; Water Polo M

MASSACHUSETTS MARITIME ACADEMY

101 Academy Dr.
Buzzards Bay, MA 02532-1803
Tel: (508)830-5000; Free: 800-544-3411
Fax: (508)830-5077
E-mail: edaly@maritime.edu
Web Site: www.maritime.edu
President/CEO: Adm. Francis X. McDonald
Admissions: Comdr. Elizabeth Daly
Financial Aid: Catherine Kedski

Type: Comprehensive **Sex:** Coed **Affiliation:** Massachusetts State University System. **Scores:** 98% SAT V 400+; 98% SAT M 400+; 77.42% ACT 18-23; 16.13% ACT 24-29 **% Accepted:** 74 **Admission Plans:** Early Decision Plan **Application Deadline:** Rolling **Application Fee:** $50.00 **H.S. Requirements:** High school diploma required; GED accepted **Costs Per Year:** Application fee: $50. State resident tuition: $1554 full-time, $307 per credit part-time. Nonresident tuition: $17,360 full-time, $965.58 per credit part-time. Mandatory fees: $6060 full-time. College room and board: $11,474. College room only: $6794. **Scholarships:** Available. **Calendar System:** 4-1-4, Summer session available **Enrollment:** Full-time 1,506, Graduate part-time 103, Part-time 65 **Faculty:** Full-time 80, Part-time 39 **Student-Faculty Ratio:** 17:1 **Exams:** SAT I or ACT; SAT II. **% Receiving Financial Aid:** 38 **% Residing in College-Owned, -Operated, or -Affiliated Housing:** 96 **Final Year or Final Semester Residency Requirement:** No **Regional Accreditation:** New England Association of Schools and Colleges **ROTC:** Army, Navy **Intercollegiate Athletics:** Baseball M; Crew M & W; Cross-Country Running M & W; Football M; Lacrosse M & W; Sailing M & W; Soccer M & W; Softball W; Track and Field M & W; Volleyball W

MASSASOIT COMMUNITY COLLEGE

1 Massasoit Blvd.
Brockton, MA 02302-3996
Tel: (508)588-9100; Free: 800-CAREERS
Fax: (508)427-1220
Web Site: www.massasoit.mass.edu
President/CEO: Charles Wall, PhD
Admissions: Michelle Hughes

Type: Two-Year College **Sex:** Coed **Admission Plans:** Open Admission; Preferred Admission **Application Deadline:** Rolling **Application Fee:** $0.00 **H.S. Requirements:** High school diploma required; GED accepted **Scholarships:** Available. **Calendar System:** Semester, Summer session available **Enrollment:** Full-time 3,631, Part-time 4,310 **Faculty:** Full-time 119, Part-time 384 **Final Year or Final Semester Residency Requirement:** Yes **Regional Accreditation:** New England Association of Schools and Colleges

Credit Hours For Degree: 60 credits, Associates **Professional Accreditation:** ACEN, ADA, CoARC, JRCERT. **Intercollegiate Athletics:** Baseball M; Basketball M & W; Soccer M & W; Softball W

MCPHS UNIVERSITY

179 Longwood Ave.
Boston, MA 02115-5896
Tel: (617)732-2800
Fax: (617)732-2801
E-mail: admissions@mcphs.edu
Web Site: www.mcphs.edu
President/CEO: Charles F. Monahan
Admissions: Sandra Hernandez
Financial Aid: Elizabeth Goreham

Type: University **Sex:** Coed **Scores:** 95% SAT V 400+; 97% SAT M 400+; 44.51% ACT 18-23; 40.85% ACT 24-29 **% Accepted:** 87 **Admission Plans:** Deferred Admission; Early Decision Plan; Open Admission **Application Deadline:** Rolling **Application Fee:** $0.00 **H.S. Requirements:** High school diploma required; GED accepted **Costs Per Year:** Application fee: $0. Comprehensive fee: $45,704 includes full-time tuition ($29,600), mandatory fees ($930), and college room and board ($15,174). College room only: $12,034. Full-time tuition and fees vary according to course load, degree level, location, program, and student level. Room and board charges vary according to board plan, housing facility, and location. Part-time tuition: $1090 per credit. Part-time mandatory fees: $245 per term. **Scholarships:** Available. **Calendar System:** Semester, Summer session available **Enrollment:** Full-time 3,717, Graduate full-time 2,665, Graduate part-time 462, Part-time 230 **Faculty:** Full-time 297, Part-time 389 **Exams:** ACT essay component not used; SAT I or ACT; SAT essay component not used. **% Receiving Financial Aid:** 78 **% Residing in College-Owned, -Operated, or -Affiliated Housing:** 27 **Regional Accreditation:** New England Association of Schools and Colleges **Credit Hours For Degree:** 120 semester hours, Bachelors **Professional Accreditation:** AACN, ACPE, ADA, JRCNMT.

MERRIMACK COLLEGE

315 Tpke. St.
North Andover, MA 01845-5800
Tel: (978)837-5000
Fax: (978)837-5222
E-mail: admission@merrimack.edu
Web Site: www.merrimack.edu
President/CEO: Dr. Christopher E. Hopey
Financial Aid: Adrienne Montgomery

Type: Comprehensive **Sex:** Coed **Affiliation:** Roman Catholic. **% Accepted:** 79 **Admission Plans:** Deferred Admission; Early Action; Early Admission; Early Decision Plan **Application Deadline:** February 15 **Application Fee:** $0.00 **H.S. Requirements:** High school diploma required; GED accepted **Costs Per Year:** Application fee: $0. Comprehensive fee: $51,170 includes full-time tuition ($35,570), mandatory fees ($2100), and college room and board ($13,500). Full-time tuition and fees vary according to degree level. Room and board charges vary according to board plan and housing facility. Part-time tuition: $1270 per credit. Part-time tuition varies according to class time, course load, and degree level. **Scholarships:** Available. **Calendar System:** Semester, Summer session available **Enrollment:** Full-time 3,058, Graduate full-time 339, Graduate part-time 114, Part-time 133 **Faculty:** Full-time 165, Part-time 227 **Student-Faculty Ratio:** 13:1 **Exams:** ACT essay component not used; SAT essay component not used; SAT Reasoning. **% Receiving Financial Aid:** 71 **% Residing in College-Owned, -Operated, or -Affiliated Housing:** 74 **Final Year or Final Semester Residency Requirement:** Yes **Regional Accreditation:** New England Association of Schools and Colleges **Credit Hours For Degree:** 124 credits, Bachelors **ROTC:** Air Force **Professional Accreditation:** ABET, JRCAT. **Intercollegiate Athletics:** Baseball M; Basketball M & W; Crew W; Cross-Country Running M & W; Field Hockey W; Football M; Golf W; Ice Hockey M & W; Lacrosse M & W; Soccer M & W; Softball W; Swimming and Diving W; Tennis M & W; Track and Field M & W; Volleyball W

MIDDLESEX COMMUNITY COLLEGE

591 Springs Rd.
Bedford, MA 01730-1655
Tel: (781)280-3200; Free: 800-818-3434
Fax: (978)656-3322
E-mail: gallaganm@middlesex.mass.edu

Web Site: www.middlesex.mass.edu
President/CEO: Carole A. Cowan
Admissions: Marilynn Gallagan
Financial Aid: Rob Baumel
Type: Two-Year College Sex: Coed Affiliation: Massachusetts Public Higher Education System. Admission Plans: Early Admission; Open Admission; Preferred Admission Application Deadline: Rolling Application Fee: $0.00 H.S. Requirements: High school diploma required; GED accepted Costs Per Year: Application fee: $0. State resident tuition: $4464 full-time. Nonresident tuition: $9408 full-time. Mandatory fees: $50 full-time. Full-time tuition and fees vary according to course load and reciprocity agreements. Scholarships: Available. Calendar System: Semester, Summer session available Enrollment: Full-time 3,537, Part-time 5,668 Exams: Other. Regional Accreditation: New England Association of Schools and Colleges Credit Hours For Degree: 60 credits, Associates ROTC: Air Force Professional Accreditation: AAMAE, ACEN, ADA, JRCEDMS, JRCERT.

MONTSERRAT COLLEGE OF ART
23 Essex St.
Beverly, MA 01915
Tel: (978)922-8222; Free: 800-836-0487
Fax: (978)922-4268
E-mail: jeffrey.newell@montserrat.edu
Web Site: www.montserrat.edu
President/CEO: Dr. Stephen D. Immerman, EdD
Admissions: Jeffrey Newell
Financial Aid: Emma Puglisi
Type: Four-Year College Sex: Coed Scores: 96% SAT V 400+; 94% SAT M 400+ % Accepted: 79 Admission Plans: Deferred Admission; Early Decision Plan Application Deadline: August 15 Application Fee: $50.00 H.S. Requirements: High school diploma required; GED accepted Scholarships: Available. Calendar System: Semester, Summer session not available Enrollment: Full-time 389, Part-time 8 Faculty: Full-time 19, Part-time 58 Student-Faculty Ratio: 12:1 Exams: ACT essay component not used; SAT I or ACT; SAT essay component not used. % Residing in College-Owned, -Operated, or -Affiliated Housing: 63 Final Year or Final Semester Residency Requirement: No Regional Accreditation: New England Association of Schools and Colleges Credit Hours For Degree: 120 credits, Bachelors Professional Accreditation: NASAD.

MOUNT HOLYOKE COLLEGE
50 College St.
South Hadley, MA 01075
Tel: (413)538-2000
Fax: (413)538-2409
E-mail: admission@mtholyoke.edu
Web Site: www.mtholyoke.edu
President/CEO: Dr. Lynn Pasquerella
Admissions: Gail Berson
Financial Aid: Kathryn Blaisdell
Type: Comprehensive Sex: Women Scores: 100% SAT V 400+; 100% SAT M 400+; 2.34% ACT 18-23; 33.59% ACT 24-29 % Accepted: 50 Admission Plans: Deferred Admission; Early Action; Early Admission Application Deadline: January 15 Application Fee: $60.00 H.S. Requirements: High school diploma required; GED accepted Costs Per Year: Application fee: $60. Comprehensive fee: $56,746 includes full-time tuition ($43,700), mandatory fees ($186), and college room and board ($12,860). College room only: $6280. Part-time tuition: $1370 per credit hour. Scholarships: Available. Calendar System: Semester, Summer session available Enrollment: Full-time 2,095, Graduate full-time 36, Graduate part-time 53, Part-time 31 Faculty: Full-time 186, Part-time 48 Student-Faculty Ratio: 10:1 Exams: ACT essay component used for admission; SAT II; SAT essay component used for admission; SAT Subject. % Receiving Financial Aid: 65 % Residing in College-Owned, -Operated, or -Affiliated Housing: 95 Final Year or Final Semester Residency Requirement: No Regional Accreditation: New England Association of Schools and Colleges Credit Hours For Degree: 128 credit hours, Bachelors ROTC: Air Force, Army Intercollegiate Athletics: Basketball W; Crew W; Cross-Country Running W; Equestrian Sports W; Field Hockey W; Golf W; Lacrosse W; Soccer W; Squash W; Swimming and Diving W; Tennis W; Track and Field W; Volleyball W

MOUNT IDA COLLEGE
777 Dedham St.
Newton, MA 02459-3310

Tel: (617)928-4500
Fax: (617)928-4507
E-mail: admissions@mountida.edu
Web Site: www.mountida.edu
President/CEO: Dr. Lance Carluccio
Admissions: Calvin Conyers
Financial Aid: David L. Goldman
Type: Comprehensive Sex: Coed Scores: 69% SAT V 400+; 69% SAT M 400+; 43% ACT 18-23; 11% ACT 24-29 % Accepted: 63 Admission Plans: Deferred Admission Application Deadline: Rolling Application Fee: $45.00 H.S. Requirements: High school diploma required; GED accepted Costs Per Year: Application fee: $45. Comprehensive fee: $46,820 includes full-time tuition ($32,300), mandatory fees ($1520), and college room and board ($13,000). Part-time tuition: $975 per credit. Scholarships: Available. Calendar System: Semester, Summer session available Faculty: Full-time 57, Part-time 112 Student-Faculty Ratio: 14:1 Exams: SAT I or ACT; SAT Reasoning; SAT Subject. % Receiving Financial Aid: 80 % Residing in College-Owned, -Operated, or -Affiliated Housing: 63 Final Year or Final Semester Residency Requirement: No Regional Accreditation: New England Association of Schools and Colleges Credit Hours For Degree: 60 credit hours, Associates; 120 credit hours, Bachelors Professional Accreditation: ABFSE, ADA, CIDA, NASAD. Intercollegiate Athletics: Baseball M; Basketball M & W; Cheerleading M & W; Cross-Country Running M & W; Equestrian Sports W; Football M; Lacrosse M & W; Soccer M & W; Softball W; Tennis W; Volleyball M & W

MOUNT WACHUSETT COMMUNITY COLLEGE
444 Green St.
Gardner, MA 01440
Tel: (978)632-6600
Fax: (978)632-8925
E-mail: admissions@mwcc.mass.edu
Web Site: www.mwcc.mass.edu
President/CEO: Dr. Daniel M. Asquino, PhD
Admissions: Marcia Rosbury-Henne
Type: Two-Year College Sex: Coed Affiliation: Massachusetts Public Higher Education System. % Accepted: 100 Admission Plans: Early Admission; Open Admission; Preferred Admission Application Deadline: Rolling Application Fee: $0.00 H.S. Requirements: High school diploma required; GED accepted Costs Per Year: Application fee: $0. State resident tuition: $600 full-time, $25 per credit hour part-time. Nonresident tuition: $5520 full-time, $230 per credit hour part-time. Mandatory fees: $4588 full-time, $177 per credit hour part-time, $170 per term part-time. Full-time tuition and fees vary according to program and reciprocity agreements. Part-time tuition and fees vary according to program and reciprocity agreements. Scholarships: Available. Calendar System: Semester, Summer session available Enrollment: Full-time 1,599, Part-time 2,475 Faculty: Full-time 74, Part-time 322 Student-Faculty Ratio: 13:1 Regional Accreditation: New England Association of Schools and Colleges Credit Hours For Degree: 60 credits, Associates ROTC: Army Professional Accreditation: AAMAE, ACEN, APTA.

NEW ENGLAND COLLEGE OF BUSINESS AND FINANCE
10 High St.
Ste. 204
Boston, MA 02111-2645
Tel: (617)951-2350; Free: 800-997-1673
Fax: (617)951-2533
E-mail: Mina.Goldman@necb.edu
Web Site: necb.edu
President/CEO: Howard Horton
Admissions: Mina Goldman
Type: Comprehensive Sex: Coed Affiliation: Whitney International University. Admission Plans: Open Admission Application Deadline: Rolling Application Fee: $0.00 H.S. Requirements: High school diploma required; GED accepted Calendar System: Miscellaneous, Summer session available Enrollment: Graduate full-time 31, Graduate part-time 20 Faculty: Full-time 1, Part-time 28 Final Year or Final Semester Residency Requirement: No Regional Accreditation: New England Association of Schools and Colleges Credit Hours For Degree: 63 credits, Associates; 121 credits, Bachelors

NEW ENGLAND CONSERVATORY OF MUSIC
290 Huntington Ave.
Boston, MA 02115-5000

Tel: (617)585-1100
Fax: (617)585-1115
E-mail: alex.powell@necmusic.edu
Web Site: necmusic.edu
President/CEO: Tom Novak
Admissions: Alex Powell
Financial Aid: Lauren G. Urbanek

Type: Comprehensive **Sex:** Coed **% Accepted:** 32 **Admission Plans:** Deferred Admission **Application Deadline:** December 1 **Application Fee:** $115.00 **H.S. Requirements:** High school diploma required; GED accepted **Costs Per Year:** Application fee: $115. Comprehensive fee: $56,295 includes full-time tuition ($42,600), mandatory fees ($455), and college room and board ($13,240). Room and board charges vary according to board plan. Part-time tuition: $1365 per credit. Part-time mandatory fees: $455 per year. **Scholarships:** Available. **Calendar System:** Semester, Summer session available **Enrollment:** Full-time 371, Graduate full-time 356, Graduate part-time 23, Part-time 38 **Faculty:** Full-time 102, Part-time 133 **Student-Faculty Ratio:** 5:1 **% Receiving Financial Aid:** 51 **% Residing in College-Owned, -Operated, or -Affiliated Housing:** 30 **Final Year or Final Semester Residency Requirement:** Yes **Regional Accreditation:** New England Association of Schools and Colleges **Credit Hours For Degree:** 120 credit hours, Bachelors **Professional Accreditation:** NASM.

NEWBURY COLLEGE
129 Fisher Ave.
Brookline, MA 02445
Tel: (617)730-7000; Free: 800-NEWBURY
Fax: (617)731-9618
E-mail: salvadore.liberto@newbury.edu
Web Site: www.newbury.edu
President/CEO: Dr. Joseph Chillo
Admissions: Salvadore Liberto
Financial Aid: Elreo Campbell

Type: Four-Year College **Sex:** Coed **Scores:** 64% SAT V 400+; 62% SAT M 400+ **% Accepted:** 70 **Application Deadline:** September 1 **Application Fee:** $0.00 **H.S. Requirements:** High school diploma required; GED accepted **Costs Per Year:** Application fee: $0. Comprehensive fee: $47,710 includes full-time tuition ($31,990), mandatory fees ($1520), and college room and board ($14,200). Full-time tuition and fees vary according to class time, course load, location, and program. Room and board charges vary according to board plan and housing facility. Part-time tuition: $1020 per credit. Part-time mandatory fees: $700 per term. Part-time tuition and fees vary according to class time, course load, location, and program. **Scholarships:** Available. **Calendar System:** Semester, Summer session available **Enrollment:** Full-time 778, Part-time 84 **Faculty:** Full-time 35, Part-time 72 **Student-Faculty Ratio:** 14:1 **Exams:** ACT essay component not used; SAT essay component not used. **% Receiving Financial Aid:** 84 **% Residing in College-Owned, -Operated, or -Affiliated Housing:** 35 **Final Year or Final Semester Residency Requirement:** Yes **Regional Accreditation:** New England Association of Schools and Colleges **Credit Hours For Degree:** 60 credits, Associates; 121 credits, Bachelors **Professional Accreditation:** CIDA. **Intercollegiate Athletics:** Baseball M; Basketball M & W; Cross-Country Running M & W; Lacrosse W; Soccer M & W; Softball W; Track and Field M & W; Volleyball M & W

NICHOLS COLLEGE
PO Box 5000
Dudley, MA 01571-5000
Tel: (508)213-1560; Free: 800-470-3379
Fax: (508)213-9885
E-mail: emily.reardon@nichols.edu
Web Site: www.nichols.edu
President/CEO: Dr. Susan Engelkemeyer, PhD
Admissions: Emily Reardon
Financial Aid: Jennifer Bianco

Type: Comprehensive **Sex:** Coed **Scores:** 87% SAT V 400+; 91% SAT M 400+; 59% ACT 18-23; 16% ACT 24-29 **Costs Per Year:** Comprehensive fee: $46,900 includes full-time tuition ($33,000), mandatory fees ($400), and college room and board ($13,500). College room only: $7000. Room and board charges vary according to board plan, housing facility, and student level. Part-time tuition: $1100 per credit. Part-time mandatory fees: $150 per term. Part-time tuition and fees vary according to course load. **Scholarships:** Available. **Calendar System:** Semester, Summer session available **Enrollment:** Full-time 1,152, Graduate full-time 1, Graduate part-time 186,

Part-time 115 **Faculty:** Full-time 44, Part-time 37 **Student-Faculty Ratio:** 18:1 **Exams:** ACT essay component not used; SAT I or ACT; SAT essay component not used. **% Receiving Financial Aid:** 81 **% Residing in College-Owned, -Operated, or -Affiliated Housing:** 80 **Final Year or Final Semester Residency Requirement:** Yes **Regional Accreditation:** New England Association of Schools and Colleges **Credit Hours For Degree:** 120 credits, Bachelors **ROTC:** Air Force, Army **Intercollegiate Athletics:** Baseball M; Basketball M & W; Field Hockey W; Football M; Golf M; Ice Hockey M & W; Lacrosse M & W; Soccer M & W; Softball W; Tennis M & W; Track and Field M & W; Volleyball W

NORTH SHORE COMMUNITY COLLEGE
1 Ferncroft Rd.
Danvers, MA 01923-4093
Tel: (978)762-4000
Fax: (978)762-4021
E-mail: gilopez@northshore.edu
Web Site: www.northshore.edu
President/CEO: Dr. Patricia A. Gentile
Admissions: Gissel Lopez
Financial Aid: Margaret Miles

Type: Two-Year College **Sex:** Coed **% Accepted:** 58 **Admission Plans:** Deferred Admission; Early Admission; Open Admission; Preferred Admission **Application Deadline:** Rolling **Application Fee:** $0.00 **H.S. Requirements:** High school diploma required; GED accepted **Costs Per Year:** Application fee: $0. State resident tuition: $600 full-time, $25 per credit hour part-time. Nonresident tuition: $6168 full-time, $257 per credit hour part-time. Mandatory fees: $3936 full-time, $164 per credit hour part-time. Full-time tuition and fees vary according to program. Part-time tuition and fees vary according to program. **Scholarships:** Available. **Calendar System:** Semester, Summer session available **Enrollment:** Full-time 2,437, Part-time 4,524 **Faculty:** Full-time 135, Part-time 351 **Student-Faculty Ratio:** 17:1 **Regional Accreditation:** New England Association of Schools and Colleges **Credit Hours For Degree:** 60 credits, Associates **Professional Accreditation:** AABI, ACEN, AOTA, APTA, CoARC, JRCERT.

NORTHEASTERN UNIVERSITY
360 Huntington Ave.
Boston, MA 02115-5096
Tel: (617)373-2000
Fax: (617)373-8780
E-mail: admissions@neu.edu
Web Site: www.northeastern.edu
President/CEO: Dr. Joseph E. Aoun
Admissions: Ronne Patrick Turner
Financial Aid: Anthony Erwin

Type: University **Sex:** Coed **Scores:** 100% SAT V 400+; 100% SAT M 400+; 1% ACT 18-23; 11% ACT 24-29 **% Accepted:** 28 **Admission Plans:** Deferred Admission; Early Action; Early Admission; Early Decision Plan **Application Deadline:** January 1 **Application Fee:** $75.00 **H.S. Requirements:** High school diploma required; GED accepted **Costs Per Year:** Application fee: $75. Comprehensive fee: $60,530 includes full-time tuition ($44,620), mandatory fees ($910), and college room and board ($15,000). College room only: $8010. Room and board charges vary according to board plan and housing facility. **Scholarships:** Available. **Calendar System:** Semester, Summer session available **Enrollment:** Full-time 17,913, Graduate full-time 6,049, Graduate part-time 905, Part-time 77 **Faculty:** Full-time 1,257, Part-time 403 **Student-Faculty Ratio:** 14:1 **Exams:** ACT essay component not used; SAT I or ACT; SAT essay component not used; SAT Reasoning. **% Receiving Financial Aid:** 37 **% Residing in College-Owned, -Operated, or -Affiliated Housing:** 48 **Final Year or Final Semester Residency Requirement:** No **Regional Accreditation:** New England Association of Schools and Colleges **ROTC:** Air Force, Army, Navy **Professional Accreditation:** AACN, AACSB, AALS, AANA, ABA, ABET, ACPE, ACPeE, AHIMA, APA, APTA, ASHA, CORE, CoARC, JRCAT, NAACLS, NASPAA. **Intercollegiate Athletics:** Baseball M; Basketball M & W; Cheerleading M & W; Crew M & W; Cross-Country Running M & W; Field Hockey W; Golf M & W; Ice Hockey M & W; Lacrosse M & W; Riflery M & W; Rugby M & W; Sailing M & W; Soccer M & W; Softball M & W; Squash M & W; Swimming and Diving W; Table Tennis M & W; Tennis M & W; Track and Field M & W; Ultimate Frisbee M & W; Volleyball W; Water Polo M & W; Weight Lifting M & W; Wrestling M

NORTHERN ESSEX COMMUNITY COLLEGE
100 Elliott St.
Haverhill, MA 01830

Tel: (978)556-3000
E-mail: nsheridan@necc.mass.edu
Web Site: www.necc.mass.edu
President/CEO: Dr. Lane Glenn
Admissions: Tina Favara
Type: Two-Year College Sex: Coed % Accepted: 99 Admission Plans: Early Admission; Open Admission; Preferred Admission Application Deadline: Rolling Application Fee: $25.00 H.S. Requirements: High school diploma required; GED accepted Costs Per Year: Application fee: $25. State resident tuition: $600 full-time, $25 per credit hour part-time. Nonresident tuition: $6384 full-time, $266 per credit hour part-time. Mandatory fees: $3960 full-time, $165 per credit hour part-time. Full-time tuition and fees vary according to program and reciprocity agreements. Part-time tuition and fees vary according to program and reciprocity agreements. Scholarships: Available. Calendar System: Semester, Summer session available Enrollment: Full-time 2,219, Part-time 4,409 Faculty: Full-time 114, Part-time 510 Exams: Other. Regional Accreditation: New England Association of Schools and Colleges Credit Hours For Degree: 60 credits, Associates ROTC: Air Force Professional Accreditation: ACEN, ADA, AHIMA, CoARC, JRCERT. Intercollegiate Athletics: Baseball M; Basketball M & W; Softball W; Volleyball M & W

NORTHPOINT BIBLE COLLEGE
320 S Main St.
Haverhill, MA 01835
Tel: (978)478-3400; Free: 800-356-4014
E-mail: admissions@zbc.edu
Web Site: northpoint.edu
President/CEO: Dr. J. David Arnett
Admissions: Helen Brouillette
Type: Four-Year College Sex: Coed Affiliation: Assembly of God Church. Admission Plans: Open Admission Application Fee: $35.00 Costs Per Year: Application fee: $35. Comprehensive fee: $19,500 includes full-time tuition ($10,200), mandatory fees ($950), and college room and board ($8350). College room only: $5550. Room and board charges vary according to board plan, housing facility, and location. Part-time tuition: $335 per credit hour. Part-time mandatory fees: $335 per term. Part-time tuition and fees vary according to course load, location, and program. Calendar System: Semester Professional Accreditation: ABHE.

PINE MANOR COLLEGE
400 Heath St.
Chestnut Hill, MA 02467
Tel: (617)731-7000; Free: 800-762-1357
Fax: (617)731-7199
Web Site: www.pmc.edu
President/CEO: Dr. Rosemary Ashby
Financial Aid: Deborah A. Gravel
Type: Comprehensive Sex: Coed % Accepted: 69 Admission Plans: Deferred Admission Application Deadline: Rolling Application Fee: $25.00 H.S. Requirements: High school diploma required; GED accepted Costs Per Year: Application fee: $25. One-time mandatory fee: $300. Comprehensive fee: $33,295 includes full-time tuition ($26,360), mandatory fees ($445), and college room and board ($6490). Full-time tuition and fees vary according to course load. Room and board charges vary according to housing facility. Part-time tuition: $760 per credit hour. Part-time mandatory fees: $545 per year, $2720 per term. Part-time tuition and fees vary according to course load. Scholarships: Available. Calendar System: Semester, Summer session available Enrollment: Full-time 438, Graduate full-time 39, Part-time 9 Faculty: Full-time 21 Student-Faculty Ratio: 15:1 Exams: SAT I or ACT; SAT Reasoning. % Receiving Financial Aid: 88 Final Year or Final Semester Residency Requirement: Yes Regional Accreditation: New England Association of Schools and Colleges Credit Hours For Degree: 64 credits, Associates Intercollegiate Athletics: Basketball M & W; Cross-Country Running M & W; Soccer M & W; Softball W; Volleyball W

QUINCY COLLEGE
1250 Hancock St.
Quincy, MA 02169
Tel: (617)984-1700; Free: 800-698-1700
Fax: (617)984-1669
E-mail: admissions@quincycollege.edu
Web Site: www.quincycollege.edu
President/CEO: Peter Tsaffaras, JD

Admissions: Tom Pham
Type: Two-Year College Sex: Coed Admission Plans: Deferred Admission; Early Admission; Open Admission Application Deadline: Rolling Application Fee: $30.00 H.S. Requirements: High school diploma or equivalent not required. For except for nursing, surgical technology programs, phlebotomy, medical laboratory technician, physical therapy assistant programs: High school diploma required; GED accepted Costs Per Year: Application fee: $30. State resident tuition: $5040 full-time, $210 per credit part-time. Nonresident tuition: $5040 full-time, $210 per credit part-time. Mandatory fees: $484 full-time, $12 per credit part-time, $98 per term part-time. Full-time tuition and fees vary according to course load and program. Part-time tuition and fees vary according to course load, program, and reciprocity agreements. Scholarships: Available. Calendar System: Semester, Summer session available Enrollment: Full-time 1,844, Part-time 2,888 Faculty: Full-time 68, Part-time 284 Student-Faculty Ratio: 18:1 Regional Accreditation: New England Association of Schools and Colleges Credit Hours For Degree: 60+ credits, depends upon major selected, Associates Professional Accreditation: ACEN.

QUINSIGAMOND COMMUNITY COLLEGE
670 W Boylston St.
Worcester, MA 01606-2092
Tel: (508)853-2300
Fax: (508)852-6943
E-mail: meyene@qcc.mass.edu
Web Site: www.qcc.edu
President/CEO: Dr. Gail Carberry
Admissions: Mishawn Davis-Eyene
Financial Aid: Paula Ogden
Type: Two-Year College Sex: Coed Affiliation: Massachusetts System of Higher Education. % Accepted: 57 Admission Plans: Open Admission Application Deadline: Rolling Application Fee: $20.00 H.S. Requirements: High school diploma required; GED accepted Costs Per Year: Application fee: $20. State resident tuition: $576 full-time, $24 per credit part-time. Nonresident tuition: $5520 full-time, $230 per credit part-time. Mandatory fees: $4866 full-time, $164 per credit part-time, $355 per term part-time. Full-time tuition and fees vary according to course load and program. Part-time tuition and fees vary according to course load and program. Scholarships: Available. Calendar System: Semester, Summer session available Enrollment: Full-time 3,040, Part-time 5,024 Faculty: Full-time 140, Part-time 442 Student-Faculty Ratio: 16:1 Regional Accreditation: New England Association of Schools and Colleges Credit Hours For Degree: 62 credits, Associates ROTC: Army Professional Accreditation: AAMAE, ACEN, ADA, AOTA, CoARC, JRCERT. Intercollegiate Athletics: Baseball M; Basketball M & W; Softball W

REGIS COLLEGE
235 Wellesley St.
Weston, MA 02493
Tel: (781)768-7000; Free: 866-438-7344
Fax: (781)768-8339
E-mail: admission@regiscollege.edu
Web Site: www.regiscollege.edu
President/CEO: Antoinette M. Hays, PhD
Admissions: Zakaree Marcus Harris
Financial Aid: Bonnie L. Quinn
Type: Comprehensive Sex: Coed Affiliation: Roman Catholic. Scores: 90% SAT V 400+; 89% SAT M 400+; 33% ACT 18-23; 38% ACT 24-29 % Accepted: 84 Admission Plans: Deferred Admission; Early Admission; Early Decision Plan Application Deadline: Rolling Application Fee: $50.00 H.S. Requirements: High school diploma required; GED accepted Costs Per Year: Application fee: $50. One-time mandatory fee: $200. Comprehensive fee: $51,920 includes full-time tuition ($37,540) and college room and board ($14,380). Full-time tuition varies according to course load. Part-time tuition: $1251 per credit hour. Part-time tuition varies according to class time. Scholarships: Available. Calendar System: Semester, Summer session available Enrollment: Full-time 958, Graduate full-time 242, Graduate part-time 477, Part-time 277 Faculty: Full-time 96, Part-time 114 Student-Faculty Ratio: 11:1 Exams: SAT I or ACT; SAT Reasoning. % Residing in College-Owned, -Operated, or -Affiliated Housing: 60 Final Year or Final Semester Residency Requirement: No Regional Accreditation: New England Association of Schools and Colleges Credit Hours For Degree: 72 credits, Associates; 36 courses, Bachelors ROTC: Army Professional Accreditation: ACEN, CSWE. Intercollegiate Athletics: Basketball M & W;

Field Hockey W; Lacrosse M & W; Soccer M & W; Softball W; Swimming and Diving M & W; Tennis M & W; Track and Field M & W; Volleyball M & W

ROXBURY COMMUNITY COLLEGE

1234 Columbus Ave.
Roxbury Crossing, MA 02120-3400
Tel: (617)427-0060
Web Site: www.rcc.mass.edu
President/CEO: Dr. Valerie Roberson
Admissions: Nancy Santos
Type: Two-Year College **Sex:** Coed **Affiliation:** Massachusetts Public Higher Education System. **% Accepted:** 83 **Admission Plans:** Deferred Admission; Open Admission; Preferred Admission **Application Deadline:** Rolling **Application Fee:** $10.00 **H.S. Requirements:** High school diploma required; GED accepted **Scholarships:** Available. **Calendar System:** Semester, Summer session available **Enrollment:** Full-time 1,124, Part-time 1,258 **Faculty:** Full-time 65, Part-time 55 **Student-Faculty Ratio:** 16:1 **Regional Accreditation:** New England Association of Schools and Colleges **Credit Hours For Degree:** 60 credits, Associates **Professional Accreditation:** ACEN. **Intercollegiate Athletics:** Baseball M; Basketball M & W; Soccer M & W; Tennis M & W

SALEM STATE UNIVERSITY

352 Lafayette St.
Salem, MA 01970-5353
Tel: (978)542-6000
Fax: (978)542-6126
E-mail: admissions@salemstate.edu
Web Site: www.salemstate.edu
President/CEO: Dr. Patricia Maguire Meservey
Admissions: Dr. Mary Dunn
Financial Aid: Mary Benda
Type: Comprehensive **Sex:** Coed **Affiliation:** Massachusetts Public Higher Education System. **% Accepted:** 72 **Admission Plans:** Early Decision Plan **Application Deadline:** May 1 **Application Fee:** $40.00 **H.S. Requirements:** High school diploma required; GED accepted **Costs Per Year:** Application fee: $40. State resident tuition: $910 full-time. Nonresident tuition: $7050 full-time. Mandatory fees: $8336 full-time. Full-time tuition and fees vary according to class time and course load. College room and board: $12,464. College room only: $8874. Room and board charges vary according to board plan and housing facility. **Scholarships:** Available. **Calendar System:** Semester, Summer session available **Enrollment:** Full-time 5,834, Graduate full-time 360, Graduate part-time 1,277, Part-time 1,830 **Student-Faculty Ratio:** 15:1 **Exams:** ACT essay component used for admission; ACT essay component used for placement; SAT I or ACT; SAT essay component used for admission; SAT essay component used for placement; SAT Reasoning. **% Residing in College-Owned, -Operated, or -Affiliated Housing:** 28 **Final Year or Final Semester Residency Requirement:** No **Regional Accreditation:** New England Association of Schools and Colleges **Credit Hours For Degree:** 120 credits, Bachelors **ROTC:** Air Force, Army **Professional Accreditation:** AACN, ABET, ACEN, AOTA, CSWE, JRCAT, JRCNMT, NASAD, NASM, NAST, NCATE. **Intercollegiate Athletics:** Baseball M; Basketball M & W; Cross-Country Running M & W; Field Hockey W; Golf M; Ice Hockey M & W; Lacrosse M & W; Soccer M & W; Softball W; Tennis M & W; Volleyball W

SALTER COLLEGE (CHICOPEE)

645 Shawinigan Dr.
Chicopee, MA 01020
Tel: (413)206-0300
Web Site: www.saltercollege.com
Type: Two-Year College **Sex:** Coed **Professional Accreditation:** ACICS.

SALTER COLLEGE (WEST BOYLSTON)

184 W Boylston St.
West Boylston, MA 01583
Web Site: www.saltercollege-us.com
Type: Two-Year College **Sex:** Coed **Professional Accreditation:** ACICS.

SCHOOL OF THE MUSEUM OF FINE ARTS, BOSTON

230 The Fenway
Boston, MA 02115
Tel: (617)267-6100
Fax: (617)369-3679

E-mail: admissions@smfa.edu
Web Site: www.smfa.edu
President/CEO: Christopher Bratton
Admissions: Angela Jones
Financial Aid: Shaun Thomas
Type: Comprehensive **Sex:** Coed **Affiliation:** Museum of Fine Arts, Boston; Tufts University. **% Accepted:** 83 **Admission Plans:** Deferred Admission; Early Admission **Application Deadline:** Rolling **Application Fee:** $65.00 **H.S. Requirements:** High school diploma required; GED accepted **Costs Per Year:** Application fee: $65. Tuition: $39,928 full-time, $1485 per credit hour part-time. Mandatory fees: $1300 full-time. Full-time tuition and fees vary according to course load, degree level, program, and student level. Part-time tuition varies according to class time, course load, program, and student level. College room only: $10,950. Room charges vary according to housing facility. **Scholarships:** Available. **Calendar System:** Semester, Summer session available **Enrollment:** Full-time 268, Graduate full-time 148, Graduate part-time 2, Part-time 81 **Faculty:** Full-time 40, Part-time 49 **Student-Faculty Ratio:** 8:1 **Exams:** Other. **% Receiving Financial Aid:** 66 **% Residing in College-Owned, -Operated, or -Affiliated Housing:** 14 **Final Year or Final Semester Residency Requirement:** Yes **Credit Hours For Degree:** 132 credits, Bachelors **Professional Accreditation:** NASAD.

SIMMONS COLLEGE

300 The Fenway
Boston, MA 02115
Tel: (617)521-2000; Free: 800-345-8468
Fax: (617)521-3199
Web Site: www.simmons.edu
President/CEO: Helen Drinan
Admissions: Ellen Johnson
Financial Aid: Heather Patenaude
Type: University **Scores:** 100% SAT V 400+; 100% SAT M 400+; 25% ACT 18-23; 58% ACT 24-29 **% Accepted:** 58 **Admission Plans:** Deferred Admission; Early Decision Plan **Application Deadline:** February 1 **Application Fee:** $55.00 **H.S. Requirements:** High school diploma required; GED accepted **Costs Per Year:** Application fee: $55. Comprehensive fee: $51,420 includes full-time tuition ($36,320), mandatory fees ($1060), and college room and board ($14,040). Full-time tuition and fees vary according to course load and program. Room and board charges vary according to location. Part-time tuition: $1135 per credit hour. Part-time mandatory fees: $260 per term. Part-time tuition and fees vary according to course load and program. **Scholarships:** Available. **Calendar System:** Semester, Summer session available **Enrollment:** Full-time 1,599, Graduate full-time 1,289, Graduate part-time 2,630, Part-time 142 **Faculty:** Full-time 218, Part-time 626 **Student-Faculty Ratio:** 10:1 **Exams:** SAT I or ACT; SAT Reasoning; SAT Subject. **% Receiving Financial Aid:** 78 **% Residing in College-Owned, -Operated, or -Affiliated Housing:** 60 **Final Year or Final Semester Residency Requirement:** No **Regional Accreditation:** New England Association of Schools and Colleges **ROTC:** Army **Professional Accreditation:** AACN, AACSB, ALA, AND, APTA, CAHME, CSWE. **Intercollegiate Athletics:** Basketball W; Crew W; Cross-Country Running W; Field Hockey W; Lacrosse W; Soccer W; Softball W; Swimming and Diving W; Tennis W; Volleyball W

SMITH COLLEGE

Northampton, MA 01063
Tel: (413)584-2700; Free: 800-383-3232
Fax: (413)585-2123
E-mail: admission@smith.edu
Web Site: www.smith.edu
President/CEO: Kathleen McCartney
Admissions: Debra Shaver
Financial Aid: David Belanger
Type: Comprehensive **Scores:** 100% SAT V 400+; 100% SAT M 400+; 6.09% ACT 18-23; 44.67% ACT 24-29 **% Accepted:** 38 **Admission Plans:** Deferred Admission; Early Action; Early Admission **Application Deadline:** January 15 **H.S. Requirements:** High school diploma or equivalent not required **Costs Per Year:** Comprehensive fee: $61,758 includes full-time tuition ($46,010), mandatory fees ($278), and college room and board ($15,470). College room only: $7740. Part-time tuition: $1440 per credit hour. **Scholarships:** Available. **Calendar System:** Semester **Enrollment:** Full-time 2,460, Graduate full-time 309, Graduate part-time 87, Part-time 18 **Exams:** ACT essay component not used; SAT I or ACT; SAT essay component not used; SAT Reasoning; SAT Subject. **% Receiving Financial**

Aid: 60 % **Residing in College-Owned, -Operated, or -Affiliated Housing:** 95 **Regional Accreditation:** New England Association of Schools and Colleges **Credit Hours For Degree:** 128 credits, Bachelors **ROTC:** Air Force, Army **Professional Accreditation:** ABET, CSWE. **Intercollegiate Athletics:** Basketball W; Crew W; Cross-Country Running W; Equestrian Sports W; Field Hockey W; Lacrosse W; Soccer W; Softball W; Squash W; Swimming and Diving W; Tennis W; Track and Field W; Volleyball W

SPRINGFIELD COLLEGE

263 Alden St.
Springfield, MA 01109-3797
Tel: (413)748-3000; Free: 800-343-1257
Fax: (413)748-3764
E-mail: admissions@spfldcol.edu
Web Site: www.springfield.edu
President/CEO: Dr. Richard Flynn
Admissions: Richard K. Veres
Financial Aid: Kinser Cancelmo

Type: Comprehensive **Sex:** Coed **Scores:** 96% SAT V 400+; 96% SAT M 400+ **% Accepted:** 64 **Admission Plans:** Deferred Admission; Early Action; Preferred Admission **Application Deadline:** April 1 **Application Fee:** $50.00 **H.S. Requirements:** High school diploma required; GED accepted **Scholarships:** Available. **Calendar System:** Semester, Summer session available **Enrollment:** Full-time 2,129, Graduate full-time 875, Graduate part-time 219, Part-time 31 **Exams:** SAT I or ACT; SAT Reasoning. **% Receiving Financial Aid:** 80 **% Residing in College-Owned, -Operated, or -Affiliated Housing:** 83 **Regional Accreditation:** New England Association of Schools and Colleges **Credit Hours For Degree:** 120 credit hours, Bachelors **ROTC:** Air Force, Army **Professional Accreditation:** AOTA, APTA, CORE, CSWE, JRCAT, NRPA. **Intercollegiate Athletics:** Baseball M; Basketball M & W; Cross-Country Running M & W; Field Hockey W; Football M; Golf M; Gymnastics M & W; Lacrosse M & W; Soccer M & W; Softball W; Swimming and Diving M & W; Tennis M & W; Track and Field M & W; Volleyball M & W; Wrestling M

SPRINGFIELD TECHNICAL COMMUNITY COLLEGE

1 Armory Sq., Ste. One
Springfield, MA 01105
Tel: (413)781-7822
Fax: (413)781-5805
E-mail: lapierce@stcc.edu
Web Site: www.stcc.edu
President/CEO: Dr. Ira Rubenzahl
Admissions: LaRue Pierce
Financial Aid: Mary Forni

Type: Two-Year College **Sex:** Coed **% Accepted:** 86 **Admission Plans:** Open Admission **Application Deadline:** Rolling **Application Fee:** $0.00 **H.S. Requirements:** High school diploma required; GED accepted **Costs Per Year:** Application fee: $0. State resident tuition: $750 full-time, $25 per credit part-time. Nonresident tuition: $7260 full-time, $242 per credit part-time. Mandatory fees: $4686 full-time, $149 per credit part-time, $108 per term part-time. Full-time tuition and fees vary according to course load and reciprocity agreements. Part-time tuition and fees vary according to course load and reciprocity agreements. Tuition guaranteed not to increase for student's term of enrollment. **Scholarships:** Available. **Calendar System:** Semester, Summer session available **Enrollment:** Full-time 2,715, Part-time 3,571 **Faculty:** Full-time 141, Part-time 333 **Student-Faculty Ratio:** 15:1 **Exams:** SAT I. **Regional Accreditation:** New England Association of Schools and Colleges **Credit Hours For Degree:** 60 credits, Associates **Professional Accreditation:** AAMAE, ABET, ACEN, ADA, AOTA, APTA, ARCST, CoARC, JRCEDMS, JRCERT, JRCNMT, NAACLS. **Intercollegiate Athletics:** Basketball M & W; Golf M; Soccer M & W; Wrestling M

STONEHILL COLLEGE

320 Washington St.
Easton, MA 02357
Tel: (508)565-1000
Fax: (508)565-1500
E-mail: admission@stonehill.edu
Web Site: www.stonehill.edu
President/CEO: Rev. John Denning, CSC
Financial Aid: Rhonda Nickley

Type: Four-Year College **Sex:** Coed **Affiliation:** Roman Catholic. **Scores:** 99% SAT V 400+; 97% SAT M 400+; 33% ACT 18-23; 58% ACT 24-29 **%**

Accepted: 75 **Admission Plans:** Deferred Admission; Early Action; Early Decision Plan **Application Deadline:** January 15 **Application Fee:** $60.00 **H.S. Requirements:** High school diploma required; GED accepted **Costs Per Year:** Application fee: $60. Comprehensive fee: $53,270 includes full-time tuition ($38,550) and college room and board ($14,720). Room and board charges vary according to board plan. Part-time tuition: $1285 per credit. Part-time tuition varies according to course load. **Scholarships:** Available. **Calendar System:** Semester, Summer session available **Enrollment:** Full-time 2,470, Part-time 24 **Faculty:** Full-time 159, Part-time 125 **Student-Faculty Ratio:** 12:1 **Exams:** ACT essay component used for admission; ACT essay component used for advising; ACT essay component used for placement; SAT essay component used for admission; SAT essay component used for advising; SAT essay component used for placement; SAT Reasoning. **% Receiving Financial Aid:** 69 **% Residing in College-Owned, -Operated, or -Affiliated Housing:** 91 **Final Year or Final Semester Residency Requirement:** No **Regional Accreditation:** New England Association of Schools and Colleges **Credit Hours For Degree:** 124 credits, Bachelors **ROTC:** Army **Intercollegiate Athletics:** Baseball M; Basketball M & W; Bowling M & W; Cheerleading M & W; Cross-Country Running M & W; Equestrian Sports W; Field Hockey W; Football M; Golf M & W; Ice Hockey M & W; Lacrosse M & W; Rugby M & W; Soccer M & W; Softball W; Tennis M & W; Track and Field M & W; Ultimate Frisbee M & W; Volleyball M & W; Wrestling M

SUFFOLK UNIVERSITY

8 Ashburton Pl.
Boston, MA 02108-2770
Tel: (617)573-8000; Free: 800-6-SUFFOLK
Fax: (617)742-4291
E-mail: admission@suffolk.edu
Web Site: www.suffolk.edu
President/CEO: Margaret McKenna
Admissions: Donna Grand Pre
Financial Aid: Christine A. Perry

Type: Comprehensive **Sex:** Coed **Scores:** 92% SAT V 400+; 93% SAT M 400+; 53.1% ACT 18-23; 31.4% ACT 24-29 **% Accepted:** 82 **Admission Plans:** Deferred Admission; Early Decision Plan **Application Deadline:** February 15 **Application Fee:** $50.00 **H.S. Requirements:** High school diploma required; GED accepted **Costs Per Year:** Application fee: $50. One-time mandatory fee: $200. Comprehensive fee: $48,582 includes full-time tuition ($33,800), mandatory fees ($134), and college room and board ($14,648). Full-time tuition and fees vary according to course level and reciprocity agreements. Room and board charges vary according to board plan and housing facility. Part-time tuition: $829 per credit hour. Part-time tuition varies according to course level, course load, and reciprocity agreements. **Scholarships:** Available. **Calendar System:** Semester, Summer session available **Enrollment:** Full-time 5,232, Graduate full-time 1,195, Graduate part-time 1,286, Part-time 333 **Faculty:** Full-time 331, Part-time 374 **Student-Faculty Ratio:** 13:1 **Exams:** ACT essay component not used; SAT I or ACT; SAT essay component not used; SAT Subject. **% Receiving Financial Aid:** 58 **% Residing in College-Owned, -Operated, or -Affiliated Housing:** 66 **Final Year or Final Semester Residency Requirement:** No **Regional Accreditation:** New England Association of Schools and Colleges **Credit Hours For Degree:** 64 semester credits, Associates; 124 semester credits, Bachelors **ROTC:** Army **Professional Accreditation:** AACSB, AALS, ABA, ABET, APA, CIDA, NASAD, NASPAA. **Intercollegiate Athletics:** Baseball M; Basketball M & W; Cross-Country Running M & W; Golf M; Ice Hockey M; Soccer M; Softball W; Tennis M & W; Volleyball W

TUFTS UNIVERSITY

Medford, MA 02155
Tel: (617)628-5000
Fax: (617)627-3860
E-mail: undergraduate.admissions@tufts.edu
Web Site: www.tufts.edu
President/CEO: Anthony Monaco
Financial Aid: Patricia C. Reilly

Type: University **Sex:** Coed **Scores:** 100% SAT V 400+; 100% SAT M 400+; 0.3% ACT 18-23; 11.4% ACT 24-29 **% Accepted:** 16 **Admission Plans:** Deferred Admission; Early Action; Early Admission **Application Deadline:** January 1 **Application Fee:** $70.00 **H.S. Requirements:** High school diploma required; GED accepted **Costs Per Year:** Application fee: $70. Comprehensive fee: $63,698 includes full-time tuition ($49,520), mandatory fees ($1084), and college room and board ($13,094). College room only:

$7134. Room and board charges vary according to board plan. **Scholarships:** Available. **Calendar System:** Semester, Summer session available **Enrollment:** Full-time 5,215, Graduate full-time 4,965, Graduate part-time 882, Part-time 75 **Faculty:** Full-time 682, Part-time 313 **Student-Faculty Ratio:** 9:1 **Exams:** SAT I and SAT II or ACT; SAT essay component used for placement; SAT Reasoning; SAT Subject. **% Receiving Financial Aid:** 37 **% Residing in College-Owned, -Operated, or -Affiliated Housing:** 65 **Final Year or Final Semester Residency Requirement:** No **Regional Accreditation:** New England Association of Schools and Colleges **Credit Hours For Degree:** 34 courses for School of Arts and Sciences, 38 courses for School of Engineering, Bachelors **ROTC:** Air Force, Army, Navy **Professional Accreditation:** ABET, ACSP, ADA, AND, AOTA, APA, AVMA, CEPH, LCME/AMA. **Intercollegiate Athletics:** Baseball M; Basketball M & W; Crew M & W; Cross-Country Running M & W; Equestrian Sports M & W; Fencing W; Field Hockey W; Football M; Golf M; Ice Hockey M; Lacrosse M & W; Rugby M & W; Sailing M & W; Soccer M & W; Softball M & W; Squash M & W; Swimming and Diving M & W; Tennis M & W; Track and Field M & W; Ultimate Frisbee M & W; Volleyball M & W; Water Polo M & W

UNIVERSITY OF MASSACHUSETTS AMHERST

Amherst, MA 01003
Tel: (413)545-0111
Fax: (413)545-4312
E-mail: mail@admissions.umass.edu
Web Site: www.umass.edu
President/CEO: Dr. Kumble R. Subbaswamy
Admissions: Jon Westover

Type: University **Sex:** Coed **Affiliation:** University of Massachusetts. **Scores:** 100% SAT V 400+; 100% SAT M 400+; 9% ACT 18-23; 62.8% ACT 24-29 **% Accepted:** 58 **Admission Plans:** Deferred Admission; Early Decision Plan **Application Deadline:** January 15 **Application Fee:** $75.00 **H.S. Requirements:** High school diploma required; GED accepted **Scholarships:** Available. **Calendar System:** Semester, Summer session available **Enrollment:** Full-time 21,098, Graduate full-time 2,241, Graduate part-time 4,280, Part-time 1,650 **Faculty:** Full-time 1,295, Part-time 178 **Student-Faculty Ratio:** 18:1 **Exams:** SAT I or ACT; SAT Reasoning. **% Receiving Financial Aid:** 58 **% Residing in College-Owned, -Operated, or -Affiliated Housing:** 58 **Final Year or Final Semester Residency Requirement:** Yes **Regional Accreditation:** New England Association of Schools and Colleges **Credit Hours For Degree:** 60 credits, Associates; 120 credits, Bachelors **ROTC:** Air Force, Army **Professional Accreditation:** AACN, AACSB, AAFCS, ABET, ACSP, AND, APA, ASHA, ASLA, CEPH, NASM, NCATE, SAF. **Intercollegiate Athletics:** Baseball M; Basketball M & W; Crew W; Cross-Country Running M & W; Field Hockey W; Football M; Ice Hockey M; Lacrosse M & W; Soccer M & W; Softball W; Swimming and Diving M & W; Tennis W; Track and Field M & W

UNIVERSITY OF MASSACHUSETTS BOSTON

100 Morrissey Blvd.
Boston, MA 02125-3393
Tel: (617)287-5000
E-mail: enrollment.info@umb.edu
Web Site: www.umb.edu
President/CEO: Dr. J. Keith Motley
Admissions: Kerry Boyd
Financial Aid: Judy L. Keyes

Type: University **Sex:** Coed **Affiliation:** University of Massachusetts. **Scores:** 96% SAT V 400+ **% Accepted:** 69 **Admission Plans:** Deferred Admission; Early Decision Plan **Application Deadline:** March 1 **Application Fee:** $60.00 **H.S. Requirements:** High school diploma required; GED accepted **Costs Per Year:** Application fee: $60. State resident tuition: $12,682 full-time. Nonresident tuition: $29,920 full-time. Full-time tuition varies according to program. **Scholarships:** Available. **Calendar System:** Semester, Summer session available **Enrollment:** Full-time 9,384, Graduate full-time 1,405, Graduate part-time 2,676, Part-time 3,565 **Faculty:** Full-time 699, Part-time 572 **Student-Faculty Ratio:** 16:1 **Exams:** ACT; SAT I; SAT I and SAT II or ACT; SAT I or ACT; SAT II; SAT Reasoning. **% Receiving Financial Aid:** 65 **Regional Accreditation:** New England Association of Schools and Colleges **Credit Hours For Degree:** 120 credits, Bachelors **ROTC:** Air Force, Army, Navy **Professional Accreditation:** AACN, AACSB, AAMFT, ABET, APA, CORE, NCATE, TEAC. **Intercollegiate Athletics:** Baseball M; Basketball M & W; Cross-Country Running M & W; Ice Hockey M & W; Lacrosse M; Soccer M & W; Softball W; Tennis M & W; Track and Field M & W; Volleyball W

UNIVERSITY OF MASSACHUSETTS DARTMOUTH

285 Old Westport Rd.
North Dartmouth, MA 02747-2300
Tel: (508)999-8000
Fax: (508)999-8755
E-mail: admissions@umassd.edu
Web Site: www.umassd.edu
President/CEO: Dr. Payton Helm
Financial Aid: Audra Callahan

Type: University **Sex:** Coed **Affiliation:** University of Massachusetts. **Scores:** 92% SAT V 400+; 94% SAT M 400+; 50% ACT 18-23; 32% ACT 24-29 **% Accepted:** 76 **Admission Plans:** Deferred Admission; Early Action; Early Admission; Early Decision Plan **Application Deadline:** Rolling **Application Fee:** $60.00 **H.S. Requirements:** High school diploma required; GED accepted **Costs Per Year:** Application fee: $60. One-time mandatory fee: $100. State resident tuition: $1417 full-time, $59.04 per credit part-time. Nonresident tuition: $8099 full-time, $337.46 per credit part-time. Mandatory fees: $11,171 full-time, $474.46 per credit part-time. Full-time tuition and fees vary according to class time, program, and reciprocity agreements. Part-time tuition and fees vary according to class time, course load, program, and reciprocity agreements. College room and board: $11,622. College room only: $7609. Room and board charges vary according to board plan and housing facility. **Scholarships:** Available. **Calendar System:** Semester, Summer session available **Enrollment:** Full-time 6,254, Graduate full-time 710, Graduate part-time 911, Part-time 1,041 **Faculty:** Full-time 392, Part-time 207 **Student-Faculty Ratio:** 18:1 **Exams:** SAT I or ACT; SAT Reasoning. **% Receiving Financial Aid:** 72 **% Residing in College-Owned, -Operated, or -Affiliated Housing:** 55 **Final Year or Final Semester Residency Requirement:** No **Regional Accreditation:** New England Association of Schools and Colleges **Credit Hours For Degree:** 120 credit hours, Bachelors **ROTC:** Army **Professional Accreditation:** AACSB, ABA, ABET, ACEN, NAACLS, NASAD. **Intercollegiate Athletics:** Baseball M; Basketball M & W; Cross-Country Running M & W; Equestrian Sports W; Field Hockey W; Football M; Golf M; Ice Hockey M; Lacrosse M & W; Sailing W; Soccer M & W; Softball W; Swimming and Diving M & W; Tennis M & W; Track and Field M & W; Volleyball W

UNIVERSITY OF MASSACHUSETTS LOWELL

1 University Ave.
Lowell, MA 01854
Tel: (978)934-4000
Fax: (978)934-3000
E-mail: admissions@uml.edu
Web Site: www.uml.edu
President/CEO: Dr. Jacqueline Moloney
Financial Aid: Joyce McLaughlin

Type: University **Sex:** Coed **Affiliation:** University of Massachusetts. **Scores:** 99% SAT V 400+; 100% SAT M 400+; 25% ACT 18-23; 55% ACT 24-29 **% Accepted:** 57 **Admission Plans:** Deferred Admission; Early Decision Plan **Application Deadline:** February 1 **Application Fee:** $60.00 **H.S. Requirements:** High school diploma required; GED accepted **Costs Per Year:** Application fee: $60. One-time mandatory fee: $200. State resident tuition: $1454 full-time, $61 per credit hour part-time. Nonresident tuition: $8567 full-time, $357 per credit hour part-time. Mandatory fees: $11,973 full-time, $499 per credit hour part-time. Part-time tuition and fees vary according to course load. College room and board: $11,670. College room only: $7710. Room and board charges vary according to board plan and housing facility. **Scholarships:** Available. **Calendar System:** Semester, Summer session available **Enrollment:** Full-time 9,743, Graduate full-time 1,261, Graduate part-time 2,923, Part-time 3,523 **Faculty:** Full-time 565, Part-time 547 **Student-Faculty Ratio:** 17:1 **Exams:** ACT essay component not used; SAT I or ACT; SAT essay component not used. **% Receiving Financial Aid:** 60 **% Residing in College-Owned, -Operated, or -Affiliated Housing:** 38 **Final Year or Final Semester Residency Requirement:** No **Regional Accreditation:** New England Association of Schools and Colleges **Credit Hours For Degree:** 60 credits, Associates; 120 credits, Bachelors **ROTC:** Air Force, Army **Professional Accreditation:** AACN, AACSB, ABET, APTA, NAACLS, NASAD, NASM, NCATE. **Intercollegiate Athletics:** Baseball M; Basketball M & W; Cross-Country Running M & W; Field Hockey W; Golf M; Ice Hockey M; Lacrosse M & W; Soccer M & W; Softball W; Track and Field M & W; Volleyball W

URBAN COLLEGE OF BOSTON

178 Tremont St.
Boston, MA 02111

Tel: (617)292-4723
Fax: (617)423-4758
Web Site: www.urbancollege.edu
President/CEO: Dr. Linda Edmonds Turner
Admissions: Dr. Henry J. Johnson

Type: Two-Year College **Sex:** Coed **Admission Plans:** Open Admission **Application Fee:** $10.00 **H.S. Requirements:** High school diploma required; GED accepted **Scholarships:** Available. **Calendar System:** Semester **Student-Faculty Ratio:** 13:1 **Regional Accreditation:** New England Association of Schools and Colleges **Credit Hours For Degree:** 65 credits, Associates

WELLESLEY COLLEGE

106 Central St.
Wellesley, MA 02481
Tel: (781)283-1000
Fax: (781)283-3678
E-mail: admission@wellesley.edu
Web Site: www.wellesley.edu
President/CEO: Paula Johnson
Financial Aid: Scott J. Juedes

Type: Four-Year College **Sex:** Women **Scores:** 100% SAT V 400+; 100% SAT M 400+ **% Accepted:** 30 **Admission Plans:** Deferred Admission; Early Action; Early Admission **Application Deadline:** January 15 **Application Fee:** $0.00 **H.S. Requirements:** High school diploma or equivalent not required **Costs Per Year:** Application fee: $0. Comprehensive fee: $63,916 includes full-time tuition ($48,510), mandatory fees ($292), and college room and board ($15,114). College room only: $7672. Part-time tuition: $6064 per course. Part-time mandatory fees: $37 per course. Part-time tuition and fees vary according to course load. **Scholarships:** Available. **Calendar System:** Semester, Summer session available **Faculty:** Full-time 298, Part-time 58 **Student-Faculty Ratio:** 7:1 **Exams:** ACT essay component not used; SAT I and SAT II or ACT; SAT essay component not used; SAT Reasoning; SAT Subject. **% Receiving Financial Aid:** 59 **% Residing in College-Owned, -Operated, or -Affiliated Housing:** 98 **Regional Accreditation:** New England Association of Schools and Colleges **Credit Hours For Degree:** 32 courses, Bachelors **ROTC:** Air Force, Army **Intercollegiate Athletics:** Basketball W; Crew W; Cross-Country Running W; Fencing W; Field Hockey W; Golf W; Lacrosse W; Rugby W; Sailing W; Skiing (Downhill) W; Soccer W; Softball W; Squash W; Swimming and Diving W; Tennis W; Track and Field W; Ultimate Frisbee W; Volleyball W

WENTWORTH INSTITUTE OF TECHNOLOGY

550 Huntington Ave.
Boston, MA 02115-5998
Tel: (617)989-4590; Free: 800-556-0610
Fax: (617)989-4010
E-mail: dufoura@wit.edu
Web Site: www.wit.edu
President/CEO: Dr. Zorica Pantic
Admissions: Amy Dufour
Financial Aid: Anne-Marie Caruso

Type: Comprehensive **Sex:** Coed **Scores:** 97% SAT V 400+; 101% SAT M 400+; 43% ACT 18-23; 48% ACT 24-29 **% Accepted:** 67 **Admission Plans:** Deferred Admission **Application Deadline:** February 15 **Application Fee:** $50.00 **H.S. Requirements:** High school diploma required; GED accepted **Costs Per Year:** Application fee: $50. Comprehensive fee: $45,890 includes full-time tuition ($30,760), mandatory fees ($1740), and college room and board ($13,390). Room and board charges vary according to board plan and housing facility. Part-time tuition: $960 per credit hour. Part-time mandatory fees: $465 per credit. Part-time tuition and fees vary according to course load. **Scholarships:** Available. **Calendar System:** Miscellaneous, Summer session available **Enrollment:** Full-time 3,902, Graduate full-time 91, Graduate part-time 161, Part-time 422 **Faculty:** Full-time 151, Part-time 220 **Student-Faculty Ratio:** 15:1 **Exams:** ACT essay component not used; SAT I or ACT; SAT essay component not used; SAT Reasoning; SAT Subject. **% Receiving Financial Aid:** 72 **% Residing in College-Owned, -Operated, or -Affiliated Housing:** 51 **Final Year or Final Semester Residency Requirement:** Yes **Regional Accreditation:** New England Association of Schools and Colleges **Credit Hours For Degree:** 64 credits, Associates; 128 credits, Bachelors **ROTC:** Air Force, Army **Professional Accreditation:** ABET, ACCE, CIDA, NAAB, NASAD. **Intercollegiate Athletics:** Baseball M; Basketball M & W; Crew M; Cross-Country Running M; Golf M; Ice Hockey

M; Lacrosse M & W; Rugby M & W; Soccer M & W; Softball W; Tennis M & W; Ultimate Frisbee M & W; Volleyball M & W

WESTERN NEW ENGLAND UNIVERSITY

1215 Wilbraham Rd.
Springfield, MA 01119
Tel: (413)782-3111; Free: 800-325-1122
Fax: (413)782-1777
E-mail: learn@wne.edu
Web Site: www.wne.edu
President/CEO: Dr. Anthony S. Caprio
Admissions: Bryan Gross
Financial Aid: Kathy M. Chambers

Type: Comprehensive **Sex:** Coed **Scores:** 96% SAT V 400+; 98% SAT M 400+; 32.9% ACT 18-23; 55.7% ACT 24-29 **% Accepted:** 81 **Admission Plans:** Deferred Admission; Early Admission **Application Deadline:** Rolling **Application Fee:** $40.00 **H.S. Requirements:** High school diploma required; GED accepted **Costs Per Year:** Application fee: $40. Comprehensive fee: $46,924 includes full-time tuition ($31,730), mandatory fees ($2300), and college room and board ($12,894). Full-time tuition and fees vary according to course load and program. Room and board charges vary according to board plan and housing facility. Part-time tuition: $598 per credit hour. Part-time tuition varies according to course load and program. **Scholarships:** Available. **Calendar System:** Semester, Summer session available **Enrollment:** Full-time 2,578, Graduate full-time 509, Graduate part-time 712, Part-time 155 **Faculty:** Full-time 229, Part-time 148 **Student-Faculty Ratio:** 12:1 **Exams:** ACT essay component not used; SAT I or ACT; SAT essay component not used; SAT Reasoning. **% Receiving Financial Aid:** 77 **% Residing in College-Owned, -Operated, or -Affiliated Housing:** 65 **Final Year or Final Semester Residency Requirement:** No **Regional Accreditation:** New England Association of Schools and Colleges **Credit Hours For Degree:** 60 semester hours, Associates; 122 semester hours, Bachelors **ROTC:** Air Force, Army **Professional Accreditation:** AACSB, AALS, ABA, ABET, ACPE, CSWE. **Intercollegiate Athletics:** Baseball M; Basketball M & W; Cross-Country Running M & W; Field Hockey W; Football M; Golf M; Ice Hockey M; Lacrosse M & W; Soccer M & W; Softball W; Swimming and Diving W; Tennis M & W; Volleyball W; Wrestling M

WESTFIELD STATE UNIVERSITY

577 Western Ave.
Westfield, MA 01086
Tel: (413)572-5300
E-mail: admission@westfield.ma.edu
Web Site: www.westfield.ma.edu
President/CEO: Dr. Ramon Torrecilha
Admissions: Dr. Kelly Hart
Financial Aid: Catherine Ryan

Type: Comprehensive **Sex:** Coed **Affiliation:** Massachusetts Public Higher Education System. **Scores:** 92% SAT V 400+; 93% SAT M 400+; 62.1% ACT 18-23; 26.4% ACT 24-29 **% Accepted:** 80 **Admission Plans:** Deferred Admission **Application Deadline:** March 1 **Application Fee:** $50.00 **H.S. Requirements:** High school diploma required; GED accepted **Costs Per Year:** Application fee: $50. State resident tuition: $970 full-time, $280 per credit hour part-time. Nonresident tuition: $7050 full-time, $280 per credit hour part-time. Mandatory fees: $7845 full-time, $75 per term part-time. Full-time tuition and fees vary according to program and reciprocity agreements. Part-time tuition and fees vary according to course load. College room and board: $10,691. Room and board charges vary according to board plan and housing facility. **Scholarships:** Available. **Calendar System:** Semester, Summer session available **Enrollment:** Full-time 4,963, Graduate full-time 260, Graduate part-time 620, Part-time 653 **Faculty:** Full-time 238, Part-time 281 **Student-Faculty Ratio:** 16:1 **Exams:** ACT essay component not used; SAT I or ACT; SAT essay component not used; SAT Reasoning. **% Receiving Financial Aid:** 64 **% Residing in College-Owned, -Operated, or -Affiliated Housing:** 54 **Final Year or Final Semester Residency Requirement:** No **Regional Accreditation:** New England Association of Schools and Colleges **Credit Hours For Degree:** 120 credit hours, Bachelors **ROTC:** Air Force, Army **Professional Accreditation:** ABET, CSWE, JRCAT, NASM, NCATE. **Intercollegiate Athletics:** Baseball M; Basketball M & W; Cheerleading W; Cross-Country Running M & W; Field Hockey W; Football M; Golf M & W; Ice Hockey M; Lacrosse W; Soccer M & W; Softball W; Swimming and Diving W; Track and Field M & W; Volleyball W

WHEATON COLLEGE

26 E Main St.
Norton, MA 02766
Tel: (508)285-7722; Free: 800-394-6003
Fax: (508)285-8271
E-mail: admission@wheatoncollege.edu
Web Site: www.wheatoncollege.edu
President/CEO: Dennis M. Hanno
Admissions: Grant M. Gosselin
Financial Aid: Susan Beard
Type: Four-Year College **Sex:** Coed **Scores:** 99% SAT V 400+; 99% SAT M 400+; 14.89% ACT 18-23; 57.45% ACT 24-29 **% Accepted:** 65 **Admission Plans:** Deferred Admission; Early Action; Early Admission; Early Decision Plan **Application Deadline:** January 15 **Application Fee:** $60.00 **H.S. Requirements:** High school diploma required; GED accepted **Costs Per Year:** Application fee: $60. Comprehensive fee: $59,865 includes full-time tuition ($47,390), mandatory fees ($310), and college room and board ($12,165). College room only: $6490. Part-time tuition: $1481 per credit hour. **Scholarships:** Available. **Calendar System:** Semester, Summer session available **Enrollment:** Full-time 1,567, Part-time 31 **Faculty:** Full-time 129, Part-time 60 **Student-Faculty Ratio:** 10:1 **Exams:** ACT essay component not used; SAT essay component not used; SAT Reasoning; SAT Subject. **% Receiving Financial Aid:** 64 **% Residing in College-Owned, -Operated, or -Affiliated Housing:** 95 **Final Year or Final Semester Residency Requirement:** Yes **Regional Accreditation:** New England Association of Schools and Colleges **Credit Hours For Degree:** 32 courses, Bachelors **ROTC:** Army **Intercollegiate Athletics:** Baseball M; Basketball M & W; Cross-Country Running M & W; Field Hockey W; Lacrosse M & W; Soccer M & W; Softball W; Swimming and Diving M & W; Tennis M & W; Track and Field M & W; Volleyball W

WHEELOCK COLLEGE

200 The Riverway
Boston, MA 02215-4176
Tel: (617)879-2000; Free: 800-734-5212
Fax: (617)566-7531
E-mail: ahaugabrook@wheelock.edu
Web Site: www.wheelock.edu
President/CEO: Jackie Jenkins-Scott
Admissions: Dr. Adrian Haugabrook
Financial Aid: Elizabeth Gorra
Type: Comprehensive **Sex:** Coed **Scores:** 82% SAT V 400+; 77% SAT M 400+; 61% ACT 18-23; 25% ACT 24-29 **% Accepted:** 95 **Admission Plans:** Deferred Admission; Early Admission; Early Decision Plan **Application Deadline:** May 1 **Application Fee:** $0.00 **H.S. Requirements:** High school diploma required; GED accepted **Costs Per Year:** Application fee: $0. Comprehensive fee: $49,225 includes full-time tuition ($33,600), mandatory fees ($1225), and college room and board ($14,400). **Scholarships:** Available. **Calendar System:** Semester, Summer session available **Enrollment:** Full-time 797, Graduate full-time 144, Graduate part-time 214, Part-time 14 **Faculty:** Full-time 75, Part-time 88 **Student-Faculty Ratio:** 10:1 **Exams:** SAT I or ACT. **% Receiving Financial Aid:** 82 **% Residing in College-Owned, -Operated, or -Affiliated Housing:** 64 **Final Year or Final Semester Residency Requirement:** No **Regional Accreditation:** New England Association of Schools and Colleges **Credit Hours For Degree:** 134 credits, Bachelors **Professional Accreditation:** CSWE, NCATE. **Intercollegiate Athletics:** Basketball M & W; Cross-Country Running M & W; Field Hockey W; Lacrosse M & W; Soccer M & W; Softball W; Tennis M

WILLIAMS COLLEGE

880 Main St.
Williamstown, MA 01267
Tel: (413)597-3131
Fax: (413)597-4018
E-mail: admission@williams.edu
Web Site: www.williams.edu
President/CEO: Pres. Adam Falk
Admissions: Richard L. Nesbitt
Financial Aid: Paul J. Boyer
Type: Comprehensive **Sex:** Coed **Scores:** 100% SAT V 400+; 100% SAT M 400+; 1% ACT 18-23; 14% ACT 24-29 **% Accepted:** 18 **Admission Plans:** Deferred Admission; Early Action; Early Admission **Application Deadline:** January 1 **Application Fee:** $65.00 **H.S. Requirements:** High school diploma or equivalent not required **Costs Per Year:** Application fee: $65.

Comprehensive fee: $63,290 includes full-time tuition ($49,780), mandatory fees ($290), and college room and board ($13,220). College room only: $6690. Room and board charges vary according to board plan. **Scholarships:** Available. **Calendar System:** 4-1-4, Summer session not available **Enrollment:** Full-time 2,065, Graduate full-time 52, Graduate part-time 2, Part-time 34 **Faculty:** Full-time 266, Part-time 84 **Student-Faculty Ratio:** 7:1 **Exams:** SAT I or ACT; SAT II; SAT Reasoning; SAT Subject. **% Receiving Financial Aid:** 49 **% Residing in College-Owned, -Operated, or -Affiliated Housing:** 93 **Regional Accreditation:** New England Association of Schools and Colleges **ROTC:** Air Force **Intercollegiate Athletics:** Baseball M; Basketball M & W; Crew M & W; Cross-Country Running M & W; Equestrian Sports M & W; Field Hockey W; Football M; Golf M & W; Ice Hockey M & W; Lacrosse M & W; Rugby M & W; Sailing M & W; Skiing (Cross-Country) M & W; Skiing (Downhill) M & W; Soccer M & W; Softball W; Squash M & W; Swimming and Diving M & W; Tennis M & W; Track and Field M & W; Ultimate Frisbee M & W; Volleyball M & W; Water Polo M & W; Wrestling M

WORCESTER POLYTECHNIC INSTITUTE

100 Institute Rd.
Worcester, MA 01609-2280
Tel: (508)831-5000
Fax: (508)831-5875
E-mail: admissions@wpi.edu
Web Site: www.wpi.edu
President/CEO: Dr. Laurie Leshin
Admissions: Jennifer A. Cluett
Financial Aid: Monica M. Blondin
Type: University **Sex:** Coed **Scores:** 100% SAT V 400+; 100% SAT M 400+; 5% ACT 18-23; 42% ACT 24-29 **% Accepted:** 49 **Admission Plans:** Deferred Admission; Early Admission; Early Decision Plan **Application Deadline:** February 1 **Application Fee:** $65.00 **H.S. Requirements:** High school diploma required; GED accepted **Costs Per Year:** Application fee: $65. One-time mandatory fee: $200. Comprehensive fee: $59,009 includes full-time tuition ($44,979), mandatory fees ($620), and college room and board ($13,410). College room only: $7654. Room and board charges vary according to board plan and housing facility. Part-time tuition: $1249 per credit hour. Part-time tuition varies according to course load. **Scholarships:** Available. **Calendar System:** Miscellaneous, Summer session available **Enrollment:** Full-time 4,158, Graduate full-time 809, Graduate part-time 1,465, Part-time 141 **Faculty:** Full-time 359, Part-time 155 **Student-Faculty Ratio:** 13:1 **Exams:** ACT essay component not used; Other; SAT I or ACT; SAT essay component not used; SAT Reasoning; SAT Subject. **% Receiving Financial Aid:** 65 **% Residing in College-Owned, -Operated, or -Affiliated Housing:** 49 **Final Year or Final Semester Residency Requirement:** No **Regional Accreditation:** New England Association of Schools and Colleges **Credit Hours For Degree:** 45 courses, Bachelors **ROTC:** Air Force, Army, Navy **Professional Accreditation:** AACSB, ABET. **Intercollegiate Athletics:** Baseball M; Basketball M & W; Crew M & W; Cross-Country Running M & W; Field Hockey W; Football M; Soccer M & W; Softball W; Swimming and Diving M & W; Track and Field M & W; Volleyball W; Water Polo M & W; Wrestling M

WORCESTER STATE UNIVERSITY

486 Chandler St.
Worcester, MA 01602-2597
Tel: (508)929-8000
Fax: (508)929-8131
E-mail: admissions@worcester.edu
Web Site: www.worcester.edu
President/CEO: Barry M. Maloney
Admissions: Sabine Dupoux
Financial Aid: Jayne McGinn
Type: Comprehensive **Sex:** Coed **Affiliation:** Massachusetts Public Higher Education System. **Scores:** 94% SAT V 400+; 96% SAT M 400+; 57.4% ACT 18-23; 33.8% ACT 24-29 **% Accepted:** 69 **Admission Plans:** Deferred Admission; Early Decision Plan **Application Deadline:** May 1 **Application Fee:** $50.00 **H.S. Requirements:** High school diploma required; GED accepted **Costs Per Year:** Application fee: $50. State resident tuition: $970 full-time, $40.42 per credit hour part-time. Nonresident tuition: $7050 full-time, $293.75 per credit hour part-time. Mandatory fees: $7887 full-time, $328.62 per credit hour part-time. Full-time tuition and fees vary according to class time, course load, degree level, and reciprocity agreements. Part-time

tuition and fees vary according to class time, course load, degree level, and reciprocity agreements. College room and board: $11,560. College room only: $7920. Room and board charges vary according to board plan and housing facility. **Scholarships:** Available. **Calendar System:** Semester, Summer session available **Enrollment:** Full-time 4,117, Graduate full-time 173, Graduate part-time 619, Part-time 1,397 **Faculty:** Full-time 203, Part-time 214 **Student-Faculty Ratio:** 18:1 **Exams:** SAT I or ACT. **% Receiving Financial Aid: 62 % Residing in College-Owned, -Operated, or**

-**Affiliated Housing:** 30 **Final Year or Final Semester Residency Requirement:** No **Regional Accreditation:** New England Association of Schools and Colleges **Credit Hours For Degree:** 120 credits, Bachelors **ROTC:** Air Force, Army, Navy **Professional Accreditation:** AACN, AOTA, ASHA, JRCNMT, TEAC. **Intercollegiate Athletics:** Baseball M; Basketball M & W; Cross-Country Running M & W; Field Hockey W; Football M; Golf M; Ice Hockey M; Lacrosse W; Soccer M & W; Softball W; Tennis W; Track and Field M & W; Volleyball W

ADRIAN COLLEGE
110 S Madison St.
Adrian, MI 49221-2575
Tel: (517)265-5161; Free: 800-877-2246
Fax: (517)265-3331
E-mail: admissions@adrian.edu
Web Site: www.adrian.edu
President/CEO: Dr. Jeffrey R. Docking
Admissions: Frank Hribar
Financial Aid: Matthew Rheinecker
Type: Comprehensive **Sex:** Coed **Affiliation:** United Methodist Church. **Scores:** 60% ACT 18-23; 32% ACT 24-29 **% Accepted:** 56 **Admission Plans:** Deferred Admission **Application Deadline:** August 1 **Application Fee:** $0.00. **H.S. Requirements:** High school diploma required; GED accepted **Scholarships:** Available. **Calendar System:** Semester, Summer session available **Enrollment:** Full-time 1,553, Graduate full-time 9, Part-time 94 **Faculty:** Full-time 94, Part-time 101 **Student-Faculty Ratio:** 10:1 **Exams:** ACT; ACT essay component not used; SAT I or ACT; SAT essay component not used; SAT Reasoning; SAT Subject. **% Receiving Financial Aid:** 87 **% Residing in College-Owned, -Operated, or -Affiliated Housing:** 92 **Final Year or Final Semester Residency Requirement:** Yes **Regional Accreditation:** North Central Association of Colleges and Schools **Credit Hours For Degree:** 62 credit hours, Associates; 124 credit hours, Bachelors **ROTC:** Army **Intercollegiate Athletics:** Baseball M; Basketball M & W; Bowling W; Cross-Country Running M & W; Equestrian Sports W; Football M; Golf M & W; Gymnastics W; Ice Hockey M & W; Lacrosse M & W; Soccer M & W; Softball W; Tennis M & W; Track and Field M & W; Volleyball M & W

ALBION COLLEGE
611 E Porter St.
Albion, MI 49224-1831
Tel: (517)629-1000; Free: 800-858-6770
Fax: (517)629-0569
E-mail: ssanders@albion.edu
Web Site: www.albion.edu
President/CEO: Dr. Mauri Ditzler
Admissions: Shar Sanders
Financial Aid: Ann Whitmer
Type: Four-Year College **Sex:** Coed **Affiliation:** Methodist. **Scores:** 91% SAT V 400+; 82% SAT M 400+; 38% ACT 18-23; 48% ACT 24-29 **% Accepted:** 79 **Admission Plans:** Deferred Admission; Early Action **Application Deadline:** Rolling **Application Fee:** $0.00. **H.S. Requirements:** High school diploma required; GED accepted **Costs Per Year:** Application fee: $0. One-time mandatory fee: $185. Comprehensive fee: $50,194 includes full-time tuition ($38,678), mandatory fees ($450), and college room and board ($11,066). College room only: $5412. Full-time tuition and fees vary according to course load. Room and board charges vary according to board plan and housing facility. Part-time tuition: $1640 per semester hour. Part-time tuition varies according to course load. **Scholarships:** Available. **Calendar System:** Semester, Summer session available **Enrollment:** Full-time 1,359, Part-time 17 **Faculty:** Full-time 97, Part-time 47 **Student-Faculty Ratio:** 12:1 **Exams:** SAT I or ACT; SAT Reasoning; SAT Subject. **% Receiving Financial Aid:** 74 **% Residing in College-Owned, -Operated, or -Affiliated Housing:** 94 **Final Year or Final Semester Residency Requirement:** Yes **Regional Accreditation:** North Central Association of

Colleges and Schools **Credit Hours For Degree:** 128 semester hours, Bachelors **Professional Accreditation:** NASM. **Intercollegiate Athletics:** Baseball M; Basketball M & W; Cross-Country Running M & W; Equestrian Sports M & W; Football M; Golf M & W; Lacrosse M & W; Soccer M & W; Softball W; Swimming and Diving M & W; Tennis M & W; Track and Field M & W; Volleyball W

ALMA COLLEGE
614 W Superior St.
Alma, MI 48801-1599
Tel: (989)463-7111; Free: 800-321-ALMA
Fax: (989)463-7057
E-mail: admissions@alma.edu
Web Site: www.alma.edu
President/CEO: Dr. Jeff Abernathy
Admissions: Craig Aimar
Financial Aid: Michelle L. McNier
Type: Four-Year College **Sex:** Coed **Affiliation:** Presbyterian. **Scores:** 100% SAT V 400+; 100% SAT M 400+; 48% ACT 18-23; 45% ACT 24-29 **% Accepted:** 68 **Application Deadline:** Rolling **Application Fee:** $25.00 **H.S. Requirements:** High school diploma required; GED accepted **Costs Per Year:** Application fee: $25. Comprehensive fee: $45,628 includes full-time tuition ($35,386), mandatory fees ($420), and college room and board ($9822). College room only: $4911. Full-time tuition and fees vary according to student level. Room and board charges vary according to board plan and housing facility. Part-time tuition: $1100 per credit hour. Part-time tuition varies according to course load and student level. **Scholarships:** Available. **Calendar System:** Miscellaneous, Summer session not available **Enrollment:** Full-time 1,335, Part-time 50 **Faculty:** Full-time 96, Part-time 71 **Student-Faculty Ratio:** 11:1 **Exams:** ACT essay component not used; SAT I or ACT; SAT essay component not used; SAT Reasoning. **% Receiving Financial Aid:** 83 **% Residing in College-Owned, -Operated, or -Affiliated Housing:** 88 **Final Year or Final Semester Residency Requirement:** No **Regional Accreditation:** North Central Association of Colleges and Schools **Credit Hours For Degree:** 136 credits, Bachelors **ROTC:** Army **Professional Accreditation:** NASM. **Intercollegiate Athletics:** Baseball M; Basketball M & W; Bowling W; Cheerleading M & W; Equestrian Sports W; Football M; Golf M & W; Lacrosse M & W; Soccer M & W; Softball W; Swimming and Diving M & W; Tennis M & W; Track and Field M & W; Volleyball W; Wrestling M

ALPENA COMMUNITY COLLEGE
665 Johnson St.
Alpena, MI 49707-1495
Tel: (989)356-9021
Fax: (989)358-7553
E-mail: kollienm@alpenacc.edu
Web Site: www.alpenacc.edu
President/CEO: Fr. Olin Joynton
Admissions: Mike Kollien
Financial Aid: Robert Roose
Type: Two-Year College **Sex:** Coed **% Accepted:** 100 **Admission Plans:** Deferred Admission; Early Admission; Open Admission **Application Deadline:** Rolling **Application Fee:** $0.00. **H.S. Requirements:** High school diploma or equivalent not required. For nursing, utility technician programs:

High school diploma required; GED accepted **Costs Per Year:** Application fee: $0. Area resident tuition: $2880 full-time, $120 per contact hour part-time. State resident tuition: $4536 full-time, $189 per contact hour part-time. Nonresident tuition: $4536 full-time, $189 per contact hour part-time. Mandatory fees: $444 full-time, $16 per contact hour part-time, $30 per term part-time. College room only: $3500. **Scholarships:** Available. **Calendar System:** Semester, Summer session available **Faculty:** Full-time 55, Part-time 70 **Student-Faculty Ratio:** 17:1 **% Residing in College-Owned, -Operated, or -Affiliated Housing:** 2 **Regional Accreditation:** North Central Association of Colleges and Schools **Credit Hours For Degree:** 60 semester hours, Associates **Professional Accreditation:** AAMAE. **Intercollegiate Athletics:** Basketball M & W; Cross-Country Running M; Softball W; Volleyball W

ANDREWS UNIVERSITY

Berrien Springs, MI 49104
Tel: (269)471-7771; Free: 800-253-2874
Fax: (269)471-3228
E-mail: enroll@andrews.edu
Web Site: www.andrews.edu
President/CEO: Dr. Niels-Erik Andreasen
Admissions: Shanna Leak
Financial Aid: Cynthia Gammon

Type: University **Sex:** Coed **Affiliation:** Seventh-day Adventist. **Scores:** 98% SAT V 400+; 99% SAT M 400+; 45% ACT 18-23; 36% ACT 24-29 **% Accepted:** 39 **Admission Plans:** Deferred Admission **Application Deadline:** Rolling **Application Fee:** $30.00 **H.S. Requirements:** High school diploma required; GED accepted **Costs Per Year:** Application fee: $30. Comprehensive fee: $35,532 includes full-time tuition ($26,128), mandatory fees ($872), and college room and board ($8532). College room only: $4432. Full-time tuition and fees vary according to course load. Room and board charges vary according to board plan. Part-time tuition: $1089 per credit hour. Part-time tuition varies according to course load. **Scholarships:** Available. **Calendar System:** Semester, Summer session available **Enrollment:** Full-time 1,415, Graduate full-time 837, Graduate part-time 796, Part-time 318 **Faculty:** Full-time 233, Part-time 67 **Student-Faculty Ratio:** 9:1 **Exams:** SAT I or ACT. **% Receiving Financial Aid:** 61 **% Residing in College-Owned, -Operated, or -Affiliated Housing:** 60 **Regional Accreditation:** North Central Association of Colleges and Schools **Credit Hours For Degree:** 62 semester hours, Associates; 124 semester hours, Bachelors **Professional Accreditation:** ABET, ACA, ACEN, AND, APTA, ATS, CSWE, NAACLS, NASM, NCATE.

AQUINAS COLLEGE

1607 Robinson Rd., SE
Grand Rapids, MI 49506-1799
Tel: (616)459-8281; Free: 800-678-9593
Fax: (616)459-2563
E-mail: admissions@aquinas.edu
Web Site: www.aquinas.edu
President/CEO: Dr. Juan R. Olivarez
Admissions: Rebecca Roberts
Financial Aid: Darcy Kampfschulte

Type: Comprehensive **Sex:** Coed **Affiliation:** Roman Catholic. **Scores:** 44.57% ACT 18-23; 46.52% ACT 24-29 **% Accepted:** 72 **Admission Plans:** Deferred Admission **Application Deadline:** Rolling **Application Fee:** $0.00 **H.S. Requirements:** High school diploma required; GED not accepted **Costs Per Year:** Application fee: $0. Comprehensive fee: $38,876 includes full-time tuition ($29,564), mandatory fees ($498), and college room and board ($8814). College room only: $4134. Full-time tuition and fees vary according to course load. Room and board charges vary according to board plan and housing facility. Part-time tuition: $498 per credit hour. Part-time tuition varies according to course load. **Scholarships:** Available. **Calendar System:** Semester, Summer session available **Enrollment:** Full-time 1,537, Graduate full-time 12, Graduate part-time 98, Part-time 155 **Faculty:** Full-time 86, Part-time 137 **Student-Faculty Ratio:** 13:1 **Exams:** SAT I or ACT; SAT II; SAT Reasoning. **% Receiving Financial Aid:** 80 **Final Year or Final Semester Residency Requirement:** No **Regional Accreditation:** North Central Association of Colleges and Schools **Credit Hours For Degree:** 64 credits, Associates; 124 credits, Bachelors **Professional Accreditation:** TEAC. **Intercollegiate Athletics:** Baseball M; Basketball M & W; Bowling M & W; Cheerleading W; Cross-Country Running M & W; Golf M & W; Ice Hockey M & W; Lacrosse M & W; Soccer M & W; Softball W; Tennis M & W; Track and Field M & W; Volleyball W

THE ART INSTITUTE OF MICHIGAN

28125 Cabot Dr.
Ste. 120
Novi, MI 48377
Tel: (248)675-3800; Free: 800-479-0087
Fax: (248)675-3830
Web Site: www.artinstitutes.edu/detroit
President/CEO: Anthony Amato

Type: Four-Year College **Sex:** Coed **Affiliation:** Education Management Corporation. **Regional Accreditation:** Southern Association of Colleges and Schools **Professional Accreditation:** ACF.

BAKER COLLEGE

Baker College System Headquarters
1050 W Bristol Rd.
Flint, MI 48507-5508
Tel: (810)766-4000; Free: 800-964-4299
Fax: (810)766-4049
E-mail: mark.heaton@baker.edu
Web Site: www.baker.edu
President/CEO: James Cummins
Admissions: Mark Heaton

Type: Comprehensive **Sex:** Coed **Affiliation:** The Baker College System. **% Accepted:** 100 **Admission Plans:** Deferred Admission; Early Admission; Open Admission **Application Deadline:** September 19 **Application Fee:** $20.00 **H.S. Requirements:** High school diploma required; GED accepted **Costs Per Year:** Application fee: $20. Tuition: $9000 full-time, $4500 per year part-time. Full-time tuition varies according to program. Part-time tuition varies according to program. College room only: $3000. **Calendar System:** Quarter, Summer session available **Enrollment:** Full-time 13,013, Graduate full-time 578, Part-time 11,086 **Faculty:** Full-time 2,170 **Student-Faculty Ratio:** 13:1 **Exams:** SAT I or ACT. **% Residing in College-Owned, -Operated, or -Affiliated Housing:** 8 **Regional Accreditation:** North Central Association of Colleges and Schools **Credit Hours For Degree:** 90 quarter hours, Associates; 180 quarter hours, Bachelors **Professional Accreditation:** AAMAE, ABET, AHIMA, APTA, ARCST.

BAY MILLS COMMUNITY COLLEGE

12214 W Lakeshore Dr.
Brimley, MI 49715
Tel: (906)248-3354; Free: 800-844-BMCC
Fax: (906)248-3351
Web Site: www.bmcc.edu
President/CEO: Michael C. Parish
Admissions: Elaine Lehre
Financial Aid: Tina Miller

Type: Two-Year College **Sex:** Coed **Admission Plans:** Early Admission; Open Admission **Application Deadline:** Rolling **H.S. Requirements:** High school diploma required; GED accepted **Scholarships:** Available. **Calendar System:** Semester **Regional Accreditation:** North Central Association of Colleges and Schools **Credit Hours For Degree:** 63 credits, Associates

BAY DE NOC COMMUNITY COLLEGE

2001 N Lincoln Rd.
Escanaba, MI 49829-2511
Tel: (906)786-5802; Free: 800-221-2001
Fax: (906)786-6555
E-mail: carterc@baycollege.edu
Web Site: www.baycollege.edu
President/CEO: Dr. Laura Coleman
Admissions: Cindy Carter
Financial Aid: Susan Hebert

Type: Two-Year College **Sex:** Coed **Affiliation:** Michigan Department of Education. **Admission Plans:** Early Admission; Open Admission **Application Deadline:** August 15 **Application Fee:** $25.00 **H.S. Requirements:** High school diploma required; GED accepted **Scholarships:** Available. **Calendar System:** Semester, Summer session available **Enrollment:** Full-time 1,400, Part-time 1,014 **Faculty:** Full-time 46, Part-time 117 **Student-Faculty Ratio:** 20:1 **% Residing in College-Owned, -Operated, or -Affiliated Housing:** 4 **Regional Accreditation:** North Central Association of Colleges and Schools **Credit Hours For Degree:** 62 credit hours, Associates **Professional Accreditation:** ACEN.

CALVIN COLLEGE
3201 Burton St., SE
Grand Rapids, MI 49546-4388
Tel: (616)526-6000; Free: 800-688-0122
Fax: (616)526-8551
E-mail: admissions@calvin.edu
Web Site: www.calvin.edu
President/CEO: Dr. Michael K. Le Roy
Admissions: Dr. Ben Arendt
Financial Aid: Craig Heerema
Type: Comprehensive **Sex:** Coed **Affiliation:** Christian Reformed. **Scores:** 98% SAT V 400+; 99% SAT M 400+; 25% ACT 18-23; 45.1% ACT 24-29 **% Accepted:** 74 **Admission Plans:** Deferred Admission **Application Deadline:** August 15 **Application Fee:** $35.00 **H.S. Requirements:** High school diploma required; GED accepted **Costs Per Year:** Application fee: $35. Comprehensive fee: $40,350 includes full-time tuition ($30,425), mandatory fees ($235), and college room and board ($9690). Full-time tuition and fees vary according to degree level, program, and student level. Room and board charges vary according to board plan and housing facility. Part-time tuition: $730 per credit hour. Part-time tuition varies according to course load, degree level, and student level. **Scholarships:** Available. **Calendar System:** 4-1-4, Summer session available **Enrollment:** Full-time 3,713, Graduate full-time 44, Graduate part-time 77, Part-time 156 **Faculty:** Full-time 262, Part-time 96 **Student-Faculty Ratio:** 13:1 **Exams:** SAT I or ACT; SAT Reasoning. **% Receiving Financial Aid:** 63 **% Residing in College-Owned, -Operated, or -Affiliated Housing:** 59 **Final Year or Final Semester Residency Requirement:** No **Regional Accreditation:** North Central Association of Colleges and Schools **Credit Hours For Degree:** 124 semester hours, Bachelors **ROTC:** Army **Professional Accreditation:** AACN, ABET, CSWE, NASM, TEAC. **Intercollegiate Athletics:** Baseball M; Basketball M & W; Cross-Country Running M & W; Equestrian Sports M & W; Golf M & W; Ice Hockey M; Lacrosse M & W; Rugby M & W; Soccer M & W; Softball W; Swimming and Diving M & W; Tennis M & W; Track and Field M & W; Ultimate Frisbee M & W; Volleyball M & W

CENTRAL MICHIGAN UNIVERSITY
Mount Pleasant, MI 48859
Tel: (989)774-4000; Free: 888-292-5366
Fax: (989)774-3537
E-mail: cmuadmit@cmich.edu
Web Site: www.cmich.edu
President/CEO: Dr. George Ross
Financial Aid: Kirk M. Yats
Type: University **Sex:** Coed **Scores:** 97% SAT V 400+; 93% SAT M 400+; 56.1% ACT 18-23; 34.5% ACT 24-29 **% Accepted:** 69 **Admission Plans:** Deferred Admission; Early Admission; Early Decision Plan **Application Deadline:** July 1 **Application Fee:** $35.00 **H.S. Requirements:** High school diploma required; GED accepted **Costs Per Year:** Application fee: $35. State resident tuition: $11,850 full-time, $395 per credit hour part-time. Nonresident tuition: $23,670 full-time, $789 per credit hour part-time. Full-time tuition varies according to location. Part-time tuition varies according to location. College room and board: $9088. College room only: $4544. Room and board charges vary according to board plan and housing facility. **Scholarships:** Available. **Calendar System:** Semester, Summer session available **Enrollment:** Full-time 17,709, Graduate full-time 2,097, Graduate part-time 4,373, Part-time 2,789 **Faculty:** Full-time 798, Part-time 338 **Student-Faculty Ratio:** 20:1 **Exams:** ACT; ACT essay component used for advising; ACT essay component used for placement; SAT I or ACT; SAT essay component used for advising; SAT essay component used for placement; SAT Reasoning. **% Receiving Financial Aid:** 60 **% Residing in College-Owned, -Operated, or -Affiliated Housing:** 34 **Final Year or Final Semester Residency Requirement:** No **Regional Accreditation:** North Central Association of Colleges and Schools **Credit Hours For Degree:** 124 credits, Bachelors **ROTC:** Air Force, Army **Professional Accreditation:** AACSB, ABET, ACEJMC, AND, APA, APTA, ASHA, CSWE, JRCAT, NASAD, NASM, NASPAA, NCATE, NRPA, TEAC. **Intercollegiate Athletics:** Baseball M; Basketball M & W; Cross-Country Running M & W; Field Hockey W; Football M; Golf W; Gymnastics W; Lacrosse W; Soccer W; Softball W; Track and Field M & W; Volleyball W; Wrestling M

CHAMBERLAIN COLLEGE OF NURSING
200 Kirts Blvd.
Ste. C
Troy, MI 48084
Tel: (248)817-4140; Free: 877-751-5783
Fax: (248)817-4237
Web Site: www.chamberlain.edu
Type: Four-Year College **Sex:** Coed **Application Fee:** $95.00 **H.S. Requirements:** High school diploma required; GED accepted **Costs Per Year:** Application fee: $95. Tuition: $17,560 full-time, $665 per credit hour part-time. Mandatory fees: $600 full-time, $300 per term part-time. **Exams:** ACT essay component used for admission; SAT I or ACT; SAT essay component used for admission. **Regional Accreditation:** North Central Association of Colleges and Schools

CLEARY UNIVERSITY
3750 Cleary Dr.
Howell, MI 48843
Tel: (517)548-3670; Free: 800-686-1883
E-mail: admissions@cleary.edu
Web Site: www.cleary.edu
President/CEO: Jayson Boyers
Admissions: Eric Brown
Financial Aid: Vesta Smith-Campbell
Type: Comprehensive **Sex:** Coed **Scores:** 50% ACT 18-23; 27% ACT 24-29 **% Accepted:** 48 **Admission Plans:** Deferred Admission; Early Admission **Application Deadline:** July 15 **Application Fee:** $35.00 **H.S. Requirements:** High school diploma required; GED accepted. For for honors track: High school diploma required; GED not accepted **Scholarships:** Available. **Calendar System:** Semester, Summer session available **Enrollment:** Full-time 268, Graduate full-time 69, Graduate part-time 17, Part-time 350 **Faculty:** Part-time 78 **Student-Faculty Ratio:** 15:1 **Exams:** SAT I or ACT; SAT II. **Final Year or Final Semester Residency Requirement:** Yes **Regional Accreditation:** North Central Association of Colleges and Schools **Credit Hours For Degree:** 60 credits, Associates; 120 credits, Bachelors **Intercollegiate Athletics:** Cross-Country Running M & W; Golf M & W; Soccer M & W; Softball W

COLLEGE FOR CREATIVE STUDIES
201 E Kirby
Detroit, MI 48202-4034
Tel: (313)664-7400; Free: 800-952-ARTS
Fax: (313)872-2739
E-mail: admissions@collegeforcreativestudies.edu
Web Site: www.collegeforcreativestudies.edu
President/CEO: Richard L. Rogers
Type: Comprehensive **Sex:** Coed **% Accepted:** 46 **Admission Plans:** Deferred Admission; Early Decision Plan **Application Fee:** $35.00 **H.S. Requirements:** High school diploma required; GED accepted **Costs Per Year:** Application fee: $35. Comprehensive fee: $47,400 includes full-time tuition ($37,560), mandatory fees ($1390), and college room and board ($8450). College room only: $5550. Room and board charges vary according to board plan and housing facility. Part-time tuition: $1252 per credit hour. **Scholarships:** Available. **Calendar System:** Semester **Enrollment:** Full-time 1,120, Graduate full-time 51, Graduate part-time 7, Part-time 281 **Faculty:** Full-time 48, Part-time 241 **Student-Faculty Ratio:** 9:1 **Exams:** ACT essay component used for advising; ACT essay component used for placement; SAT I or ACT; SAT essay component used for advising; SAT essay component used for placement. **% Residing in College-Owned, -Operated, or -Affiliated Housing:** 38 **Regional Accreditation:** North Central Association of Colleges and Schools **Credit Hours For Degree:** 126 credit hours, Bachelors **Professional Accreditation:** NASAD.

COMPASS COLLEGE OF CINEMATIC ARTS
41 Sheldon Blvd. SE
Grand Rapids, MI 49503
Tel: (616)988-1000
Web Site: www.compass.edu
Type: Four-Year College **Sex:** Coed **Professional Accreditation:** ACCSC.

CONCORDIA UNIVERSITY ANN ARBOR
4090 Geddes Rd.
Ann Arbor, MI 48105-2797
Tel: (734)995-7300; Free: 877-955-7520
Fax: (734)995-4610
E-mail: admissions@cuaa.edu
Web Site: www.cuaa.edu
President/CEO: Dr. Russell L. Nichols

Admissions: Ben Limback

Financial Aid: Steven P. Taylor

Type: Comprehensive **Sex:** Coed **Affiliation:** Lutheran Church–Missouri Synod; Concordia University System. **Scores:** 62% ACT 18-23; 20.4% ACT 24-29 **% Accepted:** 56 **Admission Plans:** Deferred Admission **Application Deadline:** Rolling **Application Fee:** $25.00 **H.S. Requirements:** High school diploma required; GED accepted **Costs Per Year:** Application fee: $25. Comprehensive fee: $36,210 includes full-time tuition ($26,840), mandatory fees ($70), and college room and board ($9300). College room only: $6900. Full-time tuition and fees vary according to course load, degree level, location, and program. Room and board charges vary according to housing facility. Part-time tuition: $1119 per credit hour. Part-time tuition varies according to course load, degree level, location, and program. **Scholarships:** Available. **Calendar System:** Semester, Summer session available **Enrollment:** Full-time 474, Graduate full-time 127, Graduate part-time 75, Part-time 35 **Faculty:** Full-time 28, Part-time 96 **Student-Faculty Ratio:** 11:1 **Exams:** ACT; SAT I or ACT; SAT Reasoning; SAT Subject. **% Receiving Financial Aid:** 88 **% Residing in College-Owned, -Operated, or -Affiliated Housing:** 79 **Regional Accreditation:** North Central Association of Colleges and Schools **Credit Hours For Degree:** 60 credit hours, Associates; 128 credit hours, Bachelors **ROTC:** Air Force, Army **Professional Accreditation:** NCATE. **Intercollegiate Athletics:** Baseball M; Basketball M & W; Bowling M & W; Cheerleading W; Cross-Country Running M & W; Football M; Golf M & W; Soccer M & W; Softball W; Track and Field M & W; Volleyball W

CORNERSTONE UNIVERSITY

1001 E Beltline Ave., NE

Grand Rapids, MI 49525-5897

Tel: (616)949-5300; Free: 800-787-9778

Fax: (616)222-1540

E-mail: admissions@cornerstone.edu

Web Site: www.cornerstone.edu

President/CEO: Dr. Joseph Stowell, III

Admissions: Lisa Link

Financial Aid: Carol S. Carpenter

Type: Comprehensive **Sex:** Coed **Affiliation:** nondenominational. **Scores:** 95% SAT V 400+; 92% SAT M 400+; 45.5% ACT 18-23; 41.8% ACT 24-29 **% Accepted:** 73 **Application Deadline:** Rolling **Application Fee:** $0.00 **H.S. Requirements:** High school diploma required; GED accepted **Costs Per Year:** Application fee: $0. Comprehensive fee: $34,660 includes full-time tuition ($25,530), mandatory fees ($570), and college room and board ($8560). Full-time tuition and fees vary according to course load and reciprocity agreements. Room and board charges vary according to board plan and housing facility. Part-time tuition: $980 per credit hour. Part-time mandatory fees: $185 per term. Part-time tuition and fees vary according to course load. **Scholarships:** Available. **Calendar System:** Semester, Summer session available **Enrollment:** Full-time 1,486, Graduate full-time 201, Graduate part-time 346, Part-time 539 **Faculty:** Full-time 69, Part-time 337 **Student-Faculty Ratio:** 18:1 **Exams:** ACT essay component used for placement; SAT I or ACT; SAT Reasoning; SAT Subject. **% Receiving Financial Aid:** 82 **% Residing in College-Owned, -Operated, or -Affiliated Housing:** 60 **Final Year or Final Semester Residency Requirement:** No **Regional Accreditation:** North Central Association of Colleges and Schools **Credit Hours For Degree:** 64 credit hours, Associates; 120 credit hours, Bachelors **ROTC:** Army **Professional Accreditation:** CSWE, NASM. **Intercollegiate Athletics:** Baseball M; Basketball M & W; Bowling M & W; Cheerleading W; Cross-Country Running M & W; Golf M & W; Soccer M & W; Softball W; Track and Field M & W; Volleyball W

DAVENPORT UNIVERSITY

6191 Kraft Ave. SE

Grand Rapids, MI 49512

Tel: (616)698-7111; Free: 866-686-1600

Fax: (616)554-5214

E-mail: amy.lucas@davenport.edu

Web Site: www.davenport.edu

President/CEO: Dr. Richard Pappas

Admissions: Amy Lucas

Financial Aid: David DeBoer

Type: Comprehensive **Sex:** Coed **Admission Plans:** Deferred Admission **Application Deadline:** Rolling **Application Fee:** $25.00 **H.S. Requirements:** High school diploma required; GED accepted **Costs Per Year:** Application fee: $25. Comprehensive fee: $26,350 includes full-time tuition

($16,458), mandatory fees ($760), and college room and board ($9132). College room only: $4868. Full-time tuition and fees vary according to location and program. Room and board charges vary according to board plan and housing facility. **Scholarships:** Available. **Calendar System:** Semester, Summer session available **Enrollment:** Full-time 2,329, Graduate full-time 1,035, Graduate part-time 1,057, Part-time 4,002 **Faculty:** Full-time 138, Part-time 717 **Student-Faculty Ratio:** 14:1 **Exams:** ACT essay component not used; SAT I or ACT; SAT essay component not used. **% Residing in College-Owned, -Operated, or -Affiliated Housing:** 6 **Regional Accreditation:** North Central Association of Colleges and Schools **Credit Hours For Degree:** 60 credit hours, Associates; 120 credit hours, Bachelors **ROTC:** Army **Professional Accreditation:** AAMAE. **Intercollegiate Athletics:** Baseball M; Basketball M & W; Bowling M & W; Cheerleading W; Cross-Country Running M & W; Football M; Golf M & W; Ice Hockey M & W; Lacrosse M & W; Rugby M & W; Soccer M & W; Softball M & W; Tennis M & W; Track and Field M & W; Volleyball W

DELTA COLLEGE

1961 Delta Rd.

University Center, MI 48710

Tel: (989)686-9000

Fax: (989)686-8736

E-mail: admit@delta.edu

Web Site: www.delta.edu

President/CEO: Dr. Jean Goodnow

Admissions: Zachary Ward

Type: Two-Year College **Sex:** Coed **% Accepted:** 100 **Admission Plans:** Deferred Admission; Early Admission; Open Admission **Application Deadline:** Rolling **Application Fee:** $0.00 **H.S. Requirements:** High school diploma or equivalent not required. For international students: High school diploma required; GED accepted **Costs Per Year:** Application fee: $0. Area resident tuition: $2509 full-time, $96.50 per credit hour part-time. State resident tuition: $4134 full-time, $159 per credit hour part-time. Nonresident tuition: $8034 full-time, $309 per credit hour part-time. Mandatory fees: $80 full-time, $40 per term part-time. Full-time tuition and fees vary according to course load. Part-time tuition and fees vary according to course load. **Scholarships:** Available. **Calendar System:** Semester, Summer session available **Enrollment:** Full-time 3,432, Part-time 5,859 **Faculty:** Full-time 213, Part-time 318 **Student-Faculty Ratio:** 22:1 **Regional Accreditation:** North Central Association of Colleges and Schools **Credit Hours For Degree:** 62 credits, Associates **Professional Accreditation:** ABET, ACEN, ADA, APTA, ARCST, CoARC, JRCEDMS, JRCERT. **Intercollegiate Athletics:** Baseball M; Basketball M & W; Golf M; Soccer W; Softball W

EASTERN MICHIGAN UNIVERSITY

Ypsilanti, MI 48197

Tel: (734)487-1849; Free: 800-GO TO EMU

Fax: (734)487-1484

Web Site: www.emich.edu

President/CEO: Dr. Donald Loppnow

Admissions: Brian Selfridge

Financial Aid: Donna Holubik

Type: Comprehensive **Sex:** Coed **Scores:** 88% SAT V 400+; 92% SAT M 400+; 53.73% ACT 18-23; 31.53% ACT 24-29 **% Accepted:** 75 **Admission Plans:** Deferred Admission **Application Deadline:** Rolling **Application Fee:** $35.00 **H.S. Requirements:** High school diploma required; GED accepted **Costs Per Year:** Application fee: $35. One-time mandatory fee: $310. State resident tuition: $8,888 full-time, $296.25 per credit hour part-time. Nonresident tuition: $26,182 full-time, $872.75 per credit hour part-time. Mandatory fees: $1,530 full-time, $47.30 per credit hour part-time, $55 per term part-time. Full-time tuition and fees vary according to course level and reciprocity agreements. Part-time tuition and fees vary according to course level and reciprocity agreements. College room and board: $9398. College room only: $4863. Room and board charges vary according to board plan, housing facility, and location. **Scholarships:** Available. **Calendar System:** Semester, Summer session available **Enrollment:** Full-time 13,071, Graduate full-time 1,030, Graduate part-time 2,824, Part-time 4,709 **Faculty:** Full-time 753, Part-time 631 **Student-Faculty Ratio:** 17:1 **Exams:** ACT essay component not used; SAT I or ACT; SAT essay component not used. **% Receiving Financial Aid:** 69 **% Residing in College-Owned, -Operated, or -Affiliated Housing:** 22 **Final Year or Final Semester Residency Requirement:** No **Regional Accreditation:** North Central Association of Colleges and Schools **Credit Hours For Degree:** 124 semester hours, Bachelors **ROTC:** Air Force, Army, Navy **Professional Accreditation:**

AACN, AACSB, ACA, ACCE, ACEN, ACSP, AND, AOTA, ASHA, ATMAE, CIDA, CSWE, JRCAT, NAACLS, NASM, NASPAA, NCATE, NRPA. **Intercollegiate Athletics:** Baseball M; Basketball M & W; Crew W; Cross-Country Running M & W; Football M; Golf M & W; Gymnastics W; Soccer W; Softball W; Swimming and Diving M & W; Tennis W; Track and Field M & W; Volleyball W; Wrestling M

FERRIS STATE UNIVERSITY

1201 S State St.
Big Rapids, MI 49307
Tel: (231)591-2000; Free: 800-433-7747
Fax: (231)591-2978
E-mail: dadayja@ferris.edu
Web Site: www.ferris.edu
President/CEO: Dr. David Eisler
Admissions: Jason Daday
Financial Aid: Nancy Wencl
Type: Comprehensive **Sex:** Coed **Scores:** 52.6% ACT 18-23; 27.5% ACT 24-29 **% Accepted:** 78 **Application Deadline:** August 1 **Application Fee:** $30.00 **H.S. Requirements:** High school diploma required; GED accepted **Costs Per Year:** Application fee: $30. One-time mandatory fee: $162. State resident tuition: $11,460 full-time, $382 per credit hour part-time. Nonresident tuition: $17,190 full-time, $573 per credit hour part-time. Full-time tuition varies according to location, program, and student level. Part-time tuition varies according to location and student level. College room and board: $9434. Room and board charges vary according to board plan and housing facility. **Scholarships:** Available. **Calendar System:** Semester, Summer session available **Enrollment:** Full-time 9,103, Graduate full-time 945, Graduate part-time 447, Part-time 4,220 **Student-Faculty Ratio:** 16:1 **Exams:** SAT I or ACT; SAT Reasoning. **% Receiving Financial Aid:** 71 **% Residing in College-Owned, -Operated, or -Affiliated Housing:** 26 **Final Year or Final Semester Residency Requirement:** Yes **Regional Accreditation:** North Central Association of Colleges and Schools **ROTC:** Army **Professional Accreditation:** ABET, ACBSP, ACCE, ACEN, ACPE, ADA, AHIMA, AOA, CSWE, CoARC, JRCERT, JRCNMT, NAACLS, NASAD, NCATE, NRPA, TEAC. **Intercollegiate Athletics:** Basketball M & W; Cross-Country Running M & W; Football M; Golf M & W; Ice Hockey M; Soccer W; Softball W; Tennis M & W; Track and Field M & W; Volleyball W

FINLANDIA UNIVERSITY

601 Quincy St.
Hancock, MI 49930-1882
Tel: (906)482-5300; Free: 877-202-5491
Fax: (906)487-7300
E-mail: admissions@finlandia.edu
Web Site: www.finlandia.edu
President/CEO: Dr. Philip Johnson
Admissions: Martin Kinard
Financial Aid: Sandra Turnquist
Type: Four-Year College **Sex:** Coed **Affiliation:** Evangelical Lutheran Church in America. **Scores:** 51% ACT 18-23; 21% ACT 24-29 **% Accepted:** 67 **Admission Plans:** Early Admission **Application Deadline:** August 25 **Application Fee:** $30.00 **H.S. Requirements:** High school diploma required; GED accepted **Scholarships:** Available. **Calendar System:** Semester, Summer session available **Enrollment:** Full-time 485, Part-time 60 **Faculty:** Full-time 42, Part-time 28 **Student-Faculty Ratio:** 10:1 **Exams:** SAT I or ACT. **% Residing in College-Owned, -Operated, or -Affiliated Housing:** 24 **Regional Accreditation:** North Central Association of Colleges and Schools **Credit Hours For Degree:** 60 credits, Associates; 129 credits, Bachelors **ROTC:** Air Force, Army **Professional Accreditation:** AACN, APTA. **Intercollegiate Athletics:** Baseball M; Basketball M & W; Cross-Country Running M & W; Ice Hockey M & W; Soccer M & W; Softball W; Volleyball W

GLEN OAKS COMMUNITY COLLEGE

62249 Shimmel Rd.
Centreville, MI 49032-9719
Tel: (269)467-9945; Free: 888-994-7818
Fax: (269)467-9068
E-mail: thowden@glenoaks.edu
Web Site: www.glenoaks.edu
President/CEO: Dr. David H. Devier
Admissions: Beverly M. Andrews
Type: Two-Year College **Sex:** Coed **Admission Plans:** Open Admission **Ap-**

plication Deadline: Rolling **Application Fee:** $0.00 **H.S. Requirements:** High school diploma or equivalent not required **Scholarships:** Available. **Calendar System:** Semester, Summer session available **Enrollment:** Full-time 531, Part-time 690 **Student-Faculty Ratio:** 16:1 **Regional Accreditation:** North Central Association of Colleges and Schools **Credit Hours For Degree:** 62 credit hours, Associates **Intercollegiate Athletics:** Baseball M; Basketball M & W; Golf M; Softball W; Track and Field M & W

GOGEBIC COMMUNITY COLLEGE

E-4946 Jackson Rd.
Ironwood, MI 49938
Tel: (906)932-4231; Free: 800-682-5910
Fax: (906)932-5541
E-mail: jeanneg@gogebic.edu
Web Site: www.gogebic.edu
President/CEO: James Lorenson
Admissions: Kim Zeckovich
Type: Two-Year College **Sex:** Coed **Affiliation:** Michigan Department of Education. **Admission Plans:** Deferred Admission; Early Admission; Open Admission **Application Deadline:** Rolling **Application Fee:** $10.00 **H.S. Requirements:** High school diploma required; GED accepted **Costs Per Year:** Application fee: $10. Area resident tuition: $3286 full-time, $106 per credit hour part-time. State resident tuition: $4650 full-time, $150 per credit hour part-time. Nonresident tuition: $5549 full-time, $179 per credit hour part-time. Mandatory fees: $1058 full-time, $10 per credit hour part-time. Full-time tuition and fees vary according to course load, program, and reciprocity agreements. Part-time tuition and fees vary according to course load and reciprocity agreements. College room and board: $6704. College room only: $4004. **Scholarships:** Available. **Calendar System:** Semester, Summer session available **Enrollment:** Full-time 647, Part-time 552 **Regional Accreditation:** North Central Association of Colleges and Schools **Credit Hours For Degree:** 63 credit hours, Associates **Professional Accreditation:** AHIMA. **Intercollegiate Athletics:** Basketball M & W; Cross-Country Running M & W; Skiing (Cross-Country) M & W; Volleyball W

GRACE BIBLE COLLEGE

1011 Aldon St. SW
Grand Rapids, MI 49509-0910
Tel: (616)538-2330; Free: 800-968-1887
Fax: (616)538-0599
E-mail: gbc@gbcol.edu
Web Site: www.gbcol.edu
President/CEO: Kenneth B. Kemper
Admissions: Kevin Gilliam
Financial Aid: Kurt Postma
Type: Four-Year College **Sex:** Coed **Affiliation:** Grace Gospel Fellowship. **Scores:** 87% SAT V 400+; 71% SAT M 400+; 44% ACT 18-23; 15% ACT 24-29 **% Accepted:** 34 **Admission Plans:** Deferred Admission; Early Admission **Application Deadline:** July 15 **Application Fee:** $0.00 **H.S. Requirements:** High school diploma required; GED accepted **Costs Per Year:** Application fee: $0. Comprehensive fee: $25,250 includes full-time tuition ($17,850) and college room and board ($7400). College room only: $3450. Room and board charges vary according to board plan and housing facility. Part-time tuition: $595 per credit hour. Part-time tuition varies according to course load. **Scholarships:** Available. **Calendar System:** Semester, Summer session not available **Enrollment:** Full-time 192, Part-time 15 **Faculty:** Full-time 7, Part-time 14 **Student-Faculty Ratio:** 17:1 **Exams:** SAT I and SAT II or ACT. **% Receiving Financial Aid:** 89 **% Residing in College-Owned, -Operated, or -Affiliated Housing:** 53 **Final Year or Final Semester Residency Requirement:** No **Regional Accreditation:** North Central Association of Colleges and Schools **Credit Hours For Degree:** 64 semester hours, Associates; 124 semester hours, Bachelors **ROTC:** Army **Professional Accreditation:** ABHE. **Intercollegiate Athletics:** Basketball M & W; Cross-Country Running M & W; Soccer M & W; Tennis M & W; Volleyball W

GRAND RAPIDS COMMUNITY COLLEGE

143 Bostwick Ave., NE
Grand Rapids, MI 49503-3201
Tel: (616)234-4000
Fax: (616)234-4005
E-mail: dpatrick@grcc.edu
Web Site: www.grcc.edu
President/CEO: Dr. Steven Ender

Admissions: Diane Patrick

Type: Two-Year College **Sex:** Coed **Affiliation:** Michigan Department of Education. **Scores:** 53% ACT 18-23; 17% ACT 24-29 **Admission Plans:** Deferred Admission; Early Admission; Open Admission **Application Deadline:** August 30 **Application Fee:** $0.00 **H.S. Requirements:** High school diploma required; GED accepted **Costs Per Year:** Application fee: $0. Area resident tuition: $3240 full-time, $108 per contact hour part-time. State resident tuition: $6960 full-time, $232 per contact hour part-time. Nonresident tuition: $10,320 full-time, $344 per contact hour part-time. Mandatory fees: $459 full-time, $15 per contact hour part-time, $90 per term part-time. Full-time tuition and fees vary according to course load and program. Part-time tuition and fees vary according to course load and program. **Scholarships:** Available. **Calendar System:** Semester, Summer session available **Enrollment:** Full-time 4,493, Part-time 10,433 **Faculty:** Full-time 245, Part-time 669 **Student-Faculty Ratio:** 21:1 **Exams:** SAT I or ACT. **Final Year or Final Semester Residency Requirement:** No **Regional Accreditation:** North Central Association of Colleges and Schools **Credit Hours For Degree:** 62 credits, Associates **Professional Accreditation:** ACEN, ACF, ADA, AOTA, JRCERT, NASAD, NASM. **Intercollegiate Athletics:** Baseball M; Basketball M & W; Cross-Country Running M & W; Golf M; Softball W; Volleyball W

GRAND VALLEY STATE UNIVERSITY

1 Campus Dr.
Allendale, MI 49401-9403
Tel: (616)331-5000; Free: 800-748-0246
Fax: (616)331-2000
E-mail: go2gvsu@gvsu.edu
Web Site: www.gvsu.edu
President/CEO: Dr. Thomas J. Haas
Admissions: Jodi Chycinski
Financial Aid: Michelle Rhodes

Type: Comprehensive **Sex:** Coed **Scores:** 47.92% ACT 18-23; 42.62% ACT 24-29 **% Accepted:** 81 **Application Deadline:** May 1 **Application Fee:** $30.00 **H.S. Requirements:** High school diploma required; GED accepted **Costs Per Year:** Application fee: $30. State resident tuition: $11,078 full-time, $462 per credit hour part-time. Nonresident tuition: $15,744 full-time, $656 per credit hour part-time. Full-time tuition varies according to course load, program, and student level. Part-time tuition varies according to course load, program, and student level. College room and board: $8360. Room and board charges vary according to board plan and housing facility. **Scholarships:** Available. **Calendar System:** Semester, Summer session available **Enrollment:** Full-time 19,377, Graduate full-time 1,405, Graduate part-time 1,948, Part-time 2,595 **Faculty:** Full-time 1,137, Part-time 612 **Student-Faculty Ratio:** 17:1 **Exams:** ACT essay component used for advising; ACT essay component used for placement; SAT I or ACT; SAT essay component used for advising; SAT essay component used for placement. **% Receiving Financial Aid:** 59 **% Residing in College-Owned, -Operated, or -Affiliated Housing:** 28 **Regional Accreditation:** North Central Association of Colleges and Schools **Credit Hours For Degree:** 120 semester hours, Bachelors **Professional Accreditation:** AACN, AACSB, ABET, AOTA, APA, APTA, CSWE, JRCAT, NAACLS, NASAD, NASM, NASPAA, NCATE. **Intercollegiate Athletics:** Baseball M; Basketball M & W; Cheerleading M & W; Crew M & W; Cross-Country Running M & W; Football M; Golf M & W; Ice Hockey M; Lacrosse M & W; Rugby M & W; Sailing M & W; Skiing (Downhill) M & W; Soccer M & W; Softball W; Swimming and Diving M & W; Tennis M & W; Track and Field M & W; Volleyball M & W; Water Polo M & W; Wrestling M

GREAT LAKES CHRISTIAN COLLEGE

6211 W Willow Hwy.
Lansing, MI 48917-1299
Tel: (517)321-0242; Free: 800-YES-GLCC
Fax: (517)321-5902
E-mail: jcarter@glcc.edu
Web Site: www.glcc.edu
President/CEO: Lawrence L. Carter
Admissions: Judy Carter

Type: Four-Year College **Sex:** Coed **Affiliation:** Christian Churches and Churches of Christ. **Scores:** 60% ACT 18-23; 17% ACT 24-29 **Application Deadline:** August 1 **Application Fee:** $30.00 **H.S. Requirements:** High school diploma required; GED accepted **Calendar System:** Semester, Summer session not available **Enrollment:** Full-time 166, Part-time 59 **Faculty:** Full-time 10, Part-time 13 **Student-Faculty Ratio:** 10:1 **Exams:** SAT I or

ACT. **Final Year or Final Semester Residency Requirement:** No **Regional Accreditation:** North Central Association of Colleges and Schools **Credit Hours For Degree:** 64 semester hours, Associates; 130 semester hours, Bachelors **Professional Accreditation:** ABHE. **Intercollegiate Athletics:** Basketball M & W; Soccer M; Volleyball W

HENRY FORD COLLEGE

5101 Evergreen Rd.
Dearborn, MI 48128-1495
Tel: (313)845-9615; Free: 800-585-HFCC
Fax: (313)845-9658
E-mail: enroll@hfcc.edu
Web Site: www.hfcc.edu
President/CEO: Gail Mee

Type: Two-Year College **Sex:** Coed **Admission Plans:** Deferred Admission; Early Admission; Open Admission **Application Deadline:** Rolling **Application Fee:** $30.00 **H.S. Requirements:** High school diploma required; GED accepted **Scholarships:** Available. **Calendar System:** Semester, Summer session available **Student-Faculty Ratio:** 24:1 **Regional Accreditation:** North Central Association of Colleges and Schools **Credit Hours For Degree:** 60 credit hours, Associates **Professional Accreditation:** ACEN, ACF, AHIMA, APTA, ARCST, CoARC. **Intercollegiate Athletics:** Basketball M & W; Golf M; Softball W; Volleyball W

HILLSDALE COLLEGE

33 E College St.
Hillsdale, MI 49242-1298
Tel: (517)437-7341
Fax: (517)437-0190
E-mail: admissions@hillsdale.edu
Web Site: www.hillsdale.edu
President/CEO: Dr. Larry Arnn
Admissions: Douglas Banbury
Financial Aid: Rich Moeggengberg

Type: Comprehensive **Sex:** Coed **Scores:** 100% SAT V 400+; 100% SAT M 400+; 2% ACT 18-23; 47% ACT 24-29 **% Accepted:** 50 **Admission Plans:** Early Action; Early Admission; Early Decision Plan **Application Deadline:** April 1 **Application Fee:** $35.00 **H.S. Requirements:** High school diploma required; GED accepted **Costs Per Year:** Application fee: $35. One-time mandatory fee: $300. Comprehensive fee: $34,352 includes full-time tuition ($23,840), mandatory fees ($752), and college room and board ($9760). College room only: $4800. Full-time tuition and fees vary according to degree level. Room and board charges vary according to board plan. Part-time tuition: $950 per credit. Part-time mandatory fees: $85 per credit, $751 per year. Part-time tuition and fees vary according to degree level. **Scholarships:** Available. **Calendar System:** Semester, Summer session available **Enrollment:** Full-time 1,451, Graduate full-time 35, Graduate part-time 1, Part-time 39 **Faculty:** Full-time 135, Part-time 49 **Student-Faculty Ratio:** 10:1 **Exams:** ACT essay component used for admission; ACT essay component used for advising; ACT essay component used for placement; SAT I or ACT; SAT II; SAT essay component used for admission; SAT essay component used for advising; SAT essay component used for placement; SAT Reasoning; SAT Subject. **% Receiving Financial Aid:** 50 **% Residing in College-Owned, -Operated, or -Affiliated Housing:** 71 **Final Year or Final Semester Residency Requirement:** Yes **Regional Accreditation:** North Central Association of Colleges and Schools **Credit Hours For Degree:** 124 credit hours, Bachelors **Intercollegiate Athletics:** Baseball M; Basketball M & W; Cheerleading W; Crew M & W; Cross-Country Running M & W; Equestrian Sports M & W; Football M; Golf M; Riflery M & W; Rugby M; Soccer M & W; Softball W; Swimming and Diving M & W; Tennis M & W; Track and Field M & W; Volleyball M & W

HOPE COLLEGE

141 E 12th St.
Holland, MI 49422-9000
Tel: (616)395-7000; Free: 800-968-7850
Fax: (616)395-7130
E-mail: admissions@hope.edu
Web Site: www.hope.edu
President/CEO: Dr. John C. Knapp
Financial Aid: Jill Nutt

Type: Four-Year College **Sex:** Coed **Affiliation:** Reformed Church in America. **Scores:** 98% SAT V 400+; 100% SAT M 400+; 23.87% ACT 18-23; 53.98% ACT 24-29 **% Accepted:** 72 **Admission Plans:** Deferred Admission; Early Admission **Application Deadline:** Rolling **Application Fee:** $35.00 **H.S. Requirements:** High school diploma required; GED accepted **Costs Per Year:** Application fee: $35. Comprehensive fee: $41,250 includes full-time tuition ($31,380), mandatory fees ($180), and college room and board ($9690). College room only: $4450. Room and board charges vary according to board plan. Part-time tuition: $1207 per semester hour. Part-time tuition varies according to course load and program. **Scholarships:** Available. **Calendar System:** Semester, Summer session available **Enrollment:** Full-time 3,216, Part-time 160 **Faculty:** Full-time 244, Part-time 139 **Student-Faculty Ratio:** 11:1 **Exams:** ACT essay component not used; SAT I or ACT; SAT essay component not used; SAT Reasoning. **% Receiving Financial Aid:** 57 **% Residing in College-Owned, -Operated, or -Affiliated Housing:** 77 **Final Year or Final Semester Residency Requirement:** Yes **Regional Accreditation:** North Central Association of Colleges and Schools **Credit Hours For Degree:** 126 credit hours, Bachelors **ROTC:** Army **Professional Accreditation:** AACN, ABET, CSWE, JRCAT, NASAD, NASD, NASM, NAST. **Intercollegiate Athletics:** Baseball M; Basketball M & W; Cheerleading M & W; Cross-Country Running M & W; Football M; Golf M & W; Ice Hockey M; Lacrosse M & W; Sailing M & W; Soccer M & W; Softball W; Swimming and Diving M & W; Tennis M & W; Track and Field M & W; Volleyball W

JACKSON COLLEGE

2111 Emmons Rd.
Jackson, MI 49201-8399
Tel: (517)787-0800; Free: 888-522-7344
E-mail: admissions@jccmi.edu
Web Site: www.jccmi.edu
President/CEO: Dr. Daniel J. Phelan, PhD
Admissions: Daniel Vainner
Financial Aid: Andrew Spohn

Type: Two-Year College **Sex:** Coed **Admission Plans:** Open Admission **Application Fee:** $0.00 **H.S. Requirements:** High school diploma or equivalent not required. For for Title IV Federal Student Aid funds: High school diploma required; GED accepted **Scholarships:** Available. **Calendar System:** Semester, Summer session available **Enrollment:** Full-time 2,389, Part-time 3,276 **Faculty:** Full-time 87, Part-time 320 **Student-Faculty Ratio:** 18:1 **Final Year or Final Semester Residency Requirement:** No **Regional Accreditation:** North Central Association of Colleges and Schools **Credit Hours For Degree:** 60 credit hours, Associates **Professional Accreditation:** AAMAE, ACBSP, JRCEDMS. **Intercollegiate Athletics:** Baseball M; Basketball M & W; Cross-Country Running M & W; Golf M & W; Soccer M & W; Softball W; Volleyball W

KALAMAZOO COLLEGE

1200 Academy St.
Kalamazoo, MI 49006-3295
Tel: (269)337-7000; Free: 800-253-3602
Fax: (269)337-7251
E-mail: admission.records@kzoo.edu
Web Site: www.kzoo.edu
President/CEO: Dr. Eileen Wilson-Oyelaran
Admissions: Kathy Gustafson
Financial Aid: Marian Stowers

Type: Four-Year College **Sex:** Coed **Affiliation:** American Baptist Churches in the U.S.A. **Scores:** 99% SAT V 400+; 99% SAT M 400+; 10.82% ACT 18-23; 52.46% ACT 24-29 **% Accepted:** 72 **Admission Plans:** Deferred Admission; Early Action; Early Decision Plan **Application Deadline:** January 15 **Application Fee:** $0.00 **H.S. Requirements:** High school diploma required; GED accepted **Costs Per Year:** Application fee: $0. Comprehensive fee: $51,732 includes full-time tuition ($42,510), mandatory fees ($336), and college room and board ($8886). College room only: $4335. Room and board charges vary according to board plan and housing facility. **Scholarships:** Available. **Calendar System:** Quarter, Summer session not available **Enrollment:** Full-time 1,434, Part-time 9 **Faculty:** Full-time 103, Part-time 23 **Student-Faculty Ratio:** 13:1 **Exams:** SAT I or ACT; SAT Reasoning. **% Receiving Financial Aid:** 68 **% Residing in College-Owned, -Operated, or -Affiliated Housing:** 66 **Final Year or Final Semester Residency Requirement:** No **Regional Accreditation:** North Central Association of Colleges and Schools **Credit Hours For Degree:** 36 units, Bachelors **ROTC:** Army **Intercollegiate Athletics:** Baseball M; Basketball M & W; Cross-Country Running M & W; Football M; Golf M & W; Lacrosse M & W; Soccer M & W; Softball W; Swimming and Diving M & W; Tennis M & W; Volleyball W

KALAMAZOO VALLEY COMMUNITY COLLEGE

PO Box 4070
Kalamazoo, MI 49003-4070
Tel: (269)488-4400
Fax: (269)448-4555
Web Site: www.kvcc.edu
President/CEO: Dr. Marilyn Schlack
Admissions: Michael McCall
Financial Aid: Sue Newington

Type: Two-Year College **Sex:** Coed **Admission Plans:** Open Admission **Application Deadline:** Rolling **Application Fee:** $0.00 **H.S. Requirements:** High school diploma required; GED accepted **Scholarships:** Available. **Calendar System:** Semester, Summer session available **Exams:** ACT. **Regional Accreditation:** North Central Association of Colleges and Schools **Credit Hours For Degree:** 62 credit hours, Associates **ROTC:** Army **Professional Accreditation:** AAMAE, ADA, CoARC. **Intercollegiate Athletics:** Baseball M; Basketball M & W; Golf M; Softball W; Tennis W; Volleyball W

KELLOGG COMMUNITY COLLEGE

450 N Ave.
Battle Creek, MI 49017-3397
Tel: (616)965-3931
Fax: (616)965-4133
E-mail: straversm@kellogg.edu
Web Site: www.kellogg.edu
President/CEO: Dennis Bona, EdD
Admissions: Meredith Stravers

Type: Two-Year College **Sex:** Coed **Affiliation:** Michigan Department of Education. **% Accepted:** 100 **Admission Plans:** Early Admission; Open Admission **Application Deadline:** Rolling **Application Fee:** $0.00 **H.S. Requirements:** High school diploma or equivalent not required. For allied health and nursing programs: High school diploma required; GED accepted **Costs Per Year:** Application fee: $0. Area resident tuition: $2388 full-time. State resident tuition: $3870 full-time. Nonresident tuition: $5538 full-time. Mandatory fees: $312 full-time. Full-time tuition and fees vary according to program. **Scholarships:** Available. **Calendar System:** Semester, Summer session available **Enrollment:** Full-time 1,268, Part-time 3,813 **Faculty:** Full-time 87, Part-time 360 **Student-Faculty Ratio:** 12:1 **Exams:** ACT; SAT I or ACT. **Final Year or Final Semester Residency Requirement:** No **Regional Accreditation:** North Central Association of Colleges and Schools **Credit Hours For Degree:** 62 credit hours, Associates **Professional Accreditation:** ADA, APTA, JRCERT, NAACLS. **Intercollegiate Athletics:** Baseball M; Basketball M & W; Soccer W; Softball W; Volleyball W

KETTERING UNIVERSITY

1700 University Ave.
Flint, MI 48504
Tel: (810)762-9500; Free: 800-955-4464
Fax: (810)762-9837
E-mail: kdarcy@kettering.edu
Web Site: www.kettering.edu
President/CEO: Dr. Robert K. McMahan
Admissions: Kip Darcy
Financial Aid: Diane Bice

Type: Comprehensive **Sex:** Coed **Scores:** 100% SAT V 400+; 100% SAT M 400+; 12.6% ACT 18-23; 64.8% ACT 24-29 **% Accepted:** 72 **Admission Plans:** Deferred Admission **Application Deadline:** Rolling **Application Fee:** $0.00 **H.S. Requirements:** High school diploma required; GED accepted **Scholarships:** Available. **Calendar System:** Semester, Summer session available **Enrollment:** Full-time 1,608, Graduate full-time 13, Graduate part-time 335, Part-time 133 **Faculty:** Full-time 119, Part-time 15 **Student-Faculty Ratio:** 13:1 **Exams:** ACT essay component not used; SAT I or ACT; SAT essay component not used; SAT Reasoning; SAT Subject. **% Receiving Financial Aid:** 75 **% Residing in College-Owned, -Operated, or -Affiliated Housing:** 34 **Final Year or Final Semester Residency Requirement:** No **Regional Accreditation:** North Central Association of Colleges and Schools **Credit Hours For Degree:** 161 credit hours, Bachelors **Professional Accreditation:** ABET, ACBSP.

KEWEENAW BAY OJIBWA COMMUNITY COLLEGE

111 Beartown Rd.
Baraga, MI 49908
Tel: (906)524-8400
Fax: (906)524-8106

E-mail: megan@kbocc.org
Web Site: www.kbocc.edu
President/CEO: Debra J. Parrish
Admissions: Megan Shanahan

Type: Two-Year College **Sex:** Coed **Application Fee:** $20.00 **Calendar System:** Semester **Enrollment:** Full-time 43, Part-time 34 **Regional Accreditation:** North Central Association of Colleges and Schools

KIRTLAND COMMUNITY COLLEGE

10775 N St. Helen Rd.
Roscommon, MI 48653-9699
Tel: (989)275-5000
Fax: (989)275-8210
E-mail: registrar@kirtland.edu
Web Site: www.kirtland.edu
President/CEO: Dr. Tom Quinn
Admissions: Michelle Vyskocil
Financial Aid: Christin Horndt

Type: Two-Year College **Sex:** Coed **Scores:** 46% ACT 18-23; 6% ACT 24-29 **% Accepted:** 100 **Admission Plans:** Open Admission **Application Deadline:** Rolling **Application Fee:** $0.00 **H.S. Requirements:** High school diploma required; GED accepted **Costs Per Year:** Application fee: $0. Area resident tuition: $3150 full-time, $105 per contact hour part-time. State resident tuition: $4380 full-time, $146 per contact hour part-time. Nonresident tuition: $7050 full-time, $235 per contact hour part-time. Mandatory fees: $575 full-time, $18 per contact hour part-time, $35 per term part-time. **Scholarships:** Available. **Calendar System:** Semester, Summer session available **Enrollment:** Full-time 520, Part-time 1,108 **Faculty:** Full-time 33, Part-time 95 **Student-Faculty Ratio:** 18:1 **Exams:** SAT I or ACT. **Regional Accreditation:** North Central Association of Colleges and Schools **Credit Hours For Degree:** 60 credit hours, Associates **Professional Accreditation:** AAMAE. **Intercollegiate Athletics:** Bowling M & W; Cross-Country Running M & W; Golf M & W

KUYPER COLLEGE

3333 E Beltline, NE
Grand Rapids, MI 49525-9749
Tel: (616)222-3000
Fax: (616)222-3045
E-mail: admissions@kuyper.edu
Web Site: www.kuyper.edu
President/CEO: Nicholas V. Kroeze
Financial Aid: Agnes Russell

Type: Four-Year College **Sex:** Coed **Affiliation:** Christian. **Scores:** 58% ACT 18-23; 18% ACT 24-29 **% Accepted:** 71 **Admission Plans:** Deferred Admission **Application Deadline:** Rolling **H.S. Requirements:** High school diploma required; GED accepted **Costs Per Year:** One-time mandatory fee: $554. Comprehensive fee: $26,344 includes full-time tuition ($18,960), mandatory fees ($584), and college room and board ($6800). Full-time tuition and fees vary according to course load and reciprocity agreements. Room and board charges vary according to board plan, housing facility, and student level. Part-time tuition: $910 per credit hour. Part-time mandatory fees: $295 per year. Part-time tuition and fees vary according to course load and reciprocity agreements. **Scholarships:** Available. **Calendar System:** Semester, Summer session available **Enrollment:** Full-time 219, Graduate part-time 2, Part-time 36 **Faculty:** Full-time 13, Part-time 28 **Student-Faculty Ratio:** 12:1 **Exams:** SAT I or ACT. **% Receiving Financial Aid:** 84 **% Residing in College-Owned, -Operated, or -Affiliated Housing:** 42 **Final Year or Final Semester Residency Requirement:** Yes **Regional Accreditation:** North Central Association of Colleges and Schools **Credit Hours For Degree:** 63 credits, Associates; 120 credits, Bachelors **ROTC:** Army **Professional Accreditation:** ABHE.

LAKE MICHIGAN COLLEGE

2755 E Napier Ave.
Benton Harbor, MI 49022-1899
Tel: (269)927-8100; Free: 800-252-1LMC
E-mail: thomas@lakemichigancollege.edu
Web Site: www.lakemichigancollege.edu
President/CEO: Dr. Robert P. Harrison
Admissions: Louis Thomas
Financial Aid: Anne Tews

Type: Two-Year College **Sex:** Coed **Affiliation:** Michigan Department of Education. **% Accepted:** 94 **Admission Plans:** Open Admission **Applica-**

tion **Deadline:** Rolling **Application Fee:** $0.00 **H.S. Requirements:** High school diploma or equivalent not required. For health science students: High school diploma required; GED accepted **Costs Per Year:** Application fee: $0. Area resident tuition: $2820 full-time, $94 per contact hour part-time. State resident tuition: $4365 full-time, $145.50 per contact hour part-time. Nonresident tuition: $4365 full-time, $145.50 per contact hour part-time. Mandatory fees: $1320 full-time, $44 per contact hour part-time. Full-time tuition and fees vary according to degree level. Part-time tuition and fees vary according to degree level. College room only: $7000. **Scholarships:** Available. **Calendar System:** Semester, Summer session available **Enrollment:** Full-time 1,508, Part-time 3,040 **Faculty:** Full-time 58, Part-time 269 **Student-Faculty Ratio:** 17:1 **Final Year or Final Semester Residency Requirement:** No **Regional Accreditation:** North Central Association of Colleges and Schools **Credit Hours For Degree:** 61 credit hours, Associates **Professional Accreditation:** ACEN, ADA, AOTA, JRCERT. **Intercollegiate Athletics:** Baseball M; Basketball M & W; Softball W; Volleyball W

LAKE SUPERIOR STATE UNIVERSITY

650 W Easterday Ave.
Sault Sainte Marie, MI 49783
Tel: (906)632-6841; Free: 888-800-LSSU
Fax: (906)635-6669
E-mail: admissions@lssu.edu
Web Site: www.lssu.edu
President/CEO: Dr. Tony McLain
Admissions: Allan R. Case
Financial Aid: Deborah Faust

Type: Comprehensive **Sex:** Coed **Scores:** 51% ACT 18-23; 35% ACT 24-29 **% Accepted:** 90 **Admission Plans:** Deferred Admission **Application Deadline:** Rolling **Application Fee:** $25.00 **H.S. Requirements:** High school diploma required; GED accepted **Costs Per Year:** Application fee: $25. One-time mandatory fee: $125. State resident tuition: $10,392 full-time, $433 per credit hour part-time. Nonresident tuition: $10,392 full-time, $433 per credit hour part-time. Mandatory fees: $245 full-time, $60 per term part-time. Full-time tuition and fees vary according to program and reciprocity agreements. Part-time tuition and fees vary according to course load, location, program, and reciprocity agreements. College room and board: $9290. Room and board charges vary according to board plan and housing facility. **Scholarships:** Available. **Calendar System:** Semester, Summer session available **Enrollment:** Full-time 1,966, Graduate part-time 6, Part-time 466 **Faculty:** Full-time 119, Part-time 59 **Student-Faculty Ratio:** 15:1 **Exams:** SAT I or ACT; SAT Reasoning; SAT Subject. **% Receiving Financial Aid:** 68 **% Residing in College-Owned, -Operated, or -Affiliated Housing:** 35 **Final Year or Final Semester Residency Requirement:** No **Regional Accreditation:** North Central Association of Colleges and Schools **Credit Hours For Degree:** 62 credit hours, Associates; 124 credit hours, Bachelors **Professional Accreditation:** ABET, ACBSP, ACEN. **Intercollegiate Athletics:** Basketball M & W; Cross-Country Running M & W; Golf M & W; Ice Hockey M; Softball W; Tennis M & W; Track and Field M & W; Volleyball W

LANSING COMMUNITY COLLEGE

PO Box 40010
Lansing, MI 48901-7210
Tel: (517)483-1957; Free: 800-644-4LCC
Fax: (517)483-9668
E-mail: grossbt@lcc.edu
Web Site: www.lcc.edu
President/CEO: Dr. Brent Knight, EdD
Admissions: Tammy Grossbauer

Type: Two-Year College **Sex:** Coed **Affiliation:** Michigan Department of Education. **Admission Plans:** Deferred Admission; Early Admission; Open Admission; Preferred Admission **Application Deadline:** August 7 **Application Fee:** $0.00 **H.S. Requirements:** High school diploma or equivalent not required. For allied health programs, international students: High school diploma required; GED accepted **Scholarships:** Available. **Calendar System:** Semester, Summer session available **Enrollment:** Full-time 6,587, Part-time 10,975 **Faculty:** Full-time 202 **Student-Faculty Ratio:** 13:1 **Final Year or Final Semester Residency Requirement:** No **Regional Accreditation:** North Central Association of Colleges and Schools **Credit Hours For Degree:** 60 semester hours, Associates **ROTC:** Air Force, Army **Professional Accreditation:** ACEN, ADA, JRCEMTP, JRCERT, NAACLS. **Intercollegiate Athletics:** Baseball M; Basketball M & W; Cross-Country Running M & W; Softball W; Track and Field M & W; Volleyball W

LAWRENCE TECHNOLOGICAL UNIVERSITY

21000 W Ten Mile Rd.
Southfield, MI 48075-1058
Tel: (248)204-4000; Free: 800-225-5588
Fax: (248)204-3727
E-mail: admissions@ltu.edu
Web Site: www.ltu.edu
President/CEO: Dr. Virinder K. Moudgil
Admissions: Jane Rohrback
Financial Aid: Susie Poli-Smith
Type: University **Sex:** Coed **Scores:** 88% SAT V 400+; 95% SAT M 400+; 27% ACT 18-23; 46% ACT 24-29 **% Accepted:** 55 **Admission Plans:** Deferred Admission **Application Deadline:** August 15 **Application Fee:** $30.00 **H.S. Requirements:** High school diploma required; GED accepted **Costs Per Year:** Application fee: $30. Comprehensive fee: $39,770 includes full-time tuition ($29,580), mandatory fees ($720), and college room and board ($9470). College room only: $5552. Full-time tuition and fees vary according to course level, degree level, location, program, and student level. Room and board charges vary according to board plan and housing facility. Part-time tuition: $986 per credit hour. Part-time mandatory fees: $360 per term. Part-time tuition and fees vary according to course level, degree level, location, program, and student level. **Scholarships:** Available. **Calendar System:** Semester, Summer session available **Enrollment:** Full-time 1,657, Graduate full-time 67, Graduate part-time 1,315, Part-time 1,122 **Faculty:** Full-time 121, Part-time 295 **Student-Faculty Ratio:** 12:1 **Exams:** ACT essay component not used; SAT I or ACT; SAT essay component not used; SAT Reasoning; SAT Subject. **% Receiving Financial Aid:** 61 **% Residing in College-Owned, -Operated, or -Affiliated Housing:** 26 **Final Year or Final Semester Residency Requirement:** No **Regional Accreditation:** North Central Association of Colleges and Schools **Credit Hours For Degree:** 60 credit hours, Associates; 120 credit hours, Bachelors **ROTC:** Air Force **Professional Accreditation:** ABET, ACBSP, CIDA, NAAB, NASAD. **Intercollegiate Athletics:** Basketball M & W; Bowling M & W; Cheerleading W; Cross-Country Running M & W; Golf M & W; Ice Hockey M; Lacrosse M & W; Soccer M & W; Tennis M & W; Volleyball M & W

MACOMB COMMUNITY COLLEGE

14500 E Twelve Mile Rd.
Warren, MI 48088-3896
Tel: (586)445-7999; Free: 866-MACOMB1
Fax: (586)445-7140
E-mail: stevensr@macomb.edu
Web Site: www.macomb.edu
President/CEO: Dr. James Jacobs
Admissions: Brian Bouwman
Financial Aid: Judy L. Florian
Type: Two-Year College **Sex:** Coed **Affiliation:** Michigan Public Community College System. **Admission Plans:** Deferred Admission; Early Admission; Open Admission **Application Deadline:** Rolling **Application Fee:** $0.00 **H.S. Requirements:** High school diploma or equivalent not required **Costs Per Year:** Application fee: $0. Area resident tuition: $2914 full-time, $94 per credit hour part-time. State resident tuition: $4960 full-time, $160 per credit hour part-time. Nonresident tuition: $6386 full-time, $206 per credit hour part-time. Mandatory fees: $255 full-time, $5 per credit hour part-time, $50 per term part-time. Full-time tuition and fees vary according to course load. Part-time tuition and fees vary according to course load. **Scholarships:** Available. **Calendar System:** Semester, Summer session available **Enrollment:** Full-time 6,894, Part-time 15,288 **Faculty:** Full-time 198, Part-time 804 **Student-Faculty Ratio:** 27:1 **Regional Accreditation:** North Central Association of Colleges and Schools **Credit Hours For Degree:** 62 semester hours, Associates **Professional Accreditation:** AAMAE, ACEN, ACF, AOTA, APTA, ARCST, CoARC. **Intercollegiate Athletics:** Baseball M; Basketball M; Cross-Country Running M & W; Soccer M; Softball W; Track and Field M & W; Volleyball W

MADONNA UNIVERSITY

36600 Schoolcraft Rd.
Livonia, MI 48150-1173
Tel: (734)432-5300; Free: 800-852-4951
Fax: (734)432-5393
E-mail: admissions@madonna.edu
Web Site: www.madonna.edu
President/CEO: Dr. Michael A. Grandillo
Admissions: Mark A. Schroeder

Financial Aid: Cathy Durham
Type: Comprehensive **Sex:** Coed **Affiliation:** Roman Catholic. **Scores:** 56% ACT 18-23; 26% ACT 24-29 **% Accepted:** 60 **Admission Plans:** Early Admission **Application Deadline:** Rolling **Application Fee:** $25.00 **H.S. Requirements:** High school diploma required; GED accepted **Costs Per Year:** Application fee: $25. Comprehensive fee: $27,970 includes full-time tuition ($18,600), mandatory fees ($140), and college room and board ($9230). College room only: $4430. Full-time tuition and fees vary according to course load. Room and board charges vary according to board plan. Part-time tuition: $620 per credit hour. Part-time mandatory fees: $70 per term. Part-time tuition and fees vary according to course load. **Scholarships:** Available. **Calendar System:** Semester, Summer session available **Enrollment:** Full-time 1,456, Graduate full-time 66, Graduate part-time 757, Part-time 1,431 **Faculty:** Full-time 105, Part-time 202 **Student-Faculty Ratio:** 11:1 **Exams:** SAT I or ACT. **% Receiving Financial Aid:** 45 **% Residing in College-Owned, -Operated, or -Affiliated Housing:** 8 **Final Year or Final Semester Residency Requirement:** No **Regional Accreditation:** North Central Association of Colleges and Schools **Credit Hours For Degree:** 60 semester hours, Associates; 120 semester hours, Bachelors **ROTC:** Army **Professional Accreditation:** AACN, CSWE, NCATE. **Intercollegiate Athletics:** Baseball M; Basketball M & W; Bowling M & W; Cross-Country Running M & W; Golf M & W; Lacrosse M & W; Soccer M & W; Softball W; Track and Field M & W; Volleyball W

MANTHANO CHRISTIAN COLLEGE

6420 N Newburgh
Westland, MI 48185-1919
Web Site: www.manthanochristian.org
Type: Two-Year College **Sex:** Coed **Professional Accreditation:** TRACS.

MARYGROVE COLLEGE

8425 W McNichols Rd.
Detroit, MI 48221-2599
Tel: (313)927-1200; Free: 866-313-1297
Fax: (313)927-1345
E-mail: info@marygrove.edu
Web Site: www.marygrove.edu
President/CEO: David Fike
Admissions: John Ambrose
Financial Aid: Donald Hurt
Type: Comprehensive **Sex:** Coed **Affiliation:** Roman Catholic. **% Accepted:** 42 **Admission Plans:** Deferred Admission; Early Admission **Application Deadline:** August 15 **Application Fee:** $25.00 **H.S. Requirements:** High school diploma required; GED accepted **Calendar System:** Semester, Summer session available **Enrollment:** Full-time 455, Part-time 325 **Faculty:** Full-time 56, Part-time 8 **Student-Faculty Ratio:** 22:1 **Exams:** ACT. **% Residing in College-Owned, -Operated, or -Affiliated Housing:** 12 **Regional Accreditation:** North Central Association of Colleges and Schools **Credit Hours For Degree:** 64 credits, Associates; 128 credits, Bachelors **Professional Accreditation:** AAFCS, CSWE, CoARC, JRCERT, NCATE, TEAC. **Intercollegiate Athletics:** Basketball M & W

MIAT COLLEGE OF TECHNOLOGY

2955 S Haggerty Rd.
Canton, MI 48188
Tel: (734)483-3758
Web Site: www.miat.edu
Type: Two-Year College **Sex:** Coed **Professional Accreditation:** ACCSC.

MICHIGAN JEWISH INSTITUTE

6890 Maple Rd.
West Bloomfield, MI 48322
Tel: (248)414-6900; Free: 888-INFO-MJI
Fax: (248)414-6907
E-mail: dstein@mji.edu
Web Site: www.mji.edu
President/CEO: Rabbi Kasriel Shemtov
Admissions: Dov Stein
Type: Four-Year College **Sex:** Coed **Admission Plans:** Deferred Admission; Early Admission; Open Admission **Application Deadline:** Rolling **Application Fee:** $50.00 **H.S. Requirements:** High school diploma required; GED accepted **Calendar System:** Semester, Summer session available **Faculty:** Full-time 6, Part-time 18 **Credit Hours For Degree:** 62 credits, Associates; 120 credits, Bachelors **Professional Accreditation:** ACICS.

MICHIGAN STATE UNIVERSITY

East Lansing, MI 48824
Tel: (517)355-1855
E-mail: admis@msu.edu
Web Site: www.msu.edu
President/CEO: Dr. LouAnna K. Simon
Admissions: James Cotter
Financial Aid: Keith Williams

Type: University **Sex:** Coed **Scores:** 90% SAT V 400+; 98% SAT M 400+; 24.6% ACT 18-23; 57.7% ACT 24-29 **% Accepted:** 66 **Admission Plans:** Early Decision Plan **Application Deadline:** Rolling **Application Fee:** $50.00 **H.S. Requirements:** High school diploma required; GED accepted **Costs Per Year:** Application fee: $50. State resident tuition: $13,560 full-time, $452 per credit hour part-time. Nonresident tuition: $36,360 full-time, $1212 per credit hour part-time. Full-time tuition varies according to course load, program, and student level. Part-time tuition varies according to course load, program, and student level. College room and board: $9474. College room only: $3912. Room and board charges vary according to board plan and housing facility. **Scholarships:** Available. **Calendar System:** Semester, Summer session available **Enrollment:** Full-time 35,645, Graduate full-time 8,381, Graduate part-time 3,019, Part-time 3,498 **Faculty:** Full-time 2,433, Part-time 406 **Student-Faculty Ratio:** 17:1 **Exams:** SAT I or ACT. **% Receiving Financial Aid:** 46 **% Residing in College-Owned, -Operated, or -Affiliated Housing:** 39 **Regional Accreditation:** North Central Association of Colleges and Schools **Credit Hours For Degree:** 120 credits, Bachelors **ROTC:** Air Force, Army **Professional Accreditation:** AACN, AACSB, AAFCS, AALE, AAMFT, AANA, ABET, ACCE, ACEJMC, ACSP, AND, AOsA, APA, ASHA, ASLA, AVMA, CIDA, CORE, CSWE, LCME/AMA, NAACLS, NASM, NASPAA, NRPA, SAF, TEAC. **Intercollegiate Athletics:** Baseball M; Basketball M & W; Cheerleading M & W; Crew M & W; Cross-Country Running M & W; Equestrian Sports M & W; Fencing M & W; Field Hockey W; Football M; Golf M & W; Gymnastics W; Ice Hockey M & W; Lacrosse M & W; Rugby M & W; Sailing M & W; Skiing (Downhill) M & W; Soccer M & W; Softball W; Swimming and Diving M & W; Table Tennis M & W; Tennis M & W; Track and Field M & W; Volleyball M & W; Water Polo M & W; Wrestling M

MICHIGAN TECHNOLOGICAL UNIVERSITY

1400 Townsend Dr.
Houghton, MI 49931
Tel: (906)487-1885; Free: 888-MTU-1885
Fax: (906)487-3343
E-mail: mtu4u@mtu.edu
Web Site: www.mtu.edu
President/CEO: Dr. Glenn D. Mroz
Admissions: Allison Carter
Financial Aid: Joseph Cooper

Type: University **Sex:** Coed **Scores:** 99% SAT V 400+; 100% SAT M 400+; 19.51% ACT 18-23; 57.07% ACT 24-29 **% Accepted:** 75 **Admission Plans:** Deferred Admission **Application Deadline:** Rolling **H.S. Requirements:** High school diploma required; GED accepted **Costs Per Year:** State resident tuition: $13,986 full-time, $529 per credit hour part-time. Nonresident tuition: $29,950 full-time, $1109 per credit hour part-time. Mandatory fees: $300 full-time, $150 per term part-time. Full-time tuition and fees vary according to program and student level. Part-time tuition and fees vary according to course load, program, and student level. College room and board: $9857. College room only: $5486. Room and board charges vary according to board plan and housing facility. **Scholarships:** Available. **Calendar System:** Semester, Summer session available **Enrollment:** Full-time 5,352, Graduate full-time 1,141, Graduate part-time 380, Part-time 369 **Faculty:** Full-time 410, Part-time 41 **Student-Faculty Ratio:** 13:1 **Exams:** ACT essay component not used; SAT I and SAT II or ACT; SAT I or ACT; SAT II; SAT essay component not used; SAT Reasoning. **% Receiving Financial Aid:** 63 **% Residing in College-Owned, -Operated, or -Affiliated Housing:** 47 **Final Year or Final Semester Residency Requirement:** Yes **Regional Accreditation:** North Central Association of Colleges and Schools **Credit Hours For Degree:** 65 credit hours, Associates; 120 credit hours, Bachelors **ROTC:** Air Force, Army **Professional Accreditation:** AACSB, ABET, SAF, TEAC. **Intercollegiate Athletics:** Archery M & W; Badminton M & W; Baseball M; Basketball M & W; Cheerleading M & W; Crew M & W; Cross-Country Running M & W; Fencing M & W; Football M; Golf M & W; Gymnastics M & W; Ice Hockey M & W; Lacrosse M & W; Racquetball M & W; Riflery M & W; Rugby M & W; Sailing M & W; Skiing (Cross-Country) M & W; Skiing (Downhill) M & W; Soccer M & W; Softball W; Swimming and Diving M & W; Tennis M & W; Track and Field M & W; Ultimate Frisbee M & W; Volleyball M & W; Water Polo M & W

MID MICHIGAN COMMUNITY COLLEGE

1375 S Clare Ave.
Harrison, MI 48625-9447
Tel: (989)386-6622
Fax: (989)386-9088
E-mail: apply@midmich.edu
Web Site: www.midmich.edu
President/CEO: Carol Churchill
Admissions: Jennifer Casebeer

Type: Two-Year College **Sex:** Coed **Affiliation:** Michigan Department of Education. **% Accepted:** 100 **Admission Plans:** Early Admission; Open Admission **Application Deadline:** Rolling **Application Fee:** $0.00 **H.S. Requirements:** High school diploma or equivalent not required **Scholarships:** Available. **Calendar System:** Semester, Summer session available **Enrollment:** Full-time 2,193, Part-time 2,692 **Faculty:** Full-time 46, Part-time 218 **Student-Faculty Ratio:** 26:1 **Final Year or Final Semester Residency Requirement:** No **Regional Accreditation:** North Central Association of Colleges and Schools **Credit Hours For Degree:** 62 credit hours, Associates **Professional Accreditation:** JRCERT. **Intercollegiate Athletics:** Basketball M & W; Ice Hockey M; Soccer M & W

MONROE COUNTY COMMUNITY COLLEGE

1555 S Raisinville Rd.
Monroe, MI 48161-9047
Tel: (734)242-7300
Fax: (734)242-9711
E-mail: mhall@monroeccc.edu
Web Site: www.monroeccc.edu
President/CEO: Dr. Kojo Quartey
Admissions: Mark V. Hall

Type: Two-Year College **Sex:** Coed **Affiliation:** Michigan Department of Education. **% Accepted:** 100 **Admission Plans:** Deferred Admission; Early Admission; Open Admission **Application Fee:** $0.00 **H.S. Requirements:** High school diploma required; GED accepted **Costs Per Year:** Application fee: $0. Area resident tuition: $2638 full-time, $120 per contact hour part-time. State resident tuition: $4270 full-time, $197 per contact hour part-time. Nonresident tuition: $4702 full-time, $217 per contact hour part-time. Mandatory fees: $204 full-time, $35 per term part-time. Full-time tuition and fees vary according to reciprocity agreements. Part-time tuition and fees vary according to reciprocity agreements. **Calendar System:** Semester, Summer session available **Faculty:** Full-time 53, Part-time 142 **Exams:** ACT; Other. **Final Year or Final Semester Residency Requirement:** No **Regional Accreditation:** North Central Association of Colleges and Schools **Credit Hours For Degree:** 60 credit hours, Associates **Professional Accreditation:** ACEN, CoARC.

MONTCALM COMMUNITY COLLEGE

2800 College Dr.
Sidney, MI 48885
Tel: (989)328-2111; Free: 877-328-2111
Fax: (989)328-2950
E-mail: admissions@montcalm.edu
Web Site: www.montcalm.edu
President/CEO: Robert Ferrentino, JD
Admissions: Debra Alexander

Type: Two-Year College **Sex:** Coed **Affiliation:** Michigan Department of Education. **Admission Plans:** Deferred Admission; Early Admission; Open Admission **Application Fee:** $0.00 **H.S. Requirements:** High school diploma or equivalent not required **Scholarships:** Available. **Calendar System:** Semester, Summer session available **Enrollment:** Full-time 538, Part-time 1,294 **Faculty:** Full-time 29, Part-time 89 **Student-Faculty Ratio:** 16:1 **Final Year or Final Semester Residency Requirement:** No **Regional Accreditation:** North Central Association of Colleges and Schools **Credit Hours For Degree:** 60 credit hours, Associates

MOTT COMMUNITY COLLEGE

1401 E Ct. St.
Flint, MI 48503-2089
Tel: (810)762-0200; Free: 800-852-8614
Fax: (810)762-0292

E-mail: regina.broomfield@mcc.edu
Web Site: www.mcc.edu
President/CEO: Dr. Beverly Walker-Griffea
Admissions: Regina Broomfield
Financial Aid: Emily Varney
Type: Two-Year College **Sex:** Coed **Admission Plans:** Deferred Admission; Early Admission; Open Admission **Application Deadline:** August 31 **Application Fee:** $0.00 **H.S. Requirements:** High school diploma or equivalent not required. For nursing, allied health programs; applicants under 19: High school diploma required; GED accepted **Costs Per Year:** Application fee: $0. Area resident tuition: $3910 full-time, $130.34 per contact hour part-time. State resident tuition: $5504 full-time, $183.48 per contact hour part-time. Nonresident tuition: $7842 full-time, $261.40 per contact hour part-time. Mandatory fees: $657 full-time, $16.51 per contact hour part-time, $130.34 per term part-time. Full-time tuition and fees vary according to course load. Part-time tuition and fees vary according to course load. **Scholarships:** Available. **Calendar System:** Semester, Summer session available **Enrollment:** Full-time 2,230, Part-time 6,387 **Faculty:** Full-time 142, Part-time 312 **Student-Faculty Ratio:** 18:1 **Final Year or Final Semester Residency Requirement:** No **Regional Accreditation:** North Central Association of Colleges and Schools **Credit Hours For Degree:** 62 credit hours, Associates **Professional Accreditation:** ACBSP, ACEN, ADA, AOTA, APTA, CoARC. **Intercollegiate Athletics:** Baseball M; Basketball M & W; Cross-Country Running M & W; Golf M; Softball W; Volleyball W

MUSKEGON COMMUNITY COLLEGE

221 S Quarterline Rd.
Muskegon, MI 49442-1493
Tel: (231)773-9131; Free: 866-711-4622
Fax: (231)777-0255
E-mail: johnathon.skidmore@muskegoncc.edu
Web Site: www.muskegoncc.edu
President/CEO: Dr. Dale K. Nesbary
Admissions: Johnathon Skidmore
Type: Two-Year College **Sex:** Coed **Affiliation:** Michigan Department of Education. **% Accepted:** 100 **Admission Plans:** Deferred Admission; Early Admission; Open Admission **Application Deadline:** Rolling **Application Fee:** $0.00 **H.S. Requirements:** High school diploma required; GED accepted **Costs Per Year:** Application fee: $0. Area resident tuition: $3960 full-time, $99 per contact hour part-time. State resident tuition: $7360 full-time, $184 per contact hour part-time. Nonresident tuition: $10,240 full-time, $256 per contact hour part-time. Mandatory fees: $1163 full-time, $25 per contact hour part-time, $35 per term part-time. **Scholarships:** Available. **Calendar System:** Semester, Summer session available **Enrollment:** Full-time 1,488, Part-time 3,018 **Faculty:** Full-time 83, Part-time 241 **Student-Faculty Ratio:** 19:1 **Regional Accreditation:** North Central Association of Colleges and Schools **Credit Hours For Degree:** 62 credit hours, Associates **Professional Accreditation:** ACEN, CoARC. **Intercollegiate Athletics:** Baseball M; Basketball M & W; Golf M & W; Softball W; Tennis M & W; Volleyball W; Wrestling M

NORTH CENTRAL MICHIGAN COLLEGE

1515 Howard St.
Petoskey, MI 49770-8717
Tel: (231)348-6600; Free: 888-298-6605
E-mail: jtobin@ncmich.edu
Web Site: www.ncmich.edu
President/CEO: Dr. Cameron Brunet-Koch
Admissions: Julieanne Tobin
Type: Two-Year College **Sex:** Coed **Admission Plans:** Open Admission **Application Deadline:** Rolling **Application Fee:** $0.00 **H.S. Requirements:** High school diploma or equivalent not required. For nursing program: High school diploma required; GED accepted **Scholarships:** Available. **Calendar System:** Semester, Summer session available **Faculty:** Full-time 31, Part-time 102 **Student-Faculty Ratio:** 17:1 **Exams:** ACT. **Regional Accreditation:** North Central Association of Colleges and Schools **Credit Hours For Degree:** 60 credit hours, Associates

NORTHERN MICHIGAN UNIVERSITY

1401 Presque Isle Ave.
Marquette, MI 49855-5301
Tel: (906)227-1000; Free: 800-682-9797
Fax: (906)227-1747
E-mail: admiss@nmu.edu

Web Site: www.nmu.edu
President/CEO: Dr. Fritz Erickson
Admissions: Gerri Daniels
Financial Aid: Michael Rotundo
Type: Comprehensive **Sex:** Coed **Scores:** 54% ACT 18-23; 28.11% ACT 24-29 **% Accepted:** 72 **Admission Plans:** Deferred Admission **Application Deadline:** Rolling **Application Fee:** $35.00 **H.S. Requirements:** High school diploma required; GED accepted **Costs Per Year:** Application fee: $35. One-time mandatory fee: $240. State resident tuition: $9556 full-time, $373 per credit hour part-time. Nonresident tuition: $14,956 full-time, $598 per credit hour part-time. Mandatory fees: $64 full-time. Full-time tuition and fees vary according to course level and program. Part-time tuition varies according to course level, course load, and program. College room and board: $9286. College room only: $4788. Room and board charges vary according to board plan and housing facility. **Scholarships:** Available. **Calendar System:** Semester, Summer session available **Enrollment:** Full-time 7,002, Graduate full-time 193, Graduate part-time 587, Part-time 999 **Faculty:** Full-time 305, Part-time 151 **Student-Faculty Ratio:** 21:1 **Exams:** ACT essay component not used; SAT I or ACT; SAT essay component not used; SAT Reasoning; SAT Subject. **% Receiving Financial Aid:** 67 **% Residing in College-Owned, -Operated, or -Affiliated Housing:** 38 **Final Year or Final Semester Residency Requirement:** No **Regional Accreditation:** North Central Association of Colleges and Schools **Credit Hours For Degree:** 62 credit hours, Associates; 124 credit hours, Bachelors **ROTC:** Army **Professional Accreditation:** AACN, AACSB, ABET, ASHA, ATMAE, CSWE, NAACLS, NASM, TEAC. **Intercollegiate Athletics:** Baseball M; Basketball M & W; Crew M & W; Cross-Country Running W; Football M; Golf M & W; Ice Hockey M & W; Lacrosse M & W; Rugby M & W; Sailing M & W; Skiing (Cross-Country) M & W; Skiing (Downhill) M & W; Soccer M & W; Swimming and Diving M & W; Track and Field M & W; Ultimate Frisbee M & W; Volleyball W

NORTHWESTERN MICHIGAN COLLEGE

1701 E Front St.
Traverse City, MI 49686-3061
Tel: (231)995-1000; Free: 800-748-0566
Fax: (231)995-1680
E-mail: c.claerhout@nmc.edu
Web Site: www.nmc.edu
President/CEO: Timothy Nelson
Admissions: Catheryn Claerhout
Financial Aid: Deb Faas
Type: Two-Year College **Sex:** Coed **% Accepted:** 55 **Admission Plans:** Deferred Admission; Early Admission; Open Admission **Application Deadline:** Rolling **Application Fee:** $20.00 **H.S. Requirements:** High school diploma required; GED accepted **Scholarships:** Available. **Calendar System:** Semester, Summer session available **Enrollment:** Full-time 2,011, Part-time 2,598 **Faculty:** Full-time 91, Part-time 189 **Student-Faculty Ratio:** 18:1 **Final Year or Final Semester Residency Requirement:** No **Regional Accreditation:** North Central Association of Colleges and Schools **Credit Hours For Degree:** 64 credits, Associates **Professional Accreditation:** ACF, ADA.

NORTHWOOD UNIVERSITY, MICHIGAN CAMPUS

4000 Whiting Dr.
Midland, MI 48640-2398
Tel: (989)837-4200; Free: 800-457-7878
Fax: (989)837-4490
E-mail: miadmit@northwood.edu
Web Site: www.northwood.edu
President/CEO: Keith A. Pretty, JD
Admissions: Keri Nieto
Financial Aid: Terri Mieler
Type: Comprehensive **Sex:** Coed **Scores:** 77% SAT V 400+; 91% SAT M 400+; 57% ACT 18-23; 32% ACT 24-29 **% Accepted:** 70 **Admission Plans:** Deferred Admission; Early Admission **Application Deadline:** August 1 **Application Fee:** $30.00 **H.S. Requirements:** High school diploma required; GED accepted **Costs Per Year:** Application fee: $30. Comprehensive fee: $33,760 includes full-time tuition ($22,940), mandatory fees ($1230), and college room and board ($9590). Full-time tuition and fees vary according to course load. Room and board charges vary according to board plan. Part-time tuition: $883 per credit hour. Part-time tuition varies according to course load. **Scholarships:** Available. **Calendar System:** Semester, Summer session available **Enrollment:** Full-time 1,363, Graduate full-time 48, Graduate

part-time 205, Part-time 53 **Faculty:** Full-time 48, Part-time 95 **Student-Faculty Ratio:** 19:1 **Exams:** ACT essay component used for advising; SAT I or ACT; SAT essay component used for advising; SAT Reasoning. **% Receiving Financial Aid:** 68 **% Residing in College-Owned, -Operated, or -Affiliated Housing:** 49 **Final Year or Final Semester Residency Requirement:** No **Regional Accreditation:** North Central Association of Colleges and Schools **Credit Hours For Degree:** 60 semester hours, Associates; 123 semester hours, Bachelors **Professional Accreditation:** ACBSP. **Intercollegiate Athletics:** Baseball M; Basketball M & W; Cheerleading M & W; Cross-Country Running M & W; Football M; Golf M & W; Soccer M & W; Softball W; Tennis M & W; Track and Field M & W; Volleyball W

OAKLAND COMMUNITY COLLEGE

2480 Opdyke Rd.
Bloomfield Hills, MI 48304-2266
Tel: (248)341-2000
Fax: (248)341-2099
E-mail: smlinden@oaklandcc.edu
Web Site: www.oaklandcc.edu
President/CEO: Dr. Timothy R. Meyer
Admissions: Stephan M. Linden
Financial Aid: Wilma Porter

Type: Two-Year College **Sex:** Coed **% Accepted:** 100 **Admission Plans:** Deferred Admission; Open Admission **Application Deadline:** Rolling **Application Fee:** $0.00 **H.S. Requirements:** High school diploma or equivalent not required. For allied health programs: High school diploma required; GED accepted **Scholarships:** Available. **Calendar System:** Semester, Summer session available **Enrollment:** Full-time 8,058, Part-time 18,347 **Faculty:** Full-time 243, Part-time 1,215 **Student-Faculty Ratio:** 22:1 **Regional Accreditation:** North Central Association of Colleges and Schools **Credit Hours For Degree:** 62 credit hours, Associates **Professional Accreditation:** AAMAE, ACEN, ACF, ADA, CoARC, JRCEDMS, JRCERT. **Intercollegiate Athletics:** Basketball M & W; Cross-Country Running M & W; Golf M; Softball W; Volleyball W

OAKLAND UNIVERSITY

Rochester, MI 48309-4401
Tel: (248)370-2100; Free: 800-OAK-UNIV
Fax: (248)370-4462
E-mail: ouinfo@oakland.edu
Web Site: www.oakland.edu
President/CEO: Dr. George W. Hynd
Admissions: Dawn M. Aubry
Financial Aid: Cindy Hermsen

Type: University **Sex:** Coed **Scores:** 49.4% ACT 18-23; 36.7% ACT 24-29 **% Accepted:** 80 **Admission Plans:** Deferred Admission **Application Deadline:** Rolling **Application Fee:** $0.00 **H.S. Requirements:** High school diploma required; GED accepted **Costs Per Year:** Application fee: $0. State resident tuition: $11,513 full-time, $383.75 per credit hour part-time. Nonresident tuition: $23,873 full-time, $795.75 per credit hour part-time. Full-time tuition varies according to program and student level. Part-time tuition varies according to program and student level. College room and board: $9250. Room and board charges vary according to housing facility. **Scholarships:** Available. **Calendar System:** Semester, Summer session available **Enrollment:** Full-time 12,887, Graduate full-time 1,688, Graduate part-time 1,780, Part-time 3,906 **Faculty:** Full-time 573, Part-time 596 **Student-Faculty Ratio:** 21:1 **Exams:** ACT essay component used for placement; SAT I and SAT II or ACT; SAT I or ACT; SAT II; SAT essay component used for placement; SAT Reasoning. **% Receiving Financial Aid:** 63 **% Residing in College-Owned, -Operated, or -Affiliated Housing:** 16 **Final Year or Final Semester Residency Requirement:** No **Regional Accreditation:** North Central Association of Colleges and Schools **Credit Hours For Degree:** 124 credits, Bachelors **ROTC:** Air Force **Professional Accreditation:** AACN, AACSB, AANA, ABET, ACA, APTA, ASC, NASD, NASM, NASPAA, NAST, TEAC. **Intercollegiate Athletics:** Baseball M; Basketball M & W; Cross-Country Running M & W; Golf M & W; Soccer M & W; Softball W; Swimming and Diving M & W; Tennis W; Track and Field M & W; Volleyball W

OLIVET COLLEGE

320 S Main St.
Olivet, MI 49076-9701
Tel: (269)749-7000; Free: 800-456-7189

Fax: (616)749-3821
Web Site: www.olivetcollege.edu
President/CEO: Steven M. Corey, PhD
Financial Aid: Libby M. Jean

Type: Comprehensive **Sex:** Coed **Affiliation:** Congregational Christian Church. **% Accepted:** 61 **Admission Plans:** Deferred Admission **Application Deadline:** Rolling **Application Fee:** $25.00 **H.S. Requirements:** High school diploma required; GED accepted **Costs Per Year:** Application fee: $25. Tuition: $22,950 full-time, $750 per semester hour part-time. Mandatory fees: $851 full-time. College room only: $3950. Room charges vary according to housing facility. **Scholarships:** Available. **Calendar System:** Miscellaneous, Summer session available **Enrollment:** Full-time 922, Graduate part-time 19, Part-time 118 **Faculty:** Full-time 44, Part-time 46 **Student-Faculty Ratio:** 17:1 **Exams:** ACT essay component used for advising; ACT essay component used for placement; SAT I or ACT; SAT essay component used for advising; SAT essay component used for placement. **% Receiving Financial Aid:** 82 **% Residing in College-Owned, -Operated, or -Affiliated Housing:** 49 **Regional Accreditation:** North Central Association of Colleges and Schools **Credit Hours For Degree:** 120 semester hours, Bachelors **ROTC:** Air Force **Professional Accreditation:** TEAC. **Intercollegiate Athletics:** Baseball M; Basketball M & W; Cross-Country Running M & W; Football M; Golf M & W; Lacrosse M & W; Soccer M & W; Softball W; Swimming and Diving M & W; Tennis W; Track and Field M & W; Volleyball W; Wrestling M

ROCHESTER COLLEGE

800 W Avon Rd.
Rochester Hills, MI 48307-2764
Tel: (248)218-2000; Free: 800-521-6010
Fax: (248)218-2005
E-mail: admissions@rc.edu
Web Site: www.rc.edu
President/CEO: Dr. Michael W. Westerfield
Admissions: Larry Norman

Type: Comprehensive **Sex:** Coed **Affiliation:** Church of Christ. **Scores:** 100% SAT V 400+; 83% SAT M 400+; 50% ACT 18-23; 32% ACT 24-29 **% Accepted:** 80 **Admission Plans:** Deferred Admission; Early Admission **Application Deadline:** Rolling **Application Fee:** $25.00 **H.S. Requirements:** High school diploma required; GED accepted **Scholarships:** Available. **Calendar System:** Semester, Summer session available **Enrollment:** Full-time 636, Part-time 334 **Faculty:** Full-time 46, Part-time 113 **Student-Faculty Ratio:** 6:1 **Exams:** SAT I or ACT. **% Residing in College-Owned, -Operated, or -Affiliated Housing:** 25 **Regional Accreditation:** North Central Association of Colleges and Schools **Credit Hours For Degree:** 64 credit hours, Associates; 128 credit hours, Bachelors **Intercollegiate Athletics:** Baseball M; Basketball M & W; Golf M; Soccer M & W; Softball W; Volleyball W

SACRED HEART MAJOR SEMINARY

2701 Chicago Blvd.
Detroit, MI 48206-1799
Tel: (313)883-8500
Web Site: www.shms.edu
President/CEO: Mgr. Jeffrey Monforton
Admissions: Fr. Michael Byrnes

Type: Comprehensive **Sex:** Coed **Affiliation:** Roman Catholic. **Scores:** 33% ACT 18-23; 67% ACT 24-29 **% Accepted:** 100 **Admission Plans:** Deferred Admission; Early Admission; Preferred Admission **Application Deadline:** August 15 **Application Fee:** $30.00 **H.S. Requirements:** High school diploma required; GED accepted **Costs Per Year:** Application fee: $30. Comprehensive fee: $19,879 includes full-time tuition ($10,010), mandatory fees ($100), and college room and board ($9769). **Scholarships:** Available. **Calendar System:** Semester **Enrollment:** Full-time 57, Graduate full-time 80, Graduate part-time 122, Part-time 207 **Faculty:** Full-time 29, Part-time 46 **Student-Faculty Ratio:** 6:1 **Exams:** ACT essay component used for admission; SAT I or ACT; SAT essay component used for admission; SAT Reasoning; SAT Subject. **% Residing in College-Owned, -Operated, or -Affiliated Housing:** 17 **Regional Accreditation:** North Central Association of Colleges and Schools **Credit Hours For Degree:** 64 credits, Associates; 120 credits, Bachelors **Professional Accreditation:** ACIPE, ATS.

SAGINAW CHIPPEWA TRIBAL COLLEGE

2274 Enterprise Dr.
Mount Pleasant, MI 48858

Tel: (989)775-4123
Fax: (989)775-4528
E-mail: flaugher.amanda@sagchip.org
Web Site: www.sagchip.edu
President/CEO: Pres. Carla Sineway
Admissions: Amanda Flaugher

Type: Two-Year College **Sex:** Coed **Costs Per Year:** Tuition: $1560 full-time, $60 per contact hour part-time. Mandatory fees: $650 full-time, $25 per credit hour part-time. Full-time tuition and fees vary according to class time, course level, course load, degree level, location, program, and student level. Part-time tuition and fees vary according to class time, course level, course load, degree level, location, program, and student level. **Calendar System:** Semester **Enrollment:** Full-time 39, Part-time 83 **Faculty:** Full-time 7, Part-time 11 **Student-Faculty Ratio:** 7:1 **Final Year or Final Semester Residency Requirement:** No **Regional Accreditation:** North Central Association of Colleges and Schools **Credit Hours For Degree:** 61 credits, Associates

SAGINAW VALLEY STATE UNIVERSITY

7400 Bay Rd.
University Center, MI 48710
Tel: (989)964-4000; Free: 800-968-9500
Fax: (989)964-0180
E-mail: admissions@svsu.edu
Web Site: www.svsu.edu
President/CEO: Dr. Donald Bachand
Admissions: Jennifer Pahl
Financial Aid: Robert Lemuel

Type: Comprehensive **Sex:** Coed **Scores:** 57.46% ACT 18-23; 33.31% ACT 24-29 **% Accepted:** 76 **Admission Plans:** Deferred Admission **Application Deadline:** Rolling **Application Fee:** $30.00 **H.S. Requirements:** High school diploma required; GED accepted **Costs Per Year:** Application fee: $30. State resident tuition: $8531 full-time, $284.35 per credit hour part-time. Nonresident tuition: $20,624 full-time, $687.45 per credit hour part-time. Mandatory fees: $438 full-time, $14.60 per credit hour part-time. Full-time tuition and fees vary according to course level, degree level, location, and program. Part-time tuition and fees vary according to course level, degree level, location, and program. College room and board: $8600. College room only: $5850. Room and board charges vary according to board plan and housing facility. **Scholarships:** Available. **Calendar System:** Semester, Summer session available **Enrollment:** Full-time 7,377, Graduate full-time 292, Graduate part-time 711, Part-time 1,386 **Faculty:** Full-time 308, Part-time 447 **Student-Faculty Ratio:** 18:1 **Exams:** SAT I or ACT. **% Receiving Financial Aid:** 66 **% Residing in College-Owned, -Operated, or -Affiliated Housing:** 31 **Final Year or Final Semester Residency Requirement:** Yes **Regional Accreditation:** North Central Association of Colleges and Schools **Credit Hours For Degree:** 124 credit hours, Bachelors **Professional Accreditation:** AACN, AACSB, ABET, AOTA, CSWE, NASM, NCATE. **Intercollegiate Athletics:** Baseball M; Basketball M & W; Bowling M & W; Cheerleading M & W; Cross-Country Running M & W; Equestrian Sports M & W; Football M; Golf M; Gymnastics M & W; Ice Hockey M & W; Lacrosse M & W; Rugby M & W; Soccer M & W; Softball W; Swimming and Diving M & W; Tennis M & W; Track and Field M & W; Volleyball W; Wrestling M

ST. CLAIR COUNTY COMMUNITY COLLEGE

323 Erie St.
Port Huron, MI 48061-5015
Tel: (810)984-3881; Free: 800-553-2427
Fax: (810)984-4730
Web Site: www.sc4.edu
President/CEO: Dr. Deborah Snyder
Admissions: Carrie Bearss

Type: Two-Year College **Sex:** Coed **Affiliation:** Michigan Department of Education. **Admission Plans:** Early Admission; Open Admission **Application Deadline:** Rolling **Application Fee:** $0.00 **H.S. Requirements:** High school diploma or equivalent not required **Costs Per Year:** Application fee: $0. Area resident tuition: $3689 full-time, $105 per contact hour part-time. State resident tuition: $6758 full-time, $204 per contact hour part-time. Nonresident tuition: $9672 full-time, $298 per contact hour part-time. Mandatory fees: $154 full-time, $14 per contact hour part-time. Full-time tuition and fees vary according to course load and location. Part-time tuition and fees vary according to course load and location. **Scholarships:** Available. **Calendar System:** Semester, Summer session available **Enrollment:** Full-

time 1,399, Part-time 2,331 **Faculty:** Full-time 74, Part-time 180 **Student-Faculty Ratio:** 19:1 **Regional Accreditation:** North Central Association of Colleges and Schools **Credit Hours For Degree:** 62 credits, Associates **Intercollegiate Athletics:** Baseball M; Basketball M & W; Golf M; Softball W; Volleyball W

SCHOOLCRAFT COLLEGE

18600 Haggerty Rd.
Livonia, MI 48152-2696
Tel: (734)462-4400
Fax: (734)462-4553
E-mail: gotoSC@schoolcraft.edu
Web Site: www.schoolcraft.edu
President/CEO: Dr. Conway Jeffress
Admissions: Nicole Wilson-Fennell

Type: Two-Year College **Sex:** Coed **Affiliation:** Michigan Department of Education. **Admission Plans:** Deferred Admission; Early Admission; Open Admission **Application Deadline:** Rolling **Application Fee:** $0.00 **H.S. Requirements:** High school diploma required; GED accepted **Costs Per Year:** Application fee: $0. Area resident tuition: $2880 full-time, $96 per semester hour part-time. State resident tuition: $4170 full-time, $139 per semester hour part-time. Nonresident tuition: $6150 full-time, $205 per semester hour part-time. Mandatory fees: $684 full-time, $20 per credit hour part-time, $42 per term part-time. **Scholarships:** Available. **Calendar System:** Semester, Summer session available **Enrollment:** Full-time 3,148, Part-time 8,539 **Faculty:** Full-time 99, Part-time 439 **Student-Faculty Ratio:** 25:1 **Regional Accreditation:** North Central Association of Colleges and Schools **Credit Hours For Degree:** 60 credit hours, Associates; 120 credit hours, Bachelors **Professional Accreditation:** ACF, AHIMA. **Intercollegiate Athletics:** Baseball M; Basketball M & W; Bowling M & W; Cross-Country Running M & W; Golf M; Soccer M & W; Softball W; Volleyball W

SIENA HEIGHTS UNIVERSITY

1247 E Siena Heights Dr.
Adrian, MI 49221-1796
Tel: (517)263-0731; Free: 800-521-0009
Fax: (517)264-7745
E-mail: tmohre@sienaheights.edu
Web Site: www.sienaheights.edu
President/CEO: Señor Peg Albert, OP, PhD
Admissions: Trudy Mohre

Type: Comprehensive **Sex:** Coed **Affiliation:** Roman Catholic. **% Accepted:** 74 **Admission Plans:** Deferred Admission **Application Deadline:** Rolling **H.S. Requirements:** High school diploma required; GED accepted **Costs Per Year:** Comprehensive fee: $33,460 includes full-time tuition ($23,320), mandatory fees ($430), and college room and board ($9710). Full-time tuition and fees vary according to course load, location, and program. Room and board charges vary according to board plan, housing facility, and location. Part-time tuition: $480 per semester hour. Part-time tuition varies according to course load, location, and program. **Scholarships:** Available. **Calendar System:** Semester, Summer session available **Enrollment:** Full-time 1,245, Graduate full-time 3, Graduate part-time 237, Part-time 1,157 **Faculty:** Full-time 85, Part-time 183 **Student-Faculty Ratio:** 12:1 **Exams:** ACT essay component not used; SAT I or ACT; SAT essay component not used; SAT Reasoning. **% Residing in College-Owned, -Operated, or -Affiliated Housing:** 25 **Final Year or Final Semester Residency Requirement:** Yes **Regional Accreditation:** North Central Association of Colleges and Schools **Credit Hours For Degree:** 60 semester hours, Associates; 120 semester hours, Bachelors **Professional Accreditation:** AACN, NASAD, TEAC. **Intercollegiate Athletics:** Baseball M; Basketball M & W; Bowling M & W; Cheerleading M & W; Cross-Country Running M & W; Football M; Golf M & W; Lacrosse M & W; Soccer M & W; Softball W; Track and Field M & W; Volleyball M & W

SOUTH UNIVERSITY

41555 Twelve Mile Rd.
Novi, MI 48377
Tel: (248)675-0200; Free: 877-693-2085
Fax: (248)675-0190
Web Site: www.southuniversity.edu/novi.aspx
President/CEO: Theodore C. Blashak

Type: Comprehensive **Sex:** Coed **Affiliation:** Education Management Corporation. **Regional Accreditation:** Southern Association of Colleges and Schools **Professional Accreditation:** ACBSP.

SOUTHWESTERN MICHIGAN COLLEGE

58900 Cherry Grove Rd.
Dowagiac, MI 49047-9793
Tel: (269)782-1000; Free: 800-456-8675
Fax: (269)782-8414
E-mail: apalsak@swmich.edu
Web Site: www.swmich.edu
President/CEO: Dr. David Mathews
Admissions: Angela Palsak

Type: Two-Year College **Sex:** Coed **% Accepted:** 99 **Admission Plans:** Deferred Admission; Open Admission **Application Deadline:** Rolling **H.S. Requirements:** High school diploma required; GED accepted **Costs Per Year:** Area resident tuition: $2938 full-time, $113 per contact hour part-time. State resident tuition: $3816 full-time, $146.75 per contact hour part-time. Nonresident tuition: $4154 full-time, $159.75 per contact hour part-time. Mandatory fees: $1190 full-time, $45.75 per contact hour part-time. College room and board: $8700. College room only: $5980. **Scholarships:** Available. **Calendar System:** Semester, Summer session available **Enrollment:** Full-time 1,122, Part-time 1,226 **Faculty:** Full-time 51, Part-time 98 **Student-Faculty Ratio:** 18:1 **% Residing in College-Owned, -Operated, or -Affiliated Housing:** 20 **Regional Accreditation:** North Central Association of Colleges and Schools **Credit Hours For Degree:** 60 credit hours, Associates

SPRING ARBOR UNIVERSITY

106 E Main St.
Spring Arbor, MI 49283-9799
Tel: (517)750-1200; Free: 800-968-0011
Fax: (517)750-1604
E-mail: admissions@arbor.edu
Web Site: www.arbor.edu
President/CEO: Dr. Brent D. Ellis
Financial Aid: Herbert Rotich

Type: Comprehensive **Sex:** Coed **Affiliation:** Free Methodist. **Scores:** 43% ACT 18-23; 40% ACT 24-29 **% Accepted:** 69 **Admission Plans:** Deferred Admission; Early Admission **Application Deadline:** August 1 **Application Fee:** $30.00 **H.S. Requirements:** High school diploma required; GED accepted **Costs Per Year:** Application fee: $30. Comprehensive fee: $34,385 includes full-time tuition ($24,910), mandatory fees ($605), and college room and board ($8870). College room only: $4130. Full-time tuition and fees vary according to course load, degree level, and program. Room and board charges vary according to board plan and housing facility. Part-time tuition: $605 per credit hour. Part-time mandatory fees: $295 per term. Part-time tuition and fees vary according to course load, degree level, program, and reciprocity agreements. **Scholarships:** Available. **Calendar System:** 4-1-4, Summer session available **Enrollment:** Full-time 1,703, Graduate full-time 587, Graduate part-time 382, Part-time 732 **Faculty:** Full-time 84, Part-time 54 **Student-Faculty Ratio:** 13:1 **Exams:** ACT; ACT essay component not used; SAT I or ACT; SAT essay component not used; SAT Reasoning. **% Receiving Financial Aid:** 84 **% Residing in College-Owned, -Operated, or -Affiliated Housing:** 70 **Final Year or Final Semester Residency Requirement:** No **Regional Accreditation:** North Central Association of Colleges and Schools **Credit Hours For Degree:** 62 credits, Associates; 124 credits, Bachelors **ROTC:** Air Force, Army **Professional Accreditation:** AACN, CSWE, TEAC. **Intercollegiate Athletics:** Baseball M; Basketball M & W; Cross-Country Running M & W; Golf M & W; Soccer M & W; Softball W; Tennis M & W; Track and Field M & W; Volleyball W

UNIVERSITY OF DETROIT MERCY

4001 W McNichols Rd.
Detroit, MI 48221
Tel: (313)993-1000; Free: 800-635-5020
Fax: (313)993-3326
E-mail: admissions@udmercy.edu
Web Site: www.udmercy.edu
President/CEO: Dr. Antoine Garibaldi
Financial Aid: Jenny McAlonan

Type: University **Sex:** Coed **Affiliation:** Roman Catholic (Jesuit). **Scores:** 82% SAT V 400+; 86% SAT M 400+; 45% ACT 18-23; 45% ACT 24-29 **% Accepted:** 73 **Admission Plans:** Deferred Admission **Application Deadline:** Rolling **Application Fee:** $0.00 **H.S. Requirements:** High school diploma required; GED accepted **Costs Per Year:** Application fee: $0. Comprehensive fee: $49,106 includes full-time tuition ($39,882) and college room and board ($9224). Full-time tuition varies according to program.

Room and board charges vary according to board plan and housing facility. Part-time tuition: $1016 per credit hour. Part-time tuition varies according to location and program. **Scholarships:** Available. **Calendar System:** Semester, Summer session available **Enrollment:** Full-time 2,081, Graduate full-time 1,580, Graduate part-time 668, Part-time 591 **Faculty:** Full-time 322, Part-time 402 **Student-Faculty Ratio:** 11:1 **Exams:** ACT essay component not used; SAT I and SAT II or ACT; SAT I or ACT; SAT II; SAT essay component not used; SAT Reasoning; SAT Subject. **% Receiving Financial Aid:** 71 **% Residing in College-Owned, -Operated, or -Affiliated Housing:** 30 **Final Year or Final Semester Residency Requirement:** No **Regional Accreditation:** North Central Association of Colleges and Schools **Credit Hours For Degree:** 126 credit hours, Bachelors **Professional Accreditation:** AACN, AACSB, AALS, AANA, ABA, ABET, ACA, ADA, APA, CSWE, NAAB, TEAC. **Intercollegiate Athletics:** Basketball M & W; Cross-Country Running M & W; Fencing M & W; Golf M & W; Lacrosse M & W; Soccer M & W; Softball W; Tennis M & W; Track and Field M & W

UNIVERSITY OF MICHIGAN

Ann Arbor, MI 48109
Tel: (734)764-1817
Fax: (734)936-0740
E-mail: yale@umich.edu
Web Site: www.umich.edu
President/CEO: Dr. Mark S. Schlissel
Admissions: Erica Sanders

Type: University **Sex:** Coed **Scores:** 101% SAT V 400+; 100% SAT M 400+; 3% ACT 18-23; 26% ACT 24-29 **% Accepted:** 26 **Admission Plans:** Deferred Admission; Early Decision Plan **Application Deadline:** February 1 **Application Fee:** $75.00 **H.S. Requirements:** High school diploma required; GED accepted **Costs Per Year:** Application fee: $75. State resident tuition: $13,528 full-time, $534 per credit hour part-time. Nonresident tuition: $43,148 full-time, $1768 per credit hour part-time. Mandatory fees: $328 full-time, $164 per term part-time. Full-time tuition and fees vary according to course load, degree level, program, and student level. Part-time tuition and fees vary according to course load, degree level, program, and student level. College room and board: $10,554. Room and board charges vary according to board plan and housing facility. **Scholarships:** Available. **Calendar System:** Trimester, Summer session available **Enrollment:** Full-time 27,258, Graduate full-time 13,856, Graduate part-time 1,483, Part-time 1,054 **Faculty:** Full-time 2,735, Part-time 593 **Student-Faculty Ratio:** 15:1 **Exams:** SAT I or ACT; SAT II; SAT Reasoning. **% Receiving Financial Aid:** 38 **% Residing in College-Owned, -Operated, or -Affiliated Housing:** 33 **Final Year or Final Semester Residency Requirement:** No **Regional Accreditation:** North Central Association of Colleges and Schools **Credit Hours For Degree:** 120 credits, Bachelors **ROTC:** Air Force, Army, Navy **Professional Accreditation:** AACN, AACSB, AALS, ABA, ABET, ACNM, ACPE, ACSP, ADA, ALA, AND, APA, ARCMI, ASLA, CAHME, CEPH, CSWE, LCME/AMA, NAAB, NASAD, NASD, NASM, SAF, TEAC. **Intercollegiate Athletics:** Baseball M; Basketball M & W; Cheerleading M & W; Crew M & W; Cross-Country Running M & W; Fencing M & W; Field Hockey W; Football M; Golf M & W; Gymnastics M & W; Ice Hockey M; Lacrosse M & W; Riflery M & W; Rugby M & W; Sailing M & W; Soccer M & W; Softball W; Swimming and Diving M & W; Table Tennis M & W; Tennis M & W; Track and Field M & W; Ultimate Frisbee M & W; Volleyball M & W; Water Polo M & W; Wrestling M

UNIVERSITY OF MICHIGAN–DEARBORN

4901 Evergreen Rd.
Dearborn, MI 48128
Tel: (313)593-5000
E-mail: admissions@umd.umich.edu
Web Site: www.umdearborn.edu
President/CEO: Dr. Daniel Little, PhD
Admissions: Deb Peffer
Financial Aid: Katherine M. Allen

Type: Comprehensive **Sex:** Coed **Affiliation:** University of Michigan System. **Scores:** 44% ACT 18-23; 43% ACT 24-29 **% Accepted:** 62 **Admission Plans:** Deferred Admission **Application Deadline:** Rolling **Application Fee:** $30.00 **H.S. Requirements:** High school diploma required; GED accepted **Costs Per Year:** Application fee: $30. One-time mandatory fee: $75. State resident tuition: $10,878 full-time, $430 per credit hour part-time. Nonresident tuition: $23,094 full-time, $919 per credit hour part-time. Mandatory fees: $826 full-time, $554 per term part-time. Full-time tuition and fees vary according to course level, course load, degree level, program, and student level. Part-time tuition and fees vary according to course level, course load, degree level, program, and student level. **Scholarships:** Available. **Calendar System:** Semester, Summer session available **Enrollment:** Full-time 5,035, Graduate full-time 516, Graduate part-time 1,348, Part-time 2,167 **Faculty:** Full-time 322, Part-time 233 **Student-Faculty Ratio:** 15:1 **Exams:** ACT essay component not used; SAT I or ACT; SAT essay component not used; SAT Reasoning. **% Receiving Financial Aid:** 67 **Final Year or Final Semester Residency Requirement:** No **Regional Accreditation:** North Central Association of Colleges and Schools **Credit Hours For Degree:** 120 credit hours, Bachelors **ROTC:** Air Force, Army, Navy **Professional Accreditation:** AACSB, ABET, TEAC. **Intercollegiate Athletics:** Basketball M & W; Bowling M & W; Cheerleading M & W; Cross-Country Running M & W; Ice Hockey M; Lacrosse M; Rugby M; Soccer M & W; Softball W; Tennis M & W; Ultimate Frisbee M; Volleyball W; Wrestling M

UNIVERSITY OF MICHIGAN–FLINT

303 E Kearsley St.
Flint, MI 48502-1950
Tel: (810)762-3300; Free: 800-942-5636
E-mail: admissions@umflint.edu
Web Site: www.umflint.edu
President/CEO: Dr. Susan E. Borrego
Admissions: Jon Davidson
Financial Aid: Lori Vedder

Type: Comprehensive **Sex:** Coed **Affiliation:** University of Michigan System. **Scores:** 92% SAT V 400+; 92% SAT M 400+; 49% ACT 18-23; 25% ACT 24-29 **% Accepted:** 74 **Admission Plans:** Deferred Admission **Application Deadline:** August 1 **Application Fee:** $30.00 **H.S. Requirements:** High school diploma required; GED accepted **Costs Per Year:** Application fee: $30. State resident tuition: $10,026 full-time, $396 per credit hour part-time. Nonresident tuition: $19,548 full-time, $790 per credit hour part-time. Mandatory fees: $432 full-time, $167 per term part-time. Full-time tuition and fees vary according to course level, course load, degree level, program, and student level. Part-time tuition and fees vary according to course level, course load, degree level, program, and student level. College room and board: $8178. College room only: $5178. Room and board charges vary according to housing facility. **Scholarships:** Available. **Calendar System:** Semester, Summer session available **Enrollment:** Full-time 4,006, Graduate full-time 633, Graduate part-time 969, Part-time 2,862 **Faculty:** Full-time 318, Part-time 266 **Student-Faculty Ratio:** 15:1 **Exams:** ACT essay component not used; SAT I or ACT; SAT essay component not used; SAT Reasoning; SAT Subject. **% Receiving Financial Aid:** 70 **% Residing in College-Owned, -Operated, or -Affiliated Housing:** 4 **Final Year or Final Semester Residency Requirement:** No **Regional Accreditation:** North Central Association of Colleges and Schools **Credit Hours For Degree:** 120 credit hours, Bachelors **ROTC:** Army **Professional Accreditation:** AACN, AACSB, AANA, APTA, CSWE, JRCERT, NASM.

UNIVERSITY OF PHOENIX–DETROIT CAMPUS

26261 Evergreen Rd.
Southfield, MI 48076
Tel: (248)675-3700; Free: 866-766-0766
Web Site: www.phoenix.edu
Type: Comprehensive **Sex:** Coed **Scholarships:** Available. **Regional Accreditation:** North Central Association of Colleges and Schools

WALSH COLLEGE OF ACCOUNTANCY AND BUSINESS ADMINISTRATION

3838 Livernois Rd.
Troy, MI 48007-7006
Tel: (248)689-8282; Free: 800-925-7401
Fax: (248)524-2520
E-mail: hrigby@walshcollege.edu
Web Site: www.walshcollege.edu
President/CEO: Stephanie W. Bergeron, MBA
Admissions: Heather Rigby
Financial Aid: Catherine Duff Berrahou

Type: Two-Year Upper Division **Sex:** Coed **Admission Plans:** Deferred Admission; Open Admission **Application Fee:** $35.00 **H.S. Requirements:** High school diploma required; GED accepted **Costs Per Year:** Application fee: $35. Tuition: $15,084 full-time, $7542 per year part-time. Mandatory fees: $375 full-time, $375 per year part-time. Full-time tuition and fees vary according to course level and degree level. Part-time tuition and fees vary according to course level and degree level. **Scholarships:** Available.

Calendar System: Miscellaneous, Summer session available **Enrollment:** Full-time 98, Graduate full-time 38, Graduate part-time 1,544, Part-time 869 **Faculty:** Full-time 23, Part-time 159 **Final Year or Final Semester Residency Requirement:** Yes **Regional Accreditation:** North Central Association of Colleges and Schools **Credit Hours For Degree:** 127 credit hours, Bachelors **Professional Accreditation:** ACBSP.

WASHTENAW COMMUNITY COLLEGE

4800 E Huron River Dr.
Ann Arbor, MI 48106
Tel: (734)973-3300
Fax: (734)677-5408
Web Site: www.wccnet.edu
President/CEO: Larry Whitworth
Admissions: Sukanya J. Jett

Type: Two-Year College **Sex:** Coed **Admission Plans:** Deferred Admission; Early Admission; Open Admission; Preferred Admission **Application Deadline:** Rolling **H.S. Requirements:** High school diploma or equivalent not required. For health occupations programs: High school diploma required; GED accepted **Scholarships:** Available. **Calendar System:** Semester, Summer session available **Student-Faculty Ratio:** 16:1 **Exams:** SAT I or ACT. **Regional Accreditation:** North Central Association of Colleges and Schools **Credit Hours For Degree:** 60 credit hours, Associates **ROTC:** Air Force, Army, Navy **Professional Accreditation:** ACEN, ACF, ADA, JRCERT.

WAYNE COUNTY COMMUNITY COLLEGE DISTRICT

801 W Fort St.
Detroit, MI 48226-3010
Tel: (313)496-2600
Fax: (313)961-2791
E-mail: aphilli1@wcccd.edu
Web Site: www.wcccd.edu
President/CEO: Dr. Curtis L. Ivery
Admissions: Adrian Phillips

Type: Two-Year College **Sex:** Coed **Admission Plans:** Deferred Admission; Early Admission; Open Admission **Application Deadline:** Rolling **H.S. Requirements:** High school diploma required; GED accepted **Costs Per Year:** Area resident tuition: $2,545 full-time. State resident tuition: $2,812 full-time. Nonresident tuition: $3,539 full-time. Mandatory fees: $268 full-time. **Scholarships:** Available. **Calendar System:** Semester, Summer session available **Enrollment:** Full-time 3,137, Part-time 13,517 **Student-Faculty Ratio:** 24:1 **Regional Accreditation:** North Central Association of Colleges and Schools **Credit Hours For Degree:** 60 credits, Associates **Professional Accreditation:** ADA, AOTA, ARCST, CoARC. **Intercollegiate Athletics:** Basketball M & W; Bowling M & W; Cross-Country Running M & W; Golf M; Volleyball W

WAYNE STATE UNIVERSITY

656 W Kirby St.
Detroit, MI 48202
Tel: (313)577-2424; Free: 877-WSU-INFO
Fax: (313)577-7536
E-mail: admissions@wayne.edu
Web Site: www.wayne.edu
President/CEO: Dr. M. Roy Wilson, MD
Admissions: La Joyce Brown
Financial Aid: Catherine Kay

Type: University **Sex:** Coed **Scores:** 47% ACT 18-23; 35% ACT 24-29 **% Accepted:** 80 **Admission Plans:** Deferred Admission **Application Deadline:** August 1 **Application Fee:** $25.00 **H.S. Requirements:** High school diploma required; GED accepted **Costs Per Year:** Application fee: $25. One-time mandatory fee: $250. State resident tuition: $11,347 full-time, $378.23 per credit hour part-time. Nonresident tuition: $26,044 full-time, $868.15 per credit hour part-time. Mandatory fees: $1,398 full-time, $32.95 per credit hour part-time, $204.85 per term part-time. Full-time tuition and fees vary according to course load, program, reciprocity agreements, and student level. Part-time tuition and fees vary according to course load, program, reciprocity agreements, and student level. College room and board: $10,061. College room only: $5901. Room and board charges vary according to board plan, housing facility, and student level. **Scholarships:** Available. **Calendar System:** Semester, Summer session available **Enrollment:** Full-time 11,907, Graduate full-time 6,066, Graduate part-time 3,487, Part-time 5,762 **Faculty:** Full-time 1,024, Part-time 775 **Student-Faculty

Ratio: 16:1 **Exams:** ACT essay component not used; SAT I or ACT; SAT essay component not used; SAT Reasoning; SAT Subject. **% Receiving Financial Aid:** 74 **% Residing in College-Owned, -Operated, or -Affiliated Housing:** 12 **Final Year or Final Semester Residency Requirement:** Yes **Regional Accreditation:** North Central Association of Colleges and Schools **Credit Hours For Degree:** 120 credit hours, Bachelors **ROTC:** Air Force, Army **Professional Accreditation:** AACN, AACSB, AALS, AANA, ABA, ABET, ABFSE, ACA, ACEN, ACNM, ACPE, ACSP, ALA, AND, AOTA, APA, APTA, ASC, ASHA, CORE, CSWE, JRCERT, LCME/AMA, NAACLS, NASD, NASM, NASPAA, NAST, TEAC. **Intercollegiate Athletics:** Baseball M; Basketball M & W; Cheerleading M & W; Cross-Country Running M & W; Fencing M & W; Football M; Golf M & W; Lacrosse M & W; Soccer M & W; Softball W; Swimming and Diving M & W; Tennis M & W; Track and Field W; Volleyball W

WEST SHORE COMMUNITY COLLEGE

PO Box 277, 3000 N Stiles Rd.
Scottville, MI 49454-0277
Tel: (231)845-6211
Fax: (231)845-0207
E-mail: admissions@westshore.edu
Web Site: www.westshore.edu
President/CEO: Charles T. Dillon
Admissions: Wendy Fought
Financial Aid: Victoria Oddo

Type: Two-Year College **Sex:** Coed **Affiliation:** Michigan Department of Education. **% Accepted:** 100 **Admission Plans:** Deferred Admission; Early Admission; Open Admission **Application Deadline:** Rolling **Application Fee:** $15.00 **H.S. Requirements:** High school diploma or equivalent not required. For nursing program: High school diploma required; GED accepted **Scholarships:** Available. **Calendar System:** Semester, Summer session available **Faculty:** Full-time 28, Part-time 72 **Regional Accreditation:** North Central Association of Colleges and Schools **Credit Hours For Degree:** 60 credits, Associates

WESTERN MICHIGAN UNIVERSITY

1903 W Michigan Ave.
Kalamazoo, MI 49008
Tel: (269)387-1000
Fax: (269)387-2096
E-mail: ask-wmu@wmich.edu
Web Site: www.wmich.edu
President/CEO: Dr. John M. Dunn
Financial Aid: Terrell Hodge

Type: University **Sex:** Coed **Scores:** 51.06% ACT 18-23; 32.11% ACT 24-29 **% Accepted:** 82 **Application Deadline:** Rolling **Application Fee:** $40.00 **H.S. Requirements:** High school diploma required; GED accepted **Costs Per Year:** Application fee: $40. One-time mandatory fee: $300. State resident tuition: $10,106 full-time, $349.47 per credit hour part-time. Nonresident tuition: $24,790 full-time, $857.32 per credit hour part-time. Mandatory fees: $923 full-time, $258.50 per term part-time. Full-time tuition and fees vary according to course load, location, program, and student level. Part-time tuition and fees vary according to course load, location, program, and student level. College room and board: $9238. College room only: $4765. Room and board charges vary according to board plan and housing facility. **Scholarships:** Available. **Calendar System:** Semester, Summer session available **Enrollment:** Full-time 15,416, Graduate full-time 1,118, Graduate part-time 3,871, Part-time 3,151 **Faculty:** Full-time 946, Part-time 494 **Student-Faculty Ratio:** 17:1 **Exams:** ACT essay component not used; SAT I or ACT; SAT essay component not used; SAT Reasoning; SAT Subject. **% Receiving Financial Aid:** 61 **% Residing in College-Owned, -Operated, or -Affiliated Housing:** 27 **Final Year or Final Semester Residency Requirement:** No **Regional Accreditation:** North Central Association of Colleges and Schools **Credit Hours For Degree:** 122 credit hours, Bachelors **ROTC:** Army **Professional Accreditation:** AABI, AACN, AACSB, AAFCS, ABET, ACA, AND, AOTA, APA, ASHA, CIDA, CORE, CSWE, NASAD, NASD, NASM, NASPAA, NAST, NCATE. **Intercollegiate Athletics:** Baseball M; Basketball M & W; Cross-Country Running W; Equestrian Sports W; Football M; Golf M & W; Gymnastics W; Ice Hockey M; Lacrosse M & W; Rugby M & W; Sailing M & W; Skiing (Downhill) M & W; Soccer M & W; Softball W; Swimming and Diving M & W; Tennis M & W; Track and Field W; Ultimate Frisbee M; Volleyball M & W; Water Polo M & W

YESHIVA BETH YEHUDA–YESHIVA GEDOLAH OF GREATER DETROIT

24600 Greenfield
Oak Park, MI 48237-1544
Tel: (248)968-3360
President/CEO: Rabbi P. Rushnawitz
Admissions: Rabbi P. Rushnawitz
Financial Aid: Rabbi P. Rushnawitz

Type: Comprehensive **Sex:** Men **Affiliation:** Jewish. **% Accepted:** 100 **H.S. Requirements:** High school diploma required; GED not accepted **Professional Accreditation:** AARTS.

ACADEMY COLLEGE
1101 E 78th St.
Bloomington, MN 55420
Tel: (952)851-0066; Free: 800-292-9149
Fax: (952)851-0094
E-mail: admissions@academycollege.edu
Web Site: www.academycollege.edu
President/CEO: Nancy Grazzini-Olson
Admissions: Tracey Schantz
Financial Aid: Kellye MacLeod
Type: Four-Year College **Sex:** Coed **Admission Plans:** Deferred Admission; Early Admission; Open Admission **Application Fee:** $30.00 **H.S. Requirements:** High school diploma required; GED accepted **Scholarships:** Available. **Calendar System:** Quarter, Summer session available **Enrollment:** Full-time 141, Part-time 9 **Faculty:** Full-time 4, Part-time 50 **Student-Faculty Ratio:** 7:1 **% Receiving Financial Aid:** 79 **Credit Hours For Degree:** 102 credit hours, Associates; 180 credit hours, Bachelors **Professional Accreditation:** ACICS.

ALEXANDRIA TECHNICAL AND COMMUNITY COLLEGE
1601 Jefferson St.
Alexandria, MN 56308-3707
Tel: (320)762-0221; Free: 888-234-1222
Fax: (320)762-4430
E-mail: info@alextech.edu
Web Site: www.alextech.edu
President/CEO: Laura Urban
Admissions: Danielle Meinert
Type: Two-Year College **Sex:** Coed **Affiliation:** Minnesota State Colleges and Universities System. **Admission Plans:** Deferred Admission; Early Admission; Open Admission **Application Deadline:** Rolling **Application Fee:** $20.00 **H.S. Requirements:** High school diploma required; GED accepted **Costs Per Year:** Application fee: $20. State resident tuition: $4,816 full-time. Nonresident tuition: $4,816 full-time. Mandatory fees: $585 full-time. **Scholarships:** Available. **Calendar System:** Semester, Summer session available **Enrollment:** Full-time 1,355, Part-time 1,347 **Faculty:** Full-time 68, Part-time 27 **Student-Faculty Ratio:** 21:1 **Final Year or Final Semester Residency Requirement:** No **Regional Accreditation:** North Central Association of Colleges and Schools **Credit Hours For Degree:** 1/3 of total credits required for the degree, Associates **Professional Accreditation:** NAACLS.

ANOKA-RAMSEY COMMUNITY COLLEGE
11200 Mississippi Blvd. NW
Coon Rapids, MN 55433-3470
Tel: (763)433-1100
Fax: (763)576-5944
E-mail: admissions@anokaramsey.edu
Web Site: www.anokaramsey.edu
President/CEO: Dr. Kent Hanson
Type: Two-Year College **Sex:** Coed **Affiliation:** Minnesota State Colleges and Universities System. **Admission Plans:** Deferred Admission; Early Admission; Open Admission **Application Deadline:** Rolling **Application Fee:** $0.00 **H.S. Requirements:** High school diploma required; GED accepted **Costs Per Year:** Application fee: $0. State resident tuition: $4,349 full-time, $144.96 per credit part-time. Nonresident tuition: $4,349 full-time, $144.96 per credit part-time. Mandatory fees: $674 full-time, $22 per credit part-time. Full-time tuition and fees vary according to course load and program. Part-time tuition and fees vary according to course load and program. **Scholarships:** Available. **Calendar System:** Semester, Summer session available **Enrollment:** Full-time 3,577, Part-time 5,717 **Faculty:** Full-time 123, Part-time 138 **Student-Faculty Ratio:** 33:1 **Regional Accreditation:** North Central Association of Colleges and Schools **Credit Hours For Degree:** 60 semester credits, Associates **ROTC:** Air Force **Professional Accreditation:** ACEN, APTA. **Intercollegiate Athletics:** Baseball M; Basketball M & W; Soccer M & W; Softball W; Volleyball W

ANOKA TECHNICAL COLLEGE
1355 W Hwy. 10
Anoka, MN 55303
Tel: (612)433-1100
E-mail: enrollmentservices@anokatech.edu
Web Site: www.anokatech.edu
President/CEO: Dean Kent Hanson
Type: Two-Year College **Sex:** Coed **Affiliation:** Minnesota State Colleges and Universities System. **Admission Plans:** Deferred Admission; Open Admission **Application Fee:** $0.00 **H.S. Requirements:** High school diploma required; GED accepted **Costs Per Year:** Application fee: $0. State resident tuition: $5,010 full-time, $166.99 per credit part-time. Nonresident tuition: $5,010 full-time, $166.99 per credit part-time. Mandatory fees: $574 full-time, $19.15 per credit part-time. Full-time tuition and fees vary according to course load, program, and reciprocity agreements. Part-time tuition and fees vary according to course load, program, and reciprocity agreements. **Scholarships:** Available. **Calendar System:** Semester, Summer session not available **Enrollment:** Full-time 885, Part-time 1,142 **Faculty:** Full-time 52, Part-time 45 **Student-Faculty Ratio:** 19:1 **Regional Accreditation:** North Central Association of Colleges and Schools **Credit Hours For Degree:** 64 credits, Associates **Professional Accreditation:** AOTA.

ARGOSY UNIVERSITY, TWIN CITIES
1515 Central Pky.
Eagan, MN 55121
Tel: (651)846-2882; Free: 888-844-2004
Fax: (952)844-0472
Web Site: www.argosy.edu/locations/twin-cities
President/CEO: Scott Tjaden, PhD
Type: University **Sex:** Coed **Affiliation:** Education Management Corporation. **H.S. Requirements:** High school diploma required; GED accepted **Calendar System:** Semester **Regional Accreditation:** Western Association of Colleges and Schools **Professional Accreditation:** AAMAE, AAMFT, ACBSP, ADA, JRCERT, NAACLS.

AUGSBURG COLLEGE
2211 Riverside Ave.
Minneapolis, MN 55454-1351
Tel: (612)330-1000; Free: 800-788-5678
Fax: (612)330-1649
E-mail: vanovers@augsburg.edu
Web Site: www.augsburg.edu

President/CEO: Paul C. Pribbenow
Admissions: Keri VanOverschelde
Financial Aid: Paul L. Terrio

Type: Comprehensive **Sex:** Coed **Affiliation:** Lutheran. **Scores:** 100% SAT V 400+; 87% SAT M 400+; 54% ACT 18-23; 29% ACT 24-29 **% Accepted:** 59 **Admission Plans:** Deferred Admission **Application Deadline:** August 1 **Application Fee:** $0.00 **H.S. Requirements:** High school diploma required; GED accepted **Costs Per Year:** Application fee: $0. Comprehensive fee: $46,075 includes full-time tuition ($35,750), mandatory fees ($665), and college room and board ($9660). College room only: $4975. Full-time tuition and fees vary according to class time and location. Room and board charges vary according to board plan and housing facility. Part-time tuition: $1117 per credit. Part-time mandatory fees: $183 per term. Part-time tuition and fees vary according to class time and location. **Scholarships:** Available. **Calendar System:** Semester, Summer session available **Enrollment:** Full-time 2,032, Graduate full-time 632, Graduate part-time 354, Part-time 504 **Faculty:** Full-time 171, Part-time 212 **Student-Faculty Ratio:** 12:1 **Exams:** ACT essay component used for admission; ACT essay component used for placement; SAT I or ACT; SAT essay component used for admission; SAT essay component used for placement; SAT Reasoning; SAT Subject. **% Receiving Financial Aid:** 71 **% Residing in College-Owned, -Operated, or -Affiliated Housing:** 37 **Final Year or Final Semester Residency Requirement:** Yes **Regional Accreditation:** North Central Association of Colleges and Schools **Credit Hours For Degree:** 32 courses, Bachelors **ROTC:** Air Force, Army, Navy **Professional Accreditation:** AACN, ACBSP, CSWE, NASM, NCATE. **Intercollegiate Athletics:** Baseball M; Basketball M & W; Cross-Country Running M & W; Football M; Golf M & W; Ice Hockey M & W; Lacrosse M; Soccer M & W; Softball W; Swimming and Diving W; Track and Field M & W; Volleyball W; Wrestling M

BEMIDJI STATE UNIVERSITY
1500 Birchmont Dr., NE
Bemidji, MN 56601-2699
Tel: (218)755-2000; Free: 800-475-2001
Fax: (218)755-2074
E-mail: LMorris@bemidjistate.edu
Web Site: www.bemidjistate.edu
President/CEO: Dr. Richard A. Hanson
Admissions: Lincoln Morris

Type: Comprehensive **Sex:** Coed **Affiliation:** Minnesota State Colleges and Universities System. **Scores:** 63.16% ACT 18-23; 23.13% ACT 24-29 **% Accepted:** 94 **Admission Plans:** Deferred Admission; Early Decision Plan **Application Fee:** $20.00 **H.S. Requirements:** High school diploma required; GED accepted **Costs Per Year:** Application fee: $20. State resident tuition: $7360 full-time, $257.35 per credit part-time. Nonresident tuition: $7360 full-time, $257.35 per credit part-time. Mandatory fees: $1006 full-time, $17.93 per credit part-time. Full-time tuition and fees vary according to course load, location, program, and reciprocity agreements. Part-time tuition and fees vary according to course load, location, program, and reciprocity agreements. College room and board: $7690. Room and board charges vary according to board plan and housing facility. **Scholarships:** Available. **Calendar System:** Semester **Enrollment:** Full-time 3,410, Graduate full-time 75, Graduate part-time 199, Part-time 1,329 **Faculty:** Full-time 174, Part-time 93 **Student-Faculty Ratio:** 19:1 **Exams:** ACT essay component not used; SAT I or ACT; SAT essay component not used; SAT Reasoning; SAT Subject. **% Receiving Financial Aid:** 62 **% Residing in College-Owned, -Operated, or -Affiliated Housing:** 28 **Regional Accreditation:** North Central Association of Colleges and Schools **Professional Accreditation:** AACN, CSWE, NASM, NCATE. **Intercollegiate Athletics:** Baseball M; Basketball M & W; Cross-Country Running W; Football M; Golf M & W; Ice Hockey M & W; Soccer W; Softball W; Tennis W; Track and Field W; Volleyball W

BETHANY GLOBAL UNIVERSITY
6820 Auto Club Rd.
Ste. C
Bloomington, MN 55438
Tel: (952)944-2121; Free: 800-323-3417
Web Site: www.bethanygu.edu

Type: Comprehensive **Sex:** Coed **Affiliation:** Christian. **Professional Accreditation:** ABHE.

BETHANY LUTHERAN COLLEGE
700 Luther Dr.
Mankato, MN 56001-6163

Tel: (507)344-7000; Free: 800-944-3066
Fax: (507)344-7376
E-mail: dtomhave@blc.edu
Web Site: www.blc.edu
President/CEO: Dr. Gene Pfeifer
Admissions: Daniel Tomhave

Type: Four-Year College **Sex:** Coed **Affiliation:** Lutheran. **Scores:** 52% ACT 18-23; 35% ACT 24-29 **% Accepted:** 85 **Application Deadline:** July 1 **Application Fee:** $0.00 **H.S. Requirements:** High school diploma required; GED accepted **Costs Per Year:** Application fee: $0. One-time mandatory fee: $130. Comprehensive fee: $32,880 includes full-time tuition ($24,720), mandatory fees ($450), and college room and board ($7710). Room and board charges vary according to board plan, housing facility, and student level. Part-time tuition: $1050 per credit hour. Part-time mandatory fees: $225 per term. Part-time tuition and fees vary according to course load. **Scholarships:** Available. **Calendar System:** Semester, Summer session available **Enrollment:** Full-time 490, Part-time 34 **Faculty:** Full-time 40, Part-time 23 **Student-Faculty Ratio:** 9:1 **Exams:** SAT I or ACT. **% Receiving Financial Aid:** 82 **% Residing in College-Owned, -Operated, or -Affiliated Housing:** 67 **Final Year or Final Semester Residency Requirement:** Yes **Regional Accreditation:** North Central Association of Colleges and Schools **Credit Hours For Degree:** 128 credits, Bachelors **ROTC:** Army **Intercollegiate Athletics:** Baseball M; Basketball M & W; Cross-Country Running M & W; Equestrian Sports M & W; Golf M & W; Soccer M & W; Softball W; Tennis M & W; Track and Field M & W; Volleyball W

BETHEL UNIVERSITY
3900 Bethel Dr.
Saint Paul, MN 55112-6999
Tel: (651)638-6400; Free: 800-255-8706
E-mail: undergrad-admissions@bethel.edu
Web Site: www.bethel.edu
President/CEO: Dr. James (Jay) H. Barnes, III
Financial Aid: Jeffrey D. Olson

Type: Comprehensive **Sex:** Coed **Affiliation:** Baptist General Conference. **Scores:** 37.33% ACT 18-23; 46.17% ACT 24-29 **% Accepted:** 95 **Admission Plans:** Early Admission **Application Deadline:** Rolling **Application Fee:** $0.00 **H.S. Requirements:** High school diploma required; GED accepted **Costs Per Year:** Application fee: $0. Comprehensive fee: $43,910 includes full-time tuition ($33,990), mandatory fees ($150), and college room and board ($9770). College room only: $5590. Room and board charges vary according to board plan. Part-time tuition: $1417 per credit. Part-time tuition varies according to course load. **Scholarships:** Available. **Calendar System:** 4-1-4, Summer session available **Enrollment:** Full-time 2,444, Graduate full-time 1,219, Graduate part-time 588, Part-time 540 **Faculty:** Full-time 174, Part-time 114 **Student-Faculty Ratio:** 12:1 **Exams:** ACT essay component not used; SAT I or ACT; SAT essay component not used. **% Receiving Financial Aid:** 73 **% Residing in College-Owned, -Operated, or -Affiliated Housing:** 72 **Final Year or Final Semester Residency Requirement:** No **Regional Accreditation:** North Central Association of Colleges and Schools **Credit Hours For Degree:** 60 credit hours, Associates; 122 credit hours, Bachelors **ROTC:** Air Force, Army **Professional Accreditation:** AACN, ATS, CSWE, JRCAT, TEAC. **Intercollegiate Athletics:** Baseball M; Basketball M & W; Cross-Country Running M & W; Football M; Golf M & W; Ice Hockey M & W; Soccer M & W; Softball W; Tennis M & W; Track and Field M & W; Volleyball M & W

CAPELLA UNIVERSITY
225 S 6th St., 9th Fl.
Minneapolis, MN 55402
Tel: (612)252-4200; Free: 866-283-7921
Fax: (612)337-5396
E-mail: info@capella.edu
Web Site: www.capella.edu
President/CEO: Scott Kinney

Type: Two-Year Upper Division **Sex:** Coed **Application Deadline:** Rolling **Application Fee:** $50.00 **H.S. Requirements:** High school diploma or equivalent not required **Scholarships:** Available. **Calendar System:** Quarter, Summer session available **Enrollment:** Full-time 1,156, Graduate full-time 1,200, Graduate part-time 27,688, Part-time 6,331 **Regional Accreditation:** North Central Association of Colleges and Schools **Professional Accreditation:** ABET, ACA, ACBSP, NCATE.

CARLETON COLLEGE
One N College St.
Northfield, MN 55057-4001

Tel: (507)646-4000; Free: 800-995-2275
Fax: (507)646-4526
E-mail: admissions@carleton.edu
Web Site: www.carleton.edu
President/CEO: Steven G. Poskanzer, JD
Admissions: Paul Thiboutot
Financial Aid: Rodney M. Oto

Type: Four-Year College **Sex:** Coed **Scores:** 100% SAT V 400+; 100% SAT M 400+; 2.08% ACT 18-23; 24.31% ACT 24-29 **% Accepted:** 21 **Admission Plans:** Deferred Admission; Early Action; Early Admission **Application Deadline:** January 15 **Application Fee:** $30.00 **H.S. Requirements:** High school diploma required; GED accepted **Costs Per Year:** Application fee: $30. Comprehensive fee: $62,046 includes full-time tuition ($48,987), mandatory fees ($276), and college room and board ($12,783). College room only: $6663. Room and board charges vary according to board plan. **Scholarships:** Available. **Calendar System:** Miscellaneous, Summer session not available **Enrollment:** Full-time 1,997, Part-time 17 **Faculty:** Full-time 205, Part-time 40 **Student-Faculty Ratio:** 9:1 **Exams:** SAT I or ACT; SAT II; SAT Reasoning; SAT Subject. **% Receiving Financial Aid:** 56 % **Residing in College-Owned, -Operated, or -Affiliated Housing:** 100 **Final Year or Final Semester Residency Requirement:** No **Regional Accreditation:** North Central Association of Colleges and Schools **Credit Hours For Degree:** 210 credits, Bachelors **Intercollegiate Athletics:** Badminton M & W; Baseball M; Basketball M & W; Cross-Country Running M & W; Equestrian Sports M & W; Fencing M & W; Field Hockey W; Football M; Golf M & W; Ice Hockey M & W; Lacrosse M & W; Rugby M & W; Sailing M & W; Skiing (Cross-Country) M & W; Skiing (Downhill) M & W; Soccer M & W; Softball W; Swimming and Diving M & W; Table Tennis M & W; Tennis M & W; Track and Field M & W; Ultimate Frisbee M & W; Volleyball M & W; Water Polo M & W

CENTRAL LAKES COLLEGE

501 W College Dr.
Brainerd, MN 56401-3904
Tel: (218)855-8000; Free: 800-933-0346
Fax: (218)855-8220
E-mail: cdaniels@clcmn.edu
Web Site: www.clcmn.edu
President/CEO: Dr. Larry Lundblad
Admissions: Rose Tretter
Financial Aid: Mike Barnaby

Type: Two-Year College **Sex:** Coed **Affiliation:** Minnesota State Colleges and Universities System. **Admission Plans:** Deferred Admission; Open Admission **Application Deadline:** Rolling **Application Fee:** $20.00 **H.S. Requirements:** High school diploma required; GED accepted **Costs Per Year:** Application fee: $20. State resident tuition: $4773 full-time, $159 per credit part-time. Nonresident tuition: $4773 full-time, $159 per credit part-time. Mandatory fees: $611 full-time, $20.91 per credit part-time. Full-time tuition and fees vary according to course load and program. Part-time tuition and fees vary according to course load and program. **Scholarships:** Available. **Calendar System:** Semester, Summer session available **Enrollment:** Full-time 1,680, Part-time 2,594 **Faculty:** Full-time 90, Part-time 65 **Student-Faculty Ratio:** 20:1 **Final Year or Final Semester Residency Requirement:** No **Regional Accreditation:** North Central Association of Colleges and Schools **Credit Hours For Degree:** 60 credits, Associates **Professional Accreditation:** ADA. **Intercollegiate Athletics:** Baseball M; Basketball M & W; Football M; Golf M & W; Softball W; Volleyball W

CENTURY COLLEGE

3300 Century Ave. N
White Bear Lake, MN 55110
Tel: (651)779-3200; Free: 800-228-1978
Fax: (651)779-5810
E-mail: admissions@century.edu
Web Site: www.century.edu
President/CEO: Dr. Patrick Opatz, PhD
Admissions: Katy Melek

Type: Two-Year College **Sex:** Coed **Affiliation:** Minnesota State Colleges and Universities System. **% Accepted:** 100 **Admission Plans:** Deferred Admission; Open Admission **Application Deadline:** Rolling **Application Fee:** $20.00 **H.S. Requirements:** High school diploma required; GED accepted **Costs Per Year:** Application fee: $20. State resident tuition: $4818 full-time, $160.60 per semester hour part-time. Nonresident tuition: $4818 full-time, $160.60 per semester hour part-time. Mandatory fees: $573 full-

time, $19.11 per semester hour part-time. Full-time tuition and fees vary according to class time, program, and reciprocity agreements. Part-time tuition and fees vary according to class time, program, and reciprocity agreements. **Scholarships:** Available. **Calendar System:** Semester, Summer session available **Enrollment:** Full-time 3,696, Part-time 5,225 **Faculty:** Full-time 177, Part-time 183 **Student-Faculty Ratio:** 22:1 **Final Year or Final Semester Residency Requirement:** No **Regional Accreditation:** North Central Association of Colleges and Schools **Credit Hours For Degree:** 60 semester credits, Associates **ROTC:** Air Force **Professional Accreditation:** ACEN, ADA, JRCEMTP. **Intercollegiate Athletics:** Baseball M; Soccer M & W; Softball W

COLLEGE OF SAINT BENEDICT

37 S College Ave.
Saint Joseph, MN 56374
Tel: (320)363-5011; Free: 800-544-1489
Fax: (320)363-5010
E-mail: admissions@csbsju.edu
Web Site: www.csbsju.edu
President/CEO: Dr. Mary Dana Hinton, PhD
Admissions: Karen Backes
Financial Aid: Stuart Perry

Type: Four-Year College **Sex:** Women **Affiliation:** Roman Catholic. **Scores:** 100% SAT V 400+; 96% SAT M 400+; 40% ACT 18-23; 45% ACT 24-29 **% Accepted:** 75 **Admission Plans:** Deferred Admission; Early Decision Plan **Application Fee:** $0.00 **H.S. Requirements:** High school diploma required; GED accepted. For home-schooled students with appropriate documentation of college preparatory curriculum: High school diploma or equivalent not required **Costs Per Year:** Application fee: $0. Comprehensive fee: $51,075 includes full-time tuition ($39,850), mandatory fees ($996), and college room and board ($10,229). College room only: $4925. Room and board charges vary according to board plan and housing facility. Part-time tuition: $1660 per credit hour. Part-time tuition varies according to course load. **Scholarships:** Available. **Calendar System:** Semester, Summer session not available **Enrollment:** Full-time 1,927, Part-time 16 **Faculty:** Full-time 142, Part-time 25 **Student-Faculty Ratio:** 12:1 **Exams:** SAT I or ACT. **% Receiving Financial Aid:** 70 % **Residing in College-Owned, -Operated, or -Affiliated Housing:** 90 **Final Year or Final Semester Residency Requirement:** No **Regional Accreditation:** North Central Association of Colleges and Schools **Credit Hours For Degree:** 124 credits, Bachelors **ROTC:** Army **Professional Accreditation:** AACN, AND, CSWE, NASM, NCATE. **Intercollegiate Athletics:** Basketball W; Crew W; Cross-Country Running W; Golf W; Ice Hockey W; Lacrosse W; Rugby W; Skiing (Cross-Country) W; Soccer W; Softball W; Swimming and Diving W; Tennis W; Track and Field W; Ultimate Frisbee W; Volleyball W

THE COLLEGE OF ST. SCHOLASTICA

1200 Kenwood Ave.
Duluth, MN 55811-4199
Tel: (218)723-6000; Free: 800-249-6412
Fax: (218)723-6290
E-mail: admissions@css.edu
Web Site: www.css.edu
President/CEO: Dr. Larry Goodwin
Admissions: Eric Berg
Financial Aid: Jon P. Erickson

Type: Comprehensive **Sex:** Coed **Affiliation:** Roman Catholic Church. **Scores:** 67% SAT V 400+; 67% SAT M 400+; 48.46% ACT 18-23; 42.08% ACT 24-29 **% Accepted:** 61 **Admission Plans:** Deferred Admission **Application Deadline:** Rolling **Application Fee:** $0.00 **H.S. Requirements:** High school diploma required; GED accepted **Costs Per Year:** Application fee: $0. Comprehensive fee: $42,926 includes full-time tuition ($33,784), mandatory fees ($210), and college room and board ($8932). College room only: $4928. Full-time tuition and fees vary according to class time and program. Room and board charges vary according to board plan and housing facility. Part-time tuition: $1056 per credit. Part-time tuition varies according to class time, course load, and program. **Scholarships:** Available. **Calendar System:** Semester, Summer session available **Enrollment:** Full-time 2,277, Graduate full-time 1,012, Graduate part-time 504, Part-time 567 **Faculty:** Full-time 185, Part-time 202 **Student-Faculty Ratio:** 15:1 **Exams:** SAT I or ACT; SAT Reasoning. **% Receiving Financial Aid:** 78 **% Residing in College-Owned, -Operated, or -Affiliated Housing:** 49 **Final Year or Final Semester Residency Requirement:** No **Regional Accreditation:** North Central Association of Colleges and Schools **Credit Hours For**

Degree: 128 credits, Bachelors **ROTC:** Air Force **Professional Accreditation:** AACN, AHIMA, AOTA, APTA, CSWE, TEAC. **Intercollegiate Athletics:** Baseball M; Basketball M & W; Cross-Country Running M & W; Football M; Golf M & W; Ice Hockey M & W; Skiing (Cross-Country) M & W; Soccer M & W; Softball W; Tennis M & W; Track and Field M & W; Volleyball W

CONCORDIA COLLEGE

901 S 8th St.
Moorhead, MN 56562
Tel: (218)299-4000; Free: 800-699-9897
Fax: (218)299-3947
E-mail: cthorson@cord.edu
Web Site: www.concordiacollege.edu
President/CEO: Dr. William J. Craft
Admissions: Carola Thorson
Financial Aid: Eric Addington

Type: Comprehensive **Sex:** Coed **Affiliation:** Evangelical Lutheran Church in America. **Scores:** 33% ACT 18-23; 48% ACT 24-29 **% Accepted:** 78 **Admission Plans:** Deferred Admission; Early Admission **Application Deadline:** Rolling **Application Fee:** $20.00 **H.S. Requirements:** High school diploma required; GED accepted **Costs Per Year:** Application fee: $20. Comprehensive fee: $44,688 includes full-time tuition ($36,650), mandatory fees ($228), and college room and board ($7810). College room only: $3360. Full-time tuition and fees vary according to course load and degree level. Room and board charges vary according to board plan and housing facility. Part-time tuition: $1380 per credit. Part-time tuition varies according to course load and degree level. **Scholarships:** Available. **Calendar System:** Semester, Summer session available **Enrollment:** Full-time 2,125, Graduate part-time 15, Part-time 171, Part-time 77 **Student-Faculty Ratio:** 11:1 **Exams:** ACT essay component not used; SAT I or ACT; SAT essay component not used; SAT Reasoning. **% Receiving Financial Aid:** 72 **% Residing in College-Owned, -Operated, or -Affiliated Housing:** 61 **Final Year or Final Semester Residency Requirement:** No **Regional Accreditation:** North Central Association of Colleges and Schools **Credit Hours For Degree:** 126 semester hours, Bachelors **ROTC:** Air Force, Army **Professional Accreditation:** AACN, AAFCS, AND, CSWE, NASM, NCATE. **Intercollegiate Athletics:** Baseball M; Basketball M & W; Cheerleading M & W; Cross-Country Running M & W; Football M; Golf M & W; Ice Hockey M & W; Soccer M & W; Softball W; Swimming and Diving W; Tennis M & W; Track and Field M & W; Volleyball M & W; Wrestling M

CONCORDIA UNIVERSITY, ST. PAUL

1282 Concordia Ave.
Saint Paul, MN 55104-5494
Tel: (651)641-8278; Free: 800-333-4705
Fax: (651)659-0207
E-mail: admission@csp.edu
Web Site: www.csp.edu
President/CEO: Rev. Thomas Ries
Admissions: Briana Eicheldinger
Financial Aid: Jeanie Peck

Type: Comprehensive **Sex:** Coed **Affiliation:** Lutheran Church–Missouri Synod. **Scores:** 54% ACT 18-23; 25% ACT 24-29 **% Accepted:** 55 **Admission Plans:** Deferred Admission; Early Admission **Application Deadline:** August 1 **Application Fee:** $30.00 **H.S. Requirements:** High school diploma required; GED accepted **Costs Per Year:** Application fee: $30. Comprehensive fee: $29,750 includes full-time tuition ($21,250) and college room and board ($8500). Full-time tuition varies according to degree level and program. Room and board charges vary according to board plan and housing facility. Part-time tuition: $600 per credit. Part-time tuition varies according to course load, degree level, and program. **Scholarships:** Available. **Calendar System:** Semester, Summer session available **Enrollment:** Full-time 1,382, Graduate full-time 1,721, Graduate part-time 92, Part-time 1,185 **Faculty:** Full-time 96, Part-time 332 **Student-Faculty Ratio:** 16:1 **Exams:** ACT essay component not used; SAT I or ACT; SAT essay component not used. **% Receiving Financial Aid:** 72 **% Residing in College-Owned, -Operated, or -Affiliated Housing:** 21 **Final Year or Final Semester Residency Requirement:** No **Regional Accreditation:** North Central Association of Colleges and Schools **Credit Hours For Degree:** 64 semester hours, Associates; 128 semester hours, Bachelors **ROTC:** Air Force, Army **Professional Accreditation:** ACBSP, NCATE. **Intercollegiate Athletics:** Baseball M; Basketball M & W; Cross-Country Running M & W; Football M; Golf M & W; Lacrosse W; Soccer W; Softball W; Track and Field M & W; Volleyball W

CROSSROADS COLLEGE

920 Mayowood Rd., SW
Rochester, MN 55902-2382
Tel: (507)288-4563; Free: 800-456-7651
Fax: (507)288-9046
E-mail: admissions@crossroadscollege.edu
Web Site: www.crossroadscollege.edu
President/CEO: Michael Kilgallin
Admissions: Todd Looney
Financial Aid: Polly Kellogg-Bradley

Type: Four-Year College **Sex:** Coed **Affiliation:** Christian Churches and Churches of Christ. **% Accepted:** 90 **Admission Plans:** Deferred Admission **Application Deadline:** August 15 **H.S. Requirements:** High school diploma required; GED accepted **Costs Per Year:** Tuition: $15,560 full-time, $450 per semester hour part-time. Mandatory fees: $480 full-time. Full-time tuition and fees vary according to class time and course load. Part-time tuition varies according to class time and course load. College room only: $4150. Room charges vary according to housing facility. **Scholarships:** Available. **Calendar System:** Semester, Summer session available **Enrollment:** Full-time 97, Part-time 12 **Student-Faculty Ratio:** 7:1 **Exams:** ACT essay component not used; SAT I or ACT; SAT essay component not used. **Final Year or Final Semester Residency Requirement:** Yes **Credit Hours For Degree:** 64 semester hours, Associates; 128 semester hours, Bachelors **Professional Accreditation:** TRACS. **Intercollegiate Athletics:** Basketball M & W; Golf M & W; Racquetball M & W; Soccer M & W; Tennis M & W; Volleyball W; Weight Lifting M & W

CROWN COLLEGE

8700 College View Dr.
Saint Bonifacius, MN 55375-9001
Tel: (952)446-4100; Free: 800-68-CROWN
Fax: (952)446-4149
E-mail: admissions@crown.edu
Web Site: www.crown.edu
President/CEO: Dr. Richard P. Mann
Admissions: Bret Hyder
Financial Aid: Shannon Schaaf

Type: Comprehensive **Sex:** Coed **Affiliation:** The Christian and Missionary Alliance. **Scores:** 96% SAT V 400+; 99% SAT M 400+; 51% ACT 18-23; 40% ACT 24-29 **% Accepted:** 56 **Admission Plans:** Deferred Admission; Early Admission **Application Deadline:** Rolling **Application Fee:** $20.00 **H.S. Requirements:** High school diploma required; GED accepted **Scholarships:** Available. **Calendar System:** Semester, Summer session available **Enrollment:** Full-time 885, Graduate full-time 143, Graduate part-time 38, Part-time 203 **Faculty:** Full-time 33, Part-time 127 **Student-Faculty Ratio:** 15:1 **Exams:** SAT I or ACT; SAT Reasoning; SAT Subject. **% Residing in College-Owned, -Operated, or -Affiliated Housing:** 79 **Final Year or Final Semester Residency Requirement:** Yes **Regional Accreditation:** North Central Association of Colleges and Schools **Credit Hours For Degree:** 66 credit hours, Associates; 125 credit hours, Bachelors **ROTC:** Army **Professional Accreditation:** AACN. **Intercollegiate Athletics:** Baseball M; Basketball M & W; Cross-Country Running M & W; Football M; Golf M; Soccer M & W; Softball W; Volleyball W

DAKOTA COUNTY TECHNICAL COLLEGE

1300 E 145th St.
Rosemount, MN 55068
Tel: (651)423-8000; Free: 877-YES-DCTC
E-mail: admissions@dctc.mnscu.edu
Web Site: www.dctc.edu
President/CEO: Ron Thomas
Admissions: Patrick Lair
Financial Aid: Scott Roelke

Type: Two-Year College **Sex:** Coed **Affiliation:** Minnesota State Colleges and Universities System. **Admission Plans:** Open Admission **Application Deadline:** Rolling **Application Fee:** $20.00 **H.S. Requirements:** High school diploma required; GED accepted **Scholarships:** Available. **Calendar System:** Semester, Summer session available **Enrollment:** Full-time 1,690, Part-time 1,982 **Faculty:** Full-time 93, Part-time 48 **Student-Faculty Ratio:** 30:1 **Regional Accreditation:** North Central Association of Colleges and Schools **Credit Hours For Degree:** 72 credits, Associates **Professional Accreditation:** AAMAE, ADA, CIDA. **Intercollegiate Athletics:** Baseball M; Basketball M; Soccer M & W; Softball W; Volleyball W

DULUTH BUSINESS UNIVERSITY

4724 Mike Colalillo Dr.
Duluth, MN 55807
Tel: (218)722-4000; Free: 800-777-8406
E-mail: markt@dbumn.edu
Web Site: www.dbumn.edu
President/CEO: James Gessner
Admissions: Mark Traux

Type: Two-Year College **Sex:** Coed **Application Fee:** $35.00 **Calendar System:** Quarter **Enrollment:** Full-time 103, Part-time 79 **Professional Accreditation:** AAMAE, ACICS, ADA.

DUNWOODY COLLEGE OF TECHNOLOGY

818 Dunwoody Blvd.
Minneapolis, MN 55403
Tel: (612)374-5800; Free: 800-292-4625
Fax: (612)374-4128
Web Site: www.dunwoody.edu
President/CEO: Dr. Rich Wagner
Admissions: Cynthia Olson
Financial Aid: Barbara Stephanie Charboneau

Type: Two-Year College **Sex:** Coed **% Accepted:** 68 **Application Deadline:** Rolling **Application Fee:** $50.00 **H.S. Requirements:** High school diploma required; GED accepted **Costs Per Year:** Application fee: $50. Tuition: $17,400 full-time, $580 per credit part-time. Mandatory fees: $1690 full-time, $1400 per term part-time. Full-time tuition and fees vary according to course load, degree level, and program. Part-time tuition and fees vary according to course load, degree level, and program. **Scholarships:** Available. **Calendar System:** Semester, Summer session available **Enrollment:** Full-time 898, Part-time 196 **Faculty:** Full-time 81, Part-time 47 **Student-Faculty Ratio:** 10:1 **Exams:** ACT essay component used for admission; SAT I or ACT; SAT essay component used for admission; SAT Reasoning; SAT Subject. **Final Year or Final Semester Residency Requirement:** No **Regional Accreditation:** North Central Association of Colleges and Schools **Credit Hours For Degree:** 60 semester credits, Associates; 120 semester credits, Bachelors

FOND DU LAC TRIBAL AND COMMUNITY COLLEGE

2101 14th St.
Cloquet, MN 55720
Tel: (218)879-0800; Free: 800-657-3712
Fax: (218)879-0814
E-mail: admissions@fdltcc.edu
Web Site: www.fdltcc.edu
President/CEO: Larry Anderson
Admissions: Kathie Jubie

Type: Two-Year College **Sex:** Coed **Affiliation:** Minnesota State Colleges and Universities System. **Admission Plans:** Deferred Admission; Early Admission; Open Admission **Application Fee:** $20.00 **H.S. Requirements:** High school diploma required; GED accepted **Costs Per Year:** Application fee: $20. State resident tuition: $4767 full-time, $158.90 per credit part-time. Nonresident tuition: $4767 full-time, $158.90 per credit part-time. Mandatory fees: $490 full-time, $16.35 per credit part-time. Full-time tuition and fees vary according to program and reciprocity agreements. Part-time tuition and fees vary according to program and reciprocity agreements. College room only: $3521. **Scholarships:** Available. **Calendar System:** Semester, Summer session available **Student-Faculty Ratio:** 29:1 **Regional Accreditation:** North Central Association of Colleges and Schools **Credit Hours For Degree:** 60 credits, Associates **Intercollegiate Athletics:** Basketball M & W; Football M; Softball W

GLOBE UNIVERSITY–MINNEAPOLIS

80 S 8th St.
Ste. 51
Minneapolis, MN 55402
Tel: (612)455-3000
Web Site: www.globeuniversity.edu
President/CEO: James Decker

Type: Comprehensive **Sex:** Coed **Affiliation:** Globe Education Network (GEN). **Admission Plans:** Open Admission **Application Deadline:** Rolling **Application Fee:** $50.00 **H.S. Requirements:** High school diploma required; GED accepted **Scholarships:** Available. **Enrollment:** Full-time 102, Graduate full-time 56, Graduate part-time 55, Part-time 24 **Faculty:** Full-time 2, Part-time 17 **Exams:** Other. **Final Year or Final Semester**

Residency Requirement: No **Credit Hours For Degree:** 90 quarter credits, Associates; 180 quarter credits, Bachelors **Professional Accreditation:** ACICS.

GLOBE UNIVERSITY–WOODBURY

8089 Globe Dr.
Woodbury, MN 55125
Tel: (651)730-5100; Free: 800-231-0660
Fax: (651)730-5151
Web Site: www.globeuniversity.edu
President/CEO: Lisa Palermo

Type: Comprehensive **Sex:** Coed **Affiliation:** Globe Education Network (GEN). **Admission Plans:** Open Admission **Application Deadline:** Rolling **Application Fee:** $50.00 **H.S. Requirements:** High school diploma required; GED accepted **Scholarships:** Available. **Calendar System:** Quarter, Summer session available **Enrollment:** Full-time 591, Graduate full-time 44, Graduate part-time 41, Part-time 307 **Faculty:** Full-time 28, Part-time 97 **Exams:** Other. **Final Year or Final Semester Residency Requirement:** No **Credit Hours For Degree:** 90 quarter credits, Associates; 180 quarter credits, Bachelors **Professional Accreditation:** AAMAE, ACICS.

GUSTAVUS ADOLPHUS COLLEGE

800 W College Ave.
Saint Peter, MN 56082-1498
Tel: (507)933-8000; Free: 800-GUSTAVU(S)
E-mail: admission@gac.edu
Web Site: www.gustavus.edu
President/CEO: Pres. Jack Ohle
Admissions: Dr. Tom M. Crady
Financial Aid: Doug Minter

Type: Four-Year College **Sex:** Coed **Affiliation:** Evangelical Lutheran Church in America. **Scores:** 100% SAT V 400+; 100% SAT M 400+; 17% ACT 18-23; 57% ACT 24-29 **% Accepted:** 67 **Admission Plans:** Deferred Admission; Early Admission; Early Decision Plan **Application Fee:** $0.00 **H.S. Requirements:** High school diploma required; GED accepted **Costs Per Year:** Application fee: $0. One-time mandatory fee: $480. Comprehensive fee: $50,508 includes full-time tuition ($41,140), mandatory fees ($192), and college room and board ($9176). College room only: $5820. Room and board charges vary according to board plan and housing facility. Part-time tuition: $7080 per course. **Scholarships:** Available. **Calendar System:** 4-1-4, Summer session available **Enrollment:** Full-time 2,342, Part-time 44 **Faculty:** Full-time 189, Part-time 51 **Student-Faculty Ratio:** 11:1 **Exams:** ACT essay component used as validity check; SAT I or ACT; SAT essay component used as validity check; SAT Reasoning. **% Receiving Financial Aid:** 72 **% Residing in College-Owned, -Operated, or -Affiliated Housing:** 88 **Regional Accreditation:** North Central Association of Colleges and Schools **Credit Hours For Degree:** 35 courses, Bachelors **ROTC:** Army **Professional Accreditation:** AACN, JRCAT, NASM, NCATE. **Intercollegiate Athletics:** Baseball M & W; Basketball M & W; Cross-Country Running M & W; Football M; Golf M & W; Gymnastics W; Ice Hockey M & W; Lacrosse M; Rugby M & W; Skiing (Cross-Country) M & W; Soccer M & W; Softball W; Swimming and Diving M & W; Tennis M & W; Track and Field M & W; Ultimate Frisbee M & W; Volleyball M & W

HAMLINE UNIVERSITY

1536 Hewitt Ave.
Saint Paul, MN 55104-1284
Tel: (651)523-2800; Free: 800-753-9753
Fax: (651)523-2458
E-mail: admission@hamline.edu
Web Site: www.hamline.edu
President/CEO: Dr. Fayneese Miller
Financial Aid: Lynette Wahl

Type: Comprehensive **Sex:** Coed **Affiliation:** United Methodist Church. **Scores:** 100% SAT V 400+; 96% SAT M 400+; 39.5% ACT 18-23; 43.4% ACT 24-29 **% Accepted:** 72 **Admission Plans:** Deferred Admission; Early Action; Early Admission; Early Decision Plan **Application Deadline:** Rolling **Application Fee:** $0.00 **H.S. Requirements:** High school diploma required; GED accepted **Costs Per Year:** Application fee: $0. Comprehensive fee: $47,622 includes full-time tuition ($36,888), mandatory fees ($998), and college room and board ($9736). College room only: $4986. Room and board charges vary according to board plan and housing facility. Part-time tuition: $1153 per credit hour. Part-time mandatory fees: $500 per year. Part-time tuition and fees vary according to course load. **Scholarships:** Available. **Calendar System:** 4-1-4, Summer session available **Enrollment:** Full-time 2,120, Graduate full-time 842, Graduate part-time 1,187, Part-time 109 **Faculty:** Full-time 163, Part-time 226 **Student-Faculty Ratio:** 13:1 **Exams:** ACT essay component used for admission; SAT I or ACT; SAT essay component used for admission; SAT Reasoning; SAT Subject. **% Receiving Financial Aid:** 83 **% Residing in College-Owned, -Operated, or -Affiliated Housing:** 41 **Final Year or Final Semester Residency Requirement:** Yes **Regional Accreditation:** North Central Association of Colleges and Schools **Credit Hours For Degree:** 128 credits, Bachelors **ROTC:** Air Force, Army **Professional Accreditation:** AALS, ABA, NASM, NCATE. **Intercollegiate Athletics:** Baseball M; Basketball M & W; Cheerleading W; Cross-Country Running M & W; Football M; Gymnastics W; Ice Hockey M & W; Lacrosse W; Soccer M & W; Softball W; Swimming and Diving M & W; Tennis M & W; Track and Field M & W; Volleyball W

HENNEPIN TECHNICAL COLLEGE

9000 Brooklyn Blvd.
Brooklyn Park, MN 55445
Tel: (952)995-1300; Free: 800-645-4655
Fax: (763)488-2944
E-mail: info@hennepintech.edu
Web Site: www.hennepintech.edu
President/CEO: Dr. Merrill Irving, Jr.

Type: Two-Year College **Sex:** Coed **Affiliation:** Minnesota State Colleges and Universities System. **% Accepted:** 100 **Admission Plans:** Open Admission **Application Deadline:** Rolling **H.S. Requirements:** High school diploma required; GED accepted **Costs Per Year:** State resident tuition: $5147 full-time, $156.70 per credit part-time. Nonresident tuition: $5147 full-time, $156.70 per credit part-time. Mandatory fees: $446 full-time, $15.25 per credit part-time. Full-time tuition and fees vary according to program. Part-time tuition and fees vary according to program. **Scholarships:** Available. **Calendar System:** Semester, Summer session available **Enrollment:** Full-time 2,004, Part-time 3,672 **Faculty:** Full-time 116, Part-time 119 **Student-Faculty Ratio:** 21:1 **Final Year or Final Semester Residency Requirement:** No **Regional Accreditation:** North Central Association of Colleges and Schools **Credit Hours For Degree:** 60 credits, Associates **Professional Accreditation:** ACBSP, ACF, ADA.

HERZING UNIVERSITY

5700 W Broadway
Minneapolis, MN 55428
Tel: (763)535-3000; Free: 800-596-0724
Fax: (763)535-9205
E-mail: info@mpls.herzing.edu
Web Site: www.herzing.edu/minneapolis
President/CEO: John Slama
Admissions: Shelly Larson

Type: Two-Year College **Sex:** Coed **Affiliation:** Herzing College. **% Accepted:** 75 **Admission Plans:** Open Admission **Application Fee:** $0.00 **H.S. Requirements:** High school diploma required; GED accepted **Calendar System:** Semester **Enrollment:** Full-time 242, Part-time 28 **Faculty:** Full-time 21, Part-time 11 **Student-Faculty Ratio:** 14:1 **Exams:** Other. **Regional Accreditation:** North Central Association of Colleges and Schools **Credit Hours For Degree:** 80 credits, Associates **Professional Accreditation:** ACCSC.

HIBBING COMMUNITY COLLEGE

1515 E 25th St.
Hibbing, MN 55746-3300
Tel: (218)262-7200; Free: 800-224-4HCC
E-mail: admissions@hibbing.edu
Web Site: www.hcc.mnscu.edu
President/CEO: Kenneth Simberg

Type: Two-Year College **Sex:** Coed **Affiliation:** Minnesota State Colleges and Universities System. **Admission Plans:** Deferred Admission; Early Admission; Open Admission **Application Deadline:** Rolling **Application Fee:** $20.00 **H.S. Requirements:** High school diploma required; GED accepted **Scholarships:** Available. **Calendar System:** Semester, Summer session available **Student-Faculty Ratio:** 17:1 **Regional Accreditation:** North Central Association of Colleges and Schools **Credit Hours For Degree:** 64 credits, Associates **Professional Accreditation:** ADA, NAACLS. **Intercollegiate Athletics:** Baseball M; Basketball M & W; Golf M & W; Softball W; Volleyball W

THE INSTITUTE OF PRODUCTION AND RECORDING

300 N 1st Ave.
Ste. 500
Minneapolis, MN 55401
Tel: (612)244-2800
Web Site: www.ipr.edu
President/CEO: Norbert Kreuzer

Type: Two-Year College **Sex:** Coed **Affiliation:** Globe Education Network (GEN). **Application Deadline:** Rolling **Application Fee:** $50.00 **H.S. Requirements:** High school diploma required; GED accepted **Scholarships:** Available. **Enrollment:** Full-time 153, Part-time 89 **Faculty:** Full-time 15, Part-time 25 **Exams:** Other. **Final Year or Final Semester Residency Requirement:** No **Credit Hours For Degree:** 90 quarter credits, Associates **Professional Accreditation:** ACCSC.

INVER HILLS COMMUNITY COLLEGE

2500 E 80th St.
Inver Grove Heights, MN 55076-3224
Tel: (651)450-8500
Fax: (651)450-8677
E-mail: admissions@inverhills.edu
Web Site: www.inverhills.edu
President/CEO: Dr. Tim Wynes
Admissions: Casey Carmody
Financial Aid: Steve Yang

Type: Two-Year College **Sex:** Coed **Affiliation:** Minnesota State Colleges and Universities System. **% Accepted:** 98 **Admission Plans:** Open Admission **Application Deadline:** August 15 **Application Fee:** $20.00 **H.S. Requirements:** High school diploma required; GED accepted **Scholarships:** Available. **Calendar System:** Semester, Summer session available **Enrollment:** Full-time 2,502, Part-time 3,840 **Faculty:** Full-time 105, Part-time 121 **Final Year or Final Semester Residency Requirement:** No **Regional Accreditation:** North Central Association of Colleges and Schools **Credit Hours For Degree:** 60 credits, Associates **ROTC:** Air Force, Army **Professional Accreditation:** ACBSP, ACEN.

ITASCA COMMUNITY COLLEGE

1851 Hwy. 169 E
Grand Rapids, MN 55744
Tel: (218)322-2300; Free: 800-996-6422
Fax: (218)327-4350
E-mail: iccinfo@itascacc.edu
Web Site: www.itascacc.edu
President/CEO: Dr. Susan Collins
Admissions: Candace Perry
Financial Aid: Nathan Wright

Type: Two-Year College **Sex:** Coed **Affiliation:** Minnesota State Colleges and Universities System, Northeastern Higher Education District. **% Accepted:** 100 **Admission Plans:** Open Admission **Application Deadline:** August 20 **Application Fee:** $0.00 **H.S. Requirements:** High school diploma required; GED accepted **Costs Per Year:** Application fee: $0. State resident tuition: $4,729 full-time, $157.62 per credit hour part-time. Nonresident tuition: $5,911 full-time, $197.02 per credit hour part-time. Mandatory fees: $596 full-time, $19.85 per credit hour part-time, $19.85. Full-time tuition and fees vary according to course load, program, and reciprocity agreements. Part-time tuition and fees vary according to course load, program, and reciprocity agreements. College room and board: $5120. College room only: $3800. Room and board charges vary according to board plan. **Scholarships:** Available. **Calendar System:** Semester, Summer session available **Enrollment:** Full-time 983, Part-time 316 **Faculty:** Full-time 43, Part-time 34 **Student-Faculty Ratio:** 17:1 **% Residing in College-Owned, -Operated, or -Affiliated Housing:** 10 **Regional Accreditation:** North Central Association of Colleges and Schools **Credit Hours For Degree:** 60 credits, Associates **Intercollegiate Athletics:** Baseball M; Basketball M & W; Football M; Softball W; Volleyball W; Wrestling M

LAKE SUPERIOR COLLEGE

2101 Trinity Rd.
Duluth, MN 55811
Tel: (218)733-7600; Free: 800-432-2884
E-mail: enroll@lsc.edu
Web Site: www.lsc.edu
President/CEO: Dr. Patrick Johns
Admissions: Melissa Leno

Financial Aid: LaNita Robinson
Type: Two-Year College **Sex:** Coed **Affiliation:** Minnesota State Colleges and Universities System. **% Accepted:** 100 **Admission Plans:** Open Admission **Application Deadline:** Rolling **Application Fee:** $20.00 **H.S. Requirements:** High school diploma or equivalent not required **Costs Per Year:** Application fee: $20. State resident tuition: $4,418 full-time. Nonresident tuition: $8,835 full-time. Mandatory fees: $721 full-time. Full-time tuition and fees vary according to course load, program, and reciprocity agreements. **Scholarships:** Available. **Calendar System:** Semester, Summer session available **Enrollment:** Full-time 2,108, Part-time 2,942 **Faculty:** Full-time 97, Part-time 154 **Student-Faculty Ratio:** 21:1 **Regional Accreditation:** North Central Association of Colleges and Schools **Credit Hours For Degree:** 60 credits, Associates **Professional Accreditation:** ADA, APTA, CoARC, NAACLS. **Intercollegiate Athletics:** Soccer M & W

LEECH LAKE TRIBAL COLLEGE
6945 Littlewolf Rd. NW
Cass Lake, MN 56633
Tel: (218)335-4200
Fax: (218)335-4282
E-mail: shelly.braford@lltc.edu
Web Site: www.lltc.edu
President/CEO: Dr. Ginny Carney
Admissions: Shelly Braford
Type: Two-Year College **Sex:** Coed **Admission Plans:** Open Admission **Application Fee:** $15.00 **H.S. Requirements:** High school diploma required; GED accepted **Calendar System:** Semester, Summer session available **Enrollment:** Full-time 190, Part-time 53 **Faculty:** Full-time 9, Part-time 19 **Student-Faculty Ratio:** 16:1 **Final Year or Final Semester Residency Requirement:** No **Regional Accreditation:** North Central Association of Colleges and Schools **Credit Hours For Degree:** 64 semester credits, Associates

MACALESTER COLLEGE
1600 Grand Ave.
Saint Paul, MN 55105-1899
Tel: (651)696-6000; Free: 800-231-7974
Fax: (651)696-6500
E-mail: admissions@macalester.edu
Web Site: www.macalester.edu
President/CEO: Dr. Brian Rosenberg
Admissions: Lorne T. Robinson
Type: Four-Year College **Sex:** Coed **Scores:** 100% SAT V 400+; 100% SAT M 400+; 1.49% ACT 18-23; 29.76% ACT 24-29 **% Accepted:** 39 **Admission Plans:** Deferred Admission; Early Action; Early Admission **Application Deadline:** January 15 **Application Fee:** $40.00 **H.S. Requirements:** High school diploma or equivalent not required **Costs Per Year:** Application fee: $40. Comprehensive fee: $61,905 includes full-time tuition ($50,418), mandatory fees ($221), and college room and board ($11,266). College room only: $6020. Full-time tuition and fees vary according to course load. Room and board charges vary according to board plan and housing facility. Part-time tuition: $1576 per credit. Part-time tuition varies according to course load. **Scholarships:** Available. **Calendar System:** Semester, Summer session available **Enrollment:** Full-time 2,138, Part-time 34 **Faculty:** Full-time 180, Part-time 77 **Student-Faculty Ratio:** 10:1 **Exams:** ACT essay component used as validity check; ACT essay component used for admission; SAT I or ACT; SAT II; SAT essay component used as validity check; SAT essay component used for admission; SAT Reasoning; SAT Subject. **% Receiving Financial Aid:** 69 **% Residing in College-Owned, -Operated, or -Affiliated Housing:** 72 **Final Year or Final Semester Residency Requirement:** Yes **Regional Accreditation:** North Central Association of Colleges and Schools **Credit Hours For Degree:** 128 semester hours, Bachelors **ROTC:** Air Force, Army, Navy **Intercollegiate Athletics:** Baseball M; Basketball M & W; Crew M & W; Cross-Country Running M & W; Football M; Golf M & W; Ice Hockey M & W; Lacrosse W; Rugby M & W; Skiing (Cross-Country) M & W; Soccer M & W; Softball W; Swimming and Diving M & W; Tennis M & W; Track and Field M & W; Ultimate Frisbee M & W; Volleyball M & W; Water Polo M & W

MARTIN LUTHER COLLEGE
1995 Luther Ct.
New Ulm, MN 56073
Tel: (507)354-8221; Free: 877-MLC-1995
Fax: (507)354-8225

E-mail: brutlaro@mlc-wels.edu
Web Site: www.mlc-wels.edu
President/CEO: Rev. Mark G. Zarling
Admissions: Prof. Mark A. Stein
Financial Aid: Mark Bauer
Type: Comprehensive **Sex:** Coed **Affiliation:** Wisconsin Evangelical Lutheran Synod. **Scores:** 39% ACT 18-23; 47% ACT 24-29 **% Accepted:** 78 **Admission Plans:** Deferred Admission **Application Fee:** $0.00 **H.S. Requirements:** High school diploma required; GED accepted **Costs Per Year:** Application fee: $0. Comprehensive fee: $19,490 includes full-time tuition ($13,980) and college room and board ($5510). Room and board charges vary according to housing facility. **Scholarships:** Available. **Calendar System:** Semester, Summer session available **Enrollment:** Full-time 705, Graduate part-time 73, Part-time 122 **Faculty:** Full-time 50, Part-time 23 **Student-Faculty Ratio:** 12:1 **Exams:** ACT; ACT essay component used for admission; ACT essay component used for advising; ACT essay component used for placement; SAT I; SAT Reasoning. **% Receiving Financial Aid:** 74 **% Residing in College-Owned, -Operated, or -Affiliated Housing:** 92 **Regional Accreditation:** North Central Association of Colleges and Schools **Credit Hours For Degree:** 134 semester hours, Bachelors **Intercollegiate Athletics:** Baseball M; Basketball M & W; Cross-Country Running M & W; Football M; Golf M; Soccer M & W; Softball W; Tennis M & W; Track and Field M & W; Volleyball W

MCNALLY SMITH COLLEGE OF MUSIC
19 Exchange St. E
Saint Paul, MN 55101
Tel: (651)291-0177; Free: 800-594-9500
Fax: (651)291-0366
E-mail: katie.marshall@mcnallysmith.edu
Web Site: www.mcnallysmith.edu
President/CEO: Harry Chalmiers
Admissions: Katie Marshall
Financial Aid: Tony Palermo
Type: Comprehensive **Sex:** Coed **Scores:** 86% SAT V 400+; 86% SAT M 400+ **% Accepted:** 43 **Application Deadline:** August 1 **Application Fee:** $75.00 **H.S. Requirements:** High school diploma required; GED accepted **Scholarships:** Available. **Calendar System:** Semester, Summer session available **Enrollment:** Full-time 383, Graduate full-time 12, Graduate part-time 8, Part-time 165 **Faculty:** Full-time 48, Part-time 48 **Student-Faculty Ratio:** 9:1 **Exams:** ACT; ACT essay component not used; SAT I or ACT; SAT essay component not used. **% Receiving Financial Aid:** 79 **% Residing in College-Owned, -Operated, or -Affiliated Housing:** 15 **Final Year or Final Semester Residency Requirement:** Yes **Regional Accreditation:** North Central Association of Colleges and Schools **Credit Hours For Degree:** 60 semester credits, Associates; 120 semester credits, Bachelors **Professional Accreditation:** NASM.

MESABI RANGE COLLEGE
1001 W Chestnut St.
Virginia, MN 55792-3448
Tel: (218)741-3095; Free: 800-657-3860
E-mail: b.kochevar@mesabirange.edu
Web Site: www.mesabirange.edu
President/CEO: Carol Helland
Admissions: Brenda Kochevar
Financial Aid: Jodi M. Pontinen
Type: Two-Year College **Sex:** Coed **Affiliation:** Minnesota State Colleges and Universities System. **Admission Plans:** Deferred Admission; Early Admission; Open Admission **Application Deadline:** Rolling **Application Fee:** $20.00 **H.S. Requirements:** High school diploma required; GED accepted. For Minnesota high school students: High school diploma or equivalent not required **Costs Per Year:** Application fee: $20. State resident tuition: $4740 full-time, $157.62 per credit part-time. Nonresident tuition: $5910 full-time, $197.02 per credit part-time. Mandatory fees: $582 full-time, $19.41 per hour part-time. Full-time tuition and fees vary according to reciprocity agreements. Part-time tuition and fees vary according to reciprocity agreements. College room only: $4036. **Scholarships:** Available. **Calendar System:** Semester, Summer session available **Student-Faculty Ratio:** 24:1 **% Residing in College-Owned, -Operated, or -Affiliated Housing:** 10 **Regional Accreditation:** North Central Association of Colleges and Schools **Credit Hours For Degree:** 60 credits, Associates **Intercollegiate Athletics:** Baseball M; Basketball M & W; Football M; Golf M & W; Softball W; Volleyball W

METROPOLITAN STATE UNIVERSITY

700 E 7th St.
Saint Paul, MN 55106-5000
Tel: (651)793-1212
Fax: (651)772-7632
E-mail: daryl.johnson@metrostate.edu
Web Site: www.metrostate.edu
President/CEO: Dr. Devinder Malhotra
Admissions: Daryl Johnson
Financial Aid: Dr. Lois J. Larson

Type: Comprehensive **Sex:** Coed **Affiliation:** Minnesota State Colleges and Universities System. **% Accepted:** 100 **Admission Plans:** Deferred Admission **Application Deadline:** June 15 **Application Fee:** $20.00 **H.S. Requirements:** High school diploma or equivalent not required. For non-transfer students: High school diploma required; GED accepted **Costs Per Year:** Application fee: $20. State resident tuition: $6,563 full-time, $218.78 per credit hour part-time. Nonresident tuition: $13,391 full-time, $446.38 per credit hour part-time. Mandatory fees: $1,003 full-time, $33.43 per credit hour part-time. Full-time tuition and fees vary according to degree level, program, and reciprocity agreements. Part-time tuition and fees vary according to degree level, program, and reciprocity agreements. **Scholarships:** Available. **Calendar System:** Semester, Summer session available **Enrollment:** Full-time 2,714, Graduate full-time 178, Graduate part-time 583, Part-time 4,879 **Exams:** SAT I or ACT. **Final Year or Final Semester Residency Requirement:** No **Regional Accreditation:** North Central Association of Colleges and Schools **Credit Hours For Degree:** 120 credits, Bachelors **Professional Accreditation:** AACN, CSWE.

MINNEAPOLIS BUSINESS COLLEGE

1711 W County Rd. B
Roseville, MN 55113
Tel: (612)636-7406; Free: 800-279-5200
Fax: (612)636-8185
Web Site: www.minneapolisbusinesscollege.edu
President/CEO: David B. Whitman

Type: Two-Year College **Sex:** Coed **% Accepted:** 87 **H.S. Requirements:** High school diploma required; GED accepted **Calendar System:** Semester **Professional Accreditation:** ACICS.

MINNEAPOLIS COLLEGE OF ART AND DESIGN

2501 Stevens Ave.
Minneapolis, MN 55404-4347
Tel: (612)874-3700; Free: 800-874-6223
Fax: (612)874-3704
E-mail: mhuybrecht@mcad.edu
Web Site: www.mcad.edu
President/CEO: Jay Coogan
Admissions: Melissa Huybrecht
Financial Aid: Laura Link

Type: Comprehensive **Sex:** Coed **Admission Plans:** Early Decision Plan **Application Deadline:** May 1 **H.S. Requirements:** High school diploma required; GED accepted **Costs Per Year:** Tuition: $36,098 full-time, $1505 per credit part-time. Mandatory fees: $450 full-time, $225 per term part-time. Part-time tuition and fees vary according to course load. College room only: $5290. Room charges vary according to housing facility. **Scholarships:** Available. **Calendar System:** Semester, Summer session available **Enrollment:** Full-time 653, Graduate full-time 28, Graduate part-time 46, Part-time 15 **Exams:** ACT essay component not used; SAT I or ACT; SAT essay component not used; SAT Reasoning. **% Receiving Financial Aid:** 79 **Final Year or Final Semester Residency Requirement:** No **Regional Accreditation:** North Central Association of Colleges and Schools **Credit Hours For Degree:** 120 credits, Bachelors **Professional Accreditation:** NASAD.

MINNEAPOLIS COMMUNITY AND TECHNICAL COLLEGE

1501 Hennepin Ave.
Minneapolis, MN 55403-1779
Tel: (612)659-6000; Free: 800-247-0911
Fax: (612)659-6210
E-mail: admissions.office@minneapolis.edu
Web Site: www.minneapolis.edu
President/CEO: Dr. Avelino Mills-Novoa

Type: Two-Year College **Sex:** Coed **Affiliation:** Minnesota State Colleges and Universities System. **Admission Plans:** Deferred Admission; Early

Admission; Open Admission **Application Deadline:** Rolling **Application Fee:** $20.00 **H.S. Requirements:** High school diploma required; GED accepted **Costs Per Year:** Application fee: $20. State resident tuition: $4,658 full-time. Nonresident tuition: $4,658 full-time. Mandatory fees: $692 full-time. Full-time tuition and fees vary according to course load and program. **Scholarships:** Available. **Calendar System:** Semester, Summer session available **Enrollment:** Full-time 3,210, Part-time 6,255 **Faculty:** Full-time 178, Part-time 219 **Final Year or Final Semester Residency Requirement:** No **Regional Accreditation:** North Central Association of Colleges and Schools **Credit Hours For Degree:** 60 credits, Associates **Professional Accreditation:** ACEN, ADA.

MINNEAPOLIS MEDIA INSTITUTE

4100 W 76th St.
Edina, MN 55435
Tel: (866)701-1310; Free: 800-236-4997
Web Site: www.mediainstitute.edu
President/CEO: Kathy Doty

Type: Two-Year College **Sex:** Coed **Calendar System:** Semester **Professional Accreditation:** ACCSC.

MINNESOTA SCHOOL OF BUSINESS–BLAINE

3680 Pheasant Ridge Dr. NE
Blaine, MN 55449
Tel: (763)225-8000
Fax: (763)225-8001
Web Site: www.msbcollege.edu
President/CEO: Susan Mago

Type: Four-Year College **Sex:** Coed **Affiliation:** Globe Education Network (GEN). **Admission Plans:** Open Admission **Application Deadline:** Rolling **Application Fee:** $50.00 **H.S. Requirements:** High school diploma required; GED accepted **Scholarships:** Available. **Enrollment:** Full-time 258, Part-time 137 **Faculty:** Full-time 11, Part-time 30 **Final Year or Final Semester Residency Requirement:** No **Credit Hours For Degree:** 90 quarter credits, Associates; 180 quarter credits, Bachelors **Professional Accreditation:** ACICS.

MINNESOTA SCHOOL OF BUSINESS–BROOKLYN CENTER

5910 Shingle Creek Pky.
Brooklyn Center, MN 55430
Tel: (763)566-7777
Fax: (763)566-7030
Web Site: www.msbcollege.edu
President/CEO: Diana Igo

Type: Two-Year College **Sex:** Coed **Affiliation:** Globe Education Network (GEN). **Admission Plans:** Open Admission **Application Deadline:** Rolling **Application Fee:** $50.00 **H.S. Requirements:** High school diploma required; GED accepted **Scholarships:** Available. **Calendar System:** Quarter, Summer session available **Enrollment:** Full-time 100, Part-time 69 **Faculty:** Full-time 7, Part-time 9 **Exams:** Other. **Final Year or Final Semester Residency Requirement:** No **Credit Hours For Degree:** 90 quarter credits, Associates; 180 quarter credits, Bachelors **Professional Accreditation:** ACICS.

MINNESOTA SCHOOL OF BUSINESS–ELK RIVER

11500 193rd Ave. NW
Elk River, MN 55330
Tel: (763)367-7000
Web Site: www.msbcollege.edu
President/CEO: Candi Janssen

Type: Four-Year College **Sex:** Coed **Affiliation:** Globe Education Network (GEN). **Admission Plans:** Open Admission **Application Deadline:** Rolling **Application Fee:** $50.00 **H.S. Requirements:** High school diploma required; GED accepted **Scholarships:** Available. **Enrollment:** Full-time 196, Part-time 95 **Faculty:** Full-time 5, Part-time 21 **Exams:** Other. **Final Year or Final Semester Residency Requirement:** No **Credit Hours For Degree:** 90 quarter credits, Associates; 180 quarter credits, Bachelors **Professional Accreditation:** ACICS.

MINNESOTA SCHOOL OF BUSINESS–LAKEVILLE

17685 Juniper Path
Lakeville, MN 55044
Tel: (952)892-9000
E-mail: bsaintey@msbcollege.edu

Web Site: www.msbcollege.edu
President/CEO: Aimee Pasko
Type: Four-Year College Sex: Coed Affiliation: Globe Education Network (GEN). Admission Plans: Open Admission Application Deadline: Rolling Application Fee: $50.00 H.S. Requirements: High school diploma required; GED accepted Scholarships: Available. Enrollment: Full-time 148, Part-time 55 Faculty: Full-time 7, Part-time 17 Exams: Other. Final Year or Final Semester Residency Requirement: No Credit Hours For Degree: 90 quarter credits, Associates; 180 quarter credits, Bachelors Professional Accreditation: ACICS.

MINNESOTA SCHOOL OF BUSINESS–PLYMOUTH

1455 Country Rd. 101 N
Plymouth, MN 55447
Tel: (763)476-2000
Web Site: www.msbcollege.edu
President/CEO: Elaine Vandenburgh
Type: Two-Year College Sex: Coed Affiliation: Globe Education Network (GEN). Admission Plans: Open Admission Application Deadline: Rolling Application Fee: $50.00 H.S. Requirements: High school diploma required; GED accepted Scholarships: Available. Calendar System: Quarter, Summer session available Enrollment: Full-time 107, Part-time 83 Faculty: Full-time 7, Part-time 29 Exams: Other. Final Year or Final Semester Residency Requirement: No Credit Hours For Degree: 90 quarter credits, Associates; 180 quarter credits, Bachelors Professional Accreditation: ACICS.

MINNESOTA SCHOOL OF BUSINESS–RICHFIELD

1401 W 76th St.
Ste. 500
Richfield, MN 55423
Tel: (612)861-2000; Free: 800-752-4223
Fax: (612)861-5548
Web Site: www.msbcollege.edu
President/CEO: Stacy Severson
Type: Four-Year College Sex: Coed Affiliation: Globe Education Network (GEN). Admission Plans: Open Admission Application Deadline: Rolling Application Fee: $50.00 H.S. Requirements: High school diploma required; GED accepted Scholarships: Available. Calendar System: Quarter, Summer session available Enrollment: Full-time 578, Part-time 369 Faculty: Full-time 21, Part-time 99 Exams: Other. Final Year or Final Semester Residency Requirement: No Credit Hours For Degree: 90 quarter credits, Associates; 180 quarter credits, Bachelors Professional Accreditation: AACN, AAMAE, ACICS.

MINNESOTA SCHOOL OF BUSINESS–ROCHESTER

2521 Pennington Dr., NW
Rochester, MN 55901
Tel: (507)536-9500; Free: 888-662-8772
Fax: (507)535-8011
Web Site: www.msbcollege.edu
President/CEO: Shan Pollitt
Type: Four-Year College Sex: Coed Affiliation: Minnesota School of Business; Globe Education Network (GEN). Admission Plans: Open Admission Application Deadline: Rolling Application Fee: $50.00 H.S. Requirements: High school diploma required; GED accepted Scholarships: Available. Calendar System: Quarter, Summer session available Enrollment: Full-time 209, Part-time 55 Faculty: Full-time 10, Part-time 33 Exams: Other. Final Year or Final Semester Residency Requirement: No Credit Hours For Degree: 90 quarter credits, Associates; 180 quarter credits, Bachelors Professional Accreditation: ACICS.

MINNESOTA SCHOOL OF BUSINESS–ST. CLOUD

1201 2nd St. S
Waite Park, MN 56387
Tel: (320)257-2000; Free: 866-403-3333
Web Site: www.msbcollege.edu
President/CEO: Jim Beck
Type: Four-Year College Sex: Coed Affiliation: Globe Education Network (GEN). Admission Plans: Open Admission Application Deadline: Rolling Application Fee: $50.00 H.S. Requirements: High school diploma required; GED accepted Scholarships: Available. Calendar System: Quarter, Summer session available Enrollment: Full-time 247, Part-time 107 Faculty: Full-time 12, Part-time 21 Exams: Other. Final Year or Final

Semester Residency Requirement: No Credit Hours For Degree: 90 quarter credits, Associates; 180 quarter credits, Bachelors Professional Accreditation: ACICS.

MINNESOTA STATE COLLEGE–SOUTHEAST TECHNICAL

1250 Homer Rd.
Winona, MN 55987
Tel: (507)453-2700; Free: 800-372-8164
Fax: (507)453-2715
E-mail: enrollmentservices@southeastmn.edu
Web Site: www.southeastmn.edu
President/CEO: Dr. Dorothy Duran
Financial Aid: Dr. Tammy Vondrasek
Type: Two-Year College Sex: Coed Affiliation: Minnesota State Colleges and Universities System. Admission Plans: Open Admission Application Deadline: Rolling Application Fee: $20.00 H.S. Requirements: High school diploma required; GED accepted Costs Per Year: Application fee: $20. State resident tuition: $5,019 full-time, $167.31 per credit part-time. Nonresident tuition: $5,019 full-time, $167.31 per credit part-time. Mandatory fees: $598 full-time, $22.28 per credit part-time. Full-time tuition and fees vary according to program. Part-time tuition and fees vary according to program. Scholarships: Available. Calendar System: Semester Enrollment: Full-time 875, Part-time 1,128 Faculty: Full-time 63, Part-time 43 Student-Faculty Ratio: 16:1 Regional Accreditation: North Central Association of Colleges and Schools

MINNESOTA STATE COMMUNITY AND TECHNICAL COLLEGE

1414 College Way
Fergus Falls, MN 56537-1009
Tel: (218)736-1500; Free: 877-450-3322
Fax: (218)739-7475
E-mail: carrie.brimhall@minnesota.edu
Web Site: www.minnesota.edu
President/CEO: Dr. Ann Valentine
Admissions: Carrie Brimhall
Financial Aid: Wendy Olds
Type: Two-Year College Sex: Coed Affiliation: Minnesota State Colleges and Universities System. Admission Plans: Deferred Admission; Early Admission; Open Admission Application Deadline: Rolling Application Fee: $20.00 H.S. Requirements: High school diploma required; GED accepted Scholarships: Available. Calendar System: Semester, Summer session available Faculty: Full-time 193, Part-time 263 Student-Faculty Ratio: 18:1 Exams: ACT essay component not used. % Residing in College-Owned, -Operated, or -Affiliated Housing: 2 Final Year or Final Semester Residency Requirement: No Regional Accreditation: North Central Association of Colleges and Schools Credit Hours For Degree: 60 semester hours, Associates Professional Accreditation: NAACLS. Intercollegiate Athletics: Baseball M; Basketball M & W; Football M; Golf M & W; Softball W; Volleyball W

MINNESOTA STATE COMMUNITY AND TECHNICAL COLLEGE–DETROIT LAKES

900 Hwy. 34, E
Detroit Lakes, MN 56501
Tel: (218)846-7444; Free: 800-492-4836
Fax: (218)847-7170
Web Site: www.minnesota.edu
President/CEO: Dr. Peggy Kennedy
Admissions: Dale Westley
Type: Two-Year College Sex: Coed Application Fee: $20.00 Costs Per Year: Application fee: $20. State resident tuition: $4824 full-time, $160.80 per credit hour part-time. Nonresident tuition: $4824 full-time, $160.80 per credit hour part-time. Mandatory fees: $514 full-time. Full-time tuition and fees vary according to location and program. Part-time tuition varies according to location and program. Calendar System: Semester Enrollment: Full-time 2,658, Part-time 3,733 Faculty: Full-time 154, Part-time 122 Regional Accreditation: North Central Association of Colleges and Schools Credit Hours For Degree: 64 credits, Associates

MINNESOTA STATE COMMUNITY AND TECHNICAL COLLEGE–MOORHEAD

1900 28th Ave., S
Moorhead, MN 56560
Tel: (218)236-6277; Free: 800-426-5603

Fax: (218)299-6584
Web Site: www.minnesota.edu
Admissions: Dale Westley

Type: Two-Year College **Sex:** Coed **Application Fee:** $20.00 **Costs Per Year:** Application fee: $20. State resident tuition: $4824 full-time, $160.80 per credit hour part-time. Nonresident tuition: $4824 full-time, $160.80 per credit hour part-time. Mandatory fees: $514 full-time. Full-time tuition and fees vary according to location and program. Part-time tuition varies according to location and program. **Calendar System:** Semester **Enrollment:** Full-time 2,658, Part-time 3,733 **Faculty:** Full-time 154, Part-time 122 **Regional Accreditation:** North Central Association of Colleges and Schools **Professional Accreditation:** ADA.

MINNESOTA STATE COMMUNITY AND TECHNICAL COLLEGE–WADENA

405 Colfax Ave., SW
Wadena, MN 56482
Tel: (218)631-7800; Free: 800-247-2007
Fax: (218)631-7901
Web Site: www.minnesota.edu
Admissions: Kyle Johnston

Type: Two-Year College **Sex:** Coed **Application Fee:** $20.00 **Costs Per Year:** Application fee: $20. State resident tuition: $4824 full-time. Nonresident tuition: $4824 full-time. Mandatory fees: $414 full-time. Full-time tuition and fees vary according to location and program. **Calendar System:** Semester **Enrollment:** Full-time 2,658, Part-time 3,733 **Faculty:** Full-time 154, Part-time 122 **Regional Accreditation:** North Central Association of Colleges and Schools

MINNESOTA STATE UNIVERSITY MANKATO

228 Wiecking Ctr.
Mankato, MN 56001
Tel: (507)389-2463; Free: 800-722-0544
E-mail: admissions@mnsu.edu
Web Site: www.mnsu.edu
President/CEO: Dr. Richard Davenport
Financial Aid: Sandra Loerts

Type: University **Sex:** Coed **Affiliation:** Minnesota State Colleges and Universities System. **Scores:** 61% ACT 18-23; 28% ACT 24-29 **Costs Per Year:** State resident tuition: $6904 full-time. Nonresident tuition: $14,648 full-time. Mandatory fees: $932 full-time. Full-time tuition and fees vary according to course load and reciprocity agreements. College room and board: $8430. Room and board charges vary according to board plan and housing facility. **Scholarships:** Available. **Calendar System:** Semester, Summer session available **Enrollment:** Full-time 11,412, Graduate full-time 669, Graduate part-time 1,279, Part-time 2,047 **Faculty:** Full-time 436, Part-time 318 **Student-Faculty Ratio:** 20:1 **Exams:** ACT essay component not used; SAT I or ACT; SAT essay component not used. **% Receiving Financial Aid:** 56 **% Residing in College-Owned, -Operated, or -Affiliated Housing:** 25 **Final Year or Final Semester Residency Requirement:** No **Regional Accreditation:** North Central Association of Colleges and Schools **Credit Hours For Degree:** 60 credits, Associates; 120 credits, Bachelors **ROTC:** Army **Professional Accreditation:** AACN, AACSB, ABET, ACA, ADA, ASHA, CORE, CSWE, JRCAT, NASAD, NASM, NCATE, NRPA. **Intercollegiate Athletics:** Baseball M; Basketball M & W; Bowling W; Cheerleading M & W; Cross-Country Running M & W; Football M; Golf M & W; Ice Hockey M & W; Soccer W; Softball W; Swimming and Diving W; Tennis M & W; Track and Field M & W; Volleyball W; Wrestling M

MINNESOTA STATE UNIVERSITY MOORHEAD

1104 7th Ave. S
Moorhead, MN 56563
Tel: (218)236-2011; Free: 800-593-7246
Fax: (218)236-2168
E-mail: admissionsoffice@mnstate.edu
Web Site: www.mnstate.edu
President/CEO: Dr. Anne Blackhurst
Financial Aid: Carolyn Zehren

Type: Comprehensive **Sex:** Coed **Affiliation:** Minnesota State Colleges and Universities System. **% Accepted:** 82 **Admission Plans:** Deferred Admission; Early Admission **Application Deadline:** August 1 **Application Fee:** $20.00 **H.S. Requirements:** High school diploma required; GED accepted **Costs Per Year:** Application fee: $20. State resident tuition: $7136 full-time, $230 per credit part-time. Nonresident tuition: $14,272 full-time, $480 per

term part-time. Mandatory fees: $960 full-time, $439 per term part-time. Full-time tuition and fees vary according to course load, program, and reciprocity agreements. Part-time tuition and fees vary according to course load, program, and reciprocity agreements. College room and board: $7798. Room and board charges vary according to board plan and housing facility. **Scholarships:** Available. **Calendar System:** Semester, Summer session available **Enrollment:** Full-time 4,324, Graduate full-time 173, Graduate part-time 418, Part-time 921 **Faculty:** Full-time 229, Part-time 138 **Student-Faculty Ratio:** 17:1 **Exams:** ACT essay component not used; SAT I or ACT; SAT essay component not used; SAT Reasoning. **% Receiving Financial Aid:** 59 **% Residing in College-Owned, -Operated, or -Affiliated Housing:** 25 **Final Year or Final Semester Residency Requirement:** Yes **Regional Accreditation:** North Central Association of Colleges and Schools **Credit Hours For Degree:** 60 credits, Associates; 120 credits, Bachelors **ROTC:** Air Force, Army **Professional Accreditation:** AACN, AACSB, ACA, ACCE, ASHA, ATMAE, CSWE, NASAD, NASM, NCATE. **Intercollegiate Athletics:** Basketball M & W; Cheerleading M & W; Cross-Country Running M & W; Football M; Golf W; Soccer W; Softball W; Swimming and Diving W; Tennis W; Track and Field M & W; Volleyball W; Wrestling M

MINNESOTA WEST COMMUNITY AND TECHNICAL COLLEGE

1314 N Hiawatha Ave.
Pipestone, MN 56164
Tel: (507)825-6800; Free: 800-658-2330
Fax: (507)825-4656
E-mail: crystal.strouth@mnwest.edu
Web Site: www.mnwest.edu
President/CEO: Dr. Terry Gaalswyk
Admissions: Crystal Strouth
Financial Aid: Jodi Landgaard

Type: Two-Year College **Sex:** Coed **Affiliation:** Minnesota State Colleges and Universities System. **Admission Plans:** Open Admission **Application Deadline:** Rolling **Application Fee:** $20.00 **H.S. Requirements:** High school diploma required; GED accepted **Costs Per Year:** Application fee: $20. One-time mandatory fee: $20. State resident tuition: $5490 full-time, $171.55 per credit part-time. Nonresident tuition: $5490 full-time, $171.55 per credit part-time. Mandatory fees: $565 full-time, $17.67 per credit part-time. Full-time tuition and fees vary according to program and reciprocity agreements. Part-time tuition and fees vary according to program and reciprocity agreements. **Scholarships:** Available. **Calendar System:** Semester, Summer session available **Enrollment:** Full-time 1,153, Part-time 2,029 **Faculty:** Full-time 97, Part-time 49 **Student-Faculty Ratio:** 21:1 **Exams:** Other. **Final Year or Final Semester Residency Requirement:** No **Regional Accreditation:** North Central Association of Colleges and Schools **Credit Hours For Degree:** 60 credits, Associates **Professional Accreditation:** AAMAE, ACEN, ADA, NAACLS. **Intercollegiate Athletics:** Baseball M; Basketball M & W; Cheerleading W; Football M; Softball W; Volleyball W; Wrestling M

NATIONAL AMERICAN UNIVERSITY (BLOOMINGTON)

7801 Metro Pky.
Ste. 200
Bloomington, MN 55425
Tel: (605)394-4800; Free: 866-628-6387
E-mail: jmichaelson@national.edu
Web Site: www.national.edu
President/CEO: Dr. Jerry Gallentine
Admissions: Jennifer Michaelson

Type: Two-Year College **Sex:** Coed **% Accepted:** 100 **Application Fee:** $25.00 **Enrollment:** Full-time 311, Part-time 163 **Faculty:** Full-time 15, Part-time 31 **Student-Faculty Ratio:** 19:1 **% Residing in College-Owned, -Operated, or -Affiliated Housing:** 18 **Regional Accreditation:** North Central Association of Colleges and Schools **ROTC:** Air Force

NATIONAL AMERICAN UNIVERSITY (BROOKLYN CENTER)

6200 Shingle Creek Pky.
Ste. 130
Brooklyn Center, MN 55430
Tel: (763)852-7500
Fax: (763)549-9955
Web Site: www.national.edu
President/CEO: Dr. Jerry Gallentine

Type: Two-Year College **Sex:** Coed **Regional Accreditation:** North Central Association of Colleges and Schools

NATIONAL AMERICAN UNIVERSITY (BURNSVILLE)

513 W Travelers Trl.
Burnsville, MN 55337
Tel: (952)563-1250; Free: 866-628-6387
Web Site: www.national.edu
Type: Four-Year College **Sex:** Coed **Regional Accreditation:** North Central Association of Colleges and Schools

NATIONAL AMERICAN UNIVERSITY (ROSEVILLE)

1500 W Hwy. 36
Roseville, MN 55113
Tel: (651)644-1265
Fax: (651)644-0690
Web Site: www.national.edu
President/CEO: Dr. Jerry Gallentine
Admissions: Steve Grunlan
Type: Four-Year College **Sex:** Coed **Affiliation:** National American University. **% Accepted:** 100 **Application Deadline:** Rolling **Application Fee:** $25.00 **Calendar System:** Quarter **Faculty:** Full-time 5, Part-time 27 **Student-Faculty Ratio:** 10:1 **Regional Accreditation:** North Central Association of Colleges and Schools

NORMANDALE COMMUNITY COLLEGE

9700 France Ave. S
Bloomington, MN 55431-4399
Tel: (952)358-8200; Free: 800-481-5412
Fax: (612)487-8101
E-mail: information@normandale.edu
Web Site: www.normandale.edu
President/CEO: Dr. Joyce Ester
Financial Aid: Susan Ant
Type: Two-Year College **Sex:** Coed **Affiliation:** Minnesota State Colleges and Universities System. **% Accepted:** 87 **Admission Plans:** Deferred Admission; Open Admission **Application Deadline:** August 10 **Application Fee:** $20.00 **H.S. Requirements:** High school diploma required; GED accepted **Costs Per Year:** Application fee: $20. State resident tuition: $5736 full-time. Nonresident tuition: $5736 full-time. Mandatory fees: $891 full-time. **Scholarships:** Available. **Calendar System:** Semester, Summer session available **Faculty:** Full-time 193, Part-time 165 **Final Year or Final Semester Residency Requirement:** No **Regional Accreditation:** North Central Association of Colleges and Schools **Credit Hours For Degree:** 60 semester hours, Associates **Professional Accreditation:** ACBSP, ACEN, ADA, NASM.

NORTH CENTRAL UNIVERSITY

910 Elliot Ave.
Minneapolis, MN 55404-1322
Tel: (612)332-3491; Free: 800-289-6222
Fax: (612)343-4778
E-mail: admissions@northcentral.edu
Web Site: www.northcentral.edu
President/CEO: Dr. Gordon L. Anderson
Admissions: Sigi Shawa
Financial Aid: Donna Jager
Type: Four-Year College **Sex:** Coed **Affiliation:** Assemblies of God. **Admission Plans:** Deferred Admission; Open Admission **Application Deadline:** June 1 **Application Fee:** $25.00 **H.S. Requirements:** High school diploma required; GED accepted **Scholarships:** Available. **Calendar System:** Semester, Summer session available **Enrollment:** Full-time 1,125 **Faculty:** Full-time 40, Part-time 62 **Student-Faculty Ratio:** 19:1 **Exams:** SAT I or ACT. **% Residing in College-Owned, -Operated, or -Affiliated Housing:** 80 **Regional Accreditation:** North Central Association of Colleges and Schools **Credit Hours For Degree:** 62 credits, Associates; 127 credits, Bachelors **ROTC:** Air Force, Army **Intercollegiate Athletics:** Baseball M; Basketball M & W; Cross-Country Running M & W; Golf M; Soccer M & W; Softball W; Tennis M & W; Track and Field M & W; Volleyball W

NORTH HENNEPIN COMMUNITY COLLEGE

7411 85th Ave. N
Brooklyn Park, MN 55445
Tel: (763)488-0391; Free: 800-818-0395
Fax: (763)424-0929
E-mail: solson2@nhcc.edu
Web Site: www.nhcc.edu

President/CEO: Dr. Barbara McDonald
Admissions: Sean Olson
Type: Two-Year College **Sex:** Coed **Affiliation:** Minnesota State Colleges and Universities System. **% Accepted:** 81 **Admission Plans:** Deferred Admission; Early Admission; Open Admission **Application Deadline:** Rolling **Application Fee:** $20.00 **H.S. Requirements:** High school diploma required; GED accepted **Costs Per Year:** Application fee: $20. State resident tuition: $3,962 full-time, $165.08 per credit part-time. Nonresident tuition: $3,962 full-time, $165.08 per credit part-time. Mandatory fees: $421 full-time, $17.55 per credit part-time, $17.55. Full-time tuition and fees vary according to location and program. Part-time tuition and fees vary according to location and program. **Scholarships:** Available. **Calendar System:** Semester, Summer session available **Enrollment:** Full-time 2,055, Part-time 4,792 **Faculty:** Full-time 132, Part-time 159 **Final Year or Final Semester Residency Requirement:** No **Regional Accreditation:** North Central Association of Colleges and Schools **Credit Hours For Degree:** 60 credits, Associates **ROTC:** Air Force, Army, Navy **Professional Accreditation:** ACBSP, ACEN, NAACLS.

NORTHLAND COMMUNITY AND TECHNICAL COLLEGE

1101 Hwy. One E
Thief River Falls, MN 56701
Tel: (218)683-8800; Free: 800-959-6282
Fax: (218)681-6405
E-mail: nicki.carlson@northlandcollege.edu
Web Site: www.northlandcollege.edu
President/CEO: Dr. Dennis Bona
Admissions: Nicki Carlson
Financial Aid: Gerald Schulte
Type: Two-Year College **Sex:** Coed **Affiliation:** Minnesota State Colleges and Universities System. **% Accepted:** 100 **Admission Plans:** Deferred Admission; Early Admission; Open Admission **Application Deadline:** August 24 **Application Fee:** $20.00 **H.S. Requirements:** High school diploma required; GED accepted **Costs Per Year:** Application fee: $20. State resident tuition: $4950 full-time, $165 per credit hour part-time. Nonresident tuition: $4950 full-time, $165 per credit hour part-time. Mandatory fees: $610 full-time, $19.45 per credit hour part-time. Full-time tuition and fees vary according to course load, program, and reciprocity agreements. Part-time tuition and fees vary according to course load, program, and reciprocity agreements. **Scholarships:** Available. **Calendar System:** Semester, Summer session available **Enrollment:** Full-time 1,389, Part-time 2,184 **Faculty:** Full-time 92, Part-time 58 **Student-Faculty Ratio:** 21:1 **Final Year or Final Semester Residency Requirement:** No **Regional Accreditation:** North Central Association of Colleges and Schools **Credit Hours For Degree:** 60 semester hours, Associates **Professional Accreditation:** ACEN. **Intercollegiate Athletics:** Baseball M; Basketball M & W; Football M; Softball W; Volleyball W; Wrestling M

NORTHWEST TECHNICAL COLLEGE

905 Grant Ave., SE
Bemidji, MN 56601
Tel: (218)333-6600; Free: 800-942-8324
E-mail: kari.kantack@ntcmn.edu
Web Site: www.ntcmn.edu
President/CEO: Dr. Richard A. Hanson, PhD
Admissions: Kari Kantack-Miller
Type: Two-Year College **Sex:** Coed **Affiliation:** Bemidji State University; Minnesota State Colleges and Universities System. **Application Fee:** $20.00 **H.S. Requirements:** High school diploma required; GED accepted **Costs Per Year:** Application fee: $20. State resident tuition: $5190 full-time, $173 per credit part-time. Nonresident tuition: $5190 full-time, $173 per credit part-time. Mandatory fees: $290 full-time, $9.68 per credit part-time. Full-time tuition and fees vary according to location, program, and reciprocity agreements. Part-time tuition and fees vary according to location, program, and reciprocity agreements. College room and board: $7690. Room and board charges vary according to board plan and housing facility. **Scholarships:** Available. **Calendar System:** Semester **Enrollment:** Full-time 336, Part-time 778 **Faculty:** Full-time 28, Part-time 45 **Student-Faculty Ratio:** 14:1 **% Residing in College-Owned, -Operated, or -Affiliated Housing:** 4 **Regional Accreditation:** North Central Association of Colleges and Schools **Credit Hours For Degree:** 60 credits, Associates **Professional Accreditation:** AAMAE, ADA, AHIMA, ARCST, CoARC, JRCERT, NAACLS.

OAK HILLS CHRISTIAN COLLEGE

1600 Oak Hills Rd., SW
Bemidji, MN 56601-8832

Tel: (218)751-8670; Free: 888-751-8670
Fax: (218)751-8825
E-mail: admissions@oakhills.edu
Web Site: www.oakhills.edu
President/CEO: Dr. Steve Hostetter
Admissions: Shelly Fast
Financial Aid: Daniel Hovestol
Type: Four-Year College Sex: Coed Affiliation: interdenominational.
Scores: 62% ACT 18-23; 8% ACT 24-29 % Accepted: 56 Admission Plans: Deferred Admission Application Deadline: Rolling Application Fee: $25.00 H.S. Requirements: High school diploma required; GED accepted Scholarships: Available. Calendar System: Semester, Summer session not available Enrollment: Full-time 134, Part-time 6 Faculty: Full-time 6, Part-time 13 Student-Faculty Ratio: 13:1 Exams: SAT I or ACT; SAT Reasoning; SAT Subject. % Receiving Financial Aid: 90 % Residing in College-Owned, -Operated, or -Affiliated Housing: 85 Credit Hours For Degree: 64 semester hours, Associates; 126 semester hours, Bachelors Professional Accreditation: ABHE. Intercollegiate Athletics: Basketball M; Volleyball W

PINE TECHNICAL AND COMMUNITY COLLEGE
900 4th St. SE
Pine City, MN 55063
Tel: (320)629-5100; Free: 800-521-7463
Fax: (320)629-5101
Web Site: www.pine.edu
President/CEO: Robert Musgrove
Admissions: Nancy Mach
Type: Two-Year College Sex: Coed Affiliation: Minnesota State Colleges and Universities System. Admission Plans: Early Admission; Open Admission Application Deadline: Rolling Application Fee: $20.00 H.S. Requirements: High school diploma required; GED accepted Costs Per Year: Application fee: $20. State resident tuition: $3676 full-time, $2144 per term part-time. Nonresident tuition: $7352 full-time, $4288 per term part-time. Mandatory fees: $390 full-time, $195 per term part-time. Scholarships: Available. Calendar System: Semester, Summer session available Enrollment: Full-time 296, Part-time 516 Faculty: Full-time 18, Part-time 21 Student-Faculty Ratio: 18:1 Regional Accreditation: North Central Association of Colleges and Schools Credit Hours For Degree: 65 credits, Associates

RAINY RIVER COMMUNITY COLLEGE
1501 Hwy. 71
International Falls, MN 56649
Tel: (218)285-7722; Free: 800-456-3996
Fax: (218)285-2239
E-mail: berta.hagen@rainyriver.edu
Web Site: www.rainyriver.edu
President/CEO: Carol Helland
Admissions: Berta Hagen
Financial Aid: Scott Riley
Type: Two-Year College Sex: Coed Affiliation: Minnesota State Colleges and Universities System. Admission Plans: Deferred Admission; Early Admission; Open Admission Application Deadline: Rolling Application Fee: $20.00 H.S. Requirements: High school diploma required; GED accepted. For applicants who demonstrate ability to benefit from college: High school diploma or equivalent not required Scholarships: Available. Calendar System: Semester, Summer session available Enrollment: Full-time 229, Part-time 49 Faculty: Full-time 10, Part-time 15 Student-Faculty Ratio: 15:1 Final Year or Final Semester Residency Requirement: No Regional Accreditation: North Central Association of Colleges and Schools Credit Hours For Degree: 60 credits, Associates Intercollegiate Athletics: Basketball M & W; Ice Hockey W; Softball W; Volleyball W

RASMUSSEN COLLEGE BLAINE
3629 95th Ave. NE
Blaine, MN 55014
Tel: (763)795-4720; Free: 888-549-6755
E-mail: susan.hammerstrom@rasmussen.edu
Web Site: www.rasmussen.edu
President/CEO: Kristi Waite
Admissions: Susan Hammerstrom
Type: Four-Year College Sex: Coed Affiliation: Rasmussen College System. Admission Plans: Deferred Admission; Early Admission Applica-

tion Deadline: Rolling Application Fee: $0.00 H.S. Requirements: High school diploma required; GED accepted Costs Per Year: Application fee: $0. Tuition: $13,455 full-time. Mandatory fees: $1800 full-time. Full-time tuition and fees vary according to course level, course load, degree level, location, and program. Tuition guaranteed not to increase for student's term of enrollment. Calendar System: Quarter, Summer session available Enrollment: Full-time 332, Part-time 588 Faculty: Full-time 8, Part-time 26 Student-Faculty Ratio: 22:1 Exams: ACT essay component not used; Other; SAT essay component not used. Final Year or Final Semester Residency Requirement: No Credit Hours For Degree: 90 credits, Associates; 180 credits, Bachelors Professional Accreditation: ACBSP.

RASMUSSEN COLLEGE BLOOMINGTON
4400 W 78th St.
Bloomington, MN 55435
Tel: (952)545-2000; Free: 888-549-6755
Web Site: www.rasmussen.edu
President/CEO: Kristi Waite
Admissions: Susan Hammerstrom
Type: Four-Year College Sex: Coed Affiliation: Rasmussen College System. Admission Plans: Deferred Admission; Early Admission Application Deadline: Rolling H.S. Requirements: High school diploma required; GED accepted Costs Per Year: Tuition: $13,455 full-time. Mandatory fees: $1800 full-time. Full-time tuition and fees vary according to course level, course load, degree level, location, and program. Tuition guaranteed not to increase for student's term of enrollment. Scholarships: Available. Calendar System: Quarter, Summer session available Enrollment: Full-time 395, Part-time 597 Faculty: Full-time 13, Part-time 61 Student-Faculty Ratio: 22:1 Exams: ACT essay component not used; Other; SAT essay component not used. Final Year or Final Semester Residency Requirement: No Regional Accreditation: North Central Association of Colleges and Schools Credit Hours For Degree: 90 credits, Associates; 180 credits, Bachelors Professional Accreditation: ACICS, AHIMA.

RASMUSSEN COLLEGE BROOKLYN PARK
8301 93rd Ave. N
Brooklyn Park, MN 55445-1512
Tel: (763)493-4500; Free: 888-549-6755
Fax: (763)425-4344
E-mail: susan.hammerstrom@rasmussen.edu
Web Site: www.rasmussen.edu
President/CEO: Kristi Waite
Admissions: Susan Hammerstrom
Type: Four-Year College Sex: Coed Affiliation: Rasmussen College System. Admission Plans: Deferred Admission; Early Admission Application Deadline: Rolling H.S. Requirements: High school diploma required; GED accepted Costs Per Year: Tuition: $13,455 full-time. Mandatory fees: $1800 full-time. Full-time tuition and fees vary according to course level, course load, degree level, location, and program. Tuition guaranteed not to increase for student's term of enrollment. Calendar System: Quarter, Summer session available Enrollment: Full-time 270, Part-time 539 Faculty: Full-time 12, Part-time 41 Student-Faculty Ratio: 22:1 Exams: ACT essay component not used; Other; SAT essay component not used. Final Year or Final Semester Residency Requirement: No Regional Accreditation: North Central Association of Colleges and Schools Credit Hours For Degree: 90 credits, Associates; 180 credits, Bachelors Professional Accreditation: ACBSP.

RASMUSSEN COLLEGE EAGAN
3500 Federal Dr.
Eagan, MN 55122-1346
Tel: (651)687-9000; Free: 888-549-6755
Fax: (651)687-0507
E-mail: susan.hammerstrom@rasmussen.edu
Web Site: www.rasmussen.edu
President/CEO: Kristi Waite
Admissions: Susan Hammerstrom
Type: Four-Year College Sex: Coed Affiliation: Rasmussen College System. Admission Plans: Deferred Admission; Early Admission Application Deadline: Rolling H.S. Requirements: High school diploma required; GED accepted Costs Per Year: Tuition: $13,455 full-time. Mandatory fees: $1800 full-time. Full-time tuition and fees vary according to course level, course load, degree level, location, and program. Tuition guaranteed not to increase for student's term of enrollment. Scholarships: Available.

Calendar System: Quarter, Summer session available **Enrollment:** Full-time 262, Part-time 524 **Faculty:** Full-time 11, Part-time 72 **Student-Faculty Ratio:** 22:1 **Exams:** ACT essay component not used; Other; SAT essay component not used. **Final Year or Final Semester Residency Requirement:** No **Regional Accreditation:** North Central Association of Colleges and Schools **Credit Hours For Degree:** 90 credits, Associates; 180 credits, Bachelors **Professional Accreditation:** ACBSP, ACICS, AHIMA.

RASMUSSEN COLLEGE LAKE ELMO/WOODBURY

8565 Eagle Point Cir.
Lake Elmo, MN 55042
Tel: (651)259-6600; Free: 888-549-6755
Fax: (651)259-6601
E-mail: susan.hammerstrom@rasmussen.edu
Web Site: www.rasmussen.edu
President/CEO: Kristi Waite
Admissions: Susan Hammerstrom

Type: Four-Year College **Sex:** Coed **Affiliation:** Rasmussen College System. **Admission Plans:** Deferred Admission; Early Admission **Application Deadline:** Rolling **Application Fee:** $0.00 **H.S. Requirements:** High school diploma required; GED accepted **Costs Per Year:** Application fee: $0. Tuition: $13,455 full-time. Mandatory fees: $1800 full-time. Full-time tuition and fees vary according to course level, course load, degree level, location, and program. Tuition guaranteed not to increase for student's term of enrollment. **Calendar System:** Quarter, Summer session available **Enrollment:** Full-time 248, Part-time 1,607 **Faculty:** Full-time 6, Part-time 17 **Student-Faculty Ratio:** 22:1 **Exams:** ACT essay component not used; Other; SAT essay component not used. **Final Year or Final Semester Residency Requirement:** No **Regional Accreditation:** North Central Association of Colleges and Schools **Credit Hours For Degree:** 90 credits, Associates; 180 credits, Bachelors **Professional Accreditation:** ACBSP.

RASMUSSEN COLLEGE MANKATO

130 Saint Andrews Dr.
Mankato, MN 56001
Tel: (507)625-6556; Free: 888-549-6755
Fax: (507)625-6557
E-mail: susan.hammerstrom@rasmussen.edu
Web Site: www.rasmussen.edu
President/CEO: Kristi Waite
Admissions: Susan Hammerstrom

Type: Four-Year College **Sex:** Coed **Affiliation:** Rasmussen College System. **Admission Plans:** Deferred Admission; Early Admission **Application Deadline:** Rolling **H.S. Requirements:** High school diploma required; GED accepted **Costs Per Year:** Tuition: $13,455 full-time. Mandatory fees: $1800 full-time. Full-time tuition and fees vary according to course level, course load, degree level, location, and program. Tuition guaranteed not to increase for student's term of enrollment. **Scholarships:** Available. **Calendar System:** Quarter, Summer session available **Enrollment:** Full-time 291, Part-time 524 **Faculty:** Full-time 18, Part-time 44 **Student-Faculty Ratio:** 22:1 **Exams:** ACT essay component not used; Other; SAT essay component not used. **Final Year or Final Semester Residency Requirement:** No **Regional Accreditation:** North Central Association of Colleges and Schools **Credit Hours For Degree:** 90 credits, Associates; 180 credits, Bachelors **Professional Accreditation:** ACBSP, ACICS, AHIMA.

RASMUSSEN COLLEGE MOORHEAD

1250 29th Ave. S
Moorhead, MN 56560
Tel: (218)304-6200; Free: 888-549-6755
Fax: (218)304-2601
E-mail: susan.hammerstrom@rasmussen.edu
Web Site: www.rasmussen.edu
President/CEO: Kristi Waite
Admissions: Susan Hammerstrom

Type: Four-Year College **Sex:** Coed **Affiliation:** Rasmussen College System. **Admission Plans:** Deferred Admission; Early Admission **Application Deadline:** Rolling **Application Fee:** $0.00 **H.S. Requirements:** High school diploma required; GED accepted **Costs Per Year:** Application fee: $0. Tuition: $13,455 full-time. Mandatory fees: $1800 full-time. Full-time tuition and fees vary according to course level, course load, degree level, location, and program. Tuition guaranteed not to increase for student's term of enrollment. **Calendar System:** Quarter, Summer session available **Enrollment:** Full-time 161, Part-time 279 **Faculty:** Full-time 8, Part-time 47

Student-Faculty Ratio: 22:1 **Exams:** ACT essay component not used; Other; SAT essay component not used. **Final Year or Final Semester Residency Requirement:** No **Regional Accreditation:** North Central Association of Colleges and Schools **Credit Hours For Degree:** 90 credits, Associates; 180 credits, Bachelors

RASMUSSEN COLLEGE ST. CLOUD

226 Park Ave. S
Saint Cloud, MN 56301-3713
Tel: (320)251-5600; Free: 888-549-6755
Fax: (320)251-3702
E-mail: susan.hammerstrom@rasmussen.edu
Web Site: www.rasmussen.edu
President/CEO: Kristi Waite
Admissions: Susan Hammerstrom

Type: Four-Year College **Sex:** Coed **Affiliation:** Rasmussen College System. **Admission Plans:** Deferred Admission; Early Admission **Application Deadline:** Rolling **H.S. Requirements:** High school diploma required; GED accepted **Costs Per Year:** Tuition: $13,455 full-time. Mandatory fees: $1800 full-time. Full-time tuition and fees vary according to course level, course load, degree level, location, and program. Tuition guaranteed not to increase for student's term of enrollment. **Scholarships:** Available. **Calendar System:** Quarter, Summer session available **Enrollment:** Full-time 370, Part-time 642 **Faculty:** Full-time 16, Part-time 46 **Student-Faculty Ratio:** 22:1 **Exams:** ACT essay component not used; Other; SAT essay component not used. **Final Year or Final Semester Residency Requirement:** No **Regional Accreditation:** North Central Association of Colleges and Schools **Credit Hours For Degree:** 90 credits, Associates; 180 credits, Bachelors **Professional Accreditation:** ACBSP, ACICS, AHIMA.

RIDGEWATER COLLEGE

2101 15th Ave. NW
Willmar, MN 56201
Tel: (320)222-5200; Free: 800-722-1151
E-mail: linda.duering@ridgewater.edu
Web Site: www.ridgewater.edu
President/CEO: Dr. Douglas Allen
Admissions: Linda Duering

Type: Two-Year College **Sex:** Coed **Affiliation:** Minnesota State Colleges and Universities System. **Admission Plans:** Open Admission **Application Fee:** $20.00 **H.S. Requirements:** High school diploma required; GED accepted **Costs Per Year:** Application fee: $20. State resident tuition: $4839 full-time, $161.30 per credit part-time. Nonresident tuition: $4839 full-time, $161.30 per credit part-time. Mandatory fees: $567 full-time, $18.90 per credit part-time. Full-time tuition and fees vary according to course load and reciprocity agreements. Part-time tuition and fees vary according to course load and reciprocity agreements. **Scholarships:** Available. **Calendar System:** Semester, Summer session available **Enrollment:** Full-time 2,002, Part-time 1,561 **Faculty:** Full-time 107, Part-time 66 **Regional Accreditation:** North Central Association of Colleges and Schools **Credit Hours For Degree:** 64 semester hours, Associates **Professional Accreditation:** ACEN, AHIMA. **Intercollegiate Athletics:** Baseball M; Basketball M & W; Football M; Soccer M; Softball W; Volleyball W; Wrestling M

RIVERLAND COMMUNITY COLLEGE

1900 8th Ave., NW
Austin, MN 55912
Tel: (507)433-0600; Free: 800-247-5039
Fax: (507)433-0515
E-mail: admissions@riverland.edu
Web Site: www.riverland.edu
President/CEO: Dr. Adenuga Atewologun
Admissions: Nel Zellar
Financial Aid: Patty Hemann

Type: Two-Year College **Sex:** Coed **Affiliation:** Minnesota State Colleges and Universities System. **Admission Plans:** Early Admission; Open Admission **Application Deadline:** Rolling **Application Fee:** $20.00 **H.S. Requirements:** High school diploma required; GED accepted **Scholarships:** Available. **Calendar System:** Semester, Summer session available **Enrollment:** Full-time 1,249, Part-time 1,765 **% Residing in College-Owned, -Operated, or -Affiliated Housing:** 2 **Regional Accreditation:** North Central Association of Colleges and Schools **Credit Hours For Degree:** 64 semester hours,

Associates **Professional Accreditation:** ACBSP, ACEN, JRCERT. **Intercollegiate Athletics:** Baseball M; Basketball M & W; Golf M & W; Softball W; Volleyball W

ROCHESTER COMMUNITY AND TECHNICAL COLLEGE

851 30th Ave., SE
Rochester, MN 55904-4999
Tel: (507)285-7210
Fax: (507)285-7496
Web Site: www.rctc.edu
President/CEO: Leslie McClellon
Admissions: Troy Tynsky
Financial Aid: Rosemary Hicks

Type: Two-Year College **Sex:** Coed **Affiliation:** Minnesota State Colleges and Universities System. **Admission Plans:** Early Admission; Open Admission **Application Deadline:** August 24 **Application Fee:** $20.00 **H.S. Requirements:** High school diploma required; GED accepted **Costs Per Year:** Application fee: $20. State resident tuition: $4923 full-time, $164.10 per credit part-time. Nonresident tuition: $4963 full-time, $164.10 per credit part-time. Mandatory fees: $713 full-time, $23.76 per credit part-time. Full-time tuition and fees vary according to course load and reciprocity agreements. Part-time tuition and fees vary according to course load and reciprocity agreements. **Scholarships:** Available. **Calendar System:** Semester, Summer session available **Regional Accreditation:** North Central Association of Colleges and Schools **Professional Accreditation:** AAMAE, ACEN, ADA, AHIMA, ARCST, CoARC. **Intercollegiate Athletics:** Baseball M; Basketball M & W; Football M; Golf M & W; Soccer W; Softball W; Volleyball W; Wrestling M

ST. CATHERINE UNIVERSITY

2004 Randolph Ave.
Saint Paul, MN 55105
Tel: (651)690-6000; Free: 800-945-4599
Fax: (651)690-6042
E-mail: stkate@stkate.edu
Web Site: www.stkate.edu
President/CEO: Dr. Andrea J. Lee, IHM
Admissions: Cory Piper-Hauswirth
Financial Aid: Beth Stevens

Type: Comprehensive **Affiliation:** Roman Catholic. **Scores:** 100% SAT V 400+; 100% SAT M 400+; 52% ACT 18-23; 38% ACT 24-29 **% Accepted:** 67 **Admission Plans:** Deferred Admission **Application Fee:** $0.00 **H.S. Requirements:** High school diploma required; GED accepted **Costs Per Year:** Application fee: $0. One-time mandatory fee: $100. Comprehensive fee: $46,592 includes full-time tuition ($37,248), mandatory fees ($594), and college room and board ($8750). College room only: $5150. Full-time tuition and fees vary according to class time and degree level. Room and board charges vary according to board plan and housing facility. Part-time tuition: $1164 per credit hour. Part-time tuition varies according to class time and degree level. **Scholarships:** Available. **Calendar System:** 4-1-4 **Enrollment:** Full-time 2,128, Graduate full-time 1,157, Graduate part-time 484, Part-time 1,192 **Faculty:** Full-time 293, Part-time 232 **Student-Faculty Ratio:** 10:1 **Exams:** ACT essay component not used; SAT I or ACT; SAT essay component not used; SAT Reasoning. **% Receiving Financial Aid:** 84 **% Residing in College-Owned, -Operated, or -Affiliated Housing:** 41 **Regional Accreditation:** North Central Association of Colleges and Schools **Credit Hours For Degree:** 130 semester credits, Bachelors **ROTC:** Air Force, Army **Professional Accreditation:** ACEN, ALA, AOTA, APTA, CSWE, JRCEDMS. **Intercollegiate Athletics:** Basketball W; Cross-Country Running W; Ice Hockey W; Soccer W; Softball W; Swimming and Diving W; Tennis W; Track and Field W; Volleyball W

ST. CLOUD STATE UNIVERSITY

720 4th Ave. S
Saint Cloud, MN 56301-4498
Tel: (320)308-0121; Free: 877-654-7278
E-mail: scsu4u@stcloudstate.edu
Web Site: www.stcloudstate.edu
President/CEO: Dr. Earl H. Potter, III
Admissions: Richard Shearer

Type: Comprehensive **Sex:** Coed **Affiliation:** Minnesota State Colleges and Universities System. **Scores:** 56.47% ACT 18-23; 22.88% ACT 24-29 **% Accepted:** 82 **Admission Plans:** Deferred Admission **Application Deadline:** August 1 **Application Fee:** $20.00 **H.S. Requirements:** High school

diploma required; GED accepted **Costs Per Year:** Application fee: $20. State resident tuition: $6820 full-time, $227.35 per credit hour part-time. Nonresident tuition: $14,738 full-time, $491.27 per credit hour part-time. Mandatory fees: $996 full-time, $39.87 per credit hour part-time. Full-time tuition and fees vary according to course load, location, and reciprocity agreements. Part-time tuition and fees vary according to course load, location, and reciprocity agreements. College room and board: $7930. College room only: $4890. Room and board charges vary according to board plan and housing facility. **Scholarships:** Available. **Calendar System:** Semester, Summer session available **Enrollment:** Full-time 9,860, Graduate full-time 589, Graduate part-time 1,015, Part-time 4,781 **Faculty:** Full-time 548, Part-time 332 **Student-Faculty Ratio:** 19:1 **Exams:** ACT essay component not used; SAT I or ACT; SAT essay component not used; SAT Reasoning; SAT Subject. **% Receiving Financial Aid:** 60 **% Residing in College-Owned, -Operated, or -Affiliated Housing:** 19 **Final Year or Final Semester Residency Requirement:** No **Regional Accreditation:** North Central Association of Colleges and Schools **Credit Hours For Degree:** 60 credit hours, Associates; 120 credit hours, Bachelors **ROTC:** Army **Professional Accreditation:** AABI, AACN, AACSB, AAMFT, ABET, ACA, ACEJMC, ASHA, CORE, CSWE, NASAD, NASM, NAST, NCATE. **Intercollegiate Athletics:** Baseball M; Basketball M & W; Bowling M & W; Cheerleading M & W; Crew M & W; Cross-Country Running M & W; Equestrian Sports M & W; Football M; Golf M & W; Ice Hockey M & W; Rock Climbing M & W; Skiing (Cross-Country) M & W; Skiing (Downhill) M & W; Soccer M & W; Softball W; Swimming and Diving M & W; Tennis M & W; Track and Field M & W; Ultimate Frisbee M & W; Volleyball M & W; Wrestling M

ST. CLOUD TECHNICAL & COMMUNITY COLLEGE

1540 Northway Dr.
Saint Cloud, MN 56303-1240
Tel: (320)654-5000; Free: 800-222-1009
Fax: (320)654-5981
E-mail: jelness@sctcc.edu
Web Site: www.sctcc.edu
President/CEO: Joyce Helens
Admissions: Jodi Elness
Financial Aid: Anita Baugh

Type: Two-Year College **Sex:** Coed **Affiliation:** Minnesota State Colleges and Universities System. **% Accepted:** 98 **Admission Plans:** Deferred Admission; Early Admission; Open Admission **Application Deadline:** Rolling **Application Fee:** $20.00 **H.S. Requirements:** High school diploma required; GED accepted **Costs Per Year:** Application fee: $20. One-time mandatory fee: $20. State resident tuition: $4,767 full-time, $158.91 per credit hour part-time. Nonresident tuition: $4,767 full-time, $158.91 per credit hour part-time. Mandatory fees: $558 full-time, $18.61 per credit hour part-time. Full-time tuition and fees vary according to location and program. Part-time tuition and fees vary according to course load, location, and program. **Scholarships:** Available. **Calendar System:** Semester, Summer session available **Enrollment:** Full-time 2,230, Part-time 2,521 **Faculty:** Full-time 96, Part-time 163 **Student-Faculty Ratio:** 22:1 **Final Year or Final Semester Residency Requirement:** No **Regional Accreditation:** North Central Association of Colleges and Schools **Credit Hours For Degree:** 60 credits, Associates **Professional Accreditation:** ADA, ARCST. **Intercollegiate Athletics:** Baseball M; Basketball M & W; Softball W; Volleyball W

SAINT JOHN'S UNIVERSITY

2850 Abbey Plz.
Collegeville, MN 56321
Tel: (320)363-2011; Free: 800-544-1489
Fax: (320)363-3206
E-mail: admissions@csbsju.edu
Web Site: www.csbsju.edu
President/CEO: Dr. Michael Hemesath, PhD
Admissions: Matt Beirne
Financial Aid: Kari Vogt

Type: Comprehensive **Affiliation:** Roman Catholic. **Scores:** 97% SAT V 400+; 97% SAT M 400+; 33% ACT 18-23; 48% ACT 24-29 **% Accepted:** 74 **Admission Plans:** Deferred Admission; Early Decision Plan **Application Fee:** $0.00 **H.S. Requirements:** High school diploma required; GED accepted. For home-schooled students with appropriate documentation of college preparatory curriculum: High school diploma or equivalent not required **Costs Per Year:** Application fee: $0. Comprehensive fee: $49,830 includes full-time tuition ($39,530), mandatory fees ($696), and college room and board ($9604). College room only: $4802. Room and board charges vary according to board plan and housing facility. Part-time tuition: $1647 per credit hour. Part-time tuition varies according to course load. **Scholarships:** Available. **Calendar System:** Semester, Summer session not available **Enrollment:** Full-time 1,712, Graduate full-time 53, Graduate part-time 74, Part-time 30 **Faculty:** Full-time 131, Part-time 28 **Student-Faculty Ratio:** 12:1 **Exams:** SAT I or ACT. **% Receiving Financial Aid:** 68 **% Residing in College-Owned, -Operated, or -Affiliated Housing:** 90 **Final Year or Final Semester Residency Requirement:** No **Regional Accreditation:** North Central Association of Colleges and Schools **Credit Hours For Degree:** 124 credits, Bachelors **ROTC:** Army **Professional Accreditation:** AACN, ATS, CSWE, NASM, NCATE. **Intercollegiate Athletics:** Baseball M; Basketball M; Crew M; Cross-Country Running M; Football M; Golf M; Ice Hockey M; Lacrosse M; Riflery M; Rugby M; Skiing (Cross-Country) M; Soccer M; Swimming and Diving M; Tennis M; Track and Field M; Ultimate Frisbee M; Volleyball M; Water Polo M; Wrestling M

SAINT MARY'S UNIVERSITY OF MINNESOTA

700 Ter. Heights
Winona, MN 55987-1399
Tel: (507)452-4430; Free: 800-635-5987
Fax: (507)457-1722
E-mail: mkormann@smumn.edu
Web Site: www.smumn.edu
President/CEO: Bro. William Mann
Admissions: Mark Kormann
Financial Aid: Jayne P. Wobig

Type: Comprehensive **Sex:** Coed **Affiliation:** Roman Catholic. **Scores:** 83% SAT V 400+; 83% SAT M 400+; 45.56% ACT 18-23; 33.2% ACT 24-29 **% Accepted:** 78 **Admission Plans:** Deferred Admission; Early Admission **Application Deadline:** May 1 **Application Fee:** $25.00 **H.S. Requirements:** High school diploma required; GED accepted **Costs Per Year:** Application fee: $25. Comprehensive fee: $41,210 includes full-time tuition ($32,060), mandatory fees ($515), and college room and board ($8635). College room only: $4865. Full-time tuition and fees vary according to course load. Room and board charges vary according to board plan and housing facility. Part-time tuition: $1070 per credit. Part-time tuition varies according to course load. **Scholarships:** Available. **Calendar System:** Semester, Summer session available **Enrollment:** Full-time 1,228, Graduate full-time 2,578, Graduate part-time 1,595, Part-time 530 **Faculty:** Full-time 99, Part-time 461 **Student-Faculty Ratio:** 18:1 **Exams:** ACT essay component used in place of application essay; SAT I or ACT; SAT essay component used in place of application essay; SAT Reasoning; SAT Subject. **% Receiving Financial Aid:** 75 **% Residing in College-Owned, -Operated, or -Affiliated Housing:** 93 **Final Year or Final Semester Residency Requirement:** Yes **Regional Accreditation:** North Central Association of Colleges and Schools **Credit Hours For Degree:** 122 credits, Bachelors **ROTC:** Army **Professional Accreditation:** AAMFT, AANA, JRCNMT, NASM. **Intercollegiate Athletics:** Baseball M; Basketball M & W; Cross-Country Running M & W; Golf M & W; Ice Hockey M & W; Soccer M & W; Softball W; Swimming and Diving M & W; Tennis M & W; Track and Field M & W; Volleyball W

ST. OLAF COLLEGE

1520 St. Olaf Ave.
Northfield, MN 55057-1098
Tel: (507)786-2222; Free: 800-800-3025
Fax: (507)646-3832
E-mail: admissions@stolaf.edu
Web Site: www.stolaf.edu
President/CEO: David R. Anderson
Admissions: Dave Wagner
Financial Aid: Sandy Sundstrom

Type: Four-Year College **Sex:** Coed **Affiliation:** Lutheran. **Scores:** 99% SAT V 400+; 100% SAT M 400+; 12.3% ACT 18-23; 40.9% ACT 24-29 **% Accepted:** 36 **Admission Plans:** Deferred Admission; Early Action **Application Deadline:** January 15 **Application Fee:** $0.00 **H.S. Requirements:** High school diploma required; GED accepted **Costs Per Year:** Application fee: $0. Comprehensive fee: $52,730 includes full-time tuition ($42,940) and college room and board ($9790). College room only: $4720. Full-time tuition varies according to course load. Room and board charges vary according to board plan. Part-time tuition: $5370 per course. Part-time tuition varies according to course load. **Scholarships:** Available. **Calendar System:** 4-1-4, Summer session available **Enrollment:** Full-time 3,005, Part-time 41 **Faculty:** Full-time 213, Part-time 120 **Student-Faculty Ratio:** 12:1 **Exams:**

ACT essay component used as validity check; SAT I and SAT II or ACT; SAT I or ACT; SAT II; SAT essay component used as validity check; SAT Reasoning. **% Receiving Financial Aid:** 68 **% Residing in College-Owned, -Operated, or -Affiliated Housing:** 93 **Final Year or Final Semester Residency Requirement:** Yes **Regional Accreditation:** North Central Association of Colleges and Schools **Credit Hours For Degree:** 35 courses, Bachelors **Professional Accreditation:** AACN, AAFCS, CSWE, NASD, NASM, NAST, NCATE. **Intercollegiate Athletics:** Baseball M; Basketball M & W; Cross-Country Running M & W; Football M; Golf M & W; Ice Hockey M & W; Skiing (Cross-Country) M & W; Skiing (Downhill) M & W; Soccer M & W; Softball W; Swimming and Diving M & W; Tennis M & W; Track and Field M & W; Volleyball W; Wrestling M

SAINT PAUL COLLEGE–A COMMUNITY & TECHNICAL COLLEGE

235 Marshall Ave.
Saint Paul, MN 55102-1800
Tel: (651)846-1600; Free: 800-227-6029
Fax: (651)221-1416
E-mail: admissions@saintpaul.edu
Web Site: www.saintpaul.edu
President/CEO: Rassoul Dastmozd
Admissions: Sarah Carrico

Type: Two-Year College **Sex:** Coed **Affiliation:** Minnesota State Colleges and Universities System. **% Accepted:** 100 **Admission Plans:** Early Admission; Open Admission **Application Deadline:** Rolling **Application Fee:** $20.00 **H.S. Requirements:** High school diploma required; GED accepted **Costs Per Year:** Application fee: $20. State resident tuition: $4852 full-time, $162 per credit hour part-time. Nonresident tuition: $4852 full-time, $162 per credit hour part-time. Mandatory fees: $628 full-time, $20.93 per credit hour part-time. Full-time tuition and fees vary according to program. Part-time tuition and fees vary according to program. **Scholarships:** Available. **Calendar System:** Semester, Summer session available **Enrollment:** Full-time 2,454, Part-time 3,474 **Faculty:** Full-time 107, Part-time 209 **Student-Faculty Ratio:** 18:1 **Exams:** Other. **Regional Accreditation:** North Central Association of Colleges and Schools **Credit Hours For Degree:** 64 semester credits, Associates **Professional Accreditation:** ACBSP, ACEN, ACF, CoARC, NAACLS.

SOUTH CENTRAL COLLEGE

1920 Lee Blvd.
North Mankato, MN 56003
Tel: (507)389-7200
Web Site: southcentral.edu
President/CEO: Keith Stover
Admissions: Beverly Herda

Type: Two-Year College **Sex:** Coed **Affiliation:** Minnesota State Colleges and Universities System. **Admission Plans:** Open Admission **Application Deadline:** August 1 **Application Fee:** $20.00 **H.S. Requirements:** High school diploma required; GED accepted **Costs Per Year:** Application fee: $20. State resident tuition: $4836 full-time, $161.20 per credit hour part-time. Nonresident tuition: $4836 full-time, $121.20 per credit hour part-time. Mandatory fees: $543 full-time, $18.10 per credit hour part-time. **Calendar System:** Semester **Student-Faculty Ratio:** 12:1 **Regional Accreditation:** North Central Association of Colleges and Schools **Credit Hours For Degree:** 72 credits, Associates **Professional Accreditation:** ADA, NAACLS.

SOUTHWEST MINNESOTA STATE UNIVERSITY

1501 State St.
Marshall, MN 56258
Tel: (507)537-7021; Free: 800-642-0684
Fax: (507)537-7154
E-mail: andrew.hlubek@smsu.edu
Web Site: www.smsu.edu
President/CEO: Dr. Ronald A. Wood
Admissions: Andrew Hlubeck
Financial Aid: David Vikander

Type: Comprehensive **Sex:** Coed **Affiliation:** Minnesota State Colleges and Universities System. **Scores:** 64% ACT 18-23; 24% ACT 24-29 **Admission Plans:** Deferred Admission; Early Admission **Application Deadline:** September 1 **Application Fee:** $20.00 **H.S. Requirements:** High school diploma required; GED accepted **Scholarships:** Available. **Calendar System:** Semester, Summer session available **Enrollment:** Full-time 2,080, Graduate full-time 277, Graduate part-time 168, Part-time 4,371 **Faculty:**

Full-time 108, Part-time 86 **Student-Faculty Ratio:** 16:1 **Exams:** ACT; ACT essay component not used; SAT I or ACT; SAT Reasoning; SAT Subject. **% Receiving Financial Aid:** 65 **% Residing in College-Owned, -Operated, or -Affiliated Housing:** 40 **Final Year or Final Semester Residency Requirement:** No **Regional Accreditation:** North Central Association of Colleges and Schools **Credit Hours For Degree:** 60 credit hours, Associates; 120 credit hours, Bachelors **Professional Accreditation:** CSWE, NASM. **Intercollegiate Athletics:** Baseball M; Basketball M & W; Football M; Golf W; Soccer W; Softball W; Tennis W; Volleyball W; Wrestling M

UNIVERSITY OF MINNESOTA, CROOKSTON

2900 University Ave.
Crookston, MN 56716-5001
Tel: (218)281-6510; Free: 800-862-6466
Fax: (218)281-8050
E-mail: cthorson@umn.edu
Web Site: www.umcrookston.edu
President/CEO: Dr. Fred Wood, PhD
Admissions: Carola Thorson
Financial Aid: Melissa Dingmann

Type: Four-Year College **Sex:** Coed **Affiliation:** University of Minnesota System. **Scores:** 95% SAT V 400+; 84% SAT M 400+; 58% ACT 18-23; 28% ACT 24-29 **% Accepted:** 78 **Admission Plans:** Deferred Admission **Application Deadline:** Rolling **Application Fee:** $30.00 **H.S. Requirements:** High school diploma required; GED accepted **Costs Per Year:** Application fee: $30. State resident tuition: $10,180 full-time, $391.54 per credit part-time. Nonresident tuition: $10,180 full-time, $391.54 per credit part-time. Mandatory fees: $1,466 full-time, $732.75 per term part-time. College room and board: $7506. College room only: $3520. Room and board charges vary according to board plan and housing facility. **Scholarships:** Available. **Calendar System:** Semester, Summer session available **Enrollment:** Full-time 1,281, Part-time 1,542 **Faculty:** Full-time 71, Part-time 45 **Student-Faculty Ratio:** 16:1 **Exams:** ACT; ACT essay component not used; SAT I or ACT; SAT essay component not used; SAT Reasoning. **% Receiving Financial Aid:** 66 **% Residing in College-Owned, -Operated, or -Affiliated Housing:** 39 **Final Year or Final Semester Residency Requirement:** No **Regional Accreditation:** North Central Association of Colleges and Schools **Credit Hours For Degree:** 120 semester hours, Bachelors **ROTC:** Air Force **Intercollegiate Athletics:** Baseball M; Basketball M & W; Equestrian Sports W; Football M; Golf M & W; Soccer W; Softball W; Tennis W; Volleyball W

UNIVERSITY OF MINNESOTA, DULUTH

1049 University Dr.
Duluth, MN 55812-2496
Tel: (218)726-8000; Free: 800-232-1339
Fax: (218)726-6394
E-mail: umdadmis@d.umn.edu
Web Site: www.d.umn.edu
President/CEO: Dr. Lendley C. Black
Financial Aid: Brenda Herzig

Type: Comprehensive **Sex:** Coed **Affiliation:** University of Minnesota System. **Scores:** 100% SAT V 400+; 94% SAT M 400+; 42.67% ACT 18-23; 47.88% ACT 24-29 **% Accepted:** 76 **Application Deadline:** August 1 **Application Fee:** $40.00 **H.S. Requirements:** High school diploma required; GED accepted **Costs Per Year:** Application fee: $40. State resident tuition: $11,896 full-time, $457.54 per credit part-time. Nonresident tuition: $15,846 full-time, $609.47 per credit part-time. Mandatory fees: $1186 full-time. Full-time tuition and fees vary according to course load, program, and reciprocity agreements. Part-time tuition varies according to course load, program, and reciprocity agreements. College room and board: $7210. Room and board charges vary according to board plan and housing facility. **Scholarships:** Available. **Calendar System:** Semester, Summer session available **Enrollment:** Full-time 8,621, Graduate full-time 644, Graduate part-time 397, Part-time 1,216 **Faculty:** Full-time 500, Part-time 111 **Student-Faculty Ratio:** 17:1 **Exams:** ACT essay component not used; SAT I or ACT; SAT essay component not used; SAT Reasoning. **% Receiving Financial Aid:** 58 **% Residing in College-Owned, -Operated, or -Affiliated Housing:** 32 **Final Year or Final Semester Residency Requirement:** No **Regional Accreditation:** North Central Association of Colleges and Schools **Credit Hours For Degree:** 120 credits, Bachelors **ROTC:** Air Force **Professional Accreditation:** AACSB, ABET, ACA, ASHA, CSWE, LCME/AMA, NASM, NCATE. **Intercollegiate Athletics:** Badminton M & W; Baseball M; Basketball M & W; Cheerleading W; Crew M & W; Cross-Country Running M

& W; Football M; Ice Hockey M & W; Lacrosse M & W; Rugby M & W; Skiing (Downhill) M & W; Soccer M & W; Softball W; Swimming and Diving M & W; Table Tennis M & W; Tennis W; Track and Field M & W; Ultimate Frisbee M & W; Volleyball M & W; Water Polo M & W; Wrestling M

UNIVERSITY OF MINNESOTA, MORRIS

600 E 4th St.
Morris, MN 56267-2134
Tel: (320)589-6035; Free: 888-866-3382
Fax: (320)589-6399
E-mail: admissions@morris.umn.edu
Web Site: www.morris.umn.edu
President/CEO: Dr. Jaqueline R. Johnson
Financial Aid: Jill Beauregard

Type: Four-Year College **Sex:** Coed **Affiliation:** University of Minnesota System. **Scores:** 100% SAT M 400+; 36.8% ACT 18-23; 50% ACT 24-29 **% Accepted:** 60 **Admission Plans:** Deferred Admission **Application Deadline:** March 15 **Application Fee:** $35.00 **H.S. Requirements:** High school diploma required; GED accepted **Costs Per Year:** Application fee: $35. State resident tuition: $11,896 full-time, $457.54 per credit hour part-time. Nonresident tuition: $11,896 full-time, $457.54 per credit hour part-time. Mandatory fees: $950 full-time. Full-time tuition and fees vary according to reciprocity agreements. Part-time tuition varies according to course load and reciprocity agreements. College room and board: $7804. College room only: $3642. Room and board charges vary according to board plan and housing facility. **Scholarships:** Available. **Calendar System:** Semester, Summer session available **Enrollment:** Full-time 1,704, Part-time 152 **Faculty:** Full-time 124, Part-time 44 **Student-Faculty Ratio:** 13:1 **Exams:** ACT essay component used for admission; SAT I or ACT; SAT essay component used for admission; SAT Reasoning; SAT Subject. **% Receiving Financial Aid:** 61 **% Residing in College-Owned, -Operated, or -Affiliated Housing:** 60 **Final Year or Final Semester Residency Requirement:** Yes **Regional Accreditation:** North Central Association of Colleges and Schools **Credit Hours For Degree:** 120 credits, Bachelors **Professional Accreditation:** NCATE. **Intercollegiate Athletics:** Baseball M; Basketball M & W; Cross-Country Running M & W; Football M; Golf M & W; Soccer M & W; Softball W; Swimming and Diving W; Tennis M & W; Track and Field M & W; Volleyball W

UNIVERSITY OF MINNESOTA ROCHESTER

111 S Broadway
Ste. 300
Rochester, MN 55904
Tel: (877)280-4699
Web Site: www.r.umn.edu
Type: Comprehensive **Sex:** Coed **Regional Accreditation:** North Central Association of Colleges and Schools

UNIVERSITY OF MINNESOTA, TWIN CITIES CAMPUS

100 Church St., SE
Minneapolis, MN 55455-0213
Tel: (612)625-5000; Free: 800-752-1000
Fax: (612)626-1693
E-mail: admissions@tc.umn.edu
Web Site: www.umn.edu/tc
President/CEO: Dr. Eric Kaler
Admissions: Rachelle Hernandez

Type: Comprehensive **Sex:** Coed **Affiliation:** University of Minnesota System. **Scores:** 99% SAT V 400+; 100% SAT M 400+; 8.3% ACT 18-23; 55.3% ACT 24-29 **% Accepted:** 45 **Admission Plans:** Deferred Admission; Early Admission **Application Deadline:** Rolling **Application Fee:** $55.00 **H.S. Requirements:** High school diploma required; GED accepted **Costs Per Year:** Application fee: $55. State resident tuition: $12,240 full-time, $471 per credit hour part-time. Nonresident tuition: $20,660 full-time, $795 per credit hour part-time. Mandatory fees: $1550 full-time. Full-time tuition and fees vary according to program and reciprocity agreements. Part-time tuition varies according to course load, program, and reciprocity agreements. College room and board: $9314. College room only: $5244. Room and board charges vary according to board plan, housing facility, and location. **Scholarships:** Available. **Calendar System:** Semester, Summer session available **Enrollment:** Full-time 29,168, Graduate full-time 9,701, Graduate part-time 6,906, Part-time 4,903 **Faculty:** Full-time 2,589, Part-time 1,102 **Student-Faculty Ratio:** 17:1 **Exams:** SAT I or ACT; SAT Reasoning; SAT Subject. **% Receiving Financial Aid:** 48 **% Residing in College-Owned,**

-Operated, or -Affiliated Housing: 23 **Regional Accreditation:** North Central Association of Colleges and Schools **Credit Hours For Degree:** 120 semester credits, Bachelors **ROTC:** Air Force, Army, Navy **Professional Accreditation:** AACN, AACSB, AALS, AAMFT, AANA, ABA, ABET, ABFSE, ACEJMC, ACEN, ACNM, ACPE, ACSP, ACIPE, ADA, AND, AOTA, APA, APTA, ASHA, ASLA, AVMA, CAHME, CEPH, CIDA, CSWE, LCME/AMA, NAAB, NAACLS, NASD, NASM, NASPAA, NAST, NCATE, NRPA, SAF. **Intercollegiate Athletics:** Baseball M; Basketball M & W; Cross-Country Running M & W; Football M; Golf M & W; Gymnastics M & W; Ice Hockey M & W; Soccer W; Softball W; Swimming and Diving M & W; Tennis M & W; Track and Field M & W; Volleyball W; Wrestling M

UNIVERSITY OF NORTHWESTERN–ST. PAUL

3003 Snelling Ave. N
Saint Paul, MN 55113-1598
Tel: (651)631-5100; Free: 800-827-6827
Fax: (651)631-5680
E-mail: admissions@unwsp.edu
Web Site: www.unwsp.edu
President/CEO: Dr. Alan S. Cureton
Financial Aid: Richard L. Blatchley
Type: Comprehensive **Sex:** Coed **Affiliation:** nondenominational. **Scores:** 100% SAT V 400+; 100% SAT M 400+; 42% ACT 18-23; 40% ACT 24-29 **% Accepted:** 70 **Admission Plans:** Deferred Admission; Early Admission **Application Deadline:** August 1 **Application Fee:** $0.00 **H.S. Requirements:** High school diploma required; GED accepted **Costs Per Year:** Application fee: $0. Comprehensive fee: $37,824 includes full-time tuition ($28,390), mandatory fees ($480), and college room and board ($8954). College room only: $5350. Full-time tuition and fees vary according to course load. Room and board charges vary according to board plan and student level. Part-time tuition: $1210 per credit. Part-time tuition varies according to course load. **Scholarships:** Available. **Calendar System:** Semester, Summer session available **Enrollment:** Full-time 1,931, Graduate full-time 7, Graduate part-time 198, Part-time 1,291 **Faculty:** Full-time 94, Part-time 114 **Student-Faculty Ratio:** 18:1 **Exams:** SAT I or ACT; SAT essay component not used; SAT Reasoning; SAT Subject. **% Receiving Financial Aid:** 83 **% Residing in College-Owned, -Operated, or -Affiliated Housing:** 65 **Final Year or Final Semester Residency Requirement:** No **Regional Accreditation:** North Central Association of Colleges and Schools **Credit Hours For Degree:** 60 semester hours, Associates; 125 semester hours, Bachelors **ROTC:** Air Force, Army **Professional Accreditation:** NASM. **Intercollegiate Athletics:** Baseball M; Basketball M & W; Cross-Country Running M & W; Football M; Golf M & W; Ice Hockey M; Lacrosse W; Soccer M & W; Softball W; Tennis M & W; Track and Field M & W; Volleyball M & W

UNIVERSITY OF ST. THOMAS

2115 Summit Ave.
Saint Paul, MN 55105-1096
Tel: (651)962-5000; Free: 800-328-6819
Fax: (651)962-6160
E-mail: admissions@stthomas.edu
Web Site: www.stthomas.edu
President/CEO: Dr. Julie Sullivan
Admissions: Dan Meyer
Financial Aid: Paula Benson
Type: University **Sex:** Coed **Affiliation:** Roman Catholic. **Scores:** 23.7% ACT 18-23; 57.6% ACT 24-29 **% Accepted:** 84 **Admission Plans:** Deferred Admission **Application Deadline:** Rolling **Application Fee:** $0.00 **H.S. Requirements:** High school diploma required; GED accepted **Costs Per Year:** Application fee: $0. Tuition: $37,264 full-time, $1,165 per credit hour part-time. Mandatory fees: $841 full-time. **Scholarships:** Available. **Calendar System:** 4-1-4, Summer session available **Enrollment:** Full-time 5,952, Graduate full-time 1,189, Graduate part-time 2,814, Part-time 288 **Student-Faculty Ratio:** 14:1 **Exams:** SAT I or ACT. **% Receiving Financial Aid:** 57 **% Residing in College-Owned, -Operated, or -Affiliated Housing:** 41 **Regional Accreditation:** North Central Association of Colleges and Schools **Credit Hours For Degree:** 132 credits, Bachelors **ROTC:** Air Force, Army, Navy **Professional Accreditation:** AACSB, ABA, ABET, ACIPE, APA, ATS, CAHME, CSWE, NASM, NCATE. **Intercollegiate Athletics:** Baseball M; Basketball M & W; Cross-Country Running M & W; Football M; Golf M & W; Ice Hockey M & W; Lacrosse M & W; Soccer M & W; Softball W; Swimming and Diving M & W; Tennis M & W; Volleyball W

VERMILION COMMUNITY COLLEGE

1900 E Camp St.
Ely, MN 55731-1996

Tel: (218)365-7200; Free: 800-657-3608
Web Site: www.vcc.edu
President/CEO: Shawn Bina
Admissions: Todd Heiman
Financial Aid: Kristi L'Allier
Type: Two-Year College **Sex:** Coed **Affiliation:** Minnesota State Colleges and Universities System. **% Accepted:** 57 **Admission Plans:** Deferred Admission; Early Admission; Open Admission **Application Deadline:** Rolling **Application Fee:** $20.00 **H.S. Requirements:** High school diploma required; GED accepted **Scholarships:** Available. **Calendar System:** Semester, Summer session available **Enrollment:** Full-time 533, Part-time 212 **Faculty:** Full-time 25, Part-time 60 **Student-Faculty Ratio:** 13:1 **% Residing in College-Owned, -Operated, or -Affiliated Housing:** 50 **Regional Accreditation:** North Central Association of Colleges and Schools **Intercollegiate Athletics:** Baseball M; Basketball M & W; Football M; Softball W; Volleyball W

WALDEN UNIVERSITY

100 Washington S, Ste. 900
Minneapolis, MN 55401
Free: 866-492-5336
E-mail: peter.scanlan@waldenu.edu
Web Site: www.waldenu.edu
President/CEO: Jonathan Kaplan, JD
Admissions: Peter Scanlan
Type: University **Sex:** Coed **Affiliation:** Laureate International Universities. **% Accepted:** 98 **Admission Plans:** Deferred Admission **Application Deadline:** Rolling **H.S. Requirements:** High school diploma required; GED accepted **Costs Per Year:** Tuition: $14,850 full-time, $330 per credit hour part-time. Mandatory fees: $480 full-time, $160 per term part-time. Full-time tuition and fees vary according to course level, course load, degree level, and program. Part-time tuition and fees vary according to course level, course load, degree level, and program. **Scholarships:** Available. **Calendar System:** Miscellaneous, Summer session available **Enrollment:** Full-time 784, Graduate full-time 25,587, Graduate part-time 18,973, Part-time 7,455 **Faculty:** Full-time 210, Part-time 2,544 **% Receiving Financial Aid:** 96 **Final Year or Final Semester Residency Requirement:** No **Regional Accreditation:** North Central Association of Colleges and Schools **Credit Hours For Degree:** 181 units, Bachelors **Professional Accreditation:** AACN, ACBSP, NCATE.

WHITE EARTH TRIBAL AND COMMUNITY COLLEGE

102 3rd St. NE
Mahnomen, MN 56557
Tel: (218)935-0417
Web Site: www.wetcc.edu
Type: Two-Year College **Sex:** Coed **Calendar System:** Semester **Regional Accreditation:** North Central Association of Colleges and Schools

WINONA STATE UNIVERSITY

175 W Mark St.
Winona, MN 55987
Tel: (507)457-5000; Free: 800-DIAL WSU
Fax: (507)457-5620
E-mail: admissions@winona.edu
Web Site: www.winona.edu
President/CEO: Dr. Scott R. Olson
Admissions: Carl Stange
Financial Aid: Mari Livingston
Type: Comprehensive **Sex:** Coed **Affiliation:** Minnesota State Colleges and Universities System. **Scores:** 60% ACT 18-23; 36% ACT 24-29 **% Accepted:** 62 **Admission Plans:** Deferred Admission **Application Deadline:** July 1 **Application Fee:** $20.00 **H.S. Requirements:** High school diploma required; GED accepted **Costs Per Year:** Application fee: $20. State resident tuition: $7103 full-time, $235 per credit hour part-time. Nonresident tuition: $12,800 full-time, $426 per credit hour part-time. Mandatory fees: $1944 full-time. Full-time tuition and fees vary according to location, program, and reciprocity agreements. Part-time tuition varies according to course load, location, program, and reciprocity agreements. College room and board: $8120. Room and board charges vary according to board plan, housing facility, and location. **Scholarships:** Available. **Calendar System:** Semester, Summer session available **Enrollment:** Full-time 7,061, Graduate full-time 322, Graduate part-time 148, Part-time 941 **Faculty:** Full-time 325, Part-time 187 **Student-Faculty Ratio:** 20:1 **Exams:** ACT essay component

not used; SAT I or ACT; SAT essay component not used; SAT Reasoning; SAT Subject. **% Receiving Financial Aid:** 58 **% Residing in College-Owned, -Operated, or -Affiliated Housing:** 30 **Final Year or Final Semester Residency Requirement:** Yes **Regional Accreditation:** North Central Association of Colleges and Schools **Credit Hours For Degree:** 60

semester hours, Associates; 120 semester hours, Bachelors **ROTC:** Army **Professional Accreditation:** AACN, AACSB, ABET, ACA, CSWE, JRCAT, NASM, NAST, NCATE. **Intercollegiate Athletics:** Baseball M; Basketball M & W; Cross-Country Running M & W; Football M; Golf M & W; Gymnastics W; Soccer W; Softball W; Tennis W; Track and Field W; Volleyball W

ALCORN STATE UNIVERSITY
1000 ASU Dr.
Lorman, MS 39096-7500
Tel: (601)877-6100; Free: 800-222-6790
Fax: (601)877-6347
E-mail: ksampson@alcorn.edu
Web Site: www.alcorn.edu
President/CEO: Dr. Alfred Rankins, Jr.
Admissions: Kantangelia Tenner
Financial Aid: Juanita M. Russell
Type: Comprehensive **Sex:** Coed **Affiliation:** Mississippi Institutions of Higher Learning. **Scores:** 75% SAT V 400+; 72% SAT M 400+; 47% ACT 18-23; 7% ACT 24-29 **% Accepted:** 81 **Admission Plans:** Deferred Admission **Application Deadline:** Rolling **Application Fee:** $0.00 **H.S. Requirements:** High school diploma required; GED accepted **Costs Per Year:** Application fee: $0. State resident tuition: $6384 full-time. Nonresident tuition: $6384 full-time. Mandatory fees: $266 per credit hour part-time. College room and board: $8996. College room only: $6138. **Scholarships:** Available. **Calendar System:** Semester, Summer session available **Enrollment:** Full-time 2,556, Graduate full-time 201, Graduate part-time 406, Part-time 355 **Faculty:** Full-time 157, Part-time 59 **Student-Faculty Ratio:** 16:1 **Exams:** ACT essay component not used; SAT I or ACT; SAT essay component not used. **% Receiving Financial Aid:** 46 **% Residing in College-Owned, -Operated, or -Affiliated Housing:** 57 **Regional Accreditation:** Southern Association of Colleges and Schools **Credit Hours For Degree:** 70 credit hours, Associates; 124 credit hours, Bachelors **ROTC:** Army **Professional Accreditation:** AACN, AAFCS, ACBSP, ACEN, AND, ATMAE, NASM, NCATE. **Intercollegiate Athletics:** Baseball M; Basketball M & W; Cross-Country Running M & W; Football M; Golf M & W; Soccer W; Softball W; Tennis M & W; Track and Field M & W; Volleyball W

ANTONELLI COLLEGE (HATTIESBURG)
1500 N 31st Ave.
Hattiesburg, MS 39401
Tel: (601)583-4100
Fax: (601)583-0839
E-mail: admissionsh@antonellicollege.edu
Web Site: www.antonellicollege.edu
President/CEO: Mary Ann Davis
Admissions: Karen Gautreau
Type: Two-Year College **Sex:** Coed **Application Fee:** $75.00 **Calendar System:** Quarter **Professional Accreditation:** ACCSC.

ANTONELLI COLLEGE (JACKSON)
2323 Lakeland Dr.
Jackson, MS 39232
Tel: (601)362-9991
Fax: (601)362-2333
E-mail: admissions.jackson@antonellicollege.edu
Web Site: www.antonellicollege.edu
President/CEO: Mary Ann Davis
Admissions: Rafael Anderson, AIA
Type: Two-Year College **Sex:** Coed **Admission Plans:** Open Admission **Application Fee:** $75.00 **Scholarships:** Available. **Calendar System:** Quarter **Professional Accreditation:** ACCSC.

BELHAVEN UNIVERSITY
1500 Peachtree St.
Jackson, MS 39202-1789
Tel: (601)968-5928; Free: 800-960-5940
Fax: (601)968-9998
E-mail: admission@belhaven.edu
Web Site: www.belhaven.edu
President/CEO: Dr. Roger Parrott
Admissions: Suzanne T. Sullivan
Financial Aid: Debbi Braswell
Type: Comprehensive **Sex:** Coed **Affiliation:** Presbyterian. **Scores:** 96% SAT V 400+; 94% SAT M 400+; 65% ACT 18-23; 28% ACT 24-29 **% Accepted:** 51 **Admission Plans:** Deferred Admission; Early Admission **Application Deadline:** Rolling **Application Fee:** $25.00 **H.S. Requirements:** High school diploma required; GED accepted **Costs Per Year:** Application fee: $25. Comprehensive fee: $29,816 includes full-time tuition ($21,626), mandatory fees ($190), and college room and board ($8000). Room and board charges vary according to housing facility. Part-time tuition: $425 per hour. Part-time tuition varies according to course load. **Scholarships:** Available. **Calendar System:** Semester, Summer session available **Enrollment:** Full-time 1,409, Graduate full-time 23, Graduate part-time 1,678, Part-time 1,342 **Faculty:** Full-time 113, Part-time 293 **Student-Faculty Ratio:** 11:1 **Exams:** ACT essay component not used; SAT I or ACT; SAT essay component not used. **% Receiving Financial Aid:** 78 **% Residing in College-Owned, -Operated, or -Affiliated Housing:** 23 **Final Year or Final Semester Residency Requirement:** No **Regional Accreditation:** Southern Association of Colleges and Schools **Credit Hours For Degree:** 62 semester hours, Associates; 124 semester hours, Bachelors **ROTC:** Air Force, Army **Professional Accreditation:** NASAD, NASD, NASM. **Intercollegiate Athletics:** Baseball M; Basketball M & W; Cross-Country Running M & W; Football M; Golf M & W; Soccer M & W; Softball W; Tennis M & W; Volleyball W

BLUE CLIFF COLLEGE–GULFPORT
12251 Bernard Pky.
Gulfport, MS 39503
Tel: (228)896-9727
Web Site: www.bluecliffcollege.edu
Type: Two-Year College **Sex:** Coed **Professional Accreditation:** ACCSC.

BLUE MOUNTAIN COLLEGE
201 W Main St.
Blue Mountain, MS 38610
Tel: (662)685-4771; Free: 800-235-0136
Fax: (662)685-4776
E-mail: lgibson@bmc.edu
Web Site: www.bmc.edu
President/CEO: Dr. Barbara McMillin
Admissions: Lynn Gibson
Financial Aid: Beverly K. Hickey
Type: Comprehensive **Sex:** Coed **Affiliation:** Southern Baptist. **Scores:** 55% ACT 18-23; 24% ACT 24-29 **% Accepted:** 38 **Admission Plans:** Deferred Admission **Application Deadline:** Rolling **Application Fee:** $10.00 **H.S. Requirements:** High school diploma required; GED accepted **Costs Per Year:** Application fee: $10. Tuition: $317 per semester hour part-time.

Mandatory fees: $575 per term part-time. Part-time tuition and fees vary according to course load, degree level, and program. **Scholarships:** Available. **Calendar System:** Semester, Summer session available **Enrollment:** Full-time 397, Graduate full-time 17, Graduate part-time 9, Part-time 60 **Faculty:** Full-time 33, Part-time 17 **Student-Faculty Ratio:** 11:1 **Exams:** ACT essay component not used; SAT I or ACT; SAT essay component not used; SAT Reasoning; SAT Subject. **% Receiving Financial Aid:** 78 **% Residing in College-Owned, -Operated, or -Affiliated Housing:** 54 **Final Year or Final Semester Residency Requirement:** Yes **Regional Accreditation:** Southern Association of Colleges and Schools **Credit Hours For Degree:** 120 semester hours, Bachelors **Intercollegiate Athletics:** Baseball M; Basketball M & W; Cross-Country Running M & W; Golf M; Softball W

COAHOMA COMMUNITY COLLEGE

3240 Friars Point Rd.
Clarksdale, MS 38614-9799
Tel: (662)627-2571; Free: 866-470-1CCC
Web Site: www.ccc.cc.ms.us
President/CEO: Dr. Vivian M. Presley
Admissions: Wanda Holmes

Type: Two-Year College **Sex:** Coed **Affiliation:** Mississippi State Board for Community and Junior Colleges. **Admission Plans:** Open Admission **Application Deadline:** Rolling **Application Fee:** $0.00 **H.S. Requirements:** High school diploma required; GED accepted **Costs Per Year:** Application fee: $0. State resident tuition: $2300 full-time, $125 per credit hour part-time. Nonresident tuition: $5400 full-time, $235 per credit hour part-time. Mandatory fees: $200 full-time, $35 per term part-time. Full-time tuition and fees vary according to class time, course load, location, and program. Part-time tuition and fees vary according to class time, course load, location, and program. College room and board: $4220. College room only: $1600. Room and board charges vary according to board plan. **Scholarships:** Available. **Calendar System:** Semester **Enrollment:** Full-time 1,962, Part-time 254 **Faculty:** Full-time 53, Part-time 64 **Student-Faculty Ratio:** 19:1 **% Residing in College-Owned, -Operated, or -Affiliated Housing:** 22 **Regional Accreditation:** Southern Association of Colleges and Schools **Credit Hours For Degree:** 65 credit hours, Associates **Intercollegiate Athletics:** Baseball M; Basketball M & W; Cheerleading W; Football M; Softball W

COPIAH-LINCOLN COMMUNITY COLLEGE

PO Box 649
Wesson, MS 39191
Tel: (601)643-5101
Fax: (601)643-8212
E-mail: gay.langham@colin.edu
Web Site: www.colin.edu
President/CEO: Dr. Ronald E. Nettles, II
Admissions: Gay Langham

Type: Two-Year College **Sex:** Coed **Affiliation:** Mississippi Community College Board. **Admission Plans:** Early Admission; Open Admission; Preferred Admission **Application Deadline:** Rolling **Application Fee:** $0.00 **H.S. Requirements:** High school diploma required; GED accepted **Costs Per Year:** Application fee: $0. State resident tuition: $2390 full-time, $119.50 per semester hour part-time. Nonresident tuition: $4390 full-time, $204.50 per semester hour part-time. Mandatory fees: $340 full-time. College room and board: $3750. College room only: $1550. Room and board charges vary according to board plan and housing facility. **Scholarships:** Available. **Calendar System:** Semester, Summer session available **Enrollment:** Full-time 2,509, Part-time 648 **% Residing in College-Owned, -Operated, or -Affiliated Housing:** 30 **Regional Accreditation:** Southern Association of Colleges and Schools **Credit Hours For Degree:** 62 semester hours, Associates **Professional Accreditation:** ACEN, JRCERT, NAACLS. **Intercollegiate Athletics:** Baseball M; Basketball M & W; Football M; Golf M & W; Softball W; Tennis M & W; Track and Field M

DELTA STATE UNIVERSITY

Hwy. 8 W
Cleveland, MS 38733-0001
Tel: (662)846-3000; Free: 800-468-6378
Fax: (662)846-4016
E-mail: admissions@deltastate.edu
Web Site: www.deltastate.edu
President/CEO: William LaForge
Admissions: Chris Gaines
Financial Aid: Christie Rocconi

Type: Comprehensive **Sex:** Coed **Affiliation:** Mississippi Institutions of Higher Learning. **% Accepted:** 92 **Admission Plans:** Deferred Admission **Application Deadline:** Rolling **Application Fee:** $25.00 **H.S. Requirements:** High school diploma required; GED accepted **Costs Per Year:** Application fee: $25. State resident tuition: $6012 full-time, $251 per hour part-time. Nonresident tuition: $6012 full-time, $251 per hour part-time. Mandatory fees: $100 full-time, $4.16. Part-time tuition and fees vary according to course load. College room and board: $7064. College room only: $4114. Room and board charges vary according to board plan and housing facility. **Scholarships:** Available. **Calendar System:** Semester, Summer session available **Enrollment:** Full-time 2,308, Graduate full-time 326, Graduate part-time 510, Part-time 470 **Faculty:** Full-time 183, Part-time 73 **Student-Faculty Ratio:** 14:1 **Exams:** ACT; ACT essay component not used; SAT I or ACT; SAT essay component not used. **% Receiving Financial Aid:** 87 **% Residing in College-Owned, -Operated, or -Affiliated Housing:** 25 **Final Year or Final Semester Residency Requirement:** No **Regional Accreditation:** Southern Association of Colleges and Schools **Credit Hours For Degree:** 124 credit hours, Bachelors **ROTC:** Army **Professional Accreditation:** AACN, AAFCS, ACA, ACBSP, AND, CSWE, NASAD, NASM, NCATE. **Intercollegiate Athletics:** Baseball M; Basketball M & W; Cheerleading M & W; Cross-Country Running W; Football M; Golf M; Soccer M & W; Softball W; Swimming and Diving M & W; Tennis M & W

EAST CENTRAL COMMUNITY COLLEGE

PO Box 129
Decatur, MS 39327-0129
Tel: (601)635-2111; Free: 877-462-3222
Fax: (601)635-2150
Web Site: www.eccc.edu
President/CEO: Billy W. Stewart
Admissions: Donna Luke

Type: Two-Year College **Sex:** Coed **Affiliation:** Mississippi State Board for Community and Junior Colleges. **Admission Plans:** Early Admission; Open Admission **Application Deadline:** Rolling **Application Fee:** $0.00 **H.S. Requirements:** High school diploma required; GED accepted **Scholarships:** Available. **Calendar System:** Semester, Summer session available **Regional Accreditation:** Southern Association of Colleges and Schools **Credit Hours For Degree:** 64 semester hours, Associates **Professional Accreditation:** ACEN, ARCST. **Intercollegiate Athletics:** Baseball M; Basketball M & W; Football M; Golf M & W; Soccer M & W; Softball W; Tennis M & W

EAST MISSISSIPPI COMMUNITY COLLEGE

PO Box 158
Scooba, MS 39358-0158
Tel: (662)476-8442
Web Site: www.eastms.edu
President/CEO: Rick Young
Admissions: Melinda Sciple

Type: Two-Year College **Sex:** Coed **Affiliation:** Mississippi State Board for Community and Junior Colleges. **Admission Plans:** Deferred Admission; Open Admission **Application Deadline:** Rolling **Application Fee:** $0.00 **H.S. Requirements:** High school diploma required; GED accepted **Scholarships:** Available. **Calendar System:** Semester, Summer session available **Regional Accreditation:** Southern Association of Colleges and Schools **Credit Hours For Degree:** 64 semester hours, Associates **Professional Accreditation:** ABFSE. **Intercollegiate Athletics:** Baseball M; Basketball M & W; Cheerleading W; Football M; Golf M; Soccer M & W; Softball W

HINDS COMMUNITY COLLEGE

PO Box 1100
Raymond, MS 39154-1100
Tel: (601)857-5261; Free: 800-HINDSCC
E-mail: randall.harris@hindscc.edu
Web Site: www.hindscc.edu
President/CEO: Dr. V. Clyde Muse
Admissions: Randall Harris

Type: Two-Year College **Sex:** Coed **Affiliation:** Mississippi Community College Board. **Scores:** 32.4% ACT 18-23; 5% ACT 24-29 **Costs Per Year:** State resident tuition: $2400 full-time, $100 per semester hour part-time. Nonresident tuition: $5000 full-time, $200 per semester hour part-time. Mandatory fees: $100 full-time, $50 per term part-time. Part-time tuition and fees vary according to course load. College room and board: $3960. Room and board charges vary according to housing facility. **Scholarships:** Available. **Calendar System:** Semester, Summer session available **Enrollment:** Full-time 7,344, Part-time 4,170 **Faculty:** Full-time 377, Part-time 442 **Student-Faculty Ratio:** 19:1 **Exams:** SAT I and SAT II or ACT. **Final Year or Final Semester Residency Requirement:** No **Regional Accreditation:** Southern Association of Colleges and Schools **Credit Hours For Degree:** 60 semester hours, Associates **ROTC:** Army **Professional Accreditation:** AAMAE, ACEN, ADA, AHIMA, APTA, CoARC, JRCERT, NAACLS. **Intercollegiate Athletics:** Baseball M; Basketball M & W; Cheerleading M & W; Football M; Golf M; Soccer M & W; Softball W; Tennis M & W; Track and Field M & W

HOLMES COMMUNITY COLLEGE

PO Box 369
Goodman, MS 39079-0369
Tel: (662)472-2312; Free: 800-HOLMES-4
Fax: (662)472-9156
Web Site: www.holmescc.edu
President/CEO: Dr. Jim Haffey
Admissions: Dr. Lynn Wright

Type: Two-Year College **Sex:** Coed **Affiliation:** Mississippi State Board for Community and Junior Colleges. **Admission Plans:** Early Admission; Open Admission **Application Deadline:** Rolling **Application Fee:** $0.00 **H.S. Requirements:** High school diploma required; GED accepted **Scholarships:** Available. **Calendar System:** Semester, Summer session available **Regional Accreditation:** Southern Association of Colleges and Schools **Credit Hours For Degree:** 64 semester hours, Associates **Professional Accreditation:** ACEN, AOTA, ARCST, JRCEMTP. **Intercollegiate Athletics:** Baseball M; Basketball M & W; Football M; Golf M; Soccer M; Softball W; Tennis W

ITAWAMBA COMMUNITY COLLEGE

602 W Hill St.
Fulton, MS 38843
Tel: (662)862-8000
Fax: (662)862-8036
E-mail: laboggs@iccms.edu
Web Site: www.iccms.edu
President/CEO: Mike Eaton
Admissions: Larry Boggs
Financial Aid: Robert D. Walker

Type: Two-Year College **Sex:** Coed **Affiliation:** Mississippi State Board for Community and Junior Colleges. **Admission Plans:** Early Admission; Open Admission **Application Deadline:** Rolling **Application Fee:** $0.00 **H.S. Requirements:** High school diploma required; GED accepted **Costs Per Year:** Application fee: $0. State resident tuition: $2500 full-time, $120 per semester hour part-time. Nonresident tuition: $4700 full-time, $120 per semester hour part-time. Mandatory fees: $120 full-time, $120. College room and board: $3510. College room only: $1500. Room and board charges vary according to board plan and housing facility. **Scholarships:** Available. **Calendar System:** Semester, Summer session available **Enrollment:** Full-time 3,605, Part-time 2,006 **Faculty:** Full-time 167, Part-time 186 **Student-Faculty Ratio:** 19:1 **Regional Accreditation:** Southern Association of Colleges and Schools **Credit Hours For Degree:** 60 semester hours, Associates **ROTC:** Army **Professional Accreditation:** ACEN, AHIMA, APTA, ARCST, CoARC, JRCERT. **Intercollegiate Athletics:** Basketball M & W; Football M; Golf M; Tennis M & W; Track and Field M

JACKSON STATE UNIVERSITY

1400 John R Lynch St.
Jackson, MS 39217
Tel: (601)979-2121; Free: 800-848-6817
Fax: (601)979-2358
E-mail: juanita.m.morris@jsums.edu
Web Site: www.jsums.edu
President/CEO: Dr. Carolyn W. Meyers
Admissions: Dr. Juanita M. Morris
Financial Aid: Betty Moncure

Type: University **Sex:** Coed **Affiliation:** Mississippi Institutions of Higher Learning. **Scores:** 53.07% ACT 18-23; 11.58% ACT 24-29 **% Accepted:** 68 **Application Deadline:** August 1 **Application Fee:** $0.00 **H.S. Requirements:** High school diploma required; GED accepted **Costs Per Year:** Application fee: $0. State resident tuition: $6866 full-time, $286 per credit hour part-time. Nonresident tuition: $16,841 full-time, $415 per credit hour part-time. Mandatory fees: $20 full-time. College room and board: $8226. Room

and board charges vary according to housing facility. **Scholarships:** Available. **Calendar System:** Semester, Summer session available **Enrollment:** Full-time 6,678, Graduate full-time 870, Graduate part-time 1,457, Part-time 797 **Faculty:** Full-time 387, Part-time 219 **Student-Faculty Ratio:** 18:1 **Exams:** ACT essay component not used; SAT I or ACT; SAT essay component not used; SAT Reasoning; SAT Subject. **% Receiving Financial Aid:** 92 **% Residing in College-Owned, -Operated, or -Affiliated Housing:** 34 **Final Year or Final Semester Residency Requirement:** Yes **Regional Accreditation:** Southern Association of Colleges and Schools **Credit Hours For Degree:** 128 credit hours, Bachelors **ROTC:** Air Force, Army **Professional Accreditation:** AACSB, ABET, ACA, ACEJMC, ACSP, APA, ASHA, ATMAE, CORE, CSWE, NASAD, NASM, NASPAA, NCATE. **Intercollegiate Athletics:** Baseball M; Basketball M & W; Bowling W; Cross-Country Running M & W; Football M; Golf M & W; Soccer W; Softball W; Tennis M & W; Track and Field M & W; Volleyball W

JONES COUNTY JUNIOR COLLEGE

900 S Ct. St.
Ellisville, MS 39437-3901
Tel: (601)477-4000
Fax: (601)477-4017
Web Site: www.jcjc.edu
President/CEO: Jesse Smith
Admissions: Dianne Speed

Type: Two-Year College **Sex:** Coed **Affiliation:** Mississippi State Board for Community and Junior Colleges. **Admission Plans:** Early Admission; Open Admission; Preferred Admission **Application Deadline:** August 26 **Application Fee:** $0.00 **H.S. Requirements:** High school diploma required; GED accepted **Scholarships:** Available. **Calendar System:** Semester, Summer session available **Faculty:** Full-time 170, Part-time 5 **Student-Faculty Ratio:** 25:1 **Exams:** SAT I or ACT. **% Residing in College-Owned, -Operated, or -Affiliated Housing:** 20 **Regional Accreditation:** Southern Association of Colleges and Schools **Credit Hours For Degree:** 64 semester hours, Associates **ROTC:** Air Force, Army **Professional Accreditation:** ACBSP, ACEN, JRCEMTP, JRCERT. **Intercollegiate Athletics:** Baseball M; Basketball M & W; Football M; Golf M; Soccer M & W; Softball W; Tennis M & W; Track and Field M

MERIDIAN COMMUNITY COLLEGE

910 Hwy. 19 N
Meridian, MS 39307
Tel: (601)483-8241; Free: 800-MCC-THE-1
E-mail: apayne@meridiancc.edu
Web Site: www.meridiancc.edu
President/CEO: Dr. Scott D. Elliott, EdD
Admissions: Angela Payne
Financial Aid: Nedra L. Bradley

Type: Two-Year College **Sex:** Coed **Affiliation:** Mississippi Community College Board. **Admission Plans:** Early Admission; Open Admission **Application Deadline:** Rolling **Application Fee:** $0.00 **H.S. Requirements:** High school diploma required; GED accepted **Costs Per Year:** Application fee: $0. State resident tuition: $2100 full-time, $100 per credit hour part-time. Nonresident tuition: $3380 full-time, $157 per credit hour part-time. Mandatory fees: $230 full-time, $6 per credit hour part-time, $25 per term part-time. Full-time tuition and fees vary according to program. Part-time tuition and fees vary according to program. College room and board: $3878. Room and board charges vary according to housing facility. **Scholarships:** Available. **Calendar System:** Semester, Summer session available **Enrollment:** Full-time 2,453, Part-time 928 **Faculty:** Full-time 154, Part-time 55 **Student-Faculty Ratio:** 18:1 **Exams:** ACT. **% Residing in College-Owned, -Operated, or -Affiliated Housing:** 12 **Final Year or Final Semester Residency Requirement:** No **Regional Accreditation:** Southern Association of Colleges and Schools **Credit Hours For Degree:** 62 semester hours, Associates **Professional Accreditation:** ACEN, ADA, AHIMA, APTA, JRCERT, NAACLS. **Intercollegiate Athletics:** Baseball M; Basketball M & W; Cross-Country Running M & W; Golf M; Soccer M & W; Softball W; Tennis M & W; Track and Field M & W

MILLER-MOTTE TECHNICAL COLLEGE

12121 Hwy. 49 N
Gulfport, MS 39503
Tel: (228)273-3400; Free: 866-297-0267
Web Site: www.miller-motte.edu

Type: Two-Year College **Sex:** Coed **Professional Accreditation:** ACICS.

MILLSAPS COLLEGE

1701 N State St.
Jackson, MS 39210-0001
Tel: (601)974-1000; Free: 800-352-1050
Fax: (601)974-1059
E-mail: admissions@millsaps.edu
Web Site: www.millsaps.edu
President/CEO: Dr. Robert W. Pearigen, PhD
Admissions: Dr. Robert Alexander
Financial Aid: Isabelle Higbee

Type: Comprehensive Sex: Coed Affiliation: United Methodist. Scores: 42.6% ACT 18-23; 38.6% ACT 24-29 % Accepted: 53 Admission Plans: Deferred Admission; Early Admission; Early Decision Plan Application Deadline: February 1 Application Fee: $0.00 H.S. Requirements: High school diploma required; GED accepted Scholarships: Available. Calendar System: Semester, Summer session available Enrollment: Full-time 750, Graduate full-time 25, Graduate part-time 24, Part-time 11 Faculty: Full-time 87, Part-time 20 Student-Faculty Ratio: 8:1 Exams: SAT I or ACT; SAT Reasoning. % Receiving Financial Aid: 60 % Residing in College-Owned, -Operated, or -Affiliated Housing: 90 Final Year or Final Semester Residency Requirement: No Regional Accreditation: Southern Association of Colleges and Schools Credit Hours For Degree: 128 semester hours, Bachelors ROTC: Air Force, Army Professional Accreditation: AACSB, NCATE. Intercollegiate Athletics: Baseball M; Basketball M & W; Cross-Country Running M & W; Football M; Golf M & W; Lacrosse M & W; Soccer M & W; Softball W; Tennis M & W; Track and Field M & W; Volleyball W

MISSISSIPPI COLLEGE

200 S Capitol St.
Clinton, MS 39058
Tel: (601)925-3000; Free: 800-738-1236
Fax: (601)925-3804
E-mail: enrollment-services@mc.edu
Web Site: www.mc.edu
President/CEO: Dr. Lee G. Royce
Admissions: William Kyle Brantley
Financial Aid: Karon Q. McMillan

Type: Comprehensive Sex: Coed Affiliation: Southern Baptist; Mississippi Baptist Convention. Scores: 95% SAT V 400+; 97% SAT M 400+; 44% ACT 18-23; 42% ACT 24-29 % Accepted: 82 Admission Plans: Deferred Admission; Early Admission Application Deadline: Rolling Application Fee: $25.00 H.S. Requirements: High school diploma required; GED accepted Costs Per Year: Application fee: $25. Comprehensive fee: $25,930 includes full-time tuition ($15,800), mandatory fees ($940), and college room and board ($9190). Room and board charges vary according to housing facility. Part-time tuition: $495 per credit. Part-time mandatory fees: $490 per term. Scholarships: Available. Calendar System: Semester, Summer session available Enrollment: Full-time 2,677, Graduate full-time 1,246, Graduate part-time 786, Part-time 327 Faculty: Full-time 228, Part-time 205 Student-Faculty Ratio: 15:1 Exams: SAT I or ACT. % Receiving Financial Aid: 52 % Residing in College-Owned, -Operated, or -Affiliated Housing: 64 Final Year or Final Semester Residency Requirement: Yes Regional Accreditation: Southern Association of Colleges and Schools Credit Hours For Degree: 130 credit hours, Bachelors ROTC: Air Force, Army Professional Accreditation: AACN, AAFCS, AALS, ABA, ACA, ACBSP, CSWE, NASM, NCATE. Intercollegiate Athletics: Baseball M; Basketball M & W; Cross-Country Running M & W; Football M; Golf M; Soccer M & W; Softball W; Tennis M & W; Track and Field M & W; Volleyball W

MISSISSIPPI DELTA COMMUNITY COLLEGE

Hwy. 3 and Cherry St.
Moorhead, MS 38761-0668
Tel: (662)246-6322
E-mail: bgregory@msdelta.edu
Web Site: www.msdelta.edu
President/CEO: Dr. Larry Nabors
Admissions: Dr. Brent Gregory

Type: Two-Year College Sex: Coed Affiliation: Mississippi State Board for Community and Junior Colleges. Scores: 27.3% ACT 18-23; 3.4% ACT 24-29 % Accepted: 100 Admission Plans: Deferred Admission; Preferred Admission Application Deadline: July 27 Application Fee: $0.00 H.S. Requirements: High school diploma required; GED accepted Scholarships: Available. Calendar System: Semester, Summer session available

Enrollment: Full-time 2,305, Part-time 645 Faculty: Full-time 112, Part-time 96 Student-Faculty Ratio: 18:1 Exams: ACT; ACT essay component not used; SAT essay component not used. % Residing in College-Owned, -Operated, or -Affiliated Housing: 25 Regional Accreditation: Southern Association of Colleges and Schools Credit Hours For Degree: 64 semester hours, Associates Professional Accreditation: ACEN, ADA, JRCERT, NAACLS. Intercollegiate Athletics: Baseball M; Basketball M & W; Football M; Softball W

MISSISSIPPI GULF COAST COMMUNITY COLLEGE

PO Box 609
Perkinston, MS 39573
Tel: (601)928-5211
Fax: (601)928-6299
Web Site: www.mgccc.edu
President/CEO: Dr. Mary S. Graham
Admissions: Nichol Green

Type: Two-Year College Sex: Coed Scholarships: Available. Calendar System: Semester, Summer session available Enrollment: Full-time 6,935, Part-time 3,139 Faculty: Full-time 287, Part-time 201 Student-Faculty Ratio: 24:1 % Residing in College-Owned, -Operated, or -Affiliated Housing: 7 Final Year or Final Semester Residency Requirement: No Regional Accreditation: Southern Association of Colleges and Schools Credit Hours For Degree: 60 semester hours most programs, Associates Professional Accreditation: ABFSE, ACEN, CoARC, JRCEMTP, JRCERT, NAACLS. Intercollegiate Athletics: Baseball M; Basketball M & W; Football M; Golf M; Soccer M & W; Softball W; Tennis M & W; Track and Field M

MISSISSIPPI STATE UNIVERSITY

Mississippi State, MS 39762
Tel: (662)325-2323
Fax: (662)325-3299
E-mail: admit@msstate.edu
Web Site: www.msstate.edu
President/CEO: Dr. Mark E. Keenum
Admissions: Lori Ball
Financial Aid: Kenneth Paul McKinney

Type: University Sex: Coed Affiliation: Mississippi Institutions of Higher Learning. Scores: 96% SAT V 400+; 96% SAT M 400+; 43.74% ACT 18-23; 36.58% ACT 24-29 % Accepted: 72 Application Deadline: August 1 Application Fee: $40.00 H.S. Requirements: High school diploma required; GED accepted Costs Per Year: Application fee: $40. State resident tuition: $7502 full-time, $312.59 per credit hour part-time. Nonresident tuition: $20,142 full-time, $839.34 per credit hour part-time. Full-time tuition varies according to degree level and location. Part-time tuition varies according to course load, degree level, and location. College room and board: $9068. College room only: $5518. Room and board charges vary according to board plan, housing facility, and student level. Scholarships: Available. Calendar System: Semester, Summer session available Enrollment: Full-time 16,023, Graduate full-time 1,850, Graduate part-time 1,602, Part-time 1,398 Faculty: Full-time 902, Part-time 151 Student-Faculty Ratio: 19:1 Exams: ACT essay component not used; SAT I or ACT; SAT essay component not used. % Receiving Financial Aid: 61 % Residing in College-Owned, -Operated, or -Affiliated Housing: 27 Final Year or Final Semester Residency Requirement: Yes Regional Accreditation: Southern Association of Colleges and Schools Credit Hours For Degree: 128 credit hours, Bachelors ROTC: Air Force, Army Professional Accreditation: AACSB, AAFCS, ABET, ACA, AND, APA, ASLA, AVMA, CIDA, CORE, CSWE, NAAB, NASAD, NASM, NASPAA, NCATE, SAF. Intercollegiate Athletics: Baseball M; Basketball M & W; Cheerleading M & W; Cross-Country Running M & W; Football M; Golf M & W; Soccer W; Softball W; Tennis M & W; Track and Field M & W; Volleyball W

MISSISSIPPI UNIVERSITY FOR WOMEN

1100 College St., MUW-1600
Columbus, MS 39701-9998
Tel: (662)329-4750; Free: 877-GO 2 THE W
Fax: (662)329-7297
E-mail: smmoss@muw.edu
Web Site: www.muw.edu
President/CEO: Dr. Jim Borsig
Admissions: Shelley Moss
Financial Aid: Nicole Patrick

Type: Comprehensive Sex: Coed Affiliation: Mississippi Institutions of

Higher Learning. **Scores:** 82% SAT V 400+; 100% SAT M 400+; 50% ACT 18-23; 26% ACT 24-29 **% Accepted:** 96 **Admission Plans:** Early Admission **Application Deadline:** Rolling **Application Fee:** $0.00 **H.S. Requirements:** High school diploma required; GED accepted **Costs Per Year:** Application fee: $0. State resident tuition: $5965 full-time, $253 per credit hour part-time. Nonresident tuition: $16,534 full-time, $693 per credit hour part-time. Mandatory fees: $100 full-time, $50 per term part-time. Part-time tuition and fees vary according to course load. College room and board: $6808. Room and board charges vary according to housing facility. **Scholarships:** Available. **Calendar System:** Semester, Summer session available **Enrollment:** Full-time 1,976, Graduate full-time 94, Graduate part-time 109, Part-time 494 **Faculty:** Full-time 137, Part-time 64 **Student-Faculty Ratio:** 14:1 **Exams:** ACT essay component not used; SAT I or ACT; SAT essay component not used; SAT Reasoning; SAT Subject. **% Receiving Financial Aid:** 79 **% Residing in College-Owned, -Operated, or -Affiliated Housing:** 27 **Final Year or Final Semester Residency Requirement:** No **Regional Accreditation:** Southern Association of Colleges and Schools **Credit Hours For Degree:** 71 semester hours, Associates; 124 semester hours, Bachelors **ROTC:** Air Force **Professional Accreditation:** AACN, ACBSP, ACEN, ASHA, NASAD, NASM, NCATE.

MISSISSIPPI VALLEY STATE UNIVERSITY

14000 Hwy. 82 W
Itta Bena, MS 38941-1400
Tel: (662)254-9041
Fax: (662)254-7900
E-mail: jawill@mvsu.edu
Web Site: www.mvsu.edu
President/CEO: Dr. William Bynum
Admissions: Jacqueline A. Williams
Financial Aid: Margaret Sherrer

Type: Comprehensive **Sex:** Coed **Affiliation:** Mississippi Institutions of Higher Learning. **Scores:** 37% ACT 18-23; 6% ACT 24-29 **% Accepted:** 76 **Admission Plans:** Deferred Admission **Application Deadline:** Rolling **Application Fee:** $0.00 **H.S. Requirements:** High school diploma required; GED accepted **Costs Per Year:** Application fee: $0. State resident tuition: $5916 full-time, $247 per credit hour part-time. Nonresident tuition: $5916 full-time, $247 per credit hour part-time. Mandatory fees: $20 full-time. Full-time tuition and fees vary according to course load. Part-time tuition varies according to course load. College room and board: $7177. College room only: $3936. Room and board charges vary according to housing facility. **Scholarships:** Available. **Calendar System:** Semester, Summer session available **Enrollment:** Full-time 1,704, Graduate full-time 161, Graduate part-time 200, Part-time 244 **Faculty:** Full-time 118, Part-time 32 **Student-Faculty Ratio:** 16:1 **Exams:** ACT essay component not used; SAT I or ACT. **% Residing in College-Owned, -Operated, or -Affiliated Housing:** 47 **Final Year or Final Semester Residency Requirement:** No **Regional Accreditation:** Southern Association of Colleges and Schools **Credit Hours For Degree:** 124 semester hours, Bachelors **ROTC:** Army **Professional Accreditation:** ABET, ACBSP, CSWE, NASAD, NASM, NCATE. **Intercollegiate Athletics:** Baseball M; Basketball M & W; Bowling W; Cross-Country Running M & W; Football M; Golf M & W; Softball W; Tennis M & W; Track and Field M & W

NORTHEAST MISSISSIPPI COMMUNITY COLLEGE

101 Cunningham Blvd.
Booneville, MS 38829
Tel: (662)728-7751; Free: 800-555-2154
Fax: (662)728-1165
E-mail: admitme@nemcc.edu
Web Site: www.nemcc.edu
President/CEO: Johnny Allen

Type: Two-Year College **Sex:** Coed **Affiliation:** Mississippi State Board for Community and Junior Colleges. **Admission Plans:** Early Admission; Open Admission **Application Deadline:** Rolling **Application Fee:** $0.00 **H.S. Requirements:** High school diploma required; GED accepted **Costs Per Year:** Application fee: $0. State resident tuition: $2250 full-time, $125 per credit hour part-time. Nonresident tuition: $4500 full-time, $250 per credit hour part-time. Mandatory fees: $131 full-time, $8 per credit hour part-time. Full-time tuition and fees vary according to program. Part-time tuition and fees vary according to course load and program. College room and board: $3450. College room only: $1600. Room and board charges vary according to board plan and housing facility. **Calendar System:** Semester, Summer session available **Exams:** SAT I or ACT. **Regional Accreditation:** Southern

Association of Colleges and Schools **Credit Hours For Degree:** 63 semester hours, Associates **Professional Accreditation:** AAMAE, ACEN, ADA, CoARC, JRCERT, NAACLS. **Intercollegiate Athletics:** Baseball M; Basketball M & W; Football M; Golf M; Softball W; Tennis M & W

NORTHWEST MISSISSIPPI COMMUNITY COLLEGE

4975 Hwy. 51 N
Senatobia, MS 38668-1701
Tel: (662)562-3200
Fax: (662)562-3911
Web Site: www.northwestms.edu
President/CEO: Gary Spears
Admissions: Deanna Ferguson

Type: Two-Year College **Sex:** Coed **Affiliation:** Mississippi State Board for Community and Junior Colleges. **% Accepted:** 100 **Admission Plans:** Deferred Admission; Early Admission; Open Admission **Application Deadline:** September 7 **Application Fee:** $0.00 **H.S. Requirements:** High school diploma required; GED accepted **Scholarships:** Available. **Calendar System:** Semester, Summer session available **Student-Faculty Ratio:** 20:1 **Regional Accreditation:** Southern Association of Colleges and Schools **Credit Hours For Degree:** 66 semester hours, Associates **ROTC:** Air Force **Professional Accreditation:** ABFSE, ACEN, CoARC. **Intercollegiate Athletics:** Baseball M; Basketball M & W; Equestrian Sports M & W; Football M; Golf M; Softball W; Tennis M & W

PEARL RIVER COMMUNITY COLLEGE

101 Hwy. 11 N
Poplarville, MS 39470
Tel: (601)403-1000
Fax: (601)403-1135
E-mail: dford@prcc.edu
Web Site: www.prcc.edu
President/CEO: William Lewis
Admissions: J. Dow Ford

Type: Two-Year College **Sex:** Coed **Affiliation:** Mississippi State Board for Community and Junior Colleges. **Admission Plans:** Deferred Admission; Early Admission; Open Admission; Preferred Admission **Application Deadline:** Rolling **Application Fee:** $0.00 **H.S. Requirements:** High school diploma required; GED accepted **Costs Per Year:** Application fee: $0. One-time mandatory fee: $180. State resident tuition: $2650 full-time, $115 per credit hour part-time. Nonresident tuition: $5048 full-time, $215 per credit hour part-time. Full-time tuition varies according to course load. Part-time tuition varies according to course load. College room and board: $4700. Room and board charges vary according to housing facility. **Scholarships:** Available. **Calendar System:** Semester, Summer session available **Faculty:** Full-time 160, Part-time 65 **% Residing in College-Owned, -Operated, or -Affiliated Housing:** 20 **Regional Accreditation:** Southern Association of Colleges and Schools **Credit Hours For Degree:** 64 semester hours, Associates **Professional Accreditation:** ACEN, ADA, AOTA, APTA, ARCST, CoARC, JRCERT, NAACLS. **Intercollegiate Athletics:** Baseball M; Basketball M & W; Football M; Golf M & W; Soccer M & W; Softball W; Tennis M & W

RUST COLLEGE

150 Rust Ave.
Holly Springs, MS 38635-2328
Tel: (662)252-8000; Free: 888-886-8492
Fax: (662)252-6107
E-mail: admissions@rustcollege.edu
Web Site: www.rustcollege.edu
President/CEO: Dr. David L. Beckley
Admissions: Braque Talley
Financial Aid: Helen L. Street

Type: Four-Year College **Sex:** Coed **Affiliation:** United Methodist. **% Accepted:** 5 **Application Deadline:** Rolling **Application Fee:** $10.00 **H.S. Requirements:** High school diploma required; GED accepted **Costs Per Year:** Application fee: $10. Comprehensive fee: $13,600 includes full-time tuition ($9500) and college room and board ($4100). College room only: $1870. Full-time tuition varies according to course load. Part-time tuition: $404 per credit hour. Part-time tuition varies according to course load. **Scholarships:** Available. **Calendar System:** Semester, Summer session available **Enrollment:** Full-time 797, Part-time 59 **Faculty:** Full-time 48, Part-time 2 **Student-Faculty Ratio:** 16:1 **Exams:** ACT; ACT essay component not used; SAT essay component not used. **% Receiving**

Financial Aid: 96 **% Residing in College-Owned, -Operated, or -Affiliated Housing:** 76 **Final Year or Final Semester Residency Requirement:** Yes **Regional Accreditation:** Southern Association of Colleges and Schools **Credit Hours For Degree:** 72 credits, Associates; 124 credits, Bachelors **Professional Accreditation:** CSWE. **Intercollegiate Athletics:** Baseball M; Basketball M & W; Cheerleading M & W; Cross-Country Running M & W; Softball W; Tennis M & W; Track and Field M & W; Volleyball M & W

SOUTHEASTERN BAPTIST COLLEGE

4229 Hwy. 15 N
Laurel, MS 39440-1096
Tel: (601)426-6346
Web Site: www.southeasternbaptist.edu
President/CEO: Dr. Medrick Savell
Admissions: Emma Bond

Type: Four-Year College **Sex:** Coed **Affiliation:** Baptist. **Admission Plans:** Deferred Admission; Early Admission; Open Admission **Application Deadline:** Rolling **Application Fee:** $25.00 **H.S. Requirements:** High school diploma required; GED accepted **Calendar System:** Semester, Summer session available **% Residing in College-Owned, -Operated, or -Affiliated Housing:** 31 **Credit Hours For Degree:** 66 semester hours, Associates; 129 semester hours, Bachelors **Professional Accreditation:** ABHE.

SOUTHWEST MISSISSIPPI COMMUNITY COLLEGE

1156 College Dr.
Summit, MS 39666
Tel: (601)276-2000
Fax: (601)276-3888
E-mail: mattc@smcc.edu
Web Site: www.smcc.cc.ms.us
President/CEO: Dr. J. Steven Bishop
Admissions: Matthew Calhoun

Type: Two-Year College **Sex:** Coed **Affiliation:** Mississippi State Board for Community and Junior Colleges. **Admission Plans:** Open Admission **Application Deadline:** August 1 **Application Fee:** $0.00 **H.S. Requirements:** High school diploma required; GED accepted **Scholarships:** Available. **Calendar System:** Semester, Summer session available **Enrollment:** Full-time 1,785, Part-time 268 **Faculty:** Full-time 71, Part-time 19 **Student-Faculty Ratio:** 24:1 **% Residing in College-Owned, -Operated, or -Affiliated Housing:** 35 **Regional Accreditation:** Southern Association of Colleges and Schools **Credit Hours For Degree:** 64 semester hours, Associates **Professional Accreditation:** ACEN. **Intercollegiate Athletics:** Baseball M; Basketball M & W; Football M; Soccer M & W; Softball W

STRAYER UNIVERSITY–JACKSON CAMPUS

460 Briarwood Dr.
Ste. 200
Jackson, MS 39206
Tel: (601)718-5900
Fax: (601)206-5788
Web Site: www.strayer.edu/mississippi/jackson
President/CEO: Brian W. Jones

Type: Comprehensive **Sex:** Coed **Regional Accreditation:** Middle States Association of Colleges and Schools

TOUGALOO COLLEGE

500 W County Line Rd.
Tougaloo, MS 39174
Tel: (601)977-7700; Free: 888-42GALOO
Fax: (601)977-7739
E-mail: jjacobs@tougaloo.edu
Web Site: www.tougaloo.edu
President/CEO: Dr. Beverly W. Hogan
Admissions: Dr. Juno Jacobs

Type: Four-Year College **Sex:** Coed **Affiliation:** United Church of Christ. **Scores:** 50% ACT 18-23; 8% ACT 24-29 **% Accepted:** 40 **Admission Plans:** Early Admission **Application Deadline:** Rolling **Application Fee:** $25.00 **H.S. Requirements:** High school diploma required; GED accepted **Costs Per Year:** Application fee: $25. One-time mandatory fee: $95. Comprehensive fee: $17,000 includes full-time tuition ($10,130), mandatory fees ($470), and college room and board ($6400). College room only: $2000. Full-time tuition and fees vary according to course load. Room and

board charges vary according to housing facility. Part-time tuition: $423 per credit hour. Part-time tuition varies according to course load. **Scholarships:** Available. **Calendar System:** Semester, Summer session available **Enrollment:** Full-time 872, Part-time 28 **Faculty:** Full-time 70, Part-time 33 **Student-Faculty Ratio:** 13:1 **Exams:** SAT I or ACT. **% Residing in College-Owned, -Operated, or -Affiliated Housing:** 66 **Final Year or Final Semester Residency Requirement:** No **Regional Accreditation:** Southern Association of Colleges and Schools **Credit Hours For Degree:** 64 hours, Associates; 124 hours, Bachelors **ROTC:** Army **Intercollegiate Athletics:** Baseball M; Basketball M & W; Cross-Country Running M & W; Golf M; Tennis M & W; Volleyball W

UNIVERSITY OF MISSISSIPPI

University, MS 38677
Tel: (662)915-7211
Fax: (662)915-5869
E-mail: admissions@olemiss.edu
Web Site: www.olemiss.edu
President/CEO: Jeffrey S. Vitter, PhD
Admissions: Martina Brewer
Financial Aid: Laura Diven-Brown

Type: University **Sex:** Coed **Affiliation:** Mississippi Institutions of Higher Learning. **Scores:** 99% SAT V 400+; 99% SAT M 400+; 39% ACT 18-23; 42% ACT 24-29 **% Accepted:** 79 **Admission Plans:** Deferred Admission **Application Deadline:** Rolling **Application Fee:** $0.00 **H.S. Requirements:** High school diploma required; GED accepted **Costs Per Year:** Application fee: $0. State resident tuition: $7344 full-time, $306 per credit hour part-time. Nonresident tuition: $20,574 full-time, $857 per credit hour part-time. Mandatory fees: $100 full-time, $4.16 per credit hour part-time. Full-time tuition and fees vary according to course load and program. Part-time tuition and fees vary according to course load and program. College room and board: $10,128. Room and board charges vary according to board plan and housing facility. **Scholarships:** Available. **Calendar System:** Semester, Summer session available **Enrollment:** Full-time 17,395, Graduate full-time 3,270, Graduate part-time 1,157, Part-time 1,390 **Faculty:** Full-time 1,007, Part-time 288 **Exams:** ACT essay component not used; SAT I or ACT; SAT essay component not used; SAT Reasoning; SAT Subject. **% Receiving Financial Aid:** 49 **% Residing in College-Owned, -Operated, or -Affiliated Housing:** 27 **Final Year or Final Semester Residency Requirement:** Yes **Regional Accreditation:** Southern Association of Colleges and Schools **Credit Hours For Degree:** Associate degrees are not offered, Associates; 120 semester hours, Bachelors **ROTC:** Air Force, Army, Navy **Professional Accreditation:** AACSB, AAFCS, AALS, ABA, ABET, ACA, ACEJMC, ACPE, AND, APA, ASHA, CSWE, NASAD, NASM, NAST, NCATE, NRPA. **Intercollegiate Athletics:** Badminton M & W; Baseball M; Basketball M & W; Cheerleading M & W; Cross-Country Running M & W; Equestrian Sports M & W; Fencing M & W; Football M; Golf M & W; Ice Hockey M; Lacrosse M & W; Riflery W; Rugby M; Soccer M & W; Softball W; Squash M & W; Swimming and Diving M & W; Tennis M & W; Track and Field M & W; Ultimate Frisbee M & W; Volleyball M & W

UNIVERSITY OF MISSISSIPPI MEDICAL CENTER

2500 N State St.
Jackson, MS 39216-4505
Tel: (601)984-1000
Fax: (601)984-1080
Web Site: www.umc.edu
President/CEO: Dr. James Keeton
Admissions: Barbara Westerfield
Financial Aid: Minetta Veazey

Type: Two-Year Upper Division **Sex:** Coed **Affiliation:** University of Mississippi. **Admission Plans:** Preferred Admission **Application Fee:** $10.00 **H.S. Requirements:** High school diploma required; GED accepted **Scholarships:** Available. **Calendar System:** Semester, Summer session not available **Enrollment:** Full-time 383, Part-time 129 **Faculty:** Full-time 698, Part-time 138 **Student-Faculty Ratio:** 2:1 **% Receiving Financial Aid:** 41 **Regional Accreditation:** Southern Association of Colleges and Schools **Credit Hours For Degree:** 133 semester hours, Bachelors **Professional Accreditation:** AACN, ADA, AHIMA, AOTA, APA, APTA, ASC, LCME/AMA, NAACLS.

UNIVERSITY OF SOUTHERN MISSISSIPPI

118 College Dr.
Hattiesburg, MS 39406-0001

Tel: (601)266-1000
E-mail: admissions@usm.edu
Web Site: www.usm.edu
President/CEO: Dr. Rodney D. Bennett
Admissions: Susan Scott
Financial Aid: David Williamson
Type: University **Sex:** Coed **Affiliation:** Mississippi Institutions of Higher Learning. **Scores:** 94% SAT V 400+; 92% SAT M 400+; 52% ACT 18-23; 30% ACT 24-29 **% Accepted:** 58 **Admission Plans:** Early Admission **Application Deadline:** June 30 **Application Fee:** $40.00 **H.S. Requirements:** High school diploma required; GED accepted **Costs Per Year:** Application fee: $40. State resident tuition: $7334 full-time, $305.59 per credit hour part-time. Nonresident tuition: $16,204 full-time, $675.59 per credit hour part-time. Mandatory fees: $4.59 per credit hour part-time, $55. Part-time tuition and fees vary according to course load and degree level. College room and board: $8610. College room only: $5040. Room and board charges vary according to board plan and housing facility. **Scholarships:** Available. **Calendar System:** Semester, Summer session available **Enrollment:** Full-time 10,300, Graduate full-time 1,435, Graduate part-time 1,276, Part-time 1,540 **Faculty:** Full-time 689, Part-time 218 **Student-Faculty Ratio:** 17:1 **Exams:** ACT essay component not used; SAT I or ACT; SAT essay component not used; SAT Subject. **% Receiving Financial Aid:** 74 **% Residing in College-Owned, -Operated, or -Affiliated Housing:** 27 **Final Year or Final Semester Residency Requirement:** Yes **Regional Accreditation:** Southern Association of Colleges and Schools **Credit Hours For Degree:** 128 semester hours, Bachelors **ROTC:** Air Force, Army **Professional Accreditation:** AACN, AACSB, AAFCS, AAMFT, ABET, ACA, ACCE, ACEJMC, ALA, AND, APA, ASHA, CEPH, CIDA, CSWE, CoA-KT, JRCAT, NAACLS, NASAD, NASD, NASM, NAST, NCATE, NRPA. **Intercollegiate Athletics:** Baseball M; Basketball M & W; Cheerleading M & W; Cross-Country Running W; Football M; Golf M & W; Soccer W; Softball W; Tennis M & W; Track and Field M & W; Volleyball W

VIRGINIA COLLEGE IN BILOXI

920 Cedar Lake Rd.
Biloxi, MS 39532
Tel: (877)207-0359
Web Site: www.vc.edu
Type: Two-Year College **Sex:** Coed **Professional Accreditation:** ACICS.

VIRGINIA COLLEGE IN JACKSON

5841 Ridgewood Rd.
Jackson, MS 39211
Tel: (601)977-0960
Fax: (601)956-4325
Web Site: www.vc.edu
President/CEO: Milton Anderson
Type: Two-Year College **Sex:** Coed **Scholarships:** Available. **Calendar System:** Quarter **Student-Faculty Ratio:** 24:1 **Exams:** Other. **Professional Accreditation:** ACICS.

WILLIAM CAREY UNIVERSITY

498 Tuscan Ave.
Hattiesburg, MS 39401-5499
Tel: (601)318-6051; Free: 800-962-5991
Fax: (601)318-6454
E-mail: admissions@wmcarey.edu
Web Site: www.wmcarey.edu
President/CEO: Tommy King
Admissions: William N. Curry
Financial Aid: Brenda Pittman
Type: Comprehensive **Sex:** Coed **Affiliation:** Southern Baptist. **% Accepted:** 93 **Admission Plans:** Deferred Admission; Early Admission **Application Deadline:** Rolling **Application Fee:** $30.00 **H.S. Requirements:** High school diploma required; GED accepted **Costs Per Year:** Application fee: $30. Comprehensive fee: $17,570 includes full-time tuition ($10,800), mandatory fees ($900), and college room and board ($5870). Full-time tuition and fees vary according to degree level and location. Room and board charges vary according to board plan, housing facility, and location. Part-time tuition: $360 per hour. Part-time mandatory fees: $300 per term. Part-time tuition and fees vary according to degree level and location. **Scholarships:** Available. **Calendar System:** Trimester, Summer session available **Student-Faculty Ratio:** 19:1 **Exams:** SAT I or ACT. **Regional Accreditation:** Southern Association of Colleges and Schools **Credit Hours For Degree:** 128 credit hours, Bachelors **ROTC:** Air Force, Army **Professional Accreditation:** AACN, NASM, NCATE. **Intercollegiate Athletics:** Baseball M; Basketball M & W; Cheerleading M & W; Golf M; Soccer M & W; Softball W

AMERICAN BUSINESS & TECHNOLOGY UNIVERSITY
2300 Frederick Ave.
Saint Joseph, MO 64506
Free: 800-908-9329
Fax: (888)890-8190
E-mail: ricahrd@acot.edu
Web Site: www.abtu.edu
President/CEO: Sam Atieh
Admissions: Richard Lingle
Type: Comprehensive **Sex:** Coed **Professional Accreditation:** DEAC.

AMERICAN TRADE SCHOOL
3925 Industrial Dr.
Saint Ann, MO 63074
Web Site: www.americantradeschool.edu
Type: Two-Year College **Sex:** Coed **Professional Accreditation:** ACCSC.

THE ART INSTITUTE OF ST. LOUIS
1520 S Fifth St.
Saint Charles, MO 63303
Tel: (636)688-3010
Web Site: www.artinstitutes.edu/st-louis
Type: Four-Year College **Sex:** Coed **Regional Accreditation:** Southern Association of Colleges and Schools **Professional Accreditation:** ACICS.

AVILA UNIVERSITY
11901 Wornall Rd.
Kansas City, MO 64145-1698
Tel: (816)942-8400; Free: 800-GO-AVILA
Fax: (816)942-3362
E-mail: bethany.bauer@avila.edu
Web Site: www.avila.edu
President/CEO: Dr. Ronald A. Slepitza
Admissions: Bethany Bauer
Financial Aid: Nancy Merz
Type: Comprehensive **Sex:** Coed **Affiliation:** Roman Catholic; The Sisters of Saint Joseph of Carondelet, St. Louis Province. **Scores:** 94% SAT V 400+; 87% SAT M 400+; 69% ACT 18-23; 26% ACT 24-29 **% Accepted:** 51 **Admission Plans:** Early Admission **Application Deadline:** August 15 **H.S. Requirements:** High school diploma required; GED accepted **Costs Per Year:** Comprehensive fee: $33,950 includes full-time tuition ($25,500), mandatory fees ($950), and college room and board ($7500). College room only: $3300. Full-time tuition and fees vary according to course load and program. Room and board charges vary according to board plan and housing facility. Part-time tuition: $665 per credit. Part-time mandatory fees: $38 per credit. Part-time tuition and fees vary according to course load and program. Tuition guaranteed not to increase for student's term of enrollment. **Scholarships:** Available. **Calendar System:** Semester, Summer session available **Enrollment:** Full-time 1,193, Graduate full-time 325, Graduate part-time 118, Part-time 230 **Faculty:** Full-time 73, Part-time 165 **Student-Faculty Ratio:** 13:1 **Exams:** SAT I or ACT; SAT Reasoning; SAT Subject. **% Receiving Financial Aid:** 93 **% Residing in College-Owned, -Operated, or -Affiliated Housing:** 31 **Regional Accreditation:** North Central Association of Colleges and Schools **Credit Hours For Degree:** 128 credit hours, Bachelors **ROTC:** Army **Professional Accreditation:** AACN, CSWE,

JRCERT. **Intercollegiate Athletics:** Baseball M; Basketball M & W; Cheerleading W; Cross-Country Running M & W; Football M; Golf M & W; Soccer M & W; Softball W; Track and Field M & W; Volleyball W

BAPTIST BIBLE COLLEGE
628 E Kearney St.
Springfield, MO 65803-3498
Tel: (417)268-6000; Free: 800-228-5754
Fax: (417)831-8029
Web Site: www.gobbc.edu
President/CEO: Jim Edge
Admissions: Terry Allcorn
Financial Aid: Bob Kotulski
Type: Comprehensive **Sex:** Coed **Affiliation:** Baptist. **% Accepted:** 76 **Admission Plans:** Deferred Admission; Early Admission; Preferred Admission **Application Deadline:** Rolling **Application Fee:** $40.00 **H.S. Requirements:** High school diploma required; GED accepted **Scholarships:** Available. **Calendar System:** Semester, Summer session available **Enrollment:** Full-time 444, Part-time 100 **Faculty:** Full-time 26, Part-time 27 **Exams:** SAT I or ACT. **% Residing in College-Owned, -Operated, or -Affiliated Housing:** 61 **Regional Accreditation:** North Central Association of Colleges and Schools **Credit Hours For Degree:** 71 hours, Associates; 131 hours, Bachelors **ROTC:** Army **Professional Accreditation:** ABHE. **Intercollegiate Athletics:** Basketball M & W; Soccer M; Volleyball W

BRYAN UNIVERSITY (COLUMBIA)
3215 LeMone Industrial Blvd.
Columbia, MO 65201
Tel: (573)777-5550; Free: 855-566-0650
Web Site: www.bryanu.edu
Type: Two-Year College **Sex:** Coed **Professional Accreditation:** ACICS.

BRYAN UNIVERSITY (SPRINGFIELD)
4255 Nature Ctr. Way
Springfield, MO 65804
Tel: (417)862-5700; Free: 855-566-0650
Web Site: www.bryanu.edu
Type: Comprehensive **Sex:** Coed **Professional Accreditation:** ACICS.

CALVARY BIBLE COLLEGE AND THEOLOGICAL SEMINARY
15800 Calvary Rd.
Kansas City, MO 64147-1341
Tel: (816)322-0110; Free: 800-326-3960
E-mail: ann.rogers@cavalry.edu
Web Site: www.calvary.edu
President/CEO: Dr. James L. Clark
Admissions: Ann Rogers
Financial Aid: Robert Crank
Type: Comprehensive **Sex:** Coed **Affiliation:** nondenominational. **Scores:** 100% SAT V 400+; 100% SAT M 400+; 44% ACT 18-23; 37% ACT 24-29 **% Accepted:** 94 **Application Deadline:** Rolling **Application Fee:** $0.00 **H.S. Requirements:** High school diploma required; GED accepted **Costs Per Year:** Application fee: $0. One-time mandatory fee: $250. Comprehensive fee: $15,510 includes full-time tuition ($9000), mandatory fees ($880), and college room and board ($5630). College room only: $2990. Room and

board charges vary according to board plan and housing facility. Part-time tuition: $375 per credit. Part-time mandatory fees: $25 per credit hour, $260 per term. **Scholarships:** Available. **Calendar System:** Semester, Summer session available **Enrollment:** Full-time 167, Graduate full-time 19, Graduate part-time 38, Part-time 95 **Faculty:** Full-time 17, Part-time 38 **Student-Faculty Ratio:** 7:1 **Exams:** SAT I or ACT. **% Receiving Financial Aid:** 81 % **Residing in College-Owned, -Operated, or -Affiliated Housing:** 47 **Final Year or Final Semester Residency Requirement:** No **Regional Accreditation:** North Central Association of Colleges and Schools **Credit Hours For Degree:** 65-66 credit hours, depending on program, Associates; 126-153 credit hours, depending on program, Bachelors **ROTC:** Army **Professional Accreditation:** ABHE. **Intercollegiate Athletics:** Basketball M & W; Soccer M; Volleyball W

CENTRAL CHRISTIAN COLLEGE OF THE BIBLE
911 Urbandale Dr. E
Moberly, MO 65270-1997
Tel: (660)263-3900; Free: 888-263-3900
Fax: (660)263-3936
E-mail: admissions@cccb.edu
Web Site: www.cccb.edu
President/CEO: Ronald L. Oakes
Admissions: Aaron Merritt
Financial Aid: Rhonda J. Dunham
Type: Four-Year College **Sex:** Coed **Affiliation:** Christian Churches and Churches of Christ. **% Accepted:** 65 **Admission Plans:** Deferred Admission; Early Admission; Preferred Admission **Application Deadline:** Rolling **Application Fee:** $25.00 **H.S. Requirements:** High school diploma required; GED accepted **Scholarships:** Available. **Calendar System:** Semester, Summer session not available **Student-Faculty Ratio:** 19:1 **Exams:** SAT I or ACT. **Regional Accreditation:** North Central Association of Colleges and Schools **Credit Hours For Degree:** 64 credits, Associates; 134 credits, Bachelors **Professional Accreditation:** ABHE. **Intercollegiate Athletics:** Basketball M & W; Soccer M; Volleyball W

CENTRAL METHODIST UNIVERSITY
411 Central Methodist Sq.
Fayette, MO 65248-1198
Tel: (660)248-3391; Free: 877-CMU-1854
Fax: (660)248-2287
E-mail: admissions@centralmethodist.edu
Web Site: www.centralmethodist.edu
President/CEO: Roger Drake
Admissions: Adam Jenkins
Financial Aid: Kristen M. Gibbs
Type: Comprehensive **Sex:** Coed **Affiliation:** Methodist; Central Methodist University - College of Graduate and Extended Studies. **Scores:** 95% SAT V 400+; 100% SAT M 400+; 64.26% ACT 18-23; 26.62% ACT 24-29 **% Accepted:** 58 **Admission Plans:** Deferred Admission **Application Deadline:** Rolling **Application Fee:** $0.00 **H.S. Requirements:** High school diploma required; GED accepted **Costs Per Year:** Application fee: $0. Comprehensive fee: $26,785 includes full-time tuition ($22,280), mandatory fees ($730), and college room and board ($3775). College room only: $1850. Full-time tuition and fees vary according to program and reciprocity agreements. Room and board charges vary according to board plan and housing facility. Part-time tuition: $210 per credit hour. Part-time tuition varies according to course load and program. **Scholarships:** Available. **Calendar System:** Semester, Summer session available **Enrollment:** Full-time 1,072, Part-time 22 **Faculty:** Full-time 64, Part-time 49 **Student-Faculty Ratio:** 13:1 **Exams:** ACT essay component not used; SAT I or ACT; SAT essay component not used; SAT Reasoning; SAT Subject. **% Receiving Financial Aid:** 79 % **Residing in College-Owned, -Operated, or -Affiliated Housing:** 61 **Final Year or Final Semester Residency Requirement:** Yes **Regional Accreditation:** North Central Association of Colleges and Schools **Credit Hours For Degree:** 62 credit hours, Associates; 124 credit hours, Bachelors **ROTC:** Air Force, Army **Professional Accreditation:** AACN, JRCAT, NASM. **Intercollegiate Athletics:** Baseball M; Basketball M & W; Cross-Country Running M & W; Football M; Soccer M & W; Softball W; Track and Field M & W; Volleyball W

CHAMBERLAIN COLLEGE OF NURSING
11830 Westline Industrial Dr.
Ste. 106
Saint Louis, MO 63146
Tel: (314)991-6200; Free: 877-751-5783
Fax: (314)991-6283
Web Site: www.chamberlain.edu
Type: Four-Year College **Sex:** Coed **Affiliation:** DeVry University. **Application Fee:** $95.00 **H.S. Requirements:** High school diploma required; GED accepted **Costs Per Year:** Application fee: $95. Tuition: $17,560 full-time, $665 per credit hour part-time. Mandatory fees: $600 full-time, $300 per term part-time. **Scholarships:** Available. **Calendar System:** Semester **Enrollment:** Full-time 294, Part-time 216 **Faculty:** Full-time 20, Part-time 30 **Student-Faculty Ratio:** 12:1 **Exams:** ACT essay component used for admission; SAT I or ACT; SAT essay component used for admission. **Regional Accreditation:** North Central Association of Colleges and Schools **Professional Accreditation:** ACEN.

CITY VISION UNIVERSITY
3101 Troost Ave., Ste. 200
Kansas City, MO 64109-1845
Tel: (816)960-2008
Fax: (816)569-0223
E-mail: newstudents@cityvision.edu
Web Site: www.cityvision.edu
President/CEO: Dr. Andrew Sears
Admissions: Nancy Young
Financial Aid: Ann Marie Cameron-Thompson
Type: Comprehensive **Sex:** Coed **Affiliation:** Christian. **% Accepted:** 100 **Admission Plans:** Open Admission **Application Deadline:** Rolling **Application Fee:** $0.00 **H.S. Requirements:** High school diploma required; GED accepted **Costs Per Year:** Application fee: $0. Tuition: $6000 full-time, $3000 per year part-time. Full-time tuition varies according to course load and degree level. Part-time tuition varies according to course load and degree level. **Scholarships:** Available. **Calendar System:** Miscellaneous, Summer session available **Enrollment:** Full-time 24, Graduate full-time 1, Graduate part-time 9, Part-time 72 **Faculty:** Part-time 21 **Student-Faculty Ratio:** 5:1 **% Receiving Financial Aid:** 83 **Final Year or Final Semester Residency Requirement:** No **Credit Hours For Degree:** 60 semester credit hours; a minimum of 30 must be from City Vision University, Associates; 120 semester credit hours; a minimum of 30 must be from City Vision University, Bachelors **Professional Accreditation:** DEAC.

COLLEGE OF THE OZARKS
PO Box 17
Point Lookout, MO 65726
Tel: (417)334-6411; Free: 800-222-0525
Fax: (417)335-2618
E-mail: admiss4@cofo.edu
Web Site: www.cofo.edu
President/CEO: Dr. Jerry C. Davis
Admissions: Gayle Groves
Type: Four-Year College **Sex:** Coed **Affiliation:** Presbyterian. **Scores:** 100% SAT V 400+; 100% SAT M 400+; 59% ACT 18-23; 34% ACT 24-29 **% Accepted:** 12 **Admission Plans:** Preferred Admission **Application Deadline:** February 15 **Application Fee:** $0.00 **H.S. Requirements:** High school diploma required; GED accepted **Costs Per Year:** Application fee: $0. Comprehensive fee: $6930 includes full-time tuition ($0), mandatory fees ($430), and college room and board ($6500). College room only: $3250. Part-time tuition: $310 per credit hour. Part-time tuition varies according to course load. Each student participates in the on-campus work program for 15 hours per week and two forty-hour work weeks. Earnings from participation in the work program, plus any federal and/or state aid for which students qualify, plus a College of the Ozarks Cost of Education Scholarship combine to meet each student's full tuition charge. **Scholarships:** Available. **Calendar System:** Semester, Summer session not available **Enrollment:** Full-time 1,442, Part-time 10 **Faculty:** Full-time 87, Part-time 56 **Student-Faculty Ratio:** 14:1 **Exams:** ACT essay component used for placement; SAT I or ACT; SAT essay component not used; SAT Reasoning; SAT Subject. **% Receiving Financial Aid:** 93 **% Residing in College-Owned, -Operated, or -Affiliated Housing:** 82 **Final Year or Final Semester Residency Requirement:** No **Regional Accreditation:** North Central Association of Colleges and Schools **Credit Hours For Degree:** 125 semester hours, Bachelors **ROTC:** Army **Professional Accreditation:** AACN. **Intercollegiate Athletics:** Baseball M; Basketball M & W; Cheerleading M & W; Cross-Country Running M & W; Volleyball W

COLUMBIA COLLEGE
1001 Rogers St.
Columbia, MO 65216-0002

Tel: (573)875-8700; Free: 800-231-2391
Fax: (573)875-7506
E-mail: admissions@ccis.edu
Web Site: www.ccis.edu
President/CEO: Dr. Scott Dalrymple
Financial Aid: Sharon Abernathy

Type: Comprehensive **Sex:** Coed **Affiliation:** Christian Church (Disciples of Christ). **Scores:** 80% SAT V 400+; 83% SAT M 400+; 39.02% ACT 18-23; 52.03% ACT 24-29 **% Accepted:** 71 **Admission Plans:** Deferred Admission **Application Deadline:** August 13 **Application Fee:** $35.00 **H.S. Requirements:** High school diploma required; GED accepted **Costs Per Year:** Application fee: $35. Comprehensive fee: $29,157 includes full-time tuition ($20,936) and college room and board ($8221). College room only: $5447. Full-time tuition varies according to class time, course load, degree level, program, reciprocity agreements, and student level. Room and board charges vary according to board plan and housing facility. Part-time tuition: $450 per credit hour. Part-time tuition varies according to class time, course load, degree level, location, and reciprocity agreements. Tuition guaranteed not to increase for student's term of enrollment. **Scholarships:** Available. **Calendar System:** Semester, Summer session available **Enrollment:** Full-time 689, Graduate full-time 57, Graduate part-time 164, Part-time 143 **Faculty:** Full-time 72, Part-time 63 **Student-Faculty Ratio:** 8:1 **Exams:** ACT essay component not used; SAT I or ACT; SAT essay component not used; SAT Reasoning; SAT Subject. **% Receiving Financial Aid:** 63 **% Residing in College-Owned, -Operated, or -Affiliated Housing:** 39 **Final Year or Final Semester Residency Requirement:** Yes **Regional Accreditation:** North Central Association of Colleges and Schools **Credit Hours For Degree:** 60 semester hours, Associates; 120 semester hours, Bachelors **ROTC:** Air Force, Army, Navy **Professional Accreditation:** CSWE. **Intercollegiate Athletics:** Baseball M; Basketball M & W; Cross-Country Running M & W; Golf M & W; Soccer M & W; Softball W; Volleyball W

CONCEPTION SEMINARY COLLEGE

PO Box 502
Conception, MO 64433-0502
Tel: (660)944-3105
Fax: (660)944-2829
E-mail: vocations@conception.edu
Web Site: www.conception.edu
President/CEO: Rev. Samuel Russell, OSB
Admissions: Bro. Luke Kral, OSB
Financial Aid: Bro. Justin Hernandez, PhD

Type: Four-Year College **Sex:** Men **Affiliation:** Roman Catholic. **Admission Plans:** Deferred Admission; Early Admission; Preferred Admission **Application Fee:** $0.00 **H.S. Requirements:** High school diploma required; GED accepted **Costs Per Year:** Application fee: $0. Comprehensive fee: $33,022 includes full-time tuition ($20,506), mandatory fees ($200), and college room and board ($12,316). College room only: $5152. Part-time tuition: $200 per credit hour. **Scholarships:** Available. **Calendar System:** Semester, Summer session not available **Student-Faculty Ratio:** 4:1 **Exams:** SAT I or ACT. **% Receiving Financial Aid:** 46 **Regional Accreditation:** North Central Association of Colleges and Schools **Credit Hours For Degree:** 126 credits, Bachelors

CONCORDE CAREER COLLEGE

3239 Broadway
Kansas City, MO 64111
Tel: (816)531-5223
Fax: (816)756-3231
E-mail: dcrow@concorde.edu
Web Site: www.concorde.edu
President/CEO: Sean McNair
Admissions: Deborah Crow

Type: Two-Year College **Sex:** Coed **% Accepted:** 100 **Student-Faculty Ratio:** 29:1 **Professional Accreditation:** ACCSC, ADA, CoARC.

COTTEY COLLEGE

1000 W Austin
Nevada, MO 64772
Tel: (417)667-8181; Free: 888-526-8839
Fax: (417)667-8103
E-mail: enrollmgt@cottey.edu
Web Site: www.cottey.edu

President/CEO: Dr. Jann Weitzel, PhD
Admissions: Judi Steege
Financial Aid: Sherry Pennington

Type: Two-Year College **Sex:** Women **Scores:** 94% SAT V 400+; 90% SAT M 400+; 48% ACT 18-23; 40% ACT 24-29 **Costs Per Year:** Comprehensive fee: $26,950 includes full-time tuition ($18,400), mandatory fees ($900), and college room and board ($7650). College room only: $4000. Room and board charges vary according to housing facility. Part-time tuition: $125 per credit hour. Part-time tuition varies according to course load. **Scholarships:** Available. **Calendar System:** Semester, Summer session not available **Enrollment:** Full-time 314, Part-time 3 **Faculty:** Full-time 36, Part-time 8 **Student-Faculty Ratio:** 9:1 **Exams:** SAT I or ACT. **% Residing in College-Owned, -Operated, or -Affiliated Housing:** 98 **Final Year or Final Semester Residency Requirement:** No **Regional Accreditation:** North Central Association of Colleges and Schools **Credit Hours For Degree:** 62 credit hours, Associates; 120 credit hours, Bachelors **Professional Accreditation:** NASM. **Intercollegiate Athletics:** Basketball W; Cross-Country Running W; Softball W; Volleyball W

COURT REPORTING INSTITUTE OF ST. LOUIS

7730 Carondelet Ave., Ste. 400
Clayton, MO 63105
Tel: (314)290-0200; Free: 888-208-6780
Web Site: www.cri.edu/st-louis-court-reporting-school.asp
Type: Two-Year College **Sex:** Coed **Calendar System:** Quarter **Professional Accreditation:** ACICS.

COX COLLEGE

1423 N Jefferson
Springfield, MO 65802
Tel: (417)269-3401
E-mail: admissions@coxcollege.edu
Web Site: www.coxcollege.edu
President/CEO: Dr. Lance Ratcliff
Admissions: Lindy Biglieni
Financial Aid: Victoria L. Jacobson

Type: Comprehensive **Sex:** Coed **% Accepted:** 59 **Admission Plans:** Early Action **Application Deadline:** January 15 **Application Fee:** $50.00 **H.S. Requirements:** High school diploma required; GED accepted **Scholarships:** Available. **Calendar System:** Semester, Summer session available **Enrollment:** Graduate full-time 81, Graduate part-time 15 **Faculty:** Full-time 102, Part-time 30 **Student-Faculty Ratio:** 9:1 **Exams:** SAT I or ACT. **Final Year or Final Semester Residency Requirement:** No **Regional Accreditation:** North Central Association of Colleges and Schools **Credit Hours For Degree:** 66 credit hours, Associates; 128 credit hours, Bachelors **Professional Accreditation:** AACN, ACEN.

CROWDER COLLEGE

601 Laclede Ave.
Neosho, MO 64850-9160
Tel: (417)451-3223; Free: 866-238-7788
Fax: (417)451-4280
E-mail: jimriggs@crowder.edu
Web Site: www.crowder.edu
President/CEO: Dr. Jennifer Methvin
Admissions: Jim Riggs

Type: Two-Year College **Sex:** Coed **Affiliation:** Missouri Coordinating Board for Higher Education. **Admission Plans:** Open Admission **Application Deadline:** Rolling **Application Fee:** $25.00 **H.S. Requirements:** High school diploma required; GED accepted **Costs Per Year:** Application fee: $25. Area resident tuition: $2460 full-time, $82 per credit hour part-time. State resident tuition: $3660 full-time, $122 per credit hour part-time. Nonresident tuition: $3660 full-time, $122 per credit hour part-time. Mandatory fees: $480 full-time, $16 per credit hour part-time. College room and board: $3200. College room only: $2200. Room and board charges vary according to board plan and housing facility. **Scholarships:** Available. **Calendar System:** Semester, Summer session available **Enrollment:** Full-time 2,638, Part-time 3,072 **Faculty:** Full-time 96, Part-time 353 **Student-Faculty Ratio:** 12:1 **% Residing in College-Owned, -Operated, or -Affiliated Housing:** 10 **Regional Accreditation:** North Central Association of Colleges and Schools **Credit Hours For Degree:** 60 semester hours, Associates **Professional Accreditation:** ATMAE. **Intercollegiate Athletics:** Baseball M; Basketball W; Soccer M

CULINARY INSTITUTE OF ST. LOUIS AT HICKEY COLLEGE
2700 N Lindbergh Blvd.
Saint Louis, MO 63114
Tel: (314)434-2212
Web Site: www.ci-stl.com
Type: Two-Year College **Sex:** Coed **% Accepted:** 81 **H.S. Requirements:** High school diploma required; GED accepted **Calendar System:** Semester

CULVER-STOCKTON COLLEGE
1 College Hill
Canton, MO 63435-1299
Tel: (573)288-6000; Free: 800-537-1883
Fax: (217)231-6611
E-mail: admissions@culver.edu
Web Site: www.culver.edu
President/CEO: Dr. Kelly M. Thompson
Admissions: Misty McBee
Financial Aid: Tina M. Wiseman
Type: Comprehensive **Sex:** Coed **Affiliation:** Christian Church (Disciples of Christ). **Scores:** 78% SAT V 400+; 89% SAT M 400+; 67% ACT 18-23; 19% ACT 24-29 **% Accepted:** 56 **Admission Plans:** Deferred Admission **Application Deadline:** Rolling **Application Fee:** $0.00 **H.S. Requirements:** High school diploma required; GED accepted **Costs Per Year:** Application fee: $0. One-time mandatory fee: $210. Comprehensive fee: $33,525 includes full-time tuition ($24,990), mandatory fees ($425), and college room and board ($8110). College room only: $3630. Room and board charges vary according to board plan and housing facility. Part-time tuition: $580 per credit hour. Part-time mandatory fees: $17.71 per credit hour. **Scholarships:** Available. **Calendar System:** Semester, Summer session available **Enrollment:** Full-time 926, Graduate full-time 17, Part-time 123 **Faculty:** Full-time 49, Part-time 45 **Student-Faculty Ratio:** 15:1 **Exams:** ACT essay component not used; SAT I or ACT; SAT essay component not used; SAT Reasoning. **% Receiving Financial Aid:** 80 **% Residing in College-Owned, -Operated, or -Affiliated Housing:** 79 **Final Year or Final Semester Residency Requirement:** No **Regional Accreditation:** North Central Association of Colleges and Schools **Credit Hours For Degree:** 120 hours, Bachelors **Professional Accreditation:** NASM. **Intercollegiate Athletics:** Baseball M; Basketball M & W; Bowling M & W; Cheerleading M & W; Cross-Country Running M & W; Football M; Golf M & W; Soccer M & W; Softball W; Track and Field M & W; Volleyball M & W

DEVRY UNIVERSITY (KANSAS CITY)
11224 Holmes Rd.
Kansas City, MO 64131
Tel: (816)943-7300; Free: 866-338-7941
Web Site: www.devry.edu
Financial Aid: Maureen Kelly
Type: Comprehensive **Sex:** Coed **Affiliation:** DeVry University. **Application Fee:** $40.00 **H.S. Requirements:** High school diploma required; GED accepted **Scholarships:** Available. **Calendar System:** Semester **Enrollment:** Full-time 173, Graduate full-time 37, Graduate part-time 83, Part-time 250 **Faculty:** Full-time 9, Part-time 66 **Student-Faculty Ratio:** 10:1 **Exams:** ACT essay component used for admission; ACT essay component used for placement; SAT essay component used for admission; SAT essay component used for placement. **% Receiving Financial Aid:** 77 **Regional Accreditation:** North Central Association of Colleges and Schools **Professional Accreditation:** ABET.

DEVRY UNIVERSITY (KANSAS CITY)
City Ctr. Sq.
1100 Main St., Ste. 118
Kansas City, MO 64105-2112
Tel: (816)221-1300; Free: 866-338-7941
Fax: (816)474-0318
Web Site: www.devry.edu
Type: Comprehensive **Sex:** Coed **Application Deadline:** Rolling **Costs Per Year:** Tuition: $17,052 full-time, $609 per credit hour part-time. Mandatory fees: $80 full-time, $40 per term part-time. **Calendar System:** Semester **Regional Accreditation:** North Central Association of Colleges and Schools **Professional Accreditation:** ACBSP.

DRURY UNIVERSITY
900 N Benton Ave.
Springfield, MO 65802

Tel: (417)873-7879; Free: 800-922-2274
Fax: (417)873-7529
E-mail: druryad@drury.edu
Web Site: www.drury.edu
President/CEO: Dr. David P. Manuel
Admissions: Jay Fedje
Financial Aid: Becky Ahrens
Type: Comprehensive **Sex:** Coed **Scores:** 31% ACT 18-23; 45% ACT 24-29 **% Accepted:** 65 **Admission Plans:** Deferred Admission **Application Deadline:** August 22 **Application Fee:** $50.00 **H.S. Requirements:** High school diploma required; GED accepted **Costs Per Year:** Application fee: $50. One-time mandatory fee: $150. Comprehensive fee: $33,905 includes full-time tuition ($24,750), mandatory fees ($1155), and college room and board ($8000). Full-time tuition and fees vary according to class time. Room and board charges vary according to board plan and housing facility. **Scholarships:** Available. **Calendar System:** Semester, Summer session available **Enrollment:** Full-time 1,291, Graduate full-time 165, Graduate part-time 91, Part-time 24 **Faculty:** Full-time 134, Part-time 24 **Student-Faculty Ratio:** 10:1 **Exams:** ACT essay component not used; SAT I or ACT; SAT essay component not used; SAT Reasoning. **% Receiving Financial Aid:** 68 **% Residing in College-Owned, -Operated, or -Affiliated Housing:** 61 **Final Year or Final Semester Residency Requirement:** Yes **Regional Accreditation:** North Central Association of Colleges and Schools **Credit Hours For Degree:** 124 semester hours, Bachelors **ROTC:** Army **Professional Accreditation:** AACSB, ACBSP, NAAB, NASM, NCATE. **Intercollegiate Athletics:** Baseball M; Basketball M & W; Cheerleading M & W; Cross-Country Running M & W; Golf M & W; Soccer M & W; Softball W; Swimming and Diving M & W; Tennis M & W; Track and Field M & W; Volleyball W; Wrestling M

EAST CENTRAL COLLEGE
1964 Prairie Dell Rd.
Union, MO 63084
Tel: (636)584-6500
Fax: (636)583-1897
E-mail: nathaniel.mitchell@eastcentral.edu
Web Site: www.eastcentral.edu
President/CEO: Dr. Jon Bauer
Admissions: Nathaniel Mitchell
Financial Aid: Karen Griffin
Type: Two-Year College **Sex:** Coed **Admission Plans:** Deferred Admission; Early Admission; Open Admission **Application Deadline:** Rolling **Application Fee:** $0.00 **H.S. Requirements:** High school diploma required; GED accepted **Costs Per Year:** Application fee: $0. Area resident tuition: $1824 full-time. State resident tuition: $2664 full-time. Nonresident tuition: $4032 full-time. Mandatory fees: $456 full-time. Full-time tuition and fees vary according to program. **Scholarships:** Available. **Calendar System:** Semester, Summer session available **Enrollment:** Full-time 1,508, Part-time 1,714 **Faculty:** Full-time 69, Part-time 162 **Student-Faculty Ratio:** 17:1 **Regional Accreditation:** North Central Association of Colleges and Schools **Credit Hours For Degree:** 60 semester hours, Associates **Professional Accreditation:** ACF. **Intercollegiate Athletics:** Soccer M; Softball W; Volleyball W

L'ECOLE CULINAIRE–KANSAS CITY
310 Ward Pky.
Kansas City, MO 64112-2110
Web Site: www.lecole.edu/kansas-city
Type: Two-Year College **Sex:** Coed **Professional Accreditation:** ACCSC.

L'ECOLE CULINAIRE–ST. LOUIS
9811 S Forty Dr.
Saint Louis, MO 63124
Web Site: www.lecole.edu/st-louis
Type: Two-Year College **Sex:** Coed **Professional Accreditation:** ACCSC, ACF.

EVANGEL UNIVERSITY
1111 N Glenstone
Springfield, MO 65802
Tel: (417)865-2811; Free: 800-382-6435
Fax: (417)865-9599
E-mail: admissions@evangel.edu
Web Site: www.evangel.edu

President/CEO: Dr. Robert H. Spence
Financial Aid: Valerie Sharp
Type: Comprehensive **Sex:** Coed **Affiliation:** Assemblies of God. **% Accepted:** 61 **Admission Plans:** Deferred Admission **H.S. Requirements:** High school diploma required; GED accepted **Costs Per Year:** Comprehensive fee: $29,018 includes full-time tuition ($20,266), mandatory fees ($1170), and college room and board ($7582). College room only: $3938. Full-time tuition and fees vary according to course load. Room and board charges vary according to board plan. Part-time tuition: $844 per credit hour. Part-time tuition varies according to course load. **Scholarships:** Available. **Calendar System:** Semester **Enrollment:** Full-time 1,559, Graduate full-time 120, Graduate part-time 114, Part-time 165 **Exams:** SAT I or ACT. **% Receiving Financial Aid:** 84 **% Residing in College-Owned, -Operated, or -Affiliated Housing:** 68 **Regional Accreditation:** North Central Association of Colleges and Schools **Credit Hours For Degree:** 60 credit hours, Associates; 124 credit hours, Bachelors **ROTC:** Army **Professional Accreditation:** ACBSP, CSWE, NASM, NCATE. **Intercollegiate Athletics:** Baseball M; Basketball M & W; Cross-Country Running M & W; Football M; Golf M & W; Softball W; Tennis M & W; Track and Field M & W; Volleyball W

EVEREST COLLEGE
1010 W Sunshine St.
Springfield, MO 65807
Tel: (417)864-7220; Free: 888-741-4270
Fax: (417)865-5697
Web Site: www.everest.edu
President/CEO: Wendy Woosley
Type: Two-Year College **Sex:** Coed **Affiliation:** Zenith Education Group. **Application Deadline:** Rolling **Application Fee:** $25.00 **H.S. Requirements:** High school diploma required; GED accepted **Scholarships:** Available. **Calendar System:** Quarter, Summer session available **Exams:** Other. **Credit Hours For Degree:** 96 credits, Associates **Professional Accreditation:** AAMAE, ACICS.

FONTBONNE UNIVERSITY
6800 Wydown Blvd.
Saint Louis, MO 63105-3098
Tel: (314)862-3456; Free: 800-205-5862
Fax: (314)719-8021
E-mail: fbyou@fontbonne.edu
Web Site: www.fontbonne.edu
President/CEO: Dr. J. Michael Pressimone
Admissions: Michelle Palumbo
Type: Comprehensive **Sex:** Coed **Affiliation:** Roman Catholic. **Scores:** 60% ACT 18-23; 34% ACT 24-29 **% Accepted:** 97 **Admission Plans:** Deferred Admission **Application Deadline:** Rolling **Application Fee:** $25.00 **H.S. Requirements:** High school diploma required; GED accepted **Costs Per Year:** Application fee: $25. Comprehensive fee: $33,717 includes full-time tuition ($24,250), mandatory fees ($360), and college room and board ($9107). Full-time tuition and fees vary according to course load and program. Room and board charges vary according to board plan and housing facility. Part-time tuition: $648 per credit. Part-time tuition varies according to course load and program. **Scholarships:** Available. **Calendar System:** Semester, Summer session available **Enrollment:** Full-time 902, Graduate full-time 278, Graduate part-time 336, Part-time 197 **Faculty:** Full-time 75, Part-time 126 **Student-Faculty Ratio:** 11:1 **Exams:** SAT I or ACT; SAT Reasoning. **Regional Accreditation:** North Central Association of Colleges and Schools **Credit Hours For Degree:** 128 credits, Bachelors **ROTC:** Air Force, Army **Professional Accreditation:** AAFCS, ACBSP, ASHA, NCATE. **Intercollegiate Athletics:** Baseball M; Basketball M & W; Bowling W; Cheerleading W; Cross-Country Running M & W; Field Hockey W; Golf M & W; Lacrosse M & W; Soccer M & W; Softball W; Tennis M & W; Track and Field M & W; Volleyball M & W

GLOBAL UNIVERSITY
1211 S Glenstone Ave.
Springfield, MO 65804
Tel: (417)862-9533; Free: 800-443-1083
Fax: (417)862-5318
E-mail: twaggoner@globaluniversity.edu
Web Site: www.globaluniversity.edu
President/CEO: Dr. Gary Seevers, Jr.
Admissions: Rev. Todd Waggoner
Type: Comprehensive **Sex:** Coed **Affiliation:** Assemblies of God. **Admis-**

sion **Plans:** Open Admission **Application Deadline:** Rolling **Application Fee:** $40.00 **H.S. Requirements:** High school diploma required; GED accepted **Calendar System:** Continuous, Summer session not available **Enrollment:** Full-time 381, Graduate full-time 60, Graduate part-time 315, Part-time 3,795 **Faculty:** Full-time 81, Part-time 552 **Student-Faculty Ratio:** 11:1 **Regional Accreditation:** North Central Association of Colleges and Schools **Credit Hours For Degree:** 64 credits, Associates; 128 credits, Bachelors **Professional Accreditation:** DEAC.

GOLDFARB SCHOOL OF NURSING AT BARNES-JEWISH COLLEGE
4483 Duncan Ave.
Saint Louis, MO 63110
Tel: (314)454-7055; Free: 800-832-9009
Fax: (314)454-5239
E-mail: mward@bjc.org
Web Site: www.barnesjewishcollege.edu
Admissions: Dr. Michael D. Ward
Financial Aid: Jason Crowe
Type: Comprehensive **Sex:** Coed **Affiliation:** Barnes Jewish Hospital. **Admission Plans:** Deferred Admission **Application Fee:** $50.00 **H.S. Requirements:** High school diploma required; GED accepted **Costs Per Year:** Application fee: $50. Tuition: $18,148 full-time, $698 per credit hour part-time. Mandatory fees: $1108 full-time, $554 per term part-time. Full-time tuition and fees vary according to course load and degree level. Part-time tuition and fees vary according to course load and degree level. **Scholarships:** Available. **Calendar System:** Trimester, Summer session available **Enrollment:** Full-time 562, Graduate full-time 63, Graduate part-time 26, Part-time 71 **Faculty:** Full-time 42, Part-time 11 **Student-Faculty Ratio:** 13:1 **Final Year or Final Semester Residency Requirement:** No **Regional Accreditation:** North Central Association of Colleges and Schools **Credit Hours For Degree:** 120 credit hours, Bachelors **Professional Accreditation:** AACN, AANA, AND, ASC, JRCERT, NAACLS. .

GRACELAND UNIVERSITY
1401 W Truman Rd.
Independence, MO 64050-3434
Tel: (816)833-0524; Free: 866-GRACELAND
E-mail: gic@graceland.edu
Web Site: www.graceland.edu
Type: Comprehensive **Sex:** Coed **Affiliation:** Community of Christ. **Calendar System:** 4-1-4 **Regional Accreditation:** North Central Association of Colleges and Schools **Professional Accreditation:** AACN.

HANNIBAL-LAGRANGE UNIVERSITY
2800 Palmyra Rd.
Hannibal, MO 63401-1999
Tel: (573)221-3675; Free: 800-HLG-1119
Fax: (573)221-6594
E-mail: admissions@hlg.edu
Web Site: www.hlg.edu
President/CEO: Dr. Anthony Allen
Admissions: Dr. Ray Summerlin
Financial Aid: Brice Baumgardner
Type: Comprehensive **Sex:** Coed **Affiliation:** Southern Baptist. **% Accepted:** 56 **Admission Plans:** Deferred Admission; Early Admission; Open Admission **Application Deadline:** Rolling **Application Fee:** $25.00 **H.S. Requirements:** High school diploma required; GED accepted **Costs Per Year:** Application fee: $25. One-time mandatory fee: $150. Comprehensive fee: $28,620 includes full-time tuition ($20,010), mandatory fees ($1000), and college room and board ($7610). Full-time tuition and fees vary according to course load, degree level, program, and student level. Room and board charges vary according to housing facility. Part-time tuition: $687 per credit. Part-time mandatory fees: $400 per year. Part-time tuition and fees vary according to course load, degree level, program, and student level. **Scholarships:** Available. **Calendar System:** Semester, Summer session available **Enrollment:** Full-time 1,303, Graduate full-time 74 **Faculty:** Full-time 62, Part-time 76 **Exams:** ACT essay component not used; SAT I or ACT; SAT essay component not used; SAT Reasoning; SAT Subject. **% Residing in College-Owned, -Operated, or -Affiliated Housing:** 47 **Final Year or Final Semester Residency Requirement:** Yes **Regional Accreditation:** North Central Association of Colleges and Schools **Credit Hours For Degree:** 64 credit hours, Associates; 124 credit hours, Bachelors **Professional Accreditation:** ACEN, CoARC. **Intercollegiate Athletics:**

Baseball M; Basketball M & W; Cheerleading M & W; Cross-Country Running M & W; Golf M & W; Soccer M & W; Softball W; Track and Field M & W; Volleyball M & W; Wrestling M

HARRIS-STOWE STATE UNIVERSITY

3026 Laclede Ave.
Saint Louis, MO 63103-2136
Tel: (314)340-3366
Fax: (314)340-3322
E-mail: admissions@hssu.edu
Web Site: www.hssu.edu
President/CEO: Dr. Dwaun J. Warmack
Admissions: Dr. Chauvette McElmurry-Green
Financial Aid: Regina Blackshear

Type: Four-Year College **Sex:** Coed **Affiliation:** Missouri Coordinating Board for Higher Education. **Scores:** 60% SAT V 400+; 54% SAT M 400+; 32% ACT 18-23; 1% ACT 24-29 **% Accepted:** 51 **Admission Plans:** Deferred Admission; Early Admission; Open Admission **Application Deadline:** July 31 **Application Fee:** $20.00 **H.S. Requirements:** High school diploma required; GED accepted **Costs Per Year:** Application fee: $20. State resident tuition: $4776 full-time, $199 per credit hour part-time. Nonresident tuition: $9409 full-time, $392.03 per credit hour part-time. Mandatory fees: $444 full-time, $222 per term part-time. Full-time tuition and fees vary according to course load. College room and board: $9250. College room only: $6500. Room and board charges vary according to housing facility. **Scholarships:** Available. **Calendar System:** Semester, Summer session available **Enrollment:** Full-time 1,036, Part-time 354 **Faculty:** Full-time 42, Part-time 132 **Student-Faculty Ratio:** 13:1 **Exams:** ACT essay component not used; SAT I or ACT; SAT essay component not used; SAT Reasoning; SAT Subject. **% Receiving Financial Aid:** 89 **% Residing in College-Owned, -Operated, or -Affiliated Housing:** 26 **Final Year or Final Semester Residency Requirement:** Yes **Regional Accreditation:** North Central Association of Colleges and Schools **Credit Hours For Degree:** 120 credit hours, Bachelors **ROTC:** Air Force, Army **Professional Accreditation:** ACBSP, NCATE. **Intercollegiate Athletics:** Baseball M; Basketball M & W; Cheerleading M & W; Soccer M & W; Softball W; Volleyball W

HERITAGE COLLEGE

1200 E 104th St.
Ste. 150
Kansas City, MO 64131
Tel: (816)942-5474; Free: 888-334-7339
Fax: (816)942-5405
E-mail: info@heritage-education.com
Web Site: www.heritagecollege.edu
President/CEO: Larry Cartmill
Type: Two-Year College **Sex:** Coed **Admission Plans:** Open Admission **Student-Faculty Ratio:** 31:1 **Professional Accreditation:** ACCSC.

HICKEY COLLEGE

940 W Port Plz.
Ste. 101
Saint Louis, MO 63146
Tel: (314)434-2212; Free: 800-777-1544
Fax: (314)434-1974
Web Site: www.hickeycollege.edu
President/CEO: Christopher A. Gearin
Type: Four-Year College **Sex:** Coed **% Accepted:** 71 **H.S. Requirements:** High school diploma required; GED accepted **Calendar System:** Semester **Professional Accreditation:** ACICS.

IHM ACADEMY OF EMS

2500 Abbott Pl.
Saint Louis, MO 63143
Tel: (314)768-1234
Fax: (314)768-1595
E-mail: info@ihmhealthstudies.edu
Web Site: www.ihmacademyofems.net
Type: Two-Year College **Sex:** Coed **Calendar System:** Trimester

JEFFERSON COLLEGE

1000 Viking Dr.
Hillsboro, MO 63050-2441
Tel: (636)797-3000

Fax: (636)789-4012
E-mail: admissions@jeffco.edu
Web Site: www.jeffco.edu
President/CEO: Dr. Raymond Cummiskey
Admissions: Dr. Kimberly Harvey
Financial Aid: Sarah Bright

Type: Two-Year College **Sex:** Coed **Admission Plans:** Early Admission; Open Admission **Application Deadline:** Rolling **Application Fee:** $25.00 **H.S. Requirements:** High school diploma required; GED accepted **Costs Per Year:** Application fee: $25. One-time mandatory fee: $25. Area resident tuition: $2910 full-time, $97 per credit hour part-time. State resident tuition: $4380 full-time, $146 per credit hour part-time. Nonresident tuition: $5820 full-time, $194 per credit hour part-time. Mandatory fees: $90 full-time, $3 per credit hour part-time, $10 per term part-time. Full-time tuition and fees vary according to course load and program. Part-time tuition and fees vary according to course load and program. College room and board: $5644. Room and board charges vary according to housing facility. **Scholarships:** Available. **Calendar System:** Semester, Summer session available **Enrollment:** Full-time 2,287, Part-time 2,418 **Faculty:** Full-time 100, Part-time 253 **Student-Faculty Ratio:** 17:1 **Final Year or Final Semester Residency Requirement:** No **Regional Accreditation:** North Central Association of Colleges and Schools **Credit Hours For Degree:** 62 semester hours, Associates **Intercollegiate Athletics:** Baseball M; Basketball W; Cheerleading M & W; Soccer M; Softball W; Volleyball W

KANSAS CITY ART INSTITUTE

4415 Warwick Blvd.
Kansas City, MO 64111-1874
Tel: (816)472-4852; Free: 800-522-5224
Fax: (816)531-6296
E-mail: admiss@kcai.edu
Web Site: www.kcai.edu
President/CEO: Pres. Tony Jones
Admissions: Gerald Valet
Financial Aid: Darchelle Renee Webster

Type: Four-Year College **Sex:** Coed **Scores:** 100% SAT V 400+; 94% SAT M 400+; 45% ACT 18-23; 42% ACT 24-29 **% Accepted:** 60 **Admission Plans:** Deferred Admission; Early Admission **Application Deadline:** August 1 **Application Fee:** $45.00 **H.S. Requirements:** High school diploma required; GED accepted **Costs Per Year:** Application fee: $45. Comprehensive fee: $45,510 includes full-time tuition ($35,120), mandatory fees ($150), and college room and board ($10,240). Full-time tuition and fees vary according to program. Room and board charges vary according to board plan. Part-time tuition: $1465 per credit hour. Part-time tuition varies according to program. **Scholarships:** Available. **Calendar System:** Semester, Summer session available **Enrollment:** Full-time 631, Part-time 14 **Faculty:** Full-time 51, Part-time 60 **Student-Faculty Ratio:** 9:1 **Exams:** ACT essay component not used; SAT I or ACT; SAT essay component not used. **% Receiving Financial Aid:** 84 **% Residing in College-Owned, -Operated, or -Affiliated Housing:** 35 **Final Year or Final Semester Residency Requirement:** Yes **Regional Accreditation:** North Central Association of Colleges and Schools **Credit Hours For Degree:** 126 credit hours, Bachelors **Professional Accreditation:** NASAD.

LINCOLN UNIVERSITY

820 Chestnut St.
Jefferson City, MO 65101
Tel: (573)681-5000
Fax: (573)681-6074
E-mail: enroll@lincolnu.edu
Web Site: www.lincolnu.edu
President/CEO: Dr. Kevin Rome
Admissions: DeRecco Lynch
Financial Aid: Alfred Robinson

Type: Comprehensive **Sex:** Coed **Affiliation:** Missouri Coordinating Board for Higher Education. **Scores:** 80% SAT V 400+; 80% SAT M 400+; 31.61% ACT 18-23; 5.35% ACT 24-29 **% Accepted:** 40 **Admission Plans:** Deferred Admission **Application Fee:** $0.00 **H.S. Requirements:** High school diploma required; GED accepted **Costs Per Year:** Application fee: $0. State resident tuition: $6150 full-time, $205 per credit hour part-time. Nonresident tuition: $12,540 full-time, $418 per credit hour part-time. Mandatory fees: $892 full-time, $6.75 per credit hour part-time, $345 per term part-time. Full-time tuition and fees vary according to course load, location, and reciprocity agreements. Part-time tuition and fees vary according to course load, location, and reciprocity agreements. College room and board: $6070. College room only: $3066. Room and board charges vary according to board plan and housing facility. **Scholarships:** Available. **Calendar System:** Semester, Summer session available **Enrollment:** Full-time 1,974, Graduate full-time 53, Graduate part-time 70, Part-time 847 **Faculty:** Full-time 124, Part-time 60 **Student-Faculty Ratio:** 17:1 **Exams:** ACT essay component not used; SAT I or ACT; SAT essay component not used. **% Receiving Financial Aid:** 84 **% Residing in College-Owned, -Operated, or -Affiliated Housing:** 33 **Final Year or Final Semester Residency Requirement:** Yes **Regional Accreditation:** North Central Association of Colleges and Schools **Credit Hours For Degree:** 61 credit hours, Associates; 121 credit hours, Bachelors **ROTC:** Air Force, Army, Navy **Professional Accreditation:** ACBSP, ACEN, NASM, NCATE. **Intercollegiate Athletics:** Baseball M; Basketball M & W; Bowling W; Cheerleading W; Cross-Country Running W; Football M; Golf M & W; Softball W; Tennis W; Track and Field M & W

LINDENWOOD UNIVERSITY

209 S Kingshighway
Saint Charles, MO 63301-1695
Tel: (636)949-2000
Fax: (636)949-4910
E-mail: cmathis@lindenwood.edu
Web Site: www.lindenwood.edu
President/CEO: Dr. Michael D. Shonrock
Admissions: Comela Mathis
Financial Aid: Lori Bode

Type: Comprehensive **Sex:** Coed **Affiliation:** Presbyterian. **Scores:** 84% SAT V 400+; 95% SAT M 400+; 62.1% ACT 18-23; 28.9% ACT 24-29 **% Accepted:** 55 **Application Deadline:** Rolling **Application Fee:** $30.00 **H.S. Requirements:** High school diploma required; GED accepted **Costs Per Year:** Application fee: $30. Comprehensive fee: $23,956 includes full-time tuition ($15,672), mandatory fees ($350), and college room and board ($7934). College room only: $4290. Full-time tuition and fees vary according to class time. Room and board charges vary according to board plan. Part-time tuition: $453 per credit hour. Part-time tuition varies according to course load. **Scholarships:** Available. **Calendar System:** 4-1-4, Summer session available **Enrollment:** Full-time 7,297, Graduate full-time 1,412, Graduate part-time 1,923, Part-time 988 **Faculty:** Full-time 301, Part-time 1,377 **Student-Faculty Ratio:** 17:1 **Exams:** SAT I or ACT; SAT Reasoning; SAT Subject. **% Receiving Financial Aid:** 57 **% Residing in College-Owned, -Operated, or -Affiliated Housing:** 56 **Final Year or Final Semester Residency Requirement:** No **Regional Accreditation:** North Central Association of Colleges and Schools **Credit Hours For Degree:** 128 credit hours, Bachelors **ROTC:** Air Force, Army **Professional Accreditation:** ACBSP, NCATE, TEAC. **Intercollegiate Athletics:** Baseball M; Basketball M & W; Bowling M & W; Cheerleading M & W; Cross-Country Running M & W; Field Hockey W; Football M; Golf M & W; Gymnastics W; Ice Hockey M & W; Lacrosse M & W; Riflery M & W; Rugby M & W; Soccer M & W; Softball W; Swimming and Diving M & W; Table Tennis M & W; Tennis M & W; Track and Field M & W; Volleyball M & W; Water Polo M & W; Weight Lifting M & W; Wrestling M & W

LOGAN UNIVERSITY

1851 Schoettler Rd.
Chesterfield, MO 63017
Tel: (636)227-2100; Free: 800-533-9210
Fax: (636)227-9338
E-mail: Admissions@logan.edu
Web Site: www.logan.edu
President/CEO: Dr. Clay McDonald, DC
Admissions: Jordan LaMarca
Financial Aid: Kerry R. Hallahan

Type: Two-Year Upper Division **Sex:** Coed **Admission Plans:** Deferred Admission; Preferred Admission **Application Fee:** $50.00 **H.S. Requirements:** High school diploma required; GED accepted **Costs Per Year:** Application fee: $50. Tuition: $6600 full-time, $275 per credit hour part-time. Mandatory fees: $160 full-time, $80 per term part-time. Full-time tuition and fees vary according to course load and degree level. Part-time tuition and fees vary according to course load and degree level. **Scholarships:** Available. **Calendar System:** Trimester, Summer session not available **Enrollment:** Full-time 34, Graduate full-time 762, Graduate part-time 98, Part-time 21 **Faculty:** Full-time 54, Part-time 43 **Student-Faculty Ratio:** 12:1 **% Receiving Financial Aid:** 68 **Regional Accreditation:** North Central Association of Colleges and Schools **Credit Hours For Degree:** 119-124 credit

hours, depending on program, Bachelors **Professional Accreditation:** CCE. **Intercollegiate Athletics:** Basketball M & W; Golf M; Soccer M; Tennis M

MARYVILLE UNIVERSITY OF SAINT LOUIS

650 Maryville University Dr.
Saint Louis, MO 63141-7299
Tel: (314)529-9300; Free: 800-627-9855
Fax: (314)529-9927
E-mail: admissions@maryville.edu
Web Site: www.maryville.edu
President/CEO: Dr. Mark Lombardi
Admissions: Shani Lenore-Jenkins
Financial Aid: Martha Harbaugh

Type: Comprehensive **Sex:** Coed **Scores:** 91% SAT V 400+; 100% SAT M 400+; 26.4% ACT 18-23; 61% ACT 24-29 **% Accepted:** 72 **Admission Plans:** Deferred Admission **Application Deadline:** August 15 **Application Fee:** $30.00 **H.S. Requirements:** High school diploma required; GED accepted **Costs Per Year:** Application fee: $30. Comprehensive fee: $37,198 includes full-time tuition ($25,558), mandatory fees ($1400), and college room and board ($10,240). College room only: $7952. Full-time tuition and fees vary according to course load. Room and board charges vary according to board plan and housing facility. Part-time tuition: $766 per credit hour. Part-time mandatory fees: $310 per term. Part-time tuition and fees vary according to class time. **Scholarships:** Available. **Calendar System:** Semester, Summer session available **Enrollment:** Full-time 1,915, Graduate full-time 274, Graduate part-time 3,345, Part-time 880 **Faculty:** Full-time 129, Part-time 465 **Student-Faculty Ratio:** 13:1 **Exams:** ACT essay component used for advising; SAT I or ACT; SAT essay component used for advising. **% Receiving Financial Aid:** 70 **% Residing in College-Owned, -Operated, or -Affiliated Housing:** 24 **Final Year or Final Semester Residency Requirement:** No **Regional Accreditation:** North Central Association of Colleges and Schools **Credit Hours For Degree:** 128 credit hours, Bachelors **ROTC:** Army **Professional Accreditation:** AACN, ACBSP, AOTA, APTA, CIDA, CORE, NASAD, NASM, NCATE. **Intercollegiate Athletics:** Baseball M; Basketball M & W; Bowling W; Cross-Country Running M & W; Golf M & W; Lacrosse M; Soccer M & W; Softball W; Swimming and Diving M & W; Tennis W; Track and Field M & W; Volleyball W; Wrestling M

METRO BUSINESS COLLEGE (CAPE GIRARDEAU)

1732 N Kingshighway
Cape Girardeau, MO 63701
Tel: (573)334-9181; Free: 888-206-4545
Fax: (573)334-0617
Web Site: www.metrobusinesscollege.edu
President/CEO: George Holske
Admissions: Kyla Evans

Type: Two-Year College **Sex:** Coed **Application Fee:** $25.00 **Scholarships:** Available. **Calendar System:** Quarter **Professional Accreditation:** ACICS.

METRO BUSINESS COLLEGE (JEFFERSON CITY)

210 El Mercado Plz.
Jefferson City, MO 65109
Tel: (573)635-6600; Free: 888-206-4545
Fax: (573)635-6999
E-mail: cheri@metrobusinesscollege.edu
Web Site: www.metrobusinesscollege.edu
President/CEO: Cheri Lee Chockley
Admissions: Cheri Chockley

Type: Two-Year College **Sex:** Coed **Costs Per Year:** Tuition: $11,250 full-time, $278 per quarter hour part-time. Mandatory fees: $125 full-time. Full-time tuition and fees vary according to program. Part-time tuition varies according to program. Tuition guaranteed not to increase for student's term of enrollment. **Calendar System:** Continuous, Summer session available **Faculty:** Full-time 6, Part-time 5 **Student-Faculty Ratio:** 11:1 **Exams:** Other. **Credit Hours For Degree:** 104 quarter credit hours, Associates **Professional Accreditation:** ACICS.

METRO BUSINESS COLLEGE (ROLLA)

1202 E Hwy. 72
Rolla, MO 65401
Tel: (573)364-8464; Free: 888-206-4545

Fax: (573)364-8077
E-mail: inforolla@metrobusinesscollege.edu
Web Site: www.metrobusinesscollege.edu
President/CEO: George Holske
Type: Two-Year College **Sex:** Coed **Application Fee:** $25.00 **Calendar System:** Quarter **Professional Accreditation:** ACICS.

METROPOLITAN COMMUNITY COLLEGE–KANSAS CITY
3200 Broadway
Kansas City, MO 64111
Tel: (816)604-1000
E-mail: tuesday.stanley@mcckc.edu
Web Site: www.mcckc.edu
President/CEO: Mark James
Admissions: Dr. Tuesday Stanley
Type: Two-Year College **Sex:** Coed **Affiliation:** Metropolitan Community Colleges System. **% Accepted:** 100 **Admission Plans:** Deferred Admission; Early Admission; Open Admission **Application Deadline:** Rolling **Application Fee:** $0.00 **H.S. Requirements:** High school diploma required; GED accepted **Scholarships:** Available. **Calendar System:** Semester, Summer session available **Enrollment:** Full-time 7,734, Part-time 11,500 **Faculty:** Full-time 218, Part-time 686 **Student-Faculty Ratio:** 26:1 **Exams:** ACT. **Regional Accreditation:** North Central Association of Colleges and Schools **Credit Hours For Degree:** 62 credit hours, Associates **Intercollegiate Athletics:** Baseball M; Basketball M & W; Cross-Country Running W; Soccer M & W; Softball W; Volleyball W

MIDWEST INSTITUTE (FENTON)
964 S Hwy. Dr.
Fenton, MO 63026
Tel: (314)965-8363; Free: 800-695-5550
Fax: (314)965-1558
Web Site: www.midwestinstitute.com
President/CEO: Christine Shreffler
Type: Two-Year College **Sex:** Coed **% Accepted:** 99

MIDWEST INSTITUTE (SAINT LOUIS)
4260 Shoreline Dr.
Saint Louis, MO 63045
Tel: (314)344-4440; Free: 800-695-5550
Fax: (314)344-0495
Web Site: www.midwestinstitute.com
Type: Two-Year College **Sex:** Coed **Professional Accreditation:** ABHES.

MIDWEST UNIVERSITY
851 Parr Rd.
Wentzville, MO 63385
Tel: (636)327-4645
Fax: (636)327-4715
E-mail: usa@midwest.edu
Web Site: www.midwest.edu
President/CEO: James Song, PhD
Admissions: Jeoung H. Ham
Type: University **Sex:** Coed **Affiliation:** interdenominational. **Application Fee:** $100.00 **Calendar System:** Semester **Student-Faculty Ratio:** 24:1 **Professional Accreditation:** ABHE.

MINERAL AREA COLLEGE
PO Box 1000
Park Hills, MO 63601-1000
Tel: (573)431-4593
E-mail: preeder@mineralarea.edu
Web Site: www.mineralarea.edu
President/CEO: Dr. Steven Kurtz
Admissions: Pam Reeder
Type: Two-Year College **Sex:** Coed **Affiliation:** Missouri Coordinating Board for Higher Education. **Admission Plans:** Early Admission; Open Admission **Application Deadline:** Rolling **Application Fee:** $15.00 **H.S. Requirements:** High school diploma or equivalent not required. For allied health programs, law enforcement programs: High school diploma required; GED accepted **Scholarships:** Available. **Calendar System:** Semester, Summer session available **Enrollment:** Full-time 2,869, Part-time 1,639 **Faculty:** Full-time 73, Part-time 243 **Student-Faculty Ratio:** 14:1 **Regional Accreditation:** North Central Association of Colleges and Schools **Credit**

Hours For Degree: 62 credit hours, Associates **Intercollegiate Athletics:** Baseball M; Basketball M & W; Golf M; Softball W; Volleyball W

MISSOURI BAPTIST UNIVERSITY
One College Park Dr.
Saint Louis, MO 63141-8660
Tel: (314)434-1115; Free: 877-434-1115
Fax: (314)434-7596
E-mail: admissions@mobap.edu
Web Site: www.mobap.edu
President/CEO: Pres. R. Alton Lacey
Admissions: Beth Kinsey
Financial Aid: John Brandt
Type: Comprehensive **Sex:** Coed **Affiliation:** Southern Baptist. **% Accepted:** 29 **Application Deadline:** Rolling **Application Fee:** $35.00 **H.S. Requirements:** High school diploma required; GED accepted **Costs Per Year:** Application fee: $35. Comprehensive fee: $33,396 includes full-time tuition ($22,690), mandatory fees ($1196), and college room and board ($9510). Full-time tuition and fees vary according to course load and location. Room and board charges vary according to board plan and housing facility. Part-time tuition: $782 per credit hour. Part-time mandatory fees: $25 per credit hour, $68 per term. Part-time tuition and fees vary according to course load and location. **Scholarships:** Available. **Calendar System:** Semester, Summer session available **Enrollment:** Full-time 1,346, Graduate full-time 215, Graduate part-time 891, Part-time 2,824 **Faculty:** Full-time 69, Part-time 221 **Student-Faculty Ratio:** 20:1 **Exams:** ACT essay component not used; SAT I or ACT; SAT essay component not used; SAT Reasoning; SAT Subject. **% Receiving Financial Aid:** 78 **% Residing in College-Owned, -Operated, or -Affiliated Housing:** 40 **Final Year or Final Semester Residency Requirement:** Yes **Regional Accreditation:** North Central Association of Colleges and Schools **Credit Hours For Degree:** 64 credit hours, Associates; 128 credit hours, Bachelors **ROTC:** Army **Professional Accreditation:** NASM, NCATE. **Intercollegiate Athletics:** Baseball M; Basketball M & W; Bowling M & W; Cheerleading M & W; Cross-Country Running M & W; Football M; Golf M & W; Lacrosse M & W; Soccer M & W; Softball W; Tennis M & W; Track and Field M & W; Volleyball M & W; Wrestling M & W

MISSOURI COLLEGE
1405 S Hanley Rd.
Brentwood, MO 63117
Tel: (314)821-7700; Free: 800-216-6732
Web Site: www.missouricollege.edu
President/CEO: Karl Petersen
Admissions: Doug Brinker
Type: Two-Year College **Sex:** Coed **Admission Plans:** Open Admission **Application Deadline:** Rolling **Application Fee:** $35.00 **H.S. Requirements:** High school diploma required; GED accepted **Scholarships:** Available. **Professional Accreditation:** ACCSC, ACICS, ADA.

MISSOURI SOUTHERN STATE UNIVERSITY
3950 E Newman Rd.
Joplin, MO 64801-1595
Tel: (417)625-9300; Free: 866-818-MSSU
Fax: (417)659-4429
E-mail: admissions@mssu.edu
Web Site: www.mssu.edu
President/CEO: Dr. Alan D. Marble
Admissions: Derek Skaggs
Financial Aid: Becca L. Diskin
Type: Comprehensive **Sex:** Coed **Scores:** 52.54% ACT 18-23; 28.5% ACT 24-29 **% Accepted:** 94 **Admission Plans:** Deferred Admission **Application Deadline:** Rolling **Application Fee:** $25.00 **H.S. Requirements:** High school diploma required; GED accepted **Costs Per Year:** Application fee: $25. State resident tuition: $5311 full-time. Nonresident tuition: $10,622 full-time. Mandatory fees: $566 full-time. College room and board: $6622. **Scholarships:** Available. **Calendar System:** Semester, Summer session available **Enrollment:** Full-time 4,210, Graduate full-time 6, Graduate part-time 45, Part-time 1,522 **Faculty:** Full-time 202, Part-time 148 **Student-Faculty Ratio:** 18:1 **Exams:** ACT; ACT essay component not used; SAT I and SAT II or ACT; SAT I or ACT; SAT Reasoning. **% Receiving Financial Aid:** 59 **% Residing in College-Owned, -Operated, or -Affiliated Housing:** 14 **Regional Accreditation:** North Central Association of Colleges and Schools **Credit Hours For Degree:** 64 credits (varies by program), Associ-

ates; 124 credits, but it varies with different programs, Bachelors **Professional Accreditation:** AACN, ABET, ACBSP, ACEN, ADA, CoARC, JRCERT, NCATE. **Intercollegiate Athletics:** Baseball M; Basketball M & W; Cross-Country Running M & W; Football M; Golf M; Soccer M & W; Softball W; Tennis W; Track and Field M & W; Volleyball W

MISSOURI STATE UNIVERSITY
901 S National
Springfield, MO 65897
Tel: (417)836-5000; Free: 800-492-7900
Fax: (417)836-6334
E-mail: info@missouristate.edu
Web Site: www.missouristate.edu
President/CEO: Clifton M. Smart, JD
Admissions: Andrew Wright
Financial Aid: Vicki Mattocks
Type: Comprehensive **Sex:** Coed **Scores:** 98% SAT V 400+; 91% SAT M 400+; 45.65% ACT 18-23; 43.16% ACT 24-29 **% Accepted:** 16 **Application Fee:** $35.00 **H.S. Requirements:** High school diploma required; GED accepted **Costs Per Year:** Application fee: $35. State resident tuition: $7060 full-time, $205 per credit hour part-time. Nonresident tuition: $13,930 full-time, $434 per credit hour part-time. Mandatory fees: $910 full-time. Full-time tuition and fees vary according to course level, course load, and program. Part-time tuition varies according to course level, course load, and program. College room and board: $8130. Room and board charges vary according to board plan, housing facility, and location. **Scholarships:** Available. **Calendar System:** Semester, Summer session available **Enrollment:** Full-time 14,540, Graduate full-time 1,608, Graduate part-time 1,685, Part-time 4,440 **Faculty:** Full-time 734, Part-time 408 **Student-Faculty Ratio:** 21:1 **Exams:** ACT essay component not used; SAT I or ACT; SAT essay component not used. **% Receiving Financial Aid:** 59 **% Residing in College-Owned, -Operated, or -Affiliated Housing:** 24 **Final Year or Final Semester Residency Requirement:** No **Regional Accreditation:** North Central Association of Colleges and Schools **Credit Hours For Degree:** 125 credit hours, Bachelors **ROTC:** Army **Professional Accreditation:** AACN, AACSB, AAFCS, AANA, ABET, ACSP, APTA, ASHA, ATMAE, CSWE, JRCAT, NASM, NASPAA, NAST, NCATE, NRPA. **Intercollegiate Athletics:** Baseball M; Basketball M & W; Bowling M & W; Cross-Country Running W; Equestrian Sports M & W; Field Hockey W; Football M; Golf M & W; Ice Hockey M; Lacrosse M; Racquetball M & W; Soccer M & W; Softball W; Swimming and Diving M & W; Track and Field W; Ultimate Frisbee M & W; Volleyball M & W; Wrestling M

MISSOURI STATE UNIVERSITY–WEST PLAINS
128 Garfield
West Plains, MO 65775
Tel: (417)255-7255; Free: 888-466-7897
E-mail: melissajett@missouristate.edu
Web Site: wp.missouristate.edu
President/CEO: Dr. Drew A. Bennett
Admissions: Melissa Jett
Type: Two-Year College **Sex:** Coed **Affiliation:** Missouri State University. **Scores:** 55% ACT 18-23; 15.5% ACT 24-29 **% Accepted:** 60 **Admission Plans:** Open Admission **Application Deadline:** Rolling **Application Fee:** $15.00 **H.S. Requirements:** High school diploma required; GED accepted **Costs Per Year:** Application fee: $15. State resident tuition: $3570 full-time, $119 per credit hour part-time. Nonresident tuition: $7140 full-time, $238 per credit hour part-time. Mandatory fees: $300 full-time. Full-time tuition and fees vary according to course load, location, and program. Part-time tuition varies according to course load and location. College room and board: $5590. Room and board charges vary according to board plan. **Scholarships:** Available. **Calendar System:** Semester, Summer session available **Enrollment:** Full-time 1,310, Part-time 813 **Faculty:** Full-time 37, Part-time 79 **Student-Faculty Ratio:** 25:1 **Exams:** ACT essay component not used; SAT essay component not used. **% Residing in College-Owned, -Operated, or -Affiliated Housing:** 4 **Final Year or Final Semester Residency Requirement:** No **Regional Accreditation:** North Central Association of Colleges and Schools **Credit Hours For Degree:** 62 credit hours, Associates **Professional Accreditation:** ACEN. **Intercollegiate Athletics:** Basketball M; Volleyball W

MISSOURI UNIVERSITY OF SCIENCE AND TECHNOLOGY
1870 Miner Cir.
Rolla, MO 65409

Tel: (573)341-4111; Free: 800-522-0938
E-mail: admissions@mst.edu
Web Site: www.mst.edu
President/CEO: Dr. Cheryl B. Schrader
Admissions: Lynn Stichnote
Financial Aid: Bridgette Betz
Type: University **Sex:** Coed **Affiliation:** University of Missouri System. **Scores:** 96% SAT V 400+; 100% SAT M 400+; 10% ACT 18-23; 50% ACT 24-29 **% Accepted:** 88 **Admission Plans:** Deferred Admission **Application Deadline:** July 1 **Application Fee:** $50.00 **H.S. Requirements:** High school diploma required; GED accepted **Costs Per Year:** Application fee: $50. State resident tuition: $8286 full-time, $276.20 per credit hour part-time. Nonresident tuition: $24,810 full-time, $827 per credit hour part-time. Mandatory fees: $1498 full-time, $55.48 per credit hour part-time. Full-time tuition and fees vary according to course load, degree level, and program. Part-time tuition and fees vary according to course load, degree level, and program. College room and board: $9464. Room and board charges vary according to board plan, housing facility, and location. **Scholarships:** Available. **Calendar System:** Semester, Summer session available **Enrollment:** Full-time 6,168, Graduate full-time 1,235, Graduate part-time 813, Part-time 673 **Faculty:** Full-time 367, Part-time 119 **Student-Faculty Ratio:** 19:1 **Exams:** ACT; ACT essay component not used; SAT I or ACT; SAT essay component not used; SAT Reasoning; SAT Subject. **% Receiving Financial Aid:** 56 **% Residing in College-Owned, -Operated, or -Affiliated Housing:** 40 **Final Year or Final Semester Residency Requirement:** Yes **Regional Accreditation:** North Central Association of Colleges and Schools **Credit Hours For Degree:** 120 credit hours, Bachelors **ROTC:** Air Force, Army **Professional Accreditation:** ABET. **Intercollegiate Athletics:** Baseball M; Basketball M & W; Cross-Country Running M & W; Football M; Soccer M & W; Softball W; Swimming and Diving M; Track and Field M & W; Volleyball W

MISSOURI VALLEY COLLEGE
500 E College
Marshall, MO 65340-3197
Tel: (660)831-4000
Fax: (660)831-4039
E-mail: admissions@moval.edu
Web Site: www.moval.edu
President/CEO: Dr. Bonnie Humphrey
Admissions: Jessica Green
Financial Aid: Rachel Kimberly Robinson
Type: Comprehensive **Sex:** Coed **Affiliation:** Presbyterian Church. **Scores:** 71% SAT V 400+; 59% ACT 18-23; 8% ACT 24-29 **% Accepted:** 46 **Admission Plans:** Deferred Admission; Early Admission **Application Deadline:** Rolling **H.S. Requirements:** High school diploma required; GED accepted **Costs Per Year:** Comprehensive fee: $28,150 includes full-time tuition ($18,500), mandatory fees ($1250), and college room and board ($8400). College room only: $4450. Room and board charges vary according to board plan, gender, housing facility, location, and student level. Part-time tuition: $350 per credit hour. **Scholarships:** Available. **Calendar System:** Semester, Summer session available **Enrollment:** Full-time 1,349, Graduate full-time 14, Graduate part-time 2, Part-time 334 **Faculty:** Full-time 86, Part-time 85 **Student-Faculty Ratio:** 16:1 **Exams:** SAT I or ACT. **% Receiving Financial Aid:** 79 **% Residing in College-Owned, -Operated, or -Affiliated Housing:** 73 **Regional Accreditation:** North Central Association of Colleges and Schools **Credit Hours For Degree:** 64 credit hours, Associates; 128 credit hours, Bachelors **ROTC:** Army **Intercollegiate Athletics:** Baseball M; Basketball M & W; Cheerleading M & W; Cross-Country Running M & W; Football M; Golf M & W; Lacrosse M & W; Soccer M & W; Softball W; Tennis M & W; Track and Field M & W; Volleyball M & W; Wrestling M & W

MISSOURI WESTERN STATE UNIVERSITY
4525 Downs Dr.
Saint Joseph, MO 64507-2294
Tel: (816)271-4200; Free: 800-662-7041
Fax: (816)271-5833
E-mail: admission@missouriwestern.edu
Web Site: www.missouriwestern.edu
President/CEO: Dr. Robert Vartabedian
Admissions: Jamie Sweiger
Financial Aid: Marilyn Baker
Type: Comprehensive **Sex:** Coed **Scores:** 55% ACT 18-23; 25% ACT 24-29

% Accepted: 61 Admission Plans: Early Admission; Open Admission Application Deadline: May 1 Application Fee: $0.00 H.S. Requirements: High school diploma required; GED accepted Costs Per Year: Application fee: $0. State resident tuition: $5,934 full-time, $197.79 per credit hour part-time. Nonresident tuition: $12,092 full-time, $403.05 per credit hour part-time. Mandatory fees: $718 full-time. Full-time tuition and fees vary according to course load, location, and program. Part-time tuition varies according to course load, location, and program. College room and board: $7590. College room only: $4376. Room and board charges vary according to board plan and housing facility. Scholarships: Available. Calendar System: Semester, Summer session available Enrollment: Full-time 3,631, Graduate full-time 67, Graduate part-time 150, Part-time 1,665 Faculty: Full-time 207, Part-time 178 Student-Faculty Ratio: 16:1 Exams: SAT I or ACT. % Residing in College-Owned, -Operated, or -Affiliated Housing: 21 Final Year or Final Semester Residency Requirement: No Regional Accreditation: North Central Association of Colleges and Schools Credit Hours For Degree: 62 credit hours, Associates; 124 credit hours, Bachelors ROTC: Army Professional Accreditation: AACN, AACSB, ABET, AHIMA, APTA, CSWE, NASM, NCATE. Intercollegiate Athletics: Baseball M; Basketball M & W; Football M; Golf M & W; Soccer W; Softball W; Tennis W; Volleyball W

MOBERLY AREA COMMUNITY COLLEGE

101 College Ave.
Moberly, MO 65270-1304
Tel: (660)263-4110; Free: 800-622-2070
Fax: (660)263-6252
E-mail: info@macc.edu
Web Site: www.macc.edu
President/CEO: Evelyn Jorgenson
Admissions: Dr. James Grant
Type: Two-Year College Sex: Coed Scores: 58% ACT 18-23; 14% ACT 24-29 Admission Plans: Open Admission Application Deadline: Rolling Application Fee: $0.00 H.S. Requirements: High school diploma required; GED accepted Scholarships: Available. Calendar System: Semester, Summer session available Enrollment: Full-time 2,023, Part-time 1,986 Faculty: Full-time 67, Part-time 166 Student-Faculty Ratio: 21:1 Exams: ACT; Other. % Residing in College-Owned, -Operated, or -Affiliated Housing: 1 Regional Accreditation: North Central Association of Colleges and Schools Credit Hours For Degree: 64 credit hours, Associates Professional Accreditation: ATMAE. Intercollegiate Athletics: Basketball M & W; Cheerleading M & W

NATIONAL AMERICAN UNIVERSITY (KANSAS CITY)

7490 NW 87th St.
Kansas City, MO 64153
Tel: (816)412-5500
E-mail: zradmissions@national.edu
Web Site: www.national.edu
President/CEO: Dr. Jerry Gallentine
Financial Aid: Mary Anderson
Type: Four-Year College Sex: Coed Affiliation: National College. Admission Plans: Deferred Admission; Early Admission; Open Admission Application Deadline: Rolling Application Fee: $25.00 H.S. Requirements: High school diploma required; GED accepted Scholarships: Available. Calendar System: Quarter, Summer session available Regional Accreditation: North Central Association of Colleges and Schools Credit Hours For Degree: 98 credits, Associates; 194 credits, Bachelors Professional Accreditation: ACEN.

NATIONAL AMERICAN UNIVERSITY (LEE'S SUMMIT)

401 NW Murray Rd.
Lee's Summit, MO 64081
Tel: (816)600-3900; Free: 866-628-1288
Web Site: www.national.edu
Type: Four-Year College Sex: Coed Regional Accreditation: North Central Association of Colleges and Schools

NORTH CENTRAL MISSOURI COLLEGE

1301 Main St.
Trenton, MO 64683-1824
Tel: (660)359-3948
E-mail: megoodin@mail.ncmissouri.edu
Web Site: www.ncmissouri.edu
President/CEO: Dr. Neil Nuttall

Admissions: Megan Goodin
Type: Two-Year College Sex: Coed % Accepted: 88 Admission Plans: Open Admission Application Deadline: Rolling Application Fee: $15.00 H.S. Requirements: High school diploma required; GED accepted Scholarships: Available. Calendar System: Semester, Summer session available Enrollment: Full-time 796, Part-time 709 Faculty: Full-time 33, Part-time 61 Student-Faculty Ratio: 16:1 Exams: Other; SAT I or ACT. Regional Accreditation: North Central Association of Colleges and Schools Credit Hours For Degree: 60 credit hours, Associates Intercollegiate Athletics: Baseball M; Basketball M & W; Softball W

NORTHWEST MISSOURI STATE UNIVERSITY

800 University Dr.
Maryville, MO 64468-6001
Tel: (660)562-1212; Free: 800-633-1175
Fax: (660)562-1121
E-mail: admissions@nwmissouri.edu
Web Site: www.nwmissouri.edu
President/CEO: Dr. John Jasinski
Admissions: Tammi Grow
Financial Aid: Charles Mayfield
Type: Comprehensive Sex: Coed Affiliation: Missouri Coordinating Board for Higher Education. Scores: 2% SAT V 400+; 39% SAT M 400+ % Accepted: 75 Admission Plans: Deferred Admission; Preferred Admission Application Deadline: Rolling Application Fee: $25.00 H.S. Requirements: High school diploma required; GED accepted Costs Per Year: Application fee: $25. State resident tuition: $5418 full-time, $180.61 per credit hour part-time. Nonresident tuition: $11,739 full-time, $391.29 per credit hour part-time. Mandatory fees: $3041 full-time, $110.35 per credit hour part-time. Full-time tuition and fees vary according to course load, location, and reciprocity agreements. Part-time tuition and fees vary according to course load and location. College room and board: $9538. College room only: $6138. Room and board charges vary according to board plan and housing facility. Scholarships: Available. Calendar System: Trimester, Summer session available Enrollment: Full-time 4,974, Graduate full-time 446, Graduate part-time 529, Part-time 644 Faculty: Full-time 260, Part-time 54 Student-Faculty Ratio: 21:1 Exams: ACT essay component not used; SAT I or ACT; SAT essay component not used; SAT Reasoning; SAT Subject. % Receiving Financial Aid: 67 % Residing in College-Owned, -Operated, or -Affiliated Housing: 41 Final Year or Final Semester Residency Requirement: No Regional Accreditation: North Central Association of Colleges and Schools Credit Hours For Degree: 124 semester hours, Bachelors ROTC: Army Professional Accreditation: AAFCS, ACBSP, NASM, NCATE. Intercollegiate Athletics: Baseball M; Basketball M & W; Cheerleading M & W; Cross-Country Running M & W; Football M; Golf W; Soccer W; Softball W; Tennis M & W; Track and Field M & W; Volleyball W

OZARK CHRISTIAN COLLEGE

1111 N Main St.
Joplin, MO 64801-4804
Tel: (417)624-2518; Free: 800-299-4622
Fax: (417)624-0090
E-mail: occadmin@occ.edu
Web Site: www.occ.edu
President/CEO: Matt Proctor
Admissions: Troy B. Nelson
Financial Aid: Jill Kaminsky
Type: Four-Year College Sex: Coed Affiliation: Christian. Application Deadline: August 5 Application Fee: $30.00 H.S. Requirements: High school diploma required; GED accepted Scholarships: Available. Calendar System: Semester, Summer session available Faculty: Full-time 30, Part-time 30 Student-Faculty Ratio: 19:1 Exams: SAT I or ACT. % Residing in College-Owned, -Operated, or -Affiliated Housing: 63 Credit Hours For Degree: 96 credits, Associates; 128 credits, Bachelors Professional Accreditation: ABHE. Intercollegiate Athletics: Basketball M & W; Cheerleading M & W; Soccer M; Volleyball W

OZARKS TECHNICAL COMMUNITY COLLEGE

1001 E Chestnut Expy.
Springfield, MO 65802
Tel: (417)447-7500
Fax: (417)895-7161
Web Site: www.otc.edu
President/CEO: Dr. Hal Higdon

Type: Two-Year College **Sex:** Coed **Affiliation:** Missouri Coordinating Board for Higher Education. **Admission Plans:** Open Admission **Application Deadline:** Rolling **Application Fee:** $0.00 **H.S. Requirements:** High school diploma required; GED accepted **Costs Per Year:** Application fee: $0. Area resident tuition: $2352 full-time, $98 per credit hour part-time. State resident tuition: $3528 full-time, $147 per credit hour part-time. Nonresident tuition: $4704 full-time, $196 per credit hour part-time. Mandatory fees: $500 full-time, $22 per credit hour part-time, $50 per term part-time. **Scholarships:** Available. **Calendar System:** Semester, Summer session available **Enrollment:** Full-time 5,950, Part-time 7,664 **Faculty:** Full-time 188, Part-time 700 **Student-Faculty Ratio:** 22:1 **Regional Accreditation:** North Central Association of Colleges and Schools **Credit Hours For Degree:** 62 credit hours, Associates **Professional Accreditation:** ACF, ADA, AHIMA, AOTA, APTA, ATMAE, CoARC.

PARK UNIVERSITY
8700 NW River Park Dr.
Parkville, MO 64152-3795
Tel: (816)741-2000; Free: 800-745-7275
Fax: (816)741-4462
E-mail: admissions@mail.park.edu
Web Site: www.park.edu
President/CEO: David Fowler
Admissions: Eric Blair
Financial Aid: Cathy Colapietro
Type: Comprehensive **Sex:** Coed **Admission Plans:** Deferred Admission; Early Admission **Application Deadline:** August 1 **Application Fee:** $25.00 **H.S. Requirements:** High school diploma required; GED accepted **Scholarships:** Available. **Calendar System:** Semester, Summer session available **Enrollment:** Full-time 1,089, Graduate full-time 48, Graduate part-time 806, Part-time 7,857 **Faculty:** Full-time 137, Part-time 37 **Student-Faculty Ratio:** 12:1 **Exams:** ACT essay component used for placement; SAT I or ACT; SAT essay component used for placement; SAT Reasoning; SAT Subject. **% Receiving Financial Aid:** 55 **% Residing in College-Owned, -Operated, or -Affiliated Housing:** 20 **Regional Accreditation:** North Central Association of Colleges and Schools **Credit Hours For Degree:** 60 credit hours, Associates; 120 credit hours, Bachelors **ROTC:** Army **Professional Accreditation:** ACBSP, ACEN, JRCAT. **Intercollegiate Athletics:** Baseball M; Basketball M & W; Cross-Country Running M & W; Golf W; Soccer M & W; Softball W; Track and Field M & W; Volleyball M & W

PINNACLE CAREER INSTITUTE (KANSAS CITY)
11500 NW Ambassador
Ste. 221
Kansas City, MO 64153
Tel: (816)270-5300
E-mail: dlang@pcitraining.edu
Web Site: www.pcitraining.edu
President/CEO: Joan Meyer
Admissions: Debbie Lang
Type: Two-Year College **Sex:** Coed **Affiliation:** Pinnacle Career Institute. **Admission Plans:** Open Admission **Application Fee:** $0.00 **H.S. Requirements:** High school diploma required; GED accepted **Calendar System:** Miscellaneous **Professional Accreditation:** ACICS.

PINNACLE CAREER INSTITUTE (KANSAS CITY)
1001 E 101st Ter.
Ste. 325
Kansas City, MO 64131
Tel: (816)331-5700; Free: 877-241-3097
Web Site: www.pcitraining.edu
President/CEO: Guy Cognet
Admissions: Ruth Matous
Type: Two-Year College **Sex:** Coed **Application Deadline:** June 1 **Application Fee:** $50.00 **Scholarships:** Available. **Professional Accreditation:** ACCSC, ACICS.

RANKEN TECHNICAL COLLEGE
4431 Finney Ave.
Saint Louis, MO 63113
Tel: (314)371-0233; Free: 866-4-RANKEN
Fax: (314)371-0241
Web Site: www.ranken.edu
President/CEO: Stan Shoun

Admissions: Elizabeth Keserauskis
Type: Two-Year College **Sex:** Coed **Application Deadline:** Rolling **Application Fee:** $25.00 **H.S. Requirements:** High school diploma required; GED accepted **Scholarships:** Available. **Calendar System:** Semester, Summer session available **Regional Accreditation:** North Central Association of Colleges and Schools **Credit Hours For Degree:** 96 semester hours, Associates; 136 semester hours, Bachelors

RESEARCH COLLEGE OF NURSING
2525 E Meyer Blvd.
Kansas City, MO 64132
Tel: (816)995-2800
Fax: (816)276-3526
E-mail: lane.ramey@rockhurst.edu
Web Site: www.researchcollege.edu
President/CEO: Dr. Nancy O. DeBasio
Admissions: Lane Ramey
Financial Aid: Stacie Withers
Type: Comprehensive **Sex:** Coed **Affiliation:** Rockhurst University. **Scores:** 44% ACT 18-23; 52% ACT 24-29 **% Accepted:** 73 **Admission Plans:** Deferred Admission **Application Deadline:** June 30 **Application Fee:** $0.00 **H.S. Requirements:** High school diploma required; GED accepted **Costs Per Year:** Application fee: $0. Comprehensive fee: $44,075 includes full-time tuition ($34,000), mandatory fees ($820), and college room and board ($9255). College room only: $5800. Room and board charges vary according to board plan, housing facility, and location. Part-time tuition: $1134 per credit hour. Part-time tuition varies according to class time. **Scholarships:** Available. **Calendar System:** Semester, Summer session available **Enrollment:** Full-time 339, Graduate full-time 4, Graduate part-time 130, Part-time 1 **Faculty:** Full-time 26, Part-time 3 **Student-Faculty Ratio:** 7:1 **Exams:** ACT essay component not used; SAT I or ACT; SAT essay component not used. **Regional Accreditation:** North Central Association of Colleges and Schools **Credit Hours For Degree:** 128 credit hours, Bachelors **ROTC:** Army **Professional Accreditation:** AACN. **Intercollegiate Athletics:** Baseball M; Basketball M & W; Golf M & W; Soccer M & W; Softball W; Tennis M & W; Volleyball W

ROCKHURST UNIVERSITY
1100 Rockhurst Rd.
Kansas City, MO 64110-2561
Tel: (816)501-4000; Free: 800-842-6776
Fax: (816)501-4241
E-mail: admission@rockhurst.edu
Web Site: www.rockhurst.edu
President/CEO: Rev. Thomas B. Curran, OSFS
Admissions: Kyle Johnson
Financial Aid: Maureen McKinnon
Type: Comprehensive **Sex:** Coed **Affiliation:** Roman Catholic (Jesuit). **Scores:** 94% SAT V 400+; 100% SAT M 400+; 31% ACT 18-23; 52% ACT 24-29 **% Accepted:** 74 **Admission Plans:** Deferred Admission **Application Deadline:** June 30 **Application Fee:** $25.00 **H.S. Requirements:** High school diploma required; GED accepted **Costs Per Year:** Application fee: $25. Comprehensive fee: $44,255 includes full-time tuition ($34,000), mandatory fees ($790), and college room and board ($9465). College room only: $5755. Full-time tuition and fees vary according to class time and course load. Room and board charges vary according to board plan and housing facility. Part-time tuition: $567 per semester hour. Part-time mandatory fees: $25 per credit hour. Part-time tuition and fees vary according to class time and course load. **Scholarships:** Available. **Calendar System:** Semester, Summer session available **Enrollment:** Full-time 1,442, Graduate full-time 403, Graduate part-time 345, Part-time 635 **Faculty:** Full-time 131, Part-time 119 **Student-Faculty Ratio:** 12:1 **Exams:** ACT essay component not used; SAT I or ACT; SAT essay component not used; SAT Reasoning; SAT Subject. **% Receiving Financial Aid:** 70 **% Residing in College-Owned, -Operated, or -Affiliated Housing:** 53 **Final Year or Final Semester Residency Requirement:** Yes **Regional Accreditation:** North Central Association of Colleges and Schools **Credit Hours For Degree:** 128 credit hours, Bachelors **ROTC:** Army **Professional Accreditation:** AACSB, AOTA, APTA, ASHA, TEAC. **Intercollegiate Athletics:** Baseball M; Basketball M & W; Cross-Country Running W; Golf M & W; Lacrosse M & W; Soccer M & W; Softball W; Tennis M & W; Volleyball W

ST. CHARLES COMMUNITY COLLEGE
4601 Mid Rivers Mall Dr.
Cottleville, MO 63376

Tel: (636)922-8000
Fax: (636)922-8236
E-mail: regist@stchas.edu
Web Site: www.stchas.edu
President/CEO: Todd Galbierz
Admissions: Kathy Brockgreitens-Gober
Financial Aid: Cassandra Hagan
Type: Two-Year College **Sex:** Coed **Affiliation:** Missouri Coordinating Board for Higher Education. **% Accepted:** 100 **Admission Plans:** Deferred Admission; Early Admission; Open Admission **Application Deadline:** Rolling **Application Fee:** $10.00 **H.S. Requirements:** High school diploma required; GED accepted **Costs Per Year:** Application fee: $10. Area resident tuition: $2352 full-time, $98 per credit part-time. State resident tuition: $3528 full-time, $147 per credit part-time. Nonresident tuition: $5160 full-time, $215 per credit part-time. Mandatory fees: $120 full-time, $5 per credit part-time. Full-time tuition and fees vary according to course load and program. Part-time tuition and fees vary according to course load and program. **Scholarships:** Available. **Calendar System:** Semester, Summer session available **Enrollment:** Full-time 3,426, Part-time 3,439 **Faculty:** Full-time 106, Part-time 274 **Student-Faculty Ratio:** 22:1 **Exams:** ACT essay component used for placement. **Final Year or Final Semester Residency Requirement:** No **Regional Accreditation:** North Central Association of Colleges and Schools **Credit Hours For Degree:** 64 semester hours, Associates **Professional Accreditation:** ACEN, AHIMA, AOTA. **Intercollegiate Athletics:** Baseball M; Soccer M & W; Softball W

SAINT LOUIS CHRISTIAN COLLEGE

1360 Grandview Dr.
Florissant, MO 63033-6499
Tel: (314)837-6777; Free: 800-887-SLCC
Fax: (314)837-8291
E-mail: bfarrar@stlchristian.edu
Web Site: www.slcconline.edu
President/CEO: Dr. Guthrie Veech
Admissions: Bob Farrar
Financial Aid: Catherine Wilhoit
Type: Four-Year College **Sex:** Coed **Affiliation:** Christian. **Scores:** 100% SAT V 400+; 100% SAT M 400+; 50% ACT 18-23; 20% ACT 24-29 **% Accepted:** 36 **Application Deadline:** August 7 **Application Fee:** $0.00 **H.S. Requirements:** High school diploma required; GED accepted **Costs Per Year:** Application fee: $0. Comprehensive fee: $14,675 includes full-time tuition ($10,075) and college room and board ($4600). Room and board charges vary according to housing facility. **Scholarships:** Available. **Calendar System:** Semester, Summer session available **Enrollment:** Full-time 126, Part-time 47 **Faculty:** Full-time 8, Part-time 20 **Student-Faculty Ratio:** 12:1 **Exams:** ACT essay component not used; SAT I or ACT; SAT essay component not used; SAT Reasoning; SAT Subject. **% Receiving Financial Aid:** 88 **% Residing in College-Owned, -Operated, or -Affiliated Housing:** 68 **Final Year or Final Semester Residency Requirement:** No **Credit Hours For Degree:** 65 credit hours, Associates; 126 credit hours, Bachelors **Professional Accreditation:** ABHE. **Intercollegiate Athletics:** Baseball M; Basketball M & W; Cross-Country Running W; Volleyball W

ST. LOUIS COLLEGE OF HEALTH CAREERS (FENTON)

1297 N Hwy. Dr.
Fenton, MO 63026
Tel: (314)845-6100
Web Site: www.slchc.com
Type: Two-Year College **Sex:** Coed **Calendar System:** Semester **Professional Accreditation:** ABHES.

ST. LOUIS COLLEGE OF HEALTH CAREERS (SAINT LOUIS)

909 S Taylor Ave.
Saint Louis, MO 63110-1511
Tel: (314)652-0300; Free: 888-789-4820
Fax: (314)652-4825
Web Site: www.slchc.com
President/CEO: Dr. Rush L. Robinson, PhD
Type: Two-Year College **Sex:** Coed **Application Fee:** $35.00 **Student-Faculty Ratio:** 12:1 **Professional Accreditation:** ABHES.

ST. LOUIS COLLEGE OF PHARMACY

4588 Parkview Pl.
Saint Louis, MO 63110-1088

Tel: (314)367-8700; Free: 800-278-5267
Fax: (314)367-2784
E-mail: connie.horrall@stlcop.edu
Web Site: www.stlcop.edu
President/CEO: Dr. John A. Pieper
Admissions: Mother Connie Horrall
Financial Aid: Dan Stiffler
Type: Comprehensive **Sex:** Coed **Scores:** 96% SAT V 400+; 100% SAT M 400+; 20.5% ACT 18-23; 60.5% ACT 24-29 **% Accepted:** 68 **Admission Plans:** Early Action **Application Deadline:** March 1 **Application Fee:** $55.00 **H.S. Requirements:** High school diploma required; GED accepted **Costs Per Year:** Application fee: $55. Comprehensive fee: $39,000 includes full-time tuition ($27,400), mandatory fees ($1555), and college room and board ($10,045). Full-time tuition and fees vary according to student level. Room and board charges vary according to board plan and housing facility. Part-time tuition: $914 per credit hour. **Scholarships:** Available. **Calendar System:** Semester, Summer session available **Enrollment:** Full-time 435, Graduate full-time 937, Graduate part-time 16, Part-time 1 **Faculty:** Full-time 91, Part-time 56 **Student-Faculty Ratio:** 9:1 **Exams:** SAT I or ACT; SAT Reasoning; SAT Subject. **% Receiving Financial Aid:** 78 **% Residing in College-Owned, -Operated, or -Affiliated Housing:** 57 **Final Year or Final Semester Residency Requirement:** Yes **Regional Accreditation:** North Central Association of Colleges and Schools **Credit Hours For Degree:** 122 semester hours, Bachelors **ROTC:** Air Force, Army, Navy **Professional Accreditation:** ACPE. **Intercollegiate Athletics:** Basketball M & W; Cross-Country Running M & W; Soccer M & W; Softball W; Tennis M & W; Track and Field M & W; Volleyball W

ST. LOUIS COMMUNITY COLLEGE

300 S Broadway
Saint Louis, MO 63102
Tel: (314)539-5000
Web Site: www.stlcc.edu
President/CEO: Jeff Pittman, PhD
Type: Two-Year College **Sex:** Coed **Affiliation:** St. Louis Community College System. **Admission Plans:** Open Admission **Application Deadline:** Rolling **Application Fee:** $0.00 **H.S. Requirements:** High school diploma required; GED accepted **Costs Per Year:** Application fee: $0. Area resident tuition: $2700 full-time, $90 per credit part-time. State resident tuition: $4080 full-time, $136 per credit part-time. Nonresident tuition: $5760 full-time, $192 per credit part-time. Mandatory fees: $390 full-time, $13 per credit part-time. Full-time tuition and fees vary according to course load. Part-time tuition and fees vary according to course load. **Calendar System:** Semester, Summer session available **Enrollment:** Full-time 7,653, Part-time 11,249 **Faculty:** Full-time 418, Part-time 967 **Student-Faculty Ratio:** 17:1 **Exams:** ACT essay component not used; SAT essay component not used. **Regional Accreditation:** North Central Association of Colleges and Schools **Credit Hours For Degree:** 64 credit hours, Associates **Intercollegiate Athletics:** Baseball M; Basketball M & W; Soccer M & W; Softball W; Volleyball W

SAINT LOUIS UNIVERSITY

One N Grand Blvd.
Saint Louis, MO 63103
Tel: (314)977-2222; Free: 800-758-3678
Fax: (314)977-7136
E-mail: admission@slu.edu
Web Site: www.slu.edu
President/CEO: Fred P. Pestello, PhD
Admissions: Jean M. Gilman
Financial Aid: Cari S. Wickliffe
Type: University **Sex:** Coed **Affiliation:** Roman Catholic (Jesuit). **Scores:** 98% SAT V 400+; 100% SAT M 400+; 12.6% ACT 18-23; 51.4% ACT 24-29 **% Accepted:** 63 **Admission Plans:** Deferred Admission **Application Deadline:** August 20 **Application Fee:** $0.00 **H.S. Requirements:** High school diploma required; GED accepted **Costs Per Year:** Application fee: $0. Comprehensive fee: $49,866 includes full-time tuition ($38,700), mandatory fees ($526), and college room and board ($10,640). College room only: $5816. Full-time tuition and fees vary according to course level, course load, degree level, location, program, and reciprocity agreements. Room and board charges vary according to board plan, housing facility, and location. Part-time tuition: $1350 per credit hour. Part-time mandatory fees: $153 per term. Part-time tuition and fees vary according to course level, course load, degree level, location, program, and reciprocity agreements. **Scholarships:** Available. **Calendar System:** Semester, Summer session available **Enroll-

ment: Full-time 7,488, Graduate full-time 4,051, Graduate part-time 615, Part-time 760 **Faculty:** Full-time 749, Part-time 420 **Student-Faculty Ratio:** 11:1 **Exams:** SAT I or ACT; SAT Reasoning. **% Receiving Financial Aid:** 57 **% Residing in College-Owned, -Operated, or -Affiliated Housing:** 51 **Regional Accreditation:** North Central Association of Colleges and Schools **Credit Hours For Degree:** 120 credit hours, Bachelors **ROTC:** Air Force, Army **Professional Accreditation:** AABI, AACN, AACSB, AALS, AAMFT, ABA, ABET, ACEN, ACIPE, AHIMA, AND, AOTA, APA, APTA, ASHA, CAHME, CEPH, CSWE, JRCNMT, LCME/AMA, NAACLS, NASPAA, NCATE. **Intercollegiate Athletics:** Badminton M & W; Baseball M; Basketball M & W; Bowling M & W; Crew M & W; Cross-Country Running M & W; Equestrian Sports M & W; Fencing M & W; Field Hockey W; Golf M & W; Ice Hockey M; Lacrosse M & W; Racquetball M & W; Rugby M; Soccer M & W; Softball W; Swimming and Diving M & W; Table Tennis M & W; Tennis M & W; Track and Field M & W; Ultimate Frisbee M & W; Volleyball M & W; Water Polo M & W

SAINT LUKE'S COLLEGE OF HEALTH SCIENCES

8320 Ward Pky., Ste. 300
Kansas City, MO 64114
Tel: (816)932-6700
Web Site: www.saintlukescollege.edu
President/CEO: Dr. Dean Hubbard
Admissions: Jennifer Wright
Financial Aid: Jennifer Wright
Type: Two-Year Upper Division **Sex:** Coed **Affiliation:** Episcopal; Saint Luke's Hospital. **Admission Plans:** Early Admission **Application Fee:** $35.00 **H.S. Requirements:** High school diploma required; GED accepted **Scholarships:** Available. **Calendar System:** Semester, Summer session available **Enrollment:** Full-time 101, Part-time 12 **Faculty:** Full-time 15 **Student-Faculty Ratio:** 8:1 **% Receiving Financial Aid:** 72 **Regional Accreditation:** North Central Association of Colleges and Schools **Credit Hours For Degree:** 124 credit hours, Bachelors **Professional Accreditation:** AACN. **Intercollegiate Athletics:** Ultimate Frisbee M & W; Volleyball M & W

SOUTHEAST MISSOURI HOSPITAL COLLEGE OF NURSING AND HEALTH SCIENCES

2001 William St.
Cape Girardeau, MO 63701
Tel: (573)334-6825
Fax: (573)339-7805
E-mail: tbuttry@sehosp.org
Web Site: www.sehcollege.edu
President/CEO: Dr. Tonya Buttry
Admissions: Dr. Tonya L. Buttry
Type: Two-Year College **Sex:** Coed **Scores:** 73% ACT 18-23; 24% ACT 24-29 **% Accepted:** 80 **Application Deadline:** Rolling **Application Fee:** $50.00 **H.S. Requirements:** High school diploma required; GED accepted **Calendar System:** Miscellaneous **Enrollment:** Full-time 25, Part-time 171 **Faculty:** Full-time 22, Part-time 9 **Student-Faculty Ratio:** 5:1 **Exams:** ACT essay component not used; Other; SAT I or ACT; SAT essay component not used. **Final Year or Final Semester Residency Requirement:** No **Regional Accreditation:** North Central Association of Colleges and Schools **Credit Hours For Degree:** 69 credits (Radiological Technology), 72 credits (Nursing), Associates **Professional Accreditation:** ACEN.

SOUTHEAST MISSOURI STATE UNIVERSITY

One University Plz.
Cape Girardeau, MO 63701-4799
Tel: (573)651-2000
E-mail: lhahn@semo.edu
Web Site: www.semo.edu
President/CEO: Dr. Carlos Vargas
Admissions: Deborah Below
Financial Aid: Karen Walker
Type: Comprehensive **Sex:** Coed **Affiliation:** Missouri Coordinating Board for Higher Education. **Scores:** 86% SAT V 400+; 86% SAT M 400+; 53.96% ACT 18-23; 33.61% ACT 24-29 **% Accepted:** 84 **Admission Plans:** Deferred Admission **Application Deadline:** July 1 **Application Fee:** $30.00 **H.S. Requirements:** High school diploma required; GED accepted **Costs Per Year:** Application fee: $30. State resident tuition: $5979 full-time, $199.30 per credit hour part-time. Nonresident tuition: $11,364 full-time, $378 per credit hour part-time. Mandatory fees: $1011 full-time, $33.70 per

credit hour part-time. Full-time tuition and fees vary according to course load and location. Part-time tuition and fees vary according to course load and location. College room and board: $8285. Room and board charges vary according to board plan and housing facility. **Scholarships:** Available. **Calendar System:** Semester, Summer session available **Enrollment:** Full-time 7,924, Graduate full-time 492, Graduate part-time 908, Part-time 2,663 **Faculty:** Full-time 407, Part-time 169 **Student-Faculty Ratio:** 21:1 **Exams:** ACT essay component not used; SAT I or ACT; SAT essay component not used. **% Receiving Financial Aid:** 61 **% Residing in College-Owned, -Operated, or -Affiliated Housing:** 31 **Final Year or Final Semester Residency Requirement:** Yes **Regional Accreditation:** North Central Association of Colleges and Schools **Credit Hours For Degree:** 60 credit hours, Associates; 120 credit hours, Bachelors **ROTC:** Air Force **Professional Accreditation:** AACN, AACSB, ABET, ACA, AND, ASHA, ATMAE, CSWE, JRCAT, NASM, NCATE, NRPA. **Intercollegiate Athletics:** Baseball M; Basketball M & W; Cheerleading M & W; Cross-Country Running M & W; Football M; Gymnastics W; Soccer W; Softball W; Tennis W; Track and Field M & W; Volleyball W

SOUTHWEST BAPTIST UNIVERSITY

1600 University Ave.
Bolivar, MO 65613-2597
Tel: (417)326-5281; Free: 800-526-5859
Fax: (417)328-1514
E-mail: dcrowder@sbuniv.edu
Web Site: www.sbuniv.edu
President/CEO: Dr. C. Pat Taylor
Admissions: Darren Crowder
Financial Aid: Brad Gamble
Type: Comprehensive **Sex:** Coed **Affiliation:** Southern Baptist. **Scores:** 48% ACT 18-23; 34% ACT 24-29 **% Accepted:** 62 **Application Deadline:** Rolling **Application Fee:** $30.00 **H.S. Requirements:** High school diploma required; GED accepted **Costs Per Year:** Application fee: $30. Comprehensive fee: $29,000 includes full-time tuition ($21,000), mandatory fees ($840), and college room and board ($7160). College room only: $3400. Full-time tuition and fees vary according to course load and location. Room and board charges vary according to board plan and housing facility. Part-time tuition: $815 per credit hour. Part-time mandatory fees: $145 per term. Part-time tuition and fees vary according to course load and location. **Scholarships:** Available. **Calendar System:** 4-1-4, Summer session available **Enrollment:** Full-time 1,934, Graduate full-time 275, Graduate part-time 459, Part-time 947 **Faculty:** Full-time 148, Part-time 153 **Student-Faculty Ratio:** 16:1 **Exams:** ACT essay component not used; SAT I or ACT; SAT essay component not used; SAT Reasoning; SAT Subject. **% Receiving Financial Aid:** 79 **% Residing in College-Owned, -Operated, or -Affiliated Housing:** 63 **Final Year or Final Semester Residency Requirement:** No **Regional Accreditation:** North Central Association of Colleges and Schools **Credit Hours For Degree:** 64 credit hours, Associates; 128 credit hours, Bachelors **ROTC:** Army **Professional Accreditation:** ACBSP, ACEN, APTA, NASM. **Intercollegiate Athletics:** Baseball M; Basketball M & W; Cheerleading M & W; Cross-Country Running M & W; Football M; Golf M; Soccer M & W; Softball W; Tennis M & W; Track and Field M & W; Volleyball W

STATE FAIR COMMUNITY COLLEGE

3201 W 16th St.
Sedalia, MO 65301-2199
Tel: (660)530-5800; Free: 877-311-7322
Fax: (660)530-5820
E-mail: astoecklein1@sfccmo.edu
Web Site: www.sfccmo.edu
President/CEO: Dr. Joanna Anderson
Admissions: Amanda L. Stoecklein
Financial Aid: Sharon Kavanaugh
Type: Two-Year College **Sex:** Coed **Affiliation:** Missouri Coordinating Board for Higher Education. **Admission Plans:** Open Admission **Application Deadline:** Rolling **H.S. Requirements:** High school diploma required; GED accepted **Costs Per Year:** Area resident tuition: $3000 full-time, $100 per credit hour part-time. State resident tuition: $4200 full-time, $140 per credit hour part-time. Nonresident tuition: $6000 full-time, $200 per credit hour part-time. Mandatory fees: $300 full-time, $10 per credit hour part-time. College room and board: $6250. Room and board charges vary according to location. **Scholarships:** Available. **Calendar System:** Semester, Summer session available **Enrollment:** Full-time 2,506, Part-time 2,477 **Faculty:**

Full-time 79, Part-time 308 **Student-Faculty Ratio:** 32:1 **Final Year or Final Semester Residency Requirement:** No **Regional Accreditation:** North Central Association of Colleges and Schools **Credit Hours For Degree:** 64 semester hours, Associates **Professional Accreditation:** ADA, ATMAE. **Intercollegiate Athletics:** Basketball M & W.

STATE TECHNICAL COLLEGE OF MISSOURI
One Technology Dr.
Linn, MO 65051-9606
Tel: (573)897-5000; Free: 800-743-TECH
E-mail: kathy.scheulen@linnstate.edu
Web Site: www.statetechmo.edu
President/CEO: Dr. Donald Claycomb
Admissions: Kathy Scheulen

Type: Two-Year College **Sex:** Coed **% Accepted:** 63 **Application Deadline:** Rolling **Application Fee:** $0.00 **H.S. Requirements:** High school diploma required; GED accepted **Scholarships:** Available. **Calendar System:** Semester, Summer session available **Enrollment:** Full-time 1,001, Part-time 167 **Faculty:** Full-time 84, Part-time 12 **Student-Faculty Ratio:** 12:1 **Exams:** ACT; ACT essay component not used; Other; SAT essay component not used. **% Residing in College-Owned, -Operated, or -Affiliated Housing:** 15 **Final Year or Final Semester Residency Requirement:** No **Regional Accreditation:** North Central Association of Colleges and Schools **Credit Hours For Degree:** 61 credit hours, Associates **ROTC:** Army **Professional Accreditation:** ABET, ATMAE.

STEPHENS COLLEGE
1200 E Broadway
Columbia, MO 65215-0002
Tel: (573)442-2211; Free: 800-876-7207
Fax: (573)876-7237
E-mail: apply@stephens.edu
Web Site: www.stephens.edu
President/CEO: Dr. Dianne Lynch
Admissions: Tiffany Goalder
Financial Aid: Kim Stonecipher-Fisher

Type: Comprehensive **Scores:** 17% ACT 18-23; 83% ACT 24-29 **% Accepted:** 54 **Admission Plans:** Deferred Admission **Application Fee:** $25.00 **H.S. Requirements:** High school diploma required; GED accepted **Costs Per Year:** Application fee: $25. Comprehensive fee: $38,994 includes full-time tuition ($28,976), mandatory fees ($200), and college room and board ($9818). College room only: $6246. Full-time tuition and fees vary according to course load, degree level, program, and reciprocity agreements. Room and board charges vary according to board plan and housing facility. **Scholarships:** Available. **Calendar System:** Semester, Summer session available **Enrollment:** Full-time 595, Graduate full-time 148, Graduate part-time 37, Part-time 111 **Faculty:** Full-time 54, Part-time 63 **Student-Faculty Ratio:** 8:1 **Exams:** ACT essay component not used; SAT I or ACT; SAT essay component not used; SAT Reasoning; SAT Subject. **% Receiving Financial Aid:** 78 **% Residing in College-Owned, -Operated, or -Affiliated Housing:** 71 **Final Year or Final Semester Residency Requirement:** No **Regional Accreditation:** North Central Association of Colleges and Schools **Credit Hours For Degree:** 60 credits, Associates; 120 credits, Bachelors **ROTC:** Air Force, Army, Navy **Professional Accreditation:** AHIMA. **Intercollegiate Athletics:** Basketball W; Cross-Country Running W; Golf W; Soccer W; Softball W; Tennis W; Volleyball W

STEVENS–THE INSTITUTE OF BUSINESS & ARTS
1521 Washington Ave.
Saint Louis, MO 63102
Tel: (314)421-0949; Free: 800-871-0949
Fax: (314)421-0304
E-mail: admission@siba.edu
Web Site: www.siba.edu
President/CEO: Cynthia Musterman, JD
Admissions: John Willmon

Type: Four-Year College **Sex:** Coed **% Accepted:** 71 **Application Deadline:** Rolling **Application Fee:** $25.00 **H.S. Requirements:** High school diploma required; GED accepted **Scholarships:** Available. **Calendar System:** Quarter, Summer session available **Enrollment:** Full-time 144, Part-time 40 **Faculty:** Full-time 7, Part-time 15 **Student-Faculty Ratio:** 10:1 **Exams:** SAT I or ACT. **Final Year or Final Semester Residency Requirement:** No **Credit Hours For Degree:** 114 quarter hours, Associates; 197 quarter hours, Bachelors **Professional Accreditation:** ACICS.

TEXAS COUNTY TECHNICAL COLLEGE
6915 S Hwy. 63
Houston, MO 65483
Tel: (417)967-5466
Web Site: www.texascountytech.edu
Type: Two-Year College **Sex:** Coed **Professional Accreditation:** ACICS.

THREE RIVERS COMMUNITY COLLEGE
2080 Three Rivers Blvd.
Poplar Bluff, MO 63901-2393
Tel: (573)840-9600; Free: 877-TRY-TRCC
E-mail: trytrcc@trcc.edu
Web Site: www.trcc.edu
President/CEO: Joseph T. Rozman, Jr.
Admissions: Marcia Fields

Type: Two-Year College **Sex:** Coed **Affiliation:** Missouri Coordinating Board for Higher Education. **% Accepted:** 100 **Admission Plans:** Early Admission; Open Admission **Application Fee:** $20.00 **H.S. Requirements:** High school diploma required; GED accepted **Scholarships:** Available. **Calendar System:** Semester, Summer session available **Enrollment:** Full-time 1,942, Part-time 1,243 **Faculty:** Full-time 60, Part-time 129 **Student-Faculty Ratio:** 23:1 **% Residing in College-Owned, -Operated, or -Affiliated Housing:** 5 **Regional Accreditation:** North Central Association of Colleges and Schools **Credit Hours For Degree:** 64 credits, Associates **Professional Accreditation:** ACBSP, ACEN, NAACLS. **Intercollegiate Athletics:** Baseball M; Basketball M & W; Cheerleading M & W; Softball W

TRUMAN STATE UNIVERSITY
100 E Normal Ave.
Kirksville, MO 63501-4221
Tel: (660)785-4000; Free: 800-892-7792
Fax: (660)785-7456
E-mail: mchamber@truman.edu
Web Site: www.truman.edu
President/CEO: Dr. Troy Paino
Admissions: Melody Chambers
Financial Aid: Kathy Elsea

Type: Comprehensive **Sex:** Coed **Scores:** 100% SAT V 400+; 98% SAT M 400+; 17.7% ACT 18-23; 54.2% ACT 24-29 **% Accepted:** 79 **Admission Plans:** Deferred Admission **Application Deadline:** Rolling **Application Fee:** $0.00 **H.S. Requirements:** High school diploma required; GED accepted **Costs Per Year:** Application fee: $0. One-time mandatory fee: $315. State resident tuition: $7152 full-time, $298 per credit hour part-time. Nonresident tuition: $13,376 full-time, $557 per credit hour part-time. Mandatory fees: $304 full-time, $304 per year part-time. Full-time tuition and fees vary according to course load, degree level, and program. Part-time tuition and fees vary according to course load, degree level, and program. College room and board: $8480. College room only: $5730. Room and board charges vary according to housing facility. **Scholarships:** Available. **Calendar System:** Semester, Summer session available **Enrollment:** Full-time 5,207, Graduate full-time 263, Graduate part-time 92, Part-time 646 **Faculty:** Full-time 329, Part-time 68 **Student-Faculty Ratio:** 16:1 **Exams:** ACT essay component not used; SAT I or ACT; SAT essay component not used. **% Receiving Financial Aid:** 53 **% Residing in College-Owned, -Operated, or -Affiliated Housing:** 48 **Final Year or Final Semester Residency Requirement:** Yes **Regional Accreditation:** North Central Association of Colleges and Schools **Credit Hours For Degree:** 124 credits, Bachelors **ROTC:** Army **Professional Accreditation:** AACN, AACSB, ACA, ASHA, JRCAT, NASM, NCATE. **Intercollegiate Athletics:** Baseball M; Basketball M & W; Bowling M & W; Cheerleading M & W; Cross-Country Running M & W; Equestrian Sports M & W; Football M; Golf W; Lacrosse W; Riflery M & W; Rock Climbing M & W; Rugby M & W; Soccer M & W; Softball W; Swimming and Diving M & W; Tennis M & W; Track and Field M & W; Ultimate Frisbee M & W; Volleyball M & W; Weight Lifting M & W; Wrestling M

UNIVERSITY OF CENTRAL MISSOURI
Warrensburg, MO 64093
Tel: (660)543-4111; Free: 800-729-8266
Fax: (660)543-8517
E-mail: admit@ucmo.edu
Web Site: www.ucmo.edu
President/CEO: Dr. Charles M. Ambrose
Admissions: Ann Nordyke
Financial Aid: Angela Karlin

Type: Comprehensive **Sex:** Coed **Scores:** 61.5% ACT 18-23; 26.24% ACT 24-29 **% Accepted:** 79 **Admission Plans:** Deferred Admission **Application Deadline:** Rolling **Application Fee:** $30.00 **H.S. Requirements:** High school diploma required; GED accepted **Costs Per Year:** Application fee: $30. State resident tuition: $6,446 full-time, $214.85 per credit hour part-time. Nonresident tuition: $12,891 full-time, $429.70 per credit hour part-time. Mandatory fees: $876 full-time, $29.20 per credit hour part-time. Full-time tuition and fees vary according to course load and location. Part-time tuition and fees vary according to location. College room and board: $8102. College room only: $5186. Room and board charges vary according to board plan, housing facility, and student level. **Scholarships:** Available. **Calendar System:** Semester, Summer session available **Enrollment:** Full-time 8,120, Graduate full-time 2,176, Graduate part-time 2,218, Part-time 1,881 **Faculty:** Full-time 513, Part-time 201 **Student-Faculty Ratio:** 20:1 **Exams:** ACT essay component not used; SAT I or ACT; SAT essay component not used. **% Receiving Financial Aid:** 61 **% Residing in College-Owned, -Operated, or -Affiliated Housing:** 34 **Final Year or Final Semester Residency Requirement:** No **Regional Accreditation:** North Central Association of Colleges and Schools **Credit Hours For Degree:** 124 credit hours, Bachelors **ROTC:** Air Force, Army **Professional Accreditation:** AABI, AACN, AACSB, AAFCS, ABET, ACCE, ASHA, ATMAE, CSWE, NASAD, NASM, NCATE. **Intercollegiate Athletics:** Baseball M; Basketball M & W; Bowling M & W; Cross-Country Running M & W; Football M; Golf M; Rock Climbing M & W; Soccer M & W; Softball W; Track and Field M & W; Volleyball W; Wrestling M

UNIVERSITY OF MISSOURI

Columbia, MO 65211
Tel: (573)882-2121
Fax: (573)882-7887
E-mail: mu4u@missouri.edu
Web Site: www.missouri.edu
President/CEO: Henry C. Foley
Admissions: Charles May
Financial Aid: Nicholas Prewett

Type: University **Sex:** Coed **Affiliation:** University of Missouri System. **Scores:** 95% SAT V 400+; 99% SAT M 400+; 27.15% ACT 18-23; 53.86% ACT 24-29 **% Accepted:** 78 **Admission Plans:** Deferred Admission **Application Deadline:** Rolling **Application Fee:** $55.00 **H.S. Requirements:** High school diploma required; GED accepted **Costs Per Year:** Application fee: $55. State resident tuition: $8286 full-time. Nonresident tuition: $23,943 full-time. Mandatory fees: $1223 full-time. Full-time tuition and fees according to course load, program, and reciprocity agreements. College room and board: $9808. College room only: $6856. Room and board charges vary according to board plan and housing facility. **Scholarships:** Available. **Calendar System:** Semester, Summer session available **Enrollment:** Full-time 26,027, Graduate full-time 4,964, Graduate part-time 2,672, Part-time 1,785 **Faculty:** Full-time 1,270, Part-time 107 **Student-Faculty Ratio:** 20:1 **Exams:** ACT; SAT I or ACT; SAT Reasoning; SAT Subject. **% Receiving Financial Aid:** 46 **% Residing in College-Owned, -Operated, or -Affiliated Housing:** 25 **Final Year or Final Semester Residency Requirement:** No **Regional Accreditation:** North Central Association of Colleges and Schools **Credit Hours For Degree:** 120 credits, Bachelors **ROTC:** Air Force, Army, Navy **Professional Accreditation:** AACN, AACSB, AAFCS, AALS, ABA, ABET, ACEJMC, ALA, AND, AOTA, APA, APTA, ASHA, AVMA, CAHME, CIDA, CORE, CSWE, CoARC, JRCERT, JRCNMT, LCME/AMA, NASM, NASPAA, NRPA, SAF, TEAC. **Intercollegiate Athletics:** Baseball M; Basketball M & W; Cheerleading M & W; Cross-Country Running M & W; Football M; Golf M & W; Gymnastics W; Soccer W; Softball W; Swimming and Diving M & W; Tennis W; Track and Field M & W; Volleyball W; Wrestling M

UNIVERSITY OF MISSOURI–KANSAS CITY

5100 Rockhill Rd.
Kansas City, MO 64110-2499
Tel: (816)235-1000; Free: 800-775-8652
Fax: (816)235-1717
E-mail: admit@umkc.edu
Web Site: www.umkc.edu
President/CEO: Leo E. Morton
Admissions: Tamera Byland
Financial Aid: Scott Young

Type: University **Sex:** Coed **Affiliation:** University of Missouri System. **Scores:** 98% SAT M 400+; 39.43% ACT 18-23; 36.65% ACT 24-29 **% Ac-**

cepted: 63 **Admission Plans:** Deferred Admission **Application Deadline:** Rolling **Application Fee:** $45.00 **H.S. Requirements:** High school diploma required; GED accepted **Costs Per Year:** Application fee: $45. State resident tuition: $8103 full-time, $272 per credit hour part-time. Nonresident tuition: $21,162 full-time, $711 per credit hour part-time. Mandatory fees: $1479 full-time, $98.62 per credit hour part-time. Full-time tuition and fees vary according to course load and program. Part-time tuition and fees vary according to course load and program. College room and board: $9815. College room only: $6769. Room and board charges vary according to board plan and housing facility. **Scholarships:** Available. **Calendar System:** Semester, Summer session available **Enrollment:** Full-time 6,636, Graduate full-time 3,381, Graduate part-time 2,065, Part-time 4,617 **Faculty:** Full-time 731, Part-time 441 **Student-Faculty Ratio:** 14:1 **Exams:** ACT essay component not used; SAT I or ACT; SAT essay component not used; SAT Reasoning. **% Receiving Financial Aid:** 64 **% Residing in College-Owned, -Operated, or -Affiliated Housing:** 25 **Final Year or Final Semester Residency Requirement:** Yes **Regional Accreditation:** North Central Association of Colleges and Schools **Credit Hours For Degree:** 120 credit hours, Bachelors **ROTC:** Air Force, Army **Professional Accreditation:** AACN, AACSB, AALS, AANA, ABA, ABET, ACPE, ADA, APA, CSWE, LCME/AMA, NASD, NASM, NASPAA, NAST, NCATE. **Intercollegiate Athletics:** Basketball M & W; Cross-Country Running M & W; Golf M & W; Soccer M & W; Softball W; Tennis M & W; Track and Field M & W; Volleyball W

UNIVERSITY OF MISSOURI–ST. LOUIS

One University Blvd.
Saint Louis, MO 63121
Tel: (314)516-5000; Free: 888-GO2-USML
Fax: (314)516-5310
E-mail: askdrew@umsl.edu
Web Site: www.umsl.edu
President/CEO: Dr. Thomas F. George
Admissions: Andrew L. Griffin
Financial Aid: Jason Bornhop

Type: University **Sex:** Coed **Affiliation:** University of Missouri System. **Scores:** 71% SAT V 400+; 100% SAT M 400+; 41% ACT 18-23; 46% ACT 24-29 **% Accepted:** 76 **Application Deadline:** Rolling **Application Fee:** $35.00 **H.S. Requirements:** High school diploma required; GED accepted **Costs Per Year:** Application fee: $35. State resident tuition: $10,065 full-time, $335.50 per credit hour part-time. Nonresident tuition: $25,512 full-time, $850.40 per credit hour part-time. Full-time tuition varies according to course level, course load, location, program, and reciprocity agreements. Part-time tuition varies according to course level, course load, location, program, and reciprocity agreements. College room and board: $9052. College room only: $5280. Room and board charges vary according to board plan and housing facility. **Scholarships:** Available. **Calendar System:** Semester, Summer session available **Enrollment:** Full-time 5,711, Graduate full-time 1,001, Graduate part-time 2,193, Part-time 7,858 **Faculty:** Full-time 467, Part-time 492 **Student-Faculty Ratio:** 17:1 **Exams:** SAT I or ACT; SAT Reasoning; SAT Subject. **% Receiving Financial Aid:** 70 **% Residing in College-Owned, -Operated, or -Affiliated Housing:** 9 **Final Year or Final Semester Residency Requirement:** Yes **Regional Accreditation:** North Central Association of Colleges and Schools **Credit Hours For Degree:** 120 credit hours, Bachelors **ROTC:** Air Force, Army **Professional Accreditation:** AACN, AACSB, ABET, ACA, AOA, APA, CSWE, NASM, NASPAA, NCATE. **Intercollegiate Athletics:** Baseball M; Basketball M & W; Cheerleading W; Golf M & W; Ice Hockey M; Soccer M & W; Softball W; Swimming and Diving M & W; Table Tennis M & W; Tennis M & W; Volleyball W

VATTEROTT COLLEGE (BERKELEY)

8580 Evans Ave.
Berkeley, MO 63134
Tel: (314)264-1000; Free: 888-553-6627
Web Site: www.vatterott.edu
President/CEO: Sean Haire
Admissions: Ann Farajallah

Type: Two-Year College **Sex:** Coed **H.S. Requirements:** High school diploma required; GED accepted **Scholarships:** Available. **Calendar System:** Continuous, Summer session not available **Credit Hours For Degree:** 72 credit hours, Associates **Professional Accreditation:** ACCSC.

VATTEROTT COLLEGE (JOPLIN)

809 Illinois Ave.
Joplin, MO 64801

Tel: (417)781-5633; Free: 800-934-6975
Fax: (417)781-6437
Web Site: www.vatterott.edu
Type: Two-Year College **Sex:** Coed **Calendar System:** Semester **Professional Accreditation:** ACCSC.

VATTEROTT COLLEGE (KANSAS CITY)

4131 N Corrington Ave.
Kansas City, MO 64117
Tel: (816)861-1000; Free: 888-553-6627
Fax: (816)861-1400
Web Site: www.vatterott.edu
President/CEO: Brian Schumann
Type: Two-Year College **Sex:** Coed **% Accepted:** 84 **Calendar System:** Semester **Professional Accreditation:** ACCSC.

VATTEROTT COLLEGE (SAINT CHARLES)

3550 W Clay St.
Saint Charles, MO 63301
Tel: (636)940-4100; Free: 888-553-6627
E-mail: ofallon@vatterott-college.edu
Web Site: www.vatterott.edu
President/CEO: Robert Donnell
Admissions: Gertrude Bogan-Jones
Type: Two-Year College **Sex:** Coed **Professional Accreditation:** ACCSC.

VATTEROTT COLLEGE (SAINT JOSEPH)

3709 Belt Hwy.
Saint Joseph, MO 64506
Tel: (816)364-5399; Free: 888-553-6627
Fax: (816)364-1593
Web Site: www.vatterott.edu
President/CEO: Brandon Deets
Type: Two-Year College **Sex:** Coed **Admission Plans:** Open Admission **Calendar System:** Semester **Student-Faculty Ratio:** 22:1 **Professional Accreditation:** ACCSC.

VATTEROTT COLLEGE (SPRINGFIELD)

3850 S Campbell Ave.
Springfield, MO 65807
Tel: (417)831-8116; Free: 888-553-6627
Fax: (417)831-5099
E-mail: springfield@vatterott-college.edu
Web Site: www.vatterott.edu
President/CEO: Pam Bell
Admissions: Scott Lester
Type: Two-Year College **Sex:** Coed **H.S. Requirements:** High school diploma required; GED accepted **Calendar System:** Quarter **Faculty:** Full-time 14, Part-time 9 **Student-Faculty Ratio:** 30:1 **Credit Hours For Degree:** 108 quarter credit hours, Associates **Professional Accreditation:** ACCSC.

VATTEROTT COLLEGE (SUNSET HILLS)

12900 Maurer Industrial Dr.
Sunset Hills, MO 63127
Tel: (314)843-4200; Free: 888-553-6627
Fax: (314)843-1709
Web Site: www.vatterott.edu
President/CEO: Brandon Ash
Type: Two-Year College **Sex:** Coed **Admission Plans:** Open Admission **Calendar System:** Semester **Student-Faculty Ratio:** 21:1 **Professional Accreditation:** ACCSC.

VET TECH INSTITUTE AT HICKEY COLLEGE

2780 N Lindbergh Blvd.
Saint Louis, MO 63114
Tel: (314)434-2212; Free: 888-884-1459
Web Site: stlouis.vettechinstitute.edu
Type: Two-Year College **Sex:** Coed **% Accepted:** 58 **Calendar System:** Semester **Professional Accreditation:** AVMA.

WASHINGTON UNIVERSITY IN ST. LOUIS

One Brookings Dr.
Saint Louis, MO 63130-4899

Tel: (314)935-5000; Free: 800-638-0700
Fax: (314)935-4290
E-mail: admissions@wustl.edu
Web Site: www.wustl.edu
President/CEO: Mark Wrighton
Admissions: Julie Shimabukuro
Financial Aid: Michael Runiewicz
Type: University **Sex:** Coed **Scores:** 100% SAT V 400+; 100% SAT M 400+; 5% ACT 24-29 **% Accepted:** 17 **Admission Plans:** Deferred Admission; Early Action; Early Admission **Application Deadline:** January 15 **Application Fee:** $75.00 **H.S. Requirements:** High school diploma required; GED accepted **Costs Per Year:** Application fee: $75. Comprehensive fee: $65,366 includes full-time tuition ($48,950), mandatory fees ($820), and college room and board ($15,596). College room only: $10,670. Room and board charges vary according to board plan and housing facility. **Scholarships:** Available. **Calendar System:** Semester, Summer session available **Enrollment:** Full-time 6,819, Graduate full-time 5,845, Graduate part-time 1,339, Part-time 685 **Faculty:** Full-time 915, Part-time 362 **Student-Faculty Ratio:** 8:1 **Exams:** ACT essay component used for admission; SAT I or ACT; SAT essay component used for admission; SAT Reasoning; SAT Subject. **% Receiving Financial Aid:** 42 **% Residing in College-Owned, -Operated, or -Affiliated Housing:** 78 **Regional Accreditation:** North Central Association of Colleges and Schools **Credit Hours For Degree:** 120 semester hours, Bachelors **ROTC:** Air Force, Army **Professional Accreditation:** AACSB, AALS, ABA, ABET, ACIPE, AOTA, APA, APTA, ASHA, CAHME, CSWE, LCME/AMA, NAAB, NASAD, NCATE. **Intercollegiate Athletics:** Baseball M; Basketball M & W; Crew M & W; Cross-Country Running M & W; Equestrian Sports M & W; Fencing M & W; Field Hockey W; Football M; Golf M & W; Gymnastics M & W; Ice Hockey M; Lacrosse M & W; Rugby M & W; Sailing M & W; Soccer M & W; Softball W; Swimming and Diving M & W; Table Tennis M & W; Tennis M & W; Track and Field M & W; Ultimate Frisbee M & W; Volleyball M & W; Water Polo M & W; Wrestling M

WEBSTER UNIVERSITY

470 E Lockwood Ave.
Saint Louis, MO 63119-3194
Tel: (314)968-6900; Free: 800-753-6765
Fax: (314)968-7115
E-mail: johnmassena24@webster.edu
Web Site: www.webster.edu
President/CEO: Dr. Elizabeth (Beth) J. Stroble
Admissions: John Massena
Type: Comprehensive **Sex:** Coed **Scores:** 41% ACT 18-23; 44% ACT 24-29 **% Accepted:** 56 **Admission Plans:** Deferred Admission; Early Admission **Application Deadline:** August 1 **Application Fee:** $35.00 **H.S. Requirements:** High school diploma required; GED accepted **Costs Per Year:** Application fee: $35. One-time mandatory fee: $125. Comprehensive fee: $36,360 includes full-time tuition ($25,300), mandatory fees ($200), and college room and board ($10,860). College room only: $5870. Full-time tuition and fees vary according to program. Room and board charges vary according to board plan and housing facility. Part-time tuition: $650 per credit hour. **Scholarships:** Available. **Calendar System:** Semester, Summer session available **Enrollment:** Full-time 2,318, Graduate full-time 478, Graduate part-time 1,230, Part-time 448 **Faculty:** Full-time 200, Part-time 407 **Student-Faculty Ratio:** 9:1 **Exams:** SAT I or ACT; SAT Reasoning; SAT Subject. **% Receiving Financial Aid:** 79 **% Residing in College-Owned, -Operated, or -Affiliated Housing:** 31 **Final Year or Final Semester Residency Requirement:** No **Regional Accreditation:** North Central Association of Colleges and Schools **Credit Hours For Degree:** 128 credit hours, Bachelors **ROTC:** Air Force, Army **Professional Accreditation:** AANA, ACBSP, ACEN, NASM, NCATE. **Intercollegiate Athletics:** Baseball M; Basketball M & W; Cross-Country Running M & W; Golf M; Soccer M & W; Softball W; Tennis M & W; Track and Field M & W; Volleyball W

WELLSPRING SCHOOL OF ALLIED HEALTH

9140 Ward Pky.
Ste. 100
Kansas City, MO 64114
Tel: (816)523-9140
Web Site: www.wellspring.edu
Type: Two-Year College **Sex:** Coed **Professional Accreditation:** ABHES.

WENTWORTH MILITARY ACADEMY AND COLLEGE

1880 Washington Ave.
Lexington, MO 64067

Tel: (660)259-2221
Fax: (660)259-2677
E-mail: admissions@wma.edu
Web Site: www.wma.edu
President/CEO: Col. William Sellers
Admissions: Capt. Mike Bellis
Financial Aid: Cindy Dawn Howard

Type: Two-Year College **Sex:** Coed **Scores:** 80% SAT V 400+; 93% SAT M 400+ **% Accepted:** 100 **Application Deadline:** Rolling **Application Fee:** $100.00 **H.S. Requirements:** High school diploma required; GED accepted **Scholarships:** Available. **Calendar System:** Semester, Summer session available **Enrollment:** Full-time 84, Part-time 857 **Faculty:** Full-time 19, Part-time 44 **Student-Faculty Ratio:** 10:1 **Exams:** ACT essay component not used; SAT I or ACT; SAT essay component not used; SAT Reasoning. **Final Year or Final Semester Residency Requirement:** No **Regional Accreditation:** North Central Association of Colleges and Schools **Credit Hours For Degree:** 64 semester hours, Associates **ROTC:** Army **Intercollegiate Athletics:** Basketball M; Cross-Country Running M & W; Soccer M; Track and Field M & W; Volleyball W; Wrestling M

WESTMINSTER COLLEGE

501 Westminster Ave.
Fulton, MO 65251-1299
Tel: (573)642-3361; Free: 800-475-3361
Fax: (573)592-5227
E-mail: admissions@westminster-mo.edu
Web Site: www.westminster-mo.edu
President/CEO: Dr. Benjamin O. Akande
Admissions: Robert Andrews
Financial Aid: Aimee Bristow

Type: Four-Year College **Sex:** Coed **Affiliation:** Presbyterian Church. **Scores:** 93% SAT V 400+; 100% SAT M 400+; 39% ACT 18-23; 41% ACT 24-29 **% Accepted:** 64 **Admission Plans:** Deferred Admission; Early Admission **Application Fee:** $0.00 **H.S. Requirements:** High school diploma required; GED accepted **Costs Per Year:** Application fee: $0. Comprehensive fee: $34,020 includes full-time tuition ($23,200), mandatory fees ($1340), and college room and board ($9480). College room only: $5120. Full-time tuition and fees vary according to reciprocity agreements. Room and board charges vary according to board plan and housing facility. Part-time tuition: $800 per credit hour. **Scholarships:** Available. **Calendar System:** Semester, Summer session available **Enrollment:** Full-time 919, Part-time 21 **Faculty:** Full-time 61, Part-time 35 **Student-Faculty Ratio:** 14:1 **Exams:** SAT I or ACT. **% Receiving Financial Aid:** 64 **% Residing in College-Owned, -Operated, or -Affiliated Housing:** 82 **Regional Accreditation:** North Central Association of Colleges and Schools **Credit Hours For Degree:** 122 credit hours, Bachelors **ROTC:** Air Force, Army **Intercollegiate Athletics:** Baseball M; Basketball M & W; Cross-Country Running M & W; Football M; Golf M & W; Soccer M & W; Softball M & W; Tennis M & W; Track and Field M & W; Volleyball W

WILLIAM JEWELL COLLEGE

500 College Hill
Liberty, MO 64068-1843
Tel: (816)781-7700; Free: 888-2JEWELL
Fax: (816)415-5027
E-mail: scheerc@william.jewell.edu
Web Site: www.jewell.edu
President/CEO: Dr. Elizabeth MacLeod Walls
Admissions: Cory Scheer

Financial Aid: Daniel Holt

Type: Comprehensive **Sex:** Coed **Scores:** 94% SAT V 400+; 100% SAT M 400+; 30% ACT 18-23; 52% ACT 24-29 **% Accepted:** 49 **Admission Plans:** Deferred Admission **Application Deadline:** August 15 **Application Fee:** $0.00 **H.S. Requirements:** High school diploma required; GED accepted **Costs Per Year:** Application fee: $0. Comprehensive fee: $42,210 includes full-time tuition ($32,210), mandatory fees ($720), and college room and board ($9280). Full-time tuition and fees vary according to program. Room and board charges vary according to board plan and housing facility. Part-time tuition: $945 per credit. **Scholarships:** Available. **Calendar System:** Semester, Summer session available **Enrollment:** Full-time 1,026, Graduate full-time 1, Graduate part-time 9, Part-time 27 **Faculty:** Full-time 80, Part-time 63 **Student-Faculty Ratio:** 10:1 **Exams:** ACT essay component used as validity check; ACT essay component used for advising; SAT I or ACT; SAT essay component used as validity check; SAT essay component used for advising; SAT Reasoning; SAT Subject. **% Receiving Financial Aid:** 72 **% Residing in College-Owned, -Operated, or -Affiliated Housing:** 84 **Final Year or Final Semester Residency Requirement:** Yes **Regional Accreditation:** North Central Association of Colleges and Schools **Credit Hours For Degree:** 124 semester hours, Bachelors **ROTC:** Army **Professional Accreditation:** AACN, NASM. **Intercollegiate Athletics:** Baseball M; Basketball M & W; Cheerleading M & W; Cross-Country Running M & W; Football M; Golf M & W; Soccer M & W; Softball W; Swimming and Diving M & W; Tennis M & W; Track and Field M & W; Volleyball W

WILLIAM WOODS UNIVERSITY

One University Ave.
Fulton, MO 65251-1098
Tel: (573)642-2251; Free: 800-995-3159
Fax: (573)592-1146
E-mail: kerry.collins@williamwoods.edu
Web Site: www.williamwoods.edu
President/CEO: Dr. Jahnae Barnett
Admissions: Kerry Collins
Financial Aid: Deana Ready

Type: Comprehensive **Sex:** Coed **Affiliation:** Christian Church (Disciples of Christ). **Scores:** 89% SAT V 400+; 95% SAT M 400+; 53% ACT 18-23; 30% ACT 24-29 **% Accepted:** 73 **Admission Plans:** Deferred Admission **Application Deadline:** August 15 **Application Fee:** $0.00 **H.S. Requirements:** High school diploma required; GED accepted **Costs Per Year:** Application fee: $0. Comprehensive fee: $31,120 includes full-time tuition ($21,370), mandatory fees ($790), and college room and board ($8960). College room only: $4600. Full-time tuition and fees vary according to degree level and program. Room and board charges vary according to board plan and housing facility. Part-time tuition: $325 per credit hour. Part-time mandatory fees: $35 per term. Part-time tuition and fees vary according to course load, degree level, and program. **Scholarships:** Available. **Calendar System:** Semester, Summer session available **Enrollment:** Full-time 843, Graduate full-time 57, Graduate part-time 1,114, Part-time 157 **Faculty:** Full-time 70, Part-time 187 **Student-Faculty Ratio:** 11:1 **Exams:** ACT essay component used for advising; SAT I or ACT; SAT essay component used for advising; SAT Reasoning; SAT Subject. **% Receiving Financial Aid:** 72 **% Residing in College-Owned, -Operated, or -Affiliated Housing:** 63 **Final Year or Final Semester Residency Requirement:** Yes **Regional Accreditation:** North Central Association of Colleges and Schools **Credit Hours For Degree:** 60 credits, Associates; 120 credits, Bachelors **ROTC:** Air Force, Army, Navy **Professional Accreditation:** CSWE. **Intercollegiate Athletics:** Baseball M; Basketball M & W; Cheerleading W; Cross-Country Running M & W; Golf M & W; Soccer M & W; Softball W; Track and Field M & W; Volleyball W

AANIIIH NAKODA COLLEGE

PO Box 159
Harlem, MT 59526-0159
Tel: (406)353-2607
Fax: (406)353-2898
E-mail: dbrockie@mail.fbcc.edu
Web Site: www.ancollege.edu
President/CEO: Carole Falcon-Chandler
Admissions: Dixie Brockie

Type: Two-Year College **Sex:** Coed **Admission Plans:** Deferred Admission; Early Admission; Open Admission **Application Deadline:** Rolling **Application Fee:** $10.00 **H.S. Requirements:** High school diploma required; GED accepted **Costs Per Year:** Application fee: $10. State resident tuition: $1740 full-time, $70 per credit part-time. Mandatory fees: $335 full-time. Part-time tuition varies according to course load. **Scholarships:** Available. **Calendar System:** Quarter, Summer session not available **Student-Faculty Ratio:** 11:1 **Credit Hours For Degree:** 92 credits, Associates **Professional Accreditation:** NCCU.

BLACKFEET COMMUNITY COLLEGE

PO Box 819
Browning, MT 59417-0819
Tel: (406)338-5441; Free: 800-549-7457
Fax: (406)338-3272
Web Site: www.bfcc.edu
President/CEO: Dr. Billie Jo Kipp
Admissions: Deana M. McNabb
Financial Aid: Margaret Ellen Bird

Type: Two-Year College **Sex:** Coed **Admission Plans:** Early Admission; Open Admission **Application Deadline:** August 29 **Application Fee:** $15.00 **H.S. Requirements:** High school diploma required; GED accepted **Scholarships:** Available. **Calendar System:** Semester, Summer session not available **Credit Hours For Degree:** 60 credit hours, Associates **Professional Accreditation:** NCCU.

CARROLL COLLEGE

1601 N Benton Ave.
Helena, MT 59625-0002
Tel: (406)447-4300; Free: 800-992-3648
Fax: (406)447-4533
E-mail: admission@carroll.edu
Web Site: www.carroll.edu
President/CEO: Dr. Thomas Evans
Financial Aid: Janet Riis

Type: Four-Year College **Sex:** Coed **Affiliation:** Roman Catholic. **Scores:** 97% SAT V 400+; 97% SAT M 400+; 33.73% ACT 18-23; 51.19% ACT 24-29 **% Accepted:** 58 **Admission Plans:** Deferred Admission **Application Deadline:** February 15 **Application Fee:** $35.00 **H.S. Requirements:** High school diploma required; GED accepted **Costs Per Year:** Application fee: $35. Comprehensive fee: $39,972 includes full-time tuition ($30,104), mandatory fees ($650), and college room and board ($9218). Full-time tuition and fees vary according to program. Room and board charges vary according to board plan. Part-time tuition: $1254 per credit hour. Part-time tuition varies according to program. **Scholarships:** Available. **Calendar System:** Semester, Summer session available **Enrollment:** Full-time 1,386,

Part-time 44 **Faculty:** Full-time 89, Part-time 76 **Student-Faculty Ratio:** 12:1 **Exams:** ACT essay component used for admission; ACT essay component used for advising; ACT essay component used for placement; SAT I or ACT; SAT II; SAT essay component used for admission; SAT essay component used for advising; SAT essay component used for placement; SAT Reasoning; SAT Subject. **% Receiving Financial Aid:** 66 **% Residing in College-Owned, -Operated, or -Affiliated Housing:** 57 **Credit Hours For Degree:** 60 semester hours, Associates; 122 semester hours, Bachelors **ROTC:** Army **Professional Accreditation:** AACN, ABET, NCCU. **Intercollegiate Athletics:** Basketball M & W; Cheerleading M & W; Cross-Country Running M & W; Football M; Golf M & W; Soccer M & W; Softball W; Track and Field M & W; Volleyball W

CHIEF DULL KNIFE COLLEGE

1 College Dr.
Lame Deer, MT 59043-0098
Tel: (406)477-6215
Fax: (406)477-6219
Web Site: www.cdkc.edu
President/CEO: Dr. Richard Littlebear

Type: Two-Year College **Sex:** Coed **Admission Plans:** Early Admission; Open Admission **Application Deadline:** Rolling **Application Fee:** $0.00 **H.S. Requirements:** High school diploma required; GED accepted **Scholarships:** Available. **Calendar System:** Semester, Summer session available **Student-Faculty Ratio:** 13:1 **Credit Hours For Degree:** 60 credit hours, Associates **Professional Accreditation:** NCCU.

DAWSON COMMUNITY COLLEGE

300 College Dr.
Glendive, MT 59330-0421
Tel: (406)377-3396; Free: 800-821-8320
Fax: (406)377-8132
E-mail: dpeterson@dawson.edu
Web Site: www.dawson.edu
President/CEO: Dr. J. Vincent Nix
Admissions: Daneen Peterson
Financial Aid: Rory Seeger

Type: Two-Year College **Sex:** Coed **% Accepted:** 100 **Admission Plans:** Deferred Admission; Open Admission **Application Deadline:** Rolling **Application Fee:** $30.00 **H.S. Requirements:** High school diploma required; GED accepted **Costs Per Year:** Application fee: $30. Area resident tuition: $1950 full-time, $65 per credit hour part-time. State resident tuition: $3345 full-time, $111.50 per credit hour part-time. Nonresident tuition: $9195 full-time, $306.50 per credit hour part-time. Mandatory fees: $1620 full-time, $54 per credit hour part-time. College room and board: $5575. College room only: $2500. **Scholarships:** Available. **Calendar System:** Semester, Summer session available **Enrollment:** Full-time 162, Part-time 142 **Faculty:** Full-time 11, Part-time 22 **Student-Faculty Ratio:** 16:1 **Credit Hours For Degree:** 60 semester hours, Associates **Professional Accreditation:** NCCU. **Intercollegiate Athletics:** Baseball M; Basketball M & W; Equestrian Sports M & W; Softball W

FLATHEAD VALLEY COMMUNITY COLLEGE

777 Grandview Dr.
Kalispell, MT 59901-2622

Tel: (406)756-3822; Free: 800-313-3822
Fax: (406)756-3815
E-mail: mstoltz@fvcc.cc.mt.us
Web Site: www.fvcc.edu
President/CEO: Dr. Jane A. Karas
Admissions: Marlene C. Stoltz
Financial Aid: Cynthia Kiefer
Type: Two-Year College **Sex:** Coed **Affiliation:** Montana University System.
Admission Plans: Deferred Admission; Early Admission; Open Admission
Application Deadline: Rolling **Application Fee:** $0.00 **H.S. Requirements:**
High school diploma required; GED accepted **Scholarships:** Available.
Calendar System: Semester, Summer session available **Enrollment:** Full-
time 1,082, Part-time 1,134 **Faculty:** Full-time 54, Part-time 152 **Student-**
Faculty Ratio: 16:1 **Exams:** ACT. **% Residing in College-Owned,**
-Operated, or -Affiliated Housing: 1 **Final Year or Final Semester**
Residency Requirement: No **Credit Hours For Degree:** 60 semester
hours, Associates **Professional Accreditation:** AAMAE, NCCU.

FORT PECK COMMUNITY COLLEGE
PO Box 398
Poplar, MT 59255-0398
Tel: (406)768-5551
Web Site: www.fpcc.edu
President/CEO: Haven Gourneau
Admissions: Robert McAnally
Financial Aid: Lanette Michelle Clark
Type: Two-Year College **Sex:** Coed **Admission Plans:** Early Admission;
Open Admission **Application Deadline:** Rolling **Application Fee:** $15.00
Scholarships: Available. **Calendar System:** Semester, Summer session
available **Credit Hours For Degree:** 60 credit hours, Associates **Profes-**
sional Accreditation: NCCU.

GREAT FALLS COLLEGE MONTANA STATE UNIVERSITY
2100 16th Ave., S
Great Falls, MT 59405
Tel: (406)771-4300; Free: 800-446-2698
Fax: (406)771-4317
E-mail: joe.simonsen@gfcmsu.edu
Web Site: www.gfcmsu.edu
President/CEO: Dr. Susan J. Wolff, EdD
Admissions: Joe Simonsen
Financial Aid: Leah J. Habel
Type: Two-Year College **Sex:** Coed **Affiliation:** Montana University System.
% Accepted: 95 **Admission Plans:** Early Admission; Open Admission **Ap-**
plication Deadline: Rolling **Application Fee:** $30.00 **H.S. Requirements:**
High school diploma required; GED accepted **Costs Per Year:** Application
fee: $30. State resident tuition: $2496 full-time, $104 per credit part-time.
Nonresident tuition: $8748 full-time, $364 per credit part-time. Mandatory
fees: $634 full-time, $89 per credit part-time. Full-time tuition and fees vary
according to course load, location, and program. Part-time tuition and fees
vary according to course load, location, and program. **Scholarships:** Available. **Calendar System:** Semester, Summer session available **Enrollment:**
Full-time 743, Part-time 914 **Faculty:** Full-time 49, Part-time 74 **Student-**
Faculty Ratio: 14:1 **Exams:** ACT essay component used for advising; ACT
essay component used for placement; SAT essay component used for advising; SAT essay component used for placement. **Final Year or Final**
Semester Residency Requirement: No **Credit Hours For Degree:** 60
credits, Associates **Professional Accreditation:** AAMAE, ADA, AHIMA,
CoARC, NCCU.

HELENA COLLEGE UNIVERSITY OF MONTANA
1115 N Roberts St.
Helena, MT 59601
Tel: (406)444-6800; Free: 800-241-4882
Fax: (406)444-6892
Web Site: www.umhelena.edu
President/CEO: Dr. Daniel Bingham
Admissions: Ryan Loomis
Type: Two-Year College **Sex:** Coed **Affiliation:** The University of Montana;
Montana University System. **% Accepted:** 87 **Admission Plans:** Deferred
Admission; Early Admission; Open Admission **Application Deadline:** Rolling
Application Fee: $30.00 **H.S. Requirements:** High school diploma
required; GED accepted **Scholarships:** Available. **Calendar System:**
Semester, Summer session available **Enrollment:** Full-time 670, Part-time

760 **Faculty:** Full-time 40, Part-time 115 **Student-Faculty Ratio:** 12:1 **Final**
Year or Final Semester Residency Requirement: No **Credit Hours For**
Degree: 60 credit hours, Associates **Professional Accreditation:** NCCU.

HIGHLANDS COLLEGE OF MONTANA TECH
25 Basin Creek Rd.
Butte, MT 59701
Tel: (406)496-3701
Fax: (406)496-3710
Web Site: www.mtech.edu/academics/highlands
Type: Two-Year College **Sex:** Coed **Costs Per Year:** State resident tuition:
$3263 full-time. Nonresident tuition: $8380 full-time. Mandatory fees: $1000
full-time. Full-time tuition and fees vary according to course load and
program. College room and board: $8562. Room and board charges vary
according to board plan.

LITTLE BIG HORN COLLEGE
Box 370
1 Forest Ln.
Crow Agency, MT 59022-0370
Tel: (406)638-3104
Web Site: www.lbhc.edu
President/CEO: Dr. David Yarlott, Jr.
Admissions: Ann Bullis
Type: Two-Year College **Sex:** Coed **Admission Plans:** Open Admission **Ap-**
plication Deadline: Rolling **H.S. Requirements:** High school diploma or
equivalent not required **Calendar System:** Quarter **Faculty:** Full-time 11,
Part-time 1 **Student-Faculty Ratio:** 25:1 **Credit Hours For Degree:** 92
quarter hours, Associates **Professional Accreditation:** NCCU. **Intercol-**
legiate Athletics: Basketball M & W

MILES COMMUNITY COLLEGE
2715 Dickinson
Miles City, MT 59301-4799
Tel: (406)874-6100; Free: 800-541-9281
Fax: (406)874-6282
E-mail: andersonh@milescc.edu
Web Site: www.milescc.edu
President/CEO: Dr. Stefani Gray Hicswa
Admissions: Haley Anderson
Type: Two-Year College **Sex:** Coed **Affiliation:** Montana University System.
% Accepted: 100 **Admission Plans:** Deferred Admission; Early Admission;
Open Admission **Application Deadline:** Rolling **Application Fee:** $30.00
H.S. Requirements: High school diploma required; GED accepted **Scholar-**
ships: Available. **Calendar System:** Semester, Summer session available
Enrollment: Full-time 280, Part-time 161 **Faculty:** Full-time 24, Part-time 26
Student-Faculty Ratio: 10:1 **Exams:** ACT essay component not used; SAT
essay component not used. **% Residing in College-Owned, -Operated, or**
-Affiliated Housing: 32 **Final Year or Final Semester Residency Require-**
ment: No **Credit Hours For Degree:** 62 semester hours, Associates
Professional Accreditation: ACEN, NCCU. **Intercollegiate Athletics:**
Baseball M; Basketball M & W; Golf M & W

MONTANA BIBLE COLLEGE
3625 S 19th Ave.
Bozeman, MT 59718
Tel: (406)586-3585; Free: 888-462-2463
Web Site: www.montanabiblecollege.edu
Type: Four-Year College **Sex:** Coed **Affiliation:** Christian. **H.S. Require-**
ments: High school diploma required; GED accepted **Calendar System:**
Semester **Exams:** SAT I or ACT. **Professional Accreditation:** ABHE.

MONTANA STATE UNIVERSITY
Bozeman, MT 59717
Tel: (406)994-0211; Free: 888-MSU-CATS
E-mail: admissions@montana.edu
Web Site: www.montana.edu
President/CEO: Dr. Waded Cruzado
Admissions: Ronda Russell
Financial Aid: Brandi Payne
Type: University **Sex:** Coed **Affiliation:** Montana University System.
Scores: 97% SAT V 400+; 97% SAT M 400+; 37% ACT 18-23; 43% ACT
24-29 **Admission Plans:** Deferred Admission; Early Admission **Application**
Deadline: Rolling **Application Fee:** $30.00 **H.S. Requirements:** High

school diploma required; GED accepted **Costs Per Year:** Application fee: $30. State resident tuition: $5330 full-time, $222 per credit hour part-time. Nonresident tuition: $20,323 full-time, $847 per credit hour part-time. Mandatory fees: $1638 full-time. Full-time tuition and fees vary according to course load, degree level, location, and program. Part-time tuition varies according to course load, degree level, location, and program. College room and board: $8650. Room and board charges vary according to board plan and housing facility. **Scholarships:** Available. **Calendar System:** Semester, Summer session available **Faculty:** Full-time 581, Part-time 403 **Student-Faculty Ratio:** 19:1 **Exams:** ACT essay component used for admission; ACT essay component used for advising; ACT essay component used for placement; SAT I or ACT; SAT essay component used for admission; SAT essay component used for advising; SAT essay component used for placement. **% Receiving Financial Aid:** 47 **% Residing in College-Owned, -Operated, or -Affiliated Housing:** 25 **Final Year or Final Semester Residency Requirement:** No **Credit Hours For Degree:** 120 credits, Bachelors **ROTC:** Air Force, Army **Professional Accreditation:** AACN, AACSB, AAFCS, ABET, ACA, APA, NAAB, NASAD, NASM, NCCU, TEAC. **Intercollegiate Athletics:** Basketball M & W; Cheerleading M & W; Cross-Country Running M & W; Football M; Golf W; Skiing (Cross-Country) M & W; Skiing (Downhill) M & W; Tennis M & W; Track and Field M & W; Volleyball W

MONTANA STATE UNIVERSITY BILLINGS

1500 University Dr.
Billings, MT 59101
Tel: (406)657-2011; Free: 800-565-6782
Fax: (406)657-2302
E-mail: tammi.watson@msubillings.edu
Web Site: www.msubillings.edu
President/CEO: Dr. Mark Nook
Admissions: Tammi Watson
Financial Aid: Emily Williamson
Type: Comprehensive **Sex:** Coed **Affiliation:** Montana University System. **Scores:** 89% SAT V 400+; 56.8% ACT 18-23; 24.17% ACT 24-29 **% Accepted:** 100 **Admission Plans:** Open Admission **Application Deadline:** Rolling **Application Fee:** $30.00 **H.S. Requirements:** High school diploma required; GED accepted **Costs Per Year:** Application fee: $30. State resident tuition: $4397 full-time, $183.20 per credit hour part-time. Nonresident tuition: $16,307 full-time, $679.45 per credit hour part-time. Mandatory fees: $1411 full-time. Full-time tuition and fees vary according to course load and location. Part-time tuition varies according to course load and location. College room and board: $7510. Room and board charges vary according to board plan and housing facility. **Scholarships:** Available. **Calendar System:** Semester, Summer session available **Enrollment:** Full-time 2,701, Graduate full-time 173, Graduate part-time 222, Part-time 1,333 **Faculty:** Full-time 174, Part-time 151 **Student-Faculty Ratio:** 17:1 **Exams:** ACT essay component not used; SAT essay component not used; SAT Reasoning; SAT Subject. **% Receiving Financial Aid:** 59 **% Residing in College-Owned, -Operated, or -Affiliated Housing:** 75 **Credit Hours For Degree:** 60 semester credits, Associates; 120 semester credits, Bachelors **ROTC:** Army **Professional Accreditation:** AACSB, CORE, NASAD, NASM, NCATE, NCCU. **Intercollegiate Athletics:** Baseball M; Basketball M & W; Cross-Country Running M & W; Golf M & W; Soccer M & W; Softball W; Volleyball W

MONTANA STATE UNIVERSITY–NORTHERN

PO Box 7751
Havre, MT 59501-7751
Tel: (406)265-3700; Free: 800-662-6132
Fax: (406)265-3777
Web Site: www.msun.edu
President/CEO: Greg Kegel
Admissions: Rosalie Spinler
Financial Aid: Cindy Small
Type: Comprehensive **Sex:** Coed **Affiliation:** Montana University System. **Scores:** 88% SAT V 400+; 82% SAT M 400+; 55.7% ACT 18-23; 10.73% ACT 24-29 **% Accepted:** 64 **Admission Plans:** Deferred Admission; Early Admission **Application Deadline:** Rolling **Application Fee:** $30.00 **H.S. Requirements:** High school diploma required; GED accepted **Scholarships:** Available. **Calendar System:** Semester **Enrollment:** Full-time 923, Graduate full-time 8, Graduate part-time 57, Part-time 285 **Faculty:** Full-time 62, Part-time 34 **Student-Faculty Ratio:** 15:1 **Exams:** SAT I or ACT; SAT essay component used for admission; SAT essay component used for advising; SAT essay component used for placement. **% Receiving Financial Aid:**

75 **% Residing in College-Owned, -Operated, or -Affiliated Housing:** 22 **Credit Hours For Degree:** 64 credits, Associates; 128 credits, Bachelors **Professional Accreditation:** ABET, ACEN, NCATE, NCCU. **Intercollegiate Athletics:** Basketball M & W; Football M; Golf W; Volleyball W; Wrestling M

MONTANA TECH OF THE UNIVERSITY OF MONTANA

1300 W Park St.
Butte, MT 59701-8997
Tel: (406)496-4101; Free: 800-445-TECH
Fax: (406)496-4710
E-mail: scrowe@mtech.edu
Web Site: www.mtech.edu
President/CEO: Dr. Donald Blackketter
Admissions: Stephanie Crowe
Financial Aid: Mike Richardson
Type: Comprehensive **Sex:** Coed **Affiliation:** Montana University System. **Scores:** 100% SAT V 400+; 100% SAT M 400+; 33% ACT 18-23; 59% ACT 24-29 **% Accepted:** 88 **Admission Plans:** Deferred Admission; Open Admission **Application Deadline:** Rolling **Application Fee:** $30.00 **H.S. Requirements:** High school diploma required; GED accepted **Costs Per Year:** Application fee: $30. State resident tuition: $5177 full-time, $216 per credit part-time. Nonresident tuition: $18,892 full-time, $784 per credit part-time. Mandatory fees: $1620 full-time, $69 per credit part-time. Full-time tuition and fees vary according to course load, degree level, location, program, and student level. Part-time tuition and fees vary according to course load, degree level, location, program, and student level. College room and board: $8562. College room only: $3798. Room and board charges vary according to board plan. **Scholarships:** Available. **Calendar System:** Semester, Summer session available **Enrollment:** Full-time 2,235, Graduate full-time 79, Graduate part-time 131, Part-time 535 **Faculty:** Full-time 148, Part-time 80 **Student-Faculty Ratio:** 15:1 **Exams:** ACT essay component used for admission; ACT essay component used for placement; SAT I or ACT; SAT essay component used for admission; SAT essay component used for placement. **% Receiving Financial Aid:** 57 **% Residing in College-Owned, -Operated, or -Affiliated Housing:** 13 **Credit Hours For Degree:** 60 credit hours, Associates; 120 credit hours, Bachelors **Professional Accreditation:** ABET, ACEN, NCCU. **Intercollegiate Athletics:** Basketball M & W; Football M; Golf M & W; Volleyball W

ROCKY MOUNTAIN COLLEGE

1511 Poly Dr.
Billings, MT 59102-1796
Tel: (406)657-1000; Free: 800-877-6259
Fax: (406)259-9751
E-mail: admissions@rocky.edu
Web Site: www.rocky.edu
President/CEO: Dr. Robert Wilmouth
Admissions: Austin Mapston
Financial Aid: Jessica Francischetti
Type: Comprehensive **Sex:** Coed **Affiliation:** interdenominational. **Scores:** 94% SAT V 400+; 93% SAT M 400+; 54% ACT 18-23; 37% ACT 24-29 **% Accepted:** 70 **Admission Plans:** Deferred Admission; Early Admission **Application Deadline:** Rolling **Application Fee:** $35.00 **H.S. Requirements:** High school diploma required; GED accepted **Costs Per Year:** Application fee: $35. Comprehensive fee: $34,798 includes full-time tuition ($26,125), mandatory fees ($540), and college room and board ($8133). College room only: $3821. Full-time tuition and fees vary according to course load, degree level, and program. Room and board charges vary according to board plan and housing facility. Part-time tuition: $1089 per credit. Part-time tuition varies according to course load, degree level, and program. **Scholarships:** Available. **Calendar System:** Semester, Summer session available **Enrollment:** Full-time 893, Graduate full-time 96, Graduate part-time 1, Part-time 45 **Faculty:** Full-time 68, Part-time 58 **Student-Faculty Ratio:** 11:1 **Exams:** SAT I or ACT. **% Receiving Financial Aid:** 75 **% Residing in College-Owned, -Operated, or -Affiliated Housing:** 51 **Final Year or Final Semester Residency Requirement:** No **Credit Hours For Degree:** 62 semester hours, Associates; 124 semester hours, Bachelors **ROTC:** Army **Professional Accreditation:** NCCU. **Intercollegiate Athletics:** Basketball M & W; Cheerleading M & W; Cross-Country Running M & W; Equestrian Sports M & W; Football M; Golf M & W; Skiing (Downhill) M & W; Soccer M & W; Track and Field M & W; Volleyball W

SALISH KOOTENAI COLLEGE

PO Box 70
Pablo, MT 59855-0117

Tel: (406)275-4800
Fax: (406)275-4801
E-mail: jackie_moran@skc.edu
Web Site: www.skc.edu
President/CEO: Robert R. DePoe, III
Admissions: Jackie Moran
Financial Aid: Chastity Wagner
Type: Two-Year College Sex: Coed % Accepted: 64 Admission Plans:
Deferred Admission; Open Admission; Preferred Admission Application
Deadline: Rolling H.S. Requirements: High school diploma required; GED
accepted Scholarships: Available. Calendar System: Quarter, Summer
session available Enrollment: Full-time 585, Part-time 503 Faculty: Full-
time 45, Part-time 35 Credit Hours For Degree: 92 credits, Associates; 180
credits, Bachelors Professional Accreditation: ACEN, ADA, NCCU.

STONE CHILD COLLEGE
RR1, Box 1082
Box Elder, MT 59521
Tel: (406)395-4313
Fax: (406)395-4836
E-mail: uanet337@quest.ocsc.montana.edu
Web Site: www.stonechild.edu
President/CEO: Nathaniel St Pierre
Admissions: Ted Whitford
Type: Two-Year College Sex: Coed % Accepted: 100 Admission Plans:
Open Admission Application Fee: $10.00 H.S. Requirements: High school
diploma required; GED accepted Scholarships: Available. Calendar
System: Semester Faculty: Full-time 10, Part-time 12 Credit Hours For
Degree: 64 semester hours, Associates Professional Accreditation:
NCCU.

UNIVERSITY OF GREAT FALLS
1301 Twentieth St. S
Great Falls, MT 59405
Tel: (406)761-8210; Free: 800-856-9544
Fax: (406)791-5209
E-mail: enroll@ugf.edu
Web Site: www.ugf.edu
President/CEO: Dr. Eugene J. McAllister
Admissions: Kelly Braun
Financial Aid: Kelli Engelhardt
Type: Comprehensive Sex: Coed Affiliation: Roman Catholic. Scores:
95% SAT V 400+; 84% SAT M 400+; 57% ACT 18-23; 18% ACT 24-29 %
Accepted: 84 Admission Plans: Deferred Admission; Early Admission Ap-
plication Fee: $35.00 H.S. Requirements: High school diploma required;
GED accepted Costs Per Year: Application fee: $35. Comprehensive fee:
$28,970 includes full-time tuition ($21,070), mandatory fees ($1100), and
college room and board ($6800). College room only: $3900. Full-time tuition
and fees vary according to course load. Room and board charges vary according to housing facility. Part-time tuition: $666 per credit hour. Part-time
tuition varies according to course load, location, and program. Scholarships: Available. Calendar System: Semester Enrollment: Full-time 610,
Graduate full-time 35, Graduate part-time 42, Part-time 442 Faculty: Full-
time 44, Part-time 72 Student-Faculty Ratio: 14:1 Exams: ACT essay
component used for admission; ACT essay component used for advising;
ACT essay component used for placement; SAT I and SAT II or ACT; SAT I
or ACT; SAT II; SAT essay component used for admission; SAT essay
component used for advising; SAT essay component used for placement;
SAT Reasoning; SAT Subject. % Receiving Financial Aid: 77 % Residing
in College-Owned, -Operated, or -Affiliated Housing: 38 Credit Hours
For Degree: 64 credits, Associates; 128 credits, Bachelors Professional
Accreditation: NCCU. Intercollegiate Athletics: Basketball M & W;
Cheerleading M & W; Cross-Country Running M & W; Equestrian Sports M
& W; Golf M & W; Soccer M & W; Softball W; Track and Field M & W; Vol-
leyball W; Wrestling M

UNIVERSITY OF MONTANA
Missoula, MT 59812-0002
Tel: (406)243-0211; Free: 800-462-8636
Fax: (406)243-5711

E-mail: admiss@umontana.edu
Web Site: www.umt.edu
President/CEO: Dr. Royce C. Engstrom
Financial Aid: Kent McGowan
Type: University Sex: Coed Affiliation: Montana University System.
Scores: 96% SAT V 400+; 95% SAT M 400+; 42% ACT 18-23; 38.7% ACT
24-29 % Accepted: 84 Admission Plans: Deferred Admission; Early
Admission Application Deadline: Rolling Application Fee: $36.00 H.S.
Requirements: High school diploma required; GED accepted. For home-
schooled applicants: High school diploma or equivalent not required Costs
Per Year: Application fee: $36. State resident tuition: $4604 full-time, $192
per credit hour part-time. Nonresident tuition: $22,720 full-time, $947 per
credit hour part-time. Mandatory fees: $1842 full-time. Full-time tuition and
fees vary according to degree level, location, program, reciprocity agreements, and student level. Part-time tuition varies according to course load,
degree level, location, and student level. College room and board: $8826.
Room and board charges vary according to board plan and housing facility.
Scholarships: Available. Calendar System: Semester, Summer session
available Enrollment: Full-time 8,683, Graduate full-time 1,167, Graduate
part-time 1,099, Part-time 2,095 Faculty: Full-time 569, Part-time 265
Student-Faculty Ratio: 17:1 Exams: ACT essay component used for
admission; ACT essay component used for advising; ACT essay component
used for placement; SAT I or ACT; SAT essay component used for admission; SAT essay component used for advising; SAT essay component used
for placement; SAT Reasoning. % Receiving Financial Aid: 59 % Residing
in College-Owned, -Operated, or -Affiliated Housing: 25 Final Year or
Final Semester Residency Requirement: Yes Credit Hours For Degree:
65 credits, Associates; 120 credits, Bachelors ROTC: Army Professional
Accreditation: AACSB, AALS, ABA, ABET, ACA, ACEJMC, ACF, ACPE,
APA, APTA, CSWE, CoARC, JRCAT, NASAD, NASM, NAST, NCATE,
NCCU, NRPA, SAF. Intercollegiate Athletics: Baseball M; Basketball M &
W; Crew M & W; Cross-Country Running M & W; Equestrian Sports M & W;
Fencing M & W; Field Hockey W; Football M; Golf W; Gymnastics W; Ice
Hockey M & W; Lacrosse M & W; Rugby M & W; Skiing (Downhill) M & W;
Soccer W; Softball W; Tennis M & W; Track and Field M & W; Ultimate
Frisbee M & W; Volleyball W

THE UNIVERSITY OF MONTANA WESTERN
710 S Atlantic
Dillon, MT 59725-3598
Tel: (406)683-7011; Free: 877-683-7331
Fax: (406)683-7493
E-mail: janet.jones@umwestern.edu
Web Site: www.umwestern.edu
President/CEO: Dr. Beth Weatherby
Admissions: Janet Jones
Financial Aid: Erica L. Jones
Type: Four-Year College Sex: Coed Affiliation: Montana University System.
Scores: 81% SAT V 400+; 75% SAT M 400+; 54% ACT 18-23; 13% ACT
24-29 % Accepted: 74 Admission Plans: Deferred Admission; Early
Admission Application Deadline: Rolling Application Fee: $30.00 H.S.
Requirements: High school diploma required; GED accepted Costs Per
Year: Application fee: $30. State resident tuition: $3699 full-time, $153 per
credit hour part-time. Nonresident tuition: $16,497 full-time, $814 per credit
hour part-time. Mandatory fees: $1,194 full-time, $153 per credit hour part-
time. Full-time tuition and fees vary according to course load, location,
program, reciprocity agreements, and student level. Part-time tuition and
fees vary according to course load, location, program, reciprocity agreements, and student level. College room and board: $7482. College room
only: $2752. Room and board charges vary according to housing facility.
Scholarships: Available. Calendar System: Semester, Summer session
available Enrollment: Full-time 1,170, Part-time 299 Faculty: Full-time 67,
Part-time 29 Student-Faculty Ratio: 15:1 Exams: ACT essay component
used for placement; SAT I or ACT; SAT essay component used for placement; SAT Reasoning; SAT Subject. % Residing in College-Owned,
-Operated, or -Affiliated Housing: 26 Final Year or Final Semester
Residency Requirement: Yes Credit Hours For Degree: 60 credits, As-
sociates; 120 credits, Bachelors Professional Accreditation: NCATE,
NCCU. Intercollegiate Athletics: Basketball M & W; Cheerleading W;
Cross-Country Running M & W; Football M; Volleyball W

BELLEVUE UNIVERSITY
1000 Galvin Rd. S
Bellevue, NE 68005-3098
Tel: (402)291-8100; Free: 800-756-7920
Fax: (402)293-2020
E-mail: nick.baker@bellevue.edu
Web Site: www.bellevue.edu
President/CEO: Dr. Mary B. Hawkins, PhD
Admissions: Nick Baker
Financial Aid: Janet Yale
Type: Comprehensive **Sex:** Coed **Admission Plans:** Deferred Admission; Open Admission **Application Deadline:** Rolling **Application Fee:** $50.00 **H.S. Requirements:** High school diploma required; GED accepted **Scholarships:** Available. **Calendar System:** Semester, Summer session available **Enrollment:** Full-time 4,978, Graduate full-time 1,482, Graduate part-time 1,994, Part-time 1,850 **Faculty:** Full-time 89, Part-time 322 **Student-Faculty Ratio:** 40:1 **% Receiving Financial Aid:** 82 **Final Year or Final Semester Residency Requirement:** No **Regional Accreditation:** North Central Association of Colleges and Schools **Credit Hours For Degree:** 127 credit hours, Bachelors **ROTC:** Air Force, Army

BRYAN COLLEGE OF HEALTH SCIENCES
5035 Everett St.
Lincoln, NE 68506-1398
Tel: (402)481 3801
Web Site: www.bryanhealth.com/CollegeofHealthSciences
Type: Comprehensive **Sex:** Coed **Costs Per Year:** Tuition: $12,360 full-time, $515 per credit hour part-time. Mandatory fees: $720 full-time, $30 per credit hour part-time. Full-time tuition and fees vary according to course load. Part-time tuition and fees vary according to course load. **Regional Accreditation:** North Central Association of Colleges and Schools **Professional Accreditation:** AANA, ACEN.

CENTRAL COMMUNITY COLLEGE–COLUMBUS CAMPUS
4500 63rd St.
Columbus, NE 68602-1027
Tel: (402)564-7132; Free: 877-CCC-0780
Fax: (402)562-1201
E-mail: eleffler@cccneb.edu
Web Site: www.cccneb.edu
President/CEO: Dr. Matt Gotschall
Admissions: Erica Leffler
Type: Two-Year College **Sex:** Coed **Affiliation:** Central Community College. **Admission Plans:** Early Admission; Open Admission **Application Deadline:** Rolling **Application Fee:** $0.00 **H.S. Requirements:** High school diploma required; GED accepted. For nursing program: High school diploma required; GED not accepted **Scholarships:** Available. **Calendar System:** Semester, Summer session available **Enrollment:** Full-time 523, Part-time 2,349 **Faculty:** Full-time 46, Part-time 53 **% Residing in College-Owned, -Operated, or -Affiliated Housing:** 17 **Final Year or Final Semester Residency Requirement:** No **Regional Accreditation:** North Central Association of Colleges and Schools **Credit Hours For Degree:** 60 credits, Associates **Intercollegiate Athletics:** Basketball M; Golf M; Softball W; Volleyball W

CENTRAL COMMUNITY COLLEGE–GRAND ISLAND CAMPUS
PO Box 4903
Grand Island, NE 68802-4903
Tel: (308)398-4222; Free: 877-CCC-0780
Fax: (308)398-7398
E-mail: mlubken@cccneb.edu
Web Site: www.cccneb.edu
President/CEO: Dr. Lynn C. Black
Admissions: Michelle Lubken
Financial Aid: Steve Millnitz
Type: Two-Year College **Sex:** Coed **Affiliation:** Central Community College. **Admission Plans:** Early Admission; Open Admission **Application Deadline:** Rolling **Application Fee:** $0.00 **H.S. Requirements:** High school diploma required; GED accepted. For nursing program and occupational therapy assistant program: High school diploma required; GED not accepted **Scholarships:** Available. **Calendar System:** Semester, Summer session available **Enrollment:** Full-time 423, Part-time 3,046 **Student-Faculty Ratio:** 15:1 **% Residing in College-Owned, -Operated, or -Affiliated Housing:** 10 **Final Year or Final Semester Residency Requirement:** No **Regional Accreditation:** North Central Association of Colleges and Schools **Credit Hours For Degree:** 60 credits, Associates **Professional Accreditation:** ADA.

CENTRAL COMMUNITY COLLEGE–HASTINGS CAMPUS
PO Box 1024
Hastings, NE 68902-1024
Tel: (402)463-9811; Free: 877-CCC-0780
E-mail: rglenn@ccneb.edu
Web Site: www.cccneb.edu
President/CEO: Bill Hitesman
Admissions: Robert Glenn
Type: Two-Year College **Sex:** Coed **Affiliation:** Central Community College. **Admission Plans:** Early Admission; Open Admission **Application Deadline:** Rolling **Application Fee:** $0.00 **H.S. Requirements:** High school diploma required; GED accepted. For nursing, dental hygiene, truck driving, medical laboratory technology programs: High school diploma required; GED not accepted **Scholarships:** Available. **Calendar System:** Semester, Summer session available **Enrollment:** Full-time 1,001, Part-time 1,965 **Faculty:** Full-time 49, Part-time 60 **Student-Faculty Ratio:** 15:1 **Final Year or Final Semester Residency Requirement:** No **Regional Accreditation:** North Central Association of Colleges and Schools **Credit Hours For Degree:** 60 credits, Associates **Professional Accreditation:** AAMAE, ADA, AHIMA, NAACLS.

CHADRON STATE COLLEGE
1000 Main St.
Chadron, NE 69337
Tel: (308)432-6000; Free: 800-242-3766
Fax: (308)432-6229
E-mail: inquire@csc.edu
Web Site: www.csc.edu
President/CEO: Janie Park
Admissions: Tena Cook
Financial Aid: Sherry Douglas
Type: Comprehensive **Sex:** Coed **Affiliation:** Nebraska State College

System. **Admission Plans:** Early Admission; Open Admission **Application Deadline:** Rolling **Application Fee:** $15.00 **H.S. Requirements:** High school diploma required; GED accepted **Scholarships:** Available. **Calendar System:** Semester, Summer session available **Student-Faculty Ratio:** 19:1 **% Receiving Financial Aid:** 97 **Regional Accreditation:** North Central Association of Colleges and Schools **Credit Hours For Degree:** 125 semester hours, Bachelors **Professional Accreditation:** AAFCS, ACBSP, CSWE, NCATE. **Intercollegiate Athletics:** Basketball M & W; Football M; Golf W; Softball W; Track and Field M & W; Volleyball W; Wrestling M

CHI HEALTH SCHOOL OF RADIOLOGIC TECHNOLOGY

7500 Mercy Rd.
Omaha, NE 68124-9832
Tel: (402)398-5527
Web Site: www.chihealth.com/school-of-radiologic-technology
Type: Two-Year College **Sex:** Coed **Professional Accreditation:** JRCERT.

CLARKSON COLLEGE

101 S 42nd St.
Omaha, NE 68131-2739
Tel: (402)552-3100; Free: 800-647-5500
Fax: (402)552-6057
E-mail: workdenise@clarksoncollege.edu
Web Site: www.clarksoncollege.edu
President/CEO: Dr. Louis Burgher
Admissions: Denise Work
Financial Aid: Pam Shelton
Type: Comprehensive **Sex:** Coed **Scores:** 61% ACT 18-23; 30% ACT 24-29 **% Accepted:** 55 **Admission Plans:** Deferred Admission **Application Deadline:** Rolling **Application Fee:** $35.00 **H.S. Requirements:** High school diploma required; GED accepted **Scholarships:** Available. **Calendar System:** Semester, Summer session available **Enrollment:** Full-time 658 **Faculty:** Full-time 48, Part-time 53 **Student-Faculty Ratio:** 8:1 **Exams:** SAT I or ACT. **% Receiving Financial Aid:** 75 **% Residing in College-Owned, -Operated, or -Affiliated Housing:** 14 **Regional Accreditation:** North Central Association of Colleges and Schools **Credit Hours For Degree:** 70 credits, Associates; 128 credits, Bachelors **ROTC:** Air Force, Army **Professional Accreditation:** AANA, ACEN, APTA, JRCERT.

COLLEGE OF SAINT MARY

7000 Mercy Rd.
Omaha, NE 68106
Tel: (402)399-2400; Free: 800-926-5534
Fax: (402)399-2412
E-mail: enroll@csm.edu
Web Site: www.csm.edu
President/CEO: Dr. Maryanne Stevens, RSM
Financial Aid: Beth Sisk
Type: Comprehensive **Sex:** Women **Affiliation:** Roman Catholic. **Scores:** 64% ACT 18-23; 29% ACT 24-29 **% Accepted:** 53 **Application Deadline:** Rolling **Application Fee:** $30.00 **H.S. Requirements:** High school diploma required; GED accepted **Costs Per Year:** Application fee: $30. Comprehensive fee: $36,364 includes full-time tuition ($28,964) and college room and board ($7400). Full-time tuition varies according to program. Part-time tuition: $950 per credit. Part-time tuition varies according to course load and program. **Scholarships:** Available. **Calendar System:** Semester, Summer session available **Enrollment:** Full-time 675, Graduate full-time 182, Graduate part-time 84, Part-time 60 **Faculty:** Full-time 62, Part-time 150 **Student-Faculty Ratio:** 6:1 **Exams:** ACT; ACT essay component not used; SAT I or ACT; SAT essay component not used. **% Receiving Financial Aid:** 84 **% Residing in College-Owned, -Operated, or -Affiliated Housing:** 34 **Final Year or Final Semester Residency Requirement:** No **Regional Accreditation:** North Central Association of Colleges and Schools **Credit Hours For Degree:** 64 credit hours, Associates; 128 credit hours, Bachelors **ROTC:** Air Force, Army **Professional Accreditation:** ACEN, AHIMA, AOTA. **Intercollegiate Athletics:** Basketball W; Cross-Country Running W; Golf W; Soccer W; Softball W; Swimming and Diving W; Tennis W; Volleyball W

CONCORDIA UNIVERSITY, NEBRASKA

800 N Columbia Ave.
Seward, NE 68434-1556
Tel: (402)643-3651; Free: 800-535-5494
Fax: (402)643-4073
E-mail: admiss@cune.edu

Web Site: www.cune.edu
President/CEO: Rev. Brian L. Friedrich
Admissions: Aaron W. Roberts
Financial Aid: Aaron W. Roberts
Type: Comprehensive **Sex:** Coed **Affiliation:** Lutheran Church–Missouri Synod. **Scores:** 87% SAT V 400+; 96% SAT M 400+; 47.6% ACT 18-23; 35.46% ACT 24-29 **% Accepted:** 78 **Admission Plans:** Deferred Admission **Application Deadline:** August 1 **Application Fee:** $0.00 **H.S. Requirements:** High school diploma required; GED accepted **Costs Per Year:** Application fee: $0. Comprehensive fee: $36,280 includes full-time tuition ($27,880), mandatory fees ($600), and college room and board ($7800). College room only: $3300. Room and board charges vary according to board plan and housing facility. Part-time tuition: $860 per credit hour. **Scholarships:** Available. **Calendar System:** Miscellaneous, Summer session available **Enrollment:** Full-time 1,215, Graduate full-time 872, Graduate part-time 107, Part-time 263 **Faculty:** Full-time 63, Part-time 177 **Student-Faculty Ratio:** 14:1 **Exams:** ACT essay component not used; SAT I or ACT; SAT essay component not used; SAT Reasoning. **% Receiving Financial Aid:** 74 **% Residing in College-Owned, -Operated, or -Affiliated Housing:** 60 **Final Year or Final Semester Residency Requirement:** No **Regional Accreditation:** North Central Association of Colleges and Schools **Credit Hours For Degree:** 120 credit hours, Bachelors **ROTC:** Air Force, Army **Professional Accreditation:** NASM, NCATE. **Intercollegiate Athletics:** Baseball M; Basketball M & W; Cheerleading W; Cross-Country Running M & W; Football M; Golf M & W; Soccer M & W; Softball W; Tennis M & W; Track and Field M & W; Volleyball W; Wrestling M

CREATIVE CENTER

10850 Emmet St.
Omaha, NE 68164
Tel: (402)898-1000; Free: 888-898-1789
Fax: (402)898-1301
E-mail: rich_c@creativecenter.edu
Web Site: www.creativecenter.edu
President/CEO: Ray Dotzler
Admissions: Richard Caldwell
Type: Four-Year College **Sex:** Coed **Costs Per Year:** One-time mandatory fee: $2800. Tuition: $25,600 full-time, $2560 per course part-time. Mandatory fees: $2055 full-time. Full-time tuition and fees vary according to course load, degree level, program, and student level. Part-time tuition and fees vary according to course load, degree level, program, and student level. **Calendar System:** Semester, Summer session not available **Enrollment:** Full-time 60, Part-time 4 **Faculty:** Full-time 3, Part-time 10 **Student-Faculty Ratio:** 11:1 **Final Year or Final Semester Residency Requirement:** No **Credit Hours For Degree:** 90 semester credit hours, Associates; 137 semester credit hours, Bachelors **Professional Accreditation:** ACCSC.

CREIGHTON UNIVERSITY

2500 California Plz.
Omaha, NE 68178-0001
Tel: (402)280-2700; Free: 800-282-5835
Fax: (402)280-2685
E-mail: admissions@creighton.edu
Web Site: www.creighton.edu
President/CEO: Rev. Daniel S. Hendrickson, SJ
Admissions: Sarah Richardson
Financial Aid: Paula S. Kohles
Type: University **Sex:** Coed **Affiliation:** Roman Catholic (Jesuit). **Scores:** 100% SAT V 400+; 100% SAT M 400+; 19.17% ACT 18-23; 55.62% ACT 24-29 **% Accepted:** 70 **Admission Plans:** Deferred Admission **Application Deadline:** February 15 **Application Fee:** $40.00 **H.S. Requirements:** High school diploma required; GED accepted **Costs Per Year:** Application fee: $40. Comprehensive fee: $46,716 includes full-time tuition ($34,810), mandatory fees ($1612), and college room and board ($10,294). Full-time tuition and fees vary according to program. Room and board charges vary according to housing facility. Part-time tuition: $1090 per credit hour. Part-time mandatory fees: $158 per term. Part-time tuition and fees vary according to course load and program. **Scholarships:** Available. **Calendar System:** Semester, Summer session available **Enrollment:** Full-time 3,909, Graduate full-time 2,877, Graduate part-time 1,395, Part-time 254 **Faculty:** Full-time 560, Part-time 285 **Student-Faculty Ratio:** 11:1 **Exams:** ACT essay component not used; SAT I or ACT; SAT essay component not used; SAT Reasoning. **% Receiving Financial Aid:** 55 **% Residing in College-Owned, -Operated, or -Affiliated Housing:** 60 **Final Year or Final**

Semester Residency Requirement: Yes **Regional Accreditation:** North Central Association of Colleges and Schools **Credit Hours For Degree:** Associate in Arts or Associate in Science degree requires 64 credits; Associate in Science in EMS degree requires 73 credits, Associates; 128 credits, Bachelors **ROTC:** Air Force, Army **Professional Accreditation:** AACN, AACSB, AALS, ABA, ACPE, ADA, AOTA, APTA, CSWE, JRCEMTP, LCME/AMA, NCATE. **Intercollegiate Athletics:** Baseball M; Basketball M & W; Crew W; Cross-Country Running M & W; Golf M & W; Soccer M & W; Softball W; Tennis M & W; Volleyball W

DOANE UNIVERSITY
1014 Boswell Ave.
Crete, NE 68333-2430
Tel: (402)826-2161; Free: 800-333-6263
Fax: (402)826-8600
E-mail: kyle.mcmurray@doane.edu
Web Site: www.doane.edu
President/CEO: Dr. Jacque Carter
Admissions: Kyle McMurray
Financial Aid: Peggy Tvrdy
Type: Comprehensive **Sex:** Coed **Affiliation:** United Church of Christ. **Scores:** 51% ACT 18-23; 42% ACT 24-29 **Costs Per Year:** Comprehensive fee: $37,140 includes full-time tuition ($28,170), mandatory fees ($620), and college room and board ($8350). Full-time tuition and fees vary according to location. Room and board charges vary according to board plan, housing facility, and location. Part-time tuition: $940 per credit hour. Part-time tuition varies according to course load and location. **Scholarships:** Available. **Calendar System:** 4-1-4, Summer session available **Enrollment:** Full-time 1,048, Part-time 9 **Faculty:** Full-time 82, Part-time 38 **Student-Faculty Ratio:** 11:1 **Exams:** SAT I or ACT. **% Receiving Financial Aid:** 77 **% Residing in College-Owned, -Operated, or -Affiliated Housing:** 82 **Final Year or Final Semester Residency Requirement:** No **Regional Accreditation:** North Central Association of Colleges and Schools **Credit Hours For Degree:** 132 credit hours, Bachelors **ROTC:** Air Force, Army **Professional Accreditation:** NCATE. **Intercollegiate Athletics:** Baseball M; Basketball M & W; Cross-Country Running M & W; Football M; Golf M & W; Soccer M & W; Softball W; Tennis M & W; Track and Field M & W; Volleyball W

GRACE UNIVERSITY
1311 S Ninth St.
Omaha, NE 68108
Tel: (402)449-2800; Free: 800-383-1422
Fax: (402)341-9587
E-mail: admissions@graceuniversity.com
Web Site: www.graceuniversity.edu
President/CEO: Dr. James P. Eckman
Admissions: Angela Wayman
Financial Aid: Marcy Pierce
Type: Comprehensive **Sex:** Coed **Affiliation:** interdenominational. **% Accepted:** 64 **Admission Plans:** Deferred Admission; Early Admission **Application Deadline:** Rolling **Application Fee:** $20.00 **H.S. Requirements:** High school diploma required; GED accepted **Scholarships:** Available. **Calendar System:** Semester, Summer session available **Enrollment:** Full-time 287, Part-time 79 **Faculty:** Full-time 25, Part-time 25 **Student-Faculty Ratio:** 18:1 **Exams:** SAT I or ACT. **% Receiving Financial Aid:** 74 **% Residing in College-Owned, -Operated, or -Affiliated Housing:** 60 **Regional Accreditation:** North Central Association of Colleges and Schools **Credit Hours For Degree:** 64 credit hours, Associates; 128 credit hours, Bachelors **ROTC:** Air Force, Army **Professional Accreditation:** ABHE. **Intercollegiate Athletics:** Basketball M & W; Soccer M; Volleyball W

HASTINGS COLLEGE
710 N Turner Ave.
Hastings, NE 68901
Tel: (402)463-2402; Free: 800-532-7642
Fax: (402)463-3002
E-mail: cschukei@hastings.edu
Web Site: www.hastings.edu
President/CEO: Don Jackson
Admissions: Chris Schukei
Financial Aid: Traci Noelle Boeve
Type: Comprehensive **Sex:** Coed **Affiliation:** Presbyterian. **Scores:** 90% SAT V 400+; 91% SAT M 400+; 52% ACT 18-23; 41% ACT 24-29 **% Accepted:** 71 **Application Deadline:** August 1 **Application Fee:** $0.00 **H.S.**

Requirements: High school diploma required; GED accepted **Costs Per Year:** Application fee: $0. Comprehensive fee: $36,570 includes full-time tuition ($27,300), mandatory fees ($1190), and college room and board ($8080). Room and board charges vary according to board plan and housing facility. Part-time tuition: $1070 per credit hour. Part-time mandatory fees: $316 per term. Part-time tuition and fees vary according to course load. **Scholarships:** Available. **Calendar System:** 4-1-4, Summer session available **Enrollment:** Full-time 1,129, Graduate full-time 23, Graduate part-time 6, Part-time 54 **Faculty:** Full-time 77, Part-time 42 **Student-Faculty Ratio:** 13:1 **Exams:** SAT I or ACT; SAT Reasoning; SAT Subject. **% Receiving Financial Aid:** 73 **% Residing in College-Owned, -Operated, or -Affiliated Housing:** 63 **Final Year or Final Semester Residency Requirement:** Yes **Regional Accreditation:** North Central Association of Colleges and Schools **Credit Hours For Degree:** 127 semester hours, Bachelors **Professional Accreditation:** NASM, NCATE. **Intercollegiate Athletics:** Baseball M; Basketball M & W; Bowling M & W; Cheerleading W; Cross-Country Running M & W; Football M; Golf M & W; Riflery M & W; Soccer M & W; Softball W; Tennis M & W; Track and Field M & W; Volleyball W; Wrestling M

KAPLAN UNIVERSITY, LINCOLN
1821 K St.
Lincoln, NE 68501-2826
Tel: (402)474-5315; Free: 800-527-5268
Fax: (402)474-5302
Web Site: www.kaplanuniversity.edu
President/CEO: Kate Packard
Type: Two-Year College **Sex:** Coed **H.S. Requirements:** High school diploma required; GED accepted **Scholarships:** Available. **Calendar System:** Quarter **Regional Accreditation:** North Central Association of Colleges and Schools **Professional Accreditation:** AAMAE, ACICS.

KAPLAN UNIVERSITY, OMAHA
5425 N 103rd St.
Omaha, NE 68134
Tel: (402)572-8500; Free: 800-527-5268
Fax: (402)573-1341
Web Site: www.kaplanuniversity.edu
President/CEO: Jeremy Brunssen
Type: Two-Year College **Sex:** Coed **H.S. Requirements:** High school diploma required; GED accepted **Calendar System:** Quarter **Regional Accreditation:** North Central Association of Colleges and Schools **Credit Hours For Degree:** 113 credit hours, Associates **Professional Accreditation:** AAMAE, ACICS.

LITTLE PRIEST TRIBAL COLLEGE
PO Box 270
Winnebago, NE 68071
Tel: (402)878-2380
Fax: (402)878-2355
E-mail: yattym@littlepriest.edu
Web Site: www.littlepriest.edu
President/CEO: Dr. Johnny Jones
Admissions: Yatty Mohammed
Type: Two-Year College **Sex:** Coed **Admission Plans:** Early Admission; Open Admission **Application Fee:** $10.00 **H.S. Requirements:** High school diploma required; GED accepted **Scholarships:** Available. **Enrollment:** Full-time 80, Part-time 42 **Faculty:** Full-time 11, Part-time 23 **Student-Faculty Ratio:** 6:1 **Final Year or Final Semester Residency Requirement:** No **Regional Accreditation:** North Central Association of Colleges and Schools **Credit Hours For Degree:** 66 credit hours, Associates

METROPOLITAN COMMUNITY COLLEGE
PO Box 3777
Omaha, NE 68103-0777
Tel: (402)457-2400; Free: 800-228-9553
Fax: (402)457-2564
E-mail: mvazquez@mccneb.edu
Web Site: www.mccneb.edu
President/CEO: Randy Schmailzl
Admissions: Maria Vazquez
Financial Aid: Wilma Hjellum
Type: Two-Year College **Sex:** Coed **Affiliation:** Nebraska Coordinating Commission for Postsecondary Education. **% Accepted:** 100 **Admission**

Plans: Early Admission; Open Admission **Application Deadline:** Rolling **Application Fee:** $0.00 **H.S. Requirements:** High school diploma or equivalent not required. For allied health programs, pre-professional associate of science: High school diploma required; GED accepted **Costs Per Year:** Application fee: $0. State resident tuition: $2745 full-time, $56 per credit hour part-time. Nonresident tuition: $4005 full-time, $84 per credit hour part-time. Mandatory fees: $225 full-time, $5 per credit hour part-time. Full-time tuition and fees vary according to course load. Part-time tuition and fees vary according to course load. College room and board: $2850. **Scholarships:** Available. **Calendar System:** Quarter, Summer session available **Enrollment:** Full-time 7,095, Part-time 9,908 **Faculty:** Full-time 198, Part-time 679 **Student-Faculty Ratio:** 16:1 **Regional Accreditation:** North Central Association of Colleges and Schools **Credit Hours For Degree:** 96 quarter hours, Associates **ROTC:** Army **Professional Accreditation:** ACBSP, ACEN, ACF, ADA, CoARC.

MID-PLAINS COMMUNITY COLLEGE
1101 Halligan Dr.
North Platte, NE 69101
Tel: (308)535-3600; Free: 800-658-4348
Fax: (308)532-8590
E-mail: driskellm@mpcc.edu
Web Site: www.mpcc.edu
President/CEO: Ryan C. Purdy
Admissions: Michael Driskell
Financial Aid: Erinn Brauer
Type: Two-Year College **Sex:** Coed **% Accepted:** 100 **Admission Plans:** Deferred Admission; Open Admission **Application Deadline:** Rolling **Application Fee:** $0.00 **H.S. Requirements:** High school diploma required; GED accepted **Costs Per Year:** Application fee: $0. State resident tuition: $2430 full-time, $81 per credit hour part-time. Nonresident tuition: $3150 full-time, $105 per credit hour part-time. Mandatory fees: $450 full-time, $15 per credit hour part-time. College room and board: $5896. Room and board charges vary according to board plan, housing facility, and location. **Scholarships:** Available. **Calendar System:** Semester, Summer session available **Enrollment:** Full-time 789, Part-time 1,446 **Faculty:** Full-time 66, Part-time 239 **Student-Faculty Ratio:** 9:1 **Exams:** ACT; ACT essay component not used; Other; SAT essay component not used. **% Residing in College-Owned, -Operated, or -Affiliated Housing:** 20 **Final Year or Final Semester Residency Requirement:** No **Regional Accreditation:** North Central Association of Colleges and Schools **Credit Hours For Degree:** 60 semester hours, Associates **Professional Accreditation:** ACEN, ADA, NAACLS. **Intercollegiate Athletics:** Baseball M; Basketball M & W; Golf M; Softball W; Volleyball W

MIDLAND UNIVERSITY
900 N Clarkson St.
Fremont, NE 68025-4200
Tel: (402)721-5480; Free: 800-642-8382
Fax: (402)721-0250
E-mail: oliver@midlandu.edu
Web Site: www.midlandu.edu
President/CEO: Dr. Stephen Fritz
Admissions: Danielle Oliver
Financial Aid: Penny James
Type: Four-Year College **Sex:** Coed **Affiliation:** Lutheran. **% Accepted:** 88 **Admission Plans:** Early Admission **Application Deadline:** Rolling **Application Fee:** $30.00 **H.S. Requirements:** High school diploma required; GED accepted **Scholarships:** Available. **Calendar System:** 4-1-4, Summer session available **Enrollment:** Full-time 808, Part-time 19 **Faculty:** Full-time 54, Part-time 27 **Student-Faculty Ratio:** 14:1 **Exams:** SAT I or ACT. **% Receiving Financial Aid:** 81 **% Residing in College-Owned, -Operated, or -Affiliated Housing:** 62 **Regional Accreditation:** North Central Association of Colleges and Schools **Credit Hours For Degree:** 64 credit hours, Associates; 128 credit hours, Bachelors **Professional Accreditation:** ACEN. **Intercollegiate Athletics:** Baseball M; Basketball M & W; Cross-Country Running M & W; Football M; Golf M & W; Soccer M & W; Softball W; Tennis M & W; Track and Field M & W; Volleyball W

MYOTHERAPY INSTITUTE
6020 S 58th St.
Lincoln, NE 68516
Tel: (402)421-7410
Fax: (402)421-6736

Web Site: www.myotherapy.edu
President/CEO: Sue A. Kozisek
Type: Two-Year College **Sex:** Coed **Application Fee:** $75.00 **Professional Accreditation:** ACCSC.

NATIONAL AMERICAN UNIVERSITY
3604 Summit Plz. Dr.
Bellevue, NE 68123
Tel: (402)972-4250; Free: 800-609-1425
Web Site: www.national.edu
Type: Four-Year College **Sex:** Coed **Regional Accreditation:** North Central Association of Colleges and Schools

NEBRASKA CHRISTIAN COLLEGE
12550 S 114th St.
Papillion, NE 68046
Tel: (402)935-9400
E-mail: dj.parkey@nechristian.edu
Web Site: www.nechristian.edu
President/CEO: Anthony D. Clark
Admissions: DJ Perkey
Financial Aid: Sarah Nigro
Type: Four-Year College **Sex:** Coed **Affiliation:** Christian Churches and Churches of Christ. **Scores:** 68% ACT 18-23; 20% ACT 24-29 **Costs Per Year:** One-time mandatory fee: $300. Comprehensive fee: $24,200 includes full-time tuition ($16,200) and college room and board ($8000). Full-time tuition varies according to course load. Room and board charges vary according to board plan and housing facility. Part-time tuition: $700 per credit hour. Part-time tuition varies according to course load. **Scholarships:** Available. **Calendar System:** Semester, Summer session not available **Enrollment:** Full-time 111, Part-time 19 **Student-Faculty Ratio:** 5:1 **Exams:** ACT; ACT essay component not used; SAT essay component not used. **% Residing in College-Owned, -Operated, or -Affiliated Housing:** 75 **Final Year or Final Semester Residency Requirement:** Yes **Credit Hours For Degree:** 64 semester hours, Associates; 122 semester hours, Bachelors **Professional Accreditation:** ABHE. **Intercollegiate Athletics:** Basketball M

NEBRASKA COLLEGE OF TECHNICAL AGRICULTURE
RR3, Box 23A
Curtis, NE 69025-9205
Tel: (308)367-4124; Free: 800-3CURTIS
Fax: (308)367-5203
Web Site: www.ncta.unl.edu
President/CEO: Dr. Weldon Sleight
Admissions: Kevin Martin
Financial Aid: Brenda Kahny-Martin
Type: Two-Year College **Sex:** Coed **Affiliation:** Institute of Agriculture and Natural Resources - University of Nebraska; University of Nebraska System. **Admission Plans:** Early Admission; Open Admission **Application Deadline:** Rolling **Application Fee:** $25.00 **H.S. Requirements:** High school diploma required; GED accepted **Scholarships:** Available. **Calendar System:** Miscellaneous, Summer session not available **Enrollment:** Full-time 246, Part-time 179 **Faculty:** Full-time 13, Part-time 8 **Student-Faculty Ratio:** 13:1 **Exams:** ACT. **% Residing in College-Owned, -Operated, or -Affiliated Housing:** 45 **Regional Accreditation:** North Central Association of Colleges and Schools **Credit Hours For Degree:** 64 semester hours, Associates **Intercollegiate Athletics:** Basketball M & W; Golf M

NEBRASKA INDIAN COMMUNITY COLLEGE
PO Box 428
Macy, NE 68039-0428
Tel: (402)494-2311; Free: 844-440-NICC
Fax: (402)878-2522
E-mail: tmunhofen@thenicc.edu
Web Site: www.thenicc.edu
President/CEO: Michael Oltrogge
Admissions: Troy Munhofen
Type: Two-Year College **Sex:** Coed **Costs Per Year:** One-time mandatory fee: $50. State resident tuition: $4080 full-time, $170 per credit hour part-time. Nonresident tuition: $4080 full-time, $170 per credit hour part-time. **Scholarships:** Available. **Calendar System:** Semester, Summer session available **Enrollment:** Full-time 54, Part-time 66 **Faculty:** Full-time 10, Part-time 6 **Student-Faculty Ratio:** 6:1 **Exams:** ACT essay component used for

placement; SAT essay component used for placement. **Regional Accreditation:** North Central Association of Colleges and Schools **Credit Hours For Degree:** 60 credit hours, Associates

NEBRASKA METHODIST COLLEGE

720 N 87th St.
Omaha, NE 68114
Tel: (402)354-7000; Free: 800-335-5510
Fax: (402)354-4819
E-mail: megan.maryott@methodistcollege.edu
Web Site: www.methodistcollege.edu
President/CEO: Dr. Dennis A. Joslin
Admissions: Megan Maryott
Financial Aid: Penny James
Type: Comprehensive **Sex:** Coed **Affiliation:** United Methodist Church. **Scores:** 100% SAT V 400+; 57% ACT 18-23; 43% ACT 24-29 **% Accepted:** 34 **Admission Plans:** Deferred Admission **Application Deadline:** Rolling **Application Fee:** $25.00 **H.S. Requirements:** High school diploma required; GED accepted **Costs Per Year:** Application fee: $25. Tuition: $17,040 full-time, $568 per credit hour part-time. Mandatory fees: $1550 full-time. Full-time tuition and fees vary according to degree level and program. Part-time tuition varies according to degree level and program. College room only: $7464. Room charges vary according to housing facility. **Scholarships:** Available. **Calendar System:** Semester, Summer session available **Enrollment:** Full-time 457, Graduate full-time 153, Graduate part-time 73, Part-time 317 **Faculty:** Full-time 58, Part-time 10 **Student-Faculty Ratio:** 12:1 **Exams:** ACT essay component not used; SAT I or ACT; SAT essay component not used. **% Receiving Financial Aid:** 76 **% Residing in College-Owned, -Operated, or -Affiliated Housing:** 8 **Final Year or Final Semester Residency Requirement:** No **Regional Accreditation:** North Central Association of Colleges and Schools **Credit Hours For Degree:** 82 credit hours, Associates; 127 credit hours, Bachelors **ROTC:** Air Force **Professional Accreditation:** AACN, CoARC, JRCEDMS.

NEBRASKA WESLEYAN UNIVERSITY

5000 Saint Paul Ave.
Lincoln, NE 68504-2796
Tel: (402)466-2371; Free: 800-541-3818
Fax: (402)465-2179
E-mail: admissions@nebrwesleyan.edu
Web Site: www.nebrwesleyan.edu
President/CEO: Dr. Frederik Ohles
Admissions: Gordie Coffin
Financial Aid: Thomas J. Ochsner
Type: Comprehensive **Sex:** Coed **Affiliation:** United Methodist. **Scores:** 100% SAT V 400+; 100% SAT M 400+; 36.67% ACT 18-23; 51.39% ACT 24-29 **% Accepted:** 78 **Admission Plans:** Deferred Admission; Early Action **Application Deadline:** August 15 **Application Fee:** $0.00 **H.S. Requirements:** High school diploma required; GED accepted **Costs Per Year:** Application fee: $0. Comprehensive fee: $38,140 includes full-time tuition ($29,200), mandatory fees ($600), and college room and board ($8340). Room and board charges vary according to board plan and housing facility. Part-time tuition: $1078 per credit hour. Part-time tuition varies according to class time and location. **Scholarships:** Available. **Calendar System:** Semester, Summer session available **Enrollment:** Full-time 1,511, Graduate full-time 38, Graduate part-time 213, Part-time 321 **Faculty:** Full-time 106, Part-time 127 **Student-Faculty Ratio:** 12:1 **Exams:** SAT I or ACT; SAT Reasoning; SAT Subject. **% Receiving Financial Aid:** 71 **% Residing in College-Owned, -Operated, or -Affiliated Housing:** 63 **Final Year or Final Semester Residency Requirement:** Yes **Regional Accreditation:** North Central Association of Colleges and Schools **Credit Hours For Degree:** 126 semester credits, Bachelors **ROTC:** Air Force, Army, Navy **Professional Accreditation:** ACBSP, ACEN, NASM, NCATE. **Intercollegiate Athletics:** Baseball M; Basketball M & W; Cheerleading W; Cross-Country Running M & W; Football M; Golf M & W; Soccer M & W; Softball W; Swimming and Diving M & W; Tennis M & W; Track and Field M & W; Volleyball W

NORTHEAST COMMUNITY COLLEGE

801 E Benjamin Ave.
Norfolk, NE 68702-0469
Tel: (402)371-2020
Fax: (402)644-0650
E-mail: admission@northeast.edu
Web Site: www.northeast.edu

President/CEO: Dr. Michael Chipps
Admissions: Tiffany Hopper
Financial Aid: Stacy Dieckman
Type: Two-Year College **Sex:** Coed **Affiliation:** Nebraska Coordinating Commission for Postsecondary Education. **Admission Plans:** Early Admission; Open Admission **Application Deadline:** Rolling **Application Fee:** $0.00 **H.S. Requirements:** High school diploma or equivalent not required **Costs Per Year:** Application fee: $0. State resident tuition: $2580 full-time, $86 per credit hour part-time. Nonresident tuition: $3630 full-time, $121 per credit hour part-time. Mandatory fees: $585 full-time, $19.50 per credit hour part-time. College room and board: $7672. College room only: $4700. Room and board charges vary according to board plan and housing facility. **Scholarships:** Available. **Calendar System:** Semester, Summer session available **Enrollment:** Full-time 2,200, Part-time 2,945 **Faculty:** Full-time 118, Part-time 168 **Student-Faculty Ratio:** 18:1 **Exams:** ACT essay component not used; SAT essay component not used. **% Residing in College-Owned, -Operated, or -Affiliated Housing:** 7 **Final Year or Final Semester Residency Requirement:** No **Regional Accreditation:** North Central Association of Colleges and Schools **Credit Hours For Degree:** 60 semester hours, Associates **Professional Accreditation:** ACEN, APTA. **Intercollegiate Athletics:** Basketball M & W; Golf M; Volleyball W

OMAHA SCHOOL OF MASSAGE AND HEALTHCARE OF HERZING UNIVERSITY

9748 Park Dr.
Omaha, NE 68127
Tel: (402)331-3694
Fax: (402)331-0280
Web Site: www.osmhc.com
President/CEO: Steve Carper
Type: Two-Year College **Sex:** Coed **Regional Accreditation:** North Central Association of Colleges and Schools

PERU STATE COLLEGE

PO Box 10
Peru, NE 68421
Tel: (402)872-3815; Free: 800-741-4412
E-mail: mwillis@peru.edu
Web Site: www.peru.edu
President/CEO: Dr. Daniel H. Hanson, PhD
Admissions: Micki Willis
Financial Aid: Diana Lind
Type: Comprehensive **Sex:** Coed **Affiliation:** Nebraska State College System. **Scores:** 58% ACT 18-23; 15% ACT 24-29 **% Accepted:** 49 **Admission Plans:** Open Admission **Application Deadline:** Rolling **Application Fee:** $0.00 **H.S. Requirements:** High school diploma required; GED accepted **Costs Per Year:** Application fee: $0. State resident tuition: $4590 full-time, $153 per credit hour part-time. Nonresident tuition: $4590 full-time, $153 per credit hour part-time. Mandatory fees: $1807 full-time. Full-time tuition and fees vary according to course level, course load, and location. Part-time tuition varies according to course level, course load, and location. College room and board: $6998. College room only: $3920. Room and board charges vary according to board plan and housing facility. **Scholarships:** Available. **Calendar System:** Semester, Summer session available **Enrollment:** Full-time 1,192, Graduate full-time 58, Graduate part-time 206, Part-time 902 **Faculty:** Full-time 47, Part-time 62 **Student-Faculty Ratio:** 24:1 **Exams:** SAT I or ACT. **% Residing in College-Owned, -Operated, or -Affiliated Housing:** 33 **Regional Accreditation:** North Central Association of Colleges and Schools **Credit Hours For Degree:** 125 semester hours, Bachelors **ROTC:** Air Force, Army **Professional Accreditation:** NCATE. **Intercollegiate Athletics:** Baseball M; Basketball M & W; Cheerleading W; Cross-Country Running W; Football M; Golf W; Softball W; Volleyball W

ST. GREGORY THE GREAT SEMINARY

800 Fletcher Rd.
Seward, NE 68434
Tel: (402)643-4052
Fax: (402)643-6964
E-mail: sggs@stgregoryseminary.edu
Web Site: www.stgregoryseminary.edu
President/CEO: Rev. John T. Folda
Admissions: Rev. Peter M. Mitchell
Type: Four-Year College **Sex:** Men **Affiliation:** Roman Catholic. **Application Fee:** $0.00 **H.S. Requirements:** High school diploma required; GED

accepted **Enrollment:** Full-time 48 **Faculty:** Full-time 7, Part-time 6 **Student-Faculty Ratio:** 5:1 **Exams:** SAT I or ACT. **% Residing in College-Owned, -Operated, or -Affiliated Housing:** 100 **Final Year or Final Semester Residency Requirement:** Yes **Regional Accreditation:** North Central Association of Colleges and Schools **Credit Hours For Degree:** 128 semester hours, Bachelors

SOUTHEAST COMMUNITY COLLEGE, BEATRICE CAMPUS
4771 W Scott Rd.
Beatrice, NE 68310
Tel: (402)228-3468; Free: 800-233-5027
Fax: (402)228-2218
Web Site: www.southeast.edu

Type: Two-Year College **Sex:** Coed **Affiliation:** Southeast Community College System. **Admission Plans:** Deferred Admission; Early Admission; Open Admission **Application Deadline:** Rolling **H.S. Requirements:** High school diploma required; GED accepted **Scholarships:** Available. **Calendar System:** Semester, Summer session available **Exams:** Other; SAT I or ACT. **Regional Accreditation:** North Central Association of Colleges and Schools **Credit Hours For Degree:** 60 credit hours, Associates **Professional Accreditation:** ACEN. **Intercollegiate Athletics:** Basketball M & W; Golf M; Volleyball W

SOUTHEAST COMMUNITY COLLEGE, LINCOLN CAMPUS
8800 O St.
Lincoln, NE 68520-1299
Tel: (402)471-3333; Free: 800-642-4075
E-mail: admissions@southeast.edu
Web Site: www.southeast.edu
President/CEO: Dr. Paul Illich

Type: Two-Year College **Sex:** Coed **Affiliation:** Southeast Community College System. **Admission Plans:** Deferred Admission; Early Admission; Open Admission **Application Deadline:** Rolling **H.S. Requirements:** High school diploma required; GED accepted **Costs Per Year:** State resident tuition: $2,722 full-time, $60.50 per quarter hour part-time. Nonresident tuition: $3,352 full-time, $74.50 per quarter hour part-time. Mandatory fees: $56 full-time, $1.25 per quarter hour part-time. Full-time tuition and fees vary according to course load. Part-time tuition and fees vary according to course load. **Scholarships:** Available. **Calendar System:** Quarter, Summer session available **Enrollment:** Full-time 4,086, Part-time 5,107 **Faculty:** Full-time 310, Part-time 397 **Student-Faculty Ratio:** 18:1 **Exams:** ACT; ACT essay component not used; SAT I; SAT essay component not used. **Final Year or Final Semester Residency Requirement:** No **Regional Accreditation:** North Central Association of Colleges and Schools **Credit Hours For Degree:** 90 quarter credits, depending on program, Associates **Professional Accreditation:** ACBSP, ACEN, ACF, ADA, ARCST, CoARC, JRCERT, NAACLS. **Intercollegiate Athletics:** Baseball M; Basketball M & W; Golf M; Softball W; Volleyball W

SOUTHEAST COMMUNITY COLLEGE, MILFORD CAMPUS
600 State St.
Milford, NE 68405
Tel: (402)761-2131; Free: 800-933-7223
E-mail: admissions@southeast.edu
Web Site: www.southeast.edu
President/CEO: Dr. Paul Illich

Type: Two-Year College **Sex:** Coed **Affiliation:** Southeast Community College System. **Admission Plans:** Deferred Admission; Early Admission; Open Admission **Application Deadline:** Rolling **H.S. Requirements:** High school diploma required; GED accepted **Costs Per Year:** State resident tuition: $2,722 full-time, $60.50 per credit hour part-time. Nonresident tuition: $3,352 full-time, $74.50 per credit hour part-time. Mandatory fees: $56 full-time, $1.25 per credit hour part-time. Full-time tuition and fees vary according to course load. Part-time tuition and fees vary according to course load. College room and board: $4647. College room only: $2355. Room and board charges vary according to gender, housing facility, and location. **Scholarships:** Available. **Calendar System:** Quarter, Summer session available **Enrollment:** Full-time 4,086, Part-time 5,107 **Faculty:** Full-time 310, Part-time 397 **Student-Faculty Ratio:** 18:1 **Exams:** ACT; ACT essay component not used; SAT I; SAT essay component not used. **Final Year or Final Semester Residency Requirement:** No **Regional Accreditation:** North Central Association of Colleges and Schools **Credit Hours For Degree:** 90 credits, depending on the program, Associates **Intercollegiate Athletics:** Baseball M; Basketball M & W; Golf M; Softball W; Volleyball W

UNION COLLEGE
3800 S 48th St.
Lincoln, NE 68506-4300
Tel: (402)486-2600; Free: 800-228-4600
Fax: (402)486-2895
E-mail: enroll@ucollege.edu
Web Site: www.ucollege.edu
President/CEO: Dr. Vinita Sauder
Admissions: Addison Hudgins
Financial Aid: Taryn A. Rouse

Type: Comprehensive **Sex:** Coed **Affiliation:** Seventh-day Adventist. **Scores:** 95% SAT M 400+; 50% ACT 18-23; 27% ACT 24-29 **% Accepted:** 56 **Application Fee:** $0.00 **H.S. Requirements:** High school diploma required; GED accepted **Costs Per Year:** Application fee: $0. Comprehensive fee: $29,304 includes full-time tuition ($21,456), mandatory fees ($1082), and college room and board ($6766). College room only: $3800. Full-time tuition and fees vary according to course load, degree level, and program. Room and board charges vary according to board plan and housing facility. Part-time tuition: $894 per credit hour. Part-time tuition varies according to program. **Scholarships:** Available. **Calendar System:** Semester, Summer session available **Enrollment:** Full-time 724, Graduate full-time 89, Part-time 90 **Faculty:** Full-time 61, Part-time 53 **Student-Faculty Ratio:** 10:1 **Exams:** SAT I or ACT; SAT Reasoning; SAT Subject. **% Receiving Financial Aid:** 72 **% Residing in College-Owned, -Operated, or -Affiliated Housing:** 74 **Regional Accreditation:** North Central Association of Colleges and Schools **Credit Hours For Degree:** 64 semester hours, Associates; 128 semester hours, Bachelors **Professional Accreditation:** AACN, NCATE. **Intercollegiate Athletics:** Basketball M & W; Golf M; Volleyball W

UNIVERSAL COLLEGE OF HEALING ARTS
8702 N 30th St.
Omaha, NE 68112-1810
Tel: (402)556-4456
Web Site: www.ucha.edu
Type: Two-Year College **Sex:** Coed **Professional Accreditation:** ABHES.

UNIVERSITY OF NEBRASKA AT KEARNEY
905 W 25th St.
Kearney, NE 68849-0001
Tel: (308)865-8441; Free: 800-532-7639
Fax: (308)865-8987
E-mail: admissionsug@unk.edu
Web Site: www.unk.edu
President/CEO: Douglas Kristensen
Admissions: Dusty Newton

Type: Comprehensive **Sex:** Coed **Affiliation:** University of Nebraska System. **Scores:** 85% SAT V 400+; 85% SAT M 400+; 52.8% ACT 18-23; 33.2% ACT 24-29 **% Accepted:** 85 **Application Deadline:** September 1 **Application Fee:** $45.00 **H.S. Requirements:** High school diploma required; GED accepted **Costs Per Year:** Application fee: $45. State resident tuition: $5325 full-time, $175 per credit hour part-time. Nonresident tuition: $11,595 full-time, $380 per credit hour part-time. Mandatory fees: $1399 full-time. Full-time tuition and fees vary according to course level, course load, degree level, location, and program. Part-time tuition varies according to course level, course load, degree level, location, and program. College room and board: $9230. College room only: $4730. Room and board charges vary according to board plan and housing facility. **Scholarships:** Available. **Calendar System:** Semester **Enrollment:** Full-time 4,432, Graduate full-time 243, Graduate part-time 1,396, Part-time 676 **Faculty:** Full-time 333, Part-time 120 **Student-Faculty Ratio:** 14:1 **Exams:** ACT essay component not used; SAT I or ACT; SAT essay component not used; SAT Reasoning. **% Receiving Financial Aid:** 63 **% Residing in College-Owned, -Operated, or -Affiliated Housing:** 90 **Final Year or Final Semester Residency Requirement:** No **Regional Accreditation:** North Central Association of Colleges and Schools **Credit Hours For Degree:** 120 semester hours, Bachelors **ROTC:** Army **Professional Accreditation:** AACSB, AAFCS, ACA, ASHA, ATMAE, CSWE, JRCAT, NASM, NCATE. **Intercollegiate Athletics:** Baseball M; Basketball M & W; Cross-Country Running M & W; Football M; Golf M & W; Soccer W; Softball W; Swimming and Diving W; Tennis M & W; Track and Field M & W; Volleyball W; Wrestling M

UNIVERSITY OF NEBRASKA MEDICAL CENTER
Nebraska Medical Ctr.
Omaha, NE 68198

Tel: (402)559-4000; Free: 800-626-8431
Fax: (402)559-6796
Web Site: www.unmc.edu
President/CEO: Dr. Harold M. Maurer
Financial Aid: Judy D. Walker
Type: Two-Year Upper Division **Sex:** Coed **Affiliation:** University of Nebraska System. **Admission Plans:** Deferred Admission; Preferred Admission **Application Fee:** $45.00 **H.S. Requirements:** High school diploma required; GED accepted **Scholarships:** Available. **Calendar System:** Semester, Summer session available **Enrollment:** Full-time 895, Graduate full-time 2,172, Graduate part-time 440, Part-time 118 **Faculty:** Full-time 1,023, Part-time 209 **Student-Faculty Ratio:** 3:1 **% Receiving Financial Aid:** 70 **Final Year or Final Semester Residency Requirement:** Yes **Regional Accreditation:** North Central Association of Colleges and Schools **Credit Hours For Degree:** 131 semester hours, Bachelors **ROTC:** Air Force, Army **Professional Accreditation:** AACN, ACPE, ACPeE, ADA, AND, APTA, CEPH, JRCEDMS, JRCERT, JRCNMT, LCME/AMA, NAACLS.

UNIVERSITY OF NEBRASKA AT OMAHA

6001 Dodge St.
Omaha, NE 68182
Tel: (402)554-2200
Fax: (402)554-3472
E-mail: cliewer@unomaha.edu
Web Site: www.unomaha.edu
President/CEO: John E. Christensen
Admissions: Chris Liewer
Financial Aid: Marty Habrock
Type: University **Sex:** Coed **Affiliation:** University of Nebraska System. **Scores:** 46% ACT 18-23; 32% ACT 24-29 **% Accepted:** 71 **Admission Plans:** Deferred Admission **Application Deadline:** August 1 **Application Fee:** $45.00 **H.S. Requirements:** High school diploma required; GED accepted **Scholarships:** Available. **Calendar System:** Semester, Summer session available **Enrollment:** Full-time 9,511, Graduate full-time 863, Graduate part-time 2,029, Part-time 2,824 **Faculty:** Full-time 520, Part-time 524 **Student-Faculty Ratio:** 17:1 **Exams:** SAT I or ACT. **% Receiving Financial Aid:** 59 **% Residing in College-Owned, -Operated, or -Affiliated Housing:** 11 **Final Year or Final Semester Residency Requirement:** No **Regional Accreditation:** North Central Association of Colleges and Schools **Credit Hours For Degree:** 125 semester hours, Bachelors **ROTC:** Air Force, Army **Professional Accreditation:** AABI, AACSB, ABET, ACA, ASHA, CEPH, CSWE, JRCAT, NASAD, NASM, NASPAA, NCATE. **Intercollegiate Athletics:** Baseball M; Basketball M & W; Golf M & W; Ice Hockey M; Soccer M & W; Softball W; Swimming and Diving W; Tennis M & W; Track and Field W; Volleyball W

UNIVERSITY OF NEBRASKA–LINCOLN

14th and R Sts.
Lincoln, NE 68588
Tel: (402)472-7211; Free: 800-742-8800
Fax: (402)472-0670
E-mail: admissions@unl.edu
Web Site: www.unl.edu
President/CEO: Harvey S. Perlman
Admissions: Amber Williams
Financial Aid: Jo Tederman
Type: University **Sex:** Coed **Affiliation:** University of Nebraska System. **Scores:** 96% SAT V 400+; 98% SAT M 400+; 35% ACT 18-23; 43% ACT 24-29 **% Accepted:** 76 **Application Deadline:** May 1 **Application Fee:** $45.00 **H.S. Requirements:** High school diploma required; GED accepted **Costs Per Year:** Application fee: $45. State resident tuition: $6593 full-time, $219.75 per credit hour part-time. Nonresident tuition: $20,760 full-time, $692 per credit hour part-time. Mandatory fees: $1686 full-time, $15 per credit hour part-time, $365 per term part-time. Full-time tuition and fees vary according to course load, program, and reciprocity agreements. Part-time tuition and fees vary according to course load, program, and reciprocity agreements. College room and board: $10,310. Room and board charges vary according to board plan and housing facility. **Scholarships:** Available. **Calendar System:** Semester, Summer session available **Enrollment:** Full-time 18,817, Graduate full-time 2,643, Graduate part-time 2,435, Part-time 1,365 **Faculty:** Full-time 1,049, Part-time 15 **Student-Faculty Ratio:** 22:1 **Exams:** ACT; ACT essay component not used; SAT I or ACT; SAT essay component not used; SAT Reasoning. **% Receiving Financial Aid:** 38 **% Residing in College-Owned, -Operated, or -Affiliated Housing:** 41 Final

Year or Final Semester Residency Requirement: Yes **Regional Accreditation:** North Central Association of Colleges and Schools **Credit Hours For Degree:** 120 credit hours, Bachelors **ROTC:** Air Force, Army, Navy **Professional Accreditation:** AACSB, AAFCS, AAMFT, ABA, ABET, ACCE, ACEJMC, ACSP, ADA, AND, APA, ASHA, CIDA, NAAB, NASAD, NASM, NAST, NCATE, TEAC. **Intercollegiate Athletics:** Baseball M; Basketball M & W; Bowling W; Cross-Country Running M & W; Football M; Golf M & W; Gymnastics M & W; Riflery W; Soccer W; Softball W; Swimming and Diving W; Tennis M & W; Track and Field M & W; Volleyball W; Wrestling M

WAYNE STATE COLLEGE

1111 Main St.
Wayne, NE 68787
Tel: (402)375-7000; Free: 866-WSC-CATS
Fax: (402)375-7204
E-mail: admit1@wsc.edu
Web Site: www.wsc.edu
President/CEO: Dr. Marysz Rames
Admissions: Kevin Halle
Financial Aid: Annette Kaus
Type: Comprehensive **Sex:** Coed **Affiliation:** Nebraska State College System. **Scores:** 37% ACT 18-23; 30% ACT 24-29 **% Accepted:** 100 **Admission Plans:** Deferred Admission; Open Admission **Application Deadline:** Rolling **H.S. Requirements:** High school diploma required; GED accepted **Costs Per Year:** State resident tuition: $4590 full-time, $153 per credit hour part-time. Nonresident tuition: $9180 full-time, $306 per credit hour part-time. Mandatory fees: $1452 full-time, $57.75 per credit hour part-time. Full-time tuition and fees vary according to course level and course load. Part-time tuition and fees vary according to course level and course load. College room and board: $6760. College room only: $3300. Room and board charges vary according to board plan and housing facility. **Scholarships:** Available. **Calendar System:** Semester, Summer session available **Enrollment:** Full-time 2,611, Graduate full-time 123, Graduate part-time 395, Part-time 302 **Faculty:** Full-time 128, Part-time 89 **Student-Faculty Ratio:** 19:1 **Exams:** SAT I or ACT. **% Receiving Financial Aid:** 67 **% Residing in College-Owned, -Operated, or -Affiliated Housing:** 46 **Final Year or Final Semester Residency Requirement:** No **Regional Accreditation:** North Central Association of Colleges and Schools **Credit Hours For Degree:** 120 semester hours, Bachelors **ROTC:** Army **Professional Accreditation:** AAFCS, NASAD, NASM, NCATE. **Intercollegiate Athletics:** Baseball M; Basketball M & W; Cheerleading M & W; Cross-Country Running M & W; Football M; Rugby M & W; Soccer M & W; Softball W; Track and Field M & W; Volleyball W; Wrestling M

WESTERN NEBRASKA COMMUNITY COLLEGE

371 College Dr.
Sidney, NE 69162
Tel: (308)254-5450; Free: 800-222-9682
Fax: (308)254-7444
E-mail: rhovey@wncc.net
Web Site: www.wncc.net
President/CEO: Todd Holcomb
Admissions: Troy Archuleta
Type: Two-Year College **Sex:** Coed **Affiliation:** Western Community College Area System. **Admission Plans:** Open Admission **Application Deadline:** Rolling **Application Fee:** $0.00 **H.S. Requirements:** High school diploma required; GED accepted **Scholarships:** Available. **Calendar System:** Semester, Summer session available **Student-Faculty Ratio:** 11:1 **Regional Accreditation:** North Central Association of Colleges and Schools **Credit Hours For Degree:** 60 semester hours, Associates **Professional Accreditation:** ACEN, AHIMA. **Intercollegiate Athletics:** Baseball M; Basketball M & W; Soccer M & W; Softball W; Volleyball W

YORK COLLEGE

1125 E 8th St.
York, NE 68467
Tel: (402)363-5600; Free: 800-950-9675
Fax: (402)363-5666
E-mail: enroll@york.edu
Web Site: www.york.edu
President/CEO: Steve Eckman
Admissions: Janae Parsons
Financial Aid: Brien Alley

Type: Four-Year College **Sex:** Coed **Affiliation:** Church of Christ. **Scores:** 90% SAT V 400+; 80% SAT M 400+; 40% ACT 18-23; 27% ACT 24-29 **% Accepted:** 60 **Admission Plans:** Deferred Admission; Early Admission **Application Deadline:** Rolling **Application Fee:** $20.00 **H.S. Requirements:** High school diploma required; GED accepted **Costs Per Year:** Application fee: $20. Comprehensive fee: $23,600 includes full-time tuition ($16,800), mandatory fees ($400), and college room and board ($6400). Full-time tuition and fees vary according to course load. Room and board charges vary according to board plan and housing facility. Part-time tuition: $580 per credit hour. Part-time tuition varies according to course load. **Scholarships:** Available. **Calendar System:** Semester, Summer session available **Enrollment:** Full-time 416, Part-time 14 **Faculty:** Full-time 22, Part-time 16 **Student-Faculty Ratio:** 11:1 **Exams:** SAT I or ACT; SAT Reasoning. **% Receiving Financial Aid:** 88 **% Residing in College-Owned, -Operated, or -Affiliated Housing:** 80 **Regional Accreditation:** North Central Association of Colleges and Schools **Credit Hours For Degree:** 64 credit hours, Associates; 128 credit hours, Bachelors **ROTC:** Air Force, Army, Navy **Professional Accreditation:** NCATE. **Intercollegiate Athletics:** Baseball M; Basketball M & W; Cross-Country Running M & W; Soccer M & W; Softball W; Track and Field M & W; Volleyball W; Wrestling M

THE ART INSTITUTE OF LAS VEGAS

2350 Corporate Cir. Dr.
Henderson, NV 89074
Tel: (702)369-9944; Free: 800-833-2678
Fax: (702)992-8558
Web Site: www.artinstitutes.edu/lasvegas
President/CEO: Mark Garland
Type: Four-Year College **Sex:** Coed **Affiliation:** Education Management Corporation. **Calendar System:** Quarter **Regional Accreditation:** Southern Association of Colleges and Schools **Professional Accreditation:** ACF, ACICS.

BRIGHTWOOD COLLEGE, LAS VEGAS CAMPUS

3535 W Sahara Ave.
Las Vegas, NV 89102
Tel: (702)368-2338; Free: 800-935-1857
Fax: (702)638-3853
Web Site: www.brightwood.edu
President/CEO: Lisia J. Moore
Type: Two-Year College **Sex:** Coed **Professional Accreditation:** ACCSC, ACICS.

CAREER COLLEGE OF NORTHERN NEVADA

1421 Pullman Dr.
Sparks, NV 89434
Tel: (775)856-2266
E-mail: lgoldhammer@ccnn4u.com
Web Site: www.ccnn.edu
President/CEO: L. Nathan Clark
Admissions: Laura Goldhammer
Type: Two-Year College **Sex:** Coed **% Accepted:** 100 **Admission Plans:** Open Admission **Application Deadline:** Rolling **Application Fee:** $25.00 **H.S. Requirements:** High school diploma required; GED accepted **Scholarships:** Available. **Calendar System:** Quarter, Summer session available **Enrollment:** Full-time 363 **Faculty:** Full-time 11, Part-time 12 **Student-Faculty Ratio:** 20:1 **Credit Hours For Degree:** 99.5 units, Associates **Professional Accreditation:** ACCSC.

CARRINGTON COLLEGE–LAS VEGAS

5740 S Eastern Ave.
Las Vegas, NV 89119
Tel: (702)688-4300
Web Site: carrington.edu
President/CEO: Janet Kent
Type: Two-Year College **Sex:** Coed **Affiliation:** Carrington Colleges Group, Inc. **Application Fee:** $0.00 **H.S. Requirements:** High school diploma required; GED accepted **Costs Per Year:** Application fee: $0. Tuition: $44,582 per degree program. **Enrollment:** Full-time 298, Part-time 72 **Faculty:** Full-time 6, Part-time 12 **Student-Faculty Ratio:** 32:1 **Professional Accreditation:** ACICS.

CARRINGTON COLLEGE–RENO

5580 Kietzke Ln.
Reno, NV 89511
Tel: (775)335-2900

E-mail: mcomo@carrington.edu
Web Site: carrington.edu
President/CEO: Terrance Harris
Admissions: Michael Como
Type: Two-Year College **Sex:** Coed **Affiliation:** Carrington Colleges Group, Inc. **H.S. Requirements:** High school diploma required; GED accepted **Costs Per Year:** Tuition: $50,599 per degree program. Part-time tuition varies according to program. **Enrollment:** Full-time 257, Part-time 70 **Faculty:** Full-time 12, Part-time 21 **Student-Faculty Ratio:** 15:1 **Professional Accreditation:** ACICS.

CHAMBERLAIN COLLEGE OF NURSING

9901 Covington Cross Dr.
Las Vegas, NV 89144
Tel: (702)786-1660; Free: 877-751-5783
Fax: (702)786-1661
Web Site: www.chamberlain.edu
Type: Four-Year College **Sex:** Coed **Application Fee:** $95.00 **H.S. Requirements:** High school diploma required; GED accepted **Costs Per Year:** Application fee: $95. Tuition: $17,560 full-time, $665 per credit hour part-time. Mandatory fees: $600 full-time, $300 per term part-time. **Exams:** ACT essay component used for admission; SAT I or ACT; SAT essay component used for admission. **Regional Accreditation:** North Central Association of Colleges and Schools

COLLEGE OF SOUTHERN NEVADA

6375 W Charleston Blvd.
Las Vegas, NV 89146
Tel: (702)651-5000
Web Site: www.csn.edu
President/CEO: Dr. Michael Richards
Type: Two-Year College **Sex:** Coed **Affiliation:** University and Community College System of Nevada. **Admission Plans:** Early Admission; Open Admission **Application Deadline:** Rolling **H.S. Requirements:** High school diploma or equivalent not required. For allied health programs: High school diploma required; GED accepted **Costs Per Year:** State resident tuition: $2196 full-time, $91.50 per credit part-time. Nonresident tuition: $8841 full-time, $193.25 per credit part-time. Mandatory fees: $132 full-time, $5.50 per credit part-time. Full-time tuition and fees vary according to course level, course load, program, and reciprocity agreements. Part-time tuition and fees vary according to course level, course load, program, and reciprocity agreements. **Scholarships:** Available. **Calendar System:** Semester, Summer session available **Credit Hours For Degree:** 60 credit hours, Associates **ROTC:** Army **Professional Accreditation:** ABET, ACBSP, ACEN, ACF, ADA, AHIMA, AOTA, APTA, COA, CoARC, JRCEDMS, NAACLS, NCCU.

DEVRY UNIVERSITY

2490 Paseo Verde Pky., Ste. 150
Henderson, NV 89074-7120
Tel: (702)933-9700; Free: 866-338-7941
Fax: (702)933-9717
Web Site: www.devry.edu
Type: Comprehensive **Sex:** Coed **Application Deadline:** Rolling **Costs Per Year:** Tuition: $13,300 full-time, $475 per credit hour part-time. Mandatory fees: $80 full-time, $40 per term part-time. **Scholarships:** Available.

Calendar System: Semester **% Receiving Financial Aid:** 74 **Regional Accreditation:** North Central Association of Colleges and Schools **Professional Accreditation:** ACBSP.

EVEREST COLLEGE
170 N Stephanie St.
Henderson, NV 89074
Tel: (702)567-1920; Free: 888-741-4270
Web Site: www.everest.edu
President/CEO: Steve Guell
Type: Two-Year College **Sex:** Coed **Affiliation:** Zenith Education Group. **Professional Accreditation:** ACICS.

GREAT BASIN COLLEGE
1500 College Pky.
Elko, NV 89801-3348
Tel: (775)738-8493
E-mail: jan.king@gbcnv.edu
Web Site: www.gbcnv.edu
President/CEO: Mark Curtis
Admissions: Jan King
Financial Aid: Scott Nielsen
Type: Two-Year College **Sex:** Coed **Affiliation:** Nevada System of Higher Education. **% Accepted:** 100 **Admission Plans:** Deferred Admission; Early Admission; Open Admission **Application Deadline:** Rolling **Application Fee:** $10.00 **H.S. Requirements:** High school diploma required; GED accepted **Costs Per Year:** Application fee: $10. State resident tuition: $2640 full-time, $88 per unit part-time. Nonresident tuition: $9450 full-time, $184.75 per unit part-time. Mandatory fees: $165 full-time, $5.50 per unit part-time. Full-time tuition and fees vary according to course level, degree level, and reciprocity agreements. Part-time tuition and fees vary according to course level, degree level, and reciprocity agreements. College room and board: $6800. Room and board charges vary according to housing facility. **Scholarships:** Available. **Calendar System:** Semester, Summer session available **Enrollment:** Full-time 948, Graduate full-time 12, Graduate part-time 10, Part-time 2,179 **Faculty:** Full-time 68, Part-time 117 **Student-Faculty Ratio:** 16:1 **Exams:** ACT essay component not used; SAT essay component not used. **% Residing in College-Owned, -Operated, or -Affiliated Housing:** 4 **Final Year or Final Semester Residency Requirement:** No **Credit Hours For Degree:** 60 semester hours, Associates; 120 semester hours, Bachelors **Professional Accreditation:** ACEN, NCCU.

NEVADA STATE COLLEGE
1125 Nevada State Dr.
Henderson, NV 89015
Tel: (702)992-2000
Fax: (702)992-2226
E-mail: admissions@nsc.nevada.edu
Web Site: www.nsc.edu
President/CEO: Bart Patterson
Admissions: Adelfa Sullivan
Financial Aid: Anthony Morrone
Type: Four-Year College **Sex:** Coed **Affiliation:** Nevada System of Higher Education. **% Accepted:** 52 **Application Deadline:** Rolling **Application Fee:** $30.00 **H.S. Requirements:** High school diploma required; GED accepted **Costs Per Year:** Application fee: $30. Area resident tuition: $4,568 full-time. State resident tuition: $4,762 full-time. Nonresident tuition: $10,686 full-time. Full-time tuition varies according to program. **Scholarships:** Available. **Calendar System:** Semester, Summer session available **Enrollment:** Full-time 1,344, Part-time 2,190 **Faculty:** Full-time 66, Part-time 187 **Exams:** ACT essay component not used; ACT essay component used for advising; ACT essay component used for placement; SAT essay component not used; SAT essay component used for advising; SAT essay component used for placement. **Final Year or Final Semester Residency Requirement:** No **Credit Hours For Degree:** 124 units, Bachelors **ROTC:** Army **Professional Accreditation:** AACN, NCCU.

NORTHWEST CAREER COLLEGE
7398 Smoke Ranch Rd.
Ste. 100
Las Vegas, NV 89128
Tel: (702)254-7577
Web Site: www.northwestcareercollege.edu
Type: Two-Year College **Sex:** Coed **Professional Accreditation:** ABHES.

PIMA MEDICAL INSTITUTE
3333 E Flamingo Rd.
Las Vegas, NV 89121
Tel: (702)458-9650; Free: 800-477-PIMA
Web Site: www.pmi.edu
President/CEO: Sam Gentile
Type: Two-Year College **Sex:** Coed **Affiliation:** Vocational Training Institutes, Inc. **H.S. Requirements:** High school diploma required; GED accepted. For some certificate programs: High school diploma or equivalent not required **Calendar System:** Miscellaneous, Summer session not available **Exams:** Other. **Professional Accreditation:** ABHES.

SIERRA NEVADA COLLEGE
999 Tahoe Blvd.
Incline Village, NV 89451
Tel: (775)831-1314
Fax: (775)831-1347
E-mail: admissions@sierranevada.edu
Web Site: www.sierranevada.edu
President/CEO: Dr. Alan Walker
Admissions: Julie Hernandez
Financial Aid: Nicole D. Ferguson
Type: Comprehensive **Sex:** Coed **Scores:** 89% SAT V 400+; 84% SAT M 400+; 42% ACT 18-23; 34% ACT 24-29 **% Accepted:** 66 **Admission Plans:** Deferred Admission **Application Deadline:** Rolling **Application Fee:** $0.00 **H.S. Requirements:** High school diploma required; GED accepted **Costs Per Year:** Application fee: $0. Comprehensive fee: $43,482 includes full-time tuition ($30,321), mandatory fees ($829), and college room and board ($12,332). College room only: $6166. Full-time tuition and fees vary according to course load, degree level, program, and reciprocity agreements. Room and board charges vary according to board plan. **Scholarships:** Available. **Calendar System:** Semester, Summer session available **Enrollment:** Full-time 475, Graduate full-time 397, Graduate part-time 140, Part-time 32 **Faculty:** Full-time 43, Part-time 114 **Student-Faculty Ratio:** 12:1 **Exams:** ACT; SAT I; SAT I and SAT II or ACT; SAT I or ACT; SAT II; SAT essay component not used; SAT Reasoning; SAT Subject. **% Residing in College-Owned, -Operated, or -Affiliated Housing:** 41 **Final Year or Final Semester Residency Requirement:** Yes **Credit Hours For Degree:** 120 semester credits, Bachelors **Professional Accreditation:** NCCU. **Intercollegiate Athletics:** Cross-Country Running M & W; Golf M & W; Lacrosse M & W; Rock Climbing M & W; Skiing (Downhill) M & W; Soccer M & W

TRUCKEE MEADOWS COMMUNITY COLLEGE
7000 Dandini Blvd.
Reno, NV 89512-3901
Tel: (775)673-7000
Fax: (775)673-7028
E-mail: ahughes@tmcc.edu
Web Site: www.tmcc.edu
President/CEO: Dr. Kyle Dalpe
Admissions: Andrew Hughes
Type: Two-Year College **Sex:** Coed **Affiliation:** Nevada System of Higher Education. **% Accepted:** 100 **Admission Plans:** Early Admission; Open Admission **Application Fee:** $10.00 **H.S. Requirements:** High school diploma or equivalent not required. For applicants under 18, allied health programs, degree-seeking students: High school diploma required; GED accepted **Costs Per Year:** Application fee: $10. State resident tuition: $3030 full-time, $91.50 per credit hour part-time. Nonresident tuition: $9675 full-time, $192.25 per credit hour part-time. Mandatory fees: $9 per credit hour part-time. Full-time tuition varies according to course load and program. Part-time tuition and fees vary according to course load and program. **Scholarships:** Available. **Calendar System:** Semester, Summer session available **Enrollment:** Full-time 3,015, Part-time 8,070 **Faculty:** Full-time 150, Part-time 401 **Student-Faculty Ratio:** 20:1 **Exams:** ACT essay component not used; SAT essay component not used. **Final Year or Final Semester Residency Requirement:** No **Credit Hours For Degree:** 60 credits, Associates **ROTC:** Army **Professional Accreditation:** ACEN, ACF, ADA, JRCERT, NCCU.

UNIVERSITY OF NEVADA, LAS VEGAS
4505 S Maryland Pky.
Las Vegas, NV 89154
Tel: (702)895-3011
Fax: (702)895-1118

E-mail: admissions@unlv.edu
Web Site: www.unlv.edu
President/CEO: Dr. Len Jessup
Financial Aid: Norm Bedford

Type: University **Sex:** Coed **Scores:** 92% SAT V 400+; 91% SAT M 400+; 54.8% ACT 18-23; 26.9% ACT 24-29 **% Accepted:** 88 **Admission Plans:** Deferred Admission; Early Admission **Application Deadline:** July 1 **Application Fee:** $60.00 **H.S. Requirements:** High school diploma required; GED not accepted **Costs Per Year:** Application fee: $60. One-time mandatory fee: $120. State resident tuition: $6,277 full-time, $199.25 per credit hour part-time. Nonresident tuition: $20,187 full-time, $410.75 per credit hour part-time. Mandatory fees: $546 full-time, $9.97 per credit hour part-time, $273 per term part-time. Full-time tuition and fees vary according to course level, program, and reciprocity agreements. Part-time tuition and fees vary according to course level, program, and reciprocity agreements. College room and board: $10,730. College room only: $5880. Room and board charges vary according to board plan. **Scholarships:** Available. **Calendar System:** Semester, Summer session available **Enrollment:** Full-time 17,575, Graduate full-time 2,485, Graduate part-time 2,319, Part-time 6,226 **Exams:** SAT I or ACT. **% Receiving Financial Aid:** 63 **% Residing in College-Owned, -Operated, or -Affiliated Housing:** 7 **Final Year or Final Semester Residency Requirement:** No **ROTC:** Air Force, Army **Professional Accreditation:** AACN, AACSB, AALS, AAMFT, ABA, ABET, ACA, ACCE, ACEN, ADA, APTA, ASLA, CIDA, CSWE, JRCAT, JRCNMT, NAAB, NAACLS, NASAD, NASM, NASPAA, NAST, NCATE, NCCU. **Intercollegiate Athletics:** Baseball M; Basketball M & W; Cheerleading M & W; Cross-Country Running W; Football M; Golf M; Soccer M & W; Softball W; Swimming and Diving M & W; Tennis M & W; Track and Field W; Volleyball W

UNIVERSITY OF NEVADA, RENO

Reno, NV 89557
Tel: (775)784-1110; Free: 866-263-8232
E-mail: asknevada@unr.edu
Web Site: www.unr.edu
President/CEO: Dr. Marc Johnson
Admissions: Dr. Steve Maples
Financial Aid: Tim Wolfe

Type: University **Sex:** Coed **Affiliation:** Nevada System of Higher Education. **Scores:** 97% SAT V 400+; 96% SAT M 400+; 46% ACT 18-23; 41% ACT 24-29 **% Accepted:** 86 **Admission Plans:** Deferred Admission; Early Admission **Application Deadline:** May 1 **Application Fee:** $60.00 **H.S. Requirements:** High school diploma required; GED not accepted **Costs Per Year:** Application fee: $60. State resident tuition: $6,578 full-time, $207.25 per credit part-time. Nonresident tuition: $20,488 full-time, $426.50 per credit part-time. Mandatory fees: $564 full-time. Full-time tuition and fees vary according to course level, course load, degree level, and program. Part-time tuition varies according to course level, course load, degree level, and program. College room and board: $10,868. College room only: $6100. Room and board charges vary according to board plan and housing facility. **Scholarships:** Available. **Calendar System:** Semester, Summer session available **Enrollment:** Full-time 14,950, Graduate full-time 1,300, Graduate part-time 1,828, Part-time 2,820 **Faculty:** Full-time 627, Part-time 539

Student-Faculty Ratio: 22:1 **Exams:** ACT essay component not used; SAT I or ACT; SAT essay component not used; SAT Reasoning. **% Receiving Financial Aid:** 53 **% Residing in College-Owned, -Operated, or -Affiliated Housing:** 22 **Credit Hours For Degree:** 120 credits, Bachelors **ROTC:** Army **Professional Accreditation:** AACN, AACSB, ABET, ACA, ACEJMC, AND, APA, ASHA, CSWE, LCME/AMA, NASM, NCATE, NCCU. **Intercollegiate Athletics:** Baseball M; Basketball M & W; Cheerleading M & W; Cross-Country Running W; Football M; Golf M & W; Riflery M & W; Soccer W; Softball W; Swimming and Diving W; Tennis M & W; Track and Field W; Volleyball W

UNIVERSITY OF PHOENIX–LAS VEGAS CAMPUS

3755 Breakthrough Way
Las Vegas, NV 89135
Tel: (702)638-7279; Free: 866-766-0766
Fax: (702)638-8035
Web Site: www.phoenix.edu
President/CEO: Timothy P. Slottow
Admissions: Marc Booker

Type: Comprehensive **Sex:** Coed **Admission Plans:** Deferred Admission; Open Admission **Application Deadline:** Rolling **Application Fee:** $0.00 **H.S. Requirements:** High school diploma required; GED accepted **Scholarships:** Available. **Calendar System:** Continuous, Summer session not available **Enrollment:** Full-time 2,301 **Faculty:** Full-time 35, Part-time 244 **Regional Accreditation:** North Central Association of Colleges and Schools **Credit Hours For Degree:** 60 credits, Associates; 120 credits, Bachelors **Professional Accreditation:** ACBSP.

WESTERN NEVADA COLLEGE

2201 W College Pky.
Carson City, NV 89703-7316
Tel: (775)445-3000
Fax: (775)887-3141
E-mail: wncc_aro@wncc.edu
Web Site: www.wnc.edu
President/CEO: Chester Burton
Financial Aid: John Lazzari

Type: Two-Year College **Sex:** Coed **Affiliation:** Nevada System of Higher Education. **% Accepted:** 100 **Admission Plans:** Early Admission; Open Admission **Application Deadline:** Rolling **Application Fee:** $15.00 **H.S. Requirements:** High school diploma required; GED accepted **Costs Per Year:** Application fee: $15. State resident tuition: $2640 full-time, $88 per unit part-time. Nonresident tuition: $9285 full-time, $184.75 per unit part-time. Mandatory fees: $165 full-time, $5.50 per credit part-time. Full-time tuition and fees vary according to course level, degree level, and reciprocity agreements. Part-time tuition and fees vary according to course level, degree level, and reciprocity agreements. **Scholarships:** Available. **Calendar System:** Semester, Summer session available **Enrollment:** Full-time 1,401, Part-time 2,438 **Exams:** SAT I or ACT. **Final Year or Final Semester Residency Requirement:** No **Credit Hours For Degree:** 60 credits, Associates; 120 credits, Bachelors **Professional Accreditation:** ACEN, NCCU. **Intercollegiate Athletics:** Baseball M; Softball W

COLBY-SAWYER COLLEGE
541 Main St.
New London, NH 03257
Tel: (603)526-3000; Free: 800-272-1015
Fax: (603)526-3452
E-mail: admissions@colby-sawyer.edu
Web Site: www.colby-sawyer.edu
President/CEO: Thomas Galligan, JD
Admissions: Jaimee Hofstetter
Financial Aid: Beth Renzulli
Type: Four-Year College **Sex:** Coed **% Accepted:** 91 **Admission Plans:** Deferred Admission; Early Admission; Early Decision Plan **Application Deadline:** April 1 **Application Fee:** $45.00 **H.S. Requirements:** High school diploma required; GED accepted **Costs Per Year:** Application fee: $45. Comprehensive fee: $51,860 includes full-time tuition ($38,610), mandatory fees ($250), and college room and board ($13,000). Room and board charges vary according to housing facility. Part-time tuition: $1287 per credit. Part-time tuition varies according to course load. Tuition guaranteed not to increase for student's term of enrollment. **Scholarships:** Available. **Calendar System:** Semester, Summer session not available **Enrollment:** Full-time 1,316, Part-time 53 **Faculty:** Full-time 81, Part-time 56 **Student-Faculty Ratio:** 14:1 **% Residing in College-Owned, -Operated, or -Affiliated Housing:** 90 **Final Year or Final Semester Residency Requirement:** No **Regional Accreditation:** New England Association of Schools and Colleges **Credit Hours For Degree:** 60 credit hours, Associates; 120 credit hours, Bachelors **ROTC:** Army **Professional Accreditation:** AACN, JRCAT. **Intercollegiate Athletics:** Baseball M; Basketball M & W; Cross-Country Running M & W; Equestrian Sports M & W; Field Hockey W; Golf M & W; Ice Hockey M & W; Lacrosse W; Rugby M & W; Skiing (Downhill) M & W; Soccer M & W; Softball W; Swimming and Diving M & W; Tennis M & W; Track and Field M & W; Volleyball W

DANIEL WEBSTER COLLEGE
20 University Dr.
Nashua, NH 03063-1300
Tel: (603)577-6000; Free: 800-325-6876
Fax: (603)577-6001
E-mail: oneill@dwc.edu
Web Site: www.dwc.edu
President/CEO: Dr. Michael Diffily
Admissions: Jennifer O'Neill
Financial Aid: Darla Ammidown
Type: Comprehensive **Sex:** Coed **% Accepted:** 62 **Admission Plans:** Deferred Admission; Early Admission **Application Deadline:** Rolling **Application Fee:** $0.00 **H.S. Requirements:** High school diploma required; GED accepted **Costs Per Year:** Application fee: $0. Comprehensive fee: $28,332 includes full-time tuition ($16,410) and college room and board ($11,922). Room and board charges vary according to housing facility. Part-time tuition: $547 per credit hour. **Scholarships:** Available. **Calendar System:** Semester, Summer session available **Enrollment:** Full-time 604, Graduate full-time 47, Part-time 35 **Faculty:** Full-time 21, Part-time 65 **Student-Faculty Ratio:** 15:1 **Exams:** ACT essay component not used; SAT I or ACT; SAT essay component not used. **% Receiving Financial Aid:** 70 **% Residing in College-Owned, -Operated, or -Affiliated Housing:** 49 **Final Year or Final Semester Residency Requirement:** Yes **Regional Accreditation:** New England Association of Schools and Colleges **Credit**

Hours For Degree: 60 semester credit hours, Associates; 120 semester credit hours, Bachelors **ROTC:** Air Force, Army, Navy **Professional Accreditation:** AABI, ABET. **Intercollegiate Athletics:** Baseball M; Basketball M & W; Cross-Country Running M & W; Field Hockey W; Golf M; Ice Hockey M & W; Lacrosse M & W; Soccer M & W; Softball W; Volleyball M & W; Wrestling M

DARTMOUTH COLLEGE
Hanover, NH 03755
Tel: (603)646-1110
Fax: (603)646-1216
E-mail: admissions.reply@dartmouth.edu
Web Site: www.dartmouth.edu
President/CEO: Philip J. Hanlon
Admissions: Paul Sunde
Financial Aid: Gordon D. Koff
Type: University **Sex:** Coed **Scores:** 100% SAT V 400+; 100% SAT M 400+ **% Accepted:** 11 **Admission Plans:** Deferred Admission; Early Action; Early Admission **Application Deadline:** January 1 **Application Fee:** $80.00 **H.S. Requirements:** High school diploma or equivalent not required **Costs Per Year:** Application fee: $80. One-time mandatory fee: $390. Comprehensive fee: $63,748 includes full-time tuition ($48,120), mandatory fees ($1386), and college room and board ($14,242). College room only: $8557. Room and board charges vary according to board plan. **Scholarships:** Available. **Calendar System:** Quarter, Summer session available **Enrollment:** Full-time 4,267, Graduate full-time 1,969, Graduate part-time 74, Part-time 40 **Faculty:** Full-time 582, Part-time 152 **Student-Faculty Ratio:** 7:1 **Exams:** ACT essay component used for admission; ACT essay component used for advising; ACT essay component used for placement; SAT I or ACT; SAT II; SAT essay component used for admission; SAT essay component used for advising; SAT essay component used for placement; SAT Reasoning; SAT Subject. **% Receiving Financial Aid:** 51 **% Residing in College-Owned, -Operated, or -Affiliated Housing:** 83 **Final Year or Final Semester Residency Requirement:** Yes **Regional Accreditation:** New England Association of Schools and Colleges **Credit Hours For Degree:** 35 courses, Bachelors **ROTC:** Army **Professional Accreditation:** AACSB, ABET, APA, CEPH, LCME/AMA, NAST. **Intercollegiate Athletics:** Badminton M & W; Baseball M; Basketball M & W; Cheerleading M & W; Crew M & W; Cross-Country Running M & W; Equestrian Sports M & W; Fencing M & W; Field Hockey W; Football M; Golf M & W; Gymnastics M & W; Ice Hockey M & W; Lacrosse M & W; Rowing M & W; Rugby M & W; Sailing M & W; Skiing (Cross-Country) M & W; Skiing (Downhill) M & W; Soccer M & W; Softball W; Squash M & W; Swimming and Diving M & W; Table Tennis M & W; Tennis M & W; Track and Field M & W; Ultimate Frisbee M & W; Volleyball M & W; Water Polo M & W; Wrestling M

FRANKLIN PIERCE UNIVERSITY
40 University Dr.
Rindge, NH 03461-0060
Tel: (603)899-4000; Free: 800-437-0048
Fax: (603)899-4372
E-mail: admissions@franklinpierce.edu
Web Site: www.franklinpierce.edu
President/CEO: Pres. Andrew H. Card, Jr.
Financial Aid: Kenneth Ferreira

Type: University **Sex:** Coed **Scores:** 84% SAT V 400+; 81% SAT M 400+; 45.16% ACT 18-23; 12.9% ACT 24-29 **% Accepted:** 80 **Admission Plans:** Deferred Admission; Early Admission **Application Deadline:** Rolling **Application Fee:** $40.00 **H.S. Requirements:** High school diploma required; GED accepted. For early entrance program: High school diploma or equivalent not required **Costs Per Year:** Application fee: $40. Comprehensive fee: $45,866 includes full-time tuition ($30,870), mandatory fees ($2450), and college room and board ($12,546). College room only: $7326. Full-time tuition and fees vary according to course load, degree level, location, and program. Room and board charges vary according to board plan, housing facility, and student level. Part-time tuition: $1030 per credit hour. Part-time tuition varies according to course load, degree level, location, and program. **Scholarships:** Available. **Calendar System:** Miscellaneous, Summer session available **Enrollment:** Full-time 1,422, Graduate full-time 353, Graduate part-time 259, Part-time 205 **Faculty:** Full-time 92, Part-time 194 **Student-Faculty Ratio:** 12:1 **Exams:** ACT essay component used for advising; ACT essay component used for placement; SAT I or ACT; SAT essay component used for advising; SAT essay component used for placement; SAT Reasoning. **% Receiving Financial Aid:** 81 **% Residing in College-Owned, -Operated, or -Affiliated Housing:** 87 **Final Year or Final Semester Residency Requirement:** No **Regional Accreditation:** New England Association of Schools and Colleges **Credit Hours For Degree:** 60 semester hours, Associates; 120 semester hours, Bachelors **ROTC:** Air Force, Army **Professional Accreditation:** ACEN, APTA. **Intercollegiate Athletics:** Baseball M; Basketball M & W; Crew M & W; Cross-Country Running M & W; Field Hockey W; Golf M; Ice Hockey M; Lacrosse M & W; Soccer M & W; Softball W; Tennis M & W; Volleyball W

GRANITE STATE COLLEGE

25 Hall St.
Concord, NH 03301
Tel: (603)228-3000; Free: 888-228-3000
Fax: (603)229-0964
E-mail: gsc.admissions@granite.edu
Web Site: www.granite.edu
President/CEO: Dr. Todd Leach
Admissions: Cortney Vachon

Type: Comprehensive **Sex:** Coed **Affiliation:** University System of New Hampshire. **% Accepted:** 100 **Admission Plans:** Open Admission **Application Deadline:** Rolling **Application Fee:** $0.00 **H.S. Requirements:** High school diploma required; GED accepted **Costs Per Year:** Application fee: $0. State resident tuition: $7032 full-time, $293 per credit part-time. Nonresident tuition: $7800 full-time, $325 per credit part-time. Mandatory fees: $225 full-time, $75 per term part-time. **Calendar System:** Trimester, Summer session available **Enrollment:** Full-time 1,021, Graduate full-time 92, Graduate part-time 218, Part-time 849 **Faculty:** Full-time 4, Part-time 186 **Student-Faculty Ratio:** 12:1 **Final Year or Final Semester Residency Requirement:** No **Regional Accreditation:** New England Association of Schools and Colleges **Credit Hours For Degree:** 60 semester hours, Associates; 120 semester hours, Bachelors **ROTC:** Air Force, Army

GREAT BAY COMMUNITY COLLEGE

320 Corporate Dr.
Portsmouth, NH 03801
Tel: (603)427-7600
E-mail: askgreatbay@ccsnh.edu
Web Site: www.greatbay.edu
President/CEO: Will Arvelo
Admissions: Matt Thornton

Type: Two-Year College **Sex:** Coed **Admission Plans:** Open Admission **Application Fee:** $20.00 **Student-Faculty Ratio:** 10:1 **Regional Accreditation:** New England Association of Schools and Colleges **Professional Accreditation:** ACBSP, ACEN.

KEENE STATE COLLEGE

229 Main St.
Keene, NH 03435
Tel: (603)352-1909; Free: 800-KSC-1909
Fax: (603)358-2767
E-mail: mrichmon@keene.edu
Web Site: www.keene.edu
President/CEO: Dr. Anne Huot
Admissions: Margaret Richmond
Financial Aid: Patricia Blodgett

Type: Comprehensive **Sex:** Coed **Affiliation:** University System of New Hampshire. **Scores:** 92% SAT V 400+; 93% SAT M 400+; 60% ACT 18-23; 20% ACT 24-29 **% Accepted:** 79 **Admission Plans:** Deferred Admission **Application Deadline:** April 1 **Application Fee:** $50.00 **H.S. Requirements:** High school diploma required; GED accepted **Costs Per Year:** Application fee: $50. State resident tuition: $10,968 full-time, $458 per credit hour part-time. Nonresident tuition: $19,352 full-time, $806 per credit hour part-time. Mandatory fees: $2645 full-time, $106 per credit hour part-time. Part-time tuition and fees vary according to course load. College room and board: $10,390. Room and board charges vary according to board plan and housing facility. **Scholarships:** Available. **Calendar System:** Semester, Summer session available **Enrollment:** Full-time 4,097, Graduate full-time 42, Graduate part-time 82, Part-time 162 **Faculty:** Full-time 215, Part-time 205 **Student-Faculty Ratio:** 15:1 **Exams:** ACT essay component used for admission; SAT I or ACT; SAT essay component used for admission; SAT Reasoning. **% Receiving Financial Aid:** 65 **% Residing in College-Owned, -Operated, or -Affiliated Housing:** 53 **Final Year or Final Semester Residency Requirement:** No **Regional Accreditation:** New England Association of Schools and Colleges **Credit Hours For Degree:** 120 credits, Bachelors **ROTC:** Air Force, Army **Professional Accreditation:** AND, JRCAT, NASM, NCATE. **Intercollegiate Athletics:** Baseball M; Basketball M & W; Cheerleading W; Cross-Country Running M & W; Field Hockey W; Ice Hockey M & W; Lacrosse M & W; Rugby M & W; Soccer M & W; Softball W; Swimming and Diving M & W; Track and Field M & W; Ultimate Frisbee M & W; Volleyball W

LAKES REGION COMMUNITY COLLEGE

379 Belmont Rd.
Laconia, NH 03246
Tel: (603)524-3207
Fax: (603)524-8084
E-mail: lrccinfo@ccsnh.edu
Web Site: www.lrcc.edu
President/CEO: Scott Kalicki, PhD
Admissions: Kathy Plummer
Financial Aid: Kristen Purrington

Type: Two-Year College **Sex:** Coed **Affiliation:** Community College System of New Hampshire. **Admission Plans:** Deferred Admission; Open Admission **Application Fee:** $20.00 **H.S. Requirements:** High school diploma required; GED accepted **Scholarships:** Available. **Calendar System:** Semester, Summer session available **Enrollment:** Full-time 490, Part-time 689 **Student-Faculty Ratio:** 9:1 **Exams:** Other. **Regional Accreditation:** New England Association of Schools and Colleges

MANCHESTER COMMUNITY COLLEGE

1066 Front St.
Manchester, NH 03102-8518
Tel: (603)668-6706
E-mail: jpoirier@nhctc.edu
Web Site: www.mccnh.edu
President/CEO: Susan Huard
Admissions: Jacquie Poirier

Type: Two-Year College **Sex:** Coed **Affiliation:** New Hampshire Community Technical College System. **Admission Plans:** Deferred Admission; Early Admission **Application Deadline:** Rolling **Application Fee:** $10.00 **H.S. Requirements:** High school diploma required; GED accepted **Scholarships:** Available. **Calendar System:** Semester, Summer session available **Faculty:** Full-time 52, Part-time 150 **Student-Faculty Ratio:** 14:1 **Regional Accreditation:** New England Association of Schools and Colleges **Credit Hours For Degree:** 64 credit hours, Associates **Professional Accreditation:** AAMAE, ACBSP, ACEN, ARCST. **Intercollegiate Athletics:** Basketball M; Skiing (Downhill) M & W; Soccer M & W; Volleyball M & W

NASHUA COMMUNITY COLLEGE

505 Amherst St.
Nashua, NH 03063-1026
Tel: (603)882-6923
Fax: (603)882-8690
E-mail: pgoodman@ccsnh.edu
Web Site: www.nashuacc.edu
President/CEO: Pres. Lucille Jordan, RD
Admissions: Patricia Goodman

Type: Two-Year College **Sex:** Coed **Affiliation:** Community College System of New Hampshire. **Admission Plans:** Deferred Admission; Open Admission **Application Deadline:** Rolling **Application Fee:** $20.00 **H.S. Requirements:** High school diploma required; GED accepted **Scholarships:** Available. **Calendar System:** Semester, Summer session available **Enrollment:** Full-time 950, Part-time 1,150 **Faculty:** Full-time 42, Part-time 66 **Exams:** Other. **Regional Accreditation:** New England Association of Schools and Colleges **Credit Hours For Degree:** 64 credits, Associates **Professional Accreditation:** ABET, ACEN, AHIMA, AOTA, CoARC, NAACLS. **Intercollegiate Athletics:** Soccer M & W

NEW ENGLAND COLLEGE

15 Main St.
Henniker, NH 03242-3293
Tel: (603)428-2211; Free: 800-521-7642
E-mail: klucier@nec.edu
Web Site: www.nec.edu
President/CEO: Dr. Michele D. Perkins
Admissions: Kay Reynolds
Financial Aid: Kristen Blase

Type: Comprehensive **Sex:** Coed **Scores:** 79% SAT V 400+; 81% SAT M 400+; 57% ACT 18-23; 25% ACT 24-29 **% Accepted:** 98 **Admission Plans:** Deferred Admission **Application Deadline:** September 5 **Application Fee:** $35.00 **H.S. Requirements:** High school diploma required; GED accepted **Costs Per Year:** Application fee: $35. Comprehensive fee: $48,558 includes full-time tuition ($34,650), mandatory fees ($640), and college room and board ($13,268). College room only: $6000. Full-time tuition and fees vary according to class time, course load, degree level, location, program, and reciprocity agreements. Room and board charges vary according to board plan and housing facility. Part-time tuition: $495 per credit. Part-time tuition varies according to class time, course load, degree level, location, and program. **Scholarships:** Available. **Calendar System:** Semester, Summer session available **Enrollment:** Full-time 1,766, Graduate full-time 540, Graduate part-time 48, Part-time 39 **Faculty:** Full-time 44, Part-time 193 **Student-Faculty Ratio:** 19:1 **Exams:** ACT; ACT essay component not used; Other; SAT I; SAT I and SAT II or ACT; SAT I or ACT; SAT II; SAT essay component not used. **% Receiving Financial Aid:** 75 **% Residing in College-Owned, -Operated, or -Affiliated Housing:** 26 **Final Year or Final Semester Residency Requirement:** Yes **Regional Accreditation:** New England Association of Schools and Colleges **Credit Hours For Degree:** 60 credits, Associates; 120 credits, Bachelors **ROTC:** Air Force, Army **Intercollegiate Athletics:** Baseball M; Basketball M & W; Cross-Country Running M & W; Field Hockey W; Ice Hockey M & W; Lacrosse M & W; Soccer M & W; Softball W

NEW HAMPSHIRE INSTITUTE OF ART

148 Concord St.
Manchester, NH 03104
Tel: (603)623-0313; Free: 866-241-4918
Fax: (603)641-1832
E-mail: bobgielow@nhia.edu
Web Site: www.nhia.edu
President/CEO: Kent Devereaux
Admissions: Bob Gielow
Financial Aid: Linda Lavallee

Type: Comprehensive **Sex:** Coed **% Accepted:** 53 **Admission Plans:** Deferred Admission; Early Decision Plan **Application Deadline:** Rolling **Application Fee:** $25.00 **H.S. Requirements:** High school diploma required; GED accepted **Costs Per Year:** Application fee: $25. Comprehensive fee: $36,760 includes full-time tuition ($23,490), mandatory fees ($2290), and college room and board ($10,980). Room and board charges vary according to board plan. Part-time tuition: $3285 per course. Part-time mandatory fees: $195 per course. Part-time tuition and fees vary according to course load. **Scholarships:** Available. **Calendar System:** Semester, Summer session available **Enrollment:** Full-time 355, Graduate full-time 65, Graduate part-time 12, Part-time 36 **Faculty:** Full-time 18, Part-time 123 **Student-Faculty Ratio:** 10:1 **Exams:** ACT essay component not used; SAT I or ACT; SAT essay component not used. **% Residing in College-Owned, -Operated, or -Affiliated Housing:** 63 **Final Year or Final Semester Residency Requirement:** Yes **Regional Accreditation:** New England Association of Schools and Colleges **Credit Hours For Degree:** 120 credits, Bachelors **Professional Accreditation:** NASAD.

NHTI, CONCORD'S COMMUNITY COLLEGE

31 College Dr.
Concord, NH 03301-7412

Tel: (603)271-6484; Free: 800-247-0179
Fax: (603)271-7734
E-mail: fmeyer@ccsnh.edu
Web Site: www.nhti.edu
President/CEO: Lynn Kilchenstein
Admissions: Francis P. Meyer
Financial Aid: Sheri Gonthier

Type: Two-Year College **Sex:** Coed **Affiliation:** Community College System of New Hampshire. **Admission Plans:** Preferred Admission **Application Deadline:** Rolling **Application Fee:** $20.00 **H.S. Requirements:** High school diploma required; GED accepted **Scholarships:** Available. **Calendar System:** Semester, Summer session available **Student-Faculty Ratio:** 15:1 **Exams:** Other; SAT I or ACT. **% Residing in College-Owned, -Operated, or -Affiliated Housing:** 23 **Final Year or Final Semester Residency Requirement:** No **Regional Accreditation:** New England Association of Schools and Colleges **Credit Hours For Degree:** 64 credit hours, Associates **Professional Accreditation:** ABET, ACBSP, ACEN, ADA, JRCEMTP, JRCERT. **Intercollegiate Athletics:** Baseball M; Basketball M & W; Gymnastics M & W; Soccer M & W; Softball W; Volleyball M & W

NORTHEAST CATHOLIC COLLEGE

511 Kearsarge Mountain Rd.
Warner, NH 03278
Tel: (603)456-2656; Free: 877-498-1723
Fax: (603)456-2660
E-mail: admissions@magdalen.edu
Web Site: www.magdalen.edu
President/CEO: Jeffrey J. Karls
Financial Aid: Marie A. Lasher

Type: Four-Year College **Sex:** Coed **Affiliation:** Roman Catholic Church. **Admission Plans:** Early Action **Application Deadline:** Rolling **Application Fee:** $35.00 **H.S. Requirements:** High school diploma required; GED accepted **Scholarships:** Available. **Calendar System:** Semester, Summer session not available **Student-Faculty Ratio:** 11:1 **Exams:** SAT I or ACT. **% Receiving Financial Aid:** 66 **% Residing in College-Owned, -Operated, or -Affiliated Housing:** 100 **Credit Hours For Degree:** 60 credit hours, Associates; 120 credit hours, Bachelors **Professional Accreditation:** AALE.

PLYMOUTH STATE UNIVERSITY

17 High St.
Plymouth, NH 03264-1595
Tel: (603)535-5000; Free: 800-842-6900
Fax: (603)535-2714
E-mail: admissions@plymouth.edu
Web Site: www.plymouth.edu
President/CEO: Dr. Donald L. Birx
Admissions: Tony Trodella
Financial Aid: Crystal Gaff

Type: Comprehensive **Sex:** Coed **Affiliation:** University System of New Hampshire. **Scores:** 89% SAT V 400+; 90% SAT M 400+; 56.41% ACT 18-23; 26.92% ACT 24-29 **% Accepted:** 74 **Admission Plans:** Deferred Admission **Application Deadline:** April 1 **Application Fee:** $50.00 **H.S. Requirements:** High school diploma required; GED accepted **Costs Per Year:** Application fee: $50. State resident tuition: $10,700 full-time, $446 per credit hour part-time. Nonresident tuition: $18,780 full-time, $783 per credit hour part-time. Mandatory fees: $2428 full-time, $101 per credit hour part-time. Full-time tuition and fees vary according to reciprocity agreements. Part-time tuition and fees vary according to reciprocity agreements. College room and board: $10,868. College room only: $6750. Room and board charges vary according to board plan and housing facility. **Scholarships:** Available. **Calendar System:** Semester, Summer session available **Enrollment:** Full-time 3,855, Graduate full-time 317, Graduate part-time 734, Part-time 250 **Faculty:** Full-time 188, Part-time 238 **Student-Faculty Ratio:** 17:1 **% Receiving Financial Aid:** 67 **% Residing in College-Owned, -Operated, or -Affiliated Housing:** 56 **Final Year or Final Semester Residency Requirement:** No **Regional Accreditation:** New England Association of Schools and Colleges **Credit Hours For Degree:** 120 semester credit hours, Bachelors **ROTC:** Air Force, Army **Professional Accreditation:** ACA, ACBSP, CSWE, JRCAT, NCATE. **Intercollegiate Athletics:** Baseball M; Basketball M & W; Cross-Country Running M & W; Field Hockey W; Football M; Ice Hockey M & W; Lacrosse M & W; Skiing (Downhill) M & W; Soccer M & W; Softball W; Swimming and Diving W; Tennis W; Track and Field M & W; Volleyball W; Wrestling M

RIVER VALLEY COMMUNITY COLLEGE

1 College Pl.
Claremont, NH 03743
Tel: (603)542-7744
Fax: (603)543-1844
E-mail: kaldrich@ccsnh.edu
Web Site: www.rivervalley.edu
President/CEO: Steven G. Budd
Admissions: Kathy Aldrich
Financial Aid: Jean Dale

Type: Two-Year College **Sex:** Coed **Affiliation:** Community College System of New Hampshire. **% Accepted:** 77 **Application Fee:** $20.00 **H.S. Requirements:** High school diploma required; GED accepted **Costs Per Year:** Application fee: $20. Area resident tuition: $300 per credit hour part-time. State resident tuition: $6720 full-time, $200 per credit hour part-time. Nonresident tuition: $15,296 full-time, $455 per credit hour part-time. Mandatory fees: $455 full-time. Full-time tuition and fees vary according to class time, course load, and program. Part-time tuition varies according to class time, course load, and program. **Scholarships:** Available. **Calendar System:** Semester, Summer session available **Enrollment:** Full-time 236, Part-time 773 **Faculty:** Full-time 36, Part-time 76 **Student-Faculty Ratio:** 6:1 **Final Year or Final Semester Residency Requirement:** No **Regional Accreditation:** New England Association of Schools and Colleges **Credit Hours For Degree:** 64 credits, Associates **Professional Accreditation:** ACBSP, ACEN.

RIVIER UNIVERSITY

420 S Main St.
Nashua, NH 03060
Tel: (603)888-1311; Free: 800-44RIVIER
Fax: (603)891-1799
E-mail: rivadmit@rivier.edu
Web Site: www.rivier.edu
President/CEO: Señor Paula Marie Buley, IHM
Admissions: Karen Schedin
Financial Aid: Valerie Patnaude

Type: Comprehensive **Sex:** Coed **Affiliation:** Roman Catholic. **Scores:** 93% SAT V 400+; 88% SAT M 400+; 62% ACT 18-23; 19% ACT 24-29 **% Accepted:** 10 **Admission Plans:** Deferred Admission **Application Deadline:** Rolling **Application Fee:** $25.00 **H.S. Requirements:** High school diploma required; GED accepted **Scholarships:** Available. **Calendar System:** Semester, Summer session available **Enrollment:** Full-time 788, Graduate full-time 322, Graduate part-time 593, Part-time 738 **Faculty:** Full-time 68, Part-time 125 **Student-Faculty Ratio:** 14:1 **Exams:** Other; SAT I or ACT. **% Receiving Financial Aid:** 85 **% Residing in College-Owned, -Operated, or -Affiliated Housing:** 48 **Final Year or Final Semester Residency Requirement:** Yes **Regional Accreditation:** New England Association of Schools and Colleges **Credit Hours For Degree:** 60 credits, Associates; 120 credits, Bachelors **ROTC:** Air Force **Professional Accreditation:** ACEN. **Intercollegiate Athletics:** Baseball M; Basketball M & W; Cross-Country Running M & W; Field Hockey W; Lacrosse M & W; Soccer M & W; Softball W; Volleyball M & W

SAINT ANSELM COLLEGE

100 Saint Anselm Dr.
Manchester, NH 03102-1310
Tel: (603)641-7000; Free: 888-4ANSELM
Fax: (603)641-7550
E-mail: admission@anselm.edu
Web Site: www.anselm.edu
President/CEO: Dr. Steven DiSalvo
Financial Aid: Elizabeth Keuffel

Type: Four-Year College **Sex:** Coed **Affiliation:** Roman Catholic. **Scores:** 100% SAT V 400+; 100% SAT M 400+; 22.5% ACT 18-23; 69% ACT 24-29 **% Accepted:** 73 **Admission Plans:** Deferred Admission; Early Admission; Early Decision Plan **Application Deadline:** February 1 **Application Fee:** $50.00 **H.S. Requirements:** High school diploma required; GED accepted **Costs Per Year:** Application fee: $50. Comprehensive fee: $51,238 includes full-time tuition ($36,724), mandatory fees ($1180), and college room and board ($13,334). College room only: $8024. Full-time tuition and fees vary according to program. Room and board charges vary according to housing facility. **Scholarships:** Available. **Calendar System:** Semester, Summer session available **Enrollment:** Full-time 1,878, Part-time 49 **Faculty:** Full-time 147, Part-time 68 **Student-Faculty Ratio:** 11:1 **Exams:** ACT essay

component used for admission; ACT essay component used for advising; ACT essay component used for placement; SAT I and SAT II or ACT; SAT I or ACT; SAT II; SAT essay component used for admission; SAT essay component used for advising; SAT essay component used for placement; SAT Reasoning; SAT Subject. **% Receiving Financial Aid:** 70 **% Residing in College-Owned, -Operated, or -Affiliated Housing:** 92 **Final Year or Final Semester Residency Requirement:** No **Regional Accreditation:** New England Association of Schools and Colleges **Credit Hours For Degree:** 120 credits, Bachelors **ROTC:** Army **Professional Accreditation:** AACN. **Intercollegiate Athletics:** Baseball M; Basketball M & W; Cross-Country Running M & W; Field Hockey W; Football M; Golf M; Ice Hockey M & W; Lacrosse M & W; Skiing (Downhill) M & W; Soccer M & W; Softball W; Tennis M & W; Volleyball W

ST. JOSEPH SCHOOL OF NURSING

5 Woodward Ave.
Nashua, NH 03060
Tel: (603)594-2567; Free: 800-370-3169
Fax: (603)594-2581
Web Site: www.sjhacademiccenter.org
Admissions: L. Nadeau

Type: Two-Year College **Sex:** Coed **Affiliation:** Roman Catholic Church; St. Joseph Hospital. **% Accepted:** 40 **Application Deadline:** July 10 **Application Fee:** $50.00 **H.S. Requirements:** High school diploma required; GED accepted **Costs Per Year:** Application fee: $50. Tuition: $870 per course part-time. Part-time tuition varies according to course load and program. **Calendar System:** Semester, Summer session available **Enrollment:** Full-time 63, Part-time 81 **Faculty:** Full-time 11, Part-time 9 **Final Year or Final Semester Residency Requirement:** No **Credit Hours For Degree:** 60 credits, Associates **Professional Accreditation:** ACCSC, ACEN.

SOUTHERN NEW HAMPSHIRE UNIVERSITY

2500 N River Rd.
Manchester, NH 03106-1045
Tel: (603)668-2211; Free: 888-327-7648
Fax: (603)645-9693
E-mail: b.perkins@snhu.edu
Web Site: www.snhu.edu
President/CEO: Dr. Paul J. LeBlanc
Admissions: Bethany Perkins

Type: University **Sex:** Coed **Scores:** 86% SAT V 400+; 89% SAT M 400+; 51.22% ACT 18-23; 36.59% ACT 24-29 **% Accepted:** 92 **Admission Plans:** Deferred Admission; Early Decision Plan **Application Deadline:** Rolling **Application Fee:** $40.00 **H.S. Requirements:** High school diploma required; GED accepted **Costs Per Year:** Application fee: $40. Comprehensive fee: $43,198 includes full-time tuition ($30,756), mandatory fees ($380), and college room and board ($12,062). College room only: $8583. Full-time tuition and fees vary according to course load. Room and board charges vary according to board plan and housing facility. Part-time tuition: $1282 per credit hour. **Scholarships:** Available. **Calendar System:** Semester, Summer session available **Enrollment:** Full-time 2,977, Graduate full-time 95, Graduate part-time 23, Part-time 52 **Faculty:** Full-time 122, Part-time 249 **Student-Faculty Ratio:** 15:1 **Exams:** ACT essay component used for advising; SAT I and SAT II or ACT; SAT I or ACT; SAT II; SAT essay component used for advising. **% Receiving Financial Aid:** 72 **% Residing in College-Owned, -Operated, or -Affiliated Housing:** 69 **Final Year or Final Semester Residency Requirement:** Yes **Regional Accreditation:** New England Association of Schools and Colleges **Credit Hours For Degree:** 60 credits, Associates; 120 credits, Bachelors **ROTC:** Air Force, Army **Professional Accreditation:** ACBSP, ACF, NCATE. **Intercollegiate Athletics:** Baseball M; Basketball M & W; Cheerleading M & W; Cross-Country Running M & W; Field Hockey W; Golf M & W; Ice Hockey M; Lacrosse M & W; Soccer M & W; Softball W; Tennis M & W; Track and Field W; Volleyball W

THOMAS MORE COLLEGE OF LIBERAL ARTS

6 Manchester St.
Merrimack, NH 03054-4818
Tel: (603)880-8308; Free: 800-880-8308
Fax: (603)880-9280
E-mail: admissions@thomasmorecollege.edu
Web Site: www.thomasmorecollege.edu
President/CEO: William E. Fahey
Admissions: Teddy Sifert
Financial Aid: Clinton A. Hanson, Jr.

Type: Four-Year College **Sex:** Coed **Affiliation:** Roman Catholic Church. **Scores:** 95% SAT V 400+; 100% SAT M 400+; 100% ACT 24-29 **% Accepted:** 70 **Application Deadline:** Rolling **Application Fee:** $0.00 **H.S. Requirements:** High school diploma required; GED accepted **Scholarships:** Available. **Calendar System:** Semester, Summer session not available **Enrollment:** Full-time 99 **Student-Faculty Ratio:** 12:1 **Exams:** SAT I or ACT. **% Receiving Financial Aid:** 81 **% Residing in College-Owned, -Operated, or -Affiliated Housing:** 97 **Regional Accreditation:** New England Association of Schools and Colleges **Credit Hours For Degree:** 120 credits, Bachelors **Professional Accreditation:** AALE.

UNIVERSITY OF NEW HAMPSHIRE

Durham, NH 03824
Tel: (603)862-1234
E-mail: admissions@unh.edu
Web Site: www.unh.edu
President/CEO: Dr. Mark Huddleston
Financial Aid: Susan K. Allen

Type: University **Sex:** Coed **Affiliation:** University System of New Hampshire. **Scores:** 98% SAT V 400+; 99% SAT M 400+; 41.31% ACT 18-23; 47.74% ACT 24-29 **% Accepted:** 79 **Admission Plans:** Deferred Admission; Early Decision Plan; Preferred Admission **Application Deadline:** February 1 **Application Fee:** $50.00 **H.S. Requirements:** High school diploma required; GED accepted **Costs Per Year:** Application fee: $50. State resident tuition: $14,050 full-time, $585 per credit hour part-time. Nonresident tuition: $27,320 full-time, $1138 per credit hour part-time. Mandatory fees: $2936 full-time, $1468 per year part-time. Full-time tuition and fees vary according to program. Part-time tuition and fees vary according to course load and program. College room and board: $10,618. College room only: $6620. Room and board charges vary according to board plan and housing facility. **Scholarships:** Available. **Calendar System:** Semester, Summer session available **Enrollment:** Full-time 12,683, Graduate full-time 1,242, Graduate part-time 1,122, Part-time 351 **Faculty:** Full-time 618, Part-time 416 **Student-Faculty Ratio:** 19:1 **Exams:** ACT essay component not used; SAT I or ACT; SAT essay component not used; SAT Reasoning. **% Receiving Financial Aid:** 66 **% Residing in College-Owned, -Operated, or -Affiliated Housing:** 56 **Final Year or Final Semester Residency Requirement:** No **Regional Accreditation:** New England Association of Schools and Colleges **Credit Hours For Degree:** 64 credits, Associates; 128 credits, Bachelors **ROTC:** Air Force, Army **Professional Accreditation:** AACN, AACSB, AAMFT, ABA, ABET, AND, AOTA, APA, ASHA, CSWE, JRCAT, NAACLS, NASM, NRPA, SAF, TEAC. **Intercollegiate Athletics:** Archery M & W; Baseball M; Basketball M & W; Crew M & W; Cross-Country Running M & W; Fencing M & W; Field Hockey W; Football M; Golf M & W; Gymnastics W; Ice Hockey M & W; Lacrosse M & W; Riflery M & W; Rock Climbing M & W; Rugby M & W; Sailing M & W; Skiing (Cross-Country) M & W; Skiing (Downhill) M & W; Soccer M & W; Softball W; Swimming and Diving W; Tennis M & W; Track and Field M & W; Ultimate Frisbee M & W; Volleyball M & W; Wrestling M & W

UNIVERSITY OF NEW HAMPSHIRE AT MANCHESTER

88 Commercial St.
Manchester, NH 03101-1113
Tel: (603)641-4321
Fax: (603)641-4125
E-mail: kim.derego@unh.edu
Web Site: www.manchester.unh.edu
President/CEO: Mike Decelle
Admissions: Kim DeRego
Financial Aid: Sharon Eaton

Type: Comprehensive **Sex:** Coed **Affiliation:** University of New Hampshire. **Scores:** 98% SAT V 400+; 96% SAT M 400+ **% Accepted:** 73 **Admission Plans:** Deferred Admission **Application Deadline:** April 1 **Application Fee:** $60.00 **H.S. Requirements:** High school diploma required; GED accepted **Costs Per Year:** Application fee: $60. State resident tuition: $13,720 full-time, $572 per credit part-time. Nonresident tuition: $26,990 full-time, $1125 per credit part-time. Mandatory fees: $412 full-time. Full-time tuition and fees vary according to course load and program. Part-time tuition varies according to course load and program. **Scholarships:** Available. **Calendar System:** Semester, Summer session available **Enrollment:** Full-time 555, Graduate full-time 3, Graduate part-time 96, Part-time 186 **Faculty:** Full-time 40, Part-time 72 **Student-Faculty Ratio:** 11:1 **Exams:** SAT I or ACT. **% Receiving Financial Aid:** 64 **Final Year or Final Semester Residency Requirement:** Yes **Regional Accreditation:** New England Association of Schools and Colleges **Credit Hours For Degree:** 64 credits, Associates; 128 credits, Bachelors **ROTC:** Air Force, Army

WHITE MOUNTAINS COMMUNITY COLLEGE

2020 Riverside Dr.
Berlin, NH 03570
Tel: (603)752-1113; Free: 800-445-4525
Fax: (603)752-6335
E-mail: kmiller@ccsnh.edu
Web Site: www.wmcc.edu
President/CEO: Matthew Wood
Admissions: Kristen Miller
Financial Aid: Angela Labonte

Type: Two-Year College **Sex:** Coed **Affiliation:** Community College System of New Hampshire. **Costs Per Year:** State resident tuition: $6000 full-time, $200 per credit part-time. Nonresident tuition: $13,500 full-time, $450 per credit part-time. Mandatory fees: $510 full-time, $17 per credit part-time. Full-time tuition and fees vary according to class time, location, and program. Part-time tuition and fees vary according to class time, location, and program. **Scholarships:** Available. **Calendar System:** Semester, Summer session available **Enrollment:** Full-time 310, Part-time 691 **Faculty:** Full-time 21, Part-time 92 **Student-Faculty Ratio:** 20:1 **Exams:** Other; SAT essay component not used. **Final Year or Final Semester Residency Requirement:** No **Regional Accreditation:** New England Association of Schools and Colleges **Credit Hours For Degree:** 64 credits, Associates

ASSUMPTION COLLEGE FOR SISTERS
350 Bernardsville Rd.
Mendham, NJ 07945-0800
Tel: (973)543-6528
Fax: (973)543-9459
E-mail: deanregistrar@acs350.org
Web Site: www.acs350.org
President/CEO: Señor Joseph Spring
Admissions: Señor Gerardine Tantsits
Type: Two-Year College **Sex:** Women **Affiliation:** Roman Catholic. **Application Fee:** $50.00 **H.S. Requirements:** High school diploma required; GED accepted **Calendar System:** Semester, Summer session available **Student-Faculty Ratio:** 7:1 **Regional Accreditation:** Middle States Association of Colleges and Schools **Credit Hours For Degree:** 66 credits, Associates

ATLANTIC CAPE COMMUNITY COLLEGE
5100 Black Horse Pke.
Mays Landing, NJ 08330-2699
Tel: (609)625-1111
Fax: (609)343-4921
E-mail: accadmit@atlantic.edu
Web Site: www.atlantic.edu
President/CEO: Dr. Peter L. Mora
Admissions: Linda McLeod
Type: Two-Year College **Sex:** Coed **Admission Plans:** Deferred Admission; Early Admission; Open Admission **Application Deadline:** July 1 **Application Fee:** $35.00 **H.S. Requirements:** High school diploma or equivalent not required **Scholarships:** Available. **Calendar System:** Semester, Summer session available **Student-Faculty Ratio:** 21:1 **Regional Accreditation:** Middle States Association of Colleges and Schools **Credit Hours For Degree:** 64 credits, Associates **Professional Accreditation:** ACEN, ACF, AOTA, APTA. **Intercollegiate Athletics:** Archery M & W; Basketball M & W

BAIS MEDRASH TORAS CHESED
910 Monmouth Ave.
Lakewood, NJ 08701
Type: Four-Year College **Sex:** Men **Affiliation:** Jewish. **Professional Accreditation:** AARTS.

BERGEN COMMUNITY COLLEGE
400 Paramus Rd.
Paramus, NJ 07652-1595
Tel: (201)447-7100
Fax: (201)444-7036
E-mail: admsoffice@bergen.edu
Web Site: www.bergen.edu
President/CEO: B. Kaye Walter
Type: Two-Year College **Sex:** Coed **Admission Plans:** Open Admission; Preferred Admission **H.S. Requirements:** High school diploma required; GED accepted **Scholarships:** Available. **Calendar System:** Semester, Summer session available **Student-Faculty Ratio:** 22:1 **Regional Accreditation:** Middle States Association of Colleges and Schools **Credit Hours For Degree:** 64 credits, Associates **Professional Accreditation:** AAMAE, ACBSP, ACEN, ADA, APTA, CoARC, JRCEDMS, JRCERT, NAACLS. **Intercollegiate Athletics:** Baseball M; Basketball M & W; Cross-

Country Running M & W; Golf M; Soccer M & W; Softball W; Tennis M; Track and Field M & W; Volleyball W; Wrestling M

BERKELEY COLLEGE–WOODLAND PARK CAMPUS
44 Rifle Camp Rd.
Woodland Park, NJ 07424-3353
Tel: (973)278-5400; Free: 800-446-5400
Fax: (973)278-2242
E-mail: info@berkeleycollege.edu
Web Site: www.berkeleycollege.edu
President/CEO: Michael J. Smith
Admissions: Carol J. Covino
Type: Comprehensive **Sex:** Coed **% Accepted:** 99 **Admission Plans:** Deferred Admission; Open Admission **Application Deadline:** Rolling **Application Fee:** $50.00 **H.S. Requirements:** High school diploma required; GED accepted **Costs Per Year:** Application fee: $50. Tuition: $23,100 full-time, $810 per credit hour part-time. Mandatory fees: $1650 full-time, $412 per term part-time. Full-time tuition and fees vary according to course load. Part-time tuition and fees vary according to course load. Tuition guaranteed not to increase for student's term of enrollment. **Scholarships:** Available. **Calendar System:** Quarter, Summer session available **Enrollment:** Full-time 3,189, Graduate part-time 41, Part-time 624 **Faculty:** Full-time 136, Part-time 276 **Student-Faculty Ratio:** 15:1 **Exams:** ACT essay component not used; SAT I or ACT; SAT essay component not used. **Final Year or Final Semester Residency Requirement:** Yes **Regional Accreditation:** Middle States Association of Colleges and Schools **Credit Hours For Degree:** 60 Semester Credits, Associates; 120 Semester Credits, Bachelors **ROTC:** Army **Intercollegiate Athletics:** Cross-Country Running M & W; Soccer M

BETH MEDRASH GOVOHA
617 Sixth St.
Lakewood, NJ 08701-2797
Tel: (732)367-1060
President/CEO: Rabbi Aaron Kotler
Type: Five-Year College **Sex:** Men **Affiliation:** Jewish. **Application Fee:** $125.00 **Costs Per Year:** Application fee: $125. Tuition: $19,240 full-time. **Calendar System:** Semester **Credit Hours For Degree:** 150 credits, Bachelors **Professional Accreditation:** AARTS.

BLOOMFIELD COLLEGE
467 Franklin St.
Bloomfield, NJ 07003-9981
Tel: (973)748-9000; Free: 800-848-4555
Fax: (973)748-0916
E-mail: nicole_cibelli@bloomfield.edu
Web Site: www.bloomfield.edu
President/CEO: Richard A. Levao
Admissions: Nicole Cibelli
Financial Aid: Breanne Simkin
Type: Comprehensive **Sex:** Coed **Affiliation:** Presbyterian Church (U.S.A.). **Scores:** 62% SAT V 400+; 72% SAT M 400+; 37% ACT 18-23; 5% ACT 24-29 **% Accepted:** 60 **Admission Plans:** Deferred Admission; Early Decision Plan **Application Deadline:** August 1 **Application Fee:** $40.00 **H.S. Requirements:** High school diploma required; GED accepted **Costs Per Year:** Application fee: $40. Comprehensive fee: $40,100 includes full-time

tuition ($28,600) and college room and board ($11,500). College room only: $5750. Full-time tuition varies according to degree level. Room and board charges vary according to housing facility. Part-time tuition: $3575 per course. Part-time tuition varies according to course load and degree level. **Scholarships:** Available. **Calendar System:** Semester, Summer session available **Enrollment:** Full-time 1,752, Graduate full-time 2, Part-time 226 **Faculty:** Full-time 73, Part-time 146 **Student-Faculty Ratio:** 15:1 **Exams:** SAT I or ACT; SAT Reasoning. **% Receiving Financial Aid:** 93 **% Residing in College-Owned, -Operated, or -Affiliated Housing:** 32 **Final Year or Final Semester Residency Requirement:** No **Regional Accreditation:** Middle States Association of Colleges and Schools **Credit Hours For Degree:** 32 courses, Bachelors **ROTC:** Army **Professional Accreditation:** AACN. **Intercollegiate Athletics:** Baseball M; Basketball M & W; Cross-Country Running M & W; Soccer M & W; Softball W; Tennis M; Volleyball W

BROOKDALE COMMUNITY COLLEGE

765 Newman Springs Rd.
Lincroft, NJ 07738-1597
Tel: (732)842-1900
Fax: (732)576-1643
Web Site: www.brookdalecc.edu
President/CEO: Dr. Maureen Murphy
Admissions: Kim Toomey

Type: Two-Year College **Sex:** Coed **Affiliation:** New Jersey Commission on Higher Education. **Admission Plans:** Deferred Admission; Early Admission; Open Admission; Preferred Admission **Application Deadline:** Rolling **Application Fee:** $25.00 **H.S. Requirements:** High school diploma required; GED accepted **Scholarships:** Available. **Calendar System:** Semester, Summer session available **Regional Accreditation:** Middle States Association of Colleges and Schools **Credit Hours For Degree:** 60 credits, Associates **ROTC:** Air Force, Army **Professional Accreditation:** ACEN, CoARC, JRCERT. **Intercollegiate Athletics:** Baseball M; Basketball M & W; Golf M; Soccer M & W; Softball W; Tennis M & W

CALDWELL UNIVERSITY

120 Bloomfield Ave.
Caldwell, NJ 07006-6195
Tel: (973)618-3000
E-mail: squinn@caldwell.edu
Web Site: www.caldwell.edu
President/CEO: Dr. Nancy H. Blattner, PhD
Admissions: Stephen Quinn
Financial Aid: Eileen Felske

Type: Comprehensive **Sex:** Coed **Affiliation:** Roman Catholic. **Scores:** 79% SAT V 400+; 86% SAT M 400+; 54% ACT 18-23; 17% ACT 24-29 **% Accepted:** 64 **Admission Plans:** Deferred Admission; Early Admission; Early Decision Plan **Application Deadline:** Rolling **Application Fee:** $40.00 **H.S. Requirements:** High school diploma required; GED accepted **Costs Per Year:** Application fee: $40. Comprehensive fee: $42,165 includes full-time tuition ($29,950), mandatory fees ($1250), and college room and board ($10,965). Full-time tuition and fees vary according to course load and location. Room and board charges vary according to housing facility. Part-time tuition: $830 per credit. Part-time mandatory fees: $200 per term. Part-time tuition and fees vary according to course load and location. **Scholarships:** Available. **Calendar System:** Semester, Summer session available **Enrollment:** Full-time 1,374, Graduate full-time 158, Graduate part-time 385, Part-time 221 **Faculty:** Full-time 89, Part-time 178 **Student-Faculty Ratio:** 12:1 **Exams:** ACT essay component used for advising; ACT essay component used for placement; SAT I or ACT; SAT essay component used for advising; SAT essay component used for placement; SAT Reasoning; SAT Subject. **% Receiving Financial Aid:** 77 **% Residing in College-Owned, -Operated, or -Affiliated Housing:** 37 **Final Year or Final Semester Residency Requirement:** Yes **Regional Accreditation:** Middle States Association of Colleges and Schools **Credit Hours For Degree:** 120 credits, Bachelors **ROTC:** Army **Professional Accreditation:** ACA, ACBSP, TEAC. **Intercollegiate Athletics:** Baseball M; Basketball M & W; Bowling W; Cross-Country Running M & W; Lacrosse W; Soccer M & W; Softball W; Tennis M & W; Track and Field M & W; Volleyball W

CAMDEN COUNTY COLLEGE

PO Box 200
Blackwood, NJ 08012-0200
Tel: (856)227-7200
E-mail: ddelaney@camdencc.edu
Web Site: www.camdencc.edu
President/CEO: Dr. Raymond Yannuzzi
Admissions: Donald Delaney

Type: Two-Year College **Sex:** Coed **Affiliation:** New Jersey Commission on Higher Education. **Admission Plans:** Early Admission; Open Admission **Application Deadline:** Rolling **Application Fee:** $0.00 **H.S. Requirements:** High school diploma required; GED accepted **Costs Per Year:** Application fee: $0. Area resident tuition: $3210 full-time, $107 per credit part-time. State resident tuition: $3330 full-time, $111 per credit part-time. Nonresident tuition: $3330 full-time, $111 per credit part-time. Mandatory fees: $1110 full-time, $37 per credit part-time. Full-time tuition and fees vary according to course load. Part-time tuition and fees vary according to course load. **Scholarships:** Available. **Calendar System:** Semester, Summer session available **Enrollment:** Full-time 5,646, Part-time 5,617 **Faculty:** Full-time 132, Part-time 546 **Final Year or Final Semester Residency Requirement:** No **Regional Accreditation:** Middle States Association of Colleges and Schools **Professional Accreditation:** ADA, COA, NAACLS. **Intercollegiate Athletics:** Baseball M; Basketball M & W; Golf M; Soccer M & W; Softball W

CENTENARY COLLEGE

400 Jefferson St.
Hackettstown, NJ 07840-2100
Tel: (908)852-1400; Free: 800-236-8679
Fax: (908)852-3454
E-mail: schierlohs@centenarycollege.edu
Web Site: www.centenarycollege.edu
President/CEO: Dr. Barbara Lewthwaite
Admissions: Stephen Schierloh
Financial Aid: Michelle Burwell

Type: Comprehensive **Sex:** Coed **Affiliation:** United Methodist Church. **Scores:** 80% SAT V 400+; 81% SAT M 400+; 64% ACT 18-23; 14% ACT 24-29 **% Accepted:** 91 **Admission Plans:** Deferred Admission **Application Deadline:** Rolling **Application Fee:** $30.00 **H.S. Requirements:** High school diploma required; GED accepted **Scholarships:** Available. **Calendar System:** Semester, Summer session available **Enrollment:** Full-time 1,610, Graduate full-time 352, Graduate part-time 340, Part-time 98 **Faculty:** Full-time 79, Part-time 147 **Student-Faculty Ratio:** 17:1 **Exams:** ACT essay component not used; SAT I or ACT; SAT essay component not used; SAT Reasoning. **% Receiving Financial Aid:** 74 **% Residing in College-Owned, -Operated, or -Affiliated Housing:** 56 **Final Year or Final Semester Residency Requirement:** No **Regional Accreditation:** Middle States Association of Colleges and Schools **Credit Hours For Degree:** 64 credit hours, Associates; 128 credit hours, Bachelors **Professional Accreditation:** TEAC. **Intercollegiate Athletics:** Baseball M; Basketball M & W; Cheerleading W; Cross-Country Running M & W; Equestrian Sports M & W; Golf M; Lacrosse M & W; Soccer M & W; Softball W; Volleyball W; Wrestling M

CHAMBERLAIN COLLEGE OF NURSING

630 US Hwy. 1
North Brunswick, NJ 08902
Tel: (732)875-1300; Free: 877-751-5783
Fax: (732)875-1394
Web Site: www.chamberlain.edu

Type: Four-Year College **Sex:** Coed **Application Fee:** $95.00 **H.S. Requirements:** High school diploma required; GED accepted **Costs Per Year:** Application fee: $95. Tuition: $17,560 full-time, $665 per credit hour part-time. Mandatory fees: $600 full-time, $300 per term part-time. **Exams:** ACT essay component used for admission; SAT I or ACT; SAT essay component used for admission. **Regional Accreditation:** North Central Association of Colleges and Schools

THE COLLEGE OF NEW JERSEY

PO Box 7718
Ewing, NJ 08628
Tel: (609)771-1855
E-mail: admiss@tcnj.edu
Web Site: www.tcnj.edu
President/CEO: Dr. R. Barbara Gitenstein
Admissions: Grecia Montero
Financial Aid: Wilbert Casaine

Type: Comprehensive **Sex:** Coed **Scores:** 99% SAT V 400+; 100% SAT M 400+; 17% ACT 18-23; 62% ACT 24-29 **% Accepted:** 49 **Admission Plans:** Deferred Admission; Early Action **Application Deadline:** February 1 **Ap-**

plication Fee: $75.00 **H.S. Requirements:** High school diploma required; GED accepted **Costs Per Year:** Application fee: $75. State resident tuition: $10,879 full-time, $385.52 per credit hour part-time. Nonresident tuition: $21,810 full-time, $771.97 per credit hour part-time. Mandatory fees: $4587 full-time, $192.74 per credit hour part-time. Part-time tuition and fees vary according to course load. College room and board: $12,498. College room only: $8621. Room and board charges vary according to board plan. **Scholarships:** Available. **Calendar System:** Semester, Summer session available **Enrollment:** Full-time 6,486, Graduate full-time 225, Graduate part-time 423, Part-time 272 **Faculty:** Full-time 355, Part-time 498 **Student-Faculty Ratio:** 13:1 **Exams:** ACT essay component used for advising; ACT essay component used for placement; SAT I or ACT; SAT essay component used as validity check; SAT essay component used for advising; SAT essay component used for placement; SAT Reasoning. **% Receiving Financial Aid:** 49 **% Residing in College-Owned, -Operated, or -Affiliated Housing:** 60 **Final Year or Final Semester Residency Requirement:** No **Regional Accreditation:** Middle States Association of Colleges and Schools **Credit Hours For Degree:** 120 semester hours, Bachelors **ROTC:** Air Force, Army **Professional Accreditation:** AACN, AACSB, ABET, ACA, ASHA, NASM, NCATE. **Intercollegiate Athletics:** Baseball M; Basketball M & W; Cross-Country Running M & W; Field Hockey W; Football M; Lacrosse W; Soccer M & W; Softball W; Swimming and Diving M & W; Tennis M & W; Track and Field M & W; Wrestling M

COLLEGE OF SAINT ELIZABETH

2 Convent Rd.
Morristown, NJ 07960-6989
Tel: (973)290-4000; Free: 800-210-7900
Fax: (973)290-4710
E-mail: apply@cse.edu
Web Site: www.cse.edu
President/CEO: Dr. Helen J. Streubert, EdD
Admissions: Adrianna Arroyo
Financial Aid: Jaquiline Weiskopff
Type: Comprehensive **Sex:** Coed **Affiliation:** Roman Catholic. **Scores:** 49% SAT V 400+; 57% SAT M 400+ **% Accepted:** 63 **Admission Plans:** Deferred Admission **Application Deadline:** Rolling **Application Fee:** $35.00 **H.S. Requirements:** High school diploma required; GED accepted **Costs Per Year:** Application fee: $35. Comprehensive fee: $44,432 includes full-time tuition ($29,732), mandatory fees ($1956), and college room and board ($12,744). Room and board charges vary according to board plan. Part-time tuition: $929 per credit hour. Part-time tuition varies according to course load and location. **Scholarships:** Available. **Calendar System:** Semester, Summer session available **Enrollment:** Full-time 534, Graduate full-time 94, Graduate part-time 348, Part-time 271 **Faculty:** Full-time 52, Part-time 106 **Student-Faculty Ratio:** 11:1 **Exams:** SAT I; SAT essay component used for admission; SAT essay component used for placement; SAT Reasoning. **% Receiving Financial Aid:** 87 **% Residing in College-Owned, -Operated, or -Affiliated Housing:** 72 **Final Year or Final Semester Residency Requirement:** No **Regional Accreditation:** Middle States Association of Colleges and Schools **Credit Hours For Degree:** 120 credits, Bachelors **Professional Accreditation:** AAFCS, ACEN, AND. **Intercollegiate Athletics:** Basketball W; Lacrosse W; Soccer W; Softball W; Tennis W; Volleyball W

COUNTY COLLEGE OF MORRIS

214 Ctr. Grove Rd.
Randolph, NJ 07869-2086
Tel: (973)328-5000
Fax: (973)328-1282
E-mail: esoltys@ccm.edu
Web Site: www.ccm.edu
President/CEO: Dr. Edward J. Yaw
Admissions: Eugene Soltys
Type: Two-Year College **Sex:** Coed **% Accepted:** 61 **Admission Plans:** Open Admission **Application Deadline:** Rolling **Application Fee:** $30.00 **H.S. Requirements:** High school diploma required; GED accepted **Costs Per Year:** Application fee: $30. Area resident tuition: $3690 full-time, $123 per credit hour part-time. State resident tuition: $7380 full-time, $246 per credit hour part-time. Nonresident tuition: $10,530 full-time, $351 per credit hour part-time. Mandatory fees: $1000 full-time, $27 per credit hour part-time, $19. Full-time tuition and fees vary according to course load, location, and program. Part-time tuition and fees vary according to course load, location, and program. **Scholarships:** Available. **Calendar System:** Semester,

Summer session available **Enrollment:** Full-time 3,946, Part-time 4,080 **Faculty:** Full-time 157, Part-time 358 **Student-Faculty Ratio:** 19:1 **Exams:** ACT essay component not used; SAT essay component not used. **Final Year or Final Semester Residency Requirement:** No **Regional Accreditation:** Middle States Association of Colleges and Schools **Credit Hours For Degree:** 62 credits, Associates **Professional Accreditation:** ABET, ACBSP, ACEN, JRCERT. **Intercollegiate Athletics:** Baseball M; Basketball M & W; Golf M; Lacrosse M; Soccer M & W; Softball W; Volleyball W

CUMBERLAND COUNTY COLLEGE

PO Box 1500, College Dr.
Vineland, NJ 08362
Tel: (856)691-8600
Fax: (856)691-6157
Web Site: www.cccnj.edu
President/CEO: Dr. Thomas Isekenegbe
Admissions: Anne Daly-Eimer
Type: Two-Year College **Sex:** Coed **Affiliation:** New Jersey Commission on Higher Education. **Admission Plans:** Deferred Admission; Early Admission; Open Admission **Application Deadline:** Rolling **H.S. Requirements:** High school diploma required; GED accepted **Costs Per Year:** Area resident tuition: $3390 full-time, $113 per credit hour part-time. State resident tuition: $3690 full-time, $123 per credit hour part-time. Nonresident tuition: $13,560 full-time, $452 per credit hour part-time. Mandatory fees: $900 full-time, $30 per credit hour part-time. Full-time tuition and fees vary according to program and reciprocity agreements. Part-time tuition and fees vary according to program and reciprocity agreements. **Scholarships:** Available. **Calendar System:** Semester, Summer session available **Enrollment:** Full-time 2,298, Part-time 1,546 **Faculty:** Full-time 43, Part-time 229 **Student-Faculty Ratio:** 23:1 **Final Year or Final Semester Residency Requirement:** No **Regional Accreditation:** Middle States Association of Colleges and Schools **Credit Hours For Degree:** about 64 credits (varies by program), Associates **Professional Accreditation:** ACEN, JRCERT. **Intercollegiate Athletics:** Baseball M; Basketball M & W; Cross-Country Running M & W; Softball W; Track and Field M

DEVRY UNIVERSITY (NORTH BRUNSWICK)

630 US Hwy. 1
North Brunswick, NJ 08902-3362
Tel: (732)729-3532; Free: 866-338-7941
Web Site: www.devry.edu
Type: Comprehensive **Sex:** Coed **Affiliation:** DeVry University. **Application Fee:** $40.00 **H.S. Requirements:** High school diploma required; GED accepted **Costs Per Year:** Application fee: $40. Tuition: $17,052 full-time, $609 per credit hour part-time. Mandatory fees: $80 full-time, $40 per term part-time. **Scholarships:** Available. **Calendar System:** Semester **Enrollment:** Full-time 467, Graduate full-time 47, Graduate part-time 99, Part-time 463 **Faculty:** Full-time 25, Part-time 121 **Student-Faculty Ratio:** 11:1 **Exams:** ACT essay component used for admission; ACT essay component used for placement; SAT essay component used for admission; SAT essay component used for placement. **Regional Accreditation:** North Central Association of Colleges and Schools **Credit Hours For Degree:** 65 credit hours, Associates; 126 credit hours, Bachelors **Professional Accreditation:** ABET, ACBSP.

DEVRY UNIVERSITY (PARAMUS)

35 Plz., 81 E State Rte. 4
Ste. 102
Paramus, NJ 07652
Tel: (201)556-2840; Free: 866-338-7941
Web Site: www.devry.edu
Type: Comprehensive **Sex:** Coed **Application Deadline:** Rolling **Costs Per Year:** Tuition: $17,052 full-time, $609 per credit hour part-time. Mandatory fees: $80 full-time, $40 per term part-time. **Regional Accreditation:** North Central Association of Colleges and Schools **Professional Accreditation:** ACBSP.

DREW UNIVERSITY

36 Madison Ave.
Madison, NJ 07940-1493
Tel: (973)408-3000
Fax: (973)408-3939
E-mail: cadm@drew.edu

Web Site: www.drew.edu
President/CEO: Dr. MaryAnn Baenninger
Admissions: James Skiff
Financial Aid: Colby McCarthy
Type: University Sex: Coed Affiliation: United Methodist Church. Scores: 98% SAT V 400+; 100% SAT M 400+; 37% ACT 18-23; 41% ACT 24-29 % Accepted: 70 Admission Plans: Deferred Admission; Early Action; Early Admission Application Deadline: February 15 Application Fee: $60.00 H.S. Requirements: High school diploma required; GED accepted Costs Per Year: Application fee: $60. Comprehensive fee: $59,056 includes full-time tuition ($45,552), mandatory fees ($832), and college room and board ($12,672). College room only: $8152. Room and board charges vary according to board plan and housing facility. Part-time tuition: $1898 per credit hour. Part-time tuition varies according to course load. Scholarships: Available. Calendar System: Semester, Summer session available Enrollment: Full-time 1,412, Graduate full-time 279, Graduate part-time 353, Part-time 38 Faculty: Full-time 146, Part-time 107 Student-Faculty Ratio: 10:1 Exams: ACT essay component not used; SAT I or ACT; SAT II; SAT essay component not used; SAT Reasoning. % Receiving Financial Aid: 72 % Residing in College-Owned, -Operated, or -Affiliated Housing: 76 Final Year or Final Semester Residency Requirement: No Regional Accreditation: Middle States Association of Colleges and Schools Credit Hours For Degree: 128 credits, Bachelors Professional Accreditation: ACIPE, ATS, TEAC. Intercollegiate Athletics: Baseball M; Basketball M & W; Cross-Country Running M & W; Equestrian Sports W; Fencing M & W; Field Hockey W; Lacrosse M & W; Rugby M & W; Soccer M & W; Softball W; Swimming and Diving M & W; Tennis M & W; Track and Field M & W

EASTERN INTERNATIONAL COLLEGE (BELLEVILLE)

251 Washington Ave.
Belleville, NJ 07109
Tel: (973)751-9051
Web Site: www.eicollege.edu
Type: Two-Year College Sex: Coed Professional Accreditation: ACCSC.

EASTERN INTERNATIONAL COLLEGE (JERSEY CITY)

684 Newark Ave.
Jersey City, NJ 07306
Tel: (201)216-9901
Web Site: www.eicollege.edu
Type: Two-Year College Sex: Coed Professional Accreditation: ACCSC.

EASTWICK COLLEGE (HACKENSACK)

250 Moore St.
Hackensack, NJ 07601
Tel: (201)488-9400
Web Site: www.eastwickcollege.edu
Type: Two-Year College Sex: Coed

EASTWICK COLLEGE (NUTLEY)

103 Park Ave.
Nutley, NJ 07110
Tel: (973)661-0600
Web Site: www.eastwickcollege.edu
Type: Two-Year College Sex: Coed

EASTWICK COLLEGE (RAMSEY)

10 S Franklin Tpke.
Ramsey, NJ 07446
Tel: (201)327-8877
Web Site: www.eastwickcollege.edu
Type: Two-Year College Sex: Coed

ESSEX COUNTY COLLEGE

303 University Ave.
Newark, NJ 07102-1798
Tel: (973)877-3000
Fax: (973)623-6449
Web Site: www.essex.edu
President/CEO: A. Zachary Yamba
Admissions: Marva Mack
Financial Aid: Mildred C. Cofer
Type: Two-Year College Sex: Coed Affiliation: New Jersey Commission on Higher Education. % Accepted: 100 Admission Plans: Deferred Admis-

sion; Open Admission Application Deadline: August 15 Application Fee: $25.00 H.S. Requirements: High school diploma or equivalent not required Costs Per Year: Application fee: $25. Area resident tuition: $3,146 full-time, $116.50 per credit hour part-time. State resident tuition: $6291 full-time, $233 per credit hour part-time. Nonresident tuition: $6291 full-time, $233 per credit hour part-time. Mandatory fees: $1,066 full-time, $39.50 per credit hour part-time. Scholarships: Available. Calendar System: Semester, Summer session available Enrollment: Full-time 6,569, Part-time 5,410 Faculty: Full-time 118, Part-time 483 Student-Faculty Ratio: 29:1 Regional Accreditation: Middle States Association of Colleges and Schools Credit Hours For Degree: 63 credit hours, Associates ROTC: Army Professional Accreditation: ABET, ACEN, APTA, COA, JRCERT. Intercollegiate Athletics: Basketball M & W; Cross-Country Running M & W; Soccer M; Track and Field M & W

FAIRLEIGH DICKINSON UNIVERSITY, COLLEGE AT FLORHAM

285 Madison Ave.
Madison, NJ 07940-1099
Tel: (973)443-8500; Free: 800-338-8803
E-mail: globaleducation@fdu.edu
Web Site: www.fdu.edu
President/CEO: Sheldon Drucker
Admissions: Jonathan Wexler
Type: Comprehensive Sex: Coed Scores: 98% SAT V 400+; 96% SAT M 400+ % Accepted: 81 Application Fee: $40.00 H.S. Requirements: High school diploma required; GED accepted Costs Per Year: Application fee: $40. Comprehensive fee: $51,724 includes full-time tuition ($38,098), mandatory fees ($994), and college room and board ($12,632). College room only: $8300. Room and board charges vary according to board plan and housing facility. Part-time tuition: $967 per credit hour. Part-time mandatory fees: $398 per year. Scholarships: Available. Calendar System: Semester, Summer session available Enrollment: Full-time 2,236, Graduate full-time 571, Graduate part-time 260, Part-time 166 Exams: SAT I or ACT. % Receiving Financial Aid: 68 % Residing in College-Owned, -Operated, or -Affiliated Housing: 62 Final Year or Final Semester Residency Requirement: No Regional Accreditation: Middle States Association of Colleges and Schools Credit Hours For Degree: 120 credits, Bachelors ROTC: Air Force, Army Professional Accreditation: AACSB, ACA. Intercollegiate Athletics: Baseball M; Basketball M & W; Cross-Country Running M & W; Field Hockey W; Football M; Golf M & W; Lacrosse M & W; Soccer M & W; Softball W; Swimming and Diving M & W; Tennis M & W; Volleyball W

FAIRLEIGH DICKINSON UNIVERSITY, METROPOLITAN CAMPUS

1000 River Rd.
Teaneck, NJ 07666-1914
Tel: (201)692-2000; Free: 800-338-8803
E-mail: globaleducation@fdu.edu
Web Site: www.fdu.edu
President/CEO: Sheldon Drucker
Admissions: Jonathan Wexler
Type: Comprehensive Sex: Coed Scores: 93% SAT V 400+; 94% SAT M 400+ % Accepted: 80 Admission Plans: Early Admission Application Fee: $40.00 H.S. Requirements: High school diploma required; GED accepted Costs Per Year: Application fee: $40. Comprehensive fee: $49,828 includes full-time tuition ($35,916), mandatory fees ($994), and college room and board ($12,918). College room only: $8586. Room and board charges vary according to board plan and housing facility. Part-time tuition: $967 per credit. Part-time mandatory fees: $398 per year. Scholarships: Available. Calendar System: Semester, Summer session available Enrollment: Full-time 2,691, Graduate full-time 1,158, Graduate part-time 1,568, Part-time 3,357 Exams: SAT I or ACT. % Receiving Financial Aid: 69 % Residing in College-Owned, -Operated, or -Affiliated Housing: 19 Final Year or Final Semester Residency Requirement: No Regional Accreditation: Middle States Association of Colleges and Schools Credit Hours For Degree: 60 credits, Associates; 120 credits, Bachelors ROTC: Air Force, Army Professional Accreditation: AACN, AACSB, ABET, APA, TEAC. Intercollegiate Athletics: Baseball M; Basketball M & W; Bowling W; Cross-Country Running M & W; Fencing W; Golf M & W; Soccer M & W; Softball W; Tennis M & W; Track and Field M & W; Volleyball W

FELICIAN UNIVERSITY

262 S Main St.
Lodi, NJ 07644-2117

Tel: (201)559-6000
Fax: (973)778-4111
E-mail: fullerc@felician.edu
Web Site: www.felician.edu
President/CEO: Dr. Anne Prisco
Admissions: Colleen Fuller
Financial Aid: Cynthia Montalvo
Type: Comprehensive **Sex:** Coed **Affiliation:** Roman Catholic. **Scores:** 72% SAT V 400+; 79% SAT M 400+ **% Accepted:** 79 **Admission Plans:** Deferred Admission; Early Decision Plan **Application Deadline:** Rolling **Application Fee:** $30.00 **H.S. Requirements:** High school diploma required; GED accepted. For nursing, elementary education programs: High school diploma required; GED not accepted **Costs Per Year:** Application fee: $30. Comprehensive fee: $45,370 includes full-time tuition ($30,680), mandatory fees ($2310), and college room and board ($12,380). Full-time tuition and fees vary according to program. Room and board charges vary according to housing facility. Part-time tuition: $1015 per credit hour. Part-time tuition varies according to course load and program. **Scholarships:** Available. **Calendar System:** Semester, Summer session available **Enrollment:** Full-time 1,388, Graduate full-time 41, Graduate part-time 307, Part-time 221 **Faculty:** Full-time 86, Part-time 126 **Student-Faculty Ratio:** 13:1 **Exams:** ACT; SAT I and SAT II or ACT; SAT I or ACT; SAT II; SAT Reasoning; SAT Subject. **% Receiving Financial Aid:** 91 **% Residing in College-Owned, -Operated, or -Affiliated Housing:** 28 **Final Year or Final Semester Residency Requirement:** No **Regional Accreditation:** Middle States Association of Colleges and Schools **Credit Hours For Degree:** 68 semester hours, Associates; 120 semester hours, Bachelors **ROTC:** Air Force, Army **Professional Accreditation:** AACN, NAACLS, TEAC. **Intercollegiate Athletics:** Baseball M; Basketball M & W; Bowling W; Cross-Country Running M & W; Golf M; Soccer M & W; Softball W; Volleyball W

GEORGIAN COURT UNIVERSITY

900 Lakewood Ave.
Lakewood, NJ 08701-2697
Tel: (732)987-2760; Free: 800-458-8422
Fax: (732)987-2000
E-mail: admissions@georgian.edu
Web Site: www.georgian.edu
President/CEO: Dr. Joseph R. Marbach, PhD
Admissions: Tracey Howard-Ubelhoer
Financial Aid: Randy Brown
Type: Comprehensive **Sex:** Coed **Affiliation:** Roman Catholic. **Scores:** 88% SAT V 400+; 84% SAT M 400+ **% Accepted:** 73 **Admission Plans:** Deferred Admission; Early Decision Plan **Application Deadline:** August 1 **Application Fee:** $40.00 **H.S. Requirements:** High school diploma required; GED accepted **Costs Per Year:** Application fee: $40. Comprehensive fee: $42,426 includes full-time tuition ($30,158), mandatory fees ($1460), and college room and board ($10,808). Full-time tuition and fees vary according to location and program. Part-time tuition: $690 per credit hour. Part-time mandatory fees: $365 per term. Part-time tuition and fees vary according to location and program. **Scholarships:** Available. **Calendar System:** Semester, Summer session available **Enrollment:** Full-time 1,249, Graduate full-time 157, Graduate part-time 437, Part-time 279 **Faculty:** Full-time 86, Part-time 161 **Student-Faculty Ratio:** 12:1 **Exams:** ACT essay component used for admission; SAT I or ACT; SAT II; SAT essay component used for admission; SAT Reasoning. **% Receiving Financial Aid:** 83 **% Residing in College-Owned, -Operated, or -Affiliated Housing:** 29 **Final Year or Final Semester Residency Requirement:** No **Regional Accreditation:** Middle States Association of Colleges and Schools **Credit Hours For Degree:** 120 credits, Bachelors **Professional Accreditation:** ACBSP, CSWE, TEAC. **Intercollegiate Athletics:** Basketball M & W; Cross-Country Running M & W; Lacrosse M & W; Soccer M & W; Softball W; Tennis W; Track and Field M & W; Volleyball W

HUDSON COUNTY COMMUNITY COLLEGE

70 Sip Ave.
Jersey City, NJ 07306
Tel: (201)714-7100
Fax: (201)714-2136
E-mail: pvida@hccc.edu
Web Site: www.hccc.edu
President/CEO: Dr. Glen Gabert
Admissions: Pete S. Vida
Type: Two-Year College **Sex:** Coed **Admission Plans:** Open Admission **Ap-**

plication Deadline: September 1 **Application Fee:** $20.00 **H.S. Requirements:** High school diploma or equivalent not required. For applicants under 18 (LEAP Program): High school diploma required; GED accepted **Costs Per Year:** Application fee: $20. Area resident tuition: $4683 full-time, $129 per credit hour part-time. State resident tuition: $8163 full-time, $258 per credit hour part-time. Nonresident tuition: $11,643 full-time, $387 per credit hour part-time. Mandatory fees: $1,422 full-time, $45.75 per credit hour part-time, $25 per term part-time. Full-time tuition and fees vary according to course load and program. Part-time tuition and fees vary according to course load and program. **Scholarships:** Available. **Calendar System:** Semester, Summer session available **Enrollment:** Full-time 5,876, Part-time 3,175 **Faculty:** Full-time 84, Part-time 577 **Final Year or Final Semester Residency Requirement:** No **Regional Accreditation:** Middle States Association of Colleges and Schools **Credit Hours For Degree:** 60 credits, Associates **Professional Accreditation:** AAMAE, ABET, ACF, AHIMA.

JERSEY COLLEGE

546 US Hwy. 46
Teterboro, NJ 07608
Tel: (201)489-5836
Web Site: www.jerseycollege.edu
Type: Two-Year College **Sex:** Coed **Professional Accreditation:** COE.

KEAN UNIVERSITY

1000 Morris Ave.
Union, NJ 07083
Tel: (908)737-KEAN
Fax: (908)737-3415
E-mail: admitme@kean.edu
Web Site: www.kean.edu
President/CEO: Dr. Dawood Farahi
Admissions: Jennifer Kanellis
Financial Aid: Sherrell Watson-Hall
Type: Comprehensive **Sex:** Coed **Affiliation:** New Jersey State College System. **Scores:** 81% SAT V 400+; 89% SAT M 400+; 51% ACT 18-23; 12% ACT 24-29 **% Accepted:** 74 **Admission Plans:** Deferred Admission; Early Decision Plan **Application Deadline:** August 15 **Application Fee:** $75.00 **H.S. Requirements:** High school diploma required; GED accepted **Costs Per Year:** Application fee: $75. State resident tuition: $7565 full-time, $295 per credit part-time. Nonresident tuition: $14,167 full-time, $500 per credit part-time. Mandatory fees: $4,016 full-time, $147 per credit part-time. Part-time tuition and fees vary according to course load. College room and board: $12,565. Room and board charges vary according to board plan, housing facility, and student level. **Scholarships:** Available. **Calendar System:** Semester, Summer session available **Enrollment:** Full-time 9,192, Graduate full-time 853, Graduate part-time 1,445, Part-time 2,622 **Faculty:** Full-time 336, Part-time 1,026 **Student-Faculty Ratio:** 17:1 **Exams:** ACT essay component used for advising; SAT I or ACT; SAT essay component used for advising; SAT Reasoning. **% Receiving Financial Aid:** 70 **% Residing in College-Owned, -Operated, or -Affiliated Housing:** 15 **Final Year or Final Semester Residency Requirement:** No **Regional Accreditation:** Middle States Association of Colleges and Schools **ROTC:** Air Force, Army **Professional Accreditation:** ACA, ACEN, AHIMA, AOTA, ASHA, ATMAE, CIDA, CSWE, JRCAT, NASAD, NASM, NASPAA, NAST, NCATE. **Intercollegiate Athletics:** Baseball M; Basketball M & W; Field Hockey W; Football M; Lacrosse M & W; Soccer M & W; Softball W; Tennis W; Volleyball M & W

MERCER COUNTY COMMUNITY COLLEGE

1200 Old Trenton Rd.
Trenton, NJ 08690-1004
Tel: (609)586-4800; Free: 800-392-MCCC
Fax: (609)586-6944
E-mail: admiss@mccc.edu
Web Site: www.mccc.edu
President/CEO: Dr. Jianping Wang
Admissions: Dr. L. Campbell
Type: Two-Year College **Sex:** Coed **Admission Plans:** Deferred Admission; Open Admission; Preferred Admission **Application Deadline:** Rolling **Application Fee:** $0.00 **H.S. Requirements:** High school diploma or equivalent not required **Costs Per Year:** Application fee: $0. Area resident tuition: $2856 full-time, $118.50 per credit hour part-time. State resident tuition: $3984 full-time, $166 per credit hour part-time. Nonresident tuition: $6096 full-time, $254 per credit hour part-time. Mandatory fees: $804 full-time, $33.50 per credit hour part-time. Full-time tuition and fees vary accord-

ing to program and reciprocity agreements. Part-time tuition and fees vary according to program and reciprocity agreements. **Scholarships:** Available. **Calendar System:** Semester, Summer session available **Enrollment:** Full-time 3,077, Part-time 4,902 **Student-Faculty Ratio:** 18:1 **Regional Accreditation:** Middle States Association of Colleges and Schools **Credit Hours For Degree:** 60 credits, Associates **ROTC:** Air Force, Army **Professional Accreditation:** AABI, ABFSE, ACEN, APTA, JRCERT, NAACLS. **Intercollegiate Athletics:** Baseball M; Basketball M & W; Golf M & W; Soccer M & W; Softball W; Tennis M & W; Track and Field M & W

MESIVTA KESER TORAH

613 Madison Ave.
Lakewood, NJ 08701
Tel: (732)681-5656

Type: Four-Year College **Sex:** Coed **Affiliation:** Jewish. **Costs Per Year:** Tuition: $13,200 full-time. Mandatory fees: $200 full-time. **Professional Accreditation:** AARTS.

MIDDLESEX COUNTY COLLEGE

2600 Woodbridge Ave.
Edison, NJ 08818-3050
Tel: (732)548-6000
Web Site: www.middlesexcc.edu
President/CEO: Dr. Joann La Perla-Morales
Admissions: Lisa Rodriguez

Type: Two-Year College **Sex:** Coed **Admission Plans:** Deferred Admission; Early Admission; Open Admission; Preferred Admission **Application Deadline:** Rolling **Application Fee:** $25.00 **H.S. Requirements:** High school diploma required; GED accepted **Costs Per Year:** Application fee: $25. One-time mandatory fee: $86. Area resident tuition: $4215 full-time, $106 per credit part-time. State resident tuition: $8430 full-time, $212 per credit part-time. Nonresident tuition: $8430 full-time, $212 per credit part-time. **Scholarships:** Available. **Calendar System:** Semester, Summer session available **Student-Faculty Ratio:** 24:1 **Exams:** Other. **Final Year or Final Semester Residency Requirement:** No **Regional Accreditation:** Middle States Association of Colleges and Schools **Credit Hours For Degree:** 60 credits, Associates **ROTC:** Army **Professional Accreditation:** ABET, ACEN, ADA, JRCERT, NAACLS. **Intercollegiate Athletics:** Baseball M; Basketball M & W; Cross-Country Running M & W; Soccer M & W; Softball W; Track and Field M & W; Wrestling M

MONMOUTH UNIVERSITY

400 Cedar Ave.
West Long Branch, NJ 07764-1898
Tel: (732)571-3400; Free: 800-543-9671
Fax: (732)263-5166
E-mail: admission@monmouth.edu
Web Site: www.monmouth.edu
President/CEO: Dr. Paul R. Brown
Admissions: Victoria Bobik
Financial Aid: Claire Alasio

Type: Comprehensive **Sex:** Coed **Scores:** 98% SAT V 400+; 98% SAT M 400+; 60.8% ACT 18-23; 33.5% ACT 24-29 **% Accepted:** 78 **Admission Plans:** Deferred Admission; Early Decision Plan **Application Deadline:** March 1 **Application Fee:** $50.00 **H.S. Requirements:** High school diploma required; GED accepted **Costs Per Year:** Application fee: $50. One-time mandatory fee: $200. Comprehensive fee: $46,234 includes full-time tuition ($33,028), mandatory fees ($700), and college room and board ($12,506). College room only: $7182. Room and board charges vary according to board plan and housing facility. Part-time tuition: $956 per credit hour. Part-time mandatory fees: $175 per term. Part-time tuition and fees vary according to course load. **Scholarships:** Available. **Calendar System:** Semester, Summer session available **Enrollment:** Full-time 4,450, Graduate full-time 737, Graduate part-time 964, Part-time 243 **Faculty:** Full-time 288, Part-time 350 **Student-Faculty Ratio:** 14:1 **Exams:** ACT essay component not used; SAT I or ACT; SAT essay component not used; SAT Reasoning. **% Receiving Financial Aid:** 72 **% Residing in College-Owned, -Operated, or -Affiliated Housing:** 46 **Final Year or Final Semester Residency Requirement:** Yes **Regional Accreditation:** Middle States Association of Colleges and Schools **Credit Hours For Degree:** 63 credits, Associates; 128 credits, Bachelors **ROTC:** Air Force, Army **Professional Accreditation:** AACN, AACSB, ABET, ACA, CSWE, NCATE. **Intercollegiate Athletics:** Baseball M; Basketball M & W; Bowling W; Cheerleading M & W; Cross-Country Run-

ning M & W; Field Hockey W; Football M; Golf M & W; Ice Hockey M; Lacrosse M & W; Sailing M & W; Soccer M & W; Softball W; Tennis M & W; Track and Field M & W

MONTCLAIR STATE UNIVERSITY

1 Normal Ave.
Montclair, NJ 07043-1624
Tel: (973)655-4000
Fax: (973)893-5455
E-mail: undergraduate.admissions@montclair.edu
Web Site: www.montclair.edu
President/CEO: Dr. Susan A. Cole
Admissions: Jeff Indiveri-Gant
Financial Aid: James T. Anderson

Type: University **Sex:** Coed **Scores:** 87% SAT V 400+; 89% SAT M 400+ **% Accepted:** 70 **Admission Plans:** Deferred Admission **Application Deadline:** March 1 **Application Fee:** $65.00 **H.S. Requirements:** High school diploma required; GED accepted **Costs Per Year:** Application fee: $65. State resident tuition: $8513 full-time, $284 per credit part-time. Nonresident tuition: $17,060 full-time, $569 per credit part-time. Mandatory fees: $3260 full-time, $109 per credit part-time. College room and board: $13,884. Room and board charges vary according to board plan and housing facility. **Scholarships:** Available. **Calendar System:** Semester, Summer session available **Enrollment:** Full-time 14,433, Graduate full-time 1,443, Graduate part-time 2,686, Part-time 1,903 **Faculty:** Full-time 604, Part-time 1,210 **Student-Faculty Ratio:** 17:1 **Exams:** SAT I or ACT. **% Receiving Financial Aid:** 63 **% Residing in College-Owned, -Operated, or -Affiliated Housing:** 32 **Final Year or Final Semester Residency Requirement:** No **Regional Accreditation:** Middle States Association of Colleges and Schools **Credit Hours For Degree:** 120 semester hours, Bachelors **Professional Accreditation:** AACSB, AAFCS, ABET, ACA, AND, ASHA, NASAD, NASD, NASM, NAST, NCATE, NRPA. **Intercollegiate Athletics:** Baseball M; Basketball M & W; Field Hockey W; Football M; Lacrosse M & W; Soccer M & W; Softball W; Swimming and Diving M & W; Track and Field M & W; Volleyball W

NEW JERSEY CITY UNIVERSITY

2039 Kennedy Blvd.
Jersey City, NJ 07305-1597
Tel: (201)200-2000; Free: 888-441-NJCU
Fax: (201)200-2044
E-mail: admissions@nicu.edu
Web Site: www.njcu.edu
President/CEO: Dr. Sue Henderson, PhD
Admissions: Jose Balda
Financial Aid: Frank Cuozzo

Type: Comprehensive **Sex:** Coed **Scores:** 58% SAT V 400+; 72% SAT M 400+ **% Accepted:** 87 **Admission Plans:** Deferred Admission **Application Deadline:** July 15 **Application Fee:** $50.00 **H.S. Requirements:** High school diploma required; GED accepted **Costs Per Year:** Application fee: $50. State resident tuition: $7936 full-time, $264.50 per credit part-time. Nonresident tuition: $16,765 full-time, $558.85 per credit part-time. Mandatory fees: $3,243 full-time, $105.60 per credit part-time. Part-time tuition and fees vary according to course load. College room and board: $10,604. College room only: $6,817. Room and board charges vary according to board plan and housing facility. **Scholarships:** Available. **Calendar System:** Semester, Summer session available **Enrollment:** Full-time 4,826, Graduate full-time 406, Graduate part-time 1,514, Part-time 1,491 **Faculty:** Full-time 251, Part-time 558 **Student-Faculty Ratio:** 14:1 **Exams:** SAT I; SAT essay component used for admission. **% Receiving Financial Aid:** 84 **% Residing in College-Owned, -Operated, or -Affiliated Housing:** 4 **Final Year or Final Semester Residency Requirement:** No **Regional Accreditation:** Middle States Association of Colleges and Schools **Credit Hours For Degree:** 120 credits, Bachelors **ROTC:** Air Force, Army **Professional Accreditation:** ACBSP, ACEN, NASAD, NASM, NCATE, TEAC. **Intercollegiate Athletics:** Baseball M; Basketball M & W; Bowling W; Cross-Country Running M & W; Golf M; Soccer M & W; Softball W; Volleyball M & W

NEW JERSEY INSTITUTE OF TECHNOLOGY

University Heights
Newark, NJ 07102
Tel: (973)596-3000; Free: 800-925-NJIT
Fax: (973)802-1854
E-mail: admissions@njit.edu

Web Site: www.njit.edu
President/CEO: Dr. Joel S. Bloom
Admissions: Stephen M. Eck
Financial Aid: Ivon Nunez
Type: University **Sex:** Coed **Scores:** 99% SAT V 400+; 100% SAT M 400+
% Accepted: 61 **Admission Plans:** Deferred Admission; Early Admission;
Preferred Admission **Application Deadline:** March 1 **Application Fee:**
$75.00 **H.S. Requirements:** High school diploma required; GED accepted
Costs Per Year: Application fee: $75. State resident tuition: $13,434 full-
time, $511 per credit part-time. Nonresident tuition: $27,652 full-time, $1182
per credit part-time. Mandatory fees: $2674 full-time, $157 per credit part-
time. Full-time tuition and fees vary according to course load and degree
level. Part-time tuition and fees vary according to course load and degree
level. College room and board: $13,300. College room only: $8900. Room
and board charges vary according to board plan and housing facility.
Scholarships: Available. **Calendar System:** Semester, Summer session
available **Enrollment:** Full-time 6,178, Graduate full-time 2,055, Graduate
part-time 1,262, Part-time 1,830 **Faculty:** Full-time 410, Part-time 391
Student-Faculty Ratio: 17:1 **Exams:** SAT I or ACT; SAT essay component
used for placement; SAT Reasoning. **% Receiving Financial Aid:** 61 %
Residing in College-Owned, -Operated, or -Affiliated Housing: 23 **Final
Year or Final Semester Residency Requirement:** No **Regional Accreditation:** Middle States Association of Colleges and Schools **Credit
Hours For Degree:** 124 credits, Bachelors **ROTC:** Air Force, Army **Profes-
sional Accreditation:** AACSB, ABET, CEPH, NAAB. **Intercollegiate Athlet-
ics:** Baseball M; Basketball M & W; Bowling M; Cross-Country Running M &
W; Fencing M & W; Ice Hockey M; Soccer M & W; Swimming and Diving M
& W; Tennis M & W; Track and Field M & W; Volleyball M & W

OCEAN COUNTY COLLEGE
College Dr.
Toms River, NJ 08754-2001
Tel: (732)255-0400
E-mail: shartigan@ocean.edu
Web Site: www.ocean.edu
President/CEO: Dr. Jon H. Larson
Admissions: Sheenah Hartigan
Type: Two-Year College **Sex:** Coed **% Accepted:** 100 **Admission Plans:**
Open Admission; Preferred Admission **Application Deadline:** Rolling **Ap-
plication Fee:** $0.00 **H.S. Requirements:** High school diploma or
equivalent not required. For nursing program: High school diploma required;
GED accepted **Costs Per Year:** Application fee: $0. Area resident tuition:
$3360 full-time, $112 per credit part-time. State resident tuition: $4050 full-
time, $135 per credit part-time. Nonresident tuition: $6750 full-time, $225 per
credit part-time. Mandatory fees: $985 full-time, $31.50 per credit part-time,
$20 per term part-time. Full-time tuition and fees vary according to program.
Part-time tuition and fees vary according to program. **Scholarships:** Available. **Calendar System:** Semester, Summer session available **Enrollment:**
Full-time 4,611, Part-time 4,052 **Faculty:** Full-time 99, Part-time 391
Student-Faculty Ratio: 25:1 **Exams:** ACT essay component used for
placement; Other. **Final Year or Final Semester Residency Requirement:**
No **Regional Accreditation:** Middle States Association of Colleges and
Schools **Credit Hours For Degree:** 64 semester hours, Associates **Profes-
sional Accreditation:** ACEN. **Intercollegiate Athletics:** Baseball M;
Basketball M & W; Cross-Country Running M & W; Golf M; Lacrosse M;
Soccer M & W; Softball W; Tennis M & W; Volleyball W

PASSAIC COUNTY COMMUNITY COLLEGE
One College Blvd.
Paterson, NJ 07505-1179
Tel: (973)684-6800
Web Site: www.pccc.cc.nj.us
President/CEO: Steven M. Rose, EdD
Admissions: Patrick Noonan
Type: Two-Year College **Sex:** Coed **% Accepted:** 100 **Admission Plans:**
Deferred Admission; Early Admission; Open Admission; Preferred Admission
Application Deadline: Rolling **H.S. Requirements:** High school diploma or
equivalent not required **Scholarships:** Available. **Calendar System:**
Semester, Summer session available **Faculty:** Full-time 78, Part-time 279
Regional Accreditation: Middle States Association of Colleges and Schools
Credit Hours For Degree: 64 credits, Associates **ROTC:** Army **Profes-
sional Accreditation:** ABET, ACEN, AHIMA, CoARC, JRCERT. **Intercol-
legiate Athletics:** Basketball M & W; Soccer M; Volleyball W

PILLAR COLLEGE
60 Park Pl., Ste. 701
Newark, NJ 07102
Tel: (973)803-5000; Free: 800-234-9305
E-mail: info@pillar.edu
Web Site: www.pillar.edu
President/CEO: Pres. David Schroeder
Admissions: Linda Aarni
Type: Four-Year College **Sex:** Coed **Affiliation:** Pillar of Fire International.
% Accepted: 48 **Admission Plans:** Deferred Admission **Application
Deadline:** Rolling **Application Fee:** $35.00 **H.S. Requirements:** High
school diploma required; GED accepted **Calendar System:** Semester, Sum-
mer session available **Enrollment:** Full-time 174, Part-time 66 **Student-
Faculty Ratio:** 15:1 **Exams:** SAT I or ACT. **Final Year or Final Semester
Residency Requirement:** No **Regional Accreditation:** Middle States As-
sociation of Colleges and Schools **Credit Hours For Degree:** 60 credits,
Associates; 120 credits, Bachelors **Professional Accreditation:** ABHE.

PRINCETON UNIVERSITY
Princeton, NJ 08544-1019
Tel: (609)258-3000
E-mail: uaoffice@princeton.edu
Web Site: www.princeton.edu
President/CEO: Christopher L. Eisgruber
Admissions: Janet Rapelye
Financial Aid: Robin Moscato
Type: University **Sex:** Coed **Scores:** 100% SAT V 400+; 100% SAT M 400+;
9.28% ACT 24-29 **% Accepted:** 7 **Admission Plans:** Deferred Admission;
Early Decision Plan **Application Deadline:** January 1 **Application Fee:**
$65.00 **H.S. Requirements:** High school diploma or equivalent not required
Costs Per Year: Application fee: $65. Comprehensive fee: $57,610 includes
full-time tuition ($43,450) and college room and board ($14,160). College
room only: $7920. Room and board charges vary according to board plan.
Scholarships: Available. **Calendar System:** Semester, Summer session
not available **Enrollment:** Full-time 5,277, Graduate full-time 2,736, Part-
time 125 **Faculty:** Full-time 919, Part-time 253 **Student-Faculty Ratio:** 5:1
Exams: ACT essay component used as validity check; ACT essay
component used for admission; ACT essay component used for advising;
SAT I or ACT; SAT II; SAT essay component used as validity check; SAT
essay component used for admission; SAT essay component used for advising; SAT Reasoning; SAT Subject. **% Receiving Financial Aid:** 59 **% Resid-
ing in College-Owned, -Operated, or -Affiliated Housing:** 98 **Final Year
or Final Semester Residency Requirement:** No **Regional Accreditation:**
Middle States Association of Colleges and Schools **Credit Hours For
Degree:** 31 courses, Bachelors **ROTC:** Air Force, Army, Navy **Professional
Accreditation:** ABET, NAAB. **Intercollegiate Athletics:** Baseball M;
Basketball M & W; Crew M & W; Cross-Country Running M & W; Fencing M
& W; Field Hockey W; Football M; Golf M & W; Ice Hockey M & W; Lacrosse
M & W; Soccer M & W; Softball W; Squash M & W; Swimming and Diving M
& W; Tennis M & W; Track and Field M & W; Volleyball M & W; Water Polo M
& W; Wrestling M

RABBI JACOB JOSEPH SCHOOL
One Plainfield Ave.
Edison, NJ 08817
Tel: (732)985-6533
President/CEO: Rabbi Joseph Eichenstein
Type: Four-Year College **Sex:** Men **Affiliation:** Jewish. **% Accepted:** 100
Costs Per Year: Comprehensive fee: $14,700 includes full-time tuition
($11,200), mandatory fees ($200), and college room and board ($3300).
Professional Accreditation: AARTS.

RABBINICAL COLLEGE OF AMERICA
226 Sussex Ave.
Morristown, NJ 07962-1996
Tel: (973)267-9404
Fax: (973)267-5208
E-mail: rca079@aol.com
Web Site: www.rca.edu
President/CEO: Rabbi Moshe Herson
Admissions: Shoshana Solomon
Type: Four-Year College **Sex:** Men **Affiliation:** Jewish. **% Accepted:** 100
Application Deadline: Rolling **Application Fee:** $150.00 **H.S. Require-
ments:** High school diploma required; GED accepted **Calendar System:**

Semester, Summer session available **Faculty:** Full-time 16 **Student-Faculty Ratio:** 12:1 **Credit Hours For Degree:** 120 credits, Bachelors **Professional Accreditation:** AARTS. **Intercollegiate Athletics:** Ultimate Frisbee M; Volleyball M

RAMAPO COLLEGE OF NEW JERSEY
505 Ramapo Valley Rd.
Mahwah, NJ 07430-1680
Tel: (201)684-7500; Free: 800-9RAMAPO
Fax: (201)684-7508
E-mail: admissions@ramapo.edu
Web Site: www.ramapo.edu
President/CEO: Dr. Peter P. Mercer
Admissions: Michael DiBartolomeo
Financial Aid: Esther Mills
Type: Comprehensive **Sex:** Coed **Affiliation:** New Jersey State College System. **Scores:** 99% SAT V 400+; 100% SAT M 400+ **% Accepted:** 53 **Admission Plans:** Deferred Admission; Early Action; Early Admission **Application Fee:** $60.00 **H.S. Requirements:** High school diploma required; GED accepted **Costs Per Year:** Application fee: $60. State resident tuition: $8,866 full-time, $277.05 per credit hour part-time. Nonresident tuition: $17,731 full-time, $554.10 per credit hour part-time. Mandatory fees: $4832 full-time, $151 per credit hour part-time. Full-time tuition and fees vary according to reciprocity agreements. Part-time tuition and fees vary according to reciprocity agreements. College room and board: $11,640. College room only: $8020. Room and board charges vary according to board plan and housing facility. **Scholarships:** Available. **Calendar System:** Semester, Summer session available **Enrollment:** Full-time 4,992, Graduate full-time 49, Graduate part-time 316, Part-time 669 **Faculty:** Full-time 215, Part-time 280 **Student-Faculty Ratio:** 17:1 **Exams:** ACT; SAT I or ACT; SAT Reasoning. **% Receiving Financial Aid:** 55 **% Residing in College-Owned, -Operated, or -Affiliated Housing:** 49 **Regional Accreditation:** Middle States Association of Colleges and Schools **Credit Hours For Degree:** 128 credits, Bachelors **ROTC:** Air Force, Army **Professional Accreditation:** AACSB, ACEN, CSWE. **Intercollegiate Athletics:** Baseball M; Basketball M & W; Cross-Country Running M & W; Field Hockey W; Lacrosse W; Soccer M & W; Softball W; Swimming and Diving M & W; Tennis M & W; Track and Field M & W; Volleyball M & W

RARITAN VALLEY COMMUNITY COLLEGE
118 Lamington Rd.
Branchburg, NJ 08876
Tel: (908)526-1200
Fax: (908)704-3442
E-mail: dpalubni@raritanval.edu
Web Site: www.raritanval.edu
President/CEO: Michael McDonough
Admissions: Daniel Palubniak
Financial Aid: Lenny Mesonas
Type: Two-Year College **Sex:** Coed **Scores:** 92% SAT V 400+; 94% SAT M 400+ **Costs Per Year:** Area resident tuition: $4110 full-time, $137 per credit hour part-time. State resident tuition: $5010 full-time, $167 per credit hour part-time. Nonresident tuition: $5010 full-time, $167 per credit hour part-time. Mandatory fees: $924 full-time, $22 per credit hour part-time, $132 per term part-time. **Scholarships:** Available. **Calendar System:** Semester, Summer session available **Enrollment:** Full-time 3,361, Part-time 4,738 **Faculty:** Full-time 124, Part-time 339 **Student-Faculty Ratio:** 21:1 **Exams:** ACT essay component used for advising; ACT essay component used for placement; SAT essay component used for advising; SAT essay component used for placement. **Final Year or Final Semester Residency Requirement:** No **Regional Accreditation:** Middle States Association of Colleges and Schools **Credit Hours For Degree:** 60 credits, Associates **ROTC:** Air Force, Army **Professional Accreditation:** ACEN, COA. **Intercollegiate Athletics:** Baseball M; Basketball M & W; Soccer M & W; Softball W; Volleyball W

RIDER UNIVERSITY
2083 Lawrenceville Rd.
Lawrenceville, NJ 08648-3001
Tel: (609)896-5000; Free: 800-257-9026
Fax: (609)895-6645
E-mail: wlarrousse@rider.edu
Web Site: www.rider.edu
President/CEO: Dr. Mordechai Rozanski
Admissions: William Larrousse

Type: Comprehensive **Sex:** Coed **Scores:** 96% SAT V 400+; 97% SAT M 400+; 51% ACT 18-23; 31% ACT 24-29 **% Accepted:** 69 **Admission Plans:** Deferred Admission; Early Admission; Early Decision Plan **Application Deadline:** Rolling **Application Fee:** $50.00 **H.S. Requirements:** High school diploma required; GED accepted **Costs Per Year:** Application fee: $50. Comprehensive fee: $54,060 includes full-time tuition ($39,090), mandatory fees ($740), and college room and board ($14,230). College room only: $9270. Room and board charges vary according to board plan and housing facility. Part-time tuition: $1140 per credit hour. Part-time mandatory fees: $16.67 per credit. Part-time tuition and fees vary according to program. **Scholarships:** Available. **Calendar System:** Semester, Summer session available **Enrollment:** Full-time 3,685, Graduate full-time 337, Graduate part-time 610, Part-time 443 **Faculty:** Full-time 252, Part-time 338 **Student-Faculty Ratio:** 12:1 **Exams:** SAT I or ACT. **% Receiving Financial Aid:** 74 **% Residing in College-Owned, -Operated, or -Affiliated Housing:** 55 **Final Year or Final Semester Residency Requirement:** No **Regional Accreditation:** Middle States Association of Colleges and Schools **Credit Hours For Degree:** 60 semester hours, Associates; 120 semester hours, Bachelors **ROTC:** Army **Professional Accreditation:** AACSB, ACA, NASM, NCATE. **Intercollegiate Athletics:** Baseball M; Basketball M & W; Cheerleading M & W; Cross-Country Running M & W; Field Hockey W; Golf M; Soccer M & W; Softball W; Swimming and Diving M & W; Tennis M & W; Track and Field M & W; Volleyball M & W; Wrestling M

ROWAN COLLEGE AT BURLINGTON COUNTY
601 Pemberton Browns Mills Rd.
Pemberton, NJ 08068
Tel: (609)894-9311
Fax: (609)894-0183
E-mail: kgasiorowski@bcc.edu
Web Site: www.rcbc.edu
President/CEO: Paul Drayton
Admissions: Kimberly Gasiorowski
Type: Two-Year College **Sex:** Coed **Admission Plans:** Deferred Admission; Early Admission; Open Admission **Application Deadline:** Rolling **Application Fee:** $20.00 **H.S. Requirements:** High school diploma required; GED accepted **Costs Per Year:** Application fee: $20. Area resident tuition: $3000 full-time, $100 per credit hour part-time. State resident tuition: $3480 full-time, $116 per credit hour part-time. Nonresident tuition: $5430 full-time, $181 per credit hour part-time. Mandatory fees: $1065 full-time, $35.50 per credit hour part-time. Full-time tuition and fees vary according to program. Part-time tuition and fees vary according to program. **Scholarships:** Available. **Calendar System:** Semester, Summer session available **Enrollment:** Full-time 4,289, Part-time 4,473 **Student-Faculty Ratio:** 26:1 **Final Year or Final Semester Residency Requirement:** No **Regional Accreditation:** Middle States Association of Colleges and Schools **Credit Hours For Degree:** 63 credit hours, Associates **Professional Accreditation:** ABET, ACEN, AHIMA. **Intercollegiate Athletics:** Baseball M; Basketball M & W; Golf M & W; Soccer M & W; Softball W

ROWAN COLLEGE AT GLOUCESTER COUNTY
1400 Tanyard Rd.
Sewell, NJ 08080
Tel: (856)468-5000
Fax: (856)468-8498
E-mail: jatkinso@gccnj.edu
Web Site: www.rcgc.edu
President/CEO: Dr. Russell Davis
Admissions: Judy Atkinson
Financial Aid: Michael J. Chando
Type: Two-Year College **Sex:** Coed **Affiliation:** New Jersey Commission on Higher Education. **Admission Plans:** Deferred Admission; Open Admission **Application Deadline:** Rolling **Application Fee:** $20.00 **H.S. Requirements:** High school diploma required; GED accepted. For those granted qualified admission: High school diploma or equivalent not required **Scholarships:** Available. **Calendar System:** Semester, Summer session available **Student-Faculty Ratio:** 28:1 **Exams:** SAT I or ACT. **Regional Accreditation:** Middle States Association of Colleges and Schools **Credit Hours For Degree:** 63 credit hours, Associates **Professional Accreditation:** ACEN, CoARC, JRCEDMS, JRCNMT. **Intercollegiate Athletics:** Baseball M; Basketball M & W; Cross-Country Running M & W; Soccer M & W; Softball W; Tennis M & W; Track and Field M & W; Wrestling M

ROWAN UNIVERSITY
201 Mullica Hill Rd.
Glassboro, NJ 08028-1701

Tel: (856)256-4500; Free: 800-447-1165N
E-mail: admissions@rowan.edu
Web Site: www.rowan.edu
President/CEO: Dr. Ali A. Houshmand, PhD
Admissions: Albert Betts
Financial Aid: Jeff Hand
Type: Comprehensive **Sex:** Coed **Affiliation:** New Jersey State College System. **Scores:** 96% SAT V 400+; 98% SAT M 400+ **% Accepted:** 56 **Admission Plans:** Deferred Admission; Early Admission **Application Deadline:** March 1 **Application Fee:** $65.00 **H.S. Requirements:** High school diploma required; GED accepted **Costs Per Year:** Application fee: $65. State resident tuition: $9256 full-time, $355 per credit part-time. Nonresident tuition: $17,370 full-time, $669 per credit part-time. Mandatory fees: $3608 full-time, $154 per credit part-time. Full-time tuition and fees vary according to course load, degree level, location, and program. Part-time tuition and fees vary according to course load, degree level, location, and program. College room and board: $11,627. College room only: $7347. Room and board charges vary according to board plan and housing facility. **Scholarships:** Available. **Calendar System:** Semester, Summer session available **Enrollment:** Full-time 11,710, Graduate full-time 1,348, Graduate part-time 1,638, Part-time 1,459 **Faculty:** Full-time 428, Part-time 1,005 **Student-Faculty Ratio:** 18:1 **Exams:** ACT essay component used for placement; SAT I or ACT; SAT essay component used for placement. **% Receiving Financial Aid:** 61 **% Residing in College-Owned, -Operated, or -Affiliated Housing:** 37 **Final Year or Final Semester Residency Requirement:** No **Regional Accreditation:** Middle States Association of Colleges and Schools **Credit Hours For Degree:** 120 credits, Bachelors **ROTC:** Army **Professional Accreditation:** AACSB, ABET, ACA, AOsA, JRCAT, NASAD, NASM, NAST, NCATE. **Intercollegiate Athletics:** Baseball M; Basketball M & W; Cross-Country Running M & W; Field Hockey W; Football M; Lacrosse M; Soccer M & W; Softball W; Swimming and Diving M & W; Track and Field M & W; Volleyball W

RUTGERS UNIVERSITY–CAMDEN

406 Penn St.
Camden, NJ 08102-1401
Tel: (856)225-1766
E-mail: bowles@ugadm.rutgers.edu
Web Site: www.camden.rutgers.edu
President/CEO: Dr. Robert L. Barchi
Admissions: Dr. Deborah Bowles
Type: University **Sex:** Coed **Affiliation:** Rutgers, The State University of New Jersey. **Scores:** 94% SAT V 400+; 95% SAT M 400+ **% Accepted:** 58 **Admission Plans:** Preferred Admission **Application Deadline:** December 1 **Application Fee:** $65.00 **H.S. Requirements:** High school diploma required; GED accepted **Costs Per Year:** Application fee: $65. State resident tuition: $11,217 full-time, $361 per credit part-time. Nonresident tuition: $26,107 full-time, $848 per credit part-time. Mandatory fees: $2783 full-time, $550.25 per term part-time. Part-time tuition and fees vary according to course load. College room and board: $11,710. College room only: $8160. Room and board charges vary according to board plan and housing facility. **Scholarships:** Available. **Calendar System:** Semester, Summer session available **Enrollment:** Full-time 3,931, Graduate full-time 745, Graduate part-time 764, Part-time 968 **Faculty:** Full-time 292, Part-time 342 **Student-Faculty Ratio:** 10:1 **Exams:** SAT I or ACT. **% Receiving Financial Aid:** 86 **% Residing in College-Owned, -Operated, or -Affiliated Housing:** 9 **Regional Accreditation:** Middle States Association of Colleges and Schools **Credit Hours For Degree:** 120 credits, Bachelors **ROTC:** Air Force, Army **Professional Accreditation:** AACN, AACSB, AALS, ABA, APTA, CSWE, NASPAA. **Intercollegiate Athletics:** Baseball M; Basketball M & W; Crew M & W; Cross-Country Running W; Golf M; Lacrosse W; Soccer M & W; Softball W; Track and Field M & W; Volleyball W

RUTGERS UNIVERSITY–NEW BRUNSWICK

65 Davidson Rd.
Rm. 202
Piscataway, NJ 08854-8097
Tel: (732)932-4636
Web Site: newbrunswick.rutgers.edu
President/CEO: Dr. Robert L. Barchi
Admissions: Diane Williams Harris
Type: University **Sex:** Coed **Affiliation:** Rutgers, The State University of New Jersey. **Scores:** 99% SAT V 400+; 100% SAT M 400+ **% Accepted:** 58 **Admission Plans:** Preferred Admission **Application Deadline:**

December 1 **Application Fee:** $65.00 **H.S. Requirements:** High school diploma required; GED accepted **Costs Per Year:** Application fee: $65. State resident tuition: $11,217 full-time, $361 per credit part-time. Nonresident tuition: $26,607 full-time, $848 per credit part-time. Mandatory fees: $2914 full-time, $362.50 per term part-time. Part-time tuition and fees vary according to course load. College room and board: $12,054. College room only: $7364. Room and board charges vary according to board plan and housing facility. **Scholarships:** Available. **Calendar System:** Semester **Enrollment:** Full-time 33,392, Graduate full-time 8,737, Graduate part-time 5,207, Part-time 2,092 **Faculty:** Full-time 2,027, Part-time 2,033 **Student-Faculty Ratio:** 13:1 **Exams:** SAT I or ACT. **% Receiving Financial Aid:** 55 **% Residing in College-Owned, -Operated, or -Affiliated Housing:** 45 **Regional Accreditation:** Middle States Association of Colleges and Schools **Credit Hours For Degree:** 120 credit hours, Bachelors **ROTC:** Air Force, Army, Navy **Professional Accreditation:** ABET, ACA, ACPE, ACSP, ALA, APA, ASLA, CSWE, LCME/AMA, NASD, NASM, NASPAA, TEAC. **Intercollegiate Athletics:** Baseball M; Basketball M & W; Crew M & W; Cross-Country Running M & W; Fencing M & W; Football M; Golf M & W; Gymnastics W; Lacrosse M & W; Soccer M & W; Softball W; Swimming and Diving M & W; Tennis M & W; Track and Field M & W; Volleyball W; Wrestling M

RUTGERS UNIVERSITY–NEWARK

249 University Ave.
Newark, NJ 07102
Tel: (973)353-1766
Fax: (973)353-1048
E-mail: chiaravalloti@ugadm.rutgers.edu
Web Site: www.newark.rutgers.edu
President/CEO: Dr. Robert L. Barchi
Admissions: Christina M. Chiaravalloti
Type: University **Sex:** Coed **Affiliation:** Rutgers, The State University of New Jersey. **Scores:** 94% SAT V 400+; 97% SAT M 400+ **% Accepted:** 65 **Admission Plans:** Preferred Admission **Application Deadline:** December 1 **Application Fee:** $65.00 **H.S. Requirements:** High school diploma required; GED accepted **Costs Per Year:** Application fee: $65. State resident tuition: $11,217 full-time, $361 per credit part-time. Nonresident tuition: $26,607 full-time, $863 per credit part-time. Mandatory fees: $2380 full-time, $430.75 per term part-time. Part-time tuition and fees vary according to course load. College room and board: $12,841. College room only: $7959. Room and board charges vary according to board plan and housing facility. **Scholarships:** Available. **Calendar System:** Semester, Summer session available **Enrollment:** Full-time 6,212, Graduate full-time 1,805, Graduate part-time 2,202, Part-time 1,501 **Faculty:** Full-time 515, Part-time 353 **Student-Faculty Ratio:** 11:1 **Exams:** SAT I or ACT. **% Receiving Financial Aid:** 83 **% Residing in College-Owned, -Operated, or -Affiliated Housing:** 20 **Regional Accreditation:** Middle States Association of Colleges and Schools **Credit Hours For Degree:** 124 credit hours, Bachelors **ROTC:** Air Force, Army, Navy **Professional Accreditation:** AACN, AACSB, AALS, AANA, ABA, ACEN, ADA, APTA, CORE, CSWE, LCME/AMA, NASPAA. **Intercollegiate Athletics:** Baseball M; Basketball M & W; Cross-Country Running M & W; Soccer M & W; Tennis M & W; Track and Field M; Volleyball M & W

SAINT PETER'S UNIVERSITY

2641 Kennedy Blvd.
Jersey City, NJ 07306-5997
Tel: (201)761-6000; Free: 888-SPC-9933
Fax: (201)432-5860
E-mail: ktillotson@saintpeters.edu
Web Site: www.saintpeters.edu
President/CEO: Dr. Eugene Cornacchia
Admissions: Kacey Tillotson
Financial Aid: Jennifer Ragsdale
Type: Comprehensive **Sex:** Coed **Affiliation:** Roman Catholic (Jesuit). **Scores:** 82% SAT V 400+; 86% SAT M 400+; 49.46% ACT 18-23; 6.45% ACT 24-29 **% Accepted:** 67 **Admission Plans:** Deferred Admission; Early Decision Plan **Application Deadline:** August 31 **Application Fee:** $0.00 **H.S. Requirements:** High school diploma required; GED accepted **Scholarships:** Available. **Calendar System:** Semester, Summer session available **Enrollment:** Full-time 2,208, Graduate full-time 242, Graduate part-time 639, Part-time 317 **Faculty:** Full-time 113, Part-time 201 **Student-Faculty Ratio:** 13:1 **Exams:** SAT I or ACT; SAT II; SAT Reasoning; SAT Subject. **% Receiving Financial Aid:** 87 **% Residing in College-Owned, -Operated,**

or -Affiliated Housing: 31 Final Year or Final Semester Residency Requirement: No Regional Accreditation: Middle States Association of Colleges and Schools Credit Hours For Degree: 60 credits, Associates; 120 credits, Bachelors ROTC: Air Force, Army Professional Accreditation: AACN, TEAC. Intercollegiate Athletics: Baseball M; Basketball M & W; Bowling M & W; Cross-Country Running M & W; Golf M; Soccer M & W; Softball W; Swimming and Diving M & W; Tennis M & W; Track and Field M & W; Volleyball W

SALEM COMMUNITY COLLEGE

460 Hollywood Ave.
Carneys Point, NJ 08069-2799
Tel: (856)299-2100
Fax: (856)299-9193
E-mail: kmcshay@salemcc.edu
Web Site: www.salemcc.edu
President/CEO: Joan Baillie
Admissions: Kelly McShay
Financial Aid: Maurice J. Thomas
Type: Two-Year College Sex: Coed Admission Plans: Deferred Admission; Early Admission; Open Admission Application Deadline: Rolling Application Fee: $27.00 H.S. Requirements: High school diploma required; GED accepted Costs Per Year: Application fee: $27. Area resident tuition: $3060 full-time, $102 per credit hour part-time. State resident tuition: $3750 full-time, $125 per credit hour part-time. Nonresident tuition: $4500 full-time, $150 per credit hour part-time. Mandatory fees: $1044 full-time, $33 per credit hour part-time, $27 per term part-time. Full-time tuition and fees vary according to course load and program. Part-time tuition and fees vary according to course load and program. Scholarships: Available. Calendar System: Semester, Summer session available Enrollment: Full-time 602, Part-time 505 Faculty: Full-time 17, Part-time 70 Student-Faculty Ratio: 19:1 Exams: ACT essay component not used; SAT essay component not used. Final Year or Final Semester Residency Requirement: No Regional Accreditation: Middle States Association of Colleges and Schools Credit Hours For Degree: 64 credits, Associates Professional Accreditation: ACEN.

SETON HALL UNIVERSITY

400 S Orange Ave.
South Orange, NJ 07079-2697
Tel: (973)761-9000; Free: 800-THE HALL
Fax: (973)761-9452
E-mail: maryclare.cullum@shu.edu
Web Site: www.shu.edu
President/CEO: Dr. Gabriel Esteban
Admissions: Mary Clare Cullum
Type: University Sex: Coed Affiliation: Roman Catholic. Scores: 100% SAT V 400+; 100% SAT M 400+; 32% ACT 18-23; 60% ACT 24-29 % Accepted: 79 Admission Plans: Deferred Admission; Early Decision Plan Application Deadline: Rolling Application Fee: $55.00 H.S. Requirements: High school diploma required; GED accepted Scholarships: Available. Calendar System: Semester, Summer session available Enrollment: Full-time 5,380, Graduate full-time 1,761, Graduate part-time 2,303, Part-time 459 Faculty: Full-time 459, Part-time 493 Student-Faculty Ratio: 14:1 Exams: SAT I or ACT; SAT Reasoning. % Receiving Financial Aid: 62 % Residing in College-Owned, -Operated, or -Affiliated Housing: 39 Final Year or Final Semester Residency Requirement: No Regional Accreditation: Middle States Association of Colleges and Schools Credit Hours For Degree: 120 credits, Bachelors ROTC: Army Professional Accreditation: AACN, AACSB, AALS, AAMFT, ABA, ACEN, ACIPE, AOTA, APA, APTA, ASHA, ATS, CAHME, CSWE, NASPAA, NCATE. Intercollegiate Athletics: Baseball M; Basketball M & W; Cross-Country Running M & W; Golf M & W; Ice Hockey M; Rugby M; Soccer M & W; Softball W; Swimming and Diving M & W; Tennis W; Volleyball M & W

STEVENS INSTITUTE OF TECHNOLOGY

Castle Point on Hudson
Hoboken, NJ 07030
Tel: (201)216-5000; Free: 800-458-5323
Fax: (201)216-8348
E-mail: jackie.williams@stevens.edu
Web Site: www.stevens.edu
President/CEO: Dr. Nariman Farvardin
Admissions: Jackie Williams

Financial Aid: Susan Gross
Type: University Sex: Coed Scores: 100% SAT V 400+; 100% SAT M 400+; 1% ACT 18-23; 33% ACT 24-29 % Accepted: 44 Admission Plans: Deferred Admission; Early Action; Early Admission Application Deadline: February 1 Application Fee: $60.00 H.S. Requirements: High school diploma required; GED accepted Costs Per Year: Application fee: $60. Comprehensive fee: $62,338 includes full-time tuition ($47,134), mandatory fees ($1704), and college room and board ($13,500). Full-time tuition and fees vary according to course load. Room and board charges vary according to board plan and housing facility. Scholarships: Available. Calendar System: Semester, Summer session available Enrollment: Full-time 2,955, Graduate full-time 2,137, Graduate part-time 1,246, Part-time 21 Faculty: Full-time 255, Part-time 149 Student-Faculty Ratio: 10:1 Exams: ACT essay component not used; SAT I and SAT II or ACT; SAT I or ACT; SAT essay component not used; SAT Reasoning. % Receiving Financial Aid: 70 % Residing in College-Owned, -Operated, or -Affiliated Housing: 71 Final Year or Final Semester Residency Requirement: No Regional Accreditation: Middle States Association of Colleges and Schools Credit Hours For Degree: 136 credits, Bachelors ROTC: Air Force, Army Professional Accreditation: ABET. Intercollegiate Athletics: Baseball M; Basketball M & W; Cross-Country Running M & W; Equestrian Sports W; Fencing M & W; Field Hockey W; Golf M; Lacrosse M & W; Soccer M & W; Softball W; Swimming and Diving M & W; Tennis M & W; Track and Field M & W; Volleyball M & W; Wrestling M

STOCKTON UNIVERSITY

101 Vera King Farris Dr.
Galloway, NJ 08205-9441
Tel: (609)652-1776
Fax: (609)748-5541
E-mail: admissions@stockton.edu
Web Site: www.stockton.edu
President/CEO: Dr. Harvey Kesselman
Admissions: John Iacovelli
Financial Aid: Jeanne S. Lewis
Type: Comprehensive Sex: Coed Affiliation: New Jersey State College System. Scores: 98% SAT V 400+; 99% SAT M 400+; 53.66% ACT 18-23; 32.93% ACT 24-29 % Accepted: 64 Admission Plans: Early Admission Application Deadline: May 1 Application Fee: $50.00 H.S. Requirements: High school diploma required; GED accepted Costs Per Year: Application fee: $50. State resident tuition: $8269 full-time, $318 per credit part-time. Nonresident tuition: $14,921 full-time, $574 per credit part-time. Mandatory fees: $4551 full-time, $175 per credit part-time, $90 per term part-time. Part-time tuition and fees vary according to course load. College room and board: $11,707. College room only: $7756. Room and board charges vary according to board plan and housing facility. Scholarships: Available. Calendar System: Semester, Summer session available Enrollment: Full-time 7,378, Graduate full-time 337, Graduate part-time 529, Part-time 430 Faculty: Full-time 315, Part-time 361 Student-Faculty Ratio: 17:1 Exams: ACT essay component used for advising; ACT essay component used for placement; SAT I or ACT; SAT essay component used for advising; SAT essay component used for placement; SAT Reasoning. % Receiving Financial Aid: 69 % Residing in College-Owned, -Operated, or -Affiliated Housing: 38 Final Year or Final Semester Residency Requirement: Yes Regional Accreditation: Middle States Association of Colleges and Schools Credit Hours For Degree: 128 credit hours, Bachelors ROTC: Army Professional Accreditation: AACN, AOTA, APTA, CSWE, TEAC. Intercollegiate Athletics: Baseball M; Basketball M & W; Cheerleading M & W; Crew W; Cross-Country Running M & W; Field Hockey W; Lacrosse M; Soccer M & W; Softball W; Tennis W; Track and Field M & W; Volleyball W

STRAYER UNIVERSITY–CHERRY HILL CAMPUS

2201 Rte. 38
Ste. 100
Cherry Hill, NJ 08002
Tel: (856)482-4200
Fax: (856)482-4230
Web Site: www.strayer.edu/new-jersey/cherry-hill
President/CEO: Brian W. Jones
Type: Comprehensive Sex: Coed Regional Accreditation: Middle States Association of Colleges and Schools

STRAYER UNIVERSITY–LAWRENCEVILLE CAMPUS

3150 Brunswick Pke.
Ste. 100

Lawrenceville, NJ 08648
Tel: (609)406-7600
Fax: (609)771-8636
Web Site: www.strayer.edu/new-jersey/lawrenceville
President/CEO: Brian W. Jones
Type: Comprehensive **Sex:** Coed **Regional Accreditation:** Middle States Association of Colleges and Schools

STRAYER UNIVERSITY–PISCATAWAY CAMPUS

242 Old New Brunswick Rd.
Ste. 220
Piscataway, NJ 08854
Tel: (732)743-3800
Fax: (732)562-1780
Web Site: www.strayer.edu/new-jersey/piscataway
President/CEO: Brian W. Jones
Type: Comprehensive **Sex:** Coed **Regional Accreditation:** Middle States Association of Colleges and Schools

STRAYER UNIVERSITY–WILLINGBORO CAMPUS

300 Willingboro Pky.
Willingboro Town Ctr., Ste. 125
Willingboro, NJ 08046
Tel: (609)835-6000
Fax: (609)835-6030
Web Site: www.strayer.edu/new-jersey/willingboro
President/CEO: Brian W. Jones
Type: Comprehensive **Sex:** Coed **Regional Accreditation:** Middle States Association of Colleges and Schools

SUSSEX COUNTY COMMUNITY COLLEGE

1 College Hill
Newton, NJ 07860
Tel: (973)300-2100
E-mail: tpoltersdorf@sussex.edu
Web Site: www.sussex.edu
President/CEO: Dr. Paul Mazur
Admissions: Todd Poltersdorf
Type: Two-Year College **Sex:** Coed **Affiliation:** New Jersey Commission on Higher Education. **Admission Plans:** Open Admission **Application Deadline:** Rolling **Application Fee:** $25.00 **H.S. Requirements:** High school diploma or equivalent not required **Scholarships:** Available. **Calendar System:** 4-1-4, Summer session available **Enrollment:** Full-time 2,059, Part-time 1,673 **Faculty:** Full-time 43, Part-time 233 **Student-Faculty Ratio:** 21:1 **Final Year or Final Semester Residency Requirement:** No **Regional Accreditation:** Middle States Association of Colleges and Schools **Credit Hours For Degree:** 60 credits, Associates **Intercollegiate Athletics:** Baseball M; Basketball M & W; Soccer M & W; Softball W

TALMUDICAL ACADEMY OF NEW JERSEY

868 Rte. 524
Adelphia, NJ 07710
Tel: (732)431-1600
President/CEO: Mordecai Gottlieb
Type: Comprehensive **Sex:** Men **Affiliation:** Jewish. **% Accepted:** 100 **H.S. Requirements:** High school diploma required; GED accepted **Costs Per Year:** Comprehensive fee: $14,700 includes full-time tuition ($12,000) and college room and board ($2700). **Calendar System:** Semester **Professional Accreditation:** AARTS.

THOMAS EDISON STATE UNIVERSITY

101 W State St.
Trenton, NJ 08608-1176
Tel: (609)984-1100; Free: 888-442-8372
Fax: (609)292-9000
E-mail: admissions@tesc.edu
Web Site: www.tesu.edu
President/CEO: Dr. George A. Pruitt
Admissions: David Hoftiezer
Financial Aid: James Owens
Type: Comprehensive **Sex:** Coed **Admission Plans:** Open Admission **Application Deadline:** Rolling **Application Fee:** $75.00 **H.S. Requirements:** High school diploma required; GED accepted **Costs Per Year:** Application fee: $75. State resident tuition: $6135 full-time, $183 per credit hour part-

time. Nonresident tuition: $9036 full-time, $247 per credit hour part-time. Mandatory fees: $131 per year part-time. **Scholarships:** Available. **Calendar System:** Continuous, Summer session available **Enrollment:** Graduate part-time 1,200, Part-time 19,406 **Final Year or Final Semester Residency Requirement:** No **Regional Accreditation:** Middle States Association of Colleges and Schools **Credit Hours For Degree:** 60 credits, Associates; 120 credits, Bachelors **Professional Accreditation:** AACN, ACBSP, ACEN.

UNION COUNTY COLLEGE

1033 Springfield Ave.
Cranford, NJ 07016
Tel: (908)709-7000
Fax: (908)709-0527
E-mail: hernandez@ucc.edu
Web Site: www.ucc.edu
President/CEO: Dr. Margaret M. McMenamin
Admissions: Nina Hernandez
Type: Two-Year College **Sex:** Coed **Affiliation:** New Jersey Commission on Higher Education. **% Accepted:** 41 **Admission Plans:** Deferred Admission; Early Admission; Open Admission **Application Deadline:** Rolling **Application Fee:** $0.00 **H.S. Requirements:** High school diploma required; GED accepted **Costs Per Year:** Application fee: $0. Area resident tuition: $4450 full-time, $177 per credit hour part-time. State resident tuition: $8900 full-time, $354 per credit hour part-time. Nonresident tuition: $8900 full-time, $354 per credit hour part-time. Full-time tuition varies according to course load. Part-time tuition varies according to course load. **Scholarships:** Available. **Calendar System:** Semester, Summer session available **Enrollment:** Full-time 5,886, Part-time 6,260 **Faculty:** Full-time 173, Part-time 346 **Student-Faculty Ratio:** 27:1 **Regional Accreditation:** Middle States Association of Colleges and Schools **Credit Hours For Degree:** 62 credits, Associates **ROTC:** Air Force **Professional Accreditation:** ACEN, APTA, CoARC. **Intercollegiate Athletics:** Baseball M; Basketball M & W; Golf M & W; Soccer M; Volleyball W

UNIVERSITY OF PHOENIX–JERSEY CITY CAMPUS

100 Town Sq. Pl.
Jersey City, NJ 07310
Tel: (201)610-1408; Free: 866-766-0766
Web Site: www.phoenix.edu
President/CEO: Timothy P. Slottow
Type: Comprehensive **Sex:** Coed **Regional Accreditation:** North Central Association of Colleges and Schools **Professional Accreditation:** ACBSP.

WARREN COUNTY COMMUNITY COLLEGE

475 Rte. 57 W
Washington, NJ 07882-4343
Tel: (908)835-9222
E-mail: shorwath@warren.edu
Web Site: www.warren.edu
President/CEO: Dr. William Austin
Admissions: Shannon Horwath
Type: Two-Year College **Sex:** Coed **Affiliation:** New Jersey Commission on Higher Education. **Admission Plans:** Deferred Admission; Early Admission; Open Admission **Application Deadline:** Rolling **Application Fee:** $25.00 **H.S. Requirements:** High school diploma or equivalent not required **Scholarships:** Available. **Calendar System:** Semester, Summer session available **Student-Faculty Ratio:** 22:1 **Regional Accreditation:** Middle States Association of Colleges and Schools **Credit Hours For Degree:** 64 credits, Associates **Professional Accreditation:** ACEN.

WILLIAM PATERSON UNIVERSITY OF NEW JERSEY

300 Pompton Rd.
Wayne, NJ 07470-8420
Tel: (973)720-2000; Free: 877-WPU-EXCEL
Fax: (973)720-2910
E-mail: leckeya@wpunj.edu
Web Site: www.wpunj.edu
President/CEO: Pres. Kathleen Waldron, PhD
Admissions: Anthony Leckey
Financial Aid: Michael Corso
Type: Comprehensive **Sex:** Coed **Scores:** 94% SAT V 400+; 97% SAT M 400+ **% Accepted:** 74 **Admission Plans:** Deferred Admission; Early Admission; Early Decision Plan **Application Deadline:** June 1 **Application Fee:**

$50.00 **H.S. Requirements:** High school diploma required; GED accepted **Costs Per Year:** Application fee: $50. State resident tuition: $9033 full-time, $288.55 per credit hour part-time. Nonresident tuition: $16,793 full-time, $544.55 per credit hour part-time. Mandatory fees: $3332 full-time, $103.45 per credit hour part-time. Full-time tuition and fees vary according to course load and location. Part-time tuition and fees vary according to course load and location. College room and board: $10,885. College room only: $6835. Room and board charges vary according to board plan and housing facility. **Scholarships:** Available. **Calendar System:** Semester, Summer session available **Enrollment:** Full-time 7,721, Graduate full-time 309, Graduate part-time 1,155, Part-time 1,677 **Faculty:** Full-time 411, Part-time 653 **Student-Faculty Ratio:** 14:1 **Exams:** SAT I or ACT; SAT essay component not used; SAT Reasoning. **% Receiving Financial Aid:** 73 **% Residing in College-Owned, -Operated, or -Affiliated Housing:** 23 **Final Year or Final Semester Residency Requirement:** Yes **Regional Accreditation:** Middle States Association of Colleges and Schools **Credit Hours For Degree:** 120 credits, Bachelors **Professional Accreditation:** AACN, AACSB, ABET, ACA, ASHA, JRCAT, NASAD, NASM, NCATE. **Intercollegiate Athletics:** Baseball M; Basketball M & W; Field Hockey W; Football M; Golf M; Soccer M & W; Softball W; Swimming and Diving M & W; Tennis W; Volleyball W

YESHIVA GEDOLAH ZICHRON LEYMA
1000 Orchard Ter.
Linden, NJ 07036

Tel: (908)587-0502
Type: Four-Year College **Sex:** Coed **Affiliation:** Jewish. **Costs Per Year:** Comprehensive fee: $14,200 includes full-time tuition ($11,500) and college room and board ($2700). **Professional Accreditation:** AARTS.

YESHIVA TORAS CHAIM
999 Ridge Ave.
Lakewood, NJ 08701
Tel: (732)942-3090

Type: Four-Year College **Sex:** Coed **Affiliation:** Jewish. **Costs Per Year:** Comprehensive fee: $17,200 includes full-time tuition ($11,650), mandatory fees ($150), and college room and board ($5400). College room only: $2400. **Professional Accreditation:** AARTS.

YESHIVAS BE'ER YITZCHOK
1391 N Ave.
Elizabeth, NJ 07208
Tel: (908)354-6057
Web Site: www.elizabethkollel.org
Type: Four-Year College **Sex:** Coed **Affiliation:** Jewish. **Professional Accreditation:** AARTS.

BROOKLINE COLLEGE

4201 Central Ave. NW
Ste. J
Albuquerque, NM 87105-1649
Tel: (505)880-2877; Free: 888-660-2428
Fax: (505)833-2087
E-mail: awebb@brooklinecollege.edu
Web Site: brooklinecollege.edu
President/CEO: Andrew Webb
Admissions: Andrew Webb
Type: Four-Year College **Sex:** Coed **Admission Plans:** Open Admission **Application Deadline:** Rolling **Application Fee:** $0.00 **H.S. Requirements:** High school diploma required; GED accepted **Costs Per Year:** Application fee: $0. Tuition: $15,225 full-time. Full-time tuition varies according to degree level and program. Tuition guaranteed not to increase for student's term of enrollment. **Calendar System:** Continuous **Faculty:** Full-time 13, Part-time 15 **Student-Faculty Ratio:** 19:1 **Credit Hours For Degree:** 60 credits, Associates **Professional Accreditation:** ACICS.

CARRINGTON COLLEGE–ALBUQUERQUE

1001 Menaul Blvd. NE
Albuquerque, NM 87107
Tel: (505)254-7777
Web Site: carrington.edu
President/CEO: Mark Lucero
Type: Two-Year College **Sex:** Coed **Affiliation:** Carrington Colleges Group, Inc. **Costs Per Year:** Tuition: $14,053 full-time. Mandatory fees: $780 full-time. Full-time tuition and fees vary according to program. **Enrollment:** Full-time 399, Part-time 43 **Faculty:** Full-time 9, Part-time 17 **Student-Faculty Ratio:** 28:1 **Regional Accreditation:** Western Association of Colleges and Schools

CENTRAL NEW MEXICO COMMUNITY COLLEGE

525 Buena Vista, SE
Albuquerque, NM 87106-4096
Tel: (505)224-3000
Fax: (505)224-4740
E-mail: gdamiani@cnm.edu
Web Site: www.cnm.edu
President/CEO: Katharine W. Winograd
Admissions: Glenn Damiani
Financial Aid: Lee M. Carrillo
Type: Two-Year College **Sex:** Coed **Admission Plans:** Open Admission **Application Deadline:** Rolling **Application Fee:** $0.00 **H.S. Requirements:** High school diploma or equivalent not required **Costs Per Year:** Application fee: $0. State resident tuition: $1224 full-time, $51 per credit hour part-time. Nonresident tuition: $6480 full-time, $270 per credit hour part-time. Mandatory fees: $224 full-time, $6 per credit hour part-time, $40 per term part-time. **Scholarships:** Available. **Calendar System:** Trimester, Summer session available **Enrollment:** Full-time 7,953, Part-time 17,935 **Faculty:** Full-time 358, Part-time 726 **Student-Faculty Ratio:** 23:1 **Regional Accreditation:** North Central Association of Colleges and Schools **Credit Hours For Degree:** 60 credit hours, Associates **ROTC:** Air Force, Army, Navy **Professional Accreditation:** ABET, ACBSP, ACCE, ACEN, ACF, ADA, CoARC, NAACLS.

CLOVIS COMMUNITY COLLEGE

417 Schepps Blvd.
Clovis, NM 88101-8381
Tel: (575)769-2811; Free: 800-769-1409
E-mail: admissions@clovis.edu
Web Site: www.clovis.edu
President/CEO: Dr. John Neibling
Admissions: Rosie Corrie
Type: Two-Year College **Sex:** Coed **% Accepted:** 100 **Admission Plans:** Open Admission **Application Deadline:** Rolling **Application Fee:** $0.00 **H.S. Requirements:** High school diploma required; GED accepted **Scholarships:** Available. **Calendar System:** Semester, Summer session available **Enrollment:** Full-time 995, Part-time 3,180 **Faculty:** Full-time 52, Part-time 130 **Student-Faculty Ratio:** 21:1 **Regional Accreditation:** North Central Association of Colleges and Schools **Credit Hours For Degree:** 64 credit hours, Associates **Professional Accreditation:** ACEN, JRCERT.

DOÑA ANA COMMUNITY COLLEGE

MSC-3DA, Box 30001
3400 S Espina St.
Las Cruces, NM 88003-8001
Tel: (505)527-7500; Free: 800-903-7503
Fax: (505)527-7515
Web Site: dacc.nmsu.edu
President/CEO: Dr. Margie Huerta
Admissions: Ricci Montes
Type: Two-Year College **Sex:** Coed **Affiliation:** New Mexico State University System. **Admission Plans:** Deferred Admission; Open Admission **Application Deadline:** Rolling **Application Fee:** $20.00 **H.S. Requirements:** High school diploma required; GED accepted **Scholarships:** Available. **Calendar System:** Semester, Summer session available **Enrollment:** Full-time 4,037, Part-time 4,854 **Student-Faculty Ratio:** 21:1 **Exams:** Other. **Regional Accreditation:** North Central Association of Colleges and Schools **Credit Hours For Degree:** 66 credits, Associates **ROTC:** Air Force, Army **Professional Accreditation:** ACBSP, ACEN, ADA, CoARC, JRCEMTP, JRCERT.

EASTERN NEW MEXICO UNIVERSITY

1500 S Ave. K
Portales, NM 88130
Tel: (575)562-1011; Free: 800-367-3668
Fax: (575)562-2118
E-mail: cody.spitz@enmu.edu
Web Site: www.enmu.edu
President/CEO: Dr. Steven Gamble
Admissions: Cody Spitz
Financial Aid: Brent Small
Type: Comprehensive **Sex:** Coed **Affiliation:** Eastern New Mexico University-Ruidoso; Eastern New Mexico University-Roswell. **Scores:** 79% SAT V 400+; 88% SAT M 400+; 53% ACT 18-23; 15% ACT 24-29 **% Accepted:** 63 **Application Deadline:** August 24 **Application Fee:** $0.00 **H.S. Requirements:** High school diploma required; GED accepted **Costs Per Year:** Application fee: $0. One-time mandatory fee: $120. State resident tuition: $3264 full-time, $136 per credit hour part-time. Nonresident tuition: $9040 full-time, $377 per credit hour part-time. Mandatory fees: $1906 full-time, $80 per credit hour part-time. Full-time tuition and fees vary according

to course load and reciprocity agreements. Part-time tuition and fees vary according to course load. College room and board: $6568. College room only: $3200. Room and board charges vary according to board plan and housing facility. **Scholarships:** Available. **Calendar System:** Semester, Summer session available **Enrollment:** Full-time 2,775, Graduate full-time 270, Graduate part-time 1,017, Part-time 1,825 **Faculty:** Full-time 156, Part-time 174 **Student-Faculty Ratio:** 19:1 **Exams:** ACT; ACT essay component not used; SAT I; SAT essay component not used; SAT Reasoning; SAT Subject. **% Receiving Financial Aid:** 59 **% Residing in College-Owned, -Operated, or -Affiliated Housing:** 16 **Final Year or Final Semester Residency Requirement:** Yes **Regional Accreditation:** North Central Association of Colleges and Schools **Credit Hours For Degree:** 64 credit hours, Associates; 128 credit hours, Bachelors **Professional Accreditation:** AAFCS, ACBSP, ACEN, ASHA, NASM, NCATE. **Intercollegiate Athletics:** Baseball M; Basketball M & W; Cross-Country Running M & W; Football M; Soccer M & W; Softball W; Track and Field M & W; Volleyball W

EASTERN NEW MEXICO UNIVERSITY–ROSWELL

PO Box 6000
Roswell, NM 88202-6000
Tel: (575)624-7000; Free: 800-624-7000
Fax: (505)624-7119
E-mail: lily.quezada@roswell.enmu.edu
Web Site: www.roswell.enmu.edu
President/CEO: Dr. John Madden
Admissions: Lilia Quezada
Financial Aid: Jessie Sjue
Type: Two-Year College **Sex:** Coed **Affiliation:** Eastern New Mexico University System. **Admission Plans:** Early Admission; Open Admission **Application Deadline:** Rolling **Application Fee:** $0.00 **H.S. Requirements:** High school diploma required; GED accepted **Scholarships:** Available. **Calendar System:** Semester, Summer session available **Student-Faculty Ratio:** 20:1 **Exams:** ACT. **Regional Accreditation:** North Central Association of Colleges and Schools **Credit Hours For Degree:** 64 credit hours, Associates **ROTC:** Air Force, Army, Navy **Professional Accreditation:** AAMAE, ACEN, AOTA, CoARC, JRCEMTP.

EC-COUNCIL UNIVERSITY

101 C Sun Ave. NE
Albuquerque, NM 87109
Tel: (505)922-2886
Web Site: www.eccu.edu
Type: Two-Year Upper Division **Sex:** Coed **Professional Accreditation:** DEAC.

INSTITUTE OF AMERICAN INDIAN ARTS

83 Avan Nu Po Rd.
Santa Fe, NM 87508
Tel: (505)424-2300
Fax: (505)424-0505
E-mail: mary.curley@iaia.edu
Web Site: www.iaia.edu
President/CEO: Dr. Robert Martin
Admissions: Mary Curley
Financial Aid: Lala M. Gallegos
Type: Comprehensive **Sex:** Coed **Costs Per Year:** State resident tuition: $4220 full-time, $175.83 per semester hour part-time. Nonresident tuition: $4220 full-time, $175.83 per semester hour part-time. Mandatory fees: $220 full-time, $110 per term part-time. College room and board: $8140. College room only: $3480. Room and board charges vary according to board plan and housing facility. **Scholarships:** Available. **Calendar System:** Semester, Summer session available **Student-Faculty Ratio:** 7:1 **Exams:** ACT essay component used for advising; ACT essay component used for placement; Other; SAT I or ACT; SAT essay component used for advising; SAT essay component used for placement. **% Receiving Financial Aid:** 93 **Final Year or Final Semester Residency Requirement:** Yes **Regional Accreditation:** North Central Association of Colleges and Schools **Credit Hours For Degree:** 60 credits, Associates; 120 credits, Bachelors **Professional Accreditation:** NASAD.

INTELLITEC COLLEGE

5001 Montgomery Blvd. NE
Ste. A24
Albuquerque, NM 87109

Tel: (505)508-5225
Web Site: www.intelliteccollege.edu
Type: Two-Year College **Sex:** Coed **Professional Accreditation:** ACCSC.

LUNA COMMUNITY COLLEGE

PO Box 1510
Las Vegas, NM 87701
Tel: (505)454-2500; Free: 800-588-7232
E-mail: hgriego@luna.cc.nm.us
Web Site: www.luna.edu
President/CEO: Dr. Pete Campos
Admissions: Henrietta Griego
Type: Two-Year College **Sex:** Coed **Admission Plans:** Open Admission **H.S. Requirements:** High school diploma required; GED accepted **Scholarships:** Available. **Calendar System:** Semester **Enrollment:** Full-time 544, Part-time 1,245 **Regional Accreditation:** North Central Association of Colleges and Schools **Credit Hours For Degree:** 66 credit hours, Associates

MESALANDS COMMUNITY COLLEGE

911 S Tenth St.
Tucumcari, NM 88401
Tel: (575)461-4413
Fax: (505)461-1901
Web Site: www.mesalands.edu
President/CEO: Thomas Newsom
Admissions: Ken Brashear
Type: Two-Year College **Sex:** Coed **Application Deadline:** Rolling **Calendar System:** Semester **Regional Accreditation:** North Central Association of Colleges and Schools

NATIONAL AMERICAN UNIVERSITY (ALBUQUERQUE)

10131 Coors Blvd. NW
Ste. I-01
Albuquerque, NM 87114
Tel: (505)348-3750
Web Site: www.national.edu
President/CEO: Dr. Jerry Gallentine
Type: Two-Year College **Sex:** Coed **Application Fee:** $25.00 **Regional Accreditation:** North Central Association of Colleges and Schools

NATIONAL AMERICAN UNIVERSITY (ALBUQUERQUE)

4775 Indian School Rd., NE, Ste. 200
Albuquerque, NM 87110
Tel: (505)265-7517; Free: 800-895-9904
Fax: (505)265-7542
E-mail: albadmissions@national.edu
Web Site: www.national.edu
President/CEO: Dr. Jerry Gallentine
Type: Four-Year College **Sex:** Coed **Admission Plans:** Open Admission **Application Deadline:** Rolling **Application Fee:** $25.00 **H.S. Requirements:** High school diploma required; GED accepted **Scholarships:** Available. **Calendar System:** Quarter, Summer session available **Regional Accreditation:** North Central Association of Colleges and Schools **Credit Hours For Degree:** 192 credits, Bachelors

NATIONAL COLLEGE OF MIDWIFERY

1041 Reed St., Ste. C
Taos, NM 87571
Tel: (575)758-8914
Fax: (505)758-0302
E-mail: info@midwiferycollege.org
Web Site: www.midwiferycollege.org
Admissions: Beth Enson
Type: Comprehensive **Sex:** Women **Calendar System:** Trimester **Professional Accreditation:** MEAC.

NAVAJO TECHNICAL UNIVERSITY

PO Box 849
Crownpoint, NM 87313
Tel: (505)786-4100
Fax: (505)786-5644
Web Site: www.navajotech.edu
President/CEO: Dr. Elmer Guy
Type: Comprehensive **Sex:** Coed **Admission Plans:** Open Admission

Scholarships: Available. **Calendar System:** Semester **Student-Faculty Ratio:** 18:1 **% Receiving Financial Aid:** 60 **Regional Accreditation:** North Central Association of Colleges and Schools

NEW MEXICO HIGHLANDS UNIVERSITY

PO Box 9000
Las Vegas, NM 87701
Tel: (505)454-3000; Free: 800-338-6648
Fax: (505)454-3311
E-mail: judycordova@nmhu.edu
Web Site: www.nmhu.edu
President/CEO: Dr. James Fries
Admissions: Fidel Trujillo
Financial Aid: Eileen Sedillo

Type: Comprehensive **Sex:** Coed **Scores:** 61% SAT V 400+; 72% SAT M 400+; 44.88% ACT 18-23; 6.83% ACT 24-29 **% Accepted:** 100 **Admission Plans:** Deferred Admission; Early Admission; Open Admission **H.S. Requirements:** High school diploma required; GED accepted **Costs Per Year:** State resident tuition: $3352 full-time, $140 per credit hour part-time. Nonresident tuition: $6086 full-time, $254 per credit hour part-time. Mandatory fees: $1448 full-time. Full-time tuition and fees vary according to course load and location. Part-time tuition varies according to course load and location. College room and board: $7164. Room and board charges vary according to board plan and housing facility. **Scholarships:** Available. **Calendar System:** Semester, Summer session available **Enrollment:** Full-time 1,474, Graduate full-time 596, Graduate part-time 734, Part-time 759 **Faculty:** Full-time 137, Part-time 145 **Student-Faculty Ratio:** 14:1 **% Receiving Financial Aid:** 74 **% Residing in College-Owned, -Operated, or -Affiliated Housing:** 21 **Regional Accreditation:** North Central Association of Colleges and Schools **Credit Hours For Degree:** 64 semester hours, Associates; 128 semester hours, Bachelors **Professional Accreditation:** AACN, ACBSP, CSWE, NCATE. **Intercollegiate Athletics:** Baseball M; Basketball M & W; Cross-Country Running M & W; Football M; Soccer W; Softball W; Track and Field M & W; Volleyball W

NEW MEXICO INSTITUTE OF MINING AND TECHNOLOGY

801 Leroy Pl.
Socorro, NM 87801
Tel: (505)835-5434; Free: 800-428-TECH
Fax: (505)835-5989
E-mail: admission@admin.nmt.edu
Web Site: www.nmt.edu
President/CEO: Dr. Daniel H. Lopez
Admissions: Tony Ortiz
Financial Aid: Marliss Monette

Type: University **Sex:** Coed **Scores:** 100% SAT V 400+; 100% SAT M 400+; 27% ACT 18-23; 50% ACT 24-29 **% Accepted:** 24 **Admission Plans:** Deferred Admission **Application Deadline:** August 1 **Application Fee:** $15.00 **H.S. Requirements:** High school diploma required; GED accepted **Costs Per Year:** Application fee: $15. State resident tuition: $5,563 full-time, $231.76 per credit hour part-time. Nonresident tuition: $18,087 full-time, $753.63 per credit hour part-time. Mandatory fees: $1050 full-time, $64.50 per credit hour part-time, $216 per term part-time. Full-time tuition and fees vary according to reciprocity agreements. Part-time tuition and fees vary according to course load. College room and board: $7586. Room and board charges vary according to board plan and housing facility. **Scholarships:** Available. **Calendar System:** Semester, Summer session available **Enrollment:** Full-time 1,423, Graduate full-time 248, Graduate part-time 285, Part-time 194 **Faculty:** Full-time 130, Part-time 42 **Student-Faculty Ratio:** 12:1 **Exams:** ACT; ACT essay component not used; SAT I; SAT I and SAT II or ACT; SAT I or ACT; SAT II; SAT essay component not used; SAT Reasoning. **% Receiving Financial Aid:** 50 **% Residing in College-Owned, -Operated, or -Affiliated Housing:** 50 **Final Year or Final Semester Residency Requirement:** Yes **Regional Accreditation:** North Central Association of Colleges and Schools **Credit Hours For Degree:** 65 credit hours, Associates; 130 credit hours, Bachelors **Professional Accreditation:** ABET. **Intercollegiate Athletics:** Golf M & W; Rugby M & W; Soccer M & W

NEW MEXICO JUNIOR COLLEGE

5317 Lovington Hwy.
Hobbs, NM 88240-9123
Tel: (575)392-4510; Free: 800-657-6260
Fax: (505)392-2527
Web Site: www.nmjc.edu

President/CEO: Steve McCleery
Admissions: Dr. Michele Clingman

Type: Two-Year College **Sex:** Coed **Affiliation:** New Mexico Commission on Higher Education. **Admission Plans:** Deferred Admission; Early Admission; Open Admission **Application Deadline:** Rolling **Application Fee:** $0.00 **H.S. Requirements:** High school diploma or equivalent not required. For automotive technology, medical laboratory technology, nursing programs: High school diploma required; GED accepted **Costs Per Year:** Application fee: $0. Area resident tuition: $1050 full-time, $35 per credit hour part-time. State resident tuition: $1620 full-time, $54 per credit hour part-time. Nonresident tuition: $1860 full-time, $62 per credit hour part-time. Mandatory fees: $510 full-time, $17 per credit hour part-time. Full-time tuition and fees vary according to course load. Part-time tuition and fees vary according to course load. College room and board: $4700. College room only: $2400. Room and board charges vary according to board plan and housing facility. **Scholarships:** Available. **Calendar System:** Semester, Summer session available **Faculty:** Full-time 65, Part-time 55 **Student-Faculty Ratio:** 19:1 **% Residing in College-Owned, -Operated, or -Affiliated Housing:** 15 **Regional Accreditation:** North Central Association of Colleges and Schools **Credit Hours For Degree:** 64 semester hours, Associates **Professional Accreditation:** ACEN. **Intercollegiate Athletics:** Baseball M; Basketball M & W; Golf M

NEW MEXICO MILITARY INSTITUTE

101 W College Blvd.
Roswell, NM 88201-5173
Tel: (575)622-6250; Free: 800-421-5376
Fax: (505)624-8067
E-mail: admissions@nmmi.edu
Web Site: www.nmmi.edu
President/CEO: Maj. Jerry W. Grizzle, PhD
Financial Aid: Sonya Rodriguez

Type: Two-Year College **Sex:** Coed **Affiliation:** New Mexico Commission on Higher Education. **% Accepted:** 62 **Admission Plans:** Deferred Admission; Early Admission; Preferred Admission **Application Deadline:** August 1 **Application Fee:** $60.00 **H.S. Requirements:** High school diploma required; GED accepted **Scholarships:** Available. **Calendar System:** Semester, Summer session available **Enrollment:** Full-time 480 **Faculty:** Full-time 65 **Student-Faculty Ratio:** 17:1 **Exams:** SAT I or ACT. **% Residing in College-Owned, -Operated, or -Affiliated Housing:** 100 **Regional Accreditation:** North Central Association of Colleges and Schools **Credit Hours For Degree:** 68 hours, Associates **ROTC:** Army **Intercollegiate Athletics:** Baseball M; Basketball M; Fencing M & W; Football M; Golf M; Riflery M & W; Tennis M & W; Track and Field M; Volleyball W

NEW MEXICO STATE UNIVERSITY

PO Box 30001
Las Cruces, NM 88003-8001
Tel: (575)646-0111; Free: 800-662-6678
E-mail: admssions@nmsu.edu
Web Site: www.nmsu.edu
President/CEO: Dr. Garrey Carruthers
Admissions: Delia DeLeon
Financial Aid: Jerry Martinez

Type: University **Sex:** Coed **Affiliation:** New Mexico State University System. **Scores:** 82% SAT V 400+; 84% SAT M 400+; 52.6% ACT 18-23; 22.3% ACT 24-29 **% Accepted:** 65 **Application Deadline:** Rolling **Application Fee:** $20.00 **H.S. Requirements:** High school diploma required; GED accepted **Costs Per Year:** Application fee: $20. One-time mandatory fee: $40. State resident tuition: $4956 full-time, $206.50 per credit hour part-time. Nonresident tuition: $18,514 full-time, $771.40 per credit hour part-time. Mandatory fees: $1138 full-time, $47.40 per credit hour part-time. Full-time tuition and fees vary according to course load and reciprocity agreements. College room and board: $8064. College room only: $4482. Room and board charges vary according to board plan and housing facility. **Scholarships:** Available. **Calendar System:** Semester, Summer session available **Enrollment:** Full-time 10,419, Graduate full-time 1,559, Graduate part-time 1,405, Part-time 2,107 **Faculty:** Full-time 690, Part-time 359 **Student-Faculty Ratio:** 16:1 **Exams:** SAT I or ACT; SAT Reasoning. **% Receiving Financial Aid:** 66 **% Residing in College-Owned, -Operated, or -Affiliated Housing:** 19 **Final Year or Final Semester Residency Requirement:** Yes **Regional Accreditation:** North Central Association of Colleges and Schools **Credit Hours For Degree:** 66 credits, Associates; 120-128 credits, depending on program, Bachelors **ROTC:** Air Force, Army **Profes-**

sional Accreditation: AACN, AACSB, AAFCS, ABET, ACA, ACEJMC, APA, ASHA, CEPH, CSWE, JRCAT, NASM, NASPAA, NCATE. **Intercollegiate Athletics:** Baseball M; Basketball M & W; Cross-Country Running M & W; Equestrian Sports W; Football M; Golf M & W; Soccer W; Softball W; Swimming and Diving W; Tennis M & W; Track and Field W; Volleyball W

NEW MEXICO STATE UNIVERSITY–ALAMOGORDO
2400 N Scenic Dr.
Alamogordo, NM 88311-0477
Tel: (505)439-3600
E-mail: advisor@nmsua.nmsu.edu
Web Site: nmsua.edu
President/CEO: Dr. Cheri Jimeno
Admissions: Elma Hernandez

Type: Two-Year College **Sex:** Coed **Affiliation:** New Mexico State University System. **% Accepted:** 79 **Admission Plans:** Deferred Admission; Early Admission; Open Admission **Application Deadline:** Rolling **Application Fee:** $20.00 **H.S. Requirements:** High school diploma required; GED accepted **Costs Per Year:** Application fee: $20. Area resident tuition: $1872 full-time, $78 per credit hour part-time. State resident tuition: $2232 full-time, $93 per credit hour part-time. Nonresident tuition: $5184 full-time, $216 per credit hour part-time. Mandatory fees: $96 full-time, $4 per credit hour part-time. Full-time tuition and fees vary according to course load. **Scholarships:** Available. **Calendar System:** Semester, Summer session available **Enrollment:** Full-time 1,005, Part-time 2,366 **Faculty:** Full-time 54, Part-time 104 **Student-Faculty Ratio:** 20:1 **Final Year or Final Semester Residency Requirement:** No **Regional Accreditation:** North Central Association of Colleges and Schools **Credit Hours For Degree:** 66 credits, Associates **Professional Accreditation:** ACEN, NAACLS.

NEW MEXICO STATE UNIVERSITY–CARLSBAD
1500 University Dr.
Carlsbad, NM 88220-3509
Tel: (575)234-9200
E-mail: eshannon@nmsu.edu
Web Site: www.cavern.nmsu.edu
President/CEO: Russell Hardy
Admissions: Everal Shannon

Type: Two-Year College **Sex:** Coed **Affiliation:** New Mexico State University System. **Scores:** 41% ACT 18-23; 2% ACT 24-29 **% Accepted:** 100 **Admission Plans:** Early Admission; Open Admission **Application Deadline:** Rolling **Application Fee:** $20.00 **H.S. Requirements:** High school diploma required; GED accepted **Scholarships:** Available. **Calendar System:** Semester, Summer session available **Enrollment:** Full-time 583, Part-time 1,415 **Faculty:** Full-time 41, Part-time 50 **Regional Accreditation:** North Central Association of Colleges and Schools **Credit Hours For Degree:** 66 credit hours, Associates **Professional Accreditation:** ACEN.

NEW MEXICO STATE UNIVERSITY–GRANTS
1500 3rd St.
Grants, NM 87020-2025
Tel: (505)287-7981
Web Site: grants.nmsu.edu
President/CEO: Felicia Casados
Admissions: Irene Lutz

Type: Two-Year College **Sex:** Coed **Affiliation:** New Mexico State University System. **Admission Plans:** Early Admission; Open Admission **Application Deadline:** July 30 **Application Fee:** $15.00 **H.S. Requirements:** High school diploma required; GED accepted **Scholarships:** Available. **Calendar System:** Semester, Summer session available **Exams:** Other. **Regional Accreditation:** North Central Association of Colleges and Schools **Credit Hours For Degree:** 66 credits, Associates

NORTHERN NEW MEXICO COLLEGE
921 Paseo de Oñate
Española, NM 87532
Tel: (505)747-2100
E-mail: dms@nnmc.edu
Web Site: www.nnmc.edu
President/CEO: Dr. Jose Griego
Admissions: Mike L. Costello

Type: Four-Year College **Sex:** Coed **% Accepted:** 100 **Admission Plans:** Deferred Admission; Early Admission; Open Admission **Application Deadline:** Rolling **Application Fee:** $0.00 **H.S. Requirements:** High school

diploma required; GED accepted **Scholarships:** Available. **Calendar System:** Semester, Summer session available **Faculty:** Full-time 45, Part-time 208 **% Residing in College-Owned, -Operated, or -Affiliated Housing:** 1 **Regional Accreditation:** North Central Association of Colleges and Schools **Credit Hours For Degree:** 64 credits, Associates **Professional Accreditation:** ACBSP, JRCERT.

PIMA MEDICAL INSTITUTE (ALBUQUERQUE)
RMTS 32, 8601 Golf Course Rd., NW
Albuquerque, NM 87114
Tel: (505)881-1234
E-mail: kmcgrath@pmi.edu
Web Site: www.pmi.edu
President/CEO: Helen Candelaria
Admissions: Karen McGrath

Type: Two-Year College **Sex:** Coed **Exams:** Other. **Professional Accreditation:** ABHES.

PIMA MEDICAL INSTITUTE (ALBUQUERQUE)
4400 Cutler Ave. NE
Albuquerque, NM 87110
Tel: (505)881-1234; Free: 888-477-PIMA
Fax: (505)884-8371
Web Site: www.pmi.edu
President/CEO: Lisa Knigge-Huntsman

Type: Two-Year College **Sex:** Coed **Affiliation:** Vocational Training Institutes, Inc. **Admission Plans:** Early Admission **Application Fee:** $0.00 **H.S. Requirements:** High school diploma required; GED accepted **Scholarships:** Available. **Calendar System:** Miscellaneous, Summer session not available **Exams:** Other. **Credit Hours For Degree:** 88.5 credits, Associates **Professional Accreditation:** ABHES, JRCERT.

ST. JOHN'S COLLEGE
1160 Camino Cruz Blanca
Santa Fe, NM 87505
Tel: (505)984-6000; Free: 800-331-5232
E-mail: santafe.admissions@sjc.edu
Web Site: www.stjohnscollege.edu
President/CEO: Michael P. Peters
Admissions: Yvette Sobky Shaffer
Financial Aid: Michael R. Rodriguez

Type: Comprehensive **Sex:** Coed **Affiliation:** St. John's College (MD). **Scores:** 100% SAT V 400+; 100% SAT M 400+; 16% ACT 18-23; 47% ACT 24-29 **% Accepted:** 81 **Admission Plans:** Deferred Admission; Early Admission; Early Decision Plan **Application Deadline:** Rolling **Application Fee:** $0.00 **H.S. Requirements:** High school diploma required; GED accepted **Costs Per Year:** Application fee: $0. Comprehensive fee: $62,513 includes full-time tuition ($49,758), mandatory fees ($1596), and college room and board ($11,159). Room and board charges vary according to board plan. Part-time tuition: $1463 per credit. **Scholarships:** Available. **Calendar System:** Semester, Summer session available **Enrollment:** Full-time 318, Graduate full-time 55, Graduate part-time 16, Part-time 6 **Faculty:** Full-time 44, Part-time 14 **Student-Faculty Ratio:** 8:1 **Exams:** ACT essay component not used; Other; SAT I or ACT; SAT essay component not used. **% Receiving Financial Aid:** 88 **% Residing in College-Owned, -Operated, or -Affiliated Housing:** 85 **Final Year or Final Semester Residency Requirement:** Yes **Regional Accreditation:** North Central Association of Colleges and Schools **Credit Hours For Degree:** 136 credits, Bachelors **Intercollegiate Athletics:** Fencing M & W

SAN JUAN COLLEGE
4601 College Blvd.
Farmington, NM 87402-4699
Tel: (505)326-3311
Fax: (505)599-3385
E-mail: calcotea@sanjuancollege.edu
Web Site: www.sanjuancollege.edu
President/CEO: Dr. Toni Hopper Pendergrass
Admissions: Abby Calcote

Type: Two-Year College **Sex:** Coed **Affiliation:** New Mexico Higher Education Department. **% Accepted:** 100 **Admission Plans:** Deferred Admission; Early Admission; Open Admission **Application Deadline:** Rolling **Application Fee:** $10.00 **H.S. Requirements:** High school diploma required; GED accepted **Costs Per Year:** Application fee: $10. State resident tuition: $1104 full-time, $46 per credit hour part-time. Nonresident tuition: $3504 full-time, $146 per credit hour part-time. Mandatory fees: $370 full-time, $77.50 per term part-time. Full-time tuition and fees vary according to reciprocity agreements. Part-time tuition and fees vary according to reciprocity agreements. **Scholarships:** Available. **Calendar System:** Semester, Summer session available **Enrollment:** Full-time 2,674, Part-time 3,018 **Faculty:** Full-time 169, Part-time 137 **Student-Faculty Ratio:** 23:1 **Final Year or Final Semester Residency Requirement:** No **Regional Accreditation:** North Central Association of Colleges and Schools **Credit Hours For Degree:** 60 credits, Associates **Professional Accreditation:** ABET, ACBSP, ACEN, ADA, AHIMA, APTA.

SANTA FE COMMUNITY COLLEGE

6401 Richards Ave.
Santa Fe, NM 87508
Tel: (505)428-1000
Fax: (505)428-1237
E-mail: rebecca.estrada@sfcc.edu
Web Site: www.sfcc.edu
President/CEO: Ana Margarita Guzman
Admissions: Rebecca Estrada
Financial Aid: Donna Cordova
Type: Two-Year College **Sex:** Coed **Admission Plans:** Deferred Admission; Early Admission; Open Admission **Application Deadline:** Rolling **Application Fee:** $0.00 **H.S. Requirements:** High school diploma or equivalent not required **Scholarships:** Available. **Calendar System:** Semester, Summer session available **Enrollment:** Full-time 1,668, Part-time 3,188 **Faculty:** Full-time 68, Part-time 270 **Student-Faculty Ratio:** 17:1 **Exams:** ACT essay component used for placement; SAT essay component used for placement. **Final Year or Final Semester Residency Requirement:** No **Regional Accreditation:** North Central Association of Colleges and Schools **Credit Hours For Degree:** 60 credits, Associates **Professional Accreditation:** ACEN, ADA.

SANTA FE UNIVERSITY OF ART AND DESIGN

1600 Saint Michael's Dr.
Santa Fe, NM 87505-7634
Tel: (505)473-6011; Free: 800-456-2673
Fax: (505)473-6127
E-mail: admissions@santafeuniversity.edu
Web Site: www.santafeuniversity.edu
President/CEO: Dr. Maria Puzziferro, PhD
Admissions: Melissa Lewis
Financial Aid: Celeste Ida Franklin
Type: Four-Year College **Sex:** Coed **Affiliation:** Laureate International Universities. **Admission Plans:** Deferred Admission **Application Deadline:** Rolling **Application Fee:** $50.00 **H.S. Requirements:** High school diploma required; GED accepted **Costs Per Year:** Application fee: $50. Comprehensive fee: $37,778 includes full-time tuition ($29,846), mandatory fees ($2500), and college room and board ($5432). College room only: $4434. Full-time tuition and fees vary according to course load and program. Room and board charges vary according to board plan and housing facility. Part-time tuition: $1119 per credit hour. Part-time mandatory fees: $12,500 per term. Part-time tuition and fees vary according to course load and program. **Scholarships:** Available. **Calendar System:** Semester, Summer session available **Enrollment:** Full-time 918, Part-time 32 **Student-Faculty Ratio:** 15:1 **% Receiving Financial Aid:** 81 **Final Year or Final Semester Residency Requirement:** Yes **Regional Accreditation:** North Central Association of Colleges and Schools **Credit Hours For Degree:** 120 semester hours, Bachelors

SOUTHWESTERN INDIAN POLYTECHNIC INSTITUTE

9169 Coors, NW, Box 10146
Albuquerque, NM 87184-0146
Tel: (505)346-2347; Free: 800-586-7474
Fax: (505)346-2343
E-mail: joseph.carpio@bie.edu
Web Site: www.sipi.edu
President/CEO: Dr. Sherry R. Allison
Admissions: Joseph M. Carpio
Financial Aid: Marilyn Pargas
Type: Two-Year College **Sex:** Coed **% Accepted:** 86 **Admission Plans:** Preferred Admission **Application Deadline:** July 30 **Application Fee:** $0.00 **H.S. Requirements:** High school diploma required; GED accepted **Costs**

Per Year: Application fee: $0. **Scholarships:** Available. **Calendar System:** Trimester, Summer session available **Enrollment:** Full-time 346, Part-time 56 **Faculty:** Full-time 23, Part-time 18 **Student-Faculty Ratio:** 16:1 **% Residing in College-Owned, -Operated, or -Affiliated Housing:** 60 **Final Year or Final Semester Residency Requirement:** No **Regional Accreditation:** North Central Association of Colleges and Schools **Credit Hours For Degree:** 64 credit hours, Associates **Professional Accreditation:** COA.

UNIVERSITY OF NEW MEXICO

Albuquerque, NM 87131-2039
Tel: (505)277-0111; Free: 800-CALL-UNM
Fax: (505)277-6686
E-mail: apply@unm.edu
Web Site: www.unm.edu
President/CEO: Dr. Robert G. Frank
Admissions: Matthew Hulett
Financial Aid: Brian Malone
Type: University **Sex:** Coed **Scores:** 95% SAT V 400+; 95% SAT M 400+; 51.67% ACT 18-23; 32.36% ACT 24-29 **% Accepted:** 50 **Admission Plans:** Deferred Admission; Early Admission **Application Deadline:** Rolling **Application Fee:** $20.00 **H.S. Requirements:** High school diploma required; GED accepted **Costs Per Year:** Application fee: $20. State resident tuition: $6447 full-time, $242.31 per credit hour part-time. Nonresident tuition: $20,644 full-time, $835.33 per credit hour part-time. Mandatory fees: $1,507 full-time, $52.33 per credit hour part-time. Full-time tuition and fees vary according to program. Part-time tuition and fees vary according to course load and program. College room and board: $8690. Room and board charges vary according to board plan and housing facility. **Scholarships:** Available. **Calendar System:** Semester, Summer session available **Enrollment:** Full-time 16,085, Graduate full-time 3,557, Graduate part-time 3,274, Part-time 4,437 **Faculty:** Full-time 1,070, Part-time 531 **Student-Faculty Ratio:** 17:1 **Exams:** ACT essay component not used; SAT I or ACT; SAT essay component not used; SAT Reasoning; SAT Subject. **% Residing in College-Owned, -Operated, or -Affiliated Housing:** 8 **Final Year or Final Semester Residency Requirement:** No **Regional Accreditation:** North Central Association of Colleges and Schools **Credit Hours For Degree:** 60 semester hours, Associates; 120 semester hours, Bachelors **ROTC:** Air Force, Army, Navy **Professional Accreditation:** AACN, AACSB, AAFCS, AALS, ABA, ABET, ACA, ACCE, ACNM, ACPE, ACSP, ADA, AND, AOTA, APA, APTA, ASHA, ASLA, CEPH, JRCAT, JRCEMTP, LCME/AMA, NAAB, NAACLS, NASD, NASM, NASPAA, NAST, NCATE. **Intercollegiate Athletics:** Baseball M; Basketball M & W; Cross-Country Running M & W; Football M; Golf M & W; Skiing (Cross-Country) M & W; Skiing (Downhill) M & W; Soccer M & W; Softball W; Swimming and Diving M & W; Tennis M & W; Track and Field M & W; Volleyball W

UNIVERSITY OF NEW MEXICO–GALLUP

200 College Rd.
Gallup, NM 87301-5603
Tel: (505)863-7500
Fax: (505)863-7532
Web Site: www.gallup.unm.edu
President/CEO: Dr. Sylvia Rodriguez-Andrew
Admissions: Pearl A. Morris
Type: Two-Year College **Sex:** Coed **Affiliation:** New Mexico Commission on Higher Education. **Admission Plans:** Open Admission **Application Deadline:** Rolling **Application Fee:** $15.00 **H.S. Requirements:** High school diploma required; GED accepted **Costs Per Year:** Application fee: $15. State resident tuition: $904 full-time, $75.30 per credit hour part-time. Nonresident tuition: $2,189 full-time, $182.80 per credit hour part-time. **Scholarships:** Available. **Calendar System:** Semester, Summer session available **Enrollment:** Full-time 1,163, Part-time 1,310 **Student-Faculty Ratio:** 20:1 **Exams:** ACT; SAT I. **Regional Accreditation:** North Central Association of Colleges and Schools **Credit Hours For Degree:** 60 credit hours, Associates; 120 credit hours, Bachelors **Professional Accreditation:** ADA, AHIMA, NAACLS.

UNIVERSITY OF NEW MEXICO–LOS ALAMOS BRANCH

4000 University Dr.
Los Alamos, NM 87544-2233
Tel: (505)662-5919
E-mail: l65130@unm.edu
Web Site: losalamos.unm.edu

President/CEO: Cedric D. Page

Admissions: Irene K. Martinez

Type: Two-Year College **Sex:** Coed **Affiliation:** New Mexico Commission on Higher Education. **Scholarships:** Available. **Calendar System:** Semester, Summer session available **Enrollment:** Full-time 191, Part-time 553 **Faculty:** Full-time 4, Part-time 84 **Student-Faculty Ratio:** 9:1 **Exams:** SAT I or ACT. **Regional Accreditation:** North Central Association of Colleges and Schools **Credit Hours For Degree:** 64 semester hours, Associates

UNIVERSITY OF NEW MEXICO–TAOS

115 Civic Plz. Dr.

Taos, NM 87571

Tel: (575)737-6200

E-mail: valvarez@unm.edu

Web Site: taos.unm.edu

President/CEO: Dr. Kate O'Neill

Admissions: Vickie Alvarez

Type: Two-Year College **Sex:** Coed **Application Fee:** $15.00 **Calendar System:** Semester **Student-Faculty Ratio:** 19:1 **Regional Accreditation:** North Central Association of Colleges and Schools

UNIVERSITY OF NEW MEXICO–VALENCIA CAMPUS

280 La Entrada

Los Lunas, NM 87031-7633

Tel: (505)925-8580

Fax: (505)925-8563

E-mail: mhulett@unm.edu

Web Site: www.unm.edu/~unmvc

President/CEO: Alic E.V. Letteney, PhD

Admissions: Richard M. Hulett

Type: Two-Year College **Sex:** Coed **Affiliation:** New Mexico Commission on Higher Education. **Admission Plans:** Deferred Admission; Early Admission; Open Admission **Application Deadline:** Rolling **Application Fee:** $15.00 **H.S. Requirements:** High school diploma required; GED accepted **Scholarships:** Available. **Calendar System:** Semester, Summer session available **Student-Faculty Ratio:** 25:1 **Regional Accreditation:** North Central Association of Colleges and Schools **Credit Hours For Degree:** 60 credit hours, Associates

UNIVERSITY OF PHOENIX–NEW MEXICO CAMPUS

5700 Pasadena Ave. NE

Albuquerque, NM 87113-1570

Tel: (505)821-4800; Free: 866-766-0766

Web Site: www.phoenix.edu

President/CEO: Timothy P. Slottow

Admissions: Marc Booker

Type: Comprehensive **Sex:** Coed **Admission Plans:** Deferred Admission; Open Admission **Application Deadline:** Rolling **Application Fee:** $0.00 **H.S. Requirements:** High school diploma required; GED accepted **Scholarships:** Available. **Calendar System:** Continuous, Summer session not available **Enrollment:** Full-time 3,452 **Faculty:** Full-time 45, Part-time 382 **Regional Accreditation:** North Central Association of Colleges and Schools **Credit Hours For Degree:** 60 credits, Associates; 120 credits, Bachelors **Professional Accreditation:** ACBSP.

UNIVERSITY OF THE SOUTHWEST

6610 Lovington Hwy.

Hobbs, NM 88240-9129

Tel: (575)392-6561; Free: 800-530-4400

E-mail: lterrazas@usw.edu

Web Site: www.usw.edu

President/CEO: Dr. Quint Thurman

Admissions: Lissete Terrazas

Financial Aid: Dawny Kringel

Type: Comprehensive **Sex:** Coed **Affiliation:** Christian. **Scores:** 63% SAT V 400+; 80% SAT M 400+; 45% ACT 18-23; 3% ACT 24-29 **% Accepted:** 74 **Admission Plans:** Deferred Admission; Early Admission **Application Deadline:** Rolling **H.S. Requirements:** High school diploma required; GED accepted **Costs Per Year:** Comprehensive fee: $20,708 includes full-time tuition ($13,248), mandatory fees ($150), and college room and board ($7310). College room only: $4300. Full-time tuition and fees vary according to course load. Room and board charges vary according to board plan and housing facility. Part-time tuition: $552 per credit hour. Part-time tuition varies according to course load. **Scholarships:** Available. **Calendar System:** Semester, Summer session available **Enrollment:** Full-time 78, Graduate full-time 282, Graduate part-time 584, Part-time 69 **Faculty:** Full-time 31, Part-time 38 **Student-Faculty Ratio:** 15:1 **Exams:** ACT essay component not used; SAT I or ACT; SAT essay component not used. **% Residing in College-Owned, -Operated, or -Affiliated Housing:** 55 **Final Year or Final Semester Residency Requirement:** No **Regional Accreditation:** North Central Association of Colleges and Schools **Credit Hours For Degree:** 120 semester hours, Bachelors **Intercollegiate Athletics:** Baseball M; Basketball M & W; Cross-Country Running M & W; Golf M & W; Soccer M & W; Softball W; Tennis M & W; Track and Field M & W; Volleyball W

WESTERN NEW MEXICO UNIVERSITY

PO Box 680

Silver City, NM 88062-0680

Tel: (575)538-6011; Free: 800-872-WNMU

Fax: (505)538-6155

E-mail: tresslerd@wnmu.edu

Web Site: www.wnmu.edu

President/CEO: Dr. John E. Counts

Admissions: Matthew Lara

Financial Aid: Debra Reyes

Type: Comprehensive **Sex:** Coed **Scores:** 43% ACT 18-23; 5% ACT 24-29 **% Accepted:** 100 **Admission Plans:** Deferred Admission; Early Admission; Open Admission **Application Deadline:** August 1 **Application Fee:** $0.00 **H.S. Requirements:** High school diploma required; GED accepted **Scholarships:** Available. **Calendar System:** Semester, Summer session available **Enrollment:** Full-time 1,363, Part-time 856 **Faculty:** Full-time 128, Part-time 131 **Student-Faculty Ratio:** 17:1 **Exams:** ACT. **% Receiving Financial Aid:** 81 **Regional Accreditation:** North Central Association of Colleges and Schools **Credit Hours For Degree:** 64 credit hours, Associates; 128 credit hours, Bachelors **Professional Accreditation:** AACN, ACBSP, ACEN, AOTA, CSWE, NCATE. **Intercollegiate Athletics:** Basketball M & W; Cheerleading M & W; Cross-Country Running M & W; Football M; Golf M & W; Rock Climbing M & W; Softball W; Tennis M & W; Volleyball W

ADELPHI UNIVERSITY

One S Ave.
Garden City, NY 11530-0701
Tel: (516)877-3000; Free: 800-ADELPHI
Fax: (516)877-3039
E-mail: admissions@adelphi.edu
Web Site: www.adelphi.edu
President/CEO: Christine M. Riordan
Admissions: Stephanie Espina
Financial Aid: Debra Evans
Type: University **Sex:** Coed **Scores:** 100% SAT V 400+; 100% SAT M 400+; 54.95% ACT 18-23; 33.66% ACT 24-29 **% Accepted:** 72 **Admission Plans:** Deferred Admission; Early Decision Plan **Application Deadline:** Rolling Application Fee: $40.00 **H.S. Requirements:** High school diploma required; GED accepted **Costs Per Year:** Application fee: $40. Comprehensive fee: $47,535 includes full-time tuition ($32,380), mandatory fees ($1645), and college room and board ($13,510). College room only: $9620. Full-time tuition and fees vary according to course level, course load, location, program, and student level. Room and board charges vary according to board plan and housing facility. Part-time tuition: $990 per credit hour. Part-time tuition varies according to course level, course load, location, program, and student level. **Scholarships:** Available. **Calendar System:** Semester, Summer session available **Enrollment:** Full-time 4,414, Graduate full-time 1,263, Graduate part-time 1,141, Part-time 438 **Faculty:** Full-time 317, Part-time 697 **Student-Faculty Ratio:** 12:1 **Exams:** ACT essay component used for admission; SAT I or ACT; SAT essay component used for admission. **% Receiving Financial Aid:** 64 **% Residing in College-Owned, -Operated, or -Affiliated Housing:** 24 **Final Year or Final Semester Residency Requirement:** No **Regional Accreditation:** Middle States Association of Colleges and Schools **Credit Hours For Degree:** 64 credits, Associates; 120 credits, Bachelors **ROTC:** Air Force, Army **Professional Accreditation:** AACN, AACSB, ACEN, APA, ASHA, CSWE, NCATE. **Intercollegiate Athletics:** Baseball M; Basketball M & W; Bowling W; Cross-Country Running M & W; Field Hockey W; Golf M & W; Lacrosse M & W; Soccer M & W; Softball W; Swimming and Diving M & W; Tennis M & W; Track and Field M & W; Volleyball W

ADIRONDACK COMMUNITY COLLEGE

640 Bay Rd.
Queensbury, NY 12804
Tel: (518)743-2200; Free: 888-SUNY-ADK
Fax: (518)745-1433
Web Site: www.sunyacc.edu
President/CEO: Kristine Duffy, EdD
Type: Two-Year College **Sex:** Coed **Affiliation:** State University of New York System. **% Accepted:** 99 **Admission Plans:** Open Admission **Application Fee:** $35.00 **H.S. Requirements:** High school diploma required; GED accepted **Costs Per Year:** Application fee: $35. State resident tuition: $3984 full-time, $166 per credit hour part-time. Nonresident tuition: $7968 full-time, $332 per credit hour part-time. Mandatory fees: $435 full-time, $15.50 per credit hour part-time. Full-time tuition and fees vary according to course load and program. Part-time tuition and fees vary according to course load and program. College room and board: $10,460. Room and board charges vary according to board plan. **Scholarships:** Available. **Calendar System:** Semester, Summer session available **Enrollment:** Full-time 2,263, Part-time 1,724 **Faculty:** Full-time 89, Part-time 187 **Student-Faculty Ratio:** 14:1

Regional Accreditation: Middle States Association of Colleges and Schools **Credit Hours For Degree:** 64 credit hours, Associates **Professional Accreditation:** ACBSP, ACEN, AHIMA. **Intercollegiate Athletics:** Baseball M; Basketball M & W; Bowling M & W; Golf M & W; Soccer M; Softball W; Tennis M & W; Volleyball W

ALBANY COLLEGE OF PHARMACY AND HEALTH SCIENCES

106 New Scotland Ave.
Albany, NY 12208
Tel: (518)445-7200; Free: 888-203-8010
Fax: (518)445-7202
E-mail: admissions@acphs.edu
Web Site: www.acphs.edu
President/CEO: Pres. Greg Dewey, PhD
Admissions: Matthew Stever
Financial Aid: Kathleen Montague
Type: Comprehensive **Sex:** Coed **Scores:** 100% SAT V 400+; 101% SAT M 400+; 30% ACT 18-23; 59% ACT 24-29 **% Accepted:** 67 **Admission Plans:** Early Action; Early Admission **Application Deadline:** February 1 **Application Fee:** $75.00 **H.S. Requirements:** High school diploma required; GED accepted **Costs Per Year:** Application fee: $75. Comprehensive fee: $41,960 includes full-time tuition ($30,300), mandatory fees ($1250), and college room and board ($10,410). College room only: $6700. Full-time tuition and fees vary according to degree level, program, and student level. Room and board charges vary according to board plan, housing facility, and location. **Scholarships:** Available. **Calendar System:** Semester, Summer session available **Enrollment:** Full-time 1,055, Graduate full-time 476, Graduate part-time 5, Part-time 23 **Faculty:** Full-time 101, Part-time 31 **Student-Faculty Ratio:** 14:1 **Exams:** ACT essay component used for admission; ACT essay component used for placement; SAT I or ACT; SAT essay component used for admission; SAT essay component used for placement; SAT Reasoning; SAT Subject. **% Receiving Financial Aid:** 82 **% Residing in College-Owned, -Operated, or -Affiliated Housing:** 58 **Final Year or Final Semester Residency Requirement:** No **Regional Accreditation:** Middle States Association of Colleges and Schools **Credit Hours For Degree:** 130 semester hours, Bachelors **Professional Accreditation:** ACPE, ASC. **Intercollegiate Athletics:** Basketball M & W; Cross-Country Running M & W; Soccer M & W; Track and Field M & W

ALFRED UNIVERSITY

One Saxon Dr.
Alfred, NY 14802-1205
Tel: (607)871-2111; Free: 800-541-9229
Fax: (607)871-2198
E-mail: admissions@alfred.edu
Web Site: www.alfred.edu
President/CEO: Dr. Charles M. Edmondson
Admissions: Jamie Marcus
Financial Aid: Earl Pierce, Jr.
Type: University **Sex:** Coed **Scores:** 95% SAT V 400+; 94% SAT M 400+; 43.6% ACT 18-23; 45.1% ACT 24-29 **% Accepted:** 68 **Admission Plans:** Deferred Admission; Early Action; Early Admission **Application Deadline:** August 1 **Application Fee:** $50.00 **H.S. Requirements:** High school diploma required; GED accepted **Costs Per Year:** Application fee: $50. Comprehensive fee: $43,266 includes full-time tuition ($30,100), mandatory

fees ($970), and college room and board ($12,196). College room only: $6140. Full-time tuition and fees vary according to program. Room and board charges vary according to board plan and housing facility. Part-time tuition: $958 per credit hour. **Scholarships:** Available. **Calendar System:** Semester, Summer session available **Enrollment:** Full-time 1,760, Graduate full-time 195, Graduate part-time 285, Part-time 46 **Faculty:** Full-time 150, Part-time 37 **Student-Faculty Ratio:** 11:1 **Exams:** ACT essay component not used; SAT I or ACT; SAT II; SAT essay component not used; SAT essay component used in place of application essay; SAT Reasoning; SAT Subject. **% Receiving Financial Aid:** 81 **% Residing in College-Owned, -Operated, or -Affiliated Housing:** 79 **Final Year or Final Semester Residency Requirement:** Yes **Regional Accreditation:** Middle States Association of Colleges and Schools **Credit Hours For Degree:** 120 to 133 credit hours (varies by program), Bachelors **ROTC:** Army **Professional Accreditation:** AACSB, ABET, APA, NASAD, TEAC. **Intercollegiate Athletics:** Basketball M & W; Cross-Country Running M & W; Equestrian Sports M & W; Football M; Lacrosse M & W; Skiing (Downhill) M & W; Soccer M & W; Softball W; Swimming and Diving M & W; Tennis M & W; Track and Field M & W; Volleyball W

AMERICAN ACADEMY OF DRAMATIC ARTS–NEW YORK
120 Madison Ave.
New York, NY 10016-7004
Tel: (212)686-9244; Free: 800-463-8990
E-mail: kreilly@aada.edu
Web Site: www.aada.edu
President/CEO: Susan Zech
Admissions: Kerin Reilly
Financial Aid: Roberto Lopez

Type: Two-Year College **Sex:** Coed **Affiliation:** American Academy of Dramatic Arts–Los Angeles. **% Accepted:** 76 **Admission Plans:** Deferred Admission **Application Deadline:** Rolling **Application Fee:** $50.00 **H.S. Requirements:** High school diploma required; GED accepted **Costs Per Year:** Application fee: $50. Tuition: $32,440 full-time. Mandatory fees: $750 full-time. **Scholarships:** Available. **Calendar System:** Semester, Summer session not available **Enrollment:** Full-time 261 **Faculty:** Full-time 10, Part-time 21 **Student-Faculty Ratio:** 13:1 **% Residing in College-Owned, -Operated, or -Affiliated Housing:** 53 **Final Year or Final Semester Residency Requirement:** No **Regional Accreditation:** Middle States Association of Colleges and Schools **Credit Hours For Degree:** 68 units, Associates **Professional Accreditation:** NAST.

AMERICAN ACADEMY MCALLISTER INSTITUTE OF FUNERAL SERVICE
619 W 54th St.
New York, NY 10019-3602
Tel: (212)757-1190; Free: 866-932-2264
Fax: (212)765-5923
Web Site: www.funeraleducation.org
President/CEO: Meg Dunn
Admissions: Norman Provost

Type: Two-Year College **Sex:** Coed **Admission Plans:** Deferred Admission; Early Admission; Open Admission **Application Deadline:** Rolling **Application Fee:** $50.00 **H.S. Requirements:** High school diploma required; GED accepted **Scholarships:** Available. **Calendar System:** Semester, Summer session not available **Student-Faculty Ratio:** 18:1 **Credit Hours For Degree:** 74 credits, Associates **Professional Accreditation:** ABFSE.

ASA COLLEGE
81 Willoughby St.
Brooklyn, NY 11201
Tel: (718)522-9073; Free: 877-679-8772
Fax: (718)834-0835
Web Site: www.asa.edu
President/CEO: Alex Shchegol

Type: Two-Year College **Sex:** Coed **Application Fee:** $25.00 **H.S. Requirements:** High school diploma required; GED accepted **Calendar System:** Semester **Regional Accreditation:** Middle States Association of Colleges and Schools **Credit Hours For Degree:** 60 credits, Associates **Professional Accreditation:** AAMAE, ACICS. **Intercollegiate Athletics:** Baseball M; Basketball M & W; Football M; Soccer M; Tennis M & W

BARD COLLEGE
PO Box 5000
Annandale-on-Hudson, NY 12504

Tel: (845)758-6822
E-mail: admission@bard.edu
Web Site: www.bard.edu
President/CEO: Dr. Leon Botstein
Admissions: Mary Inga Backlund
Financial Aid: Denise Ann Ackerman

Type: Comprehensive **Sex:** Coed **% Accepted:** 32 **Admission Plans:** Deferred Admission; Early Action; Early Admission; Early Decision Plan **Application Deadline:** January 1 **Application Fee:** $50.00 **H.S. Requirements:** High school diploma required; GED accepted **Costs Per Year:** Application fee: $50. One-time mandatory fee: $1658. Comprehensive fee: $64,024 includes full-time tuition ($49,226), mandatory fees ($680), and college room and board ($14,118). Full-time tuition and fees vary according to degree level and location. Room and board charges vary according to location. Part-time tuition: $1538 per credit hour. Part-time tuition varies according to degree level and location. **Scholarships:** Available. **Calendar System:** Semester, Summer session not available **Enrollment:** Full-time 1,946, Graduate full-time 249, Graduate part-time 18, Part-time 77 **Faculty:** Full-time 152, Part-time 121 **Student-Faculty Ratio:** 10:1 **% Receiving Financial Aid:** 67 **% Residing in College-Owned, -Operated, or -Affiliated Housing:** 73 **Final Year or Final Semester Residency Requirement:** Yes **Regional Accreditation:** Middle States Association of Colleges and Schools **Credit Hours For Degree:** 60 credits, Associates; 128 credits, Bachelors **Professional Accreditation:** TEAC. **Intercollegiate Athletics:** Baseball M; Basketball M & W; Cross-Country Running M & W; Lacrosse M & W; Soccer M & W; Squash M; Swimming and Diving M & W; Tennis M & W; Track and Field M & W; Volleyball M & W

BARNARD COLLEGE
3009 Broadway
New York, NY 10027-6598
Tel: (212)854-5262
Fax: (212)854-6220
E-mail: admissions@barnard.edu
Web Site: www.barnard.edu
President/CEO: Dr. Debora L. Spar, PhD
Admissions: Jennifer Gill Fondiller
Financial Aid: Nanette DiLauro

Type: Four-Year College **Sex:** Women **Affiliation:** Columbia University. **Scores:** 100% SAT V 400+; 100% SAT M 400+; 1.68% ACT 18-23; 33.89% ACT 24-29 **% Accepted:** 20 **Admission Plans:** Deferred Admission; Early Action; Early Admission **Application Deadline:** January 1 **Application Fee:** $75.00 **H.S. Requirements:** High school diploma required; GED accepted **Costs Per Year:** Application fee: $75. Comprehensive fee: $62,741 includes full-time tuition ($45,851), mandatory fees ($1780), and college room and board ($15,110). Room and board charges vary according to board plan and housing facility. **Scholarships:** Available. **Calendar System:** Semester, Summer session not available **Enrollment:** Full-time 2,510, Part-time 38 **Faculty:** Full-time 214, Part-time 135 **Student-Faculty Ratio:** 10:1 **Exams:** ACT essay component used for admission; SAT I and SAT II or ACT; SAT essay component used for admission; SAT Reasoning; SAT Subject. **% Receiving Financial Aid:** 41 **% Residing in College-Owned, -Operated, or -Affiliated Housing:** 91 **Final Year or Final Semester Residency Requirement:** No **Regional Accreditation:** Middle States Association of Colleges and Schools **Credit Hours For Degree:** 122 credits, Bachelors **ROTC:** Air Force, Army, Navy **Professional Accreditation:** NASD. **Intercollegiate Athletics:** Archery W; Basketball W; Crew W; Cross-Country Running W; Equestrian Sports W; Fencing W; Field Hockey W; Golf W; Ice Hockey W; Lacrosse W; Rugby W; Sailing W; Skiing (Downhill) W; Soccer W; Softball W; Squash W; Swimming and Diving W; Tennis W; Track and Field W; Volleyball W; Water Polo W

BARUCH COLLEGE OF THE CITY UNIVERSITY OF NEW YORK
1 Bernard Baruch Way
New York, NY 10010-5585
Tel: (646)312-1000
E-mail: marisa.delacruz@baruch.cuny.edu
Web Site: www.baruch.cuny.edu
President/CEO: Dr. Mitchel B. Wallerstein
Admissions: Marisa DeLaCruz
Financial Aid: Elizabeth Riquez

Type: Comprehensive **Sex:** Coed **Affiliation:** City University of New York System. **Scores:** 99% SAT V 400+; 100% SAT M 400+ **% Accepted:** 32 **Admission Plans:** Deferred Admission; Early Action; Early Admission **Ap-**

plication Deadline: February 1 **Application Fee:** $65.00 **H.S. Requirements:** High school diploma required; GED accepted **Costs Per Year:** Application fee: $65. State resident tuition: $6330 full-time, $275 per credit part-time. Nonresident tuition: $16,800 full-time, $560 per credit part-time. Mandatory fees: $531 full-time. Full-time tuition and fees vary according to course load. Part-time tuition varies according to course load. **Scholarships:** Available. **Calendar System:** Semester, Summer session available **Enrollment:** Full-time 11,233, Graduate full-time 742, Graduate part-time 2,437, Part-time 4,021 **Faculty:** Full-time 513, Part-time 711 **Student-Faculty Ratio:** 17:1 **Exams:** ACT essay component not used; SAT I or ACT; SAT essay component not used; SAT Reasoning. **% Receiving Financial Aid:** 62 % **Residing in College-Owned, -Operated, or -Affiliated Housing:** 2 **Final Year or Final Semester Residency Requirement:** No **Regional Accreditation:** Middle States Association of Colleges and Schools **Credit Hours For Degree:** 124 credits, Bachelors **ROTC:** Army **Professional Accreditation:** AACSB, CAHME, NASPAA. **Intercollegiate Athletics:** Baseball M; Basketball M & W; Cheerleading M & W; Cross-Country Running M & W; Soccer M; Softball W; Swimming and Diving M & W; Tennis M & W; Volleyball M & W

BE'ER YAAKOV TALMUDIC SEMINARY
12 Jefferson Ave.
Spring Valley, NY 10977
Tel: (845)406-9699
Type: Four-Year College **Sex:** Coed **Affiliation:** Jewish. **Professional Accreditation:** AARTS.

BEIS MEDRASH HEICHAL DOVID
257 Beach 17th St.
Far Rockaway, NY 11691
Tel: (718)868-2300
Fax: (718)868-0517
President/CEO: Rabbi Yakov Bender
Type: Comprehensive **Sex:** Men **Application Fee:** $100.00 **Professional Accreditation:** AARTS.

THE BELANGER SCHOOL OF NURSING
650 McClellan St.
Schenectady, NY 12304
Tel: (518)243-4471
E-mail: lansingc@ellismedicine.org
Web Site: www.ellismedicine.org/school-of-nursing
President/CEO: Marilyn Stapleton, PhD, RN
Admissions: Carolyn Lansing
Type: Two-Year College **Sex:** Coed **Costs Per Year:** Tuition: $9072 full-time, $6867 per year part-time. Mandatory fees: $1148 full-time, $315 per credit part-time, $728 per year part-time. Full-time tuition and fees vary according to course level, course load, and student level. Part-time tuition and fees vary according to course level, course load, and student level. **Scholarships:** Available. **Enrollment:** Full-time 32, Part-time 95 **Student-Faculty Ratio:** 6:1 **Exams:** SAT I or ACT; SAT essay component used for admission. **Credit Hours For Degree:** 72 credits, Associates **Professional Accreditation:** ACEN.

BERKELEY COLLEGE–NEW YORK CITY CAMPUS
3 E 43rd St.
New York, NY 10017-4604
Tel: (212)986-4343; Free: 800-446-5400
Fax: (212)697-3371
E-mail: info@berkeleycollege.edu
Web Site: www.berkeleycollege.edu
President/CEO: Michael J. Smith
Admissions: Michelle Gomez
Type: Four-Year College **Sex:** Coed **Admission Plans:** Deferred Admission **Application Deadline:** Rolling **Application Fee:** $50.00 **H.S. Requirements:** High school diploma required; GED accepted **Costs Per Year:** Application fee: $50. Tuition: $23,100 full-time, $810 per semester hour part-time. Mandatory fees: $1650 full-time, $412 per term part-time. Full-time tuition and fees vary according to course load. Part-time tuition and fees vary according to course load. Tuition guaranteed not to increase for student's term of enrollment. **Scholarships:** Available. **Calendar System:** Quarter, Summer session available **Enrollment:** Full-time 3,472, Part-time 496 **Student-Faculty Ratio:** 23:1 **Exams:** SAT I or ACT. **Final Year or Final Semester Residency Requirement:** Yes **Regional Accreditation:** Middle

States Association of Colleges and Schools **Credit Hours For Degree:** 60 semester hours, Associates; 120 semester hours, Bachelors **Intercollegiate Athletics:** Basketball M & W; Cross-Country Running M & W; Soccer M & W; Track and Field M & W

BERKELEY COLLEGE–WHITE PLAINS CAMPUS
99 Church St.
White Plains, NY 10601
Tel: (914)694-1122; Free: 800-446-5400
Fax: (914)694-5832
E-mail: info@berkeleycollege.edu
Web Site: www.berkeleycollege.edu
President/CEO: Michael J. Smith
Admissions: Lynn Ovimeleh
Type: Two-Year College **Sex:** Coed **Affiliation:** Berkeley College–New York City. **Admission Plans:** Deferred Admission **Application Deadline:** Rolling **Application Fee:** $50.00 **H.S. Requirements:** High school diploma required; GED accepted **Costs Per Year:** Application fee: $50. Tuition: $23,100 full-time, $810 per credit hour part-time. Mandatory fees: $1650 full-time, $412 per term part-time. Full-time tuition and fees vary according to course load. Part-time tuition and fees vary according to course load. College room only: $9000. Tuition guaranteed not to increase for student's term of enrollment. **Scholarships:** Available. **Calendar System:** Quarter, Summer session available **Enrollment:** Full-time 428, Part-time 39 **Student-Faculty Ratio:** 23:1 **Exams:** SAT I or ACT. **Final Year or Final Semester Residency Requirement:** Yes **Regional Accreditation:** Middle States Association of Colleges and Schools **Credit Hours For Degree:** 60 semester credits, Associates; 120 semester credits, Bachelors **Intercollegiate Athletics:** Basketball M & W; Cross-Country Running M & W; Soccer M & W; Tennis M & W

BETH HAMEDRASH SHAAREI YOSHER INSTITUTE
4102-10 Sixteenth Ave.
Brooklyn, NY 11204
Tel: (718)854-2290
President/CEO: Pinchos Kaff
Type: Comprehensive **Sex:** Men **Affiliation:** Jewish. **% Accepted:** 100 **H.S. Requirements:** High school diploma required; GED accepted **Calendar System:** Semester **Professional Accreditation:** AARTS.

BETH HATALMUD RABBINICAL COLLEGE
2127 Eighty-second St.
Brooklyn, NY 11214
Tel: (718)259-2525
President/CEO: Mendel Bromberg
Type: Comprehensive **Sex:** Men **Affiliation:** Jewish. **% Accepted:** 100 **H.S. Requirements:** High school diploma required; GED accepted **Calendar System:** Semester **Professional Accreditation:** AARTS.

BILL AND SANDRA POMEROY COLLEGE OF NURSING AT CROUSE HOSPITAL
765 Irving Ave.
Syracuse, NY 13210
Tel: (315)470-7481
E-mail: amygraham@crouse.org
Web Site: www.crouse.org/nursing
President/CEO: Rhonda Reader
Admissions: Amy Graham
Financial Aid: F. Peter Bullock
Type: Two-Year College **Sex:** Coed **Admission Plans:** Deferred Admission **Application Deadline:** February 1 **Application Fee:** $30.00 **H.S. Requirements:** High school diploma required; GED accepted **Scholarships:** Available. **Calendar System:** Semester, Summer session not available **Exams:** SAT I or ACT. **Credit Hours For Degree:** 70 credits, Associates **Professional Accreditation:** ACEN.

BINGHAMTON UNIVERSITY, STATE UNIVERSITY OF NEW YORK
4400 Vestal Pky. E
Vestal, NY 13850
Tel: (607)777-2000
E-mail: admit@binghamton.edu
Web Site: www.binghamton.edu
President/CEO: Dr. Harvey G. Stenger
Admissions: Randall Edouard

Financial Aid: Dennis Chavez

Type: University **Sex:** Coed **Affiliation:** State University of New York System. **Scores:** 100% SAT V 400+; 100% SAT M 400+; 2.2% ACT 18-23; 49.8% ACT 24-29 **% Accepted:** 42 **Admission Plans:** Deferred Admission; Early Admission; Early Decision Plan **Application Deadline:** Rolling **Application Fee:** $50.00 **H.S. Requirements:** High school diploma required; GED accepted **Costs Per Year:** Application fee: $50. State resident tuition: $270 per credit hour part-time. Nonresident tuition: $816 per credit hour part-time. Part-time tuition varies according to course load and program. **Scholarships:** Available. **Calendar System:** Semester, Summer session available **Enrollment:** Full-time 13,054, Graduate full-time 2,059, Graduate part-time 1,363, Part-time 437 **Faculty:** Full-time 689, Part-time 289 **Student-Faculty Ratio:** 20:1 **Exams:** ACT essay component used for admission; SAT I or ACT; SAT essay component used for admission. **% Receiving Financial Aid:** 48 **% Residing in College-Owned, -Operated, or -Affiliated Housing:** 51 **Final Year or Final Semester Residency Requirement:** No **Regional Accreditation:** Middle States Association of Colleges and Schools **Credit Hours For Degree:** 124-135 credits, depending on program, Bachelors **ROTC:** Air Force, Army **Professional Accreditation:** AACN, AACSB, ABET, APA, CSWE, NASM, NASPAA, TEAC. **Intercollegiate Athletics:** Baseball M; Basketball M & W; Cross-Country Running M & W; Golf M; Lacrosse M & W; Soccer M & W; Softball W; Swimming and Diving M & W; Tennis M & W; Track and Field M & W; Volleyball W; Wrestling M

BORICUA COLLEGE

3755 Broadway
New York, NY 10032-1560
Tel: (212)694-1000
E-mail: mpfeffer@boricuacollege.edu
Web Site: www.boricuacollege.edu
President/CEO: Dr. Victor G. Alicea
Admissions: Miriam Pfeffer
Financial Aid: Rosalia Cruz

Type: Comprehensive **Sex:** Coed **% Accepted:** 40 **Admission Plans:** Deferred Admission **Application Deadline:** Rolling **Application Fee:** $25.00 **H.S. Requirements:** High school diploma required; GED accepted **Costs Per Year:** Application fee: $25. Tuition: $10,100 full-time. **Scholarships:** Available. **Calendar System:** Miscellaneous, Summer session available **Enrollment:** Full-time 1,004 **Faculty:** Full-time 57, Part-time 76 **Student-Faculty Ratio:** 20:1 **Exams:** Other. **% Receiving Financial Aid:** 94 **Regional Accreditation:** Middle States Association of Colleges and Schools **Credit Hours For Degree:** 60 credits, Associates; 124 credits, Bachelors

BOROUGH OF MANHATTAN COMMUNITY COLLEGE OF THE CITY UNIVERSITY OF NEW YORK

199 Chambers St.
New York, NY 10007-1097
Tel: (212)220-8000; Free: 866-583-5729
Fax: (212)346-8816
E-mail: admissions@bmcc.cuny.edu
Web Site: www.bmcc.cuny.edu
President/CEO: Dr. Antonio Perez
Admissions: Dr. Eugenio Barrios

Type: Two-Year College **Sex:** Coed **Affiliation:** City University of New York System. **Scores:** 47% SAT V 400+; 47% SAT M 400+ **% Accepted:** 99 **Admission Plans:** Deferred Admission; Open Admission; Preferred Admission **Application Deadline:** Rolling **Application Fee:** $65.00 **H.S. Requirements:** High school diploma required; GED accepted **Costs Per Year:** Application fee: $65. State resident tuition: $4800 full-time, $210 per credit part-time. Nonresident tuition: $7680 full-time, $320 per credit part-time. Mandatory fees: $369 full-time, $100 per term part-time. Full-time tuition and fees vary according to course load. Part-time tuition and fees vary according to course load. **Scholarships:** Available. **Calendar System:** Semester, Summer session available **Enrollment:** Full-time 18,074, Part-time 9,235 **Faculty:** Full-time 555, Part-time 1,012 **Student-Faculty Ratio:** 24:1 **Exams:** SAT I or ACT. **Regional Accreditation:** Middle States Association of Colleges and Schools **Credit Hours For Degree:** 60 credits, Associates **Professional Accreditation:** ACEN, AHIMA, CoARC, JRCEMTP. **Intercollegiate Athletics:** Basketball M & W; Soccer M & W; Volleyball W

BRAMSON ORT COLLEGE

69-30 Austin St.
Forest Hills, NY 11375-4239

Tel: (718)261-5800
E-mail: admissions@bramsonort.edu
Web Site: www.bramsonort.edu
President/CEO: Dr. Ephraim Buhks
Financial Aid: Anna Kopit

Type: Two-Year College **Sex:** Coed **Admission Plans:** Deferred Admission; Early Admission; Open Admission **Application Deadline:** Rolling **Application Fee:** $50.00 **H.S. Requirements:** High school diploma required; GED accepted **Scholarships:** Available. **Calendar System:** Semester, Summer session available **Student-Faculty Ratio:** 22:1 **Credit Hours For Degree:** 62 credits, Associates **Professional Accreditation:** NYSBR.

BRONX COMMUNITY COLLEGE OF THE CITY UNIVERSITY OF NEW YORK

2155 University Ave.
Bronx, NY 10453
Tel: (718)289-5100
E-mail: admission@bcc.cuny.edu
Web Site: www.bcc.cuny.edu
President/CEO: Dr. Carole Berotte Joseph, PhD
Admissions: Patricia A. Ramos

Type: Two-Year College **Sex:** Coed **Affiliation:** City University of New York System. **Admission Plans:** Early Admission; Open Admission **Application Deadline:** July 1 **Application Fee:** $65.00 **H.S. Requirements:** High school diploma required; GED accepted **Calendar System:** Semester, Summer session available **Enrollment:** Full-time 6,598, Part-time 4,770 **Faculty:** Full-time 303, Part-time 103 **Student-Faculty Ratio:** 26:1 **Exams:** ACT essay component used for placement; SAT I or ACT; SAT essay component used for placement. **Final Year or Final Semester Residency Requirement:** No **Regional Accreditation:** Middle States Association of Colleges and Schools **Credit Hours For Degree:** 60 credits, Associates **Professional Accreditation:** ABET, ACBSP, ACEN, JRCERT, JRCNMT. **Intercollegiate Athletics:** Baseball M; Basketball M; Cross-Country Running M & W; Soccer M; Track and Field M & W; Volleyball W

BROOKLYN COLLEGE OF THE CITY UNIVERSITY OF NEW YORK

2900 Bedford Ave.
Brooklyn, NY 11210-2889
Tel: (718)951-5000
E-mail: adminqry@brooklyn.cuny.edu
Web Site: www.brooklyn.cuny.edu
President/CEO: Dean Karen L. Gould
Financial Aid: Ahad Farhang

Type: Comprehensive **Sex:** Coed **Affiliation:** City University of New York System. **Scores:** 96% SAT V 400+; 99% SAT M 400+ **% Accepted:** 37 **Application Deadline:** February 1 **Application Fee:** $65.00 **H.S. Requirements:** High school diploma required; GED accepted **Costs Per Year:** Application fee: $65. State resident tuition: $3165 full-time, $275 per credit part-time. Nonresident tuition: $6330 full-time, $560 per credit part-time. Mandatory fees: $505 full-time, $139.45. Full-time tuition and fees vary according to course load. Part-time tuition and fees vary according to course load. College room and board: $4210. Room and board charges vary according to housing facility. **Scholarships:** Available. **Calendar System:** Semester, Summer session available **Enrollment:** Full-time 10,175, Graduate full-time 560, Graduate part-time 2,643, Part-time 4,032 **Faculty:** Full-time 537, Part-time 711 **Student-Faculty Ratio:** 16:1 **Exams:** ACT essay component not used; SAT I or ACT; SAT essay component not used. **% Receiving Financial Aid:** 79 **Final Year or Final Semester Residency Requirement:** No **Regional Accreditation:** Middle States Association of Colleges and Schools **Credit Hours For Degree:** 120 credits, Bachelors **Professional Accreditation:** ACA, AND, ASHA, CEPH, NCATE. **Intercollegiate Athletics:** Basketball M & W; Cross-Country Running M & W; Soccer M; Softball W; Swimming and Diving M & W; Tennis M & W; Track and Field M & W; Volleyball M & W

BROOME COMMUNITY COLLEGE

PO Box 1017
Binghamton, NY 13902-1017
Tel: (607)778-5000
E-mail: admissions@sunybroome.edu
Web Site: www.sunybroome.edu
President/CEO: Dr. Kevin E. Drumm
Admissions: Jenae Norris

Type: Two-Year College **Sex:** Coed **Affiliation:** State University of New York

System. **Admission Plans:** Early Admission; Open Admission; Preferred Admission **Application Deadline:** Rolling **Application Fee:** $0.00 **H.S. Requirements:** High school diploma required; GED accepted **Scholarships:** Available. **Calendar System:** Semester, Summer session available **Enrollment:** Full-time 4,655, Part-time 2,222 **Faculty:** Full-time 141, Part-time 265 **Regional Accreditation:** Middle States Association of Colleges and Schools **Credit Hours For Degree:** 62 credit hours, Associates **Professional Accreditation:** AAMAE, ABET, ACEN, ADA, AHIMA, APTA, JRCERT, NAACLS. **Intercollegiate Athletics:** Baseball M; Basketball M & W; Cross-Country Running M & W; Golf M; Ice Hockey M; Lacrosse M; Soccer M & W; Softball W; Tennis M & W; Volleyball W

BRYANT & STRATTON COLLEGE–ALBANY CAMPUS

1259 Central Ave.
Albany, NY 12205
Tel: (518)437-1802
Fax: (518)437-1048
Web Site: www.bryantstratton.edu
President/CEO: Michael A. Gutierrez
Admissions: Robert Ferrell

Type: Two-Year College **Sex:** Coed **Affiliation:** Bryant and Stratton College, Inc. **Admission Plans:** Deferred Admission **Application Deadline:** Rolling **H.S. Requirements:** High school diploma required; GED accepted **Scholarships:** Available. **Calendar System:** Semester, Summer session available **Enrollment:** Full-time 354, Part-time 116 **Faculty:** Full-time 12, Part-time 33 **Exams:** Other; SAT I or ACT. **Regional Accreditation:** Middle States Association of Colleges and Schools **Credit Hours For Degree:** 60 credit hours, Associates **Professional Accreditation:** AAMAE.

BRYANT & STRATTON COLLEGE–AMHERST CAMPUS

3650 Millersport Hwy.
Getzville, NY 14068
Tel: (716)625-6300
E-mail: bkdioguardi@bryantstratton.edu
Web Site: www.bryantstratton.edu
President/CEO: Marvel Ross Jones, PhD
Admissions: Brian K. Dioguardi

Type: Two-Year College **Sex:** Coed **Admission Plans:** Early Admission **Application Deadline:** Rolling **H.S. Requirements:** High school diploma or equivalent not required **Scholarships:** Available. **Calendar System:** Trimester, Summer session available **Enrollment:** Full-time 277, Part-time 197 **Faculty:** Full-time 9, Part-time 58 **Exams:** Other; SAT I or ACT. **Regional Accreditation:** Middle States Association of Colleges and Schools **Credit Hours For Degree:** 60 credits, Associates; 120 credits, Bachelors

BRYANT & STRATTON COLLEGE–BUFFALO CAMPUS

465 Main St.
Ste. 400
Buffalo, NY 14203
Tel: (716)884-9120
E-mail: pjstruebel@bryantstratton.edu
Web Site: www.bryantstratton.edu
President/CEO: Jeff Tredo
Admissions: Philip J. Struebel

Type: Two-Year College **Sex:** Coed **% Accepted:** 75 **Admission Plans:** Early Admission **Application Deadline:** Rolling **H.S. Requirements:** High school diploma or equivalent not required **Scholarships:** Available. **Calendar System:** Trimester, Summer session available **Enrollment:** Full-time 473, Part-time 220 **Faculty:** Full-time 11, Part-time 42 **Exams:** Other; SAT I or ACT. **Regional Accreditation:** Middle States Association of Colleges and Schools **Credit Hours For Degree:** 60 credits, Associates; 120 credits, Bachelors **Professional Accreditation:** AAMAE.

BRYANT & STRATTON COLLEGE–GREECE CAMPUS

854 Long Pond Rd.
Rochester, NY 14612
Tel: (585)720-0660
Fax: (585)720-9226
Web Site: www.bryantstratton.edu
President/CEO: Marc Ambrosi
Admissions: John Schifano

Type: Two-Year College **Sex:** Coed **Affiliation:** Bryant and Stratton College, Inc. **Admission Plans:** Deferred Admission **Application Deadline:** Rolling **H.S. Requirements:** High school diploma required; GED accepted. For ap-

plicants 19 or over who meet entrance testing requirements: High school diploma required; GED not accepted **Scholarships:** Available. **Calendar System:** Semester, Summer session available **Enrollment:** Full-time 192, Part-time 87 **Faculty:** Full-time 8, Part-time 41 **Student-Faculty Ratio:** 10:1 **Exams:** Other; SAT I or ACT. **Regional Accreditation:** Middle States Association of Colleges and Schools **Credit Hours For Degree:** 60 semester hours, Associates **Professional Accreditation:** AAMAE.

BRYANT & STRATTON COLLEGE–HENRIETTA CAMPUS

1225 Jefferson Rd.
Rochester, NY 14623
Tel: (585)292-5627
Fax: (585)292-6015
E-mail: djprofita@bryantstratton.edu
Web Site: www.bryantstratton.edu
President/CEO: Jeffery Moore
Admissions: David Profita

Type: Two-Year College **Sex:** Coed **Affiliation:** Bryant and Stratton College, Inc. **% Accepted:** 78 **Admission Plans:** Deferred Admission **Application Deadline:** Rolling **H.S. Requirements:** High school diploma required; GED accepted. For applicants 19 or over who meet entrance testing requirements: High school diploma required; GED not accepted **Scholarships:** Available. **Calendar System:** Semester, Summer session available **Enrollment:** Full-time 288, Part-time 119 **Faculty:** Full-time 17, Part-time 47 **Student-Faculty Ratio:** 10:1 **Exams:** Other; SAT I or ACT. **Regional Accreditation:** Middle States Association of Colleges and Schools **Credit Hours For Degree:** 60 semester hours, Associates **Professional Accreditation:** AAMAE.

BRYANT & STRATTON COLLEGE–LIVERPOOL CAMPUS

8687 Carling Rd.
Liverpool, NY 13090
Tel: (315)652-6500
Web Site: www.bryantstratton.edu
President/CEO: Susan Cumoletti
Admissions: Heather Macnik

Type: Two-Year College **Sex:** Coed **Affiliation:** Bryant and Stratton Business Institute, Inc. **Admission Plans:** Deferred Admission; Open Admission **Application Deadline:** Rolling **Application Fee:** $25.00 **H.S. Requirements:** High school diploma required; GED accepted. For applicants 19 or over who meet entrance testing requirements: High school diploma required; GED not accepted **Scholarships:** Available. **Calendar System:** Semester, Summer session available **Enrollment:** Full-time 333, Part-time 164 **Faculty:** Full-time 16, Part-time 41 **Student-Faculty Ratio:** 9:1 **Exams:** Other. **Regional Accreditation:** Middle States Association of Colleges and Schools **Credit Hours For Degree:** 64 semester hours, Associates

BRYANT & STRATTON COLLEGE–ORCHARD PARK CAMPUS

200 Redtail Rd.
Orchard Park, NY 14127
Tel: (716)677-9500
E-mail: tdominiak@bryantstratton.edu
Web Site: www.bryantstratton.edu
President/CEO: Paul C. Bahr
Admissions: Tracy Dominiak

Type: Two-Year College **Sex:** Coed **Admission Plans:** Early Admission **Application Deadline:** Rolling **H.S. Requirements:** High school diploma or equivalent not required **Scholarships:** Available. **Calendar System:** Trimester, Summer session available **Enrollment:** Full-time 663, Part-time 543 **Faculty:** Full-time 23, Part-time 52 **Exams:** Other; SAT I or ACT. **Regional Accreditation:** Middle States Association of Colleges and Schools **Credit Hours For Degree:** 60 credits, Associates; 120 credits, Bachelors

BRYANT & STRATTON COLLEGE–SYRACUSE CAMPUS

953 James St.
Syracuse, NY 13203-2502
Tel: (315)472-6603
Fax: (315)474-4383
Web Site: www.bryantstratton.edu
President/CEO: Michael Sattler
Admissions: Dawn Rajkowski

Type: Two-Year College **Sex:** Coed **Affiliation:** Bryant and Stratton Business Institute, Inc. **% Accepted:** 94 **Application Deadline:** Rolling **H.S. Requirements:** High school diploma required; GED accepted. For applicants 19 or over who meet entrance testing requirements: High school diploma required; GED not accepted **Scholarships:** Available. **Calendar System:** Semester, Summer session available **Enrollment:** Full-time 494, Part-time 221 **Faculty:** Full-time 21, Part-time 34 **Student-Faculty Ratio:** 13:1 **Exams:** Other; SAT I or ACT. **% Residing in College-Owned, -Operated, or -Affiliated Housing:** 12 **Regional Accreditation:** Middle States Association of Colleges and Schools **Credit Hours For Degree:** 60 semester hours, Associates **Professional Accreditation:** AAMAE. **Intercollegiate Athletics:** Soccer M & W

BUFFALO STATE COLLEGE, STATE UNIVERSITY OF NEW YORK

1300 Elmwood Ave.
Buffalo, NY 14222-1095
Tel: (716)878-4000
Fax: (716)878-6100
E-mail: admissions@buffalostate.edu
Web Site: www.buffalostate.edu
President/CEO: Katherine Conway-Turner
Admissions: Carmella Thompson
Financial Aid: Connie F. Cooke

Type: Comprehensive **Sex:** Coed **Affiliation:** State University of New York System. **Scores:** 96% SAT V 400+; 96% SAT M 400+ **% Accepted:** 62 **Admission Plans:** Deferred Admission; Early Admission **Application Deadline:** Rolling **Application Fee:** $50.00 **H.S. Requirements:** High school diploma required; GED accepted **Costs Per Year:** Application fee: $50. State resident tuition: $6470 full-time, $270 per credit hour part-time. Nonresident tuition: $16,320 full-time, $680 per credit hour part-time. Mandatory fees: $1199 full-time. Part-time tuition varies according to course load. College room and board: $12,332. College room only: $7342. Room and board charges vary according to board plan, housing facility, and student level. **Scholarships:** Available. **Calendar System:** Semester, Summer session available **Enrollment:** Full-time 8,137, Graduate full-time 442, Graduate part-time 701, Part-time 1,050 **Faculty:** Full-time 381, Part-time 466 **Exams:** ACT essay component not used; SAT I; SAT I and SAT II or ACT; SAT I or ACT; SAT essay component used for advising; SAT essay component used for placement. **% Receiving Financial Aid:** 65 **% Residing in College-Owned, -Operated, or -Affiliated Housing:** 34 **Regional Accreditation:** Middle States Association of Colleges and Schools **Credit Hours For Degree:** 123 semester hours, Bachelors **ROTC:** Army **Professional Accreditation:** ABET, AND, ASHA, CIDA, CSWE, NASAD, NASM, NCATE. **Intercollegiate Athletics:** Baseball M; Basketball M & W; Bowling M & W; Cheerleading W; Cross-Country Running M & W; Fencing M; Football M; Ice Hockey M & W; Lacrosse M & W; Rugby M & W; Skiing (Cross-Country) M & W; Skiing (Downhill) M & W; Soccer M & W; Softball W; Swimming and Diving M & W; Tennis W; Track and Field M & W; Volleyball M & W

CANISIUS COLLEGE

2001 Main St.
Buffalo, NY 14208-1098
Tel: (716)883-7000; Free: 800-843-1517
Fax: (716)888-2377
E-mail: admissions@canisius.edu
Web Site: www.canisius.edu
President/CEO: John J. Hurley
Admissions: Justin P. Rogers
Financial Aid: Mary Koehneke

Type: Comprehensive **Sex:** Coed **Affiliation:** Roman Catholic (Jesuit). **Scores:** 96% SAT V 400+; 97% SAT M 400+; 38.97% ACT 18-23; 46.21% ACT 24-29 **% Accepted:** 87 **Admission Plans:** Deferred Admission; Early Admission **Application Deadline:** May 1 **Application Fee:** $40.00 **H.S. Requirements:** High school diploma required; GED accepted **Costs Per Year:** Application fee: $40. Comprehensive fee: $47,456 includes full-time tuition ($33,282), mandatory fees ($1408), and college room and board ($12,766). College room only: $7500. Room and board charges vary according to board plan and housing facility. Part-time tuition: $950 per credit hour. **Scholarships:** Available. **Calendar System:** Semester, Summer session available **Enrollment:** Full-time 2,538, Graduate full-time 500, Graduate part-time 733, Part-time 133 **Faculty:** Full-time 189, Part-time 242 **Student-Faculty Ratio:** 11:1 **Exams:** ACT essay component used for advising; SAT I or ACT; SAT essay component used for advising; SAT essay component used in place of application essay; SAT Reasoning. **% Receiving Financial Aid:** 77 **% Residing in College-Owned, -Operated, or -Affiliated Housing:** 54 **Final Year or Final Semester Residency Requirement:** No **Regional Accreditation:** Middle States Association of Colleges and Schools

Credit Hours For Degree: 120 credit hours, Bachelors **ROTC:** Army **Professional Accreditation:** AACSB, ACA, JRCAT, NCATE. **Intercollegiate Athletics:** Baseball M; Basketball M & W; Cross-Country Running M & W; Equestrian Sports W; Golf M; Ice Hockey M; Lacrosse M & W; Rugby M & W; Soccer M & W; Softball W; Swimming and Diving M & W; Volleyball M & W

CAYUGA COUNTY COMMUNITY COLLEGE

197 Franklin St.
Auburn, NY 13021-3099
Tel: (315)255-1743; Free: 866-598-8883
Web Site: www.cayuga-cc.edu
President/CEO: Dr. Brian Durant
Admissions: Bruce M. Blodgett

Type: Two-Year College **Sex:** Coed **Affiliation:** State University of New York System. **% Accepted:** 77 **Admission Plans:** Deferred Admission; Open Admission **Application Deadline:** Rolling **Application Fee:** $0.00 **H.S. Requirements:** High school diploma required; GED accepted **Costs Per Year:** Application fee: $0. State resident tuition: $4326 full-time, $178 per credit hour part-time. Nonresident tuition: $8652 full-time, $356 per credit hour part-time. Mandatory fees: $396 full-time. Full-time tuition and fees vary according to course load. Part-time tuition varies according to course load. **Scholarships:** Available. **Calendar System:** Semester, Summer session available **Enrollment:** Full-time 1,814, Part-time 2,616 **Faculty:** Full-time 50, Part-time 179 **Student-Faculty Ratio:** 20:1 **Exams:** SAT I or ACT. **Final Year or Final Semester Residency Requirement:** No **Regional Accreditation:** Middle States Association of Colleges and Schools **Credit Hours For Degree:** 60 credit hours, Associates **ROTC:** Air Force **Professional Accreditation:** ACEN. **Intercollegiate Athletics:** Basketball M & W; Bowling M & W; Golf M & W; Soccer M & W; Softball W; Volleyball W

CAZENOVIA COLLEGE

22 Sullivan St.
Cazenovia, NY 13035-1084
Tel: (315)655-7000; Free: 800-654-3210
Fax: (315)655-2190
E-mail: admission@cazenovia.edu
Web Site: www.cazenovia.edu
President/CEO: Pres. Mark J. Tierno
Financial Aid: Christine L. Mandel

Type: Four-Year College **Sex:** Coed **Scores:** 86% SAT V 400+; 81% SAT M 400+ **% Accepted:** 76 **Admission Plans:** Deferred Admission **Application Fee:** $30.00 **H.S. Requirements:** High school diploma required; GED accepted **Costs Per Year:** Application fee: $30. Comprehensive fee: $45,162 includes full-time tuition ($31,200), mandatory fees ($554), and college room and board ($13,408). College room only: $7190. Full-time tuition and fees vary according to class time, course load, and program. Room and board charges vary according to board plan and housing facility. Part-time tuition: $660 per credit. Part-time tuition varies according to class time and course load. **Scholarships:** Available. **Calendar System:** Semester, Summer session available **Enrollment:** Full-time 963, Part-time 128 **Faculty:** Full-time 57, Part-time 72 **Student-Faculty Ratio:** 12:1 **Exams:** ACT essay component used for advising; ACT essay component used for placement; SAT I or ACT; SAT essay component used for advising; SAT essay component used for placement; SAT Reasoning; SAT Subject. **% Receiving Financial Aid:** 91 **% Residing in College-Owned, -Operated, or -Affiliated Housing:** 94 **Final Year or Final Semester Residency Requirement:** No **Regional Accreditation:** Middle States Association of Colleges and Schools **Credit Hours For Degree:** 60 credits, Associates; 120 credits, Bachelors **ROTC:** Air Force, Army **Intercollegiate Athletics:** Baseball M; Basketball M & W; Cheerleading M & W; Crew M & W; Cross-Country Running M & W; Equestrian Sports M & W; Golf M; Lacrosse M & W; Soccer M & W; Softball W; Swimming and Diving M & W; Tennis M & W; Volleyball M & W

CENTRAL YESHIVA TOMCHEI TMIMIM-LUBAVITCH

841-853 Ocean Pky.
Brooklyn, NY 11230
Tel: (718)434-0784
President/CEO: Abraham Rosenfeld
Financial Aid: Rabbi Moshe M. Gluckowsky

Type: Comprehensive **Sex:** Men **Affiliation:** Jewish. **% Accepted:** 100 **H.S. Requirements:** High school diploma required; GED accepted **Calendar System:** Semester **Professional Accreditation:** AARTS.

CITY COLLEGE OF THE CITY UNIVERSITY OF NEW YORK

160 Convent Ave.
New York, NY 10031-9198
Tel: (212)650-7000
Fax: (212)650-6417
E-mail: admissions@ccny.cuny.edu
Web Site: www.ccny.cuny.edu
President/CEO: Pres. Lisa S. Coico
Admissions: Joseph Fantozzi
Financial Aid: Thelma Mason
Type: Comprehensive **Sex:** Coed **Affiliation:** City University of New York System. **Scores:** 94% SAT V 400+; 99% SAT M 400+ **% Accepted:** 40 **Admission Plans:** Deferred Admission; Early Admission **Application Deadline:** February 1 **Application Fee:** $65.00 **H.S. Requirements:** High school diploma required; GED accepted **Costs Per Year:** Application fee: $65. State resident tuition: $6330 full-time, $275 per credit hour part-time. Nonresident tuition: $16,800 full-time, $560 per credit hour part-time. Mandatory fees: $410 full-time, $119 per term part-time. Full-time tuition and fees vary according to course load and program. Part-time tuition and fees vary according to course load and program. **Scholarships:** Available. **Calendar System:** Semester, Summer session available **Enrollment:** Full-time 9,818, Graduate full-time 375, Graduate part-time 2,216, Part-time 3,618 **Faculty:** Full-time 563, Part-time 1,062 **Student-Faculty Ratio:** 12:1 **Exams:** SAT I or ACT. **% Receiving Financial Aid:** 87 **% Residing in College-Owned, -Operated, or -Affiliated Housing:** 1 **Regional Accreditation:** Middle States Association of Colleges and Schools **Credit Hours For Degree:** 120 credits, Bachelors **ROTC:** Army **Professional Accreditation:** ABET, APA, ASLA, NAAB, NCATE. **Intercollegiate Athletics:** Baseball M; Basketball M & W; Cross-Country Running M & W; Fencing W; Lacrosse M; Soccer M & W; Softball W; Tennis M & W; Track and Field M & W; Volleyball W

CLARKSON UNIVERSITY

Potsdam, NY 13699
Tel: (315)268-6400; Free: 800-527-6577
Fax: (315)268-7647
E-mail: admission@clarkson.edu
Web Site: www.clarkson.edu
President/CEO: Dr. Anthony G. Collins
Admissions: Brian T. Grant
Financial Aid: Pamela A. Nichols
Type: University **Sex:** Coed **Scores:** 98% SAT V 400+; 100% SAT M 400+; 21% ACT 18-23; 51% ACT 24-29 **% Accepted:** 68 **Admission Plans:** Deferred Admission; Early Action; Early Admission **Application Deadline:** January 15 **Application Fee:** $50.00 **H.S. Requirements:** High school diploma required; GED accepted **Costs Per Year:** Application fee: $50. Comprehensive fee: $60,392 includes full-time tuition ($45,132), mandatory fees ($1000), and college room and board ($14,260). College room only: $7554. Full-time tuition and fees vary according to course load. Room and board charges vary according to board plan and housing facility. Part-time tuition: $1505 per credit hour. Part-time tuition varies according to course load. **Scholarships:** Available. **Calendar System:** Semester, Summer session available **Enrollment:** Full-time 3,185, Graduate full-time 448, Graduate part-time 205, Part-time 72 **Faculty:** Full-time 229, Part-time 80 **Student-Faculty Ratio:** 15:1 **Exams:** SAT I or ACT; SAT II; SAT essay component used for admission; SAT Reasoning; SAT Subject. **% Receiving Financial Aid:** 82 **% Residing in College-Owned, -Operated, or -Affiliated Housing:** 84 **Final Year or Final Semester Residency Requirement:** No **Regional Accreditation:** Middle States Association of Colleges and Schools **Credit Hours For Degree:** 120 credit hours, Bachelors **ROTC:** Air Force, Army **Professional Accreditation:** AACSB, ABET, APTA. **Intercollegiate Athletics:** Baseball M; Basketball M & W; Cross-Country Running M & W; Golf M; Ice Hockey M & W; Lacrosse M & W; Skiing (Cross-Country) M & W; Skiing (Downhill) M & W; Soccer M & W; Softball W; Swimming and Diving M & W; Volleyball W

CLINTON COMMUNITY COLLEGE

136 Clinton Point Dr.
Plattsburgh, NY 12901-9573
Tel: (518)562-4200; Free: 800-552-1160
Fax: (518)562-8621
E-mail: Lauren.Currie@clinton.edu
Web Site: www.clinton.edu
President/CEO: Fred Smith
Admissions: Lauren Currie
Type: Two-Year College **Sex:** Coed **Affiliation:** State University of New York System. **% Accepted:** 30 **Admission Plans:** Deferred Admission; Open Admission; Preferred Admission **Application Deadline:** August 26 **Application Fee:** $0.00 **H.S. Requirements:** High school diploma required; GED accepted **Costs Per Year:** Application fee: $0. State resident tuition: $4300 full-time, $179 per credit hour part-time. Nonresident tuition: $9300 full-time, $383 per credit hour part-time. Mandatory fees: $998 full-time, $33. Full-time tuition and fees vary according to course load and program. Part-time tuition and fees vary according to course load and program. College room and board: $9310. College room only: $5170. Room and board charges vary according to board plan. **Scholarships:** Available. **Calendar System:** Semester, Summer session available **Enrollment:** Full-time 864, Part-time 381 **Faculty:** Full-time 61, Part-time 50 **Student-Faculty Ratio:** 11:1 **% Residing in College-Owned, -Operated, or -Affiliated Housing:** 10 **Final Year or Final Semester Residency Requirement:** No **Regional Accreditation:** Middle States Association of Colleges and Schools **Credit Hours For Degree:** 60 credits, Associates **Professional Accreditation:** ACEN, NAACLS. **Intercollegiate Athletics:** Baseball M; Basketball M & W; Soccer M & W

COCHRAN SCHOOL OF NURSING

967 N Broadway
Yonkers, NY 10701
Tel: (914)964-4283
E-mail: dthompson@riversidehealth.org
Web Site: www.cochranschoolofnursing.us
President/CEO: Dr. AnnMarie McAllister
Admissions: Drew Thompson
Type: Two-Year College **Sex:** Coed **Affiliation:** Mercy College. **Admission Plans:** Deferred Admission **Application Deadline:** April 15 **Application Fee:** $35.00 **H.S. Requirements:** High school diploma required; GED accepted **Costs Per Year:** Application fee: $35. Tuition: $9571 full-time, $563 per credit part-time. Mandatory fees: $1486 full-time, $734 per term part-time. Full-time tuition and fees vary according to course load and student level. Part-time tuition and fees vary according to course load and student level. **Scholarships:** Available. **Calendar System:** Semester, Summer session not available **Enrollment:** Full-time 12, Part-time 77 **Faculty:** Full-time 9, Part-time 2 **Student-Faculty Ratio:** 10:1 **Credit Hours For Degree:** 70.5 credits, Associates **Professional Accreditation:** ACEN.

COLGATE UNIVERSITY

13 Oak Dr.
Hamilton, NY 13346-1386
Tel: (315)228-1000
Fax: (315)228-7798
E-mail: admission@colgate.edu
Web Site: www.colgate.edu
President/CEO: Pres. Jill Harsin
Admissions: Gary L. Ross
Type: Comprehensive **Sex:** Coed **Scores:** 100% SAT V 400+; 100% SAT M 400+; 2% ACT 18-23; 23% ACT 24-29 **% Accepted:** 27 **Admission Plans:** Deferred Admission; Early Action **Application Deadline:** January 15 **Application Fee:** $60.00 **H.S. Requirements:** High school diploma required; GED accepted **Costs Per Year:** Application fee: $60. One-time mandatory fee: $50. Comprehensive fee: $62,540 includes full-time tuition ($49,650), mandatory fees ($320), and college room and board ($12,570). College room only: $6065. Full-time tuition and fees vary according to course load. Room and board charges vary according to board plan and housing facility. Part-time tuition: $6,206.25 per course. Part-time tuition varies according to course load. **Scholarships:** Available. **Calendar System:** Semester, Summer session not available **Enrollment:** Full-time 2,834, Graduate full-time 3, Graduate part-time 5, Part-time 19 **Faculty:** Full-time 295, Part-time 57 **Student-Faculty Ratio:** 9:1 **Exams:** ACT essay component not used; SAT I or ACT; SAT essay component not used; SAT Reasoning; SAT Subject. **% Receiving Financial Aid:** 38 **% Residing in College-Owned, -Operated, or -Affiliated Housing:** 96 **Final Year or Final Semester Residency Requirement:** No **Regional Accreditation:** Middle States Association of Colleges and Schools **Credit Hours For Degree:** 32 courses, Bachelors **ROTC:** Army **Professional Accreditation:** TEAC. **Intercollegiate Athletics:** Badminton M & W; Baseball M; Basketball M & W; Cheerleading M & W; Crew M & W; Cross-Country Running M & W; Equestrian Sports M & W; Fencing M & W; Field Hockey W; Football M; Golf M & W; Ice Hockey M & W; Lacrosse M & W; Rugby M & W; Sailing M & W; Skiing (Downhill) M & W;

Soccer M & W; Softball W; Squash M & W; Swimming and Diving M & W; Table Tennis M & W; Tennis M & W; Track and Field M & W; Volleyball M & W; Water Polo M & W

THE COLLEGE AT BROCKPORT, STATE UNIVERSITY OF NEW YORK

350 New Campus Dr.
Brockport, NY 14420-2997
Tel: (585)395-2211
Fax: (585)395-5452
E-mail: rlangsto@brockport.edu
Web Site: www.brockport.edu
President/CEO: Dr. Heidi Macpherson
Admissions: Randall J. Langston
Financial Aid: J. Scott Atkinson

Type: Comprehensive **Sex:** Coed **Affiliation:** State University of New York System. **Scores:** 97% SAT V 400+; 98% SAT M 400+; 53.4% ACT 18-23; 39.5% ACT 24-29 **% Accepted:** 53 **Admission Plans:** Deferred Admission; Preferred Admission **Application Deadline:** Rolling **Application Fee:** $50.00 **H.S. Requirements:** High school diploma required; GED accepted **Costs Per Year:** Application fee: $50. State resident tuition: $6470 full-time, $270 per credit part-time. Nonresident tuition: $15,820 full-time, $680 per credit part-time. Mandatory fees: $1434 full-time. Part-time tuition varies according to course load. College room and board: $11,540. College room only: $7180. Room and board charges vary according to board plan and housing facility. **Scholarships:** Available. **Calendar System:** Semester, Summer session available **Enrollment:** Full-time 6,353, Graduate full-time 373, Graduate part-time 719, Part-time 716 **Faculty:** Full-time 335, Part-time 284 **Student-Faculty Ratio:** 16:1 **Exams:** ACT essay component not used; SAT I or ACT; SAT essay component not used; SAT Reasoning. **% Receiving Financial Aid:** 71 **% Residing in College-Owned, -Operated, or -Affiliated Housing:** 28 **Final Year or Final Semester Residency Requirement:** No **Regional Accreditation:** Middle States Association of Colleges and Schools **Credit Hours For Degree:** 120 credit hours, Bachelors **ROTC:** Air Force, Army, Navy **Professional Accreditation:** AACN, AACSB, ABET, ACA, CSWE, JRCAT, NASD, NASPAA, NCATE, NRPA. **Intercollegiate Athletics:** Baseball M; Basketball M & W; Cross-Country Running M & W; Field Hockey W; Football M; Gymnastics W; Ice Hockey M; Lacrosse M & W; Soccer M & W; Softball W; Swimming and Diving M & W; Tennis W; Track and Field M & W; Volleyball W; Wrestling M

COLLEGE OF MOUNT SAINT VINCENT

6301 Riverdale Ave.
Riverdale, NY 10471-1093
Tel: (718)405-3200; Free: 800-665-CMSV
Fax: (718)549-7945
E-mail: jackie.williams@mountsaintvincent.edu
Web Site: www.mountsaintvincent.edu
President/CEO: Charles L. Flynn, Jr.
Admissions: Jackie Williams
Financial Aid: Emmett Cooper

Type: Comprehensive **Sex:** Coed **Scores:** 88% SAT V 400+; 83% SAT M 400+; 54.5% ACT 18-23; 20.5% ACT 24-29 **% Accepted:** 91 **Admission Plans:** Deferred Admission; Early Admission; Early Decision Plan **Application Fee:** $35.00 **H.S. Requirements:** High school diploma required; GED accepted **Costs Per Year:** Application fee: $35. Comprehensive fee: $43,770 includes full-time tuition ($34,250), mandatory fees ($800), and college room and board ($8720). **Scholarships:** Available. **Calendar System:** Semester, Summer session available **Enrollment:** Full-time 1,489, Graduate full-time 50, Graduate part-time 219, Part-time 160 **Faculty:** Full-time 80 **Student-Faculty Ratio:** 12:1 **Exams:** ACT essay component used for advising; ACT essay component used for placement; SAT I or ACT; SAT essay component used for advising; SAT essay component used for placement. **% Receiving Financial Aid:** 87 **% Residing in College-Owned, -Operated, or -Affiliated Housing:** 48 **Final Year or Final Semester Residency Requirement:** No **Regional Accreditation:** Middle States Association of Colleges and Schools **Credit Hours For Degree:** 62 credits, Associates; 120 credits, Bachelors **ROTC:** Air Force **Professional Accreditation:** AACN, ACBSP, TEAC. **Intercollegiate Athletics:** Baseball M; Basketball M & W; Cheerleading W; Cross-Country Running M & W; Lacrosse M & W; Soccer M & W; Softball W; Swimming and Diving M & W; Tennis M & W; Track and Field M & W; Volleyball M & W; Wrestling M

THE COLLEGE OF NEW ROCHELLE

29 Castle Pl.
New Rochelle, NY 10805-2308

Tel: (914)654-5000; Free: 800-933-5923
Fax: (914)654-5554
E-mail: mdipiazza@cnr.edu
Web Site: www.cnr.edu
President/CEO: Judith A. Huntington
Admissions: Michael DiPiazza
Financial Aid: Anne Pelak

Type: Comprehensive **Sex:** Coed **Scores:** 96% SAT V 400+; 91% SAT M 400+; 75% ACT 18-23; 25% ACT 24-29 **% Accepted:** 32 **Admission Plans:** Deferred Admission; Early Action; Early Admission **Application Deadline:** Rolling **Application Fee:** $35.00 **H.S. Requirements:** High school diploma required; GED accepted **Costs Per Year:** Application fee: $35. Comprehensive fee: $46,300 includes full-time tuition ($32,450), mandatory fees ($1150), and college room and board ($12,700). Full-time tuition and fees vary according to course load, location, and program. Room and board charges vary according to housing facility. Part-time tuition: $1082 per credit. Part-time mandatory fees: $350 per term. Part-time tuition and fees vary according to course load, location, and program. **Scholarships:** Available. **Calendar System:** Semester, Summer session available **Enrollment:** Full-time 649, Graduate full-time 105, Graduate part-time 510, Part-time 287 **Faculty:** Full-time 70, Part-time 114 **Student-Faculty Ratio:** 10:1 **Exams:** SAT I or ACT. **% Receiving Financial Aid:** 95 **% Residing in College-Owned, -Operated, or -Affiliated Housing:** 33 **Regional Accreditation:** Middle States Association of Colleges and Schools **Credit Hours For Degree:** 120 credits, Bachelors **Professional Accreditation:** AACN, CSWE. **Intercollegiate Athletics:** Basketball W; Cross-Country Running W; Softball W; Swimming and Diving W; Tennis W; Volleyball W

THE COLLEGE OF SAINT ROSE

432 Western Ave.
Albany, NY 12203-1419
Tel: (518)454-5111; Free: 800-637-8556
Fax: (518)451-2013
E-mail: admit@strose.edu
Web Site: www.strose.edu
President/CEO: Dr. Carolyn Stefanco
Admissions: Kathleen Lesko
Financial Aid: Steven Dwire

Type: Comprehensive **Sex:** Coed **Scores:** 98% SAT V 400+; 98% SAT M 400+; 58.89% ACT 18-23; 33.33% ACT 24-29 **% Accepted:** 82 **Admission Plans:** Deferred Admission; Early Admission; Early Decision Plan **Application Deadline:** May 1 **H.S. Requirements:** High school diploma required; GED accepted **Costs Per Year:** Comprehensive fee: $41,704 includes full-time tuition ($28,820), mandatory fees ($1006), and college room and board ($11,878). College room only: $5974. Full-time tuition and fees vary according to class time and course load. Room and board charges vary according to board plan and housing facility. Part-time tuition: $958 per credit hour. Part-time mandatory fees: $32 per credit hour. Part-time tuition and fees vary according to class time and course load. **Scholarships:** Available. **Calendar System:** Semester, Summer session available **Enrollment:** Full-time 2,540, Graduate full-time 645, Graduate part-time 1,073, Part-time 153 **Faculty:** Full-time 204, Part-time 150 **Student-Faculty Ratio:** 14:1 **Exams:** ACT; ACT essay component not used; SAT I; SAT I and SAT II or ACT; SAT I or ACT; SAT II; SAT essay component not used; SAT Reasoning. **% Receiving Financial Aid:** 83 **% Residing in College-Owned, -Operated, or -Affiliated Housing:** 48 **Final Year or Final Semester Residency Requirement:** No **Regional Accreditation:** Middle States Association of Colleges and Schools **Credit Hours For Degree:** 122 credit hours, Bachelors **ROTC:** Air Force, Army, Navy **Professional Accreditation:** ACBSP, ASHA, CSWE, NASAD, NASM, NCATE. **Intercollegiate Athletics:** Baseball M; Basketball M & W; Cross-Country Running M & W; Golf M & W; Lacrosse M; Soccer M & W; Softball W; Swimming and Diving M & W; Tennis W; Track and Field M & W; Volleyball W

COLLEGE OF STATEN ISLAND OF THE CITY UNIVERSITY OF NEW YORK

2800 Victory Blvd.
Staten Island, NY 10314-6600
Tel: (718)982-2000
Fax: (718)982-2500
E-mail: admissions@csi.cuny.edu
Web Site: www.csi.cuny.edu
President/CEO: Dr. William J. Fritz
Financial Aid: Dr. Philippe Marius

Type: Comprehensive **Sex:** Coed **Affiliation:** City University of New York System. **Scores:** 91% SAT V 400+; 97% SAT M 400+ **Costs Per Year:** State resident tuition: $6330 full-time, $275 per credit hour part-time. Nonresident tuition: $16,800 full-time, $560 per credit hour part-time. Mandatory fees: $479 full-time, $141.10 per term part-time. College room only: $13,332. Room charges vary according to housing facility. **Scholarships:** Available. **Calendar System:** Semester, Summer session available **Enrollment:** Full-time 9,693, Graduate full-time 200, Graduate part-time 769, Part-time 3,113 **Faculty:** Full-time 364, Part-time 866 **Student-Faculty Ratio:** 16:1 **Exams:** ACT essay component not used; SAT I or ACT; SAT essay component not used. **% Receiving Financial Aid:** 67 **% Residing in College-Owned, -Operated, or -Affiliated Housing:** 3 **Final Year or Final Semester Residency Requirement:** No **Regional Accreditation:** Middle States Association of Colleges and Schools **Credit Hours For Degree:** 60 credits, Associates; 120 credits, Bachelors **Professional Accreditation:** ABET, ACEN, APTA, NCATE. **Intercollegiate Athletics:** Baseball M; Basketball M & W; Cheerleading M & W; Cross-Country Running M & W; Soccer M & W; Softball W; Swimming and Diving M & W; Tennis M & W; Track and Field M & W; Volleyball M & W

THE COLLEGE OF WESTCHESTER

325 Central Ave.
White Plains, NY 10606
Tel: (914)559-2398; Free: 855-403-7722
E-mail: admissions@cw.edu
Web Site: www.cw.edu
President/CEO: Mary Beth Del Balzo
Admissions: Matt Curtis

Type: Two-Year College **Sex:** Coed **% Accepted:** 92 **Admission Plans:** Deferred Admission **Application Deadline:** Rolling **Application Fee:** $40.00 **H.S. Requirements:** High school diploma required; GED accepted **Costs Per Year:** Application fee: $40. Tuition: $20,115 full-time, $745 per credit part-time. Mandatory fees: $900 full-time. **Scholarships:** Available. **Calendar System:** Semester, Summer session available **Enrollment:** Full-time 847, Part-time 220 **Faculty:** Full-time 35, Part-time 45 **Student-Faculty Ratio:** 18:1 **Exams:** SAT I. **Regional Accreditation:** Middle States Association of Colleges and Schools **Credit Hours For Degree:** 66 credits, Associates; 120 credits, Bachelors

COLUMBIA-GREENE COMMUNITY COLLEGE

4400 Rte. 23
Hudson, NY 12534-0327
Tel: (518)828-4181
Fax: (518)828-8543
E-mail: rachel.kappel@sunycgcc.edu
Web Site: www.sunycgcc.edu
President/CEO: James R. Campion
Admissions: Rachel Kappel

Type: Two-Year College **Sex:** Coed **Affiliation:** State University of New York System. **Costs Per Year:** State resident tuition: $4200 full-time, $175 per semester hour part-time. Nonresident tuition: $8400 full-time, $350 per semester hour part-time. Mandatory fees: $352 full-time, $15 per semester hour part-time, $5 per term part-time. Full-time tuition and fees vary according to course load and program. Part-time tuition and fees vary according to course load and program. **Scholarships:** Available. **Calendar System:** Semester, Summer session available **Enrollment:** Full-time 710, Part-time 1,067 **Faculty:** Full-time 45, Part-time 53 **Student-Faculty Ratio:** 17:1 **Regional Accreditation:** Middle States Association of Colleges and Schools **Credit Hours For Degree:** 62 credits, Associates **Professional Accreditation:** ACEN. **Intercollegiate Athletics:** Baseball M & W; Basketball M; Cross-Country Running M & W; Golf M & W; Softball W; Track and Field M & W; Volleyball W

COLUMBIA UNIVERSITY

116th St. and Broadway
New York, NY 10027
Tel: (212)854-1754
Web Site: www.columbia.edu
President/CEO: Lee Bollinger
Admissions: Jessica Marinaccio
Financial Aid: Kathryn Tuman

Type: University **Sex:** Coed **Scores:** 100% SAT V 400+; 100% SAT M 400+; 7% ACT 24-29 **% Accepted:** 6 **Admission Plans:** Deferred Admission; Early Action; Early Admission **Application Deadline:** January 1 **Application**

Fee: $85.00 **H.S. Requirements:** High school diploma required; GED accepted **Costs Per Year:** Application fee: $85. Comprehensive fee: $65,860 includes full-time tuition ($50,526), mandatory fees ($2474), and college room and board ($12,860). Room and board charges vary according to board plan and housing facility. **Scholarships:** Available. **Calendar System:** Semester, Summer session available **Enrollment:** Full-time 6,102 **Student-Faculty Ratio:** 6:1 **Exams:** SAT I or ACT; SAT Reasoning; SAT Subject. **% Receiving Financial Aid:** 49 **% Residing in College-Owned, -Operated, or -Affiliated Housing:** 94 **Regional Accreditation:** Middle States Association of Colleges and Schools **Credit Hours For Degree:** 124 for CC; 128 for SEAS, Bachelors **ROTC:** Air Force, Army, Navy **Professional Accreditation:** AACN, AACSB, AALS, AANA, ABA, ABET, ACEJMC, ACEN, ACNM, ACSP, ADA, AOTA, APTA, CAHME, CEPH, CSWE, LCME/AMA, NAAB, NASPAA. **Intercollegiate Athletics:** Archery M & W; Badminton M & W; Baseball M; Basketball M & W; Crew M & W; Cross-Country Running M & W; Fencing M & W; Field Hockey W; Football M; Golf M; Ice Hockey W; Lacrosse M & W; Racquetball M & W; Rugby M & W; Skiing (Cross-Country) M & W; Skiing (Downhill) M & W; Soccer M & W; Softball W; Squash M & W; Swimming and Diving M & W; Table Tennis M & W; Tennis M & W; Track and Field M & W; Ultimate Frisbee M & W; Volleyball M & W; Water Polo M & W; Wrestling M

COLUMBIA UNIVERSITY, SCHOOL OF GENERAL STUDIES

2970 Broadway
408 Lewisohn Hall, MC 4101
New York, NY 10027-6939
Tel: (212)854-2772; Free: 800-895-1169
E-mail: gsdegree@columbia.edu
Web Site: www.gs.columbia.edu
President/CEO: Lee C. Bollinger
Admissions: Curtis M. Rodgers
Financial Aid: William Skip Bailey

Type: Four-Year College **Sex:** Coed **Affiliation:** Columbia University. **Scores:** 100% SAT V 400+; 100% SAT M 400+; 4% ACT 18-23; 23% ACT 24-29 **% Accepted:** 33 **Admission Plans:** Deferred Admission; Early Decision Plan **Application Deadline:** June 1 **Application Fee:** $80.00 **H.S. Requirements:** High school diploma required; GED accepted **Costs Per Year:** Application fee: $80. One-time mandatory fee: $105. Comprehensive fee: $61,470 includes full-time tuition ($48,900), mandatory fees ($2214), and college room and board ($10,356). College room only: $8080. Full-time tuition and fees vary according to course load and program. Room and board charges vary according to board plan and housing facility. Part-time tuition: $1630 per credit hour. Part-time tuition varies according to course load and program. **Scholarships:** Available. **Calendar System:** Semester, Summer session available **Enrollment:** Full-time 1,535, Part-time 470 **Exams:** SAT I or ACT; SAT essay component used for admission; SAT essay component used for advising; SAT essay component used for placement; SAT Reasoning; SAT Subject. **% Receiving Financial Aid:** 81 **% Residing in College-Owned, -Operated, or -Affiliated Housing:** 29 **Final Year or Final Semester Residency Requirement:** Yes **Regional Accreditation:** Middle States Association of Colleges and Schools **Credit Hours For Degree:** 124 credits, Bachelors **ROTC:** Air Force, Army, Navy **Intercollegiate Athletics:** Archery M & W; Badminton M & W; Baseball M; Basketball M & W; Crew M & W; Cross-Country Running M & W; Equestrian Sports M & W; Fencing M & W; Field Hockey W; Football M; Golf M & W; Ice Hockey M & W; Lacrosse M & W; Racquetball M & W; Rugby M & W; Sailing M & W; Skiing (Downhill) M & W; Soccer M & W; Softball W; Squash M & W; Swimming and Diving M & W; Table Tennis M & W; Tennis M & W; Track and Field M & W; Ultimate Frisbee M & W; Volleyball W; Water Polo M & W; Wrestling M

CONCORDIA COLLEGE–NEW YORK

171 White Plains Rd.
Bronxville, NY 10708-1998
Tel: (914)337-9300; Free: 800-YES-COLLEGE
Fax: (914)395-4500
E-mail: admission@concordia-ny.edu
Web Site: www.concordia-ny.edu
President/CEO: Dr. Viji George, EdD
Admissions: Donald Vos
Financial Aid: Janice Spikereit

Type: Comprehensive **Sex:** Coed **Affiliation:** Lutheran; Concordia University System. **Scores:** 89% SAT V 400+; 79% SAT M 400+; 44.4% ACT 18-23; 11.1% ACT 24-29 **% Accepted:** 76 **Admission Plans:** Deferred

Admission; Early Admission; Early Decision Plan **Application Deadline:** March 15 **Application Fee:** $50.00 **H.S. Requirements:** High school diploma required; GED accepted **Costs Per Year:** Application fee: $50. One-time mandatory fee: $100. Comprehensive fee: $40,150 includes full-time tuition ($28,855), mandatory fees ($1030), and college room and board ($10,265). Full-time tuition and fees vary according to class time, course load, degree level, and program. Room and board charges vary according to board plan. Part-time tuition: $780 per credit. Part-time tuition varies according to class time, course load, degree level, and program. **Scholarships:** Available. **Calendar System:** Semester **Faculty:** Full-time 52, Part-time 96 **Student-Faculty Ratio:** 14:1 **Exams:** Other; SAT I or ACT. **% Receiving Financial Aid:** 70 **% Residing in College-Owned, -Operated, or -Affiliated Housing:** 60 **Final Year or Final Semester Residency Requirement:** No **Regional Accreditation:** Middle States Association of Colleges and Schools **Credit Hours For Degree:** 62 credit hours, Associates; 122 credit hours, Bachelors **Professional Accreditation:** AACN, CSWE, NCATE. **Intercollegiate Athletics:** Baseball M; Basketball M & W; Cross-Country Running M & W; Golf M; Soccer M & W; Softball W; Tennis M & W; Volleyball W

COOPER UNION FOR THE ADVANCEMENT OF SCIENCE AND ART

30 Cooper Sq.
New York, NY 10003-7120
Tel: (212)353-4100
Fax: (212)353-4343
E-mail: admissions@cooper.edu
Web Site: www.cooper.edu
President/CEO: Dr. Bill Mea
Admissions: John Falls
Financial Aid: Charlie Xu

Type: Comprehensive **Sex:** Coed **Scores:** 99% SAT M 400+; 3% ACT 18-23; 19% ACT 24-29 **Costs Per Year:** Comprehensive fee: $58,210 includes full-time tuition ($40,800), mandatory fees ($1850), and college room and board ($15,560). College room only: $11,560. Room and board charges vary according to housing facility. All international students are assessed an annual fee of $2010. Like all of our enrolled students, they also receive a half-tuition scholarship worth $20,400 for the 2015-16 academic year. **Scholarships:** Available. **Calendar System:** Semester, Summer session available **Enrollment:** Full-time 893, Graduate full-time 51, Graduate part-time 22, Part-time 6 **Faculty:** Full-time 49, Part-time 167 **Student-Faculty Ratio:** 9:1 **Exams:** Other; SAT I or ACT; SAT II. **% Receiving Financial Aid:** 43 **% Residing in College-Owned, -Operated, or -Affiliated Housing:** 20 **Final Year or Final Semester Residency Requirement:** Yes **Regional Accreditation:** Middle States Association of Colleges and Schools **Credit Hours For Degree:** 128 credits, Bachelors **ROTC:** Army **Professional Accreditation:** ABET, NAAB, NASAD. **Intercollegiate Athletics:** Basketball M & W; Cross-Country Running M & W; Soccer M & W; Tennis M & W; Volleyball M & W

CORNELL UNIVERSITY

Ithaca, NY 14853-0001
Tel: (607)255-2000
Fax: (607)255-0659
E-mail: admissions@cornell.edu
Web Site: www.cornell.edu
President/CEO: Elizabeth Garrett
Financial Aid: Susan Hitchcock

Type: University **Sex:** Coed **Affiliation:** State University of New York System. **Scores:** 100% SAT V 400+; 100% SAT M 400+; 1% ACT 18-23; 17.9% ACT 24-29 **% Accepted:** 15 **Admission Plans:** Deferred Admission; Early Action **Application Deadline:** January 2 **Application Fee:** $80.00 **H.S. Requirements:** High school diploma or equivalent not required **Costs Per Year:** Application fee: $80. Comprehensive fee: $62,794 includes full-time tuition ($48,880), mandatory fees ($236), and college room and board ($13,678). College room only: $8112. Full-time tuition and fees vary according to degree level. Room and board charges vary according to board plan and housing facility. **Scholarships:** Available. **Calendar System:** Semester, Summer session available **Enrollment:** Full-time 14,315, Graduate full-time 7,589 **Faculty:** Full-time 1,783, Part-time 356 **Student-Faculty Ratio:** 9:1 **Exams:** ACT essay component used for admission; SAT I or ACT; SAT II; SAT essay component used for admission. **% Receiving Financial Aid:** 46 **% Residing in College-Owned, -Operated, or -Affiliated Housing:** 55 **Final Year or Final Semester Residency Requirement:** No **Regional Accreditation:** Middle States Association of Colleges and Schools **Credit**

Hours For Degree: 120 credit hours, Bachelors **ROTC:** Air Force, Army, Navy **Professional Accreditation:** AACSB, AAFCS, AALS, ABA, ABET, ACSP, AND, ASLA, AVMA, CAHME, CIDA, NAAB, TEAC. **Intercollegiate Athletics:** Baseball M; Basketball M & W; Crew M & W; Cross-Country Running M & W; Equestrian Sports W; Fencing W; Field Hockey W; Football M; Golf M; Gymnastics W; Ice Hockey M & W; Lacrosse M & W; Sailing W; Soccer M & W; Softball W; Squash M & W; Swimming and Diving M & W; Tennis M & W; Track and Field M & W; Ultimate Frisbee M & W; Volleyball M & W; Water Polo M & W; Wrestling M

CORNING COMMUNITY COLLEGE

One Academic Dr.
Corning, NY 14830-3297
Tel: (607)962-9CCC
Fax: (607)962-9456
E-mail: admissions@corning-cc.edu
Web Site: www.corning-cc.edu
President/CEO: Dr. Katherine P. Douglas
Admissions: Tyre Bush

Type: Two-Year College **Sex:** Coed **Affiliation:** State University of New York System. **% Accepted:** 100 **Admission Plans:** Early Admission; Open Admission; Preferred Admission **Application Deadline:** Rolling **Application Fee:** $0.00 **H.S. Requirements:** High school diploma required; GED accepted **Costs Per Year:** Application fee: $0. State resident tuition: $4230 full-time, $177 per credit hour part-time. Nonresident tuition: $8460 full-time, $354 per credit hour part-time. Mandatory fees: $544 full-time, $8.80 per credit hour part-time. Part-time tuition and fees vary according to course load. College room and board: $9000. College room only: $6200. Room and board charges vary according to housing facility. **Scholarships:** Available. **Calendar System:** Semester, Summer session available **Enrollment:** Full-time 1,929, Part-time 2,043 **Faculty:** Full-time 89, Part-time 140 **Student-Faculty Ratio:** 18:1 **% Residing in College-Owned, -Operated, or -Affiliated Housing:** 6 **Final Year or Final Semester Residency Requirement:** No **Regional Accreditation:** Middle States Association of Colleges and Schools **Credit Hours For Degree:** 62 credit hours, Associates **Professional Accreditation:** ACEN. **Intercollegiate Athletics:** Baseball M; Basketball M & W; Bowling M & W; Soccer M & W; Softball W; Volleyball W

THE CULINARY INSTITUTE OF AMERICA

1946 Campus Dr.
Hyde Park, NY 12538-1499
Tel: (845)452-9600; Free: 800-CULINARY
Fax: (845)452-8629
E-mail: admissions@culinary.edu
Web Site: www.ciachef.edu
President/CEO: Dr. L. Tim Ryan
Admissions: Rachel Birchwood
Financial Aid: Kathleen Gailor

Type: Four-Year College **Sex:** Coed **Scores:** 94% SAT V 400+; 92% SAT M 400+; 55% ACT 18-23; 23% ACT 24-29 **% Accepted:** 92 **Admission Plans:** Deferred Admission **Application Deadline:** Rolling **Application Fee:** $50.00 **H.S. Requirements:** High school diploma required; GED accepted **Costs Per Year:** Application fee: $50. Comprehensive fee: $39,615 includes full-time tuition ($27,930), mandatory fees ($1320), and college room and board ($10,365). College room only: $7565. Full-time tuition and fees vary according to location. Room and board charges vary according to board plan, housing facility, location, and student level. **Scholarships:** Available. **Calendar System:** Semester, Summer session not available **Enrollment:** Full-time 2,859 **Faculty:** Full-time 141, Part-time 48 **Student-Faculty Ratio:** 18:1 **Exams:** ACT essay component not used; SAT I or ACT; SAT essay component not used. **% Receiving Financial Aid:** 64 **% Residing in College-Owned, -Operated, or -Affiliated Housing:** 59 **Regional Accreditation:** Middle States Association of Colleges and Schools **Credit Hours For Degree:** 69 credits, Associates; 132 credits, Bachelors **Professional Accreditation:** ACCSC. **Intercollegiate Athletics:** Basketball M & W; Cross-Country Running M & W; Soccer M & W; Tennis M & W; Volleyball M & W

DAEMEN COLLEGE

4380 Main St.
Amherst, NY 14226-3592
Tel: (716)839-3600; Free: 800-462-7652
Fax: (716)839-8516
E-mail: admissions@daemen.edu

Web Site: www.daemen.edu
President/CEO: Dr. Gary A. Olson
Financial Aid: Jeffrey Pagano
Type: Comprehensive **Sex:** Coed **Scores:** 94% SAT V 400+; 96% SAT M 400+; 38.2% ACT 18-23; 50.3% ACT 24-29 **% Accepted:** 50 **Admission Plans:** Deferred Admission; Early Admission **Application Deadline:** Rolling **Application Fee:** $25.00 **H.S. Requirements:** High school diploma required; GED accepted **Costs Per Year:** Application fee: $25. Comprehensive fee: $38,045 includes full-time tuition ($25,455), mandatory fees ($540), and college room and board ($12,050). Full-time tuition and fees vary according to location and reciprocity agreements. Room and board charges vary according to board plan and housing facility. Part-time tuition: $850 per credit hour. Part-time mandatory fees: $7 per credit hour, $80 per term. Part-time tuition and fees vary according to course load, location, and reciprocity agreements. **Scholarships:** Available. **Calendar System:** Semester, Summer session available **Enrollment:** Full-time 1,678, Graduate full-time 553, Graduate part-time 186, Part-time 352 **Faculty:** Full-time 138, Part-time 159 **Student-Faculty Ratio:** 13:1 **Exams:** SAT I or ACT. **% Residing in College-Owned, -Operated, or -Affiliated Housing:** 38 **Final Year or Final Semester Residency Requirement:** Yes **Regional Accreditation:** Middle States Association of Colleges and Schools **Credit Hours For Degree:** 120 credits, Bachelors **ROTC:** Army **Professional Accreditation:** ACEN, APTA, CSWE, TEAC. **Intercollegiate Athletics:** Basketball M & W; Cross-Country Running M & W; Golf M; Soccer M & W; Tennis M & W; Track and Field M & W; Volleyball W

DAVIS COLLEGE
400 Riverside Dr.
Johnson City, NY 13790
Tel: (607)729-1581; Free: 877-949-3248
Fax: (607)729-2962
E-mail: evantol@davisny.edu
Web Site: www.davisny.edu
President/CEO: Dr. Dino Pedrone
Admissions: Elizabeth A. VanTol
Financial Aid: Sandra Conklin
Type: Four-Year College **Sex:** Coed **Affiliation:** nondenominational. **Scores:** 36% ACT 18-23; 21% ACT 24-29 **% Accepted:** 53 **Admission Plans:** Deferred Admission **Application Deadline:** Rolling **Application Fee:** $45.00 **H.S. Requirements:** High school diploma required; GED accepted **Costs Per Year:** Application fee: $45. Comprehensive fee: $9745 includes full-time tuition ($6195), mandatory fees ($450), and college room and board ($3100). Full-time tuition and fees vary according to course load and location. Room and board charges vary according to board plan and housing facility. Part-time tuition: $450 per credit hour. Part-time mandatory fees: $275 per term. Part-time tuition and fees vary according to course load and location. **Scholarships:** Available. **Calendar System:** Semester, Summer session available **Enrollment:** Full-time 396, Part-time 121 **Faculty:** Full-time 14, Part-time 17 **Student-Faculty Ratio:** 14:1 **Exams:** SAT I or ACT. **% Receiving Financial Aid:** 96 **% Residing in College-Owned, -Operated, or -Affiliated Housing:** 61 **Regional Accreditation:** Middle States Association of Colleges and Schools **Credit Hours For Degree:** 66 credits, Associates; 130 credits, Bachelors **Professional Accreditation:** ABHE. **Intercollegiate Athletics:** Basketball M & W; Soccer M; Volleyball W

DEVRY COLLEGE OF NEW YORK
180 Madison Ave., Ste. 900
New York, NY 10016-5267
Tel: (212)312-4300; Free: 866-338-7941
Web Site: www.devry.edu
Financial Aid: Elvira Senese
Type: Comprehensive **Sex:** Coed **Affiliation:** DeVry University. **Application Fee:** $30.00 **H.S. Requirements:** High school diploma required; GED accepted **Costs Per Year:** Application fee: $30. Tuition: $17,052 full-time, $609 per credit hour part-time. Mandatory fees: $460 full-time. **Scholarships:** Available. **Calendar System:** Semester **Enrollment:** Full-time 629, Graduate full-time 169, Graduate part-time 411, Part-time 286 **Faculty:** Full-time 17, Part-time 70 **Student-Faculty Ratio:** 26:1 **Exams:** ACT; ACT essay component used for admission; ACT essay component used for placement; SAT I; SAT I or ACT; SAT essay component used for admission; SAT essay component used for placement. **% Receiving Financial Aid:** 84 **Regional Accreditation:** North Central Association of Colleges and Schools **Credit Hours For Degree:** 67 credit hours, Associates; 128 credit hours, Bachelors **Professional Accreditation:** ABET.

DOMINICAN COLLEGE
470 Western Hwy.
Orangeburg, NY 10962-1210
Tel: (845)359-7800; Free: 866-432-4636
Fax: (845)359-2313
E-mail: rob.tyrrell@dc.edu
Web Site: www.dc.edu
President/CEO: Señor Mary Eileen O'Brien, PhD
Admissions: Robert Tyrrell
Financial Aid: Stacy Salinas
Type: Comprehensive **Sex:** Coed **% Accepted:** 71 **Admission Plans:** Deferred Admission **Application Deadline:** Rolling **Application Fee:** $35.00 **H.S. Requirements:** High school diploma required; GED accepted **Costs Per Year:** Application fee: $35. Comprehensive fee: $39,858 includes full-time tuition ($26,578), mandatory fees ($860), and college room and board ($12,420). Full-time tuition and fees vary according to degree level. Room and board charges vary according to board plan and housing facility. Part-time tuition: $803 per credit hour. Part-time mandatory fees: $200 per term. Part-time tuition and fees vary according to degree level and program. **Scholarships:** Available. **Calendar System:** Semester, Summer session available **Enrollment:** Full-time 1,356, Graduate full-time 195, Graduate part-time 314, Part-time 196 **Faculty:** Full-time 73, Part-time 135 **Student-Faculty Ratio:** 16:1 **Exams:** ACT essay component used for admission; ACT essay component used for advising; ACT essay component used for placement; SAT I or ACT; SAT essay component used for admission; SAT essay component used for advising; SAT essay component used for placement; SAT Reasoning. **% Residing in College-Owned, -Operated, or -Affiliated Housing:** 82 **Final Year or Final Semester Residency Requirement:** No **Regional Accreditation:** Middle States Association of Colleges and Schools **Credit Hours For Degree:** 60 credits, Associates; 120 credits, Bachelors **Professional Accreditation:** AACN, AOTA, APTA, CSWE, TEAC. **Intercollegiate Athletics:** Baseball M; Basketball M & W; Cross-Country Running M & W; Golf M; Lacrosse M & W; Soccer M & W; Softball W; Track and Field M & W; Volleyball W

DUTCHESS COMMUNITY COLLEGE
53 Pendell Rd.
Poughkeepsie, NY 12601-1595
Tel: (845)431-8000
E-mail: michael.roe@sunydutchess.edu
Web Site: www.sunydutchess.edu
President/CEO: Dr. Pamela Edington
Admissions: Michael Roe
Financial Aid: Susan L. Mead
Type: Two-Year College **Sex:** Coed **Affiliation:** State University of New York System. **Admission Plans:** Deferred Admission; Early Admission; Open Admission; Preferred Admission **Application Deadline:** Rolling **H.S. Requirements:** High school diploma required; GED accepted **Costs Per Year:** State resident tuition: $3360 full-time, $140 per credit hour part-time. Nonresident tuition: $6720 full-time, $280 per credit hour part-time. Mandatory fees: $447 full-time, $10 per hour part-time, $19 per term part-time. College room and board: $9830. Room and board charges vary according to board plan. **Scholarships:** Available. **Calendar System:** Semester, Summer session available **Enrollment:** Full-time 4,283, Part-time 5,261 **Faculty:** Full-time 125, Part-time 382 **Student-Faculty Ratio:** 25:1 **% Residing in College-Owned, -Operated, or -Affiliated Housing:** 5 **Regional Accreditation:** Middle States Association of Colleges and Schools **Credit Hours For Degree:** 64 credits, Associates **Professional Accreditation:** ACEN, NAACLS. **Intercollegiate Athletics:** Baseball M; Basketball M & W; Cross-Country Running M & W; Soccer M; Softball W; Volleyball W

D'YOUVILLE COLLEGE
320 Porter Ave.
Buffalo, NY 14201-1084
Tel: (716)829-8000; Free: 800-777-3921
Fax: (716)829-7790
Web Site: www.dyc.edu
President/CEO: Señor Denise A. Roche, GNSH
Admissions: Dr. Steve Smith
Financial Aid: Matthew R. Metz
Type: Comprehensive **Sex:** Coed **Scores:** 99% SAT V 400+; 97% SAT M 400+; 41% ACT 18-23; 54% ACT 24-29 **% Accepted:** 70 **Admission Plans:** Deferred Admission **Application Deadline:** Rolling **H.S. Requirements:** High school diploma required; GED accepted **Costs Per Year:** Comprehen-

sive fee: $35,450 includes full-time tuition ($23,900), mandatory fees ($370), and college room and board ($11,180). Full-time tuition and fees vary according to course load, degree level, and program. Room and board charges vary according to board plan and housing facility. Part-time tuition: $745 per credit hour. Part-time mandatory fees: $3 per credit, $55 per term. Part-time tuition and fees vary according to course load, degree level, and program. Tuition guaranteed not to increase for student's term of enrollment. **Scholarships:** Available. **Calendar System:** Semester, Summer session available **Enrollment:** Full-time 1,419, Graduate full-time 837, Graduate part-time 257, Part-time 396 **Faculty:** Full-time 189, Part-time 109 **Student-Faculty Ratio:** 10:1 **Exams:** ACT essay component not used; SAT I or ACT; SAT essay component not used. **% Receiving Financial Aid:** 83 **% Residing in College-Owned, -Operated, or -Affiliated Housing:** 17 **Regional Accreditation:** Middle States Association of Colleges and Schools **Credit Hours For Degree:** 120 credit hours, Bachelors **ROTC:** Army **Professional Accreditation:** AACN, ACPE, AND, AOTA, APTA, CCE, NCATE. **Intercollegiate Athletics:** Baseball M; Basketball M & W; Cheerleading W; Cross-Country Running M & W; Golf M & W; Soccer M & W; Softball W; Tennis M & W; Volleyball M & W

ELMIRA BUSINESS INSTITUTE

303 N Main St.
Elmira, NY 14901
Tel: (607)733-7177; Free: 800-843-1812
Fax: (607)733-7178
E-mail: info@ebi-college.com
Web Site: www.ebi-college.com
President/CEO: Brad C. Phillips
Admissions: Lindsay Dull
Financial Aid: Tammie S. Goodman
Type: Two-Year College **Sex:** Coed **Admission Plans:** Open Admission **Application Deadline:** Rolling **Application Fee:** $0.00 **H.S. Requirements:** High school diploma required; GED accepted **Scholarships:** Available. **Calendar System:** Semester, Summer session not available **Enrollment:** Full-time 54, Part-time 24 **Student-Faculty Ratio:** 9:1 **Credit Hours For Degree:** 61 credits, Associates **Professional Accreditation:** ACICS.

ELMIRA COLLEGE

One Park Pl.
Elmira, NY 14901
Tel: (607)735-1800; Free: 800-935-6472
Fax: (607)735-1718
E-mail: admissions@elmira.edu
Web Site: www.elmira.edu
President/CEO: Dr. Norman R. Smith
Admissions: Brett Moore
Financial Aid: Dean Kathleen L. Cohen
Type: Comprehensive **Sex:** Coed **Scores:** 93% SAT V 400+; 94% SAT M 400+; 36.4% ACT 18-23; 47.3% ACT 24-29 **% Accepted:** 76 **Admission Plans:** Deferred Admission; Early Action **Application Deadline:** Rolling **Application Fee:** $0.00 **H.S. Requirements:** High school diploma required; GED not accepted. For non-traditional adult students: High school diploma required; GED accepted **Costs Per Year:** Application fee: $0. Comprehensive fee: $53,900 includes full-time tuition ($41,900) and college room and board ($12,000). College room only: $6400. Room and board charges vary according to board plan and housing facility. Part-time tuition: $1200 per credit. Part-time tuition varies according to course load and degree level. **Scholarships:** Available. **Calendar System:** Miscellaneous, Summer session available **Enrollment:** Full-time 1,123, Graduate full-time 5, Graduate part-time 83, Part-time 165 **Faculty:** Full-time 67, Part-time 103 **Student-Faculty Ratio:** 12:1 **Exams:** SAT I or ACT; SAT Reasoning. **% Receiving Financial Aid:** 81 **% Residing in College-Owned, -Operated, or -Affiliated Housing:** 88 **Final Year or Final Semester Residency Requirement:** No **Regional Accreditation:** Middle States Association of Colleges and Schools **Credit Hours For Degree:** 60 credits, Associates; 120 credits, Bachelors **ROTC:** Air Force, Army **Professional Accreditation:** ACEN. **Intercollegiate Athletics:** Baseball M; Basketball M & W; Cheerleading W; Cross-Country Running M & W; Field Hockey W; Golf M & W; Ice Hockey M & W; Lacrosse M & W; Soccer M & W; Softball W; Tennis M & W; Volleyball M & W

ERIE COMMUNITY COLLEGE

121 Ellicott St.
Buffalo, NY 14203-2698

Tel: (716)851-1001
Fax: (716)842-1972
E-mail: admissions@ecc.edu
Web Site: www.ecc.edu
President/CEO: Jack F. Quinn, Jr.
Financial Aid: Scott Weltjen
Type: Two-Year College **Sex:** Coed **Affiliation:** State University of New York System. **Scores:** 82% SAT V 400+ **% Accepted:** 67 **Admission Plans:** Open Admission **Application Deadline:** Rolling **Application Fee:** $25.00 **H.S. Requirements:** High school diploma required; GED accepted **Costs Per Year:** Application fee: $25. One-time mandatory fee: $75. Area resident tuition: $4595 full-time, $192 per credit hour part-time. State resident tuition: $9190 full-time, $384 per credit hour part-time. Nonresident tuition: $9190 full-time, $384 per credit hour part-time. Mandatory fees: $593 full-time, $15 per credit hour part-time, $70 per term part-time. **Scholarships:** Available. **Calendar System:** Semester, Summer session available **Enrollment:** Full-time 1,965, Part-time 612 **Student-Faculty Ratio:** 26:1 **Regional Accreditation:** Middle States Association of Colleges and Schools **Credit Hours For Degree:** 60 credit hours, Associates **ROTC:** Army **Professional Accreditation:** AAMAE, ABET, COA, JRCERT. **Intercollegiate Athletics:** Baseball M; Basketball M & W; Bowling M & W; Cheerleading W; Football M; Ice Hockey M; Lacrosse W; Soccer M & W; Softball W; Volleyball W

ERIE COMMUNITY COLLEGE, NORTH CAMPUS

6205 Main St.
Williamsville, NY 14221-7095
Tel: (716)851-1002
Fax: (716)634-3802
E-mail: admissions@ecc.edu
Web Site: www.ecc.edu
President/CEO: Jack F. Quinn, Jr.
Financial Aid: Scott Weltjen
Type: Two-Year College **Sex:** Coed **Affiliation:** State University of New York System. **Scores:** 95% SAT V 400+; 96% SAT M 400+ **% Accepted:** 71 **Admission Plans:** Open Admission **Application Deadline:** Rolling **Application Fee:** $25.00 **H.S. Requirements:** High school diploma required; GED accepted **Costs Per Year:** Application fee: $25. One-time mandatory fee: $75. Area resident tuition: $4595 full-time, $192 per credit hour part-time. State resident tuition: $9190 full-time, $384 per credit hour part-time. Nonresident tuition: $9190 full-time, $384 per credit hour part-time. Mandatory fees: $593 full-time, $15 per credit hour part-time, $70 per term part-time. **Scholarships:** Available. **Calendar System:** Semester, Summer session available **Enrollment:** Full-time 3,741, Part-time 1,810 **Student-Faculty Ratio:** 26:1 **Regional Accreditation:** Middle States Association of Colleges and Schools **Credit Hours For Degree:** 60 credit hours, Associates **ROTC:** Army **Professional Accreditation:** ABET, ACEN, ADA, AHIMA, AOTA, CoARC, NAACLS. **Intercollegiate Athletics:** Baseball M; Basketball M & W; Bowling M & W; Cheerleading W; Football M; Ice Hockey M; Lacrosse W; Soccer M & W; Softball W; Volleyball W

ERIE COMMUNITY COLLEGE, SOUTH CAMPUS

4041 Southwestern Blvd.
Orchard Park, NY 14127-2199
Tel: (716)851-1003
Fax: (716)648-9953
E-mail: admissions@ecc.edu
Web Site: www.ecc.edu
President/CEO: Jack F. Quinn, Jr.
Financial Aid: Scott Weltjen
Type: Two-Year College **Sex:** Coed **Affiliation:** State University of New York System. **Scores:** 94% SAT M 400+ **% Accepted:** 82 **Admission Plans:** Open Admission **Application Deadline:** Rolling **Application Fee:** $25.00 **H.S. Requirements:** High school diploma required; GED accepted **Costs Per Year:** Application fee: $25. One-time mandatory fee: $75. Area resident tuition: $4595 full-time, $192 per credit hour part-time. State resident tuition: $9190 full-time, $384 per credit hour part-time. Nonresident tuition: $9190 full-time, $384 per credit hour part-time. Mandatory fees: $593 full-time, $15 per credit hour part-time, $70 per term part-time. **Scholarships:** Available. **Calendar System:** Semester, Summer session available **Enrollment:** Full-time 2,225, Part-time 1,669 **Student-Faculty Ratio:** 26:1 **Regional Accreditation:** Middle States Association of Colleges and Schools **Credit Hours For Degree:** 60 credit hours, Associates **ROTC:** Army **Professional Accreditation:** ADA. **Intercollegiate Athletics:** Baseball M; Basketball M &

W; Bowling M & W; Cheerleading W; Football M; Ice Hockey M; Lacrosse W; Soccer M & W; Softball W; Volleyball W

EUGENE LANG COLLEGE OF LIBERAL ARTS

65 W 11th St.
New York, NY 10011-8601
Tel: (212)229-5600; Free: 800-292-3040
Fax: (212)229-5355
E-mail: macluskc@newschool.edu
Web Site: www.newschool.edu/lang
President/CEO: David E. Van Zandt
Admissions: Candice MacLusky

Type: Four-Year College **Sex:** Coed **Affiliation:** The New School. **Scores:** 100% SAT V 400+; 98% SAT M 400+ **Costs Per Year:** Tuition: $42,080 full-time. **Scholarships:** Available. **Calendar System:** Semester, Summer session available **Enrollment:** Full-time 1,465, Part-time 85 **Faculty:** Full-time 71, Part-time 129 **Student-Faculty Ratio:** 14:1 **Exams:** Other. **% Receiving Financial Aid:** 57 **% Residing in College-Owned, -Operated, or -Affiliated Housing:** 31 **Final Year or Final Semester Residency Requirement:** No **Regional Accreditation:** Middle States Association of Colleges and Schools **Credit Hours For Degree:** 120 credits, Bachelors

EUGENIO MARÍA DE HOSTOS COMMUNITY COLLEGE OF THE CITY UNIVERSITY OF NEW YORK

500 Grand Concourse
Bronx, NY 10451
Tel: (718)518-4444
Fax: (718)518-4256
E-mail: admissions@hostos.cuny.edu
Web Site: www.hostos.cuny.edu
President/CEO: Felix V. Matos Rodriguez
Admissions: Roland Velez

Type: Two-Year College **Sex:** Coed **Affiliation:** City University of New York System. **Admission Plans:** Open Admission **Application Deadline:** Rolling **Application Fee:** $65.00 **H.S. Requirements:** High school diploma required; GED accepted **Scholarships:** Available. **Calendar System:** Semester, Summer session available **Student-Faculty Ratio:** 19:1 **Regional Accreditation:** Middle States Association of Colleges and Schools **Credit Hours For Degree:** 60 credits, Associates **Professional Accreditation:** ADA, JRCERT. **Intercollegiate Athletics:** Basketball M & W; Soccer M; Volleyball W

EXCELSIOR COLLEGE

7 Columbia Cir.
Albany, NY 12203-5159
Tel: (518)464-8500; Free: 888-647-2388
Fax: (518)464-8777
E-mail: admissions@excelsior.edu
Web Site: www.excelsior.edu
President/CEO: Dr. John F. Ebersole
Financial Aid: Christina Roarke

Type: Comprehensive **Sex:** Coed **Admission Plans:** Open Admission **Application Deadline:** Rolling **Application Fee:** $100.00 **H.S. Requirements:** High school diploma required; GED accepted **Costs Per Year:** Application fee: $100. Tuition: $490 per credit part-time. Part-time tuition varies according to reciprocity agreements. **Scholarships:** Available. **Calendar System:** Continuous **Enrollment:** Graduate part-time 3,176, Part-time 36,927 **Faculty:** Part-time 1,481 **Student-Faculty Ratio:** 11:1 **Final Year or Final Semester Residency Requirement:** No **Regional Accreditation:** Middle States Association of Colleges and Schools **Credit Hours For Degree:** 60 credits, Associates; 120 credits, Bachelors **Professional Accreditation:** ABET, ACEN.

FARMINGDALE STATE COLLEGE

2350 Broadhollow Rd.
Farmingdale, NY 11735
Tel: (631)420-2000
Fax: (631)420-2633
E-mail: admissions@farmingdale.edu
Web Site: www.farmingdale.edu
President/CEO: Dr. W. Hubert Keen
Admissions: Jim Hall

Type: Four-Year College **Sex:** Coed **Affiliation:** State University of New York System. **Scores:** 94% SAT V 400+; 97% SAT M 400+; 67% ACT 18-23; 19.6% ACT 24-29 **% Accepted:** 44 **Admission Plans:** Deferred Admission **Application Deadline:** June 1 **Application Fee:** $50.00 **H.S. Requirements:** High school diploma required; GED accepted **Costs Per Year:** Application fee: $50. State resident tuition: $6470 full-time, $270 per credit part-time. Nonresident tuition: $16,320 full-time, $680 per credit part-time. Mandatory fees: $1338 full-time, $54.15 per credit part-time, $10 per term part-time. Full-time tuition and fees vary according to program. Part-time tuition and fees vary according to course load and program. College room and board: $12,500. College room only: $7660. Room and board charges vary according to board plan and housing facility. **Scholarships:** Available. **Calendar System:** Semester, Summer session available **Enrollment:** Full-time 6,388, Part-time 2,260 **Faculty:** Full-time 212, Part-time 489 **Student-Faculty Ratio:** 19:1 **Exams:** ACT essay component used for advising; ACT essay component used for placement; SAT I or ACT; SAT essay component used for advising; SAT essay component used for placement; SAT Reasoning. **% Receiving Financial Aid:** 51 **% Residing in College-Owned, -Operated, or -Affiliated Housing:** 7 **Final Year or Final Semester Residency Requirement:** No **Regional Accreditation:** Middle States Association of Colleges and Schools **Credit Hours For Degree:** 60 credits, Associates; 120 credits, Bachelors **ROTC:** Air Force, Army, Navy **Professional Accreditation:** ABET, ACEN, ADA, NAACLS. **Intercollegiate Athletics:** Baseball M; Basketball M & W; Cross-Country Running M & W; Golf M; Ice Hockey M; Lacrosse M & W; Soccer M & W; Softball W; Tennis M & W; Track and Field M & W; Volleyball W

FASHION INSTITUTE OF TECHNOLOGY

Seventh Ave. at 27th St.
New York, NY 10001-5992
Tel: (212)217-7999
Fax: (212)217-7481
E-mail: fitinfo@fitnyc.edu
Web Site: www.fitnyc.edu
President/CEO: Dr. Joyce F. Brown
Admissions: Magda Francois

Type: Comprehensive **Sex:** Coed **Affiliation:** State University of New York System. **% Accepted:** 41 **Application Deadline:** January 1 **Application Fee:** $50.00 **H.S. Requirements:** High school diploma required; GED accepted **Costs Per Year:** Application fee: $50. State resident tuition: $6470 full-time, $270 per credit hour part-time. Nonresident tuition: $19,592 full-time, $816 per credit hour part-time. Mandatory fees: $730 full-time. Full-time tuition and fees vary according to degree level. Part-time tuition varies according to degree level. College room and board: $13,291. College room only: $8945. Room and board charges vary according to board plan and housing facility. **Scholarships:** Available. **Calendar System:** Semester, Summer session available **Enrollment:** Full-time 7,409, Graduate full-time 116, Graduate part-time 63, Part-time 1,983 **Faculty:** Full-time 232, Part-time 738 **Student-Faculty Ratio:** 17:1 **Exams:** ACT essay component not used; SAT I or ACT; SAT essay component not used. **% Receiving Financial Aid:** 52 **% Residing in College-Owned, -Operated, or -Affiliated Housing:** 21 **Final Year or Final Semester Residency Requirement:** No **Regional Accreditation:** Middle States Association of Colleges and Schools **Credit Hours For Degree:** 60 credits, Associates; 120 credits, Bachelors **Professional Accreditation:** CIDA, NASAD. **Intercollegiate Athletics:** Cross-Country Running M & W; Soccer W; Swimming and Diving M & W; Table Tennis M & W; Tennis M & W; Track and Field M & W; Volleyball W

FINGER LAKES COMMUNITY COLLEGE

3325 Marvin Sands Dr.
Canandaigua, NY 14424-8395
Tel: (585)394-3500
Fax: (585)394-5005
E-mail: admissions@flcc.edu
Web Site: www.flcc.edu
President/CEO: Dr. Barbara Risser
Admissions: Bonnie B. Ritts

Type: Two-Year College **Sex:** Coed **Affiliation:** State University of New York System. **% Accepted:** 82 **Admission Plans:** Deferred Admission; Early Admission; Open Admission **Application Deadline:** August 19 **Application Fee:** $20.00 **H.S. Requirements:** High school diploma required; GED accepted **Costs Per Year:** Application fee: $20. State resident tuition: $4180 full-time, $168 per credit hour part-time. Nonresident tuition: $8360 full-time, $336 per credit hour part-time. Mandatory fees: $524 full-time, $16 per credit hour part-time. Full-time tuition and fees vary according to course load. Part-time tuition and fees vary according to course load. **Scholarships:** Available. **Calendar System:** Semester, Summer session available **Enrollment:** Full-time 3,003, Part-time 3,758 **Faculty:** Full-time 119, Part-time 222 **Student-Faculty Ratio:** 22:1 **Exams:** ACT essay component not used; SAT essay component not used. **Final Year or Final Semester Residency Requirement:** No **Regional Accreditation:** Middle States Association of Colleges and Schools **Credit Hours For Degree:** 64 credit hours, Associates **ROTC:** Air Force **Professional Accreditation:** ACEN. **Intercollegiate Athletics:** Baseball M; Basketball M & W; Cross-Country Running M & W; Lacrosse M; Soccer M & W; Softball W; Track and Field M & W; Volleyball W

FINGER LAKES HEALTH COLLEGE OF NURSING
196 N St.
Geneva, NY 14456
Tel:.(315)787-4005
Web Site: www.flhcon.com
Type: Two-Year College **Sex:** Coed **Professional Accreditation:** ACEN.

FIORELLO H. LAGUARDIA COMMUNITY COLLEGE OF THE CITY UNIVERSITY OF NEW YORK
31-10 Thomson Ave.
Long Island City, NY 11101-3071
Tel: (718)482-7200
Fax: (718)482-5599
E-mail: admissions@lagcc.cuny.edu
Web Site: www.lagcc.cuny.edu
President/CEO: Dr. Gail O. Mellow
Admissions: LaVora Desvigne
Financial Aid: Annette Hamilton
Type: Two-Year College **Sex:** Coed **Affiliation:** City University of New York System. **% Accepted:** 100 **Admission Plans:** Deferred Admission; Early Admission; Open Admission **Application Deadline:** Rolling **Application Fee:** $65.00 **H.S. Requirements:** High school diploma required; GED accepted **Costs Per Year:** Application fee: $65. State resident tuition: $4800 full-time, $210 per credit part-time. Nonresident tuition: $9600 full-time, $320 per credit part-time. Mandatory fees: $417 full-time, $104.95 per term part-time. **Scholarships:** Available. **Calendar System:** Miscellaneous, Summer session available **Enrollment:** Full-time 10,642, Part-time 8,690 **Faculty:** Full-time 407, Part-time 719 **Student-Faculty Ratio:** 22:1 **Final Year or Final Semester Residency Requirement:** No **Regional Accreditation:** Middle States Association of Colleges and Schools **Credit Hours For Degree:** 60 units, Associates **Professional Accreditation:** ACEN, AOTA, APTA. **Intercollegiate Athletics:** Basketball M & W

FIVE TOWNS COLLEGE
305 N Service Rd.
Dix Hills, NY 11746-6055
Tel: (631)424-7000
Fax: (631)656-2172
E-mail: cynthia.catalano@ftc.edu
Web Site: www.ftc.edu
Admissions: Cynthia Catalano
Financial Aid: Jason LaBonte
Type: Comprehensive **Sex:** Coed **% Accepted:** 62 **Admission Plans:** Deferred Admission; Early Action **Application Deadline:** Rolling **Application Fee:** $35.00 **H.S. Requirements:** High school diploma required; GED accepted **Costs Per Year:** Application fee: $35. Comprehensive fee: $33,970 includes full-time tuition ($21,000), mandatory fees ($700), and college room and board ($12,270). Full-time tuition and fees vary according to course level, course load, degree level, program, and student level. Room and board charges vary according to board plan. Part-time tuition: $875 per credit. Part-time tuition varies according to course level, course load, degree level, program, and student level. **Scholarships:** Available. **Calendar System:** Semester, Summer session available **Enrollment:** Full-time 611, Graduate full-time 19, Graduate part-time 8, Part-time 43 **Faculty:** Full-time 22, Part-time 63 **Student-Faculty Ratio:** 15:1 **Exams:** ACT essay component not used; SAT I or ACT; SAT essay component not used. **% Receiving Financial Aid:** 84 **% Residing in College-Owned, -Operated, or -Affiliated Housing:** 15 **Final Year or Final Semester Residency Requirement:** No **Regional Accreditation:** Middle States Association of Colleges and Schools **Credit Hours For Degree:** 61 credits, Associates; 121 credits, Bachelors **Professional Accreditation:** NCATE.

FORDHAM UNIVERSITY
441 E Fordham Rd.
New York, NY 10458
Tel: (718)817-1000; Free: 800-FORDHAM
Fax: (718)367-9404
E-mail: peek@fordham.edu
Web Site: www.fordham.edu
President/CEO: Fr. Joseph M. McShane, SJ
Admissions: Dr. Patricia Peek
Financial Aid: Angela Van Dekker
Type: University **Sex:** Coed **Affiliation:** Roman Catholic (Jesuit). **Scores:** 100% SAT V 400+; 100% SAT M 400+; 10.01% ACT 18-23; 59.58% ACT 24-29 **% Accepted:** 48 **Admission Plans:** Deferred Admission; Early Action; Early Admission; Early Decision Plan **Application Deadline:** January 1 **Application Fee:** $70.00 **H.S. Requirements:** High school diploma required; GED accepted **Costs Per Year:** Application fee: $70. Comprehensive fee: $63,667 includes full-time tuition ($46,120), mandatory fees ($1197), and college room and board ($16,350). Room and board charges vary according to board plan, housing facility, and location. Part-time tuition: $1537 per credit hour. Part-time tuition varies according to class time and course load. **Scholarships:** Available. **Calendar System:** Semester, Summer session available **Enrollment:** Full-time 8,329, Graduate full-time 4,114, Graduate part-time 2,317, Part-time 526 **Faculty:** Full-time 737, Part-time 861 **Student-Faculty Ratio:** 14:1 **Exams:** ACT essay component used for placement; SAT I or ACT; SAT essay component not used; SAT essay component used for placement; SAT Reasoning; SAT Subject. **% Receiving Financial Aid:** 64 **% Residing in College-Owned, -Operated, or -Affiliated Housing:** 55 **Final Year or Final Semester Residency Requirement:** No **Regional Accreditation:** Middle States Association of Colleges and Schools **Credit Hours For Degree:** 124 credits, Bachelors **ROTC:** Air Force, Army, Navy **Professional Accreditation:** AACSB, AALS, ABA, APA, CSWE, NCATE. **Intercollegiate Athletics:** Baseball M; Basketball M & W; Cheerleading W; Crew W; Cross-Country Running M & W; Football M; Golf M; Ice Hockey M; Sailing M & W; Soccer M & W; Softball W; Squash M; Swimming and Diving M & W; Tennis M & W; Track and Field M & W; Volleyball W; Water Polo M

FULTON-MONTGOMERY COMMUNITY COLLEGE
2805 State Hwy. 67
Johnstown, NY 12095-3790
Tel: (518)762-4651
Fax: (518)762-6518
E-mail: llaporte@fmcc.suny.edu
Web Site: www.fmcc.suny.edu
President/CEO: Dr. Dustin Swanger
Admissions: Laura LaPorte
Type: Two-Year College **Sex:** Coed **Affiliation:** State University of New York System. **Admission Plans:** Deferred Admission; Early Admission; Open Admission **Application Deadline:** September 10 **Application Fee:** $0.00 **H.S. Requirements:** High school diploma or equivalent not required. For nursing and radiological technology programs: High school diploma required; GED accepted **Costs Per Year:** Application fee: $0. State resident tuition: $3900 full-time, $163 per credit hour part-time. Nonresident tuition: $7800 full-time, $326 per credit hour part-time. Mandatory fees: $561 full-time. College room and board: $11,000. College room only: $7250. **Scholarships:** Available. **Calendar System:** Semester, Summer session available **Enrollment:** Full-time 1,863, Part-time 970 **Faculty:** Full-time 54, Part-time 91 **Student-Faculty Ratio:** 24:1 **Regional Accreditation:** Middle States Association of Colleges and Schools **Credit Hours For Degree:** 62 credits, Associates **Intercollegiate Athletics:** Baseball M; Basketball M & W; Soccer M & W; Softball W; Volleyball W

GENESEE COMMUNITY COLLEGE
1 College Rd.
Batavia, NY 14020-9704
Tel: (585)343-0055; Free: 866-CALL GCC
Fax: (585)345-4541
E-mail: tmlanemartin@genesee.edu
Web Site: www.genesee.edu
President/CEO: Dr. James Sunser
Admissions: Tanya Lane-Martin
Financial Aid: Joseph Anthony Bailey
Type: Two-Year College **Sex:** Coed **Affiliation:** State University of New York System. **% Accepted:** 72 **Admission Plans:** Open Admission **Application**

Deadline: Rolling **Application Fee:** $0.00 **H.S. Requirements:** High school diploma required; GED accepted **Costs Per Year:** Application fee: $0. State resident tuition: $3900 full-time, $160 per credit hour part-time. Nonresident tuition: $4500 full-time, $185 per credit hour part-time. Mandatory fees: $510 full-time, $2 per credit hour part-time. Full-time tuition and fees vary according to course load. Part-time tuition and fees vary according to course load. College room and board: $8475. College room only: $6200. Room and board charges vary according to board plan and housing facility. **Scholarships:** Available. **Calendar System:** Semester, Summer session available **Enrollment:** Full-time 2,846, Part-time 3,675 **Faculty:** Full-time 90, Part-time 257 **Student-Faculty Ratio:** 18:1 **Exams:** ACT. **Final Year or Final Semester Residency Requirement:** Yes **Regional Accreditation:** Middle States Association of Colleges and Schools **Credit Hours For Degree:** 62 credit hours, Associates **ROTC:** Army **Professional Accreditation:** ACEN, AOTA, APTA, CoARC. **Intercollegiate Athletics:** Baseball M; Basketball M & W; Cheerleading M & W; Golf M & W; Lacrosse M & W; Soccer M & W; Softball W; Swimming and Diving M & W; Volleyball W

GLOBE INSTITUTE OF TECHNOLOGY
500 7th Ave.
New York, NY 10018
Tel: (212)349-4330; Free: 800-51-GLOBE
Fax: (212)227-5920
E-mail: admissions@globe.edu
Web Site: www.globe.edu
President/CEO: Martin Oliner
Admissions: Michael Scalice

Type: Four-Year College **Sex:** Coed **Admission Plans:** Open Admission **Application Deadline:** Rolling **Application Fee:** $50.00 **H.S. Requirements:** High school diploma required; GED accepted **Scholarships:** Available. **Calendar System:** Semester, Summer session available **Exams:** SAT I or ACT. **Credit Hours For Degree:** 60 credits, Associates; 120 credits, Bachelors **Professional Accreditation:** ACICS, NYSBR. **Intercollegiate Athletics:** Baseball M; Basketball M & W; Cross-Country Running M & W; Soccer M; Track and Field M & W; Volleyball W

HAMILTON COLLEGE
198 College Hill Rd.
Clinton, NY 13323-1296
Tel: (315)859-4011; Free: 800-843-2655
Fax: (315)859-4124
E-mail: admission@hamilton.edu
Web Site: www.hamilton.edu
President/CEO: Dr. Joan Hinde Stewart
Admissions: Monica Inzer

Type: Four-Year College **Sex:** Coed **Scores:** 100% SAT V 400+; 100% SAT M 400+; 14.8% ACT 24-29 **% Accepted:** 25 **Admission Plans:** Deferred Admission; Early Action **Application Deadline:** January 1 **Application Fee:** $50.00 **H.S. Requirements:** High school diploma required; GED accepted **Costs Per Year:** Application fee: $50. Comprehensive fee: $62,070 includes full-time tuition ($49,010), mandatory fees ($490), and college room and board ($12,570). College room only: $6870. Room and board charges vary according to board plan. Part-time tuition: $6,126.25 per course. **Scholarships:** Available. **Calendar System:** Semester, Summer session not available **Enrollment:** Full-time 1,862, Part-time 10 **Faculty:** Full-time 189, Part-time 43 **Student-Faculty Ratio:** 9:1 **Exams:** ACT essay component used for admission; SAT I and SAT II or ACT; SAT essay component used for admission; SAT Reasoning; SAT Subject. **% Receiving Financial Aid:** 48 **% Residing in College-Owned, -Operated, or -Affiliated Housing:** 100 **Final Year or Final Semester Residency Requirement:** Yes **Regional Accreditation:** Middle States Association of Colleges and Schools **Credit Hours For Degree:** 32 courses, Bachelors **ROTC:** Air Force, Army **Intercollegiate Athletics:** Baseball M; Basketball M & W; Crew M & W; Cross-Country Running M & W; Equestrian Sports M & W; Fencing M & W; Field Hockey W; Football M; Golf M & W; Ice Hockey M & W; Lacrosse M & W; Rugby M & W; Sailing M & W; Skiing (Cross-Country) M & W; Skiing (Downhill) M & W; Soccer M & W; Softball W; Squash M & W; Swimming and Diving M & W; Tennis M & W; Track and Field M & W; Ultimate Frisbee M & W; Volleyball M & W; Water Polo M

HARTWICK COLLEGE
One Hartwick Dr.
Oneonta, NY 13820-4020
Tel: (607)431-4200; Free: 888-HARTWICK

Fax: (607)431-4138
E-mail: admissions@hartwick.edu
Web Site: www.hartwick.edu
President/CEO: Dr. Margaret L. Drugovich
Admissions: Lisa Starkey-Wood
Financial Aid: Melissa Allen

Type: Four-Year College **Sex:** Coed **Scores:** 92% SAT V 400+; 92% SAT M 400+; 44% ACT 18-23; 41% ACT 24-29 **% Accepted:** 81 **Admission Plans:** Deferred Admission; Early Action; Early Admission **Application Deadline:** Rolling **Application Fee:** $0.00 **H.S. Requirements:** High school diploma required; GED accepted **Costs Per Year:** Application fee: $0. One-time mandatory fee: $400. Comprehensive fee: $52,560 includes full-time tuition ($40,630), mandatory fees ($810), and college room and board ($11,120). College room only: $5850. Full-time tuition and fees vary according to course load. Room and board charges vary according to board plan and housing facility. Part-time tuition: $1305 per credit hour. Part-time tuition varies according to course load. **Scholarships:** Available. **Calendar System:** 4-1-4, Summer session available **Enrollment:** Full-time 1,353, Part-time 39 **Faculty:** Full-time 106, Part-time 83 **Student-Faculty Ratio:** 10:1 **Exams:** SAT I or ACT. **% Receiving Financial Aid:** 83 **% Residing in College-Owned, -Operated, or -Affiliated Housing:** 77 **Final Year or Final Semester Residency Requirement:** No **Regional Accreditation:** Middle States Association of Colleges and Schools **Credit Hours For Degree:** 120 credit hours, Bachelors **Professional Accreditation:** AACN, NASAD, NASM. **Intercollegiate Athletics:** Basketball M & W; Cheerleading W; Cross-Country Running M & W; Equestrian Sports W; Field Hockey W; Football M; Lacrosse M & W; Soccer M & W; Swimming and Diving M & W; Tennis M & W; Volleyball W; Water Polo M & W

HELENE FULD COLLEGE OF NURSING
24 E 120th St.
New York, NY 10035
Tel: (212)616-7200
Web Site: www.helenefuld.edu
President/CEO: Margaret Wines
Admissions: Sandra Senior

Type: Two-Year College **Sex:** Coed **Admission Plans:** Deferred Admission **Application Deadline:** Rolling **Application Fee:** $110.00 **H.S. Requirements:** High school diploma required; GED accepted **Costs Per Year:** Application fee: $110. Tuition: $341 per quarter hour part-time. Part-time tuition varies according to course load, degree level, and program. **Scholarships:** Available. **Calendar System:** Quarter, Summer session available **Enrollment:** Full-time 91, Part-time 263 **Faculty:** Full-time 16, Part-time 3 **Student-Faculty Ratio:** 11:1 **Exams:** ACT essay component not used; Other; SAT essay component not used. **Final Year or Final Semester Residency Requirement:** No **Regional Accreditation:** Middle States Association of Colleges and Schools **Credit Hours For Degree:** 79.5 credits, Associates; 134, Bachelors **Professional Accreditation:** ACEN.

HERKIMER COUNTY COMMUNITY COLLEGE
100 Reservoir Rd.
Herkimer, NY 13350
Tel: (315)866-0300
Fax: (315)866-7253
E-mail: admissions@herkimer.edu
Web Site: www.herkimer.edu
President/CEO: Dr. Cathleen McColgin
Admissions: Rebecca Kohler

Type: Two-Year College **Sex:** Coed **Affiliation:** State University of New York System. **Costs Per Year:** State resident tuition: $3940 full-time, $139 per credit hour part-time. Nonresident tuition: $7000 full-time, $278 per credit hour part-time. Mandatory fees: $700 full-time, $12 per credit hour part-time, $40 per term part-time. College room and board: $9550. Room and board charges vary according to board plan and housing facility. **Scholarships:** Available. **Calendar System:** Semester, Summer session available **Enrollment:** Full-time 1,752, Part-time 1,267 **Faculty:** Full-time 51, Part-time 109 **Student-Faculty Ratio:** 21:1 **Exams:** ACT essay component not used; SAT essay component not used. **% Residing in College-Owned, -Operated, or -Affiliated Housing:** 19 **Final Year or Final Semester Residency Requirement:** No **Regional Accreditation:** Middle States Association of Colleges and Schools **Credit Hours For Degree:** 63 credit hours, Associates **ROTC:** Army **Professional Accreditation:** AOTA, APTA. **Intercollegiate Athletics:** Baseball M; Basketball M & W; Cross-Country Running M & W; Field Hockey

W; Lacrosse M & W; Soccer M & W; Softball W; Swimming and Diving M & W; Tennis M & W; Track and Field M & W; Volleyball W

HILBERT COLLEGE

5200 S Park Ave.
Hamburg, NY 14075-1597
Tel: (716)649-7900; Free: 800-649-8003
Fax: (716)649-0702
E-mail: ksperring@hilbert.edu
Web Site: www.hilbert.edu
President/CEO: Dr. Cynthia Zane
Admissions: Kim Sperring
Financial Aid: Beverly Chudy-Szczur

Type: Comprehensive **Sex:** Coed **Affiliation:** Roman Catholic. **Scores:** 92% SAT V 400+; 89% SAT M 400+; 60% ACT 18-23; 21% ACT 24-29 **% Accepted:** 82 **Admission Plans:** Deferred Admission **Application Deadline:** Rolling **Application Fee:** $25.00 **H.S. Requirements:** High school diploma required; GED accepted **Costs Per Year:** Application fee: $25. Comprehensive fee: $30,030 includes full-time tuition ($20,050), mandatory fees ($600), and college room and board ($9380). College room only: $4730. Room and board charges vary according to board plan and housing facility. Part-time tuition: $505 per credit. Part-time mandatory fees: $300 per term. **Scholarships:** Available. **Calendar System:** Semester, Summer session available **Enrollment:** Full-time 786, Graduate full-time 32, Graduate part-time 13, Part-time 102 **Faculty:** Full-time 43, Part-time 91 **Student-Faculty Ratio:** 12:1 **Exams:** ACT essay component not used; SAT I or ACT; SAT essay component not used. **% Receiving Financial Aid:** 82 % **Residing in College-Owned, -Operated, or -Affiliated Housing:** 29 **Final Year or Final Semester Residency Requirement:** No **Regional Accreditation:** Middle States Association of Colleges and Schools **Credit Hours For Degree:** 60 credit hours, Associates; 120 credit hours, Bachelors **ROTC:** Army **Intercollegiate Athletics:** Baseball M; Basketball M & W; Cross-Country Running M & W; Golf M; Lacrosse M & W; Soccer M & W; Softball W; Volleyball M & W

HOBART AND WILLIAM SMITH COLLEGES

Geneva, NY 14456-3397
Tel: (315)781-3000; Free: 800-852-2256
Fax: (315)781-5471
E-mail: murphy@hws.edu
Web Site: www.hws.edu
President/CEO: Mark D. Gearan
Admissions: Robert Murphy
Financial Aid: Beth Nepa

Type: Comprehensive **Sex:** Coed **Scores:** 100% SAT V 400+; 100% SAT M 400+; 67% ACT 24-29 **% Accepted:** 57 **Admission Plans:** Deferred Admission; Early Action; Early Admission **Application Deadline:** February 1 **Application Fee:** $45.00 **H.S. Requirements:** High school diploma required; GED accepted **Costs Per Year:** Application fee: $45. Comprehensive fee: $51,523 includes full-time tuition ($50,432), mandatory fees ($1091), and college room and board ($0). **Scholarships:** Available. **Calendar System:** Semester, Summer session not available **Enrollment:** Full-time 2,270, Graduate full-time 7, Part-time 74 **Faculty:** Full-time 223, Part-time 7 **Student-Faculty Ratio:** 10:1 **Exams:** ACT essay component used for admission; SAT I or ACT; SAT essay component used for admission; SAT Reasoning. **% Receiving Financial Aid:** 66 % **Residing in College-Owned, -Operated, or -Affiliated Housing:** 90 **Regional Accreditation:** Middle States Association of Colleges and Schools **Credit Hours For Degree:** 32 courses, Bachelors **ROTC:** Air Force, Army **Intercollegiate Athletics:** Basketball M & W; Crew M & W; Cross-Country Running M & W; Equestrian Sports M & W; Field Hockey W; Football M; Golf M & W; Ice Hockey M & W; Lacrosse M & W; Rock Climbing M & W; Rugby M & W; Sailing M & W; Skiing (Downhill) M & W; Soccer M & W; Squash M & W; Swimming and Diving W; Tennis M & W; Ultimate Frisbee M & W

HOFSTRA UNIVERSITY

100 Hofstra University
Hempstead, NY 11549
Tel: (516)463-6600; Free: 800-HOFSTRA
Fax: (516)560-7660
E-mail: admission@hofstra.edu
Web Site: www.hofstra.edu
President/CEO: Stuart Rabinowitz, JD
Admissions: Sunil A. Samuel

Financial Aid: Sandra Mervius

Type: University **Sex:** Coed **Scores:** 100% SAT V 400+; 100% SAT M 400+; 15% ACT 18-23; 64% ACT 24-29 **% Accepted:** 61 **Admission Plans:** Deferred Admission; Early Admission; Early Decision Plan **Application Deadline:** Rolling **Application Fee:** $70.00 **H.S. Requirements:** High school diploma required; GED accepted **Costs Per Year:** Application fee: $70. Comprehensive fee: $54,410 includes full-time tuition ($39,400), mandatory fees ($1060), and college room and board ($13,950). College room only: $9350. Full-time tuition and fees vary according to course load. Room and board charges vary according to board plan and housing facility. Part-time tuition: $1325 per credit hour. Part-time mandatory fees: $155 per term. Part-time tuition and fees vary according to course load. Tuition guaranteed not to increase for student's term of enrollment. **Scholarships:** Available. **Calendar System:** Semester, Summer session available **Enrollment:** Full-time 6,417, Graduate full-time 2,896, Graduate part-time 1,094, Part-time 407 **Faculty:** Full-time 498, Part-time 663 **Student-Faculty Ratio:** 13:1 **Exams:** ACT essay component used as validity check; Other; SAT essay component used as validity check. **% Receiving Financial Aid:** 66 % **Residing in College-Owned, -Operated, or -Affiliated Housing:** 47 **Final Year or Final Semester Residency Requirement:** Yes **Regional Accreditation:** Middle States Association of Colleges and Schools **Credit Hours For Degree:** 124 semester hours, Bachelors **ROTC:** Army **Professional Accreditation:** AACSB, AALS, ABA, ABET, ACEJMC, APA, ASHA, CORE, JRCAT, LCME/AMA, NCATE, TEAC. **Intercollegiate Athletics:** Baseball M; Basketball M & W; Cross-Country Running M & W; Field Hockey W; Golf M & W; Lacrosse M & W; Soccer M & W; Softball W; Tennis M & W; Volleyball W; Wrestling M

HOLY TRINITY ORTHODOX SEMINARY

PO Box 36
Jordanville, NY 13361
Tel: (315)858-0945
Fax: (315)858-0945
E-mail: ejwillmarth@hts.edu
Web Site: www.hts.edu
President/CEO: Rev. Archimandrite Luke Murianka
Admissions: Rev. Ephraim Willmarth

Type: Four-Year College **Sex:** Men **Affiliation:** Russian Orthodox. **% Accepted:** 100 **Admission Plans:** Deferred Admission **Application Deadline:** May 1 **Application Fee:** $40.00 **H.S. Requirements:** High school diploma required; GED accepted **Costs Per Year:** Application fee: $40. Comprehensive fee: $10,300 includes full-time tuition ($7000), mandatory fees ($300), and college room and board ($3000). College room only: $3000. Part-time tuition: $225 per credit hour. Part-time tuition varies according to program. **Calendar System:** Semester, Summer session not available **Enrollment:** Full-time 26, Part-time 28 **Student-Faculty Ratio:** 2:1 **% Residing in College-Owned, -Operated, or -Affiliated Housing:** 95 **Credit Hours For Degree:** 120 credit hours, Bachelors **Professional Accreditation:** NYSBR.

HOUGHTON COLLEGE

One Willard Ave.
Houghton, NY 14744
Tel: (585)567-9200; Free: 800-777-2556
Fax: (585)567-9522
E-mail: admission@houghton.edu
Web Site: www.houghton.edu
President/CEO: Dr. Shirley Mullen
Admissions: Ryan Spear
Financial Aid: Marianne Loper

Type: Comprehensive **Sex:** Coed **Affiliation:** Wesleyan. **Scores:** 96% SAT V 400+; 95% SAT M 400+; 31.65% ACT 18-23; 43.04% ACT 24-29 **% Accepted:** 94 **Admission Plans:** Deferred Admission **Application Deadline:** Rolling **Application Fee:** $40.00 **H.S. Requirements:** High school diploma required; GED accepted **Costs Per Year:** Application fee: $40. One-time mandatory fee: $100. Comprehensive fee: $37,956 includes full-time tuition ($29,258), mandatory fees ($200), and college room and board ($8498). College room only: $4558. Full-time tuition and fees vary according to course load and location. Room and board charges vary according to board plan and housing facility. Part-time tuition: $1230 per credit hour. Part-time tuition varies according to course load and location. **Scholarships:** Available. **Calendar System:** Semester, Summer session available **Enrollment:** Full-time 990, Graduate full-time 9, Graduate part-time 11, Part-time 63 **Faculty:** Full-time 73, Part-time 58 **Student-Faculty Ratio:** 11:1 **Exams:** ACT essay component used for advising; ACT essay component used for placement; SAT I or ACT; SAT essay component used for advising; SAT essay component used for placement. **% Receiving Financial Aid:** 81 % **Residing in College-Owned, -Operated, or -Affiliated Housing:** 81 **Final Year or Final Semester Residency Requirement:** Yes **Regional Accreditation:** Middle States Association of Colleges and Schools **Credit Hours For Degree:** 60 credit hours, Associates; 124 credit hours, Bachelors **ROTC:** Army **Professional Accreditation:** NASM. **Intercollegiate Athletics:** Baseball M; Basketball M & W; Cross-Country Running M & W; Field Hockey W; Lacrosse M & W; Soccer M & W; Softball W; Tennis M & W; Track and Field M & W; Volleyball W

HUDSON VALLEY COMMUNITY COLLEGE

80 Vandenburgh Ave.
Troy, NY 12180-6096
Tel: (518)629-4822; Free: 877-325-HVCC
Web Site: www.hvcc.edu
President/CEO: Andrew J. Matonak
Admissions: Marie Claire Bauer

Type: Two-Year College **Sex:** Coed **Affiliation:** State University of New York System. **Admission Plans:** Deferred Admission; Early Admission; Open Admission **Application Deadline:** Rolling **Application Fee:** $30.00 **H.S. Requirements:** High school diploma required; GED accepted **Scholarships:** Available. **Calendar System:** Semester, Summer session available **Student-Faculty Ratio:** 20:1 **Regional Accreditation:** Middle States Association of Colleges and Schools **Credit Hours For Degree:** 60 credits, Associates **ROTC:** Air Force, Army **Professional Accreditation:** ABET, ABFSE, ACCE, ACEN, ADA, CoARC, JRCEMTP, JRCERT. **Intercollegiate Athletics:** Baseball M; Basketball M & W; Bowling M & W; Cross-Country Running W; Football M; Ice Hockey M; Lacrosse M; Soccer M & W; Softball W; Tennis W; Volleyball W

HUNTER COLLEGE OF THE CITY UNIVERSITY OF NEW YORK

695 Park Ave.
New York, NY 10065-5085
Tel: (212)772-4000
E-mail: lori.janowski@hunter.cuny.edu
Web Site: www.hunter.cuny.edu
President/CEO: Jennifer J. Raab
Admissions: Lori Janowski
Financial Aid: Aristalia Cortorreal Diaz

Type: Comprehensive **Sex:** Coed **Affiliation:** City University of New York System. **Scores:** 100% SAT V 400+; 100% SAT M 400+ **% Accepted:** 39 **Admission Plans:** Early Action; Early Admission **Application Deadline:** March 15 **Application Fee:** $65.00 **H.S. Requirements:** High school diploma required; GED accepted **Costs Per Year:** Application fee: $65. State resident tuition: $275 per credit part-time. Nonresident tuition: $560 per credit part-time. Mandatory fees: $132.55 per term part-time. Part-time tuition and fees vary according to degree level and program. **Scholarships:** Available. **Calendar System:** Semester, Summer session available **Enrollment:** Full-time 12,033, Graduate full-time 1,412, Graduate part-time 4,958, Part-time 4,517 **Faculty:** Full-time 734, Part-time 1,554 **Student-Faculty Ratio:** 13:1 **Exams:** SAT I or ACT. **% Receiving Financial Aid:** 77 % **Residing in College-Owned, -Operated, or -Affiliated Housing:** 1 **Regional Accreditation:** Middle States Association of Colleges and Schools **Credit Hours For Degree:** 120 credits, Bachelors **Professional Accreditation:** AACN, ABET, ACA, ACSP, AND, APTA, ASHA, CEPH, CORE, CSWE, NCATE. **Intercollegiate Athletics:** Basketball M & W; Cross-Country Running M & W; Fencing M & W; Gymnastics W; Soccer M; Swimming and Diving W; Tennis M & W; Track and Field M & W; Volleyball M & W; Wrestling M

IONA COLLEGE

715 N Ave.
New Rochelle, NY 10801-1890
Tel: (914)633-2000; Free: 800-231-IONA
Fax: (914)633-2096
E-mail: admissions@iona.edu
Web Site: www.iona.edu
President/CEO: Dr. Joseph E. Nyre
Admissions: Alick Letang
Financial Aid: Mary Grant

Type: Comprehensive **Sex:** Coed **Affiliation:** Roman Catholic Church. **Scores:** 96% SAT V 400+; 93% SAT M 400+; 52.9% ACT 18-23; 32.7% ACT 24-29 **% Accepted:** 91 **Admission Plans:** Deferred Admission; Early Decision Plan **Application Deadline:** February 15 **Application Fee:** $50.00 **H.S.**

Requirements: High school diploma required; GED accepted **Costs Per Year:** Application fee: $50. Comprehensive fee: $49,304 includes full-time tuition ($33,124), mandatory fees ($2200), and college room and board ($13,980). Room and board charges vary according to board plan and housing facility. Part-time tuition: $1100 per credit. Part-time mandatory fees: $540 per term. Part-time tuition and fees vary according to course load. **Scholarships:** Available. **Calendar System:** Semester, Summer session available **Enrollment:** Full-time 2,959, Graduate full-time 383, Graduate part-time 323, Part-time 312 **Faculty:** Full-time 172, Part-time 169 **Student-Faculty Ratio:** 16:1 **Exams:** ACT essay component used for advising; ACT essay component used for placement; SAT I or ACT; SAT essay component used for advising; SAT essay component used for placement; SAT Reasoning. **% Receiving Financial Aid:** 81 % **Residing in College-Owned, -Operated, or -Affiliated Housing:** 41 **Final Year or Final Semester Residency Requirement:** Yes **Regional Accreditation:** Middle States Association of Colleges and Schools **Credit Hours For Degree:** 120 credits, Bachelors **ROTC:** Air Force, Army **Professional Accreditation:** AACSB, AAMFT, ABET, ACEJMC, CSWE, NCATE. **Intercollegiate Athletics:** Baseball M; Basketball M & W; Cross-Country Running M & W; Golf M; Lacrosse W; Rowing M & W; Soccer M & W; Softball W; Swimming and Diving M & W; Track and Field M & W; Volleyball W; Water Polo M & W

ISLAND DRAFTING AND TECHNICAL INSTITUTE

128 Broadway
Amityville, NY 11701
Tel: (631)691-8733
Fax: (631)691-8738
E-mail: info@idti.edu
Web Site: www.idti.edu
President/CEO: Pres. James Di Liberto
Admissions: Larry Basile
Financial Aid: Daniel Greener

Type: Two-Year College **Sex:** Coed **Admission Plans:** Early Admission; Open Admission **Application Fee:** $40.00 **H.S. Requirements:** High school diploma required; GED accepted **Costs Per Year:** Application fee: $40. Tuition: $15,750 full-time, $525 per credit part-time. Mandatory fees: $450 full-time. Tuition guaranteed not to increase for student's term of enrollment. **Scholarships:** Available. **Calendar System:** Semester, Summer session available **Enrollment:** Full-time 112 **Faculty:** Full-time 5, Part-time 6 **Student-Faculty Ratio:** 15:1 **Credit Hours For Degree:** 60 credits, Associates **Professional Accreditation:** ACCSC.

ITHACA COLLEGE

953 Danby Rd.
Ithaca, NY 14850
Tel: (607)274-3011; Free: 800-429-4274
Fax: (607)274-1900
E-mail: admission@ithaca.edu
Web Site: www.ithaca.edu
President/CEO: Dr. Thomas R. Rochon
Admissions: Nicole Eversley Bradwell
Financial Aid: Lisa Hoskey

Type: Comprehensive **Sex:** Coed **% Accepted:** 67 **Admission Plans:** Deferred Admission; Early Action; Early Admission; Early Decision Plan **Application Deadline:** February 1 **Application Fee:** $60.00 **H.S. Requirements:** High school diploma required; GED accepted **Costs Per Year:** Application fee: $60. Comprehensive fee: $55,332 includes full-time tuition ($40,658) and college room and board ($14,674). College room only: $7972. Room and board charges vary according to board plan and housing facility. Part-time tuition: $1355 per credit hour. **Scholarships:** Available. **Calendar System:** Semester, Summer session available **Enrollment:** Full-time 6,206, Graduate full-time 371, Graduate part-time 75, Part-time 117 **Faculty:** Full-time 512, Part-time 278 **Student-Faculty Ratio:** 11:1 **Exams:** SAT I or ACT; SAT II; SAT Reasoning; SAT Subject. **% Receiving Financial Aid:** 68 % **Residing in College-Owned, -Operated, or -Affiliated Housing:** 69 **Final Year or Final Semester Residency Requirement:** No **Regional Accreditation:** Middle States Association of Colleges and Schools **Credit Hours For Degree:** 120 credit hours, Bachelors **ROTC:** Air Force, Army **Professional Accreditation:** AACSB, AOTA, APTA, ASHA, JRCAT, NASM, NAST, NRPA. **Intercollegiate Athletics:** Baseball M; Basketball M & W; Crew M & W; Cross-Country Running M & W; Field Hockey W; Football M; Golf M; Gymnastics W; Lacrosse M & W; Soccer M & W; Softball W; Swimming and Diving M & W; Tennis M & W; Track and Field M & W; Volleyball W; Wrestling M

JAMESTOWN BUSINESS COLLEGE

7 Fairmount Ave., Box 429
Jamestown, NY 14702-0429
Tel: (716)664-5100
Fax: (716)664-3144
E-mail: brendasalemme@jamestownbusinesscollege.edu
Web Site: www.jamestownbusinesscollege.edu
President/CEO: Pres. David Conklin
Admissions: Brenda Salemme
Financial Aid: Diane Sturzenbecker

Type: Two-Year College **Sex:** Coed **% Accepted:** 93 **Application Deadline:** Rolling **Application Fee:** $25.00 **H.S. Requirements:** High school diploma required; GED accepted **Costs Per Year:** Application fee: $25. One-time mandatory fee: $25. Tuition: $11,400 full-time, $317 per credit hour part-time. Mandatory fees: $900 full-time. Full-time tuition and fees vary according to course load. Part-time tuition and fees vary according to course load. **Scholarships:** Available. **Calendar System:** Quarter, Summer session available **Enrollment:** Full-time 314, Part-time 4 **Faculty:** Full-time 6, Part-time 19 **Student-Faculty Ratio:** 23:1 **Final Year or Final Semester Residency Requirement:** No **Regional Accreditation:** Middle States Association of Colleges and Schools **Credit Hours For Degree:** 96 quarter hours, Associates

JAMESTOWN COMMUNITY COLLEGE

525 Falconer St.
Jamestown, NY 14701-1999
Tel: (716)338-1000; Free: 800-388-8557
E-mail: admissions@mail.sunyjcc.edu
Web Site: www.sunyjcc.edu
President/CEO: Cory L. Duckworth, JD
Admissions: Wendy Present

Type: Two-Year College **Sex:** Coed **Affiliation:** State University of New York System. **% Accepted:** 100 **Admission Plans:** Deferred Admission; Open Admission **Application Deadline:** Rolling **Application Fee:** $0.00 **H.S. Requirements:** High school diploma required; GED accepted **Costs Per Year:** Application fee: $0. One-time mandatory fee: $85. State resident tuition: $4570 full-time, $188 per credit hour part-time. Nonresident tuition: $9040 full-time, $377 per credit hour part-time. Mandatory fees: $582 full-time, $24.25 per credit hour part-time. Full-time tuition and fees vary according to course load and program. Part-time tuition and fees vary according to course load and program. College room and board: $10,740. College room only: $7540. Room and board charges vary according to board plan. **Scholarships:** Available. **Calendar System:** Semester, Summer session available **Enrollment:** Full-time 2,232, Part-time 806 **Faculty:** Full-time 86, Part-time 264 **Student-Faculty Ratio:** 16:1 **Exams:** Other. **% Residing in College-Owned, -Operated, or -Affiliated Housing:** 11 **Regional Accreditation:** Middle States Association of Colleges and Schools **Credit Hours For Degree:** 60 credit hours, Associates **Professional Accreditation:** ACEN, AOTA. **Intercollegiate Athletics:** Baseball M; Basketball M & W; Golf M & W; Soccer M & W; Softball W; Swimming and Diving M & W; Volleyball W; Wrestling M

JEFFERSON COMMUNITY COLLEGE

1220 Coffeen St.
Watertown, NY 13601
Tel: (315)786-2200; Free: 888-435-6522
Fax: (315)786-0158
E-mail: admissions@sunyjefferson.edu
Web Site: www.sunyjefferson.edu
President/CEO: Dr. Carole A. McCoy
Admissions: Rosanne N. Weir

Type: Two-Year College **Sex:** Coed **Affiliation:** State University of New York System. **Admission Plans:** Deferred Admission; Early Admission; Preferred Admission **Application Deadline:** September 6 **Application Fee:** $0.00 **H.S. Requirements:** High school diploma required; GED accepted **Costs Per Year:** Application fee: $0. State resident tuition: $4176 full-time, $174 per credit hour part-time. Nonresident tuition: $6456 full-time, $269 per credit hour part-time. Full-time tuition varies according to course load, location, and program. Part-time tuition varies according to course load, location, and program. College room and board: $10,050. Room and board charges vary according to board plan. **Scholarships:** Available. **Calendar System:** Semester, Summer session available **Enrollment:** Full-time 2,153, Part-time 1,727 **Exams:** SAT I or ACT. **Final Year or Final Semester Residency Requirement:** No **Regional Accreditation:** Middle States Association of

Colleges and Schools **Credit Hours For Degree:** 62 credit hours, Associates **Professional Accreditation:** ACEN. **Intercollegiate Athletics:** Baseball M; Basketball M & W; Lacrosse M & W; Soccer M & W; Softball W; Volleyball W

THE JEWISH THEOLOGICAL SEMINARY

3080 Broadway
New York, NY 10027-4649
Tel: (212)678-8000
Fax: (212)678-8947
E-mail: lcadmissions@jtsa.edu
Web Site: www.jtsa.edu
President/CEO: Dr. Arnold Eisen
Admissions: Sergio Lineberge
Financial Aid: Linda Levine

Type: University **Sex:** Coed **Affiliation:** Jewish. **Scores:** 100% SAT V 400+; 100% SAT M 400+; 39% ACT 24-29 **% Accepted:** 60 **Admission Plans:** Deferred Admission; Early Action; Early Admission **Application Deadline:** February 15 **Application Fee:** $65.00 **H.S. Requirements:** High school diploma required; GED accepted **Scholarships:** Available. **Calendar System:** Semester, Summer session available **Enrollment:** Full-time 182, Part-time 8 **Faculty:** Full-time 63, Part-time 67 **Student-Faculty Ratio:** 5:1 **Exams:** SAT I or ACT. **% Receiving Financial Aid:** 43 **% Residing in College-Owned, -Operated, or -Affiliated Housing:** 75 **Regional Accreditation:** Middle States Association of Colleges and Schools **Credit Hours For Degree:** 156 credits (96 in residence), Bachelors **ROTC:** Air Force, Army, Navy **Professional Accreditation:** ACIPE.

JOHN JAY COLLEGE OF CRIMINAL JUSTICE OF THE CITY UNIVERSITY OF NEW YORK

899 Tenth Ave.
New York, NY 10019-1093
Tel: (212)237-8000; Free: 877-JOHNJAY
Web Site: www.jjay.cuny.edu
President/CEO: Jeremy Travis
Financial Aid: Sylvia Lopez-Crespo

Type: Comprehensive **Sex:** Coed **Affiliation:** City University of New York System. **Scores:** 87% SAT V 400+; 92% SAT M 400+ **% Accepted:** 52 **Admission Plans:** Deferred Admission **Application Deadline:** May 31 **Application Fee:** $65.00 **H.S. Requirements:** High school diploma required; GED accepted **Scholarships:** Available. **Calendar System:** Semester, Summer session available **Enrollment:** Full-time 10,130, Graduate full-time 385, Graduate part-time 1,378, Part-time 2,839 **Exams:** ACT essay component used for placement; SAT I or ACT; SAT essay component used for admission; SAT essay component used for advising; SAT essay component used for placement; SAT Reasoning. **% Receiving Financial Aid:** 66 **Final Year or Final Semester Residency Requirement:** No **Regional Accreditation:** Middle States Association of Colleges and Schools **Credit Hours For Degree:** 60 credits, Associates; 120 credits, Bachelors **Professional Accreditation:** NASPAA. **Intercollegiate Athletics:** Baseball M; Basketball M & W; Cross-Country Running M & W; Soccer M & W; Softball W; Swimming and Diving W; Tennis M & W; Volleyball W

THE JUILLIARD SCHOOL

60 Lincoln Ctr. Plz.
New York, NY 10023-6588
Tel: (212)799-5000
Fax: (212)724-0263
E-mail: admissions@juilliard.edu
Web Site: www.juilliard.edu
President/CEO: Joseph W. Polisi
Admissions: Lee Cioppa
Financial Aid: Tina Gonzalez

Type: Comprehensive **Sex:** Coed **% Accepted:** 6 **Application Deadline:** December 1 **Application Fee:** $110.00 **H.S. Requirements:** High school diploma required; GED accepted **Costs Per Year:** Application fee: $110. Comprehensive fee: $54,860 includes full-time tuition ($39,720), mandatory fees ($350), and college room and board ($14,790). **Scholarships:** Available. **Calendar System:** Semester **Enrollment:** Full-time 488, Graduate full-time 344, Graduate part-time 20, Part-time 76 **Faculty:** Full-time 131, Part-time 220 **Student-Faculty Ratio:** 4:1 **Exams:** SAT I or ACT; SAT Reasoning; SAT Subject. **% Receiving Financial Aid:** 75 **Regional Accreditation:** Middle States Association of Colleges and Schools **Credit Hours For Degree:** 140 credits, Bachelors

KEHILATH YAKOV RABBINICAL SEMINARY

340 Illington Rd.
Ossining, NY 10562
Tel: (718)963-1212
Fax: (718)387-8586
Web Site: kehilathyakov.com
President/CEO: Joseph Weber
Type: Comprehensive **Sex:** Men **Affiliation:** Jewish. **Calendar System:** Semester **Professional Accreditation:** AARTS.

KEUKA COLLEGE

Keuka Park, NY 14478-0098
Tel: (315)279-5000; Free: 800-33-KEUKA
Fax: (315)279-5216
E-mail: admissions@keuka.edu
Web Site: www.keuka.edu
President/CEO: Prof. Jorge Diaz-Herrera, PhD
Admissions: Megan Perkins (Ryan)
Financial Aid: Jennifer Bates
Type: Comprehensive **Sex:** Coed **Affiliation:** American Baptist Churches in the U.S.A. **Scores:** 100% SAT V 400+; 98% SAT M 400+; 63% ACT 18-23; 26% ACT 24-29 **% Accepted:** 77 **Admission Plans:** Deferred Admission; Early Admission **Application Deadline:** Rolling **Application Fee:** $0.00 **H.S. Requirements:** High school diploma required; GED accepted **Costs Per Year:** Application fee: $0. One-time mandatory fee: $225. Comprehensive fee: $40,351 includes full-time tuition ($28,501), mandatory fees ($780), and college room and board ($11,070). College room only: $5258. Full-time tuition and fees vary according to degree level and program. Room and board charges vary according to board plan and housing facility. Part-time tuition: $952 per credit hour. Part-time tuition varies according to program. **Scholarships:** Available. **Calendar System:** 4-1-4, Summer session available **Enrollment:** Full-time 1,336, Graduate full-time 203, Graduate part-time 6, Part-time 388 **Faculty:** Full-time 91, Part-time 354 **Student-Faculty Ratio:** 8:1 **Exams:** ACT; SAT I; SAT I or ACT; SAT II; SAT Reasoning; SAT Subject. **% Receiving Financial Aid:** 84 **% Residing in College-Owned, -Operated, or -Affiliated Housing:** 80 **Regional Accreditation:** Middle States Association of Colleges and Schools **Credit Hours For Degree:** 120 credit hours, Bachelors **Professional Accreditation:** AACN, ACEN, AOTA, CSWE. **Intercollegiate Athletics:** Baseball M; Basketball M & W; Cheerleading M & W; Cross-Country Running M & W; Equestrian Sports M & W; Field Hockey W; Golf M & W; Lacrosse M & W; Soccer M & W; Softball W; Tennis M & W; Volleyball M & W

THE KING'S COLLEGE

56 Broadway
New York, NY 10004
Tel: (212)659-7200; Free: 888-969-7200
E-mail: lsmith@tkc.edu
Web Site: www.tkc.edu
President/CEO: Dr. Gregory Alan Thornbury, PhD
Admissions: Luke Smith
Financial Aid: Noah Hunter
Type: Four-Year College **Sex:** Coed **Affiliation:** nondenominational. **Scores:** 99% SAT V 400+; 99% SAT M 400+; 16% ACT 18-23; 60% ACT 24-29 **% Accepted:** 40 **Admission Plans:** Deferred Admission **Application Deadline:** Rolling **Application Fee:** $30.00 **H.S. Requirements:** High school diploma required; GED accepted **Costs Per Year:** Application fee: $30. Tuition: $34,320 full-time, $1410 per credit part-time. Mandatory fees: $400 full-time. Full-time tuition and fees vary according to course load. Part-time tuition varies according to course load. College room only: $13,650. Room charges vary according to location. **Scholarships:** Available. **Calendar System:** Semester, Summer session available **Enrollment:** Full-time 492, Part-time 21 **Faculty:** Full-time 26, Part-time 34 **Student-Faculty Ratio:** 13:1 **Exams:** ACT essay component not used; SAT I or ACT; SAT essay component not used. **% Receiving Financial Aid:** 73 **% Residing in College-Owned, -Operated, or -Affiliated Housing:** 90 **Final Year or Final Semester Residency Requirement:** No **Regional Accreditation:** Middle States Association of Colleges and Schools **Credit Hours For Degree:** 120 credits, Bachelors **ROTC:** Army **Intercollegiate Athletics:** Baseball M; Basketball M & W; Golf M & W; Soccer M & W; Volleyball W

KINGSBOROUGH COMMUNITY COLLEGE OF THE CITY UNIVERSITY OF NEW YORK

2001 Oriental Blvd., Manhattan Beach
Brooklyn, NY 11235
Tel: (718)368-5000
E-mail: info@kbcc.cuny.edu
Web Site: www.kbcc.cuny.edu
President/CEO: Farley Herzek
Admissions: Javier Morgades
Type: Two-Year College **Sex:** Coed **Affiliation:** City University of New York System. **Admission Plans:** Open Admission **Application Deadline:** August 15 **Application Fee:** $65.00 **H.S. Requirements:** High school diploma required; GED accepted **Costs Per Year:** Application fee: $65. State resident tuition: $4800 full-time, $210 per credit part-time. Nonresident tuition: $9600 full-time, $320 per credit part-time. Mandatory fees: $400 full-time, $92 per term part-time. **Scholarships:** Available. **Calendar System:** Semester, Summer session available **Enrollment:** Full-time 10,179, Part-time 7,316 **Regional Accreditation:** Middle States Association of Colleges and Schools **Credit Hours For Degree:** 60 credits, Associates **Professional Accreditation:** ACEN, APTA. **Intercollegiate Athletics:** Baseball M; Basketball M & W; Soccer M; Softball W; Tennis M & W; Track and Field M & W; Volleyball W

LE MOYNE COLLEGE

1419 Salt Springs Rd.
Syracuse, NY 13214
Tel: (315)445-4100; Free: 800-333-4733
Fax: (315)445-4711
E-mail: admission@lemoyne.edu
Web Site: www.lemoyne.edu
President/CEO: Linda M. LeMura, PhD
Admissions: Mary M. Chandler
Financial Aid: Sharon J. Halpin
Type: Comprehensive **Sex:** Coed **Affiliation:** Roman Catholic (Jesuit). **Scores:** 97% SAT V 400+; 98% SAT M 400+; 49% ACT 18-23; 42% ACT 24-29 **% Accepted:** 62 **Admission Plans:** Deferred Admission; Early Admission; Early Decision Plan **Application Deadline:** February 1 **Application Fee:** $35.00 **H.S. Requirements:** High school diploma required; GED accepted **Costs Per Year:** Application fee: $35. Comprehensive fee: $46,000 includes full-time tuition ($32,040), mandatory fees ($990), and college room and board ($12,970). College room only: $8120. Room and board charges vary according to board plan and housing facility. Part-time tuition: $672 per credit hour. Part-time tuition varies according to class time and course load. **Scholarships:** Available. **Calendar System:** Semester, Summer session available **Enrollment:** Full-time 2,495, Graduate full-time 196, Graduate part-time 405, Part-time 382 **Faculty:** Full-time 171, Part-time 175 **Student-Faculty Ratio:** 12:1 **Exams:** ACT essay component not used; SAT I or ACT; SAT essay component not used; SAT Reasoning. **% Receiving Financial Aid:** 83 **% Residing in College-Owned, -Operated, or -Affiliated Housing:** 59 **Final Year or Final Semester Residency Requirement:** Yes **Regional Accreditation:** Middle States Association of Colleges and Schools **Credit Hours For Degree:** 120 credit hours, Bachelors **ROTC:** Air Force, Army **Professional Accreditation:** AACN, AACSB, TEAC. **Intercollegiate Athletics:** Baseball M; Basketball M & W; Cross-Country Running M & W; Golf M & W; Lacrosse M & W; Soccer M & W; Softball W; Swimming and Diving M & W; Tennis M & W; Track and Field M & W; Volleyball W

LEHMAN COLLEGE OF THE CITY UNIVERSITY OF NEW YORK

250 Bedford Park Blvd. W
Bronx, NY 10468-1589
Tel: (718)960-8000; Free: 877-LEHMAN1
Fax: (718)960-8712
E-mail: enroll@lehman.cuny.edu
Web Site: www.lehman.cuny.edu
President/CEO: Dr. Ricardo R. Fernandez
Admissions: Laurie Austin
Financial Aid: David Martinez
Type: Comprehensive **Sex:** Coed **Affiliation:** City University of New York System. **Scores:** 89% SAT V 400+; 96% SAT M 400+ **% Accepted:** 23 **Admission Plans:** Deferred Admission **Application Deadline:** Rolling **Application Fee:** $65.00 **H.S. Requirements:** High school diploma required; GED accepted **Costs Per Year:** Application fee: $65. State resident tuition: $6330 full-time, $275 per credit hour part-time. Nonresident tuition: $13,440 full-time, $560 per credit hour part-time. Mandatory fees: $399 full-time, $117.10 per term part-time. Full-time tuition and fees vary according to course load. Part-time tuition and fees vary according to course load. **Scholarships:** Available. **Calendar System:** Semester, Summer session

available **Enrollment:** Full-time 5,646, Graduate full-time 273, Graduate part-time 1,926, Part-time 4,375 **Faculty:** Full-time 368, Part-time 544 **Student-Faculty Ratio:** 13:1 **Exams:** ACT essay component used for admission; SAT I or ACT; SAT essay component used for admission. **% Receiving Financial Aid:** 80 **Regional Accreditation:** Middle States Association of Colleges and Schools **Credit Hours For Degree:** 120 credits, Bachelors **ROTC:** Army **Professional Accreditation:** AACN, ACA, AND, ASHA, CSWE, NCATE. **Intercollegiate Athletics:** Baseball M; Basketball M & W; Cross-Country Running M & W; Racquetball M & W; Soccer M & W; Softball M & W; Swimming and Diving M & W; Table Tennis M & W; Tennis M & W; Track and Field M & W; Volleyball M & W; Water Polo M; Wrestling M

LIM COLLEGE
12 E 53rd St.
New York, NY 10022-5268
Tel: (212)752-1530; Free: 800-677-1323
Fax: (212)832-6708
E-mail: admissions@limcollege.edu
Web Site: www.limcollege.edu
President/CEO: Elizabeth S. Marcuse
Admissions: Anthony Urmey

Type: Comprehensive **Sex:** Coed **Scores:** 91% SAT V 400+; 81% SAT M 400+; 53% ACT 18-23; 25% ACT 24-29 **Costs Per Year:** Comprehensive fee: $46,075 includes full-time tuition ($24,950), mandatory fees ($775), and college room and board ($20,350). College room only: $16,350. Part-time tuition: $805 per credit. **Scholarships:** Available. **Calendar System:** Semester, Summer session available **Enrollment:** Full-time 1,428, Graduate full-time 113, Graduate part-time 72, Part-time 87 **Faculty:** Full-time 32, Part-time 164 **Student-Faculty Ratio:** 8:1 **Exams:** ACT essay component used for admission; ACT essay component used for placement; SAT I or ACT; SAT essay component used for admission; SAT essay component used for placement. **% Receiving Financial Aid:** 66 **% Residing in College-Owned, -Operated, or -Affiliated Housing:** 27 **Final Year or Final Semester Residency Requirement:** Yes **Regional Accreditation:** Middle States Association of Colleges and Schools **Credit Hours For Degree:** 67 credits, Associates; 124 credits, Bachelors **Professional Accreditation:** ACBSP.

LONG ISLAND BUSINESS INSTITUTE
136-18 39th Ave., 5th Fl.
Flushing, NY 11354
Tel: (718)939-5100
Fax: (718)939-9235
E-mail: jlin@libi.edu
Web Site: www.libi.edu
President/CEO: Monica W. Foote
Admissions: Jane Lin

Type: Two-Year College **Sex:** Coed **% Accepted:** 61 **Application Deadline:** Rolling **H.S. Requirements:** High school diploma required; GED accepted **Costs Per Year:** Tuition: $13,299 full-time, $375 per credit part-time. Mandatory fees: $1350 full-time, $450 per term part-time. **Calendar System:** Semester, Summer session available **Enrollment:** Full-time 472, Part-time 118 **Faculty:** Full-time 25, Part-time 53 **Student-Faculty Ratio:** 6:1 **Exams:** Other. **Credit Hours For Degree:** 60 credits, Associates **Professional Accreditation:** ACICS.

LONG ISLAND UNIVERSITY–LIU BROOKLYN
One University Plz.
Brooklyn, NY 11201-8423
Tel: (718)488-1000; Free: 800-LIU-PLAN
E-mail: bkln-admissions@liu.edu
Web Site: www.liu.edu
President/CEO: Dr. Kimberly R. Cline
Admissions: Richard Sunday
Financial Aid: Margaret Nelson

Type: University **Sex:** Coed **Scores:** 80% SAT V 400+; 80% SAT M 400+; 39% ACT 18-23; 34% ACT 24-29 **% Accepted:** 91 **Admission Plans:** Deferred Admission; Early Decision Plan **Application Deadline:** Rolling **Application Fee:** $50.00 **H.S. Requirements:** High school diploma required; GED accepted **Costs Per Year:** Application fee: $50. Comprehensive fee: $48,146 includes full-time tuition ($33,678), mandatory fees ($1868), and college room and board ($12,600). Full-time tuition and fees vary according to program. Room and board charges vary according to board plan and housing facility. Part-time tuition: $1051 per credit. Part-time mandatory fees:

$442 per term. Part-time tuition and fees vary according to program. **Scholarships:** Available. **Calendar System:** Semester, Summer session available **Enrollment:** Full-time 4,045, Graduate full-time 2,044, Graduate part-time 1,465, Part-time 616 **Faculty:** Full-time 238, Part-time 628 **Student-Faculty Ratio:** 15:1 **Exams:** ACT essay component used for advising; ACT essay component used for placement; SAT I or ACT; SAT essay component used for advising; SAT essay component used for placement. **% Receiving Financial Aid:** 94 **% Residing in College-Owned, -Operated, or -Affiliated Housing:** 14 **Final Year or Final Semester Residency Requirement:** Yes **Regional Accreditation:** Middle States Association of Colleges and Schools **Credit Hours For Degree:** 64 credits, Associates; 128 credits, Bachelors **ROTC:** Army **Professional Accreditation:** AACN, ACPE, AOTA, APA, APTA, ASHA, CSWE, CoARC, NASPAA, TEAC. **Intercollegiate Athletics:** Baseball M; Basketball M & W; Bowling W; Cross-Country Running M & W; Field Hockey W; Golf M & W; Lacrosse W; Soccer M & W; Softball W; Swimming and Diving W; Tennis W; Track and Field M & W; Volleyball W

LONG ISLAND UNIVERSITY–LIU POST
720 Northern Blvd.
Brookville, NY 11548-1300
Tel: (516)299-2000; Free: 800-LIU-PLAN
E-mail: post-enroll@liu.edu
Web Site: www.liu.edu
President/CEO: Dr. Kimberly R. Cline
Admissions: Marcelle Hicks
Financial Aid: Joanne Graziano

Type: Comprehensive **Sex:** Coed **Scores:** 95% SAT V 400+; 93% SAT M 400+; 58% ACT 18-23; 28% ACT 24-29 **% Accepted:** 81 **Admission Plans:** Deferred Admission; Early Decision Plan **Application Deadline:** Rolling **Application Fee:** $50.00 **H.S. Requirements:** High school diploma required; GED accepted **Costs Per Year:** Application fee: $50. Comprehensive fee: $48,684 includes full-time tuition ($33,678), mandatory fees ($1868), and college room and board ($13,138). Full-time tuition and fees vary according to program. Room and board charges vary according to board plan and housing facility. Part-time tuition: $1051 per credit. Part-time mandatory fees: $442 per term. Part-time tuition and fees vary according to program. **Scholarships:** Available. **Calendar System:** Semester, Summer session available **Enrollment:** Full-time 3,090, Graduate full-time 1,209, Graduate part-time 1,190, Part-time 3,134 **Faculty:** Full-time 278, Part-time 652 **Student-Faculty Ratio:** 12:1 **Exams:** ACT essay component not used; SAT I or ACT; SAT essay component not used. **% Receiving Financial Aid:** 83 **% Residing in College-Owned, -Operated, or -Affiliated Housing:** 31 **Final Year or Final Semester Residency Requirement:** No **Regional Accreditation:** Middle States Association of Colleges and Schools **Credit Hours For Degree:** 64 credits, Associates; 128 credits, Bachelors **ROTC:** Army **Professional Accreditation:** AACN, AACSB, ACA, AHIMA, ALA, AND, APA, ASHA, CSWE, JRCERT, NAACLS, NASPAA, TEAC. **Intercollegiate Athletics:** Baseball M; Basketball M & W; Bowling W; Cheerleading M & W; Crew M & W; Cross-Country Running M & W; Equestrian Sports M & W; Fencing W; Field Hockey W; Football W; Golf W; Ice Hockey M; Lacrosse M & W; Rugby W; Soccer M & W; Softball W; Swimming and Diving W; Tennis W; Track and Field M & W; Volleyball W; Wrestling M

MACHZIKEI HADATH RABBINICAL COLLEGE
5407 Sixteenth Ave.
Brooklyn, NY 11204-1805
Tel: (718)854-8777
President/CEO: Rabbi Yisroel Aurbach
Admissions: Rabbi Abraham M. Lezerowitz
Financial Aid: Rabbi Baruch Rozmarin

Type: Comprehensive **Sex:** Men **Affiliation:** Jewish. **Application Deadline:** Rolling **H.S. Requirements:** High school diploma required; GED not accepted **Calendar System:** Semester **Credit Hours For Degree:** 120 credits, Bachelors **Professional Accreditation:** AARTS.

MANDL SCHOOL
254 W 54th St., 9th Fl.
New York, NY 10019
Tel: (212)247-3434
Web Site: www.mandlschool.com

Type: Two-Year College **Sex:** Coed **Professional Accreditation:** ABHES.

MANHATTAN COLLEGE
4513 Manhattan College Pky.
Riverdale, NY 10471

Tel: (718)862-8000; Free: 800-622-9235
Fax: (718)862-8019
E-mail: admit@manhattan.edu
Web Site: www.manhattan.edu
President/CEO: Dr. Brennan O'Donnell
Admissions: Dr. William Bisset
Financial Aid: Denise Scalzo
Type: Comprehensive **Sex:** Coed **Affiliation:** Roman Catholic Church.
Scores: 98% SAT V 400+; 99% SAT M 400+; 36% ACT 18-23; 50% ACT
24-29 **% Accepted:** 67 **Admission Plans:** Deferred Admission; Early Action;
Early Admission **Application Deadline:** April 15 **Application Fee:** $60.00
H.S. Requirements: High school diploma required; GED accepted **Costs
Per Year:** Application fee: $60. Comprehensive fee: $53,360 includes full-
time tuition ($35,600), mandatory fees ($3330), and college room and board
($14,430). Full-time tuition and fees vary according to course load, program,
and student level. Room and board charges vary according to board plan.
Part-time tuition: $910 per credit. Part-time tuition varies according to course
load. **Scholarships:** Available. **Calendar System:** Semester, Summer session available **Enrollment:** Full-time 3,384, Graduate full-time 217, Graduate
part-time 278, Part-time 192 **Faculty:** Full-time 221, Part-time 217 **Student-
Faculty Ratio:** 13:1 **Exams:** ACT; ACT essay component used for advising;
ACT essay component used for placement; SAT I; SAT I or ACT; SAT essay
component used for advising; SAT essay component used for placement;
SAT Reasoning. **% Receiving Financial Aid:** 85 **% Residing in College-
Owned, -Operated, or -Affiliated Housing:** 67 **Final Year or Final
Semester Residency Requirement:** No **Regional Accreditation:** Middle
States Association of Colleges and Schools **Credit Hours For Degree:** 120
credit hours, Bachelors **ROTC:** Air Force, Army **Professional Accredita-
tion:** AACSB, ABET, TEAC. **Intercollegiate Athletics:** Baseball M;
Basketball M & W; Cheerleading W; Crew M & W; Cross-Country Running M
& W; Golf M; Lacrosse M & W; Rugby M; Soccer M & W; Softball W; Swim-
ming and Diving M & W; Tennis W; Track and Field M & W; Volleyball W

MANHATTAN SCHOOL OF MUSIC
120 Claremont Ave.
New York, NY 10027-4698
Tel: (212)749-2802
Fax: (212)749-5471
E-mail: aanderson@msmnyc.edu
Web Site: www.msmnyc.edu
President/CEO: Dr. James Gandre
Admissions: Amy Anderson
Financial Aid: Amy Anderson
Type: Comprehensive **Sex:** Coed **% Accepted:** 45 **Admission Plans:**
Deferred Admission **Application Deadline:** December 1 **Application Fee:**
$125.00 **H.S. Requirements:** High school diploma required; GED accepted
Costs Per Year: Application fee: $125. Comprehensive fee: $56,824
includes full-time tuition ($42,000), mandatory fees ($600), and college room
and board ($14,224). College room only: $9725. Room and board charges
vary according to board plan and housing facility. Part-time tuition: $1750 per
credit hour. Part-time mandatory fees: $600 per year. Part-time tuition and
fees vary according to course load. **Scholarships:** Available. **Calendar
System:** Semester, Summer session not available **Enrollment:** Full-time
385, Graduate full-time 566, Graduate part-time 2, Part-time 4 **Student-
Faculty Ratio:** 6:1 **Exams:** ACT essay component not used; SAT I or ACT;
SAT essay component not used. **% Residing in College-Owned,
-Operated, or -Affiliated Housing:** 67 **Regional Accreditation:** Middle
States Association of Colleges and Schools **Credit Hours For Degree:** 120
credits, Bachelors

MANHATTANVILLE COLLEGE
2900 Purchase St.
Purchase, NY 10577-2132
Tel: (914)694-2200; Free: 800-328-4553
Fax: (914)694-1732
E-mail: joseph.Cosentino@mville.edu
Web Site: www.mville.edu
President/CEO: Dr. Jon Strauss, PhD
Admissions: Joseph Cosentino
Financial Aid: Robert Gilmore
Type: Comprehensive **Sex:** Coed **Scores:** 99% SAT V 400+; 99% SAT M
400+ **% Accepted:** 74 **Admission Plans:** Deferred Admission; Early Admis-
sion; Early Decision Plan **Application Deadline:** March 1 **Application Fee:**
$50.00 **H.S. Requirements:** High school diploma required; GED accepted

Costs Per Year: Application fee: $50. Comprehensive fee: $51,440 includes
full-time tuition ($35,570), mandatory fees ($1350), and college room and
board ($14,520). College room only: $8680. Full-time tuition and fees vary
according to course load. Room and board charges vary according to board
plan. Part-time tuition: $825 per credit. Part-time mandatory fees: $60 per
term. Part-time tuition and fees vary according to course load and program.
Scholarships: Available. **Calendar System:** Semester, Summer session
available **Enrollment:** Full-time 1,714, Graduate full-time 237, Graduate
part-time 882, Part-time 88 **Faculty:** Full-time 109, Part-time 206 **Student-
Faculty Ratio:** 12:1 **Exams:** ACT; ACT essay component not used; SAT I;
SAT I and SAT II or ACT; SAT I or ACT; SAT essay component not used; SAT
Reasoning; SAT Subject. **% Receiving Financial Aid:** 68 **% Residing in
College-Owned, -Operated, or -Affiliated Housing:** 62 **Final Year or Final
Semester Residency Requirement:** No **Regional Accreditation:** Middle
States Association of Colleges and Schools **Credit Hours For Degree:** 120
credits, Bachelors **Professional Accreditation:** NCATE. **Intercollegiate
Athletics:** Baseball M; Basketball M & W; Cross-Country Running M & W;
Field Hockey W; Golf M & W; Ice Hockey M & W; Lacrosse M & W; Soccer M
& W; Softball W; Track and Field M & W; Volleyball W

MARIA COLLEGE
700 New Scotland Ave.
Albany, NY 12208-1798
Tel: (518)438-3111
E-mail: admissions@mariacollege.edu
Web Site: www.mariacollege.edu
President/CEO: Joseph Salamack, III
Admissions: John Ramoska
Type: Four-Year College **Sex:** Coed **Scores:** 79% SAT V 400+; 79% SAT M
400+; 50% ACT 18-23; 33% ACT 24-29 **% Accepted:** 46 **Admission Plans:**
Deferred Admission; Early Action; Early Admission **Application Deadline:**
March 1 **Application Fee:** $35.00 **H.S. Requirements:** High school diploma
required; GED accepted **Costs Per Year:** Application fee: $35. Tuition:
$13,020 full-time, $555 per credit hour part-time. Mandatory fees: $320 full-
time. Full-time tuition and fees vary according to course load, program, and
reciprocity agreements. Part-time tuition varies according to course load,
program, and reciprocity agreements. **Scholarships:** Available. **Calendar
System:** Semester, Summer session available **Enrollment:** Full-time 297,
Part-time 511 **Faculty:** Full-time 30, Part-time 77 **Student-Faculty Ratio:**
8:1 **Exams:** Other; SAT I or ACT; SAT Reasoning. **Final Year or Final
Semester Residency Requirement:** No **Regional Accreditation:** Middle
States Association of Colleges and Schools **Credit Hours For Degree:** 62
credits, Associates; 120 credits, Bachelors **ROTC:** Air Force **Professional
Accreditation:** ACEN, AOTA.

MARIST COLLEGE
3399 N Rd.
Poughkeepsie, NY 12601-1387
Tel: (845)575-3000; Free: 800-436-5483
Fax: (845)471-6213
E-mail: admission@marist.edu
Web Site: www.marist.edu
President/CEO: Dr. Dennis Murray
Admissions: Kent Rinehart
Financial Aid: Joseph R. Weglarz
Type: Comprehensive **Sex:** Coed **Scores:** 98% SAT V 400+; 28% ACT 18-
23; 56% ACT 24-29 **% Accepted:** 45 **Admission Plans:** Deferred Admis-
sion; Early Action; Early Admission; Early Decision Plan **Application
Deadline:** February 1 **Application Fee:** $50.00 **H.S. Requirements:** High
school diploma required; GED accepted **Costs Per Year:** Application fee:
$50. One-time mandatory fee: $100. Comprehensive fee: $48,650 includes
full-time tuition ($33,250), mandatory fees ($550), and college room and
board ($14,850). College room only: $10,480. Full-time tuition and fees vary
according to course load and location. Room and board charges vary according to board plan, housing facility, and location. Part-time tuition: $634
per credit. Part-time mandatory fees: $40 per term. Part-time tuition and fees
vary according to course load. **Scholarships:** Available. **Calendar System:**
Semester, Summer session available **Enrollment:** Full-time 4,874, Graduate
full-time 328, Graduate part-time 570, Part-time 702 **Faculty:** Full-time 234,
Part-time 385 **Student-Faculty Ratio:** 16:1 **Exams:** ACT essay component
used for placement; SAT essay component used for placement; SAT
Reasoning; SAT Subject. **% Receiving Financial Aid:** 56 **% Residing in
College-Owned, -Operated, or -Affiliated Housing:** 69 **Final Year or Final
Semester Residency Requirement:** Yes **Regional Accreditation:** Middle

States Association of Colleges and Schools **Credit Hours For Degree:** 120 credits, Bachelors **ROTC:** Army **Professional Accreditation:** AACSB, CSWE, NAACLS. **Intercollegiate Athletics:** Baseball M; Basketball M & W; Bowling M & W; Cheerleading M & W; Crew M & W; Cross-Country Running M & W; Equestrian Sports M & W; Fencing M & W; Football M; Ice Hockey M; Lacrosse M & W; Rugby M & W; Skiing (Downhill) M & W; Soccer M & W; Softball W; Swimming and Diving M & W; Tennis M & W; Track and Field M & W; Volleyball M & W; Water Polo W

MARYMOUNT MANHATTAN COLLEGE
221 E 71st St.
New York, NY 10021-4597
Tel: (212)517-0400; Free: 800-627-9668
E-mail: jrogers@mmm.edu
Web Site: www.mmm.edu
President/CEO: Kerry Walk
Admissions: Jim Rogers
Financial Aid: Christina Bennett
Type: Four-Year College **Sex:** Coed **Scores:** 97% SAT V 400+; 94% SAT M 400+; 46% ACT 18-23; 40% ACT 24-29 **% Accepted:** 84 **Admission Plans:** Deferred Admission **Application Deadline:** Rolling **Application Fee:** $60.00 **H.S. Requirements:** High school diploma required; GED accepted **Costs Per Year:** Application fee: $60. Comprehensive fee: $44,200 includes full-time tuition ($27,360), mandatory fees ($1340), and college room and board ($15,500). Full-time tuition and fees vary according to course load and program. Room and board charges vary according to board plan. Part-time tuition: $912 per credit hour. Part-time mandatory fees: $490 per term. Part-time tuition and fees vary according to course load and program. **Scholarships:** Available. **Calendar System:** Semester, Summer session available **Enrollment:** Full-time 1,711, Part-time 217 **Faculty:** Full-time 94, Part-time 212 **Student-Faculty Ratio:** 11:1 **Exams:** ACT essay component not used; SAT I or ACT; SAT essay component not used; SAT Reasoning. **% Receiving Financial Aid:** 69 **% Residing in College-Owned, -Operated, or -Affiliated Housing:** 38 **Final Year or Final Semester Residency Requirement:** No **Regional Accreditation:** Middle States Association of Colleges and Schools **Credit Hours For Degree:** 60 credits, Associates; 120 credits, Bachelors

MEDAILLE COLLEGE
18 Agassiz Cir.
Buffalo, NY 14214-2695
Tel: (716)880-2000; Free: 800-292-1582
Fax: (716)884-0291
E-mail: admissionsug@medaille.edu
Web Site: www.medaille.edu
President/CEO: Dr. Richard T. Jurasek, PhD
Admissions: Christopher LaRusso
Financial Aid: Catherine Buzanski
Type: Comprehensive **Sex:** Coed **Scores:** 71% SAT V 400+; 65% SAT M 400+ **% Accepted:** 54 **Admission Plans:** Deferred Admission; Early Admission **Application Deadline:** August 1 **Application Fee:** $25.00 **H.S. Requirements:** High school diploma required; GED not accepted **Costs Per Year:** Application fee: $25. Comprehensive fee: $37,492 includes full-time tuition ($26,252) and college room and board ($11,240). Full-time tuition varies according to location. Room and board charges vary according to board plan and housing facility. Part-time tuition: $925 per credit hour. Part-time tuition varies according to course load. **Scholarships:** Available. **Calendar System:** Semester, Summer session available **Enrollment:** Full-time 1,637, Graduate full-time 488, Graduate part-time 92, Part-time 166 **Faculty:** Full-time 87, Part-time 207 **Student-Faculty Ratio:** 14:1 **Exams:** SAT I; SAT I or ACT. **% Receiving Financial Aid:** 95 **% Residing in College-Owned, -Operated, or -Affiliated Housing:** 22 **Regional Accreditation:** Middle States Association of Colleges and Schools **Credit Hours For Degree:** 60 credit hours, Associates; 120 credit hours, Bachelors **ROTC:** Army **Professional Accreditation:** TEAC. **Intercollegiate Athletics:** Baseball M; Basketball M & W; Bowling W; Cross-Country Running M & W; Golf M; Lacrosse M & W; Soccer M & W; Softball W; Volleyball M & W

MEDGAR EVERS COLLEGE OF THE CITY UNIVERSITY OF NEW YORK
1650 Bedford Ave.
Brooklyn, NY 11225-2298
Tel: (718)270-4900
E-mail: shannon@mec.cuny.edu

Web Site: www.mec.cuny.edu
President/CEO: Dr. William L. Pollard
Admissions: Dr. Shannon Clarke-Anderson
Financial Aid: Nigel Thompson
Type: Four-Year College **Sex:** Coed **Affiliation:** City University of New York System. **Scores:** 47% SAT V 400+; 42% SAT M 400+ **% Accepted:** 91 **Admission Plans:** Deferred Admission; Open Admission; Preferred Admission **Application Deadline:** Rolling **Application Fee:** $65.00 **H.S. Requirements:** High school diploma required; GED accepted **Costs Per Year:** Application fee: $65. State resident tuition: $6330 full-time, $275 per credit part-time. Nonresident tuition: $16,800 full-time, $560 per credit part-time. Mandatory fees: $320 full-time, $100.85 per term part-time. Full-time tuition and fees vary according to course load. Part-time tuition and fees vary according to course load. **Scholarships:** Available. **Calendar System:** Semester, Summer session available **Enrollment:** Full-time 4,324, Part-time 2,377 **Faculty:** Full-time 183, Part-time 307 **Student-Faculty Ratio:** 17:1 **Exams:** SAT I and SAT II or ACT; SAT essay component used for placement. **Final Year or Final Semester Residency Requirement:** No **Regional Accreditation:** Middle States Association of Colleges and Schools **Credit Hours For Degree:** 64 credits, Associates; 120 credits, Bachelors **Professional Accreditation:** ACBSP, ACEN, NCATE. **Intercollegiate Athletics:** Basketball M & W; Cross-Country Running M & W; Soccer M & W; Tennis W; Track and Field M & W; Volleyball M & W

MEMORIAL HOSPITAL SCHOOL OF NURSING
600 Northern Blvd.
Albany, NY 12204
Tel: (518)471-3260
Fax: (518)447-3559
Web Site: www.nehealth.com/son
President/CEO: Mary-Jane Araldi
Type: Two-Year College **Sex:** Coed **Calendar System:** Semester **Professional Accreditation:** NYSBR.

MERCY COLLEGE
555 Broadway
Dobbs Ferry, NY 10522-1189
Tel: (914)693-4500; Free: 877-MERCY-GO
Fax: (914)674-7382
E-mail: admissions@mercy.edu
Web Site: www.mercy.edu
President/CEO: Dr. Timothy L. Hall
Admissions: Tara Fay-Reilly
Financial Aid: Margaret McGrail
Type: Comprehensive **Sex:** Coed **% Accepted:** 66 **Admission Plans:** Deferred Admission; Early Decision Plan **Application Deadline:** Rolling **Application Fee:** $40.00 **H.S. Requirements:** High school diploma required; GED accepted **Costs Per Year:** Application fee: $40. Comprehensive fee: $31,776 includes full-time tuition ($17,466), mandatory fees ($610), and college room and board ($13,700). College room only: $9350. Full-time tuition and fees vary according to course load. Room and board charges vary according to board plan. Part-time tuition: $735 per credit. Part-time mandatory fees: $153 per term. Part-time tuition and fees vary according to course load. **Scholarships:** Available. **Calendar System:** Semester, Summer session available **Enrollment:** Full-time 5,392, Graduate full-time 1,431, Graduate part-time 1,848, Part-time 2,624 **Faculty:** Full-time 198, Part-time 857 **Student-Faculty Ratio:** 17:1 **Exams:** ACT; ACT essay component used for advising; ACT essay component used for placement; Other; SAT I; SAT I and SAT II or ACT; SAT I or ACT; SAT II; SAT essay component used for advising; SAT essay component used for placement. **% Receiving Financial Aid:** 85 **% Residing in College-Owned, -Operated, or -Affiliated Housing:** 13 **Final Year or Final Semester Residency Requirement:** No **Regional Accreditation:** Middle States Association of Colleges and Schools **Credit Hours For Degree:** 60 credits, Associates; 120 credits, Bachelors **ROTC:** Air Force, Army **Professional Accreditation:** AACN, ACAOM, ACBSP, AOTA, APTA, ASHA, CSWE, NASAD. **Intercollegiate Athletics:** Baseball M; Basketball M & W; Field Hockey W; Lacrosse M & W; Soccer M & W; Softball W; Volleyball W

MESIVTA OF EASTERN PARKWAY–YESHIVA ZICHRON MEILECH
510 Dahill Rd.
Brooklyn, NY 11218-5559
Tel: (718)438-1002
President/CEO: Ira Liberman

Admissions: Rabbi Joseph Halberstadt
Financial Aid: Rabbi Joseph Halberstadt
Type: Five-Year College **Sex:** Men **Affiliation:** Jewish. **% Accepted:** 50 **Application Deadline:** Rolling **H.S. Requirements:** High school diploma required; GED not accepted **Calendar System:** Semester, Summer session not available **Enrollment:** Full-time 23, Graduate full-time 2 **Professional Accreditation:** AARTS.

MESIVTA TORAH VODAATH RABBINICAL SEMINARY
425 E Ninth St.
Brooklyn, NY 11218-5299
Tel: (718)941-8000
Fax: (718)941-8032
Web Site: www.torahvodaath.org
President/CEO: Chaim Leshkowitz
Admissions: Rabbi Issac Braun
Financial Aid: Kayla Goldring
Type: Comprehensive **Sex:** Men **Affiliation:** Jewish. **Admission Plans:** Deferred Admission; Early Admission; Preferred Admission **Application Deadline:** Rolling **Application Fee:** $200.00 **H.S. Requirements:** High school diploma required; GED accepted **Calendar System:** Semester, Summer session available **Credit Hours For Degree:** 128 credits, Bachelors **Professional Accreditation:** AARTS.

MESIVTHA TIFERETH JERUSALEM OF AMERICA
145 E Broadway
New York, NY 10002-6301
Tel: (212)964-2830
President/CEO: Yisrael H. Eidelman
Type: Comprehensive **Sex:** Men **Affiliation:** Jewish. **% Accepted:** 100 **Calendar System:** Semester **Professional Accreditation:** AARTS.

METROPOLITAN COLLEGE OF NEW YORK
431 Canal St.
New York, NY 10013
Tel: (212)343-1234; Free: 800-33-THINK
Fax: (212)343-8470
Web Site: www.metropolitan.edu
President/CEO: Dr. Vinton Thompson
Financial Aid: Douane Campbell
Type: Comprehensive **Sex:** Coed **% Accepted:** 53 **Admission Plans:** Deferred Admission **Application Deadline:** September 9 **Application Fee:** $30.00 **H.S. Requirements:** High school diploma required; GED accepted **Costs Per Year:** Application fee: $30. Tuition: $17,880 full-time, $747 per credit part-time. Mandatory fees: $850 full-time. Full-time tuition and fees vary according to degree level and program. Part-time tuition varies according to degree level and program. Tuition guaranteed not to increase for student's term of enrollment. **Scholarships:** Available. **Calendar System:** Miscellaneous, Summer session available **Enrollment:** Full-time 685, Graduate full-time 370, Graduate part-time 46, Part-time 94 **Exams:** Other; SAT I or ACT. **% Receiving Financial Aid:** 94 **Final Year or Final Semester Residency Requirement:** No **Regional Accreditation:** Middle States Association of Colleges and Schools **Credit Hours For Degree:** 60 credits, Associates; 120 credits, Bachelors **Professional Accreditation:** ACBSP, NCATE.

MILDRED ELLEY SCHOOL
855 Central Ave.
Albany, NY 12206
Tel: (518)786-0855; Free: 800-622-6327
Fax: (518)786-0898
Web Site: www.mildred-elley.edu
President/CEO: Faith Ann Takes
Admissions: Michael Cahalan
Type: Two-Year College **Sex:** Coed **Application Fee:** $25.00 **Scholarships:** Available. **Exams:** Other. **Professional Accreditation:** ACICS.

MILDRED ELLEY–NEW YORK CITY
25 Broadway, 16th Fl.
New York, NY 10004-1010
Tel: (212)380-9004
Web Site: www.mildred-elley.edu
Type: Two-Year College **Sex:** Coed **Professional Accreditation:** ACICS.

MIRRER YESHIVA
1795 Ocean Pky.
Brooklyn, NY 11223-2010
Tel: (718)645-0536
President/CEO: Osher Kalmanowitz
Type: Comprehensive **Sex:** Men **Affiliation:** Jewish. **% Accepted:** 100 **H.S. Requirements:** High school diploma or equivalent not required **Calendar System:** Semester **Professional Accreditation:** AARTS.

MOHAWK VALLEY COMMUNITY COLLEGE
1101 Sherman Dr.
Utica, NY 13501-5394
Tel: (315)792-5400
Fax: (315)792-5527
E-mail: nsynder@mvcc.edu
Web Site: www.mvcc.edu
President/CEO: Dr. Randall J. VanWagoner
Admissions: Nolan Snyder
Type: Two-Year College **Sex:** Coed **Affiliation:** State University of New York System. **% Accepted:** 100 **Admission Plans:** Deferred Admission; Open Admission **Application Deadline:** Rolling **Application Fee:** $0.00 **H.S. Requirements:** High school diploma or equivalent not required **Costs Per Year:** Application fee: $0. State resident tuition: $3960 full-time, $160 per credit hour part-time. Nonresident tuition: $7920 full-time, $320 per credit hour part-time. Mandatory fees: $656 full-time, $24 per credit hour part-time, $15 per term part-time. College room and board: $10,090. College room only: $6140. Room and board charges vary according to board plan. **Scholarships:** Available. **Calendar System:** Semester, Summer session available **Enrollment:** Full-time 3,632, Part-time 3,043 **Faculty:** Full-time 140, Part-time 369 **Student-Faculty Ratio:** 18:1 **% Residing in College-Owned, -Operated, or -Affiliated Housing:** 7 **Final Year or Final Semester Residency Requirement:** No **Regional Accreditation:** Middle States Association of Colleges and Schools **Credit Hours For Degree:** 63 credits, depending on program, Associates **ROTC:** Air Force, Army **Professional Accreditation:** ABET, ACEN, AHIMA, CoARC. **Intercollegiate Athletics:** Baseball M; Basketball M & W; Bowling M & W; Cross-Country Running M & W; Golf M & W; Ice Hockey M; Lacrosse M & W; Soccer M & W; Softball W; Tennis M & W; Track and Field M & W; Volleyball W

MOLLOY COLLEGE
1000 Hempstead Ave.
Rockville Centre, NY 11571-5002
Tel: (516)323-3000; Free: 888-4MOLLOY
E-mail: admissions@molloy.edu
Web Site: www.molloy.edu
President/CEO: Dr. Drew Bogner, PhD
Admissions: Marguerite Lane
Financial Aid: Ana C. Lockward
Type: Comprehensive **Sex:** Coed **Scores:** 100% SAT V 400+; 100% SAT M 400+; 54% ACT 18-23; 36% ACT 24-29 **% Accepted:** 76 **Admission Plans:** Deferred Admission; Early Decision Plan **Application Deadline:** Rolling **Application Fee:** $40.00 **H.S. Requirements:** High school diploma required; GED accepted **Costs Per Year:** Application fee: $40. Comprehensive fee: $41,970 includes full-time tuition ($26,980), mandatory fees ($1050), and college room and board ($13,940). Full-time tuition and fees vary according to degree level. Room and board charges vary according to board plan. Part-time tuition: $890 per credit hour. Part-time tuition varies according to degree level. **Scholarships:** Available. **Calendar System:** 4-1-4, Summer session available **Enrollment:** Full-time 2,753, Graduate full-time 242, Graduate part-time 1,227, Part-time 672 **Faculty:** Full-time 186, Part-time 518 **Student-Faculty Ratio:** 10:1 **Exams:** ACT essay component used for placement; SAT I or ACT; SAT essay component used for placement; SAT Reasoning. **% Receiving Financial Aid:** 74 **% Residing in College-Owned, -Operated, or -Affiliated Housing:** 8 **Final Year or Final Semester Residency Requirement:** No **Regional Accreditation:** Middle States Association of Colleges and Schools **Credit Hours For Degree:** 64 credits, Associates; 128 credits, Bachelors **ROTC:** Army, Navy **Professional Accreditation:** AACN, AHIMA, CSWE, CoARC, JRCNMT, NCATE. **Intercollegiate Athletics:** Baseball M; Basketball M & W; Bowling W; Cross-Country Running M & W; Lacrosse M & W; Soccer M & W; Softball W; Tennis W; Track and Field M & W; Volleyball W

MONROE COLLEGE
Monroe College Way
Bronx, NY 10468-5407

Tel: (718)933-6700; Free: 800-55MONROE
Web Site: www.monroecollege.edu
President/CEO: Stephen Jerome
Admissions: Craig Patrick
Financial Aid: Daniel Sharon
Type: Comprehensive **Sex:** Coed **% Accepted:** 45 **Admission Plans:** Deferred Admission; Early Action; Early Admission; Early Decision Plan **Application Deadline:** August 26 **Application Fee:** $35.00 **H.S. Requirements:** High school diploma required; GED accepted **Costs Per Year:** Application fee: $35. Comprehensive fee: $23,548 includes full-time tuition ($13,248), mandatory fees ($900), and college room and board ($9400). Room and board charges vary according to board plan and housing facility. Part-time tuition: $552 per credit hour. Part-time mandatory fees: $225 per term. **Scholarships:** Available. **Calendar System:** Semester, Summer session available **Enrollment:** Full-time 4,524, Graduate full-time 448, Graduate part-time 277, Part-time 1,613 **Faculty:** Full-time 219, Part-time 252 **Student-Faculty Ratio:** 18:1 **Exams:** SAT I or ACT. **% Receiving Financial Aid:** 96 **% Residing in College-Owned, -Operated, or -Affiliated Housing:** 13 **Final Year or Final Semester Residency Requirement:** No **Regional Accreditation:** Middle States Association of Colleges and Schools **Credit Hours For Degree:** 20 courses, Associates; 40 courses, Bachelors **ROTC:** Army **Professional Accreditation:** ACBSP, AHIMA. **Intercollegiate Athletics:** Baseball M; Basketball M & W; Cross-Country Running M & W; Football M; Soccer M & W; Softball W; Track and Field M & W; Volleyball W

MONROE COMMUNITY COLLEGE

1000 E Henrietta Rd.
Rochester, NY 14623-5780
Tel: (585)292-2000
Fax: (585)427-2749
E-mail: admissions@monroecc.edu
Web Site: www.monroecc.edu
President/CEO: Dr. Anne M. Kress
Admissions: Christine Casalinuovo-Adams
Financial Aid: Jerome St. Croix
Type: Two-Year College **Sex:** Coed **Affiliation:** State University of New York System. **Scores:** 82% SAT V 400+; 85% SAT M 400+; 42.9% ACT 18-23; 32.6% ACT 24-29 **Admission Plans:** Early Admission; Open Admission; Preferred Admission **Application Deadline:** Rolling **H.S. Requirements:** High school diploma required; GED accepted **Costs Per Year:** State resident tuition: $3800 full-time, $159 per credit hour part-time. Nonresident tuition: $7600 full-time, $318 per credit hour part-time. Mandatory fees: $604 full-time. Full-time tuition and fees vary according to program. Part-time tuition varies according to course load and program. College room only: $6170. Room charges vary according to housing facility. **Scholarships:** Available. **Calendar System:** Semester, Summer session available **Enrollment:** Full-time 8,856, Part-time 5,730 **Faculty:** Full-time 307, Part-time 501 **Student-Faculty Ratio:** 23:1 **Regional Accreditation:** Middle States Association of Colleges and Schools **Credit Hours For Degree:** 62 credits, Associates **Professional Accreditation:** ABET, ACEN, ADA, AHIMA, JRCEMTP, JRCERT. **Intercollegiate Athletics:** Baseball M; Basketball M & W; Golf M; Ice Hockey M; Lacrosse M; Soccer M & W; Softball W; Swimming and Diving M & W; Tennis M & W; Volleyball W

MONTEFIORE SCHOOL OF NURSING

53 Valentine St.
Mount Vernon, NY 10550
Tel: (914)361-6221
Fax: (914)665-7047
E-mail: hopferadmissions@sshsw.org
Web Site: www.montefiorehealthsystem.org/landing.cfm?id=19
President/CEO: Anthony Alfano
Admissions: Sandra Farrior
Type: Two-Year College **Sex:** Coed **% Accepted:** 10 **Application Fee:** $40.00 **Student-Faculty Ratio:** 5:1 **Exams:** Other. **Professional Accreditation:** ACEN.

MORRISVILLE STATE COLLEGE

PO Box 901
Morrisville, NY 13408-0901
Tel: (315)684-6000; Free: 800-258-0111
Fax: (315)684-6116
Web Site: www.morrisville.edu
President/CEO: Dr. William Murabito

Admissions: Lindsey Graham
Type: Four-Year College **Sex:** Coed **Affiliation:** State University of New York System. **Scores:** 91% SAT V 400+; 92% SAT M 400+; 62% ACT 18-23; 27% ACT 24-29 **% Accepted:** 56 **Admission Plans:** Deferred Admission **Application Deadline:** Rolling **Application Fee:** $50.00 **H.S. Requirements:** High school diploma required; GED accepted **Costs Per Year:** Application fee: $50. State resident tuition: $6470 full-time, $270 per credit hour part-time. Nonresident tuition: $10,640 full-time, $444 per credit hour part-time. Mandatory fees: $1570 full-time, $64.85 per credit hour part-time. Full-time tuition and fees vary according to course level, degree level, location, and program. Part-time tuition and fees vary according to class time, course level, course load, degree level, location, and program. College room and board: $13,488. College room only: $8298. Room and board charges vary according to board plan, housing facility, and location. **Scholarships:** Available. **Calendar System:** Semester, Summer session available **Enrollment:** Full-time 2,505, Part-time 406 **Faculty:** Full-time 143, Part-time 118 **Student-Faculty Ratio:** 11:1 **Exams:** ACT essay component used as validity check; SAT I or ACT; SAT essay component used as validity check; SAT Reasoning; SAT Subject. **% Receiving Financial Aid:** 86 **% Residing in College-Owned, -Operated, or -Affiliated Housing:** 53 **Final Year or Final Semester Residency Requirement:** No **Regional Accreditation:** Middle States Association of Colleges and Schools **Credit Hours For Degree:** 64 credits, Associates; 120 credits, Bachelors **ROTC:** Air Force, Army **Professional Accreditation:** ABET, ACBSP, ACEN. **Intercollegiate Athletics:** Basketball M & W; Cross-Country Running M & W; Equestrian Sports M & W; Field Hockey W; Football M; Golf M; Ice Hockey M & W; Lacrosse M & W; Soccer M & W; Softball W; Volleyball W

MOUNT SAINT MARY COLLEGE

330 Powell Ave.
Newburgh, NY 12550-3494
Tel: (845)561-0800; Free: 888-937-6762
Fax: (845)562-6762
E-mail: admissions@msmc.edu
Web Site: www.msmc.edu
Admissions: Nancy Scaffidi-Clark
Financial Aid: Barbara Winchell
Type: Comprehensive **Sex:** Coed **Scores:** 94% SAT V 400+; 88% SAT M 400+; 64% ACT 18-23; 28% ACT 24-29 **% Accepted:** 90 **Admission Plans:** Deferred Admission; Early Admission **Application Deadline:** August 15 **Application Fee:** $45.00 **H.S. Requirements:** High school diploma required; GED accepted **Costs Per Year:** Application fee: $45. Comprehensive fee: $42,061 includes full-time tuition ($27,233), mandatory fees ($1000), and college room and board ($13,828). College room only: $8010. Full-time tuition and fees vary according to class time, course load, location, and program. Room and board charges vary according to board plan and housing facility. Part-time tuition: $908 per credit. Part-time mandatory fees: $80 per term. Part-time tuition and fees vary according to class time, course load, location, and program. **Scholarships:** Available. **Calendar System:** Semester, Summer session available **Enrollment:** Full-time 1,780, Graduate full-time 82, Graduate part-time 269, Part-time 377 **Faculty:** Full-time 85, Part-time 191 **Student-Faculty Ratio:** 14:1 **Exams:** ACT essay component used for advising; ACT essay component used for placement; SAT I or ACT; SAT essay component used for advising; SAT essay component used for placement; SAT Reasoning; SAT Subject. **% Receiving Financial Aid:** 79 **% Residing in College-Owned, -Operated, or -Affiliated Housing:** 48 **Final Year or Final Semester Residency Requirement:** No **Regional Accreditation:** Middle States Association of Colleges and Schools **Credit Hours For Degree:** 120 credit hours, Bachelors **ROTC:** Army **Professional Accreditation:** AACN, NCATE. **Intercollegiate Athletics:** Baseball M; Basketball M & W; Cheerleading W; Cross-Country Running M & W; Golf M; Lacrosse M & W; Soccer M & W; Softball W; Swimming and Diving M & W; Tennis M & W; Track and Field M & W; Volleyball W

NASSAU COMMUNITY COLLEGE

1 Education Dr.
Garden City, NY 11530-6793
Tel: (516)572-7500
E-mail: admissions@sunynassau.edu
Web Site: www.ncc.edu
President/CEO: Dr. Kenneth K. Saunders
Admissions: Craig Wright
Financial Aid: Dr. Evangeline Manjares
Type: Two-Year College **Sex:** Coed **Affiliation:** State University of New York

System. **Admission Plans:** Deferred Admission; Open Admission **Application Deadline:** August 7 **Application Fee:** $40.00 **H.S. Requirements:** High school diploma required; GED accepted **Costs Per Year:** Application fee: $40. State resident tuition: $9070 full-time, $189 per credit hour part-time. Nonresident tuition: $9070 full-time, $378 per credit hour part-time. Mandatory fees: $140 full-time. **Scholarships:** Available. **Calendar System:** Semester, Summer session available **Enrollment:** Full-time 13,282, Part-time 9,026 **Faculty:** Full-time 497, Part-time 925 **Student-Faculty Ratio:** 21:1 **Exams:** SAT I or ACT. **Regional Accreditation:** Middle States Association of Colleges and Schools **Credit Hours For Degree:** 64 credits, Associates **Professional Accreditation:** ABET, ABFSE, ACEN, APTA, ARCST, CoARC, JRCERT, NASM. **Intercollegiate Athletics:** Baseball M; Basketball M & W; Bowling M & W; Cheerleading M & W; Cross-Country Running M & W; Football M; Golf M & W; Lacrosse M & W; Soccer M & W; Softball W; Tennis M & W; Track and Field M & W; Volleyball W; Wrestling M

NAZARETH COLLEGE OF ROCHESTER
4245 E Ave.
Rochester, NY 14618-3790
Tel: (585)389-2525; Free: 800-462-3944
Fax: (585)389-2826
E-mail: admissions@naz.edu
Web Site: www.naz.edu
President/CEO: Daan Braveman
Admissions: Ian Mortimer
Financial Aid: Janice Scheutzow
Type: Comprehensive **Sex:** Coed **Scores:** 96% SAT V 400+; 96% SAT M 400+; 33% ACT 18-23; 51% ACT 24-29 **% Accepted:** 76 **Admission Plans:** Deferred Admission; Early Action; Early Admission **Application Deadline:** February 1 **Application Fee:** $45.00 **H.S. Requirements:** High school diploma required; GED accepted **Costs Per Year:** Application fee: $45. Comprehensive fee: $44,438 includes full-time tuition ($30,120), mandatory fees ($1400), and college room and board ($12,918). College room only: $3654. **Scholarships:** Available. **Calendar System:** Semester, Summer session available **Enrollment:** Full-time 1,974, Graduate full-time 397, Graduate part-time 366, Part-time 134 **Faculty:** Full-time 178, Part-time 308 **Student-Faculty Ratio:** 9:1 **Exams:** SAT I or ACT; SAT Reasoning; SAT Subject. **% Receiving Financial Aid:** 82 **% Residing in College-Owned, -Operated, or -Affiliated Housing:** 53 **Final Year or Final Semester Residency Requirement:** No **Regional Accreditation:** Middle States Association of Colleges and Schools **Credit Hours For Degree:** 120 credit hours, Bachelors **ROTC:** Air Force, Army **Professional Accreditation:** AACN, APTA, ASHA, CSWE, NASM, TEAC. **Intercollegiate Athletics:** Basketball M & W; Cross-Country Running M & W; Equestrian Sports M & W; Field Hockey W; Golf M & W; Ice Hockey M; Lacrosse M & W; Soccer M & W; Softball W; Swimming and Diving M & W; Tennis M & W; Track and Field M & W; Volleyball M & W

THE NEW SCHOOL COLLEGE OF PERFORMING ARTS
66 W 12th St.
New York, NY 10011
Tel: (212)229-5600; Free: 800-292-3040
E-mail: schmittg@newschool.edu
Web Site: www.newschool.edu/performing-arts
President/CEO: Davied E. Van Zandt
Admissions: Georgia Schmitt
Type: Comprehensive **Sex:** Coed **Affiliation:** The New School. **Scores:** 98% SAT V 400+; 100% SAT M 400+ **% Accepted:** 59 **Admission Plans:** Deferred Admission; Early Admission; Early Decision Plan **Application Deadline:** January 15 **Application Fee:** $50.00 **H.S. Requirements:** High school diploma required; GED not accepted **Costs Per Year:** Application fee: $50. Tuition: $1430 per credit part-time. Mandatory fees: $463 per term part-time. Part-time tuition and fees vary according to course load. **Scholarships:** Available. **Calendar System:** Semester, Summer session available **Enrollment:** Full-time 509, Graduate full-time 264, Graduate part-time 1, Part-time 14 **Faculty:** Full-time 20, Part-time 395 **Student-Faculty Ratio:** 5:1 **Exams:** ACT; SAT I; SAT I and SAT II or ACT; SAT I or ACT; SAT II. **% Receiving Financial Aid:** 44 **% Residing in College-Owned, -Operated, or -Affiliated Housing:** 29 **Final Year or Final Semester Residency Requirement:** Yes **Regional Accreditation:** Middle States Association of Colleges and Schools **Credit Hours For Degree:** 120 credits, Bachelors

THE NEW SCHOOL FOR PUBLIC ENGAGEMENT
66 W 12th St.
New York, NY 10011-8603
Tel: (212)229-5600; Free: 800-292-3040
Fax: (212)645-0661
E-mail: puleioe@newschool.edu
Web Site: www.newschool.edu/public-engagement
President/CEO: David E. Van Zandt
Admissions: Elizabeth Puleio
Financial Aid: Eileen F. Doyle
Type: Comprehensive **Sex:** Coed **Affiliation:** The New School. **Scholarships:** Available. **Calendar System:** Semester, Summer session available **Enrollment:** Full-time 213, Graduate full-time 815, Graduate part-time 495, Part-time 240 **Faculty:** Full-time 81, Part-time 334 **Student-Faculty Ratio:** 5:1 **Exams:** ACT; SAT I; SAT I and SAT II or ACT; SAT I or ACT; SAT II. **% Receiving Financial Aid:** 62 **% Residing in College-Owned, -Operated, or -Affiliated Housing:** 10 **Regional Accreditation:** Middle States Association of Colleges and Schools **Credit Hours For Degree:** 120 credits, Bachelors

NEW YORK CAREER INSTITUTE
11 Park Place- 4th Fl.
New York, NY 10007
Tel: (212)962-0002
Fax: (212)385-7574
E-mail: lstieglitz@nyci.edu
Web Site: www.nyci.com
President/CEO: Dennis Byrns
Admissions: Larry Stieglitz
Type: Two-Year College **Sex:** Coed **Application Deadline:** September 7 **Application Fee:** $50.00 **H.S. Requirements:** High school diploma required; GED accepted **Costs Per Year:** Application fee: $50. Tuition: $13,500 full-time, $430 per credit hour part-time. Mandatory fees: $150 full-time, $50 per term part-time. Full-time tuition and fees vary according to class time, course load, and program. Part-time tuition and fees vary according to class time, course load, and program. **Scholarships:** Available. **Calendar System:** Trimester, Summer session available **Enrollment:** Full-time 461, Part-time 241 **Faculty:** Full-time 9, Part-time 33 **Final Year or Final Semester Residency Requirement:** No **Credit Hours For Degree:** 60 credits, Associates **Professional Accreditation:** NYSBR.

NEW YORK CITY COLLEGE OF TECHNOLOGY OF THE CITY UNIVERSITY OF NEW YORK
300 Jay St.
Brooklyn, NY 11201-2983
Tel: (718)260-5000
Fax: (718)260-5198
E-mail: achaconis@citytech.cuny.edu
Web Site: www.citytech.cuny.edu
President/CEO: Dr. Russell K. Hotzler
Admissions: Alexis Chaconis
Financial Aid: Sandra Higgins
Type: Four-Year College **Sex:** Coed **Affiliation:** City University of New York System. **Scores:** 55% SAT V 400+; 68% SAT M 400+ **% Accepted:** 38 **Admission Plans:** Deferred Admission; Open Admission **Application Deadline:** February 1 **Application Fee:** $65.00 **H.S. Requirements:** High school diploma required; GED accepted **Costs Per Year:** Application fee: $65. State resident tuition: $6330 full-time, $275 per credit part-time. Nonresident tuition: $16,800 full-time, $560 per credit part-time. Mandatory fees: $320 full-time. Full-time tuition and fees vary according to course load and program. Part-time tuition varies according to course load and program. **Scholarships:** Available. **Calendar System:** Semester, Summer session available **Enrollment:** Full-time 10,821, Part-time 6,603 **Faculty:** Full-time 445, Part-time 982 **Student-Faculty Ratio:** 17:1 **Exams:** ACT essay component used for placement; SAT I or ACT; SAT essay component used for placement; SAT Reasoning. **% Receiving Financial Aid:** 81 **Final Year or Final Semester Residency Requirement:** No **Regional Accreditation:** Middle States Association of Colleges and Schools **Credit Hours For Degree:** 60 credits, Associates; 120 credits, Bachelors **Professional Accreditation:** ABET, ACEN, ADA, COA, JRCERT, NCATE.

NEW YORK COLLEGE OF HEALTH PROFESSIONS
6801 Jericho Tpke.
Syosset, NY 11791-4413
Tel: (516)364-0808; Free: 800-922-7337
Fax: (516)364-0989
E-mail: rdodas@nycollege.edu

Web Site: www.nycollege.edu
President/CEO: Lisa Pamintuan
Admissions: Mary Rodas

Type: Comprehensive **Sex:** Coed **Admission Plans:** Deferred Admission **Application Deadline:** Rolling **Application Fee:** $85.00 **H.S. Requirements:** High school diploma required; GED accepted **Scholarships:** Available. **Calendar System:** Trimester, Summer session available **Enrollment:** Full-time 332, Part-time 469 **Faculty:** Full-time 17, Part-time 76 **Student-Faculty Ratio:** 19:1 **Credit Hours For Degree:** 72 credits, Associates **Professional Accreditation:** ACAOM.

NEW YORK INSTITUTE OF TECHNOLOGY

PO Box 8000
Old Westbury, NY 11568-8000
Tel: (516)686-7516; Free: 800-345-NYIT
Fax: (516)686-7613
E-mail: admissions@nyit.edu
Web Site: www.nyit.edu
President/CEO: Dr. Edward Guiliano
Admissions: Adeline Affonso
Financial Aid: Doreen Meyer

Type: University **Sex:** Coed **Scores:** 95% SAT V 400+; 97% SAT M 400+; 47% ACT 18-23; 35% ACT 24-29 **% Accepted:** 68 **Admission Plans:** Deferred Admission; Early Admission; Early Decision Plan **Application Deadline:** Rolling **Application Fee:** $50.00 **H.S. Requirements:** High school diploma required; GED accepted **Costs Per Year:** Application fee: $50. Comprehensive fee: $46,570 includes full-time tuition ($32,300), mandatory fees ($1180), and college room and board ($13,090). College room only: $8450. Full-time tuition and fees vary according to program. Room and board charges vary according to location. Part-time tuition: $1095 per credit. Part-time mandatory fees: $490 per term. Part-time tuition and fees vary according to course load and program. **Scholarships:** Available. **Calendar System:** Semester, Summer session available **Enrollment:** Full-time 3,540, Graduate full-time 3,085, Graduate part-time 929, Part-time 494 **Faculty:** Full-time 298, Part-time 603 **Student-Faculty Ratio:** 14:1 **Exams:** ACT essay component used for admission; SAT I or ACT; SAT II; SAT essay component used for admission; SAT Reasoning. **% Receiving Financial Aid:** 69 **% Residing in College-Owned, -Operated, or -Affiliated Housing:** 20 **Regional Accreditation:** Middle States Association of Colleges and Schools **Credit Hours For Degree:** 60 credits, Associates; 120 credits, Bachelors **ROTC:** Air Force, Army **Professional Accreditation:** AACSB, ABET, ACEN, AND, AOTA, AOsA, APTA, CIDA, NAAB, NCATE. **Intercollegiate Athletics:** Baseball M; Basketball M & W; Cross-Country Running M & W; Lacrosse M; Soccer M & W; Softball W; Tennis M & W; Volleyball W

NEW YORK SCHOOL OF INTERIOR DESIGN

170 E 70th St.
New York, NY 10021-5110
Tel: (212)472-1500; Free: 800-336-9743
Fax: (212)472-1867
E-mail: admissions@nysid.edu
Web Site: www.nysid.edu
President/CEO: David Sprouls
Admissions: Jaspreet Bains
Financial Aid: Rashmi H. Wadhvani

Type: Comprehensive **Sex:** Coed **% Accepted:** 42 **Admission Plans:** Deferred Admission **Application Deadline:** February 1 **Application Fee:** $60.00 **H.S. Requirements:** High school diploma required; GED accepted **Costs Per Year:** Application fee: $60. Tuition: $30,195 full-time, $915 per credit part-time. Mandatory fees: $750 full-time. Full-time tuition and fees vary according to course load. Part-time tuition varies according to course load. College room only: $16,000. **Scholarships:** Available. **Calendar System:** Semester, Summer session available **Enrollment:** Full-time 128, Graduate full-time 154, Graduate part-time 3, Part-time 253 **Faculty:** Full-time 5, Part-time 115 **Student-Faculty Ratio:** 8:1 **Exams:** SAT I or ACT. **% Receiving Financial Aid:** 75 **% Residing in College-Owned, -Operated, or -Affiliated Housing:** 12 **Final Year or Final Semester Residency Requirement:** No **Regional Accreditation:** Middle States Association of Colleges and Schools **Credit Hours For Degree:** 66 credits, Associates; 132 credits, Bachelors **Professional Accreditation:** CIDA, NASAD.

NEW YORK UNIVERSITY

70 Washington Sq. S
New York, NY 10012-1019

Tel: (212)998-1212
Fax: (212)995-4902
E-mail: admissions@nyu.edu
Web Site: www.nyu.edu
President/CEO: Dr. John E. Sexton
Admissions: Kristy Materasso

Type: University **Sex:** Coed **Scores:** 100% SAT V 400+; 100% SAT M 400+; 1% ACT 18-23; 39% ACT 24-29 **% Accepted:** 35 **Admission Plans:** Deferred Admission; Early Action **Application Deadline:** January 1 **Application Fee:** $70.00 **H.S. Requirements:** High school diploma required; GED accepted **Costs Per Year:** Application fee: $70. Comprehensive fee: $65,330 includes full-time tuition ($45,278), mandatory fees ($2472), and college room and board ($17,580). College room only: $12,648. Full-time tuition and fees vary according to course load and program. Room and board charges vary according to board plan and housing facility. Part-time tuition: $1334 per credit hour. Part-time mandatory fees: $66 per credit, $470 per term. Part-time tuition and fees vary according to program. **Scholarships:** Available. **Calendar System:** Semester, Summer session available **Enrollment:** Full-time 23,715, Graduate full-time 16,183, Graduate part-time 8,106, Part-time 1,270 **Faculty:** Full-time 2,843, Part-time 4,000 **Student-Faculty Ratio:** 10:1 **Exams:** ACT essay component used as validity check; Other; SAT I and SAT II or ACT; SAT essay component used as validity check; SAT Reasoning; SAT Subject. **% Receiving Financial Aid:** 51 **% Residing in College-Owned, -Operated, or -Affiliated Housing:** 47 **Final Year or Final Semester Residency Requirement:** No **Regional Accreditation:** Middle States Association of Colleges and Schools **Credit Hours For Degree:** 60 credits, Associates; 128 credits, Bachelors **ROTC:** Air Force, Army **Professional Accreditation:** AACN, AACSB, AALS, ABA, ACEJMC, ACEN, ACNM, ACSP, ACIPE, ADA, AND, AOTA, APA, APTA, ASHA, CAHME, CEPH, CORE, CSWE, JRCEDMS, LCME/AMA, MACTE, NASPAA, TEAC. **Intercollegiate Athletics:** Baseball M; Basketball M & W; Cross-Country Running M & W; Fencing M & W; Golf M & W; Soccer M & W; Softball W; Swimming and Diving M & W; Tennis M & W; Track and Field M & W; Volleyball M & W; Wrestling M

NIAGARA COUNTY COMMUNITY COLLEGE

3111 Saunders Settlement Rd.
Sanborn, NY 14132-9460
Tel: (716)614-6222
Fax: (716)731-4053
E-mail: admissions@niagaracc.suny.edu
Web Site: www.niagaracc.suny.edu
President/CEO: Dr. James P. Klyczek
Admissions: James Trimboli
Financial Aid: Jim Trimboli

Type: Two-Year College **Sex:** Coed **Affiliation:** State University of New York System. **% Accepted:** 100 **Admission Plans:** Early Admission; Open Admission **Application Fee:** $0.00 **H.S. Requirements:** High school diploma required; GED accepted **Costs Per Year:** Application fee: $0. State resident tuition: $3960 full-time, $165 per credit hour part-time. Nonresident tuition: $9900 full-time, $412.50 per credit hour part-time. Mandatory fees: $410 full-time. Full-time tuition and fees vary according to course load and program. Part-time tuition varies according to course load and program. College room and board: $11,189. College room only: $8698. Room and board charges vary according to housing facility. **Scholarships:** Available. **Calendar System:** Semester, Summer session available **Enrollment:** Full-time 3,670, Part-time 2,463 **Faculty:** Full-time 104, Part-time 256 **Student-Faculty Ratio:** 17:1 **% Residing in College-Owned, -Operated, or -Affiliated Housing:** 4 **Regional Accreditation:** Middle States Association of Colleges and Schools **Credit Hours For Degree:** 62 credit hours, Associates **ROTC:** Army **Professional Accreditation:** AAMAE, ACEN, APTA, ARCST, JRCEND, JRCERT. **Intercollegiate Athletics:** Baseball M; Basketball M & W; Golf M & W; Soccer M & W; Softball W; Volleyball W; Wrestling M

NIAGARA UNIVERSITY

Niagara University, NY 14109
Tel: (716)285-1212; Free: 800-462-2111
Fax: (716)286-8355
E-mail: admissions@niagara.edu
Web Site: www.niagara.edu
President/CEO: Rev. James J. Maher, CM
Admissions: Mark Wojnowski
Financial Aid: Katie L. Kocsis

Type: Comprehensive **Sex:** Coed **Affiliation:** Roman Catholic Church. **Scores:** 97% SAT V 400+; 97% SAT M 400+; 55.6% ACT 18-23; 36.2% ACT 24-29 **% Accepted:** 48 **Admission Plans:** Deferred Admission; Early Admission; Early Decision Plan **Application Deadline:** August 1 **H.S. Requirements:** High school diploma required; GED accepted **Costs Per Year:** Comprehensive fee: $42,200 includes full-time tuition ($28,500), mandatory fees ($1400), and college room and board ($12,300). Full-time tuition and fees vary according to program. Room and board charges vary according to housing facility. Part-time tuition: $950 per credit hour. Part-time tuition varies according to program. **Scholarships:** Available. **Calendar System:** Semester, Summer session available **Enrollment:** Full-time 2,862, Graduate full-time 508, Graduate part-time 406, Part-time 352 **Faculty:** Full-time 157, Part-time 211 **Student-Faculty Ratio:** 13:1 **Exams:** SAT I or ACT; SAT Reasoning. **% Receiving Financial Aid:** 77 **% Residing in College-Owned, -Operated, or -Affiliated Housing:** 43 **Final Year or Final Semester Residency Requirement:** No **Regional Accreditation:** Middle States Association of Colleges and Schools **Credit Hours For Degree:** 60 credit hours, Associates; 120 credit hours, Bachelors **ROTC:** Army **Professional Accreditation:** AACN, AACSB, CSWE, NCATE. **Intercollegiate Athletics:** Baseball M; Basketball M & W; Cross-Country Running M & W; Golf M & W; Ice Hockey M; Lacrosse W; Soccer M & W; Softball W; Swimming and Diving M & W; Tennis M & W; Track and Field W; Volleyball W

NORTH COUNTRY COMMUNITY COLLEGE

23 Santanoni Ave.
Saranac Lake, NY 12983-0089
Tel: (518)891-2915; Free: 888-TRY-NCCC
Fax: (518)891-2915
E-mail: info@nccc.edu
Web Site: www.nccc.edu
President/CEO: Fred Smith
Financial Aid: Edwin A. Trathen

Type: Two-Year College **Sex:** Coed **Affiliation:** State University of New York System. **Admission Plans:** Deferred Admission; Early Action; Early Admission; Open Admission; Preferred Admission **Application Deadline:** Rolling **Application Fee:** $0.00 **H.S. Requirements:** High school diploma required; GED accepted **Scholarships:** Available. **Calendar System:** Semester, Summer session available **Enrollment:** Full-time 956, Part-time 795 **Faculty:** Full-time 46, Part-time 105 **Student-Faculty Ratio:** 15:1 **Exams:** SAT I or ACT. **% Residing in College-Owned, -Operated, or -Affiliated Housing:** 7 **Regional Accreditation:** Middle States Association of Colleges and Schools **Credit Hours For Degree:** 62 semester hours, Associates **Professional Accreditation:** JRCERT. **Intercollegiate Athletics:** Basketball M & W; Ice Hockey M; Soccer M & W; Softball W; Volleyball W

NYACK COLLEGE

1 S Blvd.
Nyack, NY 10960
Tel: (845)358-1710; Free: 800-33-NYACK
Fax: (845)358-3047
E-mail: admissions@nyack.edu
Web Site: www.nyack.edu
President/CEO: Dr. Michael G. Scales
Admissions: Dan Bailey
Financial Aid: Steve Phillips

Type: Comprehensive **Sex:** Coed **Affiliation:** The Christian and Missionary Alliance. **Scores:** 73% SAT V 400+; 70% SAT M 400+; 35.71% ACT 18-23; 17.86% ACT 24-29 **% Accepted:** 99 **Admission Plans:** Deferred Admission; Early Decision Plan **Application Deadline:** Rolling **Application Fee:** $25.00 **H.S. Requirements:** High school diploma required; GED accepted **Costs Per Year:** Application fee: $25. Comprehensive fee: $34,050 includes full-time tuition ($24,500), mandatory fees ($350), and college room and board ($9200). Room and board charges vary according to board plan and housing facility. Part-time tuition: $1020 per credit hour. Part-time tuition varies according to course load. **Scholarships:** Available. **Calendar System:** Semester, Summer session available **Enrollment:** Full-time 1,300, Graduate full-time 487, Graduate part-time 632, Part-time 245 **Faculty:** Full-time 100, Part-time 184 **Student-Faculty Ratio:** 12:1 **Exams:** ACT essay component used for placement; SAT I and SAT II or ACT; SAT I or ACT; SAT essay component used for placement; SAT Reasoning; SAT Subject. **% Receiving Financial Aid:** 83 **% Residing in College-Owned, -Operated, or -Affiliated Housing:** 72 **Final Year or Final Semester Residency Requirement:** No **Regional Accreditation:** Middle States Association of Colleges and Schools **Credit Hours For Degree:** 60 credits, Associates; 120 credits,

Bachelors **Professional Accreditation:** ATS, NASM, NCATE. **Intercollegiate Athletics:** Baseball M; Basketball M & W; Cross-Country Running M & W; Golf M; Lacrosse W; Soccer M & W; Softball W; Volleyball W

OHR HAMEIR THEOLOGICAL SEMINARY

141 Furnace Woods Rd.
Cortlandt Manor, NY 10567
Tel: (914)736-1500
President/CEO: Eli Kanarek

Type: Comprehensive **Sex:** Men **Affiliation:** Jewish. **% Accepted:** 100 **H.S. Requirements:** High school diploma required; GED accepted **Calendar System:** Semester **Professional Accreditation:** AARTS.

OHR SOMAYACH/JOSEPH TANENBAUM EDUCATIONAL CENTER

PO Box 334, 244 Rte. 306
Monsey, NY 10952-0334
Tel: (845)425-1370
E-mail: ohr@os.edu
Web Site: ohr.edu
President/CEO: Rabbi Avrohom Braun
Admissions: Rabbi Avrohom Braun

Type: Comprehensive **Sex:** Men **Affiliation:** Jewish. **% Accepted:** 60 **Admission Plans:** Early Admission **Application Deadline:** Rolling **H.S. Requirements:** High school diploma required; GED accepted **Costs Per Year:** Tuition: $18,000 full-time. **Calendar System:** Semester, Summer session available **Enrollment:** Full-time 60, Graduate full-time 10 **Faculty:** Full-time 6, Part-time 6 **Credit Hours For Degree:** 132 credit hours, Bachelors **Professional Accreditation:** AARTS.

ONONDAGA COMMUNITY COLLEGE

4585 W Seneca Tpke.
Syracuse, NY 13215
Tel: (315)498-2622
Fax: (315)469-2107
E-mail: admissions@sunyocc.edu
Web Site: www.sunyocc.edu
President/CEO: Dr. Casey Crabill
Admissions: Denny Nicholson
Financial Aid: Rebecca Rose

Type: Two-Year College **Sex:** Coed **Affiliation:** State University of New York System. **% Accepted:** 66 **Admission Plans:** Open Admission; Preferred Admission **Application Fee:** $0.00 **H.S. Requirements:** High school diploma required; GED accepted. For those who demonstrate ability to benefit from program using Federal ATB testing guidelines: High school diploma or equivalent not required **Costs Per Year:** Application fee: $0. State resident tuition: $4430 full-time, $184 per credit hour part-time. Nonresident tuition: $8860 full-time, $368 per credit hour part-time. Mandatory fees: $584 full-time. Full-time tuition and fees vary according to program. Part-time tuition varies according to course load and program. College room and board: $8826. Room and board charges vary according to board plan. **Scholarships:** Available. **Calendar System:** Semester, Summer session available **Enrollment:** Full-time 5,895, Part-time 5,991 **Faculty:** Full-time 177, Part-time 468 **Student-Faculty Ratio:** 24:1 **% Residing in College-Owned, -Operated, or -Affiliated Housing:** 6 **Final Year or Final Semester Residency Requirement:** No **Regional Accreditation:** Middle States Association of Colleges and Schools **Credit Hours For Degree:** 62 credits, Associates **ROTC:** Air Force **Professional Accreditation:** ABET, ACEN, ADA, AHIMA, APTA, CoARC. **Intercollegiate Athletics:** Baseball M; Basketball M & W; Cross-Country Running M & W; Lacrosse M & W; Soccer M & W; Softball W; Tennis M & W; Volleyball W

ORANGE COUNTY COMMUNITY COLLEGE

115 S St.
Middletown, NY 10940-6437
Tel: (845)344-6222
Fax: (845)343-1228
E-mail: apply@sunyorange.edu
Web Site: www.sunyorange.edu
President/CEO: Dr. William Richards
Admissions: Michael Roe

Type: Two-Year College **Sex:** Coed **Affiliation:** State University of New York System. **Admission Plans:** Deferred Admission; Early Admission; Open Admission; Preferred Admission **Application Deadline:** August 1 **Application Fee:** $30.00 **H.S. Requirements:** High school diploma required; GED accepted. For 24 credit hour guideline program: High school diploma or equivalent not required **Scholarships:** Available. **Calendar System:** Semester, Summer session available **Student-Faculty Ratio:** 17:1 **Regional Accreditation:** Middle States Association of Colleges and Schools **Credit Hours For Degree:** 62 credits, Associates **Professional Accreditation:** ACBSP, ACEN, ADA, AOTA, APTA, NAACLS. **Intercollegiate Athletics:** Baseball M; Basketball M & W; Golf M; Soccer M; Softball W; Tennis M & W; Volleyball W

PACE UNIVERSITY

One Pace Plz.
New York, NY 10038
Tel: (212)346-1200; Free: 800-874-7223
Fax: (212)346-1040
E-mail: theilman@pace.edu
Web Site: www.pace.edu/nyc
President/CEO: Stephen J. Friedman
Admissions: Todd Heilman

Type: University **Sex:** Coed **Scores:** 97% SAT V 400+; 98% SAT M 400+; 46% ACT 18-23; 44% ACT 24-29 **% Accepted:** 85 **Admission Plans:** Deferred Admission; Early Decision Plan **Application Deadline:** February 15 **Application Fee:** $50.00 **H.S. Requirements:** High school diploma required; GED accepted **Costs Per Year:** Application fee: $50. Comprehensive fee: $59,213 includes full-time tuition ($39,728), mandatory fees ($1547), and college room and board ($17,938). Full-time tuition and fees vary according to location. Room and board charges vary according to board plan, housing facility, location, and student level. Part-time tuition: $1140 per credit hour. Part-time tuition varies according to course load and location. **Scholarships:** Available. **Calendar System:** Semester, Summer session available **Enrollment:** Full-time 5,341, Graduate full-time 1,347, Graduate part-time 1,277, Part-time 759 **Faculty:** Full-time 291, Part-time 517 **Student-Faculty Ratio:** 16:1 **Exams:** ACT essay component not used; SAT I or ACT; SAT II; SAT essay component not used. **% Receiving Financial Aid:** 72 **% Residing in College-Owned, -Operated, or -Affiliated Housing:** 39 **Regional Accreditation:** Middle States Association of Colleges and Schools **Credit Hours For Degree:** 64 credits, Associates; 128 credits, Bachelors **ROTC:** Air Force, Army **Professional Accreditation:** AACN, AACSB, AALS, ABA, ABET, APA, NCATE. **Intercollegiate Athletics:** Baseball M; Basketball M & W; Cross-Country Running M & W; Field Hockey W; Football M; Lacrosse M & W; Soccer W; Softball W; Swimming and Diving M & W; Volleyball W

PACE UNIVERSITY, PLEASANTVILLE CAMPUS

861 Bedford Rd.
Pleasantville, NY 10570
Tel: (914)773-3200; Free: 800-874-PACE
Fax: (914)773-3851
E-mail: theilman@pace.edu
Web Site: www.pace.edu/westchester
President/CEO: Stephen J. Friedman
Admissions: Todd Heilman

Type: University **Sex:** Coed **Scores:** 98% SAT V 400+; 100% SAT M 400+; 59% ACT 18-23; 33% ACT 24-29 **% Accepted:** 78 **Admission Plans:** Deferred Admission; Early Decision Plan **Application Deadline:** February 15 **Application Fee:** $50.00 **H.S. Requirements:** High school diploma required; GED accepted **Costs Per Year:** Application fee: $50. Comprehensive fee: $56,335 includes full-time tuition ($39,728), mandatory fees ($1597), and college room and board ($15,010). Full-time tuition and fees vary according to location. Room and board charges vary according to board plan, housing facility, location, and student level. Part-time tuition: $1140 per credit hour. Part-time tuition varies according to course load and location. **Calendar System:** Semester, Summer session available **Enrollment:** Full-time 2,238, Graduate full-time 797, Graduate part-time 675, Part-time 409 **Faculty:** Full-time 162, Part-time 275 **Student-Faculty Ratio:** 11:1 **Exams:** ACT essay component not used; SAT I or ACT; SAT II; SAT essay component not used. **% Residing in College-Owned, -Operated, or -Affiliated Housing:** 49 **Regional Accreditation:** Middle States Association of Colleges and Schools **Credit Hours For Degree:** 64 credits, Associates; 128 credits, Bachelors **ROTC:** Air Force, Army **Intercollegiate Athletics:** Baseball M; Basketball M & W; Cross-Country Running M & W; Field Hockey W; Football M; Lacrosse M & W; Soccer W; Softball W; Swimming and Diving M & W; Volleyball W

PARSONS SCHOOL OF DESIGN

65 Fifth Ave.
New York, NY 10011

Tel: (212)229-8900; Free: 800-292-3040
Fax: (212)229-8975
E-mail: stinee@newschool.edu
Web Site: www.newschool.edu/parsons
President/CEO: David E. Van Zandt
Admissions: Erin Stine

Type: Comprehensive **Sex:** Coed **Affiliation:** The New School. **Scores:** 97% SAT V 400+; 95% SAT M 400+; 39.39% ACT 18-23; 50% ACT 24-29 **Scholarships:** Available. **Calendar System:** Semester, Summer session available **Enrollment:** Full-time 3,775, Graduate full-time 856, Graduate part-time 67, Part-time 478 **Faculty:** Full-time 155, Part-time 962 **Student-Faculty Ratio:** 11:1 **Exams:** Other. **% Receiving Financial Aid:** 40 **% Residing in College-Owned, -Operated, or -Affiliated Housing:** 24 **Final Year or Final Semester Residency Requirement:** Yes **Regional Accreditation:** Middle States Association of Colleges and Schools **Credit Hours For Degree:** 65 credits, Associates; 120 credits, Bachelors **Professional Accreditation:** NAAB, NASAD.

PAUL SMITH'S COLLEGE

PO Box 265
Paul Smiths, NY 12970-0265
Tel: (518)327-6000; Free: 800-421-2605
Fax: (518)327-6060
E-mail: admissions@paulsmiths.edu
Web Site: www.paulsmiths.edu
President/CEO: Dr. John Mills
Financial Aid: Mary Ellen Chamberlain

Type: Four-Year College **Sex:** Coed **Scores:** 81% SAT V 400+; 85% SAT M 400+; 51% ACT 18-23; 16% ACT 24-29 **% Accepted:** 86 **Admission Plans:** Deferred Admission **Application Deadline:** Rolling **Application Fee:** $30.00 **H.S. Requirements:** High school diploma required; GED accepted **Scholarships:** Available. **Calendar System:** Semester, Summer session available **Faculty:** Full-time 57, Part-time 26 **Student-Faculty Ratio:** 14:1 **Exams:** SAT I or ACT. **% Receiving Financial Aid:** 89 **% Residing in College-Owned, -Operated, or -Affiliated Housing:** 85 **Regional Accreditation:** Middle States Association of Colleges and Schools **Credit Hours For Degree:** 60 credit hours, Associates; 120 credit hours, Bachelors **Professional Accreditation:** ABET, ACF. **Intercollegiate Athletics:** Basketball M & W; Cross-Country Running M & W; Skiing (Cross-Country) M & W; Soccer M & W; Volleyball W

PHILLIPS BETH ISRAEL SCHOOL OF NURSING

776 6th Ave.
Ste. 4
New York, NY 10001
Tel: (212)614-6110
Fax: (212)614-6109
E-mail: bstern@chpnet.org
Web Site: www.pbisn.edu
President/CEO: Dr. Todd Ambrosia
Admissions: Bernice Pass-Stern

Type: Two-Year College **Sex:** Coed **Scores:** 100% SAT V 400+; 100% SAT M 400+ **% Accepted:** 3 **Admission Plans:** Deferred Admission **Application Deadline:** April 1 **Application Fee:** $50.00 **H.S. Requirements:** High school diploma required; GED accepted **Costs Per Year:** Application fee: $50. Tuition: $17,000 full-time, $525 per credit part-time. Mandatory fees: $3100 full-time. Full-time tuition and fees vary according to degree level. Part-time tuition varies according to degree level. **Scholarships:** Available. **Calendar System:** Semester, Summer session available **Enrollment:** Full-time 34, Part-time 220 **Faculty:** Full-time 10, Part-time 20 **Student-Faculty Ratio:** 8:1 **Exams:** SAT I. **Final Year or Final Semester Residency Requirement:** No **Credit Hours For Degree:** 68 credits, Associates; 62 credits (32 credits residency), Bachelors **Professional Accreditation:** ACEN.

PLAZA COLLEGE

118-33 Queens Blvd.
Forest Hills, NY 11375
Tel: (718)779-1430
Fax: (718)779-1456
E-mail: info@plazacollege.edu
Web Site: www.plazacollege.edu
President/CEO: Charles Callahan
Admissions: Dean Vanessa Lopez

Type: Two-Year College **Sex:** Coed **Application Deadline:** Rolling **Application Fee:** $100.00 **H.S. Requirements:** High school diploma required; GED accepted **Scholarships:** Available. **Calendar System:** Semester, Summer session available **Exams:** Other. **Regional Accreditation:** Middle States Association of Colleges and Schools **Credit Hours For Degree:** 60 credits, Associates; 120 credits, Bachelors

PRATT INSTITUTE

200 Willoughby Ave.
Brooklyn, NY 11205-3899
Tel: (718)636-3600; Free: 800-331-0834
Fax: (718)636-3670
E-mail: visit@pratt.edu
Web Site: www.pratt.edu
President/CEO: Thomas F. Schutte
Admissions: Olga Burger
Financial Aid: Nedzad Goga

Type: Comprehensive **Sex:** Coed **Scores:** 99% SAT V 400+; 99% SAT M 400+; 26% ACT 18-23; 58% ACT 24-29 **% Accepted:** 66 **Admission Plans:** Deferred Admission; Early Decision Plan **Application Fee:** $50.00 **H.S. Requirements:** High school diploma required; GED accepted **Costs Per Year:** Application fee: $50. Comprehensive fee: $60,180 includes full-time tuition ($46,140), mandatory fees ($2014), and college room and board ($12,026). College room only: $7900. Full-time tuition and fees vary according to program. Room and board charges vary according to board plan and housing facility. Part-time tuition: $1488 per credit hour. Part-time tuition varies according to program. **Scholarships:** Available. **Calendar System:** Semester **Enrollment:** Full-time 3,103, Graduate full-time 1,273, Graduate part-time 118, Part-time 123 **Faculty:** Full-time 153, Part-time 960 **Student-Faculty Ratio:** 9:1 **Exams:** ACT essay component used as validity check; ACT essay component used for admission; SAT I or ACT; SAT II; SAT essay component used as validity check; SAT essay component used for admission; SAT Reasoning; SAT Subject. **% Receiving Financial Aid:** 80 **% Residing in College-Owned, -Operated, or -Affiliated Housing:** 54 **Regional Accreditation:** Middle States Association of Colleges and Schools **Credit Hours For Degree:** 66 credits, Associates; 132 credits, Bachelors **ROTC:** Army **Professional Accreditation:** ACSP, ALA, CIDA, NAAB, NASAD, TEAC. **Intercollegiate Athletics:** Basketball M; Cross-Country Running M & W; Soccer M & W; Tennis M & W; Track and Field M & W; Volleyball W

PURCHASE COLLEGE, STATE UNIVERSITY OF NEW YORK

735 Anderson Hill Rd.
Purchase, NY 10577-1400
Tel: (914)251-6000
E-mail: admission@purchase.edu
Web Site: www.purchase.edu
President/CEO: Thomas Schwarz
Admissions: Stephanie McCaine
Financial Aid: Corey York

Type: Comprehensive **Sex:** Coed **Affiliation:** State University of New York System. **Scores:** 99% SAT V 400+; 96% SAT M 400+; 39% ACT 18-23; 50% ACT 24-29 **% Accepted:** 41 **Admission Plans:** Deferred Admission; Early Admission; Early Decision Plan **Application Deadline:** July 15 **Application Fee:** $50.00 **H.S. Requirements:** High school diploma required; GED accepted **Costs Per Year:** Application fee: $50. One-time mandatory fee: $210. State resident tuition: $6470 full-time, $270 per credit part-time. Nonresident tuition: $16,320 full-time, $680 per credit part-time. Mandatory fees: $1797 full-time, $74.28 per credit part-time. Full-time tuition and fees vary according to program. Part-time tuition and fees vary according to course load and program. College room and board: $12,576. College room only: $8196. Room and board charges vary according to board plan and housing facility. **Scholarships:** Available. **Calendar System:** Semester, Summer session available **Enrollment:** Full-time 3,747, Graduate full-time 86, Graduate part-time 6, Part-time 368 **Faculty:** Full-time 172, Part-time 266 **Student-Faculty Ratio:** 15:1 **Exams:** SAT I; SAT I or ACT; SAT Reasoning. **% Receiving Financial Aid:** 57 **% Residing in College-Owned, -Operated, or -Affiliated Housing:** 67 **Regional Accreditation:** Middle States Association of Colleges and Schools **Credit Hours For Degree:** 120 credits, Bachelors **Professional Accreditation:** NASAD. **Intercollegiate Athletics:** Baseball M; Basketball M & W; Cross-Country Running M & W; Golf M; Lacrosse W; Soccer M & W; Softball W; Swimming and Diving M & W; Tennis M & W; Volleyball M & W

QUEENS COLLEGE OF THE CITY UNIVERSITY OF NEW YORK

65-30 Kissena Blvd.
Flushing, NY 11367-1597
Tel: (718)997-5000
Fax: (718)997-5617
Web Site: www.qc.cuny.edu
President/CEO: Dr. Felix V. Matos Rodriguez
Admissions: Chelsea Lavington
Financial Aid: Clifford Couloute

Type: Comprehensive **Sex:** Coed **Affiliation:** City University of New York. **Scores:** 95% SAT V 400+; 100% SAT M 400+ **% Accepted:** 40 **Admission Plans:** Deferred Admission **Application Deadline:** February 1 **Application Fee:** $65.00 **H.S. Requirements:** High school diploma required; GED accepted **Costs Per Year:** Application fee: $65. State resident tuition: $6330 full-time. Nonresident tuition: $16,800 full-time. Mandatory fees: $608 full-time. Full-time tuition and fees vary according to course load. **Scholarships:** Available. **Calendar System:** Semester, Summer session available **Enrollment:** Full-time 11,555, Graduate full-time 441, Graduate part-time 2,979, Part-time 4,545 **Faculty:** Full-time 612, Part-time 922 **Student-Faculty Ratio:** 14:1 **Exams:** SAT I or ACT; SAT II; SAT Reasoning. **% Receiving Financial Aid:** 54 **% Residing in College-Owned, -Operated, or -Affiliated Housing:** 2 **Final Year or Final Semester Residency Requirement:** No **Regional Accreditation:** Middle States Association of Colleges and Schools **Credit Hours For Degree:** 120 credits, Bachelors **ROTC:** Air Force, Army **Professional Accreditation:** AAFCS, ALA, AND, ASHA, NCATE. **Intercollegiate Athletics:** Baseball M; Basketball M & W; Cross-Country Running M & W; Fencing W; Lacrosse W; Soccer M & W; Softball W; Swimming and Diving M & W; Tennis M & W; Track and Field M & W; Volleyball W

QUEENSBOROUGH COMMUNITY COLLEGE OF THE CITY UNIVERSITY OF NEW YORK

222-05 56th Ave.
Bayside, NY 11364
Tel: (718)631-6262
Fax: (718)281-5189
Web Site: www.qcc.cuny.edu
President/CEO: Dr. Diane B. Call
Admissions: Anthony Davis

Type: Two-Year College **Sex:** Coed **Affiliation:** City University of New York System. **Admission Plans:** Deferred Admission; Open Admission **Application Deadline:** Rolling **Application Fee:** $65.00 **H.S. Requirements:** High school diploma required; GED accepted **Costs Per Year:** Application fee: $65. State resident tuition: $4800 full-time, $210 per credit part-time. Nonresident tuition: $9600 full-time, $320 per credit part-time. Mandatory fees: $640 full-time, $320 per term part-time. **Scholarships:** Available. **Calendar System:** Semester, Summer session available **Enrollment:** Full-time 9,290, Part-time 6,203 **Faculty:** Full-time 395, Part-time 560 **Student-Faculty Ratio:** 19:1 **Exams:** ACT essay component used for advising; ACT essay component used for placement. **Final Year or Final Semester Residency Requirement:** No **Regional Accreditation:** Middle States Association of Colleges and Schools **Credit Hours For Degree:** 60 credits, Associates **ROTC:** Army **Professional Accreditation:** ABET, ACBSP, ACEN. **Intercollegiate Athletics:** Baseball M; Basketball M & W; Cross-Country Running M & W; Soccer M; Softball W; Swimming and Diving M & W; Track and Field M & W; Volleyball W

RABBINICAL ACADEMY MESIVTA RABBI CHAIM BERLIN

1605 Coney Island Ave.
Brooklyn, NY 11230-4715
Tel: (718)377-0777
President/CEO: Abraham Fruchthandler

Type: Comprehensive **Sex:** Men **Affiliation:** Jewish. **% Accepted:** 100 **Calendar System:** Semester **Credit Hours For Degree:** 150 credits, Bachelors **Professional Accreditation:** AARTS.

RABBINICAL COLLEGE BETH SHRAGA

28 Saddle River Rd.
Monsey, NY 10952-3035
Tel: (914)356-1980
President/CEO: Sydney Schiff
Admissions: Rabbi Sydney Schiff

Type: Comprehensive **Sex:** Men **Affiliation:** Jewish. **% Accepted:** 100 **Calendar System:** Semester **Professional Accreditation:** AARTS.

RABBINICAL COLLEGE BOBOVER YESHIVA B'NEI ZION

1577 Forty-eighth St.
Brooklyn, NY 11219
Tel: (718)438-2018
President/CEO: Mordechai Z. Geller
Type: Comprehensive **Sex:** Men **Affiliation:** Jewish. **Calendar System:** Semester **Professional Accreditation:** AARTS.

RABBINICAL COLLEGE CH'SAN SOFER

1876 Fiftieth St.
Brooklyn, NY 11204
Tel: (718)236-1171
President/CEO: William Greenwald
Type: Comprehensive **Sex:** Men **Affiliation:** Jewish. **Calendar System:** Semester **Professional Accreditation:** AARTS.

RABBINICAL COLLEGE OF LONG ISLAND

205 W Beech St.
Long Beach, NY 11561-3305
Tel: (516)431-7414
President/CEO: Yitzchok Feigelstock
Type: Comprehensive **Sex:** Men **Affiliation:** Jewish. **% Accepted:** 100 **H.S. Requirements:** High school diploma required; GED accepted **Calendar System:** Semester **Professional Accreditation:** AARTS.

RABBINICAL COLLEGE OF OHR SHIMON YISROEL

215-217 Hewes St.
Brooklyn, NY 11211
Tel: (718)855-4092
President/CEO: Rosa Friedman
Type: Four-Year College **Sex:** Men **Affiliation:** Jewish. **Professional Accreditation:** AARTS.

RABBINICAL SEMINARY OF AMERICA

76-01 147th St.
Flushing, NY 11367
Tel: (718)268-4700
President/CEO: M. Glazer
Admissions: Rabbi Abraham Semmel
Financial Aid: Leah Eisenstein
Type: Comprehensive **Sex:** Men **Affiliation:** Jewish. **Admission Plans:** Early Admission **Application Deadline:** December 1 **Application Fee:** $0.00 **H.S. Requirements:** High school diploma required; GED accepted **Calendar System:** Semester **% Residing in College-Owned, -Operated, or -Affiliated Housing:** 90 **Credit Hours For Degree:** 150 credits, Bachelors **Professional Accreditation:** AARTS.

RENSSELAER POLYTECHNIC INSTITUTE

110 8th St.
Troy, NY 12180-3590
Tel: (518)276-6000
Fax: (518)276-4072
E-mail: admissions@rpi.edu
Web Site: www.rpi.edu
President/CEO: Dr. Shirley Ann Jackson
Admissions: Karen Long
Financial Aid: Larry Chambers
Type: University **Sex:** Coed **Scores:** 100% SAT V 400+; 100% SAT M 400+; 3% ACT 18-23; 41% ACT 24-29 **% Accepted:** 42 **Admission Plans:** Deferred Admission; Early Action; Early Admission **Application Deadline:** January 15 **Application Fee:** $70.00 **H.S. Requirements:** High school diploma required; GED accepted **Costs Per Year:** Application fee: $70. Comprehensive fee: $65,427 includes full-time tuition ($49,520), mandatory fees ($1277), and college room and board ($14,630). College room only: $8310. Room and board charges vary according to board plan and location. Part-time tuition: $2060 per credit hour. **Scholarships:** Available. **Calendar System:** Semester, Summer session available **Enrollment:** Full-time 5,845, Graduate full-time 1,024, Graduate part-time 225, Part-time 19 **Faculty:** Full-time 404, Part-time 74 **Exams:** ACT essay component used for admission; SAT I and SAT II or ACT; SAT I or ACT; SAT essay component used for admission; SAT Reasoning. **% Receiving Financial Aid:** 61 **% Residing in College-Owned, -Operated, or -Affiliated Housing:** 57 **Regional Accreditation:** Middle States Association of Colleges and Schools **Credit Hours For Degree:** 124 credit hours, Bachelors **ROTC:** Air Force, Army,

Navy **Professional Accreditation:** AACSB, ABET, NAAB. **Intercollegiate Athletics:** Archery M & W; Badminton M & W; Baseball M & W; Basketball M & W; Crew M & W; Cross-Country Running M & W; Equestrian Sports M & W; Fencing M & W; Field Hockey W; Football M; Golf M; Ice Hockey M & W; Lacrosse M & W; Racquetball M & W; Riflery M & W; Rugby M & W; Sailing M & W; Skiing (Cross-Country) M & W; Soccer M & W; Softball W; Squash M & W; Swimming and Diving M & W; Table Tennis M & W; Tennis M & W; Track and Field M & W; Ultimate Frisbee M & W; Volleyball M & W; Water Polo M & W; Weight Lifting M & W

ROBERTS WESLEYAN COLLEGE

2301 Westside Dr.
Rochester, NY 14624-1997
Tel: (585)594-6000; Free: 800-777-4RWC
Fax: (585)594-6371
E-mail: admissions@roberts.edu
Web Site: www.roberts.edu
President/CEO: Dr. Deana L. Porterfield
Admissions: JP Anderson
Type: Comprehensive **Sex:** Coed **Affiliation:** Free Methodist Church of North America. **Scores:** 99% SAT V 400+; 98% SAT M 400+; 47.3% ACT 18-23; 36.5% ACT 24-29 **% Accepted:** 66 **Admission Plans:** Deferred Admission; Early Admission **Application Deadline:** Rolling **Application Fee:** $0.00 **H.S. Requirements:** High school diploma required; GED accepted **Costs Per Year:** Application fee: $0. One-time mandatory fee: $200. Comprehensive fee: $39,752 includes full-time tuition ($28,486), mandatory fees ($1054), and college room and board ($10,212). College room only: $6480. Room and board charges vary according to board plan and housing facility. **Scholarships:** Available. **Calendar System:** Semester, Summer session available **Enrollment:** Full-time 1,215, Graduate full-time 316, Graduate part-time 72, Part-time 109 **Faculty:** Full-time 92, Part-time 175 **Student-Faculty Ratio:** 11:1 **Exams:** SAT I or ACT; SAT Reasoning. **% Receiving Financial Aid:** 85 **% Residing in College-Owned, -Operated, or -Affiliated Housing:** 65 **Final Year or Final Semester Residency Requirement:** Yes **Regional Accreditation:** Middle States Association of Colleges and Schools **Credit Hours For Degree:** 62 semester hours, Associates; 124 semester hours, Bachelors **ROTC:** Air Force, Army **Professional Accreditation:** AACN, CSWE, NASAD, NASM, TEAC. **Intercollegiate Athletics:** Basketball M & W; Cheerleading M & W; Cross-Country Running M & W; Golf M; Lacrosse M & W; Soccer M & W; Tennis M & W; Track and Field M & W; Volleyball W

ROCHESTER INSTITUTE OF TECHNOLOGY

One Lomb Memorial Dr.
Rochester, NY 14623-5603
Tel: (585)475-2411
Fax: (585)475-7424
E-mail: admissions@rit.edu
Web Site: www.rit.edu
President/CEO: Dr. William Destler
Admissions: Dr. Daniel Shelley
Financial Aid: Verna Hazen
Type: Comprehensive **Sex:** Coed **Scores:** 100% SAT V 400+; 100% SAT M 400+; 9.51% ACT 18-23; 47.17% ACT 24-29 **% Accepted:** 57 **Admission Plans:** Deferred Admission; Early Action; Early Admission **Application Deadline:** February 1 **Application Fee:** $60.00 **H.S. Requirements:** High school diploma required; GED accepted **Costs Per Year:** Application fee: $60. Comprehensive fee: $49,042 includes full-time tuition ($36,596), mandatory fees ($528), and college room and board ($11,918). College room only: $6954. Full-time tuition and fees vary according to course load. Room and board charges vary according to board plan and housing facility. Part-time tuition: $1331 per credit hour. Part-time mandatory fees: $67 per term. Part-time tuition and fees vary according to class time and course load. **Scholarships:** Available. **Calendar System:** Semester, Summer session available **Enrollment:** Full-time 12,472, Graduate full-time 2,474, Graduate part-time 623, Part-time 1,071 **Faculty:** Full-time 1,015, Part-time 468 **Student-Faculty Ratio:** 13:1 **Exams:** ACT essay component used for admission; SAT I or ACT; SAT II; SAT essay component used for admission. **% Receiving Financial Aid:** 73 **% Residing in College-Owned, -Operated, or -Affiliated Housing:** 68 **Final Year or Final Semester Residency Requirement:** Yes **Regional Accreditation:** Middle States Association of Colleges and Schools **Credit Hours For Degree:** 60 credit hours, Associates; 120 credit hours, Bachelors **ROTC:** Air Force, Army, Navy **Professional Accreditation:** AACSB, ABET, CIDA, CSWE, JRCEDMS, JRCNMT,

NASAD, TEAC. **Intercollegiate Athletics:** Baseball M; Basketball M & W; Bowling M & W; Cheerleading M & W; Crew M & W; Cross-Country Running M & W; Equestrian Sports M & W; Fencing M & W; Field Hockey W; Ice Hockey M & W; Lacrosse M & W; Skiing (Downhill) M & W; Soccer M & W; Softball W; Swimming and Diving M & W; Tennis M & W; Track and Field M & W; Ultimate Frisbee M & W; Volleyball M & W; Water Polo M & W; Wrestling M

ROCKLAND COMMUNITY COLLEGE

145 College Rd.
Suffern, NY 10901-3699
Tel: (845)574-4000; Free: 800-722-7666
E-mail: lglynn@sunyrockland.edu
Web Site: www.sunyrockland.edu
President/CEO: Cliff L. Wood
Admissions: Jude Fleurismond
Financial Aid: Debra Bouabidi

Type: Two-Year College **Sex:** Coed **Affiliation:** State University of New York System. **% Accepted:** 100 **Admission Plans:** Deferred Admission; Early Admission; Open Admission **Application Deadline:** Rolling **Application Fee:** $30.00 **H.S. Requirements:** High school diploma or equivalent not required **Costs Per Year:** Application fee: $30. State resident tuition: $4299 full-time, $180 per credit part-time. Nonresident tuition: $8598 full-time, $359 per credit part-time. Mandatory fees: $355 full-time, $13 per credit part-time. Full-time tuition and fees vary according to course load and program. Part-time tuition and fees vary according to course load and program. **Scholarships:** Available. **Calendar System:** Semester, Summer session available **Enrollment:** Full-time 4,189, Part-time 3,245 **Faculty:** Full-time 113, Part-time 377 **Student-Faculty Ratio:** 22:1 **Final Year or Final Semester Residency Requirement:** No **Regional Accreditation:** Middle States Association of Colleges and Schools **Credit Hours For Degree:** 60 credits, Associates **Professional Accreditation:** ACEN, AHIMA, AOTA. **Intercollegiate Athletics:** Baseball M; Basketball M & W; Bowling M & W; Golf M; Soccer M & W; Softball W; Tennis M & W; Volleyball W

THE SAGE COLLEGES

65 1st St.
Troy, NY 12180
Tel: (518)244-2000
E-mail: breent@sage.edu
Web Site: www.sage.edu
President/CEO: Susam Scrimshaw, PhD
Admissions: Thomas Breen

Type: Comprehensive **Sex:** Coed **Scores:** 86% SAT V 400+; 60% ACT 18-23; 24% ACT 24-29 **% Accepted:** 54 **Admission Plans:** Deferred Admission; Early Admission; Early Decision Plan **Application Deadline:** Rolling **Application Fee:** $30.00 **H.S. Requirements:** High school diploma required; GED accepted **Costs Per Year:** Application fee: $30. Comprehensive fee: $40,620 includes full-time tuition ($27,000), mandatory fees ($1400), and college room and board ($12,220). College room only: $6330. Room and board charges vary according to board plan. Part-time tuition: $900 per credit hour. **Scholarships:** Available. **Calendar System:** Semester, Summer session available **Enrollment:** Full-time 1,419, Graduate full-time 505, Graduate part-time 745, Part-time 228 **Faculty:** Full-time 139, Part-time 166 **Student-Faculty Ratio:** 13:1 **Exams:** SAT I or ACT. **% Receiving Financial Aid:** 92 **% Residing in College-Owned, -Operated, or -Affiliated Housing:** 55 **Final Year or Final Semester Residency Requirement:** No **Regional Accreditation:** Middle States Association of Colleges and Schools **Credit Hours For Degree:** 120 credits, Bachelors **ROTC:** Air Force, Army **Professional Accreditation:** AACN, AND, AOTA, APTA, NASAD, NCATE. **Intercollegiate Athletics:** Basketball M & W; Cross-Country Running M & W; Golf M; Lacrosse W; Soccer M & W; Softball W; Tennis M & W; Track and Field M & W; Volleyball M & W

ST. BONAVENTURE UNIVERSITY

3261 W State Rd.
Saint Bonaventure, NY 14778-2284
Tel: (716)375-2000; Free: 800-462-5050
Fax: (716)375-2005
E-mail: bvalento@sbu.edu
Web Site: www.sbu.edu
President/CEO: Señor Margaret Carney
Admissions: Bernard Valento
Financial Aid: Troy R. Martin

Type: Comprehensive **Sex:** Coed **Affiliation:** Roman Catholic Church. **Scores:** 94% SAT V 400+; 93% SAT M 400+; 41% ACT 18-23; 35% ACT 24-29 **% Accepted:** 66 **Admission Plans:** Deferred Admission **Application Deadline:** July 1 **Application Fee:** $0.00 **H.S. Requirements:** High school diploma required; GED accepted **Costs Per Year:** Application fee: $0. One-time mandatory fee: $100. Comprehensive fee: $42,517 includes full-time tuition ($30,424), mandatory fees ($965), and college room and board ($11,128). College room only: $5856. Room and board charges vary according to board plan and housing facility. Part-time tuition: $906 per credit hour. Part-time tuition varies according to course load. **Scholarships:** Available. **Calendar System:** Semester, Summer session available **Enrollment:** Full-time 1,633, Graduate full-time 189, Graduate part-time 135, Part-time 54 **Faculty:** Full-time 129, Part-time 93 **Student-Faculty Ratio:** 11:1 **Exams:** ACT essay component used for admission; ACT essay component used for advising; ACT essay component used for placement; SAT I and SAT II or ACT; SAT I or ACT; SAT essay component used for admission; SAT essay component used for advising; SAT essay component used for placement; SAT Reasoning; SAT Subject. **% Receiving Financial Aid:** 78 **% Residing in College-Owned, -Operated, or -Affiliated Housing:** 75 **Final Year or Final Semester Residency Requirement:** Yes **Regional Accreditation:** Middle States Association of Colleges and Schools **Credit Hours For Degree:** 120 credit hours, Bachelors **ROTC:** Army **Professional Accreditation:** AACSB, ACA, NCATE. **Intercollegiate Athletics:** Baseball M; Basketball M & W; Cross-Country Running M & W; Field Hockey W; Golf M; Gymnastics W; Ice Hockey M; Lacrosse M & W; Rugby M & W; Soccer M & W; Softball W; Swimming and Diving M & W; Tennis M & W

ST. ELIZABETH COLLEGE OF NURSING

2215 Genesee St.
Utica, NY 13501
Tel: (315)798-8144
E-mail: dernst@secon.edu
Web Site: www.secon.edu
President/CEO: Marian Kovatchitch
Admissions: Donna Ernst

Type: Two-Year College **Sex:** Coed **Affiliation:** St. Elizabeth Medical Center. **% Accepted:** 32 **Application Deadline:** Rolling **Application Fee:** $65.00 **H.S. Requirements:** High school diploma required; GED accepted **Calendar System:** Semester **Enrollment:** Full-time 72, Part-time 87 **Faculty:** Full-time 13, Part-time 5 **Student-Faculty Ratio:** 7:1 **Exams:** ACT essay component not used; SAT I or ACT; SAT essay component not used; SAT Reasoning; SAT Subject. **Final Year or Final Semester Residency Requirement:** No **Regional Accreditation:** Middle States Association of Colleges and Schools **Credit Hours For Degree:** 68 credits, Associates **Professional Accreditation:** ACEN.

ST. FRANCIS COLLEGE

180 Remsen St.
Brooklyn Heights, NY 11201-4398
Tel: (718)522-2300
Fax: (718)522-1274
E-mail: lrandazzo@sfc.edu
Web Site: www.sfc.edu
President/CEO: Brendan J. Dugan
Admissions: Lisa Randazzo
Financial Aid: Hellitz Lopez

Type: Comprehensive **Sex:** Coed **Affiliation:** Roman Catholic. **Scores:** 82% SAT V 400+; 78% SAT M 400+; 50.6% ACT 18-23; 19.2% ACT 24-29 **Scholarships:** Available. **Calendar System:** Semester, Summer session available **Enrollment:** Full-time 2,393, Graduate full-time 41, Graduate part-time 33, Part-time 205 **Faculty:** Full-time 82, Part-time 218 **Student-Faculty Ratio:** 17:1 **Exams:** ACT; SAT I; SAT essay component not used. **% Receiving Financial Aid:** 73 **% Residing in College-Owned, -Operated, or -Affiliated Housing:** 7 **Final Year or Final Semester Residency Requirement:** No **Regional Accreditation:** Middle States Association of Colleges and Schools **Credit Hours For Degree:** 64 credits, Associates; 128 credits, Bachelors **ROTC:** Air Force, Army **Professional Accreditation:** AACN. **Intercollegiate Athletics:** Basketball M & W; Cross-Country Running M & W; Golf M & W; Soccer M; Swimming and Diving M & W; Tennis M & W; Track and Field M & W; Volleyball W; Water Polo M & W

ST. JOHN FISHER COLLEGE

3690 E Ave.
Rochester, NY 14618-3597

Tel: (585)385-8000; Free: 800-444-4640
Fax: (585)385-8129
E-mail: admissions@sjfc.edu
Web Site: www.sjfc.edu
President/CEO: Dr. Gerard J. Rooney
Admissions: Stacy A. Ledermann
Financial Aid: Angela Monnat
Type: Comprehensive **Sex:** Coed **Affiliation:** Roman Catholic Church. **Scores:** 98% SAT V 400+; 98% SAT M 400+; 39.49% ACT 18-23; 53.33% ACT 24-29 **% Accepted:** 62 **Admission Plans:** Deferred Admission; Early Action **Application Deadline:** Rolling **Application Fee:** $0.00 **H.S. Requirements:** High school diploma required; GED not accepted **Costs Per Year:** Application fee: $0. Comprehensive fee: $42,150 includes full-time tuition ($30,110), mandatory fees ($580), and college room and board ($11,460). College room only: $7370. Full-time tuition and fees vary according to program. Room and board charges vary according to board plan. Part-time tuition: $820 per credit hour. Part-time mandatory fees: $10 per credit hour. Part-time tuition and fees vary according to course load and program. **Scholarships:** Available. **Calendar System:** Semester, Summer session available **Enrollment:** Full-time 2,619, Graduate full-time 644, Graduate part-time 374, Part-time 186 **Faculty:** Full-time 230, Part-time 217 **Student-Faculty Ratio:** 12:1 **Exams:** SAT I or ACT; SAT Reasoning. **% Receiving Financial Aid:** 81 **% Residing in College-Owned, -Operated, or -Affiliated Housing:** 50 **Final Year or Final Semester Residency Requirement:** No **Regional Accreditation:** Middle States Association of Colleges and Schools **Credit Hours For Degree:** 120 credit hours, Bachelors **ROTC:** Air Force, Army, Navy **Professional Accreditation:** AACN, AACSB, ACA, ACPE, NCATE. **Intercollegiate Athletics:** Baseball M; Basketball M & W; Crew W; Cross-Country Running M & W; Field Hockey W; Football M; Golf M & W; Lacrosse M & W; Soccer M & W; Softball W; Tennis M & W; Track and Field M & W; Volleyball W

ST. JOHN'S UNIVERSITY

8000 Utopia Pky.
Queens, NY 11439
Tel: (718)990-6161; Free: 888-9STJOHNS
E-mail: admission@stjohns.edu
Web Site: www.stjohns.edu
Admissions: Samantha R. Wright
Financial Aid: Jorge Rodriguez
Type: University **Sex:** Coed **Affiliation:** Roman Catholic Church. **Scores:** 99% SAT V 400+; 99% SAT M 400+; 41% ACT 18-23; 45% ACT 24-29 **% Accepted:** 65 **Admission Plans:** Deferred Admission; Early Admission **Application Deadline:** Rolling **Application Fee:** $50.00 **H.S. Requirements:** High school diploma required; GED accepted **Costs Per Year:** Application fee: $50. Comprehensive fee: $55,850 includes full-time tuition ($38,630), mandatory fees ($830), and college room and board ($16,390). College room only: $10,350. Full-time tuition and fees vary according to course load, program, and student level. Room and board charges vary according to board plan, housing facility, and location. Part-time tuition: $1288 per credit. Part-time tuition varies according to course load, program, and student level. **Scholarships:** Available. **Calendar System:** Semester, Summer session available **Enrollment:** Full-time 11,051, Graduate full-time 2,657, Graduate part-time 2,014, Part-time 5,159 **Faculty:** Full-time 611, Part-time 821 **Student-Faculty Ratio:** 17:1 **Exams:** ACT essay component not used; SAT I and SAT II or ACT; SAT I or ACT; SAT essay component not used. **% Receiving Financial Aid:** 80 **% Residing in College-Owned, -Operated, or -Affiliated Housing:** 29 **Final Year or Final Semester Residency Requirement:** No **Regional Accreditation:** Middle States Association of Colleges and Schools **Credit Hours For Degree:** 60 credits, Associates; 126 credits, Bachelors **ROTC:** Army **Professional Accreditation:** AACSB, AALS, ABA, ACA, ACPE, ACIPE, ALA, APA, ASHA, CORE, TEAC. **Intercollegiate Athletics:** Baseball M; Basketball M & W; Cross-Country Running W; Fencing M & W; Golf M & W; Lacrosse M; Soccer M & W; Softball W; Tennis M & W; Track and Field W; Volleyball W

ST. JOSEPH'S COLLEGE, LONG ISLAND CAMPUS

155 W Roe Blvd.
Patchogue, NY 11772-2399
Tel: (631)687-5100
Fax: (631)447-1734
E-mail: glamens@sjcny.edu
Web Site: www.sjcny.edu
President/CEO: Jack P. Calareso, PhD

Admissions: Gigi Lamens
Financial Aid: Amy Thompson
Type: Comprehensive **Sex:** Coed **Scores:** 96% SAT V 400+; 97% SAT M 400+; 53% ACT 18-23; 35% ACT 24-29 **% Accepted:** 75 **Admission Plans:** Deferred Admission **Application Deadline:** Rolling **Application Fee:** $25.00 **H.S. Requirements:** High school diploma required; GED accepted **Costs Per Year:** Application fee: $25. Tuition: $23,500 full-time, $760 per credit part-time. Mandatory fees: $623 full-time. Full-time tuition and fees vary according to course load and program. Part-time tuition varies according to course load and program. **Scholarships:** Available. **Calendar System:** 4-1-4, Summer session available **Enrollment:** Full-time 2,400, Graduate full-time 87, Graduate part-time 562, Part-time 488 **Faculty:** Full-time 113, Part-time 280 **Student-Faculty Ratio:** 14:1 **Exams:** ACT essay component used as validity check; ACT essay component used for advising; SAT I or ACT; SAT essay component used as validity check; SAT essay component used for advising. **% Receiving Financial Aid:** 75 **Final Year or Final Semester Residency Requirement:** No **Regional Accreditation:** Middle States Association of Colleges and Schools **Credit Hours For Degree:** 128 credits, Bachelors **Intercollegiate Athletics:** Baseball M; Basketball M & W; Cross-Country Running M & W; Equestrian Sports W; Golf M; Lacrosse M & W; Soccer M & W; Softball W; Swimming and Diving W; Tennis M & W; Track and Field M & W; Volleyball M & W

ST. JOSEPH'S COLLEGE, NEW YORK

245 Clinton Ave.
Brooklyn, NY 11205-3688
Tel: (718)940-5300
Fax: (718)636-7242
E-mail: cmurphy@sjcny.edu
Web Site: www.sjcny.edu
President/CEO: Jack P. Calareso, PhD
Admissions: Christine Murphy
Financial Aid: Amy Thompson
Type: Comprehensive **Sex:** Coed **Scores:** 86% SAT V 400+; 88% SAT M 400+; 75% ACT 18-23; 15% ACT 24-29 **% Accepted:** 61 **Admission Plans:** Deferred Admission; Early Admission **Application Deadline:** August 31 **Application Fee:** $25.00 **H.S. Requirements:** High school diploma required; GED accepted **Costs Per Year:** Application fee: $25. Tuition: $23,500 full-time, $760 per credit part-time. Mandatory fees: $613 full-time. Full-time tuition and fees vary according to course load. Part-time tuition varies according to course load. **Scholarships:** Available. **Calendar System:** Semester, Summer session available **Enrollment:** Full-time 757, Graduate full-time 41, Graduate part-time 181, Part-time 233 **Faculty:** Full-time 58, Part-time 131 **Student-Faculty Ratio:** 9:1 **Exams:** ACT essay component not used; SAT I or ACT; SAT essay component not used; SAT Reasoning. **% Receiving Financial Aid:** 78 **Final Year or Final Semester Residency Requirement:** No **Regional Accreditation:** Middle States Association of Colleges and Schools **Credit Hours For Degree:** 128 credits, Bachelors **Professional Accreditation:** ACEN, TEAC. **Intercollegiate Athletics:** Baseball M; Basketball M & W; Cross-Country Running M & W; Soccer M & W; Softball W; Swimming and Diving W; Tennis M & W; Volleyball M & W

ST. JOSEPH'S COLLEGE OF NURSING

206 Prospect Ave.
Syracuse, NY 13203
Tel: (315)448-5040
Fax: (315)448-5745
E-mail: collegeofnursing@sjhsyr.org
Web Site: www.sjhsyr.org/nursing
President/CEO: Marianne Markowitz
Admissions: Felicia Corp
Type: Two-Year College **Sex:** Coed **Affiliation:** Roman Catholic. **Scores:** 100% SAT V 400+; 100% SAT M 400+; 99% ACT 18-23; 1% ACT 24-29 **% Accepted:** 55 **Admission Plans:** Deferred Admission **Application Fee:** $50.00 **H.S. Requirements:** High school diploma required; GED accepted **Costs Per Year:** Application fee: $50. Tuition: $16,960 full-time, $530 per credit part-time. Mandatory fees: $1340 full-time. Full-time tuition and fees vary according to program. Part-time tuition varies according to program. College room only: $5500. **Scholarships:** Available. **Calendar System:** Semester, Summer session not available **Enrollment:** Full-time 166, Part-time 107 **Faculty:** Full-time 17, Part-time 13 **Student-Faculty Ratio:** 9:1 **Exams:** ACT essay component not used; SAT I or ACT; SAT essay component not used. **% Residing in College-Owned, -Operated, or -Affiliated Housing:** 20 **Final Year or Final Semester Residency Require-**

ment: No **Regional Accreditation:** Middle States Association of Colleges and Schools **Credit Hours For Degree:** 69 credit hours, Associates

ST. LAWRENCE UNIVERSITY
Canton, NY 13617-1455
Tel: (315)229-5011; Free: 800-285-1856
Fax: (315)229-5502
E-mail: jfreeman@stlawu.edu
Web Site: www.stlawu.edu
President/CEO: Dr. William L. Fox
Admissions: Jeremy Freeman
Financial Aid: Patricia J.B. Farmer

Type: Comprehensive **Sex:** Coed **Scores:** 99% SAT V 400+; 99% SAT M 400+; 14.6% ACT 18-23; 58.4% ACT 24-29 **% Accepted:** 46 **Admission Plans:** Deferred Admission; Early Action; Early Admission **Application Deadline:** February 1 **Application Fee:** $60.00 **H.S. Requirements:** High school diploma required; GED accepted **Costs Per Year:** Application fee: $60. Comprehensive fee: $62,140 includes full-time tuition ($49,060), mandatory fees ($350), and college room and board ($12,730). College room only: $6856. Room and board charges vary according to board plan. Part-time tuition: $1703 per credit hour. **Scholarships:** Available. **Calendar System:** Semester, Summer session available **Enrollment:** Full-time 2,404, Graduate full-time 48, Graduate part-time 51, Part-time 31 **Faculty:** Full-time 176, Part-time 31 **Student-Faculty Ratio:** 11:1 **Exams:** ACT essay component used for admission; SAT I and SAT II or ACT; SAT I or ACT; SAT II; SAT essay component used for admission; SAT Reasoning; SAT Subject. **% Receiving Financial Aid:** 57 **% Residing in College-Owned, -Operated, or -Affiliated Housing:** 99 **Final Year or Final Semester Residency Requirement:** No **Regional Accreditation:** Middle States Association of Colleges and Schools **Credit Hours For Degree:** 120.6 credits, Bachelors **ROTC:** Air Force, Army **Professional Accreditation:** TEAC. **Intercollegiate Athletics:** Baseball M; Basketball M & W; Cross-Country Running M & W; Equestrian Sports W; Field Hockey W; Football M; Golf M & W; Ice Hockey M & W; Lacrosse M & W; Rowing M & W; Skiing (Downhill) M & W; Soccer M & W; Softball W; Squash M & W; Swimming and Diving M & W; Tennis M & W; Track and Field M & W; Volleyball W

ST. PAUL'S SCHOOL OF NURSING (REGO PARK)
97-77 Queens Blvd.
Rego Park, NY 11374
Tel: (718)357-0500
Fax: (718)357-4683
E-mail: nwolinski@svcmcny.org
Web Site: www.stpaulsschoolofnursing.com
President/CEO: Eric Ricioppo
Admissions: Nancy Wolinski

Type: Two-Year College **Sex:** Coed **% Accepted:** 9 **Admission Plans:** Deferred Admission **Application Deadline:** April 1 **Application Fee:** $45.00 **H.S. Requirements:** High school diploma required; GED accepted **Scholarships:** Available. **Calendar System:** Semester, Summer session not available **Enrollment:** Full-time 106 **Faculty:** Full-time 8, Part-time 2 **Student-Faculty Ratio:** 10:1 **Exams:** Other. **Credit Hours For Degree:** 64 credits, Associates

ST. PAUL'S SCHOOL OF NURSING (STATEN ISLAND)
Corporate Commons Two
2 Teleport Dr., Ste. 203
Staten Island, NY 10311
Tel: (718)818-6470
Web Site: www.stpaulsschoolofnursing.com
Type: Two-Year College **Sex:** Coed **Professional Accreditation:** ABHES.

ST. THOMAS AQUINAS COLLEGE
125 Rte. 340
Sparkill, NY 10976
Tel: (845)398-4000; Free: 800-999-STAC
E-mail: sbazile@stac.edu
Web Site: www.stac.edu
President/CEO: Dr. Margaret M. Fitzpatrick, SC
Admissions: Samantha Bazile
Financial Aid: Jean Marie Mohr

Type: Comprehensive **Sex:** Coed **Scores:** 85% SAT V 400+; 87% SAT M 400+; 62.2% ACT 18-23; 14.8% ACT 24-29 **% Accepted:** 79 **Admission Plans:** Deferred Admission **Application Deadline:** Rolling **Application Fee:**

$30.00 **H.S. Requirements:** High school diploma required; GED accepted **Costs Per Year:** Application fee: $30. Comprehensive fee: $41,270 includes full-time tuition ($28,240), mandatory fees ($1000), and college room and board ($12,030). College room only: $6490. Room and board charges vary according to board plan and housing facility. Part-time tuition: $900 per credit. **Scholarships:** Available. **Calendar System:** Semester, Summer session available **Enrollment:** Full-time 1,117, Graduate full-time 45, Graduate part-time 95, Part-time 579 **Faculty:** Full-time 57, Part-time 105 **Student-Faculty Ratio:** 15:1 **Exams:** ACT essay component used for placement; SAT I or ACT; SAT essay component used for placement. **% Receiving Financial Aid:** 74 **Regional Accreditation:** Middle States Association of Colleges and Schools **Credit Hours For Degree:** 120 credits, Bachelors **ROTC:** Air Force **Professional Accreditation:** NCATE. **Intercollegiate Athletics:** Baseball M; Basketball M & W; Cross-Country Running M & W; Golf M & W; Lacrosse W; Soccer M & W; Softball W; Tennis M & W; Volleyball W

SAMARITAN HOSPITAL SCHOOL OF NURSING
2215 Burdett Ave.
Troy, NY 12180
Tel: (518)271-3285
Fax: (518)271-3303
E-mail: marronej@nehealth.com
Web Site: www.nehealth.com
President/CEO: Susan Birkhead, MPH, RN
Admissions: Diane Dyer

Type: Two-Year College **Sex:** Coed **Affiliation:** Samaritan Hospital (Troy, NY). **Application Deadline:** Rolling **H.S. Requirements:** High school diploma required; GED accepted **Scholarships:** Available. **Enrollment:** Full-time 36, Part-time 83 **Faculty:** Full-time 5, Part-time 4 **Exams:** Other; SAT I or ACT.

SARAH LAWRENCE COLLEGE
1 Mead Way
Bronxville, NY 10708-5999
Tel: (914)337-0700; Free: 800-888-2858
Fax: (914)395-2668
E-mail: slcadmit@sarahlawrence.edu
Web Site: www.sarahlawrence.edu
President/CEO: Dr. Karen R. Lawrence
Admissions: Jennifer Gayles
Financial Aid: Nicholas Salinas

Type: Comprehensive **Sex:** Coed **Scores:** 100% SAT V 400+; 99% SAT M 400+; 7% ACT 18-23; 46% ACT 24-29 **% Accepted:** 53 **Admission Plans:** Deferred Admission; Early Action; Early Admission **Application Deadline:** January 15 **Application Fee:** $60.00 **H.S. Requirements:** High school diploma required; GED accepted **Costs Per Year:** Application fee: $60. Comprehensive fee: $65,630 includes full-time tuition ($49,680), mandatory fees ($1354), and college room and board ($14,596). College room only: $9506. Full-time tuition and fees vary according to course load. Room and board charges vary according to board plan. Part-time tuition: $1656 per credit. Part-time mandatory fees: $276 per term. Part-time tuition and fees vary according to course load. **Scholarships:** Available. **Calendar System:** Semester, Summer session available **Enrollment:** Full-time 1,327, Graduate full-time 262, Graduate part-time 33, Part-time 21 **Faculty:** Full-time 103, Part-time 192 **Student-Faculty Ratio:** 10:1 **Exams:** ACT essay component not used; SAT I or ACT; SAT essay component not used; SAT Reasoning; SAT Subject. **% Receiving Financial Aid:** 58 **% Residing in College-Owned, -Operated, or -Affiliated Housing:** 82 **Final Year or Final Semester Residency Requirement:** No **Regional Accreditation:** Middle States Association of Colleges and Schools **Credit Hours For Degree:** 120 credits, Bachelors **Intercollegiate Athletics:** Basketball M & W; Crew W; Cross-Country Running M & W; Equestrian Sports M & W; Soccer M & W; Softball W; Swimming and Diving M & W; Tennis M & W; Volleyball M & W

SCHENECTADY COUNTY COMMUNITY COLLEGE
78 Washington Ave.
Schenectady, NY 12305-2294
Tel: (518)381-1200
E-mail: sampsodg@gw.sunysccc.edu
Web Site: www.sunysccc.edu
President/CEO: Martha Asselin
Admissions: David Sampson
Financial Aid: Brian McGarvey

Type: Two-Year College Sex: Coed Affiliation: State University of New York System. Admission Plans: Deferred Admission; Early Admission; Open Admission; Preferred Admission Application Deadline: Rolling Application Fee: $0.00 H.S. Requirements: High school diploma required; GED accepted Costs Per Year: Application fee: $0. State resident tuition: $3528 full-time, $147 per credit hour part-time. Nonresident tuition: $7056 full-time, $294 per credit hour part-time. Mandatory fees: $526 full-time, $22 per credit hour part-time, $4 per year part-time. Full-time tuition and fees vary according to course load and program. Part-time tuition and fees vary according to course load and program. Scholarships: Available. Calendar System: Semester, Summer session available Enrollment: Full-time 2,235, Part-time 3,916 Regional Accreditation: Middle States Association of Colleges and Schools Credit Hours For Degree: 60 credit hours, Associates Professional Accreditation: ACBSP, ACF, NASM. Intercollegiate Athletics: Baseball M; Basketball M & W; Bowling M & W; Softball W

SCHOOL OF VISUAL ARTS

209 E 23rd St.
New York, NY 10010-3994
Tel: (212)592-2000; Free: 800-436-4204
Fax: (212)592-2116
E-mail: admissions@sva.edu
Web Site: www.sva.edu
President/CEO: David Rhodes
Financial Aid: William Berrios

Type: Comprehensive Sex: Coed Scores: 93% SAT V 400+; 91% SAT M 400+; 41% ACT 18-23; 47% ACT 24-29 % Accepted: 74 Admission Plans: Deferred Admission Application Deadline: Rolling Application Fee: $50.00 H.S. Requirements: High school diploma required; GED accepted Costs Per Year: Application fee: $50. Comprehensive fee: $54,800 includes full-time tuition ($36,500) and college room and board ($18,300). College room only: $15,400. Part-time tuition: $1270 per credit hour. Scholarships: Available. Calendar System: Semester, Summer session available Enrollment: Full-time 3,466, Graduate full-time 638, Graduate part-time 62, Part-time 241 Faculty: Full-time 196, Part-time 972 Student-Faculty Ratio: 8:1 Exams: SAT I or ACT. % Receiving Financial Aid: 44 % Residing in College-Owned, -Operated, or -Affiliated Housing: 33 Regional Accreditation: Middle States Association of Colleges and Schools Credit Hours For Degree: 120 credits, Bachelors Professional Accreditation: CIDA, NASAD.

SH'OR YOSHUV RABBINICAL COLLEGE

1 Cedarlawn Ave.
Lawrence, NY 11559-1714
Tel: (718)327-2048
E-mail: mrubin@shoryoshuv.org
Web Site: www.shoryoshuv.org
President/CEO: Rabbi Naftali Jaeger
Admissions: Rabbi Moshe Rubin

Type: Comprehensive Sex: Men Affiliation: Jewish. Application Deadline: September 20 H.S. Requirements: High school diploma or equivalent not required Costs Per Year: Comprehensive fee: $15,000 includes full-time tuition ($9000) and college room and board ($6000). Calendar System: Semester, Summer session available Enrollment: Full-time 217 Faculty: Full-time 17 Student-Faculty Ratio: 15:1 % Residing in College-Owned, -Operated, or -Affiliated Housing: 84 Professional Accreditation: AARTS.

SIENA COLLEGE

515 Loudon Rd.
Loudonville, NY 12211-1462
Tel: (518)783-2300; Free: 888-AT-SIENA
Fax: (518)783-4293
E-mail: admissions@siena.edu
Web Site: www.siena.edu
President/CEO: Bro. F. Edward Coughlin, OFM
Admissions: Mary Lawyer
Financial Aid: Mary Lawyer

Type: Comprehensive Sex: Coed Affiliation: Roman Catholic. Scores: 98% SAT V 400+; 98% SAT M 400+; 42.3% ACT 18-23; 44.4% ACT 24-29 % Accepted: 59 Admission Plans: Deferred Admission; Early Action; Early Admission; Early Decision Plan Application Deadline: February 15 Application Fee: $50.00 H.S. Requirements: High school diploma required; GED accepted Costs Per Year: Application fee: $50. Comprehensive fee:

$48,716 includes full-time tuition ($34,326), mandatory fees ($285), and college room and board ($14,105). College room only: $8315. Full-time tuition and fees vary according to course load, program, and student level. Room and board charges vary according to board plan and housing facility. Part-time tuition: $500 per credit. Part-time mandatory fees: $100 per term. Part-time tuition and fees vary according to course load, program, and student level. Scholarships: Available. Calendar System: Semester, Summer session available Enrollment: Full-time 3,007, Graduate full-time 48, Graduate part-time 9, Part-time 115 Faculty: Full-time 220, Part-time 127 Student-Faculty Ratio: 12:1 Exams: ACT; ACT essay component not used; Other; SAT I; SAT I and SAT II or ACT; SAT I or ACT; SAT II; SAT essay component not used; SAT Reasoning. % Receiving Financial Aid: 73 % Residing in College-Owned, -Operated, or -Affiliated Housing: 80 Final Year or Final Semester Residency Requirement: No Regional Accreditation: Middle States Association of Colleges and Schools Credit Hours For Degree: 120 credit hours, Bachelors ROTC: Air Force, Army Professional Accreditation: AACSB, CSWE, NCATE. Intercollegiate Athletics: Baseball M; Basketball M & W; Cheerleading W; Cross-Country Running M & W; Equestrian Sports M & W; Field Hockey W; Golf M & W; Ice Hockey M; Lacrosse M & W; Rugby M & W; Soccer M & W; Softball W; Squash M & W; Swimming and Diving W; Tennis M & W; Ultimate Frisbee M & W; Volleyball M & W; Water Polo W

SKIDMORE COLLEGE

815 N Broadway
Saratoga Springs, NY 12866
Tel: (518)580-5000; Free: 800-867-6007
Fax: (518)581-7462
E-mail: admissions@skidmore.edu
Web Site: www.skidmore.edu
President/CEO: Dr. Philip A. Glotzbach
Admissions: Mary Lou Bates
Financial Aid: Beth A. Post-Lundquist

Type: Four-Year College Sex: Coed Scores: 100% SAT V 400+; 100% SAT M 400+; 7.8% ACT 18-23; 62.1% ACT 24-29 % Accepted: 36 Admission Plans: Deferred Admission; Early Action; Early Admission Application Deadline: January 15 Application Fee: $65.00 H.S. Requirements: High school diploma required; GED accepted Costs Per Year: Application fee: $65. One-time mandatory fee: $150. Comprehensive fee: $62,042 includes full-time tuition ($48,024), mandatory fees ($946), and college room and board ($13,072). College room only: $7728. Full-time tuition and fees vary according to course load. Room and board charges vary according to board plan and housing facility. Part-time tuition: $1601 per credit. Part-time mandatory fees: $25 per term. Part-time tuition and fees vary according to course load. Scholarships: Available. Calendar System: Semester, Summer session available Enrollment: Full-time 2,603, Graduate part-time 8, Part-time 31 Faculty: Full-time 277, Part-time 81 Student-Faculty Ratio: 8:1 Exams: ACT essay component used for admission; SAT I or ACT; SAT II; SAT essay component used for admission; SAT Reasoning; SAT Subject. % Receiving Financial Aid: 41 % Residing in College-Owned, -Operated, or -Affiliated Housing: 92 Regional Accreditation: Middle States Association of Colleges and Schools Credit Hours For Degree: 120 semester hours, Bachelors ROTC: Air Force, Army Professional Accreditation: CSWE, NASAD. Intercollegiate Athletics: Baseball M; Basketball M & W; Crew M & W; Equestrian Sports W; Field Hockey W; Golf M; Ice Hockey M; Lacrosse M & W; Soccer M & W; Softball W; Swimming and Diving M & W; Tennis M & W; Volleyball W

STATE UNIVERSITY OF NEW YORK COLLEGE OF AGRICULTURE AND TECHNOLOGY AT COBLESKILL

Cobleskill, NY 12043
Tel: (518)255-5011; Free: 800-295-8988
Fax: (518)255-5333
E-mail: admissions@cobleskill.edu
Web Site: www.cobleskill.edu
President/CEO: Dr. Marion Terenzio
Admissions: Lisa Starr-DeCarlo

Type: Four-Year College Sex: Coed Affiliation: State University of New York System. Scores: 71% SAT V 400+; 69% SAT M 400+; 47% ACT 18-23; 14% ACT 24-29 % Accepted: 89 Admission Plans: Deferred Admission; Early Admission Application Deadline: Rolling Application Fee: $50.00 H.S. Requirements: High school diploma required; GED accepted. For home-schooled students: High school diploma or equivalent not required Costs Per Year: Application fee: $50. State resident tuition: $6470 full-time,

$269.58 per credit hour part-time. Nonresident tuition: $16,320 full-time, $680 per credit hour part-time. Mandatory fees: $1249 full-time, $57.26 per credit hour part-time. Full-time tuition and fees vary according to degree level. Part-time tuition and fees vary according to degree level. College room and board: $12,728. College room only: $7570. Room and board charges vary according to board plan. **Scholarships:** Available. **Calendar System:** Semester, Summer session available **Enrollment:** Full-time 2,337, Part-time 109 **Faculty:** Full-time 103, Part-time 72 **Student-Faculty Ratio:** 19:1 **Exams:** ACT essay component not used; SAT I or ACT; SAT essay component not used; SAT Reasoning. **% Receiving Financial Aid:** 76 **% Residing in College-Owned, -Operated, or -Affiliated Housing:** 59 **Final Year or Final Semester Residency Requirement:** No **Regional Accreditation:** Middle States Association of Colleges and Schools **Credit Hours For Degree:** 60 credit hours, Associates; 120 credit hours, Bachelors **Professional Accreditation:** ACF, NAACLS. **Intercollegiate Athletics:** Basketball M & W; Cheerleading M & W; Cross-Country Running M & W; Golf M & W; Lacrosse M; Soccer M & W; Softball W; Swimming and Diving M & W; Tennis M & W; Track and Field M & W; Volleyball W

STATE UNIVERSITY OF NEW YORK COLLEGE AT CORTLAND

PO Box 2000
Cortland, NY 13045
Tel: (607)753-2011
Fax: (607)753-5999
E-mail: admissions@cortland.edu
Web Site: www.cortland.edu
President/CEO: Dr. Erik J. Bitterbaum
Financial Aid: Karen Gallagher
Type: Comprehensive **Sex:** Coed **Affiliation:** State University of New York System. **Scores:** 97% SAT V 400+; 98% SAT M 400+; 51.23% ACT 18-23; 42.59% ACT 24-29 **% Accepted:** 51 **Admission Plans:** Deferred Admission; Early Admission; Early Decision Plan **Application Fee:** $50.00 **H.S. Requirements:** High school diploma required; GED accepted **Costs Per Year:** Application fee: $50. State resident tuition: $6470 full-time, $270 per credit hour part-time. Nonresident tuition: $16,320 full-time, $680 per credit hour part-time. Mandatory fees: $1580 full-time. Full-time tuition and fees vary according to degree level. Part-time tuition varies according to degree level. College room and board: $12,200. College room only: $78,200. Room and board charges vary according to board plan and housing facility. **Scholarships:** Available. **Calendar System:** Semester **Enrollment:** Full-time 6,179, Graduate full-time 242, Graduate part-time 401, Part-time 104 **Faculty:** Full-time 293, Part-time 330 **Student-Faculty Ratio:** 17:1 **Exams:** ACT; SAT I; SAT I and SAT II or ACT; SAT I or ACT; SAT II. **% Receiving Financial Aid:** 62 **Regional Accreditation:** Middle States Association of Colleges and Schools **Credit Hours For Degree:** 124 credits, Bachelors **ROTC:** Air Force, Army **Professional Accreditation:** JRCAT, NCATE, NRPA. **Intercollegiate Athletics:** Baseball M; Basketball M & W; Cross-Country Running M & W; Field Hockey W; Football M & W; Golf W; Gymnastics W; Ice Hockey M & W; Lacrosse M & W; Racquetball M & W; Rugby M & W; Soccer M & W; Softball W; Swimming and Diving M & W; Tennis W; Track and Field M & W; Volleyball M & W; Wrestling M

STATE UNIVERSITY OF NEW YORK COLLEGE OF ENVIRONMENTAL SCIENCE AND FORESTRY

1 Forestry Dr.
Syracuse, NY 13210-2779
Tel: (315)470-6500
Fax: (315)470-6933
E-mail: esfinfo@esf.edu
Web Site: www.esf.edu
President/CEO: Dr. Quentin Wheeler
Admissions: Susan Sanford
Financial Aid: Mark J. Hill
Type: University **Sex:** Coed **Affiliation:** State University of New York System. **Scores:** 100% SAT V 400+; 100% SAT M 400+; 10% ACT 18-23; 67% ACT 24-29 **% Accepted:** 52 **Admission Plans:** Deferred Admission; Early Action; Early Admission **Application Deadline:** February 1 **Application Fee:** $50.00 **H.S. Requirements:** High school diploma required; GED accepted **Costs Per Year:** Application fee: $50. State resident tuition: $6170 full-time, $270 per credit hour part-time. Nonresident tuition: $15,820 full-time, $680 per credit hour part-time. Mandatory fees: $1300 full-time, $60 per term part-time. Full-time tuition and fees vary according to location. Part-time tuition and fees vary according to course load and location. College room and board: $14,490. Room and board charges vary according to board

plan, housing facility, and location. **Scholarships:** Available. **Calendar System:** Semester, Summer session available **Enrollment:** Full-time 1,731, Graduate full-time 360, Graduate part-time 185, Part-time 108 **Faculty:** Full-time 132, Part-time 42 **Student-Faculty Ratio:** 12:1 **Exams:** ACT essay component not used; SAT I or ACT; SAT II; SAT essay component not used; SAT Reasoning; SAT Subject. **% Receiving Financial Aid:** 61 **% Residing in College-Owned, -Operated, or -Affiliated Housing:** 35 **Final Year or Final Semester Residency Requirement:** No **Regional Accreditation:** Middle States Association of Colleges and Schools **Credit Hours For Degree:** 64 semester credit hours, Associates; 121 semester credit hours, Bachelors **ROTC:** Air Force, Army **Professional Accreditation:** ABET, ASLA, SAF. **Intercollegiate Athletics:** Basketball M; Cross-Country Running M & W; Golf M & W; Soccer M & W; Track and Field M & W

STATE UNIVERSITY OF NEW YORK COLLEGE AT GENESEO

1 College Cir.
Geneseo, NY 14454-1401
Tel: (585)245-5000; Free: 866-245-5211
Fax: (585)245-5005
E-mail: admissions@geneseo.edu
Web Site: www.geneseo.edu
President/CEO: Dr. Denise A. Battles
Admissions: Kevin J. Reed
Financial Aid: Archie Cureton
Type: Comprehensive **Sex:** Coed **Affiliation:** State University of New York. **Scores:** 99% SAT V 400+; 100% SAT M 400+; 9.38% ACT 18-23; 74.05% ACT 24-29 **% Accepted:** 73 **Admission Plans:** Deferred Admission; Early Action; Early Admission **Application Deadline:** January 1 **Application Fee:** $50.00 **H.S. Requirements:** High school diploma required; GED accepted **Costs Per Year:** Application fee: $50. State resident tuition: $6470 full-time, $270 per credit hour part-time. Nonresident tuition: $16,320 full-time, $680 per credit hour part-time. Mandatory fees: $1643 full-time, $67.45 per credit hour part-time. Part-time tuition and fees vary according to course load. College room and board: $11,980. College room only: $7510. Room and board charges vary according to board plan and housing facility. **Scholarships:** Available. **Calendar System:** Semester, Summer session available **Enrollment:** Full-time 5,470, Graduate full-time 50, Graduate part-time 66, Part-time 113 **Faculty:** Full-time 250, Part-time 103 **Student-Faculty Ratio:** 20:1 **Exams:** ACT; SAT I; SAT I and SAT II or ACT; SAT I or ACT; SAT II; SAT Reasoning. **% Receiving Financial Aid:** 50 **% Residing in College-Owned, -Operated, or -Affiliated Housing:** 56 **Final Year or Final Semester Residency Requirement:** Yes **Regional Accreditation:** Middle States Association of Colleges and Schools **Credit Hours For Degree:** 120 semester hours, Bachelors **ROTC:** Air Force, Army **Professional Accreditation:** AACSB, ASHA, NCATE. **Intercollegiate Athletics:** Badminton M & W; Baseball M & W; Basketball M & W; Cheerleading M & W; Crew M & W; Cross-Country Running M & W; Equestrian Sports W; Fencing M & W; Field Hockey W; Ice Hockey M & W; Lacrosse M & W; Rugby M & W; Skiing (Downhill) M & W; Soccer M & W; Softball W; Swimming and Diving M & W; Tennis M & W; Track and Field M & W; Ultimate Frisbee M & W; Volleyball M & W

STATE UNIVERSITY OF NEW YORK COLLEGE AT OLD WESTBURY

PO Box 210
Old Westbury, NY 11568-0210
Tel: (516)876-3000
Fax: (516)876-3307
E-mail: enroll@oldwestbury.edu
Web Site: www.oldwestbury.edu
President/CEO: Dr. Calvin O. Butts, III
Financial Aid: Vivian Mendonis
Type: Comprehensive **Sex:** Coed **Affiliation:** State University of New York System. **Scores:** 96% SAT V 400+; 93% SAT M 400+ **% Accepted:** 50 **Admission Plans:** Deferred Admission; Early Action; Early Admission **Application Deadline:** Rolling **Application Fee:** $50.00 **H.S. Requirements:** High school diploma required; GED accepted **Costs Per Year:** Application fee: $50. State resident tuition: $6470 full-time, $270 per credit part-time. Nonresident tuition: $16,320 full-time, $680 per credit part-time. Mandatory fees: $1173 full-time, $23.85 per credit hour part-time, $158 per term part-time. College room and board: $10,390. College room only: $7000. **Scholarships:** Available. **Calendar System:** Semester, Summer session available **Enrollment:** Full-time 3,522, Graduate full-time 134, Graduate part-time 94, Part-time 603 **Faculty:** Full-time 166, Part-time 185 **Student-Faculty Ratio:** 18:1 **Exams:** SAT I or ACT; SAT Reasoning; SAT Subject. **% Receiving**

Financial Aid: 68 % **Residing in College-Owned, -Operated, or -Affiliated Housing:** 19 **Regional Accreditation:** Middle States Association of Colleges and Schools **Credit Hours For Degree:** 120 credits, Bachelors **ROTC:** Air Force, Army **Professional Accreditation:** NCATE. **Intercollegiate Athletics:** Baseball M; Basketball M & W; Cross-Country Running M & W; Golf M; Lacrosse W; Soccer M & W; Softball W; Swimming and Diving M & W; Volleyball W

STATE UNIVERSITY OF NEW YORK COLLEGE AT ONEONTA

Ravine Pky.
Oneonta, NY 13820-4015
Tel: (607)436-3500; Free: 800-SUNY-123
Fax: (607)436-3074
E-mail: admissions@oneonta.edu
Web Site: www.oneonta.edu
President/CEO: Dr. Nancy Kleniewski
Admissions: Karen Brown
Financial Aid: Bill Goodhue
Type: Comprehensive **Sex:** Coed **Affiliation:** State University of New York System. **Scores:** 98% SAT V 400+; 99% SAT M 400+; 43.69% ACT 18-23; 53.28% ACT 24-29 **% Accepted:** 43 **Admission Plans:** Deferred Admission; Early Admission; Early Decision Plan **Application Deadline:** Rolling **Application Fee:** $50.00 **H.S. Requirements:** High school diploma required; GED accepted **Scholarships:** Available. **Calendar System:** Semester, Summer session available **Enrollment:** Full-time 5,738, Graduate full-time 92, Graduate part-time 79, Part-time 114 **Faculty:** Full-time 253, Part-time 230 **Student-Faculty Ratio:** 18:1 **Exams:** ACT essay component not used; SAT I or ACT; SAT essay component not used; SAT Reasoning. **% Receiving Financial Aid:** 59 **% Residing in College-Owned, -Operated, or -Affiliated Housing:** 59 **Regional Accreditation:** Middle States Association of Colleges and Schools **Credit Hours For Degree:** 122 semester hours, Bachelors **Professional Accreditation:** AACSB, AAFCS, AND, NASM, NCATE. **Intercollegiate Athletics:** Baseball M; Basketball M & W; Cheerleading W; Cross-Country Running M & W; Fencing M & W; Field Hockey W; Ice Hockey M; Lacrosse M & W; Rugby W; Soccer M & W; Softball W; Swimming and Diving M & W; Tennis M & W; Track and Field M & W; Volleyball W; Wrestling M

STATE UNIVERSITY OF NEW YORK COLLEGE AT POTSDAM

44 Pierrepont Ave.
Potsdam, NY 13676
Tel: (315)267-2000; Free: 877-POTSDAM
Fax: (315)267-2163
E-mail: admissions@potsdam.edu
Web Site: www.potsdam.edu
President/CEO: Dr. Krisitin G. Esterberg
Admissions: Thomas Nesbitt
Financial Aid: Susan E. Godreau
Type: Comprehensive **Sex:** Coed **Affiliation:** State University of New York System. **Scores:** 89% SAT V 400+; 38% ACT 18-23; 43% ACT 24-29 **% Accepted:** 74 **Admission Plans:** Deferred Admission; Early Admission **Application Deadline:** Rolling **Application Fee:** $50.00 **H.S. Requirements:** High school diploma required; GED accepted **Costs Per Year:** Application fee: $50. State resident tuition: $6470 full-time, $270 per credit hour part-time. Nonresident tuition: $16,320 full-time, $680 per credit hour part-time. Mandatory fees: $1453 full-time. College room and board: $11,870. College room only: $6770. Room and board charges vary according to board plan and housing facility. **Scholarships:** Available. **Calendar System:** Semester, Summer session available **Enrollment:** Full-time 3,504, Graduate full-time 190, Graduate part-time 100, Part-time 110 **Faculty:** Full-time 249, Part-time 110 **Student-Faculty Ratio:** 13:1 **Exams:** ACT essay component not used; SAT I or ACT; SAT essay component not used. **% Receiving Financial Aid:** 73 **% Residing in College-Owned, -Operated, or -Affiliated Housing:** 60 **Regional Accreditation:** Middle States Association of Colleges and Schools **ROTC:** Air Force, Army **Professional Accreditation:** NASM, NCATE. **Intercollegiate Athletics:** Basketball M & W; Cross-Country Running M & W; Golf M; Ice Hockey M & W; Lacrosse M & W; Rugby M; Soccer M & W; Softball W; Swimming and Diving M & W; Volleyball W

STATE UNIVERSITY OF NEW YORK COLLEGE OF TECHNOLOGY AT ALFRED

10 Upper College Dr.
Alfred, NY 14802
Tel: (607)587-4111; Free: 800-4-ALFRED

Fax: (607)587-4299
E-mail: admissions@alfredstate.edu
Web Site: www.alfredstate.edu
President/CEO: Dr. Irby D. Sullivan
Admissions: Goodrich Deborah
Financial Aid: Jane Gilliland
Type: Two-Year College **Sex:** Coed **Affiliation:** State University of New York System. **Scores:** 83% SAT V 400+; 86% SAT M 400+ **% Accepted:** 57 **Application Deadline:** Rolling **Application Fee:** $50.00 **H.S. Requirements:** High school diploma required; GED accepted **Costs Per Year:** Application fee: $50. One-time mandatory fee: $110. State resident tuition: $6470 full-time, $270 per credit part-time. Nonresident tuition: $9740 full-time, $406 per credit part-time. Mandatory fees: $1587 full-time, $66 per credit part-time, $10. Full-time tuition and fees vary according to course load and degree level. Part-time tuition and fees vary according to course load and degree level. College room and board: $12,010. College room only: $7080. Room and board charges vary according to board plan and housing facility. **Scholarships:** Available. **Calendar System:** Semester, Summer session available **Enrollment:** Full-time 3,378, Part-time 321 **Faculty:** Full-time 175, Part-time 51 **Student-Faculty Ratio:** 18:1 **Exams:** ACT essay component not used; SAT I or ACT; SAT essay component not used. **% Residing in College-Owned, -Operated, or -Affiliated Housing:** 64 **Final Year or Final Semester Residency Requirement:** No **Regional Accreditation:** Middle States Association of Colleges and Schools **Credit Hours For Degree:** 60 credit hours, Associates; 120 credit hours, Bachelors **ROTC:** Army **Professional Accreditation:** ABET, ACCE, ACEN, AHIMA. **Intercollegiate Athletics:** Baseball M; Basketball M & W; Cross-Country Running M & W; Football M; Lacrosse M; Soccer M & W; Softball W; Swimming and Diving M & W; Track and Field M & W; Volleyball W; Wrestling M

STATE UNIVERSITY OF NEW YORK COLLEGE OF TECHNOLOGY AT CANTON

Cornell Dr.
Canton, NY 13617
Tel: (315)386-7011; Free: 800-388-7123
Fax: (315)386-7930
E-mail: admissions@canton.edu
Web Site: www.canton.edu
President/CEO: Dr. Zvi Szafran
Admissions: Melissa Evans
Financial Aid: Kerrie Cooper
Type: Four-Year College **Sex:** Coed **Affiliation:** State University of New York System. **Scores:** 75% SAT V 400+; 77% SAT M 400+; 47.69% ACT 18-23; 15.39% ACT 24-29 **% Accepted:** 85 **Admission Plans:** Deferred Admission **Application Deadline:** July 1 **Application Fee:** $50.00 **H.S. Requirements:** High school diploma required; GED accepted **Costs Per Year:** Application fee: $50. One-time mandatory fee: $100. State resident tuition: $6470 full-time, $270 per credit hour part-time. Nonresident tuition: $16,320 full-time, $680 per credit hour part-time. Mandatory fees: $1468 full-time, $55.90 per credit hour part-time, $5 per term part-time. Full-time tuition and fees vary according to degree level. Part-time tuition and fees vary according to degree level. College room and board: $11,800. College room only: $6900. Room and board charges vary according to board plan and housing facility. **Scholarships:** Available. **Calendar System:** Semester, Summer session available **Enrollment:** Full-time 2,640, Part-time 543 **Faculty:** Full-time 124, Part-time 118 **Student-Faculty Ratio:** 17:1 **Exams:** ACT essay component not used; SAT I or ACT; SAT essay component not used; SAT Reasoning. **% Receiving Financial Aid:** 84 **% Residing in College-Owned, -Operated, or -Affiliated Housing:** 38 **Final Year or Final Semester Residency Requirement:** No **Regional Accreditation:** Middle States Association of Colleges and Schools **Credit Hours For Degree:** 60 credit hours, Associates; 120 credit hours, Bachelors **ROTC:** Air Force, Army **Professional Accreditation:** ABET, ABFSE, ACEN, AOTA, APTA. **Intercollegiate Athletics:** Baseball M; Basketball M & W; Cross-Country Running M & W; Golf M; Ice Hockey M & W; Lacrosse M & W; Soccer M & W; Softball W; Volleyball W

STATE UNIVERSITY OF NEW YORK COLLEGE OF TECHNOLOGY AT DELHI

2 Main St.
Delhi, NY 13753
Tel: (607)746-4000; Free: 800-96-DELHI
Fax: (607)746-4104
E-mail: enroll@delhi.edu

Web Site: www.delhi.edu
President/CEO: Dr. Candace Vancko
Financial Aid: Nancy B. Hughes
Type: Comprehensive **Sex:** Coed **Affiliation:** State University of New York System. **% Accepted:** 54 **Admission Plans:** Deferred Admission; Open Admission **Application Deadline:** Rolling **Application Fee:** $50.00 **H.S. Requirements:** High school diploma required; GED accepted **Costs Per Year:** Application fee: $50. State resident tuition: $6470 full-time, $270 per credit hour part-time. Nonresident tuition: $10,840 full-time, $452 per credit hour part-time. Mandatory fees: $1605 full-time. Full-time tuition and fees vary according to degree level. Part-time tuition varies according to course load and degree level. College room and board: $11,330. Room and board charges vary according to board plan and housing facility. **Scholarships:** Available. **Calendar System:** Semester, Summer session available **Enrollment:** Full-time 2,548, Graduate full-time 3, Graduate part-time 23, Part-time 876 **Faculty:** Full-time 147, Part-time 94 **Student-Faculty Ratio:** 14:1 **Exams:** ACT essay component not used; SAT I or ACT; SAT essay component not used; SAT Reasoning; SAT Subject. **% Receiving Financial Aid:** 78 **Final Year or Final Semester Residency Requirement:** No **Regional Accreditation:** Middle States Association of Colleges and Schools **Credit Hours For Degree:** 60 credit hours, Associates; 120 credit hours, Bachelors **Professional Accreditation:** ACCE, ACEN, ACF. **Intercollegiate Athletics:** Basketball M & W; Cross-Country Running M & W; Golf M & W; Lacrosse M; Soccer M & W; Softball W; Swimming and Diving M & W; Tennis M & W; Track and Field M & W; Volleyball W

STATE UNIVERSITY OF NEW YORK DOWNSTATE MEDICAL CENTER

450 Clarkson Ave.
Brooklyn, NY 11203-2098
Tel: (718)270-1000
Fax: (718)270-7592
E-mail: admissions@downstate.edu
Web Site: www.downstate.edu
President/CEO: John F. Williams
Type: Two-Year Upper Division **Sex:** Coed **Affiliation:** State University of New York System. **% Accepted:** 14 **Admission Plans:** Preferred Admission **Application Fee:** $30.00 **H.S. Requirements:** High school diploma required; GED accepted **Scholarships:** Available. **Calendar System:** Semester, Summer session available **Enrollment:** Full-time 193, Graduate full-time 1,015, Graduate part-time 336, Part-time 150 **Faculty:** Full-time 838, Part-time 143 **Regional Accreditation:** Middle States Association of Colleges and Schools **Credit Hours For Degree:** 125 credits, Bachelors **Professional Accreditation:** AACN, AANA, ACNM, AOTA, APTA, JRCEDMS, LCME/AMA.

STATE UNIVERSITY OF NEW YORK EMPIRE STATE COLLEGE

2 Union Ave.
Saratoga Springs, NY 12866-4391
Tel: (518)587-2100; Free: 800-847-3000
Fax: (518)587-2100
E-mail: admissions@esc.edu
Web Site: www.esc.edu
President/CEO: Dr. Merodie A. Hancock
Admissions: Jennifer D'Agostino
Type: Comprehensive **Sex:** Coed **Affiliation:** State University of New York System. **% Accepted:** 84 **Admission Plans:** Early Admission **Application Fee:** $50.00 **H.S. Requirements:** High school diploma required; GED accepted **Costs Per Year:** Application fee: $50. State resident tuition: $6470 full-time, $270 per credit part-time. Nonresident tuition: $16,320 full-time, $680 per credit part-time. Mandatory fees: $515 full-time. Full-time tuition and fees vary according to course load and location. Part-time tuition varies according to course load and location. **Calendar System:** Trimester, Summer session available **Enrollment:** Full-time 4,278, Graduate full-time 81, Graduate part-time 982, Part-time 6,541 **Faculty:** Full-time 182, Part-time 882 **Student-Faculty Ratio:** 15:1 **Final Year or Final Semester Residency Requirement:** No **Regional Accreditation:** Middle States Association of Colleges and Schools **Credit Hours For Degree:** 64 credits, Associates; 124 credits, Bachelors **Professional Accreditation:** AACN, ACEN, TEAC.

STATE UNIVERSITY OF NEW YORK AT FREDONIA

Fredonia, NY 14063-1136
Tel: (716)673-3111; Free: 800-252-1212
Fax: (716)673-3249

E-mail: admissions@fredonia.edu
Web Site: www.fredonia.edu
President/CEO: Dr. Virgina Horvath
Admissions: Cory M. Bezek
Financial Aid: Mark Zaffalon
Type: Comprehensive **Sex:** Coed **Affiliation:** State University of New York System. **Scores:** 96% SAT V 400+; 94% SAT M 400+; 42.2% ACT 18-23; 41.2% ACT 24-29 **% Accepted:** 59 **Admission Plans:** Deferred Admission; Early Action; Early Admission **Application Deadline:** Rolling **Application Fee:** $50.00 **H.S. Requirements:** High school diploma required; GED accepted **Costs Per Year:** Application fee: $50. State resident tuition: $6470 full-time. Nonresident tuition: $16,320 full-time. Mandatory fees: $1604 full-time. College room and board: $12,500. College room only: $7600. Room and board charges vary according to board plan and housing facility. **Scholarships:** Available. **Calendar System:** Semester, Summer session available **Enrollment:** Full-time 4,459, Graduate full-time 153, Graduate part-time 105, Part-time 128 **Faculty:** Full-time 252, Part-time 236 **Student-Faculty Ratio:** 14:1 **Exams:** SAT I or ACT. **% Receiving Financial Aid:** 68 **% Residing in College-Owned, -Operated, or -Affiliated Housing:** 53 **Regional Accreditation:** Middle States Association of Colleges and Schools **Credit Hours For Degree:** 120 credit hours, Bachelors **Professional Accreditation:** ASHA, CSWE, NASM, NAST, NCATE. **Intercollegiate Athletics:** Baseball M; Basketball M & W; Cheerleading M & W; Cross-Country Running M & W; Field Hockey M & W; Ice Hockey M; Lacrosse M & W; Rugby M & W; Soccer M & W; Softball W; Swimming and Diving M & W; Tennis M & W; Track and Field M & W; Volleyball M & W

STATE UNIVERSITY OF NEW YORK MARITIME COLLEGE

6 Pennyfield Ave.
Throggs Neck, NY 10465-4198
Tel: (718)409-7200
Fax: (718)409-7392
E-mail: rhowell@sunymaritime.edu
Web Site: www.sunymaritime.edu
President/CEO: Dr. Michael Alfultis
Admissions: Rohan Howell
Financial Aid: Andrea Damar
Type: Comprehensive **Sex:** Coed **Affiliation:** State University of New York System. **Scores:** 99% SAT V 400+; 100% SAT M 400+; 40% ACT 18-23; 50% ACT 24-29 **% Accepted:** 68 **Admission Plans:** Deferred Admission; Early Action **Application Deadline:** January 31 **Application Fee:** $50.00 **H.S. Requirements:** High school diploma required; GED accepted **Costs Per Year:** Application fee: $50. State resident tuition: $6470 full-time, $270 per credit hour part-time. Nonresident tuition: $16,320 full-time, $680 per credit hour part-time. Mandatory fees: $1339 full-time. Full-time tuition and fees vary according to course load. Part-time tuition varies according to course load. College room and board: $11,516. College room only: $7418. Room and board charges vary according to board plan and housing facility. **Scholarships:** Available. **Calendar System:** Semester, Summer session available **Enrollment:** Full-time 1,630, Graduate full-time 121, Graduate part-time 63, Part-time 46 **Faculty:** Full-time 87, Part-time 61 **Student-Faculty Ratio:** 17:1 **Exams:** ACT essay component used for placement; SAT I or ACT; SAT essay component used for placement; SAT Reasoning; SAT Subject. **% Receiving Financial Aid:** 47 **% Residing in College-Owned, -Operated, or -Affiliated Housing:** 85 **Regional Accreditation:** Middle States Association of Colleges and Schools **Credit Hours For Degree:** 80 credits, Associates; 126 credits, Bachelors **ROTC:** Army, Navy **Professional Accreditation:** ABET. **Intercollegiate Athletics:** Baseball M; Basketball M; Crew M & W; Cross-Country Running M & W; Football M; Ice Hockey M; Lacrosse M & W; Riflery M & W; Sailing M & W; Soccer M & W; Swimming and Diving M & W; Volleyball W

STATE UNIVERSITY OF NEW YORK AT NEW PALTZ

1 Hawk Dr.
New Paltz, NY 12561
Tel: (845)257-7869
Fax: (845)257-3209
E-mail: admissions@newpaltz.edu
Web Site: www.newpaltz.edu
President/CEO: Dr. Donald P. Christian
Admissions: Kimberly A. Strano
Financial Aid: Maureen Lohan-Bremer
Type: Comprehensive **Sex:** Coed **Affiliation:** State University of New York System. **Scores:** 97% SAT V 400+; 98% SAT M 400+; 29.9% ACT 18-23;

59.2% ACT 24-29 **% Accepted:** 42 **Admission Plans:** Early Admission; Early Decision Plan **Application Deadline:** May 1 **Application Fee:** $50.00 **H.S. Requirements:** High school diploma required; GED accepted **Costs Per Year:** Application fee: $50. State resident tuition: $6470 full-time, $270 per credit hour part-time. Nonresident tuition: $16,320 full-time, $680 per credit hour part-time. Mandatory fees: $1267 full-time, $36.23 per credit hour part-time, $196.50 per term part-time. College room and board: $11,480. College room only: $7620. Room and board charges vary according to board plan. **Scholarships:** Available. **Calendar System:** Semester, Summer session available **Enrollment:** Full-time 6,165, Graduate full-time 527, Graduate part-time 526, Part-time 534 **Faculty:** Full-time 360, Part-time 304 **Student-Faculty Ratio:** 15:1 **Exams:** ACT essay component used for advising; ACT essay component used for placement; SAT I or ACT; SAT essay component used for advising; SAT essay component used for placement; SAT Reasoning. **% Receiving Financial Aid:** 58 **% Residing in College-Owned, -Operated, or -Affiliated Housing:** 47 **Final Year or Final Semester Residency Requirement:** Yes **Regional Accreditation:** Middle States Association of Colleges and Schools **Credit Hours For Degree:** 120 credits, Bachelors **Professional Accreditation:** AACN, ABET, ASHA, NASAD, NASM, NAST, NCATE. **Intercollegiate Athletics:** Baseball M; Basketball M & W; Cross-Country Running M & W; Field Hockey W; Lacrosse W; Soccer M & W; Swimming and Diving M & W; Tennis W; Volleyball M & W

STATE UNIVERSITY OF NEW YORK AT OSWEGO

7060 Rte. 104
Oswego, NY 13126
Tel: (315)312-2500
Fax: (315)312-5799
E-mail: admiss@oswego.edu
Web Site: www.oswego.edu
President/CEO: Dr. Deborah Stanley
Admissions: Daniel Griffin
Financial Aid: Dr. Mark C. Humbert

Type: Comprehensive **Sex:** Coed **Affiliation:** State University of New York System. **Scores:** 100% SAT V 400+; 100% SAT M 400+; 47% ACT 18-23; 50% ACT 24-29 **% Accepted:** 51 **Admission Plans:** Deferred Admission; Early Action; Early Admission **Application Deadline:** Rolling **Application Fee:** $50.00 **H.S. Requirements:** High school diploma required; GED accepted **Costs Per Year:** Application fee: $50. State resident tuition: $6470 full-time, $270 per credit hour part-time. Nonresident tuition: $16,320 full-time, $680 per credit hour part-time. Mandatory fees: $1464 full-time, $46.31 per credit hour part-time. Part-time tuition and fees vary according to course load. College room and board: $12,990. Room and board charges vary according to board plan and housing facility. **Scholarships:** Available. **Calendar System:** Semester, Summer session available **Enrollment:** Full-time 6,778, Graduate full-time 308, Graduate part-time 525, Part-time 326 **Faculty:** Full-time 345, Part-time 255 **Student-Faculty Ratio:** 17:1 **Exams:** ACT essay component not used; SAT I or ACT; SAT essay component not used; SAT Reasoning. **% Receiving Financial Aid:** 67 **% Residing in College-Owned, -Operated, or -Affiliated Housing:** 60 **Final Year or Final Semester Residency Requirement:** No **Regional Accreditation:** Middle States Association of Colleges and Schools **Credit Hours For Degree:** 122 credit hours, Bachelors **ROTC:** Air Force, Army **Professional Accreditation:** AACSB, NASAD, NASM, NCATE. **Intercollegiate Athletics:** Baseball M; Basketball M & W; Crew M & W; Cross-Country Running M & W; Field Hockey W; Golf M; Ice Hockey M & W; Lacrosse M & W; Soccer M & W; Softball W; Swimming and Diving M & W; Tennis M & W; Track and Field M & W; Volleyball W; Wrestling M

STATE UNIVERSITY OF NEW YORK AT PLATTSBURGH

101 Broad St.
Plattsburgh, NY 12901-2681
Tel: (518)564-2000; Free: 888-673-0012
Fax: (518)564-2045
E-mail: carrie.woodward@plattsburgh.edu
Web Site: www.plattsburgh.edu
President/CEO: Dr. A. John Ettling
Admissions: Carrie Woodward
Financial Aid: Todd Moravec

Type: Comprehensive **Sex:** Coed **Affiliation:** State University of New York System. **Scores:** 99% SAT V 400+; 99% SAT M 400+; 58.8% ACT 18-23; 37.4% ACT 24-29 **% Accepted:** 50 **Admission Plans:** Deferred Admission; Early Admission **Application Deadline:** Rolling **Application Fee:** $50.00 **H.S. Requirements:** High school diploma required; GED accepted **Costs**

Per Year: Application fee: $50. State resident tuition: $6470 full-time, $270 per contact hour part-time. Nonresident tuition: $16,320 full-time, $680 per contact hour part-time. Mandatory fees: $1384 full-time, $57.83 per contact hour part-time. Full-time tuition and fees vary according to course load and location. Part-time tuition and fees vary according to course load and location. College room and board: $11,370. College room only: $7100. Room and board charges vary according to board plan and housing facility. **Scholarships:** Available. **Calendar System:** Semester, Summer session available **Enrollment:** Full-time 4,960, Graduate full-time 207, Graduate part-time 134, Part-time 417 **Faculty:** Full-time 283, Part-time 172 **Student-Faculty Ratio:** 16:1 **Exams:** SAT I or ACT. **% Receiving Financial Aid:** 62 **% Residing in College-Owned, -Operated, or -Affiliated Housing:** 46 **Final Year or Final Semester Residency Requirement:** Yes **Regional Accreditation:** Middle States Association of Colleges and Schools **Credit Hours For Degree:** 120 credits, Bachelors **Professional Accreditation:** AACN, AACSB, ACA, ASHA, CSWE, TEAC. **Intercollegiate Athletics:** Baseball M; Basketball M & W; Cross-Country Running M & W; Ice Hockey M & W; Lacrosse M; Soccer M & W; Softball W; Tennis W; Track and Field M & W; Volleyball W

STATE UNIVERSITY OF NEW YORK POLYTECHNIC INSTITUTE

100 Seymour Rd.
Utica, NY 13504-3050
Tel: (315)792-7100; Free: 866-278-6948
Fax: (315)792-7837
E-mail: admissions@sunyit.edu
Web Site: www.sunypoly.edu
President/CEO: Dr. Alain E. Kaloyeros
Admissions: Gina Liscio

Type: Comprehensive **Sex:** Coed **Affiliation:** State University of New York System. **Scores:** 99% SAT V 400+; 99% SAT M 400+; 32% ACT 18-23; 55% ACT 24-29 **% Accepted:** 60 **Admission Plans:** Deferred Admission; Early Admission; Early Decision Plan **Application Deadline:** Rolling **Application Fee:** $50.00 **H.S. Requirements:** High school diploma required; GED not accepted. For transfers with associate degrees: High school diploma or equivalent not required **Costs Per Year:** Application fee: $50. State resident tuition: $6470 full-time, $270 per credit hour part-time. Nonresident tuition: $16,320 full-time, $680 per credit hour part-time. Mandatory fees: $1289 full-time, $53.60 per credit hour part-time. Full-time tuition and fees vary according to course load. Part-time tuition and fees vary according to course load. College room and board: $11,714. Room and board charges vary according to board plan. **Scholarships:** Available. **Calendar System:** Semester, Summer session available **Enrollment:** Full-time 1,742, Graduate full-time 165, Graduate part-time 545, Part-time 340 **Faculty:** Full-time 124, Part-time 120 **Student-Faculty Ratio:** 17:1 **Exams:** SAT I or ACT; SAT II; SAT Reasoning; SAT Subject. **% Receiving Financial Aid:** 68 **% Residing in College-Owned, -Operated, or -Affiliated Housing:** 38 **Final Year or Final Semester Residency Requirement:** No **Regional Accreditation:** Middle States Association of Colleges and Schools **Credit Hours For Degree:** 124 semester hours, Bachelors **ROTC:** Air Force, Army **Professional Accreditation:** AACN, AACSB, ABET, AHIMA. **Intercollegiate Athletics:** Baseball M; Basketball M & W; Cross-Country Running M & W; Lacrosse M & W; Soccer M & W; Softball W; Volleyball M & W

STATE UNIVERSITY OF NEW YORK UPSTATE MEDICAL UNIVERSITY

766 Irving Ave.
Syracuse, NY 13210-2334
Tel: (315)464-5540; Free: 800-736-2171
Fax: (315)464-8823
E-mail: admiss@upstate.edu
Web Site: www.upstate.edu
President/CEO: Dr. David R. Smith
Admissions: Donna L. Vavonese
Financial Aid: Michael Pede

Type: Two-Year Upper Division **Sex:** Coed **Affiliation:** State University of New York System. **% Accepted:** 34 **Admission Plans:** Deferred Admission; Early Admission; Preferred Admission **Application Fee:** $50.00 **H.S. Requirements:** High school diploma required; GED accepted **Scholarships:** Available. **Calendar System:** Semester, Summer session available **Enrollment:** Full-time 213, Graduate full-time 1,040, Graduate part-time 451, Part-time 83 **Faculty:** Full-time 47, Part-time 7 **% Receiving Financial Aid:** 82 **% Residing in College-Owned, -Operated, or -Affiliated Housing:** 50 **Final Year or Final Semester Residency Requirement:** No

Regional Accreditation: Middle States Association of Colleges and Schools **Credit Hours For Degree:** 120 credits, Bachelors **ROTC:** Army **Professional Accreditation:** AACN, ACPeE, APA, APTA, ASC, CoARC, JRCERT, LCME/AMA, NAACLS.

STELLA AND CHARLES GUTTMAN COMMUNITY COLLEGE
50 W 40th St.
New York, NY 10018
Tel: (646)313-8000
Web Site: guttman.cuny.edu
Type: Two-Year College **Sex:** Coed **Regional Accreditation:** Middle States Association of Colleges and Schools

STONY BROOK UNIVERSITY, STATE UNIVERSITY OF NEW YORK
Nicolls Rd.
Stony Brook, NY 11794
Tel: (631)632-6000
E-mail: enroll@stonybrook.edu
Web Site: www.stonybrook.edu
President/CEO: Dr. Samuel L. Stanley, Jr.
Admissions: Judith Burke-Berhanan
Type: University **Sex:** Coed **Affiliation:** State University of New York System. **Scores:** 99% SAT V 400+; 100% SAT M 400+; 6.6% ACT 18-23; 55.1% ACT 24-29 **% Accepted:** 41 **Admission Plans:** Deferred Admission **Application Deadline:** January 15 **Application Fee:** $50.00 **H.S. Requirements:** High school diploma required; GED accepted **Costs Per Year:** Application fee: $50. State resident tuition: $6470 full-time, $270 per credit hour part-time. Nonresident tuition: $21,550 full-time, $898 per credit hour part-time. Mandatory fees: $2385 full-time, $118.85 per credit hour part-time. Full-time tuition and fees vary according to course load. Part-time tuition and fees vary according to course load. College room and board: $12,032. College room only: $7854. Room and board charges vary according to board plan and housing facility. **Scholarships:** Available. **Calendar System:** Semester, Summer session available **Enrollment:** Full-time 15,714, Graduate full-time 5,336, Graduate part-time 3,105, Part-time 1,117 **Faculty:** Full-time 1,124, Part-time 580 **Student-Faculty Ratio:** 16:1 **Exams:** ACT essay component used for admission; ACT essay component used for placement; SAT I or ACT; SAT essay component used for admission; SAT essay component used for placement; SAT Reasoning. **% Receiving Financial Aid:** 56 **% Residing in College-Owned, -Operated, or -Affiliated Housing:** 51 **Final Year or Final Semester Residency Requirement:** No **Regional Accreditation:** Middle States Association of Colleges and Schools **Credit Hours For Degree:** 120 credits, Bachelors **ROTC:** Air Force, Army, Navy **Professional Accreditation:** AACN, ABET, ACNM, ADA, AND, AOTA, APA, APTA, ASC, CSWE, CoARC, LCME/AMA, NAACLS, NCATE. **Intercollegiate Athletics:** Baseball M; Basketball M & W; Cross-Country Running M & W; Football M; Lacrosse M & W; Soccer M & W; Softball W; Swimming and Diving M & W; Tennis M & W; Track and Field M & W; Volleyball W

SUFFOLK COUNTY COMMUNITY COLLEGE
533 College Rd.
Selden, NY 11784-2899
Tel: (631)451-4110
Web Site: www.sunysuffolk.edu
President/CEO: Dr. Shaun McKay, AIA
Admissions: Dr. Kate B. Rowe
Type: Two-Year College **Sex:** Coed **Affiliation:** State University of New York System. **Scores:** 77% SAT V 400+; 80% SAT M 400+; 26.11% ACT 18-23; 4.08% ACT 24-29 **Admission Plans:** Deferred Admission; Open Admission; Preferred Admission **Application Deadline:** Rolling **Application Fee:** $35.00 **H.S. Requirements:** High school diploma required; GED accepted. For applicants with extenuating circumstances: High school diploma or equivalent not required **Scholarships:** Available. **Calendar System:** Semester, Summer session available **Enrollment:** Full-time 13,853, Part-time 14,441 **Student-Faculty Ratio:** 18:1 **Final Year or Final Semester Residency Requirement:** No **Regional Accreditation:** Middle States Association of Colleges and Schools **Credit Hours For Degree:** 66 credits, Associates **ROTC:** Army **Professional Accreditation:** AAMAE, ACEN, AHIMA, AOTA, APTA. **Intercollegiate Athletics:** Baseball M; Basketball M & W; Bowling M & W; Cross-Country Running M & W; Golf M & W; Lacrosse M; Soccer M; Softball W; Swimming and Diving M & W; Tennis M & W; Track and Field M & W; Volleyball W

SULLIVAN COUNTY COMMUNITY COLLEGE
112 College Rd.
Loch Sheldrake, NY 12759

Tel: (845)434-5750; Free: 800-577-5243
Fax: (845)434-4806
E-mail: sarir@sunysullivan.edu
Web Site: www.sullivan.suny.edu
President/CEO: Dr. Karin Hilgersom, PhD
Admissions: Sari Rosenheck
Financial Aid: James M. Winderl
Type: Two-Year College **Sex:** Coed **Affiliation:** State University of New York System. **% Accepted:** 92 **Admission Plans:** Deferred Admission; Early Admission; Open Admission **Application Deadline:** Rolling **H.S. Requirements:** High school diploma required; GED accepted **Costs Per Year:** State resident tuition: $4674 full-time. Nonresident tuition: $9348 full-time. Mandatory fees: $826 full-time. Full-time tuition and fees vary according to program. College room and board: $9450. College room only: $6150. Room and board charges vary according to board plan and housing facility. **Scholarships:** Available. **Calendar System:** Semester, Summer session available **Enrollment:** Full-time 809, Part-time 787 **Faculty:** Full-time 47, Part-time 53 **Student-Faculty Ratio:** 16:1 **Exams:** ACT essay component not used; SAT essay component not used. **% Residing in College-Owned, -Operated, or -Affiliated Housing:** 21 **Final Year or Final Semester Residency Requirement:** No **Regional Accreditation:** Middle States Association of Colleges and Schools **Credit Hours For Degree:** 63 credits, Associates **Professional Accreditation:** ACBSP, ACEN. **Intercollegiate Athletics:** Baseball M; Basketball M & W; Cross-Country Running M & W; Softball W; Volleyball W; Wrestling M

SWEDISH INSTITUTE, COLLEGE OF HEALTH SCIENCES
226 W 26th St.
New York, NY 10001-6700
Tel: (212)924-5900
Fax: (212)924-7600
E-mail: admissions@swedishinstitute.edu
Web Site: www.swedishinstitute.edu
President/CEO: Jeff Namian
Type: Comprehensive **Sex:** Coed **% Accepted:** 95 **Application Deadline:** November 9 **Application Fee:** $50.00 **Calendar System:** Trimester **Enrollment:** Full-time 304, Part-time 137 **Faculty:** Full-time 17, Part-time 33 **Student-Faculty Ratio:** 11:1 **Exams:** Other. **Professional Accreditation:** ACAOM, ACCSC.

SYRACUSE UNIVERSITY
Syracuse, NY 13244
Tel: (315)443-1870
E-mail: orange@syr.edu
Web Site: www.syr.edu
President/CEO: Kent D. Syverud
Type: University **Sex:** Coed **Scores:** 100% SAT V 400+; 100% SAT M 400+; 14.8% ACT 18-23; 64.4% ACT 24-29 **% Accepted:** 48 **Admission Plans:** Deferred Admission; Early Action; Early Admission **Application Deadline:** January 1 **Application Fee:** $75.00 **H.S. Requirements:** High school diploma required; GED accepted **Costs Per Year:** Application fee: $75. Comprehensive fee: $58,198 includes full-time tuition ($41,794), mandatory fees ($1524), and college room and board ($14,880). College room only: $7870. Full-time tuition and fees vary according to course load. Room and board charges vary according to board plan and housing facility. Part-time tuition: $1818 per credit hour. Part-time tuition varies according to course load. **Scholarships:** Available. **Calendar System:** Semester, Summer session available **Enrollment:** Full-time 14,566, Graduate full-time 4,765, Graduate part-time 1,828, Part-time 630 **Faculty:** Full-time 1,077, Part-time 551 **Student-Faculty Ratio:** 16:1 **Exams:** ACT essay component used for admission; SAT I or ACT; SAT essay component used for admission; SAT Reasoning. **% Receiving Financial Aid:** 55 **% Residing in College-Owned, -Operated, or -Affiliated Housing:** 75 **Final Year or Final Semester Residency Requirement:** No **Regional Accreditation:** Middle States Association of Colleges and Schools **Credit Hours For Degree:** 60 credits, Associates **ROTC:** Air Force, Army **Professional Accreditation:** AACSB, AALS, AAMFT, ABA, ABET, ACA, ACEJMC, ACEN, ALA, AND, APA, ASHA, CIDA, CORE, CSWE, NAAB, NASAD, NASM, NASPAA, NCATE. **Intercollegiate Athletics:** Badminton M & W; Baseball M; Basketball M & W; Bowling M & W; Cheerleading M & W; Crew M & W; Cross-Country Running M & W; Equestrian Sports M & W; Fencing M & W; Field Hockey W; Football M; Gymnastics M & W; Ice Hockey M & W; Lacrosse M & W; Rugby M & W; Sailing M & W; Skiing (Downhill) M & W; Soccer M & W; Softball W; Tennis M & W; Track and Field M & W; Volleyball M & W; Water Polo M & W; Wrestling M

TALMUDICAL INSTITUTE OF UPSTATE NEW YORK
769 Park Ave.
Rochester, NY 14607-3046
Tel: (716)473-2810
Fax: (716)442-0417
E-mail: yeshiva@tiuny.org
Web Site: www.tiuny.org
President/CEO: Menachem Davidowitz
Admissions: Rabbi Menachem Davidowitz
Financial Aid: Ella Berenstein
Type: Five-Year College **Sex:** Men **Affiliation:** Jewish. **% Accepted:** 100 **Admission Plans:** Early Admission **Application Deadline:** Rolling **Application Fee:** $0.00 **H.S. Requirements:** High school diploma required; GED accepted **Scholarships:** Available. **Calendar System:** Semester **Credit Hours For Degree:** 150 credits, Bachelors **Professional Accreditation:** AARTS.

TALMUDICAL SEMINARY OF BOBOV
5120 New Utrecht Ave.
Brooklyn, NY 11219
Tel: (718)436-2122
Type: Four-Year College **Sex:** Coed **Affiliation:** Jewish. **Professional Accreditation:** AARTS.

TALMUDICAL SEMINARY OHOLEI TORAH
667 Eastern Pky.
Brooklyn, NY 11213-3310
Tel: (718)774-5050
E-mail: info@oholeitorah.com
President/CEO: Rabbi Moshe Susskind
Admissions: Rabbi Yisroel Friedman
Type: Four-Year College **Sex:** Men **Affiliation:** Jewish. **% Accepted:** 100 **Admission Plans:** Deferred Admission **Application Deadline:** September 1 **H.S. Requirements:** High school diploma required; GED accepted **Calendar System:** Semester, Summer session not available **Credit Hours For Degree:** 128 credits, Bachelors **Professional Accreditation:** AARTS.

TCI–COLLEGE OF TECHNOLOGY
320 W 31st St.
New York, NY 10001-2705
Tel: (212)594-4000; Free: 800-878-8246
Fax: (212)629-3937
E-mail: mgall@tcicollege.edu
Web Site: www.tcicollege.edu
President/CEO: Dr. John J. McGrath
Admissions: Michael Gall
Type: Two-Year College **Sex:** Coed **Admission Plans:** Deferred Admission; Open Admission **Application Deadline:** Rolling **H.S. Requirements:** High school diploma required; GED accepted **Costs Per Year:** One-time mandatory fee: $100. Tuition: $13,170 full-time, $548 per credit hour part-time. Mandatory fees: $530 full-time. Part-time tuition varies according to course load. **Scholarships:** Available. **Calendar System:** Semester, Summer session available **Enrollment:** Full-time 2,640, Part-time 380 **Student-Faculty Ratio:** 24:1 **Regional Accreditation:** Middle States Association of Colleges and Schools **Credit Hours For Degree:** 65 credits, Associates **Professional Accreditation:** ABET, NYSBR.

TOMPKINS CORTLAND COMMUNITY COLLEGE
170 N St.
Dryden, NY 13053-0139
Tel: (607)844-8211; Free: 888-567-8211
Fax: (607)844-6538
E-mail: admissions@tc3.edu
Web Site: www.TC3.edu
President/CEO: Carl E. Haynes, PhD
Admissions: Sandy Drumluk
Type: Two-Year College **Sex:** Coed **Affiliation:** State University of New York System. **Admission Plans:** Deferred Admission; Early Admission; Open Admission **Application Deadline:** Rolling **H.S. Requirements:** High school diploma required; GED accepted. For nursing program: High school diploma required; GED not accepted **Costs Per Year:** State resident tuition: $4650 full-time, $164 per credit hour part-time. Nonresident tuition: $9600 full-time, $338 per credit hour part-time. Mandatory fees: $1016 full-time, $35.80 per credit hour part-time, $16 per term part-time. Part-time tuition and fees vary

according to course load. College room and board: $10,380. Room and board charges vary according to board plan and housing facility. **Scholarships:** Available. **Calendar System:** Semester, Summer session available **Enrollment:** Full-time 2,179, Part-time 906 **Faculty:** Full-time 62, Part-time 280 **Student-Faculty Ratio:** 16:1 **Regional Accreditation:** Middle States Association of Colleges and Schools **Credit Hours For Degree:** 62 credits, Associates **Professional Accreditation:** ACEN. **Intercollegiate Athletics:** Baseball M; Basketball M & W; Golf M & W; Lacrosse M; Soccer M & W; Softball W; Volleyball W

TORAH TEMIMAH TALMUDICAL SEMINARY
507 Ocean Pky.
Brooklyn, NY 11218-5913
Tel: (718)853-8500
President/CEO: Yisroel Kleinman
Type: Four-Year College **Sex:** Men **Affiliation:** Jewish. **% Accepted:** 100 **Calendar System:** Semester **Professional Accreditation:** AARTS.

TOURO COLLEGE
27-33 W 23rd St.
New York, NY 10010
Tel: (212)463-0400
Fax: (212)779-2344
E-mail: david.luk@touro.edu
Web Site: www.touro.edu
President/CEO: Dr. Alan Kadish, MD
Admissions: David Luk
Financial Aid: Karyn Wright-Moore
Type: Comprehensive **Sex:** Coed **Scores:** 90% SAT V 400+; 87% SAT M 400+ **% Accepted:** 34 **Admission Plans:** Deferred Admission; Early Admission **Application Deadline:** Rolling **Application Fee:** $50.00 **H.S. Requirements:** High school diploma required; GED accepted **Costs Per Year:** Application fee: $50. Comprehensive fee: $28,950 includes full-time tuition ($16,380), mandatory fees ($600), and college room and board ($11,970). College room only: $8320. Part-time tuition: $680 per credit hour. **Scholarships:** Available. **Calendar System:** Semester, Summer session available **Enrollment:** Full-time 5,055, Graduate full-time 2,807, Graduate part-time 2,302, Part-time 1,857 **Faculty:** Full-time 484, Part-time 851 **Student-Faculty Ratio:** 12:1 **Exams:** ACT essay component not used; SAT I and SAT II or ACT; SAT I or ACT; SAT II; SAT essay component not used; SAT Reasoning; SAT Subject. **% Receiving Financial Aid:** 85 **Regional Accreditation:** Middle States Association of Colleges and Schools **Credit Hours For Degree:** 60 credits, Associates; 120 credits, Bachelors **Professional Accreditation:** AALS, ABA, AOTA, APTA, ASHA, TEAC.

TROCAIRE COLLEGE
360 Choate Ave.
Buffalo, NY 14220-2094
Tel: (716)826-1200
Fax: (716)826-4704
E-mail: ballarom@trocaire.edu
Web Site: www.trocaire.edu
President/CEO: Dr. Bassam M. Deeb
Admissions: Mollie Bellaro
Financial Aid: Janet McGrath
Type: Two-Year College **Sex:** Coed **% Accepted:** 50 **Admission Plans:** Deferred Admission **Application Deadline:** Rolling **Application Fee:** $0.00 **H.S. Requirements:** High school diploma required; GED accepted **Costs Per Year:** Application fee: $0. Tuition: $15,970 full-time, $660 per hour part-time. Mandatory fees: $320 full-time, $27 per credit hour part-time. Full-time tuition and fees vary according to course load. Part-time tuition and fees vary according to course load. **Scholarships:** Available. **Calendar System:** Semester, Summer session available **Enrollment:** Full-time 621, Part-time 748 **Faculty:** Full-time 41, Part-time 131 **Student-Faculty Ratio:** 11:1 **Exams:** ACT essay component not used; Other; SAT essay component not used. **Regional Accreditation:** Middle States Association of Colleges and Schools **Credit Hours For Degree:** 60 credit hours, Associates **Professional Accreditation:** AAMAE, ACEN, AHIMA, ARCST, JRCERT.

ULSTER COUNTY COMMUNITY COLLEGE
491 Cottekill Rd.
Stone Ridge, NY 12484
Tel: (845)687-5000; Free: 800-724-0833
E-mail: admissionsoffice@sunyulster.edu

Web Site: www.sunyulster.edu
President/CEO: Dr. Donald C. Katt
Financial Aid: Christopher Chang
Type: Two-Year College **Sex:** Coed **Affiliation:** State University of New York System. **% Accepted:** 100 **Admission Plans:** Deferred Admission; Early Admission; Open Admission **Application Deadline:** Rolling **Application Fee:** $0.00 **H.S. Requirements:** High school diploma required; GED accepted **Costs Per Year:** Application fee: $0. State resident tuition: $4230 full-time, $159 per credit hour part-time. Nonresident tuition: $8460 full-time, $318 per credit hour part-time. Mandatory fees: $796 full-time, $65 per course part-time, $23 per term part-time. **Scholarships:** Available. **Calendar System:** Semester, Summer session available **Enrollment:** Full-time 1,759, Part-time 1,781 **Faculty:** Full-time 66, Part-time 123 **Student-Faculty Ratio:** 19:1 **Final Year or Final Semester Residency Requirement:** No **Regional Accreditation:** Middle States Association of Colleges and Schools **Credit Hours For Degree:** 60 credit hours, Associates **Professional Accreditation:** ACEN. **Intercollegiate Athletics:** Baseball M; Basketball M & W; Golf M; Soccer M; Softball W; Tennis M; Volleyball W

UNION COLLEGE
807 Union St.
Schenectady, NY 12308-2311
Tel: (518)388-6000; Free: 888-843-6688
Fax: (518)388-6986
E-mail: admissions@union.edu
Web Site: www.union.edu
President/CEO: Dr. Stephen C. Ainlay
Financial Aid: Linda Parker
Type: Four-Year College **Sex:** Coed **Scores:** 100% SAT V 400+; 100% SAT M 400+; 3% ACT 18-23; 38% ACT 24-29 **% Accepted:** 38 **Admission Plans:** Deferred Admission; Early Action; Early Admission **Application Deadline:** January 15 **H.S. Requirements:** High school diploma required; GED not accepted **Costs Per Year:** Comprehensive fee: $62,274 includes full-time tuition ($49,542), mandatory fees ($471), and college room and board ($12,261). College room only: $6723. **Scholarships:** Available. **Calendar System:** Trimester, Summer session available **Enrollment:** Full-time 2,226, Part-time 43 **Faculty:** Full-time 209, Part-time 25 **Student-Faculty Ratio:** 10:1 **Exams:** ACT essay component used for admission; Other; SAT essay component used for admission; SAT Reasoning; SAT Subject. **% Receiving Financial Aid:** 50 **% Residing in College-Owned, -Operated, or -Affiliated Housing:** 89 **Final Year or Final Semester Residency Requirement:** Yes **Regional Accreditation:** Middle States Association of Colleges and Schools **Credit Hours For Degree:** 36 courses, Bachelors **ROTC:** Air Force, Army, Navy **Professional Accreditation:** ABET. **Intercollegiate Athletics:** Baseball M; Basketball M & W; Cheerleading M & W; Crew M & W; Cross-Country Running M & W; Equestrian Sports W; Field Hockey W; Football M; Golf W; Ice Hockey M & W; Lacrosse M & W; Rugby M & W; Soccer M & W; Softball W; Swimming and Diving M & W; Tennis M & W; Track and Field M & W; Ultimate Frisbee M & W; Volleyball W

UNITED STATES MERCHANT MARINE ACADEMY
300 Steamboat Rd.
Kings Point, NY 11024-1699
Tel: (516)773-5000; Free: 866-546-4778
Fax: (516)773-5390
E-mail: admissions@usmma.edu
Web Site: www.usmma.edu
President/CEO: Adm. James Helis
Admissions: Lt. Kelly Gualtieri
Type: Comprehensive **Sex:** Coed **Scores:** 100% SAT V 400+; 100% SAT M 400+; 2% ACT 18-23; 74% ACT 24-29 **% Accepted:** 18 **Application Deadline:** March 1 **Application Fee:** $0.00 **H.S. Requirements:** High school diploma required; GED accepted **Costs Per Year:** Application fee: $0. Tuition: $0 full-time. Mandatory fees: $1107 full-time. Midshipmen at the United States Merchant Marine Academy receive from the Federal Government their education, room and board, uniforms, and books. However, midshipmen are responsible for the payment of fees for mandatory educational supplies not provided by the government. **Calendar System:** Trimester, Summer session not available **Enrollment:** Full-time 958, Graduate part-time 27 **Faculty:** Full-time 120, Part-time 25 **Student-Faculty Ratio:** 12:1 **Exams:** ACT essay component not used; SAT I or ACT; SAT essay component not used; SAT Reasoning. **% Residing in College-Owned, -Operated, or -Affiliated Housing:** 100 **Final Year or Final Semester Residency Requirement:** No **Regional Accreditation:** Middle

States Association of Colleges and Schools **Credit Hours For Degree:** 163-164 credits, depending on program, Bachelors **Professional Accreditation:** ABET. **Intercollegiate Athletics:** Baseball M; Basketball M & W; Crew M & W; Cross-Country Running M & W; Football M; Lacrosse M & W; Sailing M & W; Soccer M; Swimming and Diving M & W; Tennis M; Track and Field M & W; Volleyball W; Wrestling M

UNITED STATES MILITARY ACADEMY
600 Thayer Rd.
West Point, NY 10996
Tel: (845)938-4011
Fax: (845)938-3021
E-mail: admissions@usma.edu
Web Site: www.usma.edu
President/CEO: Lt. Gen. Robert Caslen, Jr.
Admissions: Col. Deborah J. McDonald
Type: Four-Year College **Sex:** Coed **Scores:** 100% SAT V 400+; 100% SAT M 400+; 8% ACT 18-23; 47% ACT 24-29 **Calendar System:** Semester, Summer session not available **Enrollment:** Full-time 4,348 **Faculty:** Full-time 641 **Student-Faculty Ratio:** 7:1 **Exams:** ACT essay component used for admission; SAT I or ACT; SAT essay component used for admission. **% Residing in College-Owned, -Operated, or -Affiliated Housing:** 100 **Regional Accreditation:** Middle States Association of Colleges and Schools **Credit Hours For Degree:** 40 courses, Bachelors **Professional Accreditation:** ABET. **Intercollegiate Athletics:** Baseball M; Basketball M & W; Cheerleading M & W; Crew M & W; Cross-Country Running M & W; Equestrian Sports M & W; Fencing M & W; Football M; Golf M; Gymnastics M; Ice Hockey M; Lacrosse M & W; Riflery M & W; Rugby M & W; Skiing (Cross-Country) M & W; Skiing (Downhill) M & W; Soccer M & W; Softball W; Swimming and Diving M & W; Tennis M & W; Track and Field M & W; Volleyball M & W; Water Polo M; Wrestling M

UNITED TALMUDICAL SEMINARY
191 Rodney St.
Brooklyn, NY 11211
Tel: (718)963-9260
President/CEO: Bernard Katz
Type: Comprehensive **Sex:** Men **Affiliation:** Jewish. **Admission Plans:** Open Admission **H.S. Requirements:** High school diploma required; GED accepted **Calendar System:** Semester **Professional Accreditation:** AARTS.

UNIVERSITY AT ALBANY, STATE UNIVERSITY OF NEW YORK
1400 Washington Ave.
Albany, NY 12222-0001
Tel: (518)442-3300
E-mail: ugadmissions@albany.edu
Web Site: www.albany.edu
President/CEO: Dr. Robert J. Jones
Financial Aid: Stephen Kudzin
Type: University **Sex:** Coed **Affiliation:** State University of New York System. **Scores:** 99% SAT V 400+; 100% SAT M 400+; 44.1% ACT 18-23; 47.7% ACT 24-29 **% Accepted:** 56 **Admission Plans:** Deferred Admission; Early Admission; Early Decision Plan **Application Deadline:** March 16 **Application Fee:** $50.00 **H.S. Requirements:** High school diploma required; GED accepted **Costs Per Year:** Application fee: $50. State resident tuition: $6470 full-time, $270 per credit hour part-time. Nonresident tuition: $19,590 full-time, $816 per credit hour part-time. Mandatory fees: $2526 full-time, $64.93 per credit hour part-time, $240.75 per term part-time. Part-time tuition and fees vary according to course load. College room and board: $12,422. College room only: $7732. Room and board charges vary according to board plan and housing facility. **Scholarships:** Available. **Calendar System:** Semester, Summer session available **Enrollment:** Full-time 12,223, Graduate full-time 2,218, Graduate part-time 2,052, Part-time 685 **Faculty:** Full-time 675, Part-time 494 **Student-Faculty Ratio:** 18:1 **Exams:** SAT I and SAT II or ACT; SAT I or ACT; SAT II; SAT Reasoning; SAT Subject. **% Receiving Financial Aid:** 63 **% Residing in College-Owned, -Operated, or -Affiliated Housing:** 59 **Final Year or Final Semester Residency Requirement:** Yes **Regional Accreditation:** Middle States Association of Colleges and Schools **Credit Hours For Degree:** 120 credits, Bachelors **ROTC:** Air Force, Army **Professional Accreditation:** AACSB, ACSP, ALA, APA, CEPH, CORE, CSWE, NASPAA, TEAC. **Intercollegiate Athletics:** Baseball M; Basketball M & W; Crew M & W; Cross-Country Running M &

W; Field Hockey W; Football M; Golf W; Lacrosse M & W; Rock Climbing M & W; Soccer M & W; Softball W; Tennis W; Track and Field M & W; Volleyball W

UNIVERSITY AT BUFFALO, THE STATE UNIVERSITY OF NEW YORK
Capen Hall
Buffalo, NY 14260
Tel: (716)645-2000; Free: 888-UB-ADMIT
Fax: (716)645-6411
E-mail: ub-admissions@buffalo.edu
Web Site: www.buffalo.edu
President/CEO: Dr. Satish Tripathi
Admissions: Jose Aviles
Financial Aid: John Gottardy

Type: University **Sex:** Coed **Affiliation:** State University of New York System. **Scores:** 99% SAT V 400+; 19.1% ACT 18-23; 59.6% ACT 24-29 **% Accepted:** 60 **Admission Plans:** Early Admission; Early Decision Plan **Application Fee:** $50.00 **H.S. Requirements:** High school diploma required; GED accepted **Costs Per Year:** Application fee: $50. State resident tuition: $6470 full-time, $270 per credit hour part-time. Nonresident tuition: $21,550 full-time, $898 per credit hour part-time. Mandatory fees: $2911 full-time, $241.36 per credit hour part-time. Part-time tuition and fees vary according to course load. College room and board: $13,061. College room only: $7571. Room and board charges vary according to board plan and housing facility. **Scholarships:** Available. **Calendar System:** Semester, Summer session available **Enrollment:** Full-time 18,452, Graduate full-time 6,402, Graduate part-time 3,453, Part-time 1,499 **Faculty:** Full-time 1,268, Part-time 579 **Student-Faculty Ratio:** 13:1 **Exams:** ACT essay component not used; SAT I or ACT; SAT essay component not used. **% Receiving Financial Aid:** 67 % **Residing in College-Owned, -Operated, or -Affiliated Housing:** 35 **Final Year or Final Semester Residency Requirement:** No **Regional Accreditation:** Middle States Association of Colleges and Schools **Credit Hours For Degree:** 120 credit hours, Bachelors **ROTC:** Army **Professional Accreditation:** AACN, AACSB, AALS, AANA, ABA, ABET, ACPE, ACSP, ADA, ALA, AND, AOTA, APA, APTA, ASHA, ATMAE, CORE, CSWE, JRCNMT, LCME/AMA, NAAB, NAACLS, TEAC. **Intercollegiate Athletics:** Baseball M; Basketball M & W; Crew W; Cross-Country Running M & W; Football M; Soccer M & W; Softball W; Swimming and Diving M & W; Tennis M & W; Track and Field M & W; Volleyball W; Wrestling M

UNIVERSITY OF ROCHESTER
Wilson Blvd.
Rochester, NY 14627
Tel: (585)275-2121; Free: 888-822-2256
Fax: (585)273-1118
E-mail: admit@admissions.rochester.edu
Web Site: www.rochester.edu
President/CEO: Joel Seligman
Financial Aid: Samantha Veeder

Type: University **Sex:** Coed **% Accepted:** 34 **Admission Plans:** Deferred Admission; Early Action **Application Deadline:** January 5 **Application Fee:** $50.00 **H.S. Requirements:** High school diploma required; GED accepted **Costs Per Year:** Application fee: $50. Comprehensive fee: $62,654 includes full-time tuition ($47,450), mandatory fees ($840), and college room and board ($14,364). College room only: $8834. Room and board charges vary according to board plan. Part-time tuition: $1482 per credit hour. Part-time tuition varies according to course load. **Scholarships:** Available. **Calendar System:** Semester, Summer session available **Enrollment:** Full-time 6,046, Graduate full-time 3,424, Graduate part-time 1,377, Part-time 258 **Faculty:** Full-time 606, Part-time 234 **Student-Faculty Ratio:** 10:1 **Exams:** ACT essay component used as validity check; SAT I and SAT II or ACT; SAT I or ACT; SAT II; SAT essay component used as validity check; SAT Reasoning; SAT Subject. **% Receiving Financial Aid:** 51 **% Residing in College-Owned, -Operated, or -Affiliated Housing:** 90 **Final Year or Final Semester Residency Requirement:** Yes **Regional Accreditation:** Middle States Association of Colleges and Schools **Credit Hours For Degree:** 128 credit hours, Bachelors **ROTC:** Air Force, Army, Navy **Professional Accreditation:** AACN, AACSB, AAMFT, ABET, ACA, ACIPE, APA, CEPH, LCME/AMA, NASM, NCATE. **Intercollegiate Athletics:** Archery M & W; Badminton M & W; Baseball M; Basketball M & W; Bowling M & W; Cheerleading M & W; Crew M & W; Cross-Country Running M & W; Equestrian Sports M & W; Fencing M & W; Field Hockey W; Football M; Golf M; Ice Hockey M & W; Lacrosse M & W; Rugby M & W; Sailing M & W; Skiing (Downhill) M & W; Soccer M & W; Softball W; Squash M; Swimming

and Diving M & W; Tennis M & W; Track and Field M & W; Ultimate Frisbee M & W; Volleyball M & W; Water Polo M & W

U.T.A. MESIVTA OF KIRYAS JOEL
9 Nickelsburg Rd., Unit 312
Monroe, NY 10950
Tel: (845)873-9901
Fax: (845)782-3620
President/CEO: David Schwartz
Type: Four-Year College **Sex:** Men **Affiliation:** Jewish. **Admission Plans:** Open Admission **Professional Accreditation:** AARTS.

UTICA COLLEGE
1600 Burrstone Rd.
Utica, NY 13502-4892
Tel: (315)792-3111; Free: 800-782-8884
Fax: (315)792-3003
E-mail: jtgates@utica.edu
Web Site: www.utica.edu
President/CEO: Dr. Todd S. Hutton
Admissions: Jeffrey Gates
Financial Aid: Laura Bedford

Type: Comprehensive **Sex:** Coed **Scores:** 90% SAT V 400+; 92% SAT M 400+; 56.76% ACT 18-23; 31.53% ACT 24-29 **% Accepted:** 83 **Admission Plans:** Deferred Admission; Early Action; Early Decision Plan **Application Deadline:** Rolling **Application Fee:** $40.00 **H.S. Requirements:** High school diploma required; GED accepted **Costs Per Year:** Application fee: $40. Comprehensive fee: $30,430 includes full-time tuition ($19,446), mandatory fees ($550), and college room and board ($10,434). Full-time tuition and fees vary according to course load, degree level, and location. Room and board charges vary according to board plan. Part-time tuition: $648 per credit hour. Part-time mandatory fees: $50 per term. Part-time tuition and fees vary according to course load, degree level, and location. **Scholarships:** Available. **Calendar System:** Semester, Summer session available **Enrollment:** Full-time 2,410, Graduate full-time 228, Graduate part-time 1,151, Part-time 674 **Faculty:** Full-time 146, Part-time 287 **Student-Faculty Ratio:** 11:1 **Exams:** SAT I or ACT. **% Receiving Financial Aid:** 87 **% Residing in College-Owned, -Operated, or -Affiliated Housing:** 44 **Final Year or Final Semester Residency Requirement:** No **Regional Accreditation:** Middle States Association of Colleges and Schools **Credit Hours For Degree:** 120 credit hours, Bachelors **ROTC:** Air Force, Army **Professional Accreditation:** AACN, ACEN, AOTA, APTA, TEAC. **Intercollegiate Athletics:** Baseball M; Basketball M & W; Cross-Country Running M & W; Field Hockey W; Football M; Golf M & W; Ice Hockey M & W; Lacrosse M & W; Soccer M & W; Softball W; Swimming and Diving M & W; Tennis M & W; Track and Field M & W; Volleyball W; Water Polo W

UTICA SCHOOL OF COMMERCE
201 Bleecker St.
Utica, NY 13501-2280
Tel: (315)733-2307; Free: 800-321-4USC
Fax: (315)733-9281
Web Site: www.uscny.edu
President/CEO: Philip Williams

Type: Two-Year College **Sex:** Coed **% Accepted:** 100 **Application Deadline:** Rolling **H.S. Requirements:** High school diploma required; GED accepted **Scholarships:** Available. **Calendar System:** Quarter, Summer session available **Student-Faculty Ratio:** 14:1 **Credit Hours For Degree:** 90 quarter hours, Associates **Professional Accreditation:** NYSBR.

VASSAR COLLEGE
124 Raymond Ave.
Poughkeepsie, NY 12604
Tel: (845)437-7000; Free: 800-827-7270
Fax: (845)437-7063
E-mail: admissions@vassar.edu
Web Site: www.vassar.edu
President/CEO: Pres. Catherine B. Hill
Admissions: Dean Art D. Rodriguez
Financial Aid: Jessica L. Bernier

Type: Four-Year College **Sex:** Coed **Scores:** 100% SAT V 400+; 100% SAT M 400+; 20% ACT 24-29 **% Accepted:** 26 **Admission Plans:** Deferred Admission; Early Action **Application Deadline:** January 1 **Application Fee:** $70.00 **H.S. Requirements:** High school diploma required; GED accepted

Costs Per Year: Application fee: $70. One-time mandatory fee: $80. Comprehensive fee: $65,490 includes full-time tuition ($52,320), mandatory fees ($770), and college room and board ($12,400). College room only: $6730. Room and board charges vary according to board plan and housing facility. Part-time tuition: $6230 per unit. **Scholarships:** Available. **Calendar System:** Semester, Summer session not available **Enrollment:** Full-time 2,421, Part-time 14 **Faculty:** Full-time 275, Part-time 63 **Student-Faculty Ratio:** 8:1 **Exams:** ACT essay component used as validity check; ACT essay component used for admission; SAT I and SAT II or ACT; SAT essay component used as validity check; SAT essay component used for admission; SAT Reasoning; SAT Subject. **% Receiving Financial Aid:** 60 % **Residing in College-Owned, -Operated, or -Affiliated Housing:** 96 **Final Year or Final Semester Residency Requirement:** Yes **Regional Accreditation:** Middle States Association of Colleges and Schools **Credit Hours For Degree:** 34 units, Bachelors **Intercollegiate Athletics:** Baseball M; Basketball M & W; Crew M & W; Cross-Country Running M & W; Fencing M & W; Field Hockey W; Golf W; Lacrosse M & W; Rugby M & W; Soccer M & W; Squash M & W; Swimming and Diving M & W; Tennis M & W; Track and Field M & W; Volleyball M & W

VAUGHN COLLEGE OF AERONAUTICS AND TECHNOLOGY

86-01 23rd Ave.
Flushing, NY 11369
Tel: (718)429-6600; Free: 866-6VAUGHN
Fax: (718)429-0256
E-mail: david.sookdeo@vaughn.edu
Web Site: www.vaughn.edu
President/CEO: Dr. Sharon B. DeVivo
Admissions: David Sookdeo
Financial Aid: Dorothy Martin

Type: Comprehensive **Sex:** Coed **Scores:** 98% SAT V 400+; 100% SAT M 400+; 53% ACT 18-23; 47% ACT 24-29 **% Accepted:** 74 **Admission Plans:** Open Admission **Application Deadline:** Rolling **Application Fee:** $40.00 **H.S. Requirements:** High school diploma required; GED accepted **Costs Per Year:** Application fee: $40. One-time mandatory fee: $160. Comprehensive fee: $37,350 includes full-time tuition ($22,975), mandatory fees ($800), and college room and board ($13,575). College room only: $11,175. Full-time tuition and fees vary according to course load, degree level, and program. Room and board charges vary according to board plan. Part-time tuition: $765 per credit. Part-time mandatory fees: $800 per year. Part-time tuition and fees vary according to course load, degree level, and program. **Scholarships:** Available. **Calendar System:** Semester, Summer session available **Enrollment:** Full-time 1,224, Graduate full-time 1, Graduate part-time 10, Part-time 302 **Faculty:** Full-time 42, Part-time 162 **Student-Faculty Ratio:** 14:1 **Exams:** ACT essay component used for advising; SAT I or ACT; SAT essay component used for advising. **% Receiving Financial Aid:** 83 % **Residing in College-Owned, -Operated, or -Affiliated Housing:** 10 **Final Year or Final Semester Residency Requirement:** Yes **Regional Accreditation:** Middle States Association of Colleges and Schools **Credit Hours For Degree:** 64 credits, Associates; 123 credits, Bachelors **ROTC:** Air Force, Army **Professional Accreditation:** ABET. **Intercollegiate Athletics:** Basketball M & W; Cross-Country Running M & W; Soccer M; Tennis M & W

VILLA MARIA COLLEGE

240 Pine Ridge Rd.
Buffalo, NY 14225
Tel: (716)896-0700
Fax: (716)896-0705
E-mail: admissions@villa.edu
Web Site: www.villa.edu
President/CEO: Señor Marcella Marie Garus, CSSF
Admissions: Brian Emerson
Financial Aid: Aimee Murch

Type: Four-Year College **Sex:** Coed **Affiliation:** Roman Catholic Church. **Scores:** 65% SAT V 400+; 65% SAT M 400+; 38% ACT 18-23 **Costs Per Year:** Tuition: $19,260 full-time, $645 per credit hour part-time. Mandatory fees: $650 full-time, $250 per term part-time. Full-time tuition and fees vary according to program and reciprocity agreements. Part-time tuition and fees vary according to course load, program, and reciprocity agreements. **Scholarships:** Available. **Calendar System:** Semester **Enrollment:** Full-time 418, Part-time 125 **Faculty:** Full-time 28, Part-time 61 **Student-Faculty Ratio:** 10:1 **% Receiving Financial Aid:** 97 **Regional Accreditation:** Middle States Association of Colleges and Schools **Credit Hours For**

Degree: 60 credits, Associates; 120 credits, Bachelors **Professional Accreditation:** APTA. **Intercollegiate Athletics:** Basketball M & W; Bowling W; Cross-Country Running M & W; Golf M; Soccer M & W; Swimming and Diving M & W

WAGNER COLLEGE

1 Campus Rd.
Staten Island, NY 10301-4495
Tel: (718)390-3100; Free: 800-221-1010
Fax: (718)390-3105
E-mail: jgibbons@wagner.edu
Web Site: www.wagner.edu
President/CEO: Dr. Richard Guarasci
Admissions: James Gibbons
Financial Aid: Theresa Weimer

Type: Comprehensive **Sex:** Coed **Scores:** 100% SAT V 400+; 100% SAT M 400+; 34% ACT 18-23; 51% ACT 24-29 **Costs Per Year:** Comprehensive fee: $55,480 includes full-time tuition ($42,030), mandatory fees ($450), and college room and board ($13,000). Full-time tuition and fees vary according to program. Part-time tuition: $5,253.75 per unit. **Scholarships:** Available. **Calendar System:** Semester, Summer session available **Enrollment:** Full-time 1,709, Graduate full-time 204, Graduate part-time 248, Part-time 41 **Faculty:** Full-time 96, Part-time 155 **Student-Faculty Ratio:** 15:1 **Exams:** SAT I or ACT. **% Receiving Financial Aid:** 64 % **Residing in College-Owned, -Operated, or -Affiliated Housing:** 71 **Final Year or Final Semester Residency Requirement:** Yes **Regional Accreditation:** Middle States Association of Colleges and Schools **Credit Hours For Degree:** 36 units, Bachelors **ROTC:** Army **Professional Accreditation:** ACBSP, ACEN, NCATE. **Intercollegiate Athletics:** Baseball M; Basketball M & W; Cheerleading W; Cross-Country Running M & W; Fencing W; Football M; Golf M & W; Ice Hockey M; Lacrosse M & W; Soccer W; Softball W; Swimming and Diving W; Tennis M & W; Track and Field M & W; Water Polo M & W

WEBB INSTITUTE

Crescent Beach Rd.
Glen Cove, NY 11542-1398
Tel: (516)671-2213
Fax: (516)674-9838
E-mail: admissions@webb.edu
Web Site: www.webb.edu
President/CEO: R. Keith Michel
Financial Aid: Lauri D'Ambra

Type: Four-Year College **Sex:** Coed **Scores:** 100% SAT V 400+; 100% SAT M 400+; 29% ACT 24-29 **% Accepted:** 36 **Admission Plans:** Early Action **Application Deadline:** February 15 **Application Fee:** $25.00 **H.S. Requirements:** High school diploma required; GED not accepted **Costs Per Year:** Application fee: $25. One-time mandatory fee: $2850. Comprehensive fee: $61,800 includes full-time tuition ($47,000), mandatory fees ($400), and college room and board ($14,400). Webb provides scholarships that will fully cover the tuition expenses of U.S. citizens and permanent residents. One-time required fee is for a laptop charged in the first year only. **Scholarships:** Available. **Calendar System:** Semester, Summer session not available **Enrollment:** Full-time 91 **Faculty:** Full-time 11, Part-time 3 **Student-Faculty Ratio:** 8:1 **Exams:** ACT essay component used for admission; SAT I or ACT; SAT II; SAT essay component used for admission; SAT Reasoning; SAT Subject. **% Receiving Financial Aid:** 41 % **Residing in College-Owned, -Operated, or -Affiliated Housing:** 100 **Final Year or Final Semester Residency Requirement:** No **Regional Accreditation:** Middle States Association of Colleges and Schools **Credit Hours For Degree:** 146 credits, Bachelors **Professional Accreditation:** ABET. **Intercollegiate Athletics:** Basketball M & W; Cross-Country Running M & W; Sailing M & W; Soccer M & W; Tennis M & W; Volleyball M & W

WELLS COLLEGE

170 Main St.
Aurora, NY 13026
Tel: (315)364-3266; Free: 800-952-9355
Fax: (315)364-3227
E-mail: admissions@wells.edu
Web Site: www.wells.edu
President/CEO: Dr. Jonathan Gibralter
Admissions: Susan Raith Sloan
Financial Aid: Laura Burns

Type: Four-Year College **Sex:** Coed **Scores:** 95% SAT V 400+; 93% SAT M 400+; 54% ACT 18-23; 39% ACT 24-29 **% Accepted:** 58 **Admission Plans:** Deferred Admission; Early Action; Early Admission; Early Decision Plan **Application Deadline:** March 1 **Application Fee:** $40.00 **H.S. Requirements:** High school diploma required; GED accepted **Costs Per Year:** Application fee: $40. Comprehensive fee: $51,890 includes full-time tuition ($37,030), mandatory fees ($1500), and college room and board ($13,360). Room and board charges vary according to housing facility. Part-time tuition: $700 per credit hour. Part-time mandatory fees: $150 per credit hour. Part-time tuition and fees vary according to course load. **Scholarships:** Available. **Calendar System:** Semester, Summer session not available **Enrollment:** Full-time 558, Part-time 14 **Faculty:** Full-time 38, Part-time 29 **Student-Faculty Ratio:** 11:1 **Exams:** ACT essay component not used; SAT I or ACT; SAT essay component not used; SAT Reasoning. **% Receiving Financial Aid:** 92 **% Residing in College-Owned, -Operated, or -Affiliated Housing:** 92 **Final Year or Final Semester Residency Requirement:** No **Regional Accreditation:** Middle States Association of Colleges and Schools **Credit Hours For Degree:** 120 credits, Bachelors **Intercollegiate Athletics:** Baseball M; Basketball M & W; Cross-Country Running M & W; Field Hockey W; Lacrosse M & W; Soccer M & W; Softball W; Swimming and Diving M & W; Tennis W; Volleyball M & W

WESTCHESTER COMMUNITY COLLEGE

75 Grasslands Rd.
Valhalla, NY 10595-1698
Tel: (914)785-6600
E-mail: admissions@sunywcc.edu
Web Site: www.sunywcc.edu
President/CEO: Dr. John Flynn
Admissions: Gloria Leon
Type: Two-Year College **Sex:** Coed **Affiliation:** State University of New York System. **% Accepted:** 100 **Admission Plans:** Early Admission; Open Admission **Application Fee:** $35.00 **H.S. Requirements:** High school diploma required; GED accepted **Costs Per Year:** Application fee: $35. State resident tuition: $4280 full-time, $179 per credit hour part-time. Nonresident tuition: $11,770 full-time, $493 per credit hour part-time. Mandatory fees: $443 full-time. Full-time tuition and fees vary according to location. Part-time tuition varies according to location. **Scholarships:** Available. **Calendar System:** Semester, Summer session available **Enrollment:** Full-time 7,062, Part-time 5,904 **Faculty:** Full-time 173, Part-time 881 **Regional Accreditation:** Middle States Association of Colleges and Schools **Credit Hours For Degree:** 64 credits, Associates **Professional Accreditation:** CoARC, JRCERT. **Intercollegiate Athletics:** Baseball M; Basketball M & W; Bowling M & W; Golf M; Soccer M; Softball W; Volleyball W

WOOD TOBE–COBURN SCHOOL

8 E 40th St.
New York, NY 10016
Tel: (212)686-9040; Free: 800-394-9663
Fax: (212)686-9171
Web Site: www.woodtobecoburn.edu
President/CEO: Sandi Gruninger
Type: Two-Year College **Sex:** Coed **% Accepted:** 89 **H.S. Requirements:** High school diploma required; GED accepted **Scholarships:** Available. **Calendar System:** Semester **Credit Hours For Degree:** 60 credits, Associates **Professional Accreditation:** NYSBR.

YESHIVA DERECH CHAIM

1573 39th St.
Brooklyn, NY 11218
Tel: (718)438-3070
President/CEO: Mordechai Rennert
Type: Comprehensive **Sex:** Men **Affiliation:** Jewish. **% Accepted:** 100 **H.S. Requirements:** High school diploma required; GED not accepted **Calendar System:** Semester **Professional Accreditation:** AARTS.

YESHIVA D'MONSEY RABBINICAL COLLEGE

2 Roman Blvd.
Monsey, NY 10952
Tel: (914)352-5852
Fax: (914)362-3453
President/CEO: Rabbi Aron Berger
Type: Four-Year College **Sex:** Men **Affiliation:** Jewish. **% Accepted:** 100 **Professional Accreditation:** AARTS.

YESHIVA OF FAR ROCKAWAY DERECH AYSON RABBINICAL SEMINARY

802 Hicksville Rd.
Far Rockaway, NY 11691
Tel: (718)327-7600
Web Site: www.yofr.org
Type: Four-Year College **Sex:** Men **Affiliation:** Jewish. **Professional Accreditation:** AARTS.

YESHIVA GEDOLAH IMREI YOSEF D'SPINKA

1466 56th St.
Brooklyn, NY 11219
Tel: (718)851-8721
President/CEO: Yehuda Kornreich
Type: Four-Year College **Sex:** Men **Affiliation:** Jewish. **Admission Plans:** Open Admission **Professional Accreditation:** AARTS.

YESHIVA KARLIN STOLIN RABBINICAL INSTITUTE

1818 Fifty-fourth St.
Brooklyn, NY 11204
Tel: (718)232-7800
Fax: (718)331-4833
President/CEO: Mayer Pilchick
Financial Aid: Daniel Ross
Type: Comprehensive **Sex:** Men **Affiliation:** Jewish. **% Accepted:** 100 **Admission Plans:** Preferred Admission **Application Deadline:** Rolling **H.S. Requirements:** High school diploma required; GED accepted **Scholarships:** Available. **Calendar System:** Semester, Summer session not available **Credit Hours For Degree:** 130 credits, Bachelors **Professional Accreditation:** AARTS.

YESHIVA AND KOLEL BAIS MEDRASH ELYON

73 Main St.
Monsey, NY 10952
Tel: (845)356-7064
President/CEO: Rabbi Isaac Swiatycki
Type: Four-Year College **Sex:** Men **Affiliation:** Jewish. **% Accepted:** 100 **Professional Accreditation:** AARTS.

YESHIVA AND KOLLEL HARBOTZAS TORAH

1049 E 15th St.
Brooklyn, NY 11230
Tel: (718)692-0208
President/CEO: Yekusiel Bittersfeld
Type: Four-Year College **Sex:** Men **Affiliation:** Jewish. **Professional Accreditation:** AARTS.

YESHIVA OF MACHZIKAI HADAS

1321 43rd St.
Brooklyn, NY 11219
Tel: (718)853-2442
Type: Four-Year College **Sex:** Coed **Affiliation:** Jewish. **Professional Accreditation:** AARTS.

YESHIVA OF NITRA RABBINICAL COLLEGE

Pines Bridge Rd.
Mount Kisco, NY 10549
Tel: (718)384-5460
President/CEO: Alfred Schonberger
Financial Aid: Yosef Rosen
Type: Comprehensive **Sex:** Men **Affiliation:** Jewish. **H.S. Requirements:** High school diploma required; GED accepted **Calendar System:** Semester **Professional Accreditation:** AARTS.

YESHIVA SHAAR HATORAH TALMUDIC RESEARCH INSTITUTE

117-06 84th Ave.
Kew Gardens, NY 11418-1469
Tel: (718)846-1940
President/CEO: Rabbi Yoel Yankelewitz
Financial Aid: Yoel Yankelewitz
Type: Comprehensive **Sex:** Men **Affiliation:** Jewish. **Application Fee:** $100.00 **Scholarships:** Available. **Calendar System:** Semester **Professional Accreditation:** AARTS.

YESHIVA SHAAREI TORAH OF ROCKLAND
91 W Carlton Rd.
Suffern, NY 10901
Tel: (845)352-3431
President/CEO: Rabbi Mordechai Wolmark
Type: Four-Year College **Sex:** Men **Affiliation:** Jewish. **Application Fee:** $250.00 **Professional Accreditation:** AARTS.

YESHIVA OF THE TELSHE ALUMNI
4904 Independence Ave.
Riverdale, NY 10471
Tel: (718)601-3523
President/CEO: Noson Joseph
Type: Four-Year College **Sex:** Men **Affiliation:** Jewish. **% Accepted:** 100 **Application Fee:** $50.00 **Professional Accreditation:** AARTS.

YESHIVA UNIVERSITY
500 W 185th St.
New York, NY 10033-3201
Tel: (212)960-5400
Fax: (212)960-0086
E-mail: yuadmit@yu.edu
Web Site: www.yu.edu
President/CEO: Richard Joel, JD
Admissions: Geri Mansdorf
Financial Aid: Marianela Cabral
Type: University **Sex:** Coed **Scores:** 100% SAT V 400+; 100% SAT M 400+; 23% ACT 18-23; 54% ACT 24-29 **% Accepted:** 80 **Admission Plans:** Deferred Admission; Early Action; Early Admission **Application Deadline:** February 1 **Application Fee:** $65.00 **H.S. Requirements:** High school diploma required; GED accepted **Costs Per Year:** Application fee: $65. Comprehensive fee: $52,780 includes full-time tuition ($39,930), mandatory fees ($1600), and college room and board ($11,250). Room and board charges vary according to housing facility. Part-time tuition: $1350 per credit hour. **Scholarships:** Available. **Calendar System:** Semester, Summer session available **Enrollment:** Full-time 2,691, Graduate full-time 2,549, Graduate part-time 910, Part-time 53 **Faculty:** Full-time 720, Part-time 308 **Student-Faculty Ratio:** 7:1 **Exams:** ACT essay component not used; SAT I or ACT. **% Residing in College-Owned, -Operated, or -Affiliated Housing:** 88 **Final Year or Final Semester Residency Requirement:** No **Regional Accreditation:** Middle States Association of Colleges and Schools **Credit Hours For Degree:** 128 credits, Bachelors **Professional Accreditation:** AALS, ABA, APA, CSWE, LCME/AMA, NCATE, TEAC. **Intercollegiate Athletics:** Baseball M; Basketball M & W; Cross-Country Running M & W; Fencing M & W; Golf M; Soccer M & W; Tennis M & W; Volleyball M; Wrestling M

YESHIVAS NOVOMINSK
1569 47th St.
Brooklyn, NY 11219
Tel: (718)438-2727
President/CEO: Lipa Brennan
Type: Four-Year College **Sex:** Men **Affiliation:** Jewish. **% Accepted:** 100 **Application Fee:** $100.00 **Professional Accreditation:** AARTS.

YESHIVAT MIKDASH MELECH
1326 Ocean Pky.
Brooklyn, NY 11230-5601

Tel: (718)339-1090
E-mail: mikdashmelech@verizon.net
President/CEO: Haim Benoliel
Admissions: Rabbi S. Beyda
Type: Four-Year College **Sex:** Men **Affiliation:** Jewish. **% Accepted:** 100 **Application Deadline:** Rolling **Calendar System:** Continuous **Professional Accreditation:** AARTS.

YESHIVATH VIZNITZ
25 Phyllis Ter.
Monsey, NY 10952
Tel: (914)356-1010
President/CEO: R' Gershon Neiman
Type: Comprehensive **Sex:** Men **Affiliation:** Jewish. **% Accepted:** 100 **Calendar System:** Semester **Professional Accreditation:** AARTS.

YESHIVATH ZICHRON MOSHE
Laurel Park Rd.
South Fallsburg, NY 12779
Tel: (914)434-5240
President/CEO: R' Ephraim Sher
Admissions: Rabbi Abba Gorelick
Financial Aid: Miryom R. Miller
Type: Comprehensive **Sex:** Men **Affiliation:** Jewish. **% Accepted:** 100 **Calendar System:** Semester **Professional Accreditation:** AARTS.

YORK COLLEGE OF THE CITY UNIVERSITY OF NEW YORK
94-20 Guy R Brewer Blvd.
Jamaica, NY 11451-0001
Tel: (718)262-2000
E-mail: lyates@york.cuny.edu
Web Site: www.york.cuny.edu
President/CEO: Dr. Marcia V. Keizs
Admissions: Dr. La Toro Yates
Financial Aid: Beverly Brown
Type: Comprehensive **Sex:** Coed **Affiliation:** City University of New York System. **Scores:** 68% SAT V 400+; 75% SAT M 400+ **% Accepted:** 63 **Admission Plans:** Deferred Admission; Early Admission **Application Deadline:** Rolling **Application Fee:** $65.00 **H.S. Requirements:** High school diploma required; GED accepted **Costs Per Year:** Application fee: $65. State resident tuition: $6330 full-time, $260 per credit part-time. Nonresident tuition: $16,800 full-time, $535 per credit part-time. Mandatory fees: $418 full-time, $208 per term part-time. Full-time tuition and fees vary according to degree level and student level. Part-time tuition and fees vary according to degree level and student level. **Scholarships:** Available. **Calendar System:** Semester, Summer session available **Enrollment:** Full-time 5,226, Graduate full-time 65, Part-time 3,220 **Student-Faculty Ratio:** 23:1 **Exams:** ACT; ACT essay component not used; SAT I; SAT I and SAT II or ACT; SAT II; SAT essay component not used; SAT Reasoning; SAT Subject. **% Receiving Financial Aid:** 71 **Final Year or Final Semester Residency Requirement:** No **Regional Accreditation:** Middle States Association of Colleges and Schools **Credit Hours For Degree:** 120 credits, Bachelors **ROTC:** Army **Professional Accreditation:** ACEN, AOTA, CSWE, NCATE. **Intercollegiate Athletics:** Baseball M & W; Basketball M & W; Cross-Country Running M & W; Soccer M; Softball W; Swimming and Diving M & W; Tennis M; Track and Field M & W; Volleyball M & W

ALAMANCE COMMUNITY COLLEGE
PO Box 8000
Graham, NC 27253-8000
Tel: (336)578-2002
Fax: (336)578-1987
E-mail: brehlere@alamancecc.edu
Web Site: www.alamancecc.edu
President/CEO: Dr. Algie Gatewood
Admissions: Elizabeth Brehler
Financial Aid: Elizabeth Solazzo
Type: Two-Year College **Sex:** Coed **Affiliation:** North Carolina Community College System. **% Accepted:** 100 **Admission Plans:** Open Admission **Application Deadline:** Rolling **Application Fee:** $0.00 **H.S. Requirements:** High school diploma required; GED accepted **Costs Per Year:** Application fee: $0. State resident tuition: $2432 full-time. Nonresident tuition: $8576 full-time. Mandatory fees: $30 full-time. Full-time tuition and fees vary according to course load. **Scholarships:** Available. **Calendar System:** Semester, Summer session available **Enrollment:** Full-time 2,654, Part-time 1,766 **Faculty:** Full-time 115, Part-time 320 **Student-Faculty Ratio:** 12:1 **Regional Accreditation:** Southern Association of Colleges and Schools **Credit Hours For Degree:** 64 semester hours, Associates **Professional Accreditation:** ACF, ADA, NAACLS.

APEX SCHOOL OF THEOLOGY
2945 S Miami Blvd., Ste. 114
Durham, NC 27703
Tel: (919)572-1625
Fax: (919)572-1762
E-mail: registrar@apexsot.edu
Web Site: www.apexsot.edu
President/CEO: Dr. Joseph Perkins
Admissions: Dr. Henry D. Wells, Jr.
Type: Comprehensive **Sex:** Coed **Affiliation:** interdenominational. **% Accepted:** 83 **Application Fee:** $25.00 **H.S. Requirements:** High school diploma required; GED accepted **Calendar System:** Semester **Enrollment:** Full-time 452, Graduate full-time 157, Graduate part-time 35, Part-time 77 **Faculty:** Full-time 14, Part-time 27 **Student-Faculty Ratio:** 17:1 **Final Year or Final Semester Residency Requirement:** No **Credit Hours For Degree:** 60 credit hours, Associates; 128 credit hours, Bachelors **Professional Accreditation:** TRACS.

APPALACHIAN STATE UNIVERSITY
Boone, NC 28608
Tel: (828)262-2000
Fax: (828)262-3296
E-mail: admissions@appstate.edu
Web Site: www.appstate.edu
President/CEO: Dr. Sheri N. Everts
Admissions: Alexis Pope
Financial Aid: Lori Townsend
Type: Comprehensive **Sex:** Coed **Affiliation:** University of North Carolina System. **Scores:** 100% SAT V 400+; 100% SAT M 400+; 28.64% ACT 18-23; 59.94% ACT 24-29 **% Accepted:** 66 **Admission Plans:** Deferred Admission **Application Deadline:** November 15 **Application Fee:** $55.00 **H.S. Requirements:** High school diploma required; GED accepted **Costs Per**

Year: Application fee: $55. State resident tuition: $3961 full-time, $133.50 per credit hour part-time. Nonresident tuition: $17,786 full-time, $601 per credit hour part-time. Mandatory fees: $2891 full-time, $18.13 per credit hour part-time. Part-time tuition and fees vary according to course load. College room and board: $7845. College room only: $4225. Room and board charges vary according to board plan and housing facility. **Scholarships:** Available. **Calendar System:** Semester, Summer session available **Enrollment:** Full-time 15,351, Graduate full-time 868, Graduate part-time 774, Part-time 939 **Faculty:** Full-time 930, Part-time 397 **Student-Faculty Ratio:** 16:1 **Exams:** ACT essay component not used; SAT I and SAT II or ACT; SAT I or ACT; SAT II; SAT essay component not used. **% Receiving Financial Aid:** 48 **% Residing in College-Owned, -Operated, or -Affiliated Housing:** 34 **Final Year or Final Semester Residency Requirement:** No **Regional Accreditation:** Southern Association of Colleges and Schools **Credit Hours For Degree:** 122 semester hours, Bachelors **ROTC:** Army **Professional Accreditation:** AACN, AACSB, AAFCS, AAMFT, ABET, ACA, AND, APA, ASHA, CSWE, JRCAT, NASAD, NASM, NASPAA, NAST, NCATE, NRPA. **Intercollegiate Athletics:** Archery M & W; Baseball M; Basketball M & W; Cross-Country Running M & W; Equestrian Sports W; Fencing M & W; Field Hockey W; Football M; Golf M & W; Ice Hockey M & W; Lacrosse M & W; Rock Climbing M & W; Rugby M & W; Skiing (Downhill) M & W; Soccer M & W; Softball W; Swimming and Diving M & W; Tennis M & W; Track and Field M & W; Ultimate Frisbee M & W; Volleyball W; Wrestling M

THE ART INSTITUTE OF CHARLOTTE, A CAMPUS OF SOUTH UNIVERSITY
Three LakePointe Plz.
2110 Water Ridge Pky.
Charlotte, NC 28217
Tel: (704)357-8020; Free: 800-872-4417
Fax: (704)357-1133
Web Site: www.artinstitutes.edu/charlotte
President/CEO: Asher Haines
Type: Four-Year College **Sex:** Coed **Affiliation:** Education Management Corporation. **Calendar System:** Quarter, Summer session available **Regional Accreditation:** Southern Association of Colleges and Schools **Professional Accreditation:** ACF.

THE ART INSTITUTE OF RALEIGH-DURHAM, A CAMPUS OF SOUTH UNIVERSITY
410 Blackwell St.
Ste. 200
Durham, NC 27701
Tel: (919)317-3050; Free: 888-245-9593
Web Site: www.artinstitutes.edu/raleigh-durham
President/CEO: Chris Mesecar
Type: Four-Year College **Sex:** Coed **Affiliation:** Education Management Corporation. **Regional Accreditation:** Southern Association of Colleges and Schools

ASHEVILLE-BUNCOMBE TECHNICAL COMMUNITY COLLEGE
340 Victoria Rd.
Asheville, NC 28801-4897
Tel: (828)254-1921

Fax: (828)251-6355
E-mail: admissions@abtech.edu
Web Site: www.abtech.edu
President/CEO: Hank Dunn
Type: Two-Year College **Sex:** Coed **Affiliation:** North Carolina Community College System. **Admission Plans:** Deferred Admission; Open Admission **Application Deadline:** Rolling **Application Fee:** $0.00 **H.S. Requirements:** High school diploma required; GED accepted **Scholarships:** Available. **Calendar System:** Semester, Summer session available **Student-Faculty Ratio:** 15:1 **Regional Accreditation:** Southern Association of Colleges and Schools **Credit Hours For Degree:** 64 semester hours, Associates **Professional Accreditation:** ACF, ADA, JRCERT, NAACLS.

BARTON COLLEGE
PO Box 5000
Wilson, NC 27893-7000
Tel: (252)399-6300; Free: 800-345-4973
Fax: (252)237-4957
E-mail: ahmetts@barton.edu
Web Site: www.barton.edu
President/CEO: Dr. Douglas N. Searcy
Admissions: Amanda Metts
Financial Aid: Bridget Ellis
Type: Comprehensive **Sex:** Coed **Affiliation:** Christian Church (Disciples of Christ). **Scores:** 89% SAT V 400+; 88% SAT M 400+; 58% ACT 18-23; 20% ACT 24-29 **% Accepted:** 42 **Application Deadline:** Rolling **Application Fee:** $0.00 **H.S. Requirements:** High school diploma required; GED accepted **Costs Per Year:** Application fee: $0. Comprehensive fee: $38,686 includes full-time tuition ($26,670), mandatory fees ($2382), and college room and board ($9634). College room only: $4211. Full-time tuition and fees vary according to class time, course load, and program. Room and board charges vary according to board plan and housing facility. Part-time tuition: $491 per credit hour. Part-time tuition varies according to class time, course load, and program. **Scholarships:** Available. **Calendar System:** 4-1-4, Summer session available **Enrollment:** Full-time 911, Graduate full-time 30, Graduate part-time 32, Part-time 74 **Faculty:** Full-time 69 **Student-Faculty Ratio:** 13:1 **Exams:** SAT I or ACT; SAT Reasoning. **% Receiving Financial Aid:** 89 **% Residing in College-Owned, -Operated, or -Affiliated Housing:** 43 **Final Year or Final Semester Residency Requirement:** Yes **Regional Accreditation:** Southern Association of Colleges and Schools **Credit Hours For Degree:** 126 semester hours, Bachelors **Professional Accreditation:** ACEN, CSWE, NCATE. **Intercollegiate Athletics:** Baseball M; Basketball M & W; Cross-Country Running M & W; Golf M & W; Soccer M & W; Softball W; Tennis M & W; Track and Field M & W; Volleyball M & W

BEAUFORT COUNTY COMMUNITY COLLEGE
PO Box 1069
Washington, NC 27889-1069
Tel: (252)946-6194
Fax: (252)946-0271
E-mail: garyb@beaufortccc.edu
Web Site: www.beaufortccc.edu
President/CEO: Dr. David McLawhorn
Admissions: Gary Burbage
Financial Aid: Karen Pruden
Type: Two-Year College **Sex:** Coed **Affiliation:** North Carolina Community College System. **% Accepted:** 100 **Admission Plans:** Open Admission **Application Deadline:** Rolling **Application Fee:** $0.00 **H.S. Requirements:** High school diploma required; GED accepted **Scholarships:** Available. **Calendar System:** Semester, Summer session available **Exams:** ACT essay component not used; Other; SAT I or ACT; SAT essay component not used. **Final Year or Final Semester Residency Requirement:** No **Regional Accreditation:** Southern Association of Colleges and Schools **Professional Accreditation:** NAACLS.

BELMONT ABBEY COLLEGE
100 Belmont-Mt. Holly Rd.
Belmont, NC 28012-1802
Tel: (704)825-6700; Free: 888-BAC-0110
Fax: (704)825-6670
E-mail: nicolefocareto@bac.edu
Web Site: www.belmontabbeycollege.edu
President/CEO: Dr. William K. Thierfelder

Admissions: Nicole Focareto
Financial Aid: Julie Hodge
Type: Four-Year College **Sex:** Coed **Affiliation:** Roman Catholic. **Scores:** 91% SAT V 400+; 88% SAT M 400+; 50% ACT 18-23; 34% ACT 24-29 **% Accepted:** 68 **Admission Plans:** Deferred Admission **Application Deadline:** August 1 **Application Fee:** $35.00 **H.S. Requirements:** High school diploma required; GED accepted **Costs Per Year:** Application fee: $35. One-time mandatory fee: $400. Comprehensive fee: $28,594 includes full-time tuition ($18,500) and college room and board ($10,094). College room only: $5828. Full-time tuition varies according to course load and reciprocity agreements. Room and board charges vary according to board plan and housing facility. Part-time tuition: $617 per credit hour. Part-time tuition varies according to course load and reciprocity agreements. **Scholarships:** Available. **Calendar System:** Semester, Summer session available **Enrollment:** Full-time 1,385, Part-time 110 **Faculty:** Full-time 75, Part-time 60 **Student-Faculty Ratio:** 15:1 **Exams:** ACT essay component not used; SAT I or ACT; SAT essay component not used; SAT Reasoning. **% Receiving Financial Aid:** 72 **% Residing in College-Owned, -Operated, or -Affiliated Housing:** 52 **Final Year or Final Semester Residency Requirement:** Yes **Regional Accreditation:** Southern Association of Colleges and Schools **Credit Hours For Degree:** 120 credit hours, Bachelors **ROTC:** Air Force, Army **Intercollegiate Athletics:** Baseball M; Basketball M & W; Cheerleading W; Cross-Country Running M & W; Golf M & W; Lacrosse M & W; Soccer M & W; Softball W; Tennis M & W; Track and Field M & W; Volleyball M & W; Wrestling M

BENNETT COLLEGE
900 E Washington St.
Greensboro, NC 27401-3239
Tel: (336)273-4431; Free: 800-413-5323
E-mail: jbiggs@bennett.edu
Web Site: www.bennett.edu
President/CEO: Pres. Rosalind Fuse-Hall
Admissions: Jocelyn Biggs
Financial Aid: Keisha Ragsdale
Type: Four-Year College **Sex:** Women **Affiliation:** United Methodist. **% Accepted:** 95 **Admission Plans:** Deferred Admission **Application Deadline:** Rolling **Application Fee:** $35.00 **H.S. Requirements:** High school diploma required; GED accepted **Costs Per Year:** Application fee: $35. One-time mandatory fee: $225. Comprehensive fee: $26,627 includes full-time tuition ($15,964), mandatory fees ($2549), and college room and board ($8114). College room only: $4040. Full-time tuition and fees vary according to course load. Room and board charges vary according to board plan. Part-time tuition: $633 per credit hour. Part-time mandatory fees: $1067 per term. Part-time tuition and fees vary according to course load. **Scholarships:** Available. **Calendar System:** Semester, Summer session available **Enrollment:** Full-time 502, Part-time 81 **Faculty:** Full-time 47, Part-time 14 **Student-Faculty Ratio:** 10:1 **Exams:** ACT essay component used for advising; ACT essay component used for placement; SAT I or ACT; SAT essay component used for advising; SAT essay component used for placement. **% Receiving Financial Aid:** 96 **% Residing in College-Owned, -Operated, or -Affiliated Housing:** 64 **Final Year or Final Semester Residency Requirement:** No **Regional Accreditation:** Southern Association of Colleges and Schools **Credit Hours For Degree:** 124 semester hours, Bachelors **ROTC:** Air Force, Army **Professional Accreditation:** CSWE, NCATE.

BLADEN COMMUNITY COLLEGE
PO Box 266
Dublin, NC 28332-0266
Tel: (910)879-5500
Fax: (910)879-5508
E-mail: acarterfisher@bladencc.edu
Web Site: www.bladen.cc.nc.us
President/CEO: Dr. William Findt
Admissions: Andrea Fisher
Financial Aid: Lenore Lacy
Type: Two-Year College **Sex:** Coed **Affiliation:** North Carolina Community College System. **Admission Plans:** Deferred Admission; Open Admission **Application Deadline:** August 1 **Application Fee:** $0.00 **H.S. Requirements:** High school diploma required; GED accepted **Scholarships:** Available. **Calendar System:** Semester, Summer session available **Faculty:** Full-time 35, Part-time 50 **Exams:** Other; SAT I or ACT. **Regional Accreditation:** Southern Association of Colleges and Schools **Credit Hours For Degree:** 64 semester hours, Associates

BLUE RIDGE COMMUNITY COLLEGE

180 W Campus Dr.
Flat Rock, NC 28731
Tel: (828)694-1700
Fax: (828)694-1690
E-mail: kirstenb@blueridge.edu
Web Site: www.blueridge.edu
President/CEO: Molly A. Parkhill
Admissions: Kirsten Bunch

Type: Two-Year College **Sex:** Coed **Affiliation:** North Carolina Community College System. **Admission Plans:** Early Admission; Open Admission **Application Deadline:** Rolling **H.S. Requirements:** High school diploma required; GED accepted **Scholarships:** Available. **Calendar System:** Semester, Summer session available **Enrollment:** Full-time 766, Part-time 1,722 **Regional Accreditation:** Southern Association of Colleges and Schools **Credit Hours For Degree:** 64 credit hours, Associates **Intercollegiate Athletics:** Baseball M; Volleyball W

BREVARD COLLEGE

1 Brevard College Dr.
Brevard, NC 28712-3306
Tel: (828)883-8292; Free: 800-527-9090
Fax: (828)884-3790
E-mail: admissions@brevard.edu
Web Site: www.brevard.edu
President/CEO: Dr. David C. Joyce
Admissions: David Volrath
Financial Aid: Caron Surrett

Type: Four-Year College **Sex:** Coed **Affiliation:** United Methodist. **Scores:** 88% SAT V 400+; 90% SAT M 400+; 54% ACT 18-23; 18% ACT 24-29 **% Accepted:** 43 **Admission Plans:** Deferred Admission **Application Deadline:** Rolling **Application Fee:** $0.00 **H.S. Requirements:** High school diploma required; GED accepted **Scholarships:** Available. **Calendar System:** Semester, Summer session not available **Enrollment:** Full-time 697, Part-time 8 **Faculty:** Full-time 51, Part-time 44 **Student-Faculty Ratio:** 11:1 **Exams:** ACT essay component not used; SAT I or ACT; SAT essay component not used; SAT Reasoning. **% Receiving Financial Aid:** 75 **% Residing in College-Owned, -Operated, or -Affiliated Housing:** 76 **Regional Accreditation:** Southern Association of Colleges and Schools **Credit Hours For Degree:** 124 semester hours, Bachelors **Professional Accreditation:** NASM. **Intercollegiate Athletics:** Baseball M; Basketball M & W; Cheerleading W; Cross-Country Running M & W; Football M; Golf M & W; Lacrosse M & W; Soccer M & W; Softball W; Tennis M & W; Track and Field M & W; Volleyball W

BRIGHTWOOD COLLEGE, CHARLOTTE CAMPUS

6070 E Independence Blvd.
Charlotte, NC 28212
Tel: (704)567-3700
Web Site: www.brightwood.edu
President/CEO: Tenika Glenn

Type: Two-Year College **Sex:** Coed **Professional Accreditation:** ACICS.

BRUNSWICK COMMUNITY COLLEGE

50 College Rd.
Supply, NC 28462-0030
Tel: (910)755-7300; Free: 800-754-1050
Fax: (910)754-9609
E-mail: admissions@brunswickcc.edu
Web Site: www.brunswickcc.edu
President/CEO: Dr. Stephen Greiner

Type: Two-Year College **Sex:** Coed **Affiliation:** North Carolina Community College System. **Admission Plans:** Open Admission **Application Deadline:** Rolling **Application Fee:** $0.00 **H.S. Requirements:** High school diploma required; GED accepted **Scholarships:** Available. **Calendar System:** Semester, Summer session available **Student-Faculty Ratio:** 12:1 **Regional Accreditation:** Southern Association of Colleges and Schools **Credit Hours For Degree:** 64 semester hours, Associates **Professional Accreditation:** AHIMA. **Intercollegiate Athletics:** Baseball M; Basketball M & W; Volleyball W

CABARRUS COLLEGE OF HEALTH SCIENCES

401 Medical Park Dr.
Concord, NC 28025

Tel: (704)783-1555
Fax: (704)783-1764
E-mail: mckenzie.allen@cabarruscollege.edu
Web Site: www.cabarruscollege.edu
President/CEO: Dianne Snyder
Admissions: McKenzie Allen
Financial Aid: Valerie Richard

Type: Comprehensive **Sex:** Coed **Scores:** 92% SAT V 400+; 100% SAT M 400+; 95% ACT 18-23 **% Accepted:** 94 **Application Deadline:** February 1 **Application Fee:** $50.00 **H.S. Requirements:** High school diploma required; GED accepted **Costs Per Year:** Application fee: $50. Tuition: $11,656 full-time, $375 per credit hour part-time. Mandatory fees: $320 full-time, $125 per term part-time. Full-time tuition and fees vary according to course load. Part-time tuition and fees vary according to course load. **Scholarships:** Available. **Calendar System:** Semester, Summer session not available **Enrollment:** Full-time 156, Graduate full-time 21, Part-time 275 **Faculty:** Full-time 30, Part-time 37 **Student-Faculty Ratio:** 6:1 **Exams:** ACT essay component not used; SAT I or ACT; SAT essay component not used; SAT Reasoning; SAT Subject. **Final Year or Final Semester Residency Requirement:** No **Regional Accreditation:** Southern Association of Colleges and Schools **Credit Hours For Degree:** 66 semester hours, Associates; 120 semester hours, Bachelors **Professional Accreditation:** AACN, ACEN, AOTA, ARCST.

CALDWELL COMMUNITY COLLEGE AND TECHNICAL INSTITUTE

2855 Hickory Blvd.
Hudson, NC 28638-2397
Tel: (828)726-2200
Fax: (828)726-2490
E-mail: cwoodard@cccti.edu
Web Site: www.cccti.edu
President/CEO: Dr. Kenneth A. Boham
Admissions: Carolyn Woodard

Type: Two-Year College **Sex:** Coed **Affiliation:** North Carolina Community College System. **Admission Plans:** Early Admission; Open Admission **Application Deadline:** Rolling **Application Fee:** $0.00 **H.S. Requirements:** High school diploma required; GED accepted **Costs Per Year:** Application fee: $0. State resident tuition: $1872 full-time, $72 per credit hour part-time. Nonresident tuition: $6864 full-time, $264 per credit hour part-time. Mandatory fees: $38 full-time, $9 per course part-time. Full-time tuition and fees vary according to course load and program. Part-time tuition and fees vary according to course load and program. **Scholarships:** Available. **Calendar System:** Semester, Summer session available **Enrollment:** Full-time 1,472, Part-time 2,333 **Faculty:** Full-time 130, Part-time 290 **Regional Accreditation:** Southern Association of Colleges and Schools **Credit Hours For Degree:** 65 semester hours, Associates **Professional Accreditation:** JRCEDMS, JRCERT, JRCNMT. **Intercollegiate Athletics:** Basketball M & W; Golf M; Volleyball W

CAMPBELL UNIVERSITY

450 Leslie Campbell Ave.
Buies Creek, NC 27506
Tel: (910)893-1200; Free: 800-334-4111
Fax: (910)893-1288
E-mail: adm@mailcenter.campbell.edu
Web Site: www.campbell.edu
President/CEO: Dr. Jerry M. Wallace
Admissions: Peggy Mason

Type: University **Sex:** Coed **Affiliation:** North Carolina Baptist State Convention. **Scores:** 92% SAT V 400+; 92% SAT M 400+ **% Accepted:** 60 **Admission Plans:** Deferred Admission; Early Admission **Application Deadline:** Rolling **Application Fee:** $35.00 **H.S. Requirements:** High school diploma required; GED accepted **Costs Per Year:** Application fee: $35. Comprehensive fee: $39,070 includes full-time tuition ($27,800), mandatory fees ($1020), and college room and board ($10,250). College room only: $4900. Full-time tuition and fees vary according to class time, course load, location, and program. Room and board charges vary according to board plan and housing facility. Part-time tuition: $575 per credit hour. Part-time tuition varies according to class time, course load, location, and program. **Scholarships:** Available. **Calendar System:** Semester, Summer session available **Enrollment:** Full-time 2,731, Part-time 203 **Faculty:** Full-time 196, Part-time 109 **Student-Faculty Ratio:** 14:1 **Exams:** SAT I or ACT. **% Receiving Financial Aid:** 80 **% Residing in College-Owned, -Operated, or -Affiliated Housing:** 62 **Regional Accreditation:** Southern Association of Colleges and Schools **Credit Hours For Degree:** 64 semester hours, Associates; 128 semester hours, Bachelors **ROTC:** Army **Professional Accreditation:** ABA, ACBSP, ACPE, ATS, CSWE, JRCAT, NCATE. **Intercollegiate Athletics:** Baseball M; Basketball M & W; Cheerleading W; Cross-Country Running M & W; Golf M & W; Soccer M & W; Softball W; Swimming and Diving W; Tennis M & W; Track and Field M & W; Volleyball W; Wrestling M

CAPE FEAR COMMUNITY COLLEGE

411 N Front St.
Wilmington, NC 28401-3993
Tel: (910)362-7000; Free: 877-799-2322
E-mail: admissions@cfcc.edu
Web Site: www.cfcc.edu
President/CEO: Dr. Amanda Lee
Admissions: Linda Kasyan

Type: Two-Year College **Sex:** Coed **Affiliation:** North Carolina Community College System. **% Accepted:** 54 **Admission Plans:** Early Admission; Open Admission **Application Deadline:** August 20 **Application Fee:** $0.00 **H.S. Requirements:** High school diploma required; GED accepted **Costs Per Year:** Application fee: $0. State resident tuition: $2498 full-time, $76 per credit hour part-time. Nonresident tuition: $8580 full-time, $268 per credit hour part-time. Mandatory fees: $218 full-time, $31.75 per credit hour part-time. Full-time tuition and fees vary according to course load. Part-time tuition and fees vary according to course load. **Scholarships:** Available. **Calendar System:** Semester, Summer session available **Enrollment:** Full-time 3,983, Part-time 4,868 **Faculty:** Full-time 301, Part-time 455 **Student-Faculty Ratio:** 12:1 **Final Year or Final Semester Residency Requirement:** No **Regional Accreditation:** Southern Association of Colleges and Schools **Credit Hours For Degree:** 60 semester hours, Associates **Professional Accreditation:** ACEN, ADA, AOTA. **Intercollegiate Athletics:** Basketball M & W; Cheerleading M & W; Golf M; Soccer M & W; Volleyball W

CAROLINA CHRISTIAN COLLEGE

4209 Indiana Ave.
Winston-Salem, NC 27102-0777
Tel: (336)744-0900
Fax: (336)744-0901
E-mail: katisha.blackwell@carolina.edu
Web Site: www.carolina.edu
President/CEO: LaTanya Clayton Lucas, PhD
Admissions: Dean Katisha D. Blackwell
Financial Aid: LaTanya V. Tyson

Type: Comprehensive **Sex:** Coed **Affiliation:** nondenominational. **% Accepted:** 100 **Admission Plans:** Open Admission **Application Deadline:** Rolling **Application Fee:** $50.00 **H.S. Requirements:** High school diploma required; GED accepted **Costs Per Year:** Application fee: $50. One-time mandatory fee: $100. Tuition: $7900 full-time, $325 per credit part-time. Mandatory fees: $1050 full-time, $525 per term part-time. **Scholarships:** Available. **Calendar System:** Semester **Enrollment:** Full-time 36, Graduate full-time 8 **Faculty:** Full-time 2, Part-time 10 **Student-Faculty Ratio:** 9:1 **% Receiving Financial Aid:** 97 **Final Year or Final Semester Residency Requirement:** No **Credit Hours For Degree:** 60 semester hours, Associates; 120 semester hours, Bachelors **Professional Accreditation:** ABHE.

CAROLINA COLLEGE OF BIBLICAL STUDIES

817 S McPherson Church Rd.
Fayetteville, NC 28303
Tel: (910)323-5614
Web Site: carolinabiblecollege.org

Type: Four-Year College **Sex:** Coed **Affiliation:** Christian. **Calendar System:** Quarter **Professional Accreditation:** ABHE.

CAROLINAS COLLEGE OF HEALTH SCIENCES

PO Box 32861, 1200 Blythe Blvd.
Charlotte, NC 28232-2861
Tel: (704)355-5043
Fax: (704)355-5967
E-mail: merritt.newman@carolinascollege.edu
Web Site: www.carolinascollege.edu
President/CEO: Dr. Ellen Sheppard
Admissions: Merritt Newman
Financial Aid: Jill Powell

Type: Two-Year College **Sex:** Coed **Admission Plans:** Preferred Admission **Application Fee:** $50.00 **H.S. Requirements:** High school diploma required; GED not accepted **Costs Per Year:** Application fee: $50. State resident tuition: $13,986 full-time, $333 per credit part-time. Nonresident tuition: $13,986 full-time, $333 per credit part-time. Mandatory fees: $1270 full-time, $126 per term part-time. Full-time tuition and fees vary according to course load and program. Part-time tuition and fees vary according to course load and program. **Scholarships:** Available. **Calendar System:** Semester, Summer session available **Enrollment:** Full-time 59, Part-time 415 **Student-Faculty Ratio:** 11:1 **Exams:** ACT essay component not used; SAT I or ACT; SAT essay component not used. **Final Year or Final Semester Residency Requirement:** Yes **Regional Accreditation:** Southern Association of Colleges and Schools **Credit Hours For Degree:** 60 credit hours, Associates **Professional Accreditation:** ACEN, NAACLS.

CARTERET COMMUNITY COLLEGE

3505 Arendell St.
Morehead City, NC 28557-2989
Tel: (252)222-6000
Fax: (252)222-6274
E-mail: admissions@carteret.edu
Web Site: www.carteret.edu
President/CEO: Dr. Kerry L. Youngblood
Admissions: Margie Ward
Financial Aid: Brenda J. Long

Type: Two-Year College **Sex:** Coed **Affiliation:** North Carolina Community College System. **% Accepted:** 91 **Admission Plans:** Open Admission **Application Deadline:** Rolling **Application Fee:** $0.00 **H.S. Requirements:** High school diploma required; GED accepted **Costs Per Year:** Application fee: $0. State resident tuition: $1728 full-time, $72 per credit hour part-time. Nonresident tuition: $6336 full-time, $264 per credit hour part-time. Mandatory fees: $90 full-time, $24.25 per term part-time. **Scholarships:** Available. **Calendar System:** Semester, Summer session available **Enrollment:** Full-time 804, Part-time 1,068 **Faculty:** Full-time 66, Part-time 187 **Student-Faculty Ratio:** 9:1 **Exams:** SAT I or ACT. **Regional Accreditation:** Southern Association of Colleges and Schools **Credit Hours For Degree:** 65 semester hours, Associates **Professional Accreditation:** CoARC, JRCERT.

CATAWBA COLLEGE

2300 W Innes St.
Salisbury, NC 28144-2488
Tel: (704)637-4111; Free: 800-CATAWBA
E-mail: admissions@catawba.edu
Web Site: www.catawba.edu
President/CEO: W. Brien Lewis
Admissions: Cindy Barr
Financial Aid: Kelli Hand

Type: Comprehensive **Sex:** Coed **Affiliation:** United Church of Christ. **Scores:** 89% SAT V 400+; 92% SAT M 400+; 54.17% ACT 18-23; 24.48% ACT 24-29 **% Accepted:** 32 **Admission Plans:** Deferred Admission; Early Admission **Application Deadline:** Rolling **Application Fee:** $0.00 **H.S. Requirements:** High school diploma required; GED accepted **Costs Per Year:** Application fee: $0. Comprehensive fee: $39,820 includes full-time tuition ($29,333) and college room and board ($10,487). Full-time tuition varies according to class time, course load, and degree level. **Scholarships:** Available. **Calendar System:** Semester, Summer session available **Enrollment:** Full-time 1,203, Graduate part-time 5, Part-time 67 **Faculty:** Full-time 83, Part-time 96 **Student-Faculty Ratio:** 13:1 **Exams:** ACT essay component used for admission; SAT I or ACT; SAT essay component used for admission; SAT Reasoning; SAT Subject. **% Receiving Financial Aid:** 84 **% Residing in College-Owned, -Operated, or -Affiliated Housing:** 71 **Final Year or Final Semester Residency Requirement:** Yes **Regional Accreditation:** Southern Association of Colleges and Schools **Credit Hours For Degree:** 124 semester hours, Bachelors **ROTC:** Air Force, Army **Professional Accreditation:** ACBSP, JRCAT, NCATE. **Intercollegiate Athletics:** Baseball M; Basketball M & W; Cheerleading M & W; Cross-Country Running M & W; Football M; Golf M & W; Lacrosse M & W; Soccer M & W; Softball W; Swimming and Diving M & W; Tennis M & W; Volleyball W

CATAWBA VALLEY COMMUNITY COLLEGE

2550 Hwy. 70 SE
Hickory, NC 28602-9699

Tel: (828)327-7000
Fax: (828)327-7000
E-mail: lwegner@cvcc.edu
Web Site: www.cvcc.edu
President/CEO: Dr. Garrett D. Hinshaw
Admissions: Laurie Wegner

Type: Two-Year College **Sex:** Coed **Affiliation:** North Carolina Community College System. **% Accepted:** 89 **Admission Plans:** Open Admission **Application Deadline:** Rolling **Application Fee:** $0.00 **H.S. Requirements:** High school diploma required; GED accepted. For some certificate and diploma programs: High school diploma or equivalent not required **Costs Per Year:** Application fee: $0. State resident tuition: $2128 full-time, $76 per credit hour part-time. Nonresident tuition: $7504 full-time, $268 per contact hour part-time. Mandatory fees: $122 full-time, $61.25 per contact hour part-time, $61.25 per term part-time. Part-time tuition and fees vary according to course load. **Scholarships:** Available. **Calendar System:** Semester, Summer session available **Enrollment:** Full-time 1,870, Part-time 2,701 **Faculty:** Full-time 136, Part-time 293 **Student-Faculty Ratio:** 12:1 **Exams:** Other. **Final Year or Final Semester Residency Requirement:** No **Regional Accreditation:** Southern Association of Colleges and Schools **Credit Hours For Degree:** 60 semester hours, Associates **Professional Accreditation:** ACEN, ADA, AHIMA, CoARC, JRCEMTP. **Intercollegiate Athletics:** Baseball M; Basketball M & W; Cheerleading M & W; Volleyball W

CENTRAL CAROLINA COMMUNITY COLLEGE
1105 Kelly Dr.
Sanford, NC 27330-9000
Tel: (919)775-5401; Free: 800-682-8353
Fax: (919)775-1221
Web Site: www.cccc.edu
President/CEO: Dr. T. Eston (Bud) Marchant
Admissions: Jamie Tyson Childress

Type: Two-Year College **Sex:** Coed **Affiliation:** North Carolina Community College System. **Admission Plans:** Deferred Admission; Early Admission; Open Admission **Application Deadline:** Rolling **Application Fee:** $0.00 **H.S. Requirements:** High school diploma required; GED accepted **Scholarships:** Available. **Calendar System:** Semester, Summer session available **Enrollment:** Full-time 2,138, Part-time 2,762 **Faculty:** Full-time 370, Part-time 680 **Exams:** ACT essay component not used; Other; SAT I or ACT; SAT essay component not used. **Regional Accreditation:** Southern Association of Colleges and Schools **Credit Hours For Degree:** 64 semester hours, Associates **Intercollegiate Athletics:** Basketball M & W; Golf M; Volleyball W

CENTRAL PIEDMONT COMMUNITY COLLEGE
PO Box 35009
Charlotte, NC 28235-5009
Tel: (704)330-2722
Web Site: www.cpcc.edu
President/CEO: Dr. P. Anthony Zeiss
Admissions: Linda McComb

Type: Two-Year College **Sex:** Coed **Affiliation:** North Carolina Community College System. **% Accepted:** 100 **Admission Plans:** Open Admission **Application Deadline:** Rolling **Application Fee:** $0.00 **H.S. Requirements:** High school diploma required; GED accepted. For welding program: High school diploma required; GED not accepted **Scholarships:** Available. **Calendar System:** Semester, Summer session available **Enrollment:** Full-time 7,630, Part-time 11,734 **Faculty:** Full-time 337, Part-time 1,404 **Regional Accreditation:** Southern Association of Colleges and Schools **Credit Hours For Degree:** 64 semester hours, Associates **Professional Accreditation:** AAMAE, ABET, ACF, ADA, AHIMA, APTA, CoARC, NAACLS.

CHARLOTTE CHRISTIAN COLLEGE AND THEOLOGICAL SEMINARY
3117 Whiting Ave.
Charlotte, NC 28205
Tel: (704)334-6882
Fax: (704)334-6885
Web Site: www.charlottechristian.edu
President/CEO: Dean Eddie G. Grigg
Admissions: Paula Emrich
Financial Aid: Kenneth Neal Roach

Type: Comprehensive **Sex:** Coed **Affiliation:** Christian. **% Accepted:** 100 **Admission Plans:** Open Admission **Application Fee:** $40.00 **H.S. Requirements:** High school diploma required; GED accepted **Scholarships:** Avail-

able. **Calendar System:** Quarter, Summer session available **Enrollment:** Full-time 48, Graduate full-time 8, Graduate part-time 12, Part-time 30 **Faculty:** Full-time 6, Part-time 26 **Student-Faculty Ratio:** 6:1 **% Receiving Financial Aid:** 91 **Final Year or Final Semester Residency Requirement:** No **Credit Hours For Degree:** 66 credit hours, Associates; 128 credit hours, Bachelors **Professional Accreditation:** TRACS.

CHOWAN UNIVERSITY
One University Pl.
Murfreesboro, NC 27855
Tel: (252)398-6500; Free: 888-4-CHOWAN
Fax: (252)398-1190
E-mail: parkes@chowan.edu
Web Site: www.chowan.edu
President/CEO: Dr. M. Christopher White
Admissions: Scott Parker
Financial Aid: Sharon W. Rose

Type: Comprehensive **Sex:** Coed **Affiliation:** Baptist. **Scores:** 44% SAT V 400+; 48% SAT M 400+; 20% ACT 18-23; 3% ACT 24-29 **% Accepted:** 62 **Application Deadline:** Rolling **Application Fee:** $20.00 **H.S. Requirements:** High school diploma required; GED accepted **Costs Per Year:** Application fee: $20. Comprehensive fee: $32,080 includes full-time tuition ($23,400) and college room and board ($8680). Full-time tuition varies according to class time, course load, and program. Room and board charges vary according to board plan and housing facility. Part-time tuition: $385 per credit. Part-time tuition varies according to class time and program. **Scholarships:** Available. **Calendar System:** Semester, Summer session available **Enrollment:** Full-time 1,453, Graduate part-time 10, Part-time 69 **Faculty:** Full-time 63, Part-time 32 **Student-Faculty Ratio:** 16:1 **Exams:** SAT I or ACT; SAT Reasoning; SAT Subject. **% Receiving Financial Aid:** 94 **% Residing in College-Owned, -Operated, or -Affiliated Housing:** 83 **Final Year or Final Semester Residency Requirement:** Yes **Regional Accreditation:** Southern Association of Colleges and Schools **Credit Hours For Degree:** 120 semester hours, Bachelors **Professional Accreditation:** NASM, NCATE. **Intercollegiate Athletics:** Baseball M; Basketball M & W; Bowling W; Cheerleading M & W; Cross-Country Running M & W; Football M; Golf M & W; Lacrosse M & W; Soccer M & W; Softball W; Swimming and Diving W; Tennis M & W; Volleyball W

CLEVELAND COMMUNITY COLLEGE
137 S Post Rd.
Shelby, NC 28152
Tel: (704)669-6000
E-mail: areye@clevelandcc.edu
Web Site: www.clevelandcc.edu
President/CEO: Steve L. Thornburg
Admissions: Emily Arey

Type: Two-Year College **Sex:** Coed **Affiliation:** North Carolina Community College System. **Admission Plans:** Deferred Admission; Open Admission **Application Deadline:** Rolling **Application Fee:** $0.00 **H.S. Requirements:** High school diploma required; GED accepted **Costs Per Year:** Application fee: $0. State resident tuition: $2432 full-time. Nonresident tuition: $8572 full-time. Mandatory fees: $94 full-time. Full-time tuition and fees vary according to course load. **Scholarships:** Available. **Calendar System:** Semester, Summer session available **Enrollment:** Full-time 1,029, Part-time 1,961 **Faculty:** Full-time 76, Part-time 232 **Student-Faculty Ratio:** 10:1 **Regional Accreditation:** Southern Association of Colleges and Schools **Credit Hours For Degree:** 60 semester hours, Associates **Professional Accreditation:** JRCERT.

COASTAL CAROLINA COMMUNITY COLLEGE
444 Western Blvd.
Jacksonville, NC 28546-6899
Tel: (910)455-1221
Fax: (910)455-2767
E-mail: calihanh@coastal.cc.nc.us
Web Site: www.coastalcarolina.edu
President/CEO: Dr. Ronald K. Lingle
Admissions: Heather Calihan
Financial Aid: Christina Wallace

Type: Two-Year College **Sex:** Coed **Affiliation:** North Carolina Community College System. **% Accepted:** 62 **Admission Plans:** Deferred Admission; Open Admission **Application Deadline:** Rolling **Application Fee:** $0.00 **H.S. Requirements:** High school diploma required; GED accepted **Scholar-**

ships: Available. Calendar System: Semester, Summer session available Enrollment: Full-time 1,476, Part-time 2,873 Faculty: Full-time 140, Part-time 329 Student-Faculty Ratio: 17:1 Regional Accreditation: Southern Association of Colleges and Schools Credit Hours For Degree: 64 semester hours, Associates Professional Accreditation: ADA, ARCST, NAACLS.

COLLEGE OF THE ALBEMARLE

PO Box 2327
Elizabeth City, NC 27906-2327
Tel: (252)335-0821
Fax: (252)335-2011
Web Site: www.albemarle.edu
President/CEO: Kandi W. Deitemeyer, EdD
Admissions: Angie Godfrey-Dawson
Financial Aid: Angela Godfrey-Dawson
Type: Two-Year College Sex: Coed Affiliation: North Carolina Community College System. Scores: 52% SAT V 400+; 64% SAT M 400+ Admission Plans: Deferred Admission; Early Admission; Open Admission Application Deadline: Rolling Application Fee: $0.00 H.S. Requirements: High school diploma required; GED accepted Costs Per Year: Application fee: $0. One-time mandatory fee: $147. State resident tuition: $2064 full-time, $76 per credit hour part-time. Nonresident tuition: $7252 full-time, $268 per credit hour part-time. Full-time tuition varies according to course load, location, and program. Scholarships: Available. Calendar System: Semester, Summer session available Enrollment: Full-time 715, Part-time 1,337 Faculty: Full-time 60, Part-time 62 Regional Accreditation: Southern Association of Colleges and Schools Credit Hours For Degree: 65 semester hours, Associates Professional Accreditation: ACEN. Intercollegiate Athletics: Soccer M

CRAVEN COMMUNITY COLLEGE

800 College Ct.
New Bern, NC 28562-4984
Tel: (252)638-4131
Fax: (252)638-4649
E-mail: peterz@cravencc.edu
Web Site: www.cravencc.edu
President/CEO: Dr. Raymond Staats
Admissions: Zomar Peter
Type: Two-Year College Sex: Coed Affiliation: North Carolina Community College System. Admission Plans: Open Admission Application Deadline: Rolling H.S. Requirements: High school diploma required; GED accepted Costs Per Year: State resident tuition: $1824 full-time, $76 per credit hour part-time. Nonresident tuition: $6432 full-time, $268 per credit hour part-time. Mandatory fees: $199 full-time, $99.40 per term part-time. Full-time tuition and fees vary according to course load. Part-time tuition and fees vary according to course load. Scholarships: Available. Calendar System: Semester, Summer session available Enrollment: Full-time 1,214, Part-time 1,798 Final Year or Final Semester Residency Requirement: No Regional Accreditation: Southern Association of Colleges and Schools

DAVIDSON COLLEGE

Davidson, NC 28035
Tel: (704)894-2000; Free: 800-768-0380
Fax: (704)894-2016
E-mail: admission@davidson.edu
Web Site: www.davidson.edu
President/CEO: Dr. Carol E. Quillen
Admissions: Christopher J. Gruber
Financial Aid: David R. Gelinas
Type: Four-Year College Sex: Coed Affiliation: Presbyterian. Scores: 100% SAT V 400+; 100% SAT M 400+; 2% ACT 18-23; 36% ACT 24-29 % Accepted: 22 Admission Plans: Deferred Admission; Early Action; Early Admission Application Deadline: January 2 Application Fee: $50.00 H.S. Requirements: High school diploma required; GED not accepted Costs Per Year: Application fee: $50. Comprehensive fee: $60,119 includes full-time tuition ($46,501), mandatory fees ($465), and college room and board ($13,153). College room only: $6694. Room and board charges vary according to board plan. Scholarships: Available. Calendar System: Semester, Summer session not available Enrollment: Full-time 1,784 Faculty: Full-time 176, Part-time 9 Student-Faculty Ratio: 10:1 Exams: SAT I and SAT II or ACT; SAT I or ACT; SAT Reasoning; SAT Subject. % Receiving Financial Aid: 52 % Residing in College-Owned, -Operated, or -Affiliated Hous-

ing: 94 Final Year or Final Semester Residency Requirement: No Regional Accreditation: Southern Association of Colleges and Schools Credit Hours For Degree: 32 courses, Bachelors ROTC: Air Force, Army Intercollegiate Athletics: Baseball M; Basketball M & W; Crew M & W; Cross-Country Running M & W; Fencing M & W; Field Hockey W; Football M; Golf M; Lacrosse W; Rugby M; Sailing M & W; Soccer M & W; Swimming and Diving M & W; Tennis M & W; Track and Field M & W; Ultimate Frisbee M & W; Volleyball W; Weight Lifting M & W; Wrestling M

DAVIDSON COUNTY COMMUNITY COLLEGE

PO Box 1287
Lexington, NC 27293-1287
Tel: (336)249-8186
Fax: (336)249-0379
E-mail: admissions@davidsonccc.edu
Web Site: www.davidsonccc.edu
President/CEO: Mary E. Rittling
Type: Two-Year College Sex: Coed Affiliation: North Carolina Community College System. Admission Plans: Deferred Admission; Early Admission; Open Admission Application Deadline: Rolling Application Fee: $0.00 H.S. Requirements: High school diploma or equivalent not required Scholarships: Available. Calendar System: Semester, Summer session available Student-Faculty Ratio: 20:1 Regional Accreditation: Southern Association of Colleges and Schools Credit Hours For Degree: 64 semester hours, Associates Professional Accreditation: ABET, ACEN, AHIMA, NAACLS. Intercollegiate Athletics: Basketball M; Volleyball W

DEVRY UNIVERSITY

2015 Ayrsley Town Blvd., Ste. 109
Charlotte, NC 28273-4068
Tel: (704)362-2345; Free: 866-338-7941
Fax: (704)362-2668
Web Site: www.devry.edu
Type: Comprehensive Sex: Coed Affiliation: DeVry University. Application Deadline: Rolling Costs Per Year: Tuition: $17,052 full-time, $609 per credit hour part-time. Mandatory fees: $80 full-time, $40 per term part-time. Scholarships: Available. Calendar System: Semester % Receiving Financial Aid: 78 Regional Accreditation: North Central Association of Colleges and Schools Professional Accreditation: ACBSP.

DUKE UNIVERSITY

Durham, NC 27708-0586
Tel: (919)684-8111
Fax: (919)681-8941
E-mail: askduke@admiss.duke.edu
Web Site: www.duke.edu
President/CEO: Dr. Richard Brodhead
Admissions: Christoph Guttentag
Financial Aid: Alison Rabil
Type: University Sex: Coed Affiliation: United Methodist Church. % Accepted: 13 Admission Plans: Deferred Admission; Early Action; Early Admission; Preferred Admission H.S. Requirements: High school diploma required; GED not accepted Scholarships: Available. Calendar System: Semester, Summer session available Enrollment: Full-time 6,631, Graduate full-time 8,293, Graduate part-time 438, Part-time 24 Faculty: Full-time 1,189, Part-time 146 Student-Faculty Ratio: 7:1 Exams: ACT essay component used for admission; SAT I and SAT II or ACT; SAT essay component used for admission. % Receiving Financial Aid: 43 % Residing in College-Owned, -Operated, or -Affiliated Housing: 81 Final Year or Final Semester Residency Requirement: No Regional Accreditation: Southern Association of Colleges and Schools Credit Hours For Degree: 34 courses, Bachelors ROTC: Air Force, Army, Navy Professional Accreditation: AACN, AACSB, AALS, AANA, ABA, ABET, ACIPE, APA, APTA, ATS, CAHME, LCME/AMA, NCATE, SAF. Intercollegiate Athletics: Badminton M & W; Baseball M; Basketball M & W; Crew M & W; Cross-Country Running M & W; Equestrian Sports M & W; Fencing M & W; Field Hockey M & W; Football M & W; Golf M & W; Ice Hockey M & W; Lacrosse M & W; Racquetball M & W; Rugby M & W; Sailing M & W; Skiing (Cross-Country) M & W; Skiing (Downhill) M & W; Soccer M & W; Softball M & W; Squash M & W; Swimming and Diving M & W; Table Tennis M & W; Tennis M & W; Track and Field M & W; Ultimate Frisbee M & W; Volleyball M & W; Water Polo M & W; Wrestling M

DURHAM TECHNICAL COMMUNITY COLLEGE
1637 Lawson St.
Durham, NC 27703-5023
Tel: (919)686-3300
Web Site: www.durhamtech.edu
President/CEO: William G. Ingram
Admissions: Penny Augustine
Type: Two-Year College **Sex:** Coed **Affiliation:** North Carolina Community College System. **Admission Plans:** Deferred Admission; Open Admission **Application Deadline:** Rolling **Application Fee:** $0.00 **H.S. Requirements:** High school diploma required; GED accepted **Scholarships:** Available. **Calendar System:** Semester, Summer session available **Regional Accreditation:** Southern Association of Colleges and Schools **Credit Hours For Degree:** 64 credit hours, Associates **Professional Accreditation:** ACEN, ADA, AOTA, COA, CoARC.

EAST CAROLINA UNIVERSITY
E 5th St.
Greenville, NC 27858-4353
Tel: (252)328-6131
Fax: (252)328-6495
E-mail: admis@ecu.edu
Web Site: www.ecu.edu
President/CEO: Dr. Steve C. Ballard
Financial Aid: Julie Poorman
Type: University **Sex:** Coed **Affiliation:** University of North Carolina System. **Scores:** 98% SAT V 400+; 98% SAT M 400+; 68.32% ACT 18-23; 25.65% ACT 24-29 **% Accepted:** 69 **Admission Plans:** Deferred Admission; Preferred Admission **Application Deadline:** March 1 **Application Fee:** $70.00 **H.S. Requirements:** High school diploma required; GED accepted **Costs Per Year:** Application fee: $70. State resident tuition: $4157 full-time, $173 per credit hour part-time. Nonresident tuition: $19,731 full-time, $822 per credit hour part-time. Mandatory fees: $2423 full-time. Full-time tuition and fees vary according to location. Part-time tuition varies according to course load and location. College room and board: $8984. College room only: $5060. Room and board charges vary according to board plan and housing facility. **Scholarships:** Available. **Calendar System:** Semester, Summer session available **Enrollment:** Full-time 19,336, Graduate full-time 2,505, Graduate part-time 2,745, Part-time 3,703 **Faculty:** Full-time 1,199, Part-time 262 **Student-Faculty Ratio:** 18:1 **Exams:** ACT essay component not used; SAT I or ACT; SAT II; SAT essay component not used; SAT Reasoning; SAT Subject. **% Receiving Financial Aid:** 59 **% Residing in College-Owned, -Operated, or -Affiliated Housing:** 26 **Final Year or Final Semester Residency Requirement:** No **Regional Accreditation:** Southern Association of Colleges and Schools **Credit Hours For Degree:** 120 semester hours, Bachelors **ROTC:** Air Force, Army **Professional Accreditation:** AACN, AACSB, AAFCS, AAMFT, AANA, ABET, ACCE, ACEN, ACNM, ACSP, ADA, AHIMA, AND, AOTA, APTA, ASHA, ATMAE, CIDA, CORE, CSWE, JRCAT, LCME/AMA, NAACLS, NASAD, NASM, NASPAA, NCATE, NRPA. **Intercollegiate Athletics:** Baseball M; Basketball M & W; Cross-Country Running M & W; Football M; Golf M & W; Soccer W; Softball W; Swimming and Diving M & W; Tennis M & W; Track and Field M & W; Volleyball W

ECPI UNIVERSITY (CHARLOTTE)
4800 Airport Ctr. Pky.
Charlotte, NC 28208
Tel: (704)751-4558; Free: 844-611-0624
Fax: (704)399-9144
Web Site: www.ecpi.edu
Type: Two-Year College **Sex:** Coed **Regional Accreditation:** Southern Association of Colleges and Schools

ECPI UNIVERSITY (GREENSBORO)
7802 Airport Ctr. Dr.
Greensboro, NC 27409
Tel: (336)792-7594; Free: 844-611-0702
Fax: (336)664-0801
Web Site: www.ecpi.edu
Type: Two-Year College **Sex:** Coed **Regional Accreditation:** Southern Association of Colleges and Schools

ECPI UNIVERSITY (RALEIGH)
4101 Doie Cope Rd.
Raleigh, NC 27613

Tel: (919)283-5748; Free: 844-611-0718
Fax: (919)571-0780
E-mail: swells@ecpi.edu
Web Site: www.ecpi.edu
Admissions: Susan Wells
Type: Four-Year College **Sex:** Coed **Application Deadline:** Rolling **H.S. Requirements:** High school diploma required; GED accepted **Calendar System:** Trimester, Summer session not available **Student-Faculty Ratio:** 13:1 **Exams:** SAT I; SAT I or ACT; SAT II. **Regional Accreditation:** Southern Association of Colleges and Schools **Credit Hours For Degree:** 65 credits, Associates **Professional Accreditation:** ACCSC.

EDGECOMBE COMMUNITY COLLEGE
2009 W Wilson St.
Tarboro, NC 27886-9399
Tel: (252)823-5166
Fax: (252)823-6817
Web Site: www.edgecombe.edu
President/CEO: Deborah L. Lamm
Admissions: Jackie Heath
Financial Aid: Barbara Manning
Type: Two-Year College **Sex:** Coed **Affiliation:** North Carolina Community College System. **Admission Plans:** Open Admission **Application Deadline:** Rolling **Application Fee:** $0.00 **H.S. Requirements:** High school diploma required; GED accepted **Scholarships:** Available. **Calendar System:** Semester, Summer session available **Regional Accreditation:** Southern Association of Colleges and Schools **Credit Hours For Degree:** 64 semester hours, Associates **Professional Accreditation:** AHIMA, CoARC, JRCERT.

ELIZABETH CITY STATE UNIVERSITY
1704 Weeksville Rd.
Elizabeth City, NC 27909-7806
Tel: (252)335-3400; Free: 800-347-3278
Fax: (252)335-3731
E-mail: ddeure@ecsu.edu
Web Site: www.ecsu.edu
President/CEO: Dr. Thomas Conway
Admissions: Darius Eure
Financial Aid: Jill Gable
Type: Comprehensive **Sex:** Coed **Affiliation:** University of North Carolina System. **Scores:** 63% SAT V 400+; 71% SAT M 400+; 31% ACT 18-23; 2% ACT 24-29 **% Accepted:** 70 **Admission Plans:** Deferred Admission; Preferred Admission **Application Fee:** $30.00 **H.S. Requirements:** High school diploma required; GED accepted **Costs Per Year:** Application fee: $30. State resident tuition: $2,820 full-time, $352 per credit hour part-time. Nonresident tuition: $15,173 full-time, $1,896.69 per credit hour part-time. Mandatory fees: $1,837 full-time, $229.73 per term part-time. College room and board: $7,642. College room only: $4,643. Room and board charges vary according to housing facility. **Scholarships:** Available. **Calendar System:** Semester, Summer session available **Enrollment:** Full-time 1,405, Graduate full-time 1, Graduate part-time 49, Part-time 130 **Faculty:** Full-time 107, Part-time 6 **Student-Faculty Ratio:** 15:1 **Exams:** ACT essay component used for placement; SAT I or ACT; SAT essay component used for placement; SAT Reasoning. **% Receiving Financial Aid:** 67 **% Residing in College-Owned, -Operated, or -Affiliated Housing:** 58 **Regional Accreditation:** Southern Association of Colleges and Schools **Credit Hours For Degree:** 124 credit hours, Bachelors **ROTC:** Army **Professional Accreditation:** AACSB, ATMAE, NASM, NCATE. **Intercollegiate Athletics:** Baseball M; Basketball M & W; Bowling W; Cheerleading W; Cross-Country Running M & W; Football M; Golf M; Softball W; Tennis W; Volleyball W

ELON UNIVERSITY
2700 Campus Box
Elon, NC 27244-2010
Tel: (336)278-2000; Free: 800-334-8448
Fax: (336)538-3986
E-mail: admissions@elon.edu
Web Site: www.elon.edu
President/CEO: Dr. Leo M. Lambert
Admissions: Melinda Wood
Financial Aid: Dr. Patrick Murphy
Type: Comprehensive **Sex:** Coed **Affiliation:** United Church of Christ. **Scores:** 100% SAT V 400+; 100% SAT M 400+; 15% ACT 18-23; 60% ACT

24-29 **% Accepted:** 57 **Admission Plans:** Deferred Admission; Early Action; Early Admission; Early Decision Plan **Application Deadline:** January 10 **Application Fee:** $50.00 **H.S. Requirements:** High school diploma required; GED accepted **Costs Per Year:** Application fee: $50. Comprehensive fee: $43,170 includes full-time tuition ($31,773), mandatory fees ($399), and college room and board ($10,998). College room only: $5399. Room and board charges vary according to board plan and housing facility. **Scholarships:** Available. **Calendar System:** Semester, Summer session available **Enrollment:** Full-time 5,735, Graduate full-time 631, Graduate part-time 97, Part-time 168 **Faculty:** Full-time 424, Part-time 161 **Student-Faculty Ratio:** 12:1 **Exams:** ACT essay component not used; SAT I or ACT; SAT essay component not used. **% Receiving Financial Aid:** 31 **% Residing in College-Owned, -Operated, or -Affiliated Housing:** 62 **Regional Accreditation:** Southern Association of Colleges and Schools **Credit Hours For Degree:** 132 semester hours, Bachelors **ROTC:** Air Force, Army **Professional Accreditation:** AACSB, ABA, APTA, JRCAT, NCATE. **Intercollegiate Athletics:** Baseball M; Basketball M & W; Cheerleading M & W; Cross-Country Running M & W; Equestrian Sports M & W; Field Hockey W; Football M; Golf M & W; Ice Hockey M; Lacrosse M & W; Rock Climbing M; Rugby M & W; Soccer M & W; Softball W; Swimming and Diving M & W; Tennis M & W; Track and Field W; Triathlon M & W; Ultimate Frisbee M & W; Volleyball M & W

FAYETTEVILLE STATE UNIVERSITY

1200 Murchison Rd.
Fayetteville, NC 28301-4298
Tel: (910)672-1111; Free: 800-222-2594
Fax: (910)672-1769
E-mail: admissions@uncfsu.edu
Web Site: www.uncfsu.edu
President/CEO: Dr. James A. Anderson
Admissions: Ulisa E. Bowles
Financial Aid: Keith Townsend

Type: Comprehensive **Sex:** Coed **Affiliation:** University of North Carolina System. **Scores:** 70% SAT V 400+; 76% SAT M 400+ **% Accepted:** 61 **Admission Plans:** Deferred Admission; Early Action; Early Admission; Early Decision Plan **Application Deadline:** June 30 **Application Fee:** $40.00 **H.S. Requirements:** High school diploma required; GED accepted **Costs Per Year:** Application fee: $40. State resident tuition: $2833 full-time. Nonresident tuition: $14,441 full-time. Full-time tuition varies according to course level, course load, degree level, location, and program. College room and board: $6987. College room only: $3779. Room and board charges vary according to board plan and housing facility. **Scholarships:** Available. **Calendar System:** Semester, Summer session available **Enrollment:** Full-time 4,055, Graduate full-time 319, Graduate part-time 279, Part-time 1,451 **Faculty:** Full-time 255, Part-time 87 **Student-Faculty Ratio:** 17:1 **Exams:** SAT I or ACT; SAT Reasoning. **% Receiving Financial Aid:** 85 **% Residing in College-Owned, -Operated, or -Affiliated Housing:** 17 **Regional Accreditation:** Southern Association of Colleges and Schools **Credit Hours For Degree:** 60 credit hours, Associates; 120 credit hours, Bachelors **ROTC:** Air Force, Army **Professional Accreditation:** AACN, AACSB, ABET, CSWE, NASM, NCATE. **Intercollegiate Athletics:** Basketball M & W; Bowling W; Cross-Country Running M & W; Football M; Golf M & W; Softball W; Tennis M & W; Track and Field M & W; Volleyball W

FAYETTEVILLE TECHNICAL COMMUNITY COLLEGE

2201 Hull Rd.
Fayetteville, NC 28303-0236
Tel: (910)678-8400
Fax: (910)678-8407
E-mail: castleml@faytechcc.edu
Web Site: www.faytechcc.edu
President/CEO: Dr. J. Larry Keen
Admissions: Dr. Louanna Castleman

Type: Two-Year College **Sex:** Coed **Affiliation:** North Carolina Community College System. **Scores:** 75% SAT V 400+; 63% SAT M 400+; 50% ACT 18-23; 50% ACT 24-29 **% Accepted:** 100 **Admission Plans:** Deferred Admission; Open Admission **Application Deadline:** Rolling **Application Fee:** $0.00 **H.S. Requirements:** High school diploma required; GED accepted **Costs Per Year:** Application fee: $0. One-time mandatory fee: $25. State resident tuition: $2304 full-time, $72 per credit hour part-time. Nonresident tuition: $8448 full-time, $264 per credit hour part-time. Mandatory fees: $90 full-time, $45 per term part-time. Full-time tuition and fees vary according to course load. Part-time tuition and fees vary according to course

load. **Scholarships:** Available. **Calendar System:** Semester, Summer session available **Enrollment:** Full-time 4,509, Part-time 7,037 **Faculty:** Full-time 274, Part-time 282 **Student-Faculty Ratio:** 19:1 **Exams:** ACT essay component not used; SAT essay component not used. **Final Year or Final Semester Residency Requirement:** No **Regional Accreditation:** Southern Association of Colleges and Schools **Credit Hours For Degree:** 60 semester hours, Associates **Professional Accreditation:** ABET, ABFSE, ACEN, ADA, APTA, CoARC, JRCERT.

FORSYTH TECHNICAL COMMUNITY COLLEGE

2100 Silas Creek Pky.
Winston-Salem, NC 27103-5197
Tel: (336)723-0371
Fax: (336)761-2098
E-mail: admissions@forsythtech.edu
Web Site: www.forsythtech.edu
President/CEO: Dr. Gary Green

Type: Two-Year College **Sex:** Coed **Affiliation:** North Carolina Community College System. **Costs Per Year:** State resident tuition: $1824 full-time, $72 per credit hour part-time. Nonresident tuition: $6432 full-time, $264 per credit hour part-time. Mandatory fees: $150 full-time, $75 per term part-time. Full-time tuition and fees vary according to course load. Part-time tuition and fees vary according to course load. **Scholarships:** Available. **Calendar System:** Semester, Summer session available **Enrollment:** Full-time 3,726, Part-time 5,422 **Student-Faculty Ratio:** 13:1 **Exams:** ACT essay component not used; Other; SAT essay component not used. **Final Year or Final Semester Residency Requirement:** No **Regional Accreditation:** Southern Association of Colleges and Schools **Professional Accreditation:** AAMAE, ABET, ADA, CoARC, JRCEDMS, JRCERT, JRCNMT.

GARDNER-WEBB UNIVERSITY

110 S Main St.
Boiling Springs, NC 28017
Tel: (704)406-2361; Free: 800-253-6472
Fax: (704)434-4488
E-mail: admissions@gardner-webb.edu
Web Site: www.gardner-webb.edu
President/CEO: Dr. A. Frank Bonner
Admissions: Gretchen Tucker
Financial Aid: Summer Nance

Type: University **Sex:** Coed **Affiliation:** Baptist. **Scores:** 85% SAT V 400+; 91% SAT M 400+; 52% ACT 18-23; 25% ACT 24-29 **% Accepted:** 53 **Application Deadline:** Rolling **Application Fee:** $40.00 **H.S. Requirements:** High school diploma required; GED accepted **Costs Per Year:** Application fee: $40. Comprehensive fee: $39,390 includes full-time tuition ($29,420), mandatory fees ($190), and college room and board ($9780). College room only: $4950. Room and board charges vary according to board plan. Part-time tuition: $488 per credit hour. **Scholarships:** Available. **Calendar System:** Semester, Summer session available **Enrollment:** Full-time 2,096, Graduate full-time 222, Graduate part-time 1,468, Part-time 519 **Faculty:** Full-time 165, Part-time 135 **Student-Faculty Ratio:** 13:1 **Exams:** SAT I or ACT; SAT essay component used for advising; SAT essay component used for placement; SAT Reasoning. **% Receiving Financial Aid:** 80 **% Residing in College-Owned, -Operated, or -Affiliated Housing:** 51 **Final Year or Final Semester Residency Requirement:** No **Regional Accreditation:** Southern Association of Colleges and Schools **Credit Hours For Degree:** 72 semester hours, Associates; 120 semester hours, Bachelors **ROTC:** Air Force, Army **Professional Accreditation:** ACA, ACBSP, ACEN, ACIPE, ATS, NASM, NCATE. **Intercollegiate Athletics:** Baseball M; Basketball M & W; Cheerleading M & W; Cross-Country Running M & W; Football M; Golf M & W; Soccer M & W; Softball W; Swimming and Diving M & W; Tennis M & W; Track and Field M & W; Volleyball W; Wrestling M

GASTON COLLEGE

201 Hwy. 321 S
Dallas, NC 28034-1499
Tel: (704)922-6200
Web Site: www.gaston.edu
President/CEO: Dr. Patricia Skinner
Admissions: Terry Basier

Type: Two-Year College **Sex:** Coed **Affiliation:** North Carolina Community College System. **Admission Plans:** Open Admission **Application Deadline:** Rolling **Application Fee:** $0.00 **H.S. Requirements:** High school diploma required; GED accepted. For vocational programs: High school diploma or equivalent not required **Scholarships:** Available. **Calendar System:** Semester, Summer session available **Student-Faculty Ratio:** 15:1 **Exams:** Other; SAT I and SAT II or ACT. **Regional Accreditation:** Southern Association of Colleges and Schools **Credit Hours For Degree:** 64 semester hours, Associates **Professional Accreditation:** AAMAE, ABET, ACBSP.

GRACE COLLEGE OF DIVINITY

5117 Cliffdale Rd.
Fayetteville, NC 28314
Tel: (910)221-2224
Web Site: www.gcdivinity.org
Type: Four-Year College **Sex:** Coed **Affiliation:** Christian. **Calendar System:** Semester **Professional Accreditation:** ABHE.

GREENSBORO COLLEGE

815 W Market St.
Greensboro, NC 27401-1875
Tel: (336)272-7102; Free: 800-346-8226
Fax: (336)271-6634
E-mail: admissions@greensborocollege.edu
Web Site: www.greensboro.edu
President/CEO: Dr. Larry D. Czarda
Admissions: Colleen Murphy
Financial Aid: Lindsay Latham
Type: Comprehensive **Sex:** Coed **Affiliation:** United Methodist. **Scores:** 88% SAT V 400+; 90% SAT M 400+ **% Accepted:** 41 **Admission Plans:** Deferred Admission; Early Admission; Early Decision Plan **Application Deadline:** Rolling **Application Fee:** $35.00 **H.S. Requirements:** High school diploma required; GED accepted **Costs Per Year:** Application fee: $35. Comprehensive fee: $37,000 includes full-time tuition ($26,300), mandatory fees ($600), and college room and board ($10,100). College room only: $5000. Full-time tuition and fees vary according to degree level and program. Room and board charges vary according to housing facility. Part-time tuition: $725 per credit hour. Part-time tuition varies according to course load, degree level, and program. **Scholarships:** Available. **Calendar System:** Semester, Summer session available **Enrollment:** Full-time 867, Graduate full-time 45, Graduate part-time 32, Part-time 250 **Faculty:** Full-time 62, Part-time 34 **Student-Faculty Ratio:** 13:1 **Exams:** SAT I or ACT. **% Receiving Financial Aid:** 92 **% Residing in College-Owned, -Operated, or -Affiliated Housing:** 73 **Final Year or Final Semester Residency Requirement:** Yes **Regional Accreditation:** Southern Association of Colleges and Schools **Credit Hours For Degree:** 124 semester hours, Bachelors **ROTC:** Air Force, Army **Professional Accreditation:** ACBSP, NASM, NCATE. **Intercollegiate Athletics:** Baseball M; Basketball M & W; Cheerleading M & W; Football M; Golf M & W; Lacrosse M & W; Soccer M & W; Softball W; Swimming and Diving M & W; Tennis M & W; Volleyball W; Wrestling M

GUILFORD COLLEGE

5800 W Friendly Ave.
Greensboro, NC 27410-4173
Tel: (336)316-2000; Free: 800-992-7759
Fax: (336)316-2954
E-mail: admission@guilford.edu
Web Site: www.guilford.edu
President/CEO: Dr. Jane K. Fernandes
Admissions: Arlene Cash
Financial Aid: Brian DeYoung
Type: Four-Year College **Sex:** Coed **Affiliation:** Society of Friends. **Scores:** 90% SAT V 400+; 94% SAT M 400+; 45.2% ACT 18-23; 36.36% ACT 24-29 **% Accepted:** 63 **Admission Plans:** Deferred Admission; Early Admission; Preferred Admission **Application Deadline:** February 15 **Application Fee:** $25.00 **H.S. Requirements:** High school diploma required; GED accepted **Costs Per Year:** Application fee: $25. Comprehensive fee: $43,650 includes full-time tuition ($33,710), mandatory fees ($380), and college room and board ($9560). Room and board charges vary according to board plan and housing facility. Part-time tuition: $1032 per credit hour. Part-time mandatory fees: $205 per term. Part-time tuition and fees vary according to course load. **Scholarships:** Available. **Calendar System:** 4-1-4, Summer session available **Enrollment:** Full-time 1,554, Part-time 363 **Faculty:** Full-time 104, Part-time 48 **Student-Faculty Ratio:** 14:1 **Exams:** SAT I or ACT; SAT Reasoning. **% Receiving Financial Aid:** 71 **% Residing in College-Owned, -Operated, or -Affiliated Housing:** 72 **Final Year or Final**

Semester Residency Requirement: Yes **Regional Accreditation:** Southern Association of Colleges and Schools **Credit Hours For Degree:** 128 credits, Bachelors **Professional Accreditation:** ACBSP. **Intercollegiate Athletics:** Baseball M; Basketball M & W; Cross-Country Running M & W; Football M; Golf M; Lacrosse M & W; Soccer M & W; Softball W; Swimming and Diving W; Tennis M & W; Volleyball W

GUILFORD TECHNICAL COMMUNITY COLLEGE

PO Box 309
Jamestown, NC 27282-0309
Tel: (336)334-4822
E-mail: jlcross@gtcc.edu
Web Site: www.gtcc.edu
President/CEO: Dr. Randy Parker
Admissions: Jesse L. Cross
Financial Aid: Lisa Koretoff
Type: Two-Year College **Sex:** Coed **Affiliation:** North Carolina Community College System. **% Accepted:** 100 **Admission Plans:** Deferred Admission; Early Admission; Open Admission **Application Deadline:** Rolling **Application Fee:** $0.00 **H.S. Requirements:** High school diploma required; GED accepted. For Career and College Promise: Dual- Enrollment program for High School students. A diploma is not required however, entry standards apply: High school diploma or equivalent not required **Scholarships:** Available. **Calendar System:** Semester, Summer session available **Enrollment:** Full-time 5,783, Part-time 6,647 **Faculty:** Full-time 314, Part-time 79 **Student-Faculty Ratio:** 20:1 **Final Year or Final Semester Residency Requirement:** Yes **Regional Accreditation:** Southern Association of Colleges and Schools **Credit Hours For Degree:** 64 semester hours, Associates **ROTC:** Air Force, Army **Professional Accreditation:** AAMAE, ACF, ADA, APTA. **Intercollegiate Athletics:** Baseball M; Basketball M & W; Cheerleading M & W; Volleyball W

HALIFAX COMMUNITY COLLEGE

PO Drawer 809
Weldon, NC 27890-0809
Tel: (252)536-2551
Fax: (252)536-4144
E-mail: jwashington660@halifaxcc.edu
Web Site: www.halifaxcc.edu
President/CEO: Dr. Ervin V. Griffin, Sr.
Admissions: James Washington
Type: Two-Year College **Sex:** Coed **Affiliation:** North Carolina Community College System. **Costs Per Year:** State resident tuition: $76 per credit hour part-time. Nonresident tuition: $268 per credit hour part-time. Part-time tuition varies according to course load. **Scholarships:** Available. **Calendar System:** Semester, Summer session available **Enrollment:** Full-time 666, Part-time 488 **Faculty:** Full-time 64, Part-time 120 **Student-Faculty Ratio:** 11:1 **Regional Accreditation:** Southern Association of Colleges and Schools **Credit Hours For Degree:** 60-65 semester hours, Associates **Professional Accreditation:** ADA, NAACLS.

HARRISON COLLEGE

2001 Carrington Mill Blvd.
Morrisville, NC 27560
Tel: (919)246-9394
E-mail: admissions@harrison.edu
Web Site: www.harrison.edu
President/CEO: Jason Konesco
Admissions: Jason Howanec
Type: Two-Year College **Sex:** Coed **Affiliation:** Harrison College. **% Accepted:** 100 **Application Deadline:** Rolling **Application Fee:** $0.00 **H.S. Requirements:** High school diploma required; GED accepted **Enrollment:** Full-time 159, Part-time 41 **Faculty:** Full-time 5, Part-time 9 **Student-Faculty Ratio:** 14:1 **Exams:** Other. **Final Year or Final Semester Residency Requirement:** No **Regional Accreditation:** North Central Association of Colleges and Schools

HAYWOOD COMMUNITY COLLEGE

185 Freedlander Dr.
Clyde, NC 28721-9453
Tel: (828)627-2821
Fax: (828)627-4513
E-mail: enrollment@haywood.edu
Web Site: www.haywood.edu

President/CEO: Dr. Barbara Parker
Type: Two-Year College **Sex:** Coed **Affiliation:** North Carolina Community College System. **Admission Plans:** Open Admission **Application Deadline:** Rolling **Application Fee:** $0.00 **H.S. Requirements:** High school diploma required; GED accepted **Scholarships:** Available. **Calendar System:** Semester, Summer session available **Final Year or Final Semester Residency Requirement:** No **Regional Accreditation:** Southern Association of Colleges and Schools **Credit Hours For Degree:** 65 semester hours, Associates **Professional Accreditation:** AAMAE.

HERITAGE BIBLE COLLEGE

PO Box 1628
Dunn, NC 28335-1628
Tel: (910)892-3178; Free: 800-297-6351
Fax: (910)892-1809
E-mail: pparker@heritagebiblecollege.edu
Web Site: www.heritagebiblecollege.edu
President/CEO: Dr. Elvin Butts
Admissions: Peggy Parker
Financial Aid: Kayla Sutton-Collier
Type: Four-Year College **Sex:** Coed **Affiliation:** Pentecostal Free Will Baptist. **% Accepted:** 100 **Admission Plans:** Open Admission **Application Deadline:** Rolling **Application Fee:** $25.00 **H.S. Requirements:** High school diploma required; GED accepted **Costs Per Year:** Application fee: $25. Tuition: $7200 full-time, $300 per credit hour part-time. Mandatory fees: $768 full-time, $32 per credit hour part-time. Full-time tuition and fees vary according to course load and program. Part-time tuition and fees vary according to course load and program. College room only: $3100. **Scholarships:** Available. **Calendar System:** Semester, Summer session available **Enrollment:** Full-time 34, Part-time 35 **Faculty:** Full-time 4, Part-time 14 **Student-Faculty Ratio:** 20:1 **% Receiving Financial Aid:** 93 **% Residing in College-Owned, -Operated, or -Affiliated Housing:** 13 **Final Year or Final Semester Residency Requirement:** No **Credit Hours For Degree:** 69 credit hours, Associates; 129 credit hours, Bachelors **Professional Accreditation:** TRACS.

HIGH POINT UNIVERSITY

One University Pky.
High Point, NC 27268
Tel: (336)841-9000; Free: 800-345-6993
Fax: (336)841-5123
E-mail: kramsay@highpoint.edu
Web Site: www.highpoint.edu
President/CEO: Dr. Nido Qubein
Admissions: Kerr Ramsay
Financial Aid: Ron Elmore
Type: Comprehensive **Sex:** Coed **Affiliation:** United Methodist. **Scores:** 99% SAT V 400+; 100% SAT M 400+; 46% ACT 18-23; 44% ACT 24-29 **% Accepted:** 72 **Admission Plans:** Deferred Admission; Early Action; Early Decision Plan **Application Deadline:** March 1 **Application Fee:** $50.00 **H.S. Requirements:** High school diploma required; GED accepted **Costs Per Year:** Application fee: $50. Comprehensive fee: $45,977 includes full-time tuition ($29,450), mandatory fees ($3955), and college room and board ($12,572). Full-time tuition and fees vary according to course load and reciprocity agreements. Room and board charges vary according to board plan and housing facility. **Scholarships:** Available. **Calendar System:** Semester, Summer session available **Enrollment:** Full-time 4,323, Graduate full-time 154, Graduate part-time 48, Part-time 48 **Faculty:** Full-time 276, Part-time 145 **Student-Faculty Ratio:** 13:1 **Exams:** SAT I or ACT; SAT Reasoning. **% Receiving Financial Aid:** 63 **% Residing in College-Owned, -Operated, or -Affiliated Housing:** 94 **Final Year or Final Semester Residency Requirement:** No **Regional Accreditation:** Southern Association of Colleges and Schools **Credit Hours For Degree:** 128 semester hours, Bachelors **ROTC:** Air Force, Army **Professional Accreditation:** JRCAT, NCATE. **Intercollegiate Athletics:** Baseball M; Basketball M & W; Cheerleading W; Cross-Country Running M & W; Golf M & W; Lacrosse M & W; Soccer M & W; Track and Field M & W; Volleyball W

ISOTHERMAL COMMUNITY COLLEGE

PO Box 804
Spindale, NC 28160-0804
Tel: (828)286-3636
Fax: (828)286-8109
E-mail: vsearcy@isothermal.edu

Web Site: www.isothermal.edu
President/CEO: Myra B. Johnson
Admissions: Vickie Searcy
Type: Two-Year College **Sex:** Coed **Affiliation:** North Carolina Community College System. **Admission Plans:** Deferred Admission; Early Admission; Open Admission **Application Deadline:** Rolling **Application Fee:** $0.00 **H.S. Requirements:** High school diploma required; GED accepted **Scholarships:** Available. **Calendar System:** Semester, Summer session available **Enrollment:** Full-time 988, Part-time 1,017 **Faculty:** Full-time 60, Part-time 54 **Student-Faculty Ratio:** 17:1 **Regional Accreditation:** Southern Association of Colleges and Schools **Credit Hours For Degree:** 64 semester hours, Associates

JAMES SPRUNT COMMUNITY COLLEGE

PO Box 398
Kenansville, NC 28349-0398
Tel: (910)296-2400
Fax: (910)296-1222
E-mail: wedwards@jamessprunt.edu
Web Site: www.jamessprunt.edu
President/CEO: Dr. Lawrence Rouse
Admissions: Wanda Edwards
Type: Two-Year College **Sex:** Coed **Affiliation:** North Carolina Community College System. **% Accepted:** 99 **Admission Plans:** Open Admission **Application Deadline:** Rolling **Application Fee:** $0.00 **H.S. Requirements:** High school diploma required; GED accepted **Costs Per Year:** Application fee: $0. State resident tuition: $2432 full-time, $76 per semester hour part-time. Nonresident tuition: $8576 full-time, $268 per semester hour part-time. Mandatory fees: $70 full-time, $35 per term part-time. Full-time tuition and fees vary according to course load. Part-time tuition and fees vary according to course load. **Scholarships:** Available. **Calendar System:** Semester, Summer session available **Enrollment:** Full-time 484, Part-time 711 **Faculty:** Full-time 31, Part-time 34 **Student-Faculty Ratio:** 15:1 **Regional Accreditation:** Southern Association of Colleges and Schools **Credit Hours For Degree:** 61 semester hours, Associates **Professional Accreditation:** AAMAE.

JOHN WESLEY UNIVERSITY

1215 Eastchester Dr.
High Point, NC 27265
Tel: (336)887-3000; Free: 855-528-7358
Fax: (336)889-2261
Web Site: www.johnwesley.edu
President/CEO: Dr. Stephen Condon
Admissions: Faith Cochran
Financial Aid: Shirley P. Carter
Type: Comprehensive **Sex:** Coed **Affiliation:** interdenominational. **% Accepted:** 26 **Admission Plans:** Deferred Admission; Early Admission **Application Deadline:** August 1 **Application Fee:** $20.00 **H.S. Requirements:** High school diploma required; GED accepted **Scholarships:** Available. **Calendar System:** Semester, Summer session available **Enrollment:** Full-time 102, Graduate full-time 10, Graduate part-time 23, Part-time 23 **Faculty:** Full-time 4, Part-time 15 **Student-Faculty Ratio:** 15:1 **Exams:** SAT I or ACT; SAT essay component used for admission; SAT Reasoning. **% Residing in College-Owned, -Operated, or -Affiliated Housing:** 30 **Final Year or Final Semester Residency Requirement:** No **Credit Hours For Degree:** 60 credit hours, Associates; 120 credit hours, Bachelors **Professional Accreditation:** ABHE. **Intercollegiate Athletics:** Soccer M & W; Softball W; Volleyball W

JOHNSON C. SMITH UNIVERSITY

100 Beatties Ford Rd.
Charlotte, NC 28216-5398
Tel: (704)378-1000; Free: 800-782-7303
E-mail: jburrell@jcsu.edu
Web Site: www.jcsu.edu
President/CEO: Dr. Ronald L. Carter
Admissions: James Burrell
Financial Aid: Shelline Warren
Type: Comprehensive **Sex:** Coed **Scores:** 48% SAT V 400+; 49% SAT M 400+; 25% ACT 18-23; 4% ACT 24-29 **% Accepted:** 46 **Admission Plans:** Deferred Admission; Early Admission **Application Fee:** $25.00 **H.S. Requirements:** High school diploma required; GED accepted **Costs Per Year:** Application fee: $25. Comprehensive fee: $25,336 includes full-time

tuition ($18,236) and college room and board ($7100). College room only: $4086. Full-time tuition varies according to course load. Room and board charges vary according to board plan and housing facility. Part-time tuition: $418 per credit hour. Part-time tuition varies according to course load. **Scholarships:** Available. **Calendar System:** Semester, Summer session available **Enrollment:** Full-time 1,322, Graduate full-time 63, Part-time 53 **Faculty:** Full-time 92, Part-time 68 **Student-Faculty Ratio:** 12:1 **Exams:** ACT essay component not used; SAT I or ACT; SAT essay component not used. **% Receiving Financial Aid:** 79 **% Residing in College-Owned, -Operated, or -Affiliated Housing:** 65 **Final Year or Final Semester Residency Requirement:** No **Regional Accreditation:** Southern Association of Colleges and Schools **Credit Hours For Degree:** 122 semester hours, Bachelors **Professional Accreditation:** ACBSP, CSWE, NCATE. **Intercollegiate Athletics:** Basketball M & W; Bowling W; Cheerleading W; Cross-Country Running M & W; Football M; Golf M; Softball W; Tennis M & W; Track and Field M & W; Volleyball W

JOHNSON & WALES UNIVERSITY
801 W Trade St.
Charlotte, NC 28202
Tel: (980)598-1000; Free: 866-598-2427
E-mail: clt@admissions.jwu.edu
Web Site: www.jwu.edu/charlotte
President/CEO: Arthur J. Gallagher
Admissions: Joseph Campos
Financial Aid: Lynn Robinson

Type: Four-Year College **Sex:** Coed **Scores:** 82% SAT V 400+; 76% SAT M 400+ **% Accepted:** 69 **Admission Plans:** Deferred Admission; Early Admission **Application Fee:** $0.00 **H.S. Requirements:** High school diploma required; GED accepted **Costs Per Year:** Application fee: $0. Tuition: $29,226 full-time, $196 per credit hour part-time. Mandatory fees: $350 full-time. **Scholarships:** Available. **Calendar System:** Quarter **Enrollment:** Full-time 2,207, Part-time 48 **Faculty:** Full-time 90, Part-time 30 **Student-Faculty Ratio:** 22:1 **Exams:** SAT I or ACT. **% Receiving Financial Aid:** 85 **% Residing in College-Owned, -Operated, or -Affiliated Housing:** 56 **Regional Accreditation:** New England Association of Schools and Colleges **ROTC:** Army

JOHNSTON COMMUNITY COLLEGE
PO Box 2350
Smithfield, NC 27577-2350
Tel: (919)934-3051
Fax: (919)934-2150
E-mail: pjharrell@johnstoncc.edu
Web Site: www.johnstoncc.edu
President/CEO: Dr. David N. Johnson
Admissions: Dr. Pamela J. Harrell

Type: Two-Year College **Sex:** Coed **Affiliation:** North Carolina Community College System. **Admission Plans:** Open Admission **Application Deadline:** Rolling **Application Fee:** $0.00 **H.S. Requirements:** High school diploma required; GED accepted **Costs Per Year:** Application fee: $0. State resident tuition: $2432 full-time, $76 per credit part-time. Nonresident tuition: $8576 full-time, $268 per credit part-time. Mandatory fees: $97 full-time. **Scholarships:** Available. **Calendar System:** Semester, Summer session available **Enrollment:** Full-time 1,726, Part-time 2,243 **Exams:** Other; SAT I or ACT. **Regional Accreditation:** Southern Association of Colleges and Schools **Credit Hours For Degree:** 60 credit hours, Associates **Professional Accreditation:** JRCERT. **Intercollegiate Athletics:** Golf M & W

KING'S COLLEGE
322 Lamar Ave.
Charlotte, NC 28204-2436
Tel: (704)372-0266; Free: 800-768-2255
Fax: (704)348-2029
Web Site: www.kingscollegecharlotte.edu
President/CEO: Barbara Rockecharlie

Type: Two-Year College **Sex:** Coed **% Accepted:** 77 **Calendar System:** Semester **Professional Accreditation:** ACICS.

LEES-MCRAE COLLEGE
PO Box 128
Banner Elk, NC 28604
Tel: (828)898-5241; Free: 800-280-4562
Fax: (828)898-8814

E-mail: admissions@lmc.edu
Web Site: www.lmc.edu
President/CEO: Dr. Barry M. Buxton
Admissions: Candace Silver
Financial Aid: Cathy Shell

Type: Four-Year College **Sex:** Coed **Affiliation:** Presbyterian Church (U.S. A.). **Scores:** 82% SAT V 400+; 85% SAT M 400+; 56.07% ACT 18-23; 19. 63% ACT 24-29 **% Accepted:** 62 **Admission Plans:** Early Decision Plan **Application Deadline:** Rolling **Application Fee:** $35.00 **H.S. Requirements:** High school diploma required; GED accepted **Costs Per Year:** Application fee: $35. Comprehensive fee: $34,950 includes full-time tuition ($24,154), mandatory fees ($700), and college room and board ($10,096). College room only: $4896. Full-time tuition and fees vary according to course load, location, and reciprocity agreements. Room and board charges vary according to housing facility. Part-time tuition: $670 per credit hour. Part-time tuition varies according to course load, location, and reciprocity agreements. **Scholarships:** Available. **Calendar System:** Semester, Summer session available **Enrollment:** Full-time 930, Part-time 10 **Faculty:** Full-time 48, Part-time 44 **Student-Faculty Ratio:** 15:1 **Exams:** Other; SAT I or ACT. **% Receiving Financial Aid:** 85 **% Residing in College-Owned, -Operated, or -Affiliated Housing:** 64 **Final Year or Final Semester Residency Requirement:** No **Regional Accreditation:** Southern Association of Colleges and Schools **Professional Accreditation:** AACN. **Intercollegiate Athletics:** Basketball M & W; Cross-Country Running M & W; Lacrosse M & W; Soccer M & W; Softball W; Tennis M & W; Track and Field M & W; Volleyball M & W

LENOIR COMMUNITY COLLEGE
231 Hwy. 58 S
Kinston, NC 28502-0188
Tel: (252)527-6223
E-mail: krhill01@lenoircc.edu
Web Site: www.lenoircc.edu
President/CEO: Dr. Brantley Briley
Admissions: Kim Hill

Type: Two-Year College **Sex:** Coed **Affiliation:** North Carolina Community College System. **% Accepted:** 65 **Admission Plans:** Early Admission; Open Admission **Application Deadline:** Rolling **H.S. Requirements:** High school diploma required; GED accepted **Costs Per Year:** State resident tuition: $2280 full-time, $76 per credit part-time. Nonresident tuition: $8040 full-time, $268 per credit part-time. Mandatory fees: $119 full-time. Full-time tuition and fees vary according to course load. Part-time tuition varies according to course load. **Scholarships:** Available. **Calendar System:** Semester, Summer session available **Enrollment:** Full-time 1,069, Part-time 1,688 **Faculty:** Full-time 93, Part-time 42 **Student-Faculty Ratio:** 15:1 **Exams:** SAT I or ACT. **Final Year or Final Semester Residency Requirement:** No **Regional Accreditation:** Southern Association of Colleges and Schools **Credit Hours For Degree:** 60 semester hours, Associates **Professional Accreditation:** AAMAE, ACF. **Intercollegiate Athletics:** Baseball M; Basketball M & W; Volleyball W

LENOIR-RHYNE UNIVERSITY
625 7th Ave. NE
Hickory, NC 28601
Tel: (828)328-1741; Free: 800-277-5721
Fax: (828)328-7338
E-mail: admission@lr.edu
Web Site: www.lr.edu
President/CEO: Dr. Wayne B. Powell
Admissions: Nathanael R. Summers
Financial Aid: Nick Jenkins

Type: Comprehensive **Sex:** Coed **Affiliation:** Lutheran. **Scores:** 87% SAT V 400+; 85% SAT M 400+ **% Accepted:** 84 **Admission Plans:** Deferred Admission; Early Admission; Early Decision Plan **Application Deadline:** Rolling **Application Fee:** $35.00 **H.S. Requirements:** High school diploma required; GED accepted **Costs Per Year:** Application fee: $35. Comprehensive fee: $45,330 includes full-time tuition ($33,730) and college room and board ($11,600). Room and board charges vary according to board plan. Part-time tuition: $1395 per credit. Part-time tuition varies according to class time. **Scholarships:** Available. **Calendar System:** Semester, Summer session available **Enrollment:** Full-time 1,378, Graduate full-time 348, Graduate part-time 368, Part-time 209 **Faculty:** Full-time 126, Part-time 143 **Student-Faculty Ratio:** 12:1 **Exams:** SAT I or ACT; SAT Reasoning. **% Receiving Financial Aid:** 88 **% Residing in College-Owned, -Operated, or

-**Affiliated Housing:** 51 **Regional Accreditation:** Southern Association of Colleges and Schools **Credit Hours For Degree:** 128 credit hours, Bachelors **Professional Accreditation:** AACN, ACBSP, AOTA, ATS, JRCAT, NCATE. **Intercollegiate Athletics:** Baseball M; Basketball M & W; Cheerleading M & W; Cross-Country Running M & W; Football M; Golf M & W; Lacrosse M & W; Soccer M & W; Softball W; Swimming and Diving M & W; Tennis M & W; Track and Field M & W; Volleyball W

LIVING ARTS COLLEGE

3000 Wakefield Crossing Dr.
Raleigh, NC 27614
Tel: (919)488-8500; Free: 800-288-7442
E-mail: jwenta@living-arts-college.edu
Web Site: www.living-arts-college.edu
President/CEO: Debra A. Hooper
Admissions: Julie Wenta

Type: Two-Year College **Sex:** Coed **% Accepted:** 100 **Admission Plans:** Deferred Admission; Early Action; Early Admission; Early Decision Plan **Application Deadline:** Rolling **Application Fee:** $25.00 **H.S. Requirements:** High school diploma required; GED accepted **Costs Per Year:** Application fee: $25. Tuition: $84,960 per degree program. Tuition guaranteed not to increase for student's term of enrollment. **Calendar System:** Quarter, Summer session available **Faculty:** Full-time 37, Part-time 16 **Student-Faculty Ratio:** 10:1 **Exams:** Other. **% Residing in College-Owned, -Operated, or -Affiliated Housing:** 35 **Final Year or Final Semester Residency Requirement:** No **Credit Hours For Degree:** 180 credits, Bachelors **Professional Accreditation:** ACICS, COE.

LIVINGSTONE COLLEGE

701 W Monroe St.
Salisbury, NC 28144-5298
Tel: (704)216-6000; Free: 800-835-3435
Fax: (704)216-6217
E-mail: admissions@livingstone.edu
Web Site: www.livingstone.edu
President/CEO: Dr. Jimmy R. Jenkins, Jr.
Admissions: Tony Baldwin
Financial Aid: Terry Jefferies

Type: Four-Year College **Sex:** Coed **Affiliation:** African Methodist Episcopal Zion Church. **Scores:** 54% SAT M 400+; 17.24% ACT 18-23; 3.45% ACT 24-29 **% Accepted:** 72 **Admission Plans:** Deferred Admission **Application Deadline:** Rolling **Application Fee:** $25.00 **H.S. Requirements:** High school diploma required; GED accepted **Scholarships:** Available. **Calendar System:** Semester, Summer session not available **Enrollment:** Full-time 1,164, Part-time 11 **Faculty:** Full-time 51, Part-time 22 **Student-Faculty Ratio:** 15:1 **Exams:** SAT I or ACT. **% Residing in College-Owned, -Operated, or -Affiliated Housing:** 60 **Regional Accreditation:** Southern Association of Colleges and Schools **Credit Hours For Degree:** 125 semester hours, Bachelors **ROTC:** Army **Professional Accreditation:** CSWE, NCATE. **Intercollegiate Athletics:** Basketball M & W; Bowling W; Cross-Country Running M & W; Football M; Softball W; Tennis W; Track and Field M & W; Volleyball W

LOUISBURG COLLEGE

501 N Main St.
Louisburg, NC 27549-2399
Tel: (919)496-2521; Free: 800-775-0208
Fax: (919)496-1788
E-mail: admissions@louisburg.edu
Web Site: www.louisburg.edu
President/CEO: Mark D. LaBranche
Admissions: Stephanie Tolbert

Type: Two-Year College **Sex:** Coed **Affiliation:** United Methodist. **Scores:** 47% SAT V 400+; 54% SAT M 400+; 12% ACT 18-23; 1% ACT 24-29 **% Accepted:** 62 **Admission Plans:** Deferred Admission **Application Deadline:** Rolling **Application Fee:** $25.00 **H.S. Requirements:** High school diploma required; GED accepted **Scholarships:** Available. **Calendar System:** Semester, Summer session not available **Enrollment:** Full-time 717, Part-time 13 **Faculty:** Full-time 45, Part-time 38 **Student-Faculty Ratio:** 13:1 **Exams:** SAT I or ACT. **% Residing in College-Owned, -Operated, or -Affiliated Housing:** 90 **Regional Accreditation:** Southern Association of Colleges and Schools **Credit Hours For Degree:** 64 semester hours, Associates **Intercollegiate Athletics:** Baseball M; Basketball M & W; Golf M & W; Soccer M & W; Softball W; Volleyball M & W

MARS HILL UNIVERSITY

PO Box 370
Mars Hill, NC 28754
Tel: (828)689-1307; Free: 866-648-4968
Fax: (828)689-1474
E-mail: admissions@mhu.edu
Web Site: www.mhu.edu
President/CEO: Dr. Dan Lunsford
Admissions: Kristie Vance
Financial Aid: Amanda Randolph

Type: Comprehensive **Sex:** Coed **Affiliation:** Baptist. **Scores:** 80% SAT V 400+; 85% SAT M 400+; 53% ACT 18-23; 15% ACT 24-29 **% Accepted:** 61 **Admission Plans:** Deferred Admission; Early Admission **Application Deadline:** Rolling **Application Fee:** $25.00 **H.S. Requirements:** High school diploma required; GED accepted **Costs Per Year:** Application fee: $25. Comprehensive fee: $38,306 includes full-time tuition ($26,132), mandatory fees ($3250), and college room and board ($8924). Room and board charges vary according to housing facility. Part-time tuition: $925 per credit hour. Part-time mandatory fees: $138 per credit hour. Part-time tuition and fees vary according to course load. **Scholarships:** Available. **Calendar System:** Semester, Summer session available **Enrollment:** Full-time 1,284, Graduate full-time 15, Part-time 111 **Faculty:** Full-time 91, Part-time 56 **Student-Faculty Ratio:** 12:1 **Exams:** ACT essay component not used; SAT I or ACT; SAT essay component not used. **% Receiving Financial Aid:** 42 **% Residing in College-Owned, -Operated, or -Affiliated Housing:** 69 **Final Year or Final Semester Residency Requirement:** No **Regional Accreditation:** Southern Association of Colleges and Schools **Credit Hours For Degree:** 128 credits, Bachelors **Professional Accreditation:** CSWE, JRCAT, NASM, NAST, NCATE. **Intercollegiate Athletics:** Baseball M; Basketball M & W; Cheerleading M & W; Cross-Country Running M & W; Football M; Golf M & W; Lacrosse M; Soccer M & W; Softball W; Swimming and Diving M & W; Tennis M & W; Track and Field M & W; Volleyball W

MARTIN COMMUNITY COLLEGE

1161 Kehukee Park Rd.
Williamston, NC 27892
Tel: (252)792-1521
Fax: (252)792-4425
Web Site: www.martincc.edu
President/CEO: Dr. Ann R. Britt
Admissions: Dr. Brian Busch

Type: Two-Year College **Sex:** Coed **Affiliation:** North Carolina Community College System. **Admission Plans:** Open Admission **Application Deadline:** Rolling **Application Fee:** $0.00 **H.S. Requirements:** High school diploma required; GED accepted **Scholarships:** Available. **Calendar System:** Semester, Summer session available **Final Year or Final Semester Residency Requirement:** No **Regional Accreditation:** Southern Association of Colleges and Schools **Credit Hours For Degree:** 64 semester hours, Associates **Professional Accreditation:** AAMAE, ADA, APTA.

MAYLAND COMMUNITY COLLEGE

PO Box 547
Spruce Pine, NC 28777-0547
Tel: (828)765-7351; Free: 800-462-9526
Fax: (828)765-0728
Web Site: www.mayland.edu
President/CEO: Dr. John Boyd
Admissions: Cathy Morrison

Type: Two-Year College **Sex:** Coed **Affiliation:** North Carolina Community College System. **Admission Plans:** Deferred Admission; Open Admission **Application Deadline:** Rolling **Application Fee:** $0.00 **H.S. Requirements:** High school diploma required; GED accepted **Scholarships:** Available. **Calendar System:** Semester, Summer session available **Exams:** Other. **Regional Accreditation:** Southern Association of Colleges and Schools **Credit Hours For Degree:** 65 credits, Associates **Intercollegiate Athletics:** Basketball M; Volleyball W

MCDOWELL TECHNICAL COMMUNITY COLLEGE

54 College Dr.
Marion, NC 28752-9724
Tel: (828)652-6021
Fax: (828)652-1014
E-mail: rickw@mcdowelltech.edu

Web Site: www.mcdowelltech.edu
President/CEO: Dr. Bryan Wilson
Admissions: Rick L. Wilson
Type: Two-Year College **Sex:** Coed **Affiliation:** North Carolina Community College System. **Admission Plans:** Deferred Admission; Early Admission; Open Admission **Application Deadline:** Rolling **Application Fee:** $0.00 **H.S. Requirements:** High school diploma required; GED accepted **Scholarships:** Available. **Calendar System:** Semester, Summer session available **Faculty:** Full-time 40, Part-time 18 **Regional Accreditation:** Southern Association of Colleges and Schools **Credit Hours For Degree:** 64 credit hours, Associates **Intercollegiate Athletics:** Tennis M

MEREDITH COLLEGE
3800 Hillsborough St.
Raleigh, NC 27607-5298
Tel: (919)760-8600; Free: 800-MEREDITH
Fax: (919)829-2348
E-mail: admissions@meredith.edu
Web Site: www.meredith.edu
President/CEO: Dr. Jo Allen
Admissions: Shery Boyles
Financial Aid: Kevin Michaelsen
Type: Comprehensive **Scores:** 94% SAT V 400+; 96% SAT M 400+; 44% ACT 18-23; 30% ACT 24-29 **% Accepted:** 60 **Admission Plans:** Deferred Admission; Early Action; Early Admission **Application Deadline:** February 15 **Application Fee:** $40.00 **H.S. Requirements:** High school diploma required; GED not accepted **Costs Per Year:** Application fee: $40. Comprehensive fee: $43,770 includes full-time tuition ($33,630), mandatory fees ($100), and college room and board ($10,040). Full-time tuition and fees vary according to course load. Room and board charges vary according to board plan and housing facility. Part-time tuition: $835 per credit hour. Part-time mandatory fees: $100 per year. Part-time tuition and fees vary according to course load. **Scholarships:** Available. **Calendar System:** Semester, Summer session available **Enrollment:** Full-time 1,616, Graduate full-time 60, Graduate part-time 210, Part-time 63 **Faculty:** Full-time 126, Part-time 87 **Student-Faculty Ratio:** 12:1 **Exams:** SAT I or ACT; SAT II. **% Receiving Financial Aid:** 75 **% Residing in College-Owned, -Operated, or -Affiliated Housing:** 58 **Final Year or Final Semester Residency Requirement:** No **Regional Accreditation:** Southern Association of Colleges and Schools **Credit Hours For Degree:** 124 semester hours, Bachelors **ROTC:** Air Force, Army **Professional Accreditation:** AACSB, AAFCS, AND, CIDA, CSWE, NASM, NCATE. **Intercollegiate Athletics:** Basketball W; Cross-Country Running W; Lacrosse W; Soccer W; Softball W; Tennis W; Track and Field W; Volleyball W

METHODIST UNIVERSITY
5400 Ramsey St.
Fayetteville, NC 28311-1498
Tel: (910)630-7000; Free: 800-488-7110
Fax: (910)630-7317
E-mail: admissions@methodist.edu
Web Site: www.methodist.edu
President/CEO: Dr. M. Elton Hendricks
Admissions: Jamie Legg
Financial Aid: Bonnie Adamson
Type: Comprehensive **Sex:** Coed **Affiliation:** United Methodist. **Scores:** 89% SAT V 400+; 94% SAT M 400+; 62% ACT 18-23; 18% ACT 24-29 **% Accepted:** 63 **Admission Plans:** Deferred Admission **Application Deadline:** Rolling **Application Fee:** $25.00 **H.S. Requirements:** High school diploma required; GED accepted **Scholarships:** Available. **Calendar System:** Semester, Summer session available **Enrollment:** Full-time 1,930, Graduate full-time 137, Graduate part-time 62, Part-time 287 **Faculty:** Full-time 127, Part-time 86 **Student-Faculty Ratio:** 12:1 **Exams:** SAT I or ACT. **% Receiving Financial Aid:** 79 **% Residing in College-Owned, -Operated, or -Affiliated Housing:** 57 **Regional Accreditation:** Southern Association of Colleges and Schools **Credit Hours For Degree:** 62 semester hours, Associates; 124 semester hours, Bachelors **ROTC:** Air Force, Army **Professional Accreditation:** ACBSP, CSWE, JRCAT, NCATE. **Intercollegiate Athletics:** Baseball M; Basketball M & W; Cheerleading M & W; Cross-Country Running M & W; Football M; Golf M & W; Ice Hockey M; Lacrosse M & W; Soccer M & W; Softball W; Tennis M & W; Track and Field M & W; Volleyball W

MID-ATLANTIC CHRISTIAN UNIVERSITY
715 N Poindexter St.
Elizabeth City, NC 27909-4054

Tel: (252)334-2070; Free: 866-996-MACU
Fax: (252)334-2071
E-mail: marty.riley@macuniversity.edu
Web Site: www.macuniversity.edu
President/CEO: Dr. D. Clay Perkins
Admissions: Marty Riley
Financial Aid: Jenny Rowland
Type: Four-Year College **Sex:** Coed **Affiliation:** Christian. **Scores:** 81% SAT V 400+; 74% SAT M 400+; 58% ACT 18-23 **% Accepted:** 36 **Admission Plans:** Deferred Admission; Early Admission **Application Deadline:** August 1 **Application Fee:** $50.00 **H.S. Requirements:** High school diploma required; GED accepted **Costs Per Year:** Application fee: $50. Comprehensive fee: $21,800 includes full-time tuition ($13,600) and college room and board ($8200). Full-time tuition varies according to program. Room and board charges vary according to housing facility. Part-time tuition: $425 per credit. Part-time tuition varies according to program. **Scholarships:** Available. **Calendar System:** Semester, Summer session available **Enrollment:** Full-time 175, Part-time 30 **Faculty:** Full-time 9, Part-time 29 **Student-Faculty Ratio:** 11:1 **Exams:** ACT essay component used for placement; SAT I or ACT; SAT essay component used for placement. **% Receiving Financial Aid:** 89 **% Residing in College-Owned, -Operated, or -Affiliated Housing:** 63 **Final Year or Final Semester Residency Requirement:** No **Regional Accreditation:** Southern Association of Colleges and Schools **Credit Hours For Degree:** 64 semester hours, Associates; 120 semester hours, Bachelors **ROTC:** Army **Intercollegiate Athletics:** Basketball M & W; Golf M; Soccer M; Volleyball W

MILLER-MOTTE COLLEGE (CARY)
2205 Walnut St.
Cary, NC 27518
Web Site: www.miller-motte.edu
Type: Two-Year College **Sex:** Coed **Professional Accreditation:** ACICS.

MILLER-MOTTE COLLEGE (FAYETTEVILLE)
3725 Ramsey St., Ste. 103A
Fayetteville, NC 28311
Tel: (910)354-1900
Web Site: www.miller-motte.edu
Type: Two-Year College **Sex:** Coed **Professional Accreditation:** ACICS.

MILLER-MOTTE COLLEGE (GREENVILLE)
1021 WH Smith Blvd., Ste. 102
Greenville, NC 27834
Tel: (252)215-2000
Web Site: www.miller-motte.edu
Type: Two-Year College **Sex:** Coed **Professional Accreditation:** ACICS.

MILLER-MOTTE COLLEGE (JACKSONVILLE)
1291 Hargett St.
Jacksonville, NC 28540
Tel: (910)478-4300; Free: 866-297-0267
Web Site: www.miller-motte.edu
Type: Two-Year College **Sex:** Coed **Professional Accreditation:** ACICS.

MILLER-MOTTE COLLEGE (RALEIGH)
3901 Capital Blvd., Ste. 151
Raleigh, NC 27604-6072
Tel: (919)723-2820
Web Site: www.miller-motte.edu
Type: Two-Year College **Sex:** Coed **Professional Accreditation:** ACICS.

MILLER-MOTTE COLLEGE (WILMINGTON)
5000 Market St.
Wilmington, NC 28405
Tel: (910)392-4660; Free: 800-784-2110
Fax: (910)799-6224
Web Site: www.miller-motte.edu
Type: Two-Year College **Sex:** Coed **% Accepted:** 50 **Application Fee:** $35.00 **Calendar System:** Quarter **Professional Accreditation:** AAMAE, ACICS, ARCST.

MITCHELL COMMUNITY COLLEGE
500 W Broad St.
Statesville, NC 28677

Tel: (704)878-3200
Fax: (704)878-0872
Web Site: www.mitchellcc.edu
President/CEO: Dr. James Timothy Brewer
Admissions: Dan Manning

Type: Two-Year College **Sex:** Coed **Affiliation:** North Carolina Community College System. **Admission Plans:** Open Admission **Application Deadline:** Rolling **Application Fee:** $0.00 **H.S. Requirements:** High school diploma required; GED accepted **Costs Per Year:** Application fee: $0. State resident tuition: $76 per credit hour part-time. Nonresident tuition: $268 per credit hour part-time. Mandatory fees: $1 per credit hour part-time, $17.50 per term part-time. Part-time tuition and fees vary according to course load. **Scholarships:** Available. **Calendar System:** Semester, Summer session available **Enrollment:** Full-time 1,150, Part-time 1,874 **Final Year or Final Semester Residency Requirement:** No **Regional Accreditation:** Southern Association of Colleges and Schools **Credit Hours For Degree:** 64 semester hours, Associates **ROTC:** Army **Professional Accreditation:** AAMAE, ACEN.

MONTGOMERY COMMUNITY COLLEGE

1011 Page St.
Troy, NC 27371
Tel: (910)576-6222
E-mail: housleyt@montgomery.edu
Web Site: www.montgomery.edu
President/CEO: Dr. Chad A. Bledsoe
Admissions: Tavia Housley

Type: Two-Year College **Sex:** Coed **Affiliation:** North Carolina Community College System. **Admission Plans:** Deferred Admission; Early Admission; Open Admission **Application Deadline:** Rolling **Application Fee:** $0.00 **H.S. Requirements:** High school diploma required; GED accepted **Costs Per Year:** Application fee: $0. State resident tuition: $2432 full-time, $76 per credit hour part-time. Nonresident tuition: $8576 full-time, $268 per credit hour part-time. Mandatory fees: $105 full-time, $52.60 per term part-time. Full-time tuition and fees vary according to course load. Part-time tuition and fees vary according to course load. **Scholarships:** Available. **Calendar System:** Semester, Summer session available **Enrollment:** Full-time 277, Part-time 541 **Faculty:** Full-time 36, Part-time 77 **Student-Faculty Ratio:** 7:1 **Final Year or Final Semester Residency Requirement:** Yes **Regional Accreditation:** Southern Association of Colleges and Schools **Credit Hours For Degree:** 60 semester hours, Associates **Professional Accreditation:** AAMAE.

MONTREAT COLLEGE

PO Box 1267
Montreat, NC 28757-1267
Tel: (828)669-8012; Free: 800-622-6968
Fax: (828)669-0120
E-mail: admissions@montreat.edu
Web Site: www.montreat.edu
President/CEO: Joe Kirkland
Admissions: Mandi Pike
Financial Aid: MacKenzie May

Type: Comprehensive **Sex:** Coed **Affiliation:** Presbyterian Church (U.S.A.). **Scores:** 60.8% ACT 18-23; 21.5% ACT 24-29 **% Accepted:** 54 **Admission Plans:** Deferred Admission; Early Admission **Application Fee:** $0.00 **H.S. Requirements:** High school diploma required; GED accepted **Costs Per Year:** Application fee: $0. Comprehensive fee: $32,506 includes full-time tuition ($24,040), mandatory fees ($200), and college room and board ($8,266). College room only: $4096. Full-time tuition and fees vary according to course load and degree level. Room and board charges vary according to board plan and housing facility. Part-time tuition: $620 per credit hour. Part-time tuition varies according to course load and degree level. **Scholarships:** Available. **Calendar System:** Semester, Summer session available **Enrollment:** Full-time 506, Graduate full-time 7, Graduate part-time 193, Part-time 302 **Faculty:** Full-time 31, Part-time 119 **Student-Faculty Ratio:** 12:1 **Exams:** ACT essay component not used; SAT I or ACT; SAT essay component not used; SAT Reasoning; SAT Subject. **% Receiving Financial Aid:** 81 **% Residing in College-Owned, -Operated, or -Affiliated Housing:** 80 **Regional Accreditation:** Southern Association of Colleges and Schools **Credit Hours For Degree:** 60 semester hours, Associates; 126 semester hours, Bachelors **Professional Accreditation:** NCATE. **Intercollegiate Athletics:** Baseball M; Basketball M & W; Cross-Country Running M & W; Golf M; Soccer M & W; Softball W; Tennis M & W; Track and Field M & W; Volleyball W

NASH COMMUNITY COLLEGE

522 N Old Carriage Rd.
Rocky Mount, NC 27804
Tel: (252)443-4011
Fax: (252)443-0828
E-mail: dgardner@nashcc.edu
Web Site: www.nashcc.edu
President/CEO: William S. Carver, II
Admissions: Dorothy Gardner

Type: Two-Year College **Sex:** Coed **Affiliation:** North Carolina Community College System. **Admission Plans:** Deferred Admission; Open Admission **Application Deadline:** Rolling **Application Fee:** $0.00 **H.S. Requirements:** High school diploma required; GED accepted **Scholarships:** Available. **Calendar System:** Semester, Summer session available **Exams:** Other; SAT I and SAT II or ACT; SAT I or ACT. **Regional Accreditation:** Southern Association of Colleges and Schools **Credit Hours For Degree:** 65 semester hours, Associates **Professional Accreditation:** APTA.

NORTH CAROLINA AGRICULTURAL AND TECHNICAL STATE UNIVERSITY

1601 E Market St.
Greensboro, NC 27411
Tel: (336)334-7500
Fax: (336)334-7082
E-mail: uadmit@ncat.edu
Web Site: www.ncat.edu
President/CEO: Dr. Harold L. Martin
Admissions: Cheryl Pollard-Burns
Financial Aid: Sherri Avent

Type: University **Sex:** Coed **Affiliation:** University of North Carolina System. **Scores:** 86% SAT V 400+; 90% SAT M 400+; 52.48% ACT 18-23; 8.39% ACT 24-29 **% Accepted:** 58 **Admission Plans:** Deferred Admission; Early Admission **Application Deadline:** Rolling **Application Fee:** $55.00 **H.S. Requirements:** High school diploma required; GED accepted **Costs Per Year:** Application fee: $55. State resident tuition: $3270 full-time. Nonresident tuition: $16,030 full-time. Mandatory fees: $2,265 full-time. Full-time tuition and fees vary according to course load, degree level, and program. College room and board: $6755. College room only: $6755. Room and board charges vary according to board plan and housing facility. **Scholarships:** Available. **Calendar System:** Semester, Summer session available **Enrollment:** Full-time 8,423, Graduate full-time 898, Graduate part-time 624, Part-time 780 **Faculty:** Full-time 515, Part-time 195 **Student-Faculty Ratio:** 16:1 **Exams:** SAT I or ACT; SAT Reasoning; SAT Subject. **% Receiving Financial Aid:** 79 **% Residing in College-Owned, -Operated, or -Affiliated Housing:** 41 **Final Year or Final Semester Residency Requirement:** Yes **Regional Accreditation:** Southern Association of Colleges and Schools **Credit Hours For Degree:** 124 semester hours, Bachelors **ROTC:** Air Force, Army **Professional Accreditation:** AACSB, AAFCS, ABET, ACA, ACCE, ACEN, ASLA, ATMAE, CSWE, NASM, NAST, NCATE. **Intercollegiate Athletics:** Baseball M; Basketball M & W; Bowling W; Cross-Country Running M & W; Football M; Softball W; Swimming and Diving W; Tennis W; Track and Field M & W; Volleyball W

NORTH CAROLINA CENTRAL UNIVERSITY

1801 Fayetteville St.
Durham, NC 27707-3129
Tel: (919)560-6100; Free: 877-667-7533
E-mail: admissions@nccu.edu
Web Site: www.nccu.edu
Admissions: Anthony Brooks
Financial Aid: Sharon J. Oliver

Type: Comprehensive **Sex:** Coed **Affiliation:** University of North Carolina System. **Scores:** 77% SAT V 400+; 79% SAT M 400+; 41% ACT 18-23; 7% ACT 24-29 **% Accepted:** 66 **Admission Plans:** Deferred Admission; Preferred Admission **Application Deadline:** August 1 **Application Fee:** $40.00 **H.S. Requirements:** High school diploma required; GED accepted **Costs Per Year:** Application fee: $40. State resident tuition: $3555 full-time, $444.38 per credit hour part-time. Nonresident tuition: $15,593 full-time, $1,949.13 per credit hour part-time. Mandatory fees: $2200 full-time, $1,129 per credit hour part-time. Part-time tuition and fees vary according to course load. College room and board: $8165. Room and board charges vary according to board plan, housing facility, and location. **Scholarships:** Available. **Calendar System:** Semester, Summer session available **Enrollment:** Full-time 5,247, Graduate full-time 1,275, Graduate part-time 568, Part-time

921 **Faculty:** Full-time 391, Part-time 162 **Student-Faculty Ratio:** 16:1 **Exams:** SAT I or ACT; SAT Reasoning; SAT Subject. **% Receiving Financial Aid:** 91 **% Residing in College-Owned, -Operated, or -Affiliated Housing:** 40 **Final Year or Final Semester Residency Requirement:** No **Regional Accreditation:** Southern Association of Colleges and Schools **Credit Hours For Degree:** 124 semester hours, Bachelors **ROTC:** Air Force, Army **Professional Accreditation:** AACSB, AAFCS, ABA, ACA, ACBSP, ACEN, ALA, AND, ASHA, CSWE, NASPAA, NAST, NCATE, NRPA. **Intercollegiate Athletics:** Baseball M; Basketball M & W; Bowling W; Cross-Country Running M & W; Football M; Golf M; Softball W; Tennis M & W; Track and Field M & W; Volleyball W

NORTH CAROLINA STATE UNIVERSITY

Raleigh, NC 27695
Tel: (919)515-2011
Fax: (919)515-5039
E-mail: undergrad-admissions@ncsu.edu
Web Site: www.ncsu.edu
President/CEO: Dr. Randy Woodson
Admissions: Thomas Griffin
Financial Aid: Krista Ringler
Type: University **Sex:** Coed **Affiliation:** University of North Carolina System. **Scores:** 100% SAT V 400+; 100% SAT M 400+; 3.29% ACT 18-23; 57.59% ACT 24-29 **% Accepted:** 50 **Admission Plans:** Deferred Admission; Early Decision Plan; Preferred Admission **Application Deadline:** January 15 **Application Fee:** $80.00 **H.S. Requirements:** High school diploma required; GED accepted **Costs Per Year:** Application fee: $80. State resident tuition: $6407 full-time. Nonresident tuition: $23,926 full-time. Mandatory fees: $2473 full-time. Full-time tuition and fees vary according to degree level, location, program, and reciprocity agreements. College room and board: $10,635. College room only: $6560. Room and board charges vary according to board plan and housing facility. **Scholarships:** Available. **Calendar System:** Semester, Summer session available **Enrollment:** Full-time 21,023, Graduate full-time 5,744, Graduate part-time 4,160, Part-time 3,088 **Faculty:** Full-time 1,706, Part-time 328 **Student-Faculty Ratio:** 15:1 **Exams:** ACT essay component used for admission; SAT I or ACT; SAT II; SAT essay component used for admission; SAT Reasoning. **% Receiving Financial Aid:** 47 **% Residing in College-Owned, -Operated, or -Affiliated Housing:** 32 **Final Year or Final Semester Residency Requirement:** Yes **Regional Accreditation:** Southern Association of Colleges and Schools **Credit Hours For Degree:** 60 credit hours, Associates; 120 credit hours, Bachelors **ROTC:** Air Force, Army, Navy **Professional Accreditation:** AACSB, ABET, ACA, APA, ASLA, AVMA, CSWE, NAAB, NASAD, NASPAA, NCATE, NRPA, SAF. **Intercollegiate Athletics:** Baseball M; Basketball M & W; Bowling M & W; Cheerleading M & W; Crew M & W; Cross-Country Running M & W; Equestrian Sports M & W; Fencing M & W; Field Hockey M & W; Football M; Golf M & W; Gymnastics M & W; Ice Hockey M; Lacrosse M & W; Racquetball M & W; Riflery M & W; Rugby M & W; Sailing M & W; Skiing (Downhill) M & W; Soccer M & W; Softball M & W; Swimming and Diving M & W; Table Tennis M & W; Tennis M & W; Track and Field M & W; Ultimate Frisbee M & W; Volleyball M & W; Water Polo M & W; Wrestling M

NORTH CAROLINA WESLEYAN COLLEGE

3400 N Wesleyan Blvd.
Rocky Mount, NC 27804-8677
Tel: (252)985-5100; Free: 800-488-6292
Fax: (252)985-5325
E-mail: blilley@ncwc.edu
Web Site: www.ncwc.edu
Admissions: Ben Lilley
Financial Aid: Leah Hill
Type: Four-Year College **Sex:** Coed **Affiliation:** United Methodist Church. **Scores:** 66% SAT V 400+; 67% SAT M 400+ **% Accepted:** 55 **Application Deadline:** Rolling **Application Fee:** $0.00 **H.S. Requirements:** High school diploma required; GED accepted **Costs Per Year:** Application fee: $0. Comprehensive fee: $37,674 includes full-time tuition ($28,000), mandatory fees ($150), and college room and board ($9524). College room only: $4400. Full-time tuition and fees vary according to location. Room and board charges vary according to housing facility. Part-time tuition: $425 per semester hour. Part-time tuition varies according to course load and location. **Scholarships:** Available. **Calendar System:** Semester, Summer session available **Enrollment:** Full-time 1,726, Part-time 393 **Faculty:** Full-time 58, Part-time 191 **Student-Faculty Ratio:** 15:1 **Exams:** SAT I or ACT. **%**

Receiving Financial Aid: 74 **% Residing in College-Owned, -Operated, or -Affiliated Housing:** 31 **Final Year or Final Semester Residency Requirement:** No **Regional Accreditation:** Southern Association of Colleges and Schools **Credit Hours For Degree:** 124 semester hours, Bachelors **ROTC:** Army **Professional Accreditation:** NCATE. **Intercollegiate Athletics:** Baseball M; Basketball M & W; Cross-Country Running W; Football M; Golf M; Soccer M & W; Softball W; Tennis M & W; Volleyball W

PAMLICO COMMUNITY COLLEGE

PO Box 185
Grantsboro, NC 28529-0185
Tel: (252)249-1851
Fax: (252)249-2377
Web Site: www.pamlicocc.edu
President/CEO: Cleve H. Cox, EdD
Admissions: Floyd H. Hardison
Type: Two-Year College **Sex:** Coed **Affiliation:** North Carolina Community College System. **Admission Plans:** Deferred Admission; Early Admission; Open Admission **Application Deadline:** Rolling **Application Fee:** $0.00 **H.S. Requirements:** High school diploma required; GED accepted **Scholarships:** Available. **Calendar System:** Semester, Summer session available **Faculty:** Full-time 6, Part-time 4 **Regional Accreditation:** Southern Association of Colleges and Schools **Professional Accreditation:** AAMAE.

PFEIFFER UNIVERSITY

PO Box 960
Misenheimer, NC 28109-0960
Tel: (704)463-1360; Free: 800-338-2060
Fax: (704)463-1363
E-mail: admiss@pfeiffer.edu
Web Site: www.pfeiffer.edu
President/CEO: Dr. Charles M. Ambrose
Admissions: Diane Martin
Financial Aid: Amy Brown
Type: Comprehensive **Sex:** Coed **Affiliation:** United Methodist. **Scores:** 85% SAT V 400+; 91% SAT M 400+ **% Accepted:** 71 **Admission Plans:** Deferred Admission; Early Admission **Application Deadline:** Rolling **Application Fee:** $25.00 **H.S. Requirements:** High school diploma required; GED accepted **Scholarships:** Available. **Calendar System:** Semester, Summer session available **Faculty:** Full-time 76, Part-time 74 **Student-Faculty Ratio:** 14:1 **Exams:** SAT I or ACT. **% Residing in College-Owned, -Operated, or -Affiliated Housing:** 65 **Regional Accreditation:** Southern Association of Colleges and Schools **Credit Hours For Degree:** 124 semester hours, Bachelors **ROTC:** Army **Professional Accreditation:** NASM, NCATE. **Intercollegiate Athletics:** Baseball M; Basketball M & W; Cheerleading M & W; Cross-Country Running M & W; Golf M & W; Lacrosse M & W; Soccer M & W; Softball W; Swimming and Diving M & W; Tennis M & W; Volleyball W

PIEDMONT COMMUNITY COLLEGE

PO Box 1197
Roxboro, NC 27573-1197
Tel: (336)599-1181
Fax: (336)597-3817
Web Site: www.piedmont.cc.nc.us
President/CEO: Dr. Walter C. Bartlett
Admissions: Gene Ritter
Type: Two-Year College **Sex:** Coed **Affiliation:** North Carolina Community College System. **% Accepted:** 100 **Admission Plans:** Deferred Admission; Early Admission; Open Admission **Application Deadline:** Rolling **H.S. Requirements:** High school diploma required; GED accepted **Costs Per Year:** State resident tuition: $1728 full-time, $72 per credit hour part-time. Nonresident tuition: $6336 full-time, $264 per credit hour part-time. Mandatory fees: $114 full-time, $57.25 per term part-time. Full-time tuition and fees vary according to course load. Part-time tuition and fees vary according to course load. **Scholarships:** Available. **Calendar System:** Semester, Summer session available **Enrollment:** Full-time 541, Part-time 780 **Student-Faculty Ratio:** 12:1 **Exams:** ACT essay component used for placement; SAT essay component used for placement. **Final Year or Final Semester Residency Requirement:** No **Regional Accreditation:** Southern Association of Colleges and Schools **Credit Hours For Degree:** 60-74 semester hours, depending on program, Associates

PIEDMONT INTERNATIONAL UNIVERSITY

420 S Broad St.
Winston-Salem, NC 27101-5197
Tel: (336)725-8344; Free: 800-937-5097
Fax: (336)725-5522
E-mail: stevensons@piedmontU.edu
Web Site: www.piedmontu.edu
President/CEO: Dr. Charles Petitt
Admissions: Joe Edgerton
Financial Aid: Mandy McLain

Type: Comprehensive **Sex:** Coed **Affiliation:** Baptist. **Scores:** 65% SAT V 400+; 70% SAT M 400+; 42% ACT 18-23; 21% ACT 24-29 **% Accepted:** 49 **Admission Plans:** Open Admission **Application Deadline:** Rolling **Application Fee:** $55.00 **H.S. Requirements:** High school diploma required; GED accepted **Scholarships:** Available. **Calendar System:** Semester, Summer session available **Enrollment:** Full-time 149, Graduate full-time 28, Graduate part-time 159, Part-time 48 **Student-Faculty Ratio:** 10:1 **Exams:** ACT essay component used for placement; SAT I or ACT; SAT essay component used for placement; SAT Reasoning; SAT Subject. **% Receiving Financial Aid:** 84 **% Residing in College-Owned, -Operated, or -Affiliated Housing:** 12 **Credit Hours For Degree:** 68 credit hours, Associates; 130 credit hours, Bachelors **Professional Accreditation:** TRACS. **Intercollegiate Athletics:** Basketball M; Volleyball W

PITT COMMUNITY COLLEGE

1986 Pitt Tech Rd.
Winterville, NC 28590
Tel: (252)321-4200
Fax: (252)321-4401
E-mail: pittadm@pcc.pitt.cc.nc.us
Web Site: www.pittcc.edu
President/CEO: Dr. G. Dennis Massey
Admissions: Dr. Kimberly Williamson
Financial Aid: Tamara Glaspie

Type: Two-Year College **Sex:** Coed **Affiliation:** North Carolina Community College System. **Admission Plans:** Deferred Admission; Open Admission **Application Deadline:** Rolling **Application Fee:** $0.00 **H.S. Requirements:** High school diploma required; GED accepted **Costs Per Year:** Application fee: $0. State resident tuition: $2304 full-time, $72 per credit hour part-time. Nonresident tuition: $8448 full-time, $264 per credit hour part-time. Mandatory fees: $106 full-time, $106.50 per year part-time. Part-time tuition and fees vary according to course load. **Scholarships:** Available. **Calendar System:** Semester, Summer session available **Enrollment:** Full-time 4,670, Part-time 4,232 **Faculty:** Full-time 187, Part-time 204 **Regional Accreditation:** Southern Association of Colleges and Schools **Credit Hours For Degree:** 65 semester hours, Associates **ROTC:** Army **Professional Accreditation:** AAMAE, ACEN, AHIMA, AOTA, CoARC, JRCEDMS, JRCERT. **Intercollegiate Athletics:** Baseball M; Basketball M; Golf M; Softball W; Volleyball W

QUEENS UNIVERSITY OF CHARLOTTE

1900 Selwyn Ave.
Charlotte, NC 28274-0002
Tel: (704)337-2200; Free: 800-849-0202
Fax: (704)337-2403
E-mail: admissions@queens.edu
Web Site: www.queens.edu
President/CEO: Pamela Davies, PhD
Admissions: Evan Sprinkle
Financial Aid: Nancy Buchanan

Type: Comprehensive **Sex:** Coed **Affiliation:** Presbyterian. **Scores:** 98% SAT V 400+; 97% SAT M 400+; 46.54% ACT 18-23; 41.51% ACT 24-29 **% Accepted:** 67 **Admission Plans:** Deferred Admission; Early Decision Plan **Application Deadline:** Rolling **Application Fee:** $0.00 **H.S. Requirements:** High school diploma required; GED accepted **Costs Per Year:** Application fee: $0. Comprehensive fee: $44,046 includes full-time tuition ($31,360), mandatory fees ($1200), and college room and board ($11,486). Full-time tuition and fees vary according to course load, program, and student level. Room and board charges vary according to board plan and housing facility. **Scholarships:** Available. **Calendar System:** Semester, Summer session available **Enrollment:** Full-time 1,343, Graduate full-time 92, Graduate part-time 553, Part-time 298 **Faculty:** Full-time 127, Part-time 187 **Student-Faculty Ratio:** 9:1 **Exams:** ACT essay component not used; SAT I or ACT; SAT essay component not used; SAT Reasoning; SAT Subject. **% Receiv-**

ing **Financial Aid:** 64 **% Residing in College-Owned, -Operated, or -Affiliated Housing:** 69 **Final Year or Final Semester Residency Requirement:** No **Regional Accreditation:** Southern Association of Colleges and Schools **Credit Hours For Degree:** 120 credit hours, Bachelors **Professional Accreditation:** AACN, AACSB, ACBSP, ACEN, NASM, NCATE. **Intercollegiate Athletics:** Basketball M & W; Cross-Country Running M & W; Golf M & W; Lacrosse M & W; Soccer M & W; Softball W; Swimming and Diving M & W; Tennis M & W; Track and Field M & W; Volleyball W

RANDOLPH COMMUNITY COLLEGE

629 Industrial Park Ave.
Asheboro, NC 27205
Tel: (336)633-0200
Fax: (336)629-4695
E-mail: bhagerman@randolph.edu
Web Site: www.randolph.edu
President/CEO: Dr. Robert S. Shackleford, Jr.
Admissions: Brandi F. Hagerman

Type: Two-Year College **Sex:** Coed **Affiliation:** North Carolina Community College System. **% Accepted:** 100 **Admission Plans:** Deferred Admission; Open Admission **Application Deadline:** Rolling **Application Fee:** $0.00 **H.S. Requirements:** High school diploma required; GED accepted **Costs Per Year:** Application fee: $0. State resident tuition: $2432 full-time, $76 per credit part-time. Nonresident tuition: $8576 full-time, $268 per credit part-time. Mandatory fees: $88 full-time, $2.75 per credit part-time. **Scholarships:** Available. **Calendar System:** Semester, Summer session available **Enrollment:** Full-time 978, Part-time 1,692 **Faculty:** Full-time 85, Part-time 169 **Student-Faculty Ratio:** 11:1 **Final Year or Final Semester Residency Requirement:** No **Regional Accreditation:** Southern Association of Colleges and Schools **Credit Hours For Degree:** 64 semester hours, Associates **ROTC:** Air Force **Professional Accreditation:** ACEN.

RICHMOND COMMUNITY COLLEGE

PO Box 1189
Hamlet, NC 28345-1189
Tel: (910)582-7000
Fax: (910)582-7102
E-mail: ccholmes@richmondcc.edu
Web Site: www.richmondcc.edu
President/CEO: Dr. William D. McInnis
Admissions: Cayce Holmes

Type: Two-Year College **Sex:** Coed **Affiliation:** North Carolina Community College System. **Admission Plans:** Deferred Admission; Open Admission **Application Deadline:** Rolling **Application Fee:** $0.00 **H.S. Requirements:** High school diploma required; GED accepted **Costs Per Year:** Application fee: $0. State resident tuition: $2368 full-time, $72 per credit hour part-time. Nonresident tuition: $8512 full-time, $264 per credit hour part-time. Mandatory fees: $78 full-time, $32 per term part-time. Full-time tuition and fees vary according to course load. Part-time tuition and fees vary according to course load. **Scholarships:** Available. **Calendar System:** Semester, Summer session available **Enrollment:** Full-time 1,170, Part-time 1,361 **Student-Faculty Ratio:** 15:1 **Final Year or Final Semester Residency Requirement:** No **Regional Accreditation:** Southern Association of Colleges and Schools **Credit Hours For Degree:** 64 semester hours, Associates

ROANOKE-CHOWAN COMMUNITY COLLEGE

109 Community College Rd.
Ahoskie, NC 27910
Tel: (252)862-1200
Fax: (252)862-1353
Web Site: www.roanokechowan.edu
President/CEO: Dr. Michael Elam
Admissions: Sandra Copeland

Type: Two-Year College **Sex:** Coed **Affiliation:** North Carolina Community College System. **Admission Plans:** Early Admission; Open Admission **Application Deadline:** Rolling **H.S. Requirements:** High school diploma required; GED accepted **Scholarships:** Available. **Calendar System:** Semester, Summer session available **Regional Accreditation:** Southern Association of Colleges and Schools

ROBESON COMMUNITY COLLEGE

5160 Fayetteville Rd.
Lumberton, NC 28359-1420
Tel: (910)272-3700

Fax: (910)272-3328
E-mail: plocklear@robeson.edu
Web Site: www.robeson.edu
President/CEO: Dr. Pamela Hilbert
Admissions: Patricia Locklear
Financial Aid: Teresa Tubbs
Type: Two-Year College **Sex:** Coed **Affiliation:** North Carolina Community College System. **Admission Plans:** Early Admission; Open Admission **Application Deadline:** Rolling **Application Fee:** $0.00 **H.S. Requirements:** High school diploma required; GED accepted **Scholarships:** Available. **Calendar System:** Semester **Faculty:** Full-time 44, Part-time 70 **Regional Accreditation:** Southern Association of Colleges and Schools **Credit Hours For Degree:** 65 semester hours, Associates **Professional Accreditation:** CoARC.

ROCKINGHAM COMMUNITY COLLEGE
PO Box 38
Wentworth, NC 27375-0038
Tel: (336)342-4261
E-mail: admissions@rockinghamcc.edu
Web Site: www.rockinghamcc.edu
President/CEO: Dr. Mark O. Kinlaw
Admissions: Derrick Satterfield
Type: Two-Year College **Sex:** Coed **Affiliation:** North Carolina Community College System. **Admission Plans:** Deferred Admission; Early Admission; Open Admission **Application Deadline:** Rolling **Application Fee:** $0.00 **H.S. Requirements:** High school diploma required; GED accepted **Costs Per Year:** Application fee: $0. State resident tuition: $2304 full-time. Nonresident tuition: $8448 full-time. Mandatory fees: $116 full-time. **Scholarships:** Available. **Calendar System:** Semester, Summer session available **Enrollment:** Full-time 715, Part-time 1,151 **Faculty:** Full-time 62, Part-time 65 **Student-Faculty Ratio:** 18:1 **Regional Accreditation:** Southern Association of Colleges and Schools **Intercollegiate Athletics:** Baseball M; Volleyball W

ROWAN-CABARRUS COMMUNITY COLLEGE
PO Box 1595
Salisbury, NC 28145-1595
Tel: (704)637-0760
Fax: (704)633-6804
Web Site: www.rccc.edu
President/CEO: Dr. Carol Spalding
Admissions: Gail Cummins
Type: Two-Year College **Sex:** Coed **Affiliation:** North Carolina Community College System. **% Accepted:** 99 **Admission Plans:** Open Admission **Application Deadline:** Rolling **Application Fee:** $0.00 **H.S. Requirements:** High school diploma required; GED accepted **Costs Per Year:** Application fee: $0. State resident tuition: $2368 full-time, $76 per credit hour part-time. Nonresident tuition: $8512 full-time, $268 per credit hour part-time. Mandatory fees: $138 full-time, $132 per term part-time. Full-time tuition and fees vary according to course load. Part-time tuition and fees vary according to course load. **Scholarships:** Available. **Calendar System:** Semester, Summer session available **Final Year or Final Semester Residency Requirement:** No **Regional Accreditation:** Southern Association of Colleges and Schools **Credit Hours For Degree:** 64 semester hours, Associates **Professional Accreditation:** ACEN, ADA, JRCERT.

ST. ANDREWS UNIVERSITY
1700 Dogwood Mile
Laurinburg, NC 28352-5598
Tel: (910)277-5000; Free: 800-763-0198
Fax: (910)277-5087
E-mail: admission@sapc.edu
Web Site: www.sapc.edu
President/CEO: Paul Baldasare
Admissions: Erin Balduf
Financial Aid: Shawn Caulder
Type: Comprehensive **Sex:** Coed **Affiliation:** Presbyterian Webber International University. **Scores:** 77% SAT V 400+; 82% SAT M 400+; 66% ACT 18-23; 7% ACT 24-29 **% Accepted:** 53 **Admission Plans:** Deferred Admission **Application Fee:** $35.00 **H.S. Requirements:** High school diploma required; GED accepted **Costs Per Year:** Application fee: $35. Comprehensive fee: $33,580 includes full-time tuition ($23,682) and college room and board ($9898). Full-time tuition

varies according to course load and location. Room and board charges vary according to housing facility. Part-time tuition: $274 per credit hour. Part-time tuition varies according to location. **Scholarships:** Available. **Calendar System:** Semester **Enrollment:** Full-time 649, Graduate full-time 37, Graduate part-time 8, Part-time 39 **Faculty:** Full-time 21, Part-time 26 **Student-Faculty Ratio:** 24:1 **Exams:** ACT essay component not used; ACT essay component used as validity check; ACT essay component used for admission; ACT essay component used in place of application essay; SAT I or ACT; SAT essay component not used; SAT essay component used as validity check; SAT essay component used for admission; SAT essay component used in place of application essay; SAT Reasoning. **% Receiving Financial Aid:** 73 **Final Year or Final Semester Residency Requirement:** Yes **Credit Hours For Degree:** 120 credits, Bachelors **Professional Accreditation:** NCATE. **Intercollegiate Athletics:** Baseball M; Basketball M & W; Cross-Country Running M & W; Equestrian Sports M & W; Golf M & W; Lacrosse M & W; Soccer M & W; Softball W; Wrestling M

SAINT AUGUSTINE'S UNIVERSITY
1315 Oakwood Ave.
Raleigh, NC 27610-2298
Tel: (919)516-4000; Free: 800-948-1126
Fax: (919)516-4415
E-mail: jesousa@st-aug.edu
Web Site: www.st-aug.edu
President/CEO: Dr. Everett B. Ward
Admissions: Chris J. Withers
Financial Aid: Nadine Y. Ford
Type: Four-Year College **Sex:** Coed **Affiliation:** Episcopal. **% Accepted:** 58 **Admission Plans:** Deferred Admission **Application Deadline:** Rolling **Application Fee:** $50.00 **H.S. Requirements:** High school diploma required; GED accepted **Costs Per Year:** Application fee: $50. Comprehensive fee: $25,832 includes full-time tuition ($12,890), mandatory fees ($5000), and college room and board ($7942). College room only: $3182. Full-time tuition and fees vary according to course load. Room and board charges vary according to housing facility. Part-time tuition: $537 per credit hour. Part-time mandatory fees: $208 per credit hour. Part-time tuition and fees vary according to course load. **Scholarships:** Available. **Calendar System:** Semester, Summer session available **Enrollment:** Full-time 798, Part-time 12 **Faculty:** Full-time 64 **Student-Faculty Ratio:** 11:1 **Exams:** ACT essay component used for placement; SAT I or ACT; SAT essay component used for placement; SAT Reasoning; SAT Subject. **% Receiving Financial Aid:** 98 **% Residing in College-Owned, -Operated, or -Affiliated Housing:** 75 **Final Year or Final Semester Residency Requirement:** Yes **Regional Accreditation:** Southern Association of Colleges and Schools **Credit Hours For Degree:** 120 semester hours, Bachelors **ROTC:** Air Force, Army **Professional Accreditation:** NCATE. **Intercollegiate Athletics:** Baseball M; Basketball M & W; Bowling W; Cheerleading W; Cross-Country Running M & W; Football M; Golf M; Softball W; Track and Field M & W; Volleyball W

SALEM COLLEGE
601 S Church St.
Winston-Salem, NC 27101
Tel: (336)721-2600; Free: 800-327-2536
Fax: (336)724-7102
E-mail: admissions@salem.edu
Web Site: www.salem.edu
President/CEO: Pres. D. E. Lorraine Sterritt
Admissions: Dean Katherine Knapp Watts
Financial Aid: Paul J. Coscia
Type: Comprehensive **Sex:** Coed **Affiliation:** Moravian. **Scores:** 96% SAT V 400+; 97% SAT M 400+ **Admission Plans:** Deferred Admission; Early Admission **Application Deadline:** Rolling **Application Fee:** $30.00 **H.S. Requirements:** High school diploma required; GED accepted **Costs Per Year:** Application fee: $30. Comprehensive fee: $38,060 includes full-time tuition ($25,870), mandatory fees ($366), and college room and board ($11,824). Room and board charges vary according to housing facility. Part-time tuition: $1494 per course. Part-time mandatory fees: $150 per year. **Scholarships:** Available. **Calendar System:** 4-1-4, Summer session available **Enrollment:** Full-time 768, Graduate full-time 3, Graduate part-time 146, Part-time 170 **Faculty:** Full-time 63, Part-time 79 **Student-Faculty Ratio:** 10:1 **Exams:** SAT I or ACT; SAT essay component not used. **% Residing in College-Owned, -Operated, or -Affiliated Housing:** 86 **Final Year or Final Semester Residency Requirement:** Yes **Regional Ac-**

creditation: Southern Association of Colleges and Schools Credit Hours For Degree: 120 semester hours, Bachelors ROTC: Air Force, Army Professional Accreditation: NASM, NCATE. Intercollegiate Athletics: Basketball W; Cross-Country Running W; Field Hockey W; Soccer W; Swimming and Diving W; Tennis W; Volleyball W

SAMPSON COMMUNITY COLLEGE
1801 Sunset Ave.
Hwy. 24 W
Clinton, NC 28329-0318
Tel: (910)592-8081
Fax: (910)592-8048
Web Site: www.sampsoncc.edu
President/CEO: Paul Hutchins
Admissions: William R. Jordan
Type: Two-Year College Sex: Coed Affiliation: North Carolina Community College System. % Accepted: 100 Admission Plans: Deferred Admission; Open Admission Application Deadline: Rolling Application Fee: $0.00 H.S. Requirements: High school diploma required; GED accepted Scholarships: Available. Calendar System: Semester, Summer session available Enrollment: Full-time 679, Part-time 900 Faculty: Full-time 45, Part-time 50 Student-Faculty Ratio: 20:1 Regional Accreditation: Southern Association of Colleges and Schools Credit Hours For Degree: 65 credits, Associates

SANDHILLS COMMUNITY COLLEGE
3395 Airport Rd.
Pinehurst, NC 28374-8299
Tel: (910)692-6185; Free: 800-338-3944
Fax: (910)695-1823
E-mail: robledoi@sandhills.edu
Web Site: www.sandhills.edu
President/CEO: John Dempsey
Admissions: Isai Robledo
Financial Aid: Heather M. Willett
Type: Two-Year College Sex: Coed Affiliation: North Carolina Community College System. Admission Plans: Deferred Admission; Open Admission Application Deadline: Rolling Application Fee: $0.00 H.S. Requirements: High school diploma required; GED accepted Scholarships: Available. Calendar System: Semester, Summer session available Faculty: Full-time 145, Part-time 264 Student-Faculty Ratio: 13:1 Regional Accreditation: Southern Association of Colleges and Schools Credit Hours For Degree: 64 semester hours, Associates Professional Accreditation: CoARC, JRCERT, NAACLS. Intercollegiate Athletics: Basketball M; Golf M & W; Volleyball W

SHAW UNIVERSITY
118 E S St.
Raleigh, NC 27601-2399
Tel: (919)546-8200; Free: 800-214-6683
Fax: (919)546-8271
E-mail: ssowell@shawu.edu
Web Site: www.shawu.edu
President/CEO: Dr. Tashni-Ann Dubroy
Admissions: Stacey Sowell
Financial Aid: Rochelle King
Type: Comprehensive Sex: Coed Affiliation: Baptist. Scores: 31% SAT V 400+; 16% ACT 18-23; 2% ACT 24-29 % Accepted: 60 Admission Plans: Deferred Admission; Early Admission Application Deadline: July 30 Application Fee: $25.00 H.S. Requirements: High school diploma required; GED accepted Costs Per Year: Application fee: $25. Comprehensive fee: $24,638 includes full-time tuition ($11,808), mandatory fees ($4672), and college room and board ($8158). College room only: $3842. Part-time tuition: $492 per credit hour. Scholarships: Available. Calendar System: Semester, Summer session available Enrollment: Full-time 1,407, Graduate full-time 71, Graduate part-time 66, Part-time 102 Faculty: Full-time 93, Part-time 78 Student-Faculty Ratio: 14:1 Exams: SAT I or ACT. % Receiving Financial Aid: 92 % Residing in College-Owned, -Operated, or -Affiliated Housing: 52 Final Year or Final Semester Residency Requirement: No Regional Accreditation: Southern Association of Colleges and Schools Credit Hours For Degree: 120 credit hours, Bachelors ROTC: Army Professional Accreditation: ATS, CoA-KT, NCATE. Intercollegiate Athletics: Basketball M & W; Bowling W; Cross-Country Running M & W; Football M; Softball W; Tennis M & W; Track and Field M & W; Volleyball W

SOUTH COLLEGE–ASHEVILLE
1567 Patton Ave.
Asheville, NC 28806
Tel: (828)252-2486
Web Site: www.southcollegenc.edu
President/CEO: Nick South
Type: Two-Year College Sex: Coed Admission Plans: Deferred Admission; Open Admission Application Deadline: Rolling Application Fee: $50.00 H.S. Requirements: High school diploma required; GED accepted Scholarships: Available. Calendar System: Quarter, Summer session available Student-Faculty Ratio: 8:1 Exams: Other. Credit Hours For Degree: 102 credits, Associates Professional Accreditation: ACICS.

SOUTH PIEDMONT COMMUNITY COLLEGE
PO Box 126
Polkton, NC 28135-0126
Tel: (704)272-7635; Free: 800-766-0319
E-mail: asecrest@spcc.edu
Web Site: www.spcc.edu
President/CEO: Dr. Stanley Sidor
Admissions: Amanda Secrest
Financial Aid: John P. Ratliff, Jr.
Type: Two-Year College Sex: Coed Affiliation: North Carolina Community College System. % Accepted: 84 Admission Plans: Deferred Admission; Early Admission; Open Admission Application Deadline: Rolling Application Fee: $0.00 H.S. Requirements: High school diploma required; GED accepted Costs Per Year: Application fee: $0. State resident tuition: $2304 full-time, $72 per semester hour part-time. Nonresident tuition: $8448 full-time, $264 per semester hour part-time. Mandatory fees: $169 full-time, $8.70 per semester hour part-time, $43.50 per term part-time. Full-time tuition and fees vary according to course load. Part-time tuition and fees vary according to course load. Scholarships: Available. Calendar System: Semester, Summer session available Enrollment: Full-time 732, Part-time 1,926 Student-Faculty Ratio: 17:1 Regional Accreditation: Southern Association of Colleges and Schools Credit Hours For Degree: 64 semester hours, Associates Professional Accreditation: AAMAE, AHIMA.

SOUTH UNIVERSITY
3975 Premier Dr.
High Point, NC 27265
Tel: (336)812-7200; Free: 855-268-2187
Fax: (336)812-7390
Web Site: www.southuniversity.edu/high-point.aspx
Type: Comprehensive Sex: Coed Regional Accreditation: Southern Association of Colleges and Schools Professional Accreditation: ACBSP.

SOUTHEASTERN BAPTIST THEOLOGICAL SEMINARY
PO Box 1889
Wake Forest, NC 27588-1889
Tel: (919)761-2100; Free: 800-284-6317
Web Site: www.sebts.edu
President/CEO: Dr. Jamie Dew
Admissions: Sean Robinson
Type: Comprehensive Sex: Coed Affiliation: Southern Baptist. % Accepted: 98 Admission Plans: Open Admission Application Deadline: July 20 Application Fee: $40.00 H.S. Requirements: High school diploma required; GED accepted Scholarships: Available. Calendar System: Semester, Summer session available Enrollment: Full-time 239, Graduate full-time 766, Graduate part-time 1,078, Part-time 179 Faculty: Full-time 65, Part-time 73 Student-Faculty Ratio: 20:1 Exams: ACT essay component not used; SAT I or ACT; SAT essay component not used; SAT Reasoning; SAT Subject. Regional Accreditation: Southern Association of Colleges and Schools Credit Hours For Degree: 64 credits, Associates; 128 credits, Bachelors Professional Accreditation: ACIPE, ATS.

SOUTHEASTERN COMMUNITY COLLEGE
PO Box 151
Whiteville, NC 28472-0151
Tel: (910)642-7141
Web Site: www.sccnc.edu
President/CEO: Dr. Kathy Matlock
Admissions: Sylvia McQueen
Type: Two-Year College Sex: Coed Affiliation: North Carolina Community College System. % Accepted: 100 Admission Plans: Deferred Admission;

Early Admission; Open Admission **Application Deadline:** Rolling **Application Fee:** $0.00 **H.S. Requirements:** High school diploma required; GED accepted **Scholarships:** Available. **Calendar System:** Semester, Summer session available **Enrollment:** Full-time 766, Part-time 636 **Faculty:** Full-time 75, Part-time 16 **Student-Faculty Ratio:** 20:1 **Regional Accreditation:** Southern Association of Colleges and Schools **Credit Hours For Degree:** 65 semester hours, Associates **Professional Accreditation:** NAACLS. **Intercollegiate Athletics:** Baseball M; Softball W; Squash W; Volleyball W

SOUTHWESTERN COMMUNITY COLLEGE
447 College Dr.
Sylva, NC 28779
Tel: (828)339-4000; Free: 800-447-7091
Fax: (828)586-4093
E-mail: d_benson@southwesterncc.edu
Web Site: www.southwesterncc.edu
President/CEO: Dr. Don Tomas
Admissions: Dominique Benson
Financial Aid: Andrea McCoy Garrett
Type: Two-Year College **Sex:** Coed **Affiliation:** North Carolina Community College System. **Scholarships:** Available. **Calendar System:** Semester, Summer session available **Student-Faculty Ratio:** 16:1 **Final Year or Final Semester Residency Requirement:** No **Regional Accreditation:** Southern Association of Colleges and Schools **Credit Hours For Degree:** 61 semester hours, Associates **Professional Accreditation:** AHIMA, APTA, CoARC, JRCEND, JRCERT, NAACLS.

STANLY COMMUNITY COLLEGE
141 College Dr.
Albemarle, NC 28001-7458
Tel: (704)982-0121
Fax: (704)982-0819
E-mail: dross7926@stanly.edu
Web Site: www.stanly.edu
President/CEO: Dr. Brenda S. Kays
Admissions: Denise B. Ross
Type: Two-Year College **Sex:** Coed **Affiliation:** North Carolina Community College System. **% Accepted:** 100 **Admission Plans:** Deferred Admission; Early Admission; Open Admission **Application Deadline:** Rolling **H.S. Requirements:** High school diploma required; GED accepted **Scholarships:** Available. **Calendar System:** Semester, Summer session available **Faculty:** Full-time 53, Part-time 53 **Student-Faculty Ratio:** 9:1 **Exams:** ACT essay component not used; SAT essay component not used. **Regional Accreditation:** Southern Association of Colleges and Schools **Credit Hours For Degree:** 65 semester hours, Associates **Professional Accreditation:** AAMAE, CoARC. **Intercollegiate Athletics:** Baseball M; Softball W

STRAYER UNIVERSITY–GREENSBORO CAMPUS
4900 Koger Blvd., Ste. 400
Greensboro, NC 27407
Tel: (336)315-7800
Fax: (336)315-7830
Web Site: www.strayer.edu/north-carolina/greensboro
President/CEO: Brian W. Jones
Type: Comprehensive **Sex:** Coed **Regional Accreditation:** Middle States Association of Colleges and Schools

STRAYER UNIVERSITY–HUNTERSVILLE CAMPUS
13620 Reese Blvd.
Ste. 130
Huntersville, NC 28078
Tel: (704)379-6800
Fax: (704)379-6830
Web Site: www.strayer.edu/north-carolina/huntersville
President/CEO: Brian W. Jones
Type: Comprehensive **Sex:** Coed **Regional Accreditation:** Middle States Association of Colleges and Schools

STRAYER UNIVERSITY–NORTH CHARLOTTE CAMPUS
7870 Commons Park Cir. NW
Concord, NC 28027
Tel: (704)886-6500
Fax: (704)979-3891
Web Site: www.strayer.edu/north-carolina/north-charlotte

President/CEO: Brian W. Jones
Type: Comprehensive **Sex:** Coed **Regional Accreditation:** Middle States Association of Colleges and Schools

STRAYER UNIVERSITY–NORTH RALEIGH CAMPUS
8701 Wadford Dr.
Raleigh, NC 27616
Tel: (919)878-9900
Fax: (919)878-6625
Web Site: www.strayer.edu/north-carolina/north-raleigh
President/CEO: Brian W. Jones
Type: Comprehensive **Sex:** Coed **Regional Accreditation:** Middle States Association of Colleges and Schools

STRAYER UNIVERSITY–RTP CAMPUS
4 Copley Pky.
Morrisville, NC 27560
Tel: (919)466-4400
Fax: (919)466-4430
Web Site: www.strayer.edu/north-carolina/rtp
President/CEO: Brian W. Jones
Type: Comprehensive **Sex:** Coed **Regional Accreditation:** Middle States Association of Colleges and Schools

STRAYER UNIVERSITY–SOUTH CHARLOTTE CAMPUS
9101 Kings Parade Blvd.
Ste. 200
Charlotte, NC 28273
Tel: (704)499-9200
Fax: (704)499-9230
Web Site: www.strayer.edu/north-carolina/south-charlotte
President/CEO: Brian W. Jones
Type: Comprehensive **Sex:** Coed **Regional Accreditation:** Middle States Association of Colleges and Schools

STRAYER UNIVERSITY–SOUTH RALEIGH CAMPUS
3421 Olympia Dr.
Raleigh, NC 27603
Tel: (919)890-7500
Fax: (919)662-9840
Web Site: www.strayer.edu/north-carolina/south-raleigh
President/CEO: Brian W. Jones
Type: Comprehensive **Sex:** Coed **Regional Accreditation:** Middle States Association of Colleges and Schools

SURRY COMMUNITY COLLEGE
630 S Main St.
Dobson, NC 27017
Tel: (336)386-8121
Fax: (336)386-8951
E-mail: hazelwoodr@surry.edu
Web Site: www.surry.edu
President/CEO: Dr. David Shockley
Admissions: Renita Hazelwood
Financial Aid: Kendra S. Simmons
Type: Two-Year College **Sex:** Coed **Affiliation:** North Carolina Community College System. **Admission Plans:** Deferred Admission; Early Admission; Open Admission **Application Fee:** $0.00 **H.S. Requirements:** High school diploma required; GED accepted **Scholarships:** Available. **Calendar System:** Semester, Summer session available **Faculty:** Full-time 150, Part-time 300 **Student-Faculty Ratio:** 27:1 **Exams:** Other. **Regional Accreditation:** Southern Association of Colleges and Schools **Credit Hours For Degree:** 65 semester hours, Associates **Intercollegiate Athletics:** Baseball M; Basketball M; Volleyball W

TRI-COUNTY COMMUNITY COLLEGE
21 Campus Cir.
Murphy, NC 28906-7919
Tel: (828)837-6810
Fax: (828)837-3266
E-mail: jchambers@tricountycc.edu
Web Site: www.tricountycc.edu
President/CEO: Dr. Donna Tipton-Rogers
Admissions: Dr. Jason Chambers

Type: Two-Year College **Sex:** Coed **Affiliation:** North Carolina Community College System. **Admission Plans:** Open Admission; Preferred Admission **Application Deadline:** Rolling **Application Fee:** $0.00 **H.S. Requirements:** High school diploma required; GED accepted **Costs Per Year:** Application fee: $0. State resident tuition: $1824 full-time, $76 per credit hour part-time. Nonresident tuition: $6432 full-time, $268 per credit hour part-time. Mandatory fees: $59 full-time, $29.25 per term part-time. **Scholarships:** Available. **Calendar System:** Semester, Summer session available **Faculty:** Full-time 46, Part-time 34 **Student-Faculty Ratio:** 21:1 **Exams:** SAT I and SAT II or ACT. **Final Year or Final Semester Residency Requirement:** No **Regional Accreditation:** Southern Association of Colleges and Schools

UNIVERSITY OF MOUNT OLIVE

634 Henderson St.
Mount Olive, NC 28365
Tel: (919)658-2502; Free: 800-653-0854
Fax: (919)658-8934
E-mail: admissions@moc.edu
Web Site: www.umo.edu
President/CEO: Dr. Philip Kerstetter
Admissions: Tim Woodard
Financial Aid: Katrina K. Lee

Type: Four-Year College **Sex:** Coed **Affiliation:** Free Will Baptist. **Scores:** 75% SAT V 400+; 82% SAT M 400+; 61.7% ACT 18-23; 8.51% ACT 24-29 **% Accepted:** 50 **Admission Plans:** Deferred Admission; Open Admission **Application Deadline:** August 18 **Application Fee:** $20.00 **H.S. Requirements:** High school diploma required; GED accepted **Costs Per Year:** Application fee: $20. Comprehensive fee: $25,800 includes full-time tuition ($18,400) and college room and board ($7400). Full-time tuition varies according to degree level. Room and board charges vary according to board plan. Part-time tuition: $420 per credit hour. Part-time tuition varies according to degree level. **Scholarships:** Available. **Calendar System:** Miscellaneous, Summer session available **Enrollment:** Full-time 2,955, Part-time 900 **Faculty:** Full-time 81, Part-time 102 **Student-Faculty Ratio:** 26:1 **Exams:** Other; SAT Reasoning; SAT Subject. **% Receiving Financial Aid:** 76 **% Residing in College-Owned, -Operated, or -Affiliated Housing:** 11 **Regional Accreditation:** Southern Association of Colleges and Schools **Credit Hours For Degree:** 64 semester hours, Associates; 126 semester hours, Bachelors **ROTC:** Air Force **Professional Accreditation:** ACBSP. **Intercollegiate Athletics:** Baseball M; Basketball M & W; Cheerleading W; Cross-Country Running M & W; Golf M & W; Soccer M & W; Softball W; Tennis M & W; Volleyball M & W

UNIVERSITY OF NORTH CAROLINA AT ASHEVILLE

One University Heights
Asheville, NC 28804-3299
Tel: (828)251-6600; Free: 800-531-9842
Fax: (828)251-6385
E-mail: admissions@unca.edu
Web Site: www.unca.edu
President/CEO: Mary Grant
Admissions: Shannon Earle

Type: Comprehensive **Sex:** Coed **Affiliation:** University of North Carolina System. **Scores:** 100% SAT V 400+; 100% SAT M 400+; 29.24% ACT 18-23; 53.49% ACT 24-29 **% Accepted:** 79 **Admission Plans:** Deferred Admission; Early Decision Plan **Application Deadline:** February 15 **Application Fee:** $75.00 **H.S. Requirements:** High school diploma required; GED not accepted. For applicants who can prove that they met the NC Minimum Course Requirements by successfully completing required courses: High school diploma required; GED accepted **Costs Per Year:** Application fee: $75. One-time mandatory fee: $150. State resident tuition: $4041 full-time. Nonresident tuition: $20,436 full-time. Mandatory fees: $2936 full-time. Full-time tuition and fees vary according to course load and degree level. College room and board: $8746. College room only: $4890. Room and board charges vary according to board plan and housing facility. **Scholarships:** Available. **Calendar System:** Semester, Summer session available **Enrollment:** Full-time 3,296, Graduate full-time 3, Graduate part-time 30, Part-time 562 **Faculty:** Full-time 216, Part-time 100 **Student-Faculty Ratio:** 14:1 **Exams:** SAT I or ACT; SAT II; SAT Reasoning. **% Receiving Financial Aid:** 59 **% Residing in College-Owned, -Operated, or -Affiliated Housing:** 39 **Final Year or Final Semester Residency Requirement:** Yes **Regional Accreditation:** Southern Association of Colleges and Schools **Credit Hours For Degree:** 120 semester hours, Bachelors **Professional Accreditation:** AACSB, ABET, NCATE. **Intercollegiate Athletics:** Archery M & W; Baseball M; Basketball M & W; Cross-Country Running M & W; Equestrian Sports M & W; Fencing M & W; Golf W; Rugby M & W; Soccer M & W; Swimming and Diving W; Tennis M & W; Track and Field M & W; Volleyball W

THE UNIVERSITY OF NORTH CAROLINA AT CHAPEL HILL

Chapel Hill, NC 27599
Tel: (919)962-2211
E-mail: unchelp@admissions.unc.edu
Web Site: www.unc.edu
President/CEO: Dr. Carol L. Folt
Admissions: Stephen M. Farmer
Financial Aid: Shirley A. Ort

Type: University **Sex:** Coed **Affiliation:** University of North Carolina System. **Scores:** 100% SAT V 400+; 100% SAT M 400+; 5.8% ACT 18-23; 42.2% ACT 24-29 **% Accepted:** 30 **Admission Plans:** Deferred Admission; Early Decision Plan; Preferred Admission **Application Deadline:** January 15 **Application Fee:** $80.00 **H.S. Requirements:** High school diploma required; GED not accepted **Costs Per Year:** Application fee: $80. State resident tuition: $6648 full-time. Nonresident tuition: $31,730 full-time. Mandatory fees: $1943 full-time. Full-time tuition and fees vary according to program. College room and board: $10,902. College room only: $6106. Room and board charges vary according to board plan, housing facility, and location. **Scholarships:** Available. **Calendar System:** Semester, Summer session available **Enrollment:** Full-time 17,645, Graduate full-time 6,425, Graduate part-time 4,244, Part-time 770 **Faculty:** Full-time 1,484, Part-time 177 **Student-Faculty Ratio:** 14:1 **Exams:** SAT I or ACT; SAT II; SAT Reasoning; SAT Subject. **% Receiving Financial Aid:** 45 **% Residing in College-Owned, -Operated, or -Affiliated Housing:** 52 **Final Year or Final Semester Residency Requirement:** No **Regional Accreditation:** Southern Association of Colleges and Schools **Credit Hours For Degree:** 120 credit hours, Bachelors **ROTC:** Air Force, Army, Navy **Professional Accreditation:** AACN, AACSB, AALS, ABA, ABET, ACA, ACEJMC, ACEN, ACPE, ACSP, ACIPE, ADA, ALA, AND, AOTA, APA, APTA, ASHA, CAHME, CEPH, CORE, CSWE, JRCAT, JRCERT, LCME/AMA, NAACLS, NASPAA, NCATE, NRPA. **Intercollegiate Athletics:** Badminton M & W; Baseball M; Basketball M & W; Cheerleading W; Crew M & W; Cross-Country Running M & W; Equestrian Sports M & W; Fencing M & W; Field Hockey M & W; Football M; Golf M & W; Gymnastics M & W; Ice Hockey M; Lacrosse M & W; Racquetball M & W; Rugby M & W; Sailing M & W; Skiing (Downhill) M & W; Soccer M & W; Softball W; Swimming and Diving M & W; Tennis M & W; Track and Field M & W; Triathlon M & W; Ultimate Frisbee M & W; Volleyball M & W; Water Polo M & W; Wrestling M

THE UNIVERSITY OF NORTH CAROLINA AT CHARLOTTE

9201 University City Blvd.
Charlotte, NC 28223-0001
Tel: (704)687-8622
Fax: (704)510-6483
E-mail: admissions@uncc.edu
Web Site: www.uncc.edu
President/CEO: Dr. Philip L. Dubois
Admissions: Claire Kirby
Financial Aid: Bruce Blackmon

Type: University **Sex:** Coed **Affiliation:** University of North Carolina System. **Scores:** 99% SAT V 400+; 100% SAT M 400+; 52.7% ACT 18-23; 40.49% ACT 24-29 **% Accepted:** 63 **Admission Plans:** Early Decision Plan; Preferred Admission **Application Deadline:** June 1 **Application Fee:** $60.00 **H.S. Requirements:** High school diploma required; GED accepted **Costs Per Year:** Application fee: $60. State resident tuition: $3628 full-time. Nonresident tuition: $16,799 full-time. Mandatory fees: $2904 full-time. Full-time tuition and fees vary according to course load and program. College room and board: $10,220. College room only: $5660. Room and board charges vary according to board plan and housing facility. **Scholarships:** Available. **Calendar System:** Semester, Summer session available **Enrollment:** Full-time 19,765, Graduate full-time 2,419, Graduate part-time 2,832, Part-time 2,967 **Faculty:** Full-time 1,080, Part-time 471 **Student-Faculty Ratio:** 19:1 **Exams:** ACT essay component used for admission; SAT I or ACT; SAT essay component used for admission; SAT Reasoning. **% Receiving Financial Aid:** 63 **% Residing in College-Owned, -Operated, or -Affiliated Housing:** 23 **Final Year or Final Semester Residency Requirement:** No **Regional Accreditation:** Southern Association of Colleges and Schools **Credit Hours For Degree:** 120 semester hours, Bachelors **ROTC:** Air Force, Army **Professional Accreditation:** AACN, AACSB, AANA, ABET, ACA, APA, CAHME, CSWE, NAAB, NASPAA, NCATE. **Intercollegiate**

Athletics: Baseball M; Basketball M & W; Cheerleading M & W; Cross-Country Running M & W; Football M; Golf M & W; Soccer M & W; Softball W; Tennis M & W; Track and Field M & W; Volleyball W

THE UNIVERSITY OF NORTH CAROLINA AT GREENSBORO

1400 Spring Garden St.
Greensboro, NC 27412-5001
Tel: (336)334-5000
Fax: (336)334-4180
E-mail: admissions@uncg.edu
Web Site: www.uncg.edu
President/CEO: Dr. Franklin D. Gilliam, Jr.
Financial Aid: Bruce Cabiness

Type: University **Sex:** Coed **Affiliation:** University of North Carolina System. **Scores:** 99% SAT V 400+; 100% SAT M 400+; 61.52% ACT 18-23; 34.07% ACT 24-29 **% Accepted:** 59 **Application Deadline:** March 1 **Application Fee:** $55.00 **H.S. Requirements:** High school diploma required; GED not accepted **Costs Per Year:** Application fee: $55. State resident tuition: $4130 full-time, $516.13 per credit hour part-time. Nonresident tuition: $18,991 full-time, $2,373.88 per credit hour part-time. Mandatory fees: $2574 full-time, $96.68 per credit hour part-time. Part-time tuition and fees vary according to course load. College room and board: $8252. College room only: $4996. Room and board charges vary according to board plan and housing facility. **Scholarships:** Available. **Calendar System:** Semester, Summer session available **Enrollment:** Full-time 13,450, Graduate full-time 1,598, Graduate part-time 1,844, Part-time 2,501 **Faculty:** Full-time 739, Part-time 249 **Student-Faculty Ratio:** 15:1 **Exams:** ACT essay component used for admission; SAT I or ACT; SAT essay component used for admission; SAT essay component used for placement; SAT Reasoning. **% Receiving Financial Aid:** 80 **% Residing in College-Owned, -Operated, or -Affiliated Housing:** 34 **Final Year or Final Semester Residency Requirement:** No **Regional Accreditation:** Southern Association of Colleges and Schools **Credit Hours For Degree:** 122 semester hours, Bachelors **ROTC:** Air Force, Army **Professional Accreditation:** AACN, AACSB, AAFCS, AANA, ABET, ACA, ACEN, ALA, AND, APA, ASHA, CEPH, CIDA, CSWE, NASD, NASM, NASPAA, NAST, NCATE, NRPA. **Intercollegiate Athletics:** Baseball M; Basketball M & W; Cross-Country Running M & W; Golf M & W; Soccer M & W; Softball W; Tennis M & W; Track and Field M & W; Volleyball W

THE UNIVERSITY OF NORTH CAROLINA AT PEMBROKE

One University Dr.
Pembroke, NC 28372-1510
Tel: (910)521-6000; Free: 800-949-UNCP
E-mail: lela.clark@uncp.edu
Web Site: www.uncp.edu
President/CEO: Dr. Robin G. Cummings
Admissions: Lela Clark
Financial Aid: Mildred Weber

Type: Comprehensive **Sex:** Coed **Affiliation:** University of North Carolina System. **Scores:** 87% SAT V 400+; 89% SAT M 400+; 60.94% ACT 18-23; 9.2% ACT 24-29 **% Accepted:** 74 **Admission Plans:** Deferred Admission **Application Deadline:** Rolling **Application Fee:** $45.00 **H.S. Requirements:** High school diploma required; GED accepted **Costs Per Year:** Application fee: $45. State resident tuition: $3371 full-time. Nonresident tuition: $13,819 full-time. Mandatory fees: $2193 full-time. Full-time tuition and fees vary according to course load and location. College room and board: $7377. College room only: $4750. Room and board charges vary according to board plan, housing facility, and location. **Scholarships:** Available. **Calendar System:** Semester, Summer session available **Enrollment:** Full-time 4,572, Graduate full-time 227, Graduate part-time 534, Part-time 1,108 **Faculty:** Full-time 295, Part-time 96 **Student-Faculty Ratio:** 16:1 **Exams:** ACT essay component used for admission; Other; SAT I or ACT; SAT essay component used for admission; SAT Reasoning; SAT Subject. **% Receiving Financial Aid:** 79 **% Residing in College-Owned, -Operated, or -Affiliated Housing:** 39 **Final Year or Final Semester Residency Requirement:** No **Regional Accreditation:** Southern Association of Colleges and Schools **Credit Hours For Degree:** 120 semester hours, Bachelors **ROTC:** Air Force, Army **Professional Accreditation:** AACN, CSWE, NASM, NCATE. **Intercollegiate Athletics:** Baseball M; Basketball M & W; Cheerleading M & W; Cross-Country Running M & W; Football M; Golf W; Soccer M & W; Softball W; Track and Field M & W; Volleyball W; Wrestling M

UNIVERSITY OF NORTH CAROLINA SCHOOL OF THE ARTS

1533 S Main St.
Winston-Salem, NC 27127-2738

Tel: (336)770-3399
Fax: (336)770-3370
E-mail: admissions@uncsa.edu
Web Site: www.uncsa.edu
President/CEO: Lindsay Bierman
Admissions: Sheeler Lawson
Financial Aid: Jane C. Kamiab

Type: Comprehensive **Sex:** Coed **Affiliation:** University of North Carolina system. **Scores:** 99% SAT V 400+; 97% SAT M 400+; 35.29% ACT 18-23; 52.94% ACT 24-29 **Costs Per Year:** State resident tuition: $6120 full-time, $255 per credit hour part-time. Nonresident tuition: $21,540 full-time, $897.50 per credit hour part-time. Mandatory fees: $2863 full-time, $119.29 per credit hour part-time. College room and board: $8570. College room only: $4178. Room and board charges vary according to board plan and housing facility. **Scholarships:** Available. **Calendar System:** Semester, Summer session available **Enrollment:** Full-time 838, Graduate full-time 112, Graduate part-time 2, Part-time 18 **Faculty:** Full-time 137, Part-time 50 **Student-Faculty Ratio:** 6:1 **Exams:** SAT I or ACT. **% Receiving Financial Aid:** 63 **% Residing in College-Owned, -Operated, or -Affiliated Housing:** 63 **Final Year or Final Semester Residency Requirement:** Yes **Regional Accreditation:** Southern Association of Colleges and Schools **Credit Hours For Degree:** 130 credits, Bachelors

THE UNIVERSITY OF NORTH CAROLINA WILMINGTON

601 S College Rd.
Wilmington, NC 28403-3297
Tel: (910)962-3000
Fax: (910)962-3038
E-mail: admissions@uncw.edu
Web Site: www.uncw.edu
President/CEO: Dr. Jose V. Sartarelli
Financial Aid: Frederick Holding

Type: Comprehensive **Sex:** Coed **Affiliation:** University of North Carolina System. **Scores:** 100% SAT V 400+; 100% SAT M 400+; 38.6% ACT 18-23; 54.3% ACT 24-29 **% Accepted:** 61 **Admission Plans:** Deferred Admission; Early Admission; Early Decision Plan **Application Deadline:** February 1 **Application Fee:** $75.00 **H.S. Requirements:** High school diploma required; GED accepted **Costs Per Year:** Application fee: $75. State resident tuition: $4188 full-time, $154.20 per credit hour part-time. Nonresident tuition: $18,054 full-time, $664.72 per credit hour part-time. Mandatory fees: $2503 full-time, $75.60 per credit hour part-time. Full-time tuition and fees vary according to course load and location. Part-time tuition and fees vary according to course load and location. College room and board: $9466. College room only: $5706. Room and board charges vary according to board plan and housing facility. **Scholarships:** Available. **Calendar System:** Semester, Summer session available **Enrollment:** Full-time 11,635, Graduate full-time 660, Graduate part-time 1,040, Part-time 1,583 **Faculty:** Full-time 635, Part-time 381 **Student-Faculty Ratio:** 17:1 **Exams:** ACT essay component used for admission; SAT I or ACT; SAT essay component used for admission; SAT Reasoning. **% Receiving Financial Aid:** 53 **% Residing in College-Owned, -Operated, or -Affiliated Housing:** 31 **Regional Accreditation:** Southern Association of Colleges and Schools **Credit Hours For Degree:** 124 semester hours, Bachelors **Professional Accreditation:** AACN, AACSB, ABET, ACEN, CSWE, NASM, NASPAA, NCATE, NRPA. **Intercollegiate Athletics:** Baseball M; Basketball M & W; Cheerleading M & W; Cross-Country Running M & W; Golf M & W; Soccer M & W; Softball W; Swimming and Diving M & W; Tennis M & W; Track and Field M & W; Volleyball W

UNIVERSITY OF PHOENIX–CHARLOTTE CAMPUS

3800 Arco Corporate Dr.
Charlotte, NC 28273-3409
Tel: (704)504-5409; Free: 866-766-0766
Web Site: www.phoenix.edu
President/CEO: Timothy P. Slottow
Admissions: Marc Booker

Type: Comprehensive **Sex:** Coed **Admission Plans:** Deferred Admission; Open Admission **Application Deadline:** Rolling **Application Fee:** $45.00 **H.S. Requirements:** High school diploma required; GED accepted **Scholarships:** Available. **Calendar System:** Continuous, Summer session not available **Enrollment:** Full-time 866 **Faculty:** Full-time 18, Part-time 123 **Regional Accreditation:** North Central Association of Colleges and Schools **Credit Hours For Degree:** 60 credits, Associates; 120 credits, Bachelors **Professional Accreditation:** ACBSP.

VANCE-GRANVILLE COMMUNITY COLLEGE
PO Box 917
Henderson, NC 27536-0917
Tel: (252)492-2061
Fax: (252)430-0460
Web Site: www.vgcc.edu
President/CEO: Dr. Stelfanie Williams
Admissions: Kathy Kutl

Type: Two-Year College **Sex:** Coed **Affiliation:** North Carolina Community College System. **% Accepted:** 100 **Admission Plans:** Deferred Admission; Early Admission; Open Admission; Preferred Admission **Application Deadline:** Rolling **Application Fee:** $0.00 **H.S. Requirements:** High school diploma required; GED accepted. For vocational programs: High school diploma or equivalent not required **Scholarships:** Available. **Calendar System:** Semester, Summer session available **Enrollment:** Full-time 1,718, Part-time 2,339 **Faculty:** Full-time 141, Part-time 212 **Student-Faculty Ratio:** 9:1 **Regional Accreditation:** Southern Association of Colleges and Schools **Credit Hours For Degree:** 65 semester hours, Associates **Professional Accreditation:** JRCERT.

VIRGINIA COLLEGE IN GREENSBORO
3740 S Holden Rd.
Greensboro, NC 27406
Tel: (336)398-5400
Web Site: www.vc.edu

Type: Two-Year College **Sex:** Coed **Professional Accreditation:** ACICS.

WAKE FOREST UNIVERSITY
PO Box 7373 Reynolda Station
Winston-Salem, NC 27109
Tel: (336)758-5000
Fax: (336)758-6074
E-mail: admissions@wfu.edu
Web Site: www.wfu.edu
President/CEO: Dr. Nathan O. Hatch
Admissions: Martha Allman
Financial Aid: Bill Wells

Type: University **Sex:** Coed **Scores:** 100% SAT V 400+; 100% SAT M 400+; 6.87% ACT 18-23; 38.73% ACT 24-29 **% Accepted:** 29 **Admission Plans:** Early Action; Early Admission **Application Deadline:** January 1 **Application Fee:** $50.00 **H.S. Requirements:** High school diploma required; GED accepted **Costs Per Year:** Application fee: $50. Comprehensive fee: $64,056 includes full-time tuition ($48,746), mandatory fees ($562), and college room and board ($14,748). College room only: $8750. Part-time tuition: $2020 per credit hour. **Scholarships:** Available. **Calendar System:** Semester, Summer session available **Enrollment:** Full-time 4,807, Graduate full-time 2,656, Graduate part-time 310, Part-time 64 **Faculty:** Full-time 573, Part-time 239 **Student-Faculty Ratio:** 10:1 **Exams:** ACT essay component not used; SAT I or ACT; SAT II; SAT essay component not used. **% Receiving Financial Aid:** 33 **% Residing in College-Owned, -Operated, or -Affiliated Housing:** 77 **Regional Accreditation:** Southern Association of Colleges and Schools **Credit Hours For Degree:** 120 hours, Bachelors **ROTC:** Army **Professional Accreditation:** AACSB, AALS, AANA, ABA, ACA, ACIPE, ATS, LCME/AMA, NAACLS, NCATE. **Intercollegiate Athletics:** Baseball M; Basketball M & W; Cross-Country Running M & W; Field Hockey W; Football M; Golf M & W; Soccer M & W; Tennis M & W; Track and Field M & W; Volleyball W

WAKE TECHNICAL COMMUNITY COLLEGE
9101 Fayetteville Rd.
Raleigh, NC 27603-5696
Tel: (919)662-3400
Fax: (919)662-3529
E-mail: srbloomfield@waketech.edu
Web Site: www.waketech.edu
President/CEO: Dr. Stephen Scott
Admissions: Susan Bloomfield

Type: Two-Year College **Sex:** Coed **Affiliation:** North Carolina Community College System. **Admission Plans:** Early Admission; Open Admission **Application Deadline:** Rolling **Application Fee:** $0.00 **H.S. Requirements:** High school diploma required; GED accepted **Scholarships:** Available. **Calendar System:** Semester, Summer session available **Student-Faculty Ratio:** 11:1 **Regional Accreditation:** Southern Association of Colleges and

Schools **Credit Hours For Degree:** 64 semester hours, Associates **Professional Accreditation:** ABET, ACF, ADA, JRCERT, NAACLS.

WARREN WILSON COLLEGE
PO Box 9000
Asheville, NC 28815-9000
Tel: (828)298-3325; Free: 800-934-3536
Fax: (828)298-1440
E-mail: admit@warren-wilson.edu
Web Site: www.warren-wilson.edu
President/CEO: Dr. Steven L. Solnick
Admissions: Monique Cote

Type: Comprehensive **Sex:** Coed **Affiliation:** Presbyterian Church (U.S.A.). **Scores:** 96% SAT V 400+; 92% SAT M 400+; 37% ACT 18-23; 45% ACT 24-29 **% Accepted:** 84 **Admission Plans:** Deferred Admission; Early Action; Early Admission; Early Decision Plan **Application Fee:** $0.00 **H.S. Requirements:** High school diploma required; GED accepted **Costs Per Year:** Application fee: $0. Comprehensive fee: $42,460 includes full-time tuition ($31,980), mandatory fees ($580), and college room and board ($9900). Full-time tuition and fees vary according to course load. Room and board charges vary according to board plan. Part-time tuition: $1334 per credit hour. Part-time mandatory fees: $100 per term. Part-time tuition and fees vary according to course load. **Scholarships:** Available. **Calendar System:** Semester, Summer session available **Enrollment:** Full-time 741, Graduate full-time 59, Part-time 12 **Faculty:** Full-time 63, Part-time 40 **Student-Faculty Ratio:** 10:1 **% Receiving Financial Aid:** 76 **% Residing in College-Owned, -Operated, or -Affiliated Housing:** 88 **Final Year or Final Semester Residency Requirement:** No **Regional Accreditation:** Southern Association of Colleges and Schools **Credit Hours For Degree:** 128 credit hours, Bachelors **Professional Accreditation:** CSWE. **Intercollegiate Athletics:** Basketball M & W; Cross-Country Running M & W; Soccer M & W; Swimming and Diving M & W

WAYNE COMMUNITY COLLEGE
PO Box 8002
Goldsboro, NC 27533-8002
Tel: (919)735-5151
Fax: (919)736-3204
E-mail: jbmayo@waynecc.edu
Web Site: www.waynecc.edu
President/CEO: Dr. Kay H. Albertson
Admissions: Jennifer P. Mayo

Type: Two-Year College **Sex:** Coed **Affiliation:** North Carolina Community College System. **% Accepted:** 57 **Admission Plans:** Open Admission **Application Deadline:** Rolling **Application Fee:** $0.00 **H.S. Requirements:** High school diploma required; GED accepted **Scholarships:** Available. **Calendar System:** Semester, Summer session available **Enrollment:** Full-time 1,813, Part-time 2,024 **Faculty:** Full-time 140, Part-time 193 **Student-Faculty Ratio:** 20:1 **Exams:** ACT essay component not used; SAT I or ACT; SAT essay component not used; SAT Reasoning. **Final Year or Final Semester Residency Requirement:** No **Regional Accreditation:** Southern Association of Colleges and Schools **Credit Hours For Degree:** 64 credit hours, Associates **Professional Accreditation:** AAMAE, ACEN, ADA.

WESTERN CAROLINA UNIVERSITY
Cullowhee, NC 28723
Tel: (828)227-7211; Free: 877-WCU4YOU
E-mail: admiss@email.wcu.edu
Web Site: www.wcu.edu
President/CEO: Dr. David O. Belcher
Financial Aid: Trina F. Orr

Type: Comprehensive **Sex:** Coed **Affiliation:** University of North Carolina System. **Scores:** 98% SAT V 400+; 99% SAT M 400+; 62.6% ACT 18-23; 31.8% ACT 24-29 **% Accepted:** 43 **Admission Plans:** Early Admission; Early Decision Plan **Application Fee:** $55.00 **H.S. Requirements:** High school diploma required; GED accepted **Costs Per Year:** Application fee: $55. State resident tuition: $3779 full-time. Nonresident tuition: $14,172 full-time. Mandatory fees: $3124 full-time. Full-time tuition and fees vary according to degree level. College room and board: $8131. Room and board charges vary according to board plan and housing facility. **Scholarships:** Available. **Calendar System:** Semester, Summer session available **Enrollment:** Full-time 7,373, Graduate full-time 665, Graduate part-time 930, Part-time 1,414 **Faculty:** Full-time 493, Part-time 183 **Student-Faculty Ratio:** 16:1 **Exams:** ACT essay component used for admission; SAT I or ACT; SAT essay component used for admission; SAT Reasoning. **% Receiving Financial Aid:** 67 **% Residing in College-Owned, -Operated, or -Affiliated Housing:** 42 **Regional Accreditation:** Southern Association of Colleges and Schools **Credit Hours For Degree:** 120 credit hours, Bachelors **Professional Accreditation:** AACN, AACSB, AAFCS, AANA, ABET, ACA, AHIMA, AND, APTA, ASHA, CIDA, CSWE, JRCEMTP, NAACLS, NASAD, NASM, NCATE. **Intercollegiate Athletics:** Baseball M; Basketball M & W; Cheerleading M & W; Cross-Country Running M & W; Equestrian Sports M & W; Fencing M & W; Football M; Golf M & W; Rock Climbing M & W; Rugby M; Soccer W; Softball W; Swimming and Diving M & W; Tennis M & W; Track and Field M & W; Ultimate Frisbee M & W; Volleyball W; Wrestling M

WESTERN PIEDMONT COMMUNITY COLLEGE

1001 Burkemont Ave.
Morganton, NC 28655-4511
Tel: (828)438-6000
Fax: (828)438-6015
E-mail: swilliams@wpcc.edu
Web Site: www.wpcc.edu
President/CEO: Dr. Michael Helmick
Admissions: Susan Williams
Financial Aid: Keith Conley
Type: Two-Year College **Sex:** Coed **Affiliation:** North Carolina Community College System. **Admission Plans:** Open Admission **Application Deadline:** Rolling **H.S. Requirements:** High school diploma required; GED accepted **Costs Per Year:** State resident tuition: $2368 full-time, $74 per credit hour part-time. Nonresident tuition: $8512 full-time, $266 per credit hour part-time. Mandatory fees: $145 full-time. **Scholarships:** Available. **Calendar System:** Semester, Summer session available **Final Year or Final Semester Residency Requirement:** Yes **Regional Accreditation:** Southern Association of Colleges and Schools **Credit Hours For Degree:** 64 semester hours, Associates **Professional Accreditation:** AAMAE, ACEN, ADA, NAACLS.

WILKES COMMUNITY COLLEGE

1328 Collegiate Dr.
Wilkesboro, NC 28697
Tel: (336)838-6100
Fax: (336)838-6277
E-mail: mac.warren@wilkescc.edu
Web Site: www.wilkescc.edu
President/CEO: Jeffrey Cox
Admissions: Mac Warren
Financial Aid: Vickie G. Call
Type: Two-Year College **Sex:** Coed **Affiliation:** North Carolina Community College System. **% Accepted:** 100 **Admission Plans:** Deferred Admission; Open Admission **Application Deadline:** Rolling **Application Fee:** $0.00 **H.S. Requirements:** High school diploma required; GED accepted **Scholarships:** Available. **Calendar System:** Semester, Summer session available **Faculty:** Full-time 73, Part-time 289 **Student-Faculty Ratio:** 10:1 **Regional Accreditation:** Southern Association of Colleges and Schools **Credit Hours For Degree:** 64 credit hours, Associates **Professional Accreditation:** ADA. **Intercollegiate Athletics:** Baseball M; Basketball M & W; Volleyball W

WILLIAM PEACE UNIVERSITY

15 E Peace St.
Raleigh, NC 27604-1194
Tel: (919)508-2000
Fax: (919)508-2328
E-mail: admission@peace.edu
Web Site: www.peace.edu
President/CEO: Brian C. Ralph, PhD
Financial Aid: Michelle Hemmer
Type: Four-Year College **Sex:** Coed **Affiliation:** Presbyterian Church (U.S. A.). **Scores:** 73% SAT V 400+; 76% SAT M 400+; 49.6% ACT 18-23; 8.9% ACT 24-29 **% Accepted:** 50 **Admission Plans:** Deferred Admission; Early Admission **Application Deadline:** Rolling **Application Fee:** $35.00 **H.S. Requirements:** High school diploma required; GED accepted **Costs Per Year:** Application fee: $35. Comprehensive fee: $37,430 includes full-time tuition ($26,880), mandatory fees ($200), and college room and board ($10,350). Full-time tuition and fees vary according to class time and course load. Room and board charges vary according to board plan. Part-time tuition: $896 per credit hour. Part-time tuition varies according to class time

and course load. **Scholarships:** Available. **Calendar System:** Semester, Summer session available **Enrollment:** Full-time 886, Part-time 152 **Faculty:** Full-time 26, Part-time 103 **Student-Faculty Ratio:** 15:1 **Exams:** ACT essay component not used; SAT I or ACT; SAT essay component not used; SAT Reasoning; SAT Subject. **% Receiving Financial Aid:** 90 **% Residing in College-Owned, -Operated, or -Affiliated Housing:** 66 **Final Year or Final Semester Residency Requirement:** No **Regional Accreditation:** Southern Association of Colleges and Schools **Credit Hours For Degree:** 120 semester hours, Bachelors **ROTC:** Air Force, Army, Navy **Intercollegiate Athletics:** Baseball M; Basketball M & W; Cross-Country Running M & W; Golf M; Soccer M & W; Softball W; Tennis M & W; Volleyball W

WILSON COMMUNITY COLLEGE

902 Herring Ave.
Wilson, NC 27893-3310
Tel: (252)291-1195
Fax: (252)243-7148
E-mail: mwilliams@wilsoncc.edu
Web Site: www.wilsoncc.edu
President/CEO: Dr. Rusty Stephens
Admissions: Maegan Williams
Type: Two-Year College **Sex:** Coed **Affiliation:** North Carolina Community College System. **Admission Plans:** Deferred Admission; Open Admission **Application Deadline:** Rolling **Application Fee:** $0.00 **H.S. Requirements:** High school diploma required; GED accepted **Scholarships:** Available. **Calendar System:** Semester, Summer session available **Enrollment:** Full-time 897, Part-time 940 **Faculty:** Full-time 52, Part-time 158 **Student-Faculty Ratio:** 12:1 **Regional Accreditation:** Southern Association of Colleges and Schools

WINGATE UNIVERSITY

220 N Camden St.
Wingate, NC 28174
Tel: (704)233-8000; Free: 800-755-5550
E-mail: admit@wingate.edu
Web Site: www.wingate.edu
President/CEO: Dr. Jerry McGee
Admissions: Gabe Hollingsworth
Financial Aid: Teresa G. Williams
Type: Comprehensive **Sex:** Coed **Affiliation:** Baptist. **Scores:** 95% SAT V 400+; 98% SAT M 400+; 57.1% ACT 18-23; 32% ACT 24-29 **% Accepted:** 70 **Admission Plans:** Deferred Admission **Application Deadline:** Rolling **H.S. Requirements:** High school diploma required; GED accepted **Costs Per Year:** Comprehensive fee: $39,950 includes full-time tuition ($29,170) and college room and board ($10,780). Room and board charges vary according to board plan. Part-time tuition: $915 per credit hour. Part-time tuition varies according to course load. **Scholarships:** Available. **Calendar System:** Semester, Summer session available **Enrollment:** Full-time 1,969, Graduate full-time 660, Graduate part-time 466, Part-time 54 **Faculty:** Full-time 169, Part-time 119 **Student-Faculty Ratio:** 14:1 **Exams:** SAT I or ACT; SAT Reasoning. **% Receiving Financial Aid:** 77 **% Residing in College-Owned, -Operated, or -Affiliated Housing:** 77 **Regional Accreditation:** Southern Association of Colleges and Schools **Credit Hours For Degree:** 125 credit hours, Bachelors **ROTC:** Air Force, Army **Professional Accreditation:** AAMAE, ACBSP, ACPE, JRCAT, NASM, NCATE. **Intercollegiate Athletics:** Baseball M; Basketball M & W; Cross-Country Running M & W; Football M; Golf M & W; Lacrosse M & W; Soccer M & W; Softball W; Swimming and Diving M & W; Tennis M & W; Track and Field M & W; Volleyball W

WINSTON-SALEM STATE UNIVERSITY

601 Martin Luther King Jr Dr.
Winston-Salem, NC 27110-0003
Tel: (336)750-2000; Free: 800-257-4052
Fax: (336)750-2079
E-mail: legrandet@wssu.edu
Web Site: www.wssu.edu
President/CEO: Dr. Donald Julian Reaves
Admissions: Tomikia LeGrande
Financial Aid: Raymond Solomon
Type: Comprehensive **Sex:** Coed **Affiliation:** University of North Carolina System. **Scores:** 76% SAT V 400+; 78% SAT M 400+; 39.62% ACT 18-23;

3.14% ACT 24-29 **% Accepted:** 54 **Admission Plans:** Deferred Admission **Application Deadline:** February 15 **Application Fee:** $40.00 **H.S. Requirements:** High school diploma required; GED accepted **Scholarships:** Available. **Calendar System:** Semester, Summer session available **Enrollment:** Full-time 5,327, Graduate full-time 261, Graduate part-time 206, Part-time 633 **Faculty:** Full-time 334, Part-time 2 **Student-Faculty Ratio:** 19:1 **Exams:** SAT I or ACT. **% Receiving Financial Aid:** 76 **% Residing in** **College-Owned, -Operated, or -Affiliated Housing:** 36 **Regional Accreditation:** Southern Association of Colleges and Schools **Credit Hours For Degree:** 120 semester hours, Bachelors **ROTC:** Air Force, Army **Professional Accreditation:** AACN, AACSB, ABET, AOTA, APTA, CORE, NAACLS, NASM, NCATE, NRPA. **Intercollegiate Athletics:** Basketball M & W; Bowling M & W; Cheerleading M; Cross-Country Running M & W; Football M; Golf M; Softball M & W; Tennis M & W; Volleyball W

BISMARCK STATE COLLEGE

1500 Edwards Ave.
Bismarck, ND 58506-5587
Tel: (701)224-5400; Free: 800-445-5073
Fax: (701)224-5643
E-mail: karen.erickson@bismarckstate.edu
Web Site: www.bismarckstate.edu
President/CEO: Dr. Larry Skogen, PhD
Admissions: Karen Erickson
Financial Aid: Jeff Jacobs
Type: Two-Year College **Sex:** Coed **Affiliation:** North Dakota University System. **Scores:** 53.69% ACT 18-23; 17.59% ACT 24-29 **% Accepted:** 100 **Admission Plans:** Early Admission; Open Admission **Application Deadline:** Rolling **Application Fee:** $35.00 **H.S. Requirements:** High school diploma required; GED accepted **Costs Per Year:** Application fee: $35. State resident tuition: $2,861 full-time, $119.22 per credit hour part-time. Nonresident tuition: $7,640 full-time, $318.33 per credit hour part-time. Mandatory fees: $743 full-time, $30.95 per credit hour part-time. Full-time tuition and fees vary according to course level, course load, degree level, location, program, and reciprocity agreements. Part-time tuition and fees vary according to course level, course load, degree level, location, program, and reciprocity agreements. College room and board: $7151. College room only: $2521. Room and board charges vary according to board plan and housing facility. **Scholarships:** Available. **Calendar System:** Semester, Summer session available **Enrollment:** Full-time 2,281, Part-time 1,797 **Faculty:** Full-time 133, Part-time 224 **Student-Faculty Ratio:** 14:1 **Exams:** ACT essay component not used; SAT I or ACT; SAT essay component not used; SAT Reasoning; SAT Subject. **Final Year or Final Semester Residency Requirement:** No **Regional Accreditation:** North Central Association of Colleges and Schools **Credit Hours For Degree:** 60 credits, Associates; 120 credits, Bachelors **Professional Accreditation:** ABET, ARCST, JRCEMTP, NAACLS. **Intercollegiate Athletics:** Baseball M; Basketball M & W; Golf M & W; Soccer M; Softball W; Volleyball W

CANKDESKA CIKANA COMMUNITY COLLEGE

PO Box 269
Fort Totten, ND 58335-0269
Tel: (701)766-4415; Free: 888-783-1463
Fax: (701)766-4077
Web Site: www.littlehoop.edu
President/CEO: Dr. Cynthia Lindquist
Admissions: Ermen Brown, Jr.
Type: Two-Year College **Sex:** Coed **Admission Plans:** Deferred Admission; Early Admission; Open Admission **Application Deadline:** August 22 **H.S. Requirements:** High school diploma required; GED accepted **Calendar System:** Semester, Summer session available **Student-Faculty Ratio:** 9:1 **Regional Accreditation:** North Central Association of Colleges and Schools **Credit Hours For Degree:** 61 credits, Associates

DAKOTA COLLEGE AT BOTTINEAU

105 Simrall Blvd.
Bottineau, ND 58318-1198
Tel: (701)228-2277; Free: 800-542-6866
Fax: (701)228-5499
E-mail: luann.soland@dakotacollege.edu
Web Site: www.dakotacollege.edu
President/CEO: Dr. Ken Grosz
Admissions: Luann Soland
Type: Two-Year College **Sex:** Coed **Affiliation:** Minot State University; North Dakota University System. **Admission Plans:** Deferred Admission; Early Admission; Open Admission **Application Deadline:** Rolling **Application Fee:** $35.00 **H.S. Requirements:** High school diploma required; GED accepted **Scholarships:** Available. **Calendar System:** Semester, Summer session available **Faculty:** Full-time 28, Part-time 60 **Student-Faculty Ratio:** 10:1 **Exams:** ACT; ACT essay component not used; SAT I or ACT; SAT essay component not used. **Final Year or Final Semester Residency Requirement:** Yes **Regional Accreditation:** North Central Association of Colleges and Schools **Credit Hours For Degree:** 61 credits, Associates **Intercollegiate Athletics:** Baseball M; Basketball M & W; Football M; Ice Hockey M; Softball W; Volleyball W

DICKINSON STATE UNIVERSITY

291 Campus Dr.
Dickinson, ND 58601-4896
Tel: (701)483-2507; Free: 800-279-4295
Fax: (701)483-2006
E-mail: melanie.tucker@dickinsonstate.edu
Web Site: www.dickinsonstate.edu
President/CEO: Dr. Thomas Mitzel
Admissions: Dr. Melanie Tucker
Financial Aid: Sandy Klein
Type: Four-Year College **Sex:** Coed **Affiliation:** North Dakota University System. **Scores:** 67% ACT 18-23; 19% ACT 24-29 **% Accepted:** 62 **Admission Plans:** Deferred Admission; Early Admission; Open Admission **Application Deadline:** Rolling **Application Fee:** $35.00 **H.S. Requirements:** High school diploma required; GED accepted **Costs Per Year:** Application fee: $35. State resident tuition: $5013 full-time, $208.89 per credit part-time. Nonresident tuition: $7520 full-time, $313.33 per credit part-time. Mandatory fees: $1,160 full-time, $48.31 per credit part-time, $48.31. Full-time tuition and fees vary according to course load, location, program, and reciprocity agreements. Part-time tuition and fees vary according to course load, location, program, and reciprocity agreements. College room and board: $6200. College room only: $2520. Room and board charges vary according to board plan. **Scholarships:** Available. **Calendar System:** Semester, Summer session available **Enrollment:** Full-time 896, Graduate part-time 7, Part-time 414 **Faculty:** Full-time 84, Part-time 54 **Student-Faculty Ratio:** 10:1 **Exams:** ACT essay component used for advising; ACT essay component used for placement; SAT I or ACT; SAT Reasoning; SAT Subject. **% Receiving Financial Aid:** 53 **% Residing in College-Owned, -Operated, or -Affiliated Housing:** 21 **Final Year or Final Semester Residency Requirement:** No **Regional Accreditation:** North Central Association of Colleges and Schools **Credit Hours For Degree:** 64 semester hours, Associates; 128 semester hours, Bachelors **Professional Accreditation:** ACEN, NASM, NCATE. **Intercollegiate Athletics:** Badminton M & W; Baseball M; Basketball M & W; Cheerleading M & W; Cross-Country Running M & W; Football M; Golf M & W; Softball W; Track and Field M & W; Volleyball W; Wrestling M

LAKE REGION STATE COLLEGE

1801 College Dr. N
Devils Lake, ND 58301-1598

Tel: (701)662-1600; Free: 800-443-1313
Fax: (701)662-1570
E-mail: lisa.howard@lrsc.edu
Web Site: www.lrsc.edu
President/CEO: Dr. Douglas Darling
Admissions: Lisa Howard
Financial Aid: Katie Nettell

Type: Two-Year College **Sex:** Coed **Affiliation:** North Dakota University System. **Scores:** 55% ACT 18-23; 17% ACT 24-29 **% Accepted:** 100 **Admission Plans:** Open Admission **Application Deadline:** Rolling **Application Fee:** $35.00 **H.S. Requirements:** High school diploma required; GED accepted **Costs Per Year:** Application fee: $35. State resident tuition: $3,261 full-time, $135.87 per credit part-time. Nonresident tuition: $3,261 full-time, $135.87 per credit part-time. Mandatory fees: $877 full-time, $28.78 per credit part-time. Full-time tuition and fees vary according to course load, location, and program. Part-time tuition and fees vary according to course load, location, and program. College room and board: $6055. Room and board charges vary according to board plan and housing facility. **Scholarships:** Available. **Calendar System:** Semester, Summer session available **Enrollment:** Full-time 535, Part-time 1,383 **Faculty:** Full-time 44 **Exams:** ACT essay component not used; Other; SAT I or ACT; SAT essay component not used. **% Residing in College-Owned, -Operated, or -Affiliated Housing:** 10 **Final Year or Final Semester Residency Requirement:** No **Regional Accreditation:** North Central Association of Colleges and Schools **Credit Hours For Degree:** 60 semester hours, Associates **Intercollegiate Athletics:** Baseball M; Basketball M & W; Golf M & W; Softball W; Volleyball W

MAYVILLE STATE UNIVERSITY

330 3rd St., NE
Mayville, ND 58257-1299
Tel: (701)786-2301; Free: 800-437-4104
Fax: (701)786-4748
E-mail: james.morowski@mayvillestate.edu
Web Site: www.mayvillestate.edu
President/CEO: Dr. Gary Hagen
Admissions: Jim Morowski
Financial Aid: Shirley Hanson

Type: Four-Year College **Sex:** Coed **Affiliation:** North Dakota University System. **Scores:** 52% ACT 18-23; 17% ACT 24-29 **% Accepted:** 57 **Admission Plans:** Deferred Admission; Open Admission **Application Deadline:** Rolling **Application Fee:** $35.00 **H.S. Requirements:** High school diploma required; GED accepted **Costs Per Year:** Application fee: $35. One-time mandatory fee: $35. State resident tuition: $4930 full-time, $205 per credit hour part-time. Nonresident tuition: $7395 full-time, $308 per credit hour part-time. Mandatory fees: $1450 full-time, $60 per credit hour part-time. Full-time tuition and fees vary according to course load, location, and reciprocity agreements. Part-time tuition and fees vary according to course load, location, and reciprocity agreements. College room and board: $5904. College room only: $2146. Room and board charges vary according to board plan and housing facility. **Scholarships:** Available. **Calendar System:** Semester, Summer session available **Enrollment:** Full-time 635, Graduate part-time 25, Part-time 421 **Faculty:** Full-time 46, Part-time 35 **Student-Faculty Ratio:** 13:1 **Exams:** ACT essay component not used; SAT I or ACT; SAT essay component not used; SAT Reasoning; SAT Subject. **% Receiving Financial Aid:** 65 **% Residing in College-Owned, -Operated, or -Affiliated Housing:** 41 **Final Year or Final Semester Residency Requirement:** No **Regional Accreditation:** North Central Association of Colleges and Schools **Credit Hours For Degree:** 64 semester hours, Associates; 120 semester hours, Bachelors **ROTC:** Air Force, Army **Professional Accreditation:** NCATE. **Intercollegiate Athletics:** Baseball M; Basketball M & W; Football M; Softball W; Volleyball W

MINOT STATE UNIVERSITY

500 University Ave., W
Minot, ND 58707-0002
Tel: (701)858-3000; Free: 800-777-0750
Fax: (701)839-6933
E-mail: askmsu@minotstateu.edu
Web Site: www.minotstateu.edu
President/CEO: Dr. David Fuller
Admissions: Kevin Harmon
Financial Aid: Laurie Weber

Type: Comprehensive **Sex:** Coed **Affiliation:** North Dakota University

System. **% Accepted:** 57 **Admission Plans:** Deferred Admission **Application Fee:** $35.00 **H.S. Requirements:** High school diploma required; GED accepted **Costs Per Year:** Application fee: $35. State resident tuition: $5,065 full-time, $266.26 per credit hour part-time. Nonresident tuition: $5,065 full-time, $266.26 per credit hour part-time. Mandatory fees: $1325 full-time. Full-time tuition and fees vary according to class time, course load, degree level, location, program, and reciprocity agreements. Part-time tuition varies according to class time, course load, degree level, location, program, and reciprocity agreements. College room and board: $6222. Room and board charges vary according to board plan and housing facility. **Scholarships:** Available. **Calendar System:** Semester, Summer session available **Enrollment:** Full-time 2,021, Graduate full-time 107, Graduate part-time 177, Part-time 1,043 **Faculty:** Full-time 167, Part-time 112 **Student-Faculty Ratio:** 12:1 **Exams:** ACT essay component used for admission; ACT essay component used for advising; ACT essay component used for placement; SAT I or ACT; SAT essay component used for admission; SAT essay component used for advising; SAT essay component used for placement; SAT Reasoning; SAT Subject. **% Receiving Financial Aid:** 45 **% Residing in College-Owned, -Operated, or -Affiliated Housing:** 21 **Regional Accreditation:** North Central Association of Colleges and Schools **Credit Hours For Degree:** 128 semester hours, Bachelors **Professional Accreditation:** ACEN, ASHA, CSWE, NASM, NCATE. **Intercollegiate Athletics:** Baseball M; Basketball M & W; Cheerleading W; Cross-Country Running M & W; Football M; Golf M & W; Ice Hockey M; Soccer W; Softball W; Track and Field M & W; Volleyball W; Wrestling M

NORTH DAKOTA STATE COLLEGE OF SCIENCE

800 N Sixth St.
Wahpeton, ND 58076
Tel: (701)671-2401; Free: 800-342-4325
Fax: (701)671-2332
E-mail: barb.mund@ndscs.edu
Web Site: www.ndscs.edu
President/CEO: Dr. John Richman
Admissions: Barb Mund
Financial Aid: Shelley Blome

Type: Two-Year College **Sex:** Coed **Affiliation:** North Dakota University System. **Scores:** 47% ACT 18-23; 13% ACT 24-29 **% Accepted:** 63 **Admission Plans:** Early Admission; Open Admission **Application Deadline:** Rolling **Application Fee:** $35.00 **H.S. Requirements:** High school diploma required; GED accepted **Scholarships:** Available. **Calendar System:** Semester, Summer session available **Enrollment:** Full-time 1,712, Part-time 1,456 **Faculty:** Full-time 108, Part-time 191 **Student-Faculty Ratio:** 13:1 **Exams:** ACT essay component not used; SAT Reasoning; SAT Subject. **% Residing in College-Owned, -Operated, or -Affiliated Housing:** 56 **Final Year or Final Semester Residency Requirement:** No **Regional Accreditation:** North Central Association of Colleges and Schools **Credit Hours For Degree:** 64 credits, Associates **Professional Accreditation:** ADA, AHIMA, AOTA. **Intercollegiate Athletics:** Basketball M & W; Football M; Softball W; Volleyball W

NORTH DAKOTA STATE UNIVERSITY

1340 Administration Ave.
Fargo, ND 58102
Tel: (701)231-8011; Free: 800-488-6378
Fax: (701)231-8802
E-mail: ndsu.admission@ndsu.edu
Web Site: www.ndsu.edu
President/CEO: Dr. Dean Bresciani
Admissions: Merideth Sherlin
Financial Aid: Jeanne Enebo

Type: University **Sex:** Coed **Affiliation:** North Dakota University System. **Scores:** 96% SAT V 400+; 95% SAT M 400+; 45.47% ACT 18-23; 41.93% ACT 24-29 **% Accepted:** 94 **Application Deadline:** August 1 **Application Fee:** $35.00 **H.S. Requirements:** High school diploma required; GED accepted **Costs Per Year:** Application fee: $35. One-time mandatory fee: $120. State resident tuition: $6762 full-time, $297.55 per credit hour part-time. Nonresident tuition: $18,056 full-time, $794.47 per credit hour part-time. Mandatory fees: $1216 full-time, $50.66 per credit hour part-time. Full-time tuition and fees vary according to course load, program, and reciprocity agreements. Part-time tuition and fees vary according to course load, program, and reciprocity agreements. College room and board: $7502. College room only: $3474. Room and board charges vary according to board plan and housing facility. **Scholarships:** Available. **Calendar System:**

Semester, Summer session available **Enrollment:** Full-time 10,676, Graduate full-time 1,008, Graduate part-time 1,471, Part-time 1,361 **Faculty:** Full-time 712, Part-time 141 **Student-Faculty Ratio:** 17:1 **Exams:** ACT essay component not used; SAT I or ACT; SAT essay component not used; SAT Reasoning; SAT Subject. **% Receiving Financial Aid:** 57 **% Residing in College-Owned, -Operated, or -Affiliated Housing:** 36 **Final Year or Final Semester Residency Requirement:** Yes **Regional Accreditation:** North Central Association of Colleges and Schools **Credit Hours For Degree:** 122 credits, Bachelors **ROTC:** Air Force, Army **Professional Accreditation:** AACN, AACSB, AAFCS, AAMFT, ABET, ACA, ACCE, ACPE, AND, ASLA, CIDA, CoARC, JRCAT, NAAB, NASAD, NASM, NAST, NCATE. **Intercollegiate Athletics:** Badminton M & W; Baseball M; Basketball M & W; Bowling M & W; Cross-Country Running M & W; Equestrian Sports W; Football M; Golf M & W; Ice Hockey M & W; Lacrosse M & W; Riflery M & W; Rugby M & W; Soccer M & W; Softball W; Track and Field M & W; Volleyball M & W; Wrestling M

NUETA HIDATSA SAHNISH COLLEGE

220 8th Ave. N
New Town, ND 58763-0490
Tel: (701)627-4738
Fax: (701)627-3609
Web Site: www.nhsc.edu
President/CEO: Russell D. Mason, Jr.

Type: Two-Year College **Sex:** Coed **Admission Plans:** Deferred Admission; Open Admission **Application Deadline:** Rolling **Application Fee:** $25.00 **H.S. Requirements:** High school diploma required; GED accepted. For those who demonstrate ability to benefit from program: High school diploma or equivalent not required **Scholarships:** Available. **Calendar System:** Semester, Summer session available **Student-Faculty Ratio:** 12:1 **Regional Accreditation:** North Central Association of Colleges and Schools **Credit Hours For Degree:** 64 semester hours, Associates

RASMUSSEN COLLEGE FARGO

4012 19th Ave. SW
Fargo, ND 58103
Tel: (701)277-3889; Free: 888-549-6755
Fax: (701)277-5604
E-mail: susan.hammerstrom@rasmussen.edu
Web Site: www.rasmussen.edu
President/CEO: Kristi Waite
Admissions: Susan Hammerstrom

Type: Four-Year College **Sex:** Coed **Affiliation:** Rasmussen College System. **Admission Plans:** Deferred Admission; Early Admission **Application Deadline:** Rolling **H.S. Requirements:** High school diploma required; GED accepted **Costs Per Year:** Tuition: $13,455 full-time. Mandatory fees: $1800 full-time. Full-time tuition and fees vary according to course level, course load, degree level, location, and program. Tuition guaranteed not to increase for student's term of enrollment. **Calendar System:** Quarter, Summer session available **Enrollment:** Full-time 189, Part-time 300 **Faculty:** Full-time 4, Part-time 4 **Student-Faculty Ratio:** 22:1 **Exams:** ACT essay component not used; Other; SAT essay component not used. **Final Year or Final Semester Residency Requirement:** No **Regional Accreditation:** North Central Association of Colleges and Schools **Credit Hours For Degree:** 90 credits, Associates; 180 credits, Bachelors **Professional Accreditation:** ACBSP, ACICS.

SITTING BULL COLLEGE

1341 92nd St.
Fort Yates, ND 58538-9701
Tel: (701)854-8000
Fax: (701)854-3403
E-mail: melodys@sbcl.edu
Web Site: www.sittingbull.edu
President/CEO: Laurel Vermillion
Admissions: Melody Silk
Financial Aid: Donna M. Seaboy

Type: Comprehensive **Sex:** Coed **% Accepted:** 100 **Admission Plans:** Early Admission; Open Admission **Application Deadline:** September 6 **Application Fee:** $10.00 **H.S. Requirements:** High school diploma required; GED accepted **Scholarships:** Available. **Calendar System:** Semester, Summer session not available **Faculty:** Full-time 16, Part-time 16 **Student-Faculty Ratio:** 6:1 **Regional Accreditation:** North Central Association of

Colleges and Schools **Credit Hours For Degree:** 67 credit hours, Associates **Intercollegiate Athletics:** Basketball M & W

TRINITY BIBLE COLLEGE

50 S 6th Ave.
Ellendale, ND 58436-7150
Tel: (701)349-3621; Free: 800-523-1603
Fax: (701)349-5443
E-mail: admissions@trinitybiblecollege.edu
Web Site: www.trinitybiblecollege.edu
President/CEO: Dr. Paul Alexander
Financial Aid: Mary Anne Whitman

Type: Comprehensive **Sex:** Coed **Affiliation:** Assemblies of God. **Admission Plans:** Deferred Admission **Application Deadline:** Rolling **Application Fee:** $25.00 **H.S. Requirements:** High school diploma required; GED accepted **Costs Per Year:** Application fee: $25. Comprehensive fee: $21,252 includes full-time tuition ($13,556), mandatory fees ($1950), and college room and board ($5746). College room only: $2686. Full-time tuition and fees vary according to course load. Room and board charges vary according to board plan, housing facility, and student level. Part-time tuition: $455 per credit hour. Part-time mandatory fees: $975 per semester hour. Part-time tuition and fees vary according to course load. **Scholarships:** Available. **Calendar System:** Semester, Summer session available **Enrollment:** Full-time 217 **Exams:** SAT I or ACT. **Credit Hours For Degree:** 60 credits, Associates; 120 credits, Bachelors **Professional Accreditation:** ABHE. **Intercollegiate Athletics:** Baseball M; Basketball M & W; Football M; Golf M; Track and Field M & W; Volleyball W; Wrestling M

TURTLE MOUNTAIN COMMUNITY COLLEGE

Box 340
Belcourt, ND 58316-0340
Tel: (701)477-7862
Fax: (701)477-7807
E-mail: jlafontaine@tm.edu
Web Site: my.tm.edu
President/CEO: Dr. James Davis
Admissions: Joni LaFontaine
Financial Aid: Wanda L. Laducer

Type: Two-Year College **Sex:** Coed **Admission Plans:** Deferred Admission; Early Admission; Open Admission **Application Deadline:** Rolling **H.S. Requirements:** High school diploma required; GED accepted **Scholarships:** Available. **Calendar System:** Semester, Summer session not available **Student-Faculty Ratio:** 19:1 **Exams:** ACT. **Regional Accreditation:** North Central Association of Colleges and Schools **Credit Hours For Degree:** 62 semester hours, Associates

UNITED TRIBES TECHNICAL COLLEGE

3315 University Dr.
Bismarck, ND 58504-7596
Tel: (701)255-3285
E-mail: vgillette@uttc.edu
Web Site: www.uttc.edu
President/CEO: Dr. David Gipp
Admissions: Vivian Gillette

Type: Two-Year College **Sex:** Coed **% Accepted:** 84 **Admission Plans:** Open Admission **Application Deadline:** Rolling **Application Fee:** $0.00 **H.S. Requirements:** High school diploma required; GED accepted **Scholarships:** Available. **Calendar System:** Semester, Summer session available **Enrollment:** Full-time 552, Part-time 52 **Faculty:** Full-time 49, Part-time 14 **Student-Faculty Ratio:** 8:1 **Regional Accreditation:** North Central Association of Colleges and Schools **Credit Hours For Degree:** 60 credit hours, Associates **Professional Accreditation:** AHIMA. **Intercollegiate Athletics:** Basketball M; Cross-Country Running M & W

UNIVERSITY OF JAMESTOWN

6000 College Ln.
Jamestown, ND 58405
Tel: (701)252-3467; Free: 800-336-2554
Fax: (701)253-4318
E-mail: admissions@uj.edu
Web Site: www.uj.edu
President/CEO: Dr. Robert S. Badal
Admissions: Mike Heitkamp
Financial Aid: Judy Hager

Type: Comprehensive Sex: Coed Affiliation: Presbyterian. Scores: 79% SAT V 400+; 85% SAT M 400+; 58% ACT 18-23; 27% ACT 24-29 % Accepted: 65 Admission Plans: Deferred Admission Application Deadline: Rolling Application Fee: $0.00 H.S. Requirements: High school diploma required; GED accepted Costs Per Year: Application fee: $0. Comprehensive fee: $27,546 includes full-time tuition ($19,930), mandatory fees ($550), and college room and board ($7066). College room only: $3332. Full-time tuition and fees vary according to course load, degree level, and program. Room and board charges vary according to housing facility. Part-time tuition: $435 per credit. Part-time mandatory fees: $65 per credit. Part-time tuition and fees vary according to course load, degree level, and program. Scholarships: Available. Calendar System: Semester, Summer session available Enrollment: Full-time 846, Graduate full-time 117, Graduate part-time 1, Part-time 42 Faculty: Full-time 68, Part-time 31 Student-Faculty Ratio: 13:1 Exams: ACT essay component not used; SAT I or ACT; SAT essay component not used; SAT Reasoning; SAT Subject. % Receiving Financial Aid: 64 % Residing in College-Owned, -Operated, or -Affiliated Housing: 80 Final Year or Final Semester Residency Requirement: Yes Regional Accreditation: North Central Association of Colleges and Schools Credit Hours For Degree: 128 semester hours, Bachelors Professional Accreditation: ACEN. Intercollegiate Athletics: Baseball M; Basketball M & W; Cross-Country Running M & W; Football M; Golf M & W; Ice Hockey M; Soccer M & W; Softball W; Track and Field M & W; Volleyball W; Wrestling M & W

UNIVERSITY OF MARY

7500 University Dr.
Bismarck, ND 58504-9652
Tel: (701)255-7500; Free: 800-288-6279
Fax: (701)255-7687
E-mail: mcheitkamp@umary.edu
Web Site: www.umary.edu
President/CEO: Fr. James Patrick Shea
Admissions: Curtis Ray DeGraw
Financial Aid: Janell Thomas

Type: Comprehensive Sex: Coed Affiliation: Roman Catholic. Scores: 88% SAT V 400+; 94% SAT M 400+; 47% ACT 18-23; 40% ACT 24-29 % Accepted: 96 Admission Plans: Deferred Admission; Early Admission Application Deadline: Rolling Application Fee: $25.00 H.S. Requirements: High school diploma required; GED accepted Costs Per Year: Application fee: $25. Comprehensive fee: $23,758 includes full-time tuition ($15,990), mandatory fees ($1390), and college room and board ($6378). College room only: $2966. Full-time tuition and fees vary according to course load, degree level, program, and student level. Room and board charges vary according to board plan and housing facility. Part-time tuition: $535 per credit hour. Part-time tuition and fees vary according to course load, degree level, program, and student level. Scholarships: Available. Calendar System: Semester, Summer session available Enrollment: Full-time 1,706, Graduate full-time 556, Graduate part-time 267, Part-time 343 Faculty: Full-time 124, Part-time 148 Student-Faculty Ratio: 13:1 Exams: ACT essay component not used; SAT I or ACT. % Residing in College-Owned, -Operated, or -Affiliated Housing: 35 Final Year or Final Semester Residency Requirement: No Regional Accreditation: North Central Association of Colleges and Schools Credit Hours For Degree: 64 credit hours, Associates; 128 credit hours, Bachelors Professional Accreditation: AACN, ACEN, AOTA, APTA, CSWE, CoARC, JRCAT. Intercollegiate Athletics: Baseball M; Basketball M & W; Cross-Country Running M & W; Football M; Golf M & W; Soccer M & W; Softball W; Tennis M & W; Track and Field M & W; Volleyball W; Wrestling M

UNIVERSITY OF NORTH DAKOTA

264 Centennial Dr.
Grand Forks, ND 58202
Tel: (701)777-2011; Free: 800-CALL-UND
Fax: (701)777-3650
E-mail: und.admissions@und.edu
Web Site: www.und.edu
President/CEO: Edward T. Schafer
Admissions: Jason Trainer
Financial Aid: Janelle Kilgore

Type: University Sex: Coed Affiliation: North Dakota University System. Scores: 49% ACT 18-23; 42% ACT 24-29 % Accepted: 86 Admission Plans: Deferred Admission Application Fee: $35.00 H.S. Requirements: High school diploma required; GED accepted Costs Per Year: Application

fee: $35. State resident tuition: $6548 full-time, $273 per credit hour part-time. Nonresident tuition: $17,482 full-time, $728 per credit hour part-time. Mandatory fees: $1417 full-time. Full-time tuition and fees vary according to degree level, program, and reciprocity agreements. Part-time tuition varies according to course load, degree level, program, and reciprocity agreements. College room and board: $7236. Room and board charges vary according to board plan and housing facility. Scholarships: Available. Calendar System: Semester, Summer session available Enrollment: Full-time 9,120, Graduate full-time 1,747, Graduate part-time 1,627, Part-time 2,457 Faculty: Full-time 701, Part-time 52 Student-Faculty Ratio: 19:1 Exams: ACT essay component used for advising; ACT essay component used for placement; SAT I or ACT; SAT essay component used for advising; SAT essay component used for placement. % Receiving Financial Aid: 55 % Residing in College-Owned, -Operated, or -Affiliated Housing: 29 Regional Accreditation: North Central Association of Colleges and Schools Credit Hours For Degree: 125 credit hours, Bachelors ROTC: Air Force, Army Professional Accreditation: AABI, AACN, AACSB, AALS, AANA, ABA, ABET, AND, AOTA, APA, APTA, ASC, ASHA, ATMAE, CSWE, JRCAT, LCME/AMA, NAACLS, NASAD, NASM, NASPAA, NAST, NCATE. Intercollegiate Athletics: Baseball M; Basketball M & W; Cross-Country Running M & W; Football M; Golf M & W; Ice Hockey M & W; Soccer W; Softball W; Swimming and Diving M & W; Tennis W; Track and Field M & W; Volleyball W

VALLEY CITY STATE UNIVERSITY

101 College St., SW
Valley City, ND 58072
Tel: (701)845-7990; Free: 800-532-8641
Fax: (701)845-7245
E-mail: kaleen.peterson@vcsu.edu
Web Site: www.vcsu.edu
President/CEO: Dr. Tisa Mason
Admissions: Kaleen Peterson
Financial Aid: Betty Kuss Schumacher

Type: Comprehensive Sex: Coed Affiliation: North Dakota University System. Scores: 71% SAT V 400+; 72% SAT M 400+; 56% ACT 18-23; 23% ACT 24-29 % Accepted: 86 Admission Plans: Deferred Admission; Early Admission; Open Admission Application Deadline: Rolling Application Fee: $35.00 H.S. Requirements: High school diploma required; GED accepted Costs Per Year: Application fee: $35. State resident tuition: $5153 full-time, $172 per semester hour part-time. Nonresident tuition: $13,759 full-time, $459 per semester hour part-time. Mandatory fees: $1647 full-time, $68.61 per semester hour part-time. Full-time tuition and fees vary according to course load, location, program, and reciprocity agreements. Part-time tuition and fees vary according to course load, location, program, and reciprocity agreements. College room and board: $5900. College room only: $3190. Room and board charges vary according to board plan and housing facility. Scholarships: Available. Calendar System: Semester, Summer session available Enrollment: Full-time 784, Graduate full-time 5, Graduate part-time 139, Part-time 494 Exams: ACT essay component not used; SAT I or ACT; SAT essay component not used; SAT Reasoning; SAT Subject. % Receiving Financial Aid: 57 % Residing in College-Owned, -Operated, or -Affiliated Housing: 35 Final Year or Final Semester Residency Requirement: No Regional Accreditation: North Central Association of Colleges and Schools Credit Hours For Degree: 128 semester hours, Bachelors Professional Accreditation: NASM, NCATE. Intercollegiate Athletics: Baseball M; Basketball M & W; Cross-Country Running M & W; Football M; Golf M & W; Softball W; Tennis M & W; Track and Field M & W; Volleyball W

WILLISTON STATE COLLEGE

1410 University Ave.
Williston, ND 58801
Tel: (701)774-4200; Free: 888-863-9455
Fax: (701)774-4211
E-mail: brittney.f.oneill@willistonstate.edu
Web Site: www.willistonstate.edu
President/CEO: Dr. Raymond Nadolny
Admissions: Brittney O'Neill
Financial Aid: Anna Vinger

Type: Two-Year College Sex: Coed Affiliation: North Dakota University System. % Accepted: 80 Admission Plans: Deferred Admission; Open Admission Application Deadline: Rolling Application Fee: $35.00 H.S.

Requirements: High school diploma required; GED accepted **Costs Per Year:** Application fee: $35. One-time mandatory fee: $35. State resident tuition: $2,874 full-time, $110.54 per credit hour part-time. Nonresident tuition: $2,874 full-time, $110.54 per credit hour part-time. Mandatory fees: $1,465 full-time, $56.35 per credit hour part-time. Full-time tuition and fees vary according to course load, location, program, and reciprocity agreements. Part-time tuition and fees vary according to course load, location, program, and reciprocity agreements. College room and board: $9572. College room only: $6000. Room and board charges vary according to board plan and housing facility. **Scholarships:** Available. **Calendar System:** Semester, Summer session available **Enrollment:** Full-time 603, Part-time 435 **Faculty:** Full-time 28, Part-time 2 **Student-Faculty Ratio:** 23:1 **Exams:** ACT essay component not used; SAT essay component not used. **Final Year or Final Semester Residency Requirement:** No **Regional Accreditation:** North Central Association of Colleges and Schools **Credit Hours For Degree:** 62 credit hours, Associates **Professional Accreditation:** APTA. **Intercollegiate Athletics:** Baseball M; Basketball M & W; Ice Hockey M; Softball W; Volleyball W

ALLEGHENY WESLEYAN COLLEGE
2161 Woodsdale Rd.
Salem, OH 44460
Tel: (330)337-6403; Free: 800-292-3153
Fax: (330)337-6255
E-mail: college@awc.edu
Web Site: www.awc.edu
President/CEO: Daniel R. Hardy, Sr.
Financial Aid: Esther Phelps
Type: Four-Year College **Sex:** Coed **Affiliation:** Wesleyan. **Admission Plans:** Open Admission **Application Fee:** $35.00 **Scholarships:** Available. **Calendar System:** Semester **Professional Accreditation:** ABHE.

AMERICAN INSTITUTE OF ALTERNATIVE MEDICINE
6685 Doubletree Ave.
Columbus, OH 43229
Tel: (614)825-6278
Web Site: www.aiam.edu
Type: Two-Year College **Sex:** Coed **Professional Accreditation:** ACCSC.

AMERICAN NATIONAL UNIVERSITY (CANTON)
4736 Dressler Rd. NW
Canton, OH 44718
Tel: (330)492-5300
Web Site: www.an.edu
Type: Comprehensive **Sex:** Coed **Professional Accreditation:** ACICS.

AMERICAN NATIONAL UNIVERSITY (CINCINNATI)
6871 Steger Dr.
Cincinnati, OH 45237
Tel: (513)761-1291
Web Site: www.an.edu
Admissions: Patrick M. Brown
Type: Comprehensive **Sex:** Coed **Professional Accreditation:** ACICS.

AMERICAN NATIONAL UNIVERSITY (CLEVELAND)
27557 Chardon Rd.
Cleveland, OH 44092
Tel: (440)944-0825
Web Site: www.an.edu
Type: Comprehensive **Sex:** Coed **Professional Accreditation:** ACICS.

AMERICAN NATIONAL UNIVERSITY (COLUMBUS)
5665 Forest Hills Blvd.
Columbus, OH 43231
Tel: (614)212-2800
Web Site: www.an.edu
Type: Comprehensive **Sex:** Coed **Professional Accreditation:** ACICS.

AMERICAN NATIONAL UNIVERSITY (KETTERING)
1837 Woodman Ctr. Dr.
Kettering, OH 45420
Tel: (937)299-9450
Web Site: www.an.edu
Admissions: Gregory J. Shields

Type: Comprehensive **Sex:** Coed **Professional Accreditation:** ACICS.

AMERICAN NATIONAL UNIVERSITY (STOW)
3855 Fishcreek Rd.
Stow, OH 44224
Tel: (330)676-1351
Web Site: www.an.edu
Type: Comprehensive **Sex:** Coed **Professional Accreditation:** ACICS.

AMERICAN NATIONAL UNIVERSITY (YOUNGSTOWN)
3487 Belmont Ave.
Youngstown, OH 44505
Tel: (330)759-0205
Web Site: www.an.edu
Type: Comprehensive **Sex:** Coed **Professional Accreditation:** ACICS.

ANTIOCH COLLEGE
1 Morgan Pl.
Yellow Springs, OH 45387
Tel: (937)767-1286
E-mail: hwingood@antiochcollege.org
Web Site: antiochcollege.org
President/CEO: Dr. Thomas Manley
Admissions: Harold Wingood
Type: Four-Year College **Sex:** Coed **Scores:** 100% SAT M 400+; 12% ACT 18-23; 50% ACT 24-29 **% Accepted:** 71 **Admission Plans:** Deferred Admission; Early Action; Early Admission **Application Deadline:** February 15 **Application Fee:** $0.00 **H.S. Requirements:** High school diploma required; GED accepted **Costs Per Year:** Application fee: $0. Comprehensive fee: $44,927 includes full-time tuition ($33,236), mandatory fees ($768), and college room and board ($10,923). College room only: $6934. Full-time tuition and fees vary according to reciprocity agreements. Part-time tuition: $500 per credit hour. Part-time tuition varies according to reciprocity agreements. **Calendar System:** Quarter, Summer session available **Enrollment:** Full-time 266 **Faculty:** Full-time 37, Part-time 8 **Student-Faculty Ratio:** 7:1 **Exams:** ACT essay component not used; SAT essay component not used. **% Residing in College-Owned, -Operated, or -Affiliated Housing:** 90 **Final Year or Final Semester Residency Requirement:** No **Regional Accreditation:** North Central Association of Colleges and Schools **Credit Hours For Degree:** 180 quarter credits, Bachelors

ANTIOCH UNIVERSITY MIDWEST
900 Dayton St.
Yellow Springs, OH 45387-1609
Tel: (937)769-1800
Fax: (937)769-1805
E-mail: alove@antioch.edu
Web Site: midwest.antioch.edu
President/CEO: Dr. Karen Schuster Webb
Admissions: Arlyn Love
Financial Aid: Tricia Webb
Type: Two-Year Upper Division **Sex:** Coed **Affiliation:** Antioch University. **Admission Plans:** Deferred Admission **Application Fee:** $45.00 **H.S. Requirements:** High school diploma required; GED accepted **Costs Per Year:** Application fee: $45. Tuition: $18,972 full-time, $527 per credit part-

time. Mandatory fees: $400 full-time. **Scholarships:** Available. **Calendar System:** Semester, Summer session available **Final Year or Final Semester Residency Requirement:** No **Regional Accreditation:** North Central Association of Colleges and Schools **Professional Accreditation:** NCATE.

ANTONELLI COLLEGE
124 E Seventh St.
Cincinnati, OH 45202
Tel: (513)241-4338; Free: 877-500-4304
Fax: (513)241-9396
E-mail: admissions.cincinnati@antonellicollege.edu
Web Site: www.antonellicollege.edu
President/CEO: Alex Brnilovich
Admissions: Rashawn Jones
Type: Two-Year College **Sex:** Coed **Admission Plans:** Deferred Admission; Early Admission; Open Admission **Application Deadline:** Rolling **Application Fee:** $100.00 **H.S. Requirements:** High school diploma required; GED accepted **Scholarships:** Available. **Calendar System:** Quarter, Summer session available **Credit Hours For Degree:** 95 credit hours, Associates **Professional Accreditation:** ACCSC.

ART ACADEMY OF CINCINNATI
1212 Jackson St.
Cincinnati, OH 45202
Tel: (513)562-6262; Free: 800-323-5692
Fax: (513)562-8778
E-mail: admissions@artacademy.edu
Web Site: www.artacademy.edu
President/CEO: Gregory Allgire Smith
Admissions: John J. Wadell
Financial Aid: Karen Geiger
Type: Comprehensive **Sex:** Coed **Scores:** 96% SAT V 400+; 93% SAT M 400+; 58% ACT 18-23; 21% ACT 24-29 **% Accepted:** 21 **Admission Plans:** Deferred Admission **Application Deadline:** June 30 **Application Fee:** $0.00 **H.S. Requirements:** High school diploma required; GED accepted **Costs Per Year:** Application fee: $0. Tuition: $26,908 full-time. Mandatory fees: $880 full-time, $1121 per contact hour part-time. College room only: $6350. Room charges vary according to housing facility. **Scholarships:** Available. **Calendar System:** Semester, Summer session available **Enrollment:** Full-time 153, Part-time 11 **Faculty:** Full-time 14, Part-time 30 **Student-Faculty Ratio:** 10:1 **Exams:** SAT I or ACT. **% Receiving Financial Aid:** 77 **% Residing in College-Owned, -Operated, or -Affiliated Housing:** 18 **Regional Accreditation:** North Central Association of Colleges and Schools **Credit Hours For Degree:** 65 credit hours, Associates; 132 credit hours, Bachelors **Professional Accreditation:** NASAD.

THE ART INSTITUTE OF CINCINNATI
1171 E Kemper Rd.
Cincinnati, OH 45246
Tel: (513)751-1206
Fax: (513)751-1209
Web Site: www.aic-arts.edu
President/CEO: Mother Sean M. Mendell
Admissions: Megan Orsburn
Type: Two-Year College **Sex:** Coed **Admission Plans:** Deferred Admission; Early Action; Early Admission **Application Deadline:** Rolling **Application Fee:** $100.00 **H.S. Requirements:** High school diploma required; GED accepted **Costs Per Year:** Application fee: $100. Tuition: $23,001 full-time, $511 per credit hour part-time. Mandatory fees: $1017 full-time. Full-time tuition and fees vary according to course load. Part-time tuition varies according to course load. Tuition guaranteed not to increase for student's term of enrollment. **Enrollment:** Full-time 30, Part-time 4 **Faculty:** Full-time 4, Part-time 7 **Student-Faculty Ratio:** 5:1 **Exams:** SAT I or ACT. **Final Year or Final Semester Residency Requirement:** No **Credit Hours For Degree:** 96 credits, Associates; 130 credits, Bachelors **Professional Accreditation:** ACCSC.

ASHLAND UNIVERSITY
401 College Ave.
Ashland, OH 44805-3702
Tel: (419)289-4142; Free: 800-882-1548
Fax: (419)289-5999
E-mail: enrollme@ashland.edu

Web Site: www.ashland.edu
President/CEO: Dr. Carlos Campo
Admissions: W.C. Vance
Financial Aid: Stephen C. Howell
Type: Comprehensive **Sex:** Coed **Affiliation:** Brethren Church. **Scores:** 93% SAT V 400+; 95% SAT M 400+; 55.8% ACT 18-23; 35.7% ACT 24-29 **% Accepted:** 73 **Admission Plans:** Deferred Admission **Application Deadline:** Rolling **Application Fee:** $0.00 **H.S. Requirements:** High school diploma required; GED accepted **Costs Per Year:** Application fee: $0. Comprehensive fee: $30,474 includes full-time tuition ($19,928), mandatory fees ($944), and college room and board ($9602). College room only: $5172. Full-time tuition and fees vary according to location and program. Room and board charges vary according to board plan, housing facility, and location. Part-time tuition: $886 per credit hour. Part-time mandatory fees: $23 per credit hour. Part-time tuition and fees vary according to course load, location, and program. **Scholarships:** Available. **Calendar System:** Semester, Summer session available **Enrollment:** Full-time 2,562, Graduate full-time 884, Graduate part-time 776, Part-time 1,206 **Faculty:** Full-time 263, Part-time 364 **Student-Faculty Ratio:** 10:1 **Exams:** SAT I or ACT; SAT Reasoning; SAT Subject. **% Receiving Financial Aid:** 76 **% Residing in College-Owned, -Operated, or -Affiliated Housing:** 86 **Final Year or Final Semester Residency Requirement:** Yes **Regional Accreditation:** North Central Association of Colleges and Schools **Credit Hours For Degree:** 120 credit hours, Bachelors **ROTC:** Air Force, Army **Professional Accreditation:** AACN, AAFCS, ACBSP, ATS, CSWE, NASM, NCATE. **Intercollegiate Athletics:** Baseball M; Basketball M & W; Cross-Country Running M & W; Football M; Golf M & W; Soccer M & W; Softball W; Swimming and Diving M & W; Tennis W; Track and Field M & W; Volleyball W; Wrestling M

ATS INSTITUTE OF TECHNOLOGY
325 Alpha Park
Highland Heights, OH 44143
Tel: (440)449-1700
Fax: (440)449-1389
E-mail: info@atsinstitute.edu
Web Site: www.atsinstitute.edu/cleveland
President/CEO: Yelena Bykov
Type: Two-Year College **Sex:** Coed **Admission Plans:** Open Admission **Application Fee:** $30.00 **H.S. Requirements:** High school diploma required; GED accepted **Exams:** Other. **Credit Hours For Degree:** 80.5 credits, Associates **Professional Accreditation:** ACICS.

AULTMAN COLLEGE OF NURSING AND HEALTH SCIENCES
2600 6th St., SW
Canton, OH 44710
Tel: (330)363-6347
E-mail: julie.peterson@aultmancollege.edu
Web Site: www.aultmancollege.edu
President/CEO: Rebecca Crowl
Admissions: Julie Peterson
Type: Four-Year College **Sex:** Coed **Scores:** 100% SAT V 400+; 100% SAT M 400+; 55% ACT 18-23; 45% ACT 24-29 **% Accepted:** 87 **Application Deadline:** February 1 **Application Fee:** $45.00 **H.S. Requirements:** High school diploma required; GED accepted **Costs Per Year:** Application fee: $45. Tuition: $15,690 full-time. Mandatory fees: $225 full-time. Full-time tuition and fees vary according to course load, degree level, and program. **Calendar System:** Semester, Summer session not available **Enrollment:** Full-time 69, Part-time 303 **Faculty:** Full-time 13, Part-time 41 **Student-Faculty Ratio:** 6:1 **Exams:** ACT essay component not used; SAT I or ACT; SAT essay component not used; SAT Reasoning; SAT Subject. **Final Year or Final Semester Residency Requirement:** No **Regional Accreditation:** North Central Association of Colleges and Schools **Credit Hours For Degree:** varies by degree program: Health Sciences (60 credits); Nursing or Radiography (73 credit hours), Associ; 120 credit hours for BSN Completion degree (32 of those credits are granted for an active RN license), Bachelors **Professional Accreditation:** ACEN.

BALDWIN WALLACE UNIVERSITY
275 Eastland Rd.
Berea, OH 44017-2088
Tel: (440)826-2900; Free: 877-BW-APPLY
Fax: (440)826-3830
E-mail: admission@bw.edu
Web Site: www.bw.edu

President/CEO: Dr. Robert C. Helmer
Admissions: Joyce J. Cendroski
Financial Aid: Dr. George L. Rolleston

Type: Comprehensive **Sex:** Coed **Affiliation:** Methodist. **Scores:** 95% SAT V 400+; 95% SAT M 400+; 43% ACT 18-23; 40% ACT 24-29 **% Accepted:** 60 **Admission Plans:** Deferred Admission **Application Deadline:** May 1 **Application Fee:** $25.00 **H.S. Requirements:** High school diploma required; GED accepted **Costs Per Year:** Application fee: $25. Comprehensive fee: $38,278 includes full-time tuition ($29,908) and college room and board ($8370). College room only: $4834. Full-time tuition varies according to class time, course level, course load, degree level, program, and reciprocity agreements. Room and board charges vary according to housing facility. Part-time tuition: $929 per semester hour. Part-time tuition varies according to class time, course level, course load, degree level, program, and reciprocity agreements. **Scholarships:** Available. **Calendar System:** Semester, Summer session available **Enrollment:** Full-time 3,056, Graduate full-time 385, Graduate part-time 242, Part-time 326 **Faculty:** Full-time 201, Part-time 253 **Student-Faculty Ratio:** 13:1 **Exams:** ACT essay component not used; SAT I or ACT; SAT Reasoning. **% Receiving Financial Aid:** 75 **% Residing in College-Owned, -Operated, or -Affiliated Housing:** 63 **Final Year or Final Semester Residency Requirement:** Yes **Regional Accreditation:** North Central Association of Colleges and Schools **Credit Hours For Degree:** 124 semester hours, Bachelors **ROTC:** Air Force, Army **Professional Accreditation:** NASM, NCATE. **Intercollegiate Athletics:** Baseball M; Basketball M & W; Cross-Country Running M & W; Football M; Golf M & W; Lacrosse M & W; Soccer M & W; Softball W; Swimming and Diving M & W; Tennis M & W; Track and Field M & W; Volleyball W; Wrestling M

BECKFIELD COLLEGE

225 Pictoria Dr.
Ste. 200
Cincinnati, OH 45246
Tel: (513)671-1920
Web Site: www.beckfield.edu

Type: Two-Year College **Sex:** Coed **Calendar System:** Quarter **Professional Accreditation:** ACICS.

BELMONT COLLEGE

120 Fox Shannon Pl.
Saint Clairsville, OH 43950-9735
Tel: (740)695-9500; Free: 800-423-1188
Fax: (740)695-2247
E-mail: msterling@btc.edu
Web Site: www.belmontcollege.edu
President/CEO: Dr. Paul F. Gasparro
Admissions: Michael Sterling

Type: Two-Year College **Sex:** Coed **Affiliation:** Ohio Board of Regents. **Admission Plans:** Early Admission; Open Admission **Application Deadline:** Rolling **H.S. Requirements:** High school diploma required; GED accepted **Scholarships:** Available. **Calendar System:** Quarter, Summer session available **Regional Accreditation:** North Central Association of Colleges and Schools **Credit Hours For Degree:** 90 credits, Associates **Professional Accreditation:** AAMAE.

BLUFFTON UNIVERSITY

1 University Dr.
Bluffton, OH 45817
Tel: (419)358-3000; Free: 800-488-3257
Fax: (419)358-3232
E-mail: admissions@bluffton.edu
Web Site: www.bluffton.edu
President/CEO: Dr. James M. Harder
Admissions: Robin Hopkins
Financial Aid: Chris Fowler

Type: Comprehensive **Sex:** Coed **Affiliation:** Mennonite. **Scores:** 60% ACT 18-23; 20% ACT 24-29 **% Accepted:** 54 **Admission Plans:** Deferred Admission **Application Deadline:** August 15 **Application Fee:** $20.00 **H.S. Requirements:** High school diploma required; GED accepted **Costs Per Year:** Application fee: $20. Comprehensive fee: $40,258 includes full-time tuition ($29,718), mandatory fees ($450), and college room and board ($10,090). Room and board charges vary according to board plan and housing facility. Part-time tuition: $1238 per credit hour. Part-time mandatory fees: $113 per term. **Scholarships:** Available. **Calendar System:** Semester, Summer session available **Enrollment:** Full-time 746, Graduate full-time 92,

Graduate part-time 9, Part-time 164 **Faculty:** Full-time 56, Part-time 40 **Student-Faculty Ratio:** 12:1 **Exams:** ACT essay component not used; SAT I or ACT; SAT essay component not used. **% Receiving Financial Aid:** 87 **% Residing in College-Owned, -Operated, or -Affiliated Housing:** 88 **Final Year or Final Semester Residency Requirement:** Yes **Regional Accreditation:** North Central Association of Colleges and Schools **Credit Hours For Degree:** 124 semester hours, Bachelors **Professional Accreditation:** CSWE, NASM, NCATE. **Intercollegiate Athletics:** Baseball M; Basketball M & W; Cross-Country Running M & W; Football M; Soccer M & W; Softball W; Track and Field M & W; Volleyball W

BOWLING GREEN STATE UNIVERSITY

Bowling Green, OH 43403
Tel: (419)372-2531
E-mail: choosebgsu@bgsu.edu
Web Site: www.bgsu.edu
President/CEO: Dr. Mary Ellen Mazey
Financial Aid: Eric Bucks

Type: University **Sex:** Coed **Scores:** 93% SAT V 400+; 93% SAT M 400+; 56.9% ACT 18-23; 32.5% ACT 24-29 **% Accepted:** 76 **Admission Plans:** Deferred Admission **Application Deadline:** July 15 **Application Fee:** $45.00 **H.S. Requirements:** High school diploma required; GED accepted **Costs Per Year:** Application fee: $45. State resident tuition: $9096 full-time, $379 per credit hour part-time. Nonresident tuition: $16,632 full-time, $693 per credit hour part-time. Mandatory fees: $1630 full-time, $67.25 per credit hour part-time. Full-time tuition and fees vary according to course load and location. Part-time tuition and fees vary according to course load and location. College room and board: $8496. Room and board charges vary according to board plan and housing facility. **Scholarships:** Available. **Calendar System:** Semester, Summer session available **Enrollment:** Full-time 13,214, Graduate full-time 1,405, Graduate part-time 1,169, Part-time 1,120 **Faculty:** Full-time 679, Part-time 328 **Student-Faculty Ratio:** 20:1 **Exams:** SAT I or ACT; SAT Reasoning. **% Receiving Financial Aid:** 68 **% Residing in College-Owned, -Operated, or -Affiliated Housing:** 42 **Final Year or Final Semester Residency Requirement:** No **Regional Accreditation:** North Central Association of Colleges and Schools **Credit Hours For Degree:** 122 credit hours, Bachelors **ROTC:** Air Force, Army **Professional Accreditation:** AACN, AACSB, AAFCS, ACA, ACCE, ACEJMC, AND, APA, APTA, ASHA, ATMAE, CEPH, CORE, CSWE, CoARC, NAACLS, NASAD, NASM, NAST, NCATE, NRPA. **Intercollegiate Athletics:** Baseball M; Basketball M & W; Cross-Country Running M & W; Football M; Golf M & W; Gymnastics W; Ice Hockey M; Soccer M & W; Softball W; Swimming and Diving W; Tennis W; Track and Field W; Volleyball W

BOWLING GREEN STATE UNIVERSITY–FIRELANDS COLLEGE

One University Dr.
Huron, OH 44839-9791
Tel: (419)433-5560
E-mail: divers@bgsu.edu
Web Site: www.firelands.bgsu.edu
President/CEO: Dr. Andrew J. Kurtz
Admissions: Debralee Divers

Type: Two-Year College **Sex:** Coed **Affiliation:** Bowling Green State University System. **Scores:** 75% SAT V 400+; 50% SAT M 400+; 51% ACT 18-23; 14% ACT 24-29 **Admission Plans:** Deferred Admission; Early Admission; Open Admission **Application Deadline:** August 6 **Application Fee:** $45.00 **H.S. Requirements:** High school diploma required; GED accepted **Costs Per Year:** Application fee: $45. State resident tuition: $4,706 full-time, $196.10 per credit hour part-time. Nonresident tuition: $12,014 full-time, $501.10 per credit hour part-time. Mandatory fees: $240 full-time, $9.35 per credit hour part-time, $120.20 per term part-time. Full-time tuition and fees vary according to location. Part-time tuition and fees vary according to location. **Calendar System:** Semester, Summer session available **Enrollment:** Full-time 1,114, Part-time 1,146 **Faculty:** Full-time 50, Part-time 76 **Student-Faculty Ratio:** 20:1 **Final Year or Final Semester Residency Requirement:** No **Regional Accreditation:** North Central Association of Colleges and Schools **Credit Hours For Degree:** 62 credit hours, Associates **ROTC:** Air Force, Army **Professional Accreditation:** AHIMA.

BRADFORD SCHOOL

2469 Stelzer Rd.
Columbus, OH 43219
Tel: (614)416-6200; Free: 800-678-7981
Web Site: www.bradfordschoolcolumbus.edu

President/CEO: Dennis Bartels

Type: Two-Year College **Sex:** Coed **Scholarships:** Available. **Calendar System:** Semester **Professional Accreditation:** ACICS.

BRIGHTWOOD COLLEGE, DAYTON CAMPUS

2800 E River Rd.
Dayton, OH 45439
Tel: (937)294-6155; Free: 800-935-1857
Fax: (937)294-2259
Web Site: www.brightwood.edu
President/CEO: Anthony Hibbs

Type: Two-Year College **Sex:** Coed **H.S. Requirements:** High school diploma required; GED accepted **Scholarships:** Available. **Calendar System:** Quarter **Professional Accreditation:** ACCSC, ACICS.

BROWN MACKIE COLLEGE–AKRON

755 White Pond Dr.
Ste. 101
Akron, OH 44320
Tel: (330)869-3600
Fax: (330)733-5853
Web Site: www.brownmackie.edu/akron
President/CEO: Drew Felberg

Type: Two-Year College **Sex:** Coed **Affiliation:** Education Management Corporation. **Calendar System:** Quarter **Professional Accreditation:** AAMAE, ACICS.

BROWN MACKIE COLLEGE–NORTH CANTON

4300 Munson St. NW
Canton, OH 44718-3674
Tel: (330)494-1214
Web Site: www.brownmackie.edu/northcanton
President/CEO: Peter Perkowski

Type: Two-Year College **Sex:** Coed **Affiliation:** Education Management Corporation. **Calendar System:** Quarter **Professional Accreditation:** ACICS.

BRYANT & STRATTON COLLEGE–AKRON CAMPUS

190 Montrose W Ave.
Akron, OH 44321
Tel: (330)598-2500
Web Site: www.bryantstratton.edu

Type: Four-Year College **Sex:** Coed **Regional Accreditation:** Middle States Association of Colleges and Schools

BRYANT & STRATTON COLLEGE–CLEVELAND CAMPUS

3121 Euclid Ave.
Cleveland, OH 44115
Tel: (216)771-1700
Fax: (216)771-1700
Web Site: www.bryantstratton.edu
President/CEO: James Ploskonka, PhD
Financial Aid: Bill Davenport

Type: Four-Year College **Sex:** Coed **Affiliation:** Bryant and Stratton College, Inc. **Admission Plans:** Deferred Admission **Application Deadline:** Rolling **H.S. Requirements:** High school diploma required; GED accepted **Scholarships:** Available. **Calendar System:** Semester, Summer session available **Enrollment:** Full-time 376, Part-time 148 **Faculty:** Full-time 13, Part-time 24 **Student-Faculty Ratio:** 10:1 **Exams:** Other; SAT I or ACT. **% Receiving Financial Aid:** 87 **% Residing in College-Owned, -Operated, or -Affiliated Housing:** 10 **Regional Accreditation:** Middle States Association of Colleges and Schools **Credit Hours For Degree:** 64 semester credit hours, Associates; 136 semester credit hours, Bachelors

BRYANT & STRATTON COLLEGE–EASTLAKE CAMPUS

35350 Curtis Blvd.
Eastlake, OH 44095
Tel: (440)510-1112
Web Site: www.bryantstratton.edu
President/CEO: Dr. Ted Hansen
Admissions: Melanie Pettit

Type: Two-Year College **Sex:** Coed **Affiliation:** Bryant and Stratton College, Inc. **Admission Plans:** Deferred Admission **Application Deadline:** Rolling **Application Fee:** $35.00 **H.S. Requirements:** High school diploma

required; GED accepted. For applicants 19 or over who meet entrance testing requirements: High school diploma required; GED not accepted **Scholarships:** Available. **Calendar System:** Semester, Summer session available **Enrollment:** Full-time 490, Part-time 272 **Faculty:** Full-time 24, Part-time 39 **Student-Faculty Ratio:** 12:1 **Exams:** Other; SAT I or ACT. **Regional Accreditation:** Middle States Association of Colleges and Schools **Credit Hours For Degree:** 68 semester hours, Associates **Professional Accreditation:** ACEN.

BRYANT & STRATTON COLLEGE–PARMA CAMPUS

12955 Snow Rd.
Parma, OH 44130-1005
Tel: (216)265-3151
Fax: (216)265-0325
E-mail: atinman@bryantstratton.edu
Web Site: www.bryantstratton.edu
President/CEO: Lisa Mason
Admissions: Andrea Inman

Type: Two-Year College **Sex:** Coed **Affiliation:** Bryant and Stratton College, Inc. **Admission Plans:** Deferred Admission **Application Deadline:** Rolling **H.S. Requirements:** High school diploma required; GED accepted. For applicants 19 or over who meet entrance testing requirements: High school diploma required; GED not accepted **Scholarships:** Available. **Calendar System:** Semester, Summer session available **Enrollment:** Full-time 288, Part-time 240 **Faculty:** Full-time 16, Part-time 41 **Student-Faculty Ratio:** 12:1 **Exams:** Other; SAT I or ACT. **Regional Accreditation:** Middle States Association of Colleges and Schools **Credit Hours For Degree:** 68 semester hours, Associates

CAPITAL UNIVERSITY

1 College and Main
Columbus, OH 43209-2394
Tel: (614)236-6011; Free: 866-544-6175
Fax: (614)236-6820
E-mail: asohl@capital.edu
Web Site: www.capital.edu
President/CEO: Dr. Denvy Bowman
Admissions: Amanda Sohl
Financial Aid: Susan Kannenwischer

Type: Comprehensive **Sex:** Coed **Affiliation:** Evangelical Lutheran Church in America. **Scores:** 97% SAT V 400+; 94% SAT M 400+; 40% ACT 18-23; 46% ACT 24-29 **% Accepted:** 72 **Admission Plans:** Deferred Admission **Application Deadline:** May 1 **Application Fee:** $25.00 **H.S. Requirements:** High school diploma required; GED accepted **Costs Per Year:** Application fee: $25. Comprehensive fee: $42,252 includes full-time tuition ($32,630), mandatory fees ($200), and college room and board ($9422). Full-time tuition and fees vary according to course load. Room and board charges vary according to board plan and housing facility. Part-time tuition: $1088 per credit hour. Part-time tuition varies according to course load. **Scholarships:** Available. **Calendar System:** Semester, Summer session available **Enrollment:** Full-time 2,514, Graduate full-time 450, Graduate part-time 250, Part-time 251 **Faculty:** Full-time 159, Part-time 263 **Student-Faculty Ratio:** 12:1 **Exams:** ACT essay component not used; SAT I or ACT; SAT essay component not used; SAT Reasoning. **% Receiving Financial Aid:** 81 **% Residing in College-Owned, -Operated, or -Affiliated Housing:** 59 **Final Year or Final Semester Residency Requirement:** No **Regional Accreditation:** North Central Association of Colleges and Schools **Credit Hours For Degree:** 124 semester hours, Bachelors **ROTC:** Air Force, Army **Professional Accreditation:** AACN, AALS, ABA, ACBSP, CSWE, JRCAT, NASM, NCATE. **Intercollegiate Athletics:** Baseball M; Basketball M & W; Cross-Country Running M & W; Football M; Golf M & W; Lacrosse M & W; Soccer M & W; Softball W; Tennis M & W; Track and Field M & W; Volleyball W

CASE WESTERN RESERVE UNIVERSITY

10900 Euclid Ave.
Cleveland, OH 44106
Tel: (216)368-2000
Fax: (216)368-5111
E-mail: admission@case.edu
Web Site: www.case.edu
President/CEO: Barbara R. Snyder
Admissions: Robert McCullough
Financial Aid: Venus M. Puliafico

Type: University **Sex:** Coed **Scores:** 100% SAT V 400+; 100% SAT M 400+; 1% ACT 18-23; 24% ACT 24-29 **% Accepted:** 36 **Admission Plans:** Deferred Admission; Early Action; Early Admission; Early Decision Plan **Application Deadline:** January 15 **Application Fee:** $0.00 **H.S. Requirements:** High school diploma required; GED accepted **Costs Per Year:** Application fee: $0. One-time mandatory fee: $510. Comprehensive fee: $58,410 includes full-time tuition ($44,156), mandatory fees ($404), and college room and board ($13,850). College room only: $8020. Room and board charges vary according to board plan, housing facility, and student level. Part-time tuition: $1840 per credit hour. Part-time tuition varies according to course load. **Scholarships:** Available. **Calendar System:** Semester, Summer session available **Enrollment:** Full-time 5,019, Graduate full-time 5,191, Graduate part-time 1,028, Part-time 102 **Faculty:** Full-time 759, Part-time 230 **Student-Faculty Ratio:** 11:1 **Exams:** ACT essay component used for admission; SAT I or ACT; SAT essay component used for admission; SAT Reasoning; SAT Subject. **% Receiving Financial Aid:** 51 **% Residing in College-Owned, -Operated, or -Affiliated Housing:** 80 **Final Year or Final Semester Residency Requirement:** Yes **Regional Accreditation:** North Central Association of Colleges and Schools **Credit Hours For Degree:** 120 credits, Bachelors **ROTC:** Air Force, Army **Professional Accreditation:** AACN, AACSB, AALS, AANA, ABA, ABET, ACEN, ACNM, ADA, AND, APA, ARCEAA, ASHA, CSWE, LCME/AMA, NASM, TEAC. **Intercollegiate Athletics:** Baseball M; Basketball M & W; Cross-Country Running M & W; Football M; Soccer M & W; Softball W; Swimming and Diving M & W; Tennis M & W; Track and Field M & W; Volleyball W; Wrestling M

CEDARVILLE UNIVERSITY

251 N Main St.
Cedarville, OH 45314-0601
Tel: (937)766-2211; Free: 800-233-2784
Fax: (937)766-7575
E-mail: admissions@cedarville.edu
Web Site: www.cedarville.edu
President/CEO: Dr. Thomas White
Admissions: Roscoe Smith
Financial Aid: Russell Kim Jenerette

Type: Comprehensive **Sex:** Coed **Affiliation:** Baptist. **Scores:** 99% SAT V 400+; 98% SAT M 400+; 25.58% ACT 18-23; 55.11% ACT 24-29 **% Accepted:** 74 **Admission Plans:** Deferred Admission; Early Admission **Application Deadline:** Rolling **Application Fee:** $30.00 **H.S. Requirements:** High school diploma required; GED accepted **Costs Per Year:** Application fee: $30. Comprehensive fee: $34,990 includes full-time tuition ($27,910), mandatory fees ($200), and college room and board ($6880). College room only: $3900. Room and board charges vary according to board plan and housing facility. Part-time tuition: $1056 per credit hour. Part-time mandatory fees: $50 per term. Part-time tuition and fees vary according to course load. **Scholarships:** Available. **Calendar System:** Semester, Summer session available **Enrollment:** Full-time 3,014, Graduate full-time 201, Graduate part-time 100, Part-time 339 **Faculty:** Full-time 193, Part-time 187 **Student-Faculty Ratio:** 13:1 **Exams:** SAT I or ACT; SAT Reasoning. **% Receiving Financial Aid:** 67 **% Residing in College-Owned, -Operated, or -Affiliated Housing:** 84 **Final Year or Final Semester Residency Requirement:** No **Regional Accreditation:** North Central Association of Colleges and Schools **Credit Hours For Degree:** 128 credit hours, Bachelors **ROTC:** Air Force, Army **Professional Accreditation:** AACN, ABET, ACBSP, CSWE, NASM, NCATE. **Intercollegiate Athletics:** Baseball M; Basketball M & W; Cheerleading M & W; Cross-Country Running M & W; Golf M; Soccer M & W; Softball W; Tennis M & W; Track and Field M & W; Volleyball W

CENTRAL OHIO TECHNICAL COLLEGE

1179 University Dr.
Newark, OH 43055-1767
Tel: (740)366-1351; Free: 800-9NEWARK
Fax: (740)366-5047
E-mail: bpulcini@cotc.edu
Web Site: www.cotc.edu
President/CEO: Dr. Bonnie L. Coe
Admissions: Brad Pulcini

Type: Two-Year College **Sex:** Coed **Affiliation:** Ohio Department of Higher Education. **Admission Plans:** Deferred Admission; Early Admission; Open Admission **Application Deadline:** Rolling **Application Fee:** $0.00 **H.S. Requirements:** High school diploma required; GED accepted **Costs Per Year:** Application fee: $0. One-time mandatory fee: $80. State resident tuition: $4296 full-time, $179 per semester hour part-time. Nonresident

tuition: $7056 full-time, $294 per semester hour part-time. **Scholarships:** Available. **Calendar System:** Semester, Summer session available **Enrollment:** Full-time 969, Part-time 2,597 **Faculty:** Full-time 59, Part-time 183 **Student-Faculty Ratio:** 15:1 **Final Year or Final Semester Residency Requirement:** No **Regional Accreditation:** North Central Association of Colleges and Schools **Credit Hours For Degree:** 60 semester credit hours, Associates **Professional Accreditation:** ACEN, ARCST, JRCEDMS, JRCERT.

CENTRAL STATE UNIVERSITY

1400 Brush Row Rd.
Wilberforce, OH 45384
Tel: (937)376-6011; Free: 800-388-2781
Fax: (937)376-6648
E-mail: admissions@centralstate.edu
Web Site: www.centralstate.edu
President/CEO: Dr. Cynthia Jackson-Hammond
Admissions: Stephen Williams
Financial Aid: Sonia Slomba

Type: Four-Year College **Sex:** Coed **Affiliation:** Ohio Board of Regents. **Scores:** 45% SAT V 400+; 40% SAT M 400+; 25% ACT 18-23; 1% ACT 24-29 **% Accepted:** 39 **Admission Plans:** Open Admission **Application Deadline:** June 15 **Application Fee:** $20.00 **H.S. Requirements:** High school diploma required; GED accepted **Costs Per Year:** Application fee: $20. State resident tuition: $3926 full-time, $275 per credit hour part-time. Nonresident tuition: $11,608 full-time, $625 per credit hour part-time. Mandatory fees: $2320 full-time. Full-time tuition and fees vary according to reciprocity agreements. Part-time tuition varies according to reciprocity agreements. College room and board: $9644. College room only: $5184. Room and board charges vary according to board plan and housing facility. **Scholarships:** Available. **Calendar System:** Semester, Summer session available **Enrollment:** Full-time 1,649, Graduate part-time 12, Part-time 143 **Faculty:** Full-time 94, Part-time 106 **Student-Faculty Ratio:** 13:1 **Exams:** ACT; SAT I or ACT. **% Receiving Financial Aid:** 97 **% Residing in College-Owned, -Operated, or -Affiliated Housing:** 62 **Final Year or Final Semester Residency Requirement:** No **Regional Accreditation:** North Central Association of Colleges and Schools **Credit Hours For Degree:** 124 semester hours, Bachelors **ROTC:** Army **Professional Accreditation:** ABET, NASAD, NASM, NCATE. **Intercollegiate Athletics:** Basketball M & W; Cheerleading M & W; Cross-Country Running M & W; Golf M & W; Tennis M & W; Track and Field M & W; Volleyball W

CHAMBERLAIN COLLEGE OF NURSING (CLEVELAND)

6700 Euclid Ave.
Cleveland, OH 44103
Tel: (216)361-6005; Free: 877-751-5783
Fax: (216)361-6257
Web Site: www.chamberlain.edu

Type: Four-Year College **Sex:** Coed **Application Fee:** $95.00 **H.S. Requirements:** High school diploma required; GED accepted **Costs Per Year:** Application fee: $95. Tuition: $17,560 full-time, $665 per credit hour part-time. Mandatory fees: $600 full-time, $300 per term part-time. **Enrollment:** Full-time 128, Part-time 47 **Faculty:** Full-time 9, Part-time 14 **Student-Faculty Ratio:** 11:1 **Exams:** ACT essay component used for admission; SAT I or ACT; SAT essay component used for admission. **Regional Accreditation:** North Central Association of Colleges and Schools

CHAMBERLAIN COLLEGE OF NURSING (COLUMBUS)

1350 Alum Creek Dr.
Columbus, OH 43209
Tel: (614)252-8890; Free: 877-751-5783
Fax: (614)251-6971
Web Site: www.chamberlain.edu
President/CEO: Judith Kimchi-Woods

Type: Four-Year College **Sex:** Coed **Costs Per Year:** Tuition: $17,560 full-time, $665 per credit hour part-time. Mandatory fees: $600 full-time, $300 per term part-time. Full-time tuition and fees vary according to course load. Part-time tuition and fees vary according to course load. **Calendar System:** Semester **Enrollment:** Full-time 264, Part-time 291 **Faculty:** Full-time 12, Part-time 49 **Student-Faculty Ratio:** 13:1 **Exams:** ACT essay component used for admission; SAT I or ACT; SAT essay component used for admission. **Regional Accreditation:** North Central Association of Colleges and Schools

CHATFIELD COLLEGE

20918 State Rte. 251
Saint Martin, OH 45118-9705
Tel: (513)875-3344
Fax: (513)875-3912
E-mail: admissions@chatfield.edu
Web Site: www.chatfield.edu
President/CEO: John P. Tafaro
Admissions: John Penrose
Financial Aid: Zana Smith

Type: Two-Year College **Sex:** Coed **Affiliation:** Roman Catholic Church. **% Accepted:** 94 **Admission Plans:** Deferred Admission; Early Admission; Open Admission **Application Deadline:** Rolling **Application Fee:** $10.00 **H.S. Requirements:** High school diploma required; GED accepted **Costs Per Year:** Application fee: $10. Tuition: $9698 full-time, $373 per credit hour part-time. Mandatory fees: $320 full-time, $93 per term part-time. **Scholarships:** Available. **Calendar System:** Semester, Summer session available **Enrollment:** Full-time 197, Part-time 199 **Faculty:** Full-time 5, Part-time 81 **Student-Faculty Ratio:** 8:1 **Final Year or Final Semester Residency Requirement:** No **Regional Accreditation:** North Central Association of Colleges and Schools **Credit Hours For Degree:** 64 credit hours, Associates

THE CHRIST COLLEGE OF NURSING AND HEALTH SCIENCES

2139 Auburn Ave.
Cincinnati, OH 45219
Tel: (513)585-2401
Fax: (513)585-3540
E-mail: bradley.jackson@thechristcollege.edu
Web Site: www.thechristcollege.edu
President/CEO: Dr. Nathan A. Long
Admissions: Bradley Jackson

Type: Two-Year College **Sex:** Coed **% Accepted:** 64 **Application Fee:** $45.00 **H.S. Requirements:** High school diploma required; GED accepted **Enrollment:** Full-time 202, Part-time 144 **Faculty:** Full-time 25, Part-time 16 **Student-Faculty Ratio:** 7:1 **Exams:** SAT I or ACT; SAT essay component not used. **Regional Accreditation:** North Central Association of Colleges and Schools **Credit Hours For Degree:** 72 credit hours, Associates

CINCINNATI CHRISTIAN UNIVERSITY

2700 Glenway Ave.
Cincinnati, OH 45204-3200
Tel: (513)244-8100; Free: 800-949-4CCU
Fax: (513)244-8140
E-mail: carrie.bouldin@ccuniversity.edu
Web Site: www.ccuniversity.edu
President/CEO: Ken Tracy
Admissions: Carrie Bouldin
Financial Aid: Marcella Farmer

Type: Comprehensive **Sex:** Coed **Affiliation:** Church of Christ. **Scores:** 89% SAT V 400+; 79% SAT M 400+; 44.74% ACT 18-23; 25% ACT 24-29 **% Accepted:** 59 **Admission Plans:** Deferred Admission **Application Deadline:** July 1 **Application Fee:** $40.00 **H.S. Requirements:** High school diploma required; GED accepted **Costs Per Year:** Application fee: $40. Comprehensive fee: $24,076 includes full-time tuition ($15,966), mandatory fees ($250), and college room and board ($7860). College room only: $3760. Full-time tuition and fees vary according to course load and student level. Room and board charges vary according to board plan, housing facility, and student level. Part-time tuition: $570 per semester hour. Part-time tuition varies according to course load and student level. **Scholarships:** Available. **Calendar System:** Semester, Summer session available **Enrollment:** Full-time 534, Graduate full-time 127, Graduate part-time 91, Part-time 86 **Faculty:** Full-time 34, Part-time 48 **Student-Faculty Ratio:** 15:1 **Exams:** ACT essay component not used; SAT I or ACT; SAT essay component not used; SAT Reasoning; SAT Subject. **% Receiving Financial Aid:** 83 **% Residing in College-Owned, -Operated, or -Affiliated Housing:** 45 **Final Year or Final Semester Residency Requirement:** No **Regional Accreditation:** North Central Association of Colleges and Schools **Credit Hours For Degree:** 69 semester hours, Associates; 120 semester hours, Bachelors **Professional Accreditation:** ABHE, ATS, NASM. **Intercollegiate Athletics:** Basketball M & W; Cross-Country Running M & W; Golf M; Soccer M & W; Volleyball M & W

CINCINNATI COLLEGE OF MORTUARY SCIENCE

645 W N Bend Rd.
Cincinnati, OH 45224-1462
Tel: (513)761-2020; Free: 888-377-8433
Fax: (513)761-3333
Web Site: www.ccms.edu
President/CEO: Jack Lechner
Financial Aid: Pat Leon

Type: Four-Year College **Sex:** Coed **Admission Plans:** Deferred Admission; Open Admission **Application Fee:** $50.00 **H.S. Requirements:** High school diploma required; GED accepted **Costs Per Year:** Application fee: $50. Tuition: $23,250 full-time. Tuition guaranteed not to increase for student's term of enrollment. **Scholarships:** Available. **Calendar System:** Semester, Summer session not available **Enrollment:** Full-time 100 **Faculty:** Full-time 4, Part-time 6 **Student-Faculty Ratio:** 15:1 **Exams:** ACT; Other; SAT I; SAT I and SAT II or ACT; SAT I or ACT; SAT II. **Final Year or Final Semester Residency Requirement:** Yes **Regional Accreditation:** North Central Association of Colleges and Schools **Credit Hours For Degree:** 77 semester hours, Associates; 122 Semester hours, Bachelors **Professional Accreditation:** ABFSE.

CINCINNATI STATE TECHNICAL AND COMMUNITY COLLEGE

3520 Central Pky.
Cincinnati, OH 45223-2690
Tel: (513)569-1500; Free: 877-569-0115
Fax: (513)569-1562
E-mail: adm@cincinnatistate.edu
Web Site: www.cincinnatistate.edu
President/CEO: Dr. O'dell M. Owens, Jr.
Admissions: Gabriele Boeckermann

Type: Two-Year College **Sex:** Coed **Affiliation:** Ohio Board of Regents. **Admission Plans:** Deferred Admission; Open Admission **Application Fee:** $0.00 **H.S. Requirements:** High school diploma required; GED accepted **Costs Per Year:** Application fee: $0. State resident tuition: $3567 full-time, $148.64 per credit hour part-time. Nonresident tuition: $7135 full-time, $297.28 per credit hour part-time. Mandatory fees: $258 full-time. **Scholarships:** Available. **Calendar System:** Miscellaneous, Summer session available **Enrollment:** Full-time 2,873, Part-time 6,757 **Faculty:** Full-time 196, Part-time 767 **Student-Faculty Ratio:** 11:1 **Exams:** ACT essay component not used; SAT essay component not used. **Final Year or Final Semester Residency Requirement:** No **Regional Accreditation:** North Central Association of Colleges and Schools **Credit Hours For Degree:** 60 credit hours, Associates **ROTC:** Army **Professional Accreditation:** AAMAE, ABET, ACCE, ACEN, ACF, AHIMA, AOTA, ARCST, CoARC, NAACLS. **Intercollegiate Athletics:** Basketball M & W; Golf M & W; Soccer M & W; Volleyball W

CLARK STATE COMMUNITY COLLEGE

570 E Leffel Ln.
Springfield, OH 45501-0570
Tel: (937)325-0691
E-mail: admissions@clarkstate.edu
Web Site: www.clarkstate.edu
President/CEO: Dr. Jo Alice Blondin

Type: Two-Year College **Sex:** Coed **Affiliation:** Ohio Board of Regents. **% Accepted:** 100 **Admission Plans:** Open Admission **Application Deadline:** Rolling **Application Fee:** $15.00 **H.S. Requirements:** High school diploma required; GED accepted **Costs Per Year:** Application fee: $15. State resident tuition: $2912 full-time, $139 per credit hour part-time. Nonresident tuition: $5824 full-time, $261 per credit hour part-time. Mandatory fees: $447 full-time, $7.50 per term part-time. **Scholarships:** Available. **Calendar System:** Quarter, Summer session available **Enrollment:** Full-time 1,693, Part-time 3,960 **Faculty:** Full-time 78, Part-time 394 **Student-Faculty Ratio:** 14:1 **Final Year or Final Semester Residency Requirement:** No **Regional Accreditation:** North Central Association of Colleges and Schools **Credit Hours For Degree:** 60 credit hours, Associates **ROTC:** Army **Professional Accreditation:** ACEN, APTA, NAACLS. **Intercollegiate Athletics:** Baseball M; Basketball M & W; Softball W; Volleyball W

CLEVELAND INSTITUTE OF ART

11610 Euclid Ave.
Cleveland, OH 44106
Tel: (216)421-7000; Free: 800-223-4700
Fax: (216)421-7438

E-mail: admissions@cia.edu
Web Site: www.cia.edu
President/CEO: Grafton Nunes
Financial Aid: Martin Joseph Carney, Jr.
Type: Four-Year College **Sex:** Coed **Scores:** 95% SAT V 400+; 95% SAT M 400+; 54% ACT 18-23; 36% ACT 24-29 **% Accepted:** 65 **Admission Plans:** Early Admission; Early Decision Plan **Application Deadline:** March 1 **Application Fee:** $40.00 **H.S. Requirements:** High school diploma required; GED accepted **Costs Per Year:** Application fee: $40. Comprehensive fee: $51,429 includes full-time tuition ($36,980), mandatory fees ($2595), and college room and board ($11,854). College room only: $7580. Full-time tuition and fees vary according to program, reciprocity agreements, and student level. Room and board charges vary according to board plan and housing facility. Part-time tuition: $1552 per credit. Part-time tuition varies according to course load, program, reciprocity agreements, and student level. **Scholarships:** Available. **Calendar System:** Semester, Summer session not available **Enrollment:** Full-time 600, Part-time 6 **Faculty:** Full-time 46, Part-time 62 **Student-Faculty Ratio:** 9:1 **Exams:** ACT essay component not used; SAT I or ACT; SAT essay component not used; SAT Reasoning. **% Receiving Financial Aid:** 82 **% Residing in College-Owned, -Operated, or -Affiliated Housing:** 37 **Final Year or Final Semester Residency Requirement:** Yes **Regional Accreditation:** North Central Association of Colleges and Schools **Credit Hours For Degree:** 126-135 credits, depending on program, Bachelors **Professional Accreditation:** NASAD.

CLEVELAND INSTITUTE OF MUSIC

11021 E Blvd.
Cleveland, OH 44106-1776
Tel: (216)791-5000
Fax: (216)791-1530
E-mail: william.fay@case.edu
Web Site: www.cim.edu
President/CEO: Joel Smirnoff
Admissions: William Fay
Financial Aid: Kristie Gripp
Type: Comprehensive **Sex:** Coed **% Accepted:** 44 **Admission Plans:** Deferred Admission; Early Admission **Application Deadline:** December 1 **Application Fee:** $100.00 **H.S. Requirements:** High school diploma required; GED accepted **Scholarships:** Available. **Calendar System:** Semester, Summer session available **Student-Faculty Ratio:** 7:1 **Exams:** SAT I or ACT. **% Receiving Financial Aid:** 61 **Regional Accreditation:** North Central Association of Colleges and Schools **Credit Hours For Degree:** 124 credits, Bachelors **ROTC:** Air Force, Army **Professional Accreditation:** NASM.

CLEVELAND STATE UNIVERSITY

2121 Euclid Ave.
Cleveland, OH 44115
Tel: (216)687-2000; Free: 888-CSU-OHIO
Fax: (216)687-9366
E-mail: admissions@csuohio.edu
Web Site: www.csuohio.edu
President/CEO: Dr. Ronald Berkman
Type: University **Sex:** Coed **Affiliation:** University System of Ohio. **Scores:** 89% SAT V 400+; 93% SAT M 400+; 53% ACT 18-23; 29% ACT 24-29 **% Accepted:** 91 **Admission Plans:** Deferred Admission; Early Decision Plan **Application Deadline:** May 15 **Application Fee:** $30.00 **H.S. Requirements:** High school diploma required; GED accepted **Costs Per Year:** Application fee: $30. State resident tuition: $9636 full-time, $401.50 per credit hour part-time. Nonresident tuition: $12,878 full-time, $536.60 per credit hour part-time. Mandatory fees: $60 full-time, $30 per term part-time. Full-time tuition and fees vary according to course load, degree level, and program. Part-time tuition and fees vary according to course load, degree level, and program. College room and board: $12,500. College room only: $8600. Room and board charges vary according to board plan and housing facility. **Scholarships:** Available. **Calendar System:** Semester, Summer session available **Enrollment:** Full-time 9,135, Graduate full-time 2,267, Graduate part-time 2,550, Part-time 3,308 **Faculty:** Full-time 524, Part-time 595 **Student-Faculty Ratio:** 24:1 **Exams:** SAT I or ACT; SAT Reasoning. **% Receiving Financial Aid:** 72 **% Residing in College-Owned, -Operated, or -Affiliated Housing:** 8 **Final Year or Final Semester Residency Requirement:** No **Regional Accreditation:** North Central Association of Colleges and Schools **Credit Hours For Degree:** 120 semester hours, Bachelors **ROTC:** Air Force, Army **Professional Accreditation:** AACN,

AACSB, AALS, ABA, ABET, ACA, ACSP, AOTA, APTA, ASHA, CEPH, CSWE, NASM, NASPAA, NCATE. **Intercollegiate Athletics:** Basketball M & W; Cheerleading M & W; Cross-Country Running W; Fencing M & W; Golf M & W; Soccer M & W; Softball W; Swimming and Diving M & W; Tennis M & W; Track and Field W; Volleyball W; Wrestling M

THE COLLEGE OF WOOSTER

1189 Beall Ave.
Wooster, OH 44691-2363
Tel: (330)263-2000; Free: 800-877-9905
Fax: (330)263-2621
E-mail: admissions@wooster.edu
Web Site: www.wooster.edu
President/CEO: Dr. Sarah Bolton
Admissions: Jennifer Winge
Financial Aid: Joseph Winge
Type: Four-Year College **Sex:** Coed **Affiliation:** Presbyterian Church (U.S. A.). **Scores:** 99% SAT V 400+; 100% SAT M 400+; 19% ACT 18-23; 56% ACT 24-29 **% Accepted:** 55 **Admission Plans:** Deferred Admission; Early Action; Early Admission; Early Decision Plan **Application Deadline:** February 15 **Application Fee:** $45.00 **H.S. Requirements:** High school diploma required; GED accepted **Costs Per Year:** Application fee: $45. Comprehensive fee: $55,600 includes full-time tuition ($44,520), mandatory fees ($430), and college room and board ($10,650). College room only: $5140. Full-time tuition and fees vary according to course load. Room and board charges vary according to board plan and housing facility. Part-time tuition: $1386 per credit hour. Part-time tuition varies according to course load. **Scholarships:** Available. **Calendar System:** Semester, Summer session not available **Enrollment:** Full-time 2,027, Part-time 31 **Faculty:** Full-time 171, Part-time 44 **Student-Faculty Ratio:** 11:1 **Exams:** ACT essay component used for admission; SAT I or ACT; SAT essay component used for admission; SAT Reasoning. **% Receiving Financial Aid:** 58 **% Residing in College-Owned, -Operated, or -Affiliated Housing:** 99 **Final Year or Final Semester Residency Requirement:** Yes **Regional Accreditation:** North Central Association of Colleges and Schools **Credit Hours For Degree:** 32 courses, Bachelors **Professional Accreditation:** NASM, NCATE. **Intercollegiate Athletics:** Baseball M; Basketball M & W; Cheerleading W; Cross-Country Running M & W; Equestrian Sports M & W; Field Hockey W; Football M; Golf M & W; Lacrosse M & W; Rugby M & W; Soccer M & W; Softball W; Swimming and Diving M & W; Tennis M & W; Track and Field M & W; Ultimate Frisbee M & W; Volleyball M & W

COLUMBUS COLLEGE OF ART & DESIGN

60 Cleveland Ave.
Columbus, OH 43215-1758
Tel: (614)224-9101; Free: 877-997-2223
E-mail: admissions@ccad.edu
Web Site: www.ccad.edu
President/CEO: Kevin Conlon
Financial Aid: Anna Marie Schofield
Type: Comprehensive **Sex:** Coed **Scores:** 92% SAT V 400+; 94% SAT M 400+; 50% ACT 18-23; 32% ACT 24-29 **% Accepted:** 78 **Admission Plans:** Deferred Admission **Application Deadline:** Rolling **Application Fee:** $40.00 **H.S. Requirements:** High school diploma required; GED accepted **Costs Per Year:** Application fee: $40. Comprehensive fee: $40,270 includes full-time tuition ($30,840), mandatory fees ($1040), and college room and board ($8390). Full-time tuition and fees vary according to course load. Room and board charges vary according to board plan, housing facility, location, and student level. Part-time tuition: $1285 per credit hour. Part-time tuition varies according to course load. **Scholarships:** Available. **Calendar System:** Semester, Summer session available **Enrollment:** Full-time 1,038, Graduate full-time 28, Part-time 48 **Faculty:** Full-time 69, Part-time 124 **Student-Faculty Ratio:** 10:1 **Exams:** ACT essay component not used; SAT I or ACT; SAT essay component not used. **% Receiving Financial Aid:** 77 **% Residing in College-Owned, -Operated, or -Affiliated Housing:** 37 **Regional Accreditation:** North Central Association of Colleges and Schools **Credit Hours For Degree:** 120 semester hours, Bachelors **Professional Accreditation:** CIDA, NASAD.

COLUMBUS CULINARY INSTITUTE AT BRADFORD SCHOOL

2435 Stelzer Rd.
Columbus, OH 43219
Free: 877-506-5006
Web Site: www.columbusculinary.com

Type: Two-Year College **Sex:** Coed **% Accepted:** 58 **Calendar System:** Semester

COLUMBUS STATE COMMUNITY COLLEGE

550 E Spring St.
Columbus, OH 43215
Tel: (614)287-2400; Free: 800-621-6407
Fax: (614)287-5117
E-mail: tblaney@cscc.edu
Web Site: www.cscc.edu
President/CEO: Dr. David T. Harrison
Admissions: Tari Blaney

Type: Two-Year College **Sex:** Coed **Affiliation:** Ohio Board of Regents. **% Accepted:** 91 **Admission Plans:** Deferred Admission; Early Admission; Open Admission **Application Deadline:** Rolling **Application Fee:** $50.00 **H.S. Requirements:** High school diploma or equivalent not required. For High school graduation or GED completion is required of selective admission programs in Health, Human, and Public Services: High school diploma required; GED accepted **Scholarships:** Available. **Calendar System:** Quarter, Summer session available **Enrollment:** Full-time 8,817, Part-time 16,432 **Exams:** ACT; ACT essay component not used; Other; SAT essay component not used. **Regional Accreditation:** North Central Association of Colleges and Schools **Credit Hours For Degree:** 60 semester hours, Associates **ROTC:** Air Force, Army **Professional Accreditation:** AAMAE, ABET, ACBSP, ACCE, ACEN, ACF, ADA, AHIMA, ARCST, CoARC, JRCEMTP, JRCERT, NAACLS. **Intercollegiate Athletics:** Basketball M & W; Cross-Country Running M & W; Golf M & W; Track and Field M & W; Volleyball W

CUYAHOGA COMMUNITY COLLEGE

700 Carnegie Ave.
Cleveland, OH 44115-2878
Tel: (216)987-6000; Free: 800-954-8742
Fax: (216)987-5050
Web Site: www.tri-c.edu
President/CEO: Dr. Jerry Sue Thornton
Admissions: Kevin McDaniel

Type: Two-Year College **Sex:** Coed **% Accepted:** 100 **Admission Plans:** Deferred Admission; Early Admission; Open Admission **Application Deadline:** Rolling **Application Fee:** $0.00 **H.S. Requirements:** High school diploma or equivalent not required **Costs Per Year:** Application fee: $0. Area resident tuition: $3,136 full-time, $104.54 per credit hour part-time. State resident tuition: $3,953 full-time, $131.77 per credit hour part-time. Nonresident tuition: $7,468 full-time, $248.92 per credit hour part-time. Mandatory fees: $140 full-time. **Scholarships:** Available. **Calendar System:** Semester, Summer session available **Enrollment:** Full-time 10,590, Part-time 19,475 **Faculty:** Full-time 359, Part-time 1,314 **Student-Faculty Ratio:** 18:1 **Regional Accreditation:** North Central Association of Colleges and Schools **Credit Hours For Degree:** 64 credit hours, Associates **Professional Accreditation:** ABET, ACEN, ACF, ADA, AHIMA, AOTA, APTA, ARCST, CoARC, JRCEDMS, JRCERT, JRCNMT. **Intercollegiate Athletics:** Baseball M; Basketball M; Cross-Country Running M & W; Soccer M; Softball W

DAVIS COLLEGE

4747 Monroe St.
Toledo, OH 43623-4307
Tel: (419)473-2700; Free: 800-477-7021
E-mail: tbrunner@daviscollege.edu
Web Site: daviscollege.edu
President/CEO: Pres. Diane Brunner
Admissions: Timothy Brunner

Type: Two-Year College **Sex:** Coed **Admission Plans:** Deferred Admission; Early Admission **Application Deadline:** Rolling **Application Fee:** $30.00 **H.S. Requirements:** High school diploma required; GED accepted **Costs Per Year:** Application fee: $30. Tuition: $12,600 full-time, $350 per credit hour part-time. Mandatory fees: $1050 full-time, $350 per term part-time. **Scholarships:** Available. **Calendar System:** Quarter, Summer session available **Enrollment:** Full-time 34, Part-time 125 **Faculty:** Full-time 3, Part-time 22 **Student-Faculty Ratio:** 7:1 **Regional Accreditation:** North Central Association of Colleges and Schools **Credit Hours For Degree:** 92 credit hours, Associates **Professional Accreditation:** AAMAE.

DAYMAR COLLEGE

2745 Winchester Pke.
Columbus, OH 43232
Tel: (614)643-6680; Free: 877-258-7796
E-mail: hhankinson@daymarcollege.edu
Web Site: www.daymarcollege.edu
President/CEO: Michael McMurray
Admissions: Holly Hankinson

Type: Two-Year College **Sex:** Coed **Application Fee:** $125.00 **Calendar System:** Quarter **Student-Faculty Ratio:** 11:1 **Professional Accreditation:** ACICS.

DEFIANCE COLLEGE

701 N Clinton St.
Defiance, OH 43512-1610
Tel: (419)784-4010; Free: 800-520-4632
Fax: (419)783-2468
E-mail: bharsha@defiance.edu
Web Site: www.defiance.edu
President/CEO: Dr. Richanne Mankey
Admissions: Brad Harsha
Financial Aid: Amy Francis

Type: Comprehensive **Sex:** Coed **Affiliation:** United Church of Christ. **Scores:** 77% SAT V 400+; 76% SAT M 400+; 58% ACT 18-23; 24% ACT 24-29 **% Accepted:** 66 **Admission Plans:** Deferred Admission **Application Deadline:** August 15 **Application Fee:** $25.00 **H.S. Requirements:** High school diploma required; GED accepted **Costs Per Year:** Application fee: $25. Comprehensive fee: $40,932 includes full-time tuition ($30,400), mandatory fees ($682), and college room and board ($9850). Full-time tuition and fees vary according to course load. Room and board charges vary according to housing facility. Part-time tuition: $485 per credit hour. Part-time tuition varies according to course load. **Scholarships:** Available. **Calendar System:** Semester, Summer session available **Enrollment:** Full-time 571, Graduate full-time 20, Graduate part-time 50, Part-time 95 **Faculty:** Full-time 38, Part-time 49 **Student-Faculty Ratio:** 10:1 **Exams:** ACT essay component not used; SAT I or ACT; SAT essay component not used; SAT Reasoning. **% Receiving Financial Aid:** 88 **% Residing in College-Owned, -Operated, or -Affiliated Housing:** 50 **Final Year or Final Semester Residency Requirement:** Yes **Regional Accreditation:** North Central Association of Colleges and Schools **Credit Hours For Degree:** 60 semester hours, Associates; 120 semester hours, Bachelors **Professional Accreditation:** CSWE, NCATE. **Intercollegiate Athletics:** Baseball M; Basketball M & W; Cross-Country Running M & W; Football M; Golf M & W; Lacrosse M; Soccer M & W; Softball W; Tennis M & W; Track and Field M & W; Volleyball W

DENISON UNIVERSITY

Granville, OH 43023
Tel: (740)587-0810; Free: 800-DENISON
Fax: (740)587-6306
E-mail: hills@denison.edu
Web Site: www.denison.edu
President/CEO: Pres. Adam S. Weinberg, PhD
Admissions: Michael S. Hills
Financial Aid: Laura Meek

Type: Four-Year College **Sex:** Coed **Scores:** 100% SAT V 400+; 100% SAT M 400+; 4% ACT 18-23; 56% ACT 24-29 **% Accepted:** 48 **Admission Plans:** Deferred Admission; Early Action; Early Admission **Application Deadline:** January 15 **Application Fee:** $0.00 **H.S. Requirements:** High school diploma required; GED accepted **Costs Per Year:** Application fee: $0. Comprehensive fee: $58,860 includes full-time tuition ($46,250), mandatory fees ($1040), and college room and board ($11,570). College room only: $6370. Room and board charges vary according to board plan and housing facility. Part-time tuition: $1445 per semester hour. Part-time tuition varies according to course load. **Scholarships:** Available. **Calendar System:** Semester, Summer session not available **Enrollment:** Full-time 2,253, Part-time 29 **Faculty:** Full-time 216, Part-time 30 **Student-Faculty Ratio:** 10:1 **Exams:** ACT essay component not used; SAT I or ACT; SAT essay component not used; SAT Reasoning. **% Receiving Financial Aid:** 53 **% Residing in College-Owned, -Operated, or -Affiliated Housing:** 97 **Final Year or Final Semester Residency Requirement:** No **Regional Accreditation:** North Central Association of Colleges and Schools **Credit Hours For Degree:** 127 credit hours, Bachelors **ROTC:** Army **Intercollegiate Athletics:** Baseball M; Basketball M & W; Crew M; Cross-Country

Running M & W; Equestrian Sports M & W; Field Hockey W; Football M; Golf M; Ice Hockey M; Lacrosse M & W; Riflery M & W; Rugby M & W; Sailing M & W; Skiing (Downhill) M & W; Soccer M & W; Softball W; Squash M & W; Swimming and Diving M & W; Tennis M & W; Track and Field M & W; Volleyball W

DEVRY UNIVERSITY (COLUMBUS)

1350 Alum Creek Dr.
Columbus, OH 43209-2705
Tel: (614)253-7291; Free: 866-338-7941
Web Site: www.devry.edu

Type: Comprehensive **Sex:** Coed **Application Fee:** $40.00 **H.S. Requirements:** High school diploma required; GED accepted **Costs Per Year:** Application fee: $40. Tuition: $17,052 full-time, $609 per credit hour part-time. Mandatory fees: $80 full-time, $40 per term part-time. **Scholarships:** Available. **Calendar System:** Semester **Enrollment:** Full-time 686, Graduate full-time 76, Graduate part-time 219, Part-time 990 **Faculty:** Full-time 19, Part-time 46 **Exams:** ACT essay component used for admission; ACT essay component used for placement; SAT essay component used for admission; SAT essay component used for placement. **Regional Accreditation:** North Central Association of Colleges and Schools **Professional Accreditation:** ABET, ACBSP.

DEVRY UNIVERSITY (SEVEN HILLS)

4141 Rockside Rd.
Seven Hills, OH 44131
Tel: (216)328-8754; Free: 866-338-7941
Fax: (216)328-8764
Web Site: www.devry.edu

Type: Comprehensive **Sex:** Coed **Costs Per Year:** Tuition: $17,052 full-time, $609 per credit hour part-time. Mandatory fees: $80 full-time, $40 per term part-time. **Scholarships:** Available. **Calendar System:** Semester **% Receiving Financial Aid:** 80 **Regional Accreditation:** North Central Association of Colleges and Schools **Professional Accreditation:** ACBSP.

EASTERN GATEWAY COMMUNITY COLLEGE

4000 Sunset Blvd.
Steubenville, OH 43952-3598
Tel: (740)264-5591; Free: 800-68-COLLEGE
Fax: (740)266-2706
E-mail: rogrodnik@egcc.edu
Web Site: www.egcc.edu
President/CEO: Dr. Jimmie Bruce
Admissions: Ryan Ogrodnik

Type: Two-Year College **Sex:** Coed **Affiliation:** Ohio Board of Regents. **% Accepted:** 100 **Admission Plans:** Deferred Admission; Early Admission; Open Admission **Application Fee:** $20.00 **H.S. Requirements:** High school diploma required; GED accepted **Costs Per Year:** Application fee: $20. Area resident tuition: $3330 full-time, $111 per credit hour part-time. State resident tuition: $3510 full-time, $117 per credit hour part-time. Nonresident tuition: $4350 full-time, $145 per credit hour part-time. **Scholarships:** Available. **Calendar System:** Semester, Summer session available **Enrollment:** Full-time 1,199, Part-time 1,825 **Faculty:** Full-time 40, Part-time 179 **Student-Faculty Ratio:** 23:1 **Exams:** ACT essay component not used; SAT I or ACT; SAT essay component not used. **Regional Accreditation:** North Central Association of Colleges and Schools **Credit Hours For Degree:** 60 semester hours, Associates **Professional Accreditation:** AAMAE, ADA, CoARC, JRCERT, NAACLS.

EDISON COMMUNITY COLLEGE

1973 Edison Dr.
Piqua, OH 45356-9253
Tel: (937)778-8600
Fax: (937)778-1920
E-mail: lcollins@edisonohio.edu
Web Site: www.edisonohio.edu
President/CEO: Dr. Doreen Larson
Admissions: Loleta Collins

Type: Two-Year College **Sex:** Coed **Affiliation:** Ohio Board of Regents. **Scores:** 56% ACT 18-23; 21% ACT 24-29 **% Accepted:** 86 **Admission Plans:** Open Admission **Application Deadline:** Rolling **Application Fee:** $0.00 **H.S. Requirements:** High school diploma required; GED accepted **Costs Per Year:** Application fee: $0. State resident tuition: $3609 full-time, $120.32 per credit hour part-time. Nonresident tuition: $7,219 full-time,

$240.64 per credit hour part-time. Mandatory fees: $609 full-time, $20.30 per credit hour part-time. Full-time tuition and fees vary according to class time, course level, course load, degree level, location, program, reciprocity agreements, and student level. Part-time tuition and fees vary according to class time, course level, course load, degree level, location, program, reciprocity agreements, and student level. **Calendar System:** Semester, Summer session available **Enrollment:** Full-time 806, Part-time 2,327 **Faculty:** Full-time 52, Part-time 126 **Student-Faculty Ratio:** 17:1 **Exams:** ACT essay component not used; Other; SAT essay component not used. **Final Year or Final Semester Residency Requirement:** No **Regional Accreditation:** North Central Association of Colleges and Schools **Credit Hours For Degree:** 60 credit hours, Associates **Professional Accreditation:** ACEN. **Intercollegiate Athletics:** Baseball M; Basketball M & W; Volleyball W

ETI TECHNICAL COLLEGE OF NILES

2076 Youngstown-Warren Rd.
Niles, OH 44446-4398
Tel: (330)652-9919
Fax: (330)652-4399
E-mail: dianemarsteller@eticollege.edu
Web Site: eticollege.edu
President/CEO: Renee Zuzolo
Admissions: Diane Marsteller
Financial Aid: Kay E. Madigan

Type: Two-Year College **Sex:** Coed **% Accepted:** 100 **Admission Plans:** Deferred Admission; Early Admission **Application Deadline:** Rolling **Application Fee:** $50.00 **H.S. Requirements:** High school diploma required; GED accepted **Costs Per Year:** Application fee: $50. Tuition: $11,000 full-time, $400 per credit part-time. Mandatory fees: $500 full-time, $250 per term part-time. Full-time tuition and fees vary according to course load, degree level, and program. Part-time tuition and fees vary according to course load, degree level, and program. Tuition guaranteed not to increase for student's term of enrollment. **Scholarships:** Available. **Calendar System:** Semester, Summer session not available **Enrollment:** Full-time 62, Part-time 62 **Faculty:** Full-time 8, Part-time 15 **Student-Faculty Ratio:** 5:1 **Exams:** ACT; SAT I. **Final Year or Final Semester Residency Requirement:** No **Credit Hours For Degree:** 66 credits, Associates **Professional Accreditation:** ACCSC.

FORTIS COLLEGE (CENTERVILLE)

555 E Alex Bell Rd.
Centerville, OH 45459
Tel: (937)433-3410; Free: 855-4-FORTIS
Fax: (937)435-6516
E-mail: twallace@retstechcenter.com
Web Site: www.fortis.edu
President/CEO: Dr. Richard S. Rucker, PhD
Admissions: Tony Wallace

Type: Two-Year College **Sex:** Coed **Admission Plans:** Deferred Admission; Early Admission **Application Deadline:** Rolling **Application Fee:** $100.00 **H.S. Requirements:** High school diploma required; GED accepted **Scholarships:** Available. **Calendar System:** Semester, Summer session available **Enrollment:** Full-time 533 **Faculty:** Full-time 41, Part-time 81 **Student-Faculty Ratio:** 18:1 **Professional Accreditation:** AAMAE, ACCSC, ACEN.

FORTIS COLLEGE (CINCINNATI)

11499 Chester Rd.
Ste. 200
Cincinnati, OH 45246
Tel: (513)771-2795; Free: 855-4-FORTIS
Web Site: www.fortis.edu

Type: Two-Year College **Sex:** Coed **Professional Accreditation:** ABHES.

FORTIS COLLEGE (CUYAHOGA FALLS)

2545 Bailey Rd.
Cuyahoga Falls, OH 44221
Tel: (330)923-9959; Free: 855-4-FORTIS
Fax: (330)923-0886
Web Site: www.fortis.edu
President/CEO: Carson Burke

Type: Two-Year College **Sex:** Coed **Application Fee:** $55.00 **Student-Faculty Ratio:** 13:1 **Professional Accreditation:** ACCSC.

FORTIS COLLEGE (RAVENNA)

653 Enterprise Pky.
Ravenna, OH 44266
Tel: (330)297-7319; Free: 855-4-FORTIS
Fax: (330)297-7315
Web Site: www.fortis.edu
President/CEO: Sonya Hartburg
Type: Two-Year College **Sex:** Coed **Application Fee:** $60.00 **Scholarships:** Available. **Professional Accreditation:** ACICS.

FORTIS COLLEGE (WESTERVILLE)

4151 Executive Pky.
Ste. 120
Westerville, OH 43081
Tel: (614)882-2551; Free: 855-4-FORTIS
Web Site: www.fortis.edu
Type: Two-Year College **Sex:** Coed **Professional Accreditation:** ABHES.

FRANCISCAN UNIVERSITY OF STEUBENVILLE

1235 University Blvd.
Steubenville, OH 43952-1763
Tel: (740)283-3771; Free: 800-783-6220
Fax: (740)283-6472
E-mail: admissions@franciscan.edu
Web Site: www.franciscan.edu
President/CEO: Rev. Sean O. Sheridan, TOR
Admissions: Margaret Weber
Financial Aid: John Herrmann
Type: Comprehensive **Sex:** Coed **Affiliation:** Roman Catholic. **Scores:** 100% SAT V 400+; 99% SAT M 400+; 33.07% ACT 18-23; 48.03% ACT 24-29 **% Accepted:** 79 **Admission Plans:** Deferred Admission **Application Deadline:** Rolling **Application Fee:** $20.00 **H.S. Requirements:** High school diploma required; GED accepted **Costs Per Year:** Application fee: $20. Comprehensive fee: $33,980 includes full-time tuition ($25,220), mandatory fees ($460), and college room and board ($8300). College room only: $4800. Room and board charges vary according to board plan. **Scholarships:** Available. **Calendar System:** Semester, Summer session available **Enrollment:** Full-time 2,007, Graduate full-time 141, Graduate part-time 472, Part-time 96 **Faculty:** Full-time 120, Part-time 122 **Student-Faculty Ratio:** 14:1 **Exams:** ACT essay component not used; SAT I or ACT; SAT essay component not used; SAT Reasoning. **% Receiving Financial Aid:** 63 **% Residing in College-Owned, -Operated, or -Affiliated Housing:** 83 **Final Year or Final Semester Residency Requirement:** Yes **Regional Accreditation:** North Central Association of Colleges and Schools **Credit Hours For Degree:** 60 credit hours, Associates; 124 credit hours, Bachelors **ROTC:** Air Force, Army **Professional Accreditation:** ACEN, NCATE. **Intercollegiate Athletics:** Basketball M & W; Cross-Country Running M & W; Lacrosse M & W; Rugby M; Soccer M & W; Softball W; Swimming and Diving W; Tennis M & W; Track and Field M & W; Volleyball W

FRANKLIN UNIVERSITY

201 S Grant Ave.
Columbus, OH 43215-5399
Tel: (614)797-4700; Free: 877-341-6300
Fax: (614)224-8027
E-mail: hulll@franklin.edu
Web Site: www.franklin.edu
President/CEO: Dr. David R. Decker
Admissions: Lynne Hull
Financial Aid: Marlowe Collier
Type: Comprehensive **Sex:** Coed **Admission Plans:** Deferred Admission; Open Admission **Application Deadline:** Rolling **Application Fee:** $0.00 **H.S. Requirements:** High school diploma required; GED accepted **Costs Per Year:** Application fee: $0. One-time mandatory fee: $25. Tuition: $14,520 full-time, $484 per credit hour part-time. Full-time tuition varies according to program. Part-time tuition varies according to program. **Scholarships:** Available. **Calendar System:** Trimester, Summer session available **Enrollment:** Full-time 1,571, Graduate full-time 792, Graduate part-time 266, Part-time 3,105 **Faculty:** Full-time 61, Part-time 753 **Student-Faculty Ratio:** 11:1 **% Receiving Financial Aid:** 57 **Final Year or Final Semester Residency Requirement:** No **Regional Accreditation:** North Central Association of Colleges and Schools **Credit Hours For Degree:** 64 credit hours, Associates; 124 credit hours, Bachelors **ROTC:** Air Force, Army

GALEN COLLEGE OF NURSING

100 E Business Way
Ste. 200
Cincinnati, OH 45241
Tel: (513)475-3600; Free: 877-223-7040
Web Site: www.galencollege.edu
Type: Four-Year College **Sex:** Coed **Regional Accreditation:** Southern Association of Colleges and Schools

GALLIPOLIS CAREER COLLEGE

1176 Jackson Pke.
Ste. 312
Gallipolis, OH 45631
Tel: (740)446-4367; Free: 800-214-0452
Fax: (740)446-4124
E-mail: admissions@gallipoliscareercollege.com
Web Site: gallipoliscareercollege.edu
President/CEO: Robert L. Shirey
Admissions: Jack Henson
Type: Two-Year College **Sex:** Coed **Application Deadline:** Rolling **Application Fee:** $50.00 **H.S. Requirements:** High school diploma required; GED accepted **Costs Per Year:** Application fee: $50. Tuition: $12,000 full-time. Tuition guaranteed not to increase for student's term of enrollment. **Calendar System:** Quarter, Summer session available **Enrollment:** Full-time 145, Part-time 9 **Faculty:** Full-time 2, Part-time 14 **Student-Faculty Ratio:** 22:1 **Exams:** Other. **Credit Hours For Degree:** 100 quarter hours, Associates **Professional Accreditation:** ACICS.

GOD'S BIBLE SCHOOL AND COLLEGE

1810 Young St.
Cincinnati, OH 45202-6838
Tel: (513)721-7944; Free: 800-486-4637
Fax: (513)721-3971
E-mail: hcouch@gbs.edu
Web Site: www.gbs.edu
President/CEO: Dr. Michael R. Avery
Admissions: Heather Couch
Financial Aid: Lori Waggoner
Type: Four-Year College **Sex:** Coed **Affiliation:** interdenominational. **% Accepted:** 90 **Application Deadline:** August 18 **Application Fee:** $25.00 **H.S. Requirements:** High school diploma required; GED accepted **Scholarships:** Available. **Calendar System:** Semester, Summer session available **Student-Faculty Ratio:** 12:1 **Exams:** SAT I; SAT I or ACT. **Regional Accreditation:** North Central Association of Colleges and Schools **Credit Hours For Degree:** 65 semester hours, Associates; 130 semester hours, Bachelors **Professional Accreditation:** ABHE.

GOOD SAMARITAN COLLEGE OF NURSING AND HEALTH SCIENCE

375 Dixmyth Ave.
Cincinnati, OH 45220
Tel: (513)862-2743
Fax: (513)862-3572
Web Site: www.gscollege.edu
President/CEO: Morris Cohen
Financial Aid: Linda Hayes
Type: Two-Year College **Sex:** Coed **Affiliation:** Good Samaritan College is a hospital-based program within Good Samaritan Hospital. **Scores:** 67% SAT V 400+; 70% ACT 18-23; 14% ACT 24-29 **% Accepted:** 79 **Application Fee:** $40.00 **H.S. Requirements:** High school diploma required; GED accepted **Costs Per Year:** Application fee: $40. Tuition: $13,304 full-time, $512 per credit hour part-time. Mandatory fees: $1750 full-time, $80 per credit hour part-time. **Scholarships:** Available. **Calendar System:** Semester, Summer session available **Enrollment:** Full-time 128, Part-time 225 **Faculty:** Full-time 30, Part-time 11 **Student-Faculty Ratio:** 7:1 **Exams:** SAT I or ACT. **Regional Accreditation:** North Central Association of Colleges and Schools **Credit Hours For Degree:** 73 credit hours, Associates; 121 credit hours, Bachelors **Professional Accreditation:** ACEN.

HARRISON COLLEGE

3880 Jackpot Rd.
Grove City, OH 43123
Tel: (614)539-8800; Free: 888-544-4422
E-mail: admissions@harrison.edu

Web Site: www.harrison.edu
President/CEO: Jason Konesco
Admissions: Jason Howanec
Type: Four-Year College **Sex:** Coed **Affiliation:** Harrison College. **% Accepted:** 100 **Application Deadline:** Rolling **Application Fee:** $0.00 **H.S. Requirements:** High school diploma required; GED accepted **Calendar System:** Quarter, Summer session available **Enrollment:** Full-time 169, Part-time 76 **Faculty:** Full-time 3, Part-time 11 **Student-Faculty Ratio:** 10:1 **Exams:** Other. **Final Year or Final Semester Residency Requirement:** No **Professional Accreditation:** ACICS.

HEIDELBERG UNIVERSITY
310 E Market St.
Tiffin, OH 44883-2462
Tel: (419)448-2000; Free: 800-434-3352
Fax: (419)448-2334
E-mail: mbrown@heidelberg.edu
Web Site: www.heidelberg.edu
President/CEO: Dr. Robert Huntington
Admissions: Mike Brown
Financial Aid: Juli L. Weininger
Type: Comprehensive **Sex:** Coed **Affiliation:** United Church of Christ. **Scores:** 98% SAT V 400+; 93% SAT M 400+; 57% ACT 18-23; 30% ACT 24-29 **% Accepted:** 79 **Admission Plans:** Deferred Admission **Application Deadline:** August 15 **Application Fee:** $0.00 **H.S. Requirements:** High school diploma required; GED accepted **Costs Per Year:** Application fee: $0. Comprehensive fee: $39,200 includes full-time tuition ($28,600), mandatory fees ($600), and college room and board ($10,000). College room only: $5100. Full-time tuition and fees vary according to course load and degree level. Room and board charges vary according to housing facility. Part-time tuition: $720 per contact hour. Part-time tuition varies according to course load and degree level. **Scholarships:** Available. **Calendar System:** Semester, Summer session available **Enrollment:** Full-time 1,014, Graduate full-time 37, Graduate part-time 146, Part-time 20 **Faculty:** Full-time 61, Part-time 91 **Student-Faculty Ratio:** 13:1 **Exams:** SAT I or ACT; SAT Reasoning; SAT Subject. **% Receiving Financial Aid:** 88 **% Residing in College-Owned, -Operated, or -Affiliated Housing:** 79 **Final Year or Final Semester Residency Requirement:** Yes **Regional Accreditation:** North Central Association of Colleges and Schools **Credit Hours For Degree:** 124 semester hours, Bachelors **ROTC:** Air Force, Army **Professional Accreditation:** ACA, ACBSP, NASM, NCATE. **Intercollegiate Athletics:** Baseball M; Basketball M & W; Cheerleading M & W; Cross-Country Running M & W; Football M; Golf M & W; Lacrosse M & W; Soccer M & W; Softball W; Tennis M & W; Track and Field M & W; Volleyball M & W; Wrestling M

HERZING UNIVERSITY (AKRON)
1600 S Arlington St.
Ste. 100
Akron, OH 44306
Tel: (330)724-1600; Free: 800-596-0724
Fax: (330)724-9688
Web Site: www.herzing.edu/akron
President/CEO: William Cassidy
Type: Two-Year College **Sex:** Coed **Regional Accreditation:** North Central Association of Colleges and Schools

HERZING UNIVERSITY (TOLEDO)
5212 Hill Ave.
Toledo, OH 43615
Tel: (419)776-0300; Free: 800-596-0724
Fax: (419)776-0315
Web Site: www.herzing.edu/toledo
President/CEO: William Cassidy
Type: Two-Year College **Sex:** Coed **Regional Accreditation:** North Central Association of Colleges and Schools

HIRAM COLLEGE
6832 Hinsdale St.
Hiram, OH 44234-0067
Tel: (330)569-3211; Free: 800-362-5280
Fax: (330)569-5944
E-mail: admission@hiram.edu
Web Site: www.hiram.edu
President/CEO: Lori E. Varlotta, PhD

Admissions: Sherman C. Dean, II
Financial Aid: Ann Marie Gruber
Type: Comprehensive **Sex:** Coed **Affiliation:** Christian Church (Disciples of Christ). **Scores:** 90% SAT V 400+; 93% SAT M 400+; 45% ACT 18-23; 39% ACT 24-29 **% Accepted:** 58 **Admission Plans:** Deferred Admission **Application Deadline:** Rolling **Application Fee:** $25.00 **H.S. Requirements:** High school diploma required; GED accepted **Costs Per Year:** Application fee: $25. Comprehensive fee: $41,720 includes full-time tuition ($30,230), mandatory fees ($1300), and college room and board ($10,190). College room only: $5150. Room and board charges vary according to housing facility. Part-time tuition: $435 per credit hour. Part-time mandatory fees: $125 per term. Tuition guaranteed not to increase for student's term of enrollment. **Scholarships:** Available. **Calendar System:** Semester, Summer session available **Enrollment:** Full-time 912, Graduate full-time 13, Graduate part-time 9, Part-time 188 **Faculty:** Full-time 79, Part-time 55 **Student-Faculty Ratio:** 10:1 **Exams:** ACT essay component not used; SAT I or ACT; SAT essay component not used; SAT Reasoning. **% Receiving Financial Aid:** 78 **% Residing in College-Owned, -Operated, or -Affiliated Housing:** 79 **Final Year or Final Semester Residency Requirement:** No **Regional Accreditation:** North Central Association of Colleges and Schools **Credit Hours For Degree:** 120 credit hours, Bachelors **ROTC:** Air Force, Army **Professional Accreditation:** AACN, NASM, NCATE. **Intercollegiate Athletics:** Baseball M; Basketball M & W; Football M; Golf M & W; Lacrosse M & W; Soccer M & W; Softball W; Swimming and Diving M & W; Volleyball W

HOCKING COLLEGE
3301 Hocking Pky.
Nelsonville, OH 45764-9588
Tel: (740)753-3591
Fax: (740)753-7065
E-mail: belcherm@hocking.edu
Web Site: www.hocking.edu
President/CEO: Dr. Ronald Erickson
Admissions: Deneene Merchant
Type: Two-Year College **Sex:** Coed **Affiliation:** Ohio Board of Regents. **% Accepted:** 100 **Admission Plans:** Open Admission **Application Deadline:** Rolling **Application Fee:** $15.00 **H.S. Requirements:** High school diploma required; GED accepted **Costs Per Year:** Application fee: $15. State resident tuition: $4390 full-time, $183 per credit hour part-time. Nonresident tuition: $8780 full-time, $366 per credit hour part-time. Full-time tuition varies according to course load and program. Part-time tuition varies according to program. College room and board: $6560. Room and board charges vary according to board plan and housing facility. **Scholarships:** Available. **Calendar System:** Semester, Summer session available **Enrollment:** Full-time 3,012, Part-time 1,082 **Faculty:** Full-time 173, Part-time 108 **Student-Faculty Ratio:** 16:1 **% Residing in College-Owned, -Operated, or -Affiliated Housing:** 18 **Final Year or Final Semester Residency Requirement:** No **Regional Accreditation:** North Central Association of Colleges and Schools **Credit Hours For Degree:** 60 credit hours, Associates **ROTC:** Army **Professional Accreditation:** AAMAE, ABET, ACBSP, ACEN, AHIMA, APTA.

HONDROS COLLEGE
4140 Executive Pky.
Westerville, OH 43081-3855
Tel: (614)508-7277; Free: 888-HONDROS
Fax: (614)508-7279
Web Site: www.hondros.edu
President/CEO: Carol L. Thomas
Admissions: Carol Thomas
Type: Two-Year College **Sex:** Coed **Admission Plans:** Open Admission **Application Fee:** $25.00 **Calendar System:** Quarter **Professional Accreditation:** ACICS.

INTERNATIONAL COLLEGE OF BROADCASTING
6 S Smithville Rd.
Dayton, OH 45431-1833
Tel: (937)258-8251; Free: 800-517-7284
E-mail: jstringfield@icb.edu
Web Site: www.icb.edu
President/CEO: Michael A. Lemaster
Admissions: James Stringfield
Type: Two-Year College **Sex:** Coed **Admission Plans:** Early Admission;

Open Admission **H.S. Requirements:** High school diploma required; GED accepted **Costs Per Year:** Tuition: $30,485 full-time. Full-time tuition varies according to program. Tuition guaranteed not to increase for student's term of enrollment. **Scholarships:** Available. **Calendar System:** Semester, Summer session not available **Exams:** Other. **Final Year or Final Semester Residency Requirement:** No **Credit Hours For Degree:** 69 credit hours, Associates **Professional Accreditation:** ACCSC.

JAMES A. RHODES STATE COLLEGE

4240 Campus Dr.
Lima, OH 45804-3597
Tel: (419)995-8000
Fax: (419)995-8098
E-mail: cox.t@rhodesstate.edu
Web Site: www.rhodesstate.edu
President/CEO: Debra L. McCurdy
Admissions: Traci Cox

Type: Two-Year College **Sex:** Coed **% Accepted:** 100 **Admission Plans:** Deferred Admission; Early Admission; Open Admission **Application Deadline:** Rolling **Application Fee:** $25.00 **H.S. Requirements:** High school diploma required; GED accepted **Scholarships:** Available. **Calendar System:** Quarter, Summer session available **Enrollment:** Full-time 1,548, Part-time 2,335 **Faculty:** Full-time 104, Part-time 144 **Student-Faculty Ratio:** 15:1 **Regional Accreditation:** North Central Association of Colleges and Schools **Credit Hours For Degree:** 106 credit hours, Associates **Professional Accreditation:** AAMAE, ABET, ACBSP, ACEN, ADA, AOTA, APTA, CoARC, JRCERT. **Intercollegiate Athletics:** Baseball M; Basketball M & W; Golf M

JOHN CARROLL UNIVERSITY

One John Carroll Blvd.
University Heights, OH 44118-4581
Tel: (216)397-1886; Free: 888-335-6800
Fax: (216)397-3098
E-mail: svitatoe@jcu.edu
Web Site: www.jcu.edu
President/CEO: Fr. Robert Niehoff
Admissions: Steven P. Vitatoe
Financial Aid: Claudia A. Wenzel

Type: Comprehensive **Sex:** Coed **Affiliation:** Roman Catholic (Jesuit). **Scores:** 97% SAT V 400+; 99% SAT M 400+; 40.3% ACT 18-23; 49.2% ACT 24-29 **% Accepted:** 83 **Admission Plans:** Deferred Admission; Early Admission; Early Decision Plan **Application Deadline:** February 1 **Application Fee:** $0.00 **H.S. Requirements:** High school diploma required; GED accepted **Costs Per Year:** Application fee: $0. One-time mandatory fee: $325. Comprehensive fee: $48,100 includes full-time tuition ($35,930), mandatory fees ($1250), and college room and board ($10,920). Full-time tuition and fees vary according to degree level. Room and board charges vary according to board plan and housing facility. Part-time tuition: $1095 per credit hour. Part-time tuition varies according to course load and degree level. **Scholarships:** Available. **Calendar System:** Semester, Summer session available **Enrollment:** Full-time 3,022, Graduate full-time 249, Graduate part-time 326, Part-time 103 **Faculty:** Full-time 190, Part-time 233 **Student-Faculty Ratio:** 13:1 **Exams:** SAT I or ACT; SAT Reasoning; SAT Subject. **% Receiving Financial Aid:** 72 **% Residing in College-Owned, -Operated, or -Affiliated Housing:** 57 **Final Year or Final Semester Residency Requirement:** Yes **Regional Accreditation:** North Central Association of Colleges and Schools **Credit Hours For Degree:** 128 hours, 120 credit hours (beginning with students entering in fall 2015), Bachelors **ROTC:** Army **Professional Accreditation:** AACSB, ACA, NCATE. **Intercollegiate Athletics:** Baseball M; Basketball M & W; Cheerleading W; Crew M & W; Cross-Country Running M & W; Field Hockey W; Football M; Golf M & W; Ice Hockey M; Lacrosse M & W; Rugby M & W; Sailing M & W; Skiing (Cross-Country) M & W; Skiing (Downhill) M & W; Soccer M & W; Softball W; Swimming and Diving M & W; Tennis M & W; Track and Field M & W; Ultimate Frisbee M; Volleyball M & W; Wrestling M

KENT STATE UNIVERSITY

PO Box 5190
Kent, OH 44242-0001
Tel: (330)672-3000; Free: 800-988-KENT
Fax: (330)672-2499
E-mail: admissions@kent.edu
Web Site: www.kent.edu

President/CEO: Dr. Beverly Warren
Admissions: Christopher Buttenschon
Financial Aid: Mark A. Evans

Type: University **Sex:** Coed **Affiliation:** Kent State University System. **Scores:** 81% SAT V 400+; 82% SAT M 400+; 56.95% ACT 18-23; 35.26% ACT 24-29 **% Accepted:** 85 **Application Deadline:** May 1 **Application Fee:** $45.00 **H.S. Requirements:** High school diploma required; GED accepted **Scholarships:** Available. **Calendar System:** Semester, Summer session available **Enrollment:** Full-time 20,660, Graduate full-time 3,425, Graduate part-time 2,730, Part-time 2,947 **Faculty:** Full-time 962, Part-time 800 **Student-Faculty Ratio:** 21:1 **Exams:** ACT essay component not used; SAT I or ACT; SAT essay component used for advising; SAT essay component used for placement; SAT Reasoning. **% Receiving Financial Aid:** 63 **% Residing in College-Owned, -Operated, or -Affiliated Housing:** 28 **Final Year or Final Semester Residency Requirement:** No **Regional Accreditation:** North Central Association of Colleges and Schools **Credit Hours For Degree:** 60 semester hours, Associates; 120 semester hours, Bachelors **ROTC:** Air Force, Army **Professional Accreditation:** AACN, AACSB, ACA, ACBSP, ACEJMC, ALA, AND, APA, APMA, ASHA, CEPH, CIDA, CORE, NAAB, NASAD, NASD, NASM, NASPAA, NAST, NCATE, NRPA. **Intercollegiate Athletics:** Baseball M; Basketball M & W; Cheerleading M & W; Cross-Country Running M & W; Field Hockey W; Football M; Golf M & W; Gymnastics W; Soccer W; Softball W; Track and Field M & W; Volleyball W; Wrestling M

KENT STATE UNIVERSITY AT ASHTABULA

3300 Lake Rd. W
Ashtabula, OH 44004-2299
Tel: (440)964-3322
Fax: (440)964-4269
E-mail: adolan5@kent.edu
Web Site: www.ashtabula.kent.edu
President/CEO: Dr. Susan J. Stocker
Admissions: Amanda C. Dolan
Financial Aid: Kristina Call

Type: Two-Year College **Sex:** Coed **Affiliation:** Kent State University System. **Scores:** 87% SAT V 400+; 100% SAT M 400+; 52.41% ACT 18-23; 12.66% ACT 24-29 **% Accepted:** 99 **Admission Plans:** Deferred Admission; Open Admission **Application Deadline:** August 15 **Application Fee:** $40.00 **H.S. Requirements:** High school diploma required; GED accepted **Costs Per Year:** Application fee: $40. One-time mandatory fee: $150. State resident tuition: $5664 full-time, $258 per credit hour part-time. Nonresident tuition: $13,864 full-time, $620 per credit hour part-time. Full-time tuition varies according to course level and course load. Part-time tuition varies according to course level and course load. **Scholarships:** Available. **Calendar System:** Semester, Summer session available **Enrollment:** Full-time 1,147, Graduate part-time 3, Part-time 1,138 **Faculty:** Full-time 48, Part-time 58 **Student-Faculty Ratio:** 22:1 **Exams:** ACT essay component not used; SAT I or ACT; SAT essay component not used; SAT Reasoning. **Final Year or Final Semester Residency Requirement:** No **Regional Accreditation:** North Central Association of Colleges and Schools **Credit Hours For Degree:** 60 semester hours, Associates; 120 semester hours, Bachelors **ROTC:** Air Force, Army **Professional Accreditation:** ACBSP, APTA.

KENT STATE UNIVERSITY AT EAST LIVERPOOL

400 E 4th St.
East Liverpool, OH 43920-3497
Tel: (330)385-3805
Fax: (330)385-6348
E-mail: mweekley@kent.edu
Web Site: www.eliv.kent.edu
President/CEO: Dr. Stephen Nameth
Admissions: Michelle Lingenfelter
Financial Aid: Chris Winland

Type: Two-Year College **Sex:** Coed **Affiliation:** Kent State University System. **Scores:** 58.34% ACT 18-23; 8.33% ACT 24-29 **% Accepted:** 100 **Admission Plans:** Deferred Admission; Open Admission **Application Deadline:** August 15 **Application Fee:** $40.00 **H.S. Requirements:** High school diploma required; GED accepted **Costs Per Year:** Application fee: $40. One-time mandatory fee: $150. State resident tuition: $5664 full-time, $258 per credit hour part-time. Nonresident tuition: $13,864 full-time, $620 per credit hour part-time. Full-time tuition varies according to course level and course load. Part-time tuition varies according to course level and course load. **Scholarships:** Available. **Calendar System:** Semester, Summer session available **Enrollment:** Full-time 692, Part-time 553 **Faculty:** Full-time 25, Part-time 33 **Student-Faculty Ratio:** 24:1 **Exams:** ACT essay component not used; SAT I or ACT; SAT essay component not used; SAT Reasoning. **Final Year or Final Semester Residency Requirement:** No **Regional Accreditation:** North Central Association of Colleges and Schools **Credit Hours For Degree:** 60 semester hours, Associates; 120 semester hours, Bachelors **ROTC:** Air Force, Army **Professional Accreditation:** ACBSP, AOTA, APTA.

KENT STATE UNIVERSITY AT GEAUGA

14111 Claridon-Troy Rd.
Burton, OH 44021-9500
Tel: (440)834-4187
Fax: (440)834-0919
E-mail: geaugaadmissions@kent.edu
Web Site: www.geauga.kent.edu
President/CEO: Dr. G. R. Jarrod Tudor
Financial Aid: Donna Holcomb

Type: Four-Year College **Sex:** Coed **Affiliation:** Kent State University System. **Scores:** 83% SAT V 400+; 86% SAT M 400+; 58.78% ACT 18-23; 9.16% ACT 24-29 **% Accepted:** 94 **Admission Plans:** Deferred Admission; Open Admission **Application Deadline:** August 15 **Application Fee:** $40.00 **H.S. Requirements:** High school diploma required; GED accepted **Costs Per Year:** Application fee: $40. One-time mandatory fee: $150. State resident tuition: $5664 full-time, $258 per credit hour part-time. Nonresident tuition: $13,864 full-time, $620 per credit hour part-time. Full-time tuition varies according to course level and course load. Part-time tuition varies according to course level and course load. **Scholarships:** Available. **Calendar System:** Semester, Summer session available **Enrollment:** Full-time 1,426, Part-time 1,104 **Faculty:** Full-time 41, Part-time 104 **Student-Faculty Ratio:** 24:1 **Exams:** ACT essay component not used; SAT I or ACT; SAT essay component not used; SAT Reasoning. **% Receiving Financial Aid:** 63 **Final Year or Final Semester Residency Requirement:** No **Regional Accreditation:** North Central Association of Colleges and Schools **Credit Hours For Degree:** 60 semester hours, Associates; 120 semester hours, Bachelors **ROTC:** Air Force, Army **Professional Accreditation:** ACBSP.

KENT STATE UNIVERSITY AT SALEM

2491 State Rte. 45 S
Salem, OH 44460-9412
Tel: (330)332-0361
Fax: (330)332-9256
E-mail: mweekley@kent.edu
Web Site: www.salem.kent.edu
President/CEO: Dr. Stephen Nameth
Admissions: Michelle Lingenfelter
Financial Aid: Angel Barcey

Type: Two-Year College **Sex:** Coed **Affiliation:** Kent State University System. **Scores:** 100% SAT V 400+; 100% SAT M 400+; 59.26% ACT 18-23; 14.07% ACT 24-29 **% Accepted:** 100 **Admission Plans:** Deferred Admission; Open Admission **Application Deadline:** August 15 **Application Fee:** $40.00 **H.S. Requirements:** High school diploma required; GED accepted **Costs Per Year:** Application fee: $40. One-time mandatory fee: $150. State resident tuition: $5664 full-time, $258 per credit hour part-time. Nonresident tuition: $13,864 full-time, $620 per credit hour part-time. Full-time tuition varies according to course level and course load. Part-time tuition varies according to course level and course load. **Scholarships:** Available. **Calendar System:** Semester, Summer session available **Enrollment:** Full-time 1,148, Graduate part-time 1, Part-time 590 **Faculty:** Full-time 39, Part-time 86 **Student-Faculty Ratio:** 20:1 **Exams:** ACT essay component not used; SAT I or ACT; SAT essay component not used; SAT Reasoning. **Final Year or Final Semester Residency Requirement:** No **Regional Accreditation:** North Central Association of Colleges and Schools **Credit Hours For Degree:** 60 semester hours, Associates; 120 semester hours, Bachelors **ROTC:** Air Force, Army **Professional Accreditation:** ACBSP, JRCERT, JRCNMT.

KENT STATE UNIVERSITY AT STARK

6000 Frank Ave., NW
Canton, OH 44720-7599
Tel: (330)499-9600
Fax: (330)494-6121
E-mail: starkadmissions@kent.edu
Web Site: www.stark.kent.edu

President/CEO: Dr. Denise A. Seachrist
Financial Aid: Amber Wallace

Type: Comprehensive **Sex:** Coed **Affiliation:** Kent State University System. **Scores:** 87% SAT V 400+; 100% SAT M 400+; 59.37% ACT 18-23; 14.24% ACT 24-29 **% Accepted:** 100 **Admission Plans:** Deferred Admission; Open Admission **Application Deadline:** August 15 **Application Fee:** $40.00 **H.S. Requirements:** High school diploma required; GED accepted **Costs Per Year:** Application fee: $40. One-time mandatory fee: $150. State resident tuition: $5664 full-time, $258 per credit hour part-time. Nonresident tuition: $13,864 full-time, $620 per credit hour part-time. Full-time tuition varies according to course level and course load. Part-time tuition varies according to course level and course load. **Scholarships:** Available. **Calendar System:** Semester, Summer session available **Enrollment:** Full-time 3,092, Graduate full-time 8, Graduate part-time 29, Part-time 1,628 **Faculty:** Full-time 111, Part-time 159 **Student-Faculty Ratio:** 22:1 **Exams:** ACT essay component not used; SAT I or ACT; SAT essay component not used; SAT Reasoning. **% Receiving Financial Aid:** 70 **Final Year or Final Semester Residency Requirement:** No **Regional Accreditation:** North Central Association of Colleges and Schools **Credit Hours For Degree:** 60 semester hours, Associates; 120 semester hours, Bachelors **ROTC:** Air Force, Army

KENT STATE UNIVERSITY AT TRUMBULL

4314 Mahoning Ave., NW
Warren, OH 44483-1998
Tel: (330)847-0571
E-mail: jritter0@kent.edu
Web Site: www.trumbull.kent.edu
President/CEO: Dr. Lance R. Grahn
Admissions: James Ritter
Financial Aid: Sarah Helmick

Type: Two-Year College **Sex:** Coed **Affiliation:** Kent State University System. **Scores:** 100% SAT V 400+; 100% SAT M 400+; 55.14% ACT 18-23; 13.08% ACT 24-29 **% Accepted:** 99 **Admission Plans:** Deferred Admission; Open Admission **Application Deadline:** August 15 **Application Fee:** $40.00 **H.S. Requirements:** High school diploma required; GED accepted **Costs Per Year:** Application fee: $40. One-time mandatory fee: $150. State resident tuition: $5664 full-time, $258 per credit hour part-time. Nonresident tuition: $13,864 full-time, $620 per credit hour part-time. Full-time tuition varies according to course level and course load. Part-time tuition varies according to course level and course load. **Scholarships:** Available. **Calendar System:** Semester, Summer session available **Enrollment:** Full-time 1,646, Graduate full-time 1, Graduate part-time 2, Part-time 933 **Faculty:** Full-time 52, Part-time 55 **Student-Faculty Ratio:** 28:1 **Exams:** ACT essay component not used; SAT I or ACT; SAT essay component not used; SAT Reasoning. **Final Year or Final Semester Residency Requirement:** No **Regional Accreditation:** North Central Association of Colleges and Schools **Credit Hours For Degree:** 60 credit hours, Associates; 120 credit hours, Bachelors **ROTC:** Air Force, Army **Professional Accreditation:** ACBSP.

KENT STATE UNIVERSITY AT TUSCARAWAS

330 University Dr., NE
New Philadelphia, OH 44663-9403
Tel: (330)339-3391
Fax: (330)339-3321
E-mail: info@tusc.kent.edu
Web Site: www.tusc.kent.edu
President/CEO: Dr. Bradley A. Bielski
Financial Aid: Cheryl Walker

Type: Two-Year College **Sex:** Coed **Affiliation:** Kent State University System. **Scores:** 83% SAT V 400+; 100% SAT M 400+; 58.74% ACT 18-23; 23.3% ACT 24-29 **% Accepted:** 100 **Admission Plans:** Deferred Admission; Open Admission **Application Deadline:** August 15 **Application Fee:** $40.00 **H.S. Requirements:** High school diploma required; GED accepted **Costs Per Year:** Application fee: $40. One-time mandatory fee: $150. State resident tuition: $5664 full-time, $258 per credit hour part-time. Nonresident tuition: $13,864 full-time, $620 per credit hour part-time. Full-time tuition varies according to course level and course load. Part-time tuition varies according to course level and course load. **Scholarships:** Available. **Calendar System:** Semester, Summer session available **Enrollment:** Full-time 1,323, Graduate full-time 3, Graduate part-time 29, Part-time 823 **Faculty:** Full-time 47, Part-time 60 **Student-Faculty Ratio:** 24:1 **Exams:** ACT essay component not used; SAT I or ACT; SAT essay component not used; SAT Reasoning. **Final Year or Final Semester Residency Requirement:** No **Regional Accreditation:** North Central Association of Colleges and Schools

Credit Hours For Degree: 60 semester hours, Associates; 120 semester hours, Bachelors **ROTC:** Air Force, Army **Professional Accreditation:** ABET, ACBSP.

KENYON COLLEGE
Gambier, OH 43022-9623
Tel: (740)427-5000; Free: 800-848-2468
Fax: (740)427-2634
E-mail: admissions@kenyon.edu
Web Site: www.kenyon.edu
President/CEO: Dr. Sean Decatur
Admissions: Diane Anci
Financial Aid: Craig Daugherty

Type: Four-Year College **Sex:** Coed **Scores:** 100% SAT V 400+; 100% SAT M 400+; 3% ACT 18-23; 31% ACT 24-29 **% Accepted:** 24 **Admission Plans:** Deferred Admission; Early Action; Early Admission **Application Deadline:** January 15 **Application Fee:** $0.00 **H.S. Requirements:** High school diploma required; GED accepted **Costs Per Year:** Application fee: $0. Comprehensive fee: $61,030 includes full-time tuition ($47,220), mandatory fees ($1920), and college room and board ($11,890). College room only: $5170. Full-time tuition and fees vary according to reciprocity agreements. Room and board charges vary according to housing facility and student level. **Scholarships:** Available. **Calendar System:** Semester, Summer session not available **Enrollment:** Full-time 1,698 **Faculty:** Full-time 156, Part-time 44 **Student-Faculty Ratio:** 10:1 **Exams:** ACT essay component not used; SAT I or ACT; SAT essay component not used; SAT Reasoning; SAT Subject. **% Receiving Financial Aid:** 43 **% Residing in College-Owned, -Operated, or -Affiliated Housing:** 100 **Final Year or Final Semester Residency Requirement:** Yes **Regional Accreditation:** North Central Association of Colleges and Schools **Credit Hours For Degree:** 16 units, Bachelors **Intercollegiate Athletics:** Baseball M; Basketball M & W; Cross-Country Running M & W; Equestrian Sports M & W; Field Hockey W; Football M; Golf M; Lacrosse M & W; Rugby M & W; Soccer M & W; Softball W; Squash M & W; Swimming and Diving M & W; Tennis M & W; Track and Field M & W; Ultimate Frisbee M & W; Volleyball W

KETTERING COLLEGE
3737 Southern Blvd.
Kettering, OH 45429-1299
Tel: (937)395-8601; Free: 800-433-5262
Fax: (937)395-8333
Web Site: www.kc.edu
President/CEO: Charles Scriven
Admissions: Becky McDonald

Type: Comprehensive **Sex:** Coed **Affiliation:** Seventh-day Adventist; Kettering Health Network. **Scores:** 74% ACT 18-23; 26% ACT 24-29 **% Accepted:** 50 **Admission Plans:** Early Admission **Application Deadline:** Rolling **Application Fee:** $25.00 **H.S. Requirements:** High school diploma required; GED accepted **Scholarships:** Available. **Calendar System:** Semester, Summer session available **Enrollment:** Full-time 394, Part-time 347 **Faculty:** Full-time 55, Part-time 15 **Student-Faculty Ratio:** 10:1 **Exams:** ACT; SAT I. **% Residing in College-Owned, -Operated, or -Affiliated Housing:** 15 **Regional Accreditation:** North Central Association of Colleges and Schools **Credit Hours For Degree:** 64 semester hours, Associates; 126 semester hours, Bachelors **Professional Accreditation:** ACEN, CoARC, JRCEDMS, JRCERT.

LAKE ERIE COLLEGE
391 W Washington St.
Painesville, OH 44077-3389
Tel: (440)296-1856; Free: 800-916-0904
Fax: (440)352-3533
E-mail: admissions@lec.edu
Web Site: www.lec.edu
President/CEO: Peter Gerhart, JD
Admissions: Liz Sellers
Financial Aid: Patricia Pangonis

Type: Comprehensive **Sex:** Coed **Scores:** 85% SAT V 400+; 87% SAT M 400+; 65.26% ACT 18-23; 20.53% ACT 24-29 **% Accepted:** 56 **Admission Plans:** Deferred Admission **Application Deadline:** August 1 **Application Fee:** $30.00 **H.S. Requirements:** High school diploma required; GED accepted **Costs Per Year:** Application fee: $30. One-time mandatory fee: $350. Comprehensive fee: $39,138 includes full-time tuition ($28,568), mandatory fees ($1392), and college room and board ($9178). College room

only: $4464. Full-time tuition and fees vary according to course load, degree level, and program. Room and board charges vary according to board plan. Part-time tuition: $736 per credit. Part-time mandatory fees: $51 per credit. Part-time tuition and fees vary according to course load, degree level, and program. **Scholarships:** Available. **Calendar System:** Semester, Summer session available **Enrollment:** Full-time 804, Graduate full-time 85, Graduate part-time 161, Part-time 194 **Faculty:** Full-time 45, Part-time 68 **Student-Faculty Ratio:** 15:1 **Exams:** ACT essay component not used; Other; SAT I and SAT II or ACT; SAT I or ACT; SAT essay component not used; SAT Reasoning; SAT Subject. **% Receiving Financial Aid:** 82 **% Residing in College-Owned, -Operated, or -Affiliated Housing:** 63 **Final Year or Final Semester Residency Requirement:** Yes **Regional Accreditation:** North Central Association of Colleges and Schools **Credit Hours For Degree:** 128 semester hours, Bachelors **Professional Accreditation:** NCATE, TEAC. **Intercollegiate Athletics:** Baseball M; Basketball M & W; Cross-Country Running M & W; Football M; Golf M & W; Lacrosse M & W; Soccer M & W; Softball W; Track and Field M & W; Volleyball W; Wrestling M

LAKELAND COMMUNITY COLLEGE
7700 Clocktower Dr.
Kirtland, OH 44094-5198
Tel: (440)525-7000; Free: 800-589-8520
Fax: (440)525-4330
Web Site: www.lakeland.cc.oh.us
President/CEO: Dr. Morris W. Beverage
Admissions: Tracey Cooper
Financial Aid: Lynn Axten

Type: Two-Year College **Sex:** Coed **Affiliation:** Ohio Department of Higher Education. **Admission Plans:** Deferred Admission; Early Admission; Open Admission **Application Deadline:** September 1 **Application Fee:** $15.00 **H.S. Requirements:** High school diploma required; GED accepted **Costs Per Year:** Application fee: $15. Area resident tuition: $3,286 full-time, $109.55 per credit hour part-time. State resident tuition: $4,136 full-time, $137.85 per credit hour part-time. Nonresident tuition: $9,176 full-time, $305.85 per credit hour part-time. Mandatory fees: $28 full-time, $14.25 per term part-time. Full-time tuition and fees vary according to course load. Part-time tuition and fees vary according to course load. **Scholarships:** Available. **Calendar System:** Semester, Summer session available **Enrollment:** Full-time 2,675, Part-time 5,266 **Faculty:** Full-time 116, Part-time 453 **Student-Faculty Ratio:** 17:1 **Exams:** Other. **Final Year or Final Semester Residency Requirement:** No **Regional Accreditation:** North Central Association of Colleges and Schools **Credit Hours For Degree:** 60 semester hours, Associates **Professional Accreditation:** ABET, ACEN, ADA, ARCST, CoARC, JCAHPO, JRCERT, NAACLS. **Intercollegiate Athletics:** Baseball M; Basketball M & W; Golf M; Soccer M; Softball W; Volleyball W

LORAIN COUNTY COMMUNITY COLLEGE
1005 Abbe Rd., N
Elyria, OH 44035
Tel: (440)365-5222; Free: 800-995-5222
Fax: (440)365-6519
E-mail: ssutton@lorainccc.edu
Web Site: www.lorainccc.edu
President/CEO: Dr. Roy Church
Admissions: Stephanie Sutton
Financial Aid: Virginia Biada

Type: Two-Year College **Sex:** Coed **Affiliation:** Ohio Board of Regents. **% Accepted:** 100 **Admission Plans:** Deferred Admission; Early Admission; Open Admission **Application Deadline:** Rolling **Application Fee:** $0.00 **H.S. Requirements:** High school diploma required; GED accepted **Costs Per Year:** Application fee: $0. Area resident tuition: $3077 full-time, $118.34 per credit hour part-time. State resident tuition: $3679 full-time, $141.49 per credit hour part-time. Nonresident tuition: $7302 full-time, $280.84 per credit hour part-time. **Scholarships:** Available. **Calendar System:** Semester, Summer session available **Enrollment:** Full-time 3,138, Part-time 8,382 **Faculty:** Full-time 121, Part-time 494 **Student-Faculty Ratio:** 20:1 **Regional Accreditation:** North Central Association of Colleges and Schools **Credit Hours For Degree:** 63 semester hours, Associates **Professional Accreditation:** AAMAE, ABET, ACEN, ADA, APTA, ARCST, JRCEDMS, JRCERT, NAACLS, NASAD.

LOURDES UNIVERSITY
6832 Convent Blvd.
Sylvania, OH 43560-2898

Tel: (419)885-3211; Free: 800-878-3210
Fax: (419)882-3987
Web Site: www.lourdes.edu
President/CEO: Dr. David J. Livingston
Admissions: Amy Houston
Financial Aid: Deb LaJeunesse
Type: Comprehensive **Sex:** Coed **Affiliation:** Roman Catholic. **% Accepted:** 69 **Admission Plans:** Deferred Admission; Early Admission **Application Deadline:** Rolling **Application Fee:** $25.00 **H.S. Requirements:** High school diploma required; GED accepted **Costs Per Year:** Application fee: $25. One-time mandatory fee: $400. Comprehensive fee: $29,670 includes full-time tuition ($19,920), mandatory fees ($350), and college room and board ($9400). Full-time tuition and fees vary according to course load and location. Room and board charges vary according to board plan and housing facility. Part-time tuition: $665 per credit. Part-time mandatory fees: $210 per term. Part-time tuition and fees vary according to course load and location. **Scholarships:** Available. **Calendar System:** Semester, Summer session available **Enrollment:** Full-time 878, Graduate full-time 184, Graduate part-time 109, Part-time 359 **Faculty:** Full-time 65, Part-time 121 **Student-Faculty Ratio:** 11:1 **Exams:** SAT I or ACT. **% Receiving Financial Aid:** 84 **% Residing in College-Owned, -Operated, or -Affiliated Housing:** 25 **Final Year or Final Semester Residency Requirement:** No **Regional Accreditation:** North Central Association of Colleges and Schools **Credit Hours For Degree:** 60 semester hours, Associates; 120 semester hours, Bachelors **ROTC:** Air Force, Army **Professional Accreditation:** AACN, CSWE, TEAC. **Intercollegiate Athletics:** Baseball M; Basketball M & W; Cheerleading M & W; Cross-Country Running M & W; Golf M & W; Lacrosse M & W; Soccer M & W; Softball W; Track and Field M & W; Volleyball M & W; Wrestling M

MALONE UNIVERSITY

2600 Cleveland Ave., NW
Canton, OH 44709
Tel: (330)471-8100; Free: 800-521-1146
Fax: (330)454-6977
E-mail: admissions@malone.edu
Web Site: www.malone.edu
President/CEO: Dr. David A. King
Admissions: Anissa D. Scott
Financial Aid: Pamela Pustay
Type: Comprehensive **Sex:** Coed **Affiliation:** Evangelical Friends Church–Eastern Region. **Scores:** 97% SAT V 400+; 97% SAT M 400+; 59.5% ACT 18-23; 28.7% ACT 24-29 **% Accepted:** 69 **Admission Plans:** Deferred Admission; Early Admission **Application Deadline:** Rolling **Application Fee:** $20.00 **H.S. Requirements:** High school diploma required; GED accepted **Costs Per Year:** Application fee: $20. Comprehensive fee: $36,908 includes full-time tuition ($27,104), mandatory fees ($856), and college room and board ($8948). College room only: $4524. Room and board charges vary according to board plan. Part-time tuition: $470 per credit. Part-time mandatory fees: $214 per term. Part-time tuition and fees vary according to course load. **Scholarships:** Available. **Calendar System:** Semester, Summer session available **Enrollment:** Full-time 1,171, Graduate full-time 86, Graduate part-time 273, Part-time 196 **Faculty:** Full-time 89, Part-time 81 **Student-Faculty Ratio:** 12:1 **Exams:** ACT essay component used for advising; SAT I or ACT; SAT essay component used for advising; SAT Reasoning. **% Receiving Financial Aid:** 86 **% Residing in College-Owned, -Operated, or -Affiliated Housing:** 60 **Final Year or Final Semester Residency Requirement:** Yes **Regional Accreditation:** North Central Association of Colleges and Schools **Credit Hours For Degree:** 124 credit hours, Bachelors **Professional Accreditation:** AACN, ACA, ACBSP, CSWE, NCATE. **Intercollegiate Athletics:** Baseball M; Basketball M & W; Cheerleading M & W; Cross-Country Running M & W; Football M; Golf M & W; Soccer M & W; Softball W; Swimming and Diving M & W; Track and Field M & W; Volleyball W

MARIETTA COLLEGE

215 Fifth St.
Marietta, OH 45750-4000
Tel: (740)376-4000; Free: 800-331-7896
Fax: (740)376-4896
E-mail: admit@marietta.edu
Web Site: www.marietta.edu
President/CEO: Dr. Joseph Bruno
Admissions: Scott McVicar

Financial Aid: Emily Schuck
Type: Comprehensive **Sex:** Coed **Scores:** 94% SAT V 400+; 94% SAT M 400+; 40% ACT 18-23; 46% ACT 24-29 **% Accepted:** 72 **Admission Plans:** Deferred Admission; Early Admission **Application Deadline:** July 1 **Application Fee:** $25.00 **H.S. Requirements:** High school diploma required; GED accepted **Costs Per Year:** Application fee: $25. Comprehensive fee: $46,430 includes full-time tuition ($34,340), mandatory fees ($990), and college room and board ($11,100). Full-time tuition and fees vary according to course load. Room and board charges vary according to board plan and housing facility. Part-time tuition: $1140 per hour. Part-time tuition varies according to course load. **Scholarships:** Available. **Calendar System:** Semester, Summer session available **Enrollment:** Full-time 1,177, Graduate full-time 83, Graduate part-time 2, Part-time 69 **Faculty:** Full-time 105, Part-time 55 **Student-Faculty Ratio:** 10:1 **Exams:** SAT I or ACT; SAT II; SAT Reasoning. **% Receiving Financial Aid:** 72 **% Residing in College-Owned, -Operated, or -Affiliated Housing:** 76 **Regional Accreditation:** North Central Association of Colleges and Schools **Credit Hours For Degree:** 61 credit hours, Associates; 120 credit hours, Bachelors **Professional Accreditation:** ABET, JRCAT, NCATE. **Intercollegiate Athletics:** Baseball M; Basketball M & W; Cheerleading M & W; Crew M & W; Cross-Country Running M & W; Football M; Soccer M & W; Softball W; Tennis M & W; Track and Field M & W; Volleyball W; Wrestling M & W

MARION TECHNICAL COLLEGE

1467 Mount Vernon Ave.
Marion, OH 43302-5694
Tel: (740)389-4636
Fax: (740)389-6136
E-mail: enroll@mtc.edu
Web Site: www.mtc.edu
President/CEO: Dr. Richard Bryson
Admissions: Joel Liles
Type: Two-Year College **Sex:** Coed **Affiliation:** University System of Ohio. **Admission Plans:** Deferred Admission; Early Admission; Open Admission **Application Deadline:** Rolling **Application Fee:** $20.00 **H.S. Requirements:** High school diploma required; GED accepted **Scholarships:** Available. **Calendar System:** Quarter, Summer session available **Faculty:** Full-time 35, Part-time 150 **Student-Faculty Ratio:** 18:1 **Exams:** ACT; Other. **Regional Accreditation:** North Central Association of Colleges and Schools **Credit Hours For Degree:** 60 semester hours, Associates **Professional Accreditation:** ACEN, APTA, JRCERT, NAACLS. **Intercollegiate Athletics:** Basketball M & W; Golf M & W; Rugby M; Softball W; Volleyball W

MERCY COLLEGE OF OHIO

2221 Madison Ave.
Toledo, OH 43604
Tel: (419)251-1313; Free: 888-80-MERCY
Fax: (419)251-4116
E-mail: kristen.porter@mercycollege.edu
Web Site: www.mercycollege.edu
President/CEO: Dr. Susan Wajert, PhD
Admissions: Kristen Porter
Financial Aid: Julie Leslie
Type: Four-Year College **Sex:** Coed **Affiliation:** Roman Catholic Church; Mercy Health. **Scores:** 68% ACT 18-23; 11% ACT 24-29 **% Accepted:** 52 **Admission Plans:** Deferred Admission **Application Deadline:** Rolling **Application Fee:** $25.00 **H.S. Requirements:** High school diploma required; GED accepted **Costs Per Year:** Application fee: $25. One-time mandatory fee: $85. Tuition: $11,430 full-time, $420 per semester hour part-time. Mandatory fees: $1100 full-time, $35 per semester hour part-time, $25 per term part-time. Full-time tuition and fees vary according to course load. Part-time tuition and fees vary according to course load. College room only: $5460. Room charges vary according to housing facility. **Scholarships:** Available. **Calendar System:** Semester, Summer session available **Enrollment:** Full-time 454, Part-time 789 **Faculty:** Full-time 62, Part-time 153 **Student-Faculty Ratio:** 7:1 **Exams:** ACT essay component not used; SAT I or ACT; SAT essay component not used; SAT Reasoning; SAT Subject. **% Residing in College-Owned, -Operated, or -Affiliated Housing:** 3 **Final Year or Final Semester Residency Requirement:** Yes **Regional Accreditation:** North Central Association of Colleges and Schools **Credit Hours For Degree:** 60 semester hours, Associates; 120 semester hours, Bachelors **Professional Accreditation:** AACN, ACEN, AHIMA, JRCERT, NAACLS.

MIAMI-JACOBS CAREER COLLEGE (COLUMBUS)
150 E Gay St.
Columbus, OH 43215
Tel: (614)221-7770
Web Site: www.miamijacobs.edu
Type: Two-Year College **Sex:** Coed **Professional Accreditation:** ACICS.

MIAMI-JACOBS CAREER COLLEGE (DAYTON)
401 E Third St.
Dayton, OH 45402
Tel: (937)552-4006
Web Site: www.miamijacobs.edu
President/CEO: Elizabeth Fogle-Young
Admissions: Mary Percell
Type: Two-Year College **Sex:** Coed **Admission Plans:** Deferred Admission;
Early Admission **Application Deadline:** August 15 **Application Fee:** $20.00
H.S. Requirements: High school diploma required; GED accepted **Scholar-ships:** Available. **Calendar System:** Quarter, Summer session available
Exams: ACT; Other; SAT I or ACT. **Credit Hours For Degree:** 91 credits,
Associates **Professional Accreditation:** AAMAE, ACICS.

MIAMI-JACOBS CAREER COLLEGE (INDEPENDENCE)
6400 Rockside Rd.
Independence, OH 44131
Tel: (216)834-1400; Free: 866-324-0142
Web Site: www.miamijacobs.edu
President/CEO: Patrick Resetar
Type: Two-Year College **Sex:** Coed **% Accepted:** 75 **Application Fee:**
$75.00 **Student-Faculty Ratio:** 12:1 **Professional Accreditation:** ACICS.

MIAMI-JACOBS CAREER COLLEGE (SHARONVILLE)
2 Crowne Pointe Courte
Ste. 100
Sharonville, OH 45241
Tel: (513)723-0551
Web Site: www.miamijacobs.edu
Type: Two-Year College **Sex:** Coed **Professional Accreditation:** ACICS.

MIAMI-JACOBS CAREER COLLEGE (SPRINGBORO)
875 W Central Ave.
Springboro, OH 45066
Tel: (888)666-6050
Web Site: www.miamijacobs.edu
Type: Two-Year College **Sex:** Coed **Professional Accreditation:** ACICS.

MIAMI-JACOBS CAREER COLLEGE (TROY)
865 W Market St.
Troy, OH 45373
Tel: (937)332-8580
Web Site: www.miamijacobs.edu
Type: Two-Year College **Sex:** Coed **Professional Accreditation:** ACICS.

MIAMI UNIVERSITY
Oxford, OH 45056
Tel: (513)529-1809
Fax: (513)529-1550
E-mail: admission@miamioh.edu
Web Site: miamioh.edu
President/CEO: Dr. David Hodge
Financial Aid: Brent Shock
Type: University **Sex:** Coed **Affiliation:** Miami University System. **Scores:**
98% SAT V 400+; 100% SAT M 400+; 5% ACT 18-23; 61.8% ACT 24-29 **%
Accepted:** 65 **Admission Plans:** Deferred Admission; Early Action; Early
Decision Plan **Application Deadline:** February 1 **Application Fee:** $50.00
H.S. Requirements: High school diploma required; GED accepted **Costs
Per Year:** Application fee: $50. State resident tuition: $13,533 full-time,
$563.88 per credit hour part-time. Nonresident tuition: $30,233 full-time,
$1,260 per credit hour part-time. Mandatory fees: $754 full-time. Full-time
tuition and fees vary according to location and program. Part-time tuition varies according to course load, location, and program. College room and
board: $11,644. College room only: $5994. Room and board charges vary
according to board plan and housing facility. Tuition guaranteed not to
increase for student's term of enrollment. **Scholarships:** Available.
Calendar System: Semester, Summer session available **Enrollment:** Full-

time 16,023, Graduate full-time 1,043, Graduate part-time 1,646, Part-time
364 **Faculty:** Full-time 949, Part-time 243 **Student-Faculty Ratio:** 17:1
Exams: ACT essay component not used; SAT I or ACT; SAT essay
component not used; SAT Reasoning. **% Receiving Financial Aid:** 34 **%
Residing in College-Owned, -Operated, or -Affiliated Housing:** 46 **Final
Year or Final Semester Residency Requirement:** No **Regional Ac-
creditation:** North Central Association of Colleges and Schools **Credit
Hours For Degree:** 64 credit hours, Associates; 128 credit hours, Bachelors
ROTC: Air Force, Army, Navy **Professional Accreditation:** AACSB, ABET,
APA, ASHA, CIDA, CSWE, JRCAT, NAAB, NASAD, NASM, NAST, NCATE.
Intercollegiate Athletics: Baseball M & W; Basketball M & W; Cross-
Country Running M & W; Equestrian Sports M & W; Fencing M & W; Field
Hockey M & W; Football M; Golf M; Gymnastics M & W; Ice Hockey M & W;
Lacrosse M & W; Rugby M & W; Sailing M & W; Soccer M & W; Softball M &
W; Swimming and Diving M & W; Tennis M & W; Track and Field M & W;
Ultimate Frisbee M & W; Volleyball M & W; Water Polo M & W; Weight Lifting
M & W; Wrestling M & W

MIAMI UNIVERSITY HAMILTON
1601 Peck Blvd.
Hamilton, OH 45011-3399
Tel: (513)785-3000
E-mail: nelsona3@muohio.edu
Web Site: regionals.miamioh.edu
President/CEO: Daniel E. Hall
Admissions: Archie Nelson
Type: Comprehensive **Sex:** Coed **Affiliation:** Miami University System.
Admission Plans: Open Admission **Application Deadline:** Rolling **Ap-
plication Fee:** $35.00 **H.S. Requirements:** High school diploma required;
GED accepted **Scholarships:** Available. **Calendar System:** Semester,
Summer session available **Enrollment:** Full-time 3,280, Graduate full-time
7, Graduate part-time 5, Part-time 902 **Faculty:** Full-time 84, Part-time 140
Student-Faculty Ratio: 21:1 **Regional Accreditation:** North Central As-
sociation of Colleges and Schools **Credit Hours For Degree:** 64 credits,
Associates; 128 credits, Bachelors **ROTC:** Air Force, Navy **Professional
Accreditation:** AACN, ACEN. **Intercollegiate Athletics:** Baseball M;
Basketball M & W; Cheerleading W; Golf M; Softball W; Tennis M & W; Vol-
leyball W

MIAMI UNIVERSITY MIDDLETOWN
4200 E University Blvd.
Middletown, OH 45042-3497
Tel: (513)727-3200; Free: 866-426-4643
Fax: (513)727-3223
E-mail: cantondm@muohio.edu
Web Site: regionals.miamioh.edu
President/CEO: Kelly Cowan
Admissions: Diane Cantonwine
Type: Two-Year College **Sex:** Coed **Affiliation:** Miami University System.
Admission Plans: Deferred Admission; Early Admission; Open Admission
Application Deadline: Rolling **Application Fee:** $35.00 **H.S. Require-
ments:** High school diploma required; GED accepted **Scholarships:** Avail-
able. **Calendar System:** Semester, Summer session available **Faculty:** Full-
time 79, Part-time 130 **Student-Faculty Ratio:** 13:1 **Regional
Accreditation:** North Central Association of Colleges and Schools **Credit
Hours For Degree:** 64 semester hours, Associates; 128 semester hours,
Bachelors **ROTC:** Air Force **Intercollegiate Athletics:** Baseball M;
Basketball M & W; Golf M & W; Softball W; Tennis M & W; Volleyball W

MOUNT CARMEL COLLEGE OF NURSING
127 S Davis Ave.
Columbus, OH 43222
Tel: (614)234-5800; Free: 800-556-6942
E-mail: kcampbell@mccn.edu
Web Site: www.mccn.edu
President/CEO: Dr. Christine Wynd
Admissions: Kim Campbell
Financial Aid: Todd Everett
Type: Comprehensive **Sex:** Coed **Affiliation:** Mount Carmel Health System.
Scores: 72% ACT 18-23; 24% ACT 24-29 **% Accepted:** 55 **Application
Deadline:** April 1 **Application Fee:** $30.00 **H.S. Requirements:** High
school diploma required; GED accepted **Costs Per Year:** Application fee:
$30. One-time mandatory fee: $225. Tuition: $12,245 full-time, $395 per
credit hour part-time. Full-time tuition varies according to course level,

course load, program, and student level. Part-time tuition varies according to course level, course load, program, and student level. College room only: $5000. **Scholarships:** Available. **Calendar System:** Semester, Summer session available **Enrollment:** Full-time 626, Graduate full-time 73, Graduate part-time 92, Part-time 272 **Faculty:** Full-time 51, Part-time 43 **Student-Faculty Ratio:** 15:1 **Exams:** ACT. **% Receiving Financial Aid:** 74 **% Residing in College-Owned, -Operated, or -Affiliated Housing:** 8 **Final Year or Final Semester Residency Requirement:** Yes **Regional Accreditation:** North Central Association of Colleges and Schools **Credit Hours For Degree:** 128 semester credits, Bachelors **ROTC:** Air Force, Army, Navy **Professional Accreditation:** AACN, AND.

MOUNT ST. JOSEPH UNIVERSITY

5701 Delhi Rd.
Cincinnati, OH 45233-1670
Tel: (513)244-4200; Free: 800-654-9314
Fax: (513)244-4629
E-mail: admissions@msj.edu
Web Site: www.msj.edu
President/CEO: Tony Aretz, PhD
Admissions: Peggy Minnich
Financial Aid: Kathryn Kelly

Type: Comprehensive **Sex:** Coed **Affiliation:** Roman Catholic. **Scores:** 92% SAT V 400+; 84% SAT M 400+; 60% ACT 18-23; 24% ACT 24-29 **% Accepted:** 15 **Admission Plans:** Deferred Admission **Application Deadline:** August 15 **Application Fee:** $25.00 **H.S. Requirements:** High school diploma required; GED accepted **Costs Per Year:** Application fee: $25. One-time mandatory fee: $200. Comprehensive fee: $36,310 includes full-time tuition ($26,500), mandatory fees ($1000), and college room and board ($8810). College room only: $4500. Full-time tuition and fees vary according to course load and reciprocity agreements. Room and board charges vary according to board plan and housing facility. Part-time tuition: $500 per credit hour. Part-time tuition varies according to course load and reciprocity agreements. **Scholarships:** Available. **Calendar System:** Semester, Summer session available **Enrollment:** Full-time 1,098, Graduate full-time 227, Graduate part-time 351, Part-time 307 **Faculty:** Full-time 177, Part-time 73 **Student-Faculty Ratio:** 12:1 **Exams:** SAT I or ACT; SAT Reasoning; SAT Subject. **% Receiving Financial Aid:** 62 **% Residing in College-Owned, -Operated, or -Affiliated Housing:** 25 **Regional Accreditation:** North Central Association of Colleges and Schools **Credit Hours For Degree:** 60 semester hours, Associates; 120 semester hours, Bachelors **ROTC:** Air Force, Army **Professional Accreditation:** AACN, APTA, CSWE, NASM, TEAC. **Intercollegiate Athletics:** Baseball M; Basketball M & W; Cheerleading W; Cross-Country Running M & W; Football M; Golf M & W; Lacrosse M & W; Soccer M & W; Softball W; Tennis M & W; Track and Field M & W; Volleyball M & W; Wrestling M

MOUNT VERNON NAZARENE UNIVERSITY

800 Martinsburg Rd.
Mount Vernon, OH 43050-9500
Tel: (740)392-6868; Free: 866-462-6868
E-mail: admissions@mvnu.edu
Web Site: www.mvnu.edu
President/CEO: Dr. Henry W. Spaulding, II
Admissions: Tracy Waal
Financial Aid: Jared M. Sponseller

Type: Comprehensive **Sex:** Coed **Affiliation:** Nazarene. **Scores:** 89% SAT M 400+; 49.71% ACT 18-23; 36.47% ACT 24-29 **% Accepted:** 78 **Admission Plans:** Deferred Admission **Application Deadline:** July 15 **Application Fee:** $25.00 **H.S. Requirements:** High school diploma required; GED accepted **Costs Per Year:** Application fee: $25. Comprehensive fee: $34,500 includes full-time tuition ($26,700), mandatory fees ($250), and college room and board ($7550). College room only: $4218. Full-time tuition and fees vary according to program. Part-time tuition: $742 per credit hour. Part-time tuition varies according to course load and program. **Scholarships:** Available. **Calendar System:** 4-1-4, Summer session available **Enrollment:** Full-time 1,466, Graduate full-time 234, Graduate part-time 109, Part-time 322 **Faculty:** Full-time 61, Part-time 181 **Student-Faculty Ratio:** 13:1 **Exams:** ACT essay component not used; SAT I or ACT; SAT essay component not used; SAT Reasoning; SAT Subject. **% Receiving Financial Aid:** 48 **% Residing in College-Owned, -Operated, or -Affiliated Housing:** 58 **Final Year or Final Semester Residency Requirement:** No **Regional Accreditation:** North Central Association of Colleges and Schools **Credit Hours For Degree:** 60 credit hours, Associates; 120

credit hours, Bachelors **Professional Accreditation:** AACN, ACBSP, NASM, NCATE. **Intercollegiate Athletics:** Baseball M; Basketball M & W; Cross-Country Running M & W; Golf M & W; Soccer M & W; Softball W; Track and Field M & W; Volleyball W

MUSKINGUM UNIVERSITY

163 Stormont St.
New Concord, OH 43762
Tel: (740)826-8211; Free: 800-752-6082
Fax: (740)826-8404
E-mail: adminfo@muskingum.edu
Web Site: www.muskingum.edu
President/CEO: Anne C. Steele
Admissions: Beth DaLonzo
Financial Aid: Beth DaLonzo

Type: Comprehensive **Sex:** Coed **Affiliation:** Presbyterian Church (U.S.A.). **Admission Plans:** Deferred Admission; Early Admission **Application Deadline:** June 1 **Application Fee:** $0.00 **H.S. Requirements:** High school diploma required; GED accepted **Scholarships:** Available. **Calendar System:** Semester, Summer session available **Exams:** SAT I or ACT. **% Receiving Financial Aid:** 85 **Regional Accreditation:** North Central Association of Colleges and Schools **Credit Hours For Degree:** 124 credits, Bachelors **Professional Accreditation:** NASM, NCATE. **Intercollegiate Athletics:** Baseball M; Basketball M & W; Cross-Country Running M & W; Football M; Golf M & W; Soccer M & W; Softball W; Tennis M & W; Track and Field M & W; Volleyball W; Wrestling M

NORTH CENTRAL STATE COLLEGE

2441 Kenwood Cir.
Mansfield, OH 44901-0698
Tel: (419)755-4800; Free: 888-755-4899
Fax: (419)755-4750
E-mail: nfletcher@ncstatecollege.edu
Web Site: www.ncstatecollege.edu
President/CEO: Dr. Dorey Diab
Admissions: Nikia L. Fletcher

Type: Two-Year College **Sex:** Coed **Affiliation:** Ohio Board of Regents. **Admission Plans:** Deferred Admission; Early Admission; Open Admission **Application Deadline:** Rolling **H.S. Requirements:** High school diploma required; GED accepted **Scholarships:** Available. **Calendar System:** Quarter, Summer session available **Regional Accreditation:** North Central Association of Colleges and Schools **Credit Hours For Degree:** 100 quarter hours, Associates **Professional Accreditation:** ACBSP, ACEN, APTA, CoARC, JRCERT.

NORTHWEST STATE COMMUNITY COLLEGE

22-600 State Rte. 34
Archbold, OH 43502-9542
Tel: (419)267-5511; Free: 855-267-5511
Fax: (419)267-3688
E-mail: apotts@northweststate.edu
Web Site: www.northweststate.edu
President/CEO: Dr. Thomas L. Stuckey
Admissions: Amanda Potts

Type: Two-Year College **Sex:** Coed **Affiliation:** Ohio Board of Regents. **Scores:** 54.8% ACT 18-23; 24.3% ACT 24-29 **% Accepted:** 100 **Admission Plans:** Deferred Admission; Early Admission; Open Admission **Application Deadline:** Rolling **Application Fee:** $0.00 **H.S. Requirements:** High school diploma required; GED accepted **Costs Per Year:** Application fee: $0. State resident tuition: $3768 full-time, $157 per credit part-time. Nonresident tuition: $7392 full-time, $308 per credit part-time. Mandatory fees: $70 full-time, $35 per term part-time. **Scholarships:** Available. **Calendar System:** Semester, Summer session available **Enrollment:** Full-time 713, Part-time 2,901 **Faculty:** Full-time 42, Part-time 100 **Student-Faculty Ratio:** 27:1 **Exams:** ACT essay component not used; SAT essay component not used. **Final Year or Final Semester Residency Requirement:** No **Regional Accreditation:** North Central Association of Colleges and Schools **Credit Hours For Degree:** 60 semester hours, Associates **Professional Accreditation:** ABET, ACBSP, ACEN.

NOTRE DAME COLLEGE

4545 College Rd.
South Euclid, OH 44121-4293
Tel: (216)381-1680; Free: 877-NDC-OHIO

Fax: (216)381-3802
E-mail: admissinos@ndc.edu
Web Site: www.notredamecollege.edu
President/CEO: Thomas Kruczek
Admissions: David Armstrong
Financial Aid: Dianna Roberts
Type: Comprehensive **Sex:** Coed **Affiliation:** Roman Catholic. **Scores:** 87% SAT V 400+; 84% SAT M 400+; 68% ACT 18-23; 9% ACT 24-29 **% Accepted:** 52 **Admission Plans:** Deferred Admission **Application Deadline:** Rolling **Application Fee:** $30.00 **H.S. Requirements:** High school diploma required; GED accepted **Costs Per Year:** Application fee: $30. Comprehensive fee: $36,700 includes full-time tuition ($26,820), mandatory fees ($700), and college room and board ($9180). Full-time tuition and fees vary according to course load and degree level. Room and board charges vary according to board plan and housing facility. **Scholarships:** Available. **Calendar System:** Semester, Summer session available **Enrollment:** Full-time 793, Part-time 447 **Faculty:** Full-time 34, Part-time 84 **Student-Faculty Ratio:** 13:1 **Exams:** SAT I or ACT. **% Residing in College-Owned, -Operated, or -Affiliated Housing:** 44 **Regional Accreditation:** North Central Association of Colleges and Schools **Credit Hours For Degree:** 64 semester hours, Associates; 128 semester hours, Bachelors **Professional Accreditation:** AACN, NCATE. **Intercollegiate Athletics:** Baseball M; Basketball M & W; Cross-Country Running M & W; Field Hockey W; Golf M & W; Soccer M & W; Softball W; Tennis M; Track and Field M & W; Volleyball W

OBERLIN COLLEGE

173 W Lorain St.
Oberlin, OH 44074
Tel: (440)775-8121; Free: 800-622-OBIE
Fax: (440)775-8886
E-mail: college.admissions@oberlin.edu
Web Site: www.oberlin.edu
President/CEO: Marvin Krislov
Admissions: Debra Chermonte
Financial Aid: Robert A. Reddy, Jr.
Type: Comprehensive **Sex:** Coed **Scores:** 100% SAT V 400+; 100% SAT M 400+; 3% ACT 18-23; 30% ACT 24-29 **% Accepted:** 29 **Admission Plans:** Deferred Admission; Early Action; Early Admission **Application Deadline:** January 15 **Application Fee:** $0.00 **H.S. Requirements:** High school diploma required; GED not accepted **Costs Per Year:** Application fee: $0. Comprehensive fee: $64,224 includes full-time tuition ($49,928), mandatory fees ($666), and college room and board ($13,630). College room only: $7080. Room and board charges vary according to board plan and housing facility. Part-time tuition: $2040 per credit. **Scholarships:** Available. **Calendar System:** 4-1-4, Summer session not available **Enrollment:** Full-time 2,897, Graduate full-time 17, Part-time 15 **Student-Faculty Ratio:** 10:1 **Exams:** ACT essay component used for admission; ACT essay component used for advising; SAT I and SAT II or ACT; SAT I or ACT; SAT essay component used for admission; SAT essay component used for advising; SAT Reasoning. **% Receiving Financial Aid:** 47 **% Residing in College-Owned, -Operated, or -Affiliated Housing:** 90 **Final Year or Final Semester Residency Requirement:** Yes **Regional Accreditation:** North Central Association of Colleges and Schools **Credit Hours For Degree:** 32 full courses, Bachelors **Professional Accreditation:** NASM. **Intercollegiate Athletics:** Archery M & W; Badminton M & W; Baseball M; Basketball M & W; Bowling M & W; Cross-Country Running M & W; Equestrian Sports M & W; Fencing M & W; Field Hockey W; Football M; Golf M & W; Ice Hockey M & W; Lacrosse M & W; Rugby M & W; Soccer M & W; Softball W; Swimming and Diving M & W; Tennis M & W; Track and Field M & W; Ultimate Frisbee M & W; Volleyball M & W; Water Polo M & W; Wrestling M

OHIO BUSINESS COLLEGE (HILLIARD)

4525 Trueman Blvd.
Hilliard, OH 43026
Tel: (614)891-5030; Free: 800-954-4274
Web Site: www.ohiobusinesscollege.edu
Type: Two-Year College **Sex:** Coed **Admission Plans:** Open Admission **H.S. Requirements:** High school diploma required; GED accepted **Costs Per Year:** Tuition: $8140 full-time, $225 per credit hour part-time. Full-time tuition varies according to course load. Part-time tuition varies according to course load. **Professional Accreditation:** ACICS.

OHIO BUSINESS COLLEGE (SANDUSKY)

5202 Timber Commons Dr.
Sandusky, OH 44870

Tel: (419)627-8345; Free: 888-627-8345
Fax: (419)627-1958
E-mail: sandusky@ohiobusinesscollege.edu
Web Site: www.ohiobusinesscollege.edu
President/CEO: Sharon Fain
Admissions: Brock Morgan
Type: Two-Year College **Sex:** Coed **H.S. Requirements:** High school diploma required; GED accepted **Costs Per Year:** Tuition: $8140 full-time, $225 per credit hour part-time. Full-time tuition varies according to course load. Part-time tuition varies according to course load. Tuition guaranteed not to increase for student's term of enrollment. **Calendar System:** Quarter, Summer session available **Enrollment:** Full-time 170, Part-time 95 **Faculty:** Full-time 6, Part-time 26 **Student-Faculty Ratio:** 8:1 **Credit Hours For Degree:** 92, Associates **Professional Accreditation:** ACICS.

OHIO BUSINESS COLLEGE (SHEFFIELD VILLAGE)

5095 Waterford Dr.
Sheffield Village, OH 44035
Tel: (440)934-3101; Free: 888-514-3126
Web Site: www.ohiobusinesscollege.edu
President/CEO: Rosanne Catella
Admissions: Rosemerry Nickels
Type: Two-Year College **Sex:** Coed **Affiliation:** Tri State Educational Systems. **Admission Plans:** Open Admission **Application Deadline:** Rolling **Application Fee:** $25.00 **H.S. Requirements:** High school diploma required; GED accepted **Costs Per Year:** Application fee: $25. Tuition: $8140 full-time, $225 per credit hour part-time. Full-time tuition varies according to course load. Part-time tuition varies according to course load. **Scholarships:** Available. **Calendar System:** Quarter, Summer session available **Exams:** Other. **Final Year or Final Semester Residency Requirement:** No **Professional Accreditation:** ACICS.

OHIO CHRISTIAN UNIVERSITY

1476 Lancaster Pke.
Circleville, OH 43113-9487
Tel: (740)474-8896; Free: 877-762-8669
Fax: (740)477-7755
E-mail: enroll@ohiochristian.edu
Web Site: www.ohiochristian.edu
President/CEO: Dr. Mark Smith
Admissions: Mike Egenreider
Financial Aid: Michael Fracassa
Type: Comprehensive **Sex:** Coed **Affiliation:** Churches of Christ in Christian Union. **% Accepted:** 65 **Admission Plans:** Early Admission **Application Deadline:** Rolling **Application Fee:** $25.00 **H.S. Requirements:** High school diploma required; GED accepted **Costs Per Year:** Application fee: $25. Comprehensive fee: $24,364 includes full-time tuition ($18,090), mandatory fees ($2325), and college room and board ($3949). Full-time tuition and fees vary according to course load. Room and board charges vary according to board plan and housing facility. Part-time tuition: $830 per credit hour. Part-time tuition varies according to course load. **Scholarships:** Available. **Calendar System:** Semester, Summer session available **Enrollment:** Full-time 1,613, Graduate full-time 153, Graduate part-time 167, Part-time 2,125 **Faculty:** Full-time 149, Part-time 200 **Student-Faculty Ratio:** 10:1 **Exams:** ACT; SAT I. **% Receiving Financial Aid:** 83 **Final Year or Final Semester Residency Requirement:** No **Regional Accreditation:** North Central Association of Colleges and Schools **Credit Hours For Degree:** 60 semester credit hours, Associates; 120 semester credit hours, Bachelors **ROTC:** Air Force **Professional Accreditation:** ABHE. **Intercollegiate Athletics:** Baseball M; Basketball M & W; Golf M; Soccer M; Softball W; Volleyball W

OHIO COLLEGE OF MASSOTHERAPY

225 Heritage Woods Dr.
Akron, OH 44321
Tel: (330)665-1084; Free: 888-888-4325
Fax: (330)665-5021
E-mail: johna@ocm.edu
Web Site: www.ocm.edu
President/CEO: Jeffrey S. Morrow
Admissions: John Atkins
Type: Two-Year College **Sex:** Coed **Application Fee:** $25.00 **Calendar System:** Semester **Professional Accreditation:** ACCSC.

OHIO DOMINICAN UNIVERSITY

1216 Sunbury Rd.
Columbus, OH 43219-2099
Tel: (614)253-2741; Free: 800-955-6446
Fax: (614)252-0776
E-mail: admissions@ohiodominican.edu
Web Site: www.ohiodominican.edu
President/CEO: Dr. Peter Cimbolic
Admissions: Michelle Houck
Financial Aid: Cynthia A. Hahn
Type: Comprehensive **Sex:** Coed **Affiliation:** Roman Catholic. **Scores:** 78% SAT V 400+; 96% SAT M 400+; 68.48% ACT 18-23; 26.05% ACT 24-29 **% Accepted:** 81 **Admission Plans:** Deferred Admission **Application Deadline:** Rolling **Application Fee:** $0.00 **H.S. Requirements:** High school diploma required; GED accepted **Costs Per Year:** Application fee: $0. Comprehensive fee: $40,800 includes full-time tuition ($29,690), mandatory fees ($580), and college room and board ($10,530). Room and board charges vary according to board plan and housing facility. Part-time tuition: $600 per credit hour. Part-time mandatory fees: $175 per term. Part-time tuition and fees vary according to course load. **Scholarships:** Available. **Calendar System:** Semester, Summer session available **Enrollment:** Full-time 1,147, Graduate full-time 508, Graduate part-time 175, Part-time 704 **Faculty:** Full-time 70, Part-time 173 **Student-Faculty Ratio:** 15:1 **Exams:** ACT essay component not used; SAT I or ACT; SAT essay component not used. **% Residing in College-Owned, -Operated, or -Affiliated Housing:** 42 **Final Year or Final Semester Residency Requirement:** Yes **Regional Accreditation:** North Central Association of Colleges and Schools **Credit Hours For Degree:** 60 credit hours, Associates; 120 credit hours, Bachelors **ROTC:** Air Force, Army **Professional Accreditation:** ACBSP, NCATE. **Intercollegiate Athletics:** Baseball M; Basketball M & W; Cross-Country Running M & W; Football M; Golf M & W; Soccer M & W; Softball W; Track and Field M & W; Volleyball W

OHIO NORTHERN UNIVERSITY

525 S Main
Ada, OH 45810-1599
Tel: (419)772-2000; Free: 888-408-4ONU
Fax: (419)772-2313
E-mail: admissions-ug@onu.edu
Web Site: www.onu.edu
President/CEO: Dr. Daniel DiBiasio
Admissions: Deborah Miller
Financial Aid: Melanie Weaver
Type: Comprehensive **Sex:** Coed **Affiliation:** United Methodist Church. **Scores:** 97% SAT V 400+; 98% SAT M 400+; 31.97% ACT 18-23; 52.79% ACT 24-29 **% Accepted:** 69 **Admission Plans:** Deferred Admission **Application Deadline:** August 15 **Application Fee:** $0.00 **H.S. Requirements:** High school diploma required; GED accepted **Costs Per Year:** Application fee: $0. Comprehensive fee: $39,700 includes full-time tuition ($28,250), mandatory fees ($560), and college room and board ($10,890). Full-time tuition and fees vary according to course load, degree level, and program. Room and board charges vary according to board plan, housing facility, and student level. **Scholarships:** Available. **Calendar System:** Semester, Summer session available **Enrollment:** Full-time 2,001, Graduate full-time 973, Graduate part-time 6, Part-time 258 **Faculty:** Full-time 211, Part-time 77 **Student-Faculty Ratio:** 11:1 **Exams:** SAT I or ACT; SAT Reasoning. **% Residing in College-Owned, -Operated, or -Affiliated Housing:** 68 **Final Year or Final Semester Residency Requirement:** Yes **Regional Accreditation:** North Central Association of Colleges and Schools **ROTC:** Air Force, Army **Professional Accreditation:** AACN, AACSB, AALS, ABA, ABET, ACPE, JRCAT, NASM, NCATE. **Intercollegiate Athletics:** Baseball M; Basketball M & W; Cross-Country Running M & W; Football M; Golf M & W; Lacrosse M & W; Soccer M & W; Softball W; Swimming and Diving M & W; Tennis M & W; Track and Field M & W; Volleyball M & W; Wrestling M

THE OHIO STATE UNIVERSITY

Student Academic Services Bldg.
281 W Ln. Ave.
Columbus, OH 43210
Tel: (614)292-6446
Fax: (614)292-4818
E-mail: askabuckeye@osu.edu
Web Site: www.osu.edu
President/CEO: Dr. Michael V. Drake
Financial Aid: Diane Corbett
Type: University **Sex:** Coed **Affiliation:** The Ohio State University. **Scores:** 99% SAT V 400+; 100% SAT M 400+; 6% ACT 18-23; 50% ACT 24-29 **% Accepted:** 49 **Admission Plans:** Early Decision Plan **Application Deadline:** February 1 **H.S. Requirements:** High school diploma required; GED accepted **Costs Per Year:** State resident tuition: $10,037 full-time, $454.70 per credit hour part-time. Nonresident tuition: $29,229 full-time, $1,213 per credit hour part-time. Full-time tuition varies according to course load, location, program, and reciprocity agreements. Part-time tuition varies according to course load, location, program, and reciprocity agreements. College room and board: $11,666. Room and board charges vary according to board plan, housing facility, and location. **Scholarships:** Available. **Calendar System:** Semester, Summer session available **Enrollment:** Full-time 41,117, Graduate full-time 9,861, Graduate part-time 3,513, Part-time 4,172 **Faculty:** Full-time 3,722, Part-time 1,575 **Student-Faculty Ratio:** 19:1 **Exams:** ACT essay component not used; SAT I or ACT; SAT essay component not used; SAT Reasoning. **% Receiving Financial Aid:** 48 **% Residing in College-Owned, -Operated, or -Affiliated Housing:** 26 **Final Year or Final Semester Residency Requirement:** No **Regional Accreditation:** North Central Association of Colleges and Schools **Credit Hours For Degree:** 120 semester credit hours (on average—varies by major), Bachelors **ROTC:** Air Force, Army, Navy **Professional Accreditation:** AACN, AACSB, AAFCS, AALS, AAMFT, ABA, ABET, ACNM, ACPE, ACPeE, ACSP, ACIPE, ADA, AHIMA, AND, AOA, AOTA, APA, APTA, ASHA, ASLA, AVMA, CAHME, CEPH, CIDA, CORE, CSWE, CoARC, LCME/AMA, NAAB, NAACLS, NASAD, NASD, NASM, NASPAA, NAST, NCATE, SAF. **Intercollegiate Athletics:** Baseball M; Basketball M & W; Cheerleading M & W; Cross-Country Running M & W; Fencing M & W; Field Hockey W; Football M; Golf M & W; Gymnastics M & W; Ice Hockey M & W; Lacrosse M & W; Riflery M & W; Soccer M & W; Softball W; Swimming and Diving M & W; Tennis M & W; Track and Field M & W; Volleyball M & W; Wrestling M

THE OHIO STATE UNIVERSITY AGRICULTURAL TECHNICAL INSTITUTE

1328 Dover Rd.
Wooster, OH 44691
Tel: (330)287-1331; Free: 800-647-8283
E-mail: morris.878@osu.edu
Web Site: www.ati.osu.edu
President/CEO: Dr. James Kinder
Admissions: Julia Morris
Financial Aid: Barbara LaMoreaux
Type: Two-Year College **Sex:** Coed **Affiliation:** The Ohio State University. **Scores:** 46% ACT 18-23; 11% ACT 24-29 **% Accepted:** 85 **Admission Plans:** Open Admission **Application Deadline:** June 1 **Application Fee:** $60.00 **H.S. Requirements:** High school diploma required; GED accepted **Costs Per Year:** Application fee: $60. State resident tuition: $7104 full-time, $296 per credit hour part-time. Nonresident tuition: $24,432 full-time, $1018 per credit hour part-time. Full-time tuition varies according to course load, location, and program. Part-time tuition varies according to course load, location, and program. College room and board: $8130. College room only: $6530. Room and board charges vary according to board plan and location. **Scholarships:** Available. **Calendar System:** Semester, Summer session not available **Enrollment:** Full-time 702, Part-time 55 **Faculty:** Full-time 33, Part-time 37 **Student-Faculty Ratio:** 17:1 **Exams:** ACT essay component not used; SAT I or ACT; SAT essay component not used. **Final Year or Final Semester Residency Requirement:** No **Regional Accreditation:** North Central Association of Colleges and Schools **Credit Hours For Degree:** 60 semester hours, Associates **ROTC:** Air Force, Army, Navy

THE OHIO STATE UNIVERSITY AT LIMA

4240 Campus Dr.
Lima, OH 45804
Tel: (419)995-8600
Fax: (419)995-8483
E-mail: admissions@lima.ohio-state.edu
Web Site: lima.osu.edu
President/CEO: Charlene Gilbert
Type: Comprehensive **Sex:** Coed **Affiliation:** The Ohio State University. **Scores:** 83% SAT V 400+; 100% SAT M 400+; 51% ACT 18-23; 36% ACT 24-29 **% Accepted:** 99 **Application Deadline:** June 1 **Application Fee:** $60.00 **H.S. Requirements:** High school diploma required; GED accepted **Costs Per Year:** Application fee: $60. State resident tuition: $7140 full-time,

$298 per credit hour part-time. Nonresident tuition: $24,468 full-time, $1020 per credit hour part-time. Full-time tuition varies according to course load, location, program, and reciprocity agreements. Part-time tuition varies according to course load, location, program, and reciprocity agreements. **Calendar System:** Semester, Summer session available **Enrollment:** Full-time 824, Graduate full-time 5, Graduate part-time 6, Part-time 175 **Faculty:** Full-time 34, Part-time 49 **Student-Faculty Ratio:** 18:1 **Exams:** ACT essay component not used; SAT I or ACT; SAT essay component not used; SAT Reasoning. **Final Year or Final Semester Residency Requirement:** No **Regional Accreditation:** North Central Association of Colleges and Schools **Credit Hours For Degree:** 120 semester credit hours (most majors), Bachelors **ROTC:** Air Force, Army, Navy

THE OHIO STATE UNIVERSITY AT MARION
1465 Mount Vernon Ave.
Marion, OH 43302-5695
Tel: (740)389-6786
E-mail: moreau.1@osu.edu
Web Site: osumarion.osu.edu
President/CEO: Dr. Gregory S. Rose
Admissions: Matthew Moreau

Type: Comprehensive **Sex:** Coed **Affiliation:** The Ohio State University. **Scores:** 92% SAT V 400+; 96% SAT M 400+; 50% ACT 18-23; 35% ACT 24-29 **% Accepted:** 99 **Application Deadline:** June 1 **Application Fee:** $60.00 **H.S. Requirements:** High school diploma required; GED accepted **Costs Per Year:** Application fee: $60. State resident tuition: $7140 full-time, $298 per credit hour part-time. Nonresident tuition: $24,468 full-time, $1020 per credit hour part-time. Full-time tuition varies according to course load, location, program, and reciprocity agreements. Part-time tuition varies according to course load, location, program, and reciprocity agreements. **Calendar System:** Semester, Summer session available **Enrollment:** Full-time 865, Graduate part-time 2, Part-time 218 **Faculty:** Full-time 35, Part-time 61 **Student-Faculty Ratio:** 17:1 **Exams:** ACT essay component used for admission; SAT I or ACT; SAT essay component used for admission; SAT Reasoning. **Final Year or Final Semester Residency Requirement:** No **Regional Accreditation:** North Central Association of Colleges and Schools **Credit Hours For Degree:** 60 semester hours, Associates; 120 semester hours, Bachelors **ROTC:** Air Force, Army, Navy **Intercollegiate Athletics:** Basketball M; Golf M; Volleyball W

THE OHIO STATE UNIVERSITY–MANSFIELD CAMPUS
1680 University Dr.
Mansfield, OH 44906-1599
Tel: (419)755-4011
E-mail: admissions@mansfield.ohio-state.edu
Web Site: www.mansfield.osu.edu
President/CEO: Dr. Stephen M. Gavazzi, PhD

Type: Comprehensive **Sex:** Coed **Affiliation:** The Ohio State University. **Scores:** 92% SAT V 400+; 97% SAT M 400+; 46% ACT 18-23; 37% ACT 24-29 **% Accepted:** 99 **Application Deadline:** June 1 **Application Fee:** $60.00 **H.S. Requirements:** High school diploma required; GED accepted **Costs Per Year:** Application fee: $60. State resident tuition: $7140 full-time, $298 per credit hour part-time. Nonresident tuition: $24,469 full-time, $1020 per credit hour part-time. Full-time tuition varies according to course load, location, program, and reciprocity agreements. Part-time tuition varies according to course load, location, program, and reciprocity agreements. College room and board: $7570. College room only: $5970. Room and board charges vary according to housing facility and location. **Calendar System:** Semester, Summer session available **Enrollment:** Full-time 990, Graduate full-time 2, Graduate part-time 8, Part-time 199 **Faculty:** Full-time 38, Part-time 54 **Student-Faculty Ratio:** 19:1 **Exams:** ACT essay component used for admission; SAT I or ACT; SAT essay component used for admission; SAT Reasoning. **% Residing in College-Owned, -Operated, or -Affiliated Housing:** 17 **Final Year or Final Semester Residency Requirement:** No **Regional Accreditation:** North Central Association of Colleges and Schools **Credit Hours For Degree:** 120 semester credit hours (depends my major), Bachelors **ROTC:** Air Force, Army, Navy

THE OHIO STATE UNIVERSITY–NEWARK CAMPUS
1179 University Dr.
Newark, OH 43055-1797
Tel: (740)366-3321
E-mail: barclay.3@osu.edu
Web Site: www.newark.osu.edu

President/CEO: Dr. Willilam L. MacDonald
Admissions: Ann Donahue

Type: Comprehensive **Sex:** Coed **Affiliation:** The Ohio State University. **Scores:** 96% SAT V 400+; 93% SAT M 400+; 52% ACT 18-23; 36% ACT 24-29 **% Accepted:** 99 **Application Deadline:** June 1 **Application Fee:** $60.00 **H.S. Requirements:** High school diploma required; GED accepted **Costs Per Year:** Application fee: $60. State resident tuition: $7140 full-time, $298 per credit hour part-time. Nonresident tuition: $24,468 full-time, $1020 per credit hour part-time. Full-time tuition varies according to course load, location, program, and reciprocity agreements. Part-time tuition varies according to course load, location, program, and reciprocity agreements. College room and board: $8290. College room only: $6690. Room and board charges vary according to board plan, housing facility, and location. **Calendar System:** Semester, Summer session available **Enrollment:** Full-time 2,054, Graduate full-time 2, Graduate part-time 26, Part-time 394 **Faculty:** Full-time 50, Part-time 100 **Student-Faculty Ratio:** 26:1 **Exams:** ACT essay component not used; SAT I or ACT; SAT essay component not used; SAT Reasoning. **% Residing in College-Owned, -Operated, or -Affiliated Housing:** 8 **Final Year or Final Semester Residency Requirement:** No **Regional Accreditation:** North Central Association of Colleges and Schools **Credit Hours For Degree:** 120 semester credit hours (depends by major), Bachelors **ROTC:** Air Force, Army, Navy

OHIO TECHNICAL COLLEGE
1374 E 51st St.
Cleveland, OH 44103
Tel: (216)881-1700; Free: 800-322-7000
Fax: (216)881-9145
E-mail: gkozarik@ohiotech.edu
Web Site: www.ohiotech.edu
President/CEO: Bill Hantl
Admissions: Greg Kozarik

Type: Two-Year College **Sex:** Coed **Affiliation:** PowerSport Institute. **Costs Per Year:** Comprehensive fee: $21,662 includes full-time tuition ($20,500) and college room and board ($1162). College room only: $818. Tuition guaranteed not to increase for student's term of enrollment. **Enrollment:** Full-time 1,072 **Faculty:** Full-time 42, Part-time 11 **Credit Hours For Degree:** 72 credits, Associates **Professional Accreditation:** ACCSC.

OHIO UNIVERSITY
Athens, OH 45701-2979
Tel: (740)593-1000
Fax: (740)593-4229
E-mail: admissions@ohio.edu
Web Site: www.ohio.edu
President/CEO: Dr. Roderick J. McDavis
Financial Aid: Valerie K. Miller

Type: University **Sex:** Coed **Affiliation:** Ohio Board of Regents. **Scores:** 98% SAT V 400+; 98% SAT M 400+; 46% ACT 18-23; 45% ACT 24-29 **% Accepted:** 74 **Admission Plans:** Deferred Admission; Early Admission **Application Deadline:** February 1 **Application Fee:** $50.00 **H.S. Requirements:** High school diploma required; GED accepted **Costs Per Year:** Application fee: $50. State resident tuition: $11,548 full-time, $547 per semester hour part-time. Nonresident tuition: $20,512 full-time, $989 per semester hour part-time. Full-time tuition varies according to degree level, location, program, and reciprocity agreements. Part-time tuition varies according to course load, degree level, location, program, and reciprocity agreements. College room and board: $10,864. College room only: $6370. Room and board charges vary according to board plan. Tuition guaranteed not to increase for student's term of enrollment. **Scholarships:** Available. **Calendar System:** Semester, Summer session available **Enrollment:** Full-time 17,392, Graduate full-time 2,812, Graduate part-time 2,832, Part-time 6,121 **Faculty:** Full-time 939, Part-time 384 **Student-Faculty Ratio:** 18:1 **Exams:** SAT I or ACT; SAT Reasoning; SAT Subject. **% Receiving Financial Aid:** 57 **% Residing in College-Owned, -Operated, or -Affiliated Housing:** 40 **Final Year or Final Semester Residency Requirement:** Yes **Regional Accreditation:** North Central Association of Colleges and Schools **Credit Hours For Degree:** 60 semester hours, Associates; 120 semester hours, Bachelors **ROTC:** Air Force, Army **Professional Accreditation:** AACN, AACSB, AAFCS, ABET, ACA, ACEJMC, ACEN, AOsA, APA, APTA, ASHA, CIDA, CORE, CSWE, JRCAT, NASAD, NASD, NASM, NAST, NCATE, NRPA. **Intercollegiate Athletics:** Baseball M; Basketball M & W; Cheerleading M & W; Cross-Country Running M & W; Field Hockey W;

Football M; Golf M & W; Ice Hockey M; Soccer W; Softball W; Swimming and Diving W; Track and Field W; Volleyball W; Wrestling M

OHIO UNIVERSITY–CHILLICOTHE

101 University Dr.
Chillicothe, OH 45601
Tel: (740)774-7200; Free: 877-462-6824
Fax: (740)774-7295
E-mail: evelandt@ohio.edu
Web Site: www.chillicothe.ohiou.edu
President/CEO: Dr. Roderick J. McDavis
Admissions: Neeley Allen
Financial Aid: Valerie K. Miller
Type: Comprehensive **Sex:** Coed **Affiliation:** Ohio University. **Admission Plans:** Deferred Admission; Early Admission; Open Admission **Application Deadline:** August 25 **Application Fee:** $20.00 **H.S. Requirements:** High school diploma required; GED accepted **Costs Per Year:** Application fee: $20. State resident tuition: $2530 full-time, $230 per credit hour part-time. Nonresident tuition: $4798 full-time, $419 per credit hour part-time. Mandatory fees: $60 full-time. Full-time tuition and fees vary according to course load, location, program, and student level. Part-time tuition varies according to course load, location, program, and student level. **Scholarships:** Available. **Calendar System:** Semester, Summer session available **Exams:** ACT essay component used for advising; ACT essay component used for placement; Other; SAT essay component used for advising; SAT essay component used for placement. **% Receiving Financial Aid:** 80 **Final Year or Final Semester Residency Requirement:** No **Regional Accreditation:** North Central Association of Colleges and Schools **Credit Hours For Degree:** 60 credit hours, Associates; 120 credit hours, Bachelors

OHIO UNIVERSITY–EASTERN

45425 National Rd.
Saint Clairsville, OH 43950-9724
Tel: (740)695-1720; Free: 800-648-3331
E-mail: howardn@ohio.edu
Web Site: www.eastern.ohiou.edu
President/CEO: Dr. Paul Abraham
Admissions: N. Kip Howard
Financial Aid: Valerie K. Miller
Type: Comprehensive **Sex:** Coed **Affiliation:** Ohio Board of Regents. **Admission Plans:** Deferred Admission; Early Admission; Open Admission **Application Deadline:** Rolling **Application Fee:** $20.00 **H.S. Requirements:** High school diploma required; GED accepted **Scholarships:** Available. **Calendar System:** Quarter, Summer session available **% Receiving Financial Aid:** 73 **Regional Accreditation:** North Central Association of Colleges and Schools **Credit Hours For Degree:** 96 quarter hours, Associates; 192 quarter hours, Bachelors **Intercollegiate Athletics:** Basketball M & W; Volleyball W

OHIO UNIVERSITY–LANCASTER

1570 Granville Pke.
Lancaster, OH 43130-1097
Tel: (740)654-6711; Free: 888-446-4468
Fax: (740)687-9497
E-mail: fox@ohio.edu
Web Site: www.ohiou.edu/lancaster
President/CEO: Dr. James Smith
Admissions: Pat Fox
Financial Aid: Valerie K. Miller
Type: Comprehensive **Sex:** Coed **Affiliation:** Ohio Board of Regents. **Admission Plans:** Deferred Admission; Early Admission; Open Admission **Application Deadline:** Rolling **Application Fee:** $20.00 **H.S. Requirements:** High school diploma required; GED accepted **Costs Per Year:** Application fee: $20. State resident tuition: $2497 full-time, $227 per credit hour part-time. Nonresident tuition: $4765 full-time, $416 per credit hour part-time. Mandatory fees: $33 full-time, $3 per credit hour part-time, $33. Full-time tuition and fees vary according to degree level and student level. Part-time tuition and fees vary according to degree level and student level. **Scholarships:** Available. **Calendar System:** Quarter, Summer session available **% Receiving Financial Aid:** 71 **Regional Accreditation:** North Central Association of Colleges and Schools **Credit Hours For Degree:** 96 quarter hours, Associates; 192 quarter hours, Bachelors **ROTC:** Air Force, Army **Professional Accreditation:** AAMAE.

OHIO UNIVERSITY–SOUTHERN CAMPUS

1804 Liberty Ave.
Ironton, OH 45638-2214
Tel: (740)533-4600; Free: 800-626-0513
Fax: (740)533-4632
E-mail: harlow@ohio.edu
Web Site: www.ohiou.edu
President/CEO: Dr. Nicole Pennington
Admissions: Linda Harlow
Financial Aid: Valerie K. Miller
Type: Comprehensive **Sex:** Coed **Affiliation:** Ohio Board of Regents. **% Accepted:** 100 **Admission Plans:** Deferred Admission; Early Admission; Open Admission **Application Deadline:** Rolling **Application Fee:** $20.00 **H.S. Requirements:** High school diploma required; GED accepted **Scholarships:** Available. **Calendar System:** Quarter, Summer session available **Enrollment:** Full-time 850, Part-time 849 **Exams:** ACT. **% Receiving Financial Aid:** 85 **Regional Accreditation:** North Central Association of Colleges and Schools **Credit Hours For Degree:** 96 quarter hours, Associates; 192 quarter hours, Bachelors

OHIO UNIVERSITY–ZANESVILLE

1425 Newark Rd.
Zanesville, OH 43701-2695
Tel: (740)453-0762
Fax: (740)453-6161
E-mail: ouzservices@ohio.edu
Web Site: www.zanesville.ohiou.edu
President/CEO: Jenifer Cushman
Financial Aid: Valerie K. Miller
Type: Four-Year College **Sex:** Coed **Affiliation:** Ohio University. **% Accepted:** 91 **Application Deadline:** Rolling **Application Fee:** $20.00 **H.S. Requirements:** High school diploma required; GED accepted **Scholarships:** Available. **Calendar System:** Quarter, Summer session available **Enrollment:** Full-time 885, Part-time 1,157 **Faculty:** Full-time 31, Part-time 99 **Student-Faculty Ratio:** 23:1 **Exams:** SAT I or ACT. **% Receiving Financial Aid:** 75 **Final Year or Final Semester Residency Requirement:** Yes **Regional Accreditation:** North Central Association of Colleges and Schools **Credit Hours For Degree:** 60 semester hours, Associates; 120 semester hours, Bachelors **Intercollegiate Athletics:** Baseball M; Basketball M & W; Golf M & W; Softball W; Volleyball W

OHIO VALLEY COLLEGE OF TECHNOLOGY

15258 State Rte. 170
East Liverpool, OH 43920
Tel: (330)385-1070
Web Site: www.ovct.edu
President/CEO: Scott S. Rogers
Admissions: Scott S. Rogers
Financial Aid: Mary Galeno
Type: Two-Year College **Sex:** Coed **Application Deadline:** Rolling **Application Fee:** $0.00 **H.S. Requirements:** High school diploma required; GED accepted **Costs Per Year:** Application fee: $0. Tuition: $4995 full-time. Mandatory fees: $1190 full-time. Full-time tuition and fees vary according to course load and program. **Scholarships:** Available. **Calendar System:** Semester, Summer session available **Enrollment:** Full-time 132, Part-time 15 **Faculty:** Full-time 4, Part-time 8 **Student-Faculty Ratio:** 18:1 **Exams:** Other. **Credit Hours For Degree:** 64 credits, Associates **Professional Accreditation:** AAMAE, ACICS.

OHIO WESLEYAN UNIVERSITY

61 S Sandusky St.
Delaware, OH 43015
Tel: (740)368-2000; Free: 800-922-8953
Fax: (740)368-3314
E-mail: amcouch@owu.edu
Web Site: www.owu.edu
President/CEO: Dr. Rock Jones
Admissions: Alisha Couch
Financial Aid: Kevin Paskvan
Type: Four-Year College **Sex:** Coed **Affiliation:** United Methodist. **Scores:** 96% SAT V 400+; 93% SAT M 400+; 31.3% ACT 18-23; 48.78% ACT 24-29 **% Accepted:** 75 **Admission Plans:** Deferred Admission; Early Action; Early Admission; Early Decision Plan **Application Deadline:** March 1 **Application Fee:** $0.00 **H.S. Requirements:** High school diploma required; GED ac-

cepted **Costs Per Year:** Application fee: $0. Tuition: $42,910 full-time, $1243 per credit hour part-time. Mandatory fees: $320 full-time. Full-time tuition and fees vary according to course load. Part-time tuition varies according to course load. College room only: $6230. Room charges vary according to housing facility. **Scholarships:** Available. **Calendar System:** Semester, Summer session available **Enrollment:** Full-time 1,659, Part-time 16 **Faculty:** Full-time 137, Part-time 79 **Student-Faculty Ratio:** 10:1 **Exams:** ACT essay component used as validity check; SAT I or ACT; SAT essay component used as validity check; SAT Reasoning. **% Receiving Financial Aid:** 69 **% Residing in College-Owned, -Operated, or -Affiliated Housing:** 91 **Regional Accreditation:** North Central Association of Colleges and Schools **Credit Hours For Degree:** 34 unit courses, Bachelors **ROTC:** Air Force, Army **Professional Accreditation:** NASM, NCATE. **Intercollegiate Athletics:** Baseball M; Basketball M & W; Cross-Country Running M & W; Equestrian Sports M & W; Field Hockey W; Football M; Golf M; Ice Hockey M & W; Lacrosse M & W; Rugby M & W; Sailing M & W; Soccer M & W; Softball W; Swimming and Diving M & W; Tennis M & W; Track and Field M & W; Ultimate Frisbee M & W; Volleyball M & W

OTTERBEIN UNIVERSITY

1 S Grove St.
Westerville, OH 43081
Tel: (614)890-3000; Free: 800-488-8144
Fax: (614)823-1200
E-mail: uotterb@otterbein.edu
Web Site: www.otterbein.edu
President/CEO: Dr. Kathy A. Krendl
Admissions: Mark Moffit
Financial Aid: Thomas V. Yarnell

Type: Comprehensive **Sex:** Coed **Affiliation:** United Methodist. **Scores:** 98% SAT V 400+; 95% SAT M 400+; 43.68% ACT 18-23; 43.68% ACT 24-29 **% Accepted:** 75 **Admission Plans:** Deferred Admission **Application Deadline:** March 1 **Application Fee:** $25.00 **H.S. Requirements:** High school diploma required; GED accepted **Costs Per Year:** Application fee: $25. Comprehensive fee: $43,704 includes full-time tuition ($31,424), mandatory fees ($200), and college room and board ($12,080). College room only: $5296. Room and board charges vary according to board plan and housing facility. Part-time tuition: $564 per credit hour. **Scholarships:** Available. **Calendar System:** Semester, Summer session available **Enrollment:** Full-time 2,122, Graduate full-time 207, Graduate part-time 258, Part-time 221 **Faculty:** Full-time 170, Part-time 147 **Student-Faculty Ratio:** 10:1 **Exams:** SAT I or ACT; SAT Reasoning; SAT Subject. **% Receiving Financial Aid:** 76 **% Residing in College-Owned, -Operated, or -Affiliated Housing:** 53 **Final Year or Final Semester Residency Requirement:** No **Regional Accreditation:** North Central Association of Colleges and Schools **Credit Hours For Degree:** 128 semester hours, Bachelors **ROTC:** Army **Professional Accreditation:** AACN, AANA, ACEN, JRCAT, NASM, NAST, NCATE. **Intercollegiate Athletics:** Baseball M; Basketball M & W; Cheerleading M & W; Cross-Country Running M & W; Equestrian Sports M & W; Football M; Golf M & W; Lacrosse M & W; Soccer M & W; Softball W; Tennis M & W; Track and Field M & W; Volleyball W

OWENS COMMUNITY COLLEGE

PO Box 10000
Toledo, OH 43699-1947
Tel: (419)661-7000; Free: 800-GO-OWENS
E-mail: meghan_schmidbauer@owens.edu
Web Site: www.owens.edu
President/CEO: Dr. Mike Bower, PhD
Admissions: Meghan L. Schmidbauer

Type: Two-Year College **Sex:** Coed **Scores:** 75% SAT V 400+; 70% SAT M 400+; 50.8% ACT 18-23; 8.3% ACT 24-29 **% Accepted:** 100 **Admission Plans:** Deferred Admission; Early Admission; Open Admission **Application Deadline:** Rolling **Application Fee:** $20.00 **H.S. Requirements:** High school diploma or equivalent not required **Costs Per Year:** Application fee: $20. One-time mandatory fee: $195. State resident tuition: $4284 full-time, $166.77 per credit hour part-time. Nonresident tuition: $8568 full-time, $333.54 per credit hour part-time. Mandatory fees: $54 full-time, $25 per term part-time. Full-time tuition and fees vary according to course load and reciprocity agreements. Part-time tuition and fees vary according to course load and reciprocity agreements. **Scholarships:** Available. **Calendar System:** Semester, Summer session available **Enrollment:** Full-time 4,257, Part-time 8,315 **Faculty:** Full-time 189, Part-time 1,070 **Student-Faculty Ratio:** 16:1 **Exams:** ACT essay component used for advising; ACT essay

component used for placement; SAT essay component used for advising; SAT essay component used for placement. **Final Year or Final Semester Residency Requirement:** No **Regional Accreditation:** North Central Association of Colleges and Schools **Credit Hours For Degree:** 60 semester hours, Associates **Professional Accreditation:** ABET, ACBSP, ADA, AOTA, APTA, ARCST, JRCEDMS, JRCERT. **Intercollegiate Athletics:** Baseball M; Basketball M & W; Golf M & W; Soccer M & W; Softball W; Volleyball W

PONTIFICAL COLLEGE JOSEPHINUM

7625 N High St.
Columbus, OH 43235
Tel: (614)885-5585; Free: 888-252-5812
E-mail: acrawford@pcj.edu
Web Site: www.pcj.edu
President/CEO: Rev. Paul J. Langsfeld
Admissions: Arminda Crawford
Financial Aid: Marky Leichtnam

Type: Comprehensive **Sex:** Men **Affiliation:** Roman Catholic. **Scores:** 50% SAT V 400+; 50% SAT M 400+; 50% ACT 18-23; 25% ACT 24-29 **% Accepted:** 75 **Admission Plans:** Preferred Admission **Application Deadline:** July 31 **Application Fee:** $25.00 **H.S. Requirements:** High school diploma required; GED accepted **Scholarships:** Available. **Calendar System:** Semester, Summer session not available **Enrollment:** Full-time 78, Graduate full-time 41 **Faculty:** Full-time 13, Part-time 9 **Student-Faculty Ratio:** 7:1 **Exams:** SAT I or ACT. **% Receiving Financial Aid:** 34 **% Residing in College-Owned, -Operated, or -Affiliated Housing:** 100 **Final Year or Final Semester Residency Requirement:** Yes **Regional Accreditation:** North Central Association of Colleges and Schools **Credit Hours For Degree:** 132 credit hours, Bachelors **Professional Accreditation:** ATS.

PROFESSIONAL SKILLS INSTITUTE

1505 Holland Rd.
Maumee, OH 43537
Tel: (419)531-9610
Fax: (419)531-4732
Web Site: www.proskills.edu
President/CEO: Daniel A. Finch
Admissions: Hope Finch

Type: Two-Year College **Sex:** Coed **Application Fee:** $25.00 **H.S. Requirements:** High school diploma required; GED accepted **Scholarships:** Available. **Calendar System:** Quarter, Summer session not available **Exams:** Other. **Credit Hours For Degree:** 119 quarter hours, Associates **Professional Accreditation:** ABHES, APTA.

RABBINICAL COLLEGE OF TELSHE

28400 Euclid Ave.
Wickliffe, OH 44092-2523
Tel: (216)943-5300
President/CEO: Rabbi Shlomo Eisenberger

Type: Comprehensive **Sex:** Men **Affiliation:** Jewish. **Admission Plans:** Open Admission **Application Fee:** $100.00 **Student-Faculty Ratio:** 7:1 **Professional Accreditation:** AARTS.

REMINGTON COLLEGE–CLEVELAND CAMPUS

14445 Broadway Ave.
Cleveland, OH 44125
Tel: (216)475-7520
Fax: (216)475-6055
Web Site: www.remingtoncollege.edu
President/CEO: Charles Dull

Type: Two-Year College **Sex:** Coed **H.S. Requirements:** High school diploma required; GED accepted **Calendar System:** Continuous **Credit Hours For Degree:** 96 quarter credit hours, Associates **Professional Accreditation:** ACCSC.

ROSEDALE BIBLE COLLEGE

2270 Rosedale Rd.
Irwin, OH 43029-9501
Tel: (740)857-1311
Fax: (877)857-1312
E-mail: pweber@rosedale.edu
Web Site: www.rosedale.edu
President/CEO: Christopher Jones
Admissions: John Showalter

Type: Two-Year College **Sex:** Coed **Affiliation:** Mennonite. **% Accepted:** 94 **Application Fee:** $50.00 **Calendar System:** Miscellaneous **Exams:** SAT I or ACT. **Professional Accreditation:** ABHE.

SCHOOL OF ADVERTISING ART
1725 E David Rd.
Kettering, OH 45440
Tel: (937)294-0592; Free: 877-300-9866
Fax: (937)294-5869
E-mail: abbie@saa.edu
Web Site: www.saa.edu
President/CEO: Jessica Barry
Admissions: Abigail Heaney

Type: Two-Year College **Sex:** Coed **% Accepted:** 59 **Application Fee:** $0.00 **H.S. Requirements:** High school diploma required; GED accepted **Costs Per Year:** Application fee: $0. Tuition: $25,701 full-time. Mandatory fees: $1310 full-time. Full-time tuition and fees vary according to class time, course level, course load, degree level, location, program, reciprocity agreements, and student level. **Calendar System:** Semester, Summer session not available **Enrollment:** Full-time 164, Part-time 4 **Faculty:** Full-time 10, Part-time 7 **Student-Faculty Ratio:** 14:1 **Credit Hours For Degree:** 75.5 credits, Associates **Professional Accreditation:** ACCSC.

SHAWNEE STATE UNIVERSITY
940 Second St.
Portsmouth, OH 45662-4344
Tel: (740)354-3205; Free: 800-959-2SSU
Fax: (740)355-2470
E-mail: rmerb@shawnee.edu
Web Site: www.shawnee.edu
President/CEO: Dr. Rick Kurtz
Admissions: Rick Merb
Financial Aid: Nicole Neal

Type: Comprehensive **Sex:** Coed **Affiliation:** University System of Ohio. **Scores:** 80% SAT V 400+; 75% SAT M 400+; 51% ACT 18-23; 23% ACT 24-29 **% Accepted:** 75 **Admission Plans:** Deferred Admission; Open Admission **Application Deadline:** Rolling **Application Fee:** $0.00 **H.S. Requirements:** High school diploma required; GED accepted **Costs Per Year:** Application fee: $0. State resident tuition: $6251 full-time, $260 per credit hour part-time. Nonresident tuition: $11,648 full-time, $485 per credit hour part-time. Mandatory fees: $1113 full-time, $46 per credit hour part-time. Full-time tuition and fees vary according to course load and reciprocity agreements. Part-time tuition and fees vary according to course load and reciprocity agreements. College room and board: $9766. College room only: $6168. Room and board charges vary according to board plan and housing facility. **Scholarships:** Available. **Calendar System:** Semester, Summer session available **Enrollment:** Full-time 3,098, Graduate full-time 114, Graduate part-time 38, Part-time 648 **Faculty:** Full-time 153, Part-time 181 **Student-Faculty Ratio:** 16:1 **Exams:** ACT; ACT essay component not used; SAT I or ACT; SAT essay component not used. **% Residing in College-Owned, -Operated, or -Affiliated Housing:** 24 **Final Year or Final Semester Residency Requirement:** No **Regional Accreditation:** North Central Association of Colleges and Schools **Credit Hours For Degree:** 60 semester hours, Associates; 120 semester hours, Bachelors **Professional Accreditation:** ACEN, ADA, AOTA, APTA, CoARC, JRCERT, NAACLS, NCATE. **Intercollegiate Athletics:** Baseball M; Basketball M & W; Cross-Country Running M & W; Golf M; Soccer M & W; Softball W; Tennis W; Volleyball W

SINCLAIR COMMUNITY COLLEGE
444 W Third St.
Dayton, OH 45402-1460
Tel: (937)512-2500; Free: 800-315-3000
E-mail: ssmith@sinclair.edu
Web Site: www.sinclair.edu
President/CEO: Dr. Steven Lee Johnson
Admissions: Sara Smith

Type: Two-Year College **Sex:** Coed **Affiliation:** Ohio Board of Regents. **Admission Plans:** Deferred Admission; Early Admission; Open Admission **Application Deadline:** Rolling **Application Fee:** $20.00 **H.S. Requirements:** High school diploma or equivalent not required. For allied health programs: High school diploma required; GED accepted **Scholarships:** Available. **Calendar System:** Quarter, Summer session available **Regional Accreditation:** North Central Association of Colleges and Schools **Credit**

Hours For Degree: 90 quarter hours, Associates **ROTC:** Air Force, Army **Professional Accreditation:** AAMAE, ABET, ACBSP, ACEN, ACF, ADA, AHIMA, AOTA, APTA, ARCST, ATMAE, CoARC, JRCERT, NASAD, NASM. **Intercollegiate Athletics:** Baseball M; Basketball M & W; Golf M; Tennis M & W; Volleyball W

SOUTH UNIVERSITY
4743 Richmond Rd.
Cleveland, OH 44128
Tel: (216)755-5000; Free: 855-398-9280
Web Site: www.southuniversity.edu/cleveland.aspx
Type: Comprehensive **Sex:** Coed **Regional Accreditation:** Southern Association of Colleges and Schools **Professional Accreditation:** ACBSP.

SOUTHERN STATE COMMUNITY COLLEGE
100 Hobart Dr.
Hillsboro, OH 45133-9487
Tel: (937)393-3431
Fax: (937)393-9370
E-mail: wjohnson@sscc.edu
Web Site: www.sscc.edu
President/CEO: Dr. Kevin Boys
Admissions: Wendy Johnson
Financial Aid: Janeen S. Deatley

Type: Two-Year College **Sex:** Coed **% Accepted:** 100 **Admission Plans:** Deferred Admission; Early Admission; Open Admission **Application Deadline:** Rolling **Application Fee:** $0.00 **H.S. Requirements:** High school diploma required; GED accepted. For applicants who will attend part-time: High school diploma required; GED not accepted **Costs Per Year:** Application fee: $0. State resident tuition: $162 per semester hour part-time. Nonresident tuition: $312 per semester hour part-time. Part-time tuition varies according to course load and reciprocity agreements. **Scholarships:** Available. **Calendar System:** Quarter, Summer session available **Enrollment:** Full-time 1,175, Part-time 1,256 **Faculty:** Full-time 58, Part-time 121 **Student-Faculty Ratio:** 16:1 **Regional Accreditation:** North Central Association of Colleges and Schools **Credit Hours For Degree:** 60 semester hours, Associates **Professional Accreditation:** AAMAE, ACEN. **Intercollegiate Athletics:** Basketball M & W; Soccer M; Softball W; Volleyball W

STARK STATE COLLEGE
6200 Frank Ave., NW
North Canton, OH 44720-7299
Tel: (330)494-6170; Free: 800-797-8275
Fax: (330)497-6313
E-mail: info@starkstate.edu
Web Site: www.starkstate.edu
President/CEO: Dr. Para M. Jones
Admissions: JP Cooney

Type: Two-Year College **Sex:** Coed **Affiliation:** University System of Ohio. **Scores:** 45% ACT 18-23; 9% ACT 24-29 **Costs Per Year:** One-time mandatory fee: $85. State resident tuition: $2796 full-time, $116.50 per credit hour part-time. Nonresident tuition: $4980 full-time, $207.50 per credit hour part-time. Mandatory fees: $890 full-time, $37.10 per credit hour part-time, $30 per term part-time. Full-time tuition and fees vary according to course load and program. Part-time tuition varies according to program. **Scholarships:** Available. **Calendar System:** Semester, Summer session available **Enrollment:** Full-time 3,451, Part-time 9,194 **Faculty:** Full-time 195, Part-time 363 **Student-Faculty Ratio:** 22:1 **Exams:** ACT essay component not used; SAT I or ACT; SAT essay component not used. **Final Year or Final Semester Residency Requirement:** No **Regional Accreditation:** North Central Association of Colleges and Schools **Credit Hours For Degree:** 60-65 semester hours, Associates **Professional Accreditation:** AAMAE, ABET, ACBSP, ACEN, ADA, AHIMA, AOTA, APTA, CoARC, NAACLS.

STAUTZENBERGER COLLEGE (BRECKSVILLE)
8001 Katherine Blvd.
Brecksville, OH 44141
Tel: (440)838-1999; Free: 800-437-2997
Web Site: www.sctoday.edu
Type: Two-Year College **Sex:** Coed **Professional Accreditation:** ACICS.

STAUTZENBERGER COLLEGE (MAUMEE)
1796 Indian Wood Cir.
Maumee, OH 43537

Tel: (419)866-0261; Free: 800-552-5099
Fax: (419)867-9821
E-mail: klfitzgerald@stautzenberger.com
Web Site: www.sctoday.edu/maumee
President/CEO: George Simon
Admissions: Karen Fitzgerald
Financial Aid: Angela Lewis

Type: Two-Year College **Sex:** Coed **Admission Plans:** Open Admission **Application Fee:** $25.00 **Scholarships:** Available. **Calendar System:** Quarter **Student-Faculty Ratio:** 26:1 **Professional Accreditation:** AAMAE, ACICS.

TERRA STATE COMMUNITY COLLEGE

2830 Napoleon Rd.
Fremont, OH 43420-9670
Tel: (419)334-8400; Free: 866-AT-TERRA
Fax: (419)334-9035
Web Site: www.terra.edu
President/CEO: Dr. Jerome Webster, PhD
Admissions: Heath Martin

Type: Two-Year College **Sex:** Coed **Affiliation:** Ohio Board of Regents. **% Accepted:** 100 **Admission Plans:** Deferred Admission; Early Admission; Open Admission **Application Deadline:** Rolling **Application Fee:** $0.00 **H.S. Requirements:** High school diploma required; GED accepted. For post secondary options, tech prep students: High school diploma or equivalent not required **Costs Per Year:** Application fee: $0. State resident tuition: $3876 full-time, $162 per semester hour part-time. Nonresident tuition: $8160 full-time, $341 per semester hour part-time. Mandatory fees: $408 full-time, $17 per semester hour part-time, $10 per term part-time. **Scholarships:** Available. **Calendar System:** Semester, Summer session available **Enrollment:** Full-time 822, Part-time 1,781 **Faculty:** Full-time 40, Part-time 151 **Student-Faculty Ratio:** 15:1 **Final Year or Final Semester Residency Requirement:** No **Regional Accreditation:** North Central Association of Colleges and Schools **Credit Hours For Degree:** 60 semester hours, Associates

TIFFIN UNIVERSITY

155 Miami St.
Tiffin, OH 44883-2161
Tel: (419)447-6442; Free: 800-968-6446
Fax: (419)447-9605
E-mail: depughst@tiffin.edu
Web Site: www.tiffin.edu
President/CEO: Dr. Lillian Schumacher
Admissions: Sarah Johnson
Financial Aid: Cindy Little

Type: Comprehensive **Sex:** Coed **Scores:** 79% SAT V 400+; 76% SAT M 400+; 59% ACT 18-23; 22% ACT 24-29 **% Accepted:** 93 **Application Deadline:** Rolling **Application Fee:** $20.00 **H.S. Requirements:** High school diploma required; GED accepted **Costs Per Year:** Application fee: $20. Comprehensive fee: $33,050 includes full-time tuition ($22,800), mandatory fees ($50), and college room and board ($10,200). College room only: $5300. Full-time tuition and fees vary according to course load, degree level, location, program, and reciprocity agreements. Room and board charges vary according to board plan and housing facility. Part-time tuition: $760 per credit hour. Part-time tuition varies according to course load, degree level, location, program, and reciprocity agreements. **Scholarships:** Available. **Calendar System:** Semester, Summer session available **Enrollment:** Full-time 1,821, Graduate full-time 123, Graduate part-time 929, Part-time 638 **Faculty:** Full-time 84, Part-time 281 **Student-Faculty Ratio:** 11:1 **Exams:** ACT essay component not used; SAT I or ACT; SAT II; SAT essay component not used. **% Receiving Financial Aid:** 76 **% Residing in College-Owned, -Operated, or -Affiliated Housing:** 25 **Final Year or Final Semester Residency Requirement:** No **Regional Accreditation:** North Central Association of Colleges and Schools **Credit Hours For Degree:** 60 semester hours, Associates; 121 semester hours, Bachelors **ROTC:** Air Force, Army **Professional Accreditation:** ACBSP. **Intercollegiate Athletics:** Baseball M; Basketball M & W; Cross-Country Running M & W; Football M; Golf M & W; Lacrosse W; Soccer M & W; Softball W; Swimming and Diving M & W; Tennis M & W; Track and Field M & W; Volleyball W; Wrestling M

TRI-STATE BIBLE COLLEGE

506 Margaret St.
South Point, OH 45680-8402

Tel: (740)377-2520
Fax: (740)377-0001
E-mail: recruitment@tsbc.edu
Web Site: www.tsbc.edu
President/CEO: Dr. Jack R. Finch
Financial Aid: Roberta Mercer

Type: Comprehensive **Sex:** Coed **Affiliation:** nondenominational. **Admission Plans:** Open Admission **Application Fee:** $25.00 **Scholarships:** Available. **Calendar System:** Semester **Professional Accreditation:** ABHE.

TRUMBULL BUSINESS COLLEGE

3200 Ridge Ave. SE
Warren, OH 44484
Tel: (330)369-3200; Free: 888-766-1598
Fax: (330)369-6792
E-mail: admissions@trumbull.edu
Web Site: www.trumbull.edu
President/CEO: Dennis R. Griffith

Type: Two-Year College **Sex:** Coed **% Accepted:** 72 **Admission Plans:** Open Admission **Application Deadline:** Rolling **Application Fee:** $75.00 **H.S. Requirements:** High school diploma required; GED accepted **Scholarships:** Available. **Calendar System:** Quarter, Summer session available **Enrollment:** Full-time 103, Part-time 56 **Student-Faculty Ratio:** 10:1 **Professional Accreditation:** ACICS.

UNION INSTITUTE & UNIVERSITY

440 E McMillan St.
Cincinnati, OH 45206-1925
Tel: (513)861-6400; Free: 800-486-3116
Fax: (513)861-0779
E-mail: kimbrea.browning@myunion.edu
Web Site: www.myunion.edu
President/CEO: Dr. Roger H. Sublett, PhD
Admissions: Kimbrea Browning
Financial Aid: Lisa Perdomo

Type: University **Sex:** Coed **Admission Plans:** Deferred Admission; Open Admission **Application Deadline:** Rolling **Application Fee:** $0.00 **H.S. Requirements:** High school diploma required; GED accepted **Costs Per Year:** Application fee: $0. Tuition: $12,000 full-time, $500 per semester hour part-time. Mandatory fees: $144 full-time, $36 per term part-time. Full-time tuition and fees vary according to course load and program. Part-time tuition and fees vary according to course load and program. **Scholarships:** Available. **Calendar System:** Trimester, Summer session available **Enrollment:** Full-time 554, Graduate full-time 232, Graduate part-time 134, Part-time 471 **Faculty:** Full-time 31, Part-time 258 **Student-Faculty Ratio:** 10:1 **Final Year or Final Semester Residency Requirement:** No **Regional Accreditation:** North Central Association of Colleges and Schools **Credit Hours For Degree:** 120 semester credits, Bachelors

THE UNIVERSITY OF AKRON

302 Buchtel Common
Akron, OH 44325
Tel: (330)972-7111; Free: 800-655-4884
Fax: (330)972-7676
E-mail: gentile@uakron.edu
Web Site: www.uakron.edu
President/CEO: Dr. Scott L. Scarborough
Admissions: Kimberley Gentile
Financial Aid: Michelle Ellis

Type: University **Sex:** Coed **Scores:** 100% SAT V 400+; 99% SAT M 400+; 45% ACT 18-23; 33% ACT 24-29 **% Accepted:** 97 **Admission Plans:** Deferred Admission; Early Decision Plan **Application Deadline:** August 11 **Application Fee:** $45.00 **H.S. Requirements:** High school diploma required; GED accepted **Costs Per Year:** Application fee: $45. State resident tuition: $8618 full-time, $359 per credit hour part-time. Nonresident tuition: $17,149 full-time, $715 per credit hour part-time. Mandatory fees: $1891 full-time. Full-time tuition and fees vary according to course load, degree level, location, and program. Part-time tuition varies according to course load, degree level, location, and program. College room and board: $11,322. College room only: $7374. Room and board charges vary according to board plan and housing facility. **Scholarships:** Available. **Calendar System:** Semester, Summer session available **Enrollment:** Full-time 15,175, Graduate full-time 2,475, Graduate part-time 1,534, Part-time 3,862 **Faculty:** Full-time 757, Part-time 748 **Student-Faculty Ratio:** 19:1 **Exams:**

ACT essay component used for advising; ACT essay component used for placement; SAT I or ACT; SAT essay component used for advising; SAT essay component used for placement; SAT Reasoning; SAT Subject. **% Receiving Financial Aid:** 73 **% Residing in College-Owned, -Operated, or -Affiliated Housing:** 17 **Final Year or Final Semester Residency Requirement:** No **Regional Accreditation:** North Central Association of Colleges and Schools **Credit Hours For Degree:** 64 credits, Associates; 120 credits, Bachelors **ROTC:** Air Force, Army **Professional Accreditation:** AACN, AACSB, AAFCS, AALS, AAMAE, AAMFT, AANA, ABA, ABET, ACA, ACBSP, AND, APA, ARCST, ASC, ASHA, CEPH, CIDA, CSWE, CoARC, NASAD, NASD, NASM, NCATE. **Intercollegiate Athletics:** Basketball M & W; Cheerleading M & W; Cross-Country Running M & W; Football M; Golf M & W; Riflery M & W; Soccer M & W; Softball W; Swimming and Diving W; Tennis W; Track and Field M & W; Volleyball W

THE UNIVERSITY OF AKRON WAYNE COLLEGE

1901 Smucker Rd.
Orrville, OH 44667-9192
Tel: (330)683-2010; Free: 800-221-8308
Fax: (330)684-8989
E-mail: wayneadmissions@uakron.edu
Web Site: www.wayne.uakron.edu
President/CEO: Dr. Daniel C. Deckler
Admissions: Alicia Broadus

Type: Two-Year College **Sex:** Coed **Affiliation:** The University of Akron. **Scores:** 58% ACT 18-23; 17% ACT 24-29 **% Accepted:** 77 **Admission Plans:** Deferred Admission; Early Admission; Open Admission **Application Deadline:** August 13 **Application Fee:** $40.00 **H.S. Requirements:** High school diploma required; GED accepted **Costs Per Year:** Application fee: $40. State resident tuition: $5,940 full-time, $247.52 per credit hour part-time. Nonresident tuition: $14,281 full-time, $525.55 per credit hour part-time. Mandatory fees: $176 full-time, $7.34 per credit hour part-time. Full-time tuition and fees vary according to course level, course load, location, and reciprocity agreements. Part-time tuition and fees vary according to course level, location, and reciprocity agreements. **Calendar System:** Semester, Summer session available **Enrollment:** Full-time 1,109, Part-time 1,244 **Faculty:** Full-time 24, Part-time 162 **Student-Faculty Ratio:** 20:1 **Exams:** Other; SAT I or ACT. **Regional Accreditation:** North Central Association of Colleges and Schools **Credit Hours For Degree:** 64 credits, Associates **ROTC:** Air Force, Army **Intercollegiate Athletics:** Basketball M & W; Cheerleading W; Golf M; Volleyball W

UNIVERSITY OF CINCINNATI

PO Box 210063
Cincinnati, OH 45221
Tel: (513)556-6000
E-mail: admissions@uc.edu
Web Site: www.uc.edu
President/CEO: Dr. Santa J. Ono, PhD
Admissions: Dr. Thomas Canepa
Financial Aid: Randy Ulses

Type: University **Sex:** Coed **Scores:** 98% SAT V 400+; 98% SAT M 400+; 29.6% ACT 18-23; 53.07% ACT 24-29 **% Accepted:** 86 **Admission Plans:** Deferred Admission; Early Decision Plan **Application Deadline:** March 1 **Application Fee:** $50.00 **H.S. Requirements:** High school diploma required; GED accepted **Costs Per Year:** Application fee: $50. State resident tuition: $9322 full-time, $389 per credit hour part-time. Nonresident tuition: $24,656 full-time, $1028 per credit hour part-time. Mandatory fees: $1678 full-time, $70 per credit hour part-time. Full-time tuition and fees vary according to course load, location, program, and reciprocity agreements. Part-time tuition and fees vary according to course load, location, program, and reciprocity agreements. College room and board: $10,750. College room only: $6430. Room and board charges vary according to board plan and housing facility. **Scholarships:** Available. **Calendar System:** Semester, Summer session available **Enrollment:** Full-time 21,060, Graduate full-time 5,503, Graduate part-time 5,530, Part-time 3,994 **Faculty:** Full-time 1,296, Part-time 987 **Student-Faculty Ratio:** 18:1 **Exams:** ACT essay component not used; SAT I or ACT; SAT essay component not used; SAT Reasoning. **% Receiving Financial Aid:** 51 **% Residing in College-Owned, -Operated, or -Affiliated Housing:** 20 **Final Year or Final Semester Residency Requirement:** No **Regional Accreditation:** North Central Association of Colleges and Schools **Credit Hours For Degree:** 60 credit hours, Associates; 120 credit hours, Bachelors **ROTC:** Air Force, Army **Professional Accreditation:** AABB, AACN, AACSB, AALS, AANA, ABA, ABET, ACA, ACCE,

ACNM, ACPE, ACSP, AND, APA, APTA, ASHA, CIDA, CSWE, JRCAT, JRCNMT, LCME/AMA, NAAB, NAACLS, NASAD, NASD, NASM, NAST, NCATE. **Intercollegiate Athletics:** Baseball M; Basketball M & W; Cheerleading M & W; Cross-Country Running M & W; Football M; Golf M & W; Lacrosse W; Soccer M & W; Swimming and Diving M & W; Tennis W; Track and Field M & W; Volleyball W

UNIVERSITY OF CINCINNATI BLUE ASH COLLEGE

9555 Plainfield Rd.
Cincinnati, OH 45236-1007
Tel: (513)745-5600
Fax: (513)745-5780
Web Site: www.ucblueash.edu
President/CEO: Cady Short-Thompson
Admissions: Brad Tate

Type: Two-Year College **Sex:** Coed **Affiliation:** University of Cincinnati System. **Admission Plans:** Deferred Admission; Open Admission **Application Deadline:** Rolling **Application Fee:** $50.00 **H.S. Requirements:** High school diploma required; GED accepted **Costs Per Year:** Application fee: $50. State resident tuition: $6010 full-time, $251 per quarter hour part-time. Nonresident tuition: $14,808 full-time, $617 per credit hour part-time. Mandatory fees: $736 full-time. Full-time tuition and fees vary according to course load, program, and reciprocity agreements. Part-time tuition varies according to course load and reciprocity agreements. **Scholarships:** Available. **Calendar System:** Semester, Summer session available **Enrollment:** Full-time 3,241, Part-time 1,824 **Faculty:** Full-time 168, Part-time 171 **Student-Faculty Ratio:** 16:1 **Exams:** SAT I or ACT. **Regional Accreditation:** North Central Association of Colleges and Schools **Credit Hours For Degree:** 90 credit hours, Associates **ROTC:** Air Force, Army **Professional Accreditation:** ACEN, ADA, JRCERT, NASAD.

UNIVERSITY OF CINCINNATI CLERMONT COLLEGE

4200 Clermont College Dr.
Batavia, OH 45103-1785
Tel: (513)732-5200; Free: 866-446-2822
E-mail: jamie.adkins@uc.edu
Web Site: www.ucclermont.edu
President/CEO: Dr. Jeffrey Bauer
Admissions: Jamie Adkins
Financial Aid: Vivian Renee Scott

Type: Two-Year College **Sex:** Coed **Affiliation:** University of Cincinnati System. **% Accepted:** 81 **Admission Plans:** Deferred Admission; Open Admission **Application Deadline:** Rolling **Application Fee:** $50.00 **H.S. Requirements:** High school diploma required; GED accepted **Costs Per Year:** Application fee: $50. State resident tuition: $5316 full-time, $222 per credit part-time. Nonresident tuition: $12,548 full-time, $523 per credit part-time. Full-time tuition varies according to course level, degree level, program, and reciprocity agreements. Part-time tuition varies according to course level, degree level, program, and reciprocity agreements. **Scholarships:** Available. **Calendar System:** Semester, Summer session available **Enrollment:** Full-time 1,788, Part-time 1,311 **Student-Faculty Ratio:** 14:1 **Final Year or Final Semester Residency Requirement:** No **Regional Accreditation:** North Central Association of Colleges and Schools **Credit Hours For Degree:** 60 semester hours, Associates; 120 semester hours, Bachelors **ROTC:** Air Force **Intercollegiate Athletics:** Baseball M; Basketball M & W; Cheerleading W; Golf M; Soccer M & W; Softball W; Volleyball W

UNIVERSITY OF DAYTON

300 College Park
Dayton, OH 45469
Tel: (937)229-1000; Free: 800-837-7433
Fax: (937)229-4545
E-mail: admission@udayton.edu
Web Site: www.udayton.edu
President/CEO: Dr. Daniel J. Curran
Admissions: Robert Durkle
Financial Aid: Catherine Mix

Type: University **Sex:** Coed **Affiliation:** Roman Catholic. **Scores:** 98% SAT V 400+; 99% SAT M 400+; 20% ACT 18-23; 56% ACT 24-29 **% Accepted:** 58 **Admission Plans:** Deferred Admission; Early Decision Plan **Application Fee:** $0.00 **H.S. Requirements:** High school diploma required; GED accepted **Costs Per Year:** Application fee: $0. Comprehensive fee: $51,280 includes full-time tuition ($39,090) and college room and board ($12,190).

College room only: $7310. Full-time tuition varies according to degree level. Room and board charges vary according to board plan and housing facility. Part-time tuition: $1303 per credit hour. Part-time tuition varies according to course load and degree level. **Scholarships:** Available. **Calendar System:** Semester, Summer session available **Enrollment:** Full-time 8,205, Graduate full-time 1,816, Graduate part-time 769, Part-time 460 **Faculty:** Full-time 535, Part-time 482 **Student-Faculty Ratio:** 16:1 **Exams:** SAT I or ACT; SAT Reasoning. **% Receiving Financial Aid:** 53 **% Residing in College-Owned, -Operated, or -Affiliated Housing:** 72 **Final Year or Final Semester Residency Requirement:** No **Regional Accreditation:** North Central Association of Colleges and Schools **Credit Hours For Degree:** 120 semester hours, Bachelors **ROTC:** Air Force, Army **Professional Accreditation:** AACSB, AALS, ABA, ABET, ACA, NASAD, NASM, NASPAA, NCATE. **Intercollegiate Athletics:** Baseball M; Basketball M & W; Cheerleading M & W; Crew W; Cross-Country Running M & W; Football M; Golf M & W; Soccer M & W; Softball W; Tennis M & W; Track and Field W; Volleyball W

THE UNIVERSITY OF FINDLAY

1000 N Main St.
Findlay, OH 45840-3653
Tel: (419)422-8313; Free: 800-548-0932
Fax: (419)424-4822
E-mail: ashcraft@findlay.edu
Web Site: www.findlay.edu
President/CEO: Dr. Katherine Fell, PhD
Admissions: Katie Ashcraft
Financial Aid: Edward R. Recker

Type: Comprehensive **Sex:** Coed **Affiliation:** Church of God. **Scores:** 93% SAT V 400+; 95% SAT M 400+; 50% ACT 18-23; 38% ACT 24-29 **% Accepted:** 76 **Admission Plans:** Deferred Admission **Application Deadline:** Rolling **Application Fee:** $0.00 **H.S. Requirements:** High school diploma required; GED accepted **Costs Per Year:** Application fee: $0. Comprehensive fee: $41,940 includes full-time tuition ($31,436), mandatory fees ($966), and college room and board ($9538). College room only: $4760. Full-time tuition and fees vary according to program. Room and board charges vary according to board plan and housing facility. Part-time tuition: $697 per hour. Part-time mandatory fees: $418 per term. Part-time tuition and fees vary according to course load and program. **Scholarships:** Available. **Calendar System:** Semester, Summer session available **Enrollment:** Full-time 2,704, Graduate full-time 747, Graduate part-time 570, Part-time 1,008 **Faculty:** Full-time 203, Part-time 127 **Student-Faculty Ratio:** 16:1 **Exams:** ACT essay component not used; SAT I or ACT; SAT essay component not used; SAT Reasoning. **% Receiving Financial Aid:** 64 **% Residing in College-Owned, -Operated, or -Affiliated Housing:** 40 **Final Year or Final Semester Residency Requirement:** Yes **Regional Accreditation:** North Central Association of Colleges and Schools **Credit Hours For Degree:** 62 semester hours, Associates; 124 semester hours, Bachelors **ROTC:** Air Force, Army **Professional Accreditation:** ABET, ACBSP, ACPE, AOTA, APTA, CSWE, JRCNMT, NCATE. **Intercollegiate Athletics:** Baseball M; Basketball M & W; Cross-Country Running M & W; Equestrian Sports W; Football M; Golf M & W; Lacrosse W; Soccer M & W; Softball W; Swimming and Diving M & W; Tennis M & W; Track and Field M & W; Volleyball W; Wrestling M

UNIVERSITY OF MOUNT UNION

1972 Clark Ave.
Alliance, OH 44601-3993
Tel: (330)821-5320; Free: 800-334-6682
Fax: (330)821-0425
E-mail: admission@mountunion.edu
Web Site: www.mountunion.edu
President/CEO: Dr. Richard Merriman
Admissions: Jess Canavan
Financial Aid: Emily J. Mattison

Type: Comprehensive **Sex:** Coed **Affiliation:** United Methodist. **Scores:** 95% SAT M 400+; 52% ACT 18-23; 40% ACT 24-29 **% Accepted:** 75 **Admission Plans:** Deferred Admission; Early Admission **Application Deadline:** Rolling **Application Fee:** $0.00 **H.S. Requirements:** High school diploma required; GED accepted **Costs Per Year:** Application fee: $0. Comprehensive fee: $38,090 includes full-time tuition ($28,230), mandatory fees ($320), and college room and board ($9540). Full-time tuition and fees vary according to course load and degree level. Room and board charges vary according to board plan and housing facility. Part-time tuition: $1195 per credit hour. Part-time tuition varies according to course load. **Scholarships:**

Available. **Calendar System:** Semester, Summer session available **Enrollment:** Full-time 2,058, Graduate full-time 97, Part-time 36 **Faculty:** Full-time 135, Part-time 113 **Student-Faculty Ratio:** 13:1 **Exams:** ACT essay component not used; SAT I or ACT; SAT essay component not used. **% Receiving Financial Aid:** 80 **% Residing in College-Owned, -Operated, or -Affiliated Housing:** 75 **Final Year or Final Semester Residency Requirement:** No **Regional Accreditation:** North Central Association of Colleges and Schools **Credit Hours For Degree:** 128 credits, Bachelors **ROTC:** Air Force, Army **Professional Accreditation:** JRCAT, NASM, NCATE. **Intercollegiate Athletics:** Baseball M; Basketball M & W; Cheerleading W; Cross-Country Running M & W; Football M; Golf M & W; Lacrosse M & W; Soccer M & W; Softball W; Swimming and Diving M & W; Tennis M & W; Track and Field M & W; Volleyball W; Wrestling M

UNIVERSITY OF NORTHWESTERN OHIO

1441 N Cable Rd.
Lima, OH 45805-1498
Tel: (419)227-3141
Fax: (419)229-6926
E-mail: klopp_d@unoh.edu
Web Site: www.unoh.edu
President/CEO: Dr. Jeffrey A. Jarvis
Admissions: Dan Klopp

Type: Four-Year College **Sex:** Coed **Admission Plans:** Deferred Admission; Early Admission; Open Admission **Application Deadline:** Rolling **Application Fee:** $50.00 **H.S. Requirements:** High school diploma required; GED accepted **Costs Per Year:** Application fee: $50. Tuition: $9450 full-time, $210 per credit hour part-time. Mandatory fees: $190 full-time, $190 per term part-time. Full-time tuition and fees vary according to class time, course load, and program. Part-time tuition and fees vary according to class time, course load, and program. College room only: $2700. Room charges vary according to housing facility. **Scholarships:** Available. **Calendar System:** Quarter, Summer session available **Faculty:** Full-time 93, Part-time 34 **Student-Faculty Ratio:** 20:1 **Exams:** SAT I. **% Residing in College-Owned, -Operated, or -Affiliated Housing:** 33 **Regional Accreditation:** North Central Association of Colleges and Schools **Credit Hours For Degree:** 108 credits, Associates; 180 credits, Bachelors **Professional Accreditation:** AAMAE, ACBSP.

UNIVERSITY OF RIO GRANDE

218 N College Ave.
Rio Grande, OH 45674
Tel: (740)245-5353; Free: 800-282-7201
Fax: (740)245-9220
E-mail: admissions@rio.edu
Web Site: www.rio.edu
President/CEO: Dr. Michelle Johnston
Admissions: Kristie Russell
Financial Aid: Meghann Fraley

Type: Comprehensive **Sex:** Coed **Scores:** 57% ACT 18-23; 12% ACT 24-29 **% Accepted:** 73 **Admission Plans:** Open Admission **Application Deadline:** Rolling **Application Fee:** $25.00 **H.S. Requirements:** High school diploma required; GED accepted **Costs Per Year:** Application fee: $25. Comprehensive fee: $33,780 includes full-time tuition ($23,260), mandatory fees ($600), and college room and board ($9920). Full-time tuition and fees vary according to course level, course load, degree level, and program. Part-time tuition: $970 per credit hour. Part-time tuition varies according to course level, course load, degree level, and program. **Scholarships:** Available. **Calendar System:** Semester, Summer session available **Enrollment:** Full-time 1,719, Graduate full-time 18, Graduate part-time 37, Part-time 387 **Faculty:** Full-time 86, Part-time 89 **Student-Faculty Ratio:** 19:1 **Exams:** ACT. **% Receiving Financial Aid:** 93 **% Residing in College-Owned, -Operated, or -Affiliated Housing:** 17 **Final Year or Final Semester Residency Requirement:** No **Regional Accreditation:** North Central Association of Colleges and Schools **Credit Hours For Degree:** 62 semester hours, Associates; 120 semester hours, Bachelors **Professional Accreditation:** ACEN, CSWE, NAACLS, NCATE. **Intercollegiate Athletics:** Archery M; Baseball M; Basketball M & W; Cross-Country Running M & W; Soccer M & W; Softball W; Track and Field M & W; Volleyball W

THE UNIVERSITY OF TOLEDO

2801 W Bancroft
Toledo, OH 43606-3390
Tel: (419)530-4636; Free: 800-5TOLEDO

Fax: (419)530-4940
E-mail: william.pierce@utoledo.edu
Web Site: www.utoledo.edu
President/CEO: Dr. Sharon L. Gaber
Admissions: William Pierce
Financial Aid: Stephen Schissler
Type: University **Sex:** Coed **Scores:** 44.74% ACT 18-23; 36.44% ACT 24-29 **% Accepted:** 93 **Admission Plans:** Deferred Admission; Open Admission **Application Deadline:** Rolling **Application Fee:** $40.00 **H.S. Requirements:** High school diploma required; GED accepted **Costs Per Year:** Application fee: $40. State resident tuition: $8052 full-time, $385.09 per credit hour part-time. Nonresident tuition: $17,390 full-time, $774.17 per credit hour part-time. Mandatory fees: $1508 full-time, $49.60 per credit hour part-time. Full-time tuition and fees vary according to course load, program, reciprocity agreements, and student level. Part-time tuition and fees vary according to course load, program, reciprocity agreements, and student level. College room and board: $11,494. College room only: $7712. Room and board charges vary according to board plan and housing facility. **Scholarships:** Available. **Calendar System:** Semester, Summer session available **Enrollment:** Full-time 12,714, Graduate full-time 2,996, Graduate part-time 1,317, Part-time 3,350 **Faculty:** Full-time 780, Part-time 288 **Student-Faculty Ratio:** 20:1 **Exams:** ACT essay component used for advising; SAT I or ACT; SAT essay component used for advising. **% Receiving Financial Aid:** 65 **% Residing in College-Owned, -Operated, or -Affiliated Housing:** 19 **Final Year or Final Semester Residency Requirement:** No **Regional Accreditation:** North Central Association of Colleges and Schools **Credit Hours For Degree:** 60 semester hours, Associates; 124 semester hours, Bachelors **ROTC:** Air Force, Army **Professional Accreditation:** AACN, AACSB, AALS, AAMAE, ABA, ABET, ACA, ACEN, ACPE, AOTA, APA, APTA, ASHA, CEPH, CSWE, CoA-KT, CoARC, JRCAT, JRCECT, LCME/AMA, NASAD, NASM, NASPAA, NCATE, NRPA. **Intercollegiate Athletics:** Baseball M; Basketball M & W; Cross-Country Running M & W; Football M; Golf M & W; Soccer W; Softball W; Swimming and Diving W; Tennis M & W; Track and Field W; Volleyball W

URBANA UNIVERSITY

579 College Way
Urbana, OH 43078-2091
Tel: (937)484-1400; Free: 800-7-URBANA
Fax: (937)484-1389
E-mail: admiss@urbana.edu
Web Site: www.urbana.edu
President/CEO: Stephen B. Jone, PhD
Admissions: Donnel W. Wiggins
Financial Aid: Amy M. Barnhart
Type: Comprehensive **Sex:** Coed **Affiliation:** Church of the New Jerusalem; We are a subsidiary of Franklin University, a non-profit university in Columbus, Ohio. **% Accepted:** 65 **Admission Plans:** Deferred Admission **Application Deadline:** Rolling **Application Fee:** $25.00 **H.S. Requirements:** High school diploma required; GED accepted **Scholarships:** Available. **Calendar System:** Semester, Summer session available **Enrollment:** Full-time 904, Part-time 557 **Faculty:** Full-time 55, Part-time 65 **Student-Faculty Ratio:** 16:1 **Exams:** SAT I or ACT. **% Receiving Financial Aid:** 88 **Regional Accreditation:** North Central Association of Colleges and Schools **Credit Hours For Degree:** 63 credit hours, Associates; 126 credit hours, Bachelors **Professional Accreditation:** AACN. **Intercollegiate Athletics:** Baseball M; Basketball M & W; Football M; Golf M & W; Soccer M & W; Softball W; Volleyball W

URSULINE COLLEGE

2550 Lander Rd.
Pepper Pike, OH 44124-4398
Tel: (440)449-4200; Free: 888-URSULINE
Fax: (440)449-2235
E-mail: admission@ursuline.edu
Web Site: www.ursuline.edu
President/CEO: Señor Christine De Vinne, OSU
Admissions: Carolyn Noll Sorg
Financial Aid: Mary Lynn Perri
Type: Comprehensive **Sex:** Coed **Affiliation:** Roman Catholic. **Scores:** 93% SAT V 400+; 84% SAT M 400+; 54% ACT 18-23; 29% ACT 24-29 **% Accepted:** 66 **Admission Plans:** Deferred Admission **Application Deadline:** February 1 **Application Fee:** $25.00 **H.S. Requirements:** High school diploma required; GED accepted **Costs Per Year:** Application fee:

$25. Comprehensive fee: $38,010 includes full-time tuition ($28,230), mandatory fees ($290), and college room and board ($9490). College room only: $4848. Full-time tuition and fees vary according to class time, course load, degree level, location, and program. Room and board charges vary according to board plan and housing facility. Part-time mandatory fees: $105 per term. Part-time fees vary according to class time, course load, degree level, location, and program. **Scholarships:** Available. **Calendar System:** Semester, Summer session available **Faculty:** Full-time 66, Part-time 128 **Student-Faculty Ratio:** 7:1 **Exams:** ACT essay component not used; SAT I or ACT; SAT II; SAT essay component not used; SAT Reasoning; SAT Subject. **% Receiving Financial Aid:** 87 **% Residing in College-Owned, -Operated, or -Affiliated Housing:** 25 **Final Year or Final Semester Residency Requirement:** Yes **Regional Accreditation:** North Central Association of Colleges and Schools **Credit Hours For Degree:** 128-129 semester hours, depending on program, Bachelors **ROTC:** Army **Professional Accreditation:** AACN, CSWE, NCATE. **Intercollegiate Athletics:** Basketball W; Bowling W; Cross-Country Running W; Golf W; Lacrosse W; Soccer W; Softball W; Swimming and Diving W; Tennis W; Track and Field W; Volleyball W

VATTEROTT COLLEGE

5025 E Royalton Rd.
Broadview Heights, OH 44147
Tel: (440)526-1660; Free: 888-553-6627
Fax: (440)526-1933
Web Site: www.vatterott.edu
President/CEO: Shannon McManamon
Admissions: Jack Chalk
Type: Two-Year College **Sex:** Coed **% Accepted:** 93 **Calendar System:** Semester **Professional Accreditation:** ACCSC.

VET TECH INSTITUTE AT BRADFORD SCHOOL

2469 Stelzer Rd.
Columbus, OH 43219
Tel: (614)416-6200; Free: 800-678-7981
Fax: (614)416-5197
Web Site: columbus.vettechinstitute.edu
Type: Two-Year College **Sex:** Coed **% Accepted:** 33 **Calendar System:** Semester **Professional Accreditation:** AVMA.

VIRGINIA MARTI COLLEGE OF ART AND DESIGN

11724 Detroit Ave.
Lakewood, OH 44107
Tel: (216)221-8584
E-mail: qmarti@vmcad.edu
Web Site: www.vmcad.edu
President/CEO: Dennis Marti
Admissions: Quinn Marti
Type: Two-Year College **Sex:** Coed **Admission Plans:** Deferred Admission; Early Admission **Application Deadline:** Rolling **Application Fee:** $50.00 **H.S. Requirements:** High school diploma required; GED accepted **Costs Per Year:** Application fee: $50. Tuition: $16,050 full-time, $400 per credit hour part-time. Mandatory fees: $1600 full-time, $250 per term part-time. Tuition guaranteed not to increase for student's term of enrollment. **Calendar System:** Quarter, Summer session available **Student-Faculty Ratio:** 12:1 **Exams:** Other. **Credit Hours For Degree:** 110 quarter hours, Associates **Professional Accreditation:** ACCSC.

WALSH UNIVERSITY

2020 E Maple St., NW
North Canton, OH 44720-3396
Tel: (330)490-7090; Free: 800-362-8846
Fax: (330)490-7165
E-mail: admissions@walsh.edu
Web Site: www.walsh.edu
President/CEO: Richard Jusseaume
Admissions: Melissa Schoeppner
Financial Aid: Holly Van Gilder
Type: Comprehensive **Sex:** Coed **Affiliation:** Roman Catholic. **Scores:** 100% SAT V 400+; 101% SAT M 400+; 50% ACT 18-23; 39% ACT 24-29 **% Accepted:** 80 **Admission Plans:** Deferred Admission; Early Admission **Application Deadline:** Rolling **Application Fee:** $25.00 **H.S. Requirements:** High school diploma required; GED accepted **Costs Per Year:** Application fee: $25. Comprehensive fee: $37,630 includes full-time tuition ($26,300),

mandatory fees ($1410), and college room and board ($9920). College room only: $5260. Full-time tuition and fees vary according to location. Room and board charges vary according to board plan and housing facility. Part-time tuition: $875 per credit hour. Part-time mandatory fees: $47 per credit hour. Part-time tuition and fees vary according to location. **Scholarships:** Available. **Calendar System:** Semester, Summer session available **Enrollment:** Full-time 1,878, Graduate full-time 241, Graduate part-time 344, Part-time 396 **Faculty:** Full-time 132, Part-time 150 **Student-Faculty Ratio:** 13:1 **Exams:** SAT I or ACT; SAT Reasoning. **% Receiving Financial Aid:** 90 % **Residing in College-Owned, -Operated, or -Affiliated Housing:** 48 **Final Year or Final Semester Residency Requirement:** Yes **Regional Accreditation:** North Central Association of Colleges and Schools **Credit Hours For Degree:** 60 credit hours, Associates; 125 credit hours, Bachelors **Professional Accreditation:** ACA, ACEN, APTA, NCATE. **Intercollegiate Athletics:** Baseball M; Basketball M & W; Cheerleading W; Cross-Country Running M & W; Football M; Golf M & W; Lacrosse M & W; Soccer M & W; Softball W; Tennis M & W; Track and Field M & W; Volleyball W

WASHINGTON STATE COMMUNITY COLLEGE

710 Colegate Dr.
Marietta, OH 45750-9225
Tel: (740)374-8716
Fax: (740)376-0257
E-mail: rperoni@wscc.edu
Web Site: www.wscc.edu
President/CEO: Dr. Charlotte R. Hatfield
Admissions: Rebecca Peroni

Type: Two-Year College **Sex:** Coed **Affiliation:** Ohio Board of Regents. **Admission Plans:** Deferred Admission; Early Admission; Open Admission **Application Deadline:** Rolling **H.S. Requirements:** High school diploma or equivalent not required. For medical laboratory technology, nursing programs: High school diploma required; GED accepted **Scholarships:** Available. **Calendar System:** Quarter, Summer session available **Student-Faculty Ratio:** 18:1 **Regional Accreditation:** North Central Association of Colleges and Schools **Credit Hours For Degree:** 90 credit hours, Associates **Professional Accreditation:** APTA, CoARC, NAACLS.

WILBERFORCE UNIVERSITY

1055 N Bickett Rd.
Wilberforce, OH 45384
Tel: (937)376-2911; Free: 800-367-8568
Fax: (937)376-4751
E-mail: ddriscoll@wilberforce.edu
Web Site: www.wilberforce.edu
President/CEO: Algenia Freeman, PhD
Admissions: Dadra Driscoll

Type: Comprehensive **Sex:** Coed **Affiliation:** African Methodist Episcopal Church. **% Accepted:** 38 **Admission Plans:** Deferred Admission; Early Action; Early Admission **Application Deadline:** July 1 **Application Fee:** $25.00 **H.S. Requirements:** High school diploma required; GED accepted **Scholarships:** Available. **Calendar System:** Semester, Summer session not available **Enrollment:** Full-time 290, Graduate full-time 23, Part-time 17 **Faculty:** Full-time 19, Part-time 29 **Student-Faculty Ratio:** 8:1 **Exams:** SAT I or ACT. **Regional Accreditation:** North Central Association of Colleges and Schools **Credit Hours For Degree:** 128 credit hours, Bachelors **ROTC:** Air Force, Army **Professional Accreditation:** CORE. **Intercollegiate Athletics:** Basketball M & W

WILMINGTON COLLEGE

1870 Quaker Way
Wilmington, OH 45177
Tel: (937)382-6661; Free: 800-341-9318
Fax: (937)382-7077
E-mail: admissions@wilmington.edu
Web Site: www.wilmington.edu
President/CEO: James M. Reynolds
Admissions: Tina Garland
Financial Aid: Donna Barton

Type: Comprehensive **Sex:** Coed **Affiliation:** Friends. **Scores:** 96% SAT V 400+; 82% SAT M 400+; 62.45% ACT 18-23; 20.22% ACT 24-29 **Admission Plans:** Deferred Admission **Application Deadline:** August 1 **H.S. Requirements:** High school diploma required; GED accepted **Costs Per Year:** Comprehensive fee: $34,000 includes full-time tuition ($23,800), mandatory fees ($700), and college room and board ($9500). College room only:

$4490. Full-time tuition and fees vary according to location. Room and board charges vary according to board plan and housing facility. Part-time tuition: $500 per credit hour. Part-time tuition varies according to course load and location. **Scholarships:** Available. **Calendar System:** Semester **Enrollment:** Full-time 1,179, Graduate full-time 11, Graduate part-time 15, Part-time 253 **Faculty:** Full-time 66, Part-time 53 **Student-Faculty Ratio:** 14:1 **Exams:** SAT I or ACT. **% Receiving Financial Aid:** 88 % **Residing in College-Owned, -Operated, or -Affiliated Housing:** 80 **Final Year or Final Semester Residency Requirement:** Yes **Regional Accreditation:** North Central Association of Colleges and Schools **Credit Hours For Degree:** 124 credit hours, Bachelors **ROTC:** Army **Professional Accreditation:** JRCAT, TEAC. **Intercollegiate Athletics:** Baseball M; Basketball M & W; Cross-Country Running M & W; Football M; Golf M & W; Soccer M & W; Softball W; Swimming and Diving M & W; Tennis M & W; Track and Field M & W; Volleyball W; Wrestling M

WITTENBERG UNIVERSITY

PO Box 720
Springfield, OH 45501-0720
Tel: (937)327-6231; Free: 800-677-7558
Fax: (937)327-6379
E-mail: admission@wittenberg.edu
Web Site: www.wittenberg.edu
President/CEO: Dr. Richard (Dick) Helton
Admissions: Karen Hunt
Financial Aid: J. Randy Green

Type: Comprehensive **Sex:** Coed **Affiliation:** Evangelical Lutheran Church. **Scores:** 95% SAT V 400+; 100% SAT M 400+; 33% ACT 18-23; 53% ACT 24-29 **% Accepted:** 77 **Admission Plans:** Deferred Admission; Early Action; Early Admission; Early Decision Plan; Preferred Admission **Application Fee:** $40.00 **H.S. Requirements:** High school diploma required; GED accepted **Costs Per Year:** Application fee: $40. Comprehensive fee: $48,216 includes full-time tuition ($37,230), mandatory fees ($860), and college room and board ($10,126). College room only: $5158. Room and board charges vary according to board plan and housing facility. Part-time tuition: $1241 per hour. Part-time tuition varies according to course load. **Scholarships:** Available. **Calendar System:** Semester, Summer session available **Enrollment:** Full-time 1,760, Graduate part-time 11, Part-time 105 **Faculty:** Full-time 122, Part-time 57 **Student-Faculty Ratio:** 13:1 **Exams:** ACT essay component not used; Other; SAT essay component not used. **% Receiving Financial Aid:** 79 **% Residing in College-Owned, -Operated, or -Affiliated Housing:** 86 **Final Year or Final Semester Residency Requirement:** No **Regional Accreditation:** North Central Association of Colleges and Schools **Credit Hours For Degree:** 130 credits, Bachelors **ROTC:** Air Force, Army **Professional Accreditation:** NASM, NCATE. **Intercollegiate Athletics:** Baseball M; Basketball M & W; Crew M & W; Cross-Country Running M & W; Field Hockey W; Football M; Golf M & W; Lacrosse M & W; Rugby M & W; Soccer M & W; Softball W; Swimming and Diving M & W; Tennis M & W; Track and Field M & W; Volleyball M & W

WRIGHT STATE UNIVERSITY

3640 Colonel Glenn Hwy.
Dayton, OH 45435
Tel: (937)775-3333; Free: 800-247-1770
Fax: (937)775-5795
E-mail: admissions@wright.edu
Web Site: www.wright.edu
President/CEO: Dr. David R. Hopkins

Type: University **Sex:** Coed **Affiliation:** University System of Ohio. **Scores:** 91% SAT V 400+; 90% SAT M 400+; 46% ACT 18-23; 29% ACT 24-29 **% Accepted:** 96 **Admission Plans:** Deferred Admission; Early Admission **Application Deadline:** Rolling **Application Fee:** $30.00 **H.S. Requirements:** High school diploma required; GED accepted **Costs Per Year:** Application fee: $30. State resident tuition: $8730 full-time, $394 per credit hour part-time. Nonresident tuition: $17,098 full-time, $779 per credit hour part-time. Full-time tuition varies according to course load, location, and reciprocity agreements. Part-time tuition varies according to course load, location, and reciprocity agreements. College room and board: $9304. College room only: $5878. Room and board charges vary according to board plan, housing facility, and location. **Scholarships:** Available. **Calendar System:** Semester, Summer session available **Enrollment:** Full-time 9,937, Graduate full-time 3,187, Graduate part-time 973, Part-time 2,745 **Faculty:** Full-time 658, Part-time 2 **Student-Faculty Ratio:** 22:1 **Exams:** ACT essay component not used; SAT I or ACT; SAT essay component not used; SAT Reasoning. %

Receiving Financial Aid: 63 % **Residing in College-Owned, -Operated, or -Affiliated Housing:** 20 **Final Year or Final Semester Residency Requirement:** No **Regional Accreditation:** North Central Association of Colleges and Schools **Credit Hours For Degree:** 60 credit hours, Associates; 120 credit hours, Bachelors **ROTC:** Air Force, Army **Professional Accreditation:** AACN, AACSB, ABET, ACA, APA, CORE, CSWE, JRCAT, LCME/AMA, NAACLS, NASM, NASPAA, NCATE. **Intercollegiate Athletics:** Baseball M; Basketball M & W; Cheerleading M & W; Cross-Country Running M & W; Golf M; Soccer M & W; Softball W; Swimming and Diving M & W; Tennis M & W; Track and Field W; Volleyball W

WRIGHT STATE UNIVERSITY–LAKE CAMPUS

7600 Lake Campus Dr.
Celina, OH 45822-2921
Tel: (419)586-0300; Free: 800-237-1477
Fax: (419)586-0358
E-mail: jill.puthoff@wright.edu
Web Site: www.wright.edu/lake
President/CEO: Dr. Jay Albayyari
Admissions: Jill Puthoff

Type: Comprehensive **Sex:** Coed **Affiliation:** Wright State University, Dayton; University System of Ohio. **Scores:** 71% SAT V 400+; 71% SAT M 400+; 57% ACT 18-23; 24% ACT 24-29 **% Accepted:** 99 **Admission Plans:** Deferred Admission **Application Deadline:** Rolling **Application Fee:** $30.00 **H.S. Requirements:** High school diploma required; GED accepted **Costs Per Year:** Application fee: $30. State resident tuition: $5842 full-time, $265 per credit hour part-time. Nonresident tuition: $14,210 full-time, $650 per credit hour part-time. Full-time tuition varies according to course load, location, and reciprocity agreements. Part-time tuition varies according to course load, location, and reciprocity agreements. College room and board: $9674. College room only: $4994. Room and board charges vary according to board plan, housing facility, and location. **Calendar System:** Semester, Summer session available **Enrollment:** Full-time 826, Graduate full-time 14, Part-time 332 **Faculty:** Full-time 34 **Student-Faculty Ratio:** 27:1 **Exams:** ACT essay component not used; SAT I or ACT; SAT essay component not used; SAT Reasoning. **% Residing in College-Owned, -Operated, or -Affiliated Housing:** 5 **Final Year or Final Semester Residency Requirement:** No **Regional Accreditation:** North Central Association of Colleges and Schools **Credit Hours For Degree:** 60 semester hours, Associates; 120 semester hours, Bachelors **ROTC:** Air Force, Army **Intercollegiate Athletics:** Baseball M; Basketball M & W

XAVIER UNIVERSITY

3800 Victory Pky.
Cincinnati, OH 45207
Tel: (513)745-3000; Free: 877-XUADMIT
Fax: (513)745-4319
E-mail: xuadmit@xavier.edu
Web Site: www.xavier.edu
President/CEO: Rev. Michael J. Graham, SJ

Type: University **Sex:** Coed **Affiliation:** Roman Catholic. **Scores:** 98% SAT V 400+; 98% SAT M 400+; 35.01% ACT 18-23; 52.86% ACT 24-29 **% Accepted:** 73 **Admission Plans:** Deferred Admission **Application Deadline:** February 1 **Application Fee:** $35.00 **H.S. Requirements:** High school diploma required; GED accepted **Costs Per Year:** Application fee: $35. Comprehensive fee: $46,460 includes full-time tuition ($34,050), mandatory fees ($1030), and college room and board ($11,380). College room only: $6300. Full-time tuition and fees vary according to course load, location, and program. Room and board charges vary according to board plan and housing facility. Part-time tuition: $654 per credit hour. Part-time mandatory fees: $9 per term. Part-time tuition and fees vary according to course load, location, and program. **Scholarships:** Available. **Calendar System:** Semester, Summer session available **Enrollment:** Full-time 4,270, Graduate full-time 562, Graduate part-time 1,343, Part-time 363 **Faculty:** Full-time 352, Part-time 347 **Student-Faculty Ratio:** 12:1 **Exams:** SAT I or ACT; SAT Reasoning. **% Receiving Financial Aid:** 58 **% Residing in College-Owned, -Operated, or -Affiliated Housing:** 52 **Final Year or Final Semester Residency Requirement:** No **Regional Accreditation:** North Central Association of Colleges and Schools **Credit Hours For Degree:** 60 semester

hours, Associates; 120 semester hours, Bachelors **ROTC:** Air Force, Army **Professional Accreditation:** AACN, AACSB, ACA, AOTA, APA, CAHME, CSWE, JRCAT, JRCERT, MACTE, NASM, TEAC. **Intercollegiate Athletics:** Baseball M; Basketball M & W; Cheerleading M & W; Crew M & W; Cross-Country Running M & W; Equestrian Sports M & W; Fencing M & W; Golf M & W; Gymnastics M & W; Ice Hockey M & W; Lacrosse M & W; Rugby M; Soccer M & W; Softball W; Swimming and Diving M & W; Tennis M & W; Track and Field M & W; Ultimate Frisbee M; Volleyball M & W; Water Polo M & W

YOUNGSTOWN STATE UNIVERSITY

One University Plz.
Youngstown, OH 44555-0001
Tel: (330)941-3000; Free: 877-468-6978
Fax: (330)941-1998
E-mail: enroll@ysu.edu
Web Site: www.ysu.edu
President/CEO: James P. Tressel
Admissions: Sue Davis
Financial Aid: Barbara Greene

Type: Comprehensive **Sex:** Coed **Scores:** 77% SAT V 400+; 82% SAT M 400+; 51% ACT 18-23; 23% ACT 24-29 **% Accepted:** 71 **Admission Plans:** Deferred Admission; Early Admission **Application Deadline:** August 1 **Application Fee:** $45.00 **H.S. Requirements:** High school diploma required; GED accepted **Costs Per Year:** Application fee: $45. State resident tuition: $7847 full-time, $327 per credit hour part-time. Nonresident tuition: $13,847 full-time, $577 per credit hour part-time. Mandatory fees: $470 full-time, $10 per credit hour part-time, $115. Full-time tuition and fees vary according to course load. Part-time tuition and fees vary according to course load. College room and board: $8990. Room and board charges vary according to board plan and housing facility. **Scholarships:** Available. **Calendar System:** Semester, Summer session available **Enrollment:** Full-time 8,628, Graduate full-time 683, Graduate part-time 612, Part-time 2,545 **Faculty:** Full-time 408, Part-time 639 **Student-Faculty Ratio:** 17:1 **Exams:** ACT essay component not used; SAT I or ACT; SAT essay component not used; SAT Reasoning; SAT Subject. **% Receiving Financial Aid:** 75 **% Residing in College-Owned, -Operated, or -Affiliated Housing:** 11 **Final Year or Final Semester Residency Requirement:** Yes **Regional Accreditation:** North Central Association of Colleges and Schools **Credit Hours For Degree:** 60 credits, Associates; 120 credits, Bachelors **ROTC:** Air Force, Army **Professional Accreditation:** AACSB, AAFCS, AAMAE, AANA, ABET, ACA, ACEN, ADA, AND, APTA, CEPH, CSWE, CoARC, JRCEMTP, NAACLS, NASAD, NASM, NAST, NCATE. **Intercollegiate Athletics:** Baseball M; Basketball M & W; Bowling W; Cross-Country Running M & W; Football M; Golf M & W; Soccer W; Softball W; Swimming and Diving W; Tennis M & W; Track and Field M & W; Volleyball W

ZANE STATE COLLEGE

1555 Newark Rd.
Zanesville, OH 43701-2626
Tel: (740)454-2501; Free: 800-686-8324
E-mail: pyoung@zanestate.edu
Web Site: www.zanestate.edu
President/CEO: Paul Brown
Admissions: Paul Young

Type: Two-Year College **Sex:** Coed **Admission Plans:** Early Admission; Open Admission **Application Deadline:** Rolling **Application Fee:** $25.00 **H.S. Requirements:** High school diploma required; GED accepted **Costs Per Year:** Application fee: $25. One-time mandatory fee: $50. State resident tuition: $3684 full-time, $152 per credit hour part-time. Nonresident tuition: $7332 full-time, $304 per credit hour part-time. Mandatory fees: $36 full-time. Full-time tuition and fees vary according to course load. Part-time tuition varies according to course load. **Scholarships:** Available. **Calendar System:** Quarter, Summer session available **Student-Faculty Ratio:** 19:1 **Exams:** Other; SAT I or ACT. **Regional Accreditation:** North Central Association of Colleges and Schools **Credit Hours For Degree:** 110 credits, Associates **Professional Accreditation:** AAMAE, ABET, ACBSP, ACF, AOTA, APTA, JRCERT, NAACLS. **Intercollegiate Athletics:** Baseball M; Basketball M & W; Golf M & W

BACONE COLLEGE
2299 Old Bacone Rd.
Muskogee, OK 74403-1597
Tel: (918)683-4581; Free: 888-682-5514
Fax: (918)682-5514
Web Site: www.bacone.edu
President/CEO: Franklin K. Willis
Financial Aid: Misty Oleson
Type: Four-Year College **Sex:** Coed **Affiliation:** American Baptist Churches in the U.S.A. **Admission Plans:** Deferred Admission; Early Admission **Application Deadline:** Rolling **Application Fee:** $25.00 **H.S. Requirements:** High school diploma required; GED accepted **Scholarships:** Available. **Calendar System:** Semester, Summer session available **Exams:** ACT; SAT I or ACT. **Regional Accreditation:** North Central Association of Colleges and Schools **Credit Hours For Degree:** 62 semester hours, Associates; 124 semester hours, Bachelors **Professional Accreditation:** ACEN, JRCERT.

CAMERON UNIVERSITY
2800 W Gore Blvd.
Lawton, OK 73505-6377
Tel: (580)581-2200; Free: 888-454-7600
Fax: (580)581-5514
E-mail: admissions@cameron.edu
Web Site: www.cameron.edu
President/CEO: Dr. John McArthur
Admissions: Karina Braun
Financial Aid: Gary Garoffolo
Type: Comprehensive **Sex:** Coed **Affiliation:** Oklahoma State Regents for Higher Education. **Scores:** 50.4% ACT 18-23; 18.5% ACT 24-29 **% Accepted:** 100 **Admission Plans:** Deferred Admission **Application Deadline:** Rolling **Application Fee:** $15.00 **H.S. Requirements:** High school diploma required; GED accepted **Costs Per Year:** Application fee: $15. State resident tuition: $3960 full-time, $132 per credit hour part-time. Nonresident tuition: $12,750 full-time, $419 per credit hour part-time. Mandatory fees: $1620 full-time, $54 per credit hour part-time. Full-time tuition and fees vary according to course level, course load, location, and program. Part-time tuition and fees vary according to course level, course load, location, and program. College room and board: $4888. College room only: $1872. Room and board charges vary according to board plan and housing facility. **Scholarships:** Available. **Calendar System:** Semester, Summer session available **Enrollment:** Full-time 3,190, Graduate full-time 154, Graduate part-time 282, Part-time 1,552 **Faculty:** Full-time 174, Part-time 136 **Student-Faculty Ratio:** 18:1 **Exams:** ACT essay component not used; SAT I or ACT; SAT essay component not used; SAT Reasoning. **% Receiving Financial Aid:** 66 **% Residing in College-Owned, -Operated, or -Affiliated Housing:** 9 **Final Year or Final Semester Residency Requirement:** No **Regional Accreditation:** North Central Association of Colleges and Schools **Credit Hours For Degree:** 60 semester hours, Associates; 124 semester hours, Bachelors **ROTC:** Army **Professional Accreditation:** ACBSP, NASM, NCATE. **Intercollegiate Athletics:** Baseball M; Basketball M & W; Cross-Country Running M; Golf M & W; Softball W; Tennis M & W; Volleyball W

CAREER POINT COLLEGE
3138 S Garnett Rd.
Tulsa, OK 74146

Tel: (918)622-4100
Web Site: www.careerpointcollege.edu
Type: Two-Year College **Sex:** Coed **Professional Accreditation:** ACICS.

CARL ALBERT STATE COLLEGE
1507 S McKenna
Poteau, OK 74953-5208
Tel: (918)647-1200
Fax: (918)647-1306
Web Site: www.carlalbert.edu
President/CEO: Garry M. Ivey
Admissions: Jonathan Bradley Davis
Financial Aid: Crystle McKinney
Type: Two-Year College **Sex:** Coed **Affiliation:** Oklahoma State Regents for Higher Education. **Admission Plans:** Open Admission **Application Deadline:** August 13 **Application Fee:** $0.00 **H.S. Requirements:** High school diploma or equivalent not required. For nursing, physical therapy assistant programs: High school diploma required; GED accepted **Costs Per Year:** Application fee: $0. State resident tuition: $1,572 full-time, $105.05 per credit hour part-time. Nonresident tuition: $3,042 full-time, $217.30 per credit hour part-time. Mandatory fees: $1185 full-time, $500 per term part-time. Full-time tuition and fees vary according to course load. Part-time tuition and fees vary according to course load. College room and board: $2111. College room only: $1600. Room and board charges vary according to board plan. **Scholarships:** Available. **Calendar System:** Semester **Enrollment:** Full-time 1,415, Part-time 861 **Student-Faculty Ratio:** 16:1 **% Residing in College-Owned, -Operated, or -Affiliated Housing:** 12 **Regional Accreditation:** North Central Association of Colleges and Schools **Credit Hours For Degree:** 62 credit hours, Associates **Professional Accreditation:** ACBSP, ACEN, APTA. **Intercollegiate Athletics:** Baseball M; Basketball M & W; Softball M

CLARY SAGE COLLEGE
3131 S Sheridan
Tulsa, OK 74145
Tel: (918)298-8200
Fax: (918)298-0099
E-mail: rmahlberg@clarysagecollege.com
Web Site: www.clarysagecollege.com
President/CEO: Dr. Kevin L. Kirk
Admissions: Raye Mahlberg
Type: Two-Year College **Sex:** Coed **Admission Plans:** Open Admission **Application Deadline:** Rolling **Application Fee:** $100.00 **H.S. Requirements:** High school diploma required; GED accepted **Costs Per Year:** Application fee: $100. Tuition: $12,987 full-time, $6 per credit part-time. Mandatory fees: $1209 full-time. Full-time tuition and fees vary according to class time, course level, course load, degree level, location, program, reciprocity agreements, and student level. Part-time tuition varies according to class time, course level, location, reciprocity agreements, and student level. **Calendar System:** Continuous, Summer session not available **Enrollment:** Full-time 621 **Faculty:** Full-time 32 **Student-Faculty Ratio:** 19:1 **Final Year or Final Semester Residency Requirement:** No **Credit Hours For Degree:** 60 credits, Associates **Professional Accreditation:** ACICS.

COLLEGE OF THE MUSCOGEE NATION
2170 Raven Cir.
Okmulgee, OK 74447-0917

Web Site: www.mvsktc.org
Type: Two-Year College Sex: Coed Regional Accreditation: North Central Association of Colleges and Schools

COMANCHE NATION COLLEGE

1608 SW 9th St.
Lawton, OK 73501
Tel: (580)591-0203
Web Site: www.cnc.cc.ok.us
Type: Two-Year College Sex: Coed Regional Accreditation: North Central Association of Colleges and Schools

COMMUNITY CARE COLLEGE

4242 S Sheridan Rd.
Tulsa, OK 74145
Tel: (918)610-0027
Fax: (918)610-0029
E-mail: cmeadows@communitycarecollege.edu
Web Site: www.communitycarecollege.edu
President/CEO: Dr. Kevin L. Kirk
Admissions: Dr. Celia Stall-Meadows
Financial Aid: Karissa Marcangeli
Type: Two-Year College Sex: Coed Admission Plans: Open Admission Application Deadline: Rolling H.S. Requirements: High school diploma required; GED accepted Costs Per Year: Tuition: $12,989 full-time. Mandatory fees: $1442 full-time. Full-time tuition and fees vary according to class time, course level, course load, degree level, location, program, and reciprocity agreements. Scholarships: Available. Calendar System: Continuous Enrollment: Full-time 1,002 Faculty: Full-time 28, Part-time 2 Student-Faculty Ratio: 28:1 Credit Hours For Degree: 60 credit hours, Associates Professional Accreditation: ABHES, ACICS.

CONNORS STATE COLLEGE

Rte. 1 Box 1000
Warner, OK 74469-9700
Tel: (918)463-2931
Web Site: www.connorsstate.edu
President/CEO: Dr. Timothy Faltyn
Admissions: Sonya Baker
Type: Two-Year College Sex: Coed Affiliation: Oklahoma State Regents for Higher Education. Admission Plans: Deferred Admission; Early Admission; Open Admission Application Deadline: Rolling Application Fee: $0.00 H.S. Requirements: High school diploma or equivalent not required Scholarships: Available. Calendar System: Semester, Summer session available Regional Accreditation: North Central Association of Colleges and Schools Credit Hours For Degree: 60 semester hours, Associates Professional Accreditation: ACEN. Intercollegiate Athletics: Baseball M; Basketball M & W; Softball W

DEVRY UNIVERSITY

Lakepointe Towers
4013 NW Expy. St., Ste. 100
Oklahoma City, OK 73116
Tel: (405)767-9516; Free: 866-338-7941
Web Site: www.devry.edu
Type: Comprehensive Sex: Coed Application Deadline: Rolling Costs Per Year: Tuition: $17,052 full-time, $609 per credit hour part-time. Mandatory fees: $80 full-time, $40 per term part-time. Scholarships: Available. % Receiving Financial Aid: 83 Regional Accreditation: North Central Association of Colleges and Schools

EAST CENTRAL UNIVERSITY

1100 E 14th St.
Ada, OK 74820
Tel: (580)332-8000
Fax: (580)436-5495
E-mail: kstephens@ecok.edu
Web Site: www.ecok.edu
President/CEO: Dr. John R. Hargrave
Admissions: Kylie Stephens
Financial Aid: Becky Isaacs
Type: Comprehensive Sex: Coed Affiliation: Oklahoma State Regents for Higher Education. Scores: 54% SAT V 400+; 96% SAT M 400+; 55.08% ACT 18-23; 22.72% ACT 24-29 % Accepted: 46 Admission Plans: Early

Admission Application Fee: $20.00 H.S. Requirements: High school diploma required; GED accepted Costs Per Year: Application fee: $20. State resident tuition: $4511 full-time, $150.35 per semester hour part-time. Nonresident tuition: $12,819 full-time, $427.29 per semester hour part-time. Mandatory fees: $1363 full-time, $41.80 per semester hour part-time, $54.50 per term part-time. College room and board: $5350. College room only: $2200. Room and board charges vary according to board plan and housing facility. Tuition guaranteed not to increase for student's term of enrollment. Scholarships: Available. Calendar System: Semester, Summer session available Enrollment: Full-time 3,095, Graduate full-time 247, Graduate part-time 513, Part-time 592 Faculty: Full-time 164, Part-time 107 Student-Faculty Ratio: 18:1 Exams: SAT I or ACT. % Receiving Financial Aid: 64 % Residing in College-Owned, -Operated, or -Affiliated Housing: 39 Final Year or Final Semester Residency Requirement: No Regional Accreditation: North Central Association of Colleges and Schools Credit Hours For Degree: 124 semester hours, Bachelors Professional Accreditation: ACBSP, ACEN, AHIMA, CORE, CSWE, NASM, NCATE. Intercollegiate Athletics: Baseball M; Basketball M & W; Cross-Country Running M & W; Football M; Golf M & W; Soccer W; Softball W; Tennis M & W; Track and Field M & W; Volleyball W

EASTERN OKLAHOMA STATE COLLEGE

1301 W Main
Wilburton, OK 74578-4999
Tel: (918)465-2361; Free: 855-534-3672
Fax: (918)465-2431
E-mail: lmiller@eosc.edu
Web Site: www.eosc.edu
President/CEO: Dr. Steve Smith
Admissions: Leah McLaughlin
Type: Two-Year College Sex: Coed Affiliation: Oklahoma State Regents for Higher Education. Admission Plans: Deferred Admission; Early Admission; Open Admission Application Deadline: Rolling Application Fee: $10.00 H.S. Requirements: High school diploma required; GED accepted. For state residents 18 or over: High school diploma or equivalent not required Scholarships: Available. Calendar System: Semester, Summer session available Regional Accreditation: North Central Association of Colleges and Schools Credit Hours For Degree: 64 semester hours, Associates Professional Accreditation: ACEN. Intercollegiate Athletics: Baseball M; Basketball M & W; Equestrian Sports M & W; Softball W

FAMILY OF FAITH COLLEGE

30 Kinville
Shawnee, OK 74802
Tel: (405)273-5331
Web Site: www.familyoffaithcollege.edu
Type: Four-Year College Sex: Coed Affiliation: Christian. Calendar System: Semester Professional Accreditation: ABHE.

HERITAGE COLLEGE

7202 I-35 Service Rd.
Oklahoma City, OK 73149
Tel: (405)631-3399; Free: 888-334-7339
Fax: (405)631-6711
E-mail: info@heritage-education.com
Web Site: www.heritagecollege.edu
President/CEO: Andrea Riley
Type: Two-Year College Sex: Coed Admission Plans: Open Admission Student-Faculty Ratio: 33:1 Professional Accreditation: ACCSC.

HILLSDALE FREE WILL BAPTIST COLLEGE

3701 S I-35 Service Rd.
Moore, OK 73160-1208
Tel: (405)912-9000
Fax: (405)912-9050
E-mail: recruitment@hc.edu
Web Site: www.hc.edu
President/CEO: Timothy W. Eaton
Financial Aid: Denise Conklin
Type: Comprehensive Sex: Coed Affiliation: Free Will Baptist. Admission Plans: Deferred Admission; Early Admission Application Fee: $20.00 H.S. Requirements: High school diploma required; GED accepted Costs Per Year: Application fee: $20. Comprehensive fee: $19,420 includes full-time tuition ($9580), mandatory fees ($2760), and college room and board

($7080). College room only: $2580. Full-time tuition and fees vary according to course load. Room and board charges vary according to board plan and housing facility. Part-time tuition: $400 per credit hour. Part-time mandatory fees: $40 per credit hour, $260 per term. Part-time tuition and fees vary according to course load. **Scholarships:** Available. **Calendar System:** Semester, Summer session available **Enrollment:** Full-time 186, Graduate full-time 3, Graduate part-time 5, Part-time 39 **Faculty:** Full-time 13, Part-time 34 **Exams:** SAT I or ACT. **% Receiving Financial Aid:** 79 **Final Year or Final Semester Residency Requirement:** No **Credit Hours For Degree:** 64 credit hours, Associates; 128 credit hours, Bachelors **Professional Accreditation:** TRACS. **Intercollegiate Athletics:** Baseball M; Basketball M & W; Cross-Country Running M & W; Soccer M; Softball W; Volleyball W

LANGSTON UNIVERSITY

PO Box 907
Langston, OK 73050
Tel: (405)466-2231
Fax: (405)466-3381
E-mail: jlane@langston.edu
Web Site: www.langston.edu
President/CEO: Dr. Kent Smith, Jr.
Admissions: Jeremy Lane
Financial Aid: Sheila Mcgill
Type: Comprehensive **Sex:** Coed **Affiliation:** Oklahoma A&M System. **% Accepted:** 61 **Admission Plans:** Deferred Admission **Application Deadline:** Rolling **Application Fee:** $0.00 **H.S. Requirements:** High school diploma required; GED accepted **Costs Per Year:** Application fee: $0. State resident tuition: $3467 full-time, $115.55 per credit hour part-time. Nonresident tuition: $11,054 full-time, $359.85 per credit hour part-time. Mandatory fees: $1575 full-time, $115.55 per credit hour part-time, $89.58. Full-time tuition and fees vary according to degree level and program. Part-time tuition and fees vary according to degree level and program. College room and board: $9272. College room only: $6316. Room and board charges vary according to board plan and housing facility. Tuition guaranteed not to increase for student's term of enrollment. **Scholarships:** Available. **Calendar System:** Semester, Summer session available **Enrollment:** Full-time 1,967, Graduate full-time 157, Graduate part-time 178, Part-time 193 **Faculty:** Full-time 141, Part-time 50 **Student-Faculty Ratio:** 18:1 **Exams:** ACT essay component not used; SAT I or ACT; SAT essay component not used. **% Receiving Financial Aid:** 85 **% Residing in College-Owned, -Operated, or -Affiliated Housing:** 66 **Final Year or Final Semester Residency Requirement:** Yes **Regional Accreditation:** North Central Association of Colleges and Schools **Credit Hours For Degree:** 62 credit hours, Associates; 124 credit hours, Bachelors **ROTC:** Army **Professional Accreditation:** ACBSP, ACEN, APTA, CORE, NCATE. **Intercollegiate Athletics:** Basketball M & W; Cheerleading W; Cross-Country Running M & W; Football M; Softball W; Track and Field M & W; Volleyball W

MID-AMERICA CHRISTIAN UNIVERSITY

3500 SW 119th St.
Oklahoma City, OK 73170-4504
Tel: (405)691-3800; Free: 888-436-3035
Fax: (405)692-5165
E-mail: info@macu.edu
Web Site: www.macu.edu
President/CEO: Dr. John Fozard
Admissions: Jason Duda
Financial Aid: Todd Martin
Type: Comprehensive **Sex:** Coed **Affiliation:** Church of God. **Admission Plans:** Early Admission; Open Admission **Application Deadline:** Rolling **Application Fee:** $25.00 **H.S. Requirements:** High school diploma required; GED accepted **Scholarships:** Available. **Calendar System:** Semester, Summer session available **% Receiving Financial Aid:** 86 **Regional Accreditation:** North Central Association of Colleges and Schools **Credit Hours For Degree:** 64 semester hours, Associates; 124 semester hours, Bachelors **Intercollegiate Athletics:** Baseball M; Basketball M & W; Golf M; Soccer M & W; Softball W; Volleyball W

MURRAY STATE COLLEGE

One Murray Campus
Tishomingo, OK 73460-3130
Tel: (580)371-2371
Fax: (580)371-9844
E-mail: gmarten@mscok.edu

Web Site: www.mscok.edu
President/CEO: Joy McDaniel
Admissions: Genna Marten
Type: Two-Year College **Sex:** Coed **Affiliation:** Oklahoma State Regents for Higher Education. **Admission Plans:** Early Admission; Open Admission **Application Deadline:** Rolling **H.S. Requirements:** High school diploma required; GED accepted **Scholarships:** Available. **Calendar System:** Semester, Summer session available **Enrollment:** Full-time 1,317, Part-time 1,357 **Faculty:** Full-time 57, Part-time 95 **Student-Faculty Ratio:** 20:1 **Exams:** SAT I or ACT. **% Residing in College-Owned, -Operated, or -Affiliated Housing:** 11 **Regional Accreditation:** North Central Association of Colleges and Schools **Credit Hours For Degree:** 63 credit hours, Associates **Professional Accreditation:** ACEN, APTA. **Intercollegiate Athletics:** Baseball M; Basketball M & W; Cheerleading M & W; Golf M & W; Softball W

NATIONAL AMERICAN UNIVERSITY

8040 S Sheridan Rd.
Tulsa, OK 74133
Tel: (918)879-8400
Web Site: www.national.edu
Type: Four-Year College **Sex:** Coed **Calendar System:** Quarter **Regional Accreditation:** North Central Association of Colleges and Schools

NORTHEASTERN OKLAHOMA AGRICULTURAL AND MECHANICAL COLLEGE

200 I St., NE
Miami, OK 74354-6434
Tel: (918)542-8441; Free: 800-464-6636
Fax: (918)542-9759
E-mail: neoadmission@neo.edu
Web Site: www.neo.edu
President/CEO: Dr. Glenn E. Mayle
Admissions: Amy Ishmael
Financial Aid: Aimee McMain
Type: Two-Year College **Sex:** Coed **Affiliation:** Oklahoma State Regents for Higher Education. **Admission Plans:** Open Admission **Application Deadline:** Rolling **Application Fee:** $0.00 **H.S. Requirements:** High school diploma required; GED accepted **Scholarships:** Available. **Calendar System:** Semester, Summer session available **Enrollment:** Full-time 1,396, Part-time 503 **Faculty:** Full-time 77, Part-time 33 **Student-Faculty Ratio:** 17:1 **Regional Accreditation:** North Central Association of Colleges and Schools **Credit Hours For Degree:** 60 credit hours, Associates **Professional Accreditation:** ACEN, APTA, NAACLS. **Intercollegiate Athletics:** Baseball M; Basketball M & W; Cheerleading M & W; Football M; Golf M; Soccer M & W; Softball W; Volleyball W

NORTHEASTERN STATE UNIVERSITY

600 N Grand
Tahlequah, OK 74464-2399
Tel: (918)456-5511; Free: 800-722-9614
Fax: (918)458-2342
E-mail: standleo@nsuok.edu
Web Site: www.nsuok.edu
President/CEO: Dr. Steven Turner
Admissions: Olaf Standley
Financial Aid: Dr. Teri Cochran
Type: Comprehensive **Sex:** Coed **Affiliation:** Regional University System of Oklahoma. **Scores:** 61.9% ACT 18-23; 22% ACT 24-29 **% Accepted:** 92 **Admission Plans:** Deferred Admission **Application Deadline:** August 1 **Application Fee:** $25.00 **H.S. Requirements:** High school diploma required; GED accepted **Costs Per Year:** Application fee: $25. State resident tuition: $4425 full-time, $147.50 per credit hour part-time. Nonresident tuition: $11,775 full-time, $392.50 per credit hour part-time. Mandatory fees: $1122 full-time, $37.40 per credit hour part-time. Full-time tuition and fees vary according to course load and program. Part-time tuition and fees vary according to course load and program. College room and board: $6490. College room only: $2782. Room and board charges vary according to board plan and housing facility. Tuition guaranteed not to increase for student's term of enrollment. **Scholarships:** Available. **Calendar System:** Semester, Summer session available **Enrollment:** Full-time 5,001, Graduate full-time 477, Graduate part-time 755, Part-time 2,043 **Faculty:** Full-time 306, Part-time 205 **Student-Faculty Ratio:** 17:1 **Exams:** ACT; ACT essay component not used; SAT Reasoning. **% Receiving Financial Aid:** 68 **% Residing in College-Owned, -Operated, or -Affiliated Hous-

ing: 16 **Final Year or Final Semester Residency Requirement:** Yes **Regional Accreditation:** North Central Association of Colleges and Schools **Credit Hours For Degree:** 124 semester hours, Bachelors **ROTC:** Army **Professional Accreditation:** ACBSP, ACEN, AOA, ASHA, CSWE, NASM, NCATE. **Intercollegiate Athletics:** Baseball M; Basketball M & W; Football M; Golf M & W; Soccer M & W; Softball W; Tennis W

NORTHERN OKLAHOMA COLLEGE

1220 E Grand Ave.
Tonkawa, OK 74653-0310
Tel: (580)628-6200
Fax: (580)628-6371
Web Site: www.noc.edu
President/CEO: Cheryl Evans
Admissions: Sheri Snyder
Financial Aid: Holly Lee

Type: Two-Year College **Sex:** Coed **Affiliation:** Oklahoma State Regents for Higher Education. **Admission Plans:** Early Admission; Open Admission **Application Deadline:** Rolling **Application Fee:** $25.00 **H.S. Requirements:** High school diploma required; GED accepted. For applicants 24 or over: High school diploma or equivalent not required **Scholarships:** Available. **Calendar System:** Semester, Summer session available **Faculty:** Full-time 45, Part-time 35 **Student-Faculty Ratio:** 35:1 **% Residing in College-Owned, -Operated, or -Affiliated Housing:** 20 **Regional Accreditation:** North Central Association of Colleges and Schools **Credit Hours For Degree:** 60 credit hours, Associates **Professional Accreditation:** ACBSP, ACEN. **Intercollegiate Athletics:** Baseball M; Basketball M & W; Soccer M & W; Softball W; Volleyball M & W

NORTHWESTERN OKLAHOMA STATE UNIVERSITY

709 Oklahoma Blvd.
Alva, OK 73717-2799
Tel: (580)327-1700
Fax: (580)327-1881
E-mail: plfischer@nwosu.edu
Web Site: www.nwosu.edu
President/CEO: Dr. Janet Cunningham
Admissions: Paige Fischer
Financial Aid: Rita J. Castleberry

Type: Comprehensive **Sex:** Coed **Affiliation:** Oklahoma State Regents for Higher Education. **Scores:** 59.86% ACT 18-23; 17.3% ACT 24-29 **% Accepted:** 75 **Admission Plans:** Early Admission **Application Deadline:** Rolling **Application Fee:** $15.00 **H.S. Requirements:** High school diploma required; GED accepted **Costs Per Year:** Application fee: $15. State resident tuition: $5,168 full-time. Nonresident tuition: $11,618 full-time. Mandatory fees: $945 full-time. Full-time tuition and fees vary according to course load, degree level, location, and program. College room and board: $4400. College room only: $1700. Room and board charges vary according to board plan. **Scholarships:** Available. **Calendar System:** Semester, Summer session available **Enrollment:** Full-time 1,385, Graduate full-time 81, Graduate part-time 146, Part-time 524 **Faculty:** Full-time 89, Part-time 81 **Student-Faculty Ratio:** 15:1 **Exams:** ACT essay component not used; SAT I or ACT; SAT essay component not used. **% Receiving Financial Aid:** 57 **% Residing in College-Owned, -Operated, or -Affiliated Housing:** 30 **Final Year or Final Semester Residency Requirement:** Yes **Regional Accreditation:** North Central Association of Colleges and Schools **Credit Hours For Degree:** 124 semester hours, Bachelors **Professional Accreditation:** ACBSP, ACEN, NCATE. **Intercollegiate Athletics:** Baseball M; Basketball M & W; Cheerleading M & W; Cross-Country Running M & W; Football M; Golf M & W; Soccer W; Softball W; Volleyball W

OKLAHOMA BAPTIST UNIVERSITY

500 W University
Shawnee, OK 74804
Tel: (405)275-2850; Free: 800-654-3285
Fax: (405)878-2046
E-mail: will.brantley@okbu.edu
Web Site: www.okbu.edu
President/CEO: Dr. David W. Whitlock
Admissions: Will Brantley
Financial Aid: Jonna Raney

Type: Comprehensive **Sex:** Coed **Affiliation:** Southern Baptist. **Scores:** 94% SAT V 400+; 95% SAT M 400+; 52% ACT 18-23; 33% ACT 24-29 **% Accepted:** 75 **Admission Plans:** Deferred Admission; Early Admission **Ap-**

plication Deadline: Rolling **H.S. Requirements:** High school diploma required; GED accepted **Costs Per Year:** Comprehensive fee: $32,320 includes full-time tuition ($22,710), mandatory fees ($2600), and college room and board ($7010). Room and board charges vary according to housing facility. Part-time tuition: $738 per credit hour. Part-time mandatory fees: $2600 per term. Part-time tuition and fees vary according to course load. **Scholarships:** Available. **Calendar System:** 4-1-4, Summer session available **Enrollment:** Full-time 1,774, Graduate full-time 43, Graduate part-time 36, Part-time 87 **Faculty:** Full-time 127, Part-time 60 **Student-Faculty Ratio:** 11:1 **Exams:** ACT essay component not used; SAT I or ACT; SAT essay component not used; SAT Reasoning. **% Receiving Financial Aid:** 72 **% Residing in College-Owned, -Operated, or -Affiliated Housing:** 75 **Final Year or Final Semester Residency Requirement:** No **Regional Accreditation:** North Central Association of Colleges and Schools **Credit Hours For Degree:** 64 semester credit hours, Associates; 128 credit hours, Bachelors **ROTC:** Air Force **Professional Accreditation:** AACN, ACBSP, ACEN, NASM, NCATE. **Intercollegiate Athletics:** Baseball M & W; Cross-Country Running M & W; Football M; Golf M & W; Lacrosse W; Soccer M & W; Softball W; Swimming and Diving M & W; Tennis M & W; Track and Field M & W; Volleyball W

OKLAHOMA CHRISTIAN UNIVERSITY

PO Box 11000
Oklahoma City, OK 73136-1100
Tel: (405)425-5000; Free: 800-877-5010
Fax: (405)425-5208
E-mail: info@oc.edu
Web Site: www.oc.edu
President/CEO: Dr. John deSteiguer
Admissions: Bonnie Howard
Financial Aid: Clint LaRue

Type: Comprehensive **Sex:** Coed **Affiliation:** Church of Christ. **Scores:** 94% SAT V 400+; 95% SAT M 400+; 40.11% ACT 18-23; 40.11% ACT 24-29 **% Accepted:** 59 **Admission Plans:** Deferred Admission; Early Admission **Application Deadline:** Rolling **Application Fee:** $25.00 **H.S. Requirements:** High school diploma required; GED accepted **Costs Per Year:** Application fee: $25. Comprehensive fee: $26,920 includes full-time tuition ($19,890) and college room and board ($7030). College room only: $3870. Full-time tuition varies according to course load, program, and reciprocity agreements. Room and board charges vary according to board plan and housing facility. Part-time tuition: $828 per credit hour. Part-time tuition varies according to course load, program, and reciprocity agreements. **Scholarships:** Available. **Calendar System:** Semester, Summer session available **Enrollment:** Full-time 1,910, Graduate full-time 315, Graduate part-time 267, Part-time 89 **Faculty:** Full-time 106, Part-time 127 **Student-Faculty Ratio:** 13:1 **Exams:** ACT essay component not used; SAT I or ACT; SAT essay component not used; SAT Reasoning. **% Receiving Financial Aid:** 62 **% Residing in College-Owned, -Operated, or -Affiliated Housing:** 82 **Final Year or Final Semester Residency Requirement:** Yes **Regional Accreditation:** North Central Association of Colleges and Schools **Credit Hours For Degree:** 126 semester hours, Bachelors **ROTC:** Air Force, Army **Professional Accreditation:** AACN, ABET, ACBSP, NASM, NCATE. **Intercollegiate Athletics:** Baseball M; Basketball M & W; Cross-Country Running M & W; Golf M & W; Soccer M & W; Softball W; Track and Field M & W

OKLAHOMA CITY COMMUNITY COLLEGE

7777 S May Ave.
Oklahoma City, OK 73159-4419
Tel: (405)682-1611
E-mail: mary.bodineal-sharif@occc.edu
Web Site: www.occc.edu
President/CEO: Dr. Jerry L. Steward
Admissions: Mary Bodine Al-Sharif
Financial Aid: Angela Leal

Type: Two-Year College **Sex:** Coed **Affiliation:** Oklahoma State Regents for Higher Education. **Scores:** 53% ACT 18-23; 22% ACT 24-29 **% Accepted:** 80 **Admission Plans:** Open Admission **Application Deadline:** Rolling **Application Fee:** $30.00 **H.S. Requirements:** High school diploma or equivalent not required. For nursing, emergency medical services, occupational therapy, physical therapy, speech language pathology programs: High school diploma required; GED accepted **Costs Per Year:** Application fee: $30. One-time mandatory fee: $25. State resident tuition: $2627 full-time, $87.55 per credit hour part-time. Nonresident tuition: $7661 full-time,

$255.35 per credit hour part-time. Mandatory fees: $764 full-time, $25.45 per credit hour part-time. Full-time tuition and fees vary according to class time and course level. Part-time tuition and fees vary according to class time and course level. **Scholarships:** Available. **Calendar System:** Semester, Summer session available **Enrollment:** Full-time 4,575, Part-time 8,742 **Faculty:** Full-time 138, Part-time 476 **Student-Faculty Ratio:** 22:1 **Exams:** ACT; ACT essay component used for advising; ACT essay component used for placement; SAT I or ACT; SAT essay component used for advising; SAT essay component used for placement; SAT Reasoning; SAT Subject. **Final Year or Final Semester Residency Requirement:** No **Regional Accreditation:** North Central Association of Colleges and Schools **Credit Hours For Degree:** 61 credit hours, Associates **Professional Accreditation:** ABET, ACBSP, ACEN, AOTA, APTA, CoARC, JRCEMTP.

OKLAHOMA CITY UNIVERSITY

2501 N Blackwelder
Oklahoma City, OK 73106-1402
Tel: (405)208-5000; Free: 800-633-7242
E-mail: michelle.cook@okcu.edu
Web Site: www.okcu.edu
President/CEO: Dr. Robert Henry
Admissions: Michelle Cook
Financial Aid: Denise Flis

Type: Comprehensive **Sex:** Coed **Affiliation:** United Methodist. **Scores:** 98% SAT V 400+; 97% SAT M 400+; 31% ACT 18-23; 55% ACT 24-29 **Costs Per Year:** Comprehensive fee: $39,350 includes full-time tuition ($27,276), mandatory fees ($3450), and college room and board ($8624). College room only: $4100. Full-time tuition and fees vary according to course level, course load, degree level, program, and student level. Room and board charges vary according to board plan and housing facility. Part-time tuition: $925 per credit hour. Part-time mandatory fees: $115 per credit hour. Part-time tuition and fees vary according to course level, degree level, program, and student level. **Scholarships:** Available. **Calendar System:** Semester, Summer session available **Enrollment:** Full-time 1,609, Graduate full-time 780, Graduate part-time 403, Part-time 195 **Faculty:** Full-time 193, Part-time 160 **Student-Faculty Ratio:** 11:1 **Exams:** ACT essay component not used; SAT I or ACT; SAT essay component not used. **% Receiving Financial Aid:** 63 **% Residing in College-Owned, -Operated, or -Affiliated Housing:** 53 **Final Year or Final Semester Residency Requirement:** Yes **Regional Accreditation:** North Central Association of Colleges and Schools **Credit Hours For Degree:** 124 semester hours, Bachelors **ROTC:** Air Force, Army **Professional Accreditation:** AACSB, AALS, ABA, ACBSP, ACEN, MACTE, NASM. **Intercollegiate Athletics:** Baseball M; Basketball M & W; Cheerleading M & W; Crew M & W; Golf M & W; Sailing M & W; Soccer M & W; Softball W; Track and Field M & W; Volleyball W; Wrestling M & W

OKLAHOMA PANHANDLE STATE UNIVERSITY

PO Box 430
Goodwell, OK 73939-0430
Tel: (580)349-2611; Free: 800-664-6778
Fax: (580)349-2302
E-mail: opsu@opsu.edu
Web Site: www.opsu.edu
President/CEO: David Bryant
Admissions: Bobby Jenkins
Financial Aid: Lori Ferguson

Type: Four-Year College **Sex:** Coed **Affiliation:** Oklahoma State Regents for Higher Education. **Scores:** 63% SAT V 400+; 82% SAT M 400+; 45% ACT 18-23; 12% ACT 24-29 **% Accepted:** 100 **Application Deadline:** Rolling **Application Fee:** $0.00 **H.S. Requirements:** High school diploma required; GED accepted **Costs Per Year:** Application fee: $0. State resident tuition: $4367 full-time, $146 per credit hour part-time. Nonresident tuition: $4367 full-time, $146 per credit hour part-time. Mandatory fees: $3024 full-time, $98 per credit part-time, $42 per term part-time. Full-time tuition and fees vary according to course level, program, and student level. Part-time tuition and fees vary according to course level, program, and student level. College room and board: $5344. College room only: $1306. Room and board charges vary according to board plan and housing facility. Tuition guaranteed not to increase for student's term of enrollment. **Scholarships:** Available. **Calendar System:** Semester, Summer session available **Enrollment:** Full-time 1,116, Part-time 271 **Faculty:** Full-time 65, Part-time 26 **Student-Faculty Ratio:** 16:1 **Exams:** ACT essay component used for placement; SAT I or ACT; SAT essay component used for placement.

Regional Accreditation: North Central Association of Colleges and Schools **Credit Hours For Degree:** 64 credit hours, Associates; 124 credit hours, Bachelors **Professional Accreditation:** ACEN, NCATE. **Intercollegiate Athletics:** Baseball M; Basketball M & W; Cheerleading W; Cross-Country Running M & W; Equestrian Sports W; Football M; Golf M & W; Soccer M & W; Softball W; Volleyball W

OKLAHOMA STATE UNIVERSITY

Stillwater, OK 74078
Tel: (405)744-5000; Free: 800-233-5019
Fax: (405)744-5285
E-mail: christine.crenshaw@okstate.edu
Web Site: www.okstate.edu
President/CEO: Pres. Burns Hargis
Admissions: Christine Crenshaw

Type: University **Sex:** Coed **Affiliation:** Oklahoma State University. **Scores:** 97% SAT V 400+; 98% SAT M 400+; 37.09% ACT 18-23; 45.79% ACT 24-29 **% Accepted:** 75 **Admission Plans:** Deferred Admission **Application Deadline:** Rolling **Application Fee:** $40.00 **H.S. Requirements:** High school diploma required; GED accepted **Costs Per Year:** Application fee: $40. One-time mandatory fee: $95. State resident tuition: $4620 full-time, $154 per credit hour part-time. Nonresident tuition: $17,820 full-time, $594 per credit hour part-time. Mandatory fees: $3,158 full-time, $105.25 per credit hour part-time. Full-time tuition and fees vary according to program. Part-time tuition and fees vary according to course load and program. College room and board: $8190. College room only: $4590. Room and board charges vary according to board plan and housing facility. Tuition guaranteed not to increase for student's term of enrollment. **Scholarships:** Available. **Calendar System:** Semester, Summer session available **Enrollment:** Full-time 18,336, Graduate full-time 1,877, Graduate part-time 2,883, Part-time 2,710 **Faculty:** Full-time 1,048, Part-time 306 **Student-Faculty Ratio:** 20:1 **Exams:** ACT essay component not used; SAT I or ACT; SAT II; SAT essay component not used. **% Receiving Financial Aid:** 50 **% Residing in College-Owned, -Operated, or -Affiliated Housing:** 47 **Final Year or Final Semester Residency Requirement:** Yes **Regional Accreditation:** North Central Association of Colleges and Schools **Credit Hours For Degree:** 120 credit hours, Bachelors **ROTC:** Air Force, Army **Professional Accreditation:** AACSB, AAMFT, ABET, ACEJMC, AND, APA, ASHA, ASLA, AVMA, CIDA, JRCAT, NAAB, NASM, NAST, NCATE, NRPA, SAF. **Intercollegiate Athletics:** Baseball M; Basketball M & W; Cheerleading M & W; Cross-Country Running M & W; Equestrian Sports W; Football M; Golf M & W; Soccer W; Softball W; Tennis M & W; Track and Field M & W; Wrestling M

OKLAHOMA STATE UNIVERSITY INSTITUTE OF TECHNOLOGY

1801 E Fourth St.
Okmulgee, OK 74447-3901
Tel: (918)293-4678; Free: 800-722-4471
E-mail: chenoa.worthington@okstate.edu
Web Site: www.osuit.edu
President/CEO: Dr. Bill R. Path
Admissions: Chenoa Worthington
Financial Aid: Diana Sanders

Type: Two-Year College **Sex:** Coed **Affiliation:** Oklahoma State University. **Scores:** 45% ACT 18-23; 6% ACT 24-29 **% Accepted:** 42 **Admission Plans:** Deferred Admission; Open Admission **Application Deadline:** Rolling **H.S. Requirements:** High school diploma required; GED accepted. For adult students (21 and older): High school diploma or equivalent not required **Costs Per Year:** State resident tuition: $3720 full-time, $124 per credit hour part-time. Nonresident tuition: $9330 full-time, $311 per credit hour part-time. Mandatory fees: $1140 full-time, $38 per credit hour part-time. Full-time tuition and fees vary according to course level, course load, location, program, and student level. Part-time tuition and fees vary according to course level, course load, location, program, and student level. College room and board: $6370. Room and board charges vary according to board plan and housing facility. **Scholarships:** Available. **Calendar System:** Trimester, Summer session available **Enrollment:** Full-time 1,770, Part-time 706 **Faculty:** Full-time 121, Part-time 47 **Student-Faculty Ratio:** 15:1 **Exams:** ACT; SAT I or ACT. **% Residing in College-Owned, -Operated, or -Affiliated Housing:** 29 **Final Year or Final Semester Residency Requirement:** No **Regional Accreditation:** North Central Association of Colleges and Schools **Credit Hours For Degree:** 60 credit hours, Associates; 121 credit hours, Bachelors **Professional Accreditation:** ABET, ACEN.

OKLAHOMA STATE UNIVERSITY, OKLAHOMA CITY

900 N Portland Ave.
Oklahoma City, OK 73107-6120

Tel: (405)947-4421; Free: 800-560-4099
Fax: (405)945-3277
E-mail: wilkylw@osuokc.edu
Web Site: www.osuokc.edu
President/CEO: Natalie Shirley
Admissions: Kyle Williams
Financial Aid: Karla Reiter
Type: Two-Year College **Sex:** Coed **Affiliation:** Oklahoma State University. **% Accepted:** 33 **Admission Plans:** Open Admission **Application Deadline:** Rolling **H.S. Requirements:** High school diploma required; GED accepted **Costs Per Year:** State resident tuition: $2,846 full-time, $118.60 per credit hour part-time. Nonresident tuition: $7,877 full-time, $328.20 per credit hour part-time. Mandatory fees: $89 full-time, $12 per term part-time, $65 per year part-time. Full-time tuition and fees vary according to course level, degree level, program, and student level. Part-time tuition and fees vary according to course level, degree level, program, and student level. Tuition guaranteed not to increase for student's term of enrollment. **Scholarships:** Available. **Calendar System:** Semester, Summer session available **Enrollment:** Full-time 1,878, Part-time 4,085 **Faculty:** Full-time 85, Part-time 329 **Student-Faculty Ratio:** 14:1 **Regional Accreditation:** North Central Association of Colleges and Schools **Credit Hours For Degree:** 60 semester hours, Associates; 124 semester hours, Bachelors **Professional Accreditation:** ACEN.

OKLAHOMA TECHNICAL COLLEGE

4444 S Sheridan
Tulsa, OK 74145
Tel: (918)895-7500
E-mail: jcooper@oklahomatechnicalcollege.com
Web Site: www.oklahomatechnicalcollege.com
President/CEO: Dr. Kevin L. Kirk
Admissions: Jeremy Cooper
Type: Two-Year College **Sex:** Coed **Admission Plans:** Open Admission **Application Deadline:** Rolling **Application Fee:** $100.00 **H.S. Requirements:** High school diploma required; GED accepted **Costs Per Year:** Application fee: $100. Tuition: $17,223 full-time, $6 per credit part-time. Mandatory fees: $2166 full-time. Full-time tuition and fees vary according to class time, course level, course load, degree level, location, program, and student level. Part-time tuition varies according to class time and degree level. **Calendar System:** Continuous, Summer session not available **Enrollment:** Full-time 310 **Faculty:** Full-time 12 **Student-Faculty Ratio:** 25:1 **Final Year or Final Semester Residency Requirement:** No **Credit Hours For Degree:** 60 credits, Associates **Professional Accreditation:** ACICS.

OKLAHOMA WESLEYAN UNIVERSITY

2201 Silver Lake Rd.
Bartlesville, OK 74006-6299
Tel: (918)335-6200; Free: 866-222-8226
Fax: (918)335-6229
E-mail: admissions@okwu.edu
Web Site: www.okwu.edu
President/CEO: Dr. Everett Piper
Admissions: Samantha Peterson
Financial Aid: Kandi Lyn Molder
Type: Comprehensive **Sex:** Coed **Affiliation:** Wesleyan Church. **Scores:** 82% SAT V 400+; 87% SAT M 400+; 53% ACT 18-23; 23% ACT 24-29 **% Accepted:** 85 **Admission Plans:** Open Admission **Application Deadline:** Rolling **Application Fee:** $25.00 **H.S. Requirements:** High school diploma required; GED accepted **Costs Per Year:** Application fee: $25. Comprehensive fee: $30,668 includes full-time tuition ($21,930), mandatory fees ($1250), and college room and board ($7488). College room only: $3858. Full-time tuition and fees vary according to course load. Room and board charges vary according to board plan and housing facility. Part-time tuition: $900 per credit. **Scholarships:** Available. **Calendar System:** Semester, Summer session available **Enrollment:** Full-time 593, Graduate full-time 7, Graduate part-time 291, Part-time 636 **Faculty:** Full-time 35, Part-time 76 **Student-Faculty Ratio:** 15:1 **Exams:** ACT essay component used for admission; ACT essay component used for placement; SAT I or ACT; SAT essay component used for admission; SAT essay component used for placement; SAT Reasoning. **% Receiving Financial Aid:** 77 **Final Year or Final Semester Residency Requirement:** Yes **Regional Accreditation:** North Central Association of Colleges and Schools **Credit Hours For Degree:** 64 semester hours, Associates; 126 semester hours, Bachelors **Professional Accreditation:** AACN, NCATE. **Intercollegiate Athletics:** Baseball M;

Basketball M & W; Cross-Country Running M & W; Golf M & W; Soccer M & W; Softball W; Tennis M & W; Track and Field M & W; Volleyball W

ORAL ROBERTS UNIVERSITY

7777 S Lewis Ave.
Tulsa, OK 74171
Tel: (918)495-6161; Free: 800-678-8876
Fax: (918)495-6222
E-mail: admissions@oru.edu
Web Site: www.oru.edu
President/CEO: Dr. William M. Wilson
Admissions: Chris Belcher
Type: Comprehensive **Sex:** Coed **Affiliation:** interdenominational. **Scores:** 90% SAT V 400+; 90% SAT M 400+; 54% ACT 18-23; 24% ACT 24-29 **% Accepted:** 22 **Admission Plans:** Deferred Admission **Application Fee:** $35.00 **H.S. Requirements:** High school diploma required; GED accepted **Costs Per Year:** Application fee: $35. Comprehensive fee: $34,316 includes full-time tuition ($24,750), mandatory fees ($926), and college room and board ($8640). College room only: $3650. Full-time tuition and fees vary according to degree level. Room and board charges vary according to board plan and housing facility. Part-time tuition: $1034 per credit hour. Part-time tuition varies according to degree level. **Scholarships:** Available. **Calendar System:** Semester **Enrollment:** Full-time 2,513, Graduate full-time 344, Graduate part-time 213, Part-time 544 **Faculty:** Full-time 158, Part-time 116 **Student-Faculty Ratio:** 14:1 **Exams:** ACT essay component not used; SAT I or ACT; SAT essay component not used; SAT Reasoning; SAT Subject. **% Receiving Financial Aid:** 69 **% Residing in College-Owned, -Operated, or -Affiliated Housing:** 66 **Regional Accreditation:** North Central Association of Colleges and Schools **ROTC:** Air Force **Professional Accreditation:** AACN, ABET, ACBSP, ATS, CSWE, NASM, NCATE. **Intercollegiate Athletics:** Baseball M; Basketball M & W; Cross-Country Running M & W; Golf M & W; Soccer M & W; Tennis M & W; Track and Field M & W; Volleyball W; Wrestling M

PLATT COLLEGE (MOORE)

201 N Eastern Ave.
Moore, OK 73160
Tel: (405)912-3260
Fax: (405)912-4360
Web Site: www.plattcolleges.edu
President/CEO: Robyn Criswell-Bloom
Type: Two-Year College **Sex:** Coed **% Accepted:** 100 **Application Fee:** $100.00 **Professional Accreditation:** ACCSC.

PLATT COLLEGE (OKLAHOMA CITY)

2727 W Memorial Rd.
Oklahoma City, OK 73134-8034
Web Site: www.plattcolleges.edu
Type: Four-Year College **Sex:** Coed **Professional Accreditation:** ACF.

PLATT COLLEGE (OKLAHOMA CITY)

309 S Ann Arbor Ave.
Oklahoma City, OK 73128
Tel: (405)946-7799
Fax: (405)943-2150
E-mail: klamb@plattcollege.org
Web Site: www.plattcolleges.edu
President/CEO: Jane Nowlin
Admissions: Kim Lamb
Type: Two-Year College **Sex:** Coed **Admission Plans:** Open Admission **Application Fee:** $100.00 **H.S. Requirements:** High school diploma required; GED accepted **Calendar System:** Continuous, Summer session not available **Enrollment:** Full-time 357 **Faculty:** Full-time 16, Part-time 11 **Credit Hours For Degree:** 102.75 quarter credit hours, Associates **Professional Accreditation:** ACCSC.

PLATT COLLEGE (TULSA)

3801 S Sheridan Rd.
Tulsa, OK 74145-111
Tel: (918)663-9000
Fax: (918)622-1240
E-mail: susanr@plattcollege.org
Web Site: www.plattcolleges.edu
President/CEO: Jeremy Cooper

Admissions: Susan Rone

Type: Two-Year College **Sex:** Coed **Application Fee:** $100.00 **Calendar System:** Continuous **Professional Accreditation:** ACCSC.

REDLANDS COMMUNITY COLLEGE

1300 S Country Club Rd.
El Reno, OK 73036-5304
Tel: (405)262-2552; Free: 866-415-6367
E-mail: hobsont@redlandscc.edu
Web Site: www.redlandscc.edu
President/CEO: Dr. Larry F. Devane
Admissions: Tricia Hobson

Type: Two-Year College **Sex:** Coed **Affiliation:** Oklahoma State Regents for Higher Education. **Scores:** 44.04% ACT 18-23; 11.91% ACT 24-29 **% Accepted:** 99 **Admission Plans:** Deferred Admission; Early Admission; Open Admission **Application Deadline:** Rolling **Application Fee:** $25.00 **H.S. Requirements:** High school diploma required; GED accepted **Costs Per Year:** Application fee: $25. State resident tuition: $3,882 full-time, $129.41 per credit hour part-time. Nonresident tuition: $6,026 full-time, $200.88 per credit hour part-time. Full-time tuition varies according to location, program, and reciprocity agreements. Part-time tuition varies according to location, program, and reciprocity agreements. College room only: $5110. Room charges vary according to housing facility. **Scholarships:** Available. **Calendar System:** Semester, Summer session available **Enrollment:** Full-time 915, Part-time 1,645 **Faculty:** Full-time 35, Part-time 78 **Student-Faculty Ratio:** 24:1 **Exams:** SAT I or ACT; SAT Reasoning. **% Residing in College-Owned, -Operated, or -Affiliated Housing:** 10 **Regional Accreditation:** North Central Association of Colleges and Schools **Credit Hours For Degree:** 64 semester hours, Associates **Professional Accreditation:** ACEN. **Intercollegiate Athletics:** Baseball M; Basketball M & W; Gymnastics W; Volleyball W

ROGERS STATE UNIVERSITY

1701 W Will Rogers Blvd.
Claremore, OK 74017-3252
Tel: (918)343-7777; Free: 800-256-7511
Fax: (918)343-7898
E-mail: admissions@rsu.edu
Web Site: www.rsu.edu
President/CEO: Dr. Larry Rice
Admissions: Joy Lin Hall
Financial Aid: Kelly Hicks

Type: Comprehensive **Sex:** Coed **Affiliation:** Oklahoma State Regents for Higher Education. **% Accepted:** 77 **Admission Plans:** Open Admission **Application Deadline:** Rolling **Application Fee:** $20.00 **H.S. Requirements:** High school diploma required; GED accepted **Costs Per Year:** Application fee: $20. State resident tuition: $3840 full-time. Nonresident tuition: $11,490 full-time. Mandatory fees: $2590 full-time. Full-time tuition and fees vary according to course level, course load, location, program, and student level. College room and board: $8961. College room only: $5007. Room and board charges vary according to housing facility. **Scholarships:** Available. **Calendar System:** Semester, Summer session available **Enrollment:** Full-time 2,407, Graduate full-time 5, Graduate part-time 7, Part-time 1,612 **Faculty:** Full-time 103, Part-time 163 **Student-Faculty Ratio:** 19:1 **Exams:** ACT; ACT essay component not used; SAT I or ACT; SAT essay component not used; SAT Reasoning. **% Receiving Financial Aid:** 66 **% Residing in College-Owned, -Operated, or -Affiliated Housing:** 13 **Final Year or Final Semester Residency Requirement:** No **Regional Accreditation:** North Central Association of Colleges and Schools **Credit Hours For Degree:** 60 credit hours, Associates; 120 credit hours, Bachelors **Professional Accreditation:** ACEN. **Intercollegiate Athletics:** Baseball M; Basketball M & W; Cheerleading M & W; Cross-Country Running M & W; Golf M & W; Soccer M & W; Softball W; Track and Field M & W

ROSE STATE COLLEGE

6420 SE 15th St.
Midwest City, OK 73110-2799
Tel: (405)733-7673; Free: 866-621-0987
Fax: (405)733-7399
E-mail: maitson@ms.rose.cc.ok.us
Web Site: www.rose.edu
President/CEO: Jeanie Webb
Admissions: Mechelle Aitson-Roessler

Type: Two-Year College **Sex:** Coed **Affiliation:** Oklahoma State Regents for

Higher Education. **Admission Plans:** Deferred Admission; Early Admission; Open Admission **Application Deadline:** Rolling **Application Fee:** $15.00 **H.S. Requirements:** High school diploma required; GED accepted **Scholarships:** Available. **Calendar System:** Semester, Summer session available **Faculty:** Full-time 143, Part-time 269 **Regional Accreditation:** North Central Association of Colleges and Schools **Credit Hours For Degree:** 62 credit hours, Associates **ROTC:** Air Force, Army **Professional Accreditation:** ACEN, ADA, AHIMA, CoARC, JRCERT, NAACLS. **Intercollegiate Athletics:** Baseball M; Basketball M & W; Soccer W

ST. GREGORY'S UNIVERSITY

1900 W MacArthur Dr.
Shawnee, OK 74804-2499
Tel: (405)878-5100; Free: 888-STGREGS
Fax: (405)878-5198
E-mail: admissions@stgregorys.edu
Web Site: www.stgregorys.edu
President/CEO: Gregory Main
Admissions: Sean Brown
Financial Aid: Marcia Cheers

Type: Comprehensive **Sex:** Coed **Affiliation:** Roman Catholic. **% Accepted:** 61 **Admission Plans:** Deferred Admission **Application Deadline:** Rolling **Application Fee:** $0.00 **H.S. Requirements:** High school diploma required; GED accepted **Costs Per Year:** Application fee: $0. Comprehensive fee: $29,802 includes full-time tuition ($21,632) and college room and board ($8170). College room only: $4200. Part-time tuition: $676 per credit hour. **Scholarships:** Available. **Calendar System:** Semester, Summer session available **Enrollment:** Full-time 473, Graduate full-time 44, Graduate part-time 1, Part-time 132 **Exams:** ACT essay component used for advising; ACT essay component used for placement; SAT I or ACT; SAT essay component used for advising; SAT essay component used for placement. **% Receiving Financial Aid:** 79 **% Residing in College-Owned, -Operated, or -Affiliated Housing:** 36 **Final Year or Final Semester Residency Requirement:** Yes **Regional Accreditation:** North Central Association of Colleges and Schools **Credit Hours For Degree:** 64 credit hours, Associates; 128 credit hours, Bachelors **Intercollegiate Athletics:** Baseball M; Basketball M & W; Cheerleading M & W; Lacrosse M; Soccer M & W; Softball W; Track and Field M & W; Volleyball W

SEMINOLE STATE COLLEGE

2701 Boren Blvd.
Seminole, OK 74818-0351
Tel: (405)382-9950
E-mail: c.quiett@sscok.edu
Web Site: www.sscok.edu
President/CEO: Dr. Jim Utterback
Admissions: Corey Quiett
Financial Aid: Melanie Rinehart

Type: Two-Year College **Sex:** Coed **Affiliation:** Oklahoma State Regents for Higher Education. **Scores:** 59% ACT 18-23; 17% ACT 24-29 **% Accepted:** 100 **Admission Plans:** Deferred Admission; Early Admission; Open Admission **Application Deadline:** Rolling **Application Fee:** $15.00 **H.S. Requirements:** High school diploma or equivalent not required. For applicants under 18, nursing, medical laboratory technology programs: High school diploma required; GED accepted **Costs Per Year:** Application fee: $15. One-time mandatory fee: $15. State resident tuition: $2,504 full-time, $83.45 per credit hour part-time. Nonresident tuition: $7,664 full-time, $255.45 per credit hour part-time. Mandatory fees: $1305 full-time, $43.50 per credit hour part-time. Full-time tuition and fees vary according to location and program. Part-time tuition and fees vary according to location and program. College room and board: $7070. College room only: $3900. **Scholarships:** Available. **Calendar System:** Semester, Summer session available **Enrollment:** Full-time 1,016, Part-time 811 **Faculty:** Full-time 37, Part-time 63 **Student-Faculty Ratio:** 22:1 **Exams:** ACT essay component not used; SAT essay component not used. **% Residing in College-Owned, -Operated, or -Affiliated Housing:** 8 **Final Year or Final Semester Residency Requirement:** No **Regional Accreditation:** North Central Association of Colleges and Schools **Credit Hours For Degree:** 62 credit hours, Associates **Professional Accreditation:** ACEN, NAACLS. **Intercollegiate Athletics:** Baseball M; Basketball M & W; Cheerleading W; Golf M & W; Softball W; Tennis M & W; Volleyball W

SOUTHEASTERN OKLAHOMA STATE UNIVERSITY

1405 N 4th Ave.
Durant, OK 74701-0609

Tel: (580)745-2000; Free: 800-435-1327
Fax: (580)745-7490
E-mail: crogers@se.edu
Web Site: www.se.edu
President/CEO: Sean Burrage
Admissions: Christy Rogers
Financial Aid: Tony Lehrling

Type: Comprehensive **Sex:** Coed **Affiliation:** Oklahoma State Regents for Higher Education. **Scores:** 59.42% ACT 18-23; 19.28% ACT 24-29 **% Accepted:** 70 **Admission Plans:** Open Admission **Application Deadline:** Rolling **Application Fee:** $20.00 **H.S. Requirements:** High school diploma required; GED accepted **Costs Per Year:** Application fee: $20. State resident tuition: $5,524 full-time, $184.15 per credit hour part-time. Nonresident tuition: $14,163 full-time, $472.10 per credit hour part-time. Mandatory fees: $690 full-time, $23 per credit hour part-time. Full-time tuition and fees vary according to course level, course load, degree level, location, and program. Part-time tuition and fees vary according to course level, course load, degree level, location, and program. College room and board: $6487. College room only: $3387. Room and board charges vary according to board plan, housing facility, and student level. Tuition guaranteed not to increase for student's term of enrollment. **Scholarships:** Available. **Calendar System:** Semester, Summer session available **Enrollment:** Full-time 2,451, Graduate full-time 229, Graduate part-time 310, Part-time 761 **Faculty:** Full-time 138, Part-time 132 **Student-Faculty Ratio:** 17:1 **Exams:** SAT I or ACT. **% Receiving Financial Aid:** 79 **% Residing in College-Owned, -Operated, or -Affiliated Housing:** 16 **Final Year or Final Semester Residency Requirement:** No **Regional Accreditation:** North Central Association of Colleges and Schools **Credit Hours For Degree:** 124 credit hours, Bachelors **Professional Accreditation:** AACSB, ACBSP, NASM, NCATE. **Intercollegiate Athletics:** Baseball M; Basketball M & W; Cross-Country Running W; Football M; Golf M; Softball W; Tennis M & W; Volleyball W

SOUTHERN NAZARENE UNIVERSITY

6729 NW 39th Expy.
Bethany, OK 73008
Tel: (405)789-6400; Free: 800-648-9899
Fax: (405)491-6381
E-mail: admiss@snu.edu
Web Site: www.snu.edu
President/CEO: Dr. Loren P. Gresham
Admissions: Dr. Linda Cantwell
Financial Aid: Diana Lee

Type: Comprehensive **Sex:** Coed **Affiliation:** Nazarene. **Scores:** 53% ACT 18-23; 32% ACT 24-29 **% Accepted:** 33 **Admission Plans:** Deferred Admission; Open Admission **Application Deadline:** August 15 **Application Fee:** $35.00 **H.S. Requirements:** High school diploma required; GED accepted **Scholarships:** Available. **Calendar System:** Semester, Summer session available **Enrollment:** Full-time 1,598, Graduate full-time 2,207, Graduate part-time 52, Part-time 49 **Faculty:** Full-time 92 **Student-Faculty Ratio:** 12:1 **Exams:** ACT; SAT I or ACT; SAT Reasoning; SAT Subject. **% Receiving Financial Aid:** 80 **% Residing in College-Owned, -Operated, or -Affiliated Housing:** 63 **Final Year or Final Semester Residency Requirement:** No **Regional Accreditation:** North Central Association of Colleges and Schools **Credit Hours For Degree:** 62 credit hours, Associates; 124 credit hours, Bachelors **ROTC:** Air Force, Army **Professional Accreditation:** AACN, ACBSP, NASM, NCATE. **Intercollegiate Athletics:** Baseball M; Basketball M & W; Cheerleading M & W; Cross-Country Running M & W; Equestrian Sports M & W; Football M; Golf M & W; Soccer M & W; Softball W; Tennis M & W; Track and Field M & W; Volleyball W

SOUTHWESTERN CHRISTIAN UNIVERSITY

PO Box 340
Bethany, OK 73008-0340
Tel: (405)789-7661
E-mail: admissions@swcu.edu
Web Site: www.swcu.edu
President/CEO: Dr. Ed Huckeby
Admissions: Jessie Burpo
Financial Aid: Billie Stewart

Type: Comprehensive **Sex:** Coed **Affiliation:** Pentecostal Holiness Church. **Admission Plans:** Deferred Admission; Early Admission **Application Deadline:** Rolling **Application Fee:** $0.00 **H.S. Requirements:** High school diploma required; GED accepted **Scholarships:** Available. **Calendar**

System: Semester, Summer session available **Student-Faculty Ratio:** 15:1 **Exams:** ACT essay component used for admission; ACT essay component used for advising; ACT essay component used for placement; SAT I or ACT; SAT essay component used for admission; SAT essay component used for advising; SAT essay component used for placement; SAT Reasoning; SAT Subject. **% Receiving Financial Aid:** 89 **% Residing in College-Owned, -Operated, or -Affiliated Housing:** 50 **Final Year or Final Semester Residency Requirement:** No **Regional Accreditation:** North Central Association of Colleges and Schools **Credit Hours For Degree:** 64 credits, Associates; 128 credits, Bachelors **ROTC:** Army **Intercollegiate Athletics:** Basketball M & W; Bowling M & W; Cheerleading W; Crew M & W; Cross-Country Running M & W; Golf M & W; Soccer M & W; Softball W; Tennis M & W; Track and Field M & W; Volleyball W

SOUTHWESTERN OKLAHOMA STATE UNIVERSITY

100 Campus Dr.
Weatherford, OK 73096-3098
Tel: (580)772-6611
Fax: (580)774-3795
E-mail: cassie.jones@swosu.edu
Web Site: www.swosu.edu
President/CEO: Dr. Randy Beutler
Admissions: Cassie Jones
Financial Aid: Jerome Wichert

Type: Comprehensive **Sex:** Coed **Scores:** 53.59% ACT 18-23; 25.56% ACT 24-29 **% Accepted:** 81 **Admission Plans:** Deferred Admission; Open Admission; Preferred Admission **Application Deadline:** Rolling **Application Fee:** $15.00 **H.S. Requirements:** High school diploma required; GED accepted **Costs Per Year:** Application fee: $15. One-time mandatory fee: $100. State resident tuition: $4725 full-time, $157.50 per credit hour part-time. Nonresident tuition: $11,175 full-time, $372.50 per credit hour part-time. Mandatory fees: $1365 full-time, $45.50 per credit hour part-time. Full-time tuition and fees vary according to location and program. Part-time tuition and fees vary according to location and program. College room and board: $5220. College room only: $2120. Room and board charges vary according to board plan and housing facility. **Scholarships:** Available. **Calendar System:** Semester, Summer session available **Enrollment:** Full-time 3,485, Graduate full-time 447, Graduate part-time 308, Part-time 873 **Faculty:** Full-time 206, Part-time 67 **Student-Faculty Ratio:** 18:1 **Exams:** ACT; ACT essay component not used; SAT I or ACT; SAT Reasoning. **% Receiving Financial Aid:** 53 **% Residing in College-Owned, -Operated, or -Affiliated Housing:** 27 **Final Year or Final Semester Residency Requirement:** Yes **Regional Accreditation:** North Central Association of Colleges and Schools **Credit Hours For Degree:** 59 credit hours, Associates; 120 credit hours, Bachelors **Professional Accreditation:** ABET, ACEN, ACPE, AHIMA, APTA, CSWE, NASM, NCATE. **Intercollegiate Athletics:** Baseball M; Basketball M & W; Cheerleading M & W; Cross-Country Running W; Equestrian Sports M & W; Football M; Golf M & W; Soccer W; Softball W; Volleyball W

SOUTHWESTERN OKLAHOMA STATE UNIVERSITY AT SAYRE

409 E Mississippi St.
Sayre, OK 73662-1236
Tel: (580)928-5533
E-mail: kim.seymour@swosu.edu
Web Site: www.swosu.edu/sayre
President/CEO: Dr. Randy Beutler
Admissions: Kim Seymour

Type: Two-Year College **Sex:** Coed **Affiliation:** Southwestern Oklahoma State University. **% Accepted:** 100 **Admission Plans:** Open Admission **Application Deadline:** Rolling **Application Fee:** $0.00 **H.S. Requirements:** High school diploma required; GED accepted **Costs Per Year:** Application fee: $0. State resident tuition: $191 per credit hour part-time. Nonresident tuition: $406 per credit hour part-time. Mandatory fees: $33.50 per credit hour part-time. Tuition guaranteed not to increase for student's term of enrollment. **Scholarships:** Available. **Calendar System:** Semester, Summer session available **Faculty:** Full-time 14, Part-time 4 **Student-Faculty Ratio:** 20:1 **Exams:** ACT essay component not used; SAT I or ACT; SAT essay component not used. **Final Year or Final Semester Residency Requirement:** No **Regional Accreditation:** North Central Association of Colleges and Schools **Credit Hours For Degree:** 60 credit hours, Associates **Professional Accreditation:** ABHES, AOTA, JRCERT.

SPARTAN COLLEGE OF AERONAUTICS AND TECHNOLOGY

8820 E Pine St.
Tulsa, OK 74158-2833

Tel: (918)836-6886; Free: 800-331-124
Web Site: www.spartan.edu
President/CEO: Ryan Goertzen
Admissions: Mark Fowler
Type: Two-Year College **Sex:** Coed **Application Deadline:** Rolling **Application Fee:** $100.00 **H.S. Requirements:** High school diploma required; GED accepted **Scholarships:** Available. **Calendar System:** Miscellaneous, Summer session not available **Enrollment:** Full-time 1,438 **Student-Faculty Ratio:** 14:1 **Credit Hours For Degree:** 42 credit hours, Associates **Professional Accreditation:** ACCSC.

TULSA COMMUNITY COLLEGE

6111 E Skelly Dr.
Tulsa, OK 74135-6198
Tel: (918)595-7000
Fax: (918)595-7910
E-mail: traci.heck@tulsacc.edu
Web Site: www.tulsacc.edu
President/CEO: Leigh B. Goodson, PhD
Admissions: Traci Heck
Type: Two-Year College **Sex:** Coed **Affiliation:** Oklahoma State Regents for Higher Education. **Scores:** 56.01% ACT 18-23; 18.92% ACT 24-29 **Admission Plans:** Early Admission; Open Admission **Application Deadline:** Rolling **Application Fee:** $20.00 **H.S. Requirements:** High school diploma or equivalent not required **Costs Per Year:** Application fee: $20. State resident tuition: $3,623 full-time, $90.97 per credit hour part-time. Nonresident tuition: $9,803 full-time, $2,729 per credit hour part-time. Mandatory fees: $894 full-time, $29.78 per credit hour part-time, $5 per term part-time. **Scholarships:** Available. **Calendar System:** Semester, Summer session available **Enrollment:** Full-time 5,713, Part-time 10,995 **Faculty:** Full-time 301, Part-time 566 **Student-Faculty Ratio:** 19:1 **Regional Accreditation:** North Central Association of Colleges and Schools **Credit Hours For Degree:** 60 credit hours, Associates **Professional Accreditation:** AAMAE, ACEN, ADA, AHIMA, AOTA, APTA, CoARC, JRCERT, NAACLS.

TULSA WELDING SCHOOL

2545 E 11th St.
Tulsa, OK 74104-3909
Tel: (918)587-6789; Free: 888-765-5555
Fax: (918)295-6821
E-mail: dburke@twsweld.com
Web Site: www.tulsaweldingschool.com
President/CEO: Mary Kelly
Admissions: Debbie Renee Burke
Type: Two-Year College **Sex:** Coed **Affiliation:** Tulsa Welding School, Jacksonville Branch. **H.S. Requirements:** High school diploma required; GED accepted **Calendar System:** Continuous **Enrollment:** Full-time 604 **Faculty:** Full-time 17 **Student-Faculty Ratio:** 18:1 **Credit Hours For Degree:** 62 credits, Associates **Professional Accreditation:** ACCSC.

UNIVERSITY OF CENTRAL OKLAHOMA

100 N University Dr.
Edmond, OK 73034-5209
Tel: (405)974-2000
Fax: (405)974-4964
E-mail: onestop@uco.edu
Web Site: www.uco.edu
President/CEO: Dr. Don Betz
Admissions: Dallas Caldwell
Financial Aid: Kerry Housley
Type: Comprehensive **Sex:** Coed **Affiliation:** Oklahoma State Regents for Higher Education. **Scores:** 60.81% ACT 18-23; 25.07% ACT 24-29 **% Accepted:** 70 **Admission Plans:** Deferred Admission **Application Deadline:** Rolling **Application Fee:** $90.00 **H.S. Requirements:** High school diploma required; GED accepted **Costs Per Year:** Application fee: $90. State resident tuition: $5157 full-time, $171.90 per credit hour part-time. Nonresident tuition: $14,033 full-time, $467.75 per credit hour part-time. Mandatory fees: $939 full-time, $31.30 per credit hour part-time. Full-time tuition and fees vary according to course load, degree level, location, and program. Part-time tuition and fees vary according to course load, degree level, location, and program. College room and board: $7130. College room only: $3496. Room and board charges vary according to board plan and housing facility. Tuition guaranteed not to increase for student's term of enrollment. **Scholarships:** Available. **Calendar System:** Semester, Sum-

mer session available **Enrollment:** Full-time 10,686, Graduate full-time 670, Graduate part-time 1,173, Part-time 4,381 **Faculty:** Full-time 513, Part-time 598 **Student-Faculty Ratio:** 19:1 **Exams:** ACT; ACT essay component not used; SAT I; SAT I and SAT II or ACT; SAT I or ACT; SAT II; SAT essay component not used; SAT Reasoning. **% Receiving Financial Aid:** 58 **% Residing in College-Owned, -Operated, or -Affiliated Housing:** 9 **Final Year or Final Semester Residency Requirement:** Yes **Regional Accreditation:** North Central Association of Colleges and Schools **Credit Hours For Degree:** 66 credit hours, Associates; 124 credit hours, Bachelors **ROTC:** Army **Professional Accreditation:** ABET, ABFSE, ACBSP, ACEN, AND, ASHA, CIDA, NASAD, NASM, NCATE. **Intercollegiate Athletics:** Baseball M; Basketball M & W; Cross-Country Running W; Football M; Golf M & W; Rowing W; Soccer W; Softball W; Tennis W; Volleyball W; Wrestling M

UNIVERSITY OF OKLAHOMA

660 Parrington Oval
Norman, OK 73019-0390
Tel: (405)325-0311; Free: 800-234-6868
Fax: (405)325-7478
E-mail: ou-pss@ou.edu
Web Site: www.ou.edu
President/CEO: David L. Boren
Admissions: Jeff Blahnik
Type: University **Sex:** Coed **Scores:** 99% SAT V 400+; 99% SAT M 400+; 24% ACT 18-23; 53% ACT 24-29 **% Accepted:** 78 **Application Deadline:** February 1 **Application Fee:** $40.00 **H.S. Requirements:** High school diploma required; GED accepted **Costs Per Year:** Application fee: $40. State resident tuition: $4296 full-time, $143.20 per credit hour part-time. Nonresident tuition: $17,682 full-time, $589.40 per credit hour part-time. Mandatory fees: $3769 full-time, $116.20 per credit hour part-time, $141.50 per term part-time. Full-time tuition and fees vary according to course load, location, program, and student level. Part-time tuition and fees vary according to course load, location, program, and student level. College room and board: $9742. College room only: $5474. Room and board charges vary according to board plan and housing facility. Tuition guaranteed not to increase for student's term of enrollment. **Scholarships:** Available. **Calendar System:** Semester, Summer session available **Enrollment:** Full-time 18,123, Graduate full-time 2,961, Graduate part-time 3,170, Part-time 3,174 **Faculty:** Full-time 1,191, Part-time 256 **Student-Faculty Ratio:** 18:1 **Exams:** ACT essay component not used; SAT I or ACT; SAT essay component not used. **% Receiving Financial Aid:** 45 **% Residing in College-Owned, -Operated, or -Affiliated Housing:** 31 **Final Year or Final Semester Residency Requirement:** Yes **Regional Accreditation:** North Central Association of Colleges and Schools **Credit Hours For Degree:** 120 credit hours, Bachelors **ROTC:** Air Force, Army, Navy **Professional Accreditation:** AACSB, AALS, ABA, ABET, ACCE, ACEJMC, ACSP, ALA, APA, ASLA, CIDA, CSWE, NAAB, NASM, NAST, NCATE. **Intercollegiate Athletics:** Baseball M; Basketball M & W; Cheerleading M & W; Crew W; Cross-Country Running M & W; Football M; Golf M & W; Gymnastics M & W; Rowing W; Soccer W; Softball W; Tennis M & W; Track and Field M & W; Volleyball W; Wrestling M

UNIVERSITY OF OKLAHOMA HEALTH SCIENCES CENTER

PO Box 26901
Oklahoma City, OK 73190
Tel: (405)271-4000
Fax: (405)271-2480
E-mail: jane-pippin@ouhsc.edu
Web Site: www.ouhsc.edu
President/CEO: David Boren
Admissions: Dr. Jane Pippin
Type: Two-Year Upper Division **Sex:** Coed **Affiliation:** University of Oklahoma. **Admission Plans:** Deferred Admission; Preferred Admission **H.S. Requirements:** High school diploma required; GED accepted **Calendar System:** Semester, Summer session available **Enrollment:** Full-time 787, Graduate full-time 2,314, Graduate part-time 176, Part-time 49 **Faculty:** Full-time 320, Part-time 124 **Student-Faculty Ratio:** 9:1 **% Residing in College-Owned, -Operated, or -Affiliated Housing:** 13 **Regional Accreditation:** North Central Association of Colleges and Schools **Credit Hours For Degree:** 124 credit hours, Bachelors **ROTC:** Air Force, Army **Professional Accreditation:** ABET, ACEN, ACPE, ACIPE, ADA, AND, AOTA, APA, APTA, ASHA, CAHME, CEPH, JRCEDMS, JRCERT, JRCNMT, LCME/AMA.

UNIVERSITY OF SCIENCE AND ARTS OF OKLAHOMA

1727 W Alabama
Chickasha, OK 73018
Tel: (405)224-3140; Free: 800-933-8726
Fax: (405)574-1220
E-mail: usao-admissions@usao.edu
Web Site: www.usao.edu
President/CEO: Dr. John Feaver
Admissions: Monica Trevino
Financial Aid: Laura D. Coponiti

Type: Four-Year College **Sex:** Coed **Affiliation:** Oklahoma State Regents for Higher Education. **Scores:** 70% SAT V 400+; 83% SAT M 400+; 58% ACT 18-23; 19.7% ACT 24-29 **% Accepted:** 66 **Admission Plans:** Deferred Admission **Application Deadline:** September 2 **Application Fee:** $40.00 **H.S. Requirements:** High school diploma required; GED accepted **Costs Per Year:** Application fee: $40. State resident tuition: $5100 full-time, $170 per credit hour part-time. Nonresident tuition: $14,040 full-time, $468 per credit hour part-time. Mandatory fees: $1170 full-time. College room and board: $5470. College room only: $2760. Room and board charges vary according to board plan and housing facility. **Scholarships:** Available. **Calendar System:** Trimester, Summer session available **Enrollment:** Full-time 787, Part-time 101 **Faculty:** Full-time 54, Part-time 33 **Student-Faculty Ratio:** 12:1 **Exams:** ACT essay component not used; SAT I or ACT; SAT essay component not used; SAT Reasoning; SAT Subject. **% Receiving Financial Aid:** 64 **% Residing in College-Owned, -Operated, or -Affiliated Housing:** 44 **Final Year or Final Semester Residency Requirement:** No **Regional Accreditation:** North Central Association of Colleges and Schools **Credit Hours For Degree:** 124 hours, Bachelors **Professional Accreditation:** NASM, NCATE. **Intercollegiate Athletics:** Baseball M; Basketball M & W; Cheerleading M & W; Cross-Country Running M & W; Soccer M & W; Softball W; Volleyball W

THE UNIVERSITY OF TULSA

800 S Tucker Dr.
Tulsa, OK 74104-3189
Tel: (918)631-2000; Free: 800-331-3050
Fax: (918)631-2247
E-mail: admission@utulsa.edu
Web Site: www.utulsa.edu
President/CEO: Dr. Steadman Upham
Admissions: Casey Reed
Financial Aid: Vicki Hendrickson

Type: University **Sex:** Coed **Affiliation:** Presbyterian Church (U.S.A.). **Scores:** 99% SAT V 400+; 100% SAT M 400+; 12% ACT 18-23; 40% ACT 24-29 **% Accepted:** 44 **Admission Plans:** Deferred Admission; Early Admission; Early Decision Plan **Application Deadline:** Rolling **Application Fee:** $50.00 **H.S. Requirements:** High school diploma required; GED accepted **Costs Per Year:** Application fee: $50. One-time mandatory fee: $485. Comprehensive fee: $52,140 includes full-time tuition ($40,484), mandatory fees ($540), and college room and board ($11,116). College room only: $6394. Full-time tuition and fees vary according to course load. Room and board charges vary according to board plan and housing facility. Part-time tuition: $1453 per credit. Part-time tuition varies according to course load. **Scholarships:** Available. **Calendar System:** Semester, Summer session available **Enrollment:** Full-time 3,359, Graduate full-time 763, Graduate part-time 430, Part-time 119 **Faculty:** Full-time 344, Part-time 99 **Student-Faculty Ratio:** 11:1 **Exams:** SAT I or ACT; SAT Reasoning. **% Receiving Financial Aid:** 40 **% Residing in College-Owned, -Operated, or -Affiliated Housing:** 71 **Final Year or Final Semester Residency Requirement:** Yes **Regional Accreditation:** North Central Association of Colleges and Schools **Credit Hours For Degree:** 124 credit hours, Bachelors **ROTC:** Air Force **Professional Accreditation:** AACSB, AALS, ABA, ABET, ACEN, APA, ASHA, JRCAT, NASM, NCATE, TEAC. **Intercollegiate Athletics:** Basketball M & W; Cheerleading M & W; Crew W; Cross-Country Running M & W; Football M; Golf M & W; Soccer M & W; Softball W; Tennis M & W; Track and Field M & W; Volleyball W

VATTEROTT COLLEGE (TULSA)

4343 S 118th E Ave., Ste. A
Tulsa, OK 74146
Tel: (918)835-8288; Free: 888-553-6627
Fax: (918)836-9698
E-mail: tulsa@vatterott-college.edu
Web Site: www.vatterott.edu
President/CEO: Pamela Bell
Admissions: Terry Queeno

Type: Two-Year College **Sex:** Coed **Affiliation:** Vatterott Educational Centers, Inc. **Application Fee:** $0.00 **H.S. Requirements:** High school diploma required; GED accepted **Calendar System:** Semester **Enrollment:** Full-time 146 **Faculty:** Full-time 10, Part-time 11 **Student-Faculty Ratio:** 12:1 **Professional Accreditation:** ACCSC.

VATTEROTT COLLEGE (WARR ACRES)

5537 NW Expy.
Warr Acres, OK 73132
Tel: (405)234-3600; Free: 888-553-6627
E-mail: mark.hybers@vatterott-college.edu
Web Site: www.vatterott.edu
President/CEO: Terry Dubberly
Admissions: Mark Hybers

Type: Two-Year College **Sex:** Coed **% Accepted:** 57 **Calendar System:** Semester **Enrollment:** Full-time 367 **Faculty:** Full-time 15, Part-time 21 **Student-Faculty Ratio:** 11:1 **Professional Accreditation:** ACCSC.

VIRGINIA COLLEGE IN TULSA

5124 S Peoria Ave.
Tulsa, OK 74105
Tel: (918)960-5400
Web Site: www.vc.edu

Type: Two-Year College **Sex:** Coed **Professional Accreditation:** ACICS.

WESTERN OKLAHOMA STATE COLLEGE

2801 N Main St.
Altus, OK 73521-1397
Tel: (580)477-2000
Fax: (580)477-7723
E-mail: chad.wiginton@wosc.edu
Web Site: www.wosc.edu
President/CEO: Dr. Phil Birdine
Admissions: Dean Chad E. Wiginton

Type: Two-Year College **Sex:** Coed **Affiliation:** Oklahoma State Regents for Higher Education. **% Accepted:** 100 **Admission Plans:** Early Admission; Open Admission **Application Deadline:** Rolling **Application Fee:** $15.00 **H.S. Requirements:** High school diploma required; GED accepted **Costs Per Year:** Application fee: $15. State resident tuition: $2118 full-time, $70.60 per credit hour part-time. Nonresident tuition: $6,472 full-time, $215.75 per credit hour part-time. Mandatory fees: $1,162 full-time, $38.75 per credit hour part-time. College room and board: $2125. **Scholarships:** Available. **Calendar System:** Semester, Summer session available **Enrollment:** Full-time 675, Part-time 1,015 **Faculty:** Full-time 37, Part-time 34 **Student-Faculty Ratio:** 19:1 **Exams:** ACT. **% Residing in College-Owned, -Operated, or -Affiliated Housing:** 6 **Final Year or Final Semester Residency Requirement:** No **Regional Accreditation:** North Central Association of Colleges and Schools **Credit Hours For Degree:** 64 credits, Associates **Professional Accreditation:** ACEN, JRCERT. **Intercollegiate Athletics:** Baseball M; Basketball M & W; Equestrian Sports M & W; Softball W

AMERICAN COLLEGE OF HEALTHCARE SCIENCES
5005 SW Macadam Ave.
Portland, OR 97239-3719
Tel: (503)244-0726; Free: 800-487-8839
Fax: (503)244-0727
E-mail: achs@achs.edu
Web Site: www.achs.edu
President/CEO: Dorene Petersen
Type: Two-Year College **Sex:** Coed **Application Deadline:** Rolling **Application Fee:** $35.00 **H.S. Requirements:** High school diploma required; GED accepted **Costs Per Year:** Application fee: $35. One-time mandatory fee: $200. Tuition: $7800 full-time, $325 per credit part-time. Mandatory fees: $350 per course part-time. **Professional Accreditation:** DEAC.

THE ART INSTITUTE OF PORTLAND
1122 NW Davis St.
Portland, OR 97209
Tel: (503)228-6528; Free: 888-228-6528
Fax: (503)228-4227
Web Site: www.artinstitutes.edu/portland
President/CEO: Emily E. Hill
Type: Four-Year College **Sex:** Coed **Affiliation:** Education Management Corporation. **Calendar System:** Quarter **Regional Accreditation:** Southern Association of Colleges and Schools **Professional Accreditation:** NCCU.

BIRTHINGWAY COLLEGE OF MIDWIFERY
12113 SE Foster Rd.
Portland, OR 97266
Tel: (503)760-3131
E-mail: info@birthingway.edu
Web Site: www.birthingway.edu
President/CEO: Holly Scholles
Type: Two-Year Upper Division **Sex:** Coed **Application Fee:** $50.00 **Calendar System:** Miscellaneous **Student-Faculty Ratio:** 10:1 **Professional Accreditation:** MEAC.

BLUE MOUNTAIN COMMUNITY COLLEGE
2411 NW Carden Ave.
Pendleton, OR 97801-1000
Tel: (541)276-1260
Fax: (541)278-5886
E-mail: tbosworth@bluecc.edu
Web Site: www.bluecc.edu
President/CEO: Camille Preus
Admissions: Theresa Bosworth
Type: Two-Year College **Sex:** Coed **Admission Plans:** Open Admission **Application Deadline:** Rolling **H.S. Requirements:** High school diploma or equivalent not required **Costs Per Year:** One-time mandatory fee: $35. State resident tuition: $4230 full-time, $94 per credit hour part-time. Nonresident tuition: $4230 full-time, $282 per credit hour part-time. Mandatory fees: $600 full-time, $10.50 per credit hour part-time, $18 per term part-time. Full-time tuition and fees vary according to course load, program, and reciprocity agreements. Part-time tuition and fees vary according to course load, program, and reciprocity agreements. **Scholarships:** Available. **Calendar System:** Quarter, Summer session available **Credit Hours For**

Degree: 90 credit hours, Associates **Professional Accreditation:** ABET, ADA, NCCU. **Intercollegiate Athletics:** Baseball M; Basketball M & W; Softball W; Volleyball W

CENTRAL OREGON COMMUNITY COLLEGE
2600 NW College Way
Bend, OR 97703
Tel: (541)383-7700
Fax: (541)383-7506
E-mail: welcome@cocc.edu
Web Site: www.cocc.edu
President/CEO: Dr. Shirley Metcalf
Admissions: Courtney Whetstine
Type: Two-Year College **Sex:** Coed **Affiliation:** Oregon Community College Association. **% Accepted:** 100 **Admission Plans:** Open Admission; Preferred Admission **Application Deadline:** Rolling **Application Fee:** $25.00 **H.S. Requirements:** High school diploma or equivalent not required **Costs Per Year:** Application fee: $25. Area resident tuition: $4095 full-time, $91 per credit hour part-time. State resident tuition: $5400 full-time, $120 per credit hour part-time. Nonresident tuition: $11,070 full-time, $246 per credit hour part-time. Mandatory fees: $349 full-time, $7.75 per credit hour part-time. College room and board: $10,550. Room and board charges vary according to board plan. **Scholarships:** Available. **Calendar System:** Quarter, Summer session available **Enrollment:** Full-time 2,492, Part-time 3,581 **Faculty:** Full-time 128, Part-time 201 **Student-Faculty Ratio:** 19:1 **% Residing in College-Owned, -Operated, or -Affiliated Housing:** 1 **Final Year or Final Semester Residency Requirement:** No **Credit Hours For Degree:** 93 credits, Associates **ROTC:** Army **Professional Accreditation:** ADA, AHIMA, NCCU. **Intercollegiate Athletics:** Golf M & W

CHEMEKETA COMMUNITY COLLEGE
4000 Lancaster Dr. NE
Salem, OR 97309
Tel: (503)399-5000
Fax: (503)399-3918
E-mail: admissions@chemeketa.edu
Web Site: www.chemeketa.edu
President/CEO: Dr. Cheryl Roberts, EdD
Financial Aid: Kathleen Campbell
Type: Two-Year College **Sex:** Coed **Scholarships:** Available. **Calendar System:** Quarter, Summer session available **Enrollment:** Full-time 6,225, Part-time 6,146 **Faculty:** Full-time 186, Part-time 554 **Student-Faculty Ratio:** 26:1 **Final Year or Final Semester Residency Requirement:** No **Credit Hours For Degree:** 90 credit hours, Associates **Professional Accreditation:** ACEN, ADA, JRCEMTP, NCCU. **Intercollegiate Athletics:** Baseball M; Basketball M & W; Softball W; Volleyball W

CLACKAMAS COMMUNITY COLLEGE
19600 Molalla Ave.
Oregon City, OR 97045-7998
Tel: (503)657-6958
Fax: (503)650-6654
E-mail: pattyw@clackamas.edu
Web Site: www.clackamas.edu
President/CEO: Joanne Truesdell

Admissions: Tara Sprehe

Type: Two-Year College **Sex:** Coed **Admission Plans:** Early Admission; Open Admission **Application Deadline:** Rolling **Application Fee:** $0.00 **H.S. Requirements:** High school diploma or equivalent not required **Scholarships:** Available. **Calendar System:** Quarter, Summer session available **Enrollment:** Full-time 3,205, Part-time 4,939 **Faculty:** Full-time 148, Part-time 429 **Student-Faculty Ratio:** 14:1 **Credit Hours For Degree:** 93 credit hours, Associates **Professional Accreditation:** NCCU. **Intercollegiate Athletics:** Baseball M; Basketball M & W; Cross-Country Running M & W; Soccer W; Softball W; Track and Field M & W; Volleyball W; Wrestling M

CLATSOP COMMUNITY COLLEGE

1653 Jerome
Astoria, OR 97103-3698
Tel: (503)325-0910; Free: 855-252-8767
Fax: (503)325-5738
E-mail: admissions@clatsoppcc.edu
Web Site: www.clatsoppcc.edu
President/CEO: Dr. Larry Galizio
Admissions: Monica Van Steenberg

Type: Two-Year College **Sex:** Coed **% Accepted:** 81 **Admission Plans:** Open Admission **Application Deadline:** Rolling **Application Fee:** $15.00 **H.S. Requirements:** High school diploma or equivalent not required **Costs Per Year:** Application fee: $15. State resident tuition: $3564 full-time, $99 per credit part-time. Nonresident tuition: $7128 full-time, $198 per credit part-time. Mandatory fees: $450 full-time, $10 per credit part-time, $30 per term part-time. Full-time tuition and fees vary according to course load, program, and reciprocity agreements. Part-time tuition and fees vary according to course load, program, and reciprocity agreements. **Scholarships:** Available. **Calendar System:** Quarter, Summer session available **Enrollment:** Full-time 455, Part-time 616 **Faculty:** Full-time 27, Part-time 72 **Student-Faculty Ratio:** 13:1 **Final Year or Final Semester Residency Requirement:** No **Credit Hours For Degree:** 90 credits, Associates **Professional Accreditation:** NCCU.

COLUMBIA GORGE COMMUNITY COLLEGE

400 E Scenic Dr.
The Dalles, OR 97058
Tel: (541)296-6182
Fax: (541)298-3104
E-mail: lufford@cgcc.edu
Web Site: www.cgcc.cc.or.us
President/CEO: Dr. Frank Toda
Admissions: Lori Ufford

Type: Two-Year College **Sex:** Coed **Admission Plans:** Open Admission **Costs Per Year:** State resident tuition: $3276 full-time, $91 per credit hour part-time. Nonresident tuition: $8100 full-time, $225 per credit hour part-time. Mandatory fees: $540 full-time, $15 per credit hour part-time. Full-time tuition and fees vary according to course load. Part-time tuition and fees vary according to course load. **Calendar System:** Quarter, Summer session available **Enrollment:** Full-time 542, Part-time 703 **Faculty:** Full-time 18, Part-time 107 **Final Year or Final Semester Residency Requirement:** Yes **Credit Hours For Degree:** 90 credit hours, Associates **Professional Accreditation:** NCCU.

CONCORDE CAREER COLLEGE

1425 NE Irving St.
Portland, OR 97232
Tel: (503)281-4181
Fax: (503)281-6739
Web Site: www.concorde.edu
Type: Two-Year College **Sex:** Coed **Professional Accreditation:** ACCSC.

CONCORDIA UNIVERSITY

2811 NE Holman
Portland, OR 97211-6099
Tel: (503)288-9371; Free: 800-321-9371
Fax: (503)280-8531
E-mail: admissions@cu-portland.edu
Web Site: www.cu-portland.edu
President/CEO: Dr. Charles E. Schlimpert
Admissions: Bobi Swan
Financial Aid: Robert Clarke

Type: Comprehensive **Sex:** Coed **Affiliation:** Lutheran Church–Missouri Synod; Concordia University System. **Scores:** 92% SAT V 400+; 91% SAT M 400+; 49% ACT 18-23; 28.4% ACT 24-29 **% Accepted:** 54 **Admission Plans:** Deferred Admission **Application Deadline:** Rolling **Application Fee:** $0.00 **H.S. Requirements:** High school diploma required; GED accepted **Costs Per Year:** Application fee: $0. Comprehensive fee: $36,430 includes full-time tuition ($27,900), mandatory fees ($520), and college room and board ($8010). College room only: $4210. Full-time tuition and fees vary according to program. Room and board charges vary according to board plan and housing facility. Part-time tuition: $885 per semester hour. Part-time mandatory fees: $125 per term. Part-time tuition and fees vary according to course load and program. **Scholarships:** Available. **Calendar System:** Semester, Summer session available **Enrollment:** Full-time 1,147, Graduate full-time 1,524, Graduate part-time 218, Part-time 222 **Faculty:** Full-time 65, Part-time 194 **Student-Faculty Ratio:** 19:1 **Exams:** ACT essay component not used; SAT I or ACT; SAT essay component not used; SAT essay component used in place of application essay; SAT Reasoning. **% Receiving Financial Aid:** 80 **% Residing in College-Owned, -Operated, or -Affiliated Housing:** 36 **Credit Hours For Degree:** 62 semester hours, Associates; 124 semester hours, Bachelors **ROTC:** Air Force **Professional Accreditation:** ACBSP, NCCU. **Intercollegiate Athletics:** Baseball M; Basketball M & W; Cross-Country Running M & W; Golf M & W; Soccer M & W; Softball W; Track and Field M & W; Volleyball W

CORBAN UNIVERSITY

5000 Deer Park Dr., SE
Salem, OR 97301-9392
Tel: (503)581-8600; Free: 800-845-3005
Fax: (503)585-4316
E-mail: admissions@corban.edu
Web Site: www.corban.edu
President/CEO: Dr. Reno Hoff
Admissions: Heidi Stowman
Financial Aid: Ellen Zarfas

Type: Comprehensive **Sex:** Coed **Affiliation:** Christian. **Scores:** 96% SAT V 400+; 94% SAT M 400+; 36.67% ACT 18-23; 46.67% ACT 24-29 **% Accepted:** 31 **Application Fee:** $40.00 **H.S. Requirements:** High school diploma required; GED accepted **Costs Per Year:** Application fee: $40. One-time mandatory fee: $100. Comprehensive fee: $38,880 includes full-time tuition ($28,980), mandatory fees ($660), and college room and board ($9240). College room only: $5350. Full-time tuition and fees vary according to course load, degree level, and reciprocity agreements. Room and board charges vary according to board plan. Part-time tuition: $1208 per credit hour. Part-time tuition varies according to course load, degree level, and reciprocity agreements. **Scholarships:** Available. **Calendar System:** Semester, Summer session available **Enrollment:** Full-time 949, Graduate full-time 121, Graduate part-time 49, Part-time 113 **Faculty:** Full-time 52, Part-time 63 **Student-Faculty Ratio:** 15:1 **Exams:** ACT essay component used for advising; SAT I or ACT; SAT essay component used for advising; SAT Reasoning; SAT Subject. **% Receiving Financial Aid:** 83 **% Residing in College-Owned, -Operated, or -Affiliated Housing:** 59 **Final Year or Final Semester Residency Requirement:** Yes **Credit Hours For Degree:** 64 credit hours, Associates; 128 credit hours, Bachelors **ROTC:** Army **Professional Accreditation:** NCCU. **Intercollegiate Athletics:** Baseball M; Basketball M & W; Cross-Country Running M & W; Golf M & W; Soccer M & W; Softball W; Track and Field M & W; Volleyball W

EASTERN OREGON UNIVERSITY

1 University Blvd.
La Grande, OR 97850-2899
Tel: (541)962-3672; Free: 800-452-8639
Fax: (541)962-3418
E-mail: admissions@eou.edu
Web Site: www.eou.edu
President/CEO: Thomas Insko

Type: Comprehensive **Sex:** Coed **Scores:** 81% SAT V 400+; 83% SAT M 400+; 57.7% ACT 18-23; 16.9% ACT 24-29 **% Accepted:** 97 **Admission Plans:** Deferred Admission; Early Admission; Early Decision Plan **Application Deadline:** September 1 **Application Fee:** $50.00 **H.S. Requirements:** High school diploma required; GED accepted **Costs Per Year:** Application fee: $50. State resident tuition: $6,322 full-time, $140.50 per credit hour part-time. Nonresident tuition: $16,560 full-time, $368 per credit hour part-time. Mandatory fees: $1434 full-time. Full-time tuition and fees vary according to course load, location, and reciprocity agreements. Part-time tuition varies according to course load, location, and reciprocity agreements. College room and board: $9642. College room only: $5650. Room and board charges vary according to board plan and housing facility. **Scholarships:** Available. **Calendar System:** Quarter, Summer session available **Enrollment:** Full-time 1,759, Graduate full-time 90, Graduate part-time 270, Part-time 1,369 **Faculty:** Full-time 96, Part-time 119 **Student-Faculty Ratio:** 18:1 **Exams:** SAT I or ACT; SAT Reasoning; SAT Subject. **% Receiving Financial Aid** 77 **% Residing in College-Owned, -Operated, or -Affiliated Housing:** 11 **Final Year or Final Semester Residency Requirement:** No **Credit Hours For Degree:** 90 credit hours, Associates; 180 credit hours, Bachelors **ROTC:** Army **Professional Accreditation:** NCCU. **Intercollegiate Athletics:** Basketball M & W; Cross-Country Running M & W; Football M; Soccer M & W; Softball W; Track and Field M & W; Volleyball W

GEORGE FOX UNIVERSITY

414 N Meridian
Newberg, OR 97132-2697
Tel: (503)538-8383; Free: 800-765-4369
Fax: (503)554-3830
E-mail: admissions@georgefox.edu
Web Site: www.georgefox.edu
President/CEO: Dr. Robin Baker
Admissions: Lindsay Knox
Financial Aid: Johanna Schweitzer

Type: University **Sex:** Coed **Affiliation:** Friends. **Scores:** 95% SAT V 400+; 96% SAT M 400+; 40.3% ACT 18-23; 43.73% ACT 24-29 **% Accepted:** 78 **Admission Plans:** Deferred Admission; Early Decision Plan **Application Deadline:** Rolling **Application Fee:** $40.00 **H.S. Requirements:** High school diploma required; GED accepted **Scholarships:** Available. **Calendar System:** Semester, Summer session available **Enrollment:** Full-time 2,348, Graduate full-time 567, Graduate part-time 763, Part-time 221 **Faculty:** Full-time 195, Part-time 409 **Student-Faculty Ratio:** 14:1 **Exams:** ACT essay component not used; SAT I or ACT; SAT essay component not used; SAT Reasoning. **% Receiving Financial Aid:** 75 **% Residing in College-Owned, -Operated, or -Affiliated Housing:** 55 **Final Year or Final Semester Residency Requirement:** No **Credit Hours For Degree:** 126 semester hours, Bachelors **ROTC:** Air Force **Professional Accreditation:** AACN, ABET, ACBSP, ACIPE, APA, APTA, ATS, CSWE, JRCAT, NASM, NCATE, NCCU. **Intercollegiate Athletics:** Baseball M; Basketball M & W; Cross-Country Running M & W; Football M; Golf M & W; Lacrosse W; Soccer M & W; Softball W; Tennis M & W; Track and Field M & W; Volleyball W

GUTENBERG COLLEGE

1883 University St.
Eugene, OR 97403
Tel: (541)683-5141
Fax: (541)683-6997
E-mail: tstollar@gutenberg.edu
Web Site: www.gutenberg.edu
President/CEO: Dr. David Crabtree
Admissions: Terry Stollar

Type: Four-Year College **Sex:** Coed **Affiliation:** Christian. **Scores:** 100% SAT V 400+; 86% SAT M 400+ **% Accepted:** 64 **Application Deadline:** March 1 **Application Fee:** $40.00 **H.S. Requirements:** High school diploma required; GED accepted **Enrollment:** Full-time 38 **Faculty:** Full-time 8, Part-time 2 **Student-Faculty Ratio:** 6:1 **Exams:** SAT I. **% Residing in College-Owned, -Operated, or -Affiliated Housing:** 75 **Professional Accreditation:** TRACS.

KLAMATH COMMUNITY COLLEGE

7390 S 6th St.
Klamath Falls, OR 97603
Tel: (541)882-3521
E-mail: garlock@klamathcc.edu
Web Site: www.klamathcc.edu
President/CEO: Dr. Roberto Gutierrez
Admissions: Tammi Garlock

Type: Two-Year College **Sex:** Coed **Admission Plans:** Open Admission **Application Deadline:** Rolling **H.S. Requirements:** High school diploma required; GED accepted **Calendar System:** Quarter, Summer session available **Enrollment:** Full-time 385, Part-time 763 **Faculty:** Full-time 28, Part-time 101 **Student-Faculty Ratio:** 14:1 **Final Year or Final Semester Residency Requirement:** No **Credit Hours For Degree:** 90 credit hours, Associates **Professional Accreditation:** NCCU.

LANE COMMUNITY COLLEGE

4000 E 30th Ave.
Eugene, OR 97405-0640
Tel: (541)747-4501
Fax: (541)744-3995
Web Site: www.lanecc.edu
President/CEO: Mary Spilde
Admissions: Helen Garrett

Type: Two-Year College **Sex:** Coed **Admission Plans:** Early Admission; Open Admission; Preferred Admission **Application Deadline:** Rolling **H.S. Requirements:** High school diploma or equivalent not required. For applicants under 18 admitted with a high school release to attend credit classes: High school diploma required; GED accepted **Scholarships:** Available. **Calendar System:** Quarter, Summer session available **Enrollment:** Full-time 4,996, Part-time 6,006 **Credit Hours For Degree:** 93 credit hours, Associates **Professional Accreditation:** ACF, ADA, CoARC, NCCU. **Intercollegiate Athletics:** Baseball M; Basketball M & W; Cross-Country Running M & W; Soccer W; Track and Field M & W

LEWIS & CLARK COLLEGE

0615 SW Palatine Hill Rd.
Portland, OR 97219-7899
Tel: (503)768-7000; Free: 800-444-4111
Fax: (503)768-7055
E-mail: admissions@lclark.edu
Web Site: www.lclark.edu
President/CEO: Dr. Barry Glassner
Admissions: Erica Johnson
Financial Aid: Anastacia Dillon

Type: Comprehensive **Sex:** Coed **Scores:** 100% SAT V 400+; 100% SAT M 400+; 1.1% ACT 18-23; 55.6% ACT 24-29 **% Accepted:** 63 **Admission Plans:** Deferred Admission; Early Action; Early Decision Plan **Application Deadline:** January 15 **Application Fee:** $0.00 **H.S. Requirements:** High school diploma required; GED accepted **Costs Per Year:** Application fee: $0. Comprehensive fee: $56,322 includes full-time tuition ($44,744), mandatory fees ($360), and college room and board ($11,218). College room only: $6130. Room and board charges vary according to board plan and housing facility. Part-time tuition: $2151 per credit hour. Part-time mandatory fees: $18 per credit hour. Part-time tuition and fees vary according to course load. **Scholarships:** Available. **Calendar System:** Semester, Summer session available **Enrollment:** Full-time 2,178, Graduate full-time 990, Graduate part-time 327, Part-time 31 **Faculty:** Full-time 206, Part-time 204 **Student-Faculty Ratio:** 12:1 **Exams:** ACT essay component not used; Other; SAT essay component not used; SAT Reasoning. **% Receiving Financial Aid:** 60 **% Residing in College-Owned, -Operated, or -Affiliated Housing:** 70 **Final Year or Final Semester Residency Requirement:** Yes **Credit Hours For Degree:** 128 semester hours, Bachelors **ROTC:** Army **Professional Accreditation:** AALS, AAMFT, ABA, ACA, NCATE, NCCU. **Intercollegiate Athletics:** Baseball M; Basketball M & W; Crew M & W; Cross-Country Running M & W; Football M; Golf M & W; Lacrosse W; Rugby M & W; Soccer M & W; Softball W; Swimming and Diving M & W; Tennis M & W; Track and Field M & W; Ultimate Frisbee M & W; Volleyball W

LINFIELD COLLEGE

900 SE Baker St.
McMinnville, OR 97128-6894
Tel: (503)883-2200; Free: 800-640-2287
Fax: (503)883-2472
E-mail: admission@linfield.edu
Web Site: www.linfield.edu
President/CEO: Dr. Thomas L. Hellie
Admissions: Lisa Knodle-Bragiel
Financial Aid: Keri Burke

Type: Four-Year College **Sex:** Coed **Affiliation:** American Baptist Churches in the USA. **Scores:** 98% SAT V 400+; 98% SAT M 400+; 42% ACT 18-23; 44% ACT 24-29 **% Accepted:** 84 **Admission Plans:** Deferred Admission; Early Decision Plan **Application Deadline:** February 1 **Application Fee:** $0.00 **H.S. Requirements:** High school diploma required; GED accepted **Costs Per Year:** Application fee: $0. Comprehensive fee: $49,504 includes full-time tuition ($38,300), mandatory fees ($354), and college room and board ($10,850). College room only: $5890. Full-time tuition and fees vary according to course load and location. Room and board charges vary according to board plan, housing facility, and location. Part-time tuition: $1192 per semester hour. Part-time mandatory fees: $104 per term. Part-time tuition and fees vary according to course load and location. **Scholarships:** Available. **Calendar System:** 4-1-4, Summer session available **Enrollment:** Full-time 1,663, Part-time 37 **Faculty:** Full-time 119, Part-time 85 **Student-Faculty Ratio:** 11:1 **Exams:** ACT essay component used as validity check; ACT essay component used for advising; SAT I or ACT; SAT essay component used as validity check; SAT essay component used for advising; SAT Reasoning. **% Receiving Financial Aid:** 77 **% Residing in College-Owned, -Operated, or -Affiliated Housing:** 77 **Final Year or Final Semester Residency Requirement:** Yes **Credit Hours For Degree:** 125 semester credit hours, Bachelors **ROTC:** Air Force **Professional Accreditation:** AACN, JRCAT, NASM, NCCU. **Intercollegiate Athletics:** Baseball M; Basketball M & W; Cross-Country Running M & W; Football M; Golf M & W; Lacrosse W; Soccer M & W; Softball W; Swimming and Diving M & W; Tennis M & W; Track and Field M & W; Volleyball W

LINN-BENTON COMMUNITY COLLEGE

6500 SW Pacific Blvd.
Albany, OR 97321
Tel: (541)917-4999
Fax: (541)917-4838
E-mail: admissions@linnbenton.edu
Web Site: www.linnbenton.edu
President/CEO: Dr. Greg Haman
Admissions: Kim Sullivan

Type: Two-Year College **Sex:** Coed **% Accepted:** 100 **Admission Plans:** Deferred Admission; Open Admission **Application Deadline:** Rolling **Application Fees:** $30.00 **H.S. Requirements:** High school diploma or equivalent not required **Scholarships:** Available. **Calendar System:** Quarter, Summer session available **Enrollment:** Full-time 2,604, Part-time 3,013 **Final Year or Final Semester Residency Requirement:** No **Credit Hours For Degree:** 90 quarter hours, Associates **ROTC:** Air Force, Army, Navy **Professional Accreditation:** AAMAE, ADA, NCCU. **Intercollegiate Athletics:** Basketball M; Volleyball W

MARYLHURST UNIVERSITY

17600 Pacific Hwy.
Marylhurst, OR 97036-0261
Tel: (503)636-8141; Free: 800-634-9982
Fax: (503)636-9526
E-mail: admissions@marylhurst.edu
Web Site: www.marylhurst.edu
President/CEO: Melody Rose, PhD
Admissions: Ryan Clark
Financial Aid: Tracy Reisinger

Type: Comprehensive **Sex:** Coed **Affiliation:** Roman Catholic. **% Accepted:** 100 **Admission Plans:** Deferred Admission **Application Deadline:** Rolling **Application Fee:** $50.00 **H.S. Requirements:** High school diploma required; GED accepted. For transfer students with at least 45 credits: High school diploma or equivalent not required **Costs Per Year:** Application fee: $50. Tuition: $20,835 full-time, $463 per credit hour part-time. Full-time tuition varies according to program. Part-time tuition varies according to program. **Scholarships:** Available. **Calendar System:** Quarter, Summer session available **Enrollment:** Full-time 144, Graduate full-time 115, Graduate part-time 353, Part-time 370 **% Receiving Financial Aid:** 81 **Final Year or Final Semester Residency Requirement:** No **Credit Hours For Degree:** 180 quarter hours, Bachelors **Professional Accreditation:** NASM, NCCU.

MOUNT ANGEL SEMINARY

Saint Benedict, OR 97373
Tel: (503)845-3951
E-mail: admissions@mtangel.edu
Web Site: www.mountangelabbey.org/seminary
President/CEO: Rev. Joseph Betschart
Financial Aid: Dorene Preis

Type: Comprehensive **Affiliation:** Roman Catholic. **% Accepted:** 100 **Admission Plans:** Preferred Admission **Application Deadline:** July 15 **Application Fee:** $27.00 **H.S. Requirements:** High school diploma required; GED accepted **Scholarships:** Available. **Calendar System:** Semester, Summer session not available **Exams:** SAT I. **Credit Hours For Degree:** 124 credit hours, Bachelors **Professional Accreditation:** ACIPE, ATS, NCCU.

MT. HOOD COMMUNITY COLLEGE

26000 SE Stark St.
Gresham, OR 97030-3300
Tel: (503)491-6422
Fax: (503)491-7388
Web Site: www.mhcc.edu
President/CEO: Debra Derr
Admissions: Dr. Craig Kolins

Type: Two-Year College **Sex:** Coed **Admission Plans:** Deferred Admission; Early Admission; Open Admission; Preferred Admission **Application Deadline:** Rolling **Application Fee:** $25.00 **H.S. Requirements:** High school diploma or equivalent not required. For allied health, some professional-technical programs: High school diploma required; GED accepted **Scholarships:** Available. **Calendar System:** Quarter, Summer session available **Enrollment:** Full-time 3,178, Part-time 5,593 **Faculty:** Full-time 173, Part-time 465 **Student-Faculty Ratio:** 25:1 **Credit Hours For Degree:** 90 credits, Associates **Professional Accreditation:** AAMAE, ABFSE, ADA, APTA, ARCST, CoARC, NCCU. **Intercollegiate Athletics:** Baseball M; Basketball M & W; Cross-Country Running M & W; Softball W; Track and Field M & W; Volleyball W

MULTNOMAH UNIVERSITY

8435 NE Glisan St.
Portland, OR 97220-5898
Tel: (503)255-0332; Free: 877-251-6560
Fax: (503)254-1268
E-mail: admiss@multnomah.edu
Web Site: www.multnomah.edu
President/CEO: Dr. Craig Williford
Admissions: Jenae Johnson
Financial Aid: Mary J. McGlothlan

Type: Comprehensive **Sex:** Coed **Affiliation:** interdenominational. **Scores:** 90% SAT V 400+; 84% SAT M 400+; 46.2% ACT 18-23; 23% ACT 24-29 **% Accepted:** 61 **Admission Plans:** Deferred Admission **Application Fee:** $40.00 **H.S. Requirements:** High school diploma required; GED accepted **Costs Per Year:** Application fee: $40. Comprehensive fee: $23,680 includes full-time tuition ($23,120), mandatory fees ($560), and college room and board ($0). Full-time tuition and fees vary according to course load, degree level, location, and program. Part-time tuition: $730 per credit. Part-time tuition varies according to course load, degree level, location, and program. **Scholarships:** Available. **Calendar System:** Semester, Summer session available **Enrollment:** Full-time 338, Graduate full-time 244, Graduate part-time 85, Part-time 69 **Faculty:** Full-time 31, Part-time 63 **Student-Faculty Ratio:** 13:1 **Exams:** SAT I or ACT; SAT Reasoning. **% Receiving Financial Aid:** 84 **% Residing in College-Owned, -Operated, or -Affiliated Housing:** 59 **Final Year or Final Semester Residency Requirement:** Yes **Credit Hours For Degree:** 128 semester hours, Bachelors **Professional Accreditation:** ABHE, ATS, NCCU. **Intercollegiate Athletics:** Basketball M & W; Cross-Country Running M & W; Golf M & W; Soccer M; Volleyball W

NEW HOPE CHRISTIAN COLLEGE

2155 Bailey Hill Rd.
Eugene, OR 97405
Tel: (541)485-1780; Free: 800-322-2638
Fax: (541)343-5801
E-mail: sarahslater@newhope.edu
Web Site: www.newhope.edu
President/CEO: David L. Cole
Admissions: Sarah Slater
Financial Aid: Nathan Icenhower

Type: Four-Year College **Sex:** Coed **Affiliation:** Open Bible Standard Churches. **% Accepted:** 22 **Admission Plans:** Deferred Admission **Application Deadline:** August 1 **Application Fee:** $35.00 **H.S. Requirements:** High school diploma required; GED accepted **Scholarships:** Available. **Calendar System:** Semester **Enrollment:** Full-time 134, Part-time 9 **Faculty:** Full-time 9, Part-time 16 **Student-Faculty Ratio:** 11:1 **Professional Accreditation:** ABHE. **Intercollegiate Athletics:** Basketball M; Soccer M & W; Volleyball M & W

NORTHWEST CHRISTIAN UNIVERSITY

828 E 11th Ave.
Eugene, OR 97401-3745
Tel: (541)343-1641; Free: 877-463-6622
Fax: (541)684-7317

E-mail: kgalick@nwcu.edu
Web Site: www.nwcu.edu
President/CEO: Dr. Joseph D. Womack
Admissions: Kassia Galick
Financial Aid: Jocelyn Hubbs
Type: Comprehensive **Sex:** Coed **Affiliation:** Christian. **Scores:** 96% SAT V 400+; 91% SAT M 400+; 61.29% ACT 18-23; 19.36% ACT 24-29 **% Accepted:** 68 **Admission Plans:** Deferred Admission **Application Deadline:** Rolling **Application Fee:** $0.00 **H.S. Requirements:** High school diploma required; GED accepted **Costs Per Year:** Application fee: $0. Comprehensive fee: $35,670 includes full-time tuition ($27,100), mandatory fees ($170), and college room and board ($8400). Full-time tuition and fees vary according to course load. Room and board charges vary according to housing facility. Part-time tuition: $900 per credit hour. Part-time mandatory fees: $170 per year. Part-time tuition and fees vary according to course load. **Scholarships:** Available. **Calendar System:** Quarter, Summer session available **Enrollment:** Full-time 421, Graduate full-time 182, Graduate part-time 25, Part-time 112 **Faculty:** Full-time 26, Part-time 62 **Student-Faculty Ratio:** 12:1 **Exams:** ACT essay component not used; SAT I or ACT; SAT essay component used as validity check; SAT essay component used for admission; SAT essay component used for placement. **% Receiving Financial Aid:** 80 **% Residing in College-Owned, -Operated, or -Affiliated Housing:** 48 **Final Year or Final Semester Residency Requirement:** No **Credit Hours For Degree:** 60 semester hours, Associates; 124 semester hours, Bachelors **Professional Accreditation:** NCCU. **Intercollegiate Athletics:** Basketball M & W; Cross-Country Running M & W; Golf M & W; Soccer M & W; Softball W; Track and Field M & W; Volleyball W

OREGON COAST COMMUNITY COLLEGE

400 SE College Way
Newport, OR 97366
Tel: (541)265-2283
E-mail: webinfo@occc.cc.or.us
Web Site: www.oregoncoastcc.org
President/CEO: Dr. Birgitte Ryslinge
Type: Two-Year College **Sex:** Coed **% Accepted:** 100 **Admission Plans:** Open Admission **Application Fee:** $0.00 **H.S. Requirements:** High school diploma or equivalent not required. For nursing, aquarium science, criminal justice programs: High school diploma required; GED accepted **Costs Per Year:** Application fee: $0. State resident tuition: $3564 full-time, $99 per credit part-time. Nonresident tuition: $7704 full-time, $214 per credit part-time. Mandatory fees: $252 full-time, $7 per credit part-time. Full-time tuition and fees vary according to course load and program. Part-time tuition and fees vary according to course load and program. **Calendar System:** Quarter, Summer session available **Enrollment:** Full-time 213, Part-time 290 **Faculty:** Full-time 10, Part-time 57 **Student-Faculty Ratio:** 17:1 **Exams:** Other. **Final Year or Final Semester Residency Requirement:** No **Credit Hours For Degree:** 90 credits, Associates

OREGON COLLEGE OF ART & CRAFT

8245 SW Barnes Rd.
Portland, OR 97225
Tel: (503)297-5544; Free: 800-390-0632
Fax: (503)297-3155
E-mail: aboerner@ocac.edu
Web Site: www.ocac.edu
President/CEO: Pres. Denise Mullen
Admissions: Anne Boerner
Financial Aid: Linda L. Anderson
Type: Comprehensive **Sex:** Coed **Scores:** 100% SAT V 400+; 100% SAT M 400+; 83% ACT 18-23 **% Accepted:** 16 **Admission Plans:** Deferred Admission **Application Deadline:** Rolling **Application Fee:** $35.00 **H.S. Requirements:** High school diploma required; GED accepted **Costs Per Year:** Application fee: $35. One-time mandatory fee: $30. Comprehensive fee: $37,530 includes full-time tuition ($28,000), mandatory fees ($1530), and college room and board ($8000). College room only: $5000. Full-time tuition and fees vary according to course load and degree level. Room and board charges vary according to board plan and housing facility. Part-time tuition: $1170 per credit. Part-time mandatory fees: $45 per credit, $365 per term. Part-time tuition and fees vary according to course load and degree level. **Scholarships:** Available. **Calendar System:** Semester, Summer session not available **Enrollment:** Full-time 122, Graduate full-time 24, Graduate part-time 3, Part-time 25 **Faculty:** Full-time 10, Part-time 33 **Student-Faculty Ratio:** 8:1 **Exams:** ACT; SAT I; SAT Reasoning; SAT Subject. **%**

Receiving Financial Aid: 84 **% Residing in College-Owned, -Operated, or -Affiliated Housing:** 10 **Final Year or Final Semester Residency Requirement:** No **Credit Hours For Degree:** 120 credits, Bachelors **Professional Accreditation:** NASAD, NCCU.

OREGON HEALTH & SCIENCE UNIVERSITY

3181 SW Sam Jackson Park Rd.
Portland, OR 97239-3098
Tel: (503)494-8311
Fax: (503)494-5738
E-mail: buedefel@ohsu.edu
Web Site: www.ohsu.edu
President/CEO: Dr. Joseph Robertson, MD, MBA
Admissions: Tami Buedefeldt
Financial Aid: Lea Pandozzi
Type: Two-Year Upper Division **Sex:** Coed **Application Fee:** $120.00 **H.S. Requirements:** High school diploma required; GED accepted **Costs Per Year:** Application fee: $120. State resident tuition: $10,620 full-time, $354 per credit hour part-time. Nonresident tuition: $19,470 full-time, $649 per credit hour part-time. Mandatory fees: $5,415 full-time, $4,965.09 per year part-time. Full-time tuition and fees vary according to course load, location, program, and reciprocity agreements. Part-time tuition and fees vary according to course load, location, program, and reciprocity agreements. Tuition guaranteed not to increase for student's term of enrollment. **Scholarships:** Available. **Calendar System:** Quarter, Summer session available **Enrollment:** Full-time 206, Graduate full-time 1,448, Graduate part-time 620, Part-time 621 **Faculty:** Full-time 94, Part-time 16 **% Receiving Financial Aid:** 79 **Final Year or Final Semester Residency Requirement:** No **Credit Hours For Degree:** 180 quarter hours, Bachelors **Professional Accreditation:** AACN, AANA, ACEN, ACNM, ADA, AND, APA, CEPH, JRCERT, LCME/AMA, NAACLS, NCCU.

OREGON INSTITUTE OF TECHNOLOGY

3201 Campus Dr.
Klamath Falls, OR 97601-8801
Tel: (541)885-1000; Free: 800-422-2017
Fax: (541)885-1115
E-mail: carl.thomas@oit.edu
Web Site: www.oit.edu
President/CEO: Dr. Chris Maples
Admissions: Carl Thomas
Financial Aid: Tracey Lehman
Type: Comprehensive **Sex:** Coed **Affiliation:** Oregon University System. **Scores:** 93% SAT V 400+; 92% SAT M 400+; 43% ACT 18-23; 34% ACT 24-29 **% Accepted:** 93 **Admission Plans:** Deferred Admission **Application Deadline:** October 1 **Application Fee:** $50.00 **H.S. Requirements:** High school diploma required; GED accepted **Scholarships:** Available. **Calendar System:** Quarter, Summer session available **Enrollment:** Full-time 2,148, Graduate full-time 11, Graduate part-time 19, Part-time 1,733 **Faculty:** Full-time 144, Part-time 113 **Student-Faculty Ratio:** 20:1 **Exams:** SAT I or ACT. **% Receiving Financial Aid:** 72 **% Residing in College-Owned, -Operated, or -Affiliated Housing:** 13 **Credit Hours For Degree:** 90 credit hours, Associates; 180 credit hours, Bachelors **ROTC:** Army **Professional Accreditation:** ABET, ADA, JRCERT, NAACLS, NCCU. **Intercollegiate Athletics:** Baseball M; Basketball M & W; Cross-Country Running M & W; Soccer W; Softball W; Track and Field M & W; Volleyball W

OREGON STATE UNIVERSITY

Corvallis, OR 97331
Tel: (541)737-1000; Free: 800-291-4192
Fax: (541)737-6157
E-mail: osuadmit@oregonstate.edu
Web Site: www.oregonstate.edu
President/CEO: Dr. Edward Ray
Admissions: Noah Buckley
Financial Aid: Doug Severs
Type: University **Sex:** Coed **Scores:** 96% SAT V 400+; 98% SAT M 400+; 37% ACT 18-23; 42% ACT 24-29 **% Accepted:** 78 **Admission Plans:** Deferred Admission; Early Decision Plan **Application Deadline:** February 1 **Application Fee:** $60.00 **H.S. Requirements:** High school diploma required; GED accepted **Costs Per Year:** Application fee: $60. One-time mandatory fee: $350. State resident tuition: $8535 full-time, $183 per credit hour part-time. Nonresident tuition: $27,195 full-time, $582 per credit hour part-time. Mandatory fees: $1572 full-time, $455.57 per term part-time. Full-

time tuition and fees vary according to course load, location, and program. Part-time tuition and fees vary according to course load, location, and program. College room and board: $11,691. College room only: $7878. Room and board charges vary according to board plan and housing facility. **Scholarships:** Available. **Calendar System:** Quarter, Summer session available **Enrollment:** Full-time 18,493, Graduate full-time 3,595, Graduate part-time 1,369, Part-time 6,119 **Faculty:** Full-time 1,161, Part-time 460 **Student-Faculty Ratio:** 18:1 **Exams:** SAT I or ACT; SAT II; SAT Reasoning. **% Receiving Financial Aid:** 56 **% Residing in College-Owned, -Operated, or -Affiliated Housing:** 17 **Final Year or Final Semester Residency Requirement:** No **Credit Hours For Degree:** 180 quarter hours, Bachelors **ROTC:** Air Force, Army, Navy **Professional Accreditation:** AACSB, AAFCS, ABET, ACA, ACCE, ACPE, AVMA, CEPH, JRCAT, NCATE, NCCU, SAF. **Intercollegiate Athletics:** Baseball M; Basketball M & W; Crew M & W; Cross-Country Running W; Football M; Golf M & W; Gymnastics W; Soccer M & W; Softball W; Swimming and Diving W; Track and Field W; Volleyball W; Wrestling M

OREGON STATE UNIVERSITY–CASCADES

2600 NW College Way
Bend, OR 97701
Tel: (541)322-3100
E-mail: cascadeadmit@osucascades.edu
Web Site: www.osucascades.edu
President/CEO: Becky Johnson

Type: Comprehensive **Sex:** Coed **Affiliation:** Oregon University System. **Application Deadline:** Rolling **Application Fee:** $50.00 **Calendar System:** Quarter, Summer session available **Student-Faculty Ratio:** 15:1 **Professional Accreditation:** NCCU.

PACIFIC NORTHWEST COLLEGE OF ART

511 NW Broadway
Portland, OR 97209
Tel: (503)226-4391
Fax: (503)226-3587
E-mail: admissions@pnca.edu
Web Site: www.pnca.edu
President/CEO: John Casey Mills
Admissions: Jean Hester, Jr.
Financial Aid: Peggy Burgus

Type: Comprehensive **Sex:** Coed **% Accepted:** 81 **Admission Plans:** Deferred Admission **Application Deadline:** Rolling **Application Fee:** $45.00 **H.S. Requirements:** High school diploma required; GED accepted **Costs Per Year:** Application fee: $45. One-time mandatory fee: $50. Comprehensive fee: $47,004 includes full-time tuition ($32,820), mandatory fees ($1680), and college room and board ($12,504). Part-time tuition: $1368 per credit hour. Part-time mandatory fees: $63 per contact hour, $100 per year. Part-time tuition and fees vary according to course load. **Scholarships:** Available. **Calendar System:** Semester, Summer session available **Enrollment:** Full-time 376, Graduate full-time 91, Graduate part-time 3, Part-time 31 **Faculty:** Full-time 33, Part-time 75 **Student-Faculty Ratio:** 8:1 **% Receiving Financial Aid:** 81 **% Residing in College-Owned, -Operated, or -Affiliated Housing:** 21 **Final Year or Final Semester Residency Requirement:** No **Credit Hours For Degree:** 120 semester hours, Bachelors **Professional Accreditation:** NASAD, NCCU.

PACIFIC UNIVERSITY

2043 College Way
Forest Grove, OR 97116-1797
Tel: (503)357-6151; Free: 877-722-8648
Fax: (503)352-3191
E-mail: admissions@pacificu.edu
Web Site: www.pacificu.edu
President/CEO: Dr. Leslie M. Hallick
Admissions: Karen Dunston

Type: Comprehensive **Sex:** Coed **Scores:** 98% SAT V 400+; 99% SAT M 400+; 42.02% ACT 18-23; 45.53% ACT 24-29 **% Accepted:** 79 **Admission Plans:** Deferred Admission **Application Fee:** $40.00 **H.S. Requirements:** High school diploma required; GED accepted **Costs Per Year:** Application fee: $40. Comprehensive fee: $52,876 includes full-time tuition ($40,120), mandatory fees ($934), and college room and board ($11,822). College room only: $6528. Room and board charges vary according to board plan and housing facility. Part-time tuition: $1672 per credit hour. Part-time tuition varies according to course load. **Scholarships:** Available. **Calendar**

System: Semester **Enrollment:** Full-time 1,881, Graduate full-time 1,727, Graduate part-time 159, Part-time 43 **Exams:** ACT; SAT I; SAT I and SAT II or ACT; SAT I or ACT; SAT II; SAT essay component used for admission; SAT essay component used for advising; SAT essay component used for placement. **% Receiving Financial Aid:** 79 **% Residing in College-Owned, -Operated, or -Affiliated Housing:** 59 **Credit Hours For Degree:** 124 semester hours, Bachelors **ROTC:** Air Force, Army **Professional Accreditation:** ACPE, AOA, AOTA, APA, APTA, NASM, NCATE, NCCU. **Intercollegiate Athletics:** Baseball M; Basketball M & W; Cross-Country Running M & W; Football M; Golf M & W; Lacrosse W; Soccer M & W; Softball W; Swimming and Diving M & W; Tennis M & W; Track and Field M & W; Volleyball W; Wrestling M & W

PIONEER PACIFIC COLLEGE

27501 SW Pky. Ave.
Wilsonville, OR 97070
Tel: (503)682-3903; Free: 866-PPC-INFO
Fax: (503)682-1514
E-mail: wil-info@pioneerpacific.edu
Web Site: www.pioneerpacific.edu
President/CEO: Don Moutos
Admissions: Elizabeth Cox

Type: Four-Year College **Sex:** Coed **Admission Plans:** Open Admission **Application Deadline:** Rolling **Application Fee:** $50.00 **H.S. Requirements:** High school diploma required; GED accepted **Scholarships:** Available. **Calendar System:** Continuous, Summer session not available **Exams:** Other. **Credit Hours For Degree:** 90 credit hours, Associates; 182.5 credit hours, Bachelors **Professional Accreditation:** ACICS.

PIONEER PACIFIC COLLEGE–EUGENE/SPRINGFIELD BRANCH

3800 Sports Way
Springfield, OR 97477
Free: 866-772-4636
E-mail: inquiries@pioneerpacific.edu
Web Site: www.pioneerpacific.edu

Type: Four-Year College **Sex:** Coed **H.S. Requirements:** High school diploma required; GED accepted **Exams:** Other. **Professional Accreditation:** ACICS.

PORTLAND COMMUNITY COLLEGE

PO Box 19000
Portland, OR 97280-0990
Tel: (971)722-6111; Free: 866-922-1010
Fax: (503)452-4988
Web Site: www.pcc.edu
President/CEO: Jeremy Brown

Type: Two-Year College **Sex:** Coed **Admission Plans:** Open Admission **Application Deadline:** Rolling **Application Fee:** $25.00 **H.S. Requirements:** High school diploma or equivalent not required. For career and technical programs: High school diploma required; GED not accepted **Scholarships:** Available. **Calendar System:** Quarter, Summer session available **Credit Hours For Degree:** 90 credit hours, Associates **Professional Accreditation:** ACEN, ADA, AHIMA, JCAHPO, JRCERT, NAACLS, NCCU. **Intercollegiate Athletics:** Basketball M & W

PORTLAND STATE UNIVERSITY

PO Box 751
Portland, OR 97207-0751
Tel: (503)725-3000; Free: 800-547-8887
Fax: (503)725-5525
E-mail: shannon.carr@pdx.edu
Web Site: www.pdx.edu
President/CEO: Dr. Wim Wiewel
Admissions: Shannon Carr
Financial Aid: G. Michael Johnson

Type: University **Sex:** Coed **Scores:** 93% SAT V 400+; 92% SAT M 400+; 45% ACT 18-23; 32% ACT 24-29 **% Accepted:** 86 **Admission Plans:** Deferred Admission; Early Admission **Application Deadline:** Rolling **Application Fee:** $50.00 **H.S. Requirements:** High school diploma required; GED accepted **Costs Per Year:** Application fee: $50. State resident tuition: $5400 full-time, $150 per credit hour part-time. Nonresident tuition: $18,180 full-time, $505 per credit hour part-time. Mandatory fees: $1284 full-time, $117 per credit hour part-time. Full-time tuition and fees vary according to program and reciprocity agreements. Part-time tuition and fees vary according to program and reciprocity agreements. College room and board: $10,260. College room only: $6510. Room and board charges vary according to board plan and housing facility. **Scholarships:** Available. **Calendar System:** Quarter, Summer session available **Enrollment:** Full-time 14,606, Graduate full-time 2,713, Graduate part-time 2,795, Part-time 7,374 **Faculty:** Full-time 843, Part-time 697 **Student-Faculty Ratio:** 22:1 **Exams:** SAT I or ACT. **% Receiving Financial Aid:** 66 **% Residing in College-Owned, -Operated, or -Affiliated Housing:** 10 **Final Year or Final Semester Residency Requirement:** No **Credit Hours For Degree:** 180 credit hours, Bachelors **ROTC:** Air Force, Army **Professional Accreditation:** AACSB, ABET, ACA, ACSP, ASHA, CEPH, CORE, CSWE, NASM, NASPAA, NAST, NCATE, NCCU. **Intercollegiate Athletics:** Basketball M & W; Cross-Country Running M & W; Football M; Golf W; Soccer W; Softball W; Tennis M & W; Track and Field M & W; Volleyball W

REED COLLEGE
3203 SE Woodstock Blvd.
Portland, OR 97202-8199
Tel: (503)771-1112; Free: 800-547-4750
Fax: (503)777-7553
E-mail: admission@reed.edu
Web Site: www.reed.edu
President/CEO: John R. Kroger
Financial Aid: Leslie Limper

Type: Comprehensive **Sex:** Coed **Scores:** 100% SAT V 400+; 100% SAT M 400+; 1% ACT 18-23; 25% ACT 24-29 **% Accepted:** 35 **Admission Plans:** Deferred Admission; Early Action; Early Admission **Application Deadline:** January 15 **Application Fee:** $0.00 **H.S. Requirements:** High school diploma required; GED accepted **Costs Per Year:** Application fee: $0. Comprehensive fee: $62,530 includes full-time tuition ($49,640), mandatory fees ($300), and college room and board ($12,590). College room only: $6570. Full-time tuition and fees vary according to degree level. Room and board charges vary according to board plan and housing facility. Part-time tuition: $8420 per unit. Part-time mandatory fees: $150 per term. Part-time tuition and fees vary according to course load and degree level. **Scholarships:** Available. **Calendar System:** Semester, Summer session not available **Enrollment:** Full-time 1,394, Graduate part-time 23, Part-time 36 **Faculty:** Full-time 143, Part-time 7 **Student-Faculty Ratio:** 9:1 **Exams:** ACT essay component used as validity check; ACT essay component used for admission; SAT I or ACT; SAT II; SAT essay component used as validity check; SAT essay component used for admission; SAT Reasoning; SAT Subject. **% Receiving Financial Aid:** 53 **% Residing in College-Owned, -Operated, or -Affiliated Housing:** 67 **Final Year or Final Semester Residency Requirement:** Yes **Credit Hours For Degree:** 30 courses, Bachelors **ROTC:** Air Force **Professional Accreditation:** NCCU.

ROGUE COMMUNITY COLLEGE
3345 Redwood Hwy.
Grants Pass, OR 97527-9291
Tel: (541)956-7500
E-mail: csullivan@roguecc.edu
Web Site: www.roguecc.edu
President/CEO: Dr. Peter Angstadt
Admissions: John Duarte
Financial Aid: Anna K. Manley

Type: Two-Year College **Sex:** Coed **Admission Plans:** Early Admission; Open Admission; Preferred Admission **Application Deadline:** Rolling **Application Fee:** $0.00 **H.S. Requirements:** High school diploma required; GED accepted **Costs Per Year:** Application fee: $0. State resident tuition: $3420 full-time, $95 per credit hour part-time. Nonresident tuition: $4176 full-time, $116 per credit hour part-time. Mandatory fees: $585 full-time, $5 per credit hour part-time, $135 per term part-time. Full-time tuition and fees vary according to reciprocity agreements. Part-time tuition and fees vary according to reciprocity agreements. **Scholarships:** Available. **Calendar System:** Quarter, Summer session available **Enrollment:** Full-time 1,901, Part-time 3,053 **Faculty:** Full-time 77, Part-time 395 **Student-Faculty Ratio:** 14:1 **Final Year or Final Semester Residency Requirement:** No **Credit Hours For Degree:** 90 credits, Associates **Professional Accreditation:** CoARC, NCCU. **Intercollegiate Athletics:** Soccer M & W

SOUTHERN OREGON UNIVERSITY
1250 Siskiyou Blvd.
Ashland, OR 97520
Tel: (541)552-7672; Free: 855-470-3377

Fax: (541)552-6329
E-mail: admissions@sou.edu
Web Site: www.sou.edu
President/CEO: Dr. Roy Saigo
Admissions: Kelly Moutsatson

Type: Comprehensive **Sex:** Coed **Scores:** 92% SAT V 400+; 93% SAT M 400+; 48.68% ACT 18-23; 37.28% ACT 24-29 **% Accepted:** 95 **Admission Plans:** Deferred Admission; Early Admission **Application Deadline:** Rolling **Application Fee:** $60.00 **H.S. Requirements:** High school diploma required; GED accepted **Costs Per Year:** Application fee: $60. State resident tuition: $6615 full-time, $147 per credit hour part-time. Nonresident tuition: $20,835 full-time, $463 per credit hour part-time. Mandatory fees: $1530 full-time. Full-time tuition and fees vary according to course load, program, and reciprocity agreements. Part-time tuition varies according to course load, program, and reciprocity agreements. College room and board: $11,295. College room only: $6855. Room and board charges vary according to board plan and housing facility. **Scholarships:** Available. **Calendar System:** Quarter, Summer session available **Enrollment:** Full-time 3,686, Graduate full-time 247, Graduate part-time 404, Part-time 1,715 **Faculty:** Full-time 163, Part-time 144 **Student-Faculty Ratio:** 23:1 **Exams:** SAT I and SAT II or ACT; SAT I or ACT; SAT II; SAT Reasoning; SAT Subject. **% Receiving Financial Aid:** 74 **% Residing in College-Owned, -Operated, or -Affiliated Housing:** 26 **Final Year or Final Semester Residency Requirement:** No **Credit Hours For Degree:** 180 credits, Bachelors **ROTC:** Army **Professional Accreditation:** ACBSP, NASM, NCCU. **Intercollegiate Athletics:** Basketball M & W; Cheerleading W; Football M; Lacrosse M; Rugby M & W; Soccer M & W; Softball W; Tennis M & W; Track and Field M & W; Volleyball W; Wrestling M

SOUTHWESTERN OREGON COMMUNITY COLLEGE
1988 Newmark Ave.
Coos Bay, OR 97420-2912
Tel: (541)888-2525; Free: 800-962-2838
E-mail: lwells@socc.edu
Web Site: www.socc.edu
President/CEO: Dr. Patty M. Scott, EdD
Admissions: Barb Shreckengost
Financial Aid: Avena Singh

Type: Two-Year College **Sex:** Coed **Admission Plans:** Early Admission; Open Admission **Application Deadline:** Rolling **Application Fee:** $40.00 **H.S. Requirements:** High school diploma or equivalent not required. For nursing program: High school diploma required; GED accepted **Costs Per Year:** Application fee: $40. One-time mandatory fee: $40. State resident tuition: $4095 full-time, $91 per credit part-time. Nonresident tuition: $4095 full-time, $91 per credit part-time. Mandatory fees: $1752 full-time, $29 per credit part-time, $60. Full-time tuition and fees vary according to program. Part-time tuition and fees vary according to program. College room and board: $7478. Room and board charges vary according to board plan. **Scholarships:** Available. **Calendar System:** Quarter, Summer session available **Enrollment:** Full-time 1,129, Part-time 1,209 **Faculty:** Full-time 54, Part-time 128 **Student-Faculty Ratio:** 15:1 **Exams:** ACT essay component used for advising; ACT essay component used for placement; SAT essay component used for advising; SAT essay component used for placement. **% Residing in College-Owned, -Operated, or -Affiliated Housing:** 17 **Credit Hours For Degree:** Minimum of 90 credit hours - generally 93 credits, Associates **Professional Accreditation:** ACF, NCCU. **Intercollegiate Athletics:** Baseball M; Basketball M & W; Cheerleading M & W; Cross-Country Running M & W; Golf M & W; Soccer M & W; Softball W; Swimming and Diving M & W; Track and Field M & W; Volleyball W; Wrestling M & W

SUMNER COLLEGE
15115 SW Sequoia Pky.
Ste. 200
Portland, OR 97224
Tel: (503)223-5100
Fax: (503)273-8093
Web Site: www.sumnercollege.edu
President/CEO: Joanna Russell

Type: Two-Year College **Sex:** Coed **Calendar System:** Quarter **Enrollment:** Full-time 261 **Faculty:** Full-time 12, Part-time 11 **Student-Faculty Ratio:** 15:1 **Exams:** ACT; Other; SAT I; SAT I and SAT II or ACT; SAT I or ACT; SAT II. **Final Year or Final Semester Residency Requirement:** No **Professional Accreditation:** ACICS.

TILLAMOOK BAY COMMUNITY COLLEGE

4301 Third St.
Tillamook, OR 97141
Tel: (503)842-8222
Fax: (503)842-2214
E-mail: gates@tillamookbay.cc
Web Site: www.tbcc.cc.or.us
President/CEO: Jon Carnahan
Admissions: Lori Gates
Financial Aid: Rhoda Hanson

Type: Two-Year College **Sex:** Coed **Affiliation:** Portland Community College. **Application Fee:** $0.00 **Scholarships:** Available. **Calendar System:** Quarter **Faculty:** Full-time 6, Part-time 30 **Student-Faculty Ratio:** 8:1 **Professional Accreditation:** NCCU.

TREASURE VALLEY COMMUNITY COLLEGE

650 College Blvd.
Ontario, OR 97914-3423
Tel: (541)889-6493
Fax: (541)881-2721
E-mail: kmyoung@tvcc.cc
Web Site: www.tvcc.cc
President/CEO: Dana Young
Admissions: Kelly Young

Type: Two-Year College **Sex:** Coed **% Accepted:** 100 **Admission Plans:** Deferred Admission; Early Admission; Open Admission **Application Deadline:** Rolling **Application Fee:** $0.00 **H.S. Requirements:** High school diploma or equivalent not required. For nursing program: High school diploma required; GED accepted **Costs Per Year:** Application fee: $0. State resident tuition: $4320 full-time, $96 per credit part-time. Nonresident tuition: $4770 full-time, $106 per credit part-time. Mandatory fees: $990 full-time, $22 per credit part-time. College room and board: $7069. College room only: $3763. Room and board charges vary according to board plan. **Scholarships:** Available. **Calendar System:** Quarter, Summer session available **Enrollment:** Full-time 958, Part-time 1,212 **Faculty:** Full-time 47, Part-time 39 **Student-Faculty Ratio:** 21:1 **% Residing in College-Owned, -Operated, or -Affiliated Housing:** 6 **Final Year or Final Semester Residency Requirement:** No **Credit Hours For Degree:** 90 credits, Associates **Professional Accreditation:** NCCU. **Intercollegiate Athletics:** Baseball M; Basketball M & W; Cross-Country Running M & W; Soccer M & W; Softball W; Tennis M & W; Track and Field M & W; Volleyball W

UMPQUA COMMUNITY COLLEGE

PO Box 967
Roseburg, OR 97470-0226
Tel: (541)440-4600
Fax: (541)440-4612
Web Site: www.umpqua.edu
President/CEO: Dr. Joe Olson

Type: Two-Year College **Sex:** Coed **% Accepted:** 100 **Admission Plans:** Deferred Admission; Early Admission; Open Admission **Application Deadline:** Rolling **Application Fee:** $25.00 **H.S. Requirements:** High school diploma or equivalent not required. For nursing, emergency medical technology program: High school diploma required; GED accepted **Scholarships:** Available. **Calendar System:** Quarter, Summer session available **Enrollment:** Full-time 971, Part-time 1,075 **Faculty:** Full-time 55, Part-time 94 **Student-Faculty Ratio:** 14:1 **Credit Hours For Degree:** 93 credits, Associates **Professional Accreditation:** ACEN, NCCU. **Intercollegiate Athletics:** Basketball M & W; Volleyball W

UNIVERSITY OF OREGON

Eugene, OR 97403
Tel: (541)346-1000; Free: 800-232-3825
Fax: (541)346-5815
E-mail: uoadmit@uoregon.edu
Web Site: www.uoregon.edu
President/CEO: Michael Schill
Admissions: James Rawlins
Financial Aid: Jim Brooks

Type: University **Sex:** Coed **Scores:** 97% SAT V 400+; 97% SAT M 400+; 32% ACT 18-23; 52% ACT 24-29 **% Accepted:** 74 **Admission Plans:** Early Decision Plan **Application Deadline:** January 15 **Application Fee:** $65.00 **H.S. Requirements:** High school diploma required; GED accepted **Costs Per Year:** Application fee: $65. One-time mandatory fee: $389. State

resident tuition: $8505 full-time, $189 per credit hour part-time. Nonresident tuition: $30,240 full-time, $672 per credit hour part-time. Mandatory fees: $1784 full-time. Full-time tuition and fees vary according to course load. Part-time tuition varies according to course load. College room and board: $11,785. Room and board charges vary according to board plan and housing facility. **Scholarships:** Available. **Calendar System:** Quarter, Summer session available **Enrollment:** Full-time 18,630, Graduate full-time 3,016, Graduate part-time 478, Part-time 1,908 **Faculty:** Full-time 1,080, Part-time 595 **Student-Faculty Ratio:** 18:1 **Exams:** SAT I and SAT II or ACT; SAT I or ACT; SAT Reasoning; SAT Subject. **% Receiving Financial Aid:** 43 **% Residing in College-Owned, -Operated, or -Affiliated Housing:** 20 **Final Year or Final Semester Residency Requirement:** Yes **Credit Hours For Degree:** 180 credit hours, Bachelors **ROTC:** Air Force, Army **Professional Accreditation:** AACSB, AALS, ABA, ACEJMC, ACSP, APA, ASHA, ASLA, CIDA, NAAB, NASAD, NASM, NASPAA, NCCU. **Intercollegiate Athletics:** Baseball M; Basketball M & W; Cross-Country Running M & W; Football M; Golf M & W; Lacrosse W; Soccer W; Softball W; Tennis M & W; Track and Field M & W; Volleyball W

UNIVERSITY OF PORTLAND

5000 N Willamette Blvd.
Portland, OR 97203-5798
Tel: (503)943-7911; Free: 888-627-5601
Fax: (503)943-7399
E-mail: admissions@up.edu
Web Site: www.up.edu
President/CEO: Fr. Mark Poorman, CSC
Admissions: Jason McDonald
Financial Aid: Janet Turner

Type: Comprehensive **Sex:** Coed **Affiliation:** Roman Catholic. **Scores:** 99% SAT V 400+; 99% SAT M 400+ **% Accepted:** 62 **Admission Plans:** Deferred Admission **Application Deadline:** June 1 **Application Fee:** $50.00 **H.S. Requirements:** High school diploma required; GED accepted **Costs Per Year:** Application fee: $50. Comprehensive fee: $52,152 includes full-time tuition ($40,080), mandatory fees ($170), and college room and board ($11,902). Full-time tuition and fees vary according to program. Room and board charges vary according to board plan and housing facility. Part-time tuition: $1255 per credit hour. Part-time tuition varies according to course load and program. **Scholarships:** Available. **Calendar System:** Semester, Summer session available **Enrollment:** Full-time 3,698, Graduate full-time 137, Graduate part-time 431, Part-time 72 **Faculty:** Full-time 223, Part-time 140 **Student-Faculty Ratio:** 14:1 **Exams:** ACT; SAT I; SAT I or ACT; SAT essay component not used; SAT Reasoning. **% Receiving Financial Aid:** 61 **% Residing in College-Owned, -Operated, or -Affiliated Housing:** 57 **Final Year or Final Semester Residency Requirement:** No **Credit Hours For Degree:** 120 semester hours, Bachelors **ROTC:** Air Force, Army **Professional Accreditation:** AACN, AACSB, ABET, NASM, NAST, NCATE, NCCU. **Intercollegiate Athletics:** Baseball M; Basketball M & W; Crew W; Cross-Country Running M & W; Rugby M; Soccer M & W; Tennis M & W; Track and Field M & W; Volleyball W

WARNER PACIFIC COLLEGE

2219 SE 68th Ave.
Portland, OR 97215-4099
Tel: (503)517-1000; Free: 800-804-1510
Fax: (503)788-7425
E-mail: admiss@warnerpacific.edu
Web Site: www.warnerpacific.edu
President/CEO: Dr. Andrea Cook
Admissions: Dale Seipp
Financial Aid: Cynthia D. Pollard

Type: Comprehensive **Sex:** Coed **Affiliation:** Church of God. **Scores:** 81% SAT V 400+; 76% SAT M 400+; 49% ACT 18-23; 6% ACT 24-29 **% Accepted:** 63 **Application Deadline:** Rolling **H.S. Requirements:** High school diploma required; GED accepted **Costs Per Year:** Comprehensive fee: $31,610 includes full-time tuition ($22,050), mandatory fees ($660), and college room and board ($8900). College room only: $3680. Room and board charges vary according to board plan and housing facility. Part-time tuition: $1005 per semester hour. Part-time mandatory fees: $330 per term. Part-time tuition and fees vary according to course load. **Scholarships:** Available. **Calendar System:** Semester, Summer session available **Enrollment:** Full-time 522, Graduate full-time 2, Part-time 30 **Faculty:** Full-time 22 **Student-Faculty Ratio:** 12:1 **Exams:** SAT I or ACT. **% Receiving Financial Aid:** 83 **% Residing in College-Owned, -Operated, or -Affiliated Housing: 44 **Credit Hours For Degree:** 62 semester hours, Associates; 124 semester hours, Bachelors **ROTC:** Air Force **Professional Accreditation:** NCCU. **Intercollegiate Athletics:** Basketball M & W; Cross-Country Running M & W; Golf M & W; Soccer M & W; Track and Field M & W; Volleyball W; Wrestling M & W

WESTERN OREGON UNIVERSITY

345 N Monmouth Ave.
Monmouth, OR 97361-1394
Tel: (503)838-8000; Free: 877-877-1593
Fax: (503)838-8067
E-mail: wolfgram@wou.edu
Web Site: www.wou.edu
President/CEO: Dr. Rex Fuller
Admissions: David Compton
Financial Aid: Kella Helyer
Type: Comprehensive **Sex:** Coed **Scores:** 84% SAT V 400+; 88% SAT M 400+; 56% ACT 18-23; 13% ACT 24-29 **% Accepted:** 88 **Admission Plans:** Deferred Admission **Application Deadline:** Rolling **Application Fee:** $60.00 **H.S. Requirements:** High school diploma required; GED accepted **Costs Per Year:** Application fee: $60. State resident tuition: $8796 full-time. Nonresident tuition: $22,056 full-time. Full-time tuition varies according to course load. College room and board: $9638. College room only: $7988. Room and board charges vary according to board plan and housing facility. Tuition guaranteed not to increase for student's term of enrollment. **Scholarships:** Available. **Calendar System:** Quarter, Summer session available **Enrollment:** Full-time 4,059, Graduate full-time 273, Graduate part-time 364, Part-time 749 **Faculty:** Full-time 286, Part-time 89 **Student-Faculty Ratio:** 14:1 **Exams:** SAT I and SAT II or ACT. **% Receiving Financial Aid:** 83 **% Residing in College-Owned, -Operated, or -Affiliated Housing:** 26 **Final Year or Final Semester Residency Requirement:** No **Credit Hours For Degree:** 93 credit hours, Associates; 180 credit hours, Bachelors **ROTC:** Army, Navy **Professional Accreditation:** CORE, NASM, NCATE, NCCU. **Intercollegiate Athletics:** Baseball M; Basketball M & W; Cross-Country Running M & W; Football M; Soccer W; Softball W; Track and Field M & W; Volleyball W

WILLAMETTE UNIVERSITY

900 State St.
Salem, OR 97301-3931
Tel: (503)370-6300; Free: 877-542-2787
Fax: (503)375-5363
E-mail: libarts@willamette.edu
Web Site: www.willamette.edu
President/CEO: Dr. Stephen E. Thorsett
Admissions: Ramiro Flores
Financial Aid: Patty Hoban
Type: Comprehensive **Sex:** Coed **Affiliation:** United Methodist. **Scores:** 100% SAT V 400+; 99% SAT M 400+; 13.93% ACT 18-23; 58.57% ACT 24-29 **% Accepted:** 78 **Admission Plans:** Deferred Admission; Early Decision Plan **Application Deadline:** January 15 **Application Fee:** $50.00 **H.S. Requirements:** High school diploma required; GED accepted **Costs Per Year:** Application fee: $50. Comprehensive fee: $56,817 includes full-time tuition ($45,300), mandatory fees ($317), and college room and board ($11,200). Full-time tuition and fees vary according to course load. Room and board charges vary according to board plan and housing facility. Part-time tuition: $5,662 per course. Part-time tuition varies according to course load. **Scholarships:** Available. **Calendar System:** Semester, Summer session not available **Enrollment:** Full-time 1,977, Graduate full-time 579, Graduate part-time 113, Part-time 407 **Faculty:** Full-time 217, Part-time 63 **Student-Faculty Ratio:** 10:1 **Exams:** ACT essay component used for admission; SAT I or ACT; SAT essay component used for admission; SAT Reasoning. **% Receiving Financial Aid:** 62 **% Residing in College-Owned, -Operated, or -Affiliated Housing:** 66 **Final Year or Final Semester Residency Requirement:** Yes **Credit Hours For Degree:** 124 semester hours, Bachelors **ROTC:** Air Force, Army **Professional Accreditation:** AACSB, AALS, ABA, NASM, NASPAA, NCATE, NCCU. **Intercollegiate Athletics:** Baseball M; Basketball M & W; Crew M & W; Cross-Country Running M & W; Football M; Golf M & W; Lacrosse M; Soccer M & W; Softball W; Swimming and Diving M & W; Tennis M & W; Track and Field M & W; Volleyball W

ALBRIGHT COLLEGE

13th and Bern Sts.
Reading, PA 19612-5234
Tel: (610)921-2381; Free: 800-252-1856
Fax: (610)921-7530
E-mail: admission@albright.edu
Web Site: www.albright.edu
President/CEO: Dr. Lex O. McMillan
Admissions: Gregory Eichhorn
Financial Aid: Chris Hanlon

Type: Comprehensive **Sex:** Coed **Affiliation:** United Methodist Church. **Scores:** 99% SAT V 400+; 100% SAT M 400+; 47% ACT 18-23; 39% ACT 24-29 **% Accepted:** 49 **Admission Plans:** Deferred Admission **Application Deadline:** Rolling **Application Fee:** $25.00 **H.S. Requirements:** High school diploma required; GED accepted **Costs Per Year:** Application fee: $25. Comprehensive fee: $50,620 includes full-time tuition ($38,950), mandatory fees ($900), and college room and board ($10,770). College room only: $5950. Full-time tuition and fees vary according to degree level. Room and board charges vary according to board plan and housing facility. Part-time tuition: $4869 per course. Part-time tuition varies according to degree level. **Scholarships:** Available. **Calendar System:** 4-1-4, Summer session available **Enrollment:** Full-time 1,734, Graduate part-time 33, Part-time 25 **Faculty:** Full-time 111, Part-time 60 **Student-Faculty Ratio:** 13:1 **Exams:** ACT; ACT essay component not used; SAT I; SAT I or ACT; SAT essay component not used; SAT Reasoning. **% Receiving Financial Aid:** 89 **% Residing in College-Owned, -Operated, or -Affiliated Housing:** 65 **Final Year or Final Semester Residency Requirement:** No **Regional Accreditation:** Middle States Association of Colleges and Schools **Credit Hours For Degree:** 32 courses, Bachelors **ROTC:** Army **Intercollegiate Athletics:** Badminton W; Baseball M; Basketball M & W; Cheerleading M & W; Cross-Country Running M & W; Field Hockey W; Football M; Golf M & W; Lacrosse M & W; Rugby M & W; Soccer M & W; Softball W; Swimming and Diving M & W; Tennis M & W; Track and Field M & W; Ultimate Frisbee M & W; Volleyball W

ALL-STATE CAREER SCHOOL–ESSINGTON CAMPUS

50 W Powhattan Ave.
Essington, PA 19029
Tel: (610)362-1124
Web Site: www.allstatecareer.edu
Type: Two-Year College **Sex:** Coed **Professional Accreditation:** ACCSC.

ALLEGHENY COLLEGE

520 N Main St.
Meadville, PA 16335
Tel: (814)332-3100; Free: 800-521-5293
Fax: (814)337-0431
E-mail: admissions@allegheny.edu
Web Site: www.allegheny.edu
President/CEO: Dr. James H. Mullen, Jr.
Admissions: Linda Clune
Financial Aid: Jonathan Boleratz

Type: Four-Year College **Sex:** Coed **Scores:** 98% SAT V 400+; 97% SAT M 400+; 29% ACT 18-23; 46% ACT 24-29 **% Accepted:** 68 **Admission Plans:** Deferred Admission; Early Action; Early Admission **Application Deadline:**

February 15 **H.S. Requirements:** High school diploma required; GED accepted **Costs Per Year:** Comprehensive fee: $55,420 includes full-time tuition ($43,750), mandatory fees ($500), and college room and board ($11,170). College room only: $5880. Room and board charges vary according to board plan and housing facility. Part-time tuition: $1823 per credit hour. Part-time mandatory fees: $250 per term. Part-time tuition and fees vary according to course load. **Scholarships:** Available. **Calendar System:** Semester, Summer session not available **Enrollment:** Full-time 1,890, Part-time 41 **Faculty:** Full-time 173, Part-time 24 **Student-Faculty Ratio:** 11:1 **Exams:** SAT I or ACT; SAT II; SAT Reasoning; SAT Subject. **% Receiving Financial Aid:** 72 **% Residing in College-Owned, -Operated, or -Affiliated Housing:** 91 **Final Year or Final Semester Residency Requirement:** Yes **Regional Accreditation:** Middle States Association of Colleges and Schools **Credit Hours For Degree:** 128 credit hours, Bachelors **Intercollegiate Athletics:** Baseball M; Basketball M & W; Cheerleading M & W; Crew M & W; Cross-Country Running M & W; Equestrian Sports M & W; Fencing M & W; Football M; Golf M & W; Ice Hockey M; Lacrosse M & W; Rugby M & W; Soccer M & W; Softball W; Swimming and Diving M & W; Tennis M & W; Track and Field M & W; Ultimate Frisbee M & W; Volleyball M & W

ALVERNIA UNIVERSITY

400 Saint Bernardine St.
Reading, PA 19607-1799
Tel: (610)796-8200
Fax: (610)796-8336
E-mail: admissions@alvernia.edu
Web Site: www.alvernia.edu
President/CEO: Dr. Thomas F. Flynn
Admissions: Dan Hartzman
Financial Aid: Christine Saadi

Type: Comprehensive **Sex:** Coed **Affiliation:** Roman Catholic. **Scores:** 89% SAT V 400+; 90% SAT M 400+; 47.1% ACT 18-23; 25.7% ACT 24-29 **% Accepted:** 74 **Admission Plans:** Deferred Admission **Application Deadline:** Rolling **Application Fee:** $25.00 **H.S. Requirements:** High school diploma required; GED accepted **Costs Per Year:** Application fee: $25. Comprehensive fee: $43,700 includes full-time tuition ($31,650), mandatory fees ($620), and college room and board ($11,430). College room only: $5780. Full-time tuition and fees vary according to class time and reciprocity agreements. Room and board charges vary according to board plan and housing facility. Part-time tuition: $870 per credit. Part-time tuition varies according to class time and course load. **Scholarships:** Available. **Calendar System:** Semester, Summer session available **Enrollment:** Full-time 1,765, Graduate full-time 165, Graduate part-time 333, Part-time 593 **Faculty:** Full-time 105, Part-time 223 **Student-Faculty Ratio:** 12:1 **Exams:** ACT essay component not used; SAT I or ACT; SAT essay component not used; SAT Reasoning. **% Receiving Financial Aid:** 86 **% Residing in College-Owned, -Operated, or -Affiliated Housing:** 59 **Final Year or Final Semester Residency Requirement:** No **Regional Accreditation:** Middle States Association of Colleges and Schools **Credit Hours For Degree:** 65 credits, Associates; 123 credits, Bachelors **ROTC:** Army **Professional Accreditation:** AACN, ACBSP, AOTA, CSWE, JRCAT. **Intercollegiate Athletics:** Baseball M; Basketball M & W; Cheerleading W; Cross-Country Running M & W; Field Hockey W; Golf M & W; Ice Hockey M; Lacrosse M & W; Soccer M & W; Softball W; Tennis M & W; Track and Field M & W; Volleyball W

ANTONELLI INSTITUTE
300 Montgomery Ave.
Erdenheim, PA 19038
Tel: (215)836-2222; Free: 800-722-7871
Fax: (215)836-2794
Web Site: www.antonelli.edu
President/CEO: John Hayden

Type: Two-Year College **Sex:** Coed **% Accepted:** 86 **Admission Plans:** Open Admission **H.S. Requirements:** High school diploma required; GED accepted **Scholarships:** Available. **Calendar System:** Semester **Professional Accreditation:** ACCSC.

ARCADIA UNIVERSITY
450 S Easton Rd.
Glenside, PA 19038-3295
Tel: (215)572-2900; Free: 877-ARCADIA
Fax: (215)572-4049
E-mail: admiss@arcadia.edu
Web Site: www.arcadia.edu
President/CEO: Dr. Nicolette DeVille Christensen
Admissions: Colleen Pernicello
Financial Aid: Alison Venditti

Type: Comprehensive **Sex:** Coed **Affiliation:** Presbyterian Church (U.S.A.). **Scores:** 99% SAT V 400+; 99% SAT M 400+; 38% ACT 18-23; 49% ACT 24-29 **% Accepted:** 59 **Admission Plans:** Deferred Admission **Application Deadline:** March 1 **Application Fee:** $30.00 **H.S. Requirements:** High school diploma required; GED accepted **Costs Per Year:** Application fee: $30. Comprehensive fee: $52,760 includes full-time tuition ($38,900), mandatory fees ($660), and college room and board ($13,200). College room only: $9000. Full-time tuition and fees vary according to course load, degree level, and program. Room and board charges vary according to board plan. Part-time tuition: $640 per credit. **Scholarships:** Available. **Calendar System:** Semester, Summer session available **Enrollment:** Full-time 2,380, Graduate full-time 509, Graduate part-time 835, Part-time 260 **Faculty:** Full-time 171, Part-time 322 **Student-Faculty Ratio:** 10:1 **Exams:** SAT I or ACT. **% Receiving Financial Aid:** 75 **% Residing in College-Owned, -Operated, or -Affiliated Housing:** 54 **Regional Accreditation:** Middle States Association of Colleges and Schools **Credit Hours For Degree:** 128 credits, Bachelors **Professional Accreditation:** ACBSP, APTA, NASAD. **Intercollegiate Athletics:** Baseball M; Basketball M & W; Equestrian Sports M & W; Field Hockey W; Golf M & W; Lacrosse M & W; Soccer M & W; Softball W; Swimming and Diving M & W; Tennis M & W; Volleyball W

THE ART INSTITUTE OF PHILADELPHIA
1622 Chestnut St.
Philadelphia, PA 19103
Tel: (215)567-7080; Free: 800-275-2474
Web Site: www.artinstitutes.edu/philadelphia
President/CEO: Lisa Nucci

Type: Four-Year College **Sex:** Coed **Affiliation:** Education Management Corporation. **Calendar System:** Quarter **Regional Accreditation:** Southern Association of Colleges and Schools **Professional Accreditation:** ACF, ACICS.

THE ART INSTITUTE OF PITTSBURGH
420 Blvd. of the Allies
Pittsburgh, PA 15219
Tel: (412)263-6600; Free: 800-275-2470
Fax: (412)263-6667
Web Site: www.artinstitutes.edu/pittsburgh
President/CEO: George W. Sebolt

Type: Four-Year College **Sex:** Coed **Affiliation:** Education Management Corporation. **Calendar System:** Quarter **Regional Accreditation:** Southern Association of Colleges and Schools **Professional Accreditation:** ACF, ACICS.

BERKS TECHNICAL INSTITUTE
2205 Ridgewood Rd.
Wyomissing, PA 19610-1168
Tel: (610)372-1722; Free: 866-591-8384
Fax: (610)376-4684
E-mail: abrussolo@berks.edu
Web Site: www.berks.edu

President/CEO: Joseph F. Reichard
Admissions: Allan Brussolo

Type: Two-Year College **Sex:** Coed **Affiliation:** Delta Career Education Corporation. **Admission Plans:** Early Admission **Application Fee:** $50.00 **H.S. Requirements:** High school diploma required; GED accepted **Scholarships:** Available. **Calendar System:** Semester, Summer session not available **Enrollment:** Full-time 490, Part-time 119 **Faculty:** Full-time 37, Part-time 17 **Exams:** Other. **Professional Accreditation:** AAMAE, ACCSC, ACICS.

BIDWELL TRAINING CENTER
1815 Metropolitan St.
Pittsburgh, PA 15233
Tel: (412)323-4000; Free: 800-516-1800
Fax: (412)321-2120
E-mail: admissions@mcg-btc.org
Web Site: www.bidwell-training.org
President/CEO: Valerie Njie

Type: Two-Year College **Sex:** Coed **% Accepted:** 100 **Student-Faculty Ratio:** 12:1 **Professional Accreditation:** ACCSC.

BLOOMSBURG UNIVERSITY OF PENNSYLVANIA
400 E Second St.
Bloomsburg, PA 17815-1301
Tel: (570)389-4000
E-mail: buadmiss@bloomu.edu
Web Site: www.bloomu.edu
President/CEO: Dr. David Soltz
Admissions: Christopher Lapos
Financial Aid: Amanda L. Kishbaugh

Type: Comprehensive **Sex:** Coed **Affiliation:** Pennsylvania State System of Higher Education. **Scores:** 90% SAT V 400+; 91% SAT M 400+; 55.42% ACT 18-23; 20.82% ACT 24-29 **% Accepted:** 88 **Admission Plans:** Deferred Admission; Early Admission; Early Decision Plan **Application Deadline:** Rolling **Application Fee:** $35.00 **H.S. Requirements:** High school diploma required; GED accepted **Costs Per Year:** Application fee: $35. State resident tuition: $7060 full-time, $294 per credit part-time. Nonresident tuition: $17,650 full-time, $735 per credit part-time. Mandatory fees: $2266 full-time, $79.50 per credit part-time, $75 per term part-time. Full-time tuition and fees vary according to course load and location. Part-time tuition and fees vary according to course load and location. College room and board: $8480. College room only: $5360. Room and board charges vary according to board plan and housing facility. **Scholarships:** Available. **Calendar System:** Semester, Summer session available **Enrollment:** Full-time 8,439, Graduate full-time 316, Graduate part-time 303, Part-time 719 **Faculty:** Full-time 414, Part-time 80 **Student-Faculty Ratio:** 21:1 **Exams:** ACT essay component not used; SAT I or ACT; SAT essay component not used; SAT Reasoning. **% Receiving Financial Aid:** 64 **% Residing in College-Owned, -Operated, or -Affiliated Housing:** 44 **Final Year or Final Semester Residency Requirement:** No **Regional Accreditation:** Middle States Association of Colleges and Schools **Credit Hours For Degree:** 120 credits, Bachelors **ROTC:** Air Force, Army **Professional Accreditation:** AACN, AACSB, AANA, ABET, ASHA, CSWE, NASAD, NASM, NCATE. **Intercollegiate Athletics:** Baseball M; Basketball M & W; Cross-Country Running M & W; Field Hockey W; Football M; Lacrosse W; Soccer M & W; Softball W; Swimming and Diving M & W; Tennis M & W; Track and Field M & W; Wrestling M

BRADFORD SCHOOL
125 W Station Sq. Dr.
Pittsburgh, PA 15219
Tel: (412)391-6710; Free: 800-391-6810
Fax: (412)471-6714
Web Site: www.bradfordpittsburgh.edu
President/CEO: Vincent S. Graziano

Type: Two-Year College **Sex:** Coed **% Accepted:** 84 **H.S. Requirements:** High school diploma required; GED accepted **Scholarships:** Available. **Calendar System:** Semester **Professional Accreditation:** ACICS.

BRIGHTWOOD CAREER INSTITUTE, BROOMALL CAMPUS
1991 Sproul Rd.
Ste. 42
Broomall, PA 19008
Tel: (610)353-7630; Free: 800-935-1857

Web Site: www.brightwoodcareer.edu
President/CEO: Sylvia McCray
Type: Two-Year College **Sex:** Coed **H.S. Requirements:** High school diploma required; GED accepted **Scholarships:** Available. **Calendar System:** Quarter **Professional Accreditation:** ACCSC, ACICS.

BRIGHTWOOD CAREER INSTITUTE, HARRISBURG CAMPUS

5650 Derry St.
Harrisburg, PA 17111-3518
Tel: (717)558-1300; Free: 800-935-1857
Fax: (717)564-3779
Web Site: www.brightwoodcareer.edu
President/CEO: Anthony Hibbs
Type: Two-Year College **Sex:** Coed **H.S. Requirements:** High school diploma required; GED accepted **Scholarships:** Available. **Calendar System:** Quarter **Professional Accreditation:** ACICS.

BRIGHTWOOD CAREER INSTITUTE, PHILADELPHIA CAMPUS

3010 Market St.
Philadelphia, PA 19104
Tel: (215)594-4000; Free: 800-935-1857
Web Site: www.brightwoodcareer.edu
President/CEO: Trudy Anderson
Type: Two-Year College **Sex:** Coed **Professional Accreditation:** ACICS.

BRIGHTWOOD CAREER INSTITUTE, PHILADELPHIA MILLS CAMPUS

177 Franklin Mills Blvd.
Philadelphia, PA 19154
Tel: (215)612-6600; Free: 800-935-1857
Web Site: www.brightwoodcareer.edu
President/CEO: Karen Springer
Type: Two-Year College **Sex:** Coed **H.S. Requirements:** High school diploma required; GED accepted **Scholarships:** Available. **Calendar System:** Quarter **Professional Accreditation:** ACCSC, ACICS.

BRIGHTWOOD CAREER INSTITUTE, PITTSBURGH CAMPUS

933 Penn Ave.
Pittsburgh, PA 15222
Tel: (412)261-2647; Free: 800-935-1857
Web Site: www.brightwoodcareer.edu
President/CEO: Hunter Hopkins
Type: Two-Year College **Sex:** Coed **H.S. Requirements:** High school diploma required; GED accepted **Scholarships:** Available. **Calendar System:** Continuous **Professional Accreditation:** ACICS, AOTA.

BRYN ATHYN COLLEGE OF THE NEW CHURCH

2965 College Dr.
Bryn Athyn, PA 19009-0717
Tel: (267)502-2543; Free: 800-767-9552
Fax: (267)502-2658
E-mail: admissions@brynathyn.edu
Web Site: www.brynathyn.edu
President/CEO: Pres. Brian Blair
Financial Aid: Wendy Cooper
Type: Comprehensive **Sex:** Coed **Affiliation:** Church of the New Jerusalem; Christian; The Academy of the New Church. **Scores:** 73% SAT V 400+; 74% SAT M 400+ **% Accepted:** 42 **Admission Plans:** Deferred Admission **Application Fee:** $0.00 **H.S. Requirements:** High school diploma required; GED accepted **Costs Per Year:** Application fee: $0. Comprehensive fee: $31,420 includes full-time tuition ($18,558), mandatory fees ($1324), and college room and board ($11,538). College room only: $5769. Part-time tuition: $745 per credit hour. **Scholarships:** Available. **Calendar System:** Trimester, Summer session not available **Enrollment:** Full-time 264, Graduate full-time 2, Graduate part-time 2, Part-time 9 **Faculty:** Full-time 28, Part-time 22 **Student-Faculty Ratio:** 7:1 **Exams:** ACT essay component not used; ACT essay component used for advising; SAT I or ACT; SAT essay component not used; SAT essay component used for advising. **% Receiving Financial Aid:** 49 **% Residing in College-Owned, -Operated, or -Affiliated Housing:** 61 **Final Year or Final Semester Residency Requirement:** No **Regional Accreditation:** Middle States Association of Colleges and Schools **Credit Hours For Degree:** 62 credits, Associates; 124 credits, Bachelors **ROTC:** Air Force, Army **Intercollegiate Athletics:** Basketball M &

W; Cross-Country Running M & W; Golf M; Ice Hockey M; Lacrosse M & W; Soccer M & W; Tennis M & W; Volleyball W

BRYN MAWR COLLEGE

101 N Merion Ave.
Bryn Mawr, PA 19010-2899
Tel: (610)526-5000; Free: 800-BMC-1885
Fax: (610)526-7471
E-mail: admissions@brynmawr.edu
Web Site: www.brynmawr.edu
President/CEO: Dr. Kim Cassidy
Admissions: Peaches Valdes
Financial Aid: Ethel M. Desmarais
Type: University **Scores:** 100% SAT V 400+; 100% SAT M 400+; 3.42% ACT 18-23; 46.58% ACT 24-29 **% Accepted:** 39 **Admission Plans:** Deferred Admission; Early Action; Early Admission **Application Deadline:** January 15 **Application Fee:** $50.00 **H.S. Requirements:** High school diploma required; GED accepted **Costs Per Year:** Application fee: $50. Comprehensive fee: $64,160 includes full-time tuition ($47,640), mandatory fees ($1150), and college room and board ($15,370). College room only: $8770. Part-time tuition: $5955 per course. **Scholarships:** Available. **Calendar System:** Semester, Summer session available **Enrollment:** Full-time 1,332, Graduate full-time 284, Graduate part-time 62, Part-time 14 **Faculty:** Full-time 153, Part-time 60 **Student-Faculty Ratio:** 8:1 **Exams:** SAT I and SAT II or ACT; SAT Subject. **% Receiving Financial Aid:** 51 **% Residing in College-Owned, -Operated, or -Affiliated Housing:** 93 **Regional Accreditation:** Middle States Association of Colleges and Schools **Credit Hours For Degree:** 32 courses, Bachelors **ROTC:** Air Force **Professional Accreditation:** CSWE. **Intercollegiate Athletics:** Badminton W; Basketball W; Crew W; Cross-Country Running W; Field Hockey W; Lacrosse W; Soccer W; Swimming and Diving W; Tennis W; Track and Field W; Volleyball W

BUCKNELL UNIVERSITY

One Dent Dr.
Lewisburg, PA 17837
Tel: (570)577-2000
Fax: (570)577-3760
E-mail: admissions@bucknell.edu
Web Site: www.bucknell.edu
President/CEO: Dr. John C. Bravman
Admissions: Dean Robert Springall
Financial Aid: Andrea Leithner Stauffer
Type: Comprehensive **Sex:** Coed **Scores:** 100% SAT V 400+; 100% SAT M 400+; 1.71% ACT 18-23; 42.45% ACT 24-29 **% Accepted:** 25 **Admission Plans:** Deferred Admission; Early Action; Preferred Admission **Application Deadline:** January 15 **Application Fee:** $40.00 **H.S. Requirements:** High school diploma required; GED accepted **Costs Per Year:** Application fee: $40. Comprehensive fee: $64,616 includes full-time tuition ($51,676), mandatory fees ($284), and college room and board ($12,656). College room only: $7718. Room and board charges vary according to board plan and housing facility. Part-time tuition: $1418 per semester hour. **Scholarships:** Available. **Calendar System:** Semester, Summer session available **Enrollment:** Full-time 3,533, Graduate full-time 44, Graduate part-time 12, Part-time 36 **Faculty:** Full-time 375, Part-time 50 **Student-Faculty Ratio:** 9:1 **Exams:** ACT essay component not used; SAT I or ACT; SAT II; SAT essay component not used; SAT Reasoning. **% Receiving Financial Aid:** 42 **% Residing in College-Owned, -Operated, or -Affiliated Housing:** 91 **Final Year or Final Semester Residency Requirement:** Yes **Regional Accreditation:** Middle States Association of Colleges and Schools **Credit Hours For Degree:** 32-34 courses, depending on program, Bachelors **ROTC:** Army **Professional Accreditation:** ABET, NASM. **Intercollegiate Athletics:** Baseball M; Basketball M & W; Cheerleading M & W; Crew M & W; Cross-Country Running M & W; Equestrian Sports M & W; Field Hockey W; Football M; Golf M & W; Ice Hockey M; Lacrosse M & W; Rock Climbing M & W; Rugby M & W; Sailing M & W; Skiing (Downhill) M & W; Soccer M & W; Softball W; Squash M & W; Swimming and Diving M & W; Tennis M & W; Track and Field M & W; Ultimate Frisbee M & W; Volleyball M & W; Water Polo M & W; Weight Lifting M & W; Wrestling M

BUCKS COUNTY COMMUNITY COLLEGE

275 Swamp Rd.
Newtown, PA 18940-1525
Tel: (215)968-8000

Fax: (215)968-8110
E-mail: marlene.barlow@bucks.edu
Web Site: www.bucks.edu
President/CEO: Dr. Stephanie Shanblatt
Admissions: Marlene Barlow
Financial Aid: Donna M. Wilkoski

Type: Two-Year College **Sex:** Coed **% Accepted:** 98 **Admission Plans:** Early Admission; Open Admission **Application Fee:** $0.00 **H.S. Requirements:** High school diploma required; GED accepted **Costs Per Year:** Application fee: $0. Area resident tuition: $4050 full-time, $135 per credit hour part-time. State resident tuition: $8100 full-time, $270 per credit hour part-time. Nonresident tuition: $12,150 full-time, $405 per credit hour part-time. Mandatory fees: $1160 full-time, $62 per credit hour part-time. Full-time tuition and fees vary according to program. Part-time tuition and fees vary according to program. **Scholarships:** Available. **Calendar System:** Semester, Summer session available **Enrollment:** Full-time 2,927, Part-time 5,684 **Faculty:** Full-time 151, Part-time 540 **Student-Faculty Ratio:** 16:1 **Regional Accreditation:** Middle States Association of Colleges and Schools **Credit Hours For Degree:** 60 credits, Associates **Professional Accreditation:** AAMAE, ACBSP, ACEN, NASAD, NASM. **Intercollegiate Athletics:** Baseball M; Basketball M; Equestrian Sports M & W; Golf M; Skiing (Downhill) M & W; Soccer M & W; Tennis M & W; Volleyball W

BUTLER COUNTY COMMUNITY COLLEGE

107 College Dr.
Butler, PA 16003-1203
Tel: (724)287-8711; Free: 888-826-2829
Fax: (724)285-6047
E-mail: robert.morris@bc3.edu
Web Site: www.bc3.edu
President/CEO: Dr. Nicholas Neupauer
Admissions: Robert Morris
Financial Aid: Julianne E. Louttit

Type: Two-Year College **Sex:** Coed **Admission Plans:** Open Admission **Application Deadline:** August 15 **Application Fee:** $25.00 **H.S. Requirements:** High school diploma required; GED accepted **Costs Per Year:** Application fee: $25. Area resident tuition: $4110 full-time. State resident tuition: $6990 full-time. Nonresident tuition: $9870 full-time. Mandatory fees: $930 full-time. **Scholarships:** Available. **Calendar System:** Semester, Summer session available **Enrollment:** Full-time 1,706, Part-time 1,867 **Student-Faculty Ratio:** 18:1 **Regional Accreditation:** Middle States Association of Colleges and Schools **Credit Hours For Degree:** 63 credits, Associates **Professional Accreditation:** ACBSP, ACEN, APTA, ATMAE. **Intercollegiate Athletics:** Baseball M; Basketball M; Golf M & W; Softball W; Volleyball W

CABRINI UNIVERSITY

610 King of Prussia Rd.
Radnor, PA 19087
Tel: (610)902-8100; Free: 800-848-1003
Fax: (610)902-8309
E-mail: admit@cabrini.edu
Web Site: www.cabrini.edu
President/CEO: Dr. Donald Taylor
Admissions: Shannon Zottola
Financial Aid: Elizabeth Gingerich

Type: Comprehensive **Sex:** Coed **Affiliation:** Roman Catholic. **Scores:** 68% SAT M 400+ **% Accepted:** 72 **Admission Plans:** Deferred Admission **Application Deadline:** Rolling **Application Fee:** $20.00 **H.S. Requirements:** High school diploma required; GED accepted. For transfer students with 30 or more credits: High school diploma or equivalent not required **Costs Per Year:** Application fee: $20. Comprehensive fee: $41,868 includes full-time tuition ($28,932), mandatory fees ($910), and college room and board ($12,026). Room and board charges vary according to board plan and housing facility. Part-time tuition: $525 per credit hour. Part-time tuition varies according to course load. **Scholarships:** Available. **Calendar System:** Semester, Summer session available **Enrollment:** Full-time 1,310, Graduate full-time 74, Graduate part-time 777, Part-time 267 **Faculty:** Full-time 84, Part-time 201 **Student-Faculty Ratio:** 11:1 **Exams:** SAT I or ACT; SAT Reasoning; SAT Subject. **% Receiving Financial Aid:** 80 **% Residing in College-Owned, -Operated, or -Affiliated Housing:** 64 **Final Year or Final Semester Residency Requirement:** Yes **Regional Accreditation:** Middle States Association of Colleges and Schools **Credit Hours For Degree:** 123 credits, Bachelors **ROTC:** Air Force, Army **Professional Accreditation:**

ACBSP, CSWE. **Intercollegiate Athletics:** Baseball M; Basketball M & W; Cross-Country Running M & W; Field Hockey W; Golf M; Lacrosse M & W; Rowing W; Soccer M & W; Softball W; Swimming and Diving M & W; Tennis M & W; Volleyball W

CAIRN UNIVERSITY

200 Manor Ave.
Langhorne, PA 19047-2990
Tel: (215)752-5800; Free: 800-366-0049
Fax: (215)752-5812
E-mail: admissions@cairn.edu
Web Site: cairn.edu
President/CEO: Dr. Todd J. Williams
Admissions: Rebecca Lippert
Financial Aid: Stephen Cassel

Type: Comprehensive **Sex:** Coed **Affiliation:** nondenominational. **Scores:** 90% SAT V 400+; 82% SAT M 400+; 45.7% ACT 18-23; 28.6% ACT 24-29 **% Accepted:** 99 **Admission Plans:** Deferred Admission; Early Admission **Application Deadline:** Rolling **Application Fee:** $25.00 **H.S. Requirements:** High school diploma required; GED accepted **Costs Per Year:** Application fee: $25. Comprehensive fee: $34,829 includes full-time tuition ($24,946), mandatory fees ($300), and college room and board ($9583). College room only: $5017. Full-time tuition and fees vary according to course load. Room and board charges vary according to board plan and location. Part-time tuition: $740 per credit. Part-time tuition varies according to course load. **Scholarships:** Available. **Calendar System:** Semester, Summer session available **Enrollment:** Full-time 724, Graduate full-time 56, Graduate part-time 204, Part-time 59 **Faculty:** Full-time 38, Part-time 80 **Student-Faculty Ratio:** 13:1 **Exams:** ACT essay component used as validity check; SAT I or ACT; SAT essay component used as validity check. **% Receiving Financial Aid:** 81 **% Residing in College-Owned, -Operated, or -Affiliated Housing:** 63 **Final Year or Final Semester Residency Requirement:** No **Regional Accreditation:** Middle States Association of Colleges and Schools **Credit Hours For Degree:** 126 credits, Bachelors **ROTC:** Air Force **Professional Accreditation:** ABHE, CSWE, NASM. **Intercollegiate Athletics:** Baseball M; Basketball M & W; Cross-Country Running M & W; Golf M; Soccer M & W; Softball W; Tennis W; Volleyball M & W

CALIFORNIA UNIVERSITY OF PENNSYLVANIA

250 University Ave.
California, PA 15419-1394
Tel: (724)938-4000; Free: 888-412-0479
Fax: (724)938-4138
Web Site: www.calu.edu
President/CEO: Geraldine Jones
Admissions: Stephanie Franks
Financial Aid: Jill Fernandes

Type: Comprehensive **Sex:** Coed **Affiliation:** Pennsylvania State System of Higher Education. **Scores:** 83% SAT V 400+; 83% SAT M 400+; 52% ACT 18-23; 17% ACT 24-29 **% Accepted:** 83 **Admission Plans:** Deferred Admission; Early Admission **Application Deadline:** Rolling **Application Fee:** $25.00 **H.S. Requirements:** High school diploma required; GED accepted **Costs Per Year:** Application fee: $25. State resident tuition: $7060 full-time, $294 per credit hour part-time. Nonresident tuition: $10,590 full-time, $441 per credit hour part-time. Mandatory fees: $2876 full-time. Full-time tuition and fees vary according to course load, location, and student level. Part-time tuition varies according to course load, location, and student level. College room and board: $10,086. College room only: $6592. Room and board charges vary according to board plan and housing facility. **Scholarships:** Available. **Calendar System:** Semester, Summer session available **Enrollment:** Full-time 4,995, Graduate full-time 862, Graduate part-time 1,207, Part-time 790 **Faculty:** Full-time 255, Part-time 145 **Student-Faculty Ratio:** 21:1 **Exams:** SAT I or ACT; SAT essay component used for admission; SAT essay component used for advising; SAT essay component used for placement; SAT Reasoning. **% Receiving Financial Aid:** 76 **% Residing in College-Owned, -Operated, or -Affiliated Housing:** 33 **Final Year or Final Semester Residency Requirement:** No **Regional Accreditation:** Middle States Association of Colleges and Schools **Credit Hours For Degree:** 60 credits, Associates; 120 credits, Bachelors **ROTC:** Army **Professional Accreditation:** AACN, ABET, ACA, APTA, ASHA, CSWE, JRCAT, NASAD, NCATE. **Intercollegiate Athletics:** Baseball M; Basketball M & W; Cross-Country Running M & W; Football M; Golf M & W; Soccer M & W; Softball W; Swimming and Diving W; Tennis W; Track and Field M & W; Volleyball W

CAMBRIA-ROWE BUSINESS COLLEGE (INDIANA)

422 S 13th St.
Indiana, PA 15701
Tel: (724)463-0222; Free: 800-NEW-CAREER
Fax: (724)463-7246
E-mail: sbell-leger@crbc.net
Web Site: www.crbc.edu
President/CEO: Amy Beitel
Admissions: Stacey Bell-Leger

Type: Two-Year College **Sex:** Coed **% Accepted:** 60 **Application Fee:** $30.00 **H.S. Requirements:** High school diploma required; GED accepted **Costs Per Year:** Application fee: $30. Comprehensive fee: $20,625 includes full-time tuition ($13,200) and college room and board ($7425). Full-time tuition varies according to course level and course load. Room and board charges vary according to housing facility and location. Part-time tuition: $250 per credit. Part-time tuition varies according to course level and course load. **Calendar System:** Quarter **Enrollment:** Full-time 92, Part-time 1 **Faculty:** Full-time 7 **Student-Faculty Ratio:** 13:1 **Final Year or Final Semester Residency Requirement:** No **Credit Hours For Degree:** 108 quarter credits, Associates **Professional Accreditation:** ACICS.

CAMBRIA-ROWE BUSINESS COLLEGE (JOHNSTOWN)

221 Central Ave.
Johnstown, PA 15902
Tel: (814)536-5168; Free: 800-NEWCAREER
Fax: (814)536-5160
E-mail: admissions@crbc.net
Web Site: www.crbc.edu
President/CEO: William Coward
Admissions: Riley McDonald
Financial Aid: Linda Wess

Type: Two-Year College **Sex:** Coed **% Accepted:** 90 **Admission Plans:** Early Admission **Application Deadline:** Rolling **Application Fee:** $15.00 **H.S. Requirements:** High school diploma required; GED accepted **Scholarships:** Available. **Calendar System:** Quarter, Summer session available **Enrollment:** Full-time 141, Part-time 1 **Faculty:** Full-time 10 **Student-Faculty Ratio:** 13:1 **Final Year or Final Semester Residency Requirement:** No **Credit Hours For Degree:** 106 quarter credits, Associates **Professional Accreditation:** ACICS.

CAREER TRAINING ACADEMY (LOWER BURRELL)

179 Hillcrest Shopping Ctr.
Lower Burrell, PA 15068
Tel: (724)367-7085; Free: 866-673-7773
Fax: (724)335-7140
E-mail: admissions@careeta.edu
Web Site: www.careerta.edu
President/CEO: John M. Reddy
Admissions: Tyna Pitignano

Type: Two-Year College **Sex:** Coed **Application Deadline:** Rolling **Application Fee:** $30.00 **H.S. Requirements:** High school diploma required; GED accepted **Costs Per Year:** Application fee: $30. Tuition: $10,549 full-time. Full-time tuition varies according to program. Tuition guaranteed not to increase for student's term of enrollment. **Calendar System:** Quarter **Student-Faculty Ratio:** 20:1 **Professional Accreditation:** AAMAE, ACCSC.

CAREER TRAINING ACADEMY (MONROEVILLE)

4314 Old William Penn Hwy.
Ste. 103
Monroeville, PA 15146
Tel: (412)372-3900; Free: 866-673-7773
Fax: (412)373-4262
E-mail: admissions@careerta.edu
Web Site: www.careerta.edu
President/CEO: Nicole Lane
Admissions: Cassandra Dehnel

Type: Two-Year College **Sex:** Coed **Application Fee:** $30.00 **H.S. Requirements:** High school diploma required; GED accepted **Calendar System:** Quarter **Professional Accreditation:** AAMAE, ACCSC.

CAREER TRAINING ACADEMY (PITTSBURGH)

1014 W View Park Dr.
Pittsburgh, PA 15229

Tel: (412)367-4000; Free: 866-673-7773
E-mail: admission3@careerta.edu
Web Site: www.careerta.edu
President/CEO: Carla Ryba
Admissions: Jaimie Vignone

Type: Two-Year College **Sex:** Coed **Application Deadline:** Rolling **Application Fee:** $30.00 **H.S. Requirements:** High school diploma required; GED accepted **Calendar System:** Continuous, Summer session not available **Enrollment:** Full-time 70 **Faculty:** Full-time 7, Part-time 2 **Student-Faculty Ratio:** 9:1 **Credit Hours For Degree:** 90 credits, Associates **Professional Accreditation:** ACCSC.

CARLOW UNIVERSITY

3333 Fifth Ave.
Pittsburgh, PA 15213-3165
Tel: (412)578-6000; Free: 800-333-CARLOW
Fax: (412)578-6668
E-mail: admissions@carlow.edu
Web Site: www.carlow.edu
President/CEO: Dr. Suzanne K. Mellon, PhD
Admissions: Wivina Chmura
Financial Aid: Natalie Wilson

Type: Comprehensive **Sex:** Coed **Affiliation:** Roman Catholic. **Scores:** 93% SAT V 400+; 87% SAT M 400+; 69.1% ACT 18-23; 17.6% ACT 24-29 **% Accepted:** 81 **Admission Plans:** Deferred Admission **Application Deadline:** Rolling **Application Fee:** $20.00 **H.S. Requirements:** High school diploma required; GED accepted **Costs Per Year:** Application fee: $20. Comprehensive fee: $37,404 includes full-time tuition ($26,604), mandatory fees ($228), and college room and board ($10,572). College room only: $5406. Full-time tuition and fees vary according to course load, program, and reciprocity agreements. Room and board charges vary according to board plan. Part-time tuition: $846 per credit hour. Part-time tuition varies according to course load, program, and reciprocity agreements. **Scholarships:** Available. **Calendar System:** Semester, Summer session available **Enrollment:** Full-time 1,040, Graduate full-time 653, Graduate part-time 220, Part-time 359 **Faculty:** Full-time 97, Part-time 169 **Student-Faculty Ratio:** 11:1 **Exams:** ACT; SAT I; SAT I and SAT II or ACT; SAT I or ACT; SAT II; SAT Reasoning; SAT Subject. **% Residing in College-Owned, -Operated, or -Affiliated Housing:** 31 **Final Year or Final Semester Residency Requirement:** Yes **Regional Accreditation:** Middle States Association of Colleges and Schools **Credit Hours For Degree:** 120 credits, Bachelors **ROTC:** Air Force, Army, Navy **Professional Accreditation:** AACN, ACBSP, CSWE. **Intercollegiate Athletics:** Basketball M & W; Cross-Country Running M & W; Soccer W; Softball W; Tennis W; Volleyball W

CARNEGIE MELLON UNIVERSITY

5000 Forbes Ave.
Pittsburgh, PA 15213-3891
Tel: (412)268-2000
Fax: (412)268-7838
E-mail: undergraduate-admissions@andrew.cmu.edu
Web Site: www.cmu.edu
President/CEO: Dr. Subra Suresh
Admissions: Michael Steidel
Financial Aid: Brian Hill

Type: University **Sex:** Coed **Scores:** 100% SAT V 400+; 100% SAT M 400+; 1% ACT 18-23; 13% ACT 24-29 **% Accepted:** 24 **Admission Plans:** Deferred Admission; Early Action; Early Admission **Application Deadline:** January 1 **Application Fee:** $75.00 **H.S. Requirements:** High school diploma required; GED accepted **Costs Per Year:** Application fee: $75. Comprehensive fee: $65,580 includes full-time tuition ($51,196), mandatory fees ($1114), and college room and board ($13,270). College room only: $7780. Room and board charges vary according to board plan and housing facility. Part-time tuition: $712 per unit. **Scholarships:** Available. **Calendar System:** Semester, Summer session available **Enrollment:** Full-time 6,234, Graduate full-time 6,190, Graduate part-time 1,004, Part-time 220 **Faculty:** Full-time 986, Part-time 27 **Student-Faculty Ratio:** 13:1 **Exams:** ACT essay component used for admission; SAT I or ACT; SAT II; SAT essay component used for admission; SAT Reasoning; SAT Subject. **% Receiving Financial Aid:** 43 **% Residing in College-Owned, -Operated, or -Affiliated Housing:** 61 **Regional Accreditation:** Middle States Association of Colleges and Schools **ROTC:** Air Force, Army, Navy **Professional Accreditation:** AACSB, ABET, NAAB, NASAD, NASM, NASPAA. **Intercollegiate Athletics:** Baseball M; Basketball M & W; Crew M & W; Cross-Country Running M &

W; Fencing M & W; Football M; Golf M & W; Ice Hockey M & W; Lacrosse M & W; Rowing M & W; Rugby M & W; Skiing (Downhill) M & W; Soccer M & W; Swimming and Diving M & W; Tennis M & W; Track and Field M & W; Ultimate Frisbee M & W; Volleyball M & W; Water Polo M & W

CEDAR CREST COLLEGE

100 College Dr.
Allentown, PA 18104-6196
Tel: (610)437-4471; Free: 800-360-1222
Fax: (610)606-4647
E-mail: admissions@cedarcrest.edu
Web Site: www.cedarcrest.edu
President/CEO: Carmen Twillie Ambar, JD
Admissions: Jonathan Squire
Financial Aid: Valerie D. Kreiser

Type: Comprehensive **Sex:** Coed **Affiliation:** United Church of Christ. **Scores:** 86% SAT V 400+; 86% SAT M 400+; 37% ACT 18-23; 37% ACT 24-29 **% Accepted:** 67 **Admission Plans:** Deferred Admission; Early Admission **Application Deadline:** Rolling **Application Fee:** $0.00 **H.S. Requirements:** High school diploma required; GED accepted **Costs Per Year:** Application fee: $0. Comprehensive fee: $46,365 includes full-time tuition ($35,000), mandatory fees ($600), and college room and board ($10,765). College room only: $5160. Full-time tuition and fees vary according to class time, course load, and program. Room and board charges vary according to board plan and housing facility. Part-time tuition: $1167 per credit. Part-time mandatory fees: $150 per term. Part-time tuition and fees vary according to class time, course load, and program. **Scholarships:** Available. **Calendar System:** Semester, Summer session available **Enrollment:** Full-time 775, Graduate full-time 50, Graduate part-time 153, Part-time 613 **Faculty:** Full-time 76, Part-time 112 **Student-Faculty Ratio:** 10:1 **Exams:** ACT essay component used for admission; ACT essay component used for advising; SAT I or ACT; SAT essay component used for admission; SAT essay component used for advising. **% Receiving Financial Aid:** 92 **% Residing in College-Owned, -Operated, or -Affiliated Housing:** 30 **Final Year or Final Semester Residency Requirement:** No **Regional Accreditation:** Middle States Association of Colleges and Schools **Credit Hours For Degree:** 120 credit hours, Bachelors **ROTC:** Army **Professional Accreditation:** ACBSP, ACEN, CSWE, JRCNMT. **Intercollegiate Athletics:** Basketball W; Cross-Country Running W; Equestrian Sports W; Field Hockey W; Lacrosse W; Soccer W; Softball W; Swimming and Diving W; Tennis W; Track and Field W; Volleyball W

CENTRAL PENN COLLEGE

College Hill & Valley Roads
Summerdale, PA 17093-0309
Tel: (717)732-0702; Free: 800-759-2727
Fax: (717)732-5254
E-mail: rebeccabowman@centralpenn.edu
Web Site: www.centralpenn.edu
President/CEO: Pres. Karen Scolforo, EdD
Admissions: Rebecca Bowman
Financial Aid: Kathy Shepard

Type: Comprehensive **Sex:** Coed **Application Deadline:** Rolling **Application Fee:** $0.00 **H.S. Requirements:** High school diploma required; GED accepted **Costs Per Year:** Application fee: $0. Comprehensive fee: $24,321 includes full-time tuition ($16,308), mandatory fees ($843), and college room and board ($7170). College room only: $5100. Full-time tuition and fees vary according to course load, degree level, and program. Room and board charges vary according to board plan and housing facility. Part-time tuition: $453 per credit hour. Part-time mandatory fees: $172 per term. Part-time tuition and fees vary according to course load, degree level, and program. Tuition guaranteed not to increase for student's term of enrollment. **Scholarships:** Available. **Calendar System:** Quarter, Summer session available **Enrollment:** Graduate full-time 13, Graduate part-time 35 **Faculty:** Full-time 29, Part-time 112 **Student-Faculty Ratio:** 13:1 **Exams:** SAT I or ACT. **% Residing in College-Owned, -Operated, or -Affiliated Housing:** 18 **Final Year or Final Semester Residency Requirement:** No **Regional Accreditation:** Middle States Association of Colleges and Schools **Credit Hours For Degree:** 62 credits, Associates; 125 credits, Bachelors **Professional Accreditation:** AAMAE, APTA. **Intercollegiate Athletics:** Baseball M; Basketball M & W; Cross-Country Running M & W; Soccer M & W; Volleyball W

CHATHAM UNIVERSITY

Woodland Rd.
Pittsburgh, PA 15232-2826
Tel: (412)365-1100; Free: 800-837-1290
Fax: (412)365-1609
E-mail: admission@chatham.edu
Web Site: www.chatham.edu
President/CEO: Dr. Esther L. Barazzone
Admissions: Amy M. Becher
Financial Aid: Dr. Jennifer Burns

Type: University **Sex:** Coed **Scores:** 98% SAT M 400+; 40.98% ACT 18-23; 49.18% ACT 24-29 **% Accepted:** 55 **Admission Plans:** Deferred Admission; Early Admission **Application Deadline:** August 1 **Application Fee:** $35.00 **H.S. Requirements:** High school diploma required; GED accepted **Costs Per Year:** Application fee: $35. Comprehensive fee: $46,517 includes full-time tuition ($34,195), mandatory fees ($1280), and college room and board ($11,042). College room only: $5634. Room and board charges vary according to board plan and housing facility. Part-time tuition: $829 per credit. Part-time tuition varies according to course load. **Scholarships:** Available. **Calendar System:** Miscellaneous, Summer session available **Enrollment:** Full-time 667, Graduate full-time 849, Graduate part-time 341, Part-time 367 **Faculty:** Full-time 114, Part-time 202 **Student-Faculty Ratio:** 10:1 **Exams:** ACT essay component not used; SAT essay component not used; SAT Reasoning. **% Receiving Financial Aid:** 81 **% Residing in College-Owned, -Operated, or -Affiliated Housing:** 52 **Regional Accreditation:** Middle States Association of Colleges and Schools **Credit Hours For Degree:** 120 credit hours, Bachelors **ROTC:** Air Force, Army, Navy **Professional Accreditation:** AACN, AOTA, APTA, ASLA, CIDA, CSWE. **Intercollegiate Athletics:** Baseball M; Basketball M & W; Cross-Country Running M & W; Ice Hockey W; Lacrosse M & W; Soccer W; Softball W; Swimming and Diving M & W; Track and Field M & W; Volleyball W

CHESTNUT HILL COLLEGE

9601 Germantown Ave.
Philadelphia, PA 19118-2693
Tel: (215)248-7000; Free: 800-248-0052
Fax: (215)248-7056
E-mail: williamss@chc.edu
Web Site: www.chc.edu
President/CEO: Señor Carol Jean Vale, SSJ
Admissions: Stephanie Williams
Financial Aid: Dawn Snook

Type: Comprehensive **Sex:** Coed **Affiliation:** Roman Catholic. **Scores:** 87% SAT V 400+; 86% SAT M 400+; 43.33% ACT 18-23; 26.67% ACT 24-29 **% Accepted:** 93 **Admission Plans:** Deferred Admission; Open Admission **Application Deadline:** Rolling **Application Fee:** $35.00 **H.S. Requirements:** High school diploma required; GED accepted **Costs Per Year:** Application fee: $35. One-time mandatory fee: $425. Comprehensive fee: $44,440 includes full-time tuition ($33,930), mandatory fees ($210), and college room and board ($10,300). Room and board charges vary according to board plan and housing facility. Part-time tuition: $725 per credit. **Scholarships:** Available. **Calendar System:** Semester, Summer session available **Enrollment:** Full-time 1,148, Graduate full-time 221, Graduate part-time 287, Part-time 295 **Faculty:** Full-time 92, Part-time 232 **Student-Faculty Ratio:** 9:1 **Exams:** SAT I or ACT; SAT II. **% Receiving Financial Aid:** 84 **% Residing in College-Owned, -Operated, or -Affiliated Housing:** 52 **Final Year or Final Semester Residency Requirement:** No **Regional Accreditation:** Middle States Association of Colleges and Schools **Credit Hours For Degree:** 60 semester hours, Associates; 120 semester hours, Bachelors **Professional Accreditation:** MACTE. **Intercollegiate Athletics:** Baseball M; Basketball M & W; Bowling W; Cross-Country Running M & W; Football M; Golf M & W; Lacrosse M & W; Soccer M & W; Softball W; Tennis M & W; Track and Field M & W; Volleyball W

CHEYNEY UNIVERSITY OF PENNSYLVANIA

1837 University Cir.
Cheyney, PA 19319
Tel: (610)399-2000; Free: 800-CHEYNEY
Fax: (610)399-2099
E-mail: spjeffery@cheyney.edu
Web Site: www.cheyney.edu
President/CEO: Dr. Frank G. Pogue, PhD
Admissions: Shon Jeffery
Financial Aid: James Brown

Type: Comprehensive **Sex:** Coed **Affiliation:** Pennsylvania State System of Higher Education. **Scores:** 47% SAT V 400+; 52% SAT M 400+; 46.5% ACT

18-23; 7% ACT 24-29 **% Accepted:** 85 **Admission Plans:** Deferred Admission; Preferred Admission **Application Deadline:** March 31 **Application Fee:** $20.00 **H.S. Requirements:** High school diploma required; GED accepted **Costs Per Year:** Application fee: $20. State resident tuition: $7060 full-time, $294 per credit hour part-time. Nonresident tuition: $11,650 full-time, $485 per credit hour part-time. Mandatory fees: $2284 full-time, $28 per credit hour part-time, $462 per term part-time. Full-time tuition and fees vary according to course load and location. Part-time tuition and fees vary according to course load and location. College room and board: $8660. College room only: $5008. Room and board charges vary according to board plan and housing facility. **Scholarships:** Available. **Calendar System:** Semester, Summer session available **Enrollment:** Full-time 936, Graduate full-time 6, Graduate part-time 19, Part-time 61 **Faculty:** Full-time 45, Part-time 45 **Student-Faculty Ratio:** 16:1 **Exams:** ACT; SAT I; SAT I and SAT II or ACT; SAT Reasoning; SAT Subject. **% Receiving Financial Aid:** 94 **% Residing in College-Owned, -Operated, or -Affiliated Housing:** 80 **Regional Accreditation:** Middle States Association of Colleges and Schools **Credit Hours For Degree:** 120 credit hours, Bachelors **ROTC:** Army **Intercollegiate Athletics:** Basketball M & W; Bowling W; Cross-Country Running M & W; Football M; Track and Field M & W; Volleyball W

CLARION UNIVERSITY OF PENNSYLVANIA
840 Wood St.
Clarion, PA 16214
Tel: (814)393-2000; Free: 800-672-7171
Fax: (814)393-2030
E-mail: dbehrs@clarion.edu
Web Site: www.clarion.edu
President/CEO: Dr. Karen M. Whitney
Admissions: Dr. David G. Behrs
Financial Aid: Sue A. Bloom
Type: Comprehensive **Sex:** Coed **Affiliation:** Pennsylvania State System of Higher Education. **Scores:** 83% SAT V 400+; 83% SAT M 400+; 41.67% ACT 18-23; 15.15% ACT 24-29 **Scholarships:** Available. **Calendar System:** Semester, Summer session available **Enrollment:** Full-time 4,018, Graduate full-time 173, Graduate part-time 628, Part-time 893 **Faculty:** Full-time 218, Part-time 76 **Student-Faculty Ratio:** 19:1 **Exams:** Other; SAT I or ACT. **% Receiving Financial Aid:** 78 **% Residing in College-Owned, -Operated, or -Affiliated Housing:** 35 **Final Year or Final Semester Residency Requirement:** No **Regional Accreditation:** Middle States Association of Colleges and Schools **Credit Hours For Degree:** 60 credits, Associates; 120 credits, Bachelors **ROTC:** Army **Professional Accreditation:** AACSB, ACEN, ALA, ASHA, NASAD, NASM, NCATE. **Intercollegiate Athletics:** Baseball M; Basketball M & W; Cross-Country Running W; Football M; Golf M & W; Soccer W; Softball W; Swimming and Diving M & W; Tennis W; Track and Field W; Volleyball W; Wrestling M

COMMONWEALTH TECHNICAL INSTITUTE
727 Goucher St.
Johnstown, PA 15905-3092
Tel: (814)255-8200; Free: 800-762-4211
E-mail: jgies@pa.gov
Web Site: www.portal.state.pa.us/portal/server.pt/community/commonwealth_technical_institute/10361
President/CEO: Barbara A. Petersen
Admissions: Jason Gies
Financial Aid: Sylvia A. Sabo
Type: Two-Year College **Sex:** Coed **Admission Plans:** Open Admission; Preferred Admission **Application Deadline:** Rolling **Application Fee:** $0.00 **H.S. Requirements:** High school diploma required; GED accepted **Costs Per Year:** Application fee: $0. State resident tuition: $11,224 full-time. College room and board: $5490. **Scholarships:** Available. **Calendar System:** Trimester, Summer session not available **Enrollment:** Full-time 222 **Faculty:** Full-time 27 **Student-Faculty Ratio:** 15:1 **Final Year or Final Semester Residency Requirement:** No **Credit Hours For Degree:** 63 for the AST Dental Laboratory Technology, Associates **Professional Accreditation:** ACCSC.

COMMUNITY COLLEGE OF ALLEGHENY COUNTY
800 Allegheny Ave.
Pittsburgh, PA 15233-1894
Tel: (412)323-2323
Web Site: www.ccac.edu
President/CEO: Quintin B. Bullock

Financial Aid: Margaret Barton
Type: Two-Year College **Sex:** Coed **Admission Plans:** Early Action; Early Decision Plan **Application Fee:** $0.00 **H.S. Requirements:** High school diploma required; GED accepted **Costs Per Year:** Application fee: $0. Area resident tuition: $3,142 full-time, $104.75 per credit part-time. State resident tuition: $6285 full-time, $209.50 per credit part-time. Nonresident tuition: $9,428 full-time, $314.25 per credit part-time. Full-time tuition varies according to program. Part-time tuition varies according to program. **Scholarships:** Available. **Calendar System:** Semester **Enrollment:** Full-time 6,009, Part-time 11,139 **Exams:** ACT essay component not used; SAT essay component not used. **Regional Accreditation:** Middle States Association of Colleges and Schools **Credit Hours For Degree:** 60 credits, Associates **Professional Accreditation:** AAMAE, ACEN, AHIMA, AOTA, APTA, ARCST, CoARC, JRCEDMS, JRCERT, JRCNMT, NAACLS. **Intercollegiate Athletics:** Baseball M; Basketball M & W; Bowling M & W; Golf M & W; Ice Hockey M; Softball W; Table Tennis M & W; Tennis M & W; Volleyball W

COMMUNITY COLLEGE OF BEAVER COUNTY
One Campus Dr.
Monaca, PA 15061-2588
Tel: (724)775-8561; Free: 800-335-0222
Fax: (724)728-7599
E-mail: admissions@ccbc.edu
Web Site: www.ccbc.edu
President/CEO: Dr. Joe Forrester
Type: Two-Year College **Sex:** Coed **Admission Plans:** Early Admission; Open Admission **Application Deadline:** Rolling **H.S. Requirements:** High school diploma or equivalent not required. For nursing, medical laboratory technology programs: High school diploma required; GED accepted **Scholarships:** Available. **Calendar System:** Semester, Summer session available **Student-Faculty Ratio:** 16:1 **Regional Accreditation:** Middle States Association of Colleges and Schools **Credit Hours For Degree:** 60 credits, Associates **Professional Accreditation:** ACEN.

COMMUNITY COLLEGE OF PHILADELPHIA
1700 Spring Garden St.
Philadelphia, PA 19130-3991
Tel: (215)751-8000
E-mail: admissions@ccp.edu
Web Site: www.ccp.edu
President/CEO: Dr. Donald Generals
Admissions: Warren Hilton
Type: Two-Year College **Sex:** Coed **Admission Plans:** Deferred Admission; Early Admission; Open Admission; Preferred Admission **Application Deadline:** Rolling **Application Fee:** $0.00 **H.S. Requirements:** High school diploma required; GED accepted **Costs Per Year:** Application fee: $0. Area resident tuition: $4440 full-time, $153 per credit hour part-time. State resident tuition: $8880 full-time, $306 per credit hour part-time. Nonresident tuition: $13,320 full-time, $459 per credit hour part-time. Full-time tuition varies according to course load and program. Part-time tuition varies according to course load and program. **Calendar System:** Semester, Summer session available **Faculty:** Full-time 407, Part-time 643 **Regional Accreditation:** Middle States Association of Colleges and Schools **Credit Hours For Degree:** 60 credit hours, Associates **ROTC:** Army **Professional Accreditation:** AAMAE, ACEN, ADA, AHIMA, CoARC, JRCERT, NAACLS. **Intercollegiate Athletics:** Basketball M & W; Cheerleading M & W; Cross-Country Running M & W; Tennis M & W; Track and Field M & W; Volleyball W

CONSOLIDATED SCHOOL OF BUSINESS (LANCASTER)
2124 Ambassador Cir.
Lancaster, PA 17603
Tel: (717)394-6211; Free: 800-541-8298
Fax: (717)394-6213
E-mail: lpaul@csb.edu
Web Site: www.csb.edu
President/CEO: Patricia Marcus
Admissions: Libby Paul
Type: Two-Year College **Sex:** Coed **Admission Plans:** Open Admission **Application Deadline:** Rolling **H.S. Requirements:** High school diploma required; GED accepted **Scholarships:** Available. **Calendar System:** Continuous, Summer session not available **Enrollment:** Full-time 179, Part-time 3 **Faculty:** Full-time 24, Part-time 1 **Student-Faculty Ratio:** 15:1 **Credit Hours For Degree:** 81 credit hours, Associates **Professional Accreditation:** ACICS.

CONSOLIDATED SCHOOL OF BUSINESS (YORK)

1605 Clugston Rd.
York, PA 17404
Tel: (717)764-9550; Free: 800-520-0691
Fax: (717)764-9469
E-mail: sswanger@csb.edu
Web Site: www.csb.edu
President/CEO: Bill Hoyt
Admissions: Sandra Swanger

Type: Two-Year College **Sex:** Coed **Admission Plans:** Open Admission **Application Deadline:** Rolling **H.S. Requirements:** High school diploma required; GED accepted **Scholarships:** Available. **Calendar System:** Continuous, Summer session not available **Enrollment:** Full-time 176 **Faculty:** Full-time 18, Part-time 3 **Student-Faculty Ratio:** 15:1 **Credit Hours For Degree:** 81 credit hours, Associates **Professional Accreditation:** ACICS.

CURTIS INSTITUTE OF MUSIC

1726 Locust St.
Philadelphia, PA 19103-6107
Tel: (215)893-5252
Fax: (215)893-7900
E-mail: chris.hodges@curtis.edu
Web Site: www.curtis.edu
President/CEO: Roberto Diaz
Admissions: Christopher Hodges
Financial Aid: Veronica McAuley

Type: Comprehensive **Sex:** Coed **Admission Plans:** Early Admission **Application Deadline:** December 11 **Application Fee:** $150.00 **H.S. Requirements:** High school diploma required; GED not accepted **Scholarships:** Available. **Calendar System:** Semester, Summer session not available **Regional Accreditation:** Middle States Association of Colleges and Schools **Credit Hours For Degree:** 124 semester hours, Bachelors **Professional Accreditation:** NASM.

DEAN INSTITUTE OF TECHNOLOGY

1501 W Liberty Ave.
Pittsburgh, PA 15226-1103
Tel: (412)531-4433
Fax: (412)531-4435
Web Site: www.deantech.edu
President/CEO: James Dean
Admissions: Richard D. Ali

Type: Two-Year College **Sex:** Coed **Admission Plans:** Deferred Admission; Early Admission; Open Admission **Application Deadline:** Rolling **Application Fee:** $50.00 **H.S. Requirements:** High school diploma required; GED accepted **Scholarships:** Available. **Calendar System:** Quarter, Summer session not available **Credit Hours For Degree:** 30 courses, Associates **Professional Accreditation:** ACCSC.

DELAWARE COUNTY COMMUNITY COLLEGE

901 S Media Line Rd.
Media, PA 19063-1094
Tel: (610)359-5000
E-mail: admiss@dccc.edu
Web Site: www.dccc.edu
President/CEO: Jerome S. Parker
Admissions: Hope Diehl

Type: Two-Year College **Sex:** Coed **% Accepted:** 100 **Admission Plans:** Early Admission; Open Admission; Preferred Admission **Application Deadline:** Rolling **Application Fee:** $25.00 **H.S. Requirements:** High school diploma required; GED accepted. For applicants 19 and over who demonstrate equivalent life experience: High school diploma or equivalent not required **Scholarships:** Available. **Calendar System:** Semester, Summer session available **Enrollment:** Full-time 5,360, Part-time 7,888 **Faculty:** Full-time 143, Part-time 659 **Student-Faculty Ratio:** 24:1 **Final Year or Final Semester Residency Requirement:** No **Regional Accreditation:** Middle States Association of Colleges and Schools **Credit Hours For Degree:** 60 credit hours, Associates **Professional Accreditation:** AAMAE, ACEN, ARCST, CoARC. **Intercollegiate Athletics:** Baseball M; Basketball M & W; Golf M & W; Soccer M; Softball W; Tennis M & W; Volleyball W

DELAWARE VALLEY UNIVERSITY

700 E Butler Ave.
Doylestown, PA 18901-2697
Tel: (215)345-1500; Free: 800-2DELVAL
Fax: (215)345-5277
E-mail: admitme@delval.edu
Web Site: www.delval.edu
President/CEO: Dr. Joseph Brosnan
Admissions: Dwayne Walker
Financial Aid: Joan Hock

Type: Comprehensive **Sex:** Coed **Scores:** 96% SAT V 400+; 97% SAT M 400+; 47.7% ACT 18-23; 47.7% ACT 24-29 **% Accepted:** 74 **Admission Plans:** Deferred Admission **Application Deadline:** May 1 **Application Fee:** $50.00 **H.S. Requirements:** High school diploma required; GED accepted **Costs Per Year:** Application fee: $50. Comprehensive fee: $47,874 includes full-time tuition ($33,196), mandatory fees ($2060), and college room and board ($12,618). College room only: $5736. Full-time tuition and fees vary according to class time, degree level, and program. Room and board charges vary according to board plan and housing facility. Part-time tuition: $916 per credit hour. Part-time tuition and fees vary according to class time, course load, degree level, and program. **Scholarships:** Available. **Calendar System:** Semester, Summer session available **Enrollment:** Full-time 1,761, Graduate full-time 114, Graduate part-time 230, Part-time 161 **Faculty:** Full-time 87, Part-time 120 **Student-Faculty Ratio:** 14:1 **Exams:** ACT essay component used for advising; ACT essay component used for placement; SAT I or ACT; SAT essay component used for advising; SAT essay component used for placement; SAT Reasoning; SAT Subject. **% Receiving Financial Aid:** 81 **% Residing in College-Owned, -Operated, or -Affiliated Housing:** 56 **Final Year or Final Semester Residency Requirement:** No **Regional Accreditation:** Middle States Association of Colleges and Schools **Credit Hours For Degree:** 65 credits, Associates; 126 credits, Bachelors **Professional Accreditation:** ACBSP. **Intercollegiate Athletics:** Baseball M; Basketball M & W; Cheerleading W; Cross-Country Running M & W; Field Hockey W; Football M; Golf M & W; Lacrosse M & W; Soccer M & W; Softball W; Tennis M & W; Track and Field M & W; Volleyball W; Wrestling M

DESALES UNIVERSITY

2755 Station Ave.
Center Valley, PA 18034-9568
Tel: (610)282-1100
Fax: (610)282-2254
E-mail: derrick.wetzell@desales.edu
Web Site: www.desales.edu
President/CEO: Rev. Bernard F. O'Connor, OSFS
Admissions: Derrick Wetzel
Financial Aid: Joyce Farmer

Type: Comprehensive **Sex:** Coed **Affiliation:** Roman Catholic. **Scores:** 94% SAT V 400+; 92% SAT M 400+; 32% ACT 18-23; 50% ACT 24-29 **% Accepted:** 78 **Admission Plans:** Deferred Admission **Application Deadline:** August 1 **Application Fee:** $0.00 **H.S. Requirements:** High school diploma required; GED accepted **Costs Per Year:** Application fee: $0. Comprehensive fee: $45,600 includes full-time tuition ($32,000), mandatory fees ($1550), and college room and board ($12,050). Full-time tuition and fees vary according to class time and course load. Room and board charges vary according to board plan and housing facility. Part-time tuition: $1335 per credit hour. Part-time tuition varies according to class time and course load. **Scholarships:** Available. **Calendar System:** Semester, Summer session available **Enrollment:** Full-time 1,738, Graduate full-time 349, Graduate part-time 496, Part-time 553 **Faculty:** Full-time 125, Part-time 241 **Student-Faculty Ratio:** 13:1 **Exams:** SAT I or ACT. **% Receiving Financial Aid:** 77 **% Residing in College-Owned, -Operated, or -Affiliated Housing:** 60 **Final Year or Final Semester Residency Requirement:** No **Regional Accreditation:** Middle States Association of Colleges and Schools **Credit Hours For Degree:** 40 courses, Bachelors **ROTC:** Army **Professional Accreditation:** ACBSP, ACEN. **Intercollegiate Athletics:** Baseball M; Basketball M & W; Cross-Country Running M & W; Field Hockey W; Golf M; Lacrosse M; Soccer M & W; Softball W; Track and Field M & W; Volleyball W

DEVRY UNIVERSITY (FORT WASHINGTON)

1140 Virginia Dr.
Fort Washington, PA 19034
Tel: (215)591-5700; Free: 866-338-7941

Web Site: www.devry.edu

Type: Comprehensive **Sex:** Coed **Affiliation:** DeVry University. **Application Fee:** $40.00 **H.S. Requirements:** High school diploma required; GED accepted **Costs Per Year:** Application fee: $40. Tuition: $13,300 full-time, $475 per credit hour part-time. Mandatory fees: $80 full-time, $40 per term part-time. **Scholarships:** Available. **Calendar System:** Semester **Enrollment:** Full-time 164, Graduate full-time 16, Graduate part-time 65, Part-time 272 **Faculty:** Full-time 13, Part-time 12 **Student-Faculty Ratio:** 17:1 **Exams:** ACT essay component used for admission; ACT essay component used for placement; SAT essay component used for admission; SAT essay component used for placement. **% Receiving Financial Aid:** 81 **Regional Accreditation:** North Central Association of Colleges and Schools **Professional Accreditation:** ACBSP.

DEVRY UNIVERSITY (KING OF PRUSSIA)

150 Allendale Rd., Ste. 3250
King of Prussia, PA 19406-2926
Tel: (610)205-3130; Free: 866-338-7941
Web Site: www.devry.edu

Type: Comprehensive **Sex:** Coed **Application Deadline:** Rolling **Calendar System:** Semester **Regional Accreditation:** North Central Association of Colleges and Schools **Professional Accreditation:** ACBSP.

DEVRY UNIVERSITY (PHILADELPHIA)

Philadelphia Downtown Ctr.
1800 JFK Blvd., Ste. 200
Philadelphia, PA 19103-7421
Free: 866-338-7941
Web Site: www.devry.edu

Type: Comprehensive **Sex:** Coed **Costs Per Year:** Tuition: $13,300 full-time, $475 per credit hour part-time. Mandatory fees: $80 full-time, $40 per term part-time. **Regional Accreditation:** North Central Association of Colleges and Schools

DICKINSON COLLEGE

PO Box 1773
Carlisle, PA 17013-2896
Tel: (717)243-5121; Free: 800-644-1773
Fax: (717)245-1442
E-mail: admit@dickinson.edu
Web Site: www.dickinson.edu
President/CEO: Nancy A. Roseman
Admissions: Catherine Davenport
Financial Aid: Rick A. Heckman

Type: Four-Year College **Sex:** Coed **Scores:** 100% SAT V 400+; 99% SAT M 400+; 1.09% ACT 18-23; 58.47% ACT 24-29 **% Accepted:** 47 **Admission Plans:** Deferred Admission; Early Action; Early Decision Plan **Application Deadline:** February 1 **Application Fee:** $65.00 **H.S. Requirements:** High school diploma required; GED accepted **Costs Per Year:** Application fee: $65. One-time mandatory fee: $25. Comprehensive fee: $61,826 includes full-time tuition ($49,014), mandatory fees ($450), and college room and board ($12,362). College room only: $6376. Room and board charges vary according to board plan and housing facility. Part-time tuition: $6130 per course. Part-time mandatory fees: $56 per course. **Scholarships:** Available. **Calendar System:** Semester, Summer session available **Enrollment:** Full-time 2,391, Part-time 29 **Faculty:** Full-time 221, Part-time 51 **Student-Faculty Ratio:** 9:1 **Exams:** ACT essay component not used; SAT I or ACT; SAT II; SAT essay component not used; SAT Reasoning; SAT Subject. **% Receiving Financial Aid:** 54 **% Residing in College-Owned, -Operated, or -Affiliated Housing:** 94 **Final Year or Final Semester Residency Requirement:** No **Regional Accreditation:** Middle States Association of Colleges and Schools **Credit Hours For Degree:** 32 courses, Bachelors **ROTC:** Army **Intercollegiate Athletics:** Baseball M; Basketball M & W; Cheerleading M & W; Cross-Country Running M & W; Equestrian Sports M & W; Fencing M & W; Field Hockey W; Football M; Golf M & W; Ice Hockey M & W; Lacrosse M & W; Skiing (Downhill) M & W; Soccer M & W; Softball W; Squash M & W; Swimming and Diving M & W; Tennis M & W; Track and Field M & W; Ultimate Frisbee M & W; Volleyball M & W

DOUGLAS EDUCATION CENTER

130 Seventh St.
Monessen, PA 15062
Tel: (724)684-3684; Free: 800-413-6013
Fax: (724)684-7463

Web Site: www.dec.edu
President/CEO: Jeffrey D. Imbrescia
Admissions: Sherry Lee Walters

Type: Two-Year College **Sex:** Coed **Admission Plans:** Open Admission **Application Deadline:** Rolling **Application Fee:** $50.00 **H.S. Requirements:** High school diploma required; GED accepted **Scholarships:** Available. **Enrollment:** Full-time 334 **Faculty:** Full-time 13, Part-time 24 **Student-Faculty Ratio:** 16:1 **Exams:** ACT essay component not used; Other; SAT essay component not used. **Final Year or Final Semester Residency Requirement:** No **Credit Hours For Degree:** 60 credits, Associates **Professional Accreditation:** ACICS.

DREXEL UNIVERSITY

3141 Chestnut St.
Philadelphia, PA 19104-2875
Tel: (215)895-2000; Free: 800-2-DREXEL
Fax: (215)895-5939
E-mail: randall.c.deike@drexel.edu
Web Site: www.drexel.edu
President/CEO: John Fry
Admissions: Randall C. Deike, PhD
Financial Aid: Helen Gourousis

Type: University **Sex:** Coed **Scores:** 100% SAT V 400+; 100% SAT M 400+; 19% ACT 18-23; 61% ACT 24-29 **% Accepted:** 76 **Admission Plans:** Deferred Admission; Early Admission **Application Deadline:** January 13 **Application Fee:** $50.00 **H.S. Requirements:** High school diploma required; GED accepted **Scholarships:** Available. **Calendar System:** Quarter, Summer session available **Enrollment:** Full-time 14,365, Graduate full-time 4,837, Graduate part-time 4,626, Part-time 2,531 **Faculty:** Full-time 1,174, Part-time 994 **Exams:** ACT essay component not used; SAT I or ACT; SAT essay component not used; SAT Reasoning. **% Receiving Financial Aid:** 60 **% Residing in College-Owned, -Operated, or -Affiliated Housing:** 26 **Regional Accreditation:** Middle States Association of Colleges and Schools **Credit Hours For Degree:** 180 credit hours, Bachelors **ROTC:** Air Force, Army, Navy **Professional Accreditation:** AACN, AACSB, AAMFT, AANA, ABET, ACEN, ACPeE, ALA, AND, APA, APTA, CEPH, CIDA, LCME/AMA, NAAB, NASAD. **Intercollegiate Athletics:** Basketball M & W; Crew M & W; Field Hockey W; Golf M; Lacrosse M & W; Soccer M & W; Softball W; Squash M & W; Swimming and Diving M & W; Tennis M & W; Wrestling M

DUBOIS BUSINESS COLLEGE (DUBOIS)

1 Beaver Dr.
DuBois, PA 15801
Tel: (814)371-6920; Free: 800-692-6213
Fax: (814)371-3974
E-mail: dotylj@dbcollege.com
Web Site: www.dbcollege.edu
President/CEO: Jackie Diehl Syktich
Admissions: Terry Khoury

Type: Two-Year College **Sex:** Coed **Admission Plans:** Deferred Admission **Application Deadline:** Rolling **Application Fee:** $25.00 **H.S. Requirements:** High school diploma required; GED accepted **Scholarships:** Available. **Calendar System:** Quarter, Summer session available **Credit Hours For Degree:** 90 credits, Associates **Professional Accreditation:** ACICS.

DUBOIS BUSINESS COLLEGE (HUNTINGDON)

1001 Moore St.
Huntingdon, PA 16652
Tel: (814)641-0440
Fax: (814)641-0205
Web Site: www.dbcollege.edu
Type: Two-Year College **Sex:** Coed **Professional Accreditation:** ACICS.

DUBOIS BUSINESS COLLEGE (OIL CITY)

701 E Third St.
Oil City, PA 16301
Tel: (814)677-1322
Fax: (814)677-8237
Web Site: www.dbcollege.edu
Type: Two-Year College **Sex:** Coed **Professional Accreditation:** ACICS.

DUQUESNE UNIVERSITY

600 Forbes Ave.
Pittsburgh, PA 15282-0001

Tel: (412)396-6000; Free: 800-456-0590
Fax: (412)396-5779
E-mail: admissions@duq.edu
Web Site: www.duq.edu
President/CEO: Dr. Charles J. Dougherty
Admissions: Debra Zugates
Financial Aid: Richard C. Esposito
Type: University **Sex:** Coed **Affiliation:** Roman Catholic. **Scores:** 100% SAT V 400+; 100% SAT M 400+; 25% ACT 18-23; 60% ACT 24-29 **% Accepted:** 76 **Admission Plans:** Deferred Admission; Early Action; Early Admission; Early Decision Plan **Application Deadline:** July 1 **Application Fee:** $50.00 **H.S. Requirements:** High school diploma required; GED accepted **Costs Per Year:** Application fee: $50. Comprehensive fee: $45,196 includes full-time tuition ($33,778) and college room and board ($11,418). College room only: $6226. Full-time tuition varies according to course load and program. Room and board charges vary according to board plan and housing facility. Part-time tuition: $1119 per credit. Part-time tuition varies according to course load and program. **Scholarships:** Available. **Calendar System:** Semester, Summer session available **Enrollment:** Full-time 5,720, Graduate full-time 2,857, Graduate part-time 586, Part-time 241 **Faculty:** Full-time 497, Part-time 512 **Student-Faculty Ratio:** 14:1 **Exams:** ACT essay component not used; SAT I or ACT; SAT essay component not used; SAT Reasoning. **% Receiving Financial Aid:** 68 **% Residing in College-Owned, -Operated, or -Affiliated Housing:** 56 **Final Year or Final Semester Residency Requirement:** No **Regional Accreditation:** Middle States Association of Colleges and Schools **Credit Hours For Degree:** 120 credits, Bachelors **ROTC:** Air Force, Army, Navy **Professional Accreditation:** AACN, AACSB, AALS, ABA, ACA, ACPE, AHIMA, AOTA, APA, APTA, ASHA, JRCAT, NASM, NCATE. **Intercollegiate Athletics:** Basketball M & W; Bowling W; Crew; Cross-Country Running M & W; Football M; Lacrosse W; Soccer M & W; Swimming and Diving W; Tennis M & W; Track and Field M & W; Volleyball W

EAST STROUDSBURG UNIVERSITY OF PENNSYLVANIA

200 Prospect St.
East Stroudsburg, PA 18301-2999
Tel: (570)422-3211; Free: 877-230-5547
Fax: (570)422-3933
E-mail: undergrads@po-box.esu.edu
Web Site: www.esu.edu
President/CEO: Dr. Marcia G. Welsh
Admissions: Jeff Jones
Type: Comprehensive **Sex:** Coed **Affiliation:** Pennsylvania State System of Higher Education. **Scores:** 86% SAT V 400+; 87% SAT M 400+; 52.8% ACT 18-23; 16.4% ACT 24-29 **% Accepted:** 77 **Application Deadline:** May 1 **Application Fee:** $25.00 **H.S. Requirements:** High school diploma required; GED accepted **Costs Per Year:** Application fee: $25. State resident tuition: $6820 full-time, $294 per credit hour part-time. Nonresident tuition: $17,050 full-time, $735 per credit hour part-time. Mandatory fees: $2577 full-time, $137 per credit hour part-time, $665 per term part-time. Full-time tuition and fees vary according to course load, location, and program. Part-time tuition and fees vary according to location and program. College room and board: $8058. College room only: $5372. Room and board charges vary according to board plan and housing facility. **Scholarships:** Available. **Calendar System:** Semester, Summer session available **Enrollment:** Full-time 5,644, Graduate full-time 339, Graduate part-time 323, Part-time 522 **Faculty:** Full-time 281, Part-time 59 **Student-Faculty Ratio:** 22:1 **Exams:** SAT I or ACT; SAT essay component used for advising; SAT essay component used for placement; SAT Reasoning. **% Receiving Financial Aid:** 51 **% Residing in College-Owned, -Operated, or -Affiliated Housing:** 46 **Final Year or Final Semester Residency Requirement:** No **Regional Accreditation:** Middle States Association of Colleges and Schools **Credit Hours For Degree:** 60 credits, Associates; 120 credits, Bachelors **ROTC:** Air Force, Army **Professional Accreditation:** ABET, ACEN, ASHA, CEPH, JRCAT, NCATE, NRPA. **Intercollegiate Athletics:** Baseball M; Basketball M & W; Cheerleading M & W; Cross-Country Running M & W; Equestrian Sports M & W; Field Hockey W; Football M; Golf M & W; Ice Hockey M & W; Lacrosse M & W; Rugby M & W; Soccer M & W; Softball W; Swimming and Diving W; Tennis M & W; Track and Field M & W; Ultimate Frisbee M & W; Volleyball M & W; Wrestling M

EASTERN UNIVERSITY

1300 Eagle Rd.
Saint Davids, PA 19087-3696

Tel: (610)341-5800; Free: 800-452-0996
Fax: (610)341-1723
E-mail: ugadm@eastern.edu
Web Site: www.eastern.edu
President/CEO: Dr. Robert G. Duffett
Admissions: Michael Dziedziak
Financial Aid: Christal Jennings
Type: Comprehensive **Sex:** Coed **Affiliation:** Christian. **Scores:** 95% SAT V 400+; 92% SAT M 400+; 46.4% ACT 18-23; 39.3% ACT 24-29 **% Accepted:** 68 **Admission Plans:** Deferred Admission; Early Admission **Application Deadline:** Rolling **Application Fee:** $35.00 **H.S. Requirements:** High school diploma required; GED accepted **Costs Per Year:** Application fee: $35. One-time mandatory fee: $50. Comprehensive fee: $40,780 includes full-time tuition ($30,250), mandatory fees ($340), and college room and board ($10,190). College room only: $5434. Full-time tuition and fees vary according to course load, degree level, and program. Room and board charges vary according to housing facility and location. Part-time tuition: $660 per credit. Part-time mandatory fees: $170 per term. Part-time tuition and fees vary according to course load, degree level, and program. **Scholarships:** Available. **Calendar System:** Semester, Summer session available **Enrollment:** Full-time 1,992, Graduate full-time 632, Graduate part-time 728, Part-time 410 **Faculty:** Full-time 151, Part-time 413 **Student-Faculty Ratio:** 11:1 **Exams:** SAT I or ACT. **% Receiving Financial Aid:** 92 **% Residing in College-Owned, -Operated, or -Affiliated Housing:** 75 **Final Year or Final Semester Residency Requirement:** No **Regional Accreditation:** Middle States Association of Colleges and Schools **Credit Hours For Degree:** 60 credits, Associates; 127 credits, Bachelors **ROTC:** Air Force, Army **Professional Accreditation:** AACN, ACIPE, ATS, CSWE. **Intercollegiate Athletics:** Baseball M; Basketball M & W; Cross-Country Running M & W; Field Hockey W; Golf M & W; Lacrosse M & W; Soccer M & W; Softball W; Tennis M & W; Volleyball W

EDINBORO UNIVERSITY OF PENNSYLVANIA

Edinboro, PA 16444
Tel: (814)732-2000; Free: 888-846-2676
Fax: (814)732-2420
E-mail: eup_admissions@edinboro.edu
Web Site: www.edinboro.edu
President/CEO: Dr. Julie E. Wollman
Admissions: Melissa Manning
Financial Aid: Alyssa Dobson
Type: Comprehensive **Sex:** Coed **Affiliation:** Pennsylvania State System of Higher Education. **Scores:** 82% SAT V 400+; 81% SAT M 400+; 45.33% ACT 18-23; 15.3% ACT 24-29 **% Accepted:** 99 **Admission Plans:** Deferred Admission **Application Fee:** $30.00 **H.S. Requirements:** High school diploma required; GED accepted **Costs Per Year:** Application fee: $30. State resident tuition: $7060 full-time, $294 per credit part-time. Nonresident tuition: $7414 full-time, $309 per credit part-time. Mandatory fees: $2475 full-time. Full-time tuition and fees vary according to degree level, location, and program. Part-time tuition varies according to course load, degree level, location, program, and reciprocity agreements. College room and board: $10,166. College room only: $6830. Room and board charges vary according to board plan and housing facility. **Scholarships:** Available. **Calendar System:** Semester, Summer session available **Enrollment:** Full-time 5,086, Graduate full-time 518, Graduate part-time 734, Part-time 499 **Faculty:** Full-time 317, Part-time 54 **Student-Faculty Ratio:** 19:1 **Exams:** ACT essay component not used; SAT I or ACT; SAT essay component not used; SAT Reasoning. **% Receiving Financial Aid:** 80 **% Residing in College-Owned, -Operated, or -Affiliated Housing:** 37 **Final Year or Final Semester Residency Requirement:** Yes **Regional Accreditation:** Middle States Association of Colleges and Schools **Credit Hours For Degree:** 60 credits, Associates; 120 credits, Bachelors **ROTC:** Army **Professional Accreditation:** AACN, ABET, ACA, ACBSP, AND, ASHA, CORE, CSWE, NASAD, NASM, NCATE. **Intercollegiate Athletics:** Basketball M & W; Cross-Country Running M & W; Football M; Lacrosse W; Soccer W; Softball W; Swimming and Diving M & W; Tennis M & W; Track and Field M & W; Volleyball W; Wrestling M

ELIZABETHTOWN COLLEGE

One Alpha Dr.
Elizabethtown, PA 17022-2298
Tel: (717)361-1000
E-mail: admissions@etown.edu
Web Site: www.etown.edu

President/CEO: Dr. Carl J. Strikwerda
Admissions: Lauren Deibler
Financial Aid: Melodie R. Jackson
Type: Comprehensive **Sex:** Coed **Affiliation:** Church of the Brethren. **Scores:** 99% SAT V 400+; 97% SAT M 400+; 30.2% ACT 18-23; 55.2% ACT 24-29 **% Accepted:** 71 **Admission Plans:** Deferred Admission **Application Deadline:** March 1 **Application Fee:** $30.00 **H.S. Requirements:** High school diploma required; GED accepted **Costs Per Year:** Application fee: $30. Comprehensive fee: $51,850 includes full-time tuition ($41,710) and college room and board ($10,140). College room only: $5120. Full-time tuition varies according to course load. Room and board charges vary according to board plan and housing facility. Part-time tuition: $1010 per credit hour. Part-time tuition varies according to course load. **Scholarships:** Available. **Calendar System:** Semester, Summer session available **Enrollment:** Full-time 1,755, Graduate full-time 46, Part-time 19 **Faculty:** Full-time 129, Part-time 50 **Student-Faculty Ratio:** 12:1 **Exams:** SAT I or ACT; SAT essay component used as validity check; SAT essay component used for placement; SAT Reasoning. **% Receiving Financial Aid:** 74 **% Residing in College-Owned, -Operated, or -Affiliated Housing:** 87 **Final Year or Final Semester Residency Requirement:** No **Regional Accreditation:** Middle States Association of Colleges and Schools **Credit Hours For Degree:** 125 credits, Bachelors **Professional Accreditation:** ABET, ACBSP, AOTA, CSWE, NASM. **Intercollegiate Athletics:** Baseball M; Basketball M & W; Cross-Country Running M & W; Field Hockey W; Golf M; Lacrosse M & W; Soccer M & W; Softball W; Swimming and Diving M & W; Tennis M & W; Track and Field M & W; Volleyball W; Wrestling M

ELIZABETHTOWN COLLEGE SCHOOL OF CONTINUING AND PROFESSIONAL STUDIES

One Alpha Dr.
Elizabethtown, PA 17022
Tel: (717)361-3750
E-mail: randazzob@etown.edu
Web Site: www.etowndegrees.com
President/CEO: Dr. John J. Kokolus
Admissions: Barbara A. Randazzo
Type: Comprehensive **Sex:** Coed **Affiliation:** Church of the Brethren; Elizabethtown College. **Admission Plans:** Deferred Admission **Application Deadline:** Rolling **Application Fee:** $0.00 **H.S. Requirements:** High school diploma required; GED accepted **Costs Per Year:** Application fee: $0. Tuition: $525 per credit hour part-time. Part-time tuition varies according to course load. **Calendar System:** Semester, Summer session available **Enrollment:** Graduate part-time 76, Part-time 346 **Faculty:** Part-time 57 **Student-Faculty Ratio:** 7:1 **Final Year or Final Semester Residency Requirement:** No **Credit Hours For Degree:** 125 credits, Bachelors

ERIE INSTITUTE OF TECHNOLOGY

940 Millcreek Mall
Erie, PA 16565
Tel: (814)868-9900; Free: 866-868-3743
Fax: (814)868-9977
E-mail: info@erieit.edu
Web Site: www.erieit.edu
President/CEO: Paul Fitzgerald
Admissions: Barb Bolt
Type: Two-Year College **Sex:** Coed **Admission Plans:** Open Admission **Application Fee:** $25.00 **Calendar System:** Semester **Student-Faculty Ratio:** 11:1 **Exams:** Other. **Professional Accreditation:** ACCSC.

FORTIS INSTITUTE (ERIE)

5757 W 26th St.
Erie, PA 16506
Tel: (814)838-7673; Free: 855-4-FORTIS
Fax: (814)838-8642
E-mail: geuliano@tsbi.org
Web Site: www.fortis.edu
President/CEO: Peter Correa
Admissions: Guy M. Euliano
Type: Two-Year College **Sex:** Coed **Application Fee:** $50.00 **Student-Faculty Ratio:** 17:1 **Professional Accreditation:** ACICS.

FORTIS INSTITUTE (FORTY FORT)

166 Slocum St.
Forty Fort, PA 18704

Tel: (570)288-8400; Free: 855-4-FORTIS
Fax: (717)287-7936
Web Site: www.fortis.edu
President/CEO: Ruth L. Brumagin
Type: Two-Year College **Sex:** Coed **Application Fee:** $50.00 **Professional Accreditation:** ACCSC.

FORTIS INSTITUTE (SCRANTON)

517 Ash St.
Scranton, PA 18509
Tel: (570)558-1818; Free: 855-4-FORTIS
E-mail: heatherp@markogroup.com
Web Site: www.fortis.edu
Admissions: Heather Contardi
Type: Two-Year College **Sex:** Coed **Professional Accreditation:** ACCSC.

FRANKLIN & MARSHALL COLLEGE

PO Box 3003
Lancaster, PA 17604-3003
Tel: (717)291-3911; Free: 877-678-9111
Fax: (717)291-4389
E-mail: julie.kerich@fandm.edu
Web Site: www.fandm.edu
President/CEO: Dr. Dan Porterfield
Admissions: Julie Kerich
Financial Aid: Clarke Paine
Type: Four-Year College **Sex:** Coed **Scores:** 100% SAT V 400+; 100% SAT M 400+; 56% ACT 24-29 **% Accepted:** 32 **Admission Plans:** Deferred Admission; Early Action; Early Admission **Application Deadline:** January 15 **Application Fee:** $60.00 **H.S. Requirements:** High school diploma required; GED accepted **Costs Per Year:** Application fee: $60. One-time mandatory fee: $200. Comprehensive fee: $63,170 includes full-time tuition ($50,300), mandatory fees ($100), and college room and board ($12,770). College room only: $7550. Room and board charges vary according to board plan and housing facility. Part-time tuition: $6288 per course. Part-time tuition varies according to course load. **Scholarships:** Available. **Calendar System:** Semester, Summer session available **Enrollment:** Full-time 2,217, Part-time 32 **Faculty:** Full-time 234, Part-time 48 **Student-Faculty Ratio:** 9:1 **Exams:** SAT Reasoning; SAT Subject. **% Receiving Financial Aid:** 52 **% Residing in College-Owned, -Operated, or -Affiliated Housing:** 99 **Final Year or Final Semester Residency Requirement:** Yes **Regional Accreditation:** Middle States Association of Colleges and Schools **Credit Hours For Degree:** 32 credits, Bachelors **ROTC:** Army **Intercollegiate Athletics:** Baseball M; Basketball M & W; Crew M & W; Cross-Country Running M & W; Equestrian Sports W; Field Hockey W; Football M; Golf M & W; Ice Hockey M; Lacrosse M & W; Rugby M & W; Soccer M & W; Softball W; Squash M & W; Swimming and Diving M & W; Tennis M & W; Track and Field M & W; Ultimate Frisbee M & W; Volleyball M & W; Wrestling M

GANNON UNIVERSITY

109 University Sq.
Erie, PA 16541-0001
Tel: (814)871-7000; Free: 800-GANNONU
Fax: (814)871-5803
E-mail: admissions@gannon.edu
Web Site: www.gannon.edu
President/CEO: Dr. Keith Taylor
Financial Aid: Sharon Krahe
Type: University **Sex:** Coed **Affiliation:** Roman Catholic. **Scores:** 92% SAT V 400+; 93% SAT M 400+; 51.8% ACT 18-23; 36.2% ACT 24-29 **% Accepted:** 76 **Admission Plans:** Deferred Admission **Application Deadline:** Rolling **Application Fee:** $25.00 **H.S. Requirements:** High school diploma required; GED accepted **Costs Per Year:** Application fee: $25. Comprehensive fee: $40,968 includes full-time tuition ($28,590), mandatory fees ($668), and college room and board ($11,710). College room only: $6250. Full-time tuition and fees vary according to course load and program. Room and board charges vary according to board plan and housing facility. Part-time tuition: $690 per credit hour. Part-time mandatory fees: $25 per credit hour. Part-time tuition and fees vary according to course load and program. **Scholarships:** Available. **Calendar System:** Semester, Summer session available **Enrollment:** Full-time 2,531, Graduate full-time 752, Graduate part-time 549, Part-time 584 **Faculty:** Full-time 227, Part-time 168 **Student-Faculty Ratio:** 13:1 **Exams:** ACT essay component not used; SAT I or ACT; SAT essay component not used; SAT Reasoning. **% Receiving Financial

Aid: 78 % Residing in College-Owned, -Operated, or -Affiliated Housing: 44 **Final Year or Final Semester Residency Requirement:** Yes **Regional Accreditation:** Middle States Association of Colleges and Schools **Credit Hours For Degree:** 64 credits, Associates; 128 credits, Bachelors **ROTC:** Army **Professional Accreditation:** AACN, AANA, ABET, ACA, ACBSP, AND, AOTA, APTA, CSWE, CoARC, JRCERT. **Intercollegiate Athletics:** Baseball M; Basketball M & W; Cheerleading W; Cross-Country Running M & W; Football M; Golf M & W; Gymnastics W; Ice Hockey M; Lacrosse W; Rugby M; Soccer M & W; Softball W; Swimming and Diving M & W; Volleyball W; Water Polo M & W; Wrestling M

GENEVA COLLEGE

3200 College Ave.
Beaver Falls, PA 15010-3599
Tel: (724)846-5100; Free: 800-847-8255
Fax: (724)847-6687
E-mail: admissions@geneva.edu
Web Site: www.geneva.edu
President/CEO: Dr. Kenneth A. Smith
Admissions: David Layton
Financial Aid: Steven Bell

Type: Comprehensive **Sex:** Coed **Affiliation:** Reformed Presbyterian Church of North America. **Scores:** 92% SAT V 400+; 93% SAT M 400+; 35.24% ACT 18-23; 47.62% ACT 24-29 **% Accepted:** 71 **Admission Plans:** Deferred Admission; Early Admission **Application Deadline:** Rolling **Application Fee:** $40.00 **H.S. Requirements:** High school diploma required; GED accepted **Costs Per Year:** Application fee: $40. Comprehensive fee: $35,080 includes full-time tuition ($25,450) and college room and board ($9630). Full-time tuition varies according to course load. Room and board charges vary according to board plan. Part-time tuition: $860 per credit. Part-time tuition varies according to course load. **Scholarships:** Available. **Calendar System:** Semester, Summer session available **Enrollment:** Full-time 1,247, Graduate full-time 171, Graduate part-time 79, Part-time 15 **Faculty:** Full-time 103, Part-time 90 **Student-Faculty Ratio:** 11:1 **Exams:** SAT I or ACT; SAT Reasoning. **% Receiving Financial Aid:** 82 **% Residing in College-Owned, -Operated, or -Affiliated Housing:** 72 **Final Year or Final Semester Residency Requirement:** Yes **Regional Accreditation:** Middle States Association of Colleges and Schools **Credit Hours For Degree:** 63 credits, Associates; 126 credits, Bachelors **ROTC:** Army **Professional Accreditation:** ABET, ACA, ACBSP, JRCECT. **Intercollegiate Athletics:** Baseball M; Basketball M & W; Cross-Country Running M & W; Football M; Golf M & W; Soccer M & W; Softball W; Tennis M & W; Track and Field M & W; Volleyball M & W

GETTYSBURG COLLEGE

300 N Washington St.
Gettysburg, PA 17325-1483
Tel: (717)337-6000; Free: 800-431-0803
Fax: (717)337-6008
E-mail: admiss@gettysburg.edu
Web Site: www.gettysburg.edu
President/CEO: Dr. Janet Morgan Riggs
Admissions: Gail Sweezey
Financial Aid: Christina Gormley

Type: Four-Year College **Sex:** Coed **Affiliation:** Evangelical Lutheran Church in America. **Scores:** 100% SAT V 400+; 100% SAT M 400+ **% Accepted:** 40 **Admission Plans:** Deferred Admission; Early Action; Early Admission **Application Deadline:** January 15 **Application Fee:** $60.00 **H.S. Requirements:** High school diploma required; GED accepted **Costs Per Year:** Application fee: $60. Comprehensive fee: $60,870 includes full-time tuition ($49,140) and college room and board ($11,730). **Scholarships:** Available. **Calendar System:** Semester, Summer session not available **Enrollment:** Full-time 2,430, Part-time 24 **Faculty:** Full-time 222, Part-time 86 **Student-Faculty Ratio:** 10:1 **Exams:** ACT essay component not used; SAT I or ACT; SAT II; SAT essay component not used. **% Receiving Financial Aid:** 60 **% Residing in College-Owned, -Operated, or -Affiliated Housing:** 94 **Regional Accreditation:** Middle States Association of Colleges and Schools **Credit Hours For Degree:** 32 courses, Bachelors **ROTC:** Army **Intercollegiate Athletics:** Baseball M; Basketball M & W; Cheerleading M & W; Cross-Country Running M & W; Equestrian Sports M & W; Field Hockey W; Football M; Golf M & W; Ice Hockey M; Lacrosse M & W; Rugby M & W; Soccer M & W; Softball W; Swimming and Diving M & W; Tennis M & W; Track and Field M & W; Ultimate Frisbee M & W; Volleyball W; Wrestling M

GREAT LAKES INSTITUTE OF TECHNOLOGY

5100 Peach St.
Erie, PA 16509
Tel: (814)456-6217
Fax: (814)459-4712
Web Site: www.glit.edu
Type: Two-Year College **Sex:** Coed **Professional Accreditation:** ACCSC.

GROVE CITY COLLEGE

100 Campus Dr.
Grove City, PA 16127-2104
Tel: (724)458-2000
Fax: (724)458-3395
E-mail: admissions@gcc.edu
Web Site: www.gcc.edu
President/CEO: Paul J. McNulty
Admissions: Sarah E. Gibbs
Financial Aid: Thomas G. Ball

Type: Four-Year College **Sex:** Coed **Affiliation:** Presbyterian. **Scores:** 99% SAT V 400+; 100% SAT M 400+; 21% ACT 18-23; 59% ACT 24-29 **% Accepted:** 81 **Admission Plans:** Deferred Admission; Early Action; Early Admission; Preferred Admission **Application Deadline:** February 1 **Application Fee:** $50.00 **H.S. Requirements:** High school diploma required; GED accepted. For home-schooled applicants: High school diploma or equivalent not required **Costs Per Year:** Application fee: $50. Comprehensive fee: $24,956 includes full-time tuition ($16,154) and college room and board ($8802). Room and board charges vary according to housing facility. Part-time tuition: $524 per credit hour. **Scholarships:** Available. **Calendar System:** Semester, Summer session available **Enrollment:** Full-time 2,396, Part-time 48 **Faculty:** Full-time 154, Part-time 79 **Student-Faculty Ratio:** 13:1 **Exams:** ACT essay component not used; SAT I or ACT; SAT essay component not used; SAT Reasoning. **% Receiving Financial Aid:** 42 **% Residing in College-Owned, -Operated, or -Affiliated Housing:** 92 **Final Year or Final Semester Residency Requirement:** No **Regional Accreditation:** Middle States Association of Colleges and Schools **Credit Hours For Degree:** 128 credit hours, Bachelors **Professional Accreditation:** ABET, ACBSP. **Intercollegiate Athletics:** Baseball M; Basketball M & W; Cross-Country Running M & W; Fencing M & W; Football M; Golf M & W; Lacrosse M & W; Rugby M & W; Soccer M & W; Softball W; Swimming and Diving M & W; Tennis M & W; Track and Field M & W; Ultimate Frisbee W; Volleyball M & W; Water Polo M & W

GWYNEDD MERCY UNIVERSITY

Sumneytown Pke.
Gwynedd Valley, PA 19437-0901
Tel: (215)646-7300; Free: 800-342-5462
Fax: (215)641-5556
E-mail: admissions@gmercyu.edu
Web Site: www.gmercyu.edu
President/CEO: Dr. Kathleen Owens
Admissions: Michelle Diehl
Financial Aid: Elizabeth R. Howard

Type: Comprehensive **Sex:** Coed **Affiliation:** Roman Catholic. **Scores:** 82% SAT V 400+; 87% SAT M 400+; 70% ACT 18-23; 8% ACT 24-29 **% Accepted:** 92 **Admission Plans:** Deferred Admission **Application Deadline:** Rolling **Application Fee:** $0.00 **H.S. Requirements:** High school diploma required; GED accepted **Costs Per Year:** Application fee: $0. Comprehensive fee: $43,680 includes full-time tuition ($31,780), mandatory fees ($600), and college room and board ($11,300). College room only: $5360. Full-time tuition and fees vary according to location and program. Room and board charges vary according to board plan and housing facility. Part-time tuition: $700 per credit hour. Part-time tuition varies according to location and program. **Scholarships:** Available. **Calendar System:** Semester, Summer session available **Enrollment:** Full-time 1,826, Graduate full-time 503, Graduate part-time 79, Part-time 174 **Faculty:** Full-time 75, Part-time 224 **Student-Faculty Ratio:** 16:1 **Exams:** SAT I or ACT. **% Receiving Financial Aid:** 80 **% Residing in College-Owned, -Operated, or -Affiliated Housing:** 20 **Final Year or Final Semester Residency Requirement:** No **Regional Accreditation:** Middle States Association of Colleges and Schools **Credit Hours For Degree:** 62 credits, Associates; 125 credits, Bachelors **Professional Accreditation:** ACBSP, ACEN, AHIMA, CoARC, JRCECT, JRCERT. **Intercollegiate Athletics:** Baseball M; Basketball M & W; Cheerleading W; Cross-Country Running M & W; Field

Hockey W; Golf M; Lacrosse M & W; Soccer M & W; Softball W; Tennis M & W; Track and Field M & W; Volleyball W

HARCUM COLLEGE

750 Montgomery Ave.
Bryn Mawr, PA 19010-3476
Tel: (610)525-4100
Fax: (610)526-6147
E-mail: enroll@harcum.edu
Web Site: www.harcum.edu
President/CEO: Dr. Jon Jay DeTemple
Financial Aid: Eli Moinester
Type: Two-Year College **Sex:** Coed **% Accepted:** 65 **Admission Plans:** Deferred Admission **Application Deadline:** Rolling **Application Fee:** $50.00 **H.S. Requirements:** High school diploma required; GED accepted **Scholarships:** Available. **Calendar System:** Semester, Summer session available **Faculty:** Full-time 36, Part-time 154 **Student-Faculty Ratio:** 12:1 **Exams:** SAT I or ACT. **% Residing in College-Owned, -Operated, or -Affiliated Housing:** 20 **Final Year or Final Semester Residency Requirement:** No **Regional Accreditation:** Middle States Association of Colleges and Schools **Credit Hours For Degree:** 62 credits, Associates **Professional Accreditation:** ACEN, ADA, APTA, NAACLS. **Intercollegiate Athletics:** Basketball M & W; Track and Field M & W; Volleyball W

HARRISBURG AREA COMMUNITY COLLEGE

1 HACC Dr.
Harrisburg, PA 17110-2999
Tel: (717)780-2300; Free: 800-ABC-HACC
Fax: (717)231-7674
E-mail: admit@hacc.edu
Web Site: www.hacc.edu
President/CEO: John J. Sygielski
Admissions: Matt Huber
Financial Aid: James J. Carideo
Type: Two-Year College **Sex:** Coed **% Accepted:** 100 **Admission Plans:** Deferred Admission; Early Admission; Open Admission **Application Fee:** $35.00 **H.S. Requirements:** High school diploma or equivalent not required. For allied health programs: High school diploma required; GED accepted **Costs Per Year:** Application fee: $35. Area resident tuition: $3900 full-time, $162.50 per credit hour part-time. State resident tuition: $4968 full-time, $207 per credit hour part-time. Nonresident tuition: $6000 full-time, $250 per credit hour part-time. Mandatory fees: $1032 full-time, $48 per credit hour part-time. Full-time tuition and fees vary according to location and program. Part-time tuition and fees vary according to location and program. **Scholarships:** Available. **Calendar System:** Semester, Summer session available **Enrollment:** Full-time 5,516, Part-time 13,605 **Faculty:** Full-time 335, Part-time 756 **Student-Faculty Ratio:** 17:1 **Regional Accreditation:** Middle States Association of Colleges and Schools **Credit Hours For Degree:** 61 credit hours, Associates **ROTC:** Army **Professional Accreditation:** ACBSP, ACEN, ACF, ADA, CoARC, JRCEMTP, NAACLS. **Intercollegiate Athletics:** Basketball M & W; Soccer M; Tennis M & W

HARRISBURG UNIVERSITY OF SCIENCE AND TECHNOLOGY

326 Market St.
Harrisburg, PA 17101
Tel: (717)901-5100; Free: 866-HBG-UNIV
Fax: (717)901-5150
E-mail: Connect@harrisburgu.edu
Web Site: www.HarrisburgU.edu
President/CEO: Dr. Eric D. Darr
Financial Aid: Vince P. Frank
Type: Comprehensive **Sex:** Coed **Application Deadline:** Rolling **Application Fee:** $0.00 **H.S. Requirements:** High school diploma required; GED accepted **Costs Per Year:** Application fee: $0. Tuition: $23,900 full-time, $1000 per semester hour part-time. Full-time tuition varies according to class time, course level, course load, degree level, location, program, reciprocity agreements, and student level. Part-time tuition varies according to class time, course level, course load, degree level, location, program, reciprocity agreements, and student level. College room only: $7000. Room charges vary according to housing facility. **Scholarships:** Available. **Calendar System:** Semester, Summer session available **Enrollment:** Full-time 330, Graduate full-time 1,640, Graduate part-time 25, Part-time 104 **Student-Faculty Ratio:** 26:1 **Exams:** SAT I or ACT. **% Receiving Financial Aid:** 92 **% Residing in College-Owned, -Operated, or -Affiliated Housing:** 30

Final Year or Final Semester Residency Requirement: No **Regional Accreditation:** Middle States Association of Colleges and Schools **Credit Hours For Degree:** 120 semester credit hours, Bachelors

HAVERFORD COLLEGE

370 Lancaster Ave.
Haverford, PA 19041-1392
Tel: (610)896-1000
Fax: (610)896-1338
E-mail: admission@haverford.edu
Web Site: www.haverford.edu
President/CEO: Dr. Kimberly W. Benston
Admissions: Jess Lord
Financial Aid: Michael Colahan
Type: Four-Year College **Sex:** Coed **Scores:** 100% SAT V 400+; 100% SAT M 400+; 19% ACT 24-29 **% Accepted:** 25 **Admission Plans:** Deferred Admission; Early Action; Early Admission **Application Deadline:** January 15 **Application Fee:** $65.00 **H.S. Requirements:** High school diploma required; GED accepted **Costs Per Year:** Application fee: $65. One-time mandatory fee: $230. Comprehensive fee: $63,986 includes full-time tuition ($48,656), mandatory fees ($442), and college room and board ($14,888). College room only: $8494. **Scholarships:** Available. **Calendar System:** Semester, Summer session not available **Enrollment:** Full-time 1,233 **Faculty:** Full-time 126, Part-time 38 **Student-Faculty Ratio:** 9:1 **Exams:** ACT essay component not used; SAT I and SAT II or ACT; SAT essay component not used; SAT Reasoning; SAT Subject. **% Receiving Financial Aid:** 51 **% Residing in College-Owned, -Operated, or -Affiliated Housing:** 99 **Regional Accreditation:** Middle States Association of Colleges and Schools **Credit Hours For Degree:** 32 courses, Bachelors **Intercollegiate Athletics:** Badminton W; Baseball M; Basketball M & W; Crew M & W; Cross-Country Running M & W; Fencing M & W; Field Hockey W; Golf M & W; Lacrosse M & W; Rugby M; Soccer M & W; Softball W; Squash M & W; Tennis M & W; Track and Field M & W; Ultimate Frisbee M & W; Volleyball M & W; Wrestling M

HOLY FAMILY UNIVERSITY

9801 Frankford Ave.
Philadelphia, PA 19114
Tel: (215)637-7700
Fax: (215)281-1022
E-mail: admissions@holyfamily.edu
Web Site: www.holyfamily.edu
President/CEO: Señor Maureen McGarrity, CSFN, PhD
Admissions: Lauren Campbell
Financial Aid: Janice Hetrick
Type: Comprehensive **Sex:** Coed **Affiliation:** Roman Catholic. **Scores:** 82% SAT V 400+; 78% SAT M 400+ **% Accepted:** 74 **Admission Plans:** Deferred Admission **Application Deadline:** Rolling **Application Fee:** $25.00 **H.S. Requirements:** High school diploma required; GED accepted **Costs Per Year:** Application fee: $25. Comprehensive fee: $42,744 includes full-time tuition ($28,198), mandatory fees ($970), and college room and board ($13,576). College room only: $7140. Full-time tuition and fees vary according to class time, course level, course load, degree level, program, reciprocity agreements, and student level. Room and board charges vary according to board plan and housing facility. Part-time tuition: $603 per credit hour. Part-time mandatory fees: $108 per term. Part-time tuition and fees vary according to class time, course level, course load, degree level, program, reciprocity agreements, and student level. **Scholarships:** Available. **Calendar System:** Semester, Summer session available **Enrollment:** Full-time 1,432, Graduate full-time 202, Graduate part-time 465, Part-time 613 **Faculty:** Full-time 74, Part-time 207 **Student-Faculty Ratio:** 12:1 **Exams:** ACT essay component used for placement; SAT I or ACT; SAT essay component used for placement; SAT Reasoning; SAT Subject. **% Receiving Financial Aid:** 85 **% Residing in College-Owned, -Operated, or -Affiliated Housing:** 17 **Final Year or Final Semester Residency Requirement:** No **Regional Accreditation:** Middle States Association of Colleges and Schools **Credit Hours For Degree:** 74 credits, Associates; 120 credits, Bachelors **ROTC:** Army **Professional Accreditation:** AACN, ACBSP, JRCERT, TEAC. **Intercollegiate Athletics:** Basketball M & W; Cross-Country Running M & W; Lacrosse W; Soccer M & W; Softball W; Tennis W; Track and Field M & W; Volleyball W

HUSSIAN COLLEGE, SCHOOL OF ART

The Bourse - Ste. 300
111 S Independence Mall E

Philadelphia, PA 19106
Tel: (215)981-0900
Fax: (215)864-9115
E-mail: mcernero@hussianart.edu
Web Site: www.hussianart.edu
President/CEO: Melissa Morgan
Admissions: Mark Cernero

Type: Two-Year College **Sex:** Coed **% Accepted:** 25 **Admission Plans:** Deferred Admission **Application Deadline:** Rolling **Application Fee:** $0.00 **H.S. Requirements:** High school diploma required; GED accepted **Costs Per Year:** Application fee: $0. Tuition: $18,600 full-time. Full-time tuition varies according to course load. **Scholarships:** Available. **Calendar System:** Semester, Summer session not available **Enrollment:** Full-time 82, Part-time 1 **Exams:** ACT essay component not used; SAT essay component not used. **Credit Hours For Degree:** 121, Bachelors **Professional Accreditation:** ACCSC.

IMMACULATA UNIVERSITY

1145 King Rd.
Immaculata, PA 19345
Tel: (610)647-4400; Free: 877-428-6329
Fax: (610)251-1668
E-mail: admiss@immaculata.edu
Web Site: www.immaculata.edu
President/CEO: Señor S. Patricia Fadden
Financial Aid: Robert Forest

Type: University **Sex:** Coed **Affiliation:** Roman Catholic. **Scores:** 87% SAT V 400+; 83% SAT M 400+; 63% ACT 18-23; 19% ACT 24-29 **% Accepted:** 79 **Admission Plans:** Deferred Admission **Application Deadline:** Rolling **Application Fee:** $35.00 **H.S. Requirements:** High school diploma required; GED accepted **Costs Per Year:** Application fee: $35. Comprehensive fee: $46,490 includes full-time tuition ($33,280) and college room and board ($13,210). College room only: $7100. Full-time tuition varies according to course load and student level. Room and board charges vary according to board plan and housing facility. Part-time tuition: $525 per credit. Part-time tuition varies according to course load. Tuition guaranteed not to increase for student's term of enrollment. **Scholarships:** Available. **Calendar System:** Semester, Summer session available **Enrollment:** Full-time 1,021, Graduate full-time 191, Graduate part-time 980, Part-time 769 **Faculty:** Full-time 94, Part-time 274 **Student-Faculty Ratio:** 9:1 **Exams:** ACT essay component used for advising; ACT essay component used for placement; SAT I or ACT; SAT essay component used for advising; SAT essay component used for placement; SAT Reasoning. **% Residing in College-Owned, -Operated, or -Affiliated Housing:** 42 **Final Year or Final Semester Residency Requirement:** No **Regional Accreditation:** Middle States Association of Colleges and Schools **Credit Hours For Degree:** 64 credits, Associates; 128 credits, Bachelors **ROTC:** Army **Professional Accreditation:** AACN, ACBSP, AND, APA, NASM. **Intercollegiate Athletics:** Basketball W; Cross-Country Running W; Field Hockey W; Lacrosse W; Soccer W; Softball W; Tennis W; Volleyball W

INDIANA UNIVERSITY OF PENNSYLVANIA

Indiana, PA 15705-1087
Tel: (724)357-2100; Free: 800-442-6830
Fax: (724)357-2685
E-mail: admissions-inquiry@iup.edu
Web Site: www.iup.edu
President/CEO: Dr. Michael Driscoll
Financial Aid: Ragan Griffin

Type: University **Sex:** Coed **Affiliation:** Pennsylvania State System of Higher Education. **Scores:** 89% SAT V 400+; 89% SAT M 400+ **% Accepted:** 88 **Admission Plans:** Deferred Admission; Early Admission **Application Deadline:** Rolling **Application Fee:** $50.00 **H.S. Requirements:** High school diploma required; GED accepted **Costs Per Year:** Application fee: $50. State resident tuition: $7060 full-time, $294 per credit hour part-time. Nonresident tuition: $17,650 full-time, $735 per credit hour part-time. Mandatory fees: $2,876 full-time, $99.30 per credit hour part-time, $50 per term part-time. Full-time tuition and fees vary according to course load and reciprocity agreements. Part-time tuition and fees vary according to course load and reciprocity agreements. College room and board: $11,880. College room only: $8550. Room and board charges vary according to board plan, housing facility, and location. **Scholarships:** Available. **Calendar System:** Semester, Summer session available **Enrollment:** Full-time 10,740, Graduate full-time 958, Graduate part-time 1,280, Part-time 797 **Faculty:** Full-time

603, Part-time 113 **Student-Faculty Ratio:** 17:1 **Exams:** ACT; ACT essay component not used; SAT I; SAT I and SAT II or ACT; SAT I or ACT; SAT II; SAT essay component not used; SAT Reasoning. **% Receiving Financial Aid:** 70 **% Residing in College-Owned, -Operated, or -Affiliated Housing:** 88 **Final Year or Final Semester Residency Requirement:** Yes **Regional Accreditation:** Middle States Association of Colleges and Schools **Credit Hours For Degree:** 60 semester hours, Associates; 120 semester hours, Bachelors **ROTC:** Army **Professional Accreditation:** AACN, AACSB, AAFCS, ABET, ACA, ACF, AND, APA, ASHA, CoARC, JRCAT, NASAD, NASM, NAST, NCATE. **Intercollegiate Athletics:** Baseball M; Basketball M & W; Cross-Country Running M & W; Field Hockey W; Football M; Golf M; Lacrosse W; Soccer W; Softball W; Swimming and Diving M & W; Tennis W; Track and Field M & W; Volleyball W

JNA INSTITUTE OF CULINARY ARTS

1212 S Broad St.
Philadelphia, PA 19146
Tel: (215)468-8800
Fax: (215)468-8838
Web Site: www.culinaryarts.com
President/CEO: Joseph Digironimo

Type: Two-Year College **Sex:** Coed **Costs Per Year:** One-time mandatory fee: $75. Tuition: $12,650 full-time, $375 per credit hour part-time. Full-time tuition varies according to program. Tuition guaranteed not to increase for student's term of enrollment. **Calendar System:** Continuous **Enrollment:** Full-time 59 **Professional Accreditation:** ACCSC.

JOHNSON COLLEGE

3427 N Main Ave.
Scranton, PA 18508-1495
Tel: (570)342-6404; Free: 800-2WE-WORK
Fax: (570)348-2181
E-mail: admit@johnson.edu
Web Site: www.johnson.edu
President/CEO: Dr. Ann Pipinski
Admissions: Melissa Ide

Type: Two-Year College **Sex:** Coed **Admission Plans:** Deferred Admission **Application Deadline:** May 1 **Application Fee:** $30.00 **H.S. Requirements:** High school diploma required; GED accepted **Scholarships:** Available. **Calendar System:** Semester, Summer session available **Enrollment:** Full-time 363, Part-time 13 **Faculty:** Full-time 21, Part-time 2 **Student-Faculty Ratio:** 17:1 **Exams:** SAT I. **Credit Hours For Degree:** 74 credits, Associates **Professional Accreditation:** ACCSC. **Intercollegiate Athletics:** Basketball M & W; Bowling M & W; Cross-Country Running M & W; Golf M & W

JUNIATA COLLEGE

1700 Moore St.
Huntingdon, PA 16652-2119
Tel: (814)641-3000; Free: 877-JUNIATA
Fax: (814)641-3100
E-mail: admissions@juniata.edu
Web Site: www.juniata.edu
President/CEO: Dr. James Troha
Admissions: Terri Bollman-Dalansky
Financial Aid: Shane Himes

Type: Comprehensive **Sex:** Coed **Affiliation:** Church of the Brethren. **Scores:** 98% SAT V 400+; 99% SAT M 400+; 32.05% ACT 18-23; 51.28% ACT 24-29 **% Accepted:** 77 **Admission Plans:** Deferred Admission; Early Action; Early Admission **Application Deadline:** February 15 **Application Fee:** $0.00 **H.S. Requirements:** High school diploma required; GED accepted **Costs Per Year:** Application fee: $0. Comprehensive fee: $53,760 includes full-time tuition ($41,390), mandatory fees ($780), and college room and board ($11,590). College room only: $5420. Full-time tuition and fees vary according to course load, degree level, and program. Room and board charges vary according to board plan and housing facility. Part-time tuition: $1700 per credit. Part-time tuition varies according to course load and degree level. **Scholarships:** Available. **Calendar System:** Semester, Summer session available **Enrollment:** Full-time 1,512, Graduate full-time 8, Graduate part-time 5, Part-time 58 **Faculty:** Full-time 108, Part-time 41 **Student-Faculty Ratio:** 13:1 **Exams:** SAT I or ACT; SAT Reasoning. **% Receiving Financial Aid:** 71 **% Residing in College-Owned, -Operated, or -Affiliated Housing:** 82 **Regional Accreditation:** Middle States Association of Colleges and Schools **Credit Hours For Degree:** 120 semester hours, Bachelors **Professional Accreditation:** CSWE. **Intercollegiate Athletics:** Baseball M; Basketball M & W; Cross-Country Running M & W; Field Hockey W; Football M; Lacrosse M; Rugby M & W; Soccer M & W; Softball W; Swimming and Diving W; Tennis M & W; Track and Field M & W; Ultimate Frisbee M & W; Volleyball M & W

KEYSTONE COLLEGE

One College Green
La Plume, PA 18440
Tel: (570)945-5141; Free: 877-4-COLLEGE
E-mail: admissions@keystone.edu
Web Site: www.keystone.edu
President/CEO: Dr. David L. Coppola
Admissions: Jessica Lopez

Type: Comprehensive **Sex:** Coed **Scores:** 83% SAT V 400+; 80% SAT M 400+; 47% ACT 18-23; 20% ACT 24-29 **% Accepted:** 92 **Admission Plans:** Deferred Admission; Early Admission **Application Deadline:** June 1 **Application Fee:** $30.00 **H.S. Requirements:** High school diploma required; GED accepted **Costs Per Year:** Application fee: $30. Comprehensive fee: $34,350 includes full-time tuition ($23,300), mandatory fees ($1000), and college room and board ($10,050). College room only: $5026. Room and board charges vary according to board plan, housing facility, and location. Part-time tuition: $465 per credit hour. Part-time mandatory fees: $300 per term. Part-time tuition and fees vary according to course load. **Scholarships:** Available. **Calendar System:** Semester, Summer session available **Enrollment:** Full-time 1,230, Graduate full-time 8, Graduate part-time 17, Part-time 229 **Faculty:** Full-time 65, Part-time 184 **Student-Faculty Ratio:** 11:1 **Exams:** ACT essay component used as validity check; ACT essay component used for advising; ACT essay component used for placement; SAT I or ACT; SAT essay component used as validity check; SAT essay component used for advising; SAT essay component used for placement; SAT Reasoning; SAT Subject. **% Receiving Financial Aid:** 91 **% Residing in College-Owned, -Operated, or -Affiliated Housing:** 30 **Final Year or Final Semester Residency Requirement:** No **Regional Accreditation:** Middle States Association of Colleges and Schools **Credit Hours For Degree:** 62 credit hours, Associates; 120 credit hours, Bachelors **ROTC:** Air Force, Army **Intercollegiate Athletics:** Baseball M; Basketball M & W; Cross-Country Running M & W; Field Hockey W; Golf M; Lacrosse M & W; Soccer M & W; Softball W; Tennis M & W; Track and Field M & W; Volleyball W

KEYSTONE TECHNICAL INSTITUTE

2301 Academy Dr.
Harrisburg, PA 17112
Tel: (717)545-4747; Free: 800-400-3322
Fax: (717)901-9090
E-mail: info@acadcampus.com
Web Site: www.kti.edu
President/CEO: David W. Snyder
Admissions: Tom Bogush

Type: Two-Year College **Sex:** Coed **Admission Plans:** Open Admission **Application Deadline:** Rolling **Application Fee:** $20.00 **H.S. Requirements:** High school diploma required; GED accepted **Scholarships:** Available. **Calendar System:** Continuous, Summer session not available **Credit Hours For Degree:** 64 credit hours, Associates **Professional Accreditation:** ACCSC.

KING'S COLLEGE

133 N River St.
Wilkes-Barre, PA 18711-0801
Tel: (570)208-5900; Free: 888-KINGSPA
Fax: (570)208-5971
E-mail: admissions@kings.edu
Web Site: www.kings.edu
President/CEO: Rev. John J. Ryan, CSC
Admissions: James Anderson
Financial Aid: Donna Cerza

Type: Comprehensive **Sex:** Coed **Affiliation:** Roman Catholic. **Scores:** 98% SAT V 400+; 95% SAT M 400+ **% Accepted:** 72 **Admission Plans:** Deferred Admission **Application Deadline:** Rolling **Application Fee:** $30.00 **H.S. Requirements:** High school diploma required; GED accepted **Costs Per Year:** Application fee: $30. Comprehensive fee: $45,048 includes full-time tuition ($32,640), mandatory fees ($450), and college room and board ($11,958). College room only: $5880. Room and board charges vary accord-

ing to board plan. Part-time tuition: $530 per credit hour. **Scholarships:** Available. **Calendar System:** Semester, Summer session available **Enrollment:** Full-time 1,801, Graduate full-time 89, Graduate part-time 232, Part-time 188 **Faculty:** Full-time 139, Part-time 77 **Student-Faculty Ratio:** 12:1 **Exams:** ACT essay component used as validity check; ACT essay component used for advising; SAT I or ACT; SAT essay component used as validity check; SAT essay component used for advising. **% Receiving Financial Aid:** 80 **% Residing in College-Owned, -Operated, or -Affiliated Housing:** 50 **Final Year or Final Semester Residency Requirement:** No **Regional Accreditation:** Middle States Association of Colleges and Schools **Credit Hours For Degree:** 60 credit hours, Associates; 120 credit hours, Bachelors **ROTC:** Air Force, Army **Professional Accreditation:** AACSB, CAHME, JRCAT, NCATE. **Intercollegiate Athletics:** Baseball M; Basketball M & W; Cross-Country Running M & W; Field Hockey W; Football M; Golf M; Lacrosse M & W; Soccer M & W; Softball W; Swimming and Diving M & W; Tennis M & W; Track and Field M & W; Volleyball W; Wrestling M

KUTZTOWN UNIVERSITY OF PENNSYLVANIA

15200 Kutztown Rd.
Kutztown, PA 19530-0730
Tel: (610)683-4000; Free: 877-628-1915
Fax: (610)683-1375
E-mail: admissions@kutztown.edu
Web Site: www.kutztown.edu
President/CEO: Dr. Kenneth Hawkinson
Admissions: Nancy Wunderly
Financial Aid: Bernard McCree

Type: Comprehensive **Sex:** Coed **Affiliation:** Pennsylvania State System of Higher Education. **Scores:** 93% SAT V 400+; 93% SAT M 400+; 59.3% ACT 18-23; 12.7% ACT 24-29 **% Accepted:** 82 **Admission Plans:** Deferred Admission; Early Admission **Application Deadline:** Rolling **Application Fee:** $35.00 **H.S. Requirements:** High school diploma required; GED accepted **Costs Per Year:** Application fee: $35. State resident tuition: $7060 full-time, $294 per credit hour part-time. Nonresident tuition: $17,650 full-time, $735 per credit hour part-time. Mandatory fees: $2085 full-time, $84.78 per credit hour part-time. Full-time tuition and fees vary according to course load. Part-time tuition and fees vary according to course load. College room and board: $9070. College room only: $5552. Room and board charges vary according to board plan and housing facility. **Scholarships:** Available. **Calendar System:** Semester, Summer session available **Enrollment:** Full-time 7,808, Graduate full-time 288, Graduate part-time 419, Part-time 485 **Faculty:** Full-time 417, Part-time 33 **Student-Faculty Ratio:** 19:1 **Exams:** SAT I or ACT; SAT II. **% Receiving Financial Aid:** 69 **% Residing in College-Owned, -Operated, or -Affiliated Housing:** 45 **Regional Accreditation:** Middle States Association of Colleges and Schools **Credit Hours For Degree:** 120 credits, Bachelors **ROTC:** Army **Professional Accreditation:** AACSB, ACEN, CSWE, NASAD, NASM, NCATE. **Intercollegiate Athletics:** Baseball M; Basketball M & W; Bowling W; Cheerleading W; Cross-Country Running M & W; Equestrian Sports M & W; Fencing M & W; Field Hockey W; Football M; Golf W; Ice Hockey M; Lacrosse M & W; Racquetball M & W; Rugby M & W; Soccer M & W; Softball W; Swimming and Diving W; Tennis M & W; Track and Field M & W; Ultimate Frisbee M & W; Volleyball M & W; Wrestling M

LA ROCHE COLLEGE

9000 Babcock Blvd.
Pittsburgh, PA 15237-5898
Tel: (412)367-9300; Free: 800-838-4LRC
Fax: (412)536-1075
E-mail: admissions@laroche.edu
Web Site: www.laroche.edu
President/CEO: Señor Candace Introcaso, PhD
Admissions: Terry Kizina
Financial Aid: Sharon E. Platt

Type: Comprehensive **Sex:** Coed **Affiliation:** Roman Catholic Church. **Scores:** 82% SAT V 400+; 82% SAT M 400+; 56% ACT 18-23; 16% ACT 24-29 **% Accepted:** 95 **Admission Plans:** Deferred Admission; Early Admission **Application Deadline:** Rolling **Application Fee:** $50.00 **H.S. Requirements:** High school diploma required; GED accepted **Costs Per Year:** Application fee: $50. Comprehensive fee: $36,880 includes full-time tuition ($25,500), mandatory fees ($750), and college room and board ($10,630). College room only: $6730. Room and board charges vary according to board plan and housing facility. Part-time tuition: $645 per credit hour.

Scholarships: Available. **Calendar System:** Semester, Summer session available **Enrollment:** Full-time 1,162, Graduate full-time 76, Graduate part-time 49, Part-time 236 **Faculty:** Full-time 62, Part-time 139 **Student-Faculty Ratio:** 12:1 **Exams:** SAT I or ACT. **% Receiving Financial Aid:** 68 **% Residing in College-Owned, -Operated, or -Affiliated Housing:** 46 **Final Year or Final Semester Residency Requirement:** Yes **Regional Accreditation:** Middle States Association of Colleges and Schools **Credit Hours For Degree:** 67 credit hours, Associates; 120 credit hours, Bachelors **ROTC:** Air Force, Army **Professional Accreditation:** AANA, ACBSP, ACEN, CIDA, NASAD. **Intercollegiate Athletics:** Baseball M; Basketball M & W; Cross-Country Running M & W; Golf M; Lacrosse M & W; Soccer M & W; Softball W; Tennis W; Volleyball W

LA SALLE UNIVERSITY

1900 W Olney Ave.
Philadelphia, PA 19141-1199
Tel: (215)951-1000; Free: 800-328-1910
Fax: (215)951-1656
E-mail: admiss@lasalle.edu
Web Site: www.lasalle.edu
President/CEO: Colleen M. Hanycz, PhD
Admissions: James Plunkett
Financial Aid: Joseph Alaimo

Type: Comprehensive **Sex:** Coed **Affiliation:** Roman Catholic. **Scores:** 95% SAT V 400+; 94% SAT M 400+; 55% ACT 18-23; 20% ACT 24-29 **% Accepted:** 75 **Admission Plans:** Deferred Admission; Early Admission; Early Decision Plan **Application Fee:** $35.00 **H.S. Requirements:** High school diploma required; GED accepted **Costs Per Year:** Application fee: $35. One-time mandatory fee: $150. Comprehensive fee: $55,600 includes full-time tuition ($40,400), mandatory fees ($700), and college room and board ($14,500). College room only: $7240. Full-time tuition and fees vary according to course load and program. Room and board charges vary according to board plan and housing facility. Part-time tuition: $555 per credit hour. Part-time mandatory fees: $175 per term. Part-time tuition and fees vary according to course load and program. **Scholarships:** Available. **Calendar System:** Semester, Summer session available **Enrollment:** Full-time 3,354, Graduate full-time 331, Graduate part-time 1,397, Part-time 593 **Faculty:** Full-time 242, Part-time 197 **Student-Faculty Ratio:** 12:1 **Exams:** ACT essay component not used; SAT I or ACT; SAT essay component not used. **% Receiving Financial Aid:** 82 **% Residing in College-Owned, -Operated, or -Affiliated Housing:** 56 **Final Year or Final Semester Residency Requirement:** Yes **Regional Accreditation:** Middle States Association of Colleges and Schools **Credit Hours For Degree:** 60 credit hours, Associates; 120 credit hours, Bachelors **ROTC:** Air Force, Army **Professional Accreditation:** AACN, AACSB, AAMFT, AANA, AND, APA, ASHA, CSWE. **Intercollegiate Athletics:** Baseball M; Basketball M & W; Cheerleading M & W; Crew M & W; Cross-Country Running M & W; Field Hockey W; Golf M & W; Lacrosse W; Soccer M & W; Softball W; Swimming and Diving M & W; Tennis M & W; Track and Field M & W; Volleyball W; Water Polo M & W

LACKAWANNA COLLEGE

501 Vine St.
Scranton, PA 18509
Tel: (570)961-7810; Free: 877-346-3552
Fax: (570)961-7858
E-mail: muchals@lackawanna.edu
Web Site: www.lackawanna.edu
President/CEO: Mark Volk
Admissions: Stacey Muchal
Financial Aid: Matthew Peters

Type: Two-Year College **Sex:** Coed **Scores:** 65% SAT V 400+; 62% SAT M 400+ **% Accepted:** 44 **Admission Plans:** Deferred Admission; Early Admission; Open Admission **Application Deadline:** Rolling **Application Fee:** $30.00 **H.S. Requirements:** High school diploma required; GED accepted **Costs Per Year:** Application fee: $30. Comprehensive fee: $22,410 includes full-time tuition ($13,400), mandatory fees ($710), and college room and board ($8300). College room only: $5800. Full-time tuition and fees vary according to course load. Part-time tuition: $465 per credit. Part-time mandatory fees: $105 per term. **Scholarships:** Available. **Calendar System:** Semester, Summer session available **Enrollment:** Full-time 1,158, Part-time 521 **Faculty:** Full-time 27, Part-time 141 **Student-Faculty Ratio:** 16:1 **Exams:** ACT; SAT I; SAT I or ACT. **% Residing in College-Owned, -Operated, or -Affiliated Housing:** 20 **Regional Accreditation:** Middle

States Association of Colleges and Schools **Credit Hours For Degree:** 60 credits, Associates **ROTC:** Air Force, Army **Intercollegiate Athletics:** Baseball M; Basketball M & W; Cheerleading W; Cross-Country Running M & W; Football M; Golf M & W; Soccer W; Softball W; Volleyball W

LAFAYETTE COLLEGE

Easton, PA 18042-1798
Tel: (610)330-5000
Fax: (610)330-5127
E-mail: hydem@lafayette.edu
Web Site: www.lafayette.edu
President/CEO: Dr. Alison Byerly
Admissions: Matthew Hyde
Financial Aid: Ashley Bianchi

Type: Four-Year College **Sex:** Coed **Affiliation:** Presbyterian Church (U.S. A.). **Scores:** 100% SAT V 400+; 100% SAT M 400+; 4.29% ACT 18-23; 53.8% ACT 24-29 **Costs Per Year:** One-time mandatory fee: $750. Comprehensive fee: $60,930 includes full-time tuition ($46,590), mandatory fees ($420), and college room and board ($13,920). College room only: $8610. Full-time tuition and fees vary according to course load. Room and board charges vary according to board plan, housing facility, and student level. Part-time tuition: $7765 per course. Part-time tuition varies according to course load. **Scholarships:** Available. **Calendar System:** Semester, Summer session available **Enrollment:** Full-time 2,491, Part-time 42 **Faculty:** Full-time 220, Part-time 59 **Student-Faculty Ratio:** 10:1 **Exams:** SAT I or ACT; SAT II. **% Receiving Financial Aid:** 32 **% Residing in College-Owned, -Operated, or -Affiliated Housing:** 94 **Final Year or Final Semester Residency Requirement:** Yes **Regional Accreditation:** Middle States Association of Colleges and Schools **Credit Hours For Degree:** 32-36 courses, depending on program, Bachelors **ROTC:** Army **Professional Accreditation:** ABET. **Intercollegiate Athletics:** Baseball M; Basketball M & W; Crew M & W; Cross-Country Running M & W; Equestrian Sports M & W; Fencing M & W; Field Hockey W; Football M; Ice Hockey M; Lacrosse M & W; Rugby M & W; Skiing (Downhill) M & W; Soccer M & W; Softball W; Squash M; Swimming and Diving M & W; Tennis M & W; Track and Field M & W; Volleyball W; Weight Lifting M & W; Wrestling M

LANCASTER BIBLE COLLEGE

901 Eden Rd.
Lancaster, PA 17601
Tel: (717)569-7071; Free: 800-544-7335
Fax: (717)560-8213
E-mail: admissions@lbc.edu
Web Site: www.lbc.edu
President/CEO: Peter W. Teague
Admissions: Joanne M. Roper
Financial Aid: Karen Fox

Type: Comprehensive **Sex:** Coed **Affiliation:** nondenominational. **Scores:** 98% SAT V 400+; 92% SAT M 400+; 52% ACT 18-23; 19% ACT 24-29 **% Accepted:** 57 **Admission Plans:** Deferred Admission; Early Admission **Application Deadline:** Rolling **Application Fee:** $25.00 **H.S. Requirements:** High school diploma required; GED accepted **Scholarships:** Available. **Calendar System:** Semester, Summer session available **Enrollment:** Full-time 560, Part-time 226 **Faculty:** Full-time 44, Part-time 42 **Student-Faculty Ratio:** 15:1 **Exams:** SAT I or ACT. **% Receiving Financial Aid:** 83 **% Residing in College-Owned, -Operated, or -Affiliated Housing:** 54 **Regional Accreditation:** Middle States Association of Colleges and Schools **Credit Hours For Degree:** 62 credit hours, Associates; 120 credit hours, Bachelors **Professional Accreditation:** ABHE, ATS. **Intercollegiate Athletics:** Baseball M; Basketball M & W; Lacrosse W; Soccer M & W; Volleyball M & W

LANCASTER COUNTY CAREER AND TECHNOLOGY CENTER

1730 Hans Herr Dr.
Willow Street, PA 17584
Tel: (717)464-7065
Fax: (717)464-9578
Web Site: www.lcctc.org
Type: Two-Year College **Sex:** Coed **Professional Accreditation:** COE.

LANSDALE SCHOOL OF BUSINESS

201 Church Rd.
North Wales, PA 19454-4148
Tel: (215)699-5700; Free: 800-219-0486

Fax: (215)699-8770
E-mail: mjohnson@lsb.edu
Web Site: www.lsb.edu
President/CEO: Marlon Keller
Admissions: Marianne H. Johnson
Type: Two-Year College **Sex:** Coed **Application Deadline:** Rolling **Application Fee:** $30.00 **H.S. Requirements:** High school diploma required; GED accepted **Scholarships:** Available. **Calendar System:** Semester, Summer session available **Credit Hours For Degree:** 68 credits, Associates **Professional Accreditation:** ACICS.

LAUREL BUSINESS INSTITUTE

11 E Penn St.
Uniontown, PA 15401
Tel: (724)439-4900
Fax: (724)439-3607
E-mail: ldolan@laurel.edu
Web Site: www.laurel.edu/lbi
President/CEO: Nancy Decker
Admissions: Lisa Dolan
Type: Two-Year College **Sex:** Coed **% Accepted:** 59 **Admission Plans:** Deferred Admission; Open Admission **Application Deadline:** Rolling **Application Fee:** $55.00 **H.S. Requirements:** High school diploma required; GED accepted **Costs Per Year:** Application fee: $55. One-time mandatory fee: $50. Tuition: $8794 full-time, $295 per credit hour part-time. Mandatory fees: $900 full-time. Full-time tuition and fees vary according to course load and program. Part-time tuition and fees vary according to course load and program. **Scholarships:** Available. **Calendar System:** Trimester **Enrollment:** Full-time 305 **Faculty:** Full-time 16, Part-time 9 **Student-Faculty Ratio:** 16:1 **Exams:** Other. **Professional Accreditation:** AAMAE, ACICS.

LAUREL TECHNICAL INSTITUTE

200 Sterling Ave.
Sharon, PA 16146
Tel: (724)983-0700
Fax: (724)983-8355
E-mail: info@biop.edu
Web Site: www.laurel.edu/lti
President/CEO: Nancy M. Decker
Admissions: Irene Lewis
Type: Two-Year College **Sex:** Coed **% Accepted:** 80 **H.S. Requirements:** High school diploma required; GED accepted **Scholarships:** Available. **Calendar System:** Quarter **Enrollment:** Full-time 98, Part-time 8 **Faculty:** Full-time 5, Part-time 4 **Student-Faculty Ratio:** 16:1 **Exams:** ACT. **Professional Accreditation:** ACICS.

LEBANON VALLEY COLLEGE

101 N College Ave.
Annville, PA 17003-1400
Tel: (717)867-6100; Free: 866-LVC-4ADM
Fax: (717)867-6124
E-mail: admission@lvc.edu
Web Site: www.lvc.edu
President/CEO: Dr. Lewis Evitts Thayne
Admissions: Edwin Wright
Financial Aid: Kendra M. Feigert
Type: Comprehensive **Sex:** Coed **Affiliation:** United Methodist. **Scores:** 94% SAT V 400+; 98% SAT M 400+; 42% ACT 18-23; 45% ACT 24-29 **% Accepted:** 72 **Admission Plans:** Early Action **Application Deadline:** Rolling **Application Fee:** $0.00 **H.S. Requirements:** High school diploma required; GED accepted **Costs Per Year:** Application fee: $0. Comprehensive fee: $49,540 includes full-time tuition ($37,930), mandatory fees ($1100), and college room and board ($10,510). College room only: $5080. Room and board charges vary according to board plan and housing facility. Part-time tuition: $625 per credit hour. Part-time tuition varies according to class time and degree level. **Scholarships:** Available. **Calendar System:** Semester, Summer session available **Enrollment:** Full-time 1,608, Graduate full-time 93, Graduate part-time 104, Part-time 113 **Faculty:** Full-time 108, Part-time 135 **Student-Faculty Ratio:** 11:1 **Exams:** ACT; ACT essay component not used; SAT I; SAT I and SAT II or ACT; SAT I or ACT; SAT II; SAT essay component not used. **% Receiving Financial Aid:** 86 **% Residing in College-Owned, -Operated, or -Affiliated Housing:** 80 **Final Year or Final Semester Residency Requirement:** Yes **Regional Accreditation:** Middle States Association of Colleges and Schools **Credit Hours For**

Degree: 120 credits, Bachelors **Professional Accreditation:** ACBSP, APTA, NASM. **Intercollegiate Athletics:** Baseball M; Basketball M & W; Cross-Country Running M & W; Field Hockey W; Football M; Golf M & W; Ice Hockey M & W; Lacrosse M & W; Soccer M & W; Softball W; Swimming and Diving M & W; Tennis M & W; Track and Field M & W; Volleyball W

LEHIGH CARBON COMMUNITY COLLEGE

4525 Education Park Dr.
Schnecksville, PA 18078-2598
Tel: (610)799-2121
Fax: (610)799-1527
E-mail: admissions@lccc.edu
Web Site: www.lccc.edu
President/CEO: Dr. Ann D. Bieber
Admissions: Nancy Kelley
Type: Two-Year College **Sex:** Coed **% Accepted:** 100 **Admission Plans:** Open Admission **Application Deadline:** Rolling **H.S. Requirements:** High school diploma or equivalent not required. For allied health, aviation, veterinary technician programs: High school diploma required; GED accepted **Costs Per Year:** Area resident tuition: $3000 full-time, $100 per credit part-time. State resident tuition: $6270 full-time, $209 per credit part-time. Nonresident tuition: $9540 full-time, $318 per credit part-time. Mandatory fees: $800 full-time, $37 per credit part-time. **Scholarships:** Available. **Calendar System:** Semester, Summer session available **Enrollment:** Full-time 2,577, Part-time 4,161 **Faculty:** Full-time 88, Part-time 355 **Student-Faculty Ratio:** 19:1 **Exams:** Other. **Final Year or Final Semester Residency Requirement:** No **Regional Accreditation:** Middle States Association of Colleges and Schools **Credit Hours For Degree:** 60 credits, Associates **ROTC:** Army **Professional Accreditation:** AAMAE, ACBSP, ACEN, AHIMA, AOTA, APTA. **Intercollegiate Athletics:** Baseball M; Basketball M & W; Golf M & W; Soccer M; Softball W; Volleyball W

LEHIGH UNIVERSITY

27 Memorial Dr. W
Bethlehem, PA 18015-3094
Tel: (610)758-3000
Fax: (610)758-4361
E-mail: admissions@lehigh.edu
Web Site: www.lehigh.edu
President/CEO: Dr. John D. Simon
Admissions: Bruce Bunnick
Financial Aid: Jennifer Mertz
Type: University **Sex:** Coed **Scores:** 100% SAT V 400+; 100% SAT M 400+; 2.6% ACT 18-23; 30.4% ACT 24-29 **% Accepted:** 30 **Admission Plans:** Deferred Admission; Early Action; Early Admission **Application Deadline:** January 1 **Application Fee:** $70.00 **H.S. Requirements:** High school diploma or equivalent not required **Costs Per Year:** Application fee: $70. Comprehensive fee: $58,510 includes full-time tuition ($45,860), mandatory fees ($370), and college room and board ($12,280). College room only: $7070. Room and board charges vary according to board plan and housing facility. Part-time tuition: $1915 per credit hour. **Scholarships:** Available. **Calendar System:** Semester, Summer session available **Enrollment:** Full-time 5,001, Graduate full-time 1,209, Graduate part-time 770, Part-time 74 **Faculty:** Full-time 521, Part-time 160 **Student-Faculty Ratio:** 10:1 **Exams:** SAT I or ACT; SAT II; SAT Reasoning; SAT Subject. **% Receiving Financial Aid:** 39 **% Residing in College-Owned, -Operated, or -Affiliated Housing:** 67 **Final Year or Final Semester Residency Requirement:** No **Regional Accreditation:** Middle States Association of Colleges and Schools **Credit Hours For Degree:** 120 credit hours, Bachelors **ROTC:** Army **Professional Accreditation:** AACSB, ABET, APA, NAST. **Intercollegiate Athletics:** Baseball M; Basketball M & W; Crew M & W; Cross-Country Running M & W; Equestrian Sports M & W; Fencing M & W; Field Hockey W; Football M; Golf M & W; Ice Hockey M; Lacrosse M & W; Rugby M & W; Skiing (Downhill) M & W; Soccer M & W; Softball W; Squash M & W; Swimming and Diving M & W; Tennis M & W; Track and Field M & W; Ultimate Frisbee M & W; Volleyball M & W; Water Polo M & W; Wrestling M

LINCOLN TECHNICAL INSTITUTE (ALLENTOWN)

5151 Tilghman St.
Allentown, PA 18104-3298
Tel: (610)398-5300
Web Site: www.lincolnedu.com
President/CEO: Lisa Kuntz
Type: Two-Year College **Sex:** Coed **Affiliation:** Lincoln Technical Institute,

Inc. **Admission Plans:** Early Admission; Open Admission **Application Deadline:** Rolling **Application Fee:** $25.00 **H.S. Requirements:** High school diploma required; GED accepted **Scholarships:** Available. **Calendar System:** Semester, Summer session available **Credit Hours For Degree:** 97 credits, Associates **Professional Accreditation:** ACCSC.

LINCOLN TECHNICAL INSTITUTE (PHILADELPHIA)
9191 Torresdale Ave.
Philadelphia, PA 19136-1595
Tel: (215)335-0800
Fax: (215)335-1443
E-mail: jkuntz@lincolntech.com
Web Site: www.lincolnedu.com
President/CEO: John Willie
Admissions: James Kuntz
Type: Two-Year College **Sex:** Coed **Affiliation:** Lincoln Technical Institute, Inc. **Admission Plans:** Deferred Admission; Open Admission **Application Deadline:** Rolling **Application Fee:** $25.00 **H.S. Requirements:** High school diploma required; GED accepted **Scholarships:** Available. **Calendar System:** Miscellaneous, Summer session not available **Credit Hours For Degree:** 76 credits, Associates **Professional Accreditation:** ACCSC.

LINCOLN TECHNICAL INSTITUTE (PHILADELPHIA)
2180 Hornig Rd.
Bldg. A
Philadelphia, PA 19116-4202
Web Site: www.lincolnedu.com
Type: Two-Year College **Sex:** Coed **Professional Accreditation:** ACICS.

LINCOLN UNIVERSITY
1570 Baltimore Pke.
Lincoln University, PA 19352
Tel: (484)365-8000; Free: 800-790-0191
E-mail: tharrison@lincoln.edu
Web Site: www.lincoln.edu
President/CEO: Dr. Richard I. Green
Admissions: Tiffany Harrison
Financial Aid: Kim Anderson
Type: Comprehensive **Sex:** Coed **Scores:** 66% SAT V 400+; 67% SAT M 400+; 44.23% ACT 18-23; 1.92% ACT 24-29 **% Accepted:** 91 **Admission Plans:** Deferred Admission **Application Deadline:** Rolling **Application Fee:** $20.00 **H.S. Requirements:** High school diploma required; GED accepted **Costs Per Year:** Application fee: $20. State resident tuition: $7340 full-time, $409 per credit part-time. Nonresident tuition: $12,132 full-time, $623 per credit part-time. Mandatory fees: $3378 full-time, $131 per credit part-time, $159. Full-time tuition and fees vary according to degree level, program, and student level. Part-time tuition and fees vary according to course load, degree level, program, and student level. College room and board: $9268. College room only: $5010. Room and board charges vary according to board plan and housing facility. Tuition guaranteed not to increase for student's term of enrollment. **Scholarships:** Available. **Calendar System:** Semester, Summer session available **Enrollment:** Full-time 1,549, Graduate full-time 139, Graduate part-time 65, Part-time 79 **Faculty:** Full-time 99, Part-time 64 **Student-Faculty Ratio:** 17:1 **Exams:** ACT essay component not used; SAT I or ACT; SAT essay component not used. **% Receiving Financial Aid:** 89 **% Residing in College-Owned, -Operated, or -Affiliated Housing:** 99 **Final Year or Final Semester Residency Requirement:** No **Regional Accreditation:** Middle States Association of Colleges and Schools **Credit Hours For Degree:** 120 credit hours, Bachelors **ROTC:** Air Force, Army **Professional Accreditation:** NRPA. **Intercollegiate Athletics:** Baseball M; Basketball M; Cross-Country Running M & W; Football M; Soccer W; Softball W; Track and Field M & W; Volleyball W

LOCK HAVEN UNIVERSITY OF PENNSYLVANIA
401 N Fairview St.
Lock Haven, PA 17745-2390
Tel: (570)893-2011; Free: 800-233-8978
Fax: (570)893-2201
E-mail: admissions@lhup.edu
Web Site: www.lhup.edu
President/CEO: Dr. Michael Fiorentino, Jr.
Admissions: Donna Tatarka
Financial Aid: Robert Fryer
Type: Comprehensive **Sex:** Coed **Affiliation:** Pennsylvania State System of

Higher Education. **Scores:** 86% SAT V 400+; 89% SAT M 400+; 59.63% ACT 18-23; 9.17% ACT 24-29 **% Accepted:** 92 **Admission Plans:** Deferred Admission **Application Deadline:** Rolling **Application Fee:** $25.00 **H.S. Requirements:** High school diploma required; GED accepted **Costs Per Year:** Application fee: $25. One-time mandatory fee: $30. State resident tuition: $7060 full-time, $294 per credit hour part-time. Nonresident tuition: $15,650 full-time, $652 per credit hour part-time. Mandatory fees: $2605 full-time, $139.90 per credit hour part-time, $40 per term part-time. Full-time tuition and fees vary according to course load and location. Part-time tuition and fees vary according to course load and location. College room and board: $9344. College room only: $5964. Room and board charges vary according to board plan and housing facility. **Scholarships:** Available. **Calendar System:** Semester, Summer session available **Enrollment:** Full-time 3,894, Graduate full-time 216, Graduate part-time 171, Part-time 326 **Faculty:** Full-time 214, Part-time 20 **Student-Faculty Ratio:** 19:1 **Exams:** SAT I or ACT; SAT essay component used for placement. **% Receiving Financial Aid:** 56 **% Residing in College-Owned, -Operated, or -Affiliated Housing:** 36 **Regional Accreditation:** Middle States Association of Colleges and Schools **Credit Hours For Degree:** 60 semester hours, Associates; 120 semester hours, Bachelors **ROTC:** Army **Professional Accreditation:** ACBSP, ACEN, CSWE, JRCAT, NCATE. **Intercollegiate Athletics:** Baseball M; Basketball M & W; Cross-Country Running M & W; Field Hockey W; Football M; Lacrosse W; Soccer M & W; Softball W; Swimming and Diving W; Track and Field M & W; Volleyball W; Wrestling M

LUZERNE COUNTY COMMUNITY COLLEGE
1333 S Prospect St.
Nanticoke, PA 18634-9804
Tel: (570)740-0300; Free: 800-377-5222
E-mail: admissions@luzerne.edu
Web Site: www.luzerne.edu
President/CEO: Thomas P. Leary
Admissions: Francis Curry
Type: Two-Year College **Sex:** Coed **% Accepted:** 100 **Admission Plans:** Deferred Admission; Early Admission; Open Admission **Application Fee:** $0.00 **H.S. Requirements:** High school diploma required; GED accepted. For those who demonstrate ability to benefit from program: High school diploma or equivalent not required **Scholarships:** Available. **Calendar System:** Semester, Summer session available **Enrollment:** Full-time 2,621, Part-time 3,167 **Faculty:** Full-time 112, Part-time 374 **Student-Faculty Ratio:** 17:1 **Regional Accreditation:** Middle States Association of Colleges and Schools **Credit Hours For Degree:** 60 semester hours, Associates **Professional Accreditation:** ACBSP, ACEN, ADA, ARCST. **Intercollegiate Athletics:** Baseball M; Basketball M & W; Cross-Country Running M & W; Golf M & W; Soccer M & W; Softball W; Volleyball W

LYCOMING COLLEGE
700 College Pl.
Williamsport, PA 17701-5192
Tel: (570)321-4000; Free: 800-345-3920
Fax: (570)321-4337
E-mail: admissions@lycoming.edu
Web Site: www.lycoming.edu
President/CEO: Dr. Kent C. Trachte
Admissions: Jason Moran
Financial Aid: James S. Lakis
Type: Four-Year College **Sex:** Coed **Affiliation:** United Methodist. **Scores:** 95% SAT V 400+; 95% SAT M 400+; 56.3% ACT 18-23; 31.3% ACT 24-29 **% Accepted:** 71 **Admission Plans:** Deferred Admission; Early Action; Early Decision Plan **Application Deadline:** March 1 **Application Fee:** $35.00 **H.S. Requirements:** High school diploma required; GED accepted **Costs Per Year:** Application fee: $35. One-time mandatory fee: $225. Comprehensive fee: $46,784 includes full-time tuition ($35,200), mandatory fees ($700), and college room and board ($10,884). Room and board charges vary according to board plan and housing facility. Part-time tuition: $1100 per credit hour. Part-time tuition varies according to course load. **Scholarships:** Available. **Calendar System:** Semester, Summer session available **Enrollment:** Full-time 1,272, Part-time 17 **Faculty:** Full-time 86, Part-time 36 **Student-Faculty Ratio:** 13:1 **Exams:** SAT I or ACT; SAT Reasoning; SAT Subject. **% Receiving Financial Aid:** 82 **% Residing in College-Owned, -Operated, or -Affiliated Housing:** 88 **Regional Accreditation:** Middle States Association of Colleges and Schools **Credit Hours For Degree:** 128 credits, Bachelors **ROTC:** Army **Intercollegiate Athletics:** Badminton M & W; Basketball M & W; Cheerleading M & W; Crew M & W; Cross-Country Run-

ning M & W; Equestrian Sports M & W; Fencing M & W; Football M; Golf M & W; Lacrosse M & W; Rugby M; Soccer M & W; Softball W; Swimming and Diving M & W; Tennis M & W; Ultimate Frisbee M & W; Volleyball W; Water Polo M & W; Wrestling M

MANOR COLLEGE
700 Fox Chase Rd.
Jenkintown, PA 19046
Tel: (215)885-2360
E-mail: swalker@manor.edu
Web Site: www.manor.edu
President/CEO: Dr. Jonathatn Peri
Admissions: Stephanie Walker
Financial Aid: Natalie Stusyk

Type: Two-Year College **Sex:** Coed **Affiliation:** Byzantine Catholic. **Scores:** 43% SAT V 400+; 40% SAT M 400+; 10% ACT 18-23; 10% ACT 24-29 **% Accepted:** 55 **Admission Plans:** Deferred Admission **Application Deadline:** Rolling **Application Fee:** $0.00 **H.S. Requirements:** High school diploma required; GED accepted **Costs Per Year:** Application fee: $0. Comprehensive fee: $24,050 includes full-time tuition ($15,950), mandatory fees ($600), and college room and board ($7500). Full-time tuition and fees vary according to course load and program. Part-time tuition: $599 per credit. Part-time mandatory fees: $100 per term. Part-time tuition and fees vary according to course load and program. **Scholarships:** Available. **Calendar System:** Semester, Summer session available **Enrollment:** Full-time 426, Part-time 270 **Faculty:** Full-time 25, Part-time 115 **Student-Faculty Ratio:** 8:1 **Exams:** SAT I or ACT. **% Residing in College-Owned, -Operated, or -Affiliated Housing:** 11 **Final Year or Final Semester Residency Requirement:** No **Regional Accreditation:** Middle States Association of Colleges and Schools **Credit Hours For Degree:** 60 credit hours, Associates **Professional Accreditation:** ACBSP, ADA. **Intercollegiate Athletics:** Basketball M & W; Soccer M & W

MANSFIELD UNIVERSITY OF PENNSYLVANIA
Academy St.
Mansfield, PA 16933
Tel: (570)662-4000; Free: 800-577-6826
Fax: (570)662-4121
E-mail: admissions@mnsfld.edu
Web Site: www.mansfield.edu
Admissions: Rachel Green
Financial Aid: Charles M. Scheetz

Type: Comprehensive **Sex:** Coed **Affiliation:** Pennsylvania State System of Higher Education. **Scores:** 88% SAT V 400+; 88% SAT M 400+ **% Accepted:** 86 **Admission Plans:** Deferred Admission; Early Admission **Application Fee:** $25.00 **H.S. Requirements:** High school diploma required; GED accepted **Costs Per Year:** Application fee: $25. State resident tuition: $7060 full-time, $294 per credit hour part-time. Nonresident tuition: $17,650 full-time, $735 per credit hour part-time. Mandatory fees: $2746 full-time. Part-time tuition varies according to course load. College room and board: $10,976. College room only: $7904. Room and board charges vary according to board plan and housing facility. **Scholarships:** Available. **Calendar System:** Semester **Enrollment:** Full-time 1,988, Graduate full-time 6, Graduate part-time 115, Part-time 207 **Faculty:** Full-time 113, Part-time 44 **Student-Faculty Ratio:** 17:1 **Exams:** ACT essay component not used; ACT essay component used for admission; ACT essay component used for placement; SAT I or ACT; SAT essay component not used; SAT essay component used for admission; SAT essay component used for placement. **% Receiving Financial Aid:** 83 **% Residing in College-Owned, -Operated, or -Affiliated Housing:** 51 **Regional Accreditation:** Middle States Association of Colleges and Schools **Credit Hours For Degree:** 61 credits, Associates; 120 credits, Bachelors **ROTC:** Army **Professional Accreditation:** ACEN, CSWE, CoARC, JRCERT, NASM, NCATE. **Intercollegiate Athletics:** Baseball M; Basketball M & W; Cross-Country Running M & W; Field Hockey W; Football M; Soccer W; Softball W; Swimming and Diving W; Track and Field M & W

MARYWOOD UNIVERSITY
2300 Adams Ave.
Scranton, PA 18509-1598
Tel: (570)348-6211; Free: 866-279-9663
Fax: (570)961-4763
E-mail: yourfuture@marywood.edu
Web Site: www.marywood.edu

President/CEO: Señor Anne Munley, IHM, PhD
Admissions: Christian DiGregorio
Financial Aid: Barbara Schmitt

Type: Comprehensive **Sex:** Coed **Affiliation:** Roman Catholic. **Scores:** 98% SAT V 400+; 98% SAT M 400+ **% Accepted:** 71 **Admission Plans:** Deferred Admission; Early Admission **Application Deadline:** Rolling **Application Fee:** $35.00 **H.S. Requirements:** High school diploma required; GED accepted **Costs Per Year:** Application fee: $35. Comprehensive fee: $46,592 includes full-time tuition ($30,942), mandatory fees ($1750), and college room and board ($13,900). College room only: $7822. Full-time tuition and fees vary according to course load. Room and board charges vary according to board plan and housing facility. Part-time tuition: $630 per credit. Part-time mandatory fees: $450 per term. Part-time tuition and fees vary according to course load. **Scholarships:** Available. **Calendar System:** Semester, Summer session available **Enrollment:** Full-time 1,768, Graduate full-time 904, Graduate part-time 173, Part-time 165 **Faculty:** Full-time 160, Part-time 244 **Student-Faculty Ratio:** 11:1 **Exams:** ACT essay component used for admission; SAT I or ACT; SAT essay component used for admission; SAT Reasoning. **% Receiving Financial Aid:** 81 **% Residing in College-Owned, -Operated, or -Affiliated Housing:** 36 **Final Year or Final Semester Residency Requirement:** No **Regional Accreditation:** Middle States Association of Colleges and Schools **Credit Hours For Degree:** 126 credits, Bachelors **ROTC:** Air Force, Army **Professional Accreditation:** AAFCS, ACA, ACBSP, ACEN, AND, ASHA, CSWE, NASAD, NASM, NCATE. **Intercollegiate Athletics:** Baseball M; Basketball M & W; Cross-Country Running M & W; Field Hockey W; Golf M; Lacrosse M & W; Soccer M & W; Softball W; Swimming and Diving M & W; Tennis M & W; Track and Field M & W; Volleyball W

MCCANN SCHOOL OF BUSINESS & TECHNOLOGY (HAZLETON)
370 Maplewood Dr.
Hazleton, PA 18202
Web Site: www.mccann.edu

Type: Two-Year College **Sex:** Coed **Professional Accreditation:** ACICS.

MCCANN SCHOOL OF BUSINESS & TECHNOLOGY (LEWISBURG)
7495 Westbranch Hwy.
Lewisburg, PA 17837
Tel: (570)497-8014
Web Site: www.mccann.edu

Type: Two-Year College **Sex:** Coed **Professional Accreditation:** ACICS.

MCCANN SCHOOL OF BUSINESS & TECHNOLOGY (POTTSVILLE)
2650 Woodglen Rd.
Pottsville, PA 17901
Tel: (570)622-7622
Fax: (570)622-7770
Web Site: www.mccann.edu
President/CEO: Shannon M. Brennan
Admissions: Amelia Hopkins

Type: Two-Year College **Sex:** Coed **Admission Plans:** Open Admission **Application Deadline:** Rolling **Application Fee:** $40.00 **H.S. Requirements:** High school diploma required; GED accepted **Scholarships:** Available. **Calendar System:** Quarter, Summer session available **Exams:** Other. **Credit Hours For Degree:** 90 credits, Associates **Professional Accreditation:** ACICS.

MERCYHURST NORTH EAST
16 W Division St.
North East, PA 16428
Tel: (717)725-6100; Free: 866-846-6042
E-mail: neadmiss@mercyhurst.edu
Web Site: northeast.mercyhurst.edu
President/CEO: Dr. Thomas J. Gamble
Admissions: Travis Lindahl
Financial Aid: Steve Gregg

Type: Two-Year College **Sex:** Coed **Affiliation:** Roman Catholic. **Scholarships:** Available. **Calendar System:** Miscellaneous **Regional Accreditation:** Middle States Association of Colleges and Schools **Intercollegiate Athletics:** Baseball M; Basketball M & W; Lacrosse M; Soccer M & W; Softball W; Volleyball W; Wrestling M

MERCYHURST UNIVERSITY
501 E 38th St.
Erie, PA 16546

Tel: (814)824-2000; Free: 800-825-1926
Fax: (814)824-2071
E-mail: cbeyer@mercyhurst.edu
Web Site: www.mercyhurst.edu
President/CEO: Michael T. Victor
Admissions: Christian Beyer
Financial Aid: Carrie Newman
Type: Comprehensive **Sex:** Coed **Affiliation:** Roman Catholic. **Scores:** 89% SAT V 400+; 89% SAT M 400+; 40% ACT 18-23; 40% ACT 24-29 **% Accepted:** 80 **Admission Plans:** Deferred Admission **Application Deadline:** Rolling **Application Fee:** $0.00 **H.S. Requirements:** High school diploma required; GED accepted **Costs Per Year:** Application fee: $0. Comprehensive fee: $44,546 includes full-time tuition ($31,320), mandatory fees ($1994), and college room and board ($11,232). College room only: $5694. Full-time tuition and fees vary according to class time, course load, degree level, location, and program. Room and board charges vary according to board plan, housing facility, and location. Part-time tuition: $3132 per course. Part-time mandatory fees: $65 per term. Part-time tuition and fees vary according to class time, course load, degree level, location, and program. **Scholarships:** Available. **Calendar System:** Semester, Summer session available **Enrollment:** Full-time 2,403, Graduate full-time 169, Graduate part-time 146, Part-time 88 **Faculty:** Full-time 165, Part-time 96 **Student-Faculty Ratio:** 13:1 **Exams:** ACT; SAT I; SAT I and SAT II or ACT; SAT I or ACT; SAT II; SAT Reasoning; SAT Subject. **% Receiving Financial Aid:** 71 **% Residing in College-Owned, -Operated, or -Affiliated Housing:** 68 **Final Year or Final Semester Residency Requirement:** No **Regional Accreditation:** Middle States Association of Colleges and Schools **Credit Hours For Degree:** 60 credits, Associates; 121 credits, Bachelors **ROTC:** Air Force, Army **Professional Accreditation:** AAFCS, ACEN, AND, APTA, CSWE, JRCAT, NASD, NASM. **Intercollegiate Athletics:** Baseball M; Basketball M & W; Crew M & W; Cross-Country Running M & W; Field Hockey W; Football M; Golf M & W; Ice Hockey M & W; Lacrosse M & W; Soccer M & W; Softball W; Tennis M & W; Volleyball W; Water Polo M & W; Wrestling M

MESSIAH COLLEGE

One College Ave.
Mechanicsburg, PA 17055
Tel: (717)766-2511; Free: 800-233-4220
Fax: (717)796-5374
E-mail: admiss@messiah.edu
Web Site: www.messiah.edu
President/CEO: Dr. Kim S. Phipps
Admissions: Dr. John Chopka
Financial Aid: Michael Strite
Type: Comprehensive **Sex:** Coed **Affiliation:** interdenominational. **Scores:** 99% SAT V 400+; 99% SAT M 400+; 38.38% ACT 18-23; 39.9% ACT 24-29 **% Accepted:** 79 **Application Deadline:** Rolling **Application Fee:** $20.00 **H.S. Requirements:** High school diploma required; GED accepted **Costs Per Year:** Application fee: $20. Comprehensive fee: $43,100 includes full-time tuition ($32,350), mandatory fees ($830), and college room and board ($9920). College room only: $5250. Room and board charges vary according to board plan and housing facility. Part-time tuition: $1350 per credit hour. **Scholarships:** Available. **Calendar System:** Semester, Summer session available **Enrollment:** Full-time 2,681, Graduate full-time 328, Graduate part-time 155, Part-time 138 **Faculty:** Full-time 192, Part-time 149 **Student-Faculty Ratio:** 12:1 **Exams:** SAT I or ACT; SAT essay component used for placement. **% Receiving Financial Aid:** 71 **% Residing in College-Owned, -Operated, or -Affiliated Housing:** 86 **Final Year or Final Semester Residency Requirement:** No **Regional Accreditation:** Middle States Association of Colleges and Schools **Credit Hours For Degree:** 123 credits, Bachelors **Professional Accreditation:** AACN, ABET, ACA, ACBSP, JRCAT, NASAD, NASM. **Intercollegiate Athletics:** Baseball M; Basketball M & W; Cross-Country Running M & W; Field Hockey W; Golf M; Ice Hockey M; Lacrosse M & W; Soccer M & W; Softball W; Swimming and Diving M & W; Tennis M & W; Track and Field M & W; Ultimate Frisbee M & W; Volleyball W; Wrestling M

METROPOLITAN CAREER CENTER COMPUTER TECHNOLOGY INSTITUTE

100 S Broad St.
Ste. 830
Philadelphia, PA 19110
Tel: (215)568-9215

Fax: (215)568-3511
Web Site: www.careersinit.org
President/CEO: Amy Miller
Type: Two-Year College **Sex:** Coed **% Accepted:** 53 **Calendar System:** Semester **Student-Faculty Ratio:** 16:1 **Professional Accreditation:** ACCSC.

MILLERSVILLE UNIVERSITY OF PENNSYLVANIA

1 S George St.
Millersville, PA 17551-0302
Tel: (717)871-4636; Free: 800-MU-ADMIT
E-mail: admissions@millersville.edu
Web Site: www.millersville.edu
President/CEO: Dr. John M. Anderson
Admissions: Katy A. Ferrier
Financial Aid: Dwight G. Horsey
Type: Comprehensive **Sex:** Coed **Affiliation:** Pennsylvania State System of Higher Education. **Scores:** 95% SAT V 400+; 94% SAT M 400+; 60% ACT 18-23; 23% ACT 24-29 **% Accepted:** 73 **Admission Plans:** Deferred Admission; Early Admission **Application Deadline:** Rolling **Application Fee:** $50.00 **H.S. Requirements:** High school diploma required; GED accepted **Costs Per Year:** Application fee: $50. State resident tuition: $8460 full-time, $282 per credit part-time. Nonresident tuition: $17,650 full-time, $735 per credit part-time. Mandatory fees: $2458 full-time, $84.25 per credit part-time, $19. Full-time tuition and fees vary according to course load and program. Part-time tuition and fees vary according to course load and program. College room and board: $12,188. College room only: $8034. Room and board charges vary according to board plan and housing facility. **Scholarships:** Available. **Calendar System:** 4-1-4, Summer session available **Enrollment:** Full-time 6,152, Graduate full-time 225, Graduate part-time 679, Part-time 932 **Faculty:** Full-time 290, Part-time 159 **Student-Faculty Ratio:** 20:1 **Exams:** SAT I or ACT. **% Receiving Financial Aid:** 67 **% Residing in College-Owned, -Operated, or -Affiliated Housing:** 33 **Final Year or Final Semester Residency Requirement:** No **Regional Accreditation:** Middle States Association of Colleges and Schools **Credit Hours For Degree:** 60 Credits, Associates; 120 credits, Bachelors **ROTC:** Army **Professional Accreditation:** ABET, ACBSP, ACEN, ATMAE, CSWE, CoARC, NASAD, NASM, NCATE. **Intercollegiate Athletics:** Baseball M; Basketball M & W; Cross-Country Running W; Field Hockey W; Football M; Golf M & W; Lacrosse W; Soccer M & W; Softball W; Swimming and Diving W; Tennis M & W; Track and Field W; Volleyball W; Wrestling M

MISERICORDIA UNIVERSITY

301 Lake St.
Dallas, PA 18612-1098
Tel: (570)674-6400; Free: 866-262-6363
Fax: (570)675-2441
E-mail: admiss@misericordia.edu
Web Site: www.misericordia.edu
President/CEO: Dr. Thomas J. Botzman
Admissions: Glenn Bozinski
Financial Aid: Jane Dessoye
Type: Comprehensive **Sex:** Coed **Affiliation:** Roman Catholic. **Scores:** 99% SAT V 400+; 99% SAT M 400+; 45% ACT 18-23; 50% ACT 24-29 **% Accepted:** 71 **Admission Plans:** Deferred Admission; Early Admission **Application Deadline:** Rolling **Application Fee:** $35.00 **H.S. Requirements:** High school diploma required; GED accepted **Costs Per Year:** Application fee: $35. Comprehensive fee: $43,890 includes full-time tuition ($29,150), mandatory fees ($1590), and college room and board ($13,150). College room only: $7160. Full-time tuition and fees vary according to degree level. Room and board charges vary according to board plan and housing facility. Part-time tuition: $575 per credit. Part-time tuition varies according to class time and location. **Scholarships:** Available. **Calendar System:** Semester, Summer session available **Enrollment:** Full-time 1,792, Graduate full-time 194, Graduate part-time 471, Part-time 608 **Faculty:** Full-time 134, Part-time 183 **Student-Faculty Ratio:** 12:1 **Exams:** ACT essay component not used; SAT I or ACT; SAT essay component not used. **% Receiving Financial Aid:** 80 **% Residing in College-Owned, -Operated, or -Affiliated Housing:** 42 **Final Year or Final Semester Residency Requirement:** No **Regional Accreditation:** Middle States Association of Colleges and Schools **Credit Hours For Degree:** 120 credits, Bachelors **ROTC:** Air Force, Army **Professional Accreditation:** AACN, AOTA, APTA, ASHA, CSWE, JRCERT, NCATE. **Intercollegiate Athletics:** Baseball M; Basketball M & W; Cross-Country Running M & W; Field Hockey W; Football M; Golf M & W; Lacrosse

M & W; Soccer M & W; Softball W; Swimming and Diving M & W; Tennis M & W; Track and Field M & W; Volleyball W

MONTGOMERY COUNTY COMMUNITY COLLEGE

340 DeKalb Pke.
Blue Bell, PA 19422-0796
Tel: (215)641-6300
Fax: (215)653-0585
E-mail: admrec@admin.mc3.edu
Web Site: www.mc3.edu
President/CEO: Dr. Kevin Pollock

Type: Two-Year College **Sex:** Coed **% Accepted:** 100 **Admission Plans:** Deferred Admission; Early Admission; Open Admission; Preferred Admission **H.S. Requirements:** High school diploma required; GED accepted. For early admissions program: High school diploma or equivalent not required **Costs Per Year:** Area resident tuition: $4020 full-time, $134 per credit part-time. State resident tuition: $8340 full-time, $268 per credit part-time. Nonresident tuition: $12,660 full-time, $402 per credit part-time. Mandatory fees: $900 full-time, $30 per credit part-time. Full-time tuition and fees vary according to program. Part-time tuition and fees vary according to program. **Scholarships:** Available. **Calendar System:** Semester, Summer session available **Enrollment:** Full-time 3,897, Part-time 8,475 **Faculty:** Full-time 176, Part-time 547 **Student-Faculty Ratio:** 19:1 **Regional Accreditation:** Middle States Association of Colleges and Schools **Credit Hours For Degree:** 60 credits, Associates **Professional Accreditation:** ACEN, ADA, NAACLS. **Intercollegiate Athletics:** Baseball M; Basketball M & W; Soccer M & W; Softball W; Volleyball W

MOORE COLLEGE OF ART & DESIGN

20th and the Pky.
Philadelphia, PA 19103
Tel: (215)965-4000; Free: 800-523-2025
E-mail: enroll@moore.edu
Web Site: www.moore.edu
President/CEO: Cecelia Fitzgibbon
Admissions: Jasmine Zateeny
Financial Aid: MIchelle Shonleber

Type: Comprehensive **Scores:** 91% SAT V 400+; 78% SAT M 400+; 12% ACT 18-23; 38% ACT 24-29 **% Accepted:** 56 **Admission Plans:** Deferred Admission **Application Deadline:** August 15 **Application Fee:** $60.00 **H.S. Requirements:** High school diploma required; GED accepted **Costs Per Year:** Application fee: $60. Comprehensive fee: $50,664 includes full-time tuition ($35,608), mandatory fees ($1220), and college room and board ($13,836). College room only: $8330. Full-time tuition and fees vary according to course load. Room and board charges vary according to board plan. Part-time tuition: $1486 per credit. Part-time tuition varies according to course load. **Scholarships:** Available. **Calendar System:** Semester, Summer session available **Enrollment:** Full-time 392, Graduate full-time 26, Graduate part-time 8, Part-time 14 **Faculty:** Full-time 24, Part-time 115 **Student-Faculty Ratio:** 7:1 **Exams:** SAT I or ACT. **% Residing in College-Owned, -Operated, or -Affiliated Housing:** 38 **Final Year or Final Semester Residency Requirement:** No **Regional Accreditation:** Middle States Association of Colleges and Schools **Credit Hours For Degree:** 126 credits, Bachelors **Professional Accreditation:** CIDA, NASAD.

MORAVIAN COLLEGE

1200 Main St.
Bethlehem, PA 18018-6650
Tel: (610)861-1300; Free: 800-441-3191
Fax: (610)861-3956
E-mail: admission@moravian.edu
Web Site: www.moravian.edu
President/CEO: Dr. Bryon Grigsby
Admissions: Steven Soba
Financial Aid: Dr. Dennis P. Levy

Type: Comprehensive **Sex:** Coed **Affiliation:** Moravian Church. **Scores:** 92% SAT V 400+; 94% SAT M 400+; 60.4% ACT 18-23; 29.7% ACT 24-29 **% Accepted:** 75 **Admission Plans:** Deferred Admission **Application Deadline:** March 1 **Application Fee:** $0.00 **H.S. Requirements:** High school diploma required; GED accepted **Costs Per Year:** Application fee: $0. One-time mandatory fee: $140. Comprehensive fee: $50,468 includes full-time tuition ($37,251), mandatory fees ($1581), and college room and board ($11,636). College room only: $6560. Room and board charges vary according to board plan and housing facility. Part-time tuition: $1,034.75 per

credit. Part-time tuition varies according to class time. **Scholarships:** Available. **Calendar System:** Semester, Summer session available **Enrollment:** Full-time 1,691, Graduate full-time 93, Graduate part-time 337, Part-time 140 **Faculty:** Full-time 113, Part-time 84 **Student-Faculty Ratio:** 12:1 **Exams:** ACT; ACT essay component used for admission; ACT essay component used for advising; ACT essay component used for placement; SAT I; SAT I and SAT II or ACT; SAT I or ACT; SAT II; SAT essay component used for admission; SAT essay component used for advising; SAT essay component used for placement; SAT Reasoning; SAT Subject. **% Receiving Financial Aid:** 81 **% Residing in College-Owned, -Operated, or -Affiliated Housing:** 70 **Final Year or Final Semester Residency Requirement:** No **Regional Accreditation:** Middle States Association of Colleges and Schools **Credit Hours For Degree:** 128 credits, Bachelors **ROTC:** Army **Professional Accreditation:** AACN, ACBSP, NASM. **Intercollegiate Athletics:** Baseball M; Basketball M & W; Bowling M; Cheerleading W; Cross-Country Running M & W; Equestrian Sports W; Field Hockey W; Football M; Golf M & W; Ice Hockey M & W; Lacrosse M & W; Rugby M & W; Soccer M & W; Softball W; Tennis M & W; Track and Field M & W; Ultimate Frisbee W; Volleyball W; Wrestling M

MOUNT ALOYSIUS COLLEGE

7373 Admiral Peary Hwy.
Cresson, PA 16630-1999
Tel: (814)886-4131; Free: 888-823-2220
Fax: (814)886-2978
E-mail: admissions@mtaloy.edu
Web Site: www.mtaloy.edu
President/CEO: Dr. Thomas P. Foley, JD
Admissions: Frank C. Crouse, Jr.
Financial Aid: Stacy L. Schenk

Type: Comprehensive **Sex:** Coed **Affiliation:** Roman Catholic. **Scores:** 91% SAT V 400+; 89% SAT M 400+; 57% ACT 18-23; 11% ACT 24-29 **% Accepted:** 73 **Admission Plans:** Deferred Admission; Early Admission **Application Deadline:** Rolling **Application Fee:** $30.00 **H.S. Requirements:** High school diploma required; GED accepted **Costs Per Year:** Application fee: $30. Comprehensive fee: $31,790 includes full-time tuition ($20,710), mandatory fees ($1140), and college room and board ($9940). College room only: $5000. Part-time tuition: $770 per credit hour. **Scholarships:** Available. **Calendar System:** Semester, Summer session available **Enrollment:** Full-time 1,176, Graduate full-time 41, Graduate part-time 33, Part-time 627 **Faculty:** Full-time 72, Part-time 131 **Student-Faculty Ratio:** 12:1 **Exams:** ACT; ACT essay component not used; SAT I; SAT I or ACT; SAT essay component used for advising. **% Receiving Financial Aid:** 88 **% Residing in College-Owned, -Operated, or -Affiliated Housing:** 34 **Regional Accreditation:** Middle States Association of Colleges and Schools **Professional Accreditation:** AAMAE, ACBSP, ACEN, AOTA, APTA, ARCST. **Intercollegiate Athletics:** Baseball M; Basketball M & W; Cross-Country Running M & W; Golf M & W; Soccer M & W; Softball W; Tennis M & W; Volleyball W

MUHLENBERG COLLEGE

2400 Chew St.
Allentown, PA 18104-5586
Tel: (484)664-3100
Fax: (484)664-3234
E-mail: adm@muhlenberg.edu
Web Site: www.muhlenberg.edu
President/CEO: Pres. John I. Williams
Admissions: Christopher Hooker-Haring
Financial Aid: Greg Mitton

Type: Four-Year College **Sex:** Coed **Affiliation:** Lutheran Church. **Scores:** 100% SAT V 400+; 100% SAT M 400+; 9.1% ACT 18-23; 59.8% ACT 24-29 **% Accepted:** 48 **Admission Plans:** Deferred Admission; Early Action; Early Admission **Application Deadline:** February 15 **Application Fee:** $50.00 **H.S. Requirements:** High school diploma required; GED accepted **Costs Per Year:** Application fee: $50. Comprehensive fee: $56,645 includes full-time tuition ($45,590), mandatory fees ($285), and college room and board ($10,770). College room only: $5850. Room and board charges vary according to board plan, housing facility, and location. **Scholarships:** Available. **Calendar System:** Semester, Summer session available **Enrollment:** Full-time 2,307, Part-time 90 **Faculty:** Full-time 177, Part-time 108 **Student-Faculty Ratio:** 11:1 **Exams:** ACT essay component used for admission; ACT essay component used for advising; ACT essay component used for placement; SAT I or ACT; SAT essay component used for admission; SAT essay component used for advising; SAT essay component used for placement; SAT Reasoning. **% Receiving Financial Aid:** 47 **% Residing in College-Owned, -Operated, or -Affiliated Housing:** 91 **Regional Accreditation:** Middle States Association of Colleges and Schools **Credit Hours For Degree:** 34 courses, Bachelors **ROTC:** Army **Intercollegiate Athletics:** Baseball M; Basketball M & W; Cheerleading M & W; Cross-Country Running M & W; Field Hockey W; Football M; Golf M & W; Lacrosse M & W; Soccer M & W; Softball W; Tennis M & W; Track and Field M & W; Volleyball W; Wrestling M

NEUMANN UNIVERSITY

One Neumann Dr.
Aston, PA 19014-1298
Tel: (610)459-0905; Free: 800-963-8626
E-mail: neumann@neumann.edu
Web Site: www.neumann.edu
President/CEO: Dr. Rosalie Mirenda
Admissions: Chris Mayerski
Financial Aid: Deborah Cawley

Type: Comprehensive **Sex:** Coed **Affiliation:** Roman Catholic. **Scores:** 76% SAT V 400+; 75% SAT M 400+; 48.7% ACT 18-23; 10.3% ACT 24-29 **% Accepted:** 91 **Admission Plans:** Deferred Admission **Application Deadline:** Rolling **Application Fee:** $35.00 **H.S. Requirements:** High school diploma required; GED accepted **Costs Per Year:** Application fee: $35. Comprehensive fee: $38,672 includes full-time tuition ($25,792), mandatory fees ($1126), and college room and board ($11,754). College room only: $7114. Room and board charges vary according to board plan and housing facility. Part-time tuition: $589 per credit hour. Part-time mandatory fees: $70 per term. **Scholarships:** Available. **Calendar System:** Semester, Summer session available **Enrollment:** Full-time 1,806, Graduate full-time 136, Graduate part-time 362, Part-time 597 **Faculty:** Full-time 97, Part-time 206 **Student-Faculty Ratio:** 14:1 **Exams:** ACT; ACT essay component not used; SAT I; SAT I and SAT II or ACT; SAT I or ACT; SAT II; SAT essay component not used; SAT Reasoning. **% Receiving Financial Aid:** 77 **% Residing in College-Owned, -Operated, or -Affiliated Housing:** 32 **Final Year or Final Semester Residency Requirement:** No **Regional Accreditation:** Middle States Association of Colleges and Schools **Credit Hours For Degree:** 60 credits, Associates; 120 credits, Bachelors **ROTC:** Air Force, Army **Professional Accreditation:** ACBSP, ACEN, APTA, NAACLS. **Intercollegiate Athletics:** Baseball M; Basketball M & W; Cross-Country Running M & W; Field Hockey W; Golf M & W; Ice Hockey M & W; Lacrosse M & W; Rugby M & W; Soccer M & W; Softball W; Tennis M & W; Track and Field M & W; Volleyball W

NEW CASTLE SCHOOL OF TRADES

4117 Pulaski Rd.
New Castle, PA 16101
Tel: (724)964-8811; Free: 800-837-8299
Web Site: www.ncstrades.com
President/CEO: Jim Buttermore
Admissions: Joe Blazak

Type: Two-Year College **Sex:** Coed **Scholarships:** Available. **Calendar System:** Quarter, Summer session not available **Enrollment:** Full-time 503 **Faculty:** Full-time 30, Part-time 16 **Student-Faculty Ratio:** 11:1 **Exams:** Other. **Final Year or Final Semester Residency Requirement:** No **Credit Hours For Degree:** 90 quarter credits, Associates **Professional Accreditation:** ACCSC.

NORTHAMPTON COMMUNITY COLLEGE

3835 Green Pond Rd.
Bethlehem, PA 18020-7599
Tel: (610)861-5300
E-mail: jrmccarthy@northampton.edu
Web Site: www.northampton.edu
President/CEO: Dr. Mark H. Erickson
Admissions: James McCarthy
Financial Aid: Cindy King

Type: Two-Year College **Sex:** Coed **% Accepted:** 100 **Admission Plans:** Deferred Admission; Open Admission **Application Deadline:** Rolling **Application Fee:** $25.00 **H.S. Requirements:** High school diploma required; GED accepted **Costs Per Year:** Application fee: $25. Area resident tuition: $2820 full-time, $94 per credit hour part-time. State resident tuition: $5640 full-time, $188 per credit hour part-time. Nonresident tuition: $8460 full-time, $282 per credit hour part-time. Mandatory fees: $1170 full-time, $39 per

credit hour part-time. Full-time tuition and fees vary according to course load. Part-time tuition and fees vary according to course load. College room and board: $8092. College room only: $5000. Room and board charges vary according to board plan and housing facility. **Scholarships:** Available. **Calendar System:** Semester, Summer session available **Enrollment:** Full-time 4,594, Part-time 5,675 **Faculty:** Full-time 122, Part-time 585 **Student-Faculty Ratio:** 20:1 **% Residing in College-Owned, -Operated, or -Affiliated Housing:** 6 **Final Year or Final Semester Residency Requirement:** No **Regional Accreditation:** Middle States Association of Colleges and Schools **Credit Hours For Degree:** 60 credit hours, Associates **Professional Accreditation:** ABFSE, ACBSP, ACEN, ADA, JRCERT. **Intercollegiate Athletics:** Baseball M; Basketball M & W; Cross-Country Running M & W; Golf M; Lacrosse M; Soccer M & W; Softball W; Tennis W; Volleyball W

PEIRCE COLLEGE

1420 Pine St.
Philadelphia, PA 19102-4699
Tel: (215)545-6400; Free: 888-467-3472
Fax: (215)546-5996
E-mail: info@peirce.edu
Web Site: www.peirce.edu
President/CEO: James J. Mergiotti
Admissions: Paul Ballentine
Financial Aid: Chanel Greene

Type: Comprehensive **Sex:** Coed **Admission Plans:** Open Admission **Application Fee:** $50.00 **H.S. Requirements:** High school diploma required; GED accepted **Costs Per Year:** Application fee: $50. Tuition: $13,584 full-time, $566 per credit hour part-time. Mandatory fees: $600 full-time. Full-time tuition and fees vary according to course load and reciprocity agreements. Part-time tuition varies according to course load and reciprocity agreements. **Scholarships:** Available. **Calendar System:** Semester, Summer session available **Enrollment:** Full-time 304, Graduate full-time 1, Graduate part-time 64, Part-time 1,339 **Faculty:** Full-time 30, Part-time 91 **Student-Faculty Ratio:** 13:1 **% Receiving Financial Aid:** 77 **Final Year or Final Semester Residency Requirement:** No **Regional Accreditation:** Middle States Association of Colleges and Schools **Credit Hours For Degree:** 61 credits, Associates; 121 credits, Bachelors **Professional Accreditation:** ACBSP.

PENN COMMERCIAL BUSINESS AND TECHNICAL SCHOOL

242 Oak Spring Rd.
Washington, PA 15301
Tel: (724)222-5330; Free: 888-309-7484
Fax: (724)222-4722
E-mail: mjoyce@penn-commercial.com
Web Site: www.penncommercial.net
President/CEO: Robert S. Bazant
Admissions: Michael John Joyce
Financial Aid: Cynthia A. Galloway

Type: Two-Year College **Sex:** Coed **Admission Plans:** Deferred Admission; Early Admission; Open Admission **Application Deadline:** Rolling **Application Fee:** $100.00 **H.S. Requirements:** High school diploma required; GED accepted **Scholarships:** Available. **Calendar System:** Quarter, Summer session available **Credit Hours For Degree:** 1500 hours, Associates **Professional Accreditation:** AAMAE, ACICS.

PENN STATE ABINGTON

1600 Woodland Rd.
Abington, PA 19001
Tel: (215)881-7300
E-mail: abingtonadmissions@psu.edu
Web Site: www.abington.psu.edu
President/CEO: Karen Wiley Sandler

Type: Four-Year College **Sex:** Coed **Affiliation:** Pennsylvania State University. **Scores:** 82% SAT V 400+; 88% SAT M 400+; 49.21% ACT 18-23; 30.16% ACT 24-29 **% Accepted:** 82 **Admission Plans:** Deferred Admission; Early Admission **Application Deadline:** Rolling **Application Fee:** $50.00 **H.S. Requirements:** High school diploma required; GED accepted **Costs Per Year:** Application fee: $50. State resident tuition: $13,012 full-time, $535 per credit hour part-time. Nonresident tuition: $20,324 full-time, $847 per credit hour part-time. Mandatory fees: $942 full-time. Full-time tuition and fees vary according to course level, degree level, location, program, and student level. Part-time tuition varies according to course level, course load, degree level, location, program, and student level. **Scholar-**

ships: Available. **Calendar System:** Semester **Enrollment:** Full-time 3,113, Graduate part-time 5, Part-time 848 **Faculty:** Full-time 136, Part-time 168 **Student-Faculty Ratio:** 18:1 **Exams:** SAT I or ACT. **% Receiving Financial Aid:** 69 **Regional Accreditation:** Middle States Association of Colleges and Schools **Credit Hours For Degree:** 60 credits, Associates; 120 credits, Bachelors **ROTC:** Air Force, Army **Intercollegiate Athletics:** Baseball M; Basketball M & W; Golf M; Soccer M & W; Softball W; Tennis M & W; Volleyball W

PENN STATE ALTOONA

3000 Ivyside Park
Altoona, PA 16601-3760
Tel: (814)949-5000; Free: 800-848-9843
Fax: (814)949-5011
E-mail: aaadmit@psu.edu
Web Site: www.altoona.psu.edu
Financial Aid: David Pearlman

Type: Four-Year College **Sex:** Coed **Affiliation:** Pennsylvania State University. **Scores:** 92% SAT V 400+; 92% SAT M 400+; 62.28% ACT 18-23; 28.07% ACT 24-29 **% Accepted:** 89 **Admission Plans:** Deferred Admission; Early Admission **Application Deadline:** Rolling **Application Fee:** $50.00 **H.S. Requirements:** High school diploma required; GED accepted **Costs Per Year:** Application fee: $50. State resident tuition: $13,658 full-time, $569 per credit hour part-time. Nonresident tuition: $21,392 full-time, $891 per credit hour part-time. Mandatory fees: $952 full-time. Full-time tuition and fees vary according to course level, degree level, location, program, and student level. Part-time tuition varies according to course level, course load, degree level, location, program, and student level. College room and board: $10,920. College room only: $5720. Room and board charges vary according to board plan, housing facility, and location. **Scholarships:** Available. **Calendar System:** Semester **Enrollment:** Full-time 3,684, Graduate part-time 1, Part-time 154 **Faculty:** Full-time 203, Part-time 99 **Student-Faculty Ratio:** 16:1 **Exams:** ACT essay component not used; SAT I or ACT; SAT essay component not used. **% Receiving Financial Aid:** 67 **% Residing in College-Owned, -Operated, or -Affiliated Housing:** 25 **Regional Accreditation:** Middle States Association of Colleges and Schools **Credit Hours For Degree:** 60 credits, Associates; 120 credits, Bachelors **ROTC:** Air Force, Army **Professional Accreditation:** ABET. **Intercollegiate Athletics:** Baseball M; Basketball M & W; Cross-Country Running M & W; Golf M & W; Soccer M & W; Softball W; Swimming and Diving M & W; Tennis M & W

PENN STATE BEAVER

100 University Dr.
Monaca, PA 15061
Tel: (724)773-3800
Fax: (724)773-3557
E-mail: br-admissions@psu.edu
Web Site: www.br.psu.edu
President/CEO: Donna J. Kuga
Financial Aid: Gail Gray

Type: Four-Year College **Sex:** Coed **Affiliation:** Pennsylvania State University. **Scores:** 85% SAT V 400+; 89% SAT M 400+; 45% ACT 18-23; 25% ACT 24-29 **% Accepted:** 82 **Admission Plans:** Deferred Admission; Early Admission **Application Deadline:** Rolling **Application Fee:** $50.00 **H.S. Requirements:** High school diploma required; GED accepted **Costs Per Year:** Application fee: $50. State resident tuition: $12,718 full-time, $524 per credit hour part-time. Nonresident tuition: $19,404 full-time, $809 per credit hour part-time. Mandatory fees: $942 full-time. Full-time tuition and fees vary according to course level, degree level, location, program, and student level. Part-time tuition varies according to course level, course load, degree level, location, program, and student level. College room and board: $10,920. College room only: $5720. Room and board charges vary according to board plan, housing facility, and location. **Scholarships:** Available. **Calendar System:** Semester **Enrollment:** Full-time 619, Part-time 86 **Faculty:** Full-time 32, Part-time 27 **Student-Faculty Ratio:** 16:1 **Exams:** ACT essay component not used; SAT I or ACT; SAT essay component not used. **% Receiving Financial Aid:** 74 **% Residing in College-Owned, -Operated, or -Affiliated Housing:** 23 **Regional Accreditation:** Middle States Association of Colleges and Schools **Credit Hours For Degree:** 60 credits, Associates **Professional Accreditation:** ABET. **Intercollegiate Athletics:** Baseball M; Basketball M; Softball M & W; Volleyball W

PENN STATE BERKS

Tulpehocken Rd.
Reading, PA 19610-6009

Tel: (610)396-6000
E-mail: admissionsbk@psu.edu
Web Site: www.bk.psu.edu
Financial Aid: Judith A. Rile

Type: Four-Year College **Sex:** Coed **Affiliation:** Pennsylvania State University. **Scores:** 85% SAT V 400+; 86% SAT M 400+; 51.67% ACT 18-23; 28.33% ACT 24-29 **% Accepted:** 85 **Admission Plans:** Deferred Admission; Early Admission **Application Deadline:** Rolling **Application Fee:** $50.00 **H.S. Requirements:** High school diploma required; GED accepted **Costs Per Year:** Application fee: $50. State resident tuition: $13,658 full-time, $569 per credit hour part-time. Nonresident tuition: $21,392 full-time, $891 per credit hour part-time. Mandatory fees: $952 full-time. Full-time tuition and fees vary according to course level, degree level, location, program, and student level. Part-time tuition varies according to course level, course load, degree level, location, program, and student level. College room and board: $11,950. College room only: $6750. Room and board charges vary according to board plan, housing facility, and location. **Scholarships:** Available. **Calendar System:** Semester **Enrollment:** Full-time 2,602, Part-time 304 **Faculty:** Full-time 136, Part-time 84 **Student-Faculty Ratio:** 17:1 **Exams:** ACT essay component not used; SAT I or ACT; SAT essay component not used. **% Receiving Financial Aid:** 70 **% Residing in College-Owned, -Operated, or -Affiliated Housing:** 28 **Regional Accreditation:** Middle States Association of Colleges and Schools **Credit Hours For Degree:** 60 credits, Associates; 120 credits, Bachelors **ROTC:** Army **Professional Accreditation:** ABET, AOTA. **Intercollegiate Athletics:** Baseball M; Basketball M & W; Cheerleading M & W; Cross-Country Running M & W; Golf M; Soccer M & W; Softball W; Tennis M & W; Volleyball W

PENN STATE BRANDYWINE

25 Yearsley Mill Rd.
Media, PA 19063-5596
Tel: (610)892-1200
E-mail: bwadmissions@psu.edu
Web Site: www.brandywine.psu.edu
President/CEO: Kristin R. Woolever

Type: Four-Year College **Sex:** Coed **Affiliation:** Pennsylvania State University. **Scores:** 88% SAT V 400+; 89% SAT M 400+; 35% ACT 18-23; 40% ACT 24-29 **% Accepted:** 83 **Admission Plans:** Deferred Admission; Early Admission **Application Deadline:** Rolling **Application Fee:** $50.00 **H.S. Requirements:** High school diploma required; GED accepted **Costs Per Year:** Application fee: $50. State resident tuition: $13,012 full-time, $535 per credit hour part-time. Nonresident tuition: $20,206 full-time, $842 per credit hour part-time. Mandatory fees: $952 full-time. Full-time tuition and fees vary according to course level, degree level, location, program, and student level. Part-time tuition varies according to course level, course load, degree level, location, program, and student level. **Scholarships:** Available. **Calendar System:** Semester **Enrollment:** Full-time 1,250, Part-time 207 **Faculty:** Full-time 68, Part-time 67 **Student-Faculty Ratio:** 15:1 **Exams:** ACT essay component not used; SAT I or ACT; SAT essay component not used. **% Receiving Financial Aid:** 65 **Regional Accreditation:** Middle States Association of Colleges and Schools **Credit Hours For Degree:** 60 credits, Associates; 120 credits, Bachelors **ROTC:** Air Force, Army **Intercollegiate Athletics:** Baseball M; Basketball M & W; Soccer M & W; Tennis M & W; Volleyball W

PENN STATE DUBOIS

1 College Pl.
DuBois, PA 15801
Tel: (814)375-4700; Free: 800-346-7627
E-mail: duboisinfo@psi.edu
Web Site: www.ds.psu.edu
President/CEO: Melanie L. Hatch

Type: Two-Year College **Sex:** Coed **Affiliation:** Pennsylvania State University. **Scores:** 81% SAT V 400+; 83% SAT M 400+; 66.67% ACT 18-23; 33.33% ACT 24-29 **% Accepted:** 85 **Admission Plans:** Deferred Admission; Early Admission **Application Deadline:** Rolling **Application Fee:** $50.00 **H.S. Requirements:** High school diploma required; GED accepted **Costs Per Year:** Application fee: $50. State resident tuition: $12,718 full-time, $524 per credit hour part-time. Nonresident tuition: $19,404 full-time, $809 per credit hour part-time. Mandatory fees: $828 full-time. Full-time tuition and fees vary according to course level, degree level, location, program, and student level. Part-time tuition varies according to course level, course load, degree level, location, program, and student level. **Scholarships:** Available. **Calendar System:** Semester **Enrollment:** Full-time 497,

Part-time 105 **Faculty:** Full-time 42, Part-time 16 **Student-Faculty Ratio:** 11:1 **Exams:** ACT essay component not used; SAT I or ACT; SAT essay component not used. **Regional Accreditation:** Middle States Association of Colleges and Schools **Credit Hours For Degree:** 60 credits, Associates **Professional Accreditation:** ABET, AOTA, APTA. **Intercollegiate Athletics:** Basketball M; Cross-Country Running M & W; Golf M & W; Volleyball W

PENN STATE ERIE, THE BEHREND COLLEGE

4701 College Dr.
Erie, PA 16563-0001
Tel: (814)898-6000; Free: 866-374-3378
E-mail: behrend.admissions@psu.edu
Web Site: www.pserie.psu.edu
Financial Aid: Jane Brady

Type: Comprehensive **Sex:** Coed **Affiliation:** Pennsylvania State University. **Scores:** 94% SAT V 400+; 96% SAT M 400+; 44.58% ACT 18-23; 40.36% ACT 24-29 **% Accepted:** 87 **Admission Plans:** Deferred Admission; Early Admission **Application Deadline:** Rolling **Application Fee:** $50.00 **H.S. Requirements:** High school diploma required; GED accepted **Costs Per Year:** Application fee: $50. State resident tuition: $13,658 full-time, $569 per credit hour part-time. Nonresident tuition: $21,392 full-time, $891 per credit hour part-time. Mandatory fees: $952 full-time. Full-time tuition and fees vary according to course level, degree level, location, program, and student level. Part-time tuition varies according to course level, course load, degree level, location, program, and student level. College room and board: $10,920. College room only: $5720. Room and board charges vary according to board plan, housing facility, and location. **Scholarships:** Available. **Calendar System:** Semester **Enrollment:** Full-time 3,955, Graduate full-time 31, Graduate part-time 121, Part-time 220 **Faculty:** Full-time 260, Part-time 70 **Student-Faculty Ratio:** 15:1 **Exams:** ACT essay component not used; SAT I or ACT; SAT essay component not used. **% Receiving Financial Aid:** 69 % **Residing in College-Owned, -Operated, or -Affiliated Housing:** 41 **Regional Accreditation:** Middle States Association of Colleges and Schools **Credit Hours For Degree:** 60 credits, Associates; 124 credits, Bachelors **ROTC:** Army **Professional Accreditation:** AACSB, ABET. **Intercollegiate Athletics:** Baseball M; Basketball M & W; Cheerleading M & W; Cross-Country Running M & W; Golf M & W; Ice Hockey M; Lacrosse M; Skiing (Downhill) M & W; Soccer M & W; Softball W; Swimming and Diving M & W; Tennis M & W; Track and Field M & W; Volleyball M & W; Water Polo M & W

PENN STATE FAYETTE, THE EBERLY CAMPUS

2201 University Dr.
Lemont Furnace, PA 15456
Tel: (724)430-4100; Free: 877-568-4130
Fax: (724)430-4184
E-mail: feadm@psu.edu
Web Site: www.fe.psu.edu
President/CEO: W. Charles Patrick

Type: Two-Year College **Sex:** Coed **Affiliation:** Pennsylvania State University. **Scores:** 75% SAT V 400+; 80% SAT M 400+; 60% ACT 18-23 **% Accepted:** 81 **Admission Plans:** Deferred Admission; Early Admission **Application Deadline:** Rolling **Application Fee:** $50.00 **H.S. Requirements:** High school diploma required; GED accepted **Costs Per Year:** Application fee: $50. State resident tuition: $12,718 full-time, $524 per credit hour part-time. Nonresident tuition: $19,404 full-time, $809 per credit hour part-time. Mandatory fees: $890 full-time. Full-time tuition and fees vary according to course level, degree level, location, program, and student level. Part-time tuition varies according to course level, course load, degree level, location, program, and student level. **Scholarships:** Available. **Calendar System:** Semester **Enrollment:** Full-time 592, Part-time 112 **Faculty:** Full-time 44, Part-time 25 **Student-Faculty Ratio:** 12:1 **Exams:** ACT essay component not used; SAT I or ACT; SAT essay component not used. **Regional Accreditation:** Middle States Association of Colleges and Schools **Credit Hours For Degree:** 60 credits, Associates **Professional Accreditation:** ABET. **Intercollegiate Athletics:** Baseball M; Basketball M; Softball W; Volleyball W

PENN STATE GREATER ALLEGHENY

4000 University Dr.
McKeesport, PA 15132-7698
Tel: (412)675-9000
E-mail: psuga@psu.edu
Web Site: www.ga.psu.edu
President/CEO: Nancy L. Herron

Type: Comprehensive **Sex:** Coed **Affiliation:** Pennsylvania State University. **Scores:** 73% SAT V 400+; 79% SAT M 400+; 36.36% ACT 24-29 **% Accepted:** 79 **Admission Plans:** Deferred Admission; Early Admission **Application Deadline:** Rolling **Application Fee:** $50.00 **H.S. Requirements:** High school diploma required; GED accepted **Costs Per Year:** Application fee: $50. State resident tuition: $12,718 full-time, $524 per credit hour part-time. Nonresident tuition: $19,404 full-time, $809 per credit hour part-time. Mandatory fees: $942 full-time. Full-time tuition and fees vary according to course level, degree level, location, program, and student level. Part-time tuition varies according to course level, course load, degree level, location, program, and student level. College room and board: $10,920. College room only: $5720. Room and board charges vary according to board plan, housing facility, and location. **Scholarships:** Available. **Calendar System:** Semester **Enrollment:** Full-time 504, Part-time 73 **Faculty:** Full-time 34, Part-time 43 **Student-Faculty Ratio:** 11:1 **Exams:** ACT essay component not used; SAT I or ACT; SAT essay component not used. **% Receiving Financial Aid:** 77 % **Residing in College-Owned, -Operated, or -Affiliated Housing:** 22 **Regional Accreditation:** Middle States Association of Colleges and Schools **Credit Hours For Degree:** 60 credits, Associates **Intercollegiate Athletics:** Baseball M; Basketball M; Softball W; Volleyball W

PENN STATE HARRISBURG

777 W Harrisburg Pke.
Middletown, PA 17057-4898
Tel: (717)948-6000; Free: 800-222-2056
E-mail: hbgadmit@psu.edu
Web Site: www.hbg.psu.edu

Type: Comprehensive **Sex:** Coed **Affiliation:** Pennsylvania State University. **Scores:** 91% SAT V 400+; 95% SAT M 400+; 48% ACT 18-23; 33.33% ACT 24-29 **% Accepted:** 85 **Admission Plans:** Deferred Admission; Early Admission **Application Deadline:** Rolling **Application Fee:** $50.00 **H.S. Requirements:** High school diploma required; GED accepted **Costs Per Year:** Application fee: $50. State resident tuition: $13,658 full-time, $569 per credit hour part-time. Nonresident tuition: $21,392 full-time, $891 per credit hour part-time. Mandatory fees: $952 full-time. Full-time tuition and fees vary according to course level, degree level, location, program, and student level. Part-time tuition varies according to course level, course load, degree level, location, program, and student level. College room and board: $12,450. College room only: $7250. Room and board charges vary according to board plan, housing facility, and location. **Scholarships:** Available. **Calendar System:** Semester **Enrollment:** Full-time 3,439, Graduate full-time 229, Graduate part-time 583, Part-time 427 **Faculty:** Full-time 229, Part-time 142 **Student-Faculty Ratio:** 15:1 **Exams:** ACT essay component not used; SAT I or ACT; SAT essay component not used. **% Receiving Financial Aid:** 65 % **Residing in College-Owned, -Operated, or -Affiliated Housing:** 11 **Regional Accreditation:** Middle States Association of Colleges and Schools **Credit Hours For Degree:** 60 credits, Associates; 120 credits, Bachelors **ROTC:** Army **Professional Accreditation:** AACSB, ABET, NASPAA, NCATE. **Intercollegiate Athletics:** Baseball M; Basketball M & W; Cross-Country Running M & W; Golf M & W; Soccer M & W; Softball W; Tennis M & W; Volleyball W

PENN STATE HAZLETON

76 University Dr.
Hazleton, PA 18202
Tel: (570)450-3000; Free: 800-279-8495
E-mail: admissions-hn@psu.edu
Web Site: www.hn.psu.edu
President/CEO: Gary M. Lawler
Financial Aid: Sarah Evancho

Type: Four-Year College **Sex:** Coed **Affiliation:** Pennsylvania State University. **Scores:** 81% SAT V 400+; 86% SAT M 400+; 40% ACT 18-23; 33.33% ACT 24-29 **% Accepted:** 84 **Admission Plans:** Deferred Admission; Early Admission **Application Deadline:** Rolling **Application Fee:** $50.00 **H.S. Requirements:** High school diploma required; GED accepted **Costs Per Year:** Application fee: $50. State resident tuition: $13,012 full-time, $535 per credit hour part-time. Nonresident tuition: $20,206 full-time, $842 per credit hour part-time. Mandatory fees: $890 full-time. Full-time tuition and fees vary according to course level, degree level, location, program, and student level. Part-time tuition varies according to course level, course load, degree level, location, program, and student level. College room and board: $10,920. College room only: $5720. Room and board charges vary according to board plan, housing facility, and location.

Scholarships: Available. **Calendar System:** Semester **Enrollment:** Full-time 725, Part-time 106 **Faculty:** Full-time 50, Part-time 21 **Student-Faculty Ratio:** 13:1 **Exams:** ACT essay component not used; SAT I or ACT; SAT essay component not used. **% Receiving Financial Aid:** 81 **% Residing in College-Owned, -Operated, or -Affiliated Housing:** 41 **Regional Accreditation:** Middle States Association of Colleges and Schools **Credit Hours For Degree:** 60 credits, Associates **ROTC:** Air Force **Professional Accreditation:** ABET, APTA, NAACLS. **Intercollegiate Athletics:** Baseball M; Basketball M & W; Cheerleading M & W; Soccer M; Softball W; Tennis M & W; Volleyball M & W

PENN STATE LEHIGH VALLEY

2809 Saucon Valley Rd.
Center Valley, PA 18034-8447
Tel: (610)285-5000
E-mail: admissions-lv@psu.edu
Web Site: www.lv.psu.edu
President/CEO: Ann M. Williams
Financial Aid: Maryann Hubick

Type: Four-Year College **Sex:** Coed **Affiliation:** Pennsylvania State University. **Scores:** 91% SAT V 400+; 90% SAT M 400+; 43.75% ACT 18-23; 37.5% ACT 24-29 **% Accepted:** 86 **Admission Plans:** Deferred Admission; Early Admission **Application Fee:** $50.00 **H.S. Requirements:** High school diploma required; GED accepted **Costs Per Year:** Application fee: $50. State resident tuition: $13,012 full-time, $535 per credit hour part-time. Nonresident tuition: $20,206 full-time, $842 per credit hour part-time. Mandatory fees: $952 full-time. Full-time tuition and fees vary according to course level, degree level, location, program, and student level. Part-time tuition varies according to course level, course load, degree level, location, program, and student level. **Scholarships:** Available. **Calendar System:** Semester **Enrollment:** Full-time 712, Graduate part-time 31, Part-time 150 **Faculty:** Full-time 43, Part-time 41 **Student-Faculty Ratio:** 14:1 **Exams:** ACT essay component not used; SAT I or ACT; SAT essay component not used. **% Receiving Financial Aid:** 66 **Regional Accreditation:** Middle States Association of Colleges and Schools **Credit Hours For Degree:** 60 credits, Associates; 120 credits, Bachelors **ROTC:** Army **Intercollegiate Athletics:** Baseball M; Basketball M & W; Bowling M & W; Cheerleading M & W; Cross-Country Running M & W; Football M; Golf M & W; Ice Hockey M & W; Skiing (Downhill) M & W; Soccer M & W; Tennis M & W; Volleyball M & W

PENN STATE MONT ALTO

1 Campus Dr.
Mont Alto, PA 17237-9703
Tel: (717)749-6000; Free: 800-392-6173
E-mail: psuma@psu.edu
Web Site: www.ma.psu.edu
President/CEO: Francis K. Achampong

Type: Two-Year College **Sex:** Coed **Affiliation:** Pennsylvania State University. **Scores:** 86% SAT V 400+; 87% SAT M 400+; 28.57% ACT 18-23; 28.57% ACT 24-29 **% Accepted:** 79 **Admission Plans:** Deferred Admission; Early Admission **Application Deadline:** Rolling **Application Fee:** $50.00 **H.S. Requirements:** High school diploma required; GED accepted **Costs Per Year:** Application fee: $50. State resident tuition: $12,718 full-time, $524 per credit hour part-time. Nonresident tuition: $19,404 full-time, $809 per credit hour part-time. Mandatory fees: $952 full-time. Full-time tuition and fees vary according to course level, degree level, location, program, and student level. Part-time tuition varies according to course level, course load, degree level, location, program, and student level. College room and board: $10,920. College room only: $5720. Room and board charges vary according to board plan, housing facility, and location. **Scholarships:** Available. **Calendar System:** Semester **Enrollment:** Full-time 661, Part-time 232 **Faculty:** Full-time 56, Part-time 36 **Student-Faculty Ratio:** 11:1 **Exams:** ACT essay component not used; SAT I or ACT; SAT essay component not used. **% Residing in College-Owned, -Operated, or -Affiliated Housing:** 26 **Regional Accreditation:** Middle States Association of Colleges and Schools **Credit Hours For Degree:** 60 credits, Associates **ROTC:** Army **Professional Accreditation:** AOTA, APTA. **Intercollegiate Athletics:** Basketball M & W; Cheerleading M & W; Cross-Country Running M & W; Golf M & W; Soccer M & W; Softball W; Tennis M & W; Volleyball W

PENN STATE NEW KENSINGTON

3550 Seventh St. Rd.
New Kensington, PA 15068

Tel: (724)334-5466; Free: 888-968-7297
Fax: (724)334-6111
E-mail: nkadmissions@psu.edu
Web Site: www.nk.psu.edu
President/CEO: Kevin J.G. Snider

Type: Four-Year College **Sex:** Coed **Affiliation:** Pennsylvania State University. **Scores:** 86% SAT V 400+; 86% SAT M 400+; 62.5% ACT 18-23; 12.5% ACT 24-29 **% Accepted:** 79 **Admission Plans:** Deferred Admission; Early Admission **Application Deadline:** Rolling **Application Fee:** $50.00 **H.S. Requirements:** High school diploma required; GED accepted **Costs Per Year:** Application fee: $50. State resident tuition: $12,718 full-time, $524 per credit hour part-time. Nonresident tuition: $19,404 full-time, $809 per credit hour part-time. Mandatory fees: $890 full-time. Full-time tuition and fees vary according to course level, degree level, location, program, and student level. Part-time tuition varies according to course level, course load, degree level, location, program, and student level. **Scholarships:** Available. **Calendar System:** Semester **Enrollment:** Full-time 512, Part-time 144 **Faculty:** Full-time 35, Part-time 37 **Student-Faculty Ratio:** 12:1 **Exams:** ACT essay component not used; SAT I or ACT; SAT essay component not used. **% Receiving Financial Aid:** 74 **Regional Accreditation:** Middle States Association of Colleges and Schools **Credit Hours For Degree:** 60 credits, Associates **ROTC:** Air Force **Professional Accreditation:** ABET, JRCERT, NAACLS. **Intercollegiate Athletics:** Baseball M; Basketball M & W; Cheerleading M & W; Golf M & W; Softball W; Volleyball W

PENN STATE SCHUYLKILL

200 University Dr.
Schuylkill Haven, PA 17972-2208
Tel: (570)385-6000
E-mail: sl-admissions@psu.edu
Web Site: www.sl.psu.edu
President/CEO: Kelly M. Austin

Type: Four-Year College **Sex:** Coed **Affiliation:** Pennsylvania State University. **Scores:** 79% SAT V 400+; 83% SAT M 400+; 32% ACT 18-23 **% Accepted:** 73 **Admission Plans:** Deferred Admission; Early Admission **Application Deadline:** Rolling **Application Fee:** $50.00 **H.S. Requirements:** High school diploma required; GED accepted **Costs Per Year:** Application fee: $50. State resident tuition: $13,012 full-time, $535 per credit hour part-time. Nonresident tuition: $20,206 full-time, $842 per credit hour part-time. Mandatory fees: $890 full-time. Full-time tuition and fees vary according to course level, degree level, location, program, and student level. Part-time tuition varies according to course level, course load, degree level, location, program, and student level. College room and board: $8060. College room only: $6060. Room and board charges vary according to board plan, housing facility, and location. **Scholarships:** Available. **Calendar System:** Semester **Enrollment:** Full-time 626, Part-time 157 **Faculty:** Full-time 43, Part-time 28 **Student-Faculty Ratio:** 13:1 **Exams:** ACT essay component not used; SAT I or ACT; SAT essay component not used. **% Receiving Financial Aid:** 83 **% Residing in College-Owned, -Operated, or -Affiliated Housing:** 30 **Regional Accreditation:** Middle States Association of Colleges and Schools **Credit Hours For Degree:** 60 credits, Associates; 120 credits, Bachelors **Professional Accreditation:** ABET, JRCERT. **Intercollegiate Athletics:** Basketball M; Cross-Country Running M & W; Golf M; Soccer M; Softball W; Volleyball W

PENN STATE SHENANGO

147 Shenango Ave.
Sharon, PA 16146-1537
Tel: (724)983-2803
Fax: (724)983-2820
E-mail: psushenango@psu.edu
Web Site: www.shenango.psu.edu
President/CEO: Jo Anne Carrick
Financial Aid: Shawn O'Neill

Type: Two-Year College **Sex:** Coed **Affiliation:** Pennsylvania State University. **Scores:** 92% SAT V 400+; 90% SAT M 400+; 70% ACT 18-23; 10% ACT 24-29 **% Accepted:** 68 **Admission Plans:** Deferred Admission; Early Admission **Application Deadline:** Rolling **Application Fee:** $50.00 **H.S. Requirements:** High school diploma required; GED accepted **Costs Per Year:** Application fee: $50. State resident tuition: $12,474 full-time, $504 per credit hour part-time. Nonresident tuition: $19,030 full-time, $793 per credit hour part-time. Mandatory fees: $880 full-time. Full-time tuition and fees vary according to course level, degree level, location, program, and student level. Part-time tuition varies according to course level, course load, degree level, location, program, and student level. **Scholarships:** Available. **Calendar System:** Semester **Enrollment:** Full-time 280, Part-time 228 **Faculty:** Full-time 28, Part-time 16 **Student-Faculty Ratio:** 11:1 **Exams:** ACT essay component not used; SAT I or ACT; SAT essay component not used. **Regional Accreditation:** Middle States Association of Colleges and Schools **Credit Hours For Degree:** 60 credits, Associates **Professional Accreditation:** ABET, APTA.

PENN STATE UNIVERSITY PARK
201 Old Main
University Park, PA 16802
Tel: (814)865-4700
E-mail: admissions@psu.edu
Web Site: www.psu.edu
President/CEO: Dr. Eric J. Barron
Admissions: Clark V. Brigger
Financial Aid: Anna M. Griswold

Type: University **Sex:** Coed **Affiliation:** The Pennsylvania State University. **Scores:** 99% SAT V 400+; 100% SAT M 400+; 13.04% ACT 18-23; 61.58% ACT 24-29 **% Accepted:** 51 **Admission Plans:** Deferred Admission; Early Admission **Application Deadline:** Rolling **Application Fee:** $50.00 **H.S. Requirements:** High school diploma required; GED accepted **Costs Per Year:** Application fee: $50. State resident tuition: $16,572 full-time, $691 per credit hour part-time. Nonresident tuition: $30,404 full-time, $1267 per credit hour part-time. Mandatory fees: $942 full-time. Full-time tuition and fees vary according to course level, degree level, location, program, and student level. Part-time tuition varies according to course level, course load, degree level, location, program, and student level. College room and board: $10,920. College room only: $5720. Room and board charges vary according to board plan, housing facility, and location. **Scholarships:** Available. **Calendar System:** Semester, Summer session available **Enrollment:** Full-time 39,520, Graduate full-time 5,890, Graduate part-time 675, Part-time 1,222 **Faculty:** Full-time 2,740, Part-time 359 **Student-Faculty Ratio:** 16:1 **Exams:** SAT I or ACT. **% Receiving Financial Aid:** 47 **% Residing in College-Owned, -Operated, or -Affiliated Housing:** 34 **Final Year or Final Semester Residency Requirement:** No **Regional Accreditation:** Middle States Association of Colleges and Schools **Credit Hours For Degree:** 60 credits, Associates; 120 credits, Bachelors **ROTC:** Air Force, Army, Navy **Professional Accreditation:** AACN, AACSB, ABA, ABET, ACA, ACEJMC, ACEN, AND, APA, ASHA, ASLA, CAHME, CORE, JRCAT, NAAB, NASAD, NASM, NAST, NCATE, SAF. **Intercollegiate Athletics:** Baseball M; Basketball M & W; Cross-Country Running M & W; Fencing M & W; Field Hockey W; Football M; Golf M & W; Gymnastics M & W; Ice Hockey M & W; Lacrosse M & W; Soccer M & W; Softball W; Swimming and Diving M & W; Tennis M & W; Track and Field M & W; Volleyball M & W; Wrestling M

PENN STATE WILKES-BARRE
Old Rte. 115
Lehman, PA 18627
Tel: (570)675-2171
E-mail: wbadmissions@psu.edu
Web Site: www.wb.psu.edu
President/CEO: Charles H. Davis
Financial Aid: Stacey Zelinka

Type: Four-Year College **Sex:** Coed **Affiliation:** Pennsylvania State University. **Scores:** 90% SAT V 400+; 90% SAT M 400+; 66.67% ACT 18-23; 33.33% ACT 24-29 **% Accepted:** 88 **Admission Plans:** Deferred Admission; Early Admission **Application Deadline:** Rolling **Application Fee:** $50.00 **H.S. Requirements:** High school diploma required; GED accepted **Costs Per Year:** Application fee: $50. State resident tuition: $12,718 full-time, $524 per credit hour part-time. Nonresident tuition: $19,404 full-time, $809 per credit hour part-time. Mandatory fees: $880 full-time. Full-time tuition and fees vary according to course level, degree level, location, program, and student level. Part-time tuition varies according to course level, course load, degree level, location, program, and student level. **Scholarships:** Available. **Calendar System:** Semester **Enrollment:** Full-time 440, Graduate part-time 8, Part-time 53 **Faculty:** Full-time 30, Part-time 19 **Student-Faculty Ratio:** 13:1 **Exams:** ACT essay component not used; SAT I or ACT; SAT essay component not used. **% Receiving Financial Aid:** 72 **Regional Accreditation:** Middle States Association of Colleges and Schools **Credit Hours For Degree:** 60 credits, Associates **ROTC:** Air Force, Army **Professional Accreditation:** ABET. **Intercollegiate Athletics:** Baseball M; Basketball M; Cross-Country Running M & W; Golf M & W; Soccer M & W; Volleyball W

PENN STATE WORTHINGTON SCRANTON
120 Ridge View Dr.
Dunmore, PA 18512-1699
Tel: (570)963-2500
Fax: (570)963-2535
E-mail: wsadmissions@psu.edu
Web Site: www.sn.psu.edu
President/CEO: Mary Beth Krogh-Jespersen

Type: Four-Year College **Sex:** Coed **Affiliation:** Pennsylvania State University. **Scores:** 87% SAT V 400+; 86% SAT M 400+; 42.86% ACT 18-23; 14.29% ACT 24-29 **% Accepted:** 81 **Admission Plans:** Deferred Admission; Early Admission **Application Deadline:** Rolling **Application Fee:** $50.00 **H.S. Requirements:** High school diploma required; GED accepted **Costs Per Year:** Application fee: $50. State resident tuition: $13,012 full-time, $535 per credit hour part-time. Nonresident tuition: $20,206 full-time, $842 per credit hour part-time. Mandatory fees: $890 full-time. Full-time tuition and fees vary according to course level, degree level, location, program, and student level. Part-time tuition varies according to course level, course load, degree level, location, program, and student level. **Scholarships:** Available. **Calendar System:** Semester **Enrollment:** Full-time 880, Part-time 154 **Faculty:** Full-time 50, Part-time 47 **Student-Faculty Ratio:** 14:1 **Exams:** ACT essay component not used; SAT I or ACT; SAT essay component not used. **% Receiving Financial Aid:** 79 **Regional Accreditation:** Middle States Association of Colleges and Schools **Credit Hours For Degree:** 60 credits, Associates **ROTC:** Air Force, Army **Professional Accreditation:** ABET. **Intercollegiate Athletics:** Baseball M; Basketball M & W; Cheerleading M & W; Cross-Country Running M & W; Soccer M; Softball W; Volleyball W

PENN STATE YORK
1031 Edgecomb Ave.
York, PA 17403
Tel: (717)771-4000; Free: 800-778-6227
Fax: (717)771-4062
E-mail: ykadmission@psu.edu
Web Site: www.yk.psu.edu
President/CEO: David W. Chown

Type: Comprehensive **Sex:** Coed **Affiliation:** Pennsylvania State University. **Scores:** 91% SAT V 400+; 93% SAT M 400+; 25.81% ACT 18-23; 58.06% ACT 24-29 **% Accepted:** 86 **Admission Plans:** Deferred Admission; Early Admission **Application Deadline:** Rolling **Application Fee:** $50.00 **H.S. Requirements:** High school diploma required; GED accepted **Costs Per Year:** Application fee: $50. State resident tuition: $13,012 full-time, $535 per credit hour part-time. Nonresident tuition: $20,206 full-time, $842 per credit hour part-time. Mandatory fees: $952 full-time. Full-time tuition and fees vary according to course level, degree level, location, program, and student level. Part-time tuition varies according to course level, course load, degree level, location, program, and student level. **Scholarships:** Available. **Calendar System:** Semester **Enrollment:** Full-time 841, Graduate part-time 18, Part-time 246 **Faculty:** Full-time 50, Part-time 43 **Student-Faculty Ratio:** 15:1 **Exams:** ACT essay component not used; SAT I or ACT; SAT essay component not used. **% Receiving Financial Aid:** 61 **Regional Accreditation:** Middle States Association of Colleges and Schools **Credit Hours For Degree:** 60 credits, Associates **Professional Accreditation:** ABET.

PENNCO TECH
3815 Otter St.
Bristol, PA 19007-3696
Tel: (215)824-3200; Free: 800-575-9399
E-mail: admissions@penncotech.com
Web Site: www.penncotech.com
President/CEO: Alfred William Parcells, Jr.
Admissions: John Keenan

Type: Two-Year College **Sex:** Coed **Affiliation:** Pennco Institutes, Inc. **Application Deadline:** Rolling **Application Fee:** $100.00 **H.S. Requirements:** High school diploma required; GED accepted. For applicants who demonstrate ability to benefit from college: High school diploma or equivalent not required **Scholarships:** Available. **Calendar System:** Miscellaneous, Summer session not available **Enrollment:** Full-time 245, Part-time 155 **Faculty:** Full-time 30, Part-time 10 **Student-Faculty Ratio:** 18:1 **% Residing in College-Owned, -Operated, or -Affiliated Housing:** 3 **Final Year or Final Semester Residency Requirement:** No **Credit Hours For Degree:** 2100 clock hours, Associates **Professional Accreditation:** ACCSC.

PENNSYLVANIA ACADEMY OF THE FINE ARTS

128 N Broad St.
Philadelphia, PA 19102
Tel: (215)972-7600
E-mail: avandeputte@pafa.edu
Web Site: www.pafa.edu
Admissions: André van de Putte
Financial Aid: Dana Moore

Type: Comprehensive **Sex:** Coed **Application Deadline:** February 15 **Application Fee:** $60.00 **Costs Per Year:** Application fee: $60. Tuition: $32,960 full-time. Mandatory fees: $1450 full-time. Full-time tuition and fees vary according to course load and degree level. Tuition guaranteed not to increase for student's term of enrollment. **Scholarships:** Available. **Calendar System:** Semester **Exams:** Other. **Regional Accreditation:** Middle States Association of Colleges and Schools **Professional Accreditation:** NASAD.

PENNSYLVANIA COLLEGE OF ART & DESIGN

204 N Prince St.
Lancaster, PA 17608-0059
Tel: (717)396-7833; Free: 800-689-0379
Fax: (717)396-1339
E-mail: admissions@pcad.edu
Web Site: www.pcad.edu
President/CEO: Mary Colleen Heil
Financial Aid: J. David Hershey

Type: Four-Year College **Sex:** Coed **% Accepted:** 40 **Admission Plans:** Deferred Admission **Application Deadline:** Rolling **Application Fee:** $40.00 **H.S. Requirements:** High school diploma required; GED accepted **Costs Per Year:** Application fee: $40. Tuition: $21,300 full-time, $888 per credit part-time. Mandatory fees: $1500 full-time. Full-time tuition and fees vary according to course load and program. Part-time tuition varies according to course load and program. **Scholarships:** Available. **Calendar System:** Semester, Summer session not available **Enrollment:** Full-time 209, Part-time 11 **Faculty:** Full-time 11, Part-time 34 **Student-Faculty Ratio:** 11:1 **Exams:** ACT; SAT I. **Regional Accreditation:** Middle States Association of Colleges and Schools **Credit Hours For Degree:** 120 credits, Bachelors **Professional Accreditation:** NASAD.

PENNSYLVANIA COLLEGE OF HEALTH SCIENCES

410 N Lime St.
Lancaster, PA 17602
Tel: (717)544-4912; Free: 800-622-5443
Fax: (717)290-5970
E-mail: admission@pacollege.edu
Web Site: www.pacollege.edu
President/CEO: Dr. Mary Grace Rose Simcox

Type: Comprehensive **Sex:** Coed **% Accepted:** 53 **Admission Plans:** Deferred Admission **Application Deadline:** February 1 **Application Fee:** $35.00 **H.S. Requirements:** High school diploma required; GED accepted **Costs Per Year:** Application fee: $35. Tuition: $23,178 full-time, $512 per credit hour part-time. Mandatory fees: $1275 full-time. **Calendar System:** Semester, Summer session available **Enrollment:** Full-time 491, Graduate part-time 38, Part-time 848 **Faculty:** Full-time 64, Part-time 156 **Student-Faculty Ratio:** 8:1 **Exams:** ACT essay component not used; SAT I or ACT; SAT essay component not used; SAT Reasoning; SAT Subject. **Final Year or Final Semester Residency Requirement:** No **Regional Accreditation:** Middle States Association of Colleges and Schools **Credit Hours For Degree:** 64-69 credits, depending on program, Associates; 120 credits, Bachelors **Professional Accreditation:** ACEN.

PENNSYLVANIA COLLEGE OF TECHNOLOGY

One College Ave.
Williamsport, PA 17701-5778
Tel: (570)326-3761; Free: 800-367-9222
Fax: (570)321-5551
E-mail: admissions@pct.edu
Web Site: www.pct.edu
President/CEO: Dr. Davie Jane Gilmour
Admissions: Dennis L. Correll
Financial Aid: Dennis Correll

Type: Four-Year College **Sex:** Coed **Affiliation:** The Pennsylvania State University. **% Accepted:** 85 **Admission Plans:** Deferred Admission; Early Admission; Open Admission **Application Deadline:** July 1 **Application Fee:**

$50.00 **H.S. Requirements:** High school diploma required; GED accepted **Costs Per Year:** Application fee: $50. State resident tuition: $13,320 full-time, $444 per credit hour part-time. Nonresident tuition: $19,980 full-time, $666 per credit hour part-time. Mandatory fees: $2490 full-time, $83 per credit hour part-time. Full-time tuition and fees vary according to course load and program. Part-time tuition and fees vary according to course load and program. College room and board: $11,108. College room only: $6392. Room and board charges vary according to board plan and housing facility. **Scholarships:** Available. **Calendar System:** Semester, Summer session available **Enrollment:** Full-time 4,619, Part-time 895 **Faculty:** Full-time 293, Part-time 179 **Student-Faculty Ratio:** 18:1 **Exams:** ACT essay component not used; SAT I; SAT essay component not used. **% Receiving Financial Aid:** 91 **% Residing in College-Owned, -Operated, or -Affiliated Housing:** 31 **Final Year or Final Semester Residency Requirement:** No **Regional Accreditation:** Middle States Association of Colleges and Schools **Credit Hours For Degree:** 60 credits, Associates; 120 credits, Bachelors **ROTC:** Army **Professional Accreditation:** ABET, ACBSP, ACEN, ACF, ADA, AOTA, JRCEMTP, JRCERT. **Intercollegiate Athletics:** Archery M & W; Baseball M; Basketball M & W; Bowling M & W; Cross-Country Running M & W; Golf M & W; Soccer M & W; Softball W; Tennis M & W; Volleyball M & W; Wrestling M

PENNSYLVANIA HIGHLANDS COMMUNITY COLLEGE

101 Community College Way
Johnstown, PA 15904
Tel: (814)262-6400; Free: 888-385-7325
E-mail: jmaul@pennhighlands.edu
Web Site: www.pennhighlands.edu
President/CEO: Dr. Walter J. Asonevich
Admissions: Jeff Maul

Type: Two-Year College **Sex:** Coed **% Accepted:** 100 **Admission Plans:** Open Admission **Application Deadline:** Rolling **Application Fee:** $20.00 **H.S. Requirements:** High school diploma required; GED accepted **Costs Per Year:** Application fee: $20. Area resident tuition: $3810 full-time, $127 per credit part-time. State resident tuition: $5850 full-time, $195 per credit part-time. Nonresident tuition: $8790 full-time, $293 per credit part-time. Mandatory fees: $1860 full-time, $62 per credit part-time. Full-time tuition and fees vary according to course load. Part-time tuition and fees vary according to course load. **Scholarships:** Available. **Calendar System:** Semester, Summer session available **Enrollment:** Full-time 866, Part-time 1,590 **Faculty:** Full-time 27, Part-time 81 **Student-Faculty Ratio:** 26:1 **Regional Accreditation:** Middle States Association of Colleges and Schools **Credit Hours For Degree:** 61 credits, Associates **Intercollegiate Athletics:** Basketball M; Bowling M & W; Cross-Country Running M & W; Volleyball W

PENNSYLVANIA INSTITUTE OF HEALTH AND TECHNOLOGY

1015 Mount Braddock Rd.
Mount Braddock, PA 15465
Tel: (724)437-4600
Web Site: www.piht.edu
Type: Two-Year College **Sex:** Coed **Professional Accreditation:** ACICS.

PENNSYLVANIA INSTITUTE OF TECHNOLOGY

800 Manchester Ave.
Media, PA 19063
Tel: (610)892-1500; Free: 800-422-0025
Fax: (610)892-1510
E-mail: info@pit.edu
Web Site: www.pit.edu
President/CEO: Walter R. Garrison
Admissions: John DeTurris

Type: Two-Year College **Sex:** Coed **Admission Plans:** Deferred Admission; Open Admission **Application Deadline:** September 9 **Application Fee:** $25.00 **H.S. Requirements:** High school diploma required; GED accepted **Costs Per Year:** Application fee: $25. Tuition: $11,250 full-time, $375 per credit hour part-time. Mandatory fees: $1950 full-time, $65 per credit hour part-time. Full-time tuition and fees vary according to program. Part-time tuition and fees vary according to course load and program. **Scholarships:** Available. **Calendar System:** Semester, Summer session available **Enrollment:** Full-time 306, Part-time 290 **Faculty:** Full-time 19, Part-time 55 **Student-Faculty Ratio:** 14:1 **Regional Accreditation:** Middle States Association of Colleges and Schools **Credit Hours For Degree:** 60 credits, Associates

PHILADELPHIA UNIVERSITY
4201 Henry Ave.
Philadelphia, PA 19144
Tel: (215)951-2700
Fax: (215)951-2907
E-mail: admissions@philau.edu
Web Site: www.philau.edu
President/CEO: Dr. Stephen Spinelli, Jr.
Admissions: Greg Potts
Financial Aid: Lisa J. Cooper

Type: Comprehensive **Sex:** Coed **Scores:** 99% SAT V 400+; 100% SAT M 400+; 50.8% ACT 18-23; 39.7% ACT 24-29 **% Accepted:** 64 **Admission Plans:** Deferred Admission **Application Fee:** $40.00 **H.S. Requirements:** High school diploma required; GED accepted **Costs Per Year:** Application fee: $40. Comprehensive fee: $48,660 includes full-time tuition ($35,620), mandatory fees ($900), and college room and board ($12,140). College room only: $5670. Full-time tuition and fees vary according to course load, degree level, program, and student level. Room and board charges vary according to board plan and housing facility. Part-time tuition: $605 per credit hour. Part-time mandatory fees: $20 per credit hour. Part-time tuition and fees vary according to class time, course load, degree level, program, and reciprocity agreements. **Scholarships:** Available. **Calendar System:** Semester **Enrollment:** Full-time 2,557, Graduate full-time 446, Graduate part-time 405, Part-time 349 **Exams:** SAT I or ACT; SAT Reasoning. **% Receiving Financial Aid:** 78 **% Residing in College-Owned, -Operated, or -Affiliated Housing:** 50 **Regional Accreditation:** Middle States Association of Colleges and Schools **Credit Hours For Degree:** 124 credits, Bachelors **Professional Accreditation:** ABET, ACNM, AOTA, CIDA, NAAB, NASAD. **Intercollegiate Athletics:** Baseball M; Basketball M & W; Cross-Country Running M & W; Golf M; Lacrosse W; Soccer M & W; Softball W; Tennis M & W; Volleyball W

PITTSBURGH CAREER INSTITUTE
421 Seventh Ave.
Pittsburgh, PA 15219-1907
Tel: (412)281-2600; Free: 888-270-6333
Fax: (412)281-0319
Web Site: www.pci.edu
President/CEO: Patti Yakshe
Admissions: Bruce E. Jones

Type: Two-Year College **Sex:** Coed **Admission Plans:** Deferred Admission; Early Admission **Application Fee:** $25.00 **H.S. Requirements:** High school diploma required; GED accepted **Scholarships:** Available. **Calendar System:** Continuous, Summer session not available **Exams:** SAT I or ACT; SAT II. **Credit Hours For Degree:** 65 credits, Associates **Professional Accreditation:** ACCSC, ACICS, CoARC, JRCEDMS, JRCERT.

PITTSBURGH INSTITUTE OF AERONAUTICS
PO Box 10897
Pittsburgh, PA 15236-0897
Tel: (412)462-9011; Free: 800-444-1440
Fax: (412)466-0513
E-mail: admissions@pia.edu
Web Site: www.pia.edu
President/CEO: John Graham, III
Admissions: Steven J. Sabold

Type: Two-Year College **Sex:** Coed **% Accepted:** 100 **Admission Plans:** Deferred Admission; Open Admission **Application Deadline:** Rolling **Application Fee:** $150.00 **H.S. Requirements:** High school diploma required; GED accepted **Calendar System:** Quarter **Enrollment:** Full-time 368 **Faculty:** Full-time 31, Part-time 6 **Student-Faculty Ratio:** 17:1 **Credit Hours For Degree:** 2520 hours, Associates **Professional Accreditation:** ACCSC.

PITTSBURGH INSTITUTE OF MORTUARY SCIENCE, INCORPORATED
5808 Baum Blvd.
Pittsburgh, PA 15206-3706
Tel: (412)362-8500
Fax: (412)362-1684
E-mail: pims5808@aol.com
Web Site: www.pims.edu
President/CEO: Eugene Ogrodnik
Admissions: Karen Rocco

Financial Aid: Janice Benna

Type: Two-Year College **Sex:** Coed **Admission Plans:** Open Admission **Application Deadline:** Rolling **Application Fee:** $40.00 **H.S. Requirements:** High school diploma required; GED accepted **Scholarships:** Available. **Calendar System:** Trimester **Enrollment:** Full-time 85, Part-time 108 **Faculty:** Full-time 2, Part-time 22 **Student-Faculty Ratio:** 13:1 **Credit Hours For Degree:** 96 credits, Associates **Professional Accreditation:** ABFSE.

PITTSBURGH TECHNICAL INSTITUTE
1111 McKee Rd.
Oakdale, PA 15071
Tel: (412)809-5100; Free: 800-784-9675
Fax: (412)809-5388
E-mail: goodlin.nancy@pti.edu
Web Site: www.pti.edu
President/CEO: Greg DeFeo
Admissions: Nancy Goodlin

Type: Two-Year College **Sex:** Coed **Admission Plans:** Deferred Admission; Open Admission **Application Deadline:** Rolling **Application Fee:** $0.00 **H.S. Requirements:** High school diploma required; GED accepted **Costs Per Year:** Application fee: $0. Comprehensive fee: $27,527 includes full-time tuition ($16,664), mandatory fees ($1350), and college room and board ($9513). College room only: $7137. Full-time tuition and fees vary according to course load and program. Room and board charges vary according to housing facility. Tuition guaranteed not to increase for student's term of enrollment. **Calendar System:** Quarter **Enrollment:** Full-time 1,936 **Faculty:** Full-time 76, Part-time 45 **Student-Faculty Ratio:** 16:1 **Exams:** ACT essay component not used; Other; SAT essay component not used. **% Residing in College-Owned, -Operated, or -Affiliated Housing:** 40 **Final Year or Final Semester Residency Requirement:** No **Regional Accreditation:** Middle States Association of Colleges and Schools **Credit Hours For Degree:** 100 credits, Associates

POINT PARK UNIVERSITY
201 Wood St.
Pittsburgh, PA 15222-1984
Tel: (412)391-4100; Free: 800-321-0129
Fax: (412)391-1980
E-mail: enroll@pointpark.edu
Web Site: www.pointpark.edu
President/CEO: Dr. Paul Hennigan
Admissions: Joell Minford

Type: Comprehensive **Sex:** Coed **Scores:** 92% SAT V 400+; 85% SAT M 400+; 50% ACT 18-23; 32% ACT 24-29 **% Accepted:** 74 **Admission Plans:** Deferred Admission **Application Deadline:** Rolling **Application Fee:** $40.00 **H.S. Requirements:** High school diploma required; GED accepted **Costs Per Year:** Application fee: $40. Comprehensive fee: $38,870 includes full-time tuition ($27,000), mandatory fees ($1250), and college room and board ($10,620). College room only: $5000. Full-time tuition and fees vary according to program. Room and board charges vary according to board plan and housing facility. Part-time tuition: $766 per credit. Part-time mandatory fees: $50 per credit. Part-time tuition and fees vary according to program. **Scholarships:** Available. **Calendar System:** Semester, Summer session available **Enrollment:** Full-time 2,551, Graduate full-time 250, Graduate part-time 365, Part-time 675 **Faculty:** Full-time 136, Part-time 318 **Student-Faculty Ratio:** 13:1 **Exams:** SAT I or ACT; SAT essay component used for advising. **% Receiving Financial Aid:** 91 **% Residing in College-Owned, -Operated, or -Affiliated Housing:** 25 **Final Year or Final Semester Residency Requirement:** Yes **Regional Accreditation:** Middle States Association of Colleges and Schools **Credit Hours For Degree:** 60 credits, Associates; 120 credits, Bachelors **ROTC:** Air Force, Army **Professional Accreditation:** ABET, NASD. **Intercollegiate Athletics:** Baseball M; Basketball M & W; Cross-Country Running M & W; Golf M & W; Soccer M & W; Softball W; Volleyball W

READING AREA COMMUNITY COLLEGE
PO Box 1706
Reading, PA 19603-1706
Tel: (610)372-4721
Fax: (610)375-8255
E-mail: dhettinger@racc.edu
Web Site: www.racc.edu
President/CEO: Dr. Anna Weitz

Admissions: Debbie Hettinger

Type: Two-Year College **Sex:** Coed **% Accepted:** 100 **Admission Plans:** Early Admission; Open Admission **Application Deadline:** Rolling **Application Fee:** $0.00 **H.S. Requirements:** High school diploma required; GED accepted **Costs Per Year:** Application fee: $0. Area resident tuition: $3750 full-time, $125 per credit part-time. State resident tuition: $7500 full-time, $250 per credit part-time. Nonresident tuition: $11,250 full-time, $375 per credit part-time. Mandatory fees: $1560 full-time, $52 per credit part-time. Full-time tuition and fees vary according to course load and program. Part-time tuition and fees vary according to course load and program. **Scholarships:** Available. **Calendar System:** Semester, Summer session available **Enrollment:** Full-time 936, Part-time 3,154 **Faculty:** Full-time 58, Part-time 154 **Student-Faculty Ratio:** 18:1 **Exams:** ACT; Other; SAT I. **Final Year or Final Semester Residency Requirement:** No **Regional Accreditation:** Middle States Association of Colleges and Schools **Credit Hours For Degree:** 60 credits, Associates **Professional Accreditation:** ACEN, CoARC, NAACLS.

THE RESTAURANT SCHOOL AT WALNUT HILL COLLEGE

4207 Walnut St.
Philadelphia, PA 19104-3518
Tel: (215)222-4200
Fax: (215)222-4219
E-mail: jenglish@walnuthillcollege.edu
Web Site: www.walnuthillcollege.edu
President/CEO: Daniel Literatoscioli
Admissions: John English
Financial Aid: Caitlin Snedeker

Type: Two-Year College **Sex:** Coed **% Accepted:** 97 **Admission Plans:** Deferred Admission; Early Action; Early Admission; Open Admission **Application Deadline:** Rolling **Application Fee:** $50.00 **H.S. Requirements:** High school diploma required; GED accepted **Costs Per Year:** Application fee: $50. One-time mandatory fee: $200. Tuition: $19,050 full-time. Mandatory fees: $3850 full-time. College room only: $5400. Room charges vary according to housing facility. **Scholarships:** Available. **Calendar System:** Quarter, Summer session not available **Faculty:** Full-time 18, Part-time 1 **Student-Faculty Ratio:** 22:1 **Exams:** SAT I or ACT. **Final Year or Final Semester Residency Requirement:** No **Professional Accreditation:** ACCSC.

ROBERT MORRIS UNIVERSITY

6001 University Blvd.
Moon Township, PA 15108-1189
Tel: (412)397-3000; Free: 800-762-0097
Fax: (412)262-8619
E-mail: admissionsoffice@rmu.edu
Web Site: www.rmu.edu
President/CEO: Dr. Christopher B. Howard
Financial Aid: Stephanie Hendershot

Type: University **Sex:** Coed **Scores:** 97% SAT V 400+; 97% SAT M 400+; 51.76% ACT 18-23; 35.18% ACT 24-29 **% Accepted:** 78 **Admission Plans:** Deferred Admission **Application Deadline:** Rolling **Application Fee:** $30.00 **H.S. Requirements:** High school diploma required; GED accepted **Costs Per Year:** Application fee: $30. Comprehensive fee: $39,324 includes full-time tuition ($26,330), mandatory fees ($864), and college room and board ($12,130). College room only: $5760. Full-time tuition and fees vary according to degree level and program. Room and board charges vary according to board plan and housing facility. Part-time tuition: $845 per credit hour. Part-time mandatory fees: $70 per credit hour. Part-time tuition and fees vary according to course load, degree level, and program. **Scholarships:** Available. **Calendar System:** Semester, Summer session available **Enrollment:** Full-time 3,965, Graduate part-time 880, Part-time 532 **Faculty:** Full-time 214, Part-time 274 **Student-Faculty Ratio:** 15:1 **Exams:** SAT I or ACT; SAT Reasoning; SAT Subject. **% Receiving Financial Aid:** 71 **% Residing in College-Owned, -Operated, or -Affiliated Housing:** 51 **Final Year or Final Semester Residency Requirement:** No **Regional Accreditation:** Middle States Association of Colleges and Schools **Credit Hours For Degree:** 126 credits, Bachelors **ROTC:** Air Force, Army, Navy **Professional Accreditation:** AACN, AACSB, ABET, JRCERT, TEAC. **Intercollegiate Athletics:** Basketball M & W; Crew W; Cross-Country Running W; Football M; Golf M; Ice Hockey M & W; Lacrosse M & W; Soccer M & W; Softball W; Track and Field W; Volleyball W

ROSEDALE TECHNICAL INSTITUTE

215 Beecham Dr.
Ste. 2

Pittsburgh, PA 15205-9791
Tel: (412)521-6200; Free: 800-521-6262
Fax: (412)521-9277
E-mail: admissions@rosedaletech.org
Web Site: www.rosedaletech.org
President/CEO: Dennis Wilke
Admissions: Debbie Bier

Type: Two-Year College **Sex:** Coed **% Accepted:** 65 **Calendar System:** Semester **Enrollment:** Full-time 200 **Faculty:** Full-time 14, Part-time 4 **Student-Faculty Ratio:** 13:1 **Professional Accreditation:** ACCSC.

ROSEMONT COLLEGE

1400 Montgomery Ave.
Rosemont, PA 19010-1699
Tel: (610)527-0200; Free: 888-2-ROSEMONT
Fax: (610)527-1041
E-mail: bettsy.thommen@rosemont.edu
Web Site: www.rosemont.edu
President/CEO: Dr. Sharon Latchaw Hirsh, PhD
Admissions: Bettsy Thommen
Financial Aid: Deborah A. Cawley

Type: Comprehensive **Sex:** Coed **Affiliation:** Roman Catholic. **Scores:** 77% SAT V 400+; 69% SAT M 400+; 42% ACT 18-23; 6% ACT 24-29 **% Accepted:** 71 **Admission Plans:** Deferred Admission **Application Deadline:** Rolling **Application Fee:** $0.00 **H.S. Requirements:** High school diploma required; GED accepted **Costs Per Year:** Application fee: $0. Comprehensive fee: $30,980 includes full-time tuition ($18,500), mandatory fees ($980), and college room and board ($11,500). Room and board charges vary according to board plan. Part-time tuition: $1200 per credit hour. **Scholarships:** Available. **Calendar System:** Semester, Summer session available **Enrollment:** Full-time 456, Graduate full-time 116, Graduate part-time 242, Part-time 73 **Faculty:** Full-time 25, Part-time 121 **Student-Faculty Ratio:** 10:1 **Exams:** SAT I or ACT. **% Receiving Financial Aid:** 89 **% Residing in College-Owned, -Operated, or -Affiliated Housing:** 79 **Final Year or Final Semester Residency Requirement:** No **Regional Accreditation:** Middle States Association of Colleges and Schools **Credit Hours For Degree:** 120 credits, Associates **Intercollegiate Athletics:** Basketball M & W; Cross-Country Running M & W; Golf M; Lacrosse M & W; Soccer M & W; Softball W; Tennis M & W; Volleyball W

SAINT CHARLES BORROMEO SEMINARY, OVERBROOK

100 E Wynnewood Rd.
Wynnewood, PA 19096
Tel: (610)667-3394
E-mail: jshenosky@scs.edu
Web Site: www.scs.edu
President/CEO: Rev. Timothy C. Senior
Admissions: Rev. Joseph Shenosky
Financial Aid: Nora M. Downey

Type: Comprehensive **Sex:** Coed **Affiliation:** Roman Catholic. **Scores:** 100% SAT V 400+; 100% SAT M 400+ **% Accepted:** 100 **Admission Plans:** Deferred Admission **Application Deadline:** July 15 **Application Fee:** $0.00 **H.S. Requirements:** High school diploma required; GED accepted **Scholarships:** Available. **Calendar System:** Semester, Summer session available **Enrollment:** Full-time 74, Graduate full-time 85, Graduate part-time 29, Part-time 24 **Faculty:** Full-time 16, Part-time 17 **Student-Faculty Ratio:** 6:1 **Exams:** ACT essay component not used; SAT I or ACT; SAT essay component not used. **% Receiving Financial Aid:** 22 **% Residing in College-Owned, -Operated, or -Affiliated Housing:** 100 **Final Year or Final Semester Residency Requirement:** Yes **Regional Accreditation:** Middle States Association of Colleges and Schools **Credit Hours For Degree:** 125 credits, Bachelors **Professional Accreditation:** ATS.

SAINT FRANCIS UNIVERSITY

117 Evergreen Dr.
Loretto, PA 15940-0600
Tel: (814)472-3000; Free: 866-DIAL-SFU
Fax: (814)472-3044
E-mail: rbeener@francis.edu
Web Site: www.francis.edu
President/CEO: Rev. Malachi Van Tassell
Admissions: Robert Beener
Financial Aid: Jamie Kosh

Type: Comprehensive **Sex:** Coed **Affiliation:** Roman Catholic. **Scores:**

98% SAT V 400+; 98% SAT M 400+; 49% ACT 18-23; 38% ACT 24-29 **% Accepted:** 74 **Admission Plans:** Deferred Admission **Application Deadline:** Rolling **Application Fee:** $30.00 **H.S. Requirements:** High school diploma required; GED accepted **Costs Per Year:** Application fee: $30. One-time mandatory fee: $100. Comprehensive fee: $44,868 includes full-time tuition ($32,244), mandatory fees ($1100), and college room and board ($11,524). College room only: $5734. Full-time tuition and fees vary according to course load, degree level, program, and student level. Room and board charges vary according to board plan and housing facility. Part-time tuition: $1007 per credit hour. Part-time mandatory fees: $476 per credit hour. Part-time tuition and fees vary according to class time, degree level, and program. **Scholarships:** Available. **Calendar System:** Semester, Summer session available **Enrollment:** Full-time 1,604, Graduate full-time 228, Graduate part-time 384, Part-time 120 **Faculty:** Full-time 130, Part-time 106 **Student-Faculty Ratio:** 14:1 **Exams:** ACT essay component used for advising; SAT I or ACT; SAT essay component used for advising; SAT Reasoning; SAT Subject. **% Receiving Financial Aid:** 81 **% Residing in College-Owned, -Operated, or -Affiliated Housing:** 88 **Final Year or Final Semester Residency Requirement:** No **Regional Accreditation:** Middle States Association of Colleges and Schools **Credit Hours For Degree:** 63 credits, Associates; 128 credits, Bachelors **ROTC:** Army **Professional Accreditation:** AACN, AOTA, APTA, CSWE, TEAC. **Intercollegiate Athletics:** Basketball M & W; Bowling M & W; Cross-Country Running M & W; Field Hockey W; Football M; Golf M & W; Lacrosse W; Soccer M & W; Softball W; Swimming and Diving M & W; Tennis M & W; Track and Field M & W; Volleyball M & W

SAINT JOSEPH'S UNIVERSITY

5600 City Ave.
Philadelphia, PA 19131-1395
Tel: (610)660-1000; Free: 800-BE-A-HAWK
E-mail: admit@sju.edu
Web Site: www.sju.edu
President/CEO: Dr. Mark C. Reed
Financial Aid: Eileen M. Tucker

Type: Comprehensive **Sex:** Coed **Affiliation:** Roman Catholic (Jesuit). **Scores:** 100% SAT V 400+; 100% SAT M 400+; 26.1% ACT 18-23; 61.6% ACT 24-29 **% Accepted:** 82 **Admission Plans:** Deferred Admission; Early Decision Plan **Application Deadline:** February 1 **Application Fee:** $50.00 **H.S. Requirements:** High school diploma required; GED accepted **Costs Per Year:** Application fee: $50. Comprehensive fee: $57,108 includes full-time tuition ($42,000), mandatory fees ($180), and college room and board ($14,928). College room only: $9748. Full-time tuition and fees vary according to course load. Room and board charges vary according to board plan and housing facility. Part-time tuition: $557 per credit. Part-time tuition varies according to course load. **Scholarships:** Available. **Calendar System:** Semester, Summer session available **Enrollment:** Full-time 4,624, Graduate full-time 553, Graduate part-time 2,681, Part-time 771 **Faculty:** Full-time 298, Part-time 430 **Student-Faculty Ratio:** 13:1 **Exams:** ACT essay component not used; SAT I or ACT; SAT essay component not used; SAT Reasoning. **% Receiving Financial Aid:** 53 **% Residing in College-Owned, -Operated, or -Affiliated Housing:** 59 **Final Year or Final Semester Residency Requirement:** Yes **Regional Accreditation:** Middle States Association of Colleges and Schools **Credit Hours For Degree:** 60 credit hours, Associates; 120 credit hours, Bachelors **ROTC:** Air Force, Army, Navy **Professional Accreditation:** AACSB, AANA, NCATE. **Intercollegiate Athletics:** Baseball M; Basketball M & W; Cheerleading M & W; Crew M & W; Cross-Country Running M & W; Field Hockey W; Golf M; Lacrosse M & W; Soccer M & W; Softball W; Tennis M & W; Track and Field M & W

SAINT VINCENT COLLEGE

300 Fraser Purchase Rd.
Latrobe, PA 15650-2690
Tel: (724)532-6600; Free: 800-782-5549
Fax: (724)537-4554
E-mail: admission@stvincent.edu
Web Site: www.stvincent.edu
President/CEO: Bro. Norman W. Hipps, OSB
Admissions: Stephen Neitz
Financial Aid: Mary Gazal

Type: Comprehensive **Sex:** Coed **Affiliation:** Roman Catholic. **Scores:** 98% SAT V 400+; 96% SAT M 400+; 48% ACT 18-23; 41% ACT 24-29 **% Accepted:** 70 **Admission Plans:** Deferred Admission; Early Admission Ap-

plication **Deadline:** May 1 **Application Fee:** $25.00 **H.S. Requirements:** High school diploma required; GED accepted **Costs Per Year:** Application fee: $25. Comprehensive fee: $43,563 includes full-time tuition ($31,534), mandatory fees ($1236), and college room and board ($10,793). College room only: $5821. Full-time tuition and fees vary according to course load and degree level. Room and board charges vary according to board plan and housing facility. Part-time tuition: $986 per credit hour. Part-time tuition varies according to course load and degree level. **Scholarships:** Available. **Calendar System:** Semester, Summer session available **Enrollment:** Full-time 1,590, Graduate full-time 108, Graduate part-time 97, Part-time 62 **Faculty:** Full-time 102, Part-time 120 **Student-Faculty Ratio:** 12:1 **Exams:** SAT I or ACT. **% Receiving Financial Aid:** 78 **% Residing in College-Owned, -Operated, or -Affiliated Housing:** 75 **Final Year or Final Semester Residency Requirement:** Yes **Regional Accreditation:** Middle States Association of Colleges and Schools **Credit Hours For Degree:** 124 credits, Bachelors **ROTC:** Air Force, Army **Professional Accreditation:** ACBSP, ATS. **Intercollegiate Athletics:** Baseball M; Basketball M & W; Cheerleading W; Cross-Country Running M & W; Equestrian Sports M & W; Fencing M & W; Football M; Golf M & W; Ice Hockey M; Lacrosse M & W; Soccer M & W; Softball W; Swimming and Diving M & W; Tennis M & W; Track and Field M & W; Volleyball W

SETON HILL UNIVERSITY

Seton Hill Dr.
Greensburg, PA 15601
Tel: (724)834-2200; Free: 800-826-6234
Fax: (724)830-4611
E-mail: admit@setonhill.edu
Web Site: www.setonhill.edu
President/CEO: Dr. Mary Finger
Admissions: Allison Sasso
Financial Aid: Tracey Snyder de Baez

Type: Comprehensive **Sex:** Coed **Affiliation:** Roman Catholic. **Scores:** 96% SAT V 400+; 93% SAT M 400+; 40% ACT 18-23; 40% ACT 24-29 **% Accepted:** 76 **Admission Plans:** Deferred Admission **Application Deadline:** Rolling **Application Fee:** $35.00 **H.S. Requirements:** High school diploma required; GED accepted **Costs Per Year:** Application fee: $35. Comprehensive fee: $43,032 includes full-time tuition ($31,420), mandatory fees ($1000), and college room and board ($10,612). Full-time tuition and fees vary according to course load, degree level, and program. Room and board charges vary according to board plan and housing facility. Part-time tuition: $842 per credit. Part-time mandatory fees: $25 per credit. Part-time tuition and fees vary according to course load, degree level, and program. **Scholarships:** Available. **Calendar System:** Semester, Summer session available **Enrollment:** Full-time 1,493, Graduate full-time 286, Graduate part-time 110, Part-time 127 **Faculty:** Full-time 106, Part-time 90 **Student-Faculty Ratio:** 14:1 **Exams:** ACT essay component used for placement; SAT I or ACT; SAT essay component used for placement; SAT Reasoning. **% Receiving Financial Aid:** 87 **% Residing in College-Owned, -Operated, or -Affiliated Housing:** 56 **Final Year or Final Semester Residency Requirement:** Yes **Regional Accreditation:** Middle States Association of Colleges and Schools **Credit Hours For Degree:** 120 credits, Bachelors **ROTC:** Army **Professional Accreditation:** AAFCS, AAMFT, AND, CSWE, NASM. **Intercollegiate Athletics:** Baseball M; Basketball M & W; Cross-Country Running M & W; Equestrian Sports W; Field Hockey W; Football M; Golf W; Lacrosse M & W; Soccer M & W; Softball W; Tennis W; Track and Field M & W; Volleyball W; Wrestling M

SHIPPENSBURG UNIVERSITY OF PENNSYLVANIA

1871 Old Main Dr.
Shippensburg, PA 17257-2299
Tel: (717)477-7447
Fax: (717)477-1273
E-mail: admiss@ship.edu
Web Site: www.ship.edu
President/CEO: Dr. Jody F. Harpster
Admissions: William H. Washabaugh
Financial Aid: Trina M. Snyder

Type: Comprehensive **Sex:** Coed **Affiliation:** Pennsylvania State System of Higher Education. **Scores:** 92% SAT V 400+; 92% SAT M 400+; 54.4% ACT 18-23; 19.7% ACT 24-29 **% Accepted:** 89 **Admission Plans:** Deferred Admission; Early Admission; Early Decision Plan **Application Fee:** $45.00 **H.S. Requirements:** High school diploma required; GED accepted **Costs Per Year:** Application fee: $45. State resident tuition: $7060 full-time, $294 per credit hour part-time. Nonresident tuition: $15,886 full-time, $662 per credit hour part-time. Mandatory fees: $2992 full-time, $125 per credit hour part-time. College room and board: $11,428. College room only: $7482. Room and board charges vary according to board plan and housing facility. **Scholarships:** Available. **Calendar System:** Semester, Summer session available **Enrollment:** Full-time 5,665, Graduate full-time 365, Graduate part-time 666, Part-time 362 **Faculty:** Full-time 294, Part-time 71 **Student-Faculty Ratio:** 19:1 **Exams:** ACT essay component used for advising; ACT essay component used for placement; SAT I or ACT; SAT essay component used for advising; SAT essay component used for placement; SAT Reasoning. **% Receiving Financial Aid:** 69 **% Residing in College-Owned, -Operated, or -Affiliated Housing:** 34 **Final Year or Final Semester Residency Requirement:** No **Regional Accreditation:** Middle States Association of Colleges and Schools **Credit Hours For Degree:** 120 credit hours, Bachelors **ROTC:** Army **Professional Accreditation:** AACSB, ABET, ACA, CSWE, NCATE. **Intercollegiate Athletics:** Baseball M; Basketball M & W; Cross-Country Running M & W; Field Hockey W; Football M; Lacrosse W; Soccer M & W; Softball W; Swimming and Diving M & W; Tennis W; Track and Field M & W; Volleyball W; Wrestling M

SLIPPERY ROCK UNIVERSITY OF PENNSYLVANIA

1 Morrow Way
Slippery Rock, PA 16057-1383
Tel: (724)738-9000; Free: 800-SRU-9111
Fax: (724)738-2098
E-mail: asktherock@sru.edu
Web Site: www.sru.edu
President/CEO: Dr. Cheryl Norton
Admissions: Michael May
Financial Aid: Alyssa Dobson

Type: Comprehensive **Sex:** Coed **Affiliation:** Pennsylvania State System of Higher Education. **Scores:** 92% SAT V 400+; 100% SAT M 400+; 62.33% ACT 18-23; 26.46% ACT 24-29 **% Accepted:** 68 **Admission Plans:** Deferred Admission **Application Deadline:** Rolling **Application Fee:** $30.00 **H.S. Requirements:** High school diploma required; GED accepted **Costs Per Year:** Application fee: $30. State resident tuition: $7060 full-time, $294 per credit hour part-time. Nonresident tuition: $10,590 full-time, $441 per credit hour part-time. Mandatory fees: $2585 full-time, $108.53 per credit hour part-time. Full-time tuition and fees vary according to course load. Part-time tuition and fees vary according to course load. College room and board: $10,022. College room only: $6620. Room and board charges vary according to board plan and housing facility. **Scholarships:** Available. **Calendar System:** Semester, Summer session available **Enrollment:** Full-time 7,057, Graduate full-time 370, Graduate part-time 675, Part-time 526 **Faculty:** Full-time 338, Part-time 65 **Student-Faculty Ratio:** 21:1 **Exams:** ACT; ACT essay component not used; SAT I; SAT I and SAT II or ACT; SAT I or ACT; SAT II; SAT essay component used for placement; SAT Reasoning. **% Receiving Financial Aid:** 68 **% Residing in College-Owned, -Operated, or -Affiliated Housing:** 36 **Final Year or Final Semester Residency Requirement:** Yes **Regional Accreditation:** Middle States Association of Colleges and Schools **Credit Hours For Degree:** 120 credits, Bachelors **ROTC:** Army **Professional Accreditation:** ABET, ACA, ACBSP, ACEN, APTA, CSWE, JRCAT, NASAD, NASD, NASM, NCATE, NRPA. **Intercollegiate Athletics:** Baseball M; Basketball M & W; Cheerleading M & W; Cross-Country Running M & W; Equestrian Sports M & W; Field Hockey W; Football M; Ice Hockey M & W; Lacrosse M & W; Rugby M & W; Soccer M & W; Softball W; Tennis M & W; Track and Field M & W; Volleyball M & W

SOUTH HILLS SCHOOL OF BUSINESS & TECHNOLOGY (ALTOONA)

541 58th St.
Altoona, PA 16602
Tel: (814)944-6134
Fax: (814)944-4684
E-mail: hemerick@southhills.edu
Web Site: www.southhills.edu
President/CEO: S. Paul Mazza
Admissions: Holly J. Emerick

Type: Two-Year College **Sex:** Coed **% Accepted:** 60 **Application Deadline:** September 1 **Application Fee:** $25.00 **H.S. Requirements:** High school diploma required; GED accepted **Scholarships:** Available. **Calendar System:** Trimester, Summer session available **Enrollment:** Full-time 189 **Faculty:** Full-time 10, Part-time 1 **Student-Faculty Ratio:** 13:1 **Exams:** Other. **Credit Hours For Degree:** 90 credits, Associates **Professional Accreditation:** ACICS.

SOUTH HILLS SCHOOL OF BUSINESS & TECHNOLOGY (STATE COLLEGE)

480 Waupelani Dr.
State College, PA 16801-4516
Tel: (814)234-7755; Free: 888-282-7427
Fax: (814)234-0926
E-mail: admissions@southhills.edu
Web Site: www.southhills.edu
President/CEO: Mark Maggs
Admissions: Troy R. Otradovec

Type: Two-Year College **Sex:** Coed **% Accepted:** 92 **Application Deadline:** Rolling **Application Fee:** $0.00 **H.S. Requirements:** High school diploma required; GED accepted **Costs Per Year:** Application fee: $0. Tuition: $16,521 full-time, $459 per credit part-time. Full-time tuition varies according to program. Part-time tuition varies according to course load. **Scholarships:** Available. **Calendar System:** Quarter, Summer session not available **Enrollment:** Full-time 574, Part-time 56 **Faculty:** Full-time 41, Part-time 24 **Student-Faculty Ratio:** 13:1 **Exams:** Other. **Credit Hours For Degree:** 90 credits, Associates **Professional Accreditation:** ACICS, AHIMA.

STRAYER UNIVERSITY–ALLENTOWN CAMPUS

3800 Sierra Cir.
Ste. 300
Center Valley, PA 18034
Tel: (484)809-7770
Fax: (610)791-0210
Web Site: www.strayer.edu/pennsylvania/allentown
President/CEO: Brian W. Jones

Type: Comprehensive **Sex:** Coed **Regional Accreditation:** Middle States Association of Colleges and Schools

STRAYER UNIVERSITY–CENTER CITY CAMPUS

1601 Cherry St., Ste. 100
Philadelphia, PA 19102
Tel: (267)256-0200
Fax: (267)256-0230
Web Site: www.strayer.edu/pennsylvania/center-city
President/CEO: Brian W. Jones

Type: Comprehensive **Sex:** Coed **Regional Accreditation:** Middle States Association of Colleges and Schools

STRAYER UNIVERSITY–DELAWARE COUNTY CAMPUS

760 W Sproul Rd., Ste. 200
Springfield, PA 19064-1215
Tel: (610)604-7700
Fax: (610)543-6599
Web Site: www.strayer.edu/pennsylvania/delaware-county
President/CEO: Brian W. Jones

Type: Comprehensive **Sex:** Coed **Regional Accreditation:** Middle States Association of Colleges and Schools

STRAYER UNIVERSITY–KING OF PRUSSIA CAMPUS

234 Mall Blvd.
Ste. G-50
King of Prussia, PA 19406
Tel: (610)992-1700
Fax: (610)992-9777
Web Site: www.strayer.edu/pennsylvania/king-prussia
President/CEO: Brian W. Jones

Type: Comprehensive **Sex:** Coed **Regional Accreditation:** Middle States Association of Colleges and Schools

STRAYER UNIVERSITY–LOWER BUCKS COUNTY CAMPUS

3800 Horizon Blvd., Ste. 100
Trevose, PA 19053
Tel: (215)953-5999
Fax: (215)953-9464
Web Site: www.strayer.edu/pennsylvania/lower-bucks-county
President/CEO: Brian W. Jones

Type: Comprehensive **Sex:** Coed **Regional Accreditation:** Middle States Association of Colleges and Schools

STRAYER UNIVERSITY–WARRENDALE CAMPUS
802 Warrendale Village Dr.
Warrendale, PA 15086
Tel: (724)799-2900
Fax: (724)933-7877
Web Site: www.strayer.edu/pennsylvania/warrendale
President/CEO: Brian W. Jones
Type: Comprehensive **Sex:** Coed **Regional Accreditation:** Middle States Association of Colleges and Schools

SUMMIT UNIVERSITY
538 Venard Rd.
Clarks Summit, PA 18411-1297
Tel: (570)586-2400; Free: 800-451-7664
Fax: (570)585-9400
E-mail: admissions@bbc.edu
Web Site: www.summitu.edu
President/CEO: Dr. Jim Jeffery
Admissions: Kellyn Lovell
Financial Aid: Steven E. Brown
Type: Comprehensive **Sex:** Coed **Affiliation:** Baptist. **Scores:** 97% SAT V 400+; 88% SAT M 400+; 54% ACT 18-23; 27% ACT 24-29 **% Accepted:** 38 **Admission Plans:** Deferred Admission; Early Admission **Application Deadline:** August 15 **Application Fee:** $40.00 **H.S. Requirements:** High school diploma required; GED accepted **Costs Per Year:** Application fee: $40. Comprehensive fee: $27,650 includes full-time tuition ($21,850) and college room and board ($5800). College room only: $2200. Room and board charges vary according to board plan. Part-time tuition: $650 per credit. Part-time mandatory fees: $43 per credit. Tuition guaranteed not to increase for student's term of enrollment. **Scholarships:** Available. **Calendar System:** Semester, Summer session available **Enrollment:** Full-time 568, Graduate full-time 139, Graduate part-time 140, Part-time 154 **Faculty:** Full-time 41, Part-time 6 **Student-Faculty Ratio:** 11:1 **Exams:** SAT I or ACT. **% Receiving Financial Aid:** 90 **% Residing in College-Owned, -Operated, or -Affiliated Housing:** 91 **Final Year or Final Semester Residency Requirement:** No **Regional Accreditation:** Middle States Association of Colleges and Schools **Credit Hours For Degree:** 64 semester hours, Associates; 124 semester hours, Bachelors **ROTC:** Air Force, Army, Navy **Professional Accreditation:** ABHE. **Intercollegiate Athletics:** Baseball M; Basketball M & W; Cheerleading W; Cross-Country Running M & W; Golf M; Soccer M & W; Softball W; Tennis W; Track and Field M & W; Volleyball W

SUSQUEHANNA UNIVERSITY
514 University Ave.
Selinsgrove, PA 17870
Tel: (570)374-0101; Free: 800-326-9672
Fax: (570)372-2722
E-mail: suadmiss@susqu.edu
Web Site: www.susqu.edu
President/CEO: Dr. L. Jay Lemons
Admissions: Philip Betz
Financial Aid: Erin M. Wolfe
Type: Four-Year College **Sex:** Coed **Affiliation:** Evangelical Lutheran Church in America. **Scores:** 99% SAT V 400+; 99% SAT M 400+; 30.2% ACT 18-23; 57% ACT 24-29 **% Accepted:** 76 **Admission Plans:** Deferred Admission; Early Action; Early Admission; Early Decision Plan **Application Deadline:** Rolling **Application Fee:** $0.00 **H.S. Requirements:** High school diploma required; GED accepted **Costs Per Year:** Application fee: $0. Comprehensive fee: $55,960 includes full-time tuition ($43,780), mandatory fees ($560), and college room and board ($11,620). College room only: $6080. Room and board charges vary according to board plan. Part-time tuition: $1375 per credit hour. **Scholarships:** Available. **Calendar System:** Semester, Summer session available **Enrollment:** Full-time 2,114, Graduate full-time 4, Graduate part-time 3, Part-time 82 **Faculty:** Full-time 133, Part-time 127 **Student-Faculty Ratio:** 12:1 **Exams:** ACT essay component not used; SAT I or ACT; SAT essay component not used; SAT Reasoning. **% Receiving Financial Aid:** 77 **% Residing in College-Owned, -Operated, or -Affiliated Housing:** 92 **Final Year or Final Semester Residency Requirement:** Yes **Regional Accreditation:** Middle States Association of Colleges and Schools **Credit Hours For Degree:** 130 semester hours, Bachelors **ROTC:** Army **Professional Accreditation:** AACSB, NASM. **Intercollegiate Athletics:** Baseball M; Basketball M & W; Cheerleading M & W; Crew M & W; Cross-Country Running M & W; Equestrian Sports M & W; Field Hockey W; Football M; Golf M & W; Lacrosse M & W; Rugby M & W; Soccer M & W; Softball W; Swimming and Diving M & W; Tennis M & W; Track and Field M & W; Volleyball M & W

SWARTHMORE COLLEGE
500 College Ave.
Swarthmore, PA 19081-1397
Tel: (610)328-8000; Free: 800-667-3110
Fax: (610)328-8673
Web Site: www.swarthmore.edu
President/CEO: Dr. Valerie Smith
Financial Aid: Varo L. Duffins
Type: Four-Year College **Sex:** Coed **Scores:** 100% SAT V 400+; 100% SAT M 400+; 22.3% ACT 24-29 **Costs Per Year:** Comprehensive fee: $61,400 includes full-time tuition ($47,070), mandatory fees ($372), and college room and board ($13,958). College room only: $7160. Room and board charges vary according to board plan. **Scholarships:** Available. **Calendar System:** Semester **Enrollment:** Full-time 1,571, Part-time 10 **Faculty:** Full-time 183, Part-time 29 **Student-Faculty Ratio:** 8:1 **Exams:** ACT essay component not used; SAT I and SAT II or ACT; SAT essay component not used. **% Receiving Financial Aid:** 52 **% Residing in College-Owned, -Operated, or -Affiliated Housing:** 95 **Final Year or Final Semester Residency Requirement:** No **Regional Accreditation:** Middle States Association of Colleges and Schools **Credit Hours For Degree:** 32 courses, Bachelors **ROTC:** Air Force, Army, Navy **Professional Accreditation:** ABET. **Intercollegiate Athletics:** Badminton M & W; Baseball M; Basketball M & W; Cross-Country Running M & W; Fencing M & W; Field Hockey W; Golf M; Ice Hockey M & W; Lacrosse M & W; Rugby M & W; Soccer M & W; Softball W; Squash M & W; Swimming and Diving M & W; Tennis M & W; Track and Field M & W; Ultimate Frisbee M & W; Volleyball M & W; Water Polo M & W

TALMUDICAL YESHIVA OF PHILADELPHIA
6063 Drexel Rd.
Philadelphia, PA 19131-1296
Tel: (215)473-1212
Fax: (215)477-5065
President/CEO: Rabbi Shmuel Kamenetsky
Admissions: Rabbi Shmuel Kamenetsky
Type: Four-Year College **Sex:** Men **Affiliation:** Jewish. **Admission Plans:** Deferred Admission; Early Admission **Application Deadline:** July 15 **H.S. Requirements:** High school diploma required; GED accepted **Scholarships:** Available. **Calendar System:** Trimester, Summer session not available **Enrollment:** Full-time 124 **% Receiving Financial Aid:** 63 **Credit Hours For Degree:** 170 credit hours, Bachelors **Professional Accreditation:** AARTS.

TEMPLE UNIVERSITY
1801 N Broad St.
Philadelphia, PA 19122-6096
Tel: (215)204-7000; Free: 888-340-2222
Fax: (215)204-5694
E-mail: tuadm@temple.edu
Web Site: www.temple.edu
President/CEO: Dr. Neil D. Theobald
Admissions: Karin Mormando
Financial Aid: Craig Fennell
Type: University **Sex:** Coed **Affiliation:** Commonwealth System of Higher Education. **Scores:** 98% SAT V 400+; 99% SAT M 400+; 24% ACT 18-23; 52% ACT 24-29 **% Accepted:** 56 **Admission Plans:** Deferred Admission; Early Decision Plan **Application Deadline:** March 1 **Application Fee:** $55.00 **H.S. Requirements:** High school diploma required; GED accepted **Costs Per Year:** Application fee: $55. State resident tuition: $14,898 full-time, $573 per credit hour part-time. Nonresident tuition: $25,204 full-time, $899 per credit hour part-time. Mandatory fees: $790 full-time. Full-time tuition and fees vary according to course load, degree level, location, program, reciprocity agreements, and student level. Part-time tuition varies according to course load, degree level, location, program, reciprocity agreements, and student level. College room and board: $11,146. College room only: $7340. Room and board charges vary according to board plan and housing facility. **Scholarships:** Available. **Calendar System:** Semester, Summer session available **Enrollment:** Full-time 25,318, Graduate full-time 4,590, Graduate part-time 4,828, Part-time 3,291 **Faculty:** Full-time 1,440, Part-time 1,426 **Student-Faculty Ratio:** 14:1 **Exams:** SAT I or ACT; SAT essay component used for admission; SAT Reasoning. **% Receiving**

Financial Aid: 69 % **Residing in College-Owned, -Operated, or -Affiliated Housing:** 21 **Final Year or Final Semester Residency Requirement:** No **Regional Accreditation:** Middle States Association of Colleges and Schools **Credit Hours For Degree:** 60 semester hours, Associates; 120 semester hours, Bachelors **ROTC:** Air Force, Army, Navy **Professional Accreditation:** AACN, AACSB, AALS, ABA, ABET, ACEJMC, ACPE, ACSP, ADA, AHIMA, AOTA, APA, APMA, APTA, ASHA, ASLA, CAHME, CEPH, CSWE, JRCAT, LCME/AMA, NAAB, NASAD, NASD, NASM, NAST, NRPA, TEAC. **Intercollegiate Athletics:** Basketball M & W; Crew M & W; Cross-Country Running M & W; Fencing W; Field Hockey W; Football M; Golf M; Gymnastics W; Lacrosse W; Soccer M & W; Tennis M & W; Track and Field W; Volleyball W

THADDEUS STEVENS COLLEGE OF TECHNOLOGY
750 E King St.
Lancaster, PA 17602-3198
Tel: (717)299-7730; Free: 800-842-3832
Fax: (717)391-6929
E-mail: kwiatkowski@stevenscollege.edu
Web Site: www.stevenscollege.edu
President/CEO: Dr. William E. Griscom
Admissions: Amy Kwiatkowski

Type: Two-Year College **Sex:** Coed **% Accepted:** 31 **Admission Plans:** Deferred Admission; Preferred Admission **Application Deadline:** June 30 **Application Fee:** $45.00 **H.S. Requirements:** High school diploma required; GED accepted **Costs Per Year:** Application fee: $45. State resident tuition: $7400 full-time, $308 per credit hour part-time. Mandatory fees: $30 full-time. College room and board: $8620. College room only: $4500. Room and board charges vary according to board plan. Pennsylvania residency is required for admission. **Scholarships:** Available. **Calendar System:** Semester, Summer session not available **Faculty:** Full-time 58, Part-time 22 **Student-Faculty Ratio:** 12:1 **Exams:** ACT essay component not used; Other; SAT essay component not used; SAT Reasoning; SAT Subject. **% Residing in College-Owned, -Operated, or -Affiliated Housing:** 45 **Final Year or Final Semester Residency Requirement:** No **Regional Accreditation:** Middle States Association of Colleges and Schools **Credit Hours For Degree:** 68 credits, Associates **Intercollegiate Athletics:** Basketball M; Cross-Country Running M; Football M; Track and Field M; Wrestling M

THIEL COLLEGE
75 College Ave.
Greenville, PA 16125-2181
Tel: (724)589-2000; Free: 800-248-4435
Fax: (724)589-2013
E-mail: admissions@thiel.edu
Web Site: www.thiel.edu
President/CEO: Dr. Troy VanAken
Admissions: Stephen Lazowski
Financial Aid: Cynthia H. Farrell

Type: Four-Year College **Sex:** Coed **Affiliation:** Evangelical Lutheran Church in America. **% Accepted:** 61 **Admission Plans:** Deferred Admission **Application Deadline:** Rolling **Application Fee:** $0.00 **H.S. Requirements:** High school diploma required; GED accepted **Costs Per Year:** Application fee: $0. Comprehensive fee: $41,440 includes full-time tuition ($27,910), mandatory fees ($1830), and college room and board ($11,700). College room only: $5850. Full-time tuition and fees vary according to course load. Room and board charges vary according to housing facility. **Scholarships:** Available. **Calendar System:** Semester, Summer session available **Enrollment:** Full-time 903, Part-time 23 **Faculty:** Full-time 59, Part-time 34 **Student-Faculty Ratio:** 13:1 **Exams:** SAT I or ACT; SAT Reasoning; SAT Subject. **% Receiving Financial Aid:** 86 **% Residing in College-Owned, -Operated, or -Affiliated Housing:** 95 **Final Year or Final Semester Residency Requirement:** Yes **Regional Accreditation:** Middle States Association of Colleges and Schools **Credit Hours For Degree:** 64 credit hours, Associates; 124 credit hours, Bachelors **Intercollegiate Athletics:** Baseball M; Basketball M & W; Bowling W; Cheerleading W; Cross-Country Running M & W; Football M; Golf M & W; Lacrosse M & W; Soccer M & W; Softball W; Tennis M & W; Track and Field M & W; Volleyball M & W; Wrestling M

THOMAS JEFFERSON UNIVERSITY
Eleventh and Walnut Sts.
Philadelphia, PA 19107
Tel: (215)955-6000; Free: 877-533-3247
Fax: (215)503-7241
E-mail: chpadmissions@mail.tju.edu
Web Site: www.jefferson.edu/university.html
President/CEO: Stephen K. Klasko, MD
Admissions: Karen Jacobs
Financial Aid: Susan McFadden

Type: University **Sex:** Coed **Admission Plans:** Deferred Admission **Application Deadline:** Rolling **Application Fee:** $50.00 **H.S. Requirements:** High school diploma required; GED accepted **Scholarships:** Available. **Calendar System:** Semester, Summer session not available **Student-Faculty Ratio:** 15:1 **Exams:** Other; SAT I or ACT. **Regional Accreditation:** Middle States Association of Colleges and Schools **Credit Hours For Degree:** 126 credits, Bachelors **ROTC:** Air Force **Professional Accreditation:** AACN, AAMFT, AANA, ACPE, ACIPE, AOTA, APTA, ASC, JRCEDMS, JRCERT, LCME/AMA, NAACLS. **Intercollegiate Athletics:** Rugby M

TRIANGLE TECH, BETHLEHEM
3184 Airport Rd.
Bethlehem, PA 18017
Tel: (610)691-1300
Web Site: www.triangle-tech.edu
President/CEO: Michael Biechy

Type: Two-Year College **Sex:** Coed **% Accepted:** 99 **Admission Plans:** Open Admission **Application Fee:** $0.00 **H.S. Requirements:** High school diploma required; GED accepted **Enrollment:** Full-time 140 **Faculty:** Full-time 8, Part-time 2 **Student-Faculty Ratio:** 15:1 **Credit Hours For Degree:** 72 credits, Associates **Professional Accreditation:** ACCSC.

TRIANGLE TECH, DUBOIS
225 Tannery Row Rd.
Falls Creek, PA 15840
Tel: (814)371-2090; Free: 800-874-8324
Fax: (814)371-9227
E-mail: tkucic@triangle-tech.com
Web Site: www.triangle-tech.edu
President/CEO: Stephanie Craig
Admissions: Terry Kucic

Type: Two-Year College **Sex:** Coed **Affiliation:** Triangle Tech Group, Inc. **% Accepted:** 100 **Admission Plans:** Deferred Admission **Application Deadline:** Rolling **Application Fee:** $0.00 **H.S. Requirements:** High school diploma required; GED accepted **Scholarships:** Available. **Calendar System:** Semester, Summer session not available **Enrollment:** Full-time 329 **Faculty:** Full-time 21 **Student-Faculty Ratio:** 15:1 **Credit Hours For Degree:** 72 credits, Associates **Professional Accreditation:** ACCSC.

TRIANGLE TECH, ERIE
2000 Liberty St.
Erie, PA 16502-2594
Tel: (814)453-6016; Free: 800-TRI-TECH
Fax: (814)454-2818
Web Site: www.triangle-tech.edu
President/CEO: Timothy J. McMahon

Type: Two-Year College **Sex:** Coed **Affiliation:** Triangle Tech Group, Inc. **% Accepted:** 100 **Admission Plans:** Deferred Admission **Application Deadline:** Rolling **Application Fee:** $75.00 **H.S. Requirements:** High school diploma required; GED accepted **Scholarships:** Available. **Calendar System:** Semester **Enrollment:** Full-time 176 **Faculty:** Full-time 14, Part-time 2 **Student-Faculty Ratio:** 12:1 **Credit Hours For Degree:** 72 credits, Associates **Professional Accreditation:** ACCSC.

TRIANGLE TECH, GREENSBURG
222 E Pittsburgh St.
Ste. A
Greensburg, PA 15601-3304
Tel: (724)832-1050; Free: 800-874-8324
Web Site: www.triangle-tech.edu
President/CEO: Timothy J. McMahon
Admissions: John Mazzarese
Financial Aid: Chrissy Detore

Type: Two-Year College **Sex:** Coed **Affiliation:** Triangle Tech Group, Inc. **% Accepted:** 100 **Admission Plans:** Deferred Admission **Application Deadline:** Rolling **Application Fee:** $75.00 **H.S. Requirements:** High school diploma required; GED accepted **Scholarships:** Available. **Calendar**

System: Semester, Summer session available **Enrollment:** Full-time 260 **Faculty:** Full-time 21 **Student-Faculty Ratio:** 12:1 **Credit Hours For Degree:** 72 credits, Associates **Professional Accreditation:** ACCSC.

TRIANGLE TECH, PITTSBURGH
1940 Perrysville Ave.
Pittsburgh, PA 15214-3897
Tel: (412)359-1000; Free: 800-874-8324
Fax: (412)359-1012
E-mail: info@triangle-tech.edu
Web Site: www.triangle-tech.edu
President/CEO: Kenneth Adams
Type: Two-Year College **Sex:** Coed **Affiliation:** Triangle Tech Group, Inc. **Application Deadline:** Rolling **H.S. Requirements:** High school diploma required; GED accepted **Scholarships:** Available. **Calendar System:** Semester, Summer session not available **Enrollment:** Full-time 103 **Student-Faculty Ratio:** 12:1 **Credit Hours For Degree:** 72 credits, Associates **Professional Accreditation:** ACCSC.

TRIANGLE TECH, SUNBURY
191 Performance Rd.
Sunbury, PA 17801
Tel: (570)988-0700
Web Site: www.triangle-tech.edu
President/CEO: Joseph Drumm
Admissions: John Mazzarese
Type: Two-Year College **Sex:** Coed **% Accepted:** 100 **H.S. Requirements:** High school diploma required; GED accepted **Calendar System:** Semester, Summer session not available **Enrollment:** Full-time 170 **Faculty:** Full-time 14, Part-time 1 **Student-Faculty Ratio:** 12:1 **Credit Hours For Degree:** 72 credits, Associates **Professional Accreditation:** ACCSC.

THE UNIVERSITY OF THE ARTS
320 S Broad St.
Philadelphia, PA 19102-4944
Tel: (215)717-6000; Free: 800-616-ARTS
Fax: (215)717-6045
E-mail: admissions@uarts.edu
Web Site: www.uarts.edu
President/CEO: David Yager
Admissions: Liz Gensemer
Type: Comprehensive **Sex:** Coed **% Accepted:** 74 **Admission Plans:** Deferred Admission **Application Deadline:** Rolling **Application Fee:** $60.00 **H.S. Requirements:** High school diploma required; GED accepted **Costs Per Year:** Application fee: $60. Comprehensive fee: $54,460 includes full-time tuition ($39,908) and college room and board ($14,552). College room only: $9396. Room and board charges vary according to board plan and housing facility. Part-time tuition: $1663 per credit hour. Part-time tuition varies according to course load. **Scholarships:** Available. **Calendar System:** Semester, Summer session available **Enrollment:** Full-time 1,671, Graduate full-time 112, Graduate part-time 52, Part-time 41 **Faculty:** Full-time 99, Part-time 412 **Student-Faculty Ratio:** 8:1 **Exams:** ACT essay component not used; SAT I or ACT; SAT essay component not used. **% Residing in College-Owned, -Operated, or -Affiliated Housing:** 34 **Final Year or Final Semester Residency Requirement:** No **Regional Accreditation:** Middle States Association of Colleges and Schools **Credit Hours For Degree:** 123 credits, Bachelors **Professional Accreditation:** NASAD, NASM.

UNIVERSITY OF PENNSYLVANIA
3451 Walnut St.
Philadelphia, PA 19104
Tel: (215)898-5000
Web Site: www.upenn.edu
President/CEO: Amy Gutmann
Financial Aid: Elaine Papas Varas
Type: University **Sex:** Coed **Scores:** 100% SAT V 400+; 100% SAT M 400+; 10% ACT 24-29 **% Accepted:** 10 **Admission Plans:** Deferred Admission; Early Action; Early Admission **Application Deadline:** January 5 **Application Fee:** $75.00 **H.S. Requirements:** High school diploma or equivalent not required **Costs Per Year:** Application fee: $75. Comprehensive fee: $63,526 includes full-time tuition ($43,838), mandatory fees ($5698), and college room and board ($13,990). College room only: $9060. Room and board charges vary according to board plan and housing facility. Part-time tuition: $1399 per credit hour. Part-time tuition varies according to course load.

Scholarships: Available. **Calendar System:** Semester, Summer session available **Enrollment:** Full-time 9,444, Graduate full-time 10,523, Graduate part-time 1,146, Part-time 282 **Faculty:** Full-time 1,458, Part-time 627 **Student-Faculty Ratio:** 6:1 **Exams:** ACT essay component used as validity check; ACT essay component used for admission; SAT I and SAT II or ACT; SAT essay component used as validity check; SAT essay component used for admission; SAT Reasoning; SAT Subject. **% Receiving Financial Aid:** 47 **% Residing in College-Owned, -Operated, or -Affiliated Housing:** 54 **Regional Accreditation:** Middle States Association of Colleges and Schools **Credit Hours For Degree:** 16 course units, Bachelors **ROTC:** Air Force, Army, Navy **Professional Accreditation:** AACN, AACSB, AALS, AANA, ABA, ABET, ACEN, ACNM, ACSP, ACIPE, ADA, APA, ASLA, AVMA, CAHME, CSWE, LCME/AMA, NAAB. **Intercollegiate Athletics:** Baseball M; Basketball M & W; Crew M & W; Cross-Country Running M & W; Fencing M & W; Field Hockey W; Football M; Golf M & W; Gymnastics W; Lacrosse M & W; Soccer M & W; Softball W; Squash M & W; Swimming and Diving M & W; Tennis M & W; Track and Field M & W; Volleyball W; Wrestling M

UNIVERSITY OF PHOENIX–PHILADELPHIA CAMPUS
30 S 17th St.
Philadelphia, PA 19103
Tel: (267)234-2000
Web Site: www.phoenix.edu
Type: Comprehensive **Sex:** Coed **Regional Accreditation:** North Central Association of Colleges and Schools

UNIVERSITY OF PITTSBURGH
4200 Fifth Ave.
Pittsburgh, PA 15260
Tel: (412)624-4141
Fax: (412)648-8815
E-mail: oafa@pitt.edu
Web Site: www.pitt.edu
President/CEO: Dr. Patrick Gallagher
Admissions: Marc L. Harding
Financial Aid: Marc L. Harding
Type: University **Sex:** Coed **Affiliation:** Commonwealth System of Higher Education. **Scores:** 100% SAT V 400+; 100% SAT M 400+; 3% ACT 18-23; 56% ACT 24-29 **% Accepted:** 54 **Application Deadline:** Rolling **Application Fee:** $45.00 **H.S. Requirements:** High school diploma required; GED not accepted **Costs Per Year:** Application fee: $45. State resident tuition: $17,292 full-time, $720 per credit hour part-time. Nonresident tuition: $28,058 full-time, $1169 per credit hour part-time. Mandatory fees: $900 full-time, $214 per term part-time. Full-time tuition and fees vary according to location and program. Part-time tuition and fees vary according to location and program. College room and board: $10,900. College room only: $6300. Room and board charges vary according to board plan, housing facility, and location. **Scholarships:** Available. **Calendar System:** Semester, Summer session available **Enrollment:** Full-time 17,887, Graduate full-time 7,577, Graduate part-time 2,164, Part-time 1,021 **Exams:** ACT essay component used for admission; SAT I or ACT; SAT essay component used for admission. **% Receiving Financial Aid:** 53 **% Residing in College-Owned, -Operated, or -Affiliated Housing:** 44 **Final Year or Final Semester Residency Requirement:** No **Regional Accreditation:** Middle States Association of Colleges and Schools **Credit Hours For Degree:** 120 credits, Bachelors **ROTC:** Air Force, Army, Navy **Professional Accreditation:** AACN, AACSB, AALS, AANA, ABA, ABET, ACA, ACPE, ADA, AHIMA, ALA, AND, AOTA, APA, APTA, ASHA, CAHME, CEPH, CORE, CSWE, JRCAT, JRCEMTP, LCME/AMA, NASPAA, NAST, NCATE, TEAC. **Intercollegiate Athletics:** Baseball M; Basketball M & W; Cross-Country Running M & W; Football M; Gymnastics W; Soccer M & W; Softball W; Swimming and Diving M & W; Tennis W; Track and Field M & W; Volleyball W; Wrestling M

UNIVERSITY OF PITTSBURGH AT BRADFORD
300 Campus Dr.
Bradford, PA 16701-2812
Tel: (814)362-7500; Free: 800-872-1787
Fax: (814)362-7578
E-mail: monti@pitt.edu
Web Site: www.upb.pitt.edu
President/CEO: Dr. Livingston Alexander
Admissions: Vicky Pingie
Financial Aid: Melissa Ibanez
Type: Four-Year College **Sex:** Coed **Affiliation:** University of Pittsburgh

System. **Scores:** 89% SAT V 400+; 92% SAT M 400+; 56% ACT 18-23; 16% ACT 24-29 **% Accepted:** 58 **Admission Plans:** Deferred Admission **Application Deadline:** Rolling **Application Fee:** $45.00 **H.S. Requirements:** High school diploma required; GED accepted **Costs Per Year:** Application fee: $45. One-time mandatory fee: $90. State resident tuition: $12,452 full-time, $518 per credit hour part-time. Nonresident tuition: $23,268 full-time, $969 per credit hour part-time. Mandatory fees: $920 full-time, $155 per term part-time. Full-time tuition and fees vary according to course load and program. Part-time tuition and fees vary according to course load and program. College room and board: $8592. College room only: $5228. Room and board charges vary according to board plan and housing facility. **Scholarships:** Available. **Calendar System:** Semester, Summer session available **Enrollment:** Full-time 1,342, Part-time 119 **Faculty:** Full-time 71, Part-time 92 **Student-Faculty Ratio:** 17:1 **Exams:** ACT essay component not used; SAT I or ACT; SAT essay component not used; SAT Reasoning. **% Receiving Financial Aid:** 82 **% Residing in College-Owned, -Operated, or -Affiliated Housing:** 68 **Final Year or Final Semester Residency Requirement:** Yes **Regional Accreditation:** Middle States Association of Colleges and Schools **Credit Hours For Degree:** 60 credits, Associates; 120 credits, Bachelors **ROTC:** Army **Professional Accreditation:** ACEN. **Intercollegiate Athletics:** Baseball M; Basketball M & W; Cross-Country Running M & W; Golf M; Soccer M & W; Softball W; Swimming and Diving M & W; Tennis M & W; Volleyball W

UNIVERSITY OF PITTSBURGH AT GREENSBURG

150 Finoli Dr.
Greensburg, PA 15601-5860
Tel: (724)837-7040
Fax: (724)836-9901
E-mail: upgadmit@pitt.edu
Web Site: www.greensburg.pitt.edu
President/CEO: Dr. Sharon P. Smith
Admissions: Heather Kabala
Financial Aid: Brandi S. Darr
Type: Four-Year College **Sex:** Coed **Affiliation:** University of Pittsburgh System. **Scores:** 96% SAT V 400+; 95% SAT M 400+; 51% ACT 18-23; 33% ACT 24-29 **% Accepted:** 71 **Admission Plans:** Deferred Admission; Early Admission **Application Deadline:** Rolling **Application Fee:** $45.00 **H.S. Requirements:** High school diploma required; GED accepted **Costs Per Year:** Application fee: $45. State resident tuition: $12,452 full-time, $518 per credit hour part-time. Nonresident tuition: $23,268 full-time, $969 per credit hour part-time. Mandatory fees: $930 full-time. College room and board: $9750. College room only: $5990. Room and board charges vary according to board plan and housing facility. **Scholarships:** Available. **Calendar System:** Semester, Summer session available **Enrollment:** Full-time 1,471, Part-time 91 **Faculty:** Full-time 76, Part-time 82 **Student-Faculty Ratio:** 15:1 **Exams:** ACT essay component used for placement; SAT I or ACT; SAT essay component used for placement; SAT Reasoning. **% Receiving Financial Aid:** 73 **% Residing in College-Owned, -Operated, or -Affiliated Housing:** 40 **Final Year or Final Semester Residency Requirement:** No **Regional Accreditation:** Middle States Association of Colleges and Schools **Credit Hours For Degree:** 120 credits, Bachelors **ROTC:** Air Force, Army **Intercollegiate Athletics:** Baseball M; Basketball M & W; Cross-Country Running M & W; Golf M; Soccer M & W; Softball W; Tennis M & W; Volleyball W

UNIVERSITY OF PITTSBURGH AT JOHNSTOWN

450 Schoolhouse Rd.
Johnstown, PA 15904-2990
Tel: (814)269-7000; Free: 800-765-4875
Fax: (814)269-7044
E-mail: upjadmit@pitt.edu
Web Site: www.upj.pitt.edu
President/CEO: Dr. Jem Spectar
Financial Aid: Joni L. Trovato
Type: Four-Year College **Sex:** Coed **Affiliation:** University of Pittsburgh System. **Scores:** 93% SAT V 400+; 94% SAT M 400+; 56% ACT 18-23; 28% ACT 24-29 **% Accepted:** 88 **Admission Plans:** Deferred Admission; Early Admission **Application Deadline:** Rolling **Application Fee:** $45.00 **H.S. Requirements:** High school diploma required; GED accepted **Scholarships:** Available. **Calendar System:** Semester, Summer session available **Enrollment:** Full-time 2,849, Part-time 108 **Exams:** ACT essay component used for advising; SAT I or ACT; SAT essay component used for advising; SAT Reasoning. **% Receiving Financial Aid:** 73 **% Residing in College-**

Owned, -Operated, or -Affiliated Housing: 59 **Final Year or Final Semester Residency Requirement:** No **Regional Accreditation:** Middle States Association of Colleges and Schools **Credit Hours For Degree:** 65 credits, Associates; 120 credits, Bachelors **Professional Accreditation:** ABET, CoARC. **Intercollegiate Athletics:** Baseball M; Basketball M & W; Cheerleading W; Cross-Country Running W; Golf M & W; Soccer M & W; Track and Field W; Volleyball W; Wrestling M

UNIVERSITY OF PITTSBURGH AT TITUSVILLE

504 E Main St.
Titusville, PA 16354
Tel: (814)827-4400; Free: 888-878-0462
Fax: (814)827-4448
E-mail: motter@pitt.edu
Web Site: www.upt.pitt.edu
President/CEO: Dr. Livingston Alexander
Admissions: Colleen R. Motter
Type: Two-Year College **Sex:** Coed **Affiliation:** University of Pittsburgh System. **Scores:** 76% SAT V 400+; 72% SAT M 400+; 62% ACT 18-23; 7% ACT 24-29 **Costs Per Year:** One-time mandatory fee: $60. State resident tuition: $10,754 full-time, $448 per credit part-time. Nonresident tuition: $20,316 full-time, $846 per credit part-time. Mandatory fees: $830 full-time, $135 per term part-time. Full-time tuition and fees vary according to program. Part-time tuition and fees vary according to program. College room and board: $10,224. College room only: $5292. Room and board charges vary according to board plan. **Scholarships:** Available. **Calendar System:** Semester, Summer session available **Enrollment:** Full-time 313, Part-time 75 **Faculty:** Full-time 25, Part-time 23 **Student-Faculty Ratio:** 15:1 **Exams:** SAT I or ACT. **% Residing in College-Owned, -Operated, or -Affiliated Housing:** 57 **Final Year or Final Semester Residency Requirement:** No **Regional Accreditation:** Middle States Association of Colleges and Schools **Credit Hours For Degree:** 60 credits, Associates **Professional Accreditation:** ACEN, APTA. **Intercollegiate Athletics:** Basketball M & W; Cheerleading M & W; Volleyball W

UNIVERSITY OF THE SCIENCES

600 S 43rd St.
Philadelphia, PA 19104-4495
Tel: (215)596-8800; Free: 888-996-8747
Fax: (215)895-1100
E-mail: admit@usciences.edu
Web Site: www.usciences.edu
President/CEO: Dr. Kathleen Mayes
Financial Aid: Pamela Ramanathan
Type: University **Sex:** Coed **Scores:** 100% SAT V 400+; 101% SAT M 400+; 31% ACT 18-23; 54% ACT 24-29 **% Accepted:** 58 **Admission Plans:** Deferred Admission **Application Deadline:** August 15 **Application Fee:** $45.00 **H.S. Requirements:** High school diploma required; GED accepted **Costs Per Year:** Application fee: $45. Comprehensive fee: $54,038 includes full-time tuition ($36,962), mandatory fees ($1888), and college room and board ($15,188). College room only: $9280. Full-time tuition and fees vary according to program and student level. Room and board charges vary according to board plan and housing facility. **Scholarships:** Available. **Calendar System:** Semester, Summer session available **Enrollment:** Full-time 2,215, Graduate full-time 205, Graduate part-time 213, Part-time 31 **Faculty:** Full-time 189, Part-time 230 **Student-Faculty Ratio:** 9:1 **Exams:** ACT essay component not used; Other; SAT I or ACT; SAT essay component not used; SAT Reasoning; SAT Subject. **% Receiving Financial Aid:** 83 **Final Year or Final Semester Residency Requirement:** Yes **Regional Accreditation:** Middle States Association of Colleges and Schools **Credit Hours For Degree:** 120 credits, Bachelors **ROTC:** Air Force, Army **Professional Accreditation:** ACPE, AOTA, APTA. **Intercollegiate Athletics:** Baseball M; Basketball M & W; Cross-Country Running M & W; Golf M & W; Riflery M & W; Softball W; Tennis M & W; Volleyball W

THE UNIVERSITY OF SCRANTON

800 Linden St.
Scranton, PA 18510
Tel: (570)941-7400; Free: 888-SCRANTON
Fax: (570)941-5928
E-mail: admissions@scranton.edu
Web Site: www.scranton.edu
President/CEO: Rev. Kevin P. Quinn, SJ
Admissions: Joseph Roback

Financial Aid: William R. Burke

Type: Comprehensive **Sex:** Coed **Affiliation:** Roman Catholic (Jesuit). **Scores:** 100% SAT V 400+; 99% SAT M 400+; 34% ACT 18-23; 56% ACT 24-29 **% Accepted:** 72 **Admission Plans:** Deferred Admission; Early Admission; Early Decision Plan **Application Deadline:** March 1 **Application Fee:** $0.00 **H.S. Requirements:** High school diploma required; GED accepted **Costs Per Year:** Application fee: $0. Comprehensive fee: $54,962 includes full-time tuition ($40,644), mandatory fees ($400), and college room and board ($13,918). College room only: $8152. Room and board charges vary according to board plan and housing facility. **Scholarships:** Available. **Calendar System:** 4-1-4, Summer session available **Enrollment:** Full-time 3,713, Graduate full-time 502, Graduate part-time 1,010, Part-time 197 **Faculty:** Full-time 295, Part-time 253 **Student-Faculty Ratio:** 10:1 **Exams:** ACT essay component not used; SAT I or ACT; SAT essay component not used; SAT Reasoning. **% Receiving Financial Aid:** 72 **% Residing in College-Owned, -Operated, or -Affiliated Housing:** 64 **Final Year or Final Semester Residency Requirement:** No **Regional Accreditation:** Middle States Association of Colleges and Schools **Credit Hours For Degree:** 60 credit hours, Associates; 130 credit hours, Bachelors **ROTC:** Air Force, Army **Professional Accreditation:** AACN, AACSB, AANA, ABET, ACA, AOTA, APTA, CAHME, CORE, NCATE, TEAC. **Intercollegiate Athletics:** Baseball M; Basketball M & W; Crew M & W; Cross-Country Running M & W; Equestrian Sports M & W; Fencing M & W; Field Hockey W; Golf M; Ice Hockey M; Lacrosse M & W; Rugby M & W; Soccer M & W; Softball W; Swimming and Diving M & W; Tennis M & W; Ultimate Frisbee M & W; Volleyball M & W; Wrestling M

UNIVERSITY OF VALLEY FORGE

1401 Charlestown Rd.
Phoenixville, PA 19460
Tel: (610)935-0450; Free: 800-432-8322
E-mail: admissions@valleyforge.edu
Web Site: www.valleyforge.edu
President/CEO: Pres. Don Meyer, PhD
Admissions: Rev. Joseph Ocasio
Financial Aid: Linda Stein

Type: Comprehensive **Sex:** Coed **Affiliation:** Assemblies of God. **Scores:** 84% SAT V 400+; 74% SAT M 400+; 34% ACT 18-23; 28% ACT 24-29 **% Accepted:** 95 **Admission Plans:** Deferred Admission; Early Admission; Open Admission **Application Deadline:** August 1 **Application Fee:** $25.00 **H.S. Requirements:** High school diploma required; GED accepted **Costs Per Year:** Application fee: $25. Comprehensive fee: $29,054 includes full-time tuition ($19,244), mandatory fees ($1450), and college room and board ($8360). College room only: $4780. Full-time tuition and fees vary according to course load and location. Room and board charges vary according to board plan and housing facility. **Scholarships:** Available. **Calendar System:** Semester, Summer session available **Enrollment:** Full-time 620, Graduate full-time 4, Graduate part-time 66, Part-time 276 **Faculty:** Full-time 35, Part-time 57 **Student-Faculty Ratio:** 13:1 **Exams:** ACT essay component not used; SAT I or ACT; SAT essay component not used; SAT Reasoning; SAT Subject. **% Receiving Financial Aid:** 88 **% Residing in College-Owned, -Operated, or -Affiliated Housing:** 81 **Final Year or Final Semester Residency Requirement:** No **Regional Accreditation:** Middle States Association of Colleges and Schools **Credit Hours For Degree:** 60 credit hours, Associates; 120 credit hours, Bachelors **Intercollegiate Athletics:** Baseball M; Basketball M & W; Cross-Country Running M & W; Golf M; Soccer M & W; Softball W; Volleyball W

URSINUS COLLEGE

601 E Main St.
Collegeville, PA 19426
Tel: (610)409-3000
Fax: (610)489-0627
E-mail: admissions@ursinus.edu
Web Site: www.ursinus.edu
President/CEO: Dr. S. Brock Blomberg
Admissions: Dana Matassino
Financial Aid: Suzanne Sparrow

Type: Four-Year College **Sex:** Coed **Scores:** 99% SAT V 400+; 99% SAT M 400+; 26% ACT 18-23; 45.8% ACT 24-29 **% Accepted:** 83 **Admission Plans:** Deferred Admission; Early Action; Early Decision Plan **Application Deadline:** November 1 **Application Fee:** $0.00 **H.S. Requirements:** High school diploma required; GED accepted **Costs Per Year:** Application fee: $0. Comprehensive fee: $59,600 includes full-time tuition ($47,500), manda-

tory fees ($200), and college room and board ($11,900). Part-time tuition: $1484 per credit hour. **Scholarships:** Available. **Calendar System:** Semester, Summer session not available **Enrollment:** Full-time 1,632, Part-time 11 **Faculty:** Full-time 117, Part-time 62 **Student-Faculty Ratio:** 12:1 **Exams:** SAT I or ACT; SAT Reasoning; SAT Subject. **% Receiving Financial Aid:** 75 **% Residing in College-Owned, -Operated, or -Affiliated Housing:** 96 **Final Year or Final Semester Residency Requirement:** No **Regional Accreditation:** Middle States Association of Colleges and Schools **Credit Hours For Degree:** 128 credits, Bachelors **Intercollegiate Athletics:** Baseball M; Basketball M & W; Cross-Country Running M & W; Field Hockey W; Football M; Golf M & W; Gymnastics W; Lacrosse M & W; Soccer M & W; Softball W; Swimming and Diving M & W; Tennis M & W; Track and Field M & W; Volleyball W; Wrestling M

VALLEY FORGE MILITARY COLLEGE

1001 Eagle Rd.
Wayne, PA 19087-3695
Tel: (610)989-1200; Free: 800-234-8362
Fax: (610)688-1545
E-mail: admissions@vfmac.edu
Web Site: www.vfmac.edu
President/CEO: William Gallagher
Admissions: Maj. Greg Potts

Type: Two-Year College **Sex:** Coed **Scores:** 82% SAT V 400+ **Admission Plans:** Deferred Admission; Early Admission **Application Deadline:** August 2 **Application Fee:** $25.00 **H.S. Requirements:** High school diploma required; GED accepted **Scholarships:** Available. **Calendar System:** 4-1-4, Summer session not available **Faculty:** Full-time 16, Part-time 10 **Student-Faculty Ratio:** 10:1 **Exams:** SAT I or ACT. **% Residing in College-Owned, -Operated, or -Affiliated Housing:** 100 **Regional Accreditation:** Middle States Association of Colleges and Schools **Credit Hours For Degree:** 60 credits, Associates **ROTC:** Air Force, Army **Intercollegiate Athletics:** Basketball M; Cross-Country Running M; Equestrian Sports M; Football M; Golf M; Lacrosse M; Riflery M; Soccer M; Tennis M; Wrestling M

VET TECH INSTITUTE

125 7th St.
Pittsburgh, PA 15222-3400
Tel: (412)391-7021; Free: 800-570-0693
Fax: (412)232-4348
Web Site: pittsburgh.vettechinstitute.edu
President/CEO: Jackie Flynn
Financial Aid: Donna Durr

Type: Two-Year College **Sex:** Coed **% Accepted:** 64 **H.S. Requirements:** High school diploma required; GED accepted **Scholarships:** Available. **Calendar System:** Semester **Professional Accreditation:** ACCSC, ADA.

VILLANOVA UNIVERSITY

800 Lancaster Ave.
Villanova, PA 19085-1699
Tel: (610)519-4500
Fax: (610)519-6450
E-mail: gotovu@villanova.edu
Web Site: www.villanova.edu
President/CEO: Rev. Peter M. Donohue, OSA
Admissions: Michael Gaynor
Financial Aid: Bonnie Lee Behm

Type: Comprehensive **Sex:** Coed **Affiliation:** Roman Catholic. **Scores:** 100% SAT V 400+; 100% SAT M 400+; 3.39% ACT 18-23; 36.26% ACT 24-29 **% Accepted:** 48 **Admission Plans:** Deferred Admission; Early Admission; Early Decision Plan **Application Deadline:** January 15 **Application Fee:** $80.00 **H.S. Requirements:** High school diploma required; GED accepted **Costs Per Year:** Application fee: $80. One-time mandatory fee: $150. Comprehensive fee: $60,323 includes full-time tuition ($46,966), mandatory fees ($650), and college room and board ($12,707). College room only: $6737. Full-time tuition and fees vary according to degree level and location. Room and board charges vary according to board plan and housing facility. Part-time tuition: $1960 per credit hour. Part-time mandatory fees: $15 per semester hour. Part-time tuition and fees vary according to class time, course load, degree level, location, and program. **Scholarships:** Available. **Calendar System:** Semester, Summer session available **Enrollment:** Full-time 6,614, Graduate full-time 2,497, Graduate part-time 1,237, Part-time 577 **Faculty:** Full-time 622, Part-time 410 **Student-Faculty Ratio:** 12:1 **Exams:** SAT I or ACT; SAT Reasoning. **% Receiving Financial Aid:** 48

% Residing in College-Owned, -Operated, or -Affiliated Housing: 69 **Final Year or Final Semester Residency Requirement:** Yes **Regional Accreditation:** Middle States Association of Colleges and Schools **Credit Hours For Degree:** 60 credit hours, Associates; 122 credit hours, Bachelors **ROTC:** Air Force, Army, Navy **Professional Accreditation:** AACN, AACSB, AALS, AANA, ABA, ABET, NASPAA. **Intercollegiate Athletics:** Baseball M; Basketball M & W; Cheerleading M & W; Crew M & W; Cross-Country Running M & W; Equestrian Sports W; Field Hockey W; Football M; Golf M; Ice Hockey M & W; Lacrosse M & W; Sailing M & W; Skiing (Downhill) M & W; Soccer M & W; Softball W; Swimming and Diving M & W; Tennis M & W; Track and Field M & W; Volleyball M & W; Water Polo M & W

WASHINGTON & JEFFERSON COLLEGE

60 S Lincoln St.
Washington, PA 15301
Tel: (724)222-4400; Free: 888-WANDJAY
Fax: (724)223-5271
E-mail: admission@washjeff.edu
Web Site: www.washjeff.edu
President/CEO: Dr. Tori Haring-Smith
Admissions: Robert J. Gould
Financial Aid: Michelle Anderson
Type: Comprehensive **Sex:** Coed **Scores:** 100% SAT V 400+; 100% SAT M 400+; 30% ACT 18-23; 53% ACT 24-29 **% Accepted:** 43 **Admission Plans:** Deferred Admission; Early Action; Early Admission; Early Decision Plan **Application Deadline:** March 1 **Application Fee:** $25.00 **H.S. Requirements:** High school diploma required; GED accepted **Costs Per Year:** Application fee: $25. Comprehensive fee: $54,632 includes full-time tuition ($42,656), mandatory fees ($570), and college room and board ($11,406). College room only: $6694. Full-time tuition and fees vary according to reciprocity agreements. Room and board charges vary according to board plan and housing facility. Part-time tuition: $1075 per credit hour. Part-time tuition varies according to course load. **Scholarships:** Available. **Calendar System:** 4-1-4, Summer session available **Enrollment:** Full-time 1,342, Part-time 8 **Faculty:** Full-time 110, Part-time 44 **Student-Faculty Ratio:** 11:1 **Exams:** ACT essay component not used; SAT I or ACT; SAT II; SAT essay component not used; SAT Reasoning; SAT Subject. **% Receiving Financial Aid:** 79 **% Residing in College-Owned, -Operated, or -Affiliated Housing:** 91 **Final Year or Final Semester Residency Requirement:** No **Regional Accreditation:** Middle States Association of Colleges and Schools **Credit Hours For Degree:** 34 courses, Bachelors **ROTC:** Air Force, Army **Intercollegiate Athletics:** Baseball M; Basketball M & W; Cheerleading M & W; Cross-Country Running M & W; Equestrian Sports M & W; Field Hockey W; Football M; Golf M & W; Ice Hockey M; Lacrosse M & W; Rugby M & W; Soccer M & W; Softball W; Swimming and Diving M & W; Tennis M & W; Track and Field M & W; Ultimate Frisbee M & W; Volleyball M & W; Water Polo M & W; Wrestling M

WAYNESBURG UNIVERSITY

51 W College St.
Waynesburg, PA 15370-1222
Tel: (724)627-8191; Free: 800-225-7393
Fax: (724)627-8124
E-mail: admissions@waynesburg.edu
Web Site: www.waynesburg.edu
President/CEO: Douglas Lee
Admissions: Jacqueline Palko
Financial Aid: Matthew C. Stokan
Type: Comprehensive **Sex:** Coed **Affiliation:** Presbyterian Church (U.S.A.). **% Accepted:** 86 **Admission Plans:** Early Admission **Application Deadline:** Rolling **Application Fee:** $20.00 **H.S. Requirements:** High school diploma required; GED accepted **Costs Per Year:** Application fee: $20. Comprehensive fee: $31,200 includes full-time tuition ($21,620), mandatory fees ($410), and college room and board ($9170). College room only: $4640. Full-time tuition and fees vary according to class time. Room and board charges vary according to board plan and housing facility. Part-time tuition: $900 per credit hour. Part-time mandatory fees: $16 per credit hour. Part-time tuition and fees vary according to class time, course load, and location. **Scholarships:** Available. **Calendar System:** Semester, Summer session available **Enrollment:** Full-time 1,329, Graduate full-time 115, Graduate part-time 324, Part-time 101 **Faculty:** Full-time 80, Part-time 150 **Student-Faculty Ratio:** 12:1 **Exams:** ACT essay component used for placement; SAT I or ACT; SAT essay component used for placement; SAT Reasoning; SAT Subject. **% Receiving Financial Aid:** 71 **% Residing in College-Owned, -Operated,**

or -Affiliated Housing: 77 **Final Year or Final Semester Residency Requirement:** No **Regional Accreditation:** Middle States Association of Colleges and Schools **Credit Hours For Degree:** 124 credit hours, Bachelors **ROTC:** Army **Professional Accreditation:** AACN, JRCAT. **Intercollegiate Athletics:** Baseball M; Basketball M & W; Cross-Country Running M & W; Football M; Golf M & W; Lacrosse W; Soccer M & W; Softball W; Tennis M & W; Track and Field M & W; Volleyball W; Wrestling M

WEST CHESTER UNIVERSITY OF PENNSYLVANIA

University Ave. and High St.
West Chester, PA 19383
Tel: (610)436-1000
E-mail: ugadmiss@wcupa.edu
Web Site: www.wcupa.edu
President/CEO: Dr. Christopher Fiorentino
Admissions: Marsha Haug
Financial Aid: Dana Parker
Type: Comprehensive **Sex:** Coed **Affiliation:** Pennsylvania State System of Higher Education. **Scores:** 97% SAT V 400+; 96% SAT M 400+; 48% ACT 18-23; 40% ACT 24-29 **% Accepted:** 59 **Application Deadline:** Rolling **Application Fee:** $45.00 **H.S. Requirements:** High school diploma required; GED accepted **Costs Per Year:** Application fee: $45. State resident tuition: $7060 full-time, $294 per credit part-time. Nonresident tuition: $17,650 full-time, $735 per credit part-time. Mandatory fees: $2,402 full-time, $100.90 per credit part-time. Full-time tuition and fees vary according to course load. Part-time tuition and fees vary according to course load. College room and board: $8,427. College room only: $5148. Room and board charges vary according to board plan and housing facility. **Scholarships:** Available. **Calendar System:** Semester, Summer session available **Enrollment:** Full-time 12,781, Graduate full-time 856, Graduate part-time 1,529, Part-time 1,440 **Exams:** ACT essay component used for placement; SAT I or ACT; SAT essay component used for placement; SAT Reasoning. **% Receiving Financial Aid:** 61 **% Residing in College-Owned, -Operated, or -Affiliated Housing:** 36 **Final Year or Final Semester Residency Requirement:** Yes **Regional Accreditation:** Middle States Association of Colleges and Schools **Credit Hours For Degree:** 120 credits, Bachelors **ROTC:** Air Force, Army **Professional Accreditation:** AACN, AACSB, ABET, ACA, ASHA, CEPH, CSWE, CoARC, JRCAT, NASM, NCATE. **Intercollegiate Athletics:** Baseball M; Basketball M & W; Bowling M & W; Cheerleading W; Cross-Country Running M & W; Equestrian Sports M & W; Fencing M & W; Field Hockey W; Football M; Golf M & W; Gymnastics W; Ice Hockey M & W; Lacrosse M & W; Rugby M & W; Skiing (Downhill) M & W; Soccer M & W; Softball W; Swimming and Diving M & W; Tennis M & W; Track and Field M & W; Ultimate Frisbee M; Volleyball M & W; Water Polo W; Wrestling M

WESTMINSTER COLLEGE

319 S Market St.
New Wilmington, PA 16172-0001
Tel: (724)946-8761; Free: 800-942-8033
Fax: (724)946-7171
E-mail: steinth@westminster.edu
Web Site: www.westminster.edu
President/CEO: Dr. Richard H. Dorman
Admissions: Dr. Thomas Stein
Financial Aid: Cheryl A. Gerber
Type: Comprehensive **Sex:** Coed **Affiliation:** Presbyterian Church (U.S.A.). **Scores:** 93% SAT V 400+; 95% SAT M 400+; 46% ACT 18-23; 39% ACT 24-29 **% Accepted:** 94 **Admission Plans:** Deferred Admission **Application Deadline:** May 1 **Application Fee:** $35.00 **H.S. Requirements:** High school diploma required; GED accepted **Costs Per Year:** Application fee: $35. Comprehensive fee: $45,900 includes full-time tuition ($33,810), mandatory fees ($1400), and college room and board ($10,690). Full-time tuition and fees vary according to degree level. Room and board charges vary according to board plan and housing facility. Part-time tuition: $1090 per credit. Part-time mandatory fees: $15 per credit. **Scholarships:** Available. **Calendar System:** Semester, Summer session available **Enrollment:** Full-time 1,093, Graduate full-time 12, Graduate part-time 176, Part-time 29 **Faculty:** Full-time 93, Part-time 55 **Student-Faculty Ratio:** 10:1 **Exams:** ACT essay component not used; SAT I or ACT; SAT essay component not used; SAT Reasoning; SAT Subject. **% Receiving Financial Aid:** 83 **% Residing in College-Owned, -Operated, or -Affiliated Housing:** 71 **Final Year or Final Semester Residency Requirement:** No **Regional Accreditation:** Middle States Association of Colleges and Schools **Credit Hours For Degree:** 128 semester hours, Bachelors **ROTC:** Army **Profes-**

sional **Accreditation:** NASM. **Intercollegiate Athletics:** Baseball M; Basketball M & W; Cross-Country Running M & W; Equestrian Sports M & W; Football M; Golf M & W; Ice Hockey M; Lacrosse M; Rock Climbing M & W; Skiing (Downhill) M & W; Soccer M & W; Softball W; Swimming and Diving M & W; Tennis M & W; Track and Field M & W; Ultimate Frisbee M & W; Volleyball W

WESTMORELAND COUNTY COMMUNITY COLLEGE

145 Pavilion Ln.
Youngwood, PA 15697
Tel: (724)925-4000; Free: 800-262-2103
Fax: (724)925-1150
E-mail: littles@wccc.edu
Web Site: www.wccc.edu
President/CEO: Dr. Tuesday L. Stanley
Admissions: Shawna Little
Type: Two-Year College **Sex:** Coed **% Accepted:** 100 **Admission Plans:** Early Admission; Open Admission **Application Deadline:** Rolling **Application Fee:** $0.00 **H.S. Requirements:** High school diploma or equivalent not required **Costs Per Year:** Application fee: $0. Area resident tuition: $3660 full-time, $122 per credit part-time. State resident tuition: $7320 full-time, $244 per credit part-time. Nonresident tuition: $10,980 full-time, $366 per credit part-time. Mandatory fees: $1410 full-time, $47 per credit part-time. Full-time tuition and fees vary according to course load. Part-time tuition and fees vary according to course load. **Scholarships:** Available. **Calendar System:** Semester, Summer session available **Enrollment:** Full-time 2,531, Part-time 2,986 **Faculty:** Full-time 81, Part-time 308 **Student-Faculty Ratio:** 18:1 **Regional Accreditation:** Middle States Association of Colleges and Schools **Credit Hours For Degree:** 60 credits, Associates **Professional Accreditation:** ACEN, ACF, ADA. **Intercollegiate Athletics:** Baseball M; Basketball M & W; Bowling M & W; Cross-Country Running M & W; Golf M & W; Soccer M & W; Softball W; Volleyball W

WIDENER UNIVERSITY

One University Pl.
Chester, PA 19013-5792
Tel: (610)499-4000; Free: 888-WIDENER
Fax: (610)499-4676
E-mail: admissions.office@widener.edu
Web Site: www.widener.edu
President/CEO: Dr. Julie E. Wollman
Financial Aid: Thomas K. Malloy
Type: Comprehensive **Sex:** Coed **Scores:** 96% SAT V 400+; 97% SAT M 400+; 57% ACT 18-23; 33% ACT 24-29 **% Accepted:** 68 **Admission Plans:** Deferred Admission **Application Deadline:** Rolling **Application Fee:** $35.00 **H.S. Requirements:** High school diploma required; GED accepted **Costs Per Year:** Application fee: $35. Tuition: $1346 per credit part-time. **Scholarships:** Available. **Calendar System:** Semester, Summer session available **Enrollment:** Full-time 2,954, Graduate full-time 1,455, Graduate part-time 1,209, Part-time 600 **Faculty:** Full-time 297, Part-time 335 **Student-Faculty Ratio:** 12:1 **Exams:** ACT essay component not used; SAT I or ACT; SAT essay component not used. **% Receiving Financial Aid:** 78 **% Residing in College-Owned, -Operated, or -Affiliated Housing:** 47 **Final Year or Final Semester Residency Requirement:** Yes **Regional Accreditation:** Middle States Association of Colleges and Schools **Credit Hours For Degree:** 120 credits, Bachelors **ROTC:** Air Force, Army, Navy **Professional Accreditation:** AACN, AACSB, AALS, ABA, ABET, APA, APTA, CAHME, CSWE, NCATE. **Intercollegiate Athletics:** Baseball M; Basketball M & W; Cheerleading W; Cross-Country Running M & W; Field Hockey W; Football M; Golf M; Lacrosse M & W; Soccer M & W; Softball W; Swimming and Diving M & W; Track and Field M & W; Volleyball W

WILKES UNIVERSITY

84 W S St.
Wilkes-Barre, PA 18766-0002
Tel: (570)408-5000; Free: 800-945-5378
Fax: (570)408-7820
E-mail: admissions@wilkes.edu
Web Site: www.wilkes.edu
President/CEO: Dr. Patrick Leahy
Admissions: Melanie Wade
Financial Aid: Chanel Greene
Type: Comprehensive **Sex:** Coed **Scores:** 91% SAT V 400+; 93% SAT M 400+ **% Accepted:** 82 **Admission Plans:** Deferred Admission; Early Admis-

sion **Application Deadline:** Rolling **Application Fee:** $40.00 **H.S. Requirements:** High school diploma required; GED accepted **Costs Per Year:** Application fee: $40. Comprehensive fee: $45,622 includes full-time tuition ($30,792), mandatory fees ($1564), and college room and board ($13,266). College room only: $7974. Room and board charges vary according to board plan and housing facility. Part-time tuition: $855 per credit hour. **Scholarships:** Available. **Calendar System:** Semester, Summer session available **Enrollment:** Full-time 2,254, Graduate full-time 482, Graduate part-time 2,150, Part-time 167 **Faculty:** Full-time 173, Part-time 170 **Student-Faculty Ratio:** 15:1 **Exams:** SAT I or ACT. **% Receiving Financial Aid:** 80 **% Residing in College-Owned, -Operated, or -Affiliated Housing:** 41 **Final Year or Final Semester Residency Requirement:** No **Regional Accreditation:** Middle States Association of Colleges and Schools **Credit Hours For Degree:** 120 credits, Bachelors **ROTC:** Air Force, Army **Professional Accreditation:** AACN, ABET, ACBSP, ACPE. **Intercollegiate Athletics:** Baseball M; Basketball M & W; Cross-Country Running M & W; Field Hockey W; Football M; Golf M & W; Lacrosse M & W; Soccer M & W; Softball W; Swimming and Diving M & W; Tennis M & W; Volleyball W; Wrestling M

WILLIAMSON COLLEGE OF THE TRADES

106 S New Middletown Rd.
Media, PA 19063
Tel: (610)566-1776
Fax: (610)566-6502
E-mail: jmerillat@williamson.edu
Web Site: www.williamson.edu
President/CEO: Michael Rounds
Admissions: Jay Merillat
Type: Two-Year College **Sex:** Men **% Accepted:** 26 **Admission Plans:** Preferred Admission **Application Deadline:** February 22 **Application Fee:** $0.00 **H.S. Requirements:** High school diploma required; GED accepted **Costs Per Year:** Application fee: $0. Tuition: $0 full-time. Mandatory fees: $800 full-time. All Williamson students attend on full scholarships covering tuition, room, board, and textbooks. **Scholarships:** Available. **Calendar System:** Semester **Enrollment:** Full-time 270 **Faculty:** Full-time 29 **Student-Faculty Ratio:** 12:1 **Exams:** Other. **% Residing in College-Owned, -Operated, or -Affiliated Housing:** 100 **Professional Accreditation:** ACCSC. **Intercollegiate Athletics:** Baseball M; Basketball M; Cross-Country Running M; Football M; Lacrosse M; Soccer M; Tennis M; Wrestling M

WILSON COLLEGE

1015 Philadelphia Ave.
Chambersburg, PA 17201-1285
Tel: (717)264-4141; Free: 800-421-8402
Fax: (717)264-1578
E-mail: admissions@wilson.edu
Web Site: www.wilson.edu
President/CEO: Dr. Barbara K. Mistick, PhD
Admissions: Patricia Beidel
Financial Aid: Linda Brittain
Type: Comprehensive **Sex:** Coed **Affiliation:** Presbyterian Church (U.S.A.). **Scores:** 88% SAT V 400+; 86% SAT M 400+; 66.7% ACT 18-23; 33.3% ACT 24-29 **% Accepted:** 53 **Admission Plans:** Deferred Admission; Early Admission **Application Deadline:** Rolling **Application Fee:** $0.00 **H.S. Requirements:** High school diploma required; GED accepted **Costs Per Year:** Application fee: $0. Comprehensive fee: $35,304 includes full-time tuition ($23,745), mandatory fees ($647), and college room and board ($10,912). College room only: $5390. Full-time tuition and fees vary according to location and program. Room and board charges vary according to board plan and housing facility. Part-time tuition: $792 per semester hour. Part-time mandatory fees: $105 per semester hour. Part-time tuition and fees vary according to course load, location, and program. **Scholarships:** Available. **Calendar System:** 4-1-4, Summer session available **Enrollment:** Full-time 330, Graduate full-time 1, Graduate part-time 90, Part-time 241 **Faculty:** Full-time 39, Part-time 55 **Student-Faculty Ratio:** 8:1 **Exams:** ACT essay component not used; Other; SAT I or ACT; SAT essay component not used. **% Receiving Financial Aid:** 74 **% Residing in College-Owned, -Operated, or -Affiliated Housing:** 48 **Final Year or Final Semester Residency Requirement:** Yes **Regional Accreditation:** Middle States Association of Colleges and Schools **Credit Hours For Degree:** 18 course credits, Associates; 36 course credits, Bachelors **ROTC:** Army **Intercollegiate Athletics:** Basketball M & W; Cross-Country Running M & W; Field Hockey W; Golf M; Lacrosse W; Soccer M & W; Softball W; Volleyball M

WYOTECH BLAIRSVILLE

500 Innovation Dr.
Blairsville, PA 15717
Tel: (724)459-9500; Free: 888-577-7559
Fax: (724)459-6499
E-mail: tsmyers@wyotech.edu
Web Site: www.wyotech.edu
President/CEO: Stephen Whitson
Admissions: Tim Smyers
Type: Two-Year College **Sex:** Coed **Affiliation:** Zenith Education Group.
Application Fee: $100.00 **Calendar System:** Miscellaneous **Professional Accreditation:** ACCSC.

YESHIVA BETH MOSHE

930 Hickory St.
Scranton, PA 18505-2124
Tel: (717)346-1747
President/CEO: Avrohom Pressman
Type: Comprehensive **Sex:** Men **Affiliation:** Jewish. **Admission Plans:** Open Admission **H.S. Requirements:** High school diploma required; GED not accepted **Calendar System:** Semester **Professional Accreditation:** AARTS.

YORK COLLEGE OF PENNSYLVANIA

York, PA 17405-7199
Tel: (717)846-7788; Free: 800-455-8018
E-mail: admissions@ycp.edu
Web Site: www.ycp.edu
President/CEO: Dr. Pamela Gunter-Smith
Admissions: Ines Ramirez
Financial Aid: Calvin Williams
Type: Comprehensive **Sex:** Coed **Scores:** 99% SAT V 400+; 98% SAT M 400+; 56.14% ACT 18-23; 35.53% ACT 24-29 **% Accepted:** 43 **Admission Plans:** Deferred Admission **Application Fee:** $0.00 **H.S. Requirements:** High school diploma required; GED accepted **Costs Per Year:** Application fee: $0. Comprehensive fee: $29,240 includes full-time tuition ($16,970),

mandatory fees ($1810), and college room and board ($10,460). Full-time tuition and fees vary according to program. Room and board charges vary according to board plan and housing facility. Part-time tuition: $525 per credit hour. **Scholarships:** Available. **Calendar System:** Semester, Summer session available **Enrollment:** Full-time 4,077, Graduate full-time 40, Graduate part-time 162, Part-time 460 **Faculty:** Full-time 173, Part-time 296 **Student-Faculty Ratio:** 16:1 **Exams:** ACT essay component not used; SAT I or ACT; SAT essay component not used; SAT Reasoning; SAT Subject. **% Receiving Financial Aid:** 66 **% Residing in College-Owned, -Operated, or -Affiliated Housing:** 57 **Final Year or Final Semester Residency Requirement:** No **Regional Accreditation:** Middle States Association of Colleges and Schools **Credit Hours For Degree:** 60 credit hours, Associates; 122 credit hours, Bachelors **Professional Accreditation:** AACN, AANA, ABET, ACBSP, ACEN, CoARC, NASM, NRPA. **Intercollegiate Athletics:** Baseball M; Basketball M & W; Cheerleading M & W; Cross-Country Running M & W; Field Hockey W; Golf M; Lacrosse M & W; Soccer M & W; Softball W; Swimming and Diving M & W; Tennis M & W; Track and Field M & W; Volleyball W; Wrestling M

YTI CAREER INSTITUTE–ALTOONA

2900 Fairway Dr.
Altoona, PA 16602
Tel: (814)944-5643
Web Site: www.yti.edu
Type: Two-Year College **Sex:** Coed **Professional Accreditation:** ACCSC.

YTI CAREER INSTITUTE–YORK

1405 Williams Rd.
York, PA 17402-9017
Tel: (717)757-1100; Free: 800-557-6335
Fax: (717)757-4964
Web Site: www.yti.edu
President/CEO: Mark Millen
Type: Two-Year College **Sex:** Coed **Affiliation:** York Technical Institute, LLC. **H.S. Requirements:** High school diploma required; GED accepted **Scholarships:** Available. **Calendar System:** Continuous **Professional Accreditation:** ACCSC.

BROWN UNIVERSITY

One Prospect St.
Providence, RI 02912
Tel: (401)863-1000
Fax: (401)863-9300
E-mail: admission_undergraduate@brown.edu
Web Site: www.brown.edu
President/CEO: Christina H. Paxon
Admissions: James Miller

Type: University **Sex:** Coed **Scores:** 100% SAT V 400+; 100% SAT M 400+; 0.71% ACT 18-23; 15.58% ACT 24-29 **% Accepted:** 9 **Admission Plans:** Deferred Admission; Early Action **Application Deadline:** January 1 **Application Fee:** $75.00 **H.S. Requirements:** High school diploma required; GED accepted **Costs Per Year:** Application fee: $75. Comprehensive fee: $64,566 includes full-time tuition ($50,224), mandatory fees ($1142), and college room and board ($13,200). College room only: $8284. Room and board charges vary according to board plan. Part-time tuition: $6278 per credit. **Scholarships:** Available. **Calendar System:** Semester, Summer session available **Enrollment:** Full-time 6,318, Graduate full-time 2,576, Graduate part-time 230, Part-time 334 **Faculty:** Full-time 770, Part-time 115 **Student-Faculty Ratio:** 9:1 **Exams:** SAT I and SAT II or ACT; SAT Reasoning; SAT Subject. **% Receiving Financial Aid:** 45 **% Residing in College-Owned, -Operated, or -Affiliated Housing:** 76 **Final Year or Final Semester Residency Requirement:** No **Regional Accreditation:** New England Association of Schools and Colleges **Credit Hours For Degree:** 30 credits (1 credit = 4 semester hours), Bachelors **ROTC:** Air Force, Army, Navy **Professional Accreditation:** ABET, APA, CEPH, LCME/AMA. **Intercollegiate Athletics:** Baseball M; Basketball M & W; Crew M & W; Cross-Country Running M & W; Equestrian Sports W; Fencing M & W; Field Hockey W; Football M; Golf M & W; Gymnastics W; Ice Hockey M & W; Lacrosse M & W; Rugby M & W; Sailing M & W; Skiing (Downhill) M & W; Soccer M & W; Softball W; Squash M & W; Swimming and Diving M & W; Tennis M & W; Track and Field M & W; Volleyball M & W; Water Polo M & W; Wrestling M

BRYANT UNIVERSITY

1150 Douglas Pke.
Smithfield, RI 02917
Tel: (401)232-6000; Free: 800-622-7001
Fax: (401)232-6741
E-mail: admission@bryant.edu
Web Site: www.bryant.edu
President/CEO: Ronald K. Machtley
Admissions: Michelle Cloutier
Financial Aid: John B. Canning

Type: Comprehensive **Sex:** Coed **Scores:** 100% SAT V 400+; 100% SAT M 400+; 25.45% ACT 18-23; 64.85% ACT 24-29 **% Accepted:** 72 **Admission Plans:** Deferred Admission; Early Action; Early Decision Plan **Application Deadline:** February 1 **Application Fee:** $50.00 **H.S. Requirements:** High school diploma required; GED accepted **Costs Per Year:** Application fee: $50. Comprehensive fee: $55,937 includes full-time tuition ($40,564), mandatory fees ($398), and college room and board ($14,975). College room only: $8790. Room and board charges vary according to board plan and housing facility. Part-time tuition: $1005 per credit hour. Part-time tuition varies according to course load. **Scholarships:** Available. **Calendar System:** Semester, Summer session available **Enrollment:** Full-time 3,379,

Graduate full-time 118, Graduate part-time 93, Part-time 80 **Faculty:** Full-time 166, Part-time 115 **Student-Faculty Ratio:** 13:1 **Exams:** ACT essay component not used; SAT essay component not used; SAT Reasoning. **% Receiving Financial Aid:** 62 **% Residing in College-Owned, -Operated, or -Affiliated Housing:** 82 **Final Year or Final Semester Residency Requirement:** Yes **Regional Accreditation:** New England Association of Schools and Colleges **Credit Hours For Degree:** 123 credits, Bachelors **ROTC:** Army **Professional Accreditation:** AACSB. **Intercollegiate Athletics:** Baseball M; Basketball M & W; Bowling M & W; Cheerleading W; Crew W; Cross-Country Running M & W; Field Hockey W; Football M; Golf M; Ice Hockey M; Lacrosse M & W; Racquetball M & W; Rowing W; Rugby M & W; Soccer M & W; Softball W; Squash M & W; Swimming and Diving M & W; Tennis M & W; Track and Field M & W; Ultimate Frisbee M & W; Volleyball M & W

COMMUNITY COLLEGE OF RHODE ISLAND

400 E Ave.
Warwick, RI 02886-1807
Tel: (401)825-1000
Fax: (401)825-2418
E-mail: webadmission@ccri.edu
Web Site: www.ccri.edu
President/CEO: Dr. Meghan Hughes

Type: Two-Year College **Sex:** Coed **% Accepted:** 100 **Admission Plans:** Deferred Admission; Open Admission; Preferred Admission **Application Deadline:** Rolling **Application Fee:** $20.00 **H.S. Requirements:** High school diploma required; GED accepted. For nursing, dental, allied health programs: High school diploma required; GED not accepted **Costs Per Year:** Application fee: $20. State resident tuition: $3950 full-time, $180 per credit hour part-time. Nonresident tuition: $11,180 full-time, $534 per credit hour part-time. Mandatory fees: $316 full-time, $12 per credit hour part-time. Full-time tuition and fees vary according to program. Part-time tuition and fees vary according to course load and program. **Scholarships:** Available. **Calendar System:** Semester, Summer session available **Enrollment:** Full-time 4,836, Part-time 11,359 **Faculty:** Full-time 327, Part-time 496 **Student-Faculty Ratio:** 18:1 **Regional Accreditation:** New England Association of Schools and Colleges **Credit Hours For Degree:** 60 credits, Associates **ROTC:** Army **Professional Accreditation:** ACBSP, ACEN, ADA, AOTA, APTA, CoARC, JRCERT, NAACLS. **Intercollegiate Athletics:** Baseball M; Basketball M & W; Golf M & W; Soccer M & W; Softball W; Tennis M & W; Track and Field M & W; Volleyball W

JOHNSON & WALES UNIVERSITY

8 Abbott Park Pl.
Providence, RI 02903-3703
Tel: (401)598-1000; Free: 800-342-5598
Fax: (401)598-1835
E-mail: pvd@admissions.jwu.edu
Web Site: www.jwu.edu/providence
President/CEO: Dr. Irving Schneider
Admissions: Amy Podbelski
Financial Aid: Lynn Robinson

Type: Comprehensive **Sex:** Coed **% Accepted:** 82 **Admission Plans:** Deferred Admission; Early Admission **H.S. Requirements:** High school diploma required; GED accepted **Costs Per Year:** Tuition: $30,396 full-time.

Mandatory fees: $350 full-time. College room only: $8268. **Scholarships:** Available. **Calendar System:** Quarter, Summer session available **Enrollment:** Full-time 8,145, Graduate full-time 622, Graduate part-time 114, Part-time 573 **Faculty:** Full-time 294, Part-time 323 **Student-Faculty Ratio:** 20:1 **% Receiving Financial Aid:** 71 **% Residing in College-Owned, -Operated, or -Affiliated Housing:** 44 **Regional Accreditation:** New England Association of Schools and Colleges **Credit Hours For Degree:** 90 credit hours, Associates; 180 credit hours, Bachelors **ROTC:** Army **Intercollegiate Athletics:** Baseball M; Basketball M & W; Cross-Country Running M & W; Equestrian Sports M & W; Golf M & W; Ice Hockey M; Sailing M & W; Soccer M & W; Softball W; Tennis M & W; Volleyball M & W; Wrestling M

MATER ECCLESIAE COLLEGE

60 Austin Ave.
Greenville, RI 02828
Tel: (401)949-2820
E-mail: info@mecollege.org
Web Site: www.mecollege.edu
President/CEO: Maria Lourdes Fernandez, PhD

Type: Four-Year College **Sex:** Women **Affiliation:** Roman Catholic. **Exams:** SAT I or ACT. **Regional Accreditation:** New England Association of Schools and Colleges

NEW ENGLAND INSTITUTE OF TECHNOLOGY

One New England Tech Blvd.
East Greenwich, RI 02818
Tel: (401)467-7744; Free: 800-736-7744
E-mail: mcaruso@neit.edu
Web Site: www.neit.edu
President/CEO: Richard I. Gouse
Admissions: Michael Caruso

Type: Comprehensive **Sex:** Coed **Admission Plans:** Deferred Admission; Early Admission; Open Admission **Application Deadline:** Rolling **Application Fee:** $25.00 **H.S. Requirements:** High school diploma required; GED accepted **Costs Per Year:** Application fee: $25. Tuition: $22,995 full-time. Mandatory fees: $1656 full-time. Full-time tuition and fees vary according to course level, degree level, and program. Tuition guaranteed not to increase for student's term of enrollment. **Scholarships:** Available. **Calendar System:** Quarter, Summer session available **Enrollment:** Full-time 2,369, Graduate full-time 55, Graduate part-time 51, Part-time 444 **Faculty:** Full-time 133, Part-time 212 **Student-Faculty Ratio:** 13:1 **Final Year or Final Semester Residency Requirement:** No **Regional Accreditation:** New England Association of Schools and Colleges **Credit Hours For Degree:** 90 credits, Associates; 180 credits, Bachelors **Professional Accreditation:** ABET, AOTA, ARCST.

PROVIDENCE COLLEGE

1 Cunningham Sq.
Providence, RI 02918
Tel: (401)865-1000; Free: 800-721-6444
Fax: (401)865-2826
E-mail: pcadmiss@providence.edu
Web Site: www.providence.edu
President/CEO: Rev. Brian Shanley, OP
Admissions: Raul Fonts
Financial Aid: Sandra J. Oliveira

Type: Comprehensive **Sex:** Coed **Affiliation:** Roman Catholic. **Scores:** 99% SAT V 400+; 99% SAT M 400+; 29.3% ACT 18-23; 55% ACT 24-29 **Costs Per Year:** Comprehensive fee: $58,790 includes full-time tuition ($44,520), mandatory fees ($880), and college room and board ($13,390). College room only: $7720. Full-time tuition and fees vary according to class time and degree level. Room and board charges vary according to board plan and housing facility. Part-time tuition: $1590 per credit hour. Part-time tuition varies according to class time and degree level. **Scholarships:** Available. **Calendar System:** Semester, Summer session available **Enrollment:** Full-time 3,911, Graduate full-time 219, Graduate part-time 315, Part-time 290 **Faculty:** Full-time 297, Part-time 233 **Student-Faculty Ratio:** 12:1 **Exams:** ACT essay component used for advising; ACT essay component used for placement; Other; SAT essay component used for advising; SAT essay component used for placement. **% Receiving Financial Aid:** 56 **% Residing in College-Owned, -Operated, or -Affiliated Housing:** 72 **Final Year or Final Semester Residency Requirement:** No **Regional Accreditation:** New England Association of Schools and Colleges **Credit Hours For Degree:** 60 credits, Associates; 120 credits, Bachelors **ROTC:**

Army **Professional Accreditation:** CSWE, NASM. **Intercollegiate Athletics:** Basketball M & W; Cross-Country Running M & W; Field Hockey W; Ice Hockey M & W; Lacrosse M; Soccer M & W; Softball W; Swimming and Diving M & W; Tennis W; Track and Field M & W; Volleyball W

RHODE ISLAND COLLEGE

600 Mount Pleasant Ave.
Providence, RI 02908-1991
Tel: (401)456-8000; Free: 800-669-5760
Fax: (401)456-8379
E-mail: admissions@ric.edu
Web Site: www.ric.edu
President/CEO: Dr. Nancy Carriuolo
Admissions: John McLaughlin
Financial Aid: Kenneth Ferus

Type: Comprehensive **Sex:** Coed **Scores:** 78% SAT V 400+; 81% SAT M 400+; 50.9% ACT 18-23; 7.3% ACT 24-29 **% Accepted:** 72 **Admission Plans:** Early Admission **Application Deadline:** March 15 **Application Fee:** $50.00 **H.S. Requirements:** High school diploma required; GED accepted **Costs Per Year:** Application fee: $50. State resident tuition: $7118 full-time, $280 per credit part-time. Nonresident tuition: $18,434 full-time, $690 per credit part-time. Mandatory fees: $1079 full-time, $32 per credit part-time, $74 per term part-time. Part-time tuition and fees vary according to course load. College room and board: $10,394. College room only: $5914. Room and board charges vary according to housing facility. **Scholarships:** Available. **Calendar System:** Semester, Summer session available **Enrollment:** Full-time 5,581, Graduate full-time 195, Graduate part-time 871, Part-time 1,865 **Faculty:** Full-time 335, Part-time 437 **Student-Faculty Ratio:** 14:1 **Exams:** ACT essay component not used; ACT essay component used for advising; SAT I or ACT; SAT essay component not used; SAT essay component used for advising; SAT Reasoning; SAT Subject. **% Receiving Financial Aid:** 66 **% Residing in College-Owned, -Operated, or -Affiliated Housing:** 15 **Final Year or Final Semester Residency Requirement:** No **Regional Accreditation:** New England Association of Schools and Colleges **Credit Hours For Degree:** 120 semester hours, Bachelors **ROTC:** Army **Professional Accreditation:** AACN, AACSB, CSWE, NASAD, NASM, NCATE. **Intercollegiate Athletics:** Baseball M; Basketball M & W; Cross-Country Running M & W; Golf M & W; Gymnastics W; Lacrosse W; Soccer M & W; Softball W; Swimming and Diving W; Tennis M & W; Track and Field M & W; Volleyball W; Wrestling M

RHODE ISLAND SCHOOL OF DESIGN

2 College St.
Providence, RI 02903-2784
Tel: (401)454-6100; Free: 800-364-7473
Fax: (401)454-6309
E-mail: admissions@risd.edu
Web Site: www.risd.edu
President/CEO: Prof. Rosanne Somerson
Admissions: Edward Newhall
Financial Aid: Anthony Gallonio

Type: Comprehensive **Sex:** Coed **Scores:** 100% SAT V 400+; 100% SAT M 400+ **Costs Per Year:** Comprehensive fee: $58,440 includes full-time tuition ($45,530), mandatory fees ($310), and college room and board ($12,600). College room only: $7200. Room and board charges vary according to board plan and housing facility. **Scholarships:** Available. **Calendar System:** 4-1-4, Summer session not available **Enrollment:** Full-time 2,014, Graduate full-time 467 **Faculty:** Full-time 168, Part-time 302 **Student-Faculty Ratio:** 9:1 **Exams:** SAT I or ACT. **% Receiving Financial Aid:** 39 **% Residing in College-Owned, -Operated, or -Affiliated Housing:** 60 **Final Year or Final Semester Residency Requirement:** No **Regional Accreditation:** New England Association of Schools and Colleges **Credit Hours For Degree:** 126 credits, Bachelors **ROTC:** Army **Professional Accreditation:** ASLA, NAAB, NASAD.

ROGER WILLIAMS UNIVERSITY

1 Old Ferry Rd.
Bristol, RI 02809
Tel: (401)253-1040; Free: 800-458-7144
Fax: (401)254-3557
E-mail: admit@rwu.edu
Web Site: www.rwu.edu
President/CEO: Donald J. Farish, PhD
Financial Aid: Diane Usher

Type: Comprehensive **Sex:** Coed **Scores:** 100% SAT V 400+; 99% SAT M 400+; 31.1% ACT 18-23; 63.7% ACT 24-29 **% Accepted:** 78 **Admission Plans:** Deferred Admission; Early Decision Plan **Application Deadline:** February 1 **Application Fee:** $50.00 **H.S. Requirements:** High school diploma required; GED accepted **Costs Per Year:** Application fee: $50. Comprehensive fee: $46,646 includes full-time tuition ($29,976), mandatory fees ($1824), and college room and board ($14,846). College room only: $7990. **Scholarships:** Available. **Calendar System:** Semester, Summer session available **Enrollment:** Full-time 3,956, Graduate full-time 185, Graduate part-time 68, Part-time 599 **Faculty:** Full-time 206, Part-time 299 **Student-Faculty Ratio:** 14:1 **Exams:** ACT; ACT essay component not used; SAT I; SAT I and SAT II or ACT; SAT I or ACT; SAT II; SAT essay component not used; SAT Reasoning. **% Receiving Financial Aid:** 57 **% Residing in College-Owned, -Operated, or -Affiliated Housing:** 75 **Final Year or Final Semester Residency Requirement:** No **Regional Accreditation:** New England Association of Schools and Colleges **Credit Hours For Degree:** 60 credits, Associates; 120 credits, Bachelors **ROTC:** Army **Professional Accreditation:** AACSB, ABA, ABET, ACCE, NAAB. **Intercollegiate Athletics:** Baseball M; Basketball M & W; Cheerleading M & W; Crew M & W; Cross-Country Running M & W; Equestrian Sports M & W; Field Hockey W; Golf M; Lacrosse M & W; Rugby M & W; Sailing M & W; Soccer M & W; Softball W; Swimming and Diving M & W; Tennis M & W; Track and Field M & W; Volleyball M & W; Wrestling M

SALVE REGINA UNIVERSITY

100 Ochre Point Ave.
Newport, RI 02840-4192
Tel: (401)847-6650; Free: 888-GO SALVE
Fax: (401)848-2823
E-mail: sruadmis@salve.edu
Web Site: www.salve.edu
President/CEO: Señor Jane Gerety, PhD
Admissions: Dean Colleen Emerson
Financial Aid: Anne McDermott
Type: Comprehensive **Sex:** Coed **Affiliation:** Roman Catholic. **Scores:** 100% SAT V 400+; 100% SAT M 400+; 35% ACT 18-23; 61% ACT 24-29 **% Accepted:** 73 **Admission Plans:** Deferred Admission; Early Decision Plan **Application Deadline:** February 1 **Application Fee:** $50.00 **H.S. Requirements:** High school diploma required; GED accepted **Costs Per Year:** Application fee: $50. Comprehensive fee: $49,990 includes full-time tuition ($36,190), mandatory fees ($550), and college room and board ($13,250). Full-time tuition and fees vary according to location. Room and board charges vary according to board plan and housing facility. Part-time tuition: $1206 per credit. Part-time mandatory fees: $50 per term. Part-time tuition and fees vary according to course load and location. **Scholarships:** Available. **Calendar System:** Semester, Summer session available **Enrollment:** Full-time 1,995, Graduate full-time 184, Graduate part-time 416, Part-time

163 **Faculty:** Full-time 122, Part-time 182 **Student-Faculty Ratio:** 13:1 **Exams:** ACT essay component not used; SAT I; SAT I or ACT; SAT essay component not used; SAT Reasoning. **% Receiving Financial Aid:** 77 **% Residing in College-Owned, -Operated, or -Affiliated Housing:** 60 **Final Year or Final Semester Residency Requirement:** No **Regional Accreditation:** New England Association of Schools and Colleges **Credit Hours For Degree:** 60 credit hours, Associates; 120 credit hours, Bachelors **ROTC:** Army **Professional Accreditation:** ACEN, CORE, CSWE, NASAD. **Intercollegiate Athletics:** Baseball M; Basketball M & W; Cross-Country Running M & W; Field Hockey W; Football M; Ice Hockey M & W; Lacrosse M & W; Rugby M & W; Sailing M & W; Soccer M & W; Softball W; Tennis M & W; Track and Field W; Volleyball W

UNIVERSITY OF RHODE ISLAND

Kingston, RI 02881
Tel: (401)874-1000
Fax: (401)874-5523
E-mail: lynch@uri.edu
Web Site: www.uri.edu
President/CEO: Dr. David M. Dooley
Admissions: Joanne Lynch
Type: University **Sex:** Coed **Scores:** 99% SAT V 400+; 99% SAT M 400+; 39.9% ACT 18-23; 51.6% ACT 24-29 **% Accepted:** 71 **Admission Plans:** Deferred Admission; Early Admission; Early Decision Plan **Application Deadline:** February 1 **Application Fee:** $65.00 **H.S. Requirements:** High school diploma required; GED accepted **Costs Per Year:** Application fee: $65. State resident tuition: $11,128 full-time, $464 per credit hour part-time. Nonresident tuition: $27,118 full-time, $1130 per credit hour part-time. Mandatory fees: $1734 full-time, $44 per credit hour part-time, $58 per term part-time. Full-time tuition and fees vary according to course load, location, and reciprocity agreements. Part-time tuition and fees vary according to course load, location, and reciprocity agreements. College room and board: $7400. College room only: $4300. Room and board charges vary according to board plan and housing facility. **Scholarships:** Available. **Calendar System:** Semester, Summer session available **Enrollment:** Full-time 12,293, Graduate full-time 1,835, Graduate part-time 1,137, Part-time 1,348 **Faculty:** Full-time 699, Part-time 407 **Student-Faculty Ratio:** 16:1 **Exams:** ACT essay component not used; ACT essay component used for admission; SAT I or ACT; SAT Reasoning. **% Receiving Financial Aid:** 73 **% Residing in College-Owned, -Operated, or -Affiliated Housing:** 44 **Regional Accreditation:** New England Association of Schools and Colleges **Credit Hours For Degree:** 120 credits, Bachelors **ROTC:** Army **Professional Accreditation:** AACN, AACSB, AAMFT, ABET, ACNM, ACPE, ACSP, ALA, AND, APA, APTA, ASHA, ASLA, NASM, NCATE. **Intercollegiate Athletics:** Baseball M; Basketball M; Crew M; Cross-Country Running M & W; Football M; Golf M; Soccer M & W; Softball W; Swimming and Diving W; Tennis W; Track and Field M & W; Volleyball W

AIKEN TECHNICAL COLLEGE
2276 J. Davis Hwy.
Graniteville, SC 29829
Tel: (803)593-9231
E-mail: moonj@atc.edu
Web Site: www.atc.edu
President/CEO: Dr. Susan A. Winsor
Admissions: Jessica Moon
Type: Two-Year College **Sex:** Coed **Affiliation:** South Carolina State Board for Technical and Comprehensive Education. **% Accepted:** 55 **Admission Plans:** Deferred Admission; Open Admission **Application Deadline:** Rolling **Application Fee:** $0.00 **H.S. Requirements:** High school diploma required; GED accepted **Costs Per Year:** Application fee: $0. Area resident tuition: $4352 full-time. State resident tuition: $4712 full-time. Nonresident tuition: $8224 full-time. **Scholarships:** Available. **Calendar System:** Semester, Summer session available **Enrollment:** Full-time 694, Part-time 1,663 **Faculty:** Full-time 57, Part-time 143 **Final Year or Final Semester Residency Requirement:** No **Regional Accreditation:** Southern Association of Colleges and Schools **Credit Hours For Degree:** 64 semester hours, Associates **Professional Accreditation:** ABET, ACBSP, ACEN, ADA.

ALLEN UNIVERSITY
1530 Harden St.
Columbia, SC 29204
Tel: (803)254-4165; Free: 877-625-5368
Fax: (803)376-5731
E-mail: tparker@allenuniversity.edu
Web Site: www.allenuniversity.edu
President/CEO: Charles E. Young
Admissions: Terri Parker
Financial Aid: Donna Foster
Type: Four-Year College **Sex:** Coed **Affiliation:** African Methodist Episcopal. **Scores:** 44% SAT V 400+; 44% SAT M 400+ **% Accepted:** 72 **Admission Plans:** Open Admission **Application Deadline:** July 31 **Application Fee:** $20.00 **H.S. Requirements:** High school diploma required; GED accepted **Scholarships:** Available. **Calendar System:** Semester, Summer session available **Enrollment:** Full-time 804, Part-time 23 **Faculty:** Full-time 29, Part-time 12 **Exams:** SAT I or ACT. **% Receiving Financial Aid:** 80 **Regional Accreditation:** Southern Association of Colleges and Schools **Credit Hours For Degree:** 125 credit hours, Bachelors **ROTC:** Army **Intercollegiate Athletics:** Basketball M & W; Cross-Country Running M & W; Golf M & W; Track and Field M & W; Volleyball W

ANDERSON UNIVERSITY
316 Blvd.
Anderson, SC 29621-4035
Tel: (864)231-2000; Free: 800-542-3594
Fax: (864)231-2004
E-mail: admissions@andersonuniversity.edu
Web Site: www.andersonuniversity.edu
President/CEO: Dr. Evans P. Whitaker
Admissions: Pam Bryant-Ross
Financial Aid: Allison Sullivan
Type: Comprehensive **Sex:** Coed **Affiliation:** Baptist. **Scores:** 97% SAT V 400+; 96% SAT M 400+; 43.52% ACT 18-23; 43.52% ACT 24-29 **% Ac-**cepted: 55 **Admission Plans:** Deferred Admission **Application Deadline:** August 1 **Application Fee:** $25.00 **H.S. Requirements:** High school diploma required; GED accepted **Costs Per Year:** Application fee: $25. Comprehensive fee: $35,054 includes full-time tuition ($23,470), mandatory fees ($2410), and college room and board ($9174). College room only: $4670. Full-time tuition and fees vary according to course load and program. Room and board charges vary according to board plan and housing facility. **Scholarships:** Available. **Calendar System:** Semester, Summer session available **Enrollment:** Full-time 2,397, Graduate full-time 317, Graduate part-time 71, Part-time 427 **Faculty:** Full-time 124, Part-time 191 **Student-Faculty Ratio:** 16:1 **Exams:** SAT I or ACT. **% Receiving Financial Aid:** 80 **% Residing in College-Owned, -Operated, or -Affiliated Housing:** 47 **Final Year or Final Semester Residency Requirement:** No **Regional Accreditation:** Southern Association of Colleges and Schools **Credit Hours For Degree:** 128 semester hours, Bachelors **ROTC:** Air Force, Army **Professional Accreditation:** ACBSP, NASAD, NASM, NCATE. **Intercollegiate Athletics:** Baseball M; Basketball M & W; Cheerleading W; Cross-Country Running M & W; Golf M & W; Soccer M & W; Softball W; Tennis M & W; Track and Field M & W; Volleyball W; Wrestling M

THE ART INSTITUTE OF CHARLESTON, A BRANCH OF THE ART INSTITUTE OF ATLANTA
24 N Market St.
Charleston, SC 29401
Tel: (843)727-3500; Free: 866-211-0107
Fax: (843)727-3440
Web Site: www.artinstitutes.edu/charleston
President/CEO: Todd Cunningham
Type: Four-Year College **Sex:** Coed **Affiliation:** Education Management Corporation. **Calendar System:** Quarter **Regional Accreditation:** Southern Association of Colleges and Schools

BENEDICT COLLEGE
1600 Harden St.
Columbia, SC 29204
Tel: (803)256-4220; Free: 800-868-6598
Fax: (803)253-5167
E-mail: thompsop@benedict.edu
Web Site: www.benedict.edu
President/CEO: David H. Swinton
Admissions: Phyllis Thompson
Financial Aid: Bichevia Green
Type: Four-Year College **Sex:** Coed **Affiliation:** Baptist. **Admission Plans:** Deferred Admission; Early Admission; Open Admission **Application Deadline:** Rolling **Application Fee:** $25.00 **H.S. Requirements:** High school diploma required; GED accepted **Scholarships:** Available. **Calendar System:** Semester, Summer session available **Regional Accreditation:** Southern Association of Colleges and Schools **Credit Hours For Degree:** 125 semester hours, Bachelors **ROTC:** Air Force, Army **Professional Accreditation:** ACBSP, CSWE, NCATE. **Intercollegiate Athletics:** Baseball M; Basketball M & W; Cheerleading W; Football M; Golf M; Softball W; Tennis M; Track and Field M; Volleyball W

BOB JONES UNIVERSITY
1700 Wade Hampton Blvd.
Greenville, SC 29614

Tel: (864)242-5100; Free: 800-252-6363
E-mail: admission@bju.edu
Web Site: www.bju.edu
President/CEO: Dr. Stephen Pettit
Admissions: Gary Deedrick

Type: University **Sex:** Coed **Affiliation:** Christian. **Scores:** 37% ACT 18-23; 43% ACT 24-29 **% Accepted:** 81 **Application Deadline:** August 1 **Application Fee:** $0.00 **H.S. Requirements:** High school diploma required; GED accepted **Costs Per Year:** Application fee: $0. Comprehensive fee: $21,180 includes full-time tuition ($14,250), mandatory fees ($650), and college room and board ($6280). Full-time tuition and fees vary according to course load and program. Part-time tuition: $680 per credit hour. Part-time tuition varies according to course load and program. **Scholarships:** Available. **Calendar System:** Semester, Summer session available **Enrollment:** Full-time 2,496, Graduate full-time 121, Graduate part-time 266, Part-time 225 **Faculty:** Full-time 190, Part-time 30 **Student-Faculty Ratio:** 14:1 **Exams:** ACT. **% Receiving Financial Aid:** 100 **% Residing in College-Owned, -Operated, or -Affiliated Housing:** 74 **Final Year or Final Semester Residency Requirement:** Yes **Credit Hours For Degree:** 90 credits, Associates; 128 credits, Bachelors **Professional Accreditation:** TRACS. **Intercollegiate Athletics:** Basketball M & W; Cross-Country Running M & W; Golf M & W; Soccer M & W

CENTRAL CAROLINA TECHNICAL COLLEGE

506 N Guignard Dr.
Sumter, SC 29150-2499
Tel: (803)778-1961; Free: 800-221-8711
Fax: (803)773-4859
E-mail: wrightb@cctech.edu
Web Site: www.cctech.edu
President/CEO: Dr. Blon Tim Hardee, EdD
Admissions: Barbara Wright
Financial Aid: Cynthia Walker

Type: Two-Year College **Sex:** Coed **Affiliation:** South Carolina State Board for Technical and Comprehensive Education. **Admission Plans:** Open Admission **Application Deadline:** Rolling **Application Fee:** $0.00 **H.S. Requirements:** High school diploma required; GED accepted. For nursing programs and early childhood development programs: High school diploma required; GED not accepted **Scholarships:** Available. **Calendar System:** Semester, Summer session available **Enrollment:** Full-time 1,607, Part-time 2,915 **Faculty:** Full-time 99, Part-time 159 **Student-Faculty Ratio:** 17:1 **Exams:** ACT; Other; SAT I; SAT I or ACT. **Final Year or Final Semester Residency Requirement:** No **Regional Accreditation:** Southern Association of Colleges and Schools **Credit Hours For Degree:** 60 semester hours, Associates **Professional Accreditation:** ABET, ACEN.

CENTURA COLLEGE

7500 Two Notch Rd.
Columbia, SC 29223
Tel: (803)754-7544
Web Site: www.centuracollege.edu
Type: Two-Year College **Sex:** Coed **Professional Accreditation:** ACCSC.

CHARLESTON SOUTHERN UNIVERSITY

PO Box 118087
Charleston, SC 29423-8087
Tel: (843)863-7000; Free: 800-947-7474
E-mail: enroll@csuniv.edu
Web Site: www.charlestonsouthern.edu
President/CEO: Dr. Jairy C. Hunter, Jr.
Admissions: Jim Rhoden
Financial Aid: Jim Rhoden

Type: Comprehensive **Sex:** Coed **Affiliation:** Baptist. **% Accepted:** 60 **Application Deadline:** Rolling **Application Fee:** $40.00 **H.S. Requirements:** High school diploma required; GED accepted **Costs Per Year:** Application fee: $40. Comprehensive fee: $32,710 includes full-time tuition ($23,400), mandatory fees ($40), and college room and board ($9270). Full-time tuition and fees vary according to program. Room and board charges vary according to board plan. Part-time tuition: $470 per credit hour. Part-time tuition varies according to program. **Scholarships:** Available. **Calendar System:** Miscellaneous, Summer session available **Enrollment:** Full-time 2,796, Graduate full-time 55, Graduate part-time 385, Part-time 385 **Faculty:** Full-time 163, Part-time 129 **Student-Faculty Ratio:** 15:1 **Exams:** ACT essay component not used; SAT I or ACT; SAT essay component not used. **%**

Receiving Financial Aid: 82 **% Residing in College-Owned, -Operated, or -Affiliated Housing:** 42 **Final Year or Final Semester Residency Requirement:** No **Regional Accreditation:** Southern Association of Colleges and Schools **Credit Hours For Degree:** 125 credit hours, Bachelors **ROTC:** Air Force, Army **Professional Accreditation:** ACEN, NASM, NCATE. **Intercollegiate Athletics:** Baseball M; Basketball M & W; Cheerleading M & W; Cross-Country Running M & W; Football M; Golf M & W; Soccer W; Softball W; Tennis W; Track and Field M & W; Volleyball W

THE CITADEL, THE MILITARY COLLEGE OF SOUTH CAROLINA

171 Moultrie St.
Charleston, SC 29409
Tel: (843)225-3294; Free: 800-868-1842
Fax: (843)953-7084
E-mail: john.powell@citadel.edu
Web Site: www.citadel.edu
President/CEO: Lt. Gen. John W. Rosa, USAF (Ret)
Admissions: Lt. Col. John W. Powell, Jr.
Financial Aid: Lt. Col. Hank M. Fuller

Type: Comprehensive **Sex:** Coed **Scores:** 100% SAT V 400+; 99% SAT M 400+; 59% ACT 18-23; 35% ACT 24-29 **% Accepted:** 77 **Admission Plans:** Preferred Admission **Application Deadline:** Rolling **Application Fee:** $40.00 **H.S. Requirements:** High school diploma required; GED accepted **Costs Per Year:** Application fee: $40. State resident tuition: $11,364 full-time, $442 per credit hour part-time. Nonresident tuition: $31,780 full-time, $820 per credit hour part-time. Mandatory fees: $1660 full-time. Full-time tuition and fees vary according to class time, degree level, and student level. Part-time tuition varies according to class time. College room and board: $6381. College room only: $2780. **Scholarships:** Available. **Calendar System:** Semester, Summer session available **Enrollment:** Full-time 2,461, Graduate full-time 165, Graduate part-time 670, Part-time 210 **Faculty:** Full-time 192, Part-time 96 **Student-Faculty Ratio:** 13:1 **Exams:** ACT essay component not used; SAT I or ACT; SAT essay component not used. **% Receiving Financial Aid:** 55 **% Residing in College-Owned, -Operated, or -Affiliated Housing:** 100 **Final Year or Final Semester Residency Requirement:** No **Regional Accreditation:** Southern Association of Colleges and Schools **ROTC:** Air Force, Army, Navy **Professional Accreditation:** AACSB, ABET, ACA, NCATE. **Intercollegiate Athletics:** Baseball M; Basketball M; Cross-Country Running M & W; Football M; Golf W; Ice Hockey M; Lacrosse M; Riflery M & W; Rugby M & W; Soccer M & W; Tennis M; Track and Field M & W; Volleyball W; Wrestling M

CLAFLIN UNIVERSITY

400 Magnolia St.
Orangeburg, SC 29115
Tel: (803)535-5097; Free: 800-922-1276
Fax: (803)531-2860
E-mail: mike.zeigler.@claflin.edu
Web Site: www.claflin.edu
President/CEO: Dr. Henry N. Tisdale
Admissions: Michael Zeigler
Financial Aid: Yolanda Frazier

Type: Comprehensive **Sex:** Coed **Affiliation:** United Methodist. **Scores:** 61% SAT V 400+; 56% SAT M 400+; 32% ACT 18-23; 7% ACT 24-29 **% Accepted:** 60 **Admission Plans:** Deferred Admission **Application Deadline:** Rolling **Application Fee:** $30.00 **H.S. Requirements:** High school diploma required; GED accepted **Scholarships:** Available. **Calendar System:** Semester, Summer session available **Enrollment:** Full-time 1,769, Graduate full-time 40, Graduate part-time 10, Part-time 67 **Student-Faculty Ratio:** 14:1 **Exams:** ACT essay component not used; SAT I or ACT; SAT essay component not used; SAT Reasoning. **% Receiving Financial Aid:** 92 **% Residing in College-Owned, -Operated, or -Affiliated Housing:** 70 **Final Year or Final Semester Residency Requirement:** No **Regional Accreditation:** Southern Association of Colleges and Schools **Credit Hours For Degree:** 124 semester hours, Bachelors **ROTC:** Army **Professional Accreditation:** ACBSP, NASM, NCATE. **Intercollegiate Athletics:** Baseball M; Basketball M & W; Cheerleading M & W; Cross-Country Running M & W; Softball W; Track and Field M & W; Volleyball W

CLEMSON UNIVERSITY

Clemson, SC 29634
Tel: (864)656-3311
Fax: (864)656-2464
E-mail: cuadmissions@clemson.edu

Web Site: www.clemson.edu
President/CEO: Dr. James P. Clements
Admissions: Audrey R. Bodell
Financial Aid: Jennifer Williams

Type: University **Sex:** Coed **Scores:** 99% SAT V 400+; 100% SAT M 400+; 7.5% ACT 18-23; 50.6% ACT 24-29 **% Accepted:** 51 **Admission Plans:** Preferred Admission **Application Deadline:** May 1 **Application Fee:** $70.00 **H.S. Requirements:** High school diploma required; GED accepted **Costs Per Year:** Application fee: $70. State resident tuition: $13,882 full-time, $601 per credit hour part-time. Nonresident tuition: $32,800 full-time, $1423 per credit hour part-time. Full-time tuition varies according to course level, course load, location, program, and student level. Part-time tuition varies according to course level, course load, location, program, and student level. College room and board: $8718. Room and board charges vary according to board plan, housing facility, and location. **Scholarships:** Available. **Calendar System:** Semester, Summer session available **Enrollment:** Full-time 17,238, Graduate full-time 2,887, Graduate part-time 1,795, Part-time 778 **Faculty:** Full-time 1,134, Part-time 129 **Student-Faculty Ratio:** 18:1 **Exams:** ACT essay component not used; SAT I or ACT; SAT essay component not used; SAT Reasoning; SAT Subject. **% Receiving Financial Aid:** 44 **% Residing in College-Owned, -Operated, or -Affiliated Housing:** 37 **Final Year or Final Semester Residency Requirement:** No **Regional Accreditation:** Southern Association of Colleges and Schools **Credit Hours For Degree:** 128 hours, Bachelors **ROTC:** Air Force, Army **Professional Accreditation:** AACN, AACSB, ABET, ACA, ACCE, ACSP, AND, ASLA, NAAB, NASAD, NCATE, NRPA, SAF. **Intercollegiate Athletics:** Baseball M; Basketball M & W; Bowling M & W; Cheerleading M & W; Crew M & W; Cross-Country Running M & W; Equestrian Sports M & W; Fencing M & W; Field Hockey M & W; Football M; Golf M; Ice Hockey M & W; Lacrosse M & W; Riflery M & W; Rugby M & W; Sailing M & W; Soccer M & W; Softball W; Tennis M & W; Track and Field M & W; Ultimate Frisbee M & W; Volleyball M & W; Weight Lifting M & W; Wrestling M

CLINTON COLLEGE
1029 Crawford Rd.
Rock Hill, SC 29730
Tel: (803)327-7402; Free: 877-837-9645
Fax: (803)327-3261
E-mail: rcopeland@clintonjrcollege.org
Web Site: www.clintoncollege.edu
President/CEO: Elaine Johnson, PhD
Admissions: Robert M. Copeland

Type: Two-Year College **Sex:** Coed **Affiliation:** African Methodist Episcopal Zion Church. **Application Fee:** $25.00 **Calendar System:** Semester **Student-Faculty Ratio:** 15:1 **Professional Accreditation:** TRACS. **Intercollegiate Athletics:** Basketball M & W

COASTAL CAROLINA UNIVERSITY
PO Box 261954
Conway, SC 29528-6054
Tel: (843)347-3161; Free: 800-277-7000
Fax: (843)349-2127
E-mail: admissions@coastal.edu
Web Site: www.coastal.edu
President/CEO: Dr. David A. DeCenzo
Admissions: Amanda E. Craddock
Financial Aid: Wendy H. Watts

Type: Comprehensive **Sex:** Coed **Scores:** 99% SAT V 400+; 98% SAT M 400+; 67.4% ACT 18-23; 28.6% ACT 24-29 **% Accepted:** 60 **Admission Plans:** Deferred Admission; Preferred Admission **Application Deadline:** Rolling **Application Fee:** $45.00 **H.S. Requirements:** High school diploma required; GED accepted **Costs Per Year:** Application fee: $45. State resident tuition: $10,270 full-time, $442 per credit hour part-time. Nonresident tuition: $24,060 full-time, $1010 per credit hour part-time. Mandatory fees: $260 full-time. Full-time tuition and fees vary according to course load and degree level. Part-time tuition varies according to course load and degree level. College room and board: $8690. College room only: $5440. Room and board charges vary according to board plan and housing facility. **Scholarships:** Available. **Calendar System:** Semester, Summer session available **Enrollment:** Full-time 8,771, Graduate full-time 195, Graduate part-time 453, Part-time 844 **Faculty:** Full-time 433, Part-time 281 **Student-Faculty Ratio:** 18:1 **Exams:** ACT essay component used for placement; SAT I or ACT; SAT essay component used for placement; SAT Reasoning. **% Receiving Financial Aid:** 71 **% Residing in College-**

Owned, -Operated, or -Affiliated Housing: 42 **Final Year or Final Semester Residency Requirement:** No **Regional Accreditation:** Southern Association of Colleges and Schools **Credit Hours For Degree:** 120 semester hours, Bachelors **ROTC:** Army **Professional Accreditation:** AACSB, ABET, NASAD, NASM, NCATE. **Intercollegiate Athletics:** Baseball M; Basketball M & W; Bowling M & W; Cheerleading M & W; Cross-Country Running M & W; Equestrian Sports M & W; Field Hockey M & W; Football M; Golf M & W; Lacrosse M & W; Rugby M & W; Soccer M & W; Softball W; Swimming and Diving M & W; Tennis M & W; Track and Field M & W; Volleyball M & W; Weight Lifting M & W; Wrestling M

COKER COLLEGE
300 E College Ave.
Hartsville, SC 29550
Tel: (843)383-8000; Free: 800-950-1908
Fax: (843)383-8056
E-mail: admissions@coker.edu
Web Site: www.coker.edu
President/CEO: Dr. Robert Wyatt
Admissions: Adam Connolly
Financial Aid: Betty Williams

Type: Comprehensive **Sex:** Coed **Scores:** 96% SAT V 400+; 96% SAT M 400+; 61% ACT 18-23; 18% ACT 24-29 **% Accepted:** 51 **Admission Plans:** Deferred Admission **Application Deadline:** August 1 **Application Fee:** $25.00 **H.S. Requirements:** High school diploma required; GED accepted **Costs Per Year:** Application fee: $25. Comprehensive fee: $34,810 includes full-time tuition ($26,568) and college room and board ($8242). College room only: $3800. Full-time tuition varies according to course load, degree level, location, and program. Room and board charges vary according to board plan and housing facility. Part-time tuition: $1107 per credit hour. Part-time tuition varies according to course load, degree level, location, and program. **Scholarships:** Available. **Calendar System:** Semester, Summer session available **Enrollment:** Full-time 967, Graduate part-time 54, Part-time 198 **Faculty:** Full-time 64, Part-time 41 **Student-Faculty Ratio:** 13:1 **Exams:** SAT I or ACT; SAT Reasoning; SAT Subject. **% Receiving Financial Aid:** 73 **% Residing in College-Owned, -Operated, or -Affiliated Housing:** 48 **Final Year or Final Semester Residency Requirement:** Yes **Regional Accreditation:** Southern Association of Colleges and Schools **Credit Hours For Degree:** 120 semester hours, Bachelors **Professional Accreditation:** NASM. **Intercollegiate Athletics:** Baseball M; Basketball M & W; Cross-Country Running M & W; Golf M & W; Lacrosse M & W; Soccer M & W; Softball W; Tennis M & W; Track and Field M & W; Volleyball M & W; Wrestling M

COLLEGE OF CHARLESTON
66 George St.
Charleston, SC 29424-0001
Tel: (843)953-5507
E-mail: admissions@cofc.edu
Web Site: www.cofc.edu
President/CEO: Glenn F. McConnell
Admissions: Suzette Stille
Financial Aid: Derwin Simpson

Type: Comprehensive **Sex:** Coed **Scores:** 99% SAT V 400+; 99% SAT M 400+; 32.2% ACT 18-23; 54.6% ACT 24-29 **% Accepted:** 77 **Admission Plans:** Deferred Admission; Early Decision Plan **Application Deadline:** February 1 **Application Fee:** $50.00 **H.S. Requirements:** High school diploma required; GED accepted **Costs Per Year:** Application fee: $50. State resident tuition: $10,900 full-time, $454 per credit hour part-time. Nonresident tuition: $28,444 full-time, $1185 per credit hour part-time. Mandatory fees: $460 full-time, $16.25 per term part-time, $15 per term part-time. Full-time tuition and fees vary according to student level. Part-time tuition and fees vary according to course load and student level. College room and board: $11,629. College room only: $7839. Room and board charges vary according to board plan and housing facility. **Scholarships:** Available. **Calendar System:** Semester, Summer session available **Enrollment:** Full-time 9,590, Graduate full-time 288, Graduate part-time 775, Part-time 878 **Faculty:** Full-time 573, Part-time 415 **Student-Faculty Ratio:** 15:1 **Exams:** SAT I or ACT; SAT Reasoning. **% Receiving Financial Aid:** 47 **% Residing in College-Owned, -Operated, or -Affiliated Housing:** 31 **Final Year or Final Semester Residency Requirement:** Yes **Regional Accreditation:** Southern Association of Colleges and Schools **Credit Hours For Degree:** 122 semester hours, Bachelors **ROTC:** Air Force **Professional Accreditation:** AACSB, ABET, JRCAT, NASM, NASPAA, NCATE. **Intercol-**

legiate Athletics: Baseball M; Basketball M & W; Cheerleading M & W; Cross-Country Running M & W; Equestrian Sports W; Golf M & W; Sailing M & W; Soccer M & W; Softball W; Tennis M & W; Volleyball W

COLUMBIA COLLEGE
1301 Columbia College Dr.
Columbia, SC 29203-5998
Tel: (803)786-3012; Free: 800-277-1301
Fax: (803)786-3674
E-mail: juking@columbiasc.edu
Web Site: www.columbiasc.edu
President/CEO: Dr. Elizabeth A. Dinndorf, JD
Admissions: Julie King
Financial Aid: Anita Kaminer Elliott

Type: Comprehensive Sex: Coed Affiliation: United Methodist. Scores: 88% SAT V 400+; 83% SAT M 400+; 48% ACT 18-23; 23% ACT 24-29 % Accepted: 89 Application Deadline: August 1 H.S. Requirements: High school diploma required; GED accepted Costs Per Year: Comprehensive fee: $35,500 includes full-time tuition ($28,100) and college room and board ($7400). College room only: $3700. Full-time tuition varies according to class time. Room and board charges vary according to board plan and housing facility. Part-time tuition: $725 per credit hour. Part-time tuition varies according to course load. Scholarships: Available. Calendar System: Semester, Summer session available Enrollment: Full-time 994, Graduate full-time 93, Graduate part-time 3, Part-time 560 Faculty: Full-time 79, Part-time 96 Student-Faculty Ratio: 13:1 Exams: SAT I or ACT; SAT Reasoning. % Receiving Financial Aid: 78 % Residing in College-Owned, -Operated, or -Affiliated Housing: 47 Final Year or Final Semester Residency Requirement: No Regional Accreditation: Southern Association of Colleges and Schools Credit Hours For Degree: 127 semester hours, Bachelors ROTC: Air Force, Army, Navy Professional Accreditation: CSWE, NASAD, NASD, NASM, NCATE. Intercollegiate Athletics: Basketball W; Cross-Country Running W; Golf W; Lacrosse W; Soccer W; Softball W; Swimming and Diving W; Tennis W; Track and Field W; Volleyball W

COLUMBIA INTERNATIONAL UNIVERSITY
PO Box 3122
Columbia, SC 29230-3122
Tel: (803)754-4100; Free: 800-777-2227
Fax: (803)786-4209
E-mail: yesciu@ciu.edu
Web Site: www.ciu.edu
President/CEO: Dr. Bill Jones
Admissions: Jen Johnson
Financial Aid: Patty Jean Hix

Type: University Sex: Coed Affiliation: nondenominational. Scores: 100% SAT V 400+; 91% SAT M 400+; 50% ACT 18-23; 38.1% ACT 24-29 % Accepted: 34 Admission Plans: Deferred Admission Application Deadline: August 1 Application Fee: $0.00 H.S. Requirements: High school diploma required; GED accepted Costs Per Year: Application fee: $0. Comprehensive fee: $29,180 includes full-time tuition ($20,880), mandatory fees ($540), and college room and board ($7760). Full-time tuition and fees vary according to course load, program, and reciprocity agreements. Room and board charges vary according to board plan and housing facility. Part-time tuition: $870 per semester hour. Part-time mandatory fees: $10 per semester hour, $120 per term. Part-time tuition and fees vary according to course load, program, and reciprocity agreements. Scholarships: Available. Calendar System: Semester, Summer session available Enrollment: Full-time 495, Graduate full-time 187, Graduate part-time 267, Part-time 54 Faculty: Full-time 45, Part-time 36 Student-Faculty Ratio: 15:1 Exams: ACT essay component not used; SAT I or ACT; SAT essay component not used; SAT Reasoning. % Receiving Financial Aid: 78 % Residing in College-Owned, -Operated, or -Affiliated Housing: 65 Final Year or Final Semester Residency Requirement: Yes Regional Accreditation: Southern Association of Colleges and Schools Credit Hours For Degree: 62 semester hours, Associates; 126 semester hours, Bachelors Professional Accreditation: ABHE, ATS. Intercollegiate Athletics: Basketball M & W; Cross-Country Running M & W; Golf M; Soccer M & W

CONVERSE COLLEGE
580 E Main St.
Spartanburg, SC 29302-0006
Tel: (864)596-9000; Free: 800-766-1125
Fax: (864)596-9158
E-mail: admissions@converse.edu
Web Site: www.converse.edu
President/CEO: Dr. Elizabeth Fleming
Financial Aid: James W. Kellam

Type: Comprehensive Scores: 99% SAT V 400+; 96% SAT M 400+; 47% ACT 18-23; 45% ACT 24-29 % Accepted: 58 Admission Plans: Deferred Admission Application Deadline: Rolling Application Fee: $0.00 H.S. Requirements: High school diploma required; GED accepted Costs Per Year: Application fee: $0. Comprehensive fee: $27,300 includes full-time tuition ($16,000), mandatory fees ($1000), and college room and board ($10,300). Full-time tuition and fees vary according to course load and program. Room and board charges vary according to board plan. Scholarships: Available. Calendar System: Miscellaneous, Summer session available Enrollment: Full-time 745, Graduate full-time 113, Graduate part-time 275, Part-time 49 Faculty: Full-time 79, Part-time 3 Student-Faculty Ratio: 12:1 Exams: ACT essay component not used; SAT I or ACT; SAT essay component not used; SAT Reasoning. % Receiving Financial Aid: 83 % Residing in College-Owned, -Operated, or -Affiliated Housing: 80 Final Year or Final Semester Residency Requirement: No Regional Accreditation: Southern Association of Colleges and Schools Credit Hours For Degree: 120 credit hours, Bachelors ROTC: Army Professional Accreditation: AAMFT, NASAD, NASM, NCATE. Intercollegiate Athletics: Basketball W; Cross-Country Running W; Equestrian Sports W; Golf W; Lacrosse W; Soccer W; Swimming and Diving W; Tennis W; Track and Field W; Volleyball W

DENMARK TECHNICAL COLLEGE
1126 Solomon Blatt Blvd.
Denmark, SC 29042-0327
Tel: (803)793-5100
Fax: (803)793-5942
E-mail: troyk@denmarktech.edu
Web Site: www.denmarktech.edu
President/CEO: Dr. Leonard A. McIntyre
Admissions: Kara Troy

Type: Two-Year College Sex: Coed Affiliation: South Carolina State Board for Technical and Comprehensive Education. Admission Plans: Deferred Admission; Early Admission; Open Admission Application Deadline: Rolling Application Fee: $10.00 H.S. Requirements: High school diploma required; GED accepted. For BCT, PLB, culinary arts, welding certificate programs: High school diploma or equivalent not required Costs Per Year: Application fee: $10. State resident tuition: $2616 full-time, $109 per credit hour part-time. Nonresident tuition: $5232 full-time, $218 per credit hour part-time. Mandatory fees: $310 full-time. College room and board: $3958. College room only: $1932. Scholarships: Available. Calendar System: Semester, Summer session available Enrollment: Full-time 655, Part-time 388 Faculty: Full-time 37, Part-time 26 Student-Faculty Ratio: 20:1 Exams: ACT essay component not used; Other; SAT I or ACT; SAT essay component not used. Regional Accreditation: Southern Association of Colleges and Schools Credit Hours For Degree: 60 credit hours, Associates Professional Accreditation: ABET, ACBSP. Intercollegiate Athletics: Basketball M & W; Cheerleading W

ECPI UNIVERSITY (COLUMBIA)
250 Berryhill Rd., No.300
Columbia, SC 29210
Tel: (803)610-4111; Free: 844-611-0668
Fax: (803)772-2922
Web Site: www.ecpi.edu

Type: Two-Year College Sex: Coed Regional Accreditation: Southern Association of Colleges and Schools

ECPI UNIVERSITY (GREENVILLE)
1001 Keys Dr., No.100
Greenville, SC 29615
Tel: (864)438-5018; Free: 844-611-0627
Fax: (864)288-2930
Web Site: www.ecpi.edu

Type: Two-Year College Sex: Coed Regional Accreditation: Southern Association of Colleges and Schools

ECPI UNIVERSITY (NORTH CHARLESTON)
7410 Northside Dr., No.100
North Charleston, SC 29420

Tel: (843)606-5902; Free: 844-611-0642
Fax: (843)572-8085
Web Site: www.ecpi.edu
Type: Two-Year College **Sex:** Coed **Regional Accreditation:** Southern Association of Colleges and Schools

ERSKINE COLLEGE
2 Washington St.
Due West, SC 29639
Tel: (864)379-2131; Free: 800-241-8721
Fax: (864)379-8759
Web Site: www.erskine.edu
President/CEO: Dr. Paul D. Kooistra
Admissions: Tobe Frierson
Financial Aid: Becky Pressley
Type: Comprehensive **Sex:** Coed **Affiliation:** Associate Reformed Presbyterian Church; Erskine Theological Seminary. **Scores:** 97% SAT V 400+; 97% SAT M 400+; 51% ACT 18-23; 39% ACT 24-29 **% Accepted:** 64 **Admission Plans:** Deferred Admission; Early Admission; Early Decision Plan; Preferred Admission **Application Deadline:** Rolling **Application Fee:** $0.00 **H.S. Requirements:** High school diploma required; GED accepted **Costs Per Year:** Application fee: $0. Comprehensive fee: $44,210 includes full-time tuition ($31,345), mandatory fees ($2365), and college room and board ($10,500). College room only: $5400. Full-time tuition and fees vary according to program. Room and board charges vary according to board plan. **Scholarships:** Available. **Calendar System:** 4-1-4, Summer session available **Enrollment:** Full-time 615, Graduate full-time 17, Graduate part-time 122, Part-time 7 **Faculty:** Full-time 59, Part-time 23 **Student-Faculty Ratio:** 12:1 **Exams:** SAT I or ACT; SAT Reasoning. **% Receiving Financial Aid:** 69 **% Residing in College-Owned, -Operated, or -Affiliated Housing:** 89 **Final Year or Final Semester Residency Requirement:** Yes **Regional Accreditation:** Southern Association of Colleges and Schools **Credit Hours For Degree:** 124 semester hours, Bachelors **Professional Accreditation:** NCATE. **Intercollegiate Athletics:** Baseball M; Basketball M & W; Cross-Country Running M & W; Equestrian Sports W; Golf M & W; Lacrosse W; Soccer M & W; Softball W; Tennis M & W; Volleyball W

FLORENCE-DARLINGTON TECHNICAL COLLEGE
2715 W Lucas St.
Florence, SC 29501-0548
Tel: (843)661-8324; Free: 800-228-5745
Fax: (843)661-8306
E-mail: shelley.fortin@fdtc.edu
Web Site: www.fdtc.edu
President/CEO: Charles Gould
Admissions: Shelley Fortin
Financial Aid: Joseph M. DuRant
Type: Two-Year College **Sex:** Coed **Affiliation:** South Carolina State Board for Technical and Comprehensive Education. **Admission Plans:** Deferred Admission; Open Admission **Application Deadline:** August 1 **H.S. Requirements:** High school diploma or equivalent not required. For nursing, dental services, chemical engineering technology, surgical technology, health information management, medical laboratory technology programs: High school diploma required; GED accepted **Scholarships:** Available. **Calendar System:** Semester, Summer session available **Student-Faculty Ratio:** 26:1 **Regional Accreditation:** Southern Association of Colleges and Schools **Credit Hours For Degree:** 61 credit hours, Associates **ROTC:** Army **Professional Accreditation:** ABET, ACBSP, ACEN, ADA, AHIMA, CoARC, JRCERT, NAACLS.

FORREST COLLEGE
601 E River St.
Anderson, SC 29624
Tel: (864)225-7653
Fax: (864)261-7471
E-mail: janieturmon@forrestcollege.edu
Web Site: www.forrestcollege.edu
President/CEO: Dr. Cosmo John Re, PhD
Admissions: Janie Turmon
Financial Aid: Kathryn Childress
Type: Two-Year College **Sex:** Coed **Costs Per Year:** Tuition: $11,760 full-time, $245 per credit hour part-time. Mandatory fees: $375 full-time, $125 per term part-time. Full-time tuition and fees vary according to class time, course level, course load, degree level, program, reciprocity agreements,

and student level. Part-time tuition and fees vary according to class time, course level, course load, degree level, program, reciprocity agreements, and student level. **Scholarships:** Available. **Calendar System:** Quarter, Summer session available **Enrollment:** Full-time 85, Part-time 14 **Faculty:** Full-time 11, Part-time 17 **Student-Faculty Ratio:** 4:1 **Exams:** ACT; Other; SAT I; SAT I and SAT II or ACT; SAT I or ACT; SAT II. **Final Year or Final Semester Residency Requirement:** No **Credit Hours For Degree:** 96 quarter hours, Associates **Professional Accreditation:** ACICS.

FORTIS COLLEGE
246 Stoneridge Dr.
Ste. 101
Columbia, SC 29210
Tel: (803)678-4800; Free: 855-4-FORTIS
Web Site: www.fortis.edu
Type: Two-Year College **Sex:** Coed **Professional Accreditation:** ABHES.

FRANCIS MARION UNIVERSITY
PO Box 100547
Florence, SC 29502-0547
Tel: (843)661-1362; Free: 800-368-7551
Fax: (843)661-4635
E-mail: admissions@fmarion.edu
Web Site: www.fmarion.edu
President/CEO: Dr. Fred Carter
Admissions: Perry Wilson
Financial Aid: Kim Ellisor
Type: Comprehensive **Sex:** Coed **Scores:** 84% SAT V 400+; 82% SAT M 400+; 53.2% ACT 18-23; 15.3% ACT 24-29 **% Accepted:** 59 **Admission Plans:** Deferred Admission; Early Admission **Application Deadline:** August 1 **Application Fee:** $37.00 **H.S. Requirements:** High school diploma required; GED accepted **Costs Per Year:** Application fee: $37. State resident tuition: $9568 full-time, $478.40 per credit hour part-time. Nonresident tuition: $19,136 full-time, $956.80 per credit hour part-time. Mandatory fees: $532 full-time, $14.40 per credit hour part-time, $70.50 per term part-time. Full-time tuition and fees vary according to degree level and program. Part-time tuition and fees vary according to course load, degree level, and program. College room and board: $7472. College room only: $4222. Room and board charges vary according to board plan and housing facility. **Scholarships:** Available. **Calendar System:** Semester, Summer session available **Enrollment:** Full-time 3,172, Graduate full-time 102, Graduate part-time 261, Part-time 412 **Faculty:** Full-time 204, Part-time 87 **Student-Faculty Ratio:** 15:1 **Exams:** SAT I or ACT; SAT essay component used for advising; SAT essay component used for placement; SAT Reasoning. **% Receiving Financial Aid:** 77 **% Residing in College-Owned, -Operated, or -Affiliated Housing:** 45 **Final Year or Final Semester Residency Requirement:** No **Regional Accreditation:** Southern Association of Colleges and Schools **Credit Hours For Degree:** 120 semester hours, Bachelors **ROTC:** Army **Professional Accreditation:** AACSB, ACEN, NASAD, NAST, NCATE. **Intercollegiate Athletics:** Baseball M; Basketball M & W; Cheerleading W; Cross-Country Running M & W; Golf M; Soccer M & W; Softball W; Tennis M & W; Track and Field M & W; Volleyball W

FURMAN UNIVERSITY
3300 Poinsett Hwy.
Greenville, SC 29613
Tel: (864)294-2000
Fax: (864)294-3127
E-mail: admissions@furman.edu
Web Site: www.furman.edu
President/CEO: Dr. Elizabeth Davis
Admissions: Brad Pochard
Financial Aid: Forrest Stuart
Type: Comprehensive **Sex:** Coed **Scores:** 100% SAT V 400+; 100% SAT M 400+; 10.42% ACT 18-23; 57% ACT 24-29 **% Accepted:** 65 **Admission Plans:** Early Action; Early Decision Plan; Preferred Admission **Application Deadline:** January 15 **Application Fee:** $50.00 **H.S. Requirements:** High school diploma required; GED accepted **Costs Per Year:** Application fee: $50. Comprehensive fee: $57,534 includes full-time tuition ($45,632), mandatory fees ($380), and college room and board ($11,522). College room only: $6202. Room and board charges vary according to board plan and housing facility. Part-time tuition: $1426 per credit. Part-time tuition varies according to course load. **Scholarships:** Available. **Calendar System:**

Miscellaneous, Summer session available **Enrollment:** Full-time 2,623, Graduate full-time 54, Graduate part-time 99, Part-time 108 **Faculty:** Full-time 234, Part-time 23 **Student-Faculty Ratio:** 11:1 **Exams:** ACT essay component used for admission; SAT I or ACT; SAT essay component used for admission; SAT Reasoning. **% Receiving Financial Aid:** 43 **% Residing in College-Owned, -Operated, or -Affiliated Housing:** 96 **Regional Accreditation:** Southern Association of Colleges and Schools **Credit Hours For Degree:** 128 credits, Bachelors **ROTC:** Army **Professional Accreditation:** NASM, NCATE. **Intercollegiate Athletics:** Baseball M; Basketball M & W; Cheerleading M & W; Crew M & W; Cross-Country Running M & W; Equestrian Sports W; Fencing M & W; Football M; Golf M & W; Ice Hockey M; Lacrosse M & W; Rugby M & W; Soccer M & W; Softball W; Swimming and Diving M & W; Tennis M & W; Track and Field M & W; Ultimate Frisbee M & W; Volleyball W; Weight Lifting M & W; Wrestling M

GOLF ACADEMY OF AMERICA

3268 Waccamaw Blvd.
Myrtle Beach, SC 29579
Tel: (843)236-0481
Web Site: www.golfacademy.edu
Type: Two-Year College **Sex:** Coed **Calendar System:** Semester **Professional Accreditation:** ACICS.

GREENVILLE TECHNICAL COLLEGE

PO Box 5616
Greenville, SC 29606-5616
Tel: (864)250-8000; Free: 800-723-0673
Fax: (864)250-8534
E-mail: carolyn.watkins@gvltec.edu
Web Site: www.gvltec.edu
President/CEO: Dr. Keith Miller
Admissions: Carolyn Watkins
Financial Aid: DJ Wetzel
Type: Two-Year College **Sex:** Coed **Affiliation:** South Carolina State Board for Technical and Comprehensive Education. **% Accepted:** 100 **Admission Plans:** Deferred Admission; Early Admission; Open Admission **Application Deadline:** Rolling **Application Fee:** $35.00 **H.S. Requirements:** High school diploma required; GED accepted **Costs Per Year:** Application fee: $35. Area resident tuition: $5370 full-time. State resident tuition: $5820 full-time. Nonresident tuition: $10,710 full-time. Full-time tuition varies according to course load and program. **Scholarships:** Available. **Calendar System:** Semester, Summer session available **Enrollment:** Full-time 4,793, Part-time 7,487 **Faculty:** Full-time 341, Part-time 476 **Student-Faculty Ratio:** 15:1 **Exams:** ACT essay component used for advising; ACT essay component used for placement; Other; SAT essay component used for advising; SAT essay component used for placement; SAT Reasoning; SAT Subject. **Final Year or Final Semester Residency Requirement:** No **Regional Accreditation:** Southern Association of Colleges and Schools **Credit Hours For Degree:** 60 semester hours, Associates **Professional Accreditation:** ABET, ACBSP, ACEN, ACF, ADA, AHIMA, AOTA, APTA, CoARC, JRCEMTP, JRCERT, NAACLS.

HORRY-GEORGETOWN TECHNICAL COLLEGE

2050 Hwy. 501
Conway, SC 29528-6066
Tel: (843)347-3186
Fax: (843)347-4207
E-mail: george.swindoll@hgtc.edu
Web Site: www.hgtc.edu
President/CEO: Neyle Wilson
Admissions: George Swindoll
Financial Aid: Rachel Mabry
Type: Two-Year College **Sex:** Coed **Affiliation:** South Carolina State Board for Technical and Comprehensive Education. **Admission Plans:** Early Admission; Open Admission **Application Deadline:** Rolling **Application Fee:** $25.00 **H.S. Requirements:** High school diploma or equivalent not required. For health science programs: High school diploma required; GED accepted **Costs Per Year:** Application fee: $25. Area resident tuition: $1793 full-time, $150 per hour part-time. State resident tuition: $2250 full-time, $188 per hour part-time. Nonresident tuition: $3229 full-time, $270 per hour part-time. Mandatory fees: $402 full-time. **Scholarships:** Available. **Calendar System:** Semester, Summer session available **Enrollment:** Full-time 2,911, Part-time 4,749 **Faculty:** Full-time 148, Part-time 204 **Student-Faculty Ratio:** 21:1 **Regional Accreditation:** Southern Association of Col-

leges and Schools **Credit Hours For Degree:** 63 semester hours, Associates **Professional Accreditation:** ABET, ACBSP, ACEN, ACF, ADA, JRCERT.

LANDER UNIVERSITY

320 Stanley Ave.
Greenwood, SC 29649-2099
Tel: (864)388-8000; Free: 888-452-6337
Fax: (864)388-8125
E-mail: admissions@lander.edu
Web Site: www.lander.edu
President/CEO: Dr. Daniel W. Ball
Admissions: Jennifer M. Mathis
Type: Comprehensive **Sex:** Coed **Affiliation:** South Carolina Commission on Higher Education. **Scores:** 90% SAT V 400+; 96% SAT M 400+; 62.8% ACT 18-23; 17.8% ACT 24-29 **% Accepted:** 42 **Application Deadline:** Rolling **Application Fee:** $35.00 **H.S. Requirements:** High school diploma required; GED accepted **Costs Per Year:** Application fee: $35. State resident tuition: $10,752 full-time, $448 per credit hour part-time. Nonresident tuition: $20,370 full-time, $849 per credit hour part-time. Mandatory fees: $880 full-time. Full-time tuition and fees vary according to course load, degree level, program, and reciprocity agreements. Part-time tuition varies according to course load, degree level, and program. College room and board: $8246. Room and board charges vary according to board plan and housing facility. **Scholarships:** Available. **Calendar System:** Semester, Summer session available **Enrollment:** Full-time 2,706, Graduate full-time 7, Graduate part-time 73, Part-time 263 **Faculty:** Full-time 164, Part-time 85 **Student-Faculty Ratio:** 16:1 **Exams:** SAT I or ACT. **% Receiving Financial Aid:** 39 **% Residing in College-Owned, -Operated, or -Affiliated Housing:** 45 **Regional Accreditation:** Southern Association of Colleges and Schools **Credit Hours For Degree:** 121 semester hours, Bachelors **ROTC:** Army **Professional Accreditation:** AACSB, ACEN, MACTE, NASAD, NASM, NAST, NCATE. **Intercollegiate Athletics:** Baseball M; Basketball M & W; Golf M & W; Soccer M & W; Softball W; Tennis M & W; Volleyball W

LIMESTONE COLLEGE

1115 College Dr.
Gaffney, SC 29340-3799
Tel: (864)489-7151; Free: 800-795-7151
Fax: (864)487-8706
E-mail: lhobbs@limestone.edu
Web Site: www.limestone.edu
President/CEO: Dr. Walt Griffin
Admissions: Lisa Hobbs
Financial Aid: Bobby Greer
Type: Comprehensive **Sex:** Coed **Scores:** 78% SAT V 400+; 83% SAT M 400+; 48% ACT 18-23; 8% ACT 24-29 **% Accepted:** 52 **Application Deadline:** Rolling **Application Fee:** $25.00 **H.S. Requirements:** High school diploma required; GED accepted **Costs Per Year:** Application fee: $25. Comprehensive fee: $32,450 includes full-time tuition ($23,900) and college room and board ($8550). College room only: $4300. Full-time tuition varies according to class time and course load. Room and board charges vary according to board plan and housing facility. **Scholarships:** Available. **Calendar System:** Semester, Summer session available **Enrollment:** Full-time 1,227, Graduate full-time 53 **Faculty:** Full-time 81, Part-time 36 **Student-Faculty Ratio:** 13:1 **Exams:** ACT essay component not used; Other; SAT I or ACT; SAT essay component not used; SAT Reasoning. **% Receiving Financial Aid:** 80 **% Residing in College-Owned, -Operated, or -Affiliated Housing:** 62 **Final Year or Final Semester Residency Requirement:** No **Regional Accreditation:** Southern Association of Colleges and Schools **Credit Hours For Degree:** 62 semester hours, Associates; 123 semester hours, Bachelors **ROTC:** Army **Professional Accreditation:** CSWE, NASM, NCATE. **Intercollegiate Athletics:** Baseball M; Basketball M & W; Cheerleading M & W; Cross-Country Running M & W; Field Hockey W; Football M; Golf M & W; Lacrosse M & W; Soccer M & W; Softball W; Swimming and Diving M & W; Tennis M & W; Track and Field M & W; Volleyball M & W; Wrestling M

MEDICAL UNIVERSITY OF SOUTH CAROLINA

179 Ashley Ave.
Charleston, SC 29425
Tel: (843)792-2300
Fax: (843)792-3764
E-mail: hudsonly@musc.edu

Web Site: www.musc.edu
President/CEO: David Cole
Admissions: Lyla E. Hudson
Financial Aid: Joseph M. DuRant
Type: Two-Year Upper Division **Sex:** Coed **Admission Plans:** Deferred Admission; Preferred Admission **Application Fee:** $95.00 **H.S. Requirements:** High school diploma required; GED accepted **Scholarships:** Available. **Calendar System:** Semester, Summer session not available **Enrollment:** Full-time 203, Graduate full-time 2,390, Graduate part-time 180, Part-time 2 **Faculty:** Full-time 153, Part-time 70 **Student-Faculty Ratio:** 2:1 **% Receiving Financial Aid:** 72 **Regional Accreditation:** Southern Association of Colleges and Schools **ROTC:** Air Force **Professional Accreditation:** AACN, AANA, ACEN, ACNM, ACPE, ACPeE, ADA, AND, AOTA, APA, APTA, ASC, ASHA, CAHME, LCME/AMA.

MIDLANDS TECHNICAL COLLEGE
PO Box 2408
Columbia, SC 29202-2408
Tel: (803)738-1400; Free: 800-922-8038
Fax: (803)738-7784
E-mail: admissions@midlandstech.edu
Web Site: www.midlandstech.edu
President/CEO: Dr. Ronald Rhames
Admissions: Sylvia Littlejohn
Type: Two-Year College **Sex:** Coed **Affiliation:** South Carolina State Board for Technical and Comprehensive Education. **% Accepted:** 65 **Admission Plans:** Deferred Admission; Early Admission; Open Admission **Application Fee:** $35.00 **H.S. Requirements:** High school diploma or equivalent not required **Costs Per Year:** Application fee: $35. One-time mandatory fee: $35. Area resident tuition: $3840 full-time, $160 per credit hour part-time. State resident tuition: $4800 full-time, $200 per credit hour part-time. Nonresident tuition: $11,520 full-time, $480 per credit hour part-time. Mandatory fees: $1044 full-time, $30 per credit hour part-time, $162 per term part-time. Full-time tuition and fees vary according to course load. Part-time tuition and fees vary according to course load. **Scholarships:** Available. **Calendar System:** Semester, Summer session available **Enrollment:** Full-time 4,981, Part-time 5,965 **Faculty:** Full-time 223, Part-time 435 **Student-Faculty Ratio:** 20:1 **Exams:** ACT essay component used for admission; Other; SAT I or ACT; SAT essay component used for admission. **Regional Accreditation:** Southern Association of Colleges and Schools **Credit Hours For Degree:** 60 semester hours, Associates **ROTC:** Air Force, Army, Navy **Professional Accreditation:** ABET, ACBSP, ACEN, ADA, AHIMA, APTA, CoARC, JRCERT, NAACLS.

MILLER-MOTTE TECHNICAL COLLEGE (CONWAY)
2451 Hwy. 501 E
Conway, SC 29526
Tel: (843)591-1100; Free: 866-297-0267
Web Site: www.miller-motte.edu
Type: Two-Year College **Sex:** Coed **Professional Accreditation:** ACICS.

MILLER-MOTTE TECHNICAL COLLEGE (NORTH CHARLESTON)
8085 Rivers Ave.
Ste. E
North Charleston, SC 29406
Tel: (843)574-0101; Free: 800-923-4162
Fax: (843)266-3434
E-mail: juliasc@miller-mott.net
Web Site: www.miller-motte.edu
President/CEO: Sara Eichelman
Admissions: Elaine Cue
Type: Two-Year College **Sex:** Coed **Affiliation:** Delta Career Education Corporation. **Admission Plans:** Open Admission **Application Fee:** $35.00 **H.S. Requirements:** High school diploma required; GED accepted **Calendar System:** Quarter **Exams:** Other. **Credit Hours For Degree:** 96 quarter credits, Associates **Professional Accreditation:** ACICS.

MORRIS COLLEGE
100 W College St.
Sumter, SC 29150-3599
Tel: (803)934-3200; Free: 866-853-1345
Fax: (803)773-3687
E-mail: gscriven@morris.edu
Web Site: www.morris.edu

President/CEO: Dr. Luns C. Richardson
Admissions: Gloria Scriven
Financial Aid: Sandra S. Gibson
Type: Four-Year College **Sex:** Coed **Affiliation:** Baptist Educational and Missionary Convention of South Carolina. **% Accepted:** 78 **Admission Plans:** Deferred Admission; Open Admission **Application Deadline:** Rolling **H.S. Requirements:** High school diploma required; GED accepted **Costs Per Year:** Comprehensive fee: $17,865 includes full-time tuition ($11,294), mandatory fees ($1355), and college room and board ($5216). College room only: $2224. Part-time tuition: $471 per credit hour. **Scholarships:** Available. **Calendar System:** Semester, Summer session available **Enrollment:** Full-time 760, Part-time 14 **Faculty:** Full-time 43, Part-time 18 **Student-Faculty Ratio:** 13:1 **% Receiving Financial Aid:** 96 **% Residing in College-Owned, -Operated, or -Affiliated Housing:** 78 **Final Year or Final Semester Residency Requirement:** No **Regional Accreditation:** Southern Association of Colleges and Schools **Credit Hours For Degree:** 124 credit hours, Bachelors **ROTC:** Army **Professional Accreditation:** ACBSP, NCATE. **Intercollegiate Athletics:** Baseball M; Basketball M & W; Cheerleading M & W; Cross-Country Running M & W; Softball W; Track and Field M & W; Volleyball W

NEWBERRY COLLEGE
2100 College St.
Newberry, SC 29108-2197
Tel: (803)276-5010; Free: 800-845-4955
E-mail: admissions@newberry.edu
Web Site: www.newberry.edu
President/CEO: Dr. Maurice William Scherrens
Admissions: Joel Vander Horst
Financial Aid: Danielle Bell
Type: Four-Year College **Sex:** Coed **Affiliation:** Evangelical Lutheran. **Scores:** 89% SAT V 400+; 90% SAT M 400+; 61.4% ACT 18-23; 16.1% ACT 24-29 **% Accepted:** 56 **Admission Plans:** Deferred Admission **Application Deadline:** Rolling **Application Fee:** $30.00 **H.S. Requirements:** High school diploma required; GED accepted **Costs Per Year:** Application fee: $30. Comprehensive fee: $34,550 includes full-time tuition ($23,000), mandatory fees ($2000), and college room and board ($9550). Full-time tuition and fees vary according to course load and student level. Room and board charges vary according to board plan and housing facility. Part-time tuition: $735 per credit hour. Part-time mandatory fees: $67 per credit hour. Part-time tuition and fees vary according to course load and student level. Tuition guaranteed not to increase for student's term of enrollment. **Scholarships:** Available. **Calendar System:** Semester, Summer session available **Enrollment:** Full-time 1,031, Part-time 33 **Faculty:** Full-time 65, Part-time 66 **Student-Faculty Ratio:** 12:1 **Exams:** ACT essay component used for placement; SAT I or ACT; SAT essay component used for placement. **% Receiving Financial Aid:** 87 **% Residing in College-Owned, -Operated, or -Affiliated Housing:** 82 **Final Year or Final Semester Residency Requirement:** Yes **Regional Accreditation:** Southern Association of Colleges and Schools **Credit Hours For Degree:** 126 semester hours, Bachelors **ROTC:** Army **Professional Accreditation:** NASM, NCATE. **Intercollegiate Athletics:** Baseball M; Basketball M & W; Cheerleading M & W; Cross-Country Running M & W; Field Hockey W; Football M; Golf M & W; Lacrosse W; Soccer M & W; Softball W; Tennis M & W; Volleyball W; Wrestling M

NORTH GREENVILLE UNIVERSITY
PO Box 1892
Tigerville, SC 29688-1892
Tel: (864)977-7000; Free: 800-468-6642
Fax: (864)977-7177
E-mail: ksewell@ngu.edu
Web Site: www.ngu.edu
President/CEO: Dr. Randall J. Pannell
Admissions: Keli Sewell
Financial Aid: Mike Jordan
Type: Comprehensive **Sex:** Coed **Affiliation:** Southern Baptist. **Scores:** 99% SAT V 400+; 98% SAT M 400+; 42% ACT 18-23; 45% ACT 24-29 **% Accepted:** 58 **Admission Plans:** Deferred Admission; Early Admission; Preferred Admission **Application Deadline:** August 22 **Application Fee:** $25.00 **H.S. Requirements:** High school diploma required; GED accepted **Costs Per Year:** Application fee: $25. Comprehensive fee: $27,486 includes full-time tuition ($17,594) and college room and board ($9892). Full-time tuition varies according to course load. Room and board charges vary ac-

cording to housing facility. Part-time tuition: $425 per credit. **Scholarships:** Available. **Calendar System:** Semester, Summer session available **Enrollment:** Full-time 2,209, Graduate full-time 105, Graduate part-time 105, Part-time 272 **Faculty:** Full-time 137, Part-time 72 **Student-Faculty Ratio:** 14:1 **Exams:** ACT essay component used for advising; Other; SAT I or ACT; SAT essay component used for advising; SAT Reasoning; SAT Subject. **% Receiving Financial Aid:** 57 **% Residing in College-Owned, -Operated, or -Affiliated Housing:** 68 **Final Year or Final Semester Residency Requirement:** No **Regional Accreditation:** Southern Association of Colleges and Schools **Credit Hours For Degree:** 64 semester hours, Associates; 120 semester hours, Bachelors **ROTC:** Army **Professional Accreditation:** NASM, NCATE. **Intercollegiate Athletics:** Baseball M; Basketball M & W; Cheerleading M & W; Cross-Country Running M & W; Football M; Golf M & W; Lacrosse M & W; Soccer M & W; Softball W; Tennis M & W; Track and Field M & W; Volleyball M & W

NORTHEASTERN TECHNICAL COLLEGE

1201 Chesterfield Hwy.
Cheraw, SC 29520-1007
Tel: (843)921-6900; Free: 800-921-7399
Fax: (843)537-6148
E-mail: mpace@netc.edu
Web Site: www.netc.edu
President/CEO: Dr. Ron Bartley
Admissions: Mary K. Newton

Type: Two-Year College **Sex:** Coed **Affiliation:** South Carolina State Board for Technical and Comprehensive Education. **% Accepted:** 100 **Admission Plans:** Early Admission; Open Admission **Application Deadline:** August 4 **Application Fee:** $25.00 **H.S. Requirements:** High school diploma required; GED accepted **Costs Per Year:** Application fee: $25. Area resident tuition: $2385 full-time, $159 per credit hour part-time. State resident tuition: $2520 full-time, $168 per credit hour part-time. Nonresident tuition: $4020 full-time, $268 per credit hour part-time. Full-time tuition varies according to class time, course level, course load, degree level, program, reciprocity agreements, and student level. Part-time tuition varies according to class time, course level, course load, degree level, program, reciprocity agreements, and student level. **Scholarships:** Available. **Calendar System:** Semester **Enrollment:** Full-time 446, Part-time 530 **Student-Faculty Ratio:** 25:1 **Exams:** Other; SAT I. **Regional Accreditation:** Southern Association of Colleges and Schools **Credit Hours For Degree:** 60 semester hours, Associates

ORANGEBURG-CALHOUN TECHNICAL COLLEGE

3250 St. Matthews Rd., NE
Orangeburg, SC 29118-8299
Tel: (803)536-0311; Free: 800-813-6519
Fax: (803)535-1388
Web Site: www.octech.edu
President/CEO: Dr. Anne Crook
Admissions: Dana Rickards

Type: Two-Year College **Sex:** Coed **Affiliation:** State Board for Technical and Comprehensive Education, South Carolina. **Admission Plans:** Open Admission **Application Deadline:** Rolling **Application Fee:** $15.00 **H.S. Requirements:** High school diploma required; GED accepted **Costs Per Year:** Application fee: $15. Area resident tuition: $3840 full-time, $160 per credit hour part-time. State resident tuition: $4776 full-time, $199 per credit hour part-time. Nonresident tuition: $6552 full-time, $273 per credit hour part-time. Mandatory fees: $85 full-time. Full-time tuition and fees vary according to course load. Part-time tuition varies according to course load. **Scholarships:** Available. **Calendar System:** Semester, Summer session available **Enrollment:** Full-time 1,538, Part-time 1,681 **Faculty:** Full-time 75, Part-time 88 **Student-Faculty Ratio:** 20:1 **Regional Accreditation:** Southern Association of Colleges and Schools **Credit Hours For Degree:** 60 semester hours, Associates **Professional Accreditation:** ABET, ACBSP, ACEN, JRCERT, NAACLS.

PIEDMONT TECHNICAL COLLEGE

620 N Emerald Rd.
Greenwood, SC 29648-1467
Tel: (864)941-8324; Free: 800-868-5528
Fax: (864)941-8555
Web Site: www.ptc.edu
President/CEO: Ray Brooks
Admissions: Steve Coleman

Type: Two-Year College **Sex:** Coed **Affiliation:** South Carolina State Board for Technical and Comprehensive Education. **% Accepted:** 100 **Admission Plans:** Deferred Admission; Early Admission; Open Admission **Application Deadline:** Rolling **Application Fee:** $25.00 **H.S. Requirements:** High school diploma required; GED accepted **Scholarships:** Available. **Calendar System:** Semester, Summer session available **Faculty:** Full-time 103, Part-time 130 **Student-Faculty Ratio:** 18:1 **Regional Accreditation:** Southern Association of Colleges and Schools **Credit Hours For Degree:** 60 credits, Associates **Professional Accreditation:** ABET, ABFSE, ACEN, CoARC, JRCERT.

PRESBYTERIAN COLLEGE

503 S Broad St.
Clinton, SC 29325
Tel: (864)833-2820; Free: 800-960-7583
Fax: (864)833-8481
E-mail: bjfortman@presby.edu
Web Site: www.presby.edu
President/CEO: Dr. Claude C. Lilly
Admissions: Brian J. Fortman
Financial Aid: Linda J. McAnnally

Type: Comprehensive **Sex:** Coed **Affiliation:** Presbyterian Church (U.S.A.). **Scores:** 95% SAT V 400+; 97% SAT M 400+; 47% ACT 18-23; 37% ACT 24-29 **% Accepted:** 62 **Admission Plans:** Deferred Admission; Early Action; Early Decision Plan **Application Deadline:** June 30 **Application Fee:** $0.00 **H.S. Requirements:** High school diploma required; GED accepted **Costs Per Year:** Application fee: $0. Comprehensive fee: $45,880 includes full-time tuition ($33,200), mandatory fees ($2930), and college room and board ($9750). College room only: $4750. Full-time tuition and fees vary according to course load and reciprocity agreements. Room and board charges vary according to board plan and housing facility. Part-time tuition: $1384 per credit hour. Part-time tuition varies according to course load and program. **Scholarships:** Available. **Calendar System:** Semester, Summer session available **Enrollment:** Full-time 990, Graduate full-time 312, Graduate part-time 3, Part-time 74 **Faculty:** Full-time 77, Part-time 36 **Student-Faculty Ratio:** 12:1 **Exams:** ACT essay component used for placement; SAT I or ACT; SAT essay component used for placement; SAT Reasoning; SAT Subject. **% Receiving Financial Aid:** 77 **% Residing in College-Owned, -Operated, or -Affiliated Housing:** 98 **Final Year or Final Semester Residency Requirement:** Yes **Regional Accreditation:** Southern Association of Colleges and Schools **Credit Hours For Degree:** 122 semester hours, Bachelors **ROTC:** Army **Professional Accreditation:** NASM, NCATE. **Intercollegiate Athletics:** Baseball M; Basketball M & W; Cheerleading M & W; Cross-Country Running M & W; Football M; Golf M & W; Lacrosse W; Soccer M & W; Softball W; Tennis M & W; Volleyball W

SOUTH CAROLINA STATE UNIVERSITY

300 College St. NE
Orangeburg, SC 29117-0001
Tel: (803)536-7000; Free: 800-260-5956
Fax: (803)536-8990
E-mail: admissions@scsu.edu
Web Site: www.scsu.edu
President/CEO: Dr. W. Franklin Evans
Admissions: Anthony Wright
Financial Aid: Sandra S. Davis

Type: Comprehensive **Sex:** Coed **Affiliation:** South Carolina Commission on Higher Education. **Scores:** 43% SAT V 400+; 41% SAT M 400+; 11% ACT 18-23; 3% ACT 24-29 **% Accepted:** 95 **Admission Plans:** Deferred Admission **Application Deadline:** July 31 **Application Fee:** $25.00 **H.S. Requirements:** High school diploma required; GED accepted **Costs Per Year:** Application fee: $25. State resident tuition: $8906 full-time, $420 per credit hour part-time. Nonresident tuition: $18,674 full-time, $827 per credit hour part-time. Mandatory fees: $1182 full-time. Full-time tuition and fees vary according to course load, program, and reciprocity agreements. Part-time tuition varies according to course load, program, and reciprocity agreements. College room and board: $9402. College room only: $6300. Room and board charges vary according to board plan and housing facility. **Scholarships:** Available. **Calendar System:** Semester, Summer session available **Enrollment:** Full-time 2,303, Graduate full-time 200, Graduate part-time 204, Part-time 347 **Faculty:** Full-time 136, Part-time 67 **Student-Faculty Ratio:** 17:1 **Exams:** SAT I or ACT; SAT II. **% Residing in College-Owned, -Operated, or -Affiliated Housing:** 57 **Regional Accreditation:** Southern Association of Colleges and Schools **Credit Hours For Degree:**

120 semester hours, Bachelors **ROTC:** Air Force, Army **Professional Accreditation:** AACN, AACSB, AAFCS, ABET, ACA, ASHA, CORE, CSWE, NASAD, NASM, NCATE. **Intercollegiate Athletics:** Basketball M & W; Cross-Country Running M & W; Football M; Soccer W; Softball W; Tennis M & W; Track and Field M & W; Volleyball W

SOUTH UNIVERSITY
9 Science Ct.
Columbia, SC 29203
Tel: (803)799-9082; Free: 866-629-3031
Fax: (803)799-9038
Web Site: www.southuniversity.edu/columbia
President/CEO: David Shoop
Type: Comprehensive **Sex:** Coed **Affiliation:** Education Management Corporation. **Calendar System:** Quarter **Regional Accreditation:** Southern Association of Colleges and Schools **Professional Accreditation:** ACBSP.

SOUTHERN WESLEYAN UNIVERSITY
907 Wesleyan Dr.
Central, SC 29630-1020
Tel: (864)644-5000; Free: 800-CU-AT-SWU
Fax: (864)644-5900
E-mail: broe@swu.edu
Web Site: www.swu.edu
President/CEO: Dr. David J. Spittal
Admissions: Beth Roe
Financial Aid: Laura Hedden
Type: Comprehensive **Sex:** Coed **Affiliation:** Wesleyan Church. **Scores:** 92% SAT V 400+; 92% SAT M 400+; 65% ACT 18-23; 13% ACT 24-29 **% Accepted:** 94 **Admission Plans:** Deferred Admission **Application Deadline:** August 1 **Application Fee:** $25.00 **H.S. Requirements:** High school diploma required; GED accepted **Scholarships:** Available. **Calendar System:** Semester, Summer session available **Enrollment:** Full-time 1,440, Graduate full-time 427, Part-time 16 **Faculty:** Full-time 57, Part-time 136 **Student-Faculty Ratio:** 18:1 **Exams:** SAT I or ACT; SAT Reasoning; SAT Subject. **% Receiving Financial Aid:** 88 **% Residing in College-Owned, -Operated, or -Affiliated Housing:** 55 **Final Year or Final Semester Residency Requirement:** Yes **Regional Accreditation:** Southern Association of Colleges and Schools **Credit Hours For Degree:** 64 hours, Associates; 120 hours, Bachelors **ROTC:** Air Force, Army **Professional Accreditation:** NASM, NCATE. **Intercollegiate Athletics:** Baseball M; Basketball M & W; Cheerleading M & W; Cross-Country Running M & W; Golf M; Soccer M & W; Softball W; Volleyball W

SPARTANBURG COMMUNITY COLLEGE
107 Community College Dr.
Spartanburg, SC 29303
Tel: (864)592-4600; Free: 866-591-3700
E-mail: admissions@sccsc.edu
Web Site: www.sccsc.edu
President/CEO: Henry C. Giles, Jr.
Admissions: Sabrina Sims
Financial Aid: Jeff O. Boyle
Type: Two-Year College **Sex:** Coed **Affiliation:** South Carolina State Board for Technical and Comprehensive Education. **Admission Plans:** Early Admission; Open Admission **Application Deadline:** Rolling **Application Fee:** $25.00 **H.S. Requirements:** High school diploma required; GED accepted. For industrial technology programs: High school diploma or equivalent not required **Costs Per Year:** Application fee: $25. Area resident tuition: $4092 full-time, $171 per credit hour part-time. State resident tuition: $5110 full-time, $213 per credit hour part-time. Nonresident tuition: $8372 full-time, $349 per credit hour part-time. Mandatory fees: $100 full-time, $50 per term part-time. Full-time tuition and fees vary according to course load and location. Part-time tuition and fees vary according to location. **Scholarships:** Available. **Calendar System:** Semester, Summer session available **Enrollment:** Full-time 2,232, Part-time 2,696 **Faculty:** Full-time 107, Part-time 238 **Student-Faculty Ratio:** 16:1 **Exams:** SAT I or ACT. **Final Year or Final Semester Residency Requirement:** No **Regional Accreditation:** Southern Association of Colleges and Schools **Credit Hours For Degree:** 60 semester hours, Associates **Professional Accreditation:** ABET, ACBSP, ACEN, ADA, CoARC, JRCERT, NAACLS.

SPARTANBURG METHODIST COLLEGE
1000 Powell Mill Rd.
Spartanburg, SC 29301

Tel: (864)587-4000; Free: 800-772-7286
Fax: (864)587-4355
E-mail: admiss@smcsc.edu
Web Site: www.smcsc.edu
President/CEO: Dr. Colleen P. Keith
Admissions: Daniel L. Philbeck
Type: Two-Year College **Sex:** Coed **Affiliation:** Methodist. **Scores:** 65% SAT V 400+; 69% SAT M 400+; 41% ACT 18-23; 5% ACT 24-29 **% Accepted:** 70 **Admission Plans:** Deferred Admission **Application Deadline:** Rolling **Application Fee:** $25.00 **H.S. Requirements:** High school diploma required; GED accepted **Costs Per Year:** Application fee: $25. One-time mandatory fee: $175. Comprehensive fee: $26,578 includes full-time tuition ($16,538), mandatory fees ($950), and college room and board ($9090). Full-time tuition and fees vary according to course load. **Scholarships:** Available. **Calendar System:** Semester, Summer session available **Enrollment:** Full-time 762, Part-time 9 **Faculty:** Full-time 28, Part-time 45 **Student-Faculty Ratio:** 19:1 **Exams:** ACT essay component not used; SAT I or ACT; SAT essay component not used. **% Residing in College-Owned, -Operated, or -Affiliated Housing:** 65 **Final Year or Final Semester Residency Requirement:** No **Regional Accreditation:** Southern Association of Colleges and Schools **Credit Hours For Degree:** 63 semester hours, Associates **Intercollegiate Athletics:** Baseball M; Basketball M & W; Cross-Country Running M & W; Golf M & W; Soccer M & W; Softball W; Tennis M & W; Volleyball W; Wrestling M

STRAYER UNIVERSITY–CHARLESTON CAMPUS
5010 Wetland Crossing
North Charleston, SC 29418
Tel: (843)746-5100
Fax: (843)746-5130
Web Site: www.strayer.edu/south-carolina/charleston
President/CEO: Brian W. Jones
Type: Comprehensive **Sex:** Coed **Regional Accreditation:** Middle States Association of Colleges and Schools

STRAYER UNIVERSITY–COLUMBIA CAMPUS
200 Ctr. Point Cir., Ste. 300
Columbia, SC 29210
Tel: (803)750-2500
Fax: (803)750-2530
Web Site: www.strayer.edu/south-carolina/columbia
President/CEO: Brian W. Jones
Type: Comprehensive **Sex:** Coed **Regional Accreditation:** Middle States Association of Colleges and Schools

STRAYER UNIVERSITY–GREENVILLE CAMPUS
555 N Pleasantburg Dr.
Ste. 300
Greenville, SC 29607
Tel: (864)250-7000
Fax: (864)232-3611
Web Site: www.strayer.edu/south-carolina/greenville
President/CEO: Brian W. Jones
Type: Comprehensive **Sex:** Coed **Regional Accreditation:** Middle States Association of Colleges and Schools

TECHNICAL COLLEGE OF THE LOWCOUNTRY
921 Ribaut Rd.
Beaufort, SC 29901-1288
Tel: (843)525-8324
E-mail: rcole@tcl.edu
Web Site: www.tcl.edu
President/CEO: Thomas Leitzel
Admissions: Rhonda Cole
Type: Two-Year College **Sex:** Coed **Affiliation:** South Carolina Technical and Comprehensive Education System. **Admission Plans:** Deferred Admission; Early Admission **Application Deadline:** Rolling **Application Fee:** $25.00 **H.S. Requirements:** High school diploma required; GED accepted **Costs Per Year:** Application fee: $25. Area resident tuition: $3984 full-time, $166 per credit hour part-time. State resident tuition: $4584 full-time, $191 per credit hour part-time. Nonresident tuition: $8880 full-time, $370 per credit hour part-time. Mandatory fees: $196 full-time. **Scholarships:** Available. **Calendar System:** Semester, Summer session available **Enrollment:** Full-time 665, Part-time 1,667 **Student-Faculty Ratio:** 15:1 **Exams:** Other; SAT

I and SAT II or ACT. **Regional Accreditation:** Southern Association of Colleges and Schools **Credit Hours For Degree:** 64 credit hours, Associates **Professional Accreditation:** ACBSP, ACEN.

TRI-COUNTY TECHNICAL COLLEGE

PO Box 587, 7900 Hwy. 76
Pendleton, SC 29670-0587
Tel: (864)646-8361
E-mail: infocent@tctc.edu
Web Site: www.tctc.edu
President/CEO: Dr. Ronnie Booth
Admissions: Renae Frazier

Type: Two-Year College **Sex:** Coed **Affiliation:** South Carolina State Board for Technical and Comprehensive Education. **Admission Plans:** Early Admission; Open Admission **Application Deadline:** Rolling **Application Fee:** $30.00 **H.S. Requirements:** High school diploma required; GED accepted. For welding, industrial mechanics programs: High school diploma or equivalent not required **Scholarships:** Available. **Calendar System:** Semester, Summer session available **Enrollment:** Full-time 3,451, Part-time 2,677 **Student-Faculty Ratio:** 21:1 **Regional Accreditation:** Southern Association of Colleges and Schools **Credit Hours For Degree:** 60 credits, Associates **ROTC:** Air Force, Army **Professional Accreditation:** ABET, ACBSP, ACEN, ADA, NAACLS. **Intercollegiate Athletics:** Golf M; Soccer M

TRIDENT TECHNICAL COLLEGE

PO Box 118067
Charleston, SC 29423-8067
Tel: (843)574-6111
Fax: (843)574-6109
E-mail: clara.martin@tridenttech.edu
Web Site: www.tridenttech.edu
President/CEO: Dr. Mary Thornley
Admissions: Clara Martin
Financial Aid: Ellen Green

Type: Two-Year College **Sex:** Coed **Affiliation:** South Carolina State Board for Technical and Comprehensive Education. **Admission Plans:** Early Admission; Open Admission **Application Deadline:** August 6 **Application Fee:** $30.00 **H.S. Requirements:** High school diploma required; GED accepted **Costs Per Year:** Application fee: $30. Area resident tuition: $3912 full-time. State resident tuition: $4340 full-time. Nonresident tuition: $7404 full-time. Full-time tuition varies according to course load and program. **Scholarships:** Available. **Calendar System:** Semester, Summer session available **Enrollment:** Full-time 7,183, Part-time 8,953 **Faculty:** Full-time 339, Part-time 781 **Student-Faculty Ratio:** 17:1 **Final Year or Final Semester Residency Requirement:** No **Regional Accreditation:** Southern Association of Colleges and Schools **Credit Hours For Degree:** 60 credit hours, Associates **Professional Accreditation:** ABET, ACBSP, ACEN, ACF, ADA, AOTA, APTA, CoARC, JRCERT, NAACLS.

UNIVERSITY OF SOUTH CAROLINA

Columbia, SC 29208
Tel: (803)777-7000; Free: 800-868-5872
E-mail: admissions-ugrad@sc.edu
Web Site: www.sc.edu
President/CEO: Dr. Harris Pastides
Admissions: Dr. Mary Wagner
Financial Aid: Joey C. Derrick

Type: University **Sex:** Coed **Affiliation:** University of South Carolina System. **Scores:** 100% SAT V 400+; 100% SAT M 400+; 13% ACT 18-23; 63% ACT 24-29 **% Accepted:** 65 **Admission Plans:** Early Decision Plan **Application Fee:** $50.00 **H.S. Requirements:** High school diploma required; GED accepted **Costs Per Year:** Application fee: $50. State resident tuition: $11,082 full-time, $461.75 per credit hour part-time. Nonresident tuition: $29,898 full-time, $1,245.75 per credit hour part-time. Mandatory fees: $400 full-time. Full-time tuition and fees vary according to program and reciprocity agreements. Part-time tuition varies according to course load. College room and board: $9872. College room only: $6627. Room and board charges vary according to board plan, housing facility, and location. Scholarships: Available. **Calendar System:** Semester, Summer session available **Enrollment:** Full-time 23,177, Graduate full-time 5,726, Graduate part-time 2,382, Part-time 1,686 **Faculty:** Full-time 1,525, Part-time 848 **Student-Faculty Ratio:** 18:1 **Exams:** ACT essay component used for admission; SAT I or ACT; SAT essay component used for admission; SAT Reasoning. **% Receiving Financial Aid:** 51 **% Residing in College-**

Owned, -Operated, or -Affiliated Housing: 29 **Final Year or Final Semester Residency Requirement:** Yes **Regional Accreditation:** Southern Association of Colleges and Schools **Credit Hours For Degree:** 60 credit hours, Associates; 120 credit hours, Bachelors **ROTC:** Air Force, Army, Navy **Professional Accreditation:** AACN, AACSB, AALS, AANA, ABA, ABET, ACA, ACEJMC, ACPE, ALA, APA, APTA, ASHA, CAHME, CEPH, CORE, CSWE, JRCAT, LCME/AMA, NASAD, NASM, NASPAA, NAST, NCATE. **Intercollegiate Athletics:** Baseball M; Basketball M & W; Cross-Country Running W; Equestrian Sports W; Football M; Golf M & W; Soccer M & W; Softball W; Swimming and Diving M & W; Tennis M & W; Track and Field M & W; Volleyball W

UNIVERSITY OF SOUTH CAROLINA AIKEN

471 University Pky.
Aiken, SC 29801
Tel: (803)648-6851; Free: 888-WOW-USCA
Fax: (803)641-3727
E-mail: admit@usca.edu
Web Site: www.usca.edu
President/CEO: Dr. Sandra J. Jordan
Admissions: Andrew Hendrix
Financial Aid: Linda Aubrey-Higgins

Type: Comprehensive **Sex:** Coed **Affiliation:** University of South Carolina System. **Scores:** 93% SAT V 400+; 93% SAT M 400+; 63% ACT 18-23; 17% ACT 24-29 **% Accepted:** 57 **Admission Plans:** Deferred Admission; Early Admission **Application Deadline:** August 1 **Application Fee:** $45.00 **H.S. Requirements:** High school diploma required; GED accepted **Costs Per Year:** Application fee: $45. State resident tuition: $9588 full-time, $399.50 per credit hour part-time. Nonresident tuition: $19,182 full-time, $799.25 per credit hour part-time. Mandatory fees: $290 full-time, $9 per credit hour part-time, $25 per term part-time. Full-time tuition and fees vary according to reciprocity agreements. Part-time tuition and fees vary according to course load and reciprocity agreements. College room and board: $7290. Room and board charges vary according to board plan and housing facility. **Scholarships:** Available. **Calendar System:** Semester, Summer session available **Enrollment:** Full-time 2,594, Graduate full-time 20, Graduate part-time 72, Part-time 762 **Faculty:** Full-time 142, Part-time 124 **Student-Faculty Ratio:** 16:1 **Exams:** SAT I or ACT; SAT Reasoning. **% Receiving Financial Aid:** 69 **% Residing in College-Owned, -Operated, or -Affiliated Housing:** 29 **Final Year or Final Semester Residency Requirement:** No **Regional Accreditation:** Southern Association of Colleges and Schools **Credit Hours For Degree:** 120 semester hours, Bachelors **Professional Accreditation:** AACSB, ACEN, NASM, NCATE. **Intercollegiate Athletics:** Baseball M; Basketball M & W; Cross-Country Running W; Golf M; Soccer M & W; Softball W; Tennis M & W; Volleyball W

UNIVERSITY OF SOUTH CAROLINA BEAUFORT

One University Blvd.
Bluffton, SC 29909
Tel: (843)208-8000
E-mail: monicaw@sc.edu
Web Site: www.uscb.edu
President/CEO: Dr. Al M. Panu
Admissions: Monica Williams
Financial Aid: Heather Robinson

Type: Four-Year College **Sex:** Coed **Affiliation:** University of South Carolina system. **Scores:** 89% SAT V 400+; 84% SAT M 400+; 56% ACT 18-23; 15% ACT 24-29 **% Accepted:** 63 **Admission Plans:** Deferred Admission **Application Deadline:** Rolling **Application Fee:** $40.00 **H.S. Requirements:** High school diploma required; GED accepted **Costs Per Year:** Application fee: $40. One-time mandatory fee: $175. State resident tuition: $9462 full-time, $394.25 per credit hour part-time. Nonresident tuition: $19,596 full-time, $816.50 per credit hour part-time. Mandatory fees: $386 full-time, $14 per credit hour part-time, $25. Full-time tuition and fees vary according to course load, program, and reciprocity agreements. Part-time tuition and fees vary according to course load, program, and reciprocity agreements. College room and board: $7400. College room only: $5100. Room and board charges vary according to board plan, housing facility, location, and student level. **Scholarships:** Available. **Calendar System:** Semester, Summer session available **Enrollment:** Full-time 1,705, Part-time 275 **Exams:** ACT essay component not used; SAT I or ACT; SAT essay component not used. **% Residing in College-Owned, -Operated, or -Affiliated Housing:** 37 **Final Year or Final Semester Residency Requirement:** Yes **Regional Accreditation:** Southern Association of Colleges and Schools **Credit Hours**

For Degree: 60 semester hours, Associates; 120 semester hours, Bachelors **Professional Accreditation:** NCATE. **Intercollegiate Athletics:** Baseball M; Cross-Country Running M & W; Golf M & W; Soccer W; Softball W; Track and Field M & W

UNIVERSITY OF SOUTH CAROLINA LANCASTER

PO Box 889
Lancaster, SC 29721-0889
Tel: (803)313-7000
Fax: (803)313-7106
E-mail: vinsons@mailbox.sc.edu
Web Site: usclancaster.sc.edu
President/CEO: Dr. John Catalano
Admissions: Susan Vinson
Financial Aid: Kenneth Tobey Cole

Type: Two-Year College **Sex:** Coed **Affiliation:** University of South Carolina System. **% Accepted:** 100 **Admission Plans:** Early Admission; Open Admission **Application Deadline:** Rolling **Application Fee:** $40.00 **H.S. Requirements:** High school diploma required; GED accepted **Scholarships:** Available. **Calendar System:** Semester, Summer session not available **Enrollment:** Full-time 794, Part-time 799 **Faculty:** Full-time 63, Part-time 42 **Student-Faculty Ratio:** 14:1 **Exams:** ACT essay component not used; SAT I or ACT; SAT essay component not used. **Final Year or Final Semester Residency Requirement:** Yes **Regional Accreditation:** Southern Association of Colleges and Schools **Credit Hours For Degree:** 60 semester hours, Associates **Professional Accreditation:** ACBSP, ACEN. **Intercollegiate Athletics:** Baseball M; Golf M; Soccer W; Tennis M & W

UNIVERSITY OF SOUTH CAROLINA SALKEHATCHIE

PO Box 617
Allendale, SC 29810-0617
Tel: (803)584-3446; Free: 800-922-5500
E-mail: cdbrown@mailbox.sc.edu
Web Site: uscsalkehatchie.sc.edu
President/CEO: Ann C. Carmichael
Admissions: Carmen Brown
Financial Aid: Julie Hadwin

Type: Two-Year College **Sex:** Coed **Affiliation:** University of South Carolina System. **% Accepted:** 59 **Application Deadline:** Rolling **Application Fee:** $40.00 **H.S. Requirements:** High school diploma required; GED accepted **Scholarships:** Available. **Calendar System:** Semester, Summer session available **Student-Faculty Ratio:** 17:1 **Exams:** ACT essay component not used; SAT I or ACT; SAT essay component not used. **Final Year or Final Semester Residency Requirement:** Yes **Regional Accreditation:** Southern Association of Colleges and Schools **Credit Hours For Degree:** 60 semester hours, Associates; 120 semester hours, Bachelors **Intercollegiate Athletics:** Baseball M; Basketball M; Soccer M & W; Softball W

UNIVERSITY OF SOUTH CAROLINA SUMTER

200 Miller Rd.
Sumter, SC 29150-2498
Tel: (803)775-8727
E-mail: kbritton@usc.sumter.edu
Web Site: www.uscsumter.edu
President/CEO: C. Leslie Carpenter, PhD
Admissions: Keith Britton
Financial Aid: Sue Sims

Type: Two-Year College **Sex:** Coed **Affiliation:** University of South Carolina System. **Scores:** 85% SAT V 400+; 85% SAT M 400+; 57.4% ACT 18-23; 3.7% ACT 24-29 **% Accepted:** 58 **Application Deadline:** August 8 **Application Fee:** $40.00 **H.S. Requirements:** High school diploma required; GED accepted **Costs Per Year:** Application fee: $40. One-time mandatory fee: $50. State resident tuition: $6486 full-time, $270.25 per credit hour part-time. Nonresident tuition: $16,206 full-time, $675.25 per credit hour part-time. Mandatory fees: $392 full-time, $15 per credit hour part-time, $25 per term part-time. Full-time tuition and fees vary according to student level. Part-time tuition and fees vary according to location and student level. **Scholarships:** Available. **Calendar System:** Semester, Summer session available **Faculty:** Full-time 41, Part-time 25 **Student-Faculty Ratio:** 19:1 **Exams:** SAT I or ACT. **Regional Accreditation:** Southern Association of Colleges and Schools **Credit Hours For Degree:** 60 semester hours, Associates **ROTC:** Air Force, Army

UNIVERSITY OF SOUTH CAROLINA UNION

PO Drawer 729
Union, SC 29379-0729
Tel: (864)427-3681
E-mail: tyoung@gwm.sc.edu
Web Site: uscunion.sc.edu
President/CEO: Dr. John Catalano
Admissions: Michael B. Greer

Type: Two-Year College **Sex:** Coed **Affiliation:** University of South Carolina System. **Application Deadline:** Rolling **Application Fee:** $40.00 **H.S. Requirements:** High school diploma required; GED accepted **Costs Per Year:** Application fee: $40. State resident tuition: $3243 full-time, $270.25 per credit hour part-time. Nonresident tuition: $8103 full-time, $675.25 per credit hour part-time. Mandatory fees: $361 full-time, $180 per term part-time. Full-time tuition and fees vary according to course load, degree level, and student level. Part-time tuition and fees vary according to student level. **Scholarships:** Available. **Calendar System:** Semester **Enrollment:** Full-time 435, Part-time 322 **Faculty:** Full-time 10, Part-time 28 **Student-Faculty Ratio:** 18:1 **Exams:** ACT essay component not used; SAT I or ACT; SAT essay component not used. **Final Year or Final Semester Residency Requirement:** No **Regional Accreditation:** Southern Association of Colleges and Schools **Credit Hours For Degree:** 60 semester hours, Associates

UNIVERSITY OF SOUTH CAROLINA UPSTATE

800 University Way
Spartanburg, SC 29303-4999
Tel: (864)503-5000; Free: 800-277-8727
Fax: (864)503-5201
E-mail: dstewart@uscupstate.edu
Web Site: www.uscupstate.edu
President/CEO: Dr. Thomas F. Moore
Admissions: Donette Stewart
Financial Aid: Bonnie Carson-Durham

Type: Comprehensive **Sex:** Coed **Affiliation:** University of South Carolina System. **Scores:** 90% SAT V 400+; 93% SAT M 400+; 64% ACT 18-23; 15% ACT 24-29 **% Accepted:** 53 **Admission Plans:** Deferred Admission **Application Fee:** $40.00 **H.S. Requirements:** High school diploma required; GED accepted **Scholarships:** Available. **Calendar System:** Semester, Summer session available **Enrollment:** Full-time 4,232, Graduate full-time 11, Graduate part-time 164, Part-time 1,102 **Faculty:** Full-time 212, Part-time 217 **Student-Faculty Ratio:** 16:1 **Exams:** SAT I or ACT. **% Receiving Financial Aid:** 77 **% Residing in College-Owned, -Operated, or -Affiliated Housing:** 19 **Regional Accreditation:** Southern Association of Colleges and Schools **Credit Hours For Degree:** 71 semester hours, Associates; 120 semester hours, Bachelors **ROTC:** Army **Professional Accreditation:** AACN, AACSB, ABET, ACEN, NASAD, NCATE. **Intercollegiate Athletics:** Baseball M; Basketball M & W; Cheerleading M & W; Cross-Country Running M & W; Golf M & W; Soccer M & W; Softball W; Tennis M & W; Track and Field M & W; Volleyball W

VIRGINIA COLLEGE IN CHARLESTON

6185 Rivers Ave.
North Charleston, SC 29406
Tel: (843)614-4300
Web Site: www.vc.edu
Type: Two-Year College **Sex:** Coed **Professional Accreditation:** ACICS.

VIRGINIA COLLEGE IN COLUMBIA

7201 Two Notch Rd., Ste. 1000
Columbia, SC 29223
Tel: (803)509-4725
Web Site: www.vc.edu
Type: Two-Year College **Sex:** Coed **Professional Accreditation:** ACICS.

VIRGINIA COLLEGE IN FLORENCE

2400 David H. McLeod Blvd.
Florence, SC 29501
Tel: (843)407-2200
Web Site: www.vc.edu
Type: Two-Year College **Sex:** Coed **Professional Accreditation:** ACICS.

VIRGINIA COLLEGE IN GREENVILLE
78 Global Dr.
Ste. 200
Greenville, SC 29607
Tel: (864)679-4900
Web Site: www.vc.edu
Type: Two-Year College **Sex:** Coed **Professional Accreditation:** ACICS.

VIRGINIA COLLEGE IN SPARTANBURG
8150 Warren H. Abernathy Hwy.
Spartanburg, SC 29301
Tel: (864)504-3200
Web Site: www.vc.edu
Type: Two-Year College **Sex:** Coed **Calendar System:** Quarter **Professional Accreditation:** ACICS.

VOORHEES COLLEGE
213 Wiggins Dr.
Denmark, SC 29042
Tel: (803)780-1234; Free: 866-237-4570
Fax: (803)793-5773
E-mail: west@voorhees.edu
Web Site: www.voorhees.edu
President/CEO: Dr. Cleveland Sellers
Admissions: Adrain West
Financial Aid: Augusta L. Kitchen
Type: Four-Year College **Sex:** Coed **Affiliation:** Episcopal. **Scores:** 3% ACT 18-23 **% Accepted:** 50 **Admission Plans:** Deferred Admission **Application Deadline:** Rolling **Application Fee:** $25.00 **H.S. Requirements:** High school diploma required; GED accepted **Costs Per Year:** Application fee: $25. Comprehensive fee: $19,976 includes full-time tuition ($11,630), mandatory fees ($1000), and college room and board ($7346). College room only: $3676. Part-time tuition: $484 per hour. **Scholarships:** Available. **Calendar System:** Semester, Summer session available **Enrollment:** Full-time 452, Part-time 16 **Faculty:** Full-time 39, Part-time 5 **Exams:** SAT I or ACT. **% Receiving Financial Aid:** 91 **% Residing in College-Owned, -Operated, or -Affiliated Housing:** 70 **Regional Accreditation:** Southern Association of Colleges and Schools **Credit Hours For Degree:** 124 credit hours, Bachelors **ROTC:** Army **Professional Accreditation:** ACBSP. **Intercollegiate Athletics:** Baseball M; Basketball M & W; Cheerleading W; Cross-Country Running M & W; Softball W; Track and Field M & W

WILLIAMSBURG TECHNICAL COLLEGE
601 Martin Luther King, Jr Ave.
Kingstree, SC 29556-4197
Tel: (843)355-4110; Free: 800-768-2021
Fax: (843)355-4296
E-mail: wrighta@wiltech.edu
Web Site: www.wiltech.edu
President/CEO: Dr. Patricia A. Lee
Admissions: Dr. Alexis DuBose
Financial Aid: Jean M. Boos
Type: Two-Year College **Sex:** Coed **Affiliation:** South Carolina State Board for Technical and Comprehensive Education. **Admission Plans:** Deferred Admission; Early Admission; Open Admission **Application Deadline:** Rolling **Application Fee:** $0.00 **H.S. Requirements:** High school diploma required; GED accepted **Costs Per Year:** Application fee: $0. Area resident tuition: $3816 full-time, $159 per credit hour part-time. State resident tuition: $3936 full-time, $164 per credit hour part-time. Nonresident tuition: $7416 full-time, $309 per credit hour part-time. Mandatory fees: $192 full-time, $8 per credit hour part-time. **Scholarships:** Available. **Calendar System:** Semester, Summer session available **Enrollment:** Full-time 199, Part-time 494 **Faculty:** Full-time 19, Part-time 28 **Student-Faculty Ratio:** 14:1 **Regional Accreditation:** Southern Association of Colleges and Schools **Credit Hours For Degree:** 62 semester hours, Associates **Professional Accreditation:** ACBSP.

WINTHROP UNIVERSITY
701 Oakland Ave.
Rock Hill, SC 29733
Tel: (803)323-2211; Free: 800-763-0230
Fax: (803)323-2137
E-mail: admissions@winthrop.edu
Web Site: www.winthrop.edu

President/CEO: Dr. Daniel F. Mahony, PhD
Admissions: Debi Barber
Financial Aid: Michelle K. Hare
Type: Comprehensive **Sex:** Coed **Affiliation:** South Carolina Commission on Higher Education. **Scores:** 97% SAT V 400+; 97% SAT M 400+; 52.1% ACT 18-23; 35.7% ACT 24-29 **% Accepted:** 67 **Admission Plans:** Deferred Admission **Application Deadline:** May 1 **Application Fee:** $40.00 **H.S. Requirements:** High school diploma required; GED accepted **Costs Per Year:** Application fee: $40. State resident tuition: $14,156 full-time, $590 per credit hour part-time. Nonresident tuition: $27,404 full-time, $1142 per credit hour part-time. Mandatory fees: $300 full-time. Full-time tuition and fees vary according to degree level, reciprocity agreements, and student level. Part-time tuition varies according to degree level and student level. College room and board: $8320. College room only: $5140. Room and board charges vary according to board plan and housing facility. **Scholarships:** Available. **Calendar System:** Semester, Summer session available **Enrollment:** Full-time 4,551, Graduate full-time 466, Graduate part-time 492, Part-time 522 **Faculty:** Full-time 282, Part-time 273 **Student-Faculty Ratio:** 14:1 **Exams:** SAT I or ACT; SAT Reasoning. **% Receiving Financial Aid:** 74 **% Residing in College-Owned, -Operated, or -Affiliated Housing:** 51 **Final Year or Final Semester Residency Requirement:** Yes **Regional Accreditation:** Southern Association of Colleges and Schools **Credit Hours For Degree:** 120 semester hours, Bachelors **ROTC:** Air Force, Army **Professional Accreditation:** AACSB, ABET, ACA, ACEJMC, AND, CIDA, CSWE, NASAD, NASD, NASM, NAST, NCATE. **Intercollegiate Athletics:** Baseball M; Basketball M & W; Cheerleading M & W; Cross-Country Running M & W; Fencing M & W; Golf M & W; Lacrosse M & W; Rugby M; Soccer M & W; Softball W; Tennis M & W; Track and Field M & W; Volleyball W

WOFFORD COLLEGE
429 N Church St.
Spartanburg, SC 29303-3663
Tel: (864)597-4000
Fax: (864)597-4149
E-mail: admission@wofford.edu
Web Site: www.wofford.edu
President/CEO: Dr. Nayef H. Samhat
Admissions: Ashley S. Hill
Financial Aid: Carolyn B. Sparks
Type: Four-Year College **Sex:** Coed **Affiliation:** United Methodist Church. **Scores:** 100% SAT V 400+; 100% SAT M 400+; 29% ACT 18-23; 53% ACT 24-29 **% Accepted:** 72 **Admission Plans:** Deferred Admission; Early Action; Early Admission; Early Decision Plan **Application Fee:** $35.00 **H.S. Requirements:** High school diploma required; GED accepted **Costs Per Year:** Application fee: $35. Comprehensive fee: $49,885 includes full-time tuition ($38,705) and college room and board ($11,180). **Scholarships:** Available. **Calendar System:** 4-1-4, Summer session available **Enrollment:** Full-time 1,573, Part-time 40 **Faculty:** Full-time 136, Part-time 19 **Student-Faculty Ratio:** 11:1 **Exams:** ACT essay component not used; SAT I or ACT; SAT essay component not used. **% Receiving Financial Aid:** 61 **% Residing in College-Owned, -Operated, or -Affiliated Housing:** 96 **Regional Accreditation:** Southern Association of Colleges and Schools **Credit Hours For Degree:** 124 semester hours, Bachelors **ROTC:** Army **Intercollegiate Athletics:** Baseball M; Basketball M & W; Cheerleading W; Cross-Country Running M & W; Football M; Golf M & W; Riflery M & W; Soccer M & W; Tennis M & W; Track and Field M & W; Volleyball W

YORK TECHNICAL COLLEGE
452 S Anderson Rd.
Rock Hill, SC 29730-3395
Tel: (803)327-8000
Fax: (803)327-8059
E-mail: kaldridge@yorktech.com
Web Site: www.yorktech.com
President/CEO: Dr. Greg Rutherford
Admissions: Kenny Aldridge
Financial Aid: Elizabeth Rollins
Type: Two-Year College **Sex:** Coed **Affiliation:** South Carolina State Board for Technical and Comprehensive Education. **Admission Plans:** Open Admission **Application Deadline:** Rolling **Application Fee:** $0.00 **H.S. Requirements:** High school diploma or equivalent not required. For health and human services program applicants: High school diploma required; GED accepted **Scholarships:** Available. **Calendar System:** Semester, Summer session available **Enrollment:** Full-time 2,279, Part-time 2,452 **Faculty:**

Full-time 128, Part-time 139 **Student-Faculty Ratio:** 16:1 **Exams:** Other. **Regional Accreditation:** Southern Association of Colleges and Schools

Credit Hours For Degree: 62 semester hours, Associates **Professional Accreditation:** ABET, ACBSP, ACEN, ADA, JRCERT, NAACLS.

AUGUSTANA UNIVERSITY

2001 S Summit Ave.
Sioux Falls, SD 57197
Tel: (605)274-0770; Free: 800-727-2844
Fax: (605)274-5518
E-mail: admission@augie.edu
Web Site: www.augie.edu
President/CEO: Robert C. Oliver
Admissions: Nancy Davidson
Financial Aid: Tresse J. Evenson
Type: Comprehensive **Sex:** Coed **Affiliation:** Evangelical Lutheran Church in America. **Scores:** 32.3% ACT 18-23; 52.9% ACT 24-29 **% Accepted:** 65 **Admission Plans:** Deferred Admission **Application Deadline:** Rolling **Application Fee:** $0.00 **H.S. Requirements:** High school diploma required; GED accepted **Costs Per Year:** Application fee: $0. Comprehensive fee: $38,424 includes full-time tuition ($30,454), mandatory fees ($490), and college room and board ($7480). College room only: $3360. Full-time tuition and fees vary according to course load and degree level. Room and board charges vary according to board plan and housing facility. Part-time tuition: $450 per credit hour. Part-time tuition varies according to course load and degree level. **Scholarships:** Available. **Calendar System:** 4-1-4, Summer session available **Enrollment:** Full-time 1,516, Graduate full-time 1, Graduate part-time 223, Part-time 97 **Faculty:** Full-time 136, Part-time 25 **Student-Faculty Ratio:** 11:1 **Exams:** ACT essay component not used; SAT I or ACT; SAT essay component not used; SAT Reasoning. **% Receiving Financial Aid:** 60 **% Residing in College-Owned, -Operated, or -Affiliated Housing:** 72 **Final Year or Final Semester Residency Requirement:** No **Regional Accreditation:** North Central Association of Colleges and Schools **Credit Hours For Degree:** 124 credit hours, Bachelors **ROTC:** Air Force, Army **Professional Accreditation:** AACN, CSWE, JRCAT, NASM, NCATE. **Intercollegiate Athletics:** Baseball M; Basketball M & W; Cheerleading M & W; Cross-Country Running M & W; Football M; Golf M & W; Rugby W; Soccer M & W; Softball W; Swimming and Diving W; Tennis M & W; Track and Field M & W; Ultimate Frisbee M & W; Volleyball W; Wrestling M

BLACK HILLS STATE UNIVERSITY

1200 University St.
Spearfish, SD 57799
Tel: (605)642-6011; Free: 800-255-2478
E-mail: admissions@bhsu.edu
Web Site: www.bhsu.edu
President/CEO: Dr. Tom Jackson, Jr.
Admissions: Beth Oaks
Financial Aid: Deb Henriksen
Type: Comprehensive **Sex:** Coed **Affiliation:** South Dakota Board of Regents. **Scores:** 60.81% ACT 18-23; 21.17% ACT 24-29 **Costs Per Year:** State resident tuition: $8004 full-time. Nonresident tuition: $10,586 full-time. Full-time tuition varies according to course load, location, program, and reciprocity agreements. College room and board: $6458. College room only: $3361. Room and board charges vary according to board plan and housing facility. **Scholarships:** Available. **Calendar System:** Semester, Summer session available **Enrollment:** Full-time 2,279, Graduate full-time 32, Graduate part-time 437, Part-time 1,741 **Student-Faculty Ratio:** 19:1 **Exams:** ACT essay component not used; SAT I or ACT; SAT essay component not used. **Regional Accreditation:** North Central Association of Colleges and Schools **Credit Hours For Degree:** 60 Credits, Associates; 120 credits, Bachelors **ROTC:** Army **Professional Accreditation:** AACSB, NASM, NCATE. **Intercollegiate Athletics:** Basketball M & W; Cross-Country Running M & W; Football M; Golf W; Track and Field M & W; Volleyball W

DAKOTA STATE UNIVERSITY

820 N Washington
Madison, SD 57042-1799
Tel: (605)256-5111; Free: 888-DSU-9988
Fax: (605)256-5316
E-mail: admissions@dsu.edu
Web Site: www.dsu.edu
President/CEO: Dr. Jose-Marie Griffiths
Admissions: Tory Bickett
Financial Aid: Denise Grayson
Type: Comprehensive **Sex:** Coed **Affiliation:** South Dakota Board of Regents. **Scores:** 95% SAT V 400+; 95% SAT M 400+; 47.1% ACT 18-23; 38% ACT 24-29 **% Accepted:** 81 **Admission Plans:** Deferred Admission **Application Deadline:** Rolling **Application Fee:** $20.00 **H.S. Requirements:** High school diploma required; GED accepted **Costs Per Year:** Application fee: $20. State resident tuition: $4170 full-time, $139 per credit hour part-time. Nonresident tuition: $6258 full-time, $209 per credit hour part-time. Mandatory fees: $4584 full-time. Full-time tuition and fees vary according to location and reciprocity agreements. Part-time tuition varies according to location and reciprocity agreements. College room and board: $6060. College room only: $3281. Room and board charges vary according to board plan and housing facility. **Scholarships:** Available. **Calendar System:** Semester, Summer session available **Enrollment:** Full-time 1,251, Graduate full-time 85, Graduate part-time 240, Part-time 1,569 **Faculty:** Full-time 91, Part-time 50 **Student-Faculty Ratio:** 18:1 **Exams:** ACT essay component not used; SAT I or ACT; SAT essay component not used; SAT Reasoning. **% Receiving Financial Aid:** 70 **% Residing in College-Owned, -Operated, or -Affiliated Housing:** 32 **Final Year or Final Semester Residency Requirement:** No **Regional Accreditation:** North Central Association of Colleges and Schools **Credit Hours For Degree:** 60 credit hours, Associates; 120 credit hours, Bachelors **ROTC:** Air Force, Army **Professional Accreditation:** ACBSP, AHIMA, CoARC, NCATE. **Intercollegiate Athletics:** Baseball M; Basketball M & W; Cheerleading M & W; Cross-Country Running M & W; Football M; Softball W; Track and Field M & W; Volleyball W

DAKOTA WESLEYAN UNIVERSITY

1200 W University Ave.
Mitchell, SD 57301-4398
Tel: (605)995-2600; Free: 800-333-8506
Fax: (605)995-2699
E-mail: admissions@dwu.edu
Web Site: www.dwu.edu
President/CEO: Dr. Robert G. Duffett
Admissions: Melissa Herr-Valburg
Financial Aid: Kristy O'Kief
Type: Comprehensive **Sex:** Coed **Affiliation:** United Methodist. **Scores:** 92% SAT V 400+; 92% SAT M 400+; 50% ACT 18-23; 35% ACT 24-29 **% Accepted:** 73 **Application Deadline:** August 27 **Application Fee:** $25.00 **H.S. Requirements:** High school diploma required; GED accepted **Scholarships:** Available. **Calendar System:** Semester, Summer session available

Enrollment: Full-time 688, Graduate full-time 9, Graduate part-time 68, Part-time 71 **Faculty:** Full-time 50, Part-time 20 **Student-Faculty Ratio:** 11:1 **Exams:** SAT I or ACT. **% Receiving Financial Aid:** 80 **% Residing in College-Owned, -Operated, or -Affiliated Housing:** 45 **Final Year or Final Semester Residency Requirement:** No **Regional Accreditation:** North Central Association of Colleges and Schools **Credit Hours For Degree:** 62 semester hours, Associates; 125 semester hours, Bachelors **ROTC:** Army **Professional Accreditation:** ACEN, JRCAT. **Intercollegiate Athletics:** Baseball M; Basketball M & W; Cheerleading M & W; Cross-Country Running M & W; Football M; Golf M & W; Softball W; Track and Field M & W; Volleyball W; Wrestling M

GLOBE UNIVERSITY–SIOUX FALLS

5101 S Broadband Ln.
Sioux Falls, SD 57108-2208
Tel: (605)977-0705; Free: 866-437-0705
Fax: (605)977-0784
Web Site: www.globeuniversity.edu
President/CEO: Aimee Miritello

Type: Four-Year College **Sex:** Coed **Affiliation:** Globe Education Network (GEN). **Admission Plans:** Open Admission **Application Deadline:** Rolling **Application Fee:** $50.00 **H.S. Requirements:** High school diploma required; GED accepted **Scholarships:** Available. **Enrollment:** Full-time 139, Part-time 32 **Faculty:** Full-time 7, Part-time 28 **Exams:** Other. **Final Year or Final Semester Residency Requirement:** No **Credit Hours For Degree:** 90 quarter credits, Associates; 180 quarter credits, Bachelors **Professional Accreditation:** ACICS.

LAKE AREA TECHNICAL INSTITUTE

1201 Arrow Ave.
Watertown, SD 57201
Tel: (605)882-5284; Free: 800-657-4344
E-mail: straitl@lakeareatech.edu
Web Site: www.lakeareatech.edu
President/CEO: Col. Michael Cartney, Retd.
Admissions: LuAnn Strait

Type: Two-Year College **Sex:** Coed **Affiliation:** South Dakota Department of Education. **Admission Plans:** Open Admission **Application Deadline:** Rolling **Application Fee:** $25.00 **H.S. Requirements:** High school diploma required; GED accepted **Costs Per Year:** Application fee: $25. State resident tuition: $2616 full-time, $109 per credit hour part-time. Nonresident tuition: $2616 full-time, $109 per credit hour part-time. Mandatory fees: $2545 full-time. Full-time tuition and fees vary according to course load and program. Part-time tuition varies according to course load and program. **Scholarships:** Available. **Calendar System:** Semester, Summer session available **Enrollment:** Full-time 1,548, Part-time 298 **Faculty:** Full-time 101, Part-time 67 **Student-Faculty Ratio:** 16:1 **Exams:** ACT; ACT essay component not used; Other; SAT essay component not used. **Final Year or Final Semester Residency Requirement:** No **Regional Accreditation:** North Central Association of Colleges and Schools **Credit Hours For Degree:** 60 credits, Associates **Professional Accreditation:** AAMAE, ADA, AOTA, APTA, NAACLS.

MITCHELL TECHNICAL INSTITUTE

1800 E Spruce St.
Mitchell, SD 57301
Tel: (605)995-3024; Free: 800-684-1969
Fax: (605)996-3299
E-mail: clayton.deuter@mitchelltech.edu
Web Site: www.mitchelltech.edu
President/CEO: Mark Wilson
Admissions: Clayton Deuter
Financial Aid: Morgan Huber

Type: Two-Year College **Sex:** Coed **Affiliation:** South Dakota Board of Regents. **Scores:** 49.73% ACT 18-23; 19.89% ACT 24-29 **% Accepted:** 55 **Admission Plans:** Open Admission **Application Deadline:** Rolling **H.S. Requirements:** High school diploma required; GED accepted **Costs Per Year:** State resident tuition: $3270 full-time, $109 per credit hour part-time. Nonresident tuition: $3270 full-time, $109 per credit hour part-time. Mandatory fees: $2610 full-time, $87 per credit hour part-time. Full-time tuition and fees vary according to course load and program. Part-time tuition and fees vary according to course load and program. **Scholarships:** Available. **Calendar System:** Semester, Summer session available **Enrollment:** Full-time 852, Part-time 410 **Faculty:** Full-time 80, Part-time 13 **Student-Faculty**

Ratio: 12:1 **Exams:** ACT; ACT essay component not used; Other; SAT Reasoning; SAT Subject. **Final Year or Final Semester Residency Requirement:** No **Regional Accreditation:** North Central Association of Colleges and Schools **Credit Hours For Degree:** 65 credits, Associates **Professional Accreditation:** AAMAE, NAACLS. **Intercollegiate Athletics:** Equestrian Sports M & W

MOUNT MARTY COLLEGE

1105 W 8th St.
Yankton, SD 57078-3724
Tel: (605)668-1011; Free: 800-658-4552
Fax: (605)668-1607
E-mail: jpaulson@mtmc.edu
Web Site: www.mtmc.edu
President/CEO: Dr. Marcus Long
Admissions: Jill Paulson
Financial Aid: Ken Kocer

Type: Comprehensive **Sex:** Coed **Affiliation:** Roman Catholic. **Scores:** 59% ACT 18-23; 26% ACT 24-29 **% Accepted:** 73 **Admission Plans:** Deferred Admission; Early Admission **Application Deadline:** Rolling **Application Fee:** $35.00 **H.S. Requirements:** High school diploma required; GED accepted **Costs Per Year:** Application fee: $35. Comprehensive fee: $31,632 includes full-time tuition ($22,336), mandatory fees ($1970), and college room and board ($7326). Full-time tuition and fees vary according to degree level, location, and program. Room and board charges vary according to board plan. Part-time tuition: $492 per credit hour. Part-time mandatory fees: $45 per credit hour. Part-time tuition and fees vary according to course load, degree level, location, and program. **Scholarships:** Available. **Calendar System:** Semester, Summer session available **Enrollment:** Full-time 494, Graduate full-time 108, Graduate part-time 35, Part-time 553 **Faculty:** Full-time 46, Part-time 9 **Student-Faculty Ratio:** 9:1 **Exams:** ACT essay component not used; SAT I or ACT; SAT essay component not used; SAT Reasoning; SAT Subject. **% Receiving Financial Aid:** 76 **% Residing in College-Owned, -Operated, or -Affiliated Housing:** 62 **Final Year or Final Semester Residency Requirement:** Yes **Regional Accreditation:** North Central Association of Colleges and Schools **Credit Hours For Degree:** 64 credit hours, Associates; 128 credit hours, Bachelors **ROTC:** Army **Professional Accreditation:** AANA, AND. **Intercollegiate Athletics:** Archery M & W; Baseball M; Basketball M & W; Cross-Country Running M & W; Golf M & W; Riflery M & W; Soccer M & W; Softball W; Tennis W; Track and Field M & W; Volleyball W

NATIONAL AMERICAN UNIVERSITY (ELLSWORTH AFB)

1000 Ellsworth St.
Ste. 2400B
Ellsworth AFB, SD 57706
Tel: (605)718-6550
Web Site: www.national.edu
President/CEO: Dr. Jerry Gallentine

Type: Two-Year College **Sex:** Coed **Application Fee:** $25.00 **Regional Accreditation:** North Central Association of Colleges and Schools

NATIONAL AMERICAN UNIVERSITY (RAPID CITY)

5301 S Hwy. 16
Rapid City, SD 57701
Tel: (605)394-4800; Free: 800-209-4090
Fax: (605)394-4871
E-mail: abeck@national.edu
Web Site: www.national.edu
President/CEO: Dr. Jerry Gallentine
Admissions: Angela Beck

Type: Comprehensive **Sex:** Coed **Affiliation:** National College. **Admission Plans:** Deferred Admission; Early Admission; Open Admission **Application Deadline:** Rolling **Application Fee:** $25.00 **H.S. Requirements:** High school diploma required; GED accepted **Scholarships:** Available. **Calendar System:** Quarter, Summer session available **Enrollment:** Full-time 350, Part-time 131 **Faculty:** Full-time 13, Part-time 34 **Student-Faculty Ratio:** 26:1 **Exams:** ACT. **% Residing in College-Owned, -Operated, or -Affiliated Housing:** 21 **Regional Accreditation:** North Central Association of Colleges and Schools **Credit Hours For Degree:** 97 credit hours, Associates; 193 credit hours, Bachelors **ROTC:** Army **Professional Accreditation:** AAMAE. **Intercollegiate Athletics:** Equestrian Sports M & W; Ultimate Frisbee M & W; Volleyball M & W

NATIONAL AMERICAN UNIVERSITY (SIOUX FALLS)

5801 S Corporate Pl.
Sioux Falls, SD 57108
Tel: (605)334-5430; Free: 800-388-5430
E-mail: lhoutsma@national.edu
Web Site: www.national.edu
President/CEO: Dr. Jerry Gallentine
Admissions: Lisa Houtsma
Financial Aid: Rhonda Kohnen

Type: Comprehensive **Sex:** Coed **Affiliation:** National College. **% Accepted:** 100 **Admission Plans:** Deferred Admission; Open Admission **Application Deadline:** Rolling **Application Fee:** $25.00 **H.S. Requirements:** High school diploma required; GED accepted **Scholarships:** Available. **Calendar System:** Quarter, Summer session available **Faculty:** Part-time 35 **Regional Accreditation:** North Central Association of Colleges and Schools **Credit Hours For Degree:** 91 credit hours, Associates; 184 credit hours, Bachelors

NORTHERN STATE UNIVERSITY

1200 S Jay St.
Aberdeen, SD 57401-7198
Tel: (605)626-3011; Free: 800-678-5330
Fax: (605)626-3022
E-mail: admission2@northern.edu
Web Site: www.northern.edu
President/CEO: Dr. James Smith
Admissions: Joellen Lindner
Financial Aid: Sharon Kienow

Type: Comprehensive **Sex:** Coed **Affiliation:** South Dakota Board of Regents. **Scores:** 85% SAT V 400+; 86% SAT M 400+; 52% ACT 18-23; 29% ACT 24-29 **% Accepted:** 83 **Admission Plans:** Deferred Admission; Early Admission **Application Fee:** $20.00 **H.S. Requirements:** High school diploma required; GED accepted **Costs Per Year:** Application fee: $20. State resident tuition: $3993 full-time, $133 per credit hour part-time. Nonresident tuition: $5992 full-time, $200 per credit hour part-time. Mandatory fees: $4050 full-time. Full-time tuition and fees vary according to course level, course load, location, and reciprocity agreements. Part-time tuition varies according to course level, course load, location, and reciprocity agreements. College room and board: $6942. College room only: $3155. Room and board charges vary according to board plan. **Scholarships:** Available. **Calendar System:** Semester, Summer session available **Enrollment:** Full-time 1,477, Graduate full-time 56, Graduate part-time 474, Part-time 1,524 **Faculty:** Full-time 90, Part-time 79 **Student-Faculty Ratio:** 21:1 **Exams:** ACT essay component not used; SAT I or ACT; SAT essay component not used; SAT Reasoning. **% Receiving Financial Aid:** 64 **% Residing in College-Owned, -Operated, or -Affiliated Housing:** 41 **Regional Accreditation:** North Central Association of Colleges and Schools **Credit Hours For Degree:** 60 credit hours, Associates; 120 credit hours, Bachelors **Professional Accreditation:** ACBSP, NASM, NCATE. **Intercollegiate Athletics:** Baseball M; Basketball M & W; Cross-Country Running M & W; Football M; Soccer W; Softball W; Swimming and Diving W; Track and Field M & W; Volleyball W; Wrestling M

OGLALA LAKOTA COLLEGE

490 Piya Wiconi Rd.
Kyle, SD 57752-0490
Tel: (605)455-6000
Fax: (605)455-2787
E-mail: lmeseteth@olc.edu
Web Site: www.olc.edu
President/CEO: Thomas Shortbull

Type: Comprehensive **Sex:** Coed **Admission Plans:** Early Admission; Open Admission; Preferred Admission **Application Fee:** $0.00 **H.S. Requirements:** High school diploma required; GED accepted **Scholarships:** Available. **Calendar System:** Semester, Summer session available **Regional Accreditation:** North Central Association of Colleges and Schools **Credit Hours For Degree:** 65 credit hours, Associates; 128 credit hours, Bachelors

PRESENTATION COLLEGE

1500 N Main St.
Aberdeen, SD 57401-1299
Tel: (605)225-1634; Free: 800-437-6060
Fax: (605)229-8518

E-mail: admit@presentation.edu
Web Site: www.presentation.edu
President/CEO: Dr. Margaret Huber
Admissions: Robert Schuchardt
Financial Aid: Janel Wagner

Type: Four-Year College **Sex:** Coed **Affiliation:** Roman Catholic. **Scores:** 63% SAT V 400+; 63% SAT M 400+; 50% ACT 18-23; 22% ACT 24-29 **% Accepted:** 74 **Application Deadline:** Rolling **Application Fee:** $25.00 **H.S. Requirements:** High school diploma required; GED accepted **Scholarships:** Available. **Calendar System:** Semester, Summer session available **Enrollment:** Full-time 465, Part-time 283 **Faculty:** Full-time 46, Part-time 27 **Student-Faculty Ratio:** 10:1 **Exams:** ACT essay component not used; SAT I or ACT; SAT essay component not used; SAT Reasoning; SAT Subject. **% Receiving Financial Aid:** 95 **% Residing in College-Owned, -Operated, or -Affiliated Housing:** 21 **Final Year or Final Semester Residency Requirement:** No **Regional Accreditation:** North Central Association of Colleges and Schools **Credit Hours For Degree:** 60 credit hours, Associates; 120 credit hours, Bachelors **Professional Accreditation:** AAMAE, ACEN, ARCST, CSWE, JRCERT, NAACLS. **Intercollegiate Athletics:** Baseball M; Basketball M & W; Football M; Golf M & W; Soccer M & W; Softball W; Track and Field M; Volleyball W

SINTE GLESKA UNIVERSITY

101 Antelope Lake Cir.
Mission, SD 57555
Tel: (605)856-8100
Fax: (605)747-2098
Web Site: www.sintegleska.edu
President/CEO: Lionel R. Bordeaux
Admissions: Jack Herman

Type: Comprehensive **Sex:** Coed **Admission Plans:** Open Admission **Application Deadline:** August 20 **Application Fee:** $20.00 **H.S. Requirements:** High school diploma required; GED accepted **Scholarships:** Available. **Calendar System:** Semester, Summer session available **Regional Accreditation:** North Central Association of Colleges and Schools **Credit Hours For Degree:** 68 credits, Associates; 128 credits, Bachelors

SISSETON-WAHPETON COLLEGE

Old Agency Box 689
Sisseton, SD 57262
Tel: (605)698-3966
E-mail: dredday@swc.tc
Web Site: www.swc.tc
President/CEO: Diana Canku
Admissions: Darlene Redday
Financial Aid: Sylvan John Flute

Type: Two-Year College **Sex:** Coed **% Accepted:** 94 **Admission Plans:** Open Admission **Application Deadline:** Rolling **Application Fee:** $0.00 **H.S. Requirements:** High school diploma required; GED accepted **Costs Per Year:** Application fee: $0. One-time mandatory fee: $540. State resident tuition: $3000 full-time, $125 per credit hour part-time. Nonresident tuition: $3000 full-time, $125 per credit hour part-time. Mandatory fees: $590 full-time, $265. College room and board: $6000. College room only: $6000. Tuition guaranteed not to increase for student's term of enrollment. **Scholarships:** Available. **Calendar System:** Semester, Summer session available **Enrollment:** Full-time 101, Part-time 64 **Faculty:** Full-time 10, Part-time 20 **Student-Faculty Ratio:** 10:1 **Exams:** Other. **Regional Accreditation:** North Central Association of Colleges and Schools **Credit Hours For Degree:** 64 semester hours, Associates

SOUTH DAKOTA SCHOOL OF MINES AND TECHNOLOGY

501 E Saint Joseph St.
Rapid City, SD 57701-3995
Tel: (605)394-2511; Free: 800-544-8162
Fax: (605)394-2914
E-mail: admissions@sdsmt.edu
Web Site: www.sdsmt.edu
President/CEO: Dr. Heather Wilson
Admissions: Genene Sigler
Financial Aid: David W. Martin

Type: University **Sex:** Coed **Affiliation:** South Dakota Board of Regents. **Scores:** 98% SAT V 400+; 100% SAT M 400+; 22% ACT 18-23; 58% ACT 24-29 **% Accepted:** 84 **Application Deadline:** Rolling **Application Fee:** $20.00 **H.S. Requirements:** High school diploma required; GED accepted

Costs Per Year: Application fee: $20. State resident tuition: $4530 full-time, $151 per credit hour part-time. Nonresident tuition: $7590 full-time, $253 per credit hour part-time. Mandatory fees: $6640 full-time, $224.65 per credit hour part-time. Full-time tuition and fees vary according to course load, program, and reciprocity agreements. Part-time tuition and fees vary according to course load, program, and reciprocity agreements. College room and board: $7300. College room only: $3800. Room and board charges vary according to board plan and housing facility. **Scholarships:** Available. **Calendar System:** Semester, Summer session available **Enrollment:** Full-time 2,055, Graduate full-time 190, Graduate part-time 168, Part-time 430 **Faculty:** Full-time 149, Part-time 26 **Student-Faculty Ratio:** 15:1 **Exams:** ACT essay component not used; SAT I or ACT; SAT essay component not used; SAT Reasoning; SAT Subject. **% Receiving Financial Aid:** 60 % **Residing in College-Owned, -Operated, or -Affiliated Housing:** 60 **Final Year or Final Semester Residency Requirement:** No **Regional Accreditation:** North Central Association of Colleges and Schools **Credit Hours For Degree:** 64 semester hours, Associates; 128 semester hours, Bachelors **ROTC:** Army **Professional Accreditation:** ABET. **Intercollegiate Athletics:** Basketball M & W; Cross-Country Running M & W; Football M; Golf M & W; Soccer M; Track and Field M & W; Volleyball W

SOUTH DAKOTA STATE UNIVERSITY
Box 2201
Brookings, SD 57007
Tel: (605)688-4151; Free: 800-952-3541
Fax: (605)688-6384
E-mail: sdsu.admissions@sdstate.edu
Web Site: www.sdstate.edu
President/CEO: David L. Chicoine
Admissions: Michelle Kuebler
Financial Aid: Carolyn Halgerson

Type: University **Sex:** Coed **Affiliation:** South Dakota Board of Regents. **Scores:** 87% SAT V 400+; 99% SAT M 400+; 47% ACT 18-23; 40% ACT 24-29 **% Accepted:** 92 **Application Deadline:** Rolling **Application Fee:** $20.00 **H.S. Requirements:** High school diploma required; GED accepted **Costs Per Year:** Application fee: $20. State resident tuition: $4341 full-time, $144.70 per credit hour part-time. Nonresident tuition: $6512 full-time, $217.05 per credit hour part-time. Mandatory fees: $3831 full-time. Full-time tuition and fees vary according to course level, course load, degree level, location, program, and reciprocity agreements. Part-time tuition varies according to course level, course load, degree level, location, program, and reciprocity agreements. College room and board: $7462. College room only: $3595. Room and board charges vary according to board plan and housing facility. **Scholarships:** Available. **Calendar System:** Semester, Summer session available **Enrollment:** Full-time 8,559, Graduate full-time 531, Graduate part-time 1,051, Part-time 2,448 **Faculty:** Full-time 546, Part-time 144 **Student-Faculty Ratio:** 17:1 **Exams:** ACT essay component not used; SAT I or ACT; SAT essay component not used; SAT Reasoning. **% Receiving Financial Aid:** 61 **Regional Accreditation:** North Central Association of Colleges and Schools **Credit Hours For Degree:** 60 credits, Associates; 120 credits, Bachelors **ROTC:** Air Force, Army **Professional Accreditation:** AACN, AAFCS, ABET, ACA, ACEJMC, ACPE, JRCAT, NASM, NCATE. **Intercollegiate Athletics:** Baseball M; Basketball M & W; Bowling M & W; Cheerleading M & W; Cross-Country Running M & W; Equestrian Sports W; Football M; Golf M & W; Ice Hockey M & W; Soccer W; Softball W; Swimming and Diving M & W; Tennis M & W; Track and Field M & W; Volleyball W; Wrestling M

SOUTHEAST TECHNICAL INSTITUTE
2320 N Career Ave.
Sioux Falls, SD 57107-1301
Tel: (605)367-7624; Free: 800-247-0789
E-mail: scott.dorman@southeasttech.edu
Web Site: www.southeasttech.edu
President/CEO: Jeff Holcomb
Admissions: Scott Dorman

Type: Two-Year College **Sex:** Coed **% Accepted:** 42 **Application Deadline:** Rolling **Application Fee:** $35.00 **H.S. Requirements:** High school diploma required; GED accepted **Costs Per Year:** Application fee: $35. State resident tuition: $3270 full-time, $109 per credit part-time. Nonresident tuition: $3270 full-time, $109 per credit part-time. Mandatory fees: $3330 full-time, $111 per credit part-time, $111. Full-time tuition and fees vary according to program. Part-time tuition and fees vary according to program. College room only: $4750. **Scholarships:** Available. **Calendar System:** Semester,

Summer session available **Enrollment:** Full-time 1,304, Part-time 743 **Faculty:** Full-time 88, Part-time 113 **Student-Faculty Ratio:** 15:1 **Exams:** ACT. **% Residing in College-Owned, -Operated, or -Affiliated Housing:** 2 **Final Year or Final Semester Residency Requirement:** No **Regional Accreditation:** North Central Association of Colleges and Schools **Credit Hours For Degree:** 63 credits, Associates **Professional Accreditation:** JRCECT, JRCNMT.

UNIVERSITY OF SIOUX FALLS
1101 W 22nd St.
Sioux Falls, SD 57105-1699
Tel: (605)331-5000; Free: 800-888-1047
Fax: (605)331-6615
E-mail: admissions@usiouxfalls.edu
Web Site: www.usiouxfalls.edu
President/CEO: Dr. Mark Benedetto
Admissions: Aimee Vander Feen
Financial Aid: Rachel Gunn

Type: Comprehensive **Sex:** Coed **Affiliation:** American Baptist Churches in the USA. **Scores:** 89% SAT V 400+; 89% SAT M 400+; 51% ACT 18-23; 36% ACT 24-29 **% Accepted:** 97 **Application Deadline:** Rolling **Application Fee:** $25.00 **H.S. Requirements:** High school diploma required; GED accepted **Scholarships:** Available. **Calendar System:** 4-1-4, Summer session available **Enrollment:** Full-time 1,011, Part-time 232 **Faculty:** Full-time 60, Part-time 80 **Student-Faculty Ratio:** 15:1 **Exams:** ACT essay component not used; SAT I or ACT; SAT essay component not used. **% Residing in College-Owned, -Operated, or -Affiliated Housing:** 47 **Final Year or Final Semester Residency Requirement:** No **Regional Accreditation:** North Central Association of Colleges and Schools **Credit Hours For Degree:** 64 semester hours, Associates; 128 semester hours, Bachelors **ROTC:** Air Force **Professional Accreditation:** CSWE, NCATE. **Intercollegiate Athletics:** Baseball M; Basketball M & W; Cheerleading M & W; Cross-Country Running M & W; Football M; Golf M & W; Soccer M & W; Softball W; Tennis M & W; Track and Field M & W; Volleyball W; Wrestling M

THE UNIVERSITY OF SOUTH DAKOTA
414 E Clark St.
Vermillion, SD 57069-2390
Tel: (605)677-5011; Free: 877-269-6837
Fax: (605)677-6753
E-mail: admiss@usd.edu
Web Site: www.usd.edu
President/CEO: James W. Abbott
Admissions: Travis Vlasman
Financial Aid: Julie Pier

Type: University **Sex:** Coed **Affiliation:** South Dakota Board of Regents. **Scores:** 89% SAT V 400+; 94% SAT M 400+; 51% ACT 18-23; 39% ACT 24-29 **% Accepted:** 89 **Admission Plans:** Deferred Admission; Early Admission **Application Deadline:** Rolling **Application Fee:** $20.00 **H.S. Requirements:** High school diploma required; GED accepted **Scholarships:** Available. **Calendar System:** Semester, Summer session available **Enrollment:** Full-time 4,876, Graduate full-time 1,260, Graduate part-time 1,260, Part-time 2,665 **Faculty:** Full-time 453, Part-time 142 **Student-Faculty Ratio:** 17:1 **Exams:** SAT I or ACT; SAT Reasoning; SAT Subject. **% Receiving Financial Aid:** 59 **% Residing in College-Owned, -Operated, or -Affiliated Housing:** 28 **Final Year or Final Semester Residency Requirement:** No **Regional Accreditation:** North Central Association of Colleges and Schools **Credit Hours For Degree:** 64 credit hours, Associates; 128 credit hours, Bachelors **ROTC:** Army **Professional Accreditation:** AACSB, AALS, ABA, ACA, ACEJMC, ACEN, ADA, AND, AOTA, APA, APTA, ASHA, CSWE, LCME/AMA, NASAD, NASM, NASPAA, NAST, NCATE. **Intercollegiate Athletics:** Basketball M & W; Cross-Country Running M & W; Football M; Golf M & W; Soccer W; Softball W; Swimming and Diving M & W; Tennis W; Track and Field M & W; Volleyball W

WESTERN DAKOTA TECHNICAL INSTITUTE
800 Mickelson Dr.
Rapid City, SD 57703
Tel: (605)394-4034; Free: 800-544-8765
E-mail: jill.elder@wdt.edu
Web Site: www.wdt.edu
President/CEO: Pres. Mark Wilson
Admissions: Jill Elder

Financial Aid: Sharon M. Martin

Type: Two-Year College **Sex:** Coed **% Accepted:** 67 **Admission Plans:** Open Admission **Application Deadline:** August 1 **Application Fee:** $20.00 **H.S. Requirements:** High school diploma required; GED accepted **Costs Per Year:** Application fee: $20. One-time mandatory fee: $170. State resident tuition: $3924 full-time, $109 per credit hour part-time. Nonresident tuition: $3924 full-time, $109 per credit hour part-time. Mandatory fees: $3096 full-time, $86 per credit hour part-time. Full-time tuition and fees vary according to course load and program. Part-time tuition and fees vary according to course load. **Scholarships:** Available. **Calendar System:** Semester, Summer session available **Enrollment:** Full-time 681, Part-time 195 **Faculty:** Full-time 33, Part-time 38 **Student-Faculty Ratio:** 16:1 **Exams:** ACT essay component not used; SAT I or ACT; SAT essay component not used. **Final Year or Final Semester Residency Requirement:** No **Regional Accreditation:** North Central Association of Colleges and Schools **Credit Hours For Degree:** 60 credits, Associates

AMERICAN BAPTIST COLLEGE

1800 Baptist World Ctr. Dr.
Nashville, TN 37207
Tel: (615)256-1463
E-mail: admissions@abcnash.edu
Web Site: www.abcnash.edu
President/CEO: Dr. Forrest E. Harris, Sr.
Financial Aid: Sharonda Campbell

Type: Four-Year College **Sex:** Coed **Affiliation:** Baptist. **% Accepted:** 82 **Admission Plans:** Deferred Admission; Open Admission **Application Deadline:** Rolling **Application Fee:** $30.00 **H.S. Requirements:** High school diploma required; GED accepted **Costs Per Year:** Application fee: $30. Comprehensive fee: $13,800 includes full-time tuition ($8760) and college room and board ($5040). College room only: $3840. Room and board charges vary according to board plan and housing facility. Part-time tuition: $380 per credit hour. **Scholarships:** Available. **Calendar System:** Semester, Summer session available **Enrollment:** Full-time 114, Part-time 38 **Faculty:** Full-time 4, Part-time 14 **Student-Faculty Ratio:** 12:1 **Exams:** ACT essay component not used; Other; SAT essay component not used. **% Receiving Financial Aid:** 100 **% Residing in College-Owned, -Operated, or -Affiliated Housing:** 30 **Final Year or Final Semester Residency Requirement:** No **Credit Hours For Degree:** 60 credit hours, Associates; 120 credit hours, Bachelors **Professional Accreditation:** ABHE.

AQUINAS COLLEGE

4210 Harding Pke.
Nashville, TN 37205-2005
Tel: (615)297-7545; Free: 800-649-9956
Fax: (615)297-7970
E-mail: hansomc@aquinascollege.edu
Web Site: www.aquinascollege.edu
President/CEO: Señor Mary Sarah Galbraith, OP
Admissions: Connie Hansom
Financial Aid: Kylie Pruitt

Type: Comprehensive **Sex:** Coed **Affiliation:** Roman Catholic; The Dominican Sisters of the Saint Cecilia Congregation. **Scores:** 100% SAT V 400+; 100% SAT M 400+; 50% ACT 18-23; 41% ACT 24-29 **% Accepted:** 52 **Admission Plans:** Deferred Admission **Application Deadline:** Rolling **Application Fee:** $0.00 **H.S. Requirements:** High school diploma required; GED accepted **Costs Per Year:** Application fee: $0. Comprehensive fee: $30,850 includes full-time tuition ($21,350), mandatory fees ($600), and college room and board ($8900). College room only: $5700. Full-time tuition and fees vary according to course load and program. Part-time tuition: $730 per credit hour. Part-time tuition varies according to course load and program. **Scholarships:** Available. **Calendar System:** Semester, Summer session available **Enrollment:** Full-time 196, Graduate full-time 19, Graduate part-time 28, Part-time 141 **Faculty:** Full-time 28, Part-time 45 **Student-Faculty Ratio:** 8:1 **Exams:** ACT essay component not used; SAT I or ACT; SAT essay component not used; SAT Reasoning; SAT Subject. **% Residing in College-Owned, -Operated, or -Affiliated Housing:** 15 **Final Year or Final Semester Residency Requirement:** Yes **Regional Accreditation:** Southern Association of Colleges and Schools **Credit Hours For Degree:** 63 semester hours, Associates; 120 semester hours, Bachelors **Professional Accreditation:** ACEN.

ARGOSY UNIVERSITY, NASHVILLE

100 Centerview Dr., Ste. 225
Nashville, TN 37214
Tel: (615)525-2800; Free: 866-833-6598
Fax: (615)369-0601
Web Site: www.argosy.edu/locations/nashville
President/CEO: Roger Widmer

Type: University **Sex:** Coed **Calendar System:** Semester **Regional Accreditation:** Western Association of Colleges and Schools **Professional Accreditation:** ACBSP.

THE ART INSTITUTE OF TENNESSEE–NASHVILLE, A BRANCH OF THE ART INSTITUTE OF ATLANTA

100 Centerview Dr., Ste. 250
Nashville, TN 37214
Tel: (615)874-1067; Free: 866-747-5770
Web Site: www.artinstitutes.edu/nashville
President/CEO: Carol Menck

Type: Four-Year College **Sex:** Coed **Affiliation:** Education Management Corporation. **Regional Accreditation:** Southern Association of Colleges and Schools

AUSTIN PEAY STATE UNIVERSITY

601 College St.
Clarksville, TN 37044
Tel: (931)221-7011; Free: 800-844-2778
Fax: (931)221-5994
E-mail: admissions@apsu.edu
Web Site: www.apsu.edu
President/CEO: Alisa White
Admissions: Amy Corlew
Financial Aid: Donna Price

Type: Comprehensive **Sex:** Coed **Affiliation:** Tennessee Board of Regents. **Scores:** 92% SAT V 400+; 92% SAT M 400+; 58% ACT 18-23; 23% ACT 24-29 **% Accepted:** 88 **Admission Plans:** Deferred Admission **Application Deadline:** August 5 **Application Fee:** $15.00 **H.S. Requirements:** High school diploma required; GED accepted **Costs Per Year:** Application fee: $15. One-time mandatory fee: $75. State resident tuition: $6048 full-time, $252 per credit hour part-time. Nonresident tuition: $20,880 full-time, $870 per credit hour part-time. Mandatory fees: $1453 full-time. Full-time tuition and fees vary according to location and program. Part-time tuition varies according to location and program. College room and board: $8350. College room only: $5100. Room and board charges vary according to board plan and housing facility. **Scholarships:** Available. **Calendar System:** Semester, Summer session available **Enrollment:** Full-time 6,751, Graduate full-time 255, Graduate part-time 660, Part-time 2,433 **Faculty:** Full-time 363, Part-time 234 **Student-Faculty Ratio:** 18:1 **Exams:** ACT essay component not used; SAT I or ACT; SAT essay component not used; SAT Reasoning; SAT Subject. **% Receiving Financial Aid:** 80 **% Residing in College-Owned, -Operated, or -Affiliated Housing:** 16 **Final Year or Final Semester Residency Requirement:** No **Regional Accreditation:** Southern Association of Colleges and Schools **Credit Hours For Degree:** 60 semester hours, Associates; 120 semester hours, Bachelors **ROTC:** Air Force, Army **Professional Accreditation:** ABET, ACEN, CSWE, NAACLS, NASAD, NASM, NCATE. **Intercollegiate Athletics:** Baseball M; Basketball M & W;

Cheerleading M & W; Cross-Country Running M & W; Football M; Golf M & W; Soccer W; Softball W; Tennis M & W; Track and Field W; Volleyball W

BAPTIST COLLEGE OF HEALTH SCIENCES

1003 Monroe Ave.
Memphis, TN 38104
Tel: (901)227-4330; Free: 866-575-2247
E-mail: Lissa.Morgan@bchs.edu
Web Site: www.bchs.edu
President/CEO: Dr. Betty Sue McGarvey
Admissions: Lissa Morgan
Financial Aid: Leanne Smith
Type: Four-Year College **Sex:** Coed **Affiliation:** Southern Baptist; Baptist Memorial Health Care. **Scores:** 55% ACT 18-23; 35% ACT 24-29 **% Accepted:** 27 **Application Deadline:** May 1 **Application Fee:** $25.00 **H.S. Requirements:** High school diploma required; GED not accepted **Scholarships:** Available. **Calendar System:** Trimester, Summer session available **Enrollment:** Full-time 489, Part-time 554 **Faculty:** Full-time 59, Part-time 48 **Student-Faculty Ratio:** 9:1 **Exams:** ACT; ACT essay component not used; SAT essay component not used; SAT Reasoning; SAT Subject. **% Residing in College-Owned, -Operated, or -Affiliated Housing:** 10 **Final Year or Final Semester Residency Requirement:** Yes **Regional Accreditation:** Southern Association of Colleges and Schools **Credit Hours For Degree:** 122 credits, Bachelors **Professional Accreditation:** AACN, CoARC, JRCEDMS, JRCNMT.

BELHAVEN UNIVERSITY

5100 Poplar Ave., Ste. 200
Memphis, TN 38137
Tel: (901)888-3343
Fax: (901)888-0771
E-mail: memphisadmission@belhaven.edu
Web Site: memphis.belhaven.edu
President/CEO: Dr. Roger Parrott
Admissions: Don Jones
Type: Comprehensive **Sex:** Coed **Affiliation:** Presbyterian. **Application Fee:** $25.00 **Calendar System:** Semester **Regional Accreditation:** Southern Association of Colleges and Schools

BELMONT UNIVERSITY

1900 Belmont Blvd.
Nashville, TN 37212-3757
Tel: (615)460-6000
E-mail: david.mee@belmont.edu
Web Site: www.belmont.edu
President/CEO: Dr. Robert C. Fisher
Admissions: David Mee
Financial Aid: Pat Smedley
Type: University **Sex:** Coed **Affiliation:** Christian. **Scores:** 100% SAT V 400+; 99% SAT M 400+; 29% ACT 18-23; 54% ACT 24-29 **% Accepted:** 80 **Admission Plans:** Deferred Admission; Early Admission **Application Deadline:** August 1 **Application Fee:** $50.00 **H.S. Requirements:** High school diploma required; GED accepted **Costs Per Year:** Application fee: $50. Comprehensive fee: $40,970 includes full-time tuition ($28,600), mandatory fees ($1400), and college room and board ($10,970). College room only: $6050. Full-time tuition and fees vary according to course load. Room and board charges vary according to board plan and housing facility. Part-time tuition: $1090 per credit hour. Part-time tuition varies according to course load. **Scholarships:** Available. **Calendar System:** Semester, Summer session available **Enrollment:** Full-time 5,639, Graduate full-time 1,244, Graduate part-time 123, Part-time 344 **Faculty:** Full-time 342, Part-time 437 **Student-Faculty Ratio:** 15:1 **Exams:** ACT essay component not used; SAT I or ACT; SAT essay component not used; SAT Reasoning. **% Receiving Financial Aid:** 54 **% Residing in College-Owned, -Operated, or -Affiliated Housing:** 50 **Regional Accreditation:** Southern Association of Colleges and Schools **Credit Hours For Degree:** 128 semester hours, Bachelors **ROTC:** Air Force, Army, Navy **Professional Accreditation:** AACN, AACSB, ABA, ABET, ACPE, AOTA, APTA, CSWE, NASM, NCATE. **Intercollegiate Athletics:** Baseball M; Basketball M & W; Cross-Country Running M & W; Golf M & W; Soccer M & W; Softball W; Tennis M & W; Track and Field M & W; Volleyball W

BETHEL UNIVERSITY

325 Cherry Ave.
McKenzie, TN 38201

Tel: (731)352-4000
Fax: (731)352-4069
E-mail: hodgest@bethelu.edu
Web Site: www.bethelu.edu
President/CEO: Dr. Walter Bulter
Admissions: Tina Hodges
Financial Aid: Laura Bateman
Type: Comprehensive **Sex:** Coed **Affiliation:** Cumberland Presbyterian. **% Accepted:** 62 **Admission Plans:** Deferred Admission; Early Admission; Open Admission **Application Deadline:** Rolling **Application Fee:** $30.00 **H.S. Requirements:** High school diploma required; GED accepted **Scholarships:** Available. **Calendar System:** Semester, Summer session available **Enrollment:** Full-time 3,606, Graduate full-time 1,220, Graduate part-time 94, Part-time 633 **Faculty:** Full-time 152, Part-time 268 **Student-Faculty Ratio:** 13:1 **Exams:** SAT I or ACT. **% Residing in College-Owned, -Operated, or -Affiliated Housing:** 29 **Regional Accreditation:** Southern Association of Colleges and Schools **Credit Hours For Degree:** 128 semester hours, Bachelors **Professional Accreditation:** AACN. **Intercollegiate Athletics:** Baseball M; Basketball M & W; Bowling M & W; Cheerleading M & W; Cross-Country Running M & W; Football M; Golf M & W; Riflery M & W; Soccer M & W; Softball W; Tennis M & W; Track and Field M & W; Volleyball W

BRIGHTWOOD COLLEGE, NASHVILLE CAMPUS

750 Envious Ln.
Nashville, TN 37217
Tel: (615)279-8300; Free: 800-935-1857
Fax: (615)297-6678
Web Site: www.brightwood.edu
President/CEO: Haley Johnson
Type: Two-Year College **Sex:** Coed **H.S. Requirements:** High school diploma required; GED accepted **Professional Accreditation:** ACICS, COE.

BRYAN COLLEGE

721 Bryan Dr.
Dayton, TN 37321
Tel: (423)775-2041; Free: 800-277-9522
Fax: (423)775-7330
E-mail: admissions@bryan.edu
Web Site: www.bryan.edu
President/CEO: Dr. Stephen D. Livesay
Admissions: Andrew Smith
Financial Aid: Rick Taphorn
Type: Comprehensive **Sex:** Coed **Affiliation:** interdenominational. **Scores:** 84% SAT V 400+; 89% SAT M 400+; 52.9% ACT 18-23; 35.51% ACT 24-29 **% Accepted:** 46 **Admission Plans:** Deferred Admission; Early Decision Plan **Application Deadline:** Rolling **Application Fee:** $35.00 **H.S. Requirements:** High school diploma required; GED accepted **Costs Per Year:** Application fee: $35. Comprehensive fee: $29,990 includes full-time tuition ($23,300) and college room and board ($6690). College room only: $4190. Room and board charges vary according to housing facility. Part-time tuition: $990 per credit hour. **Scholarships:** Available. **Calendar System:** Semester, Summer session available **Enrollment:** Full-time 838, Graduate full-time 73, Graduate part-time 57, Part-time 582 **Faculty:** Full-time 37, Part-time 87 **Exams:** ACT essay component used for placement; SAT I or ACT; SAT essay component used for placement; SAT Reasoning. **% Receiving Financial Aid:** 74 **% Residing in College-Owned, -Operated, or -Affiliated Housing:** 74 **Regional Accreditation:** Southern Association of Colleges and Schools **Credit Hours For Degree:** 60 semester hours, Associates; 124 semester hours, Bachelors **Intercollegiate Athletics:** Baseball M; Basketball M & W; Cross-Country Running M & W; Golf M & W; Soccer M & W; Softball W; Track and Field M & W; Volleyball M & W

CARSON-NEWMAN UNIVERSITY

1646 Russell Ave.
Jefferson City, TN 37760
Tel: (865)471-2000; Free: 800-678-9061
Fax: (865)471-3502
E-mail: cnadmiss@cn.edu
Web Site: www.cn.edu
President/CEO: Dr. Randall O'Brien
Admissions: Aaron Porter
Financial Aid: Danette Seale

Type: Comprehensive **Sex:** Coed **Affiliation:** Southern Baptist. **Scores:** 92% SAT V 400+; 91% SAT M 400+; 45.45% ACT 18-23; 32.73% ACT 24-29 **% Accepted:** 59 **Admission Plans:** Deferred Admission **Application Deadline:** August 1 **Application Fee:** $0.00 **H.S. Requirements:** High school diploma required; GED accepted **Costs Per Year:** Application fee: $0. Comprehensive fee: $34,790 includes full-time tuition ($25,200), mandatory fees ($1160), and college room and board ($8430). College room only: $3930. Full-time tuition and fees vary according to class time and course load. Room and board charges vary according to board plan, gender, and housing facility. Part-time tuition: $1050 per credit hour. Part-time mandatory fees: $355 per term. **Scholarships:** Available. **Calendar System:** Semester, Summer session available **Enrollment:** Full-time 1,691, Graduate full-time 114, Graduate part-time 662, Part-time 61 **Faculty:** Full-time 119, Part-time 96 **Student-Faculty Ratio:** 11:1 **Exams:** SAT I or ACT; SAT essay component not used. **% Receiving Financial Aid:** 83 **% Residing in College-Owned, -Operated, or -Affiliated Housing:** 56 **Regional Accreditation:** Southern Association of Colleges and Schools **Credit Hours For Degree:** 128 semester hours, Bachelors **ROTC:** Army **Professional Accreditation:** AACN, AAFCS, NASAD, NASM, NCATE. **Intercollegiate Athletics:** Baseball M; Basketball M & W; Cross-Country Running M & W; Football M; Golf M & W; Soccer M & W; Softball W; Swimming and Diving M & W; Tennis M & W; Track and Field M & W; Volleyball W

CHATTANOOGA COLLEGE–MEDICAL, DENTAL AND TECHNICAL CAREERS

248 Northgate Mall Dr., Ste. 130
Chattanooga, TN 37415
Tel: (423)624-0078; Free: 877-313-2373
Web Site: www.chattanoogacollege.edu
President/CEO: William G. Faour
Admissions: Toney McFadden

Type: Two-Year College **Sex:** Coed **Admission Plans:** Open Admission **Application Fee:** $25.00 **Scholarships:** Available. **Professional Accreditation:** ACCSC.

CHATTANOOGA STATE COMMUNITY COLLEGE

4501 Amnicola Hwy.
Chattanooga, TN 37406-1097
Tel: (423)697-4400; Free: 866-547-3733
Fax: (423)697-4709
E-mail: brad.mccormick@chattanoogastate.edu
Web Site: www.chattanoogastate.edu
President/CEO: Dr. James Catanzaro
Admissions: Brad McCormick

Type: Two-Year College **Sex:** Coed **Affiliation:** Tennessee Board of Regents. **% Accepted:** 100 **Admission Plans:** Deferred Admission; Early Admission; Open Admission **Application Deadline:** Rolling **Application Fee:** $15.00 **H.S. Requirements:** High school diploma required; GED accepted **Scholarships:** Available. **Calendar System:** Semester, Summer session available **Enrollment:** Full-time 4,775, Part-time 5,663 **Faculty:** Full-time 224, Part-time 475 **Student-Faculty Ratio:** 19:1 **Final Year or Final Semester Residency Requirement:** Yes **Regional Accreditation:** Southern Association of Colleges and Schools **Credit Hours For Degree:** 60 semester hours, Associates **Professional Accreditation:** ABET, ACBSP, ACEN, ADA, AHIMA, APTA, CoARC. **Intercollegiate Athletics:** Baseball M; Basketball M & W; Softball W

CHRISTIAN BROTHERS UNIVERSITY

650 E Pky. S
Memphis, TN 38104-5581
Tel: (901)321-3000; Free: 877-321-4CBU
Fax: (901)321-3202
E-mail: admissions@cbu.edu
Web Site: www.cbu.edu
President/CEO: Dr. John Smarrelli, Jr.
Admissions: Kristi Forman
Financial Aid: John H. Lewis, IV

Type: Comprehensive **Sex:** Coed **Affiliation:** Roman Catholic. **Scores:** 48% ACT 18-23; 43% ACT 24-29 **% Accepted:** 46 **Admission Plans:** Deferred Admission **Application Deadline:** August 1 **Application Fee:** $25.00 **H.S. Requirements:** High school diploma required; GED accepted **Costs Per Year:** Application fee: $25. Comprehensive fee: $37,106 includes full-time tuition ($29,316), mandatory fees ($790), and college room and board ($7000). Full-time tuition and fees vary according to class time, course

load, and program. Room and board charges vary according to board plan and housing facility. Part-time tuition: $1,050.63 per credit. Part-time mandatory fees: $225 per term. Part-time tuition and fees vary according to class time, course load, and program. **Scholarships:** Available. **Calendar System:** Semester, Summer session available **Enrollment:** Full-time 1,300, Graduate full-time 188, Graduate part-time 244, Part-time 110 **Faculty:** Full-time 104, Part-time 75 **Student-Faculty Ratio:** 10:1 **Exams:** ACT essay component not used; SAT I or ACT; SAT essay component not used; SAT Reasoning. **% Receiving Financial Aid:** 78 **% Residing in College-Owned, -Operated, or -Affiliated Housing:** 40 **Final Year or Final Semester Residency Requirement:** No **Regional Accreditation:** Southern Association of Colleges and Schools **Credit Hours For Degree:** 66 semester hours, Associates; 122 semester hours, Bachelors **ROTC:** Air Force, Army, Navy **Professional Accreditation:** ABET, NCATE. **Intercollegiate Athletics:** Baseball M; Basketball M & W; Cross-Country Running M & W; Golf M & W; Soccer M & W; Softball W; Tennis M & W; Track and Field M & W; Volleyball W

CLEVELAND STATE COMMUNITY COLLEGE

PO Box 3570
Cleveland, TN 37320-3570
Tel: (423)472-7141; Free: 800-604-2722
Fax: (423)478-6255
E-mail: sbayne@clevelandstatecc.edu
Web Site: www.clevelandstatecc.edu
President/CEO: Dr. William Seymour
Admissions: Suzanne Bayne

Type: Two-Year College **Sex:** Coed **Affiliation:** Tennessee Board of Regents. **Scores:** 59% ACT 18-23; 10% ACT 24-29 **% Accepted:** 50 **Admission Plans:** Deferred Admission; Early Admission; Open Admission **Application Deadline:** Rolling **Application Fee:** $20.00 **H.S. Requirements:** High school diploma required; GED accepted **Costs Per Year:** Application fee: $20. State resident tuition: $3828 full-time, $152 per credit hour part-time. Nonresident tuition: $15,618 full-time, $627 per credit hour part-time. Mandatory fees: $299 full-time, $14.25 per credit hour part-time, $27 per term part-time. Full-time tuition and fees vary according to course load. **Scholarships:** Available. **Calendar System:** Semester, Summer session available **Enrollment:** Full-time 1,785, Part-time 1,737 **Faculty:** Full-time 70, Part-time 104 **Student-Faculty Ratio:** 23:1 **Regional Accreditation:** Southern Association of Colleges and Schools **Credit Hours For Degree:** 64 semester hours, Associates **Professional Accreditation:** AAMAE, ACBSP, ACEN, ATMAE. **Intercollegiate Athletics:** Baseball M; Basketball M & W; Softball W

COLUMBIA STATE COMMUNITY COLLEGE

1665 Hampshire Pke.
Columbia, TN 38401
Tel: (931)540-2722
Fax: (931)540-2535
E-mail: scruggs@coscc.cc.tn.us
Web Site: www.columbiastate.edu
President/CEO: Janet F. Smith
Admissions: Joey Scruggs
Financial Aid: Paulette Burns

Type: Two-Year College **Sex:** Coed **% Accepted:** 100 **Admission Plans:** Early Admission **Application Deadline:** Rolling **Application Fee:** $10.00 **H.S. Requirements:** High school diploma required; GED accepted **Costs Per Year:** Application fee: $10. One-time mandatory fee: $10. State resident tuition: $3648 full-time, $152 per credit hour part-time. Nonresident tuition: $15,048 full-time, $627 per credit hour part-time. Mandatory fees: $271 full-time, $13.83 per credit hour part-time, $83 per term part-time. Full-time tuition and fees vary according to course load and program. Part-time tuition and fees vary according to program. **Scholarships:** Available. **Calendar System:** Semester, Summer session available **Regional Accreditation:** Southern Association of Colleges and Schools **Credit Hours For Degree:** 66 semester hours, Associates **Professional Accreditation:** ACBSP, ACEN, CoARC, JRCEMTP, JRCERT. **Intercollegiate Athletics:** Baseball M; Basketball M & W; Softball W

CONCORDE CAREER COLLEGE

5100 Poplar Ave.
Ste. 132
Memphis, TN 38137
Tel: (901)761-9494

Fax: (901)761-3293
E-mail: dvickers@concorde.edu
Web Site: www.concorde.edu
President/CEO: Tommy Stewart
Admissions: Dee Vickers

Type: Two-Year College **Sex:** Coed **% Accepted:** 100 **Student-Faculty Ratio:** 24:1 **Professional Accreditation:** COE.

CUMBERLAND UNIVERSITY

1 Cumberland Sq.
Lebanon, TN 37087
Tel: (615)444-2562; Free: 800-467-0562
Fax: (615)444-2569
E-mail: admissions@cumberland.edu
Web Site: www.cumberland.edu
President/CEO: Dr. Harvill C. Eaton
Admissions: Beatrice LaChance
Financial Aid: Beatrice LaChance

Type: Comprehensive **Sex:** Coed **Scores:** 100% SAT V 400+; 100% SAT M 400+; 53% ACT 18-23; 35% ACT 24-29 **% Accepted:** 46 **Admission Plans:** Deferred Admission **Application Deadline:** Rolling **Application Fee:** $25.00 **H.S. Requirements:** High school diploma required; GED accepted **Costs Per Year:** Application fee: $25. One-time mandatory fee: $100. Comprehensive fee: $28,760 includes full-time tuition ($20,160), mandatory fees ($1050), and college room and board ($7550). Full-time tuition and fees vary according to degree level. Room and board charges vary according to housing facility. Part-time tuition: $840 per credit hour. Part-time tuition varies according to course load and degree level. **Scholarships:** Available. **Calendar System:** Semester, Summer session available **Enrollment:** Full-time 984, Graduate full-time 50, Graduate part-time 177, Part-time 270 **Faculty:** Full-time 56, Part-time 103 **Student-Faculty Ratio:** 14:1 **Exams:** ACT essay component not used; SAT I; SAT I or ACT; SAT essay component not used. **% Receiving Financial Aid:** 86 **% Residing in College-Owned, -Operated, or -Affiliated Housing:** 30 **Regional Accreditation:** Southern Association of Colleges and Schools **Credit Hours For Degree:** 64 semester hours, Associates; 120 semester hours, Bachelors **ROTC:** Army **Professional Accreditation:** ACBSP, ACEN, NCATE. **Intercollegiate Athletics:** Baseball M; Basketball M & W; Bowling M & W; Cheerleading M & W; Cross-Country Running M & W; Football M; Golf M & W; Soccer M & W; Softball W; Tennis M & W; Volleyball W; Wrestling M

DAYMAR COLLEGE (CLARKSVILLE)

2691 Trenton Rd.
Clarksville, TN 37040
Tel: (931)552-7600
Fax: (931)552-3624
E-mail: aprather@daymarinstitute.edu
Web Site: www.daymarcollege.edu
President/CEO: Katharine Purnell
Admissions: Alphonse Prather

Type: Two-Year College **Sex:** Coed **Admission Plans:** Open Admission **Application Deadline:** Rolling **Application Fee:** $0.00 **H.S. Requirements:** High school diploma required; GED accepted **Scholarships:** Available. **Calendar System:** Quarter **Enrollment:** Full-time 381, Part-time 151 **Faculty:** Full-time 20, Part-time 19 **Student-Faculty Ratio:** 7:1 **Final Year or Final Semester Residency Requirement:** No **Credit Hours For Degree:** 96 quarter credits, Associates; 180 quarter credits, Bachelors **Professional Accreditation:** ACICS.

DAYMAR COLLEGE (MURFREESBORO)

415 Golden Bear Ct.
Murfreesboro, TN 37128
Tel: (615)217-9347
Web Site: www.daymarcollege.edu

Type: Two-Year College **Sex:** Coed **Professional Accreditation:** ACICS.

DAYMAR COLLEGE (NASHVILLE)

560 Royal Pky.
Nashville, TN 37214
Tel: (615)361-7555
Web Site: www.daymarcollege.edu
President/CEO: Steve Allen

Type: Two-Year College **Sex:** Coed **Admission Plans:** Deferred Admission; Open Admission **Application Deadline:** Rolling **H.S. Requirements:** High school diploma required; GED accepted **Scholarships:** Available. **Calendar System:** Semester, Summer session available **Credit Hours For Degree:** 60 semester hours, Associates **Professional Accreditation:** ACICS.

DEVRY UNIVERSITY

3343 Perimeter Hill Dr., Ste. 200
Nashville, TN 37211-4147
Tel: (615)445-3456; Free: 866-338-7941
Web Site: www.devry.edu

Type: Comprehensive **Sex:** Coed **Application Deadline:** Rolling **Costs Per Year:** Tuition: $17,052 full-time, $609 per credit hour part-time. Mandatory fees: $80 full-time, $40 per term part-time. **Regional Accreditation:** North Central Association of Colleges and Schools **Professional Accreditation:** ACBSP.

DYERSBURG STATE COMMUNITY COLLEGE

1510 Lake Rd.
Dyersburg, TN 38024
Tel: (731)286-3200
Fax: (731)286-3325
E-mail: mjones@dscc.edu
Web Site: www.dscc.edu
President/CEO: Dr. Karen A. Bowyer
Admissions: Margaret Jones
Financial Aid: Sandra Rockett

Type: Two-Year College **Sex:** Coed **Affiliation:** Tennessee Board of Regents. **Scores:** 51% ACT 18-23; 12% ACT 24-29 **Costs Per Year:** State resident tuition: $3648 full-time, $152 per credit hour part-time. Nonresident tuition: $15,048 full-time, $627 per credit hour part-time. Mandatory fees: $299 full-time, $149.50 per term part-time. Full-time tuition and fees vary according to course load. Part-time tuition and fees vary according to course load. **Scholarships:** Available. **Calendar System:** Semester, Summer session available **Enrollment:** Full-time 1,226, Part-time 1,631 **Faculty:** Full-time 53, Part-time 129 **Student-Faculty Ratio:** 8:1 **Exams:** ACT essay component not used; Other; SAT I or ACT; SAT essay component not used. **Final Year or Final Semester Residency Requirement:** No **Regional Accreditation:** Southern Association of Colleges and Schools **Credit Hours For Degree:** 60 semester hours, Associates **Professional Accreditation:** ACBSP, ACEN. **Intercollegiate Athletics:** Baseball M; Basketball M & W; Cheerleading M & W; Softball W

EAST TENNESSEE STATE UNIVERSITY

1276 Gilbreath Dr.
Johnson City, TN 37614
Tel: (423)439-1000; Free: 800-462-3878
Fax: (423)439-5770
E-mail: go2etsu@etsu.edu
Web Site: www.etsu.edu
President/CEO: Dr. Brian E. Noland
Admissions: Brian Henley

Type: University **Sex:** Coed **Affiliation:** State University and Community College System of Tennessee; Tennessee Board of Regents. **Scores:** 81% SAT V 400+; 92% SAT M 400+; 46.12% ACT 18-23; 37.3% ACT 24-29 **% Accepted:** 79 **Admission Plans:** Early Admission **Application Deadline:** Rolling **Application Fee:** $25.00 **H.S. Requirements:** High school diploma required; GED accepted **Costs Per Year:** Application fee: $25. State resident tuition: $6828 full-time, $271 per credit hour part-time. Nonresident tuition: $24,498 full-time, $972 per credit hour part-time. Mandatory fees: $1649 full-time, $103 per credit hour part-time. Full-time tuition and fees vary according to course load and program. Part-time tuition and fees vary according to course load and program. College room and board: $7952. College room only: $4602. Room and board charges vary according to board plan and housing facility. **Scholarships:** Available. **Calendar System:** Semester, Summer session available **Enrollment:** Full-time 9,455, Graduate full-time 1,857, Graduate part-time 1,085, Part-time 1,937 **Faculty:** Full-time 575, Part-time 342 **Student-Faculty Ratio:** 17:1 **Exams:** ACT essay component not used; SAT I or ACT; SAT essay component not used; SAT Reasoning. **% Receiving Financial Aid:** 81 **% Residing in College-Owned, -Operated, or -Affiliated Housing:** 20 **Final Year or Final Semester Residency Requirement:** Yes **Regional Accreditation:** Southern Association of Colleges and Schools **Credit Hours For Degree:** 120 semester hours, Bachelors **ROTC:** Army **Professional Accreditation:** AACN, AACSB, AAFCS, AAMAE, ABET, ACA, ACEJMC, ACPE, ADA, AND, APTA, ASHA, CEPH, CSWE, CoARC, JRCERT, LCME/AMA, NAACLS,

NASAD, NASM, NCATE. **Intercollegiate Athletics:** Baseball M; Basketball M & W; Cross-Country Running M & W; Football M; Golf M & W; Soccer M & W; Softball W; Tennis M & W; Track and Field M & W; Volleyball W

L'ECOLE CULINAIRE–MEMPHIS
1245 N Germantown Pky.
Cordova, TN 38016
Tel: (901)754-7115
Web Site: www.lecole.edu/memphis
Type: Two-Year College **Sex:** Coed **Professional Accreditation:** ACCSC.

FISK UNIVERSITY
1000 17th Ave., N
Nashville, TN 37208-3051
Tel: (615)329-8500; Free: 888-702-0022
Fax: (615)329-8576
E-mail: lmcdonald@fisk.edu
Web Site: www.fisk.edu
President/CEO: Pres. Frank Sims
Admissions: Loretta McDonald
Financial Aid: Mary Chambliss
Type: Comprehensive **Sex:** Coed **Affiliation:** United Church of Christ. **Scores:** 89% SAT V 400+; 90% SAT M 400+; 55% ACT 18-23; 23% ACT 24-29 **% Accepted:** 81 **Admission Plans:** Early Action; Early Admission **Application Deadline:** August 1 **Application Fee:** $25.00 **H.S. Requirements:** High school diploma required; GED accepted **Costs Per Year:** Application fee: $25. Comprehensive fee: $31,756 includes full-time tuition ($19,624), mandatory fees ($1856), and college room and board ($10,276). College room only: $5868. Full-time tuition and fees vary according to course load and degree level. Room and board charges vary according to board plan. Part-time tuition: $817 per credit hour. Tuition guaranteed not to increase for student's term of enrollment. **Scholarships:** Available. **Calendar System:** Semester, Summer session available **Enrollment:** Full-time 738, Graduate full-time 28, Graduate part-time 21, Part-time 67 **Faculty:** Full-time 46, Part-time 34 **Student-Faculty Ratio:** 13:1 **Exams:** ACT essay component used for admission; SAT I or ACT; SAT essay component used for admission. **% Receiving Financial Aid:** 90 **% Residing in College-Owned, -Operated, or -Affiliated Housing:** 82 **Final Year or Final Semester Residency Requirement:** No **Regional Accreditation:** Southern Association of Colleges and Schools **Credit Hours For Degree:** 120 credit hours, Bachelors **ROTC:** Air Force, Army, Navy **Professional Accreditation:** NASM. **Intercollegiate Athletics:** Basketball M & W; Cross-Country Running M & W; Softball W; Tennis M & W; Track and Field M & W; Volleyball W

FORTIS INSTITUTE (COOKEVILLE)
1025 Hwy. 111
Cookeville, TN 38501
Tel: (931)526-3660; Free: 855-4-FORTIS
Fax: (931)372-2603
Web Site: www.fortis.edu
President/CEO: James Williamson
Admissions: Sharon Mellott
Type: Two-Year College **Sex:** Coed **Application Deadline:** Rolling **Application Fee:** $25.00 **H.S. Requirements:** High school diploma required; GED accepted **Scholarships:** Available. **Calendar System:** Quarter, Summer session not available **Exams:** Other. **Credit Hours For Degree:** 96 quarter hours, Associates **Professional Accreditation:** COE, NAACLS.

FORTIS INSTITUTE (NASHVILLE)
3354 Perimeter Hill Dr.
Ste. 105
Nashville, TN 37211
Tel: (615)320-5917; Free: 855-4-FORTIS
Web Site: www.fortis.edu
Type: Two-Year College **Sex:** Coed **Professional Accreditation:** ABHES.

FOUNTAINHEAD COLLEGE OF TECHNOLOGY
10208 Technology Dr.
Knoxville, TN 37932
Tel: (865)688-9422; Free: 888-218-7335
Fax: (865)688-2419
E-mail: joel.southern@fountainheadcollege.edu
Web Site: www.fountainheadcollege.edu

President/CEO: Richard Rackley
Admissions: Joel B. Southern
Type: Two-Year College **Sex:** Coed **Admission Plans:** Open Admission **Application Deadline:** Rolling **H.S. Requirements:** High school diploma required; GED accepted **Scholarships:** Available. **Calendar System:** Semester, Summer session available **Enrollment:** Full-time 180 **Faculty:** Full-time 13, Part-time 7 **Student-Faculty Ratio:** 8:1 **Exams:** ACT essay component used for admission; ACT essay component used in place of application essay; Other; SAT I or ACT. **Final Year or Final Semester Residency Requirement:** No **Credit Hours For Degree:** 60 credits, Associates; 120 credits, Bachelors **Professional Accreditation:** ACCSC.

FREED-HARDEMAN UNIVERSITY
158 E Main St.
Henderson, TN 38340-2399
Tel: (731)989-6000; Free: 800-FHU-FHU-1
Fax: (731)989-6047
E-mail: jaskew@fhu.edu
Web Site: www.fhu.edu
President/CEO: Dr. Joe Wiley
Admissions: Joe Askew
Financial Aid: Summer Judd
Type: Comprehensive **Sex:** Coed **Affiliation:** Church of Christ. **Scores:** 100% SAT V 400+; 95% SAT M 400+; 39% ACT 18-23; 44% ACT 24-29 **% Accepted:** 92 **Admission Plans:** Deferred Admission **Application Deadline:** Rolling **Application Fee:** $0.00 **H.S. Requirements:** High school diploma required; GED accepted **Scholarships:** Available. **Calendar System:** Semester, Summer session available **Enrollment:** Full-time 1,217, Graduate full-time 91, Graduate part-time 375, Part-time 145 **Faculty:** Full-time 91, Part-time 59 **Student-Faculty Ratio:** 13:1 **Exams:** ACT essay component not used; SAT I or ACT; SAT essay component not used; SAT Reasoning. **% Receiving Financial Aid:** 78 **% Residing in College-Owned, -Operated, or -Affiliated Housing:** 85 **Final Year or Final Semester Residency Requirement:** No **Regional Accreditation:** Southern Association of Colleges and Schools **Credit Hours For Degree:** 126 semester hours, Bachelors **Professional Accreditation:** ACBSP, ATS, CSWE, NCATE. **Intercollegiate Athletics:** Baseball M; Basketball M & W; Cheerleading W; Cross-Country Running M & W; Golf M & W; Rugby M; Soccer M & W; Softball W; Volleyball W

HIWASSEE COLLEGE
225 Hiwassee College Dr.
Madisonville, TN 37354
Tel: (423)442-2001; Free: 800-356-2187
Fax: (423)442-3520
Web Site: www.hiwassee.edu
Admissions: Jamie Williamson
Type: Two-Year College **Sex:** Coed **Affiliation:** Methodist. **Scores:** 64% SAT V 400+; 73% SAT M 400+; 48% ACT 18-23; 14% ACT 24-29 **% Accepted:** 70 **Admission Plans:** Deferred Admission; Early Admission **Application Deadline:** Rolling **Application Fee:** $0.00 **H.S. Requirements:** High school diploma required; GED accepted **Scholarships:** Available. **Calendar System:** Semester, Summer session available **Enrollment:** Full-time 350, Part-time 48 **Faculty:** Full-time 21, Part-time 7 **Student-Faculty Ratio:** 15:1 **Exams:** SAT I or ACT. **% Residing in College-Owned, -Operated, or -Affiliated Housing:** 40 **Credit Hours For Degree:** 66 semester hours, Associates **Professional Accreditation:** TRACS. **Intercollegiate Athletics:** Baseball M; Basketball M & W; Cross-Country Running M & W; Golf M & W; Soccer M & W; Softball W

HUNTINGTON COLLEGE OF HEALTH SCIENCES
117 Legacy View Way
Knoxville, TN 37918
Tel: (865)524-8079; Free: 800-290-4226
Fax: (865)524-8339
E-mail: studentservices@hchs.edu
Web Site: www.hchs.edu
President/CEO: Dr. Arthur Presser
Admissions: Kim Galyon
Type: Comprehensive **Sex:** Coed **% Accepted:** 52 **Admission Plans:** Deferred Admission; Open Admission **Application Deadline:** Rolling **Application Fee:** $75.00 **H.S. Requirements:** High school diploma required; GED accepted **Costs Per Year:** Application fee: $75. Tuition: $5880 full-time. **Calendar System:** Continuous, Summer session available **Enroll-

ment: Graduate part-time 10, Part-time 288 **Faculty:** Full-time 3, Part-time 19 **Student-Faculty Ratio:** 13:1 **Final Year or Final Semester Residency Requirement:** No **Credit Hours For Degree:** 61 credit hours, Associates; 129 credit hours, Bachelors **Professional Accreditation:** DEAC.

JACKSON STATE COMMUNITY COLLEGE
2046 N Pky.
Jackson, TN 38301-3797
Tel: (731)424-3520; Free: 800-355-5722
Fax: (731)425-2647
E-mail: awinchester@jscc.edu
Web Site: www.jscc.edu
President/CEO: Dr. Bruce Blanding
Admissions: Andrea Winchester
Financial Aid: Lori Thorne
Type: Two-Year College **Sex:** Coed **Affiliation:** Tennessee Board of Regents. **% Accepted:** 76 **Admission Plans:** Open Admission; Preferred Admission **Application Deadline:** August 23 **Application Fee:** $0.00 **H.S. Requirements:** High school diploma required; GED accepted **Costs Per Year:** Application fee: $0. State resident tuition: $4560 full-time, $152 per credit hour part-time. Nonresident tuition: $14,250 full-time, $475 per credit hour part-time. Mandatory fees: $285 full-time, $9 per credit hour part-time, $30 per term part-time. Full-time tuition and fees vary according to course load and program. Part-time tuition and fees vary according to course load and program. **Scholarships:** Available. **Calendar System:** Semester, Summer session available **Faculty:** Full-time 88, Part-time 197 **Student-Faculty Ratio:** 19:1 **Exams:** ACT; Other; SAT I or ACT. **Final Year or Final Semester Residency Requirement:** Yes **Regional Accreditation:** Southern Association of Colleges and Schools **Credit Hours For Degree:** 60 semester hours, Associates **ROTC:** Army **Professional Accreditation:** ACBSP, ACEN, APTA, ATMAE, CoARC, JRCEMTP, JRCERT, NAACLS. **Intercollegiate Athletics:** Baseball M; Basketball M & W; Softball W

JOHN A. GUPTON COLLEGE
1616 Church St.
Nashville, TN 37203-2920
Tel: (615)327-3927
Fax: (615)321-4518
E-mail: purcell@guptoncollege.edu
Web Site: www.guptoncollege.edu
President/CEO: B. Steven Spann
Admissions: Terri Purcell
Type: Two-Year College **Sex:** Coed **Admission Plans:** Deferred Admission **Application Deadline:** Rolling **Application Fee:** $50.00 **H.S. Requirements:** High school diploma required; GED accepted **Costs Per Year:** Application fee: $50. Tuition: $9920 full-time, $310 per semester hour part-time. Mandatory fees: $70 full-time. Full-time tuition and fees vary according to course load. Part-time tuition varies according to course load. College room only: $3600. **Scholarships:** Available. **Calendar System:** Semester **Enrollment:** Full-time 70, Part-time 50 **Faculty:** Full-time 3, Part-time 10 **Exams:** ACT. **% Residing in College-Owned, -Operated, or -Affiliated Housing:** 11 **Final Year or Final Semester Residency Requirement:** No **Regional Accreditation:** Southern Association of Colleges and Schools **Credit Hours For Degree:** 62 semester hours, Associates **Professional Accreditation:** ABFSE.

JOHNSON UNIVERSITY
7900 Johnson Dr.
Knoxville, TN 37998-1001
Tel: (865)573-4517; Free: 800-827-2122
Fax: (865)251-2337
E-mail: twingfield@jbc.edu
Web Site: www.johnsonu.edu
President/CEO: Gary Weedman
Admissions: Tim Wingfield
Financial Aid: Lawrence Rector, CPA
Type: Comprehensive **Sex:** Coed **Affiliation:** Christian Churches and Churches of Christ. **Scores:** 55% ACT 18-23; 30% ACT 24-29 **% Accepted:** 55 **Admission Plans:** Deferred Admission **Application Deadline:** July 1 **Application Fee:** $35.00 **H.S. Requirements:** High school diploma required; GED accepted **Scholarships:** Available. **Calendar System:** Semester, Summer session available **Enrollment:** Full-time 781, Graduate full-time 78, Graduate part-time 123, Part-time 49 **Faculty:** Full-time 38, Part-time 47 **Student-Faculty Ratio:** 17:1 **Exams:** ACT; SAT I or ACT. **%**

Receiving Financial Aid: 84 **% Residing in College-Owned, -Operated, or -Affiliated Housing:** 85 **Final Year or Final Semester Residency Requirement:** No **Regional Accreditation:** Southern Association of Colleges and Schools **Credit Hours For Degree:** 62 semester hours, Associates; 124 semester hours, Bachelors **Professional Accreditation:** ABHE. **Intercollegiate Athletics:** Baseball M; Basketball M & W; Cheerleading M & W; Cross-Country Running M & W; Soccer M & W; Volleyball W

KING UNIVERSITY
1350 King College Rd.
Bristol, TN 37620-2699
Tel: (423)968-1187; Free: 800-362-0014
Fax: (423)968-4456
E-mail: admissions@king.edu
Web Site: www.king.edu
President/CEO: Dr. Richard A. Ray
Admissions: Tom VerDow
Financial Aid: Richard J. Brand
Type: Comprehensive **Sex:** Coed **Affiliation:** Presbyterian Church (U.S.A.). **Scores:** 83% SAT V 400+; 84% SAT M 400+; 51.16% ACT 18-23; 34.88% ACT 24-29 **% Accepted:** 44 **Admission Plans:** Deferred Admission **Application Deadline:** Rolling **Application Fee:** $25.00 **H.S. Requirements:** High school diploma required; GED accepted **Costs Per Year:** Application fee: $25. One-time mandatory fee: $125. Comprehensive fee: $35,456 includes full-time tuition ($25,798), mandatory fees ($1478), and college room and board ($8180). College room only: $4108. Full-time tuition and fees vary according to class time, course load, degree level, location, and program. Room and board charges vary according to board plan and housing facility. Part-time tuition: $600 per credit. Part-time mandatory fees: $120 per term. Part-time tuition and fees vary according to class time, course load, degree level, location, and program. **Scholarships:** Available. **Calendar System:** Semester, Summer session available **Enrollment:** Full-time 2,244, Graduate full-time 347, Graduate part-time 106, Part-time 223 **Faculty:** Full-time 135, Part-time 169 **Student-Faculty Ratio:** 14:1 **Exams:** ACT essay component not used; SAT I or ACT; SAT essay component not used; SAT Reasoning; SAT Subject. **% Receiving Financial Aid:** 87 **% Residing in College-Owned, -Operated, or -Affiliated Housing:** 42 **Final Year or Final Semester Residency Requirement:** No **Regional Accreditation:** Southern Association of Colleges and Schools **Credit Hours For Degree:** 60 semester hours, Associates; 124 semester hours, Bachelors **Professional Accreditation:** AACN, ACBSP. **Intercollegiate Athletics:** Baseball M; Basketball M & W; Cheerleading M & W; Cross-Country Running M & W; Golf M & W; Soccer M & W; Softball W; Swimming and Diving M & W; Tennis M & W; Track and Field M & W; Volleyball M & W; Wrestling M & W

LANE COLLEGE
545 Ln. Ave.
Jackson, TN 38301-4598
Tel: (731)426-7500; Free: 800-960-7533
Fax: (731)426-7559
E-mail: mclayborne@lanecollege.edu
Web Site: www.lanecollege.edu
President/CEO: Dr. Logan C. Hampton
Admissions: Dr. Monica C. Scott
Financial Aid: Tony Calhoun
Type: Four-Year College **Sex:** Coed **Affiliation:** Christian Methodist Episcopal Church. **Scores:** 85% SAT V 400+; 13% ACT 18-23; 1% ACT 24-29 **% Accepted:** 55 **Admission Plans:** Deferred Admission **Application Deadline:** Rolling **Application Fee:** $0.00 **H.S. Requirements:** High school diploma required; GED accepted **Costs Per Year:** Application fee: $0. Comprehensive fee: $16,550 includes full-time tuition ($8980), mandatory fees ($950), and college room and board ($6620). Full-time tuition and fees vary according to course load. Part-time tuition: $375 per credit hour. Part-time tuition varies according to course load. **Scholarships:** Available. **Calendar System:** Semester, Summer session available **Enrollment:** Full-time 1,351, Part-time 25 **Faculty:** Full-time 65, Part-time 8 **Student-Faculty Ratio:** 21:1 **Exams:** SAT I or ACT; SAT Reasoning. **% Receiving Financial Aid:** 99 **% Residing in College-Owned, -Operated, or -Affiliated Housing:** 63 **Regional Accreditation:** Southern Association of Colleges and Schools **Credit Hours For Degree:** 124 semester hours, Bachelors **ROTC:** Army **Intercollegiate Athletics:** Baseball M; Basketball M & W; Cheerleading W; Cross-Country Running M & W; Football M; Softball W; Tennis M & W; Track and Field M & W; Volleyball W

LEE UNIVERSITY
PO Box 3450
Cleveland, TN 37320-3450
Tel: (423)614-8000; Free: 800-533-9930
Fax: (423)614-8533
E-mail: admissions@leeuniversity.edu
Web Site: www.leeuniversity.edu
President/CEO: Dr. C. Paul Conn, PhD
Admissions: Phillip Cook
Financial Aid: Marian Dill
Type: Comprehensive **Sex:** Coed **Affiliation:** Church of God. **Scores:** 91% SAT V 400+; 88% SAT M 400+; 35.38% ACT 18-23; 43.5% ACT 24-29 **Costs Per Year:** Comprehensive fee: $23,650 includes full-time tuition ($15,170), mandatory fees ($600), and college room and board ($7880). College room only: $4330. Full-time tuition and fees vary according to course load, location, and program. Room and board charges vary according to board plan and housing facility. Part-time tuition: $632 per credit hour. Part-time mandatory fees: $60 per term. Part-time tuition and fees vary according to course load, location, and program. **Scholarships:** Available. **Calendar System:** Semester, Summer session available **Enrollment:** Full-time 3,785, Graduate full-time 227, Graduate part-time 254, Part-time 775 **Faculty:** Full-time 171, Part-time 248 **Student-Faculty Ratio:** 17:1 **Exams:** ACT; ACT essay component not used; SAT I; SAT I and SAT II or ACT; SAT I or ACT; SAT II; SAT essay component not used. **% Receiving Financial Aid:** 70 **% Residing in College-Owned, -Operated, or -Affiliated Housing:** 46 **Final Year or Final Semester Residency Requirement:** Yes **Regional Accreditation:** Southern Association of Colleges and Schools **Credit Hours For Degree:** 120 semester hours, Bachelors **Professional Accreditation:** ACBSP, NASM, NCATE. **Intercollegiate Athletics:** Baseball M; Basketball M & W; Cross-Country Running M & W; Golf M & W; Soccer M & W; Softball W; Tennis M & W; Track and Field M & W; Volleyball W

LEMOYNE-OWEN COLLEGE
807 Walker Ave.
Memphis, TN 38126-6595
Tel: (901)435-1000; Free: 800-737-7778
Fax: (901)942-6272
E-mail: samuel_king@loc.edu
Web Site: www.loc.edu
President/CEO: Dr. Andrea Lewis Miller
Admissions: Samuel King
Type: Four-Year College **Sex:** Coed **Affiliation:** United Church of Christ. **% Accepted:** 100 **Admission Plans:** Open Admission **Application Deadline:** April 1 **Application Fee:** $25.00 **H.S. Requirements:** High school diploma required; GED accepted **Costs Per Year:** Application fee: $25. Comprehensive fee: $16,810 includes full-time tuition ($10,680), mandatory fees ($220), and college room and board ($5910). College room only: $3600. Full-time tuition and fees vary according to course load. Room and board charges vary according to housing facility. Part-time tuition: $436 per credit hour. **Scholarships:** Available. **Calendar System:** Semester, Summer session available **Enrollment:** Full-time 836, Part-time 109 **Faculty:** Full-time 55, Part-time 33 **Student-Faculty Ratio:** 14:1 **Exams:** SAT I or ACT. **% Receiving Financial Aid:** 95 **% Residing in College-Owned, -Operated, or -Affiliated Housing:** 31 **Regional Accreditation:** Southern Association of Colleges and Schools **Credit Hours For Degree:** 120 credit hours, Bachelors **ROTC:** Air Force, Army **Professional Accreditation:** NCATE. **Intercollegiate Athletics:** Baseball M; Basketball M & W; Cross-Country Running M & W; Golf M & W; Softball W; Tennis M & W; Volleyball W

LINCOLN COLLEGE OF TECHNOLOGY
1524 Gallatin Ave.
Nashville, TN 37206-3298
Tel: (615)226-3990; Free: 800-228-6232
Fax: (615)262-8488
E-mail: tlegg-smith@lincolntech.com
Web Site: www.lincolnedu.com/campus/nashville-tn
President/CEO: James Coakley
Admissions: Tanya Smith
Type: Two-Year College **Sex:** Coed **% Accepted:** 89 **Admission Plans:** Deferred Admission **Application Deadline:** Rolling **Application Fee:** $100.00 **H.S. Requirements:** High school diploma required; GED accepted **Scholarships:** Available. **Calendar System:** Continuous, Summer session not available **Enrollment:** Full-time 1,375 **Faculty:** Full-time 59, Part-time 4

Student-Faculty Ratio: 30:1 **Exams:** SAT I or ACT. **% Residing in College-Owned, -Operated, or -Affiliated Housing:** 21 **Professional Accreditation:** ACCSC.

LINCOLN MEMORIAL UNIVERSITY
6965 Cumberland Gap Pky.
Harrogate, TN 37752-1901
Tel: (423)869-3611; Free: 800-325-0900
Fax: (423)869-6250
E-mail: admissions@lmunet.edu
Web Site: www.lmunet.edu
President/CEO: Dr. B. James Dawson
Admissions: Sherry McCreary
Financial Aid: Bryan Erslan
Type: Comprehensive **Sex:** Coed **Scores:** 89% SAT V 400+; 94% SAT M 400+; 58% ACT 18-23; 29% ACT 24-29 **% Accepted:** 74 **Application Deadline:** Rolling **Application Fee:** $25.00 **H.S. Requirements:** High school diploma required; GED accepted **Costs Per Year:** Application fee: $25. Comprehensive fee: $27,846 includes full-time tuition ($20,016), mandatory fees ($530), and college room and board ($7300). Room and board charges vary according to board plan and housing facility. Part-time tuition: $834 per credit hour. Part-time tuition varies according to course load. **Scholarships:** Available. **Calendar System:** Semester, Summer session available **Enrollment:** Full-time 1,298, Graduate full-time 1,612, Graduate part-time 424, Part-time 401 **Faculty:** Full-time 206, Part-time 84 **Student-Faculty Ratio:** 13:1 **Exams:** ACT essay component not used; SAT I or ACT; SAT essay component not used. **% Receiving Financial Aid:** 85 **% Residing in College-Owned, -Operated, or -Affiliated Housing:** 36 **Regional Accreditation:** Southern Association of Colleges and Schools **Credit Hours For Degree:** 64 semester hours, Associates; 128 semester hours, Bachelors **Professional Accreditation:** AANA, ABA, ACBSP, ACEN, AOsA, CSWE, JRCAT, NAACLS. **Intercollegiate Athletics:** Baseball M; Basketball M & W; Cross-Country Running M & W; Golf M & W; Lacrosse M & W; Soccer M & W; Softball W; Tennis M & W; Volleyball W

LIPSCOMB UNIVERSITY
One University Park Dr.
Nashville, TN 37204-3951
Tel: (615)966-1000; Free: 877-582-4766
Fax: (615)966-1804
E-mail: admissions@lipscomb.edu
Web Site: www.lipscomb.edu
President/CEO: Dr. L. Randolph Lowry, III
Admissions: Johnathan Akin
Financial Aid: Tiffany Summers
Type: Comprehensive **Sex:** Coed **Affiliation:** Church of Christ. **Scores:** 98% SAT V 400+; 99% SAT M 400+; 30.07% ACT 18-23; 48% ACT 24-29 **% Accepted:** 61 **Admission Plans:** Deferred Admission; Early Admission **Application Deadline:** Rolling **Application Fee:** $50.00 **H.S. Requirements:** High school diploma required; GED accepted **Costs Per Year:** Application fee: $50. Comprehensive fee: $39,656 includes full-time tuition ($26,428), mandatory fees ($2196), and college room and board ($11,032). College room only: $6192. Full-time tuition and fees vary according to course load. Room and board charges vary according to board plan and housing facility. Part-time tuition: $1110 per credit hour. Part-time tuition varies according to course load. **Scholarships:** Available. **Calendar System:** Semester, Summer session available **Enrollment:** Full-time 2,726, Graduate full-time 859, Graduate part-time 791, Part-time 304 **Faculty:** Full-time 206, Part-time 368 **Student-Faculty Ratio:** 12:1 **Exams:** SAT I or ACT; SAT Reasoning; SAT Subject. **% Receiving Financial Aid:** 63 **% Residing in College-Owned, -Operated, or -Affiliated Housing:** 51 **Final Year or Final Semester Residency Requirement:** Yes **Regional Accreditation:** Southern Association of Colleges and Schools **Credit Hours For Degree:** 63 semester hours, Associates; 126 semester hours, Bachelors **ROTC:** Air Force, Army **Professional Accreditation:** ABET, ACBSP, ACEN, ACPE, AND, ATS, CSWE, JRCAT, NASM, NCATE. **Intercollegiate Athletics:** Baseball M; Basketball M & W; Cross-Country Running M & W; Golf M & W; Soccer M & W; Softball W; Tennis M & W; Track and Field M & W; Volleyball W

MARTIN METHODIST COLLEGE
433 W Madison St.
Pulaski, TN 38478-2716
Tel: (931)363-9868; Free: 800-467-1273
Fax: (931)363-9818

E-mail: admit@martinmethodist.edu
Web Site: www.martinmethodist.edu
President/CEO: Ted Brown
Admissions: Lisa Smith
Financial Aid: Anita Beecham

Type: Four-Year College **Sex:** Coed **Affiliation:** United Methodist. **Admission Plans:** Deferred Admission; Early Admission **Application Deadline:** August 26 **Application Fee:** $25.00 **H.S. Requirements:** High school diploma required; GED accepted **Scholarships:** Available. **Calendar System:** Semester, Summer session available **Exams:** SAT I or ACT. **% Receiving Financial Aid:** 54 **Regional Accreditation:** Southern Association of Colleges and Schools **Credit Hours For Degree:** 63 hours, Associates; 120 hours, Bachelors **Professional Accreditation:** AACN. **Intercollegiate Athletics:** Baseball M; Basketball M & W; Bowling M & W; Cheerleading W; Golf M & W; Soccer M & W; Softball W; Tennis M & W; Volleyball W

MARYVILLE COLLEGE

502 E Lamar Alexander Pky.
Maryville, TN 37804-5907
Tel: (865)981-8000; Free: 800-597-2687
Fax: (865)983-0581
E-mail: admissions@maryvillecollege.edu
Web Site: www.maryvillecollege.edu
President/CEO: Dr. W. Tom Bogart
Admissions: Linda L. Moore
Financial Aid: Alayne Bowman

Type: Four-Year College **Sex:** Coed **Affiliation:** Presbyterian. **Scores:** 91% SAT V 400+; 90% SAT M 400+; 45% ACT 18-23; 40% ACT 24-29 **% Accepted:** 67 **Admission Plans:** Deferred Admission; Early Admission **Application Deadline:** March 1 **Application Fee:** $0.00 **H.S. Requirements:** High school diploma required; GED accepted **Costs Per Year:** Application fee: $0. Comprehensive fee: $43,308 includes full-time tuition ($32,104), mandatory fees ($762), and college room and board ($10,442). College room only: $5182. Full-time tuition and fees vary according to course load. Room and board charges vary according to board plan and housing facility. Part-time tuition: $825 per credit hour. Part-time tuition varies according to course load. **Scholarships:** Available. **Calendar System:** 4-1-4, Summer session available **Enrollment:** Full-time 1,178, Part-time 35 **Faculty:** Full-time 76, Part-time 43 **Student-Faculty Ratio:** 13:1 **Exams:** ACT essay component used for advising; SAT I or ACT; SAT essay component used for advising; SAT Reasoning. **% Receiving Financial Aid:** 85 **% Residing in College-Owned, -Operated, or -Affiliated Housing:** 73 **Final Year or Final Semester Residency Requirement:** Yes **Regional Accreditation:** Southern Association of Colleges and Schools **Credit Hours For Degree:** 128 semester hours, Bachelors **Professional Accreditation:** NASM. **Intercollegiate Athletics:** Baseball M; Basketball M & W; Cheerleading M & W; Cross-Country Running M & W; Equestrian Sports M & W; Football M; Golf M & W; Soccer M & W; Softball W; Swimming and Diving M & W; Tennis M & W; Ultimate Frisbee M & W; Volleyball W

MEMPHIS COLLEGE OF ART

Overton Park, 1930 Poplar Ave.
Memphis, TN 38104-2764
Tel: (901)272-5100; Free: 800-727-1088
Fax: (901)272-5104
E-mail: gmassey@mca.edu
Web Site: www.mca.edu
President/CEO: Dr. Ron Jones
Admissions: Gail Massey
Financial Aid: Aaron White

Type: Comprehensive **Sex:** Coed **Scores:** 65% ACT 18-23; 23% ACT 24-29 **% Accepted:** 38 **Admission Plans:** Deferred Admission **Application Deadline:** Rolling **Application Fee:** $0.00 **H.S. Requirements:** High school diploma required; GED accepted **Costs Per Year:** Application fee: $0. Comprehensive fee: $38,750 includes full-time tuition ($29,550), mandatory fees ($700), and college room and board ($8500). College room only: $6500. Full-time tuition and fees vary according to degree level and reciprocity agreements. Room and board charges vary according to housing facility. **Scholarships:** Available. **Calendar System:** Semester, Summer session available **Enrollment:** Full-time 332, Graduate full-time 28, Graduate part-time 41, Part-time 34 **Faculty:** Full-time 26, Part-time 35 **Student-Faculty Ratio:** 10:1 **Exams:** SAT I or ACT. **% Receiving Financial Aid:** 90 **% Residing in College-Owned, -Operated, or -Affiliated Housing:** 44 **Final Year or Final Semester Residency Requirement:** Yes **Regional Accreditation:** Southern Association of Colleges and Schools **Credit Hours For Degree:** 120 credit hours, Bachelors **Professional Accreditation:** NASAD.

MID-AMERICA BAPTIST THEOLOGICAL SEMINARY

2095 Appling Rd.
Cordova, TN 38016
Tel: (901)751-8453; Free: 800-968-4508
Fax: (901)751-8454
E-mail: info@mabts.edu
Web Site: www.mabts.edu
Admissions: Duffy Guyton

Type: Comprehensive **Sex:** Men **Affiliation:** Southern Baptist. **Admission Plans:** Open Admission **Application Deadline:** August 4 **Application Fee:** $25.00 **H.S. Requirements:** High school diploma required; GED accepted **Calendar System:** Semester, Summer session available **Enrollment:** Full-time 29, Part-time 22 **Faculty:** Full-time 27 **Student-Faculty Ratio:** 15:1 **Regional Accreditation:** Southern Association of Colleges and Schools **Credit Hours For Degree:** 64 semester hours, Associates

MID-SOUTH CHRISTIAN COLLEGE

3097 Knight Rd.
Memphis, TN 38118-3151
E-mail: wendylambert@midsouthcc.org
Web Site: www.midsouthchristian.edu
President/CEO: Larry A. Griffin
Admissions: Wendy Lambert

Type: Four-Year College **Sex:** Coed **Scores:** 100% ACT 18-23 **Costs Per Year:** Comprehensive fee: $10,058 includes full-time tuition ($5568), mandatory fees ($1090), and college room and board ($3400). College room only: $1800. Tuition guaranteed not to increase for student's term of enrollment. **Calendar System:** Semester, Summer session not available **Enrollment:** Full-time 21, Part-time 1 **Faculty:** Full-time 2, Part-time 11 **Student-Faculty Ratio:** 4:1 **Exams:** ACT; SAT I or ACT. **% Residing in College-Owned, -Operated, or -Affiliated Housing:** 95 **Final Year or Final Semester Residency Requirement:** Yes **Credit Hours For Degree:** 66 hours, Associates; 133 hours, Bachelors **Professional Accreditation:** ABHE.

MIDDLE TENNESSEE STATE UNIVERSITY

1301 E Main St.
Murfreesboro, TN 37132
Tel: (615)898-2300; Free: 800-331-MTSU
E-mail: admissions@mtsu.edu
Web Site: www.mtsu.edu
President/CEO: Dr. Sidney A. McPhee
Financial Aid: Stephen White

Type: University **Sex:** Coed **Affiliation:** Tennessee Board of Regents. **Scores:** 88% SAT V 400+; 91% SAT M 400+; 53.94% ACT 18-23; 28.54% ACT 24-29 **% Accepted:** 73 **Application Fee:** $25.00 **H.S. Requirements:** High school diploma required; GED accepted **Costs Per Year:** Application fee: $25. State resident tuition: $6756 full-time, $268 per credit hour part-time. Nonresident tuition: $24,324 full-time, $965 per credit hour part-time. Mandatory fees: $1648 full-time, $69 per credit hour part-time. Full-time tuition and fees vary according to course load. Part-time tuition and fees vary according to course load. College room and board: $8550. Room and board charges vary according to board plan and housing facility. **Scholarships:** Available. **Calendar System:** Semester **Enrollment:** Full-time 16,167, Graduate full-time 794, Graduate part-time 1,577, Part-time 3,973 **Faculty:** Full-time 918, Part-time 329 **Student-Faculty Ratio:** 18:1 **Exams:** ACT essay component not used; SAT I or ACT; SAT essay component not used; SAT Reasoning; SAT Subject. **% Receiving Financial Aid:** 68 **% Residing in College-Owned, -Operated, or -Affiliated Housing:** 15 **Regional Accreditation:** Southern Association of Colleges and Schools **Credit Hours For Degree:** 65 semester hours, Associates; 120 semester hours, Bachelors **ROTC:** Air Force, Army **Professional Accreditation:** AABI, AACN, AACSB, AAFCS, ABET, ACA, ACEJMC, ACEN, ATMAE, CIDA, CSWE, NASAD, NASM, NCATE, NRPA. **Intercollegiate Athletics:** Baseball M; Basketball M & W; Cheerleading M & W; Cross-Country Running M & W; Equestrian Sports M & W; Football M; Golf M; Soccer W; Softball W; Tennis M & W; Track and Field M & W; Volleyball W

MILLER-MOTTE TECHNICAL COLLEGE (CHATTANOOGA)

6397 Lee Hwy.
Ste. 100

Chattanooga, TN 37421
Tel: (423)414-3247
Web Site: www.miller-motte.edu
Type: Two-Year College **Sex:** Coed **Professional Accreditation:** ACICS.

MILLER-MOTTE TECHNICAL COLLEGE (CLARKSVILLE)
1820 Business Park Dr.
Clarksville, TN 37040
Tel: (931)553-0071
Fax: (931)552-2916
E-mail: lisateague@hotmail.com
Web Site: www.miller-motte.edu
President/CEO: Kala Fielder
Admissions: Joseph Kuchno
Type: Two-Year College **Sex:** Coed **Scholarships:** Available. **Calendar System:** Quarter **Professional Accreditation:** AAMAE, ACICS.

MILLER-MOTTE TECHNICAL COLLEGE (MADISON)
1515 Gallatin Pke. N
Madison, TN 37115
Tel: (931)553-0071
Fax: (931)552-2916
Web Site: www.miller-motte.edu
Type: Two-Year College **Sex:** Coed **Professional Accreditation:** ACICS.

MILLIGAN COLLEGE
PO Box 500
Milligan College, TN 37682
Tel: (423)461-8700; Free: 800-262-8337
Fax: (423)461-8960
E-mail: admissions@milligan.edu
Web Site: www.milligan.edu
President/CEO: Dr. Bill Greer
Admissions: Kristin Wright
Financial Aid: Diane Keasling
Type: Comprehensive **Sex:** Coed **Affiliation:** Christian. **Scores:** 95% SAT V 400+; 42% ACT 18-23; 42% ACT 24-29 **% Accepted:** 65 **Admission Plans:** Deferred Admission **Application Deadline:** August 1 **Application Fee:** $30.00 **H.S. Requirements:** High school diploma required; GED accepted **Costs Per Year:** Application fee: $30. One-time mandatory fee: $75. Comprehensive fee: $36,330 includes full-time tuition ($28,800), mandatory fees ($1030), and college room and board ($6500). Full-time tuition and fees vary according to course load and degree level. Room and board charges vary according to housing facility. Part-time tuition: $800 per credit hour. Part-time tuition varies according to course load and degree level. **Scholarships:** Available. **Calendar System:** Semester, Summer session available **Enrollment:** Full-time 785, Graduate full-time 229, Graduate part-time 73, Part-time 107 **Faculty:** Full-time 79, Part-time 71 **Student-Faculty Ratio:** 9:1 **Exams:** SAT I or ACT. **% Receiving Financial Aid:** 81 **% Residing in College-Owned, -Operated, or -Affiliated Housing:** 74 **Final Year or Final Semester Residency Requirement:** Yes **Regional Accreditation:** Southern Association of Colleges and Schools **Credit Hours For Degree:** 128 semester hours, Bachelors **Professional Accreditation:** AACN, ACBSP, AOTA, ATS, NCATE. **Intercollegiate Athletics:** Baseball M; Basketball M & W; Cross-Country Running M & W; Golf M & W; Soccer M & W; Softball W; Swimming and Diving M & W; Tennis M & W; Track and Field M & W; Volleyball W

MOTLOW STATE COMMUNITY COLLEGE
PO Box 8500
Lynchburg, TN 37352-8500
Tel: (931)393-1500; Free: 800-654-4877
Fax: (931)393-1681
E-mail: smason@mscc.edu
Web Site: www.mscc.edu
President/CEO: Dr. Mary Lou Apple
Admissions: Sheri Mason
Type: Two-Year College **Sex:** Coed **Affiliation:** Tennessee Board of Regents. **Admission Plans:** Deferred Admission; Early Admission; Open Admission **Application Deadline:** August 13 **Application Fee:** $10.00 **H.S. Requirements:** High school diploma required; GED accepted **Scholarships:** Available. **Calendar System:** Semester, Summer session available **Faculty:** Full-time 95, Part-time 166 **Regional Accreditation:** Southern Association of Colleges and Schools **Credit Hours For Degree:** 60 semester

hours, Associates **Professional Accreditation:** ACBSP, ACEN. **Intercollegiate Athletics:** Baseball M; Basketball M & W; Softball W

NASHVILLE STATE COMMUNITY COLLEGE
120 White Bridge Rd.
Nashville, TN 37209-4515
Tel: (615)353-3333; Free: 800-272-7363
Fax: (615)353-3243
E-mail: jennifer.evernham@nscc.edu
Web Site: www.nscc.edu
President/CEO: Dr. George H. Van Allen
Admissions: Jennifer Evernham
Financial Aid: James Joshua Moran
Type: Two-Year College **Sex:** Coed **Affiliation:** Tennessee Board of Regents. **Admission Plans:** Open Admission; Preferred Admission **Application Deadline:** Rolling **Application Fee:** $20.00 **H.S. Requirements:** High school diploma required; GED accepted **Costs Per Year:** Application fee: $20. State resident tuition: $4560 full-time, $152 per credit hour part-time. Nonresident tuition: $18,110 full-time, $627 per credit hour part-time. Mandatory fees: $10 per credit hour part-time. Full-time tuition varies according to course load. Part-time tuition and fees vary according to course load. **Scholarships:** Available. **Calendar System:** Semester, Summer session available **Student-Faculty Ratio:** 19:1 **Exams:** ACT essay component used for placement; SAT I or ACT; SAT essay component used for placement. **Final Year or Final Semester Residency Requirement:** No **Regional Accreditation:** Southern Association of Colleges and Schools **Credit Hours For Degree:** 60 credit hours, Associates **Professional Accreditation:** ABET, ACBSP, ACF, AOTA.

NATIONAL COLLEGE (BRISTOL)
1328 Hwy. 11 W
Bristol, TN 37620
Tel: (423)878-4440; Free: 888-9-JOBREADY
Web Site: www.national-college.edu
Admissions: Patrick DeMesa
Type: Two-Year College **Sex:** Coed **Affiliation:** National College of Business and Technology. **Admission Plans:** Open Admission **Application Deadline:** Rolling **H.S. Requirements:** High school diploma required; GED accepted **Scholarships:** Available. **Calendar System:** Quarter, Summer session available **Credit Hours For Degree:** 96 quarter hours, Associates **Professional Accreditation:** AAMAE, ACICS.

NATIONAL COLLEGE (KNOXVILLE)
8415 Kingston Pke.
Knoxville, TN 37919
Tel: (865)539-2011; Free: 888-9-JOBREADY
Fax: (865)539-2049
Web Site: www.national-college.edu
Admissions: Frank Alvey
Type: Two-Year College **Sex:** Coed **Affiliation:** National College of Business and Technology. **Calendar System:** Quarter **Professional Accreditation:** ACICS.

NATIONAL COLLEGE (NASHVILLE)
1638 Bell Rd.
Nashville, TN 37211
Tel: (615)333-3344; Free: 888-9-JOBREADY
Web Site: www.national-college.edu
President/CEO: Frank Longaker
Admissions: Jerry Lafferty
Type: Two-Year College **Sex:** Coed **Affiliation:** National College of Business and Technology. **Admission Plans:** Open Admission **Application Deadline:** Rolling **H.S. Requirements:** High school diploma required; GED accepted **Scholarships:** Available. **Calendar System:** Quarter, Summer session available **Credit Hours For Degree:** 96 credit hours, Associates **Professional Accreditation:** AAMAE, ACICS.

NORTH CENTRAL INSTITUTE
168 Jack Miller Blvd.
Clarksville, TN 37042
Tel: (931)431-9700; Free: 800-603-4116
Fax: (931)431-9771
E-mail: admissions@nci.edu
Web Site: www.nci.edu

President/CEO: Dr. John McCurdy
Admissions: Dale Wood

Type: Two-Year College **Sex:** Coed **Admission Plans:** Early Admission; Open Admission **Application Deadline:** Rolling **Application Fee:** $35.00 **H.S. Requirements:** High school diploma required; GED accepted **Costs Per Year:** Application fee: $35. Tuition: $292 per course part-time. **Scholarships:** Available. **Calendar System:** Continuous, Summer session available **Student-Faculty Ratio:** 10:1 **Credit Hours For Degree:** 62 credits, Associates **Professional Accreditation:** COE.

NORTHEAST STATE COMMUNITY COLLEGE

PO Box 246
Blountville, TN 37617-0246
Tel: (423)323-3191; Free: 800-836-7822
Fax: (423)323-0215
E-mail: jpharr@northeaststate.edu
Web Site: www.northeaststate.edu
President/CEO: Janice H. Gilliam
Admissions: Dr. Jon P. Harr

Type: Two-Year College **Sex:** Coed **Affiliation:** Tennessee Board of Regents. **Scores:** 48.6% ACT 18-23; 7.1% ACT 24-29 **% Accepted:** 100 **Admission Plans:** Open Admission; Preferred Admission **Application Deadline:** Rolling **Application Fee:** $10.00 **H.S. Requirements:** High school diploma required; GED accepted **Scholarships:** Available. **Calendar System:** Semester, Summer session available **Enrollment:** Full-time 2,927, Part-time 2,543 **Faculty:** Full-time 107, Part-time 161 **Student-Faculty Ratio:** 11:1 **Regional Accreditation:** Southern Association of Colleges and Schools **Credit Hours For Degree:** 60 semester hours, Associates **Professional Accreditation:** AAMAE, ACBSP, ACEN, ADA, ATMAE, NAACLS.

NOSSI COLLEGE OF ART

590 Cheron Rd.
Nashville, TN 37115
Tel: (615)514-2787; Free: 888-986-ARTS
Fax: (615)851-1087
E-mail: admissions@nossi.edu
Web Site: www.nossi.edu
President/CEO: Cyrus Vatandoost
Admissions: Mary Alexander
Financial Aid: Mary P. Kidd

Type: Four-Year College **Sex:** Coed **Admission Plans:** Early Admission **Application Deadline:** Rolling **Application Fee:** $100.00 **H.S. Requirements:** High school diploma required; GED accepted **Costs Per Year:** Application fee: $100. Tuition: $17,700 full-time. Mandatory fees: $100 full-time. Tuition guaranteed not to increase for student's term of enrollment. **Scholarships:** Available. **Calendar System:** Semester **Enrollment:** Full-time 276 **Faculty:** Full-time 4, Part-time 27 **Student-Faculty Ratio:** 9:1 **Exams:** ACT; ACT essay component not used; SAT essay component not used. **Final Year or Final Semester Residency Requirement:** No **Credit Hours For Degree:** 75 credits, Associates; 133 credits, Bachelors **Professional Accreditation:** ACCSC.

O'MORE COLLEGE OF DESIGN

423 S Margin St.
Franklin, TN 37064-2816
Tel: (615)794-4254; Free: 888-662-1970
Fax: (615)790-1662
E-mail: tbagsby@omorecollege.edu
Web Site: www.omorecollege.edu
President/CEO: Dr. David Rosen
Admissions: Tori Bagsby
Financial Aid: Sara Martin

Type: Four-Year College **Sex:** Coed **Scores:** 60% ACT 18-23; 9% ACT 24-29 **% Accepted:** 80 **Admission Plans:** Deferred Admission **Application Deadline:** July 31 **Application Fee:** $50.00 **H.S. Requirements:** High school diploma required; GED accepted **Costs Per Year:** Application fee: $50. Tuition: $27,360 full-time, $1140 per credit hour part-time. Full-time tuition varies according to course load. **Scholarships:** Available. **Calendar System:** Semester, Summer session available **Enrollment:** Full-time 149, Part-time 18 **Faculty:** Full-time 14, Part-time 28 **Student-Faculty Ratio:** 7:1 **Exams:** ACT; ACT essay component not used; SAT I; SAT I and SAT II or ACT; SAT I or ACT; SAT II; SAT essay component not used; SAT Reasoning; SAT Subject. **% Receiving Financial Aid:** 72 **Final Year or Final Semester**

Residency Requirement: No **Credit Hours For Degree:** 136 credits, Bachelors **Professional Accreditation:** ACCSC, CIDA.

PELLISSIPPI STATE COMMUNITY COLLEGE

PO Box 22990
Knoxville, TN 37933-0990
Tel: (865)694-6400
Web Site: www.pstcc.edu
President/CEO: Allen Edwards

Type: Two-Year College **Sex:** Coed **Affiliation:** Tennessee Board of Regents. **% Accepted:** 100 **Admission Plans:** Deferred Admission; Early Admission; Open Admission **Application Deadline:** Rolling **Application Fee:** $20.00 **H.S. Requirements:** High school diploma required; GED accepted. For non-degree seeking applicants 21 or over: High school diploma or equivalent not required **Scholarships:** Available. **Calendar System:** Semester, Summer session available **Student-Faculty Ratio:** 24:1 **Exams:** SAT I or ACT. **Regional Accreditation:** Southern Association of Colleges and Schools **Credit Hours For Degree:** 64 semester hours, Associates **Professional Accreditation:** ABET, ACBSP.

REMINGTON COLLEGE–MEMPHIS CAMPUS

2710 Nonconnah Blvd.
Memphis, TN 38132
Tel: (901)291-4200
Fax: (901)396-8310
E-mail: randal.hayes@remingtoncollege.edu
Web Site: www.remingtoncollege.edu
President/CEO: Lori May
Admissions: Randal Hayes

Type: Two-Year College **Sex:** Coed **Scholarships:** Available. **Calendar System:** Quarter **Professional Accreditation:** ACCSC.

REMINGTON COLLEGE–NASHVILLE CAMPUS

441 Donelson Pke.
Ste. 150
Nashville, TN 37214
Tel: (615)889-5520
Fax: (615)889-5528
E-mail: frank.vivelo@remingtoncollege.edu
Web Site: www.remingtoncollege.edu
President/CEO: James Saulsbury
Admissions: Frank Vivelo

Type: Two-Year College **Sex:** Coed **Calendar System:** Quarter **Professional Accreditation:** ACCSC.

RHODES COLLEGE

2000 N Pky.
Memphis, TN 38112-1690
Tel: (901)843-3000; Free: 800-844-5969
Fax: (901)843-3719
E-mail: adminfo@rhodes.edu
Web Site: www.rhodes.edu
President/CEO: Dr. William E. Troutt
Admissions: Carey Thompson
Financial Aid: Michael Morgan

Type: Comprehensive **Sex:** Coed **Affiliation:** Presbyterian. **Scores:** 100% SAT V 400+; 100% SAT M 400+; 3.78% ACT 18-23; 47.61% ACT 24-29 **% Accepted:** 47 **Admission Plans:** Deferred Admission; Early Action; Early Admission; Early Decision Plan **Application Deadline:** January 15 **H.S. Requirements:** High school diploma required; GED accepted **Costs Per Year:** Comprehensive fee: $56,010 includes full-time tuition ($44,632), mandatory fees ($310), and college room and board ($11,068). College room only: $5534. Room and board charges vary according to board plan and housing facility. Part-time tuition: $1865 per credit hour. **Scholarships:** Available. **Calendar System:** Semester, Summer session available **Enrollment:** Full-time 2,032, Graduate full-time 17, Part-time 14 **Faculty:** Full-time 183, Part-time 41 **Student-Faculty Ratio:** 10:1 **Exams:** ACT essay component not used; SAT I or ACT; SAT essay component not used; SAT Reasoning. **% Receiving Financial Aid:** 39 **% Residing in College-Owned, -Operated, or -Affiliated Housing:** 71 **Final Year or Final Semester Residency Requirement:** Yes **Regional Accreditation:** Southern Association of Colleges and Schools **Credit Hours For Degree:** 128 credit hours, Bachelors **ROTC:** Air Force, Army, Navy **Intercollegiate Athletics:** Badminton M & W; Baseball M; Basketball M & W; Cheerleading

W; Crew M & W; Cross-Country Running M & W; Fencing M & W; Field Hockey W; Football M; Golf M & W; Lacrosse M & W; Rugby M; Soccer M & W; Softball W; Swimming and Diving M & W; Tennis M & W; Track and Field M & W; Ultimate Frisbee M & W; Volleyball W

ROANE STATE COMMUNITY COLLEGE

276 Patton Ln.
Harriman, TN 37748-5011
Tel: (865)354-3000; Free: 866-462-7722
Fax: (865)882-4562
E-mail: admissionsrecords@roanestate.edu
Web Site: www.roanestate.edu
President/CEO: Chris Whaley
Financial Aid: Jennifer Fugate
Type: Two-Year College **Sex:** Coed **Affiliation:** Tennessee Board of Regents. **Scores:** 50.5% ACT 18-23; 6.5% ACT 24-29 **% Accepted:** 97 **Admission Plans:** Deferred Admission; Early Admission; Open Admission **Application Deadline:** Rolling **Application Fee:** $20.00 **H.S. Requirements:** High school diploma required; GED accepted **Costs Per Year:** Application fee: $20. State resident tuition: $3528 full-time. Nonresident tuition: $14,592 full-time. Mandatory fees: $303 full-time. **Scholarships:** Available. **Calendar System:** Semester, Summer session available **Enrollment:** Full-time 2,358, Part-time 3,474 **Faculty:** Full-time 121, Part-time 264 **Student-Faculty Ratio:** 17:1 **Final Year or Final Semester Residency Requirement:** No **Regional Accreditation:** Southern Association of Colleges and Schools **Credit Hours For Degree:** 60 semester hours, Associates **ROTC:** Air Force, Army **Professional Accreditation:** ACBSP, ACEN, ADA, AHIMA, AOTA, APTA, COA, CoARC, JRCERT. **Intercollegiate Athletics:** Baseball M; Basketball M & W; Softball W

SAE INSTITUTE NASHVILLE

7 Music Cir. N
Nashville, TN 37203
Tel: (615)244-5848
Web Site: www.sae.edu
Type: Two-Year College **Sex:** Coed **Professional Accreditation:** ACCSC.

SEWANEE: THE UNIVERSITY OF THE SOUTH

735 University Ave.
Sewanee, TN 37383-1000
Tel: (931)598-1000; Free: 800-522-2234
Fax: (931)598-1145
E-mail: admiss@sewanee.edu
Web Site: www.sewanee.edu
President/CEO: Dr. John M. McCardell, Jr.
Admissions: Lisa Burns
Financial Aid: Beth A. Cragar
Type: Comprehensive **Sex:** Coed **Affiliation:** Episcopal. **Scores:** 100% SAT V 400+; 100% SAT M 400+; 4.82% ACT 18-23; 59.04% ACT 24-29 **% Accepted:** 41 **Admission Plans:** Deferred Admission; Early Action; Early Admission; Early Decision Plan **Application Deadline:** February 1 **Application Fee:** $0.00 **H.S. Requirements:** High school diploma required; GED not accepted **Costs Per Year:** Application fee: $0. Comprehensive fee: $54,500 includes full-time tuition ($42,128), mandatory fees ($272), and college room and board ($12,100). College room only: $6270. Full-time tuition and fees vary according to student level. Room and board charges vary according to student level. Part-time tuition: $1375 per credit hour. Part-time tuition varies according to student level. Tuition guaranteed not to increase for student's term of enrollment. **Scholarships:** Available. **Calendar System:** Semester, Summer session available **Enrollment:** Full-time 1,685, Graduate full-time 74, Graduate part-time 13, Part-time 25 **Faculty:** Full-time 160, Part-time 63 **Student-Faculty Ratio:** 10:1 **Exams:** ACT essay component used for admission; Other; SAT I or ACT; SAT essay component used for admission; SAT Reasoning; SAT Subject. **% Receiving Financial Aid:** 48 **% Residing in College-Owned, -Operated, or -Affiliated Housing:** 98 **Final Year or Final Semester Residency Requirement:** Yes **Regional Accreditation:** Southern Association of Colleges and Schools **Credit Hours For Degree:** 128 semester hours, Bachelors **Professional Accreditation:** ACIPE, ATS. **Intercollegiate Athletics:** Baseball M; Basketball M & W; Cheerleading W; Crew M & W; Cross-Country Running M & W; Equestrian Sports M & W; Fencing M & W; Field Hockey W; Football M; Golf M & W; Ice Hockey M & W; Lacrosse M & W; Rugby M & W; Soccer M & W; Softball W; Squash M & W; Swimming and Diving M & W; Tennis M & W; Track and Field M & W; Volleyball W

SOUTH COLLEGE

720 N Fifth Ave.
Knoxville, TN 37917
Tel: (865)524-3043
Fax: (865)673-8019
E-mail: whosea@southcollegetn.edu
Web Site: www.southcollegetn.edu
President/CEO: Stephen A. South
Admissions: Walter Hosea
Type: Comprehensive **Sex:** Coed **% Accepted:** 100 **Admission Plans:** Deferred Admission; Early Admission **Application Deadline:** October 1 **Application Fee:** $50.00 **H.S. Requirements:** High school diploma required; GED accepted **Scholarships:** Available. **Calendar System:** Quarter, Summer session available **Student-Faculty Ratio:** 16:1 **Regional Accreditation:** Southern Association of Colleges and Schools **Credit Hours For Degree:** 94 quarter hours, Associates **Professional Accreditation:** AAMAE, ACEN, AOTA, APTA.

SOUTHERN ADVENTIST UNIVERSITY

PO Box 370
Collegedale, TN 37315-0370
Tel: (423)236-2000; Free: 800-768-8437
Fax: (423)236-1000
E-mail: emilyfreck@southern.edu
Web Site: www.southern.edu
President/CEO: Gordon Bietz
Admissions: Emily Freck
Financial Aid: Marc Grundy
Type: Comprehensive **Sex:** Coed **Affiliation:** Seventh-day Adventist. **Scores:** 95% SAT V 400+; 93% SAT M 400+; 50% ACT 18-23; 34% ACT 24-29 **% Accepted:** 60 **Admission Plans:** Deferred Admission **Application Deadline:** Rolling **Application Fee:** $25.00 **H.S. Requirements:** High school diploma required; GED accepted **Costs Per Year:** Application fee: $25. Comprehensive fee: $27,600 includes full-time tuition ($20,300), mandatory fees ($850), and college room and board ($6450). College room only: $4050. Full-time tuition and fees vary according to course load. Room and board charges vary according to board plan. Part-time tuition: $850 per credit hour. Part-time mandatory fees: $850 per term. Part-time tuition and fees vary according to course load. **Scholarships:** Available. **Calendar System:** Semester, Summer session available **Enrollment:** Full-time 2,225, Graduate full-time 205, Graduate part-time 247, Part-time 448 **Faculty:** Full-time 172, Part-time 2 **Student-Faculty Ratio:** 15:1 **Exams:** SAT I or ACT; SAT Reasoning; SAT Subject. **% Receiving Financial Aid:** 70 **Final Year or Final Semester Residency Requirement:** Yes **Regional Accreditation:** Southern Association of Colleges and Schools **Credit Hours For Degree:** 64 semester hours, Associates; 124 semester hours, Bachelors **Professional Accreditation:** ABET, ACEN, CSWE, NASM, NCATE.

SOUTHWEST TENNESSEE COMMUNITY COLLEGE

PO Box 780
Memphis, TN 38101-0780
Tel: (901)333-5000; Free: 877-717-STCC
Fax: (901)333-4273
E-mail: vdowdy@southwest.tn.edu
Web Site: www.southwest.tn.edu
President/CEO: Dr. Tracy Hall
Admissions: Vanessa Dowdy
Type: Two-Year College **Sex:** Coed **Affiliation:** Tennessee Board of Regents. **% Accepted:** 100 **Admission Plans:** Deferred Admission; Early Admission; Open Admission **Application Fee:** $10.00 **H.S. Requirements:** High school diploma required; GED accepted **Scholarships:** Available. **Calendar System:** Semester, Summer session available **Enrollment:** Full-time 4,183, Part-time 5,984 **Regional Accreditation:** Southern Association of Colleges and Schools **Credit Hours For Degree:** 64 semester hours, Associates **ROTC:** Air Force, Army **Professional Accreditation:** ABET, ACBSP, ACEN, APTA, JRCERT, NAACLS.

STRAYER UNIVERSITY–KNOXVILLE CAMPUS

10118 Parkside Dr.
Ste. 200
Knoxville, TN 37922
Tel: (865)288-6000
Fax: (865)288-6030
Web Site: www.strayer.edu/tennessee/knoxville

President/CEO: Brian W. Jones
Type: Comprehensive **Sex:** Coed **Regional Accreditation:** Middle States Association of Colleges and Schools

STRAYER UNIVERSITY–NASHVILLE CAMPUS

1809 Dabbs Ave.
Nashville, TN 37210
Tel: (615)871-2260
Fax: (615)391-5330
Web Site: www.strayer.edu/tennessee/nashville
President/CEO: Brian W. Jones
Type: Comprehensive **Sex:** Coed **Regional Accreditation:** Middle States Association of Colleges and Schools

STRAYER UNIVERSITY–SHELBY CAMPUS

7275 Appling Farms Pky.
Memphis, TN 38133
Tel: (901)383-6750
Fax: (901)373-8700
Web Site: www.strayer.edu/tennessee/shelby
President/CEO: Brian W. Jones
Type: Comprehensive **Sex:** Coed **Regional Accreditation:** Middle States Association of Colleges and Schools

STRAYER UNIVERSITY–THOUSAND OAKS CAMPUS

2620 Thousand Oaks Blvd.
Ste. 1100
Memphis, TN 38118
Tel: (901)369-0835
Fax: (901)565-9400
Web Site: www.strayer.edu/tennessee/thousand-oaks
President/CEO: Brian W. Jones
Type: Comprehensive **Sex:** Coed **Regional Accreditation:** Middle States Association of Colleges and Schools

TENNESSEE STATE UNIVERSITY

3500 John A Merritt Blvd.
Nashville, TN 37209-1561
Tel: (615)963-5000
Fax: (615)963-5108
E-mail: jcade@tnstate.edu
Web Site: www.tnstate.edu
President/CEO: Dr. Glenda Baskin Glover
Admissions: Dr. John Cade
Financial Aid: Amy Wood
Type: Comprehensive **Sex:** Coed **Affiliation:** Tennessee Board of Regents. **Scores:** 50% SAT V 400+; 64% SAT M 400+; 43% ACT 18-23; 6% ACT 24-29 **% Accepted:** 61 **Admission Plans:** Preferred Admission **Application Deadline:** August 1 **Application Fee:** $25.00 **H.S. Requirements:** High school diploma required; GED accepted **Costs Per Year:** Application fee: $25. State resident tuition: $246 full-time. Nonresident tuition: $776 full-time. **Scholarships:** Available. **Calendar System:** Semester, Summer session available **Enrollment:** Full-time 5,975, Graduate full-time 830, Graduate part-time 1,073, Part-time 1,289 **Faculty:** Full-time 398, Part-time 140 **Student-Faculty Ratio:** 17:1 **Exams:** SAT I or ACT. **% Receiving Financial Aid:** 85 **Regional Accreditation:** Southern Association of Colleges and Schools **Credit Hours For Degree:** 65 semester hours, Associates; 132 semester hours, Bachelors **ROTC:** Air Force, Army, Navy **Professional Accreditation:** AACSB, AAFCS, ABET, ACEN, ADA, AHIMA, AOTA, APA, APTA, ASHA, CSWE, CoARC, NAACLS, NASAD, NASM, NASPAA, NCATE. **Intercollegiate Athletics:** Basketball M & W; Cross-Country Running M & W; Football M; Golf M; Softball W; Tennis M & W; Track and Field M & W; Volleyball W

TENNESSEE TECHNOLOGICAL UNIVERSITY

N Dixie Ave.
Cookeville, TN 38505
Tel: (931)372-3101; Free: 800-255-8881
Fax: (931)372-6250
E-mail: admissions@tntech.edu
Web Site: www.tntech.edu
President/CEO: Dr. Phillip Oldham
Admissions: Alexis Pope
Financial Aid: Lester C. McKenzie, III

Type: University **Sex:** Coed **Affiliation:** Tennessee Board of Regents. **Scores:** 95% SAT V 400+; 94% SAT M 400+; 52% ACT 18-23; 36% ACT 24-29 **% Accepted:** 93 **Admission Plans:** Deferred Admission; Early Admission; Preferred Admission **Application Deadline:** August 1 **Application Fee:** $25.00 **H.S. Requirements:** High school diploma required; GED accepted **Costs Per Year:** Application fee: $25. State resident tuition: $6840 full-time, $358 per credit hour part-time. Nonresident tuition: $22,272 full-time, $1001 per credit hour part-time. Mandatory fees: $1171 full-time. Full-time tuition and fees vary according to course load and program. Part-time tuition varies according to course load and program. College room and board: $8700. College room only: $4590. Room and board charges vary according to board plan and housing facility. **Scholarships:** Available. **Calendar System:** Semester, Summer session available **Enrollment:** Full-time 9,140, Graduate full-time 381, Graduate part-time 685, Part-time 912 **Faculty:** Full-time 417, Part-time 263 **Student-Faculty Ratio:** 22:1 **Exams:** ACT; SAT I or ACT. **% Receiving Financial Aid:** 70 **% Residing in College-Owned, -Operated, or -Affiliated Housing:** 30 **Regional Accreditation:** Southern Association of Colleges and Schools **Credit Hours For Degree:** 120 semester hours, Bachelors **ROTC:** Air Force, Army **Professional Accreditation:** AACN, AACSB, AAFCS, ABET, ATMAE, NASAD, NASM, NCATE. **Intercollegiate Athletics:** Baseball M; Basketball M & W; Cheerleading M & W; Cross-Country Running M & W; Football M; Golf M & W; Soccer W; Softball W; Tennis M; Track and Field W; Volleyball W

TENNESSEE WESLEYAN COLLEGE

204 E College St.
Athens, TN 37303
Tel: (423)745-7504; Free: 800-PICK-TWC
Fax: (423)744-9968
E-mail: admissions@twcnet.edu
Web Site: www.tnwesleyan.edu
President/CEO: Dr. Harley Knowles
Admissions: Joanne Landers
Financial Aid: Lacey Weese
Type: Comprehensive **Sex:** Coed **Affiliation:** United Methodist. **Scores:** 79% SAT V 400+; 83% SAT M 400+; 52.58% ACT 18-23; 32.99% ACT 24-29 **% Accepted:** 65 **Admission Plans:** Deferred Admission **Application Deadline:** Rolling **Application Fee:** $30.00 **H.S. Requirements:** High school diploma required; GED accepted **Costs Per Year:** Application fee: $30. Comprehensive fee: $30,540 includes full-time tuition ($22,000), mandatory fees ($1000), and college room and board ($7540). Full-time tuition and fees vary according to class time and degree level. Room and board charges vary according to board plan and housing facility. Part-time tuition: $570 per credit. Part-time tuition varies according to class time, course load, degree level, location, and program. **Scholarships:** Available. **Calendar System:** Semester, Summer session available **Enrollment:** Full-time 955, Graduate full-time 3, Graduate part-time 19, Part-time 71 **Faculty:** Full-time 59, Part-time 63 **Student-Faculty Ratio:** 12:1 **Exams:** SAT I or ACT; SAT Subject. **% Receiving Financial Aid:** 67 **% Residing in College-Owned, -Operated, or -Affiliated Housing:** 35 **Final Year or Final Semester Residency Requirement:** No **Regional Accreditation:** Southern Association of Colleges and Schools **Credit Hours For Degree:** 120 semester hours, Bachelors **Professional Accreditation:** AACN. **Intercollegiate Athletics:** Baseball M; Basketball M & W; Bowling M & W; Cheerleading M & W; Cross-Country Running M & W; Golf M & W; Lacrosse M & W; Soccer M & W; Softball W; Tennis M & W; Track and Field M & W; Volleyball W

TREVECCA NAZARENE UNIVERSITY

333 Murfreesboro Rd.
Nashville, TN 37210-2877
Tel: (615)248-1200; Free: 888-210-4TNU
Fax: (615)248-7728
E-mail: admissions_und@trevecca.edu
Web Site: www.trevecca.edu
President/CEO: Dr. Dan Boone
Admissions: Melinda Miller
Financial Aid: Eddie White
Type: Comprehensive **Sex:** Coed **Affiliation:** Nazarene. **Scores:** 87% SAT V 400+; 95% SAT M 400+; 49.83% ACT 18-23; 33.22% ACT 24-29 **% Accepted:** 73 **Admission Plans:** Deferred Admission; Early Admission **Application Deadline:** August 1 **Application Fee:** $25.00 **H.S. Requirements:** High school diploma required; GED accepted **Costs Per Year:** Application fee: $25. Comprehensive fee: $32,048 includes full-time tuition

($23,248), mandatory fees ($500), and college room and board ($8300). College room only: $4150. Full-time tuition and fees vary according to course load and program. Room and board charges vary according to board plan. Part-time tuition: $898 per credit hour. Part-time tuition varies according to course load and program. **Scholarships:** Available. **Calendar System:** Semester, Summer session available **Enrollment:** Full-time 1,244, Graduate full-time 592, Graduate part-time 217, Part-time 587 **Faculty:** Full-time 81, Part-time 128 **Student-Faculty Ratio:** 17:1 **Exams:** ACT essay component not used; SAT I or ACT; SAT essay component not used; SAT Reasoning. **% Residing in College-Owned, -Operated, or -Affiliated Housing:** 45 **Regional Accreditation:** Southern Association of Colleges and Schools **Credit Hours For Degree:** 60 semester hours, Associates; 120 semester hours, Bachelors **ROTC:** Army **Professional Accreditation:** AACN, NASM, NCATE. **Intercollegiate Athletics:** Baseball M; Basketball M & W; Cross-Country Running M & W; Golf M & W; Soccer M & W; Softball W; Track and Field M & W; Volleyball W

TUSCULUM COLLEGE

60 Shiloh Rd.
Greeneville, TN 37743-9997
Tel: (423)636-7300; Free: 800-729-0256
Fax: (423)638-7166
E-mail: admissions@tusculum.edu
Web Site: www.tusculum.edu
President/CEO: Dr. Nancy B. Moody
Admissions: Andrew Starnes
Financial Aid: Karen Sartain

Type: Comprehensive **Sex:** Coed **Affiliation:** Presbyterian. **Scores:** 86% SAT M 400+; 57% ACT 18-23; 20% ACT 24-29 **% Accepted:** 69 **Admission Plans:** Deferred Admission; Early Admission **Application Deadline:** Rolling **Application Fee:** $0.00 **H.S. Requirements:** High school diploma required; GED accepted **Costs Per Year:** Application fee: $0. Comprehensive fee: $31,625 includes full-time tuition ($23,125) and college room and board ($8500). College room only: $5610. Part-time tuition: $718 per credit hour. **Scholarships:** Available. **Calendar System:** Semester, Summer session available **Enrollment:** Full-time 1,505, Graduate full-time 109, Graduate part-time 81, Part-time 114 **Faculty:** Full-time 71, Part-time 81 **Student-Faculty Ratio:** 17:1 **Exams:** SAT I or ACT. **% Receiving Financial Aid:** 84 **% Residing in College-Owned, -Operated, or -Affiliated Housing:** 46 **Final Year or Final Semester Residency Requirement:** No **Regional Accreditation:** Southern Association of Colleges and Schools **Credit Hours For Degree:** 128 credit hours, Bachelors **Intercollegiate Athletics:** Baseball M; Basketball M & W; Cheerleading W; Cross-Country Running M & W; Football M; Golf M & W; Lacrosse M & W; Soccer M & W; Softball W; Tennis M & W; Volleyball W

UNION UNIVERSITY

1050 Union University Dr.
Jackson, TN 38305-3697
Tel: (731)668-1818; Free: 800-33-UNION
Fax: (731)661-5187
E-mail: rgraves@uu.edu
Web Site: www.uu.edu
President/CEO: Dr. Samuel (Dub) W. Oliver
Admissions: Robbie Graves
Financial Aid: John Windham

Type: Comprehensive **Sex:** Coed **Affiliation:** Southern Baptist. **Scores:** 97% SAT V 400+; 100% SAT M 400+; 34.97% ACT 18-23; 45.09% ACT 24-29 **% Accepted:** 68 **Admission Plans:** Deferred Admission; Early Admission **Application Deadline:** Rolling **Application Fee:** $35.00 **H.S. Requirements:** High school diploma required; GED accepted **Costs Per Year:** Application fee: $35. Comprehensive fee: $38,630 includes full-time tuition ($28,200), mandatory fees ($990), and college room and board ($9440). Full-time tuition and fees vary according to class time, course load, degree level, location, and program. Room and board charges vary according to board plan and housing facility. Part-time tuition: $940 per credit hour. Part-time mandatory fees: $42 per credit hour. Part-time tuition and fees vary according to class time, course load, degree level, location, and program. **Scholarships:** Available. **Calendar System:** 4-1-4, Summer session available **Enrollment:** Full-time 1,872, Graduate full-time 810, Graduate part-time 253, Part-time 638 **Faculty:** Full-time 239, Part-time 3 **Student-Faculty Ratio:** 8:1 **Exams:** ACT essay component not used; SAT I or ACT; SAT essay component not used. **% Receiving Financial Aid:** 66 **Regional Accreditation:** Southern Association of Colleges and Schools **Credit Hours**

For Degree: 66 semester hours, Associates; 128 semester hours, Bachelors **ROTC:** Army **Professional Accreditation:** AACN, AANA, ABET, CSWE, NASAD, NASM, NCATE. **Intercollegiate Athletics:** Baseball M; Basketball M & W; Cheerleading W; Cross-Country Running M & W; Golf M; Soccer M & W; Softball W; Track and Field M & W; Volleyball W

UNIVERSITY OF MEMPHIS

Memphis, TN 38152
Tel: (901)678-2000; Free: 800-669-2678
Fax: (901)678-3053
E-mail: admissions@memphis.edu
Web Site: www.memphis.edu
President/CEO: David Rudd
Admissions: Gloria W. Moore
Financial Aid: Richard Ritzman

Type: University **Sex:** Coed **Affiliation:** Tennessee Board of Regents. **Scores:** 92% SAT V 400+; 95% SAT M 400+; 56.25% ACT 18-23; 32.87% ACT 24-29 **% Accepted:** 92 **Admission Plans:** Early Admission **Application Deadline:** July 1 **Application Fee:** $25.00 **H.S. Requirements:** High school diploma required; GED accepted **Costs Per Year:** Application fee: $25. State resident tuition: $7686 full-time, $305 per credit hour part-time. Nonresident tuition: $19,398 full-time, $793 per credit hour part-time. Mandatory fees: $1583 full-time. Full-time tuition and fees vary according to course load, degree level, program, and reciprocity agreements. Part-time tuition varies according to course load, degree level, and program. College room and board: $9061. College room only: $5437. Room and board charges vary according to board plan, housing facility, and location. **Scholarships:** Available. **Calendar System:** Semester, Summer session available **Enrollment:** Full-time 12,053, Graduate full-time 1,967, Graduate part-time 1,979, Part-time 4,586 **Faculty:** Full-time 881, Part-time 554 **Student-Faculty Ratio:** 15:1 **Exams:** SAT I or ACT; SAT Reasoning. **% Receiving Financial Aid:** 67 **% Residing in College-Owned, -Operated, or -Affiliated Housing:** 14 **Final Year or Final Semester Residency Requirement:** Yes **Regional Accreditation:** Southern Association of Colleges and Schools **Credit Hours For Degree:** 120 semester hours, Bachelors **ROTC:** Air Force, Army, Navy **Professional Accreditation:** AACN, AACSB, AAFCS, AALS, ABA, ABET, ACA, ACEJMC, ACSP, AND, APA, ASHA, CAHME, CIDA, CORE, CSWE, NASAD, NASM, NASPAA, NAST, NCATE. **Intercollegiate Athletics:** Baseball M; Basketball M & W; Cheerleading M & W; Cross-Country Running M & W; Football M; Golf M & W; Racquetball M & W; Riflery M & W; Soccer M & W; Softball W; Swimming and Diving M & W; Tennis M & W; Track and Field M & W; Volleyball W

THE UNIVERSITY OF TENNESSEE

Knoxville, TN 37996
Tel: (865)974-1000
E-mail: admissions@utk.edu
Web Site: www.utk.edu
President/CEO: Dr. Jimmy G. Cheek
Admissions: Norma Harrington
Financial Aid: Jeffery Gerkin

Type: University **Sex:** Coed **Affiliation:** University of Tennessee System. **Scores:** 99% SAT V 400+; 99% SAT M 400+; 18% ACT 18-23; 54% ACT 24-29 **% Accepted:** 76 **Application Deadline:** December 1 **Application Fee:** $50.00 **H.S. Requirements:** High school diploma required; GED accepted. For architecture, engineering, nursing programs: High school diploma required; GED not accepted **Costs Per Year:** Application fee: $50. State resident tuition: $10,678 full-time, $359 per hour part-time. Nonresident tuition: $28,868 full-time, $1110 per hour part-time. Mandatory fees: $1758 full-time, $84 per hour part-time. Full-time tuition and fees vary according to course level, location, program, reciprocity agreements, and student level. Part-time tuition and fees vary according to course level, location, program, reciprocity agreements, and student level. College room and board: $9926. Room and board charges vary according to board plan and housing facility. **Scholarships:** Available. **Calendar System:** Semester, Summer session available **Enrollment:** Full-time 20,569, Graduate full-time 3,894, Graduate part-time 2,088, Part-time 1,294 **Faculty:** Full-time 1,526, Part-time 205 **Student-Faculty Ratio:** 17:1 **Exams:** ACT essay component not used; SAT I or ACT; SAT essay component not used; SAT Reasoning. **% Receiving Financial Aid:** 59 **% Residing in College-Owned, -Operated, or -Affiliated Housing:** 33 **Final Year or Final Semester Residency Requirement:** Yes **Regional Accreditation:** Southern Association of Colleges and Schools **Credit Hours For Degree:** 120-128 semester hours, depending on program, Bachelors **ROTC:** Air Force, Army **Professional Accreditation:**

AACN, AACSB, AAFCS, AALS, AANA, ABA, ABET, ACA, ACEJMC, ACSP, ACIPE, ALA, AND, APA, ASHA, ASLA, AVMA, CEPH, CIDA, CORE, CSWE, JRCNMT, NAAB, NAACLS, NASAD, NASM, NASPAA, NAST, NCATE, NRPA, SAF. **Intercollegiate Athletics:** Baseball M; Basketball M & W; Crew W; Cross-Country Running M & W; Football M; Golf M & W; Soccer W; Softball W; Swimming and Diving M & W; Tennis M & W; Track and Field M & W; Volleyball W

THE UNIVERSITY OF TENNESSEE AT CHATTANOOGA

615 McCallie Ave.
Chattanooga, TN 37403-2598
Tel: (423)425-4111; Free: 800-882-6627
Fax: (423)425-4157
E-mail: admissions@utc.edu
Web Site: www.utc.edu
President/CEO: Steve Angle
Admissions: Lee Pierce
Financial Aid: Jennifer Buckles
Type: Comprehensive **Sex:** Coed **Affiliation:** University of Tennessee System. **Scores:** 95% SAT V 400+; 94% SAT M 400+; 55.2% ACT 18-23; 37.7% ACT 24-29 **% Accepted:** 79 **Admission Plans:** Deferred Admission; Early Admission **Application Deadline:** May 1 **Application Fee:** $100.00 **H.S. Requirements:** High school diploma required; GED accepted **Costs Per Year:** Application fee: $100. State resident tuition: $6624 full-time, $276 per credit hour part-time. Nonresident tuition: $22,742 full-time, $948 per credit hour part-time. Mandatory fees: $1732 full-time, $253 per credit hour part-time. Full-time tuition and fees vary according to degree level. Part-time tuition and fees vary according to degree level. College room and board: $8388. College room only: $5068. Room and board charges vary according to board plan, housing facility, and location. **Scholarships:** Available. **Calendar System:** Semester, Summer session available **Enrollment:** Full-time 8,763, Graduate full-time 606, Graduate part-time 698, Part-time 1,321 **Faculty:** Full-time 431, Part-time 260 **Student-Faculty Ratio:** 20:1 **Exams:** ACT essay component not used; SAT I or ACT; SAT essay component not used; SAT Reasoning; SAT Subject. **% Receiving Financial Aid:** 61 **% Residing in College-Owned, -Operated, or -Affiliated Housing:** 30 **Final Year or Final Semester Residency Requirement:** No **Regional Accreditation:** Southern Association of Colleges and Schools **Credit Hours For Degree:** 120 semester hours, Bachelors **ROTC:** Army **Professional Accreditation:** AACN, AACSB, AANA, ABET, ACA, ACEJMC, APTA, CIDA, CSWE, NASAD, NASM, NASPAA, NCATE. **Intercollegiate Athletics:** Basketball M & W; Cross-Country Running M & W; Football M; Golf M & W; Soccer W; Softball W; Tennis M & W; Track and Field M & W; Volleyball W; Wrestling M

THE UNIVERSITY OF TENNESSEE AT MARTIN

554 University St.
Martin, TN 38238
Tel: (731)881-7000; Free: 800-829-8861
Fax: (731)881-7029
E-mail: jdmantooth@utm.edu
Web Site: www.utm.edu
President/CEO: Dr. Robert M. Smith
Admissions: Dr. James Mantooth
Financial Aid: Amy J. Mistric
Type: Comprehensive **Sex:** Coed **Affiliation:** University of Tennessee System. **Scores:** 60.1% ACT 18-23; 32.53% ACT 24-29 **% Accepted:** 70 **Admission Plans:** Deferred Admission; Early Admission **Application Fee:** $30.00 **H.S. Requirements:** High school diploma required; GED accepted **Costs Per Year:** Application fee: $30. State resident tuition: $6918 full-time, $288 per credit hour part-time. Nonresident tuition: $20,862 full-time, $869 per credit hour part-time. Mandatory fees: $1408 full-time, $59 per credit hour part-time. Part-time tuition and fees vary according to course load. College room and board: $5896. College room only: $2780. Room and board charges vary according to board plan and housing facility. **Scholarships:** Available. **Calendar System:** Semester, Summer session available **Enrollment:** Full-time 5,401, Graduate full-time 61, Graduate part-time 331, Part-time 1,034 **Faculty:** Full-time 289, Part-time 221 **Student-Faculty Ratio:** 16:1 **Exams:** ACT essay component not used; SAT I or ACT; SAT Reasoning; SAT Subject. **% Receiving Financial Aid:** 73 **% Residing in College-Owned, -Operated, or -Affiliated Housing:** 30 **Final Year or Final Semester Residency Requirement:** Yes **Regional Accreditation:** Southern Association of Colleges and Schools **Credit Hours For Degree:** 120 semester hours, Bachelors **ROTC:** Army **Professional Accreditation:**

AACSB, AAFCS, ABET, ACEJMC, ACEN, AND, CSWE, NASM, NCATE. **Intercollegiate Athletics:** Baseball M; Basketball M & W; Cheerleading W; Cross-Country Running M & W; Equestrian Sports W; Football M; Golf M; Riflery M & W; Soccer W; Softball W; Tennis W; Volleyball W

VANDERBILT UNIVERSITY

Nashville, TN 37240-1001
Tel: (615)322-7311; Free: 800-288-0432
Fax: (615)343-7765
E-mail: admissions@vanderbilt.edu
Web Site: www.vanderbilt.edu
President/CEO: Nicholas S. Zeppos
Admissions: John O. Gaines
Financial Aid: Brent Tener
Type: University **Sex:** Coed **Scores:** 100% SAT V 400+; 100% SAT M 400+; 2.27% ACT 18-23; 5.52% ACT 24-29 **% Accepted:** 12 **Admission Plans:** Deferred Admission; Early Action; Early Admission **Application Deadline:** January 1 **Application Fee:** $50.00 **H.S. Requirements:** High school diploma required; GED accepted **Costs Per Year:** Application fee: $50. Comprehensive fee: $59,382 includes full-time tuition ($43,620), mandatory fees ($1092), and college room and board ($14,670). College room only: $9580. Room and board charges vary according to board plan. Part-time tuition: $1818 per credit hour. **Scholarships:** Available. **Calendar System:** Semester, Summer session available **Enrollment:** Full-time 6,822, Graduate full-time 4,985, Graduate part-time 699, Part-time 61 **Faculty:** Full-time 920, Part-time 259 **Student-Faculty Ratio:** 8:1 **Exams:** ACT; SAT I; SAT I and SAT II or ACT; SAT I or ACT; SAT II; SAT Reasoning; SAT Subject. **% Receiving Financial Aid:** 48 **% Residing in College-Owned, -Operated, or -Affiliated Housing:** 92 **Final Year or Final Semester Residency Requirement:** No **Regional Accreditation:** Southern Association of Colleges and Schools **Credit Hours For Degree:** 120 semester hours, Bachelors **ROTC:** Air Force, Army, Navy **Professional Accreditation:** AACSB, AALS, ABA, ABET, ACA, ACEN, ACNM, ACIPE, AND, APA, ASHA, ATS, JRCNMT, LCME/AMA, NAACLS, NASM, NCATE. **Intercollegiate Athletics:** Baseball M; Basketball M & W; Bowling W; Cross-Country Running M & W; Football M; Golf M & W; Lacrosse W; Soccer W; Swimming and Diving W; Tennis M & W; Track and Field W

VATTEROTT COLLEGE (MEMPHIS)

2655 Dividend Dr.
Memphis, TN 38132
Tel: (901)761-5730; Free: 888-553-6627
Fax: (901)763-2897
Web Site: www.vatterott.edu
President/CEO: Christinetta Shelton
Type: Two-Year College **Sex:** Coed **% Accepted:** 45 **Calendar System:** Semester **Professional Accreditation:** ACCSC.

VATTEROTT COLLEGE (MEMPHIS)

6991 Appling Farms Pky.
Memphis, TN 38133
Tel: (901)372-2399
Web Site: www.vatterott.edu
Type: Two-Year College **Sex:** Coed **Professional Accreditation:** ACCSC.

VIRGINIA COLLEGE IN CHATTANOOGA

721 Eastgate Loop Rd.
Chattanooga, TN 37411
Tel: (888)232-7887
Web Site: www.vc.edu
Type: Two-Year College **Sex:** Coed **Professional Accreditation:** ACICS.

VIRGINIA COLLEGE IN KNOXVILLE

5003 N Broadway St.
Knoxville, TN 37918
Tel: (865)745-4500
Web Site: www.vc.edu
Type: Two-Year College **Sex:** Coed **Professional Accreditation:** ACICS.

VISIBLE MUSIC COLLEGE

200 Madison Ave.
Memphis, TN 38103
Tel: (901)381-3939
Web Site: visible.edu

Type: Four-Year College **Sex:** Coed **Professional Accreditation:** TRACS.

VOLUNTEER STATE COMMUNITY COLLEGE

1480 Nashville Pke.
Gallatin, TN 37066-3188
Tel: (615)452-8600; Free: 888-335-8722
Fax: (615)230-3577
E-mail: admissions@volstate.edu
Web Site: www.volstate.edu
President/CEO: Dr. Jerry Faulkner
Admissions: Tim Amyx
Financial Aid: Sue Pedigo
Type: Two-Year College **Sex:** Coed **Affiliation:** Tennessee Board of Regents. **% Accepted:** 100 **Admission Plans:** Deferred Admission; Early Admission; Open Admission **Application Deadline:** August 25 **Application Fee:** $20.00 **H.S. Requirements:** High school diploma required; GED accepted **Costs Per Year:** Application fee: $20. State resident tuition: $3648 full-time, $152 per credit hour part-time. Nonresident tuition: $15,048 full-time, $627 per credit hour part-time. Mandatory fees: $277 full-time, $9 per hour part-time, $26 per term part-time. Full-time tuition and fees vary according to course load. Part-time tuition and fees vary according to course load. **Scholarships:** Available. **Calendar System:** Semester, Summer session available **Enrollment:** Full-time 4,267, Part-time 3,801 **Faculty:** Full-time 169, Part-time 242 **Student-Faculty Ratio:** 22:1 **Exams:** SAT I or ACT; SAT essay component not used; SAT Reasoning; SAT Subject. **Final Year or Final Semester Residency Requirement:** No **Regional Accreditation:** Southern Association of Colleges and Schools **Credit Hours For Degree:** 60 semester hours, Associates **Professional Accreditation:** ACBSP, ADA, AHIMA, APTA, CoARC, JRCEMTP, JRCERT. **Intercollegiate Athletics:** Baseball M; Basketball M & W; Softball W

WALTERS STATE COMMUNITY COLLEGE

500 S Davy Crockett Pky.
Morristown, TN 37813-6899
Tel: (423)585-2600; Free: 800-225-4770
E-mail: mike.campbell@ws.edu
Web Site: www.ws.edu
President/CEO: Dr. Wade B. McCamey
Admissions: Michael Campbell
Financial Aid: Terri Janeen Stansberry
Type: Two-Year College **Sex:** Coed **Affiliation:** Tennessee Board of Regents. **Scores:** 54% ACT 18-23; 14% ACT 24-29 **% Accepted:** 44 **Admission Plans:** Early Admission; Open Admission **Application Deadline:** Rolling **Application Fee:** $0.00 **H.S. Requirements:** High school diploma required; GED accepted **Costs Per Year:** Application fee: $0. State resident tuition: $3936 full-time, $152 per credit hour part-time. Nonresident tuition: $15,336 full-time, $627 per credit hour part-time. Mandatory fees: $288 full-time, $16 per credit hour part-time, $19.50 per term part-time. Full-time tuition and fees vary according to course load and program. Part-time tuition and fees vary according to course load and program. **Scholarships:** Available. **Calendar System:** Semester, Summer session available **Enrollment:** Full-time 3,227, Part-time 2,720 **Faculty:** Full-time 164, Part-time 208 **Student-Faculty Ratio:** 18:1 **Exams:** ACT essay component not used; SAT essay component not used. **Final Year or Final Semester Residency Requirement:** No **Regional Accreditation:** Southern Association of Colleges and Schools **Credit Hours For Degree:** 60 semester hours, Associates **Professional Accreditation:** ACBSP, ACEN, ACF, APTA, ATMAE, CoARC. **Intercollegiate Athletics:** Baseball M; Basketball M & W; Golf M; Softball W; Volleyball W

WATKINS COLLEGE OF ART, DESIGN, & FILM

2298 Rosa L. Parks Blvd.
Nashville, TN 37228
Tel: (615)383-4848
Fax: (615)383-4849
E-mail: admissions@watkins.edu
Web Site: www.watkins.edu
President/CEO: Ellen L. Meyer
Admissions: Linda E. Schwab
Financial Aid: Lyle Jones
Type: Four-Year College **Sex:** Coed **Scores:** 59% ACT 18-23; 20% ACT

24-29 **% Accepted:** 94 **Admission Plans:** Deferred Admission; Early Admission **Application Deadline:** July 15 **Application Fee:** $50.00 **H.S. Requirements:** High school diploma required; GED accepted **Scholarships:** Available. **Calendar System:** Semester, Summer session available **Enrollment:** Full-time 251, Part-time 111 **Faculty:** Full-time 20, Part-time 36 **Student-Faculty Ratio:** 13:1 **Exams:** ACT essay component not used; SAT I or ACT; SAT essay component not used; SAT Reasoning; SAT Subject. **% Residing in College-Owned, -Operated, or -Affiliated Housing:** 24 **Final Year or Final Semester Residency Requirement:** Yes **Regional Accreditation:** Southern Association of Colleges and Schools **Credit Hours For Degree:** 120 credit hours, Bachelors **Professional Accreditation:** CIDA, NASAD.

WELCH COLLEGE

3606 W End Ave.
Nashville, TN 37205-2498
Tel: (615)844-5000; Free: 800-763-9222
Fax: (615)269-6028
E-mail: dmouser@welch.edu
Web Site: www.welch.edu
President/CEO: Dr. J. Matthew Pinson
Admissions: Debbie Mouser
Financial Aid: Angie Edgmon
Type: Four-Year College **Sex:** Coed **Affiliation:** Free Will Baptist. **Scores:** 88% SAT V 400+; 89% SAT M 400+ **% Accepted:** 69 **Admission Plans:** Deferred Admission; Early Admission; Open Admission; Preferred Admission **Application Deadline:** Rolling **Application Fee:** $35.00 **H.S. Requirements:** High school diploma required; GED accepted **Costs Per Year:** Application fee: $35. Comprehensive fee: $24,446 includes full-time tuition ($17,398) and college room and board ($7048). Room and board charges vary according to board plan. Part-time tuition: $595 per credit hour. **Scholarships:** Available. **Calendar System:** Semester, Summer session available **Enrollment:** Full-time 220, Part-time 107 **Faculty:** Full-time 16, Part-time 42 **Student-Faculty Ratio:** 8:1 **Exams:** SAT I or ACT; SAT Reasoning. **% Receiving Financial Aid:** 82 **% Residing in College-Owned, -Operated, or -Affiliated Housing:** 52 **Final Year or Final Semester Residency Requirement:** Yes **Regional Accreditation:** Southern Association of Colleges and Schools **Credit Hours For Degree:** 66 semester hours, Associates; 124 semester hours, Bachelors **ROTC:** Air Force, Army **Professional Accreditation:** ABHE. **Intercollegiate Athletics:** Basketball M & W; Golf M & W; Volleyball W

WEST TENNESSEE BUSINESS COLLEGE

1186 Hwy. 45 Byp.
Jackson, TN 38343
Tel: (731)668-7240
Web Site: www.wtbc.edu
Type: Two-Year College **Sex:** Coed

WILLIAMSON COLLEGE

274 Mallory Station Rd.
Franklin, TN 37067
Tel: (615)771-7821
Fax: (615)771-7810
E-mail: laura@williamsoncc.edu
Web Site: www.williamsoncc.edu
President/CEO: Dr. Kenneth W. Oosting
Admissions: Laura Flowers
Financial Aid: Jeanie Maguire
Type: Comprehensive **Sex:** Coed **Affiliation:** interdenominational. **Admission Plans:** Deferred Admission; Early Admission **Application Deadline:** September 1 **Application Fee:** $25.00 **H.S. Requirements:** High school diploma required; GED accepted **Costs Per Year:** Application fee: $25. Tuition: $10,800 full-time, $425 per credit hour part-time. Mandatory fees: $500 full-time, $500 per year part-time. Full-time tuition and fees vary according to course load. **Scholarships:** Available. **Calendar System:** Semester, Summer session not available **Enrollment:** Full-time 61, Graduate full-time 10, Part-time 1 **Faculty:** Full-time 5, Part-time 12 **Student-Faculty Ratio:** 5:1 **Exams:** SAT I or ACT. **% Receiving Financial Aid:** 18 **Credit Hours For Degree:** 60 credits, Associates; 124 credits, Bachelors **Professional Accreditation:** ABHE.

ABILENE CHRISTIAN UNIVERSITY

ACU Box 29100
Abilene, TX 79699-9100
Tel: (325)674-2000; Free: 800-460-6228
E-mail: info@admissions.acu.edu
Web Site: www.acu.edu
President/CEO: Dr. Phil Schubert

Type: University **Sex:** Coed **Affiliation:** Church of Christ. **Scores:** 95% SAT V 400+; 97% SAT M 400+; 39.11% ACT 18-23; 48.63% ACT 24-29 **% Accepted:** 50 **Admission Plans:** Early Admission; Early Decision Plan **Application Deadline:** February 15 **Application Fee:** $50.00 **H.S. Requirements:** High school diploma required; GED accepted **Costs Per Year:** Application fee: $50. Comprehensive fee: $40,140 includes full-time tuition ($30,780), mandatory fees ($50), and college room and board ($9310). College room only: $4390. Full-time tuition and fees vary according to course load. Room and board charges vary according to board plan and housing facility. Part-time tuition: $1280 per credit hour. Part-time tuition varies according to course load. **Scholarships:** Available. **Calendar System:** Semester, Summer session available **Enrollment:** Full-time 3,582, Graduate full-time 318, Graduate part-time 466, Part-time 178 **Faculty:** Full-time 253, Part-time 151 **Student-Faculty Ratio:** 14:1 **Exams:** ACT essay component used for admission; ACT essay component used in place of application essay; SAT I or ACT; SAT essay component used for admission; SAT essay component used in place of application essay; SAT Reasoning; SAT Subject. **% Receiving Financial Aid:** 66 **% Residing in College-Owned, -Operated, or -Affiliated Housing:** 48 **Final Year or Final Semester Residency Requirement:** Yes **Regional Accreditation:** Southern Association of Colleges and Schools **Credit Hours For Degree:** 64 semester hours, Associates; 128 semester hours, Bachelors **Professional Accreditation:** AACN, AACSB, AAFCS, AAMFT, ACEJMC, ASHA, ATS, CSWE, NASM, TEAC. **Intercollegiate Athletics:** Baseball M; Basketball M & W; Cross-Country Running M & W; Football M; Golf M; Soccer W; Softball W; Tennis M & W; Track and Field M & W; Volleyball W

ALVIN COMMUNITY COLLEGE

3110 Mustang Rd.
Alvin, TX 77511-4898
Tel: (281)756-3500
Fax: (281)756-3854
E-mail: info@alvincollege.edu
Web Site: www.alvincollege.edu
President/CEO: Dr. Christal Albrecht
Admissions: Stephanie Stockstill

Type: Two-Year College **Sex:** Coed **Costs Per Year:** Area resident tuition: $1080 full-time, $45 per credit hour part-time. State resident tuition: $2160 full-time, $90 per credit hour part-time. Nonresident tuition: $3360 full-time, $140 per credit hour part-time. Mandatory fees: $434 full-time, $5 per credit hour part-time, $157 per term part-time. Full-time tuition and fees vary according to course load and program. Part-time tuition and fees vary according to course load and program. **Scholarships:** Available. **Calendar System:** Semester, Summer session available **Faculty:** Full-time 106, Part-time 191 **Student-Faculty Ratio:** 17:1 **Regional Accreditation:** Southern Association of Colleges and Schools **Credit Hours For Degree:** 60 credits, Associates **Professional Accreditation:** ACEN, CoARC. **Intercollegiate Athletics:** Baseball M; Softball W

AMARILLO COLLEGE

PO Box 447
Amarillo, TX 79178-0001
Tel: (806)371-5000; Free: 800-227-8784
Fax: (806)371-5370
E-mail: askac@actx.edu
Web Site: www.actx.edu
President/CEO: Dr. Russell D. Lowery-Hart

Type: Two-Year College **Sex:** Coed **Admission Plans:** Deferred Admission; Early Admission; Open Admission **Application Fee:** $0.00 **H.S. Requirements:** High school diploma or equivalent not required **Costs Per Year:** Application fee: $0. Area resident tuition: $2010 full-time, $83.75 per semester hour part-time. State resident tuition: $3042 full-time, $126.75 per semester hour part-time. Nonresident tuition: $4578 full-time, $190.75 per credit hour part-time. Full-time tuition varies according to course load. Part-time tuition varies according to course load. **Scholarships:** Available. **Calendar System:** Semester, Summer session available **Faculty:** Full-time 219, Part-time 210 **Regional Accreditation:** Southern Association of Colleges and Schools **Credit Hours For Degree:** 60 semester hours, Associates **Professional Accreditation:** ABET, ABFSE, ACEN, ADA, AOTA, APTA, ARCST, CoARC, JRCERT, JRCNMT, NAACLS, NASM.

AMBERTON UNIVERSITY

1700 Eastgate Dr.
Garland, TX 75041-5595
Tel: (972)279-6511
Fax: (972)279-9773
E-mail: advisor@amberton.edu
Web Site: www.amberton.edu
President/CEO: Dr. Melinda Reagan

Type: Two-Year Upper Division **Sex:** Coed **Affiliation:** nondenominational. **Admission Plans:** Deferred Admission **Application Fee:** $0.00 **Costs Per Year:** Application fee: $0. Tuition: $7500 full-time, $250 per credit hour part-time. **Calendar System:** Miscellaneous, Summer session available **Enrollment:** Full-time 33, Graduate full-time 91, Graduate part-time 1,057, Part-time 198 **Faculty:** Full-time 15, Part-time 25 **Student-Faculty Ratio:** 25:1 **Regional Accreditation:** Southern Association of Colleges and Schools **Credit Hours For Degree:** 126 semester hours, Bachelors

AMERICAN INTERCONTINENTAL UNIVERSITY HOUSTON

9999 Richmond Ave.
Houston, TX 77042
Tel: (832)201-3600; Free: 888-607-9888
Fax: (832)242-5775
Web Site: www.aiuniv.edu
President/CEO: Stephen J. Tober

Type: Comprehensive **Sex:** Coed **Affiliation:** American InterContinental University. **Admission Plans:** Deferred Admission **Application Deadline:** Rolling **Application Fee:** $50.00 **H.S. Requirements:** High school diploma required; GED accepted **Calendar System:** Miscellaneous **Enrollment:** Full-time 330, Part-time 85 **Regional Accreditation:** North Central Association of Colleges and Schools **Professional Accreditation:** ACBSP.

ANGELINA COLLEGE

PO Box 1768
Lufkin, TX 75902-1768

Tel: (936)639-1301
Fax: (936)639-4299
E-mail: jthomas@angelina.edu
Web Site: www.angelina.cc.tx.us
President/CEO: Larry M. Phillips
Admissions: Jerry Thomas
Financial Aid: Susan Jones

Type: Two-Year College Sex: Coed Admission Plans: Deferred Admission; Early Admission; Open Admission Application Deadline: Rolling H.S. Requirements: High school diploma required; GED accepted Scholarships: Available. Calendar System: Semester, Summer session available Student-Faculty Ratio: 8:1 Regional Accreditation: Southern Association of Colleges and Schools Credit Hours For Degree: 70 semester hours, Associates ROTC: Army Professional Accreditation: CoARC, JRCERT. Intercollegiate Athletics: Baseball M; Basketball M & W; Softball W

ANGELO STATE UNIVERSITY
2601 W Ave. N
San Angelo, TX 76909
Tel: (325)942-2555; Free: 800-946-8627
Fax: (325)942-2038
E-mail: admissions@angelo.edu
Web Site: www.angelo.edu
President/CEO: Dr. Brian J. May
Admissions: Sharla Adam
Financial Aid: William R. Bloom

Type: Comprehensive Sex: Coed Affiliation: Texas Tech University System. Scores: 84% SAT V 400+; 90% SAT M 400+; 38% ACT 18-23; 29% ACT 24-29 % Accepted: 77 Admission Plans: Deferred Admission; Early Admission Application Deadline: Rolling Application Fee: $35.00 H.S. Requirements: High school diploma required; GED accepted Costs Per Year: Application fee: $35. State resident tuition: $4860 full-time, $162 per credit hour part-time. Nonresident tuition: $16,560 full-time, $552 per credit hour part-time. Mandatory fees: $3004 full-time. Full-time tuition and fees vary according to course load. Part-time tuition varies according to course load. College room and board: $7702. Room and board charges vary according to board plan and housing facility. Tuition guaranteed not to increase for student's term of enrollment. Scholarships: Available. Calendar System: Semester, Summer session available Enrollment: Full-time 4,755, Graduate full-time 623, Graduate part-time 607, Part-time 2,498 Faculty: Full-time 263, Part-time 62 Student-Faculty Ratio: 23:1 Exams: ACT essay component not used; SAT I or ACT; SAT essay component not used; SAT Reasoning. % Receiving Financial Aid: 65 % Residing in College-Owned, -Operated, or -Affiliated Housing: 32 Final Year or Final Semester Residency Requirement: No Regional Accreditation: Southern Association of Colleges and Schools Credit Hours For Degree: 120 semester hours, Bachelors ROTC: Air Force Professional Accreditation: ACBSP, ACEN, APTA, NASM, NCATE. Intercollegiate Athletics: Baseball M; Basketball M & W; Cross-Country Running M & W; Football M; Golf W; Soccer W; Softball W; Track and Field M & W; Volleyball W

ARGOSY UNIVERSITY, DALLAS
5001 Lyndon B. Johnson Fwy.
Heritage Sq.
Farmers Branch, TX 75244
Tel: (214)890-9900; Free: 866-954-9900
Fax: (214)656-3900
Web Site: www.argosy.edu/dallas-texas/default.aspx
President/CEO: Ronald Hyson

Type: University Sex: Coed Affiliation: Education Management Corporation. Calendar System: Semester Regional Accreditation: Western Association of Colleges and Schools

ARLINGTON BAPTIST COLLEGE
3001 W Division
Arlington, TX 76012-3425
Tel: (817)461-8741
Fax: (817)274-1138
E-mail: jtaylor@arlingtonbaptistcollege.edu
Web Site: www.arlingtonbaptistcollege.edu
President/CEO: Dr. D. L. Moody
Admissions: Kim Marvin
Financial Aid: David B. Clogston, Jr.

Type: Comprehensive Sex: Coed Affiliation: Baptist. % Accepted: 100

Admission Plans: Deferred Admission; Early Admission; Preferred Admission Application Deadline: Rolling Application Fee: $25.00 H.S. Requirements: High school diploma required; GED accepted Costs Per Year: Application fee: $25. Comprehensive fee: $17,700 includes full-time tuition ($11,000), mandatory fees ($900), and college room and board ($5800). Full-time tuition and fees vary according to course load. Part-time tuition: $335 per credit hour. Part-time tuition and fees vary according to course load. Scholarships: Available. Calendar System: Semester, Summer session available Enrollment: Full-time 165, Graduate full-time 18, Graduate part-time 1, Part-time 28 Faculty: Full-time 10, Part-time 23 Student-Faculty Ratio: 12:1 % Receiving Financial Aid: 67 % Residing in College-Owned, -Operated, or -Affiliated Housing: 46 Final Year or Final Semester Residency Requirement: Yes Credit Hours For Degree: 128 semester hours, Bachelors Professional Accreditation: ABHE. Intercollegiate Athletics: Baseball M; Basketball M & W; Cross-Country Running M & W; Volleyball W

THE ART INSTITUTE OF AUSTIN, A BRANCH OF THE ART INSTITUTE OF HOUSTON
101 W Louis Henna Blvd.
Ste. 100
Austin, TX 78728
Tel: (512)691-1707; Free: 866-583-7952
Web Site: www.artinstitutes.edu/austin
President/CEO: Monica Jeffs

Type: Four-Year College Sex: Coed Affiliation: Education Management Corporation. Regional Accreditation: Southern Association of Colleges and Schools

THE ART INSTITUTE OF DALLAS, A CAMPUS OF SOUTH UNIVERSITY
8080 Park Ln.
Ste. 100
Dallas, TX 75231-5993
Tel: (214)692-8080; Free: 800-275-4243
Fax: (214)750-9460
Web Site: www.artinstitutes.edu/dallas
President/CEO: John Willis

Type: Comprehensive Sex: Coed Affiliation: Education Management Corporation. Calendar System: Quarter Regional Accreditation: Southern Association of Colleges and Schools Professional Accreditation: ACF, CIDA, NASAD.

THE ART INSTITUTE OF HOUSTON
4140 SW Fwy.
Houston, TX 77027
Tel: (713)623-2040; Free: 800-275-4244
Fax: (713)966-2797
Web Site: www.artinstitutes.edu/houston
President/CEO: Susanne Behrens

Type: Four-Year College Sex: Coed Affiliation: Education Management Corporation. Calendar System: Quarter Regional Accreditation: Southern Association of Colleges and Schools Professional Accreditation: ACF.

THE ART INSTITUTE OF SAN ANTONIO, A BRANCH OF THE ART INSTITUTE OF HOUSTON
1000 IH-10 W, Ste. 200
San Antonio, TX 78230
Tel: (210)338-7320; Free: 888-222-0040
Fax: (210)338-7321
Web Site: www.artinstitutes.edu/san-antonio
President/CEO: Josh Pond

Type: Four-Year College Sex: Coed Regional Accreditation: Southern Association of Colleges and Schools

AUGUSTE ESCOFFIER SCHOOL OF CULINARY ARTS
6020-B Dillard
Austin, TX 78752
Tel: (512)451-5743
Web Site: www.escoffier.edu

Type: Two-Year College Sex: Coed Professional Accreditation: COE.

AUSTIN COLLEGE

900 N Grand Ave.
Sherman, TX 75090-4400
Tel: (903)813-2000; Free: 800-526-4276
Fax: (903)813-3198
E-mail: admission@austincollege.edu
Web Site: www.austincollege.edu
President/CEO: Dr. Marjorie Hass
Admissions: Nan Davis
Financial Aid: Laurie Coulter

Type: Comprehensive **Sex:** Coed **Affiliation:** Presbyterian. **Scores:** 98% SAT V 400+; 100% SAT M 400+; 30% ACT 18-23; 54% ACT 24-29 **% Accepted:** 54 **Admission Plans:** Deferred Admission; Early Action; Early Admission; Early Decision Plan **Application Deadline:** March 1 **Application Fee:** $0.00 **H.S. Requirements:** High school diploma required; GED accepted **Costs Per Year:** Application fee: $0. One-time mandatory fee: $25. Comprehensive fee: $48,023 includes full-time tuition ($36,045), mandatory fees ($185), and college room and board ($11,793). College room only: $5525. Full-time tuition and fees vary according to student level. Room and board charges vary according to board plan and housing facility. Part-time tuition: $5130 per course. Part-time mandatory fees: $90 per term. **Scholarships:** Available. **Calendar System:** 4-1-4, Summer session available **Enrollment:** Full-time 1,242, Graduate full-time 17, Part-time 13 **Faculty:** Full-time 91, Part-time 29 **Student-Faculty Ratio:** 13:1 **Exams:** ACT essay component used as validity check; SAT I or ACT; SAT essay component used as validity check. **% Receiving Financial Aid:** 65 **% Residing in College-Owned, -Operated, or -Affiliated Housing:** 82 **Final Year or Final Semester Residency Requirement:** No **Regional Accreditation:** Southern Association of Colleges and Schools **Credit Hours For Degree:** 34 course credit units, Bachelors **Intercollegiate Athletics:** Baseball M; Basketball M & W; Cheerleading M & W; Cross-Country Running M & W; Football M; Soccer M & W; Softball W; Swimming and Diving M & W; Tennis M & W; Volleyball W

AUSTIN COMMUNITY COLLEGE DISTRICT

5930 Middle Fiskville Rd.
Austin, TX 78752-4390
Tel: (512)223-7000
Fax: (512)223-7665
E-mail: admission@austincc.edu
Web Site: www.austincc.edu
President/CEO: Dr. Richard M. Rhodes
Admissions: Linda Kluck
Financial Aid: Rosario Juarez

Type: Two-Year College **Sex:** Coed **Admission Plans:** Open Admission **Application Deadline:** Rolling **Application Fee:** $0.00 **H.S. Requirements:** High school diploma required; GED accepted **Costs Per Year:** Application fee: $0. Area resident tuition: $2010 full-time, $67 per credit hour part-time. State resident tuition: $8670 full-time, $289 per credit hour part-time. Nonresident tuition: $10,800 full-time, $360 per credit hour part-time. Mandatory fees: $540 full-time, $18 per credit hour part-time. Full-time tuition and fees vary according to course load. Part-time tuition and fees vary according to course load. **Scholarships:** Available. **Calendar System:** Semester, Summer session available **Enrollment:** Full-time 9,031, Part-time 32,543 **Faculty:** Full-time 536, Part-time 1,332 **Student-Faculty Ratio:** 20:1 **Final Year or Final Semester Residency Requirement:** No **Regional Accreditation:** Southern Association of Colleges and Schools **Credit Hours For Degree:** 60 semester hours, Associates **ROTC:** Air Force, Army **Professional Accreditation:** ACBSP, ACEN, ACF, ADA, AOTA, APTA, ARCST, JRCEDMS, JRCEMTP, JRCERT, NAACLS.

AUSTIN GRADUATE SCHOOL OF THEOLOGY

7640 Guadalupe St.
Austin, TX 78752
Tel: (512)476-2772; Free: 866-AUS-GRAD
Fax: (512)476-3919
E-mail: registrar@austingrad.edu
Web Site: www.austingrad.edu
President/CEO: Dr. Stan Reid
Admissions: Dawn Bond
Financial Aid: David Arthur

Type: Two-Year Upper Division **Sex:** Coed **Affiliation:** Church of Christ. **Admission Plans:** Deferred Admission; Early Admission; Open Admission **Application Fee:** $0.00 **H.S. Requirements:** High school diploma required;

GED accepted **Costs Per Year:** Application fee: $0. Tuition: $8400 full-time, $350 per credit hour part-time. Mandatory fees: $350 full-time, $175 per term part-time. **Scholarships:** Available. **Calendar System:** Semester, Summer session available **Enrollment:** Full-time 6, Graduate full-time 11, Graduate part-time 19, Part-time 24 **Faculty:** Full-time 4, Part-time 6 **Regional Accreditation:** Southern Association of Colleges and Schools **Credit Hours For Degree:** 120 semester hours, Bachelors

BAPTIST HEALTH SYSTEM SCHOOL OF HEALTH PROFESSIONS

8400 Datapoint Dr.
San Antonio, TX 78229
Tel: (210)297-9636
Web Site: www.bshp.edu
Type: Four-Year College **Sex:** Coed

BAPTIST MISSIONARY ASSOCIATION THEOLOGICAL SEMINARY

1530 E Pine St.
Jacksonville, TX 75766-5407
Tel: (903)586-2501; Free: 800-259-5673
E-mail: attebery@bmats.edu
Web Site: www.bmats.edu
President/CEO: Dr. Charley Holmes
Admissions: Dr. Philip Attebery
Financial Aid: Dr. Philip Attebery

Type: Comprehensive **Sex:** Coed **Affiliation:** Baptist. **Admission Plans:** Open Admission **Application Deadline:** July 25 **Application Fee:** $35.00 **H.S. Requirements:** High school diploma required; GED accepted. For applicants to the associate's degree program 25 or over: High school diploma or equivalent not required **Scholarships:** Available. **Calendar System:** Semester, Summer session available **Enrollment:** Full-time 23, Graduate full-time 28, Graduate part-time 33, Part-time 33 **Faculty:** Full-time 5, Part-time 6 **% Receiving Financial Aid:** 95 **% Residing in College-Owned, -Operated, or -Affiliated Housing:** 29 **Final Year or Final Semester Residency Requirement:** No **Regional Accreditation:** Southern Association of Colleges and Schools **Credit Hours For Degree:** 66 semester hours, Associates; 126 semester hours, Bachelors **Professional Accreditation:** ATS.

BAPTIST UNIVERSITY OF THE AMERICAS

8019 S Pan Am Expy.
San Antonio, TX 78224-2701
Tel: (210)924-4338; Free: 800-721-1396
Fax: (210)924-2701
E-mail: admissions@bua.edu
Web Site: www.bua.edu
President/CEO: Pres. Rene Maciel
Financial Aid: Araceli G. Acosta

Type: Four-Year College **Sex:** Coed **Affiliation:** Baptist. **Costs Per Year:** Tuition: $5280 full-time, $220 per credit part-time. Mandatory fees: $720 full-time. College room only: $2500. Room charges vary according to housing facility. **Scholarships:** Available. **Calendar System:** Semester, Summer session not available **Enrollment:** Full-time 128, Part-time 67 **Faculty:** Full-time 9, Part-time 31 **Student-Faculty Ratio:** 7:1 **Exams:** ACT; ACT essay component not used; ACT essay component used for admission; ACT essay component used for advising; ACT essay component used for placement; Other; SAT I; SAT I and SAT II or ACT; SAT I or ACT; SAT essay component not used; SAT essay component used for admission; SAT essay component used for advising; SAT essay component used for placement. **% Residing in College-Owned, -Operated, or -Affiliated Housing:** 40 **Final Year or Final Semester Residency Requirement:** No **Credit Hours For Degree:** 62 credit hours, Associates; 123 credit hours, Bachelors **Professional Accreditation:** ABHE.

BAYLOR UNIVERSITY

Waco, TX 76798
Tel: (254)710-1011; Free: 800-BAYLORU
E-mail: admissions@baylor.edu
Web Site: www.baylor.edu
President/CEO: Dr. Ken W. Starr
Admissions: Jessica King Gereghty

Type: University **Sex:** Coed **Affiliation:** Baptist. **Scores:** 99% SAT V 400+; 100% SAT M 400+; 10% ACT 18-23; 59% ACT 24-29 **% Accepted:** 44 **Admission Plans:** Early Admission; Early Decision Plan **Application Deadline:** February 1 **Application Fee:** $0.00 **H.S. Requirements:** High school diploma required; GED accepted **Costs Per Year:** Application fee: $0. Comprehensive fee: $53,760 includes full-time tuition ($37,996), mandatory fees ($4010), and college room and board ($11,754). College room only: $6400. Room and board charges vary according to board plan and housing facility. Part-time tuition: $1583 per hour. **Scholarships:** Available. **Calendar System:** Semester, Summer session available **Enrollment:** Full-time 13,946, Graduate full-time 2,172, Graduate part-time 426, Part-time 243 **Faculty:** Full-time 988, Part-time 262 **Student-Faculty Ratio:** 15:1 **Exams:** ACT essay component used in place of application essay; SAT I or ACT; SAT essay component used in place of application essay; SAT Reasoning. **% Receiving Financial Aid:** 54 **% Residing in College-Owned, -Operated, or -Affiliated Housing:** 36 **Final Year or Final Semester Residency Requirement:** Yes **Regional Accreditation:** Southern Association of Colleges and Schools **Credit Hours For Degree:** 124 semester hours, Bachelors **ROTC:** Air Force, Army **Professional Accreditation:** AACN, AACSB, AAFCS, AALE, AALS, ABA, ABET, ACEJMC, ACIPE, AND, APA, APTA, ASHA, ATS, CAHME, CSWE, NASM, NAST, NCATE. **Intercollegiate Athletics:** Baseball M; Basketball M & W; Cheerleading M & W; Crew M & W; Cross-Country Running M & W; Equestrian Sports W; Fencing M & W; Football M; Golf M & W; Gymnastics M & W; Ice Hockey M; Lacrosse M & W; Rock Climbing M & W; Rugby M; Sailing M & W; Skiing (Downhill) M & W; Soccer M & W; Softball W; Tennis M & W; Track and Field M & W; Ultimate Frisbee M; Volleyball M & W; Water Polo M & W

BLINN COLLEGE
902 College Ave.
Brenham, TX 77833-4049
Tel: (979)830-4000
E-mail: jennifer.bynum@blinn.edu
Web Site: www.blinn.edu
President/CEO: Dr. Mary Hensley
Admissions: Jennifer Bynum
Financial Aid: Brent Williford
Type: Two-Year College **Sex:** Coed **Admission Plans:** Deferred Admission; Early Admission; Open Admission **Application Deadline:** Rolling **Application Fee:** $0.00 **H.S. Requirements:** High school diploma required; GED accepted **Costs Per Year:** Application fee: $0. Area resident tuition: $1440 full-time, $48 per credit hour part-time. State resident tuition: $3510 full-time, $117 per credit hour part-time. Nonresident tuition: $6000 full-time, $200 per credit hour part-time. Mandatory fees: $1380 full-time, $46 per credit hour part-time. Full-time tuition and fees vary according to course load. Part-time tuition and fees vary according to course load. College room and board: $6700. College room only: $4400. Room and board charges vary according to board plan, gender, and housing facility. **Scholarships:** Available. **Calendar System:** Semester, Summer session available **Enrollment:** Full-time 10,360, Part-time 9,420 **Faculty:** Full-time 398, Part-time 250 **Student-Faculty Ratio:** 29:1 **% Residing in College-Owned, -Operated, or -Affiliated Housing:** 9 **Regional Accreditation:** Southern Association of Colleges and Schools **Credit Hours For Degree:** 63 credit hours, Associates **Professional Accreditation:** ACEN, ADA, APTA, JRCERT. **Intercollegiate Athletics:** Baseball M; Basketball M & W; Cheerleading M & W; Football M; Softball W; Volleyball W

BRAZOSPORT COLLEGE
500 College Dr.
Lake Jackson, TX 77566-3199
Tel: (979)230-3000
Fax: (979)230-3443
E-mail: wade.wilson@brazosport.edu
Web Site: www.brazosport.edu
President/CEO: Millicent M. Vanek
Admissions: Wade Wilson
Type: Two-Year College **Sex:** Coed **Admission Plans:** Deferred Admission; Early Admission; Open Admission **Application Deadline:** August 15 **Application Fee:** $0.00 **H.S. Requirements:** High school diploma required; GED accepted **Scholarships:** Available. **Calendar System:** Semester, Summer session available **Student-Faculty Ratio:** 17:1 **Regional Accreditation:** Southern Association of Colleges and Schools **Credit Hours For Degree:** 62 semester hours, Associates

BRIGHTWOOD COLLEGE, ARLINGTON CAMPUS
2241 S Watson Rd.
Arlington, TX 76010
Free: 800-935-1857

Web Site: www.brightwood.edu
President/CEO: Debbie Wiggins
Type: Two-Year College **Sex:** Coed **H.S. Requirements:** High school diploma required; GED accepted **Professional Accreditation:** ACICS, COE.

BRIGHTWOOD COLLEGE, BEAUMONT CAMPUS
6115 Eastex Fwy.
Beaumont, TX 77706
Tel: (409)347-5900; Free: 800-935-1857
Web Site: www.brightwood.edu
President/CEO: Debbie Schroller
Type: Two-Year College **Sex:** Coed **Calendar System:** Continuous **Professional Accreditation:** ACICS.

BRIGHTWOOD COLLEGE, BROWNSVILLE CAMPUS
1900 N Expy.
Ste. O
Brownsville, TX 78521
Tel: (956)547-8200
Web Site: www.brightwood.edu
President/CEO: Colin Ellis
Type: Two-Year College **Sex:** Coed **Professional Accreditation:** ACICS.

BRIGHTWOOD COLLEGE, CORPUS CHRISTI CAMPUS
1620 S Padre Island Dr.
Ste. 600
Corpus Christi, TX 78416
Tel: (361)852-2900
Web Site: www.brightwood.edu
President/CEO: Jeriann Hix
Type: Two-Year College **Sex:** Coed **Calendar System:** Miscellaneous **Professional Accreditation:** ACICS.

BRIGHTWOOD COLLEGE, DALLAS CAMPUS
12005 Ford Rd.
Ste. 100
Dallas, TX 75234
Tel: (972)385-1446; Free: 800-935-1857
Fax: (972)385-0641
Web Site: www.brightwood.edu
President/CEO: Jeff Thorud
Type: Two-Year College **Sex:** Coed **H.S. Requirements:** High school diploma required; GED accepted **Professional Accreditation:** ACICS, COE.

BRIGHTWOOD COLLEGE, EL PASO CAMPUS
8360 Burnham Rd.
Ste. 100
El Paso, TX 79907
Web Site: www.brightwood.edu
President/CEO: Dawn Michell
Type: Two-Year College **Sex:** Coed **Professional Accreditation:** ACICS.

BRIGHTWOOD COLLEGE, FORT WORTH CAMPUS
2001 Beach St.
Ste. 201
Fort Worth, TX 76103
Tel: (817)413-2000
Web Site: www.brightwood.edu
President/CEO: Shaheen Mamdani
Type: Two-Year College **Sex:** Coed **Professional Accreditation:** ACICS.

BRIGHTWOOD COLLEGE, FRIENDSWOOD CAMPUS
3208 Farm to Market Rd. 528
Friendswood, TX 77546
Web Site: www.brightwood.edu
President/CEO: Ann Gibson
Type: Two-Year College **Sex:** Coed **Professional Accreditation:** ACICS.

BRIGHTWOOD COLLEGE, HOUSTON CAMPUS
711 E Airtex Dr.
Houston, TX 77073
Tel: (281)443-8900

Web Site: www.brightwood.edu
President/CEO: Ann Gibson
Type: Two-Year College **Sex:** Coed **Professional Accreditation:** ACICS.

BRIGHTWOOD COLLEGE, LAREDO CAMPUS
6410 McPherson Rd.
Laredo, TX 78041
Tel: (956)717-5909; Free: 800-935-1857
Web Site: www.brightwood.edu
President/CEO: Jorge Hinojosa
Type: Two-Year College **Sex:** Coed **Professional Accreditation:** ACICS.

BRIGHTWOOD COLLEGE, MCALLEN CAMPUS
1500 S Jackson Rd.
McAllen, TX 78503
Tel: (956)630-1499; Free: 800-935-1857
Web Site: www.brightwood.edu
Type: Two-Year College **Sex:** Coed **Professional Accreditation:** ACICS.

BRIGHTWOOD COLLEGE, SAN ANTONIO INGRAM CAMPUS
6441 NW Loop 410
San Antonio, TX 78238
Tel: (210)308-8584; Free: 800-935-1857
Web Site: www.brightwood.edu
President/CEO: Liza Canchola
Type: Two-Year College **Sex:** Coed **Professional Accreditation:** ACICS.

BRIGHTWOOD COLLEGE, SAN ANTONIO SAN PEDRO CAMPUS
7142 San Pedro Ave.
Ste. 100
San Antonio, TX 78216
Tel: (210)733-0777; Free: 800-935-1857
Web Site: www.brightwood.edu
President/CEO: Rene Candelaria
Type: Two-Year College **Sex:** Coed **Professional Accreditation:** ACICS.

BROOKHAVEN COLLEGE
3939 Valley View Ln.
Farmers Branch, TX 75244-4997
Tel: (972)860-4700
Fax: (972)860-4897
E-mail: bhcAdmissions@dcccd.edu
Web Site: www.brookhavencollege.edu
President/CEO: Thomas D. Chesney, PhD
Type: Two-Year College **Sex:** Coed **Affiliation:** Dallas County Community College District System. **Admission Plans:** Deferred Admission; Early Admission; Open Admission **Application Deadline:** Rolling **Application Fee:** $0.00 **H.S. Requirements:** High school diploma or equivalent not required **Costs Per Year:** Application fee: $0. Area resident tuition: $1770 full-time, $59 per credit part-time. State resident tuition: $3330 full-time, $111 per credit part-time. Nonresident tuition: $5220 full-time, $174 per credit part-time. **Calendar System:** Semester, Summer session available **Enrollment:** Full-time 2,125, Part-time 10,384 **Faculty:** Full-time 133, Part-time 440 **Student-Faculty Ratio:** 20:1 **Final Year or Final Semester Residency Requirement:** No **Regional Accreditation:** Southern Association of Colleges and Schools **Credit Hours For Degree:** 60 semester hours, Associates **Professional Accreditation:** ACEN. **Intercollegiate Athletics:** Baseball M; Basketball M; Soccer W; Volleyball W

CAREER POINT COLLEGE
4522 Fredericksburg Rd.
San Antonio, TX 78201
Tel: (210)732-3000
Web Site: www.careerpointcollege.edu
Type: Four-Year College **Sex:** Coed **Professional Accreditation:** ACICS.

CEDAR VALLEY COLLEGE
3030 N Dallas Ave.
Lancaster, TX 75134-3799
Tel: (972)860-8201
Web Site: www.cedarvalleycollege.edu
President/CEO: Dr. Jennifer Wimbish
Type: Two-Year College **Sex:** Coed **Affiliation:** Dallas County Community College District System. **Costs Per Year:** Area resident tuition: $1180 full-

time, $59 per credit hour part-time. State resident tuition: $2220 full-time, $111 per credit hour part-time. Nonresident tuition: $3480 full-time, $200 per credit hour part-time. Full-time tuition varies according to class time, course level, course load, degree level, location, program, reciprocity agreements, and student level. Part-time tuition varies according to class time, course level, course load, degree level, location, program, reciprocity agreements, and student level. Tuition guaranteed not to increase for student's term of enrollment. **Scholarships:** Available. **Calendar System:** Semester, Summer session available **Enrollment:** Full-time 1,564, Part-time 5,112 **Faculty:** Full-time 75, Part-time 221 **Student-Faculty Ratio:** 24:1 **Exams:** ACT essay component used for admission; ACT essay component used for advising; ACT essay component used for placement; Other; SAT I and SAT II or ACT; SAT I or ACT; SAT essay component used for admission; SAT essay component used for advising; SAT essay component used for placement. **Regional Accreditation:** Southern Association of Colleges and Schools **Credit Hours For Degree:** 60 semester hours, Associates **Intercollegiate Athletics:** Baseball M; Basketball M; Soccer W; Volleyball W

CENTER FOR ADVANCED LEGAL STUDIES
800 W Sam Houston Pky. S, Ste. 100
Houston, TX 77042
Tel: (713)529-2778; Free: 800-446-6931
Fax: (713)523-2715
E-mail: james.scheffer@paralegal.edu
Web Site: www.paralegal.edu
President/CEO: Doyle Happe
Admissions: James Scheffer
Type: Two-Year College **Sex:** Coed **Application Deadline:** Rolling **Application Fee:** $100.00 **H.S. Requirements:** High school diploma required; GED accepted **Costs Per Year:** Application fee: $100. Tuition: $300 per semester hour part-time. Part-time tuition varies according to class time and course load. Tuition guaranteed not to increase for student's term of enrollment. **Enrollment:** Full-time 176 **Faculty:** Full-time 2, Part-time 23 **Student-Faculty Ratio:** 17:1 **Exams:** Other. **Professional Accreditation:** COE.

CENTRAL TEXAS COLLEGE
PO Box 1800
Killeen, TX 76540-1800
Tel: (254)526-7161; Free: 800-792-3348
E-mail: admissions@ctcd.edu
Web Site: www.ctcd.edu
President/CEO: Jim Yenopolus
Type: Two-Year College **Sex:** Coed **Admission Plans:** Deferred Admission; Early Admission; Open Admission **Application Deadline:** Rolling **Application Fee:** $0.00 **H.S. Requirements:** High school diploma required; GED accepted **Costs Per Year:** Application fee: $0. Area resident tuition: $2280 full-time, $76 per credit part-time. State resident tuition: $2940 full-time, $98 per credit part-time. Nonresident tuition: $6420 full-time, $214 per credit part-time. Full-time tuition varies according to location and program. Part-time tuition varies according to location and program. College room and board: $5031. Room and board charges vary according to housing facility. **Scholarships:** Available. **Calendar System:** Semester, Summer session available **Enrollment:** Full-time 4,362, Part-time 15,200 **Faculty:** Full-time 229, Part-time 1,311 **Student-Faculty Ratio:** 16:1 **% Residing in College-Owned, -Operated, or -Affiliated Housing:** 1 **Regional Accreditation:** Southern Association of Colleges and Schools **Credit Hours For Degree:** 60 semester hours, Associates **ROTC:** Army **Professional Accreditation:** ACEN, NAACLS.

CHAMBERLAIN COLLEGE OF NURSING (HOUSTON)
11025 Equity Dr.
Houston, TX 77041
Tel: (713)277-9800; Free: 877-751-5783
Fax: (713)277-9980
Web Site: www.chamberlain.edu
President/CEO: Vivian Lilly
Type: Four-Year College **Sex:** Coed **Application Fee:** $95.00 **H.S. Requirements:** High school diploma required; GED accepted **Costs Per Year:** Application fee: $95. Tuition: $17,560 full-time, $665 per credit hour part-time. Mandatory fees: $600 full-time, $300 per term part-time. Full-time tuition and fees vary according to course load. Part-time tuition and fees vary according to course load. **Enrollment:** Full-time 218, Part-time 143 **Faculty:** Full-time 9, Part-time 71 **Student-Faculty Ratio:** 8:1 **Exams:** ACT essay component

used for admission; SAT I or ACT; SAT essay component used for admission. **Regional Accreditation:** North Central Association of Colleges and Schools

CHAMBERLAIN COLLEGE OF NURSING (PEARLAND)

12000 Shadow Creek Pky.
Pearland, TX 77584
Tel: (832)664-7000; Free: 877-751-5783
Fax: (832)664-7001
Web Site: www.chamberlain.edu
Type: Four-Year College **Sex:** Coed **Application Fee:** $95.00 **H.S. Requirements:** High school diploma required; GED accepted **Costs Per Year:** Application fee: $95. Tuition: $17,560 full-time, $665 per credit hour part-time. Mandatory fees: $600 full-time, $300 per term part-time. **Enrollment:** Full-time 27, Part-time 11 **Faculty:** Full-time 2 **Student-Faculty Ratio:** 15:1 **Exams:** SAT I or ACT. **Regional Accreditation:** North Central Association of Colleges and Schools

CISCO COLLEGE

101 College Heights
Cisco, TX 76437-9321
Tel: (254)442-5000
Fax: (254)442-5100
E-mail: oodom@cjc.edu
Web Site: www.cisco.edu
President/CEO: Bobby Smith
Admissions: Olin O. Odom, III
Financial Aid: Dianne Pharr
Type: Two-Year College **Sex:** Coed **% Accepted:** 100 **Admission Plans:** Early Admission; Open Admission **Application Deadline:** Rolling **Application Fee:** $0.00 **H.S. Requirements:** High school diploma required; GED accepted **Scholarships:** Available. **Calendar System:** Semester, Summer session available **Enrollment:** Full-time 1,601, Part-time 2,421 **Student-Faculty Ratio:** 18:1 **Exams:** ACT; SAT I. **% Residing in College-Owned, -Operated, or -Affiliated Housing:** 12 **Regional Accreditation:** Southern Association of Colleges and Schools **Credit Hours For Degree:** 63 credit hours, Associates **ROTC:** Army **Professional Accreditation:** AAMAE, ACEN. **Intercollegiate Athletics:** Baseball M; Basketball W; Cheerleading M & W; Football M; Soccer M; Softball W; Volleyball W

CLARENDON COLLEGE

PO Box 968
Clarendon, TX 79226-0968
Tel: (806)874-3571; Free: 800-687-9737
E-mail: martha.smith@clarendoncollege.edu
Web Site: www.clarendoncollege.edu
President/CEO: Dr. Phil Shirley
Admissions: Martha Smith
Financial Aid: Michele Copelin
Type: Two-Year College **Sex:** Coed **% Accepted:** 100 **Admission Plans:** Early Admission; Open Admission **Application Deadline:** Rolling **Application Fee:** $0.00 **H.S. Requirements:** High school diploma required; GED accepted **Costs Per Year:** Application fee: $0. State resident tuition: $1128 full-time, $47 per credit hour part-time. Nonresident tuition: $1872 full-time, $78 per credit hour part-time. Mandatory fees: $1296 full-time, $30 per credit hour part-time, $24. College room and board: $2,088. Room and board charges vary according to housing facility. **Scholarships:** Available. **Calendar System:** Semester, Summer session available **Enrollment:** Full-time 576, Part-time 638 **Faculty:** Full-time 36, Part-time 58 **Student-Faculty Ratio:** 19:1 **% Residing in College-Owned, -Operated, or -Affiliated Housing:** 21 **Final Year or Final Semester Residency Requirement:** No **Regional Accreditation:** Southern Association of Colleges and Schools **Credit Hours For Degree:** 62 semester hours, Associates **Intercollegiate Athletics:** Baseball M; Basketball M & W; Cheerleading M & W; Cross-Country Running M & W; Softball W; Volleyball W

COASTAL BEND COLLEGE

3800 Charco Rd.
Beeville, TX 78102-2197
Tel: (361)358-2838; Free: 866-262-2838
Fax: (361)354-2254
E-mail: tadams@coastalbend.edu
Web Site: www.coastalbend.edu
President/CEO: Dr. Beatriz Espinoza

Admissions: Tammy Adams
Type: Two-Year College **Sex:** Coed **% Accepted:** 100 **Admission Plans:** Deferred Admission; Open Admission **Application Deadline:** Rolling **Application Fee:** $0.00 **H.S. Requirements:** High school diploma required; GED accepted **Scholarships:** Available. **Calendar System:** Semester, Summer session available **Enrollment:** Full-time 1,353, Part-time 2,423 **Faculty:** Full-time 73, Part-time 84 **Student-Faculty Ratio:** 13:1 **% Residing in College-Owned, -Operated, or -Affiliated Housing:** 5 **Regional Accreditation:** Southern Association of Colleges and Schools **Credit Hours For Degree:** 62 semester hours, Associates **Professional Accreditation:** ADA, AHIMA. **Intercollegiate Athletics:** Basketball M; Volleyball W

COLLEGE OF BIBLICAL STUDIES–HOUSTON

7000 Regency Sq. Blvd.
Houston, TX 77036
Tel: (713)785-5995; Free: 844-227-9673
Fax: (713)785-5998
E-mail: admissions@cbshouston.edu
Web Site: www.cbshouston.edu
President/CEO: Dr. Bill Blocker
Admissions: Maggie Rodriguez
Financial Aid: Roshanna Hardison
Type: Four-Year College **Sex:** Coed **Affiliation:** nondenominational. **% Accepted:** 46 **Admission Plans:** Open Admission **Application Deadline:** Rolling **Application Fee:** $40.00 **H.S. Requirements:** High school diploma required; GED accepted **Costs Per Year:** Application fee: $40. Tuition: $6946 full-time, $274 per credit hour part-time. Mandatory fees: $370 full-time, $185 per term part-time. Full-time tuition and fees vary according to program. Part-time tuition and fees vary according to program. **Scholarships:** Available. **Calendar System:** Semester, Summer session available **Enrollment:** Full-time 69, Part-time 354 **Final Year or Final Semester Residency Requirement:** No **Regional Accreditation:** Southern Association of Colleges and Schools **Credit Hours For Degree:** 64 credits, Associates; 120 credits, Bachelors **Professional Accreditation:** ABHE.

THE COLLEGE OF HEALTH CARE PROFESSIONS (AUSTIN)

6505 Airport Blvd.
Austin, TX 78752
Tel: (512)892-2835
Web Site: www.chcp.edu
Type: Two-Year College **Sex:** Coed **Calendar System:** Continuous **Professional Accreditation:** ABHES.

THE COLLEGE OF HEALTH CARE PROFESSIONS (FORT WORTH)

4248 N Fwy.
Fort Worth, TX 76137-5021
Tel: (817)632-5900
Web Site: www.chcp.edu
Type: Two-Year College **Sex:** Coed **Professional Accreditation:** ABHES.

THE COLLEGE OF HEALTH CARE PROFESSIONS (HOUSTON)

240 NW Mall Blvd.
Houston, TX 77092
Tel: (713)862-2633; Free: 800-487-6728
Fax: (713)746-5466
Web Site: www.chcp.edu
President/CEO: Eric Bing
Type: Two-Year College **Sex:** Coed **Calendar System:** Semester **Professional Accreditation:** ABHES.

THE COLLEGE OF HEALTH CARE PROFESSIONS (SAN ANTONIO)

4738 NW Loop 410
San Antonio, TX 78229
Tel: (210)298-3600
Web Site: www.chcp.edu
Type: Two-Year College **Sex:** Coed **Professional Accreditation:** ABHES.

COLLEGE OF THE MAINLAND

1200 Amburn Rd.
Texas City, TX 77591-2499
Tel: (409)938-1211; Free: 888-258-8859
Fax: (409)938-1306
E-mail: mperez@com.edu
Web Site: www.com.edu

President/CEO: Dr. Beth Lewis
Admissions: Martin Perez
Financial Aid: Carl Gordon
Type: Two-Year College **Sex:** Coed **% Accepted:** 47 **Admission Plans:** Deferred Admission; Early Admission; Open Admission **Application Deadline:** Rolling **Application Fee:** $0.00 **H.S. Requirements:** High school diploma required; GED accepted **Scholarships:** Available. **Calendar System:** Semester, Summer session available **Enrollment:** Full-time 1,121, Part-time 3,067 **Faculty:** Full-time 108, Part-time 162 **Student-Faculty Ratio:** 15:1 **Exams:** SAT I or ACT. **Regional Accreditation:** Southern Association of Colleges and Schools **Credit Hours For Degree:** 60 credit hours, Associates **ROTC:** Air Force **Professional Accreditation:** ACEN. **Intercollegiate Athletics:** Basketball M; Soccer M; Volleyball W

COLLIN COUNTY COMMUNITY COLLEGE DISTRICT

3452 Spur 399
McKinney, TX 75069
Tel: (972)548-6790
Fax: (972)758-5468
E-mail: tfields@collin.edu
Web Site: www.collin.edu
President/CEO: Dr. H. Neil Matkin
Admissions: Todd Fields
Financial Aid: Debra Wilkison
Type: Two-Year College **Sex:** Coed **% Accepted:** 100 **Application Deadline:** Rolling **Application Fee:** $0.00 **H.S. Requirements:** High school diploma required; GED accepted **Costs Per Year:** Application fee: $0. Area resident tuition: $960 full-time, $39 per credit hour part-time. State resident tuition: $2130 full-time, $78 per credit hour part-time. Nonresident tuition: $3930 full-time, $138 per credit hour part-time. Mandatory fees: $214 full-time, $7 per credit hour part-time, $2 per term part-time. **Scholarships:** Available. **Calendar System:** Semester, Summer session available **Enrollment:** Full-time 9,427, Part-time 18,760 **Faculty:** Full-time 420, Part-time 797 **Student-Faculty Ratio:** 23:1 **Final Year or Final Semester Residency Requirement:** No **Regional Accreditation:** Southern Association of Colleges and Schools **Credit Hours For Degree:** 60 credit hours, Associates **ROTC:** Air Force **Professional Accreditation:** ACEN, ADA, CoARC. **Intercollegiate Athletics:** Basketball M & W; Tennis M & W

COMMONWEALTH INSTITUTE OF FUNERAL SERVICE

415 Barren Springs Dr.
Houston, TX 77090
Tel: (281)873-0262; Free: 800-628-1580
Fax: (281)873-5232
E-mail: p.moreno@commonwealth.edu
Web Site: www.commonwealth.edu
President/CEO: Jason Altieri
Admissions: Patricia Moreno
Type: Two-Year College **Sex:** Coed **% Accepted:** 100 **Application Deadline:** Rolling **Application Fee:** $50.00 **H.S. Requirements:** High school diploma required; GED accepted **Scholarships:** Available. **Calendar System:** Quarter, Summer session not available **Exams:** Other; SAT I or ACT. **Credit Hours For Degree:** 97 quarter hours, Associates **Professional Accreditation:** ABFSE.

CONCORDE CAREER COLLEGE (DALLAS)

12606 Greenville Ave.
Ste. 130
Dallas, TX 75243
Tel: (469)221-3400
Web Site: www.concorde.edu
Type: Two-Year College **Sex:** Coed **Professional Accreditation:** ACCSC.

CONCORDE CAREER COLLEGE (GRAND PRAIRIE)

3015 W Interstate 20
Grand Prairie, TX 75052
Tel: (469)348-2500; Free: 800-693-7010
Web Site: www.concorde.edu
Type: Two-Year College **Sex:** Coed **Professional Accreditation:** ACCSC.

CONCORDE CAREER COLLEGE (SAN ANTONIO)

4803 NW Loop 410
Ste. 200
San Antonio, TX 78229
Tel: (210)428-2000
Web Site: www.concorde.edu
Type: Two-Year College **Sex:** Coed **Professional Accreditation:** ACCSC.

CONCORDIA UNIVERSITY TEXAS

11400 Concordia University Dr.
Austin, TX 78726
Tel: (512)313-3000; Free: 800-865-4282
Fax: (512)459-8517
E-mail: admissions@concordia.edu
Web Site: www.concordia.edu
Admissions: Kristin Coulter
Financial Aid: Russell Jeffrey
Type: Comprehensive **Sex:** Coed **Affiliation:** Lutheran Church–Missouri Synod; Concordia University System. **Scores:** 95% SAT V 400+; 98% SAT M 400+; 60.87% ACT 18-23; 24.35% ACT 24-29 **% Accepted:** 83 **Admission Plans:** Deferred Admission; Early Admission **Application Deadline:** Rolling **Application Fee:** $25.00 **H.S. Requirements:** High school diploma required; GED accepted **Costs Per Year:** Application fee: $25. Comprehensive fee: $37,444 includes full-time tuition ($27,600), mandatory fees ($560), and college room and board ($9284). College room only: $4954. Full-time tuition and fees vary according to course load, degree level, and program. Room and board charges vary according to board plan. Part-time tuition: $905 per credit hour. Part-time tuition varies according to course load, degree level, and program. **Scholarships:** Available. **Calendar System:** Semester, Summer session available **Enrollment:** Full-time 1,192, Graduate full-time 39, Graduate part-time 898, Part-time 375 **Faculty:** Full-time 71, Part-time 231 **Student-Faculty Ratio:** 11:1 **Exams:** ACT essay component not used; SAT I or ACT; SAT essay component not used; SAT Reasoning. **% Receiving Financial Aid:** 69 **% Residing in College-Owned, -Operated, or -Affiliated Housing:** 13 **Final Year or Final Semester Residency Requirement:** No **Regional Accreditation:** Southern Association of Colleges and Schools **Credit Hours For Degree:** 64 semester hours, Associates; 128 semester hours, Bachelors **ROTC:** Air Force, Army **Intercollegiate Athletics:** Baseball M; Basketball M & W; Cross-Country Running M & W; Golf M & W; Soccer M & W; Softball W; Track and Field M & W; Volleyball W

CRISWELL COLLEGE

4010 Gaston Ave.
Dallas, TX 75246-1537
Tel: (214)821-5433; Free: 800-899-0012
Fax: (214)818-1310
Web Site: www.criswell.edu
President/CEO: Dr. Lamar E. Cooper, Sr.
Financial Aid: TaLisa Pollard
Type: Comprehensive **Sex:** Coed **Affiliation:** Southern Baptist Convention. **Application Fee:** $35.00 **H.S. Requirements:** High school diploma required; GED accepted **Costs Per Year:** Application fee: $35. Tuition: $7560 full-time, $315 per credit hour part-time. Mandatory fees: $670 full-time, $670 per year part-time. Full-time tuition and fees vary according to course load and degree level. Part-time tuition and fees vary according to course load and degree level. **Scholarships:** Available. **Calendar System:** Semester, Summer session available **% Receiving Financial Aid:** 77 **Regional Accreditation:** Southern Association of Colleges and Schools **Credit Hours For Degree:** 63 semester hours, Associates; 129 semester hours, Bachelors

CULINARY INSTITUTE LENOTRE

7070 Allensby
Houston, TX 77022-4322
Tel: (713)692-0077; Free: 888-LENOTRE
Fax: (713)692-7399
Web Site: www.culinaryinstitute.edu
President/CEO: Mark Stroeh
Type: Two-Year College **Sex:** Coed **Application Fee:** $50.00 **H.S. Requirements:** High school diploma required; GED accepted **Enrollment:** Full-time 248, Part-time 155 **Faculty:** Full-time 12, Part-time 15 **Student-Faculty Ratio:** 12:1 **Final Year or Final Semester Residency Requirement:** No **Professional Accreditation:** ACCSC, ACF.

DALLAS BAPTIST UNIVERSITY

3000 Mountain Creek Pky.
Dallas, TX 75211-9299
Tel: (214)333-7100; Free: 800-460-1328

Fax: (214)333-5447
E-mail: admiss@dbu.edu
Web Site: www.dbu.edu
President/CEO: Dr. Gary Cook
Admissions: Bobby Soto
Financial Aid: Lee Ferguson
Type: Comprehensive **Sex:** Coed **Affiliation:** Baptist General Convention of Texas. **Scores:** 100% SAT V 400+; 100% SAT M 400+; 62% ACT 18-23; 27% ACT 24-29 **% Accepted:** 42 **Admission Plans:** Deferred Admission; Early Admission **Application Deadline:** Rolling **Application Fee:** $25.00 **H.S. Requirements:** High school diploma required; GED accepted **Costs Per Year:** Application fee: $25. Comprehensive fee: $32,216 includes full-time tuition ($24,390), mandatory fees ($500), and college room and board ($7326). College room only: $3590. Room and board charges vary according to board plan and housing facility. Part-time tuition: $813 per credit hour. Part-time mandatory fees: $250 per term. **Scholarships:** Available. **Calendar System:** 4-1-4, Summer session available **Enrollment:** Full-time 2,421, Graduate full-time 707, Graduate part-time 1,297, Part-time 894 **Faculty:** Full-time 126, Part-time 503 **Student-Faculty Ratio:** 13:1 **Exams:** SAT I or ACT. **% Receiving Financial Aid:** 58 **% Residing in College-Owned, -Operated, or -Affiliated Housing:** 59 **Final Year or Final Semester Residency Requirement:** Yes **Regional Accreditation:** Southern Association of Colleges and Schools **Credit Hours For Degree:** 62 credit hours, Associates; 120 credit hours, Bachelors **ROTC:** Air Force, Army **Professional Accreditation:** ACBSP, NASM. **Intercollegiate Athletics:** Baseball M; Basketball M; Cheerleading W; Cross-Country Running M & W; Golf M & W; Ice Hockey M; Lacrosse M; Soccer M & W; Tennis M & W; Track and Field M & W; Volleyball W

DALLAS CHRISTIAN COLLEGE

2700 Christian Pky.
Dallas, TX 75234-7299
Tel: (972)241-3371; Free: 800-688-1029
Fax: (972)241-8021
E-mail: bcondra@dallas.edu
Web Site: www.dallas.edu
President/CEO: Dustin D. Rubeck
Admissions: Brian Condra
Financial Aid: Robin L. Walker
Type: Four-Year College **Sex:** Coed **Affiliation:** Christian Churches and Churches of Christ. **% Accepted:** 64 **Admission Plans:** Deferred Admission; Preferred Admission **Application Deadline:** Rolling **Application Fee:** $25.00 **H.S. Requirements:** High school diploma required; GED accepted **Scholarships:** Available. **Calendar System:** Semester, Summer session available **Enrollment:** Full-time 227, Part-time 95 **Faculty:** Full-time 8, Part-time 48 **Student-Faculty Ratio:** 16:1 **Exams:** ACT essay component used for admission; ACT essay component used for advising; ACT essay component used for placement; SAT I or ACT; SAT essay component used for admission; SAT essay component used for advising; SAT essay component used for placement. **% Residing in College-Owned, -Operated, or -Affiliated Housing:** 41 **Credit Hours For Degree:** 61 semester hours, Associates; 129 semester hours, Bachelors **Professional Accreditation:** ABHE. **Intercollegiate Athletics:** Baseball M; Basketball M & W; Soccer M & W; Volleyball W

DALLAS INSTITUTE OF FUNERAL SERVICE

3909 S Buckner Blvd.
Dallas, TX 75227
Tel: (214)388-5466; Free: 800-235-5444
Fax: (214)388-0316
E-mail: difs@dallasinstitute.edu
Web Site: www.dallasinstitute.edu
President/CEO: James M. Shoemake
Financial Aid: Robert Clark
Type: Two-Year College **Sex:** Coed **Affiliation:** Pierce Mortuary Colleges, Inc. **Admission Plans:** Open Admission **Application Deadline:** Rolling **Application Fee:** $50.00 **H.S. Requirements:** High school diploma required; GED accepted **Scholarships:** Available. **Calendar System:** Quarter, Summer session not available **Enrollment:** Full-time 141 **Faculty:** Full-time 5, Part-time 6 **Student-Faculty Ratio:** 17:1 **Credit Hours For Degree:** 99 quarter hours, Associates **Professional Accreditation:** ABFSE.

DALLAS NURSING INSTITUTE

12170 N Abrams Rd.
Ste. 200

Dallas, TX 75243
Tel: (214)351-0223
Web Site: www.dni.edu
Type: Two-Year College **Sex:** Coed **Professional Accreditation:** ABHES.

DEL MAR COLLEGE

101 Baldwin Blvd.
Corpus Christi, TX 78404-3897
Tel: (361)698-1200; Free: 800-652-3357
Fax: (361)698-1559
E-mail: fjordan@delmar.edu
Web Site: www.delmar.edu
President/CEO: Dr. Mark Escamilla
Admissions: Frances P. Jordan
Type: Two-Year College **Sex:** Coed **Admission Plans:** Deferred Admission; Early Admission; Open Admission **Application Deadline:** Rolling **Application Fee:** $0.00 **H.S. Requirements:** High school diploma required; GED accepted **Scholarships:** Available. **Calendar System:** Semester, Summer session available **Enrollment:** Full-time 3,722, Part-time 8,285 **Faculty:** Full-time 267, Part-time 293 **Student-Faculty Ratio:** 18:1 **Final Year or Final Semester Residency Requirement:** No **Regional Accreditation:** Southern Association of Colleges and Schools **Credit Hours For Degree:** 62 semester hours, Associates **ROTC:** Army **Professional Accreditation:** ABET, ACEN, ACF, ADA, AHIMA, AOTA, APTA, ARCST, CoARC, JRCEDMS, JRCERT, NAACLS, NASAD, NASM, NAST.

DEVRY UNIVERSITY (AUSTIN)

Stratum Executive Ctr.
11044 Research Blvd., Ste. B100
Austin, TX 78759
Tel: (512)231-2500
Fax: (512)342-1716
Web Site: www.devry.edu
Type: Comprehensive **Sex:** Coed **Costs Per Year:** Tuition: $17,052 full-time, $609 per credit hour part-time. Mandatory fees: $80 full-time, $40 per term part-time. **Regional Accreditation:** North Central Association of Colleges and Schools

DEVRY UNIVERSITY (IRVING)

4800 Regent Blvd.
Irving, TX 75063-2439
Tel: (972)929-6777; Free: 866-338-7941
Web Site: www.devry.edu
Type: Comprehensive **Sex:** Coed **Affiliation:** DeVry University. **Application Fee:** $40.00 **H.S. Requirements:** High school diploma required; GED accepted **Costs Per Year:** Application fee: $40. Tuition: $13,300 full-time, $475 per credit hour part-time. Mandatory fees: $80 full-time, $40 per term part-time. **Scholarships:** Available. **Calendar System:** Semester **Enrollment:** Full-time 204, Graduate full-time 57, Graduate part-time 183, Part-time 374 **Faculty:** Full-time 21, Part-time 75 **Student-Faculty Ratio:** 10:1 **Exams:** ACT essay component used for admission; ACT essay component used for placement; SAT essay component used for admission; SAT essay component used for placement. **Regional Accreditation:** North Central Association of Colleges and Schools **Credit Hours For Degree:** 66 credit hours, Associates; 122 credit hours, Bachelors **Professional Accreditation:** ABET, ACBSP.

DEVRY UNIVERSITY (SAN ANTONIO)

618 NW Loop
Ste. 202
San Antonio, TX 78216
Tel: (210)524-5400
Fax: (210)979-9960
Web Site: www.devry.edu
Type: Comprehensive **Sex:** Coed **Costs Per Year:** Tuition: $17,052 full-time, $609 per credit hour part-time. Mandatory fees: $80 full-time, $40 per term part-time. **Regional Accreditation:** North Central Association of Colleges and Schools

EAST TEXAS BAPTIST UNIVERSITY

One Tiger Dr.
Marshall, TX 75670-1498
Tel: (903)935-7963; Free: 800-804-ETBU
Fax: (903)938-1705

E-mail: admissions@etbu.edu
Web Site: www.etbu.edu
President/CEO: Dr. J. Blair Blackburn
Admissions: Kevin Caffey
Financial Aid: Tommy Young
Type: Comprehensive **Sex:** Coed **Affiliation:** Baptist. **Scores:** 92% SAT V 400+; 94% SAT M 400+; 66% ACT 18-23; 19% ACT 24-29 **% Accepted:** 55 **Application Deadline:** September 1 **Application Fee:** $25.00 **H.S. Requirements:** High school diploma required; GED accepted **Costs Per Year:** Application fee: $25. Comprehensive fee: $32,847 includes full-time tuition ($23,250), mandatory fees ($968), and college room and board ($8629). College room only: $4576. Room and board charges vary according to board plan and housing facility. Part-time tuition: $775 per credit hour. Part-time mandatory fees: $41 per credit hour. **Scholarships:** Available. **Calendar System:** Semester, Summer session available **Enrollment:** Full-time 1,096, Graduate full-time 26, Graduate part-time 49, Part-time 137 **Faculty:** Full-time 73, Part-time 46 **Student-Faculty Ratio:** 14:1 **Exams:** ACT essay component not used; SAT I or ACT; SAT essay component not used; SAT Reasoning. **% Receiving Financial Aid:** 88 **% Residing in College-Owned, -Operated, or -Affiliated Housing:** 85 **Final Year or Final Semester Residency Requirement:** No **Regional Accreditation:** Southern Association of Colleges and Schools **Credit Hours For Degree:** 120 semester hours, Bachelors **Professional Accreditation:** AACN, NASM. **Intercollegiate Athletics:** Baseball M; Basketball M & W; Cross-Country Running M & W; Football M; Soccer M & W; Softball W; Tennis M & W; Track and Field M & W; Volleyball W

EASTFIELD COLLEGE
3737 Motley Dr.
Mesquite, TX 75150-2099
Tel: (972)860-7100
Fax: (972)860-8373
E-mail: efc@dcccd.edu
Web Site: www.efc.dcccd.edu
President/CEO: Dr. Jean Conway
Admissions: Glynis Miller
Type: Two-Year College **Sex:** Coed **Affiliation:** Dallas County Community College District System. **% Accepted:** 100 **Admission Plans:** Deferred Admission; Early Admission; Open Admission **Application Deadline:** Rolling **Application Fee:** $0.00 **H.S. Requirements:** High school diploma required; GED accepted **Scholarships:** Available. **Calendar System:** Semester, Summer session available **Enrollment:** Full-time 3,026, Part-time 9,377 **Faculty:** Full-time 121, Part-time 443 **Student-Faculty Ratio:** 24:1 **Regional Accreditation:** Southern Association of Colleges and Schools **Credit Hours For Degree:** 61 credit hours, Associates **Intercollegiate Athletics:** Baseball M; Basketball M; Golf M; Soccer W; Tennis M & W; Volleyball M & W

EL CENTRO COLLEGE
801 Main St.
Dallas, TX 75202-3604
Tel: (214)860-2037
Fax: (214)860-2335
E-mail: rgarza@dcccd.edu
Web Site: www.elcentrocollege.edu
President/CEO: Dr. Jose Adames
Admissions: Rebecca Garza
Type: Two-Year College **Sex:** Coed **Affiliation:** Dallas County Community College District System. **Scholarships:** Available. **Calendar System:** Semester, Summer session available **Enrollment:** Full-time 2,314, Part-time 7,787 **Faculty:** Full-time 135, Part-time 358 **Student-Faculty Ratio:** 19:1 **Regional Accreditation:** Southern Association of Colleges and Schools **Credit Hours For Degree:** 61 credit hours, Associates **ROTC:** Army **Professional Accreditation:** ACEN, ACF, CIDA, CoARC, JRCECT, JRCEDMS, JRCERT, NAACLS.

EL PASO COMMUNITY COLLEGE
PO Box 20500
El Paso, TX 79998-0500
Tel: (915)831-2000
Fax: (915)831-6145
E-mail: daryleh@epcc.edu
Web Site: www.epcc.edu
President/CEO: Dr. Ernst E. Roberts

Admissions: Daryle Hendry
Financial Aid: Raul H. Lerma
Type: Two-Year College **Sex:** Coed **Admission Plans:** Deferred Admission; Early Admission; Open Admission **Application Deadline:** August 3 **Application Fee:** $10.00 **H.S. Requirements:** High school diploma required; GED accepted **Costs Per Year:** Application fee: $10. State resident tuition: $2376 full-time, $84 per credit hour part-time. Nonresident tuition: $4032 full-time, $200 per credit hour part-time. Mandatory fees: $180 full-time, $15 per credit hour part-time, $15. Full-time tuition and fees vary according to course load. Part-time tuition and fees vary according to course load. **Scholarships:** Available. **Calendar System:** Semester, Summer session available **Enrollment:** Full-time 11,886, Part-time 18,837 **Faculty:** Full-time 415, Part-time 1,037 **Regional Accreditation:** Southern Association of Colleges and Schools **Credit Hours For Degree:** 60 credit hours, Associates **ROTC:** Army **Professional Accreditation:** AAMAE, ACEN, ADA, AHIMA, APTA, ARCST, COA, CoARC, NAACLS. **Intercollegiate Athletics:** Baseball M; Softball W; Track and Field M & W

EVEREST COLLEGE (ARLINGTON)
300 Six Flags Dr.
Ste. 100
Arlington, TX 76011
Tel: (817)652-7790
Fax: (817)649-6033
Web Site: www.everest.edu
President/CEO: Nikki Smith
Type: Two-Year College **Sex:** Coed **Affiliation:** Zenith Education Group. **% Accepted:** 75 **Calendar System:** Miscellaneous **Student-Faculty Ratio:** 18:1 **Professional Accreditation:** ACICS.

EVEREST COLLEGE (FORT WORTH)
4200 S Fwy.
Ste. 1940
Fort Worth, TX 76115
Tel: (817)566-7700
Web Site: www.everest.edu
Type: Two-Year College **Sex:** Coed **Affiliation:** Zenith Education Group. **Professional Accreditation:** ACICS.

FRANK PHILLIPS COLLEGE
Box 5118
Borger, TX 79008-5118
Tel: (806)457-4200
Fax: (806)274-6835
E-mail: mstevens@fpctx.edu
Web Site: www.fpctx.edu
President/CEO: Dr. Jud Hicks
Admissions: Michele Stevens
Type: Two-Year College **Sex:** Coed **Admission Plans:** Deferred Admission; Early Admission; Open Admission **Application Deadline:** August 25 **Application Fee:** $0.00 **H.S. Requirements:** High school diploma required; GED accepted **Costs Per Year:** Application fee: $0. Area resident tuition: $1290 full-time, $43 per credit hour part-time. State resident tuition: $2040 full-time, $68 per credit hour part-time. Nonresident tuition: $2280 full-time, $76 per credit hour part-time. Mandatory fees: $1762 full-time, $53 per credit hour part-time, $48 per term part-time. Full-time tuition and fees vary according to course load. Part-time tuition and fees vary according to course load. College room and board: $3360. Room and board charges vary according to housing facility. **Scholarships:** Available. **Calendar System:** Semester, Summer session available **Enrollment:** Full-time 501, Part-time 647 **Faculty:** Full-time 35, Part-time 40 **Student-Faculty Ratio:** 16:1 **% Residing in College-Owned, -Operated, or -Affiliated Housing:** 20 **Regional Accreditation:** Southern Association of Colleges and Schools **Credit Hours For Degree:** 64 credit hours, Associates **Intercollegiate Athletics:** Baseball M; Basketball M & W; Softball W; Volleyball W

GALVESTON COLLEGE
4015 Ave. Q
Galveston, TX 77550
Tel: (409)944-4242
Fax: (409)944-1500
E-mail: sbranum@gc.edu
Web Site: www.gc.edu
President/CEO: Dr. W. Myles Shelton, EdD

Admissions: Scott Branum

Type: Two-Year College **Sex:** Coed **Admission Plans:** Open Admission **Application Deadline:** Rolling **Application Fee:** $0.00 **H.S. Requirements:** High school diploma required; GED accepted **Costs Per Year:** Application fee: $0. Area resident tuition: $1110 full-time, $37 per credit hour part-time. State resident tuition: $1590 full-time, $53 per credit hour part-time. Nonresident tuition: $3480 full-time, $116 per credit hour part-time. Mandatory fees: $790 full-time, $20 per credit hour part-time, $95 per term part-time. Full-time tuition and fees vary according to course load. Part-time tuition and fees vary according to course load. **Scholarships:** Available. **Calendar System:** Semester, Summer session available **Enrollment:** Full-time 504, Part-time 1,567 **Faculty:** Full-time 55, Part-time 44 **Student-Faculty Ratio:** 15:1 **Exams:** Other. **Regional Accreditation:** Southern Association of Colleges and Schools **Credit Hours For Degree:** 60 credit hours, Associates **Professional Accreditation:** ACEN, JRCEMTP, JRCERT, JRCNMT. **Intercollegiate Athletics:** Baseball M; Softball W

GOLF ACADEMY OF AMERICA

1861 Valley View Ln.
Ste. 100
Farmers Branch, TX 75234
Tel: (972)763-8100; Free: 800-342-7342
Web Site: www.golfacademy.edu
Type: Two-Year College **Sex:** Coed **Professional Accreditation:** ACICS.

GRACE SCHOOL OF THEOLOGY

3705 College Park Dr. Ste. 140
Conroe, TX 77384-4894
Web Site: www.gsot.edu
Type: Four-Year College **Sex:** Coed **Professional Accreditation:** ATS.

GRAYSON COLLEGE

6101 Grayson Dr.
Denison, TX 75020-8299
Tel: (903)465-6030
Fax: (903)463-5284
E-mail: lesliec@grayson.edu
Web Site: www.grayson.edu
President/CEO: Dr. Jeremy P. McMillen, PhD
Admissions: Charles Leslie
Type: Two-Year College **Sex:** Coed **Admission Plans:** Deferred Admission; Early Admission; Open Admission **Application Deadline:** August 31 **Application Fee:** $0.00 **H.S. Requirements:** High school diploma required; GED accepted **Costs Per Year:** Application fee: $0. Area resident tuition: $1176 full-time, $49 per credit hour part-time. State resident tuition: $2088 full-time, $87 per credit hour part-time. Nonresident tuition: $3192 full-time, $133 per credit hour part-time. Mandatory fees: $552 full-time, $23 per credit hour part-time, $12 per term part-time. Full-time tuition and fees vary according to course load. Part-time tuition and fees vary according to course load. College room and board: $5299. **Scholarships:** Available. **Calendar System:** Semester, Summer session available **Enrollment:** Full-time 2,101, Part-time 2,913 **Faculty:** Full-time 105, Part-time 135 **Student-Faculty Ratio:** 26:1 **% Residing in College-Owned, -Operated, or -Affiliated Housing:** 17 **Final Year or Final Semester Residency Requirement:** No **Regional Accreditation:** Southern Association of Colleges and Schools **Credit Hours For Degree:** 62 semester hours, Associates **Professional Accreditation:** ACEN, ADA, NAACLS. **Intercollegiate Athletics:** Baseball M; Softball W

HALLMARK UNIVERSITY

10401 IH 10 W
San Antonio, TX 78230
Tel: (210)690-9000; Free: 800-880-6600
Fax: (210)697-8225
E-mail: slross@hallmarkuniversity.edu
Web Site: www.hallmarkuniversity.edu
President/CEO: Joe Fisher
Admissions: Sal Ross
Type: Comprehensive **Sex:** Coed **% Accepted:** 100 **Admission Plans:** Early Admission **Application Deadline:** Rolling **H.S. Requirements:** High school diploma required; GED accepted **Scholarships:** Available. **Calendar System:** Continuous **Enrollment:** Full-time 582, Graduate full-time 33 **Faculty:** Full-time 31, Part-time 29 **Student-Faculty Ratio:** 15:1 **Exams:**

Other. **Credit Hours For Degree:** 60-72, depending on program, Associates; 120-126 credit hours, depending on program, Bachelors **Professional Accreditation:** ACCSC.

HARDIN-SIMMONS UNIVERSITY

2200 Hickory St.
Abilene, TX 79698-0001
Tel: (325)670-1000; Free: 877-464-7889
Fax: (325)677-8351
E-mail: visit@hsutx.edu
Web Site: www.hsutx.edu
President/CEO: Dr. Lanny Hall
Admissions: Bobbie Turner
Financial Aid: Bridget Moore
Type: Comprehensive **Sex:** Coed **Affiliation:** Baptist. **Scores:** 96% SAT V 400+; 97% SAT M 400+; 52.87% ACT 18-23; 33.44% ACT 24-29 **% Accepted:** 60 **Admission Plans:** Deferred Admission **Application Deadline:** Rolling **H.S. Requirements:** High school diploma required; GED accepted **Costs Per Year:** Comprehensive fee: $33,518 includes full-time tuition ($25,230) and college room and board ($8288). College room only: $3900. Full-time tuition varies according to program. Room and board charges vary according to board plan and housing facility. Part-time tuition: $770 per credit hour. Part-time mandatory fees: $200 per term. Part-time tuition and fees vary according to course load and program. Tuition guaranteed not to increase for student's term of enrollment. **Scholarships:** Available. **Calendar System:** Semester, Summer session available **Enrollment:** Full-time 1,475, Graduate full-time 238, Graduate part-time 236, Part-time 163 **Faculty:** Full-time 134, Part-time 70 **Student-Faculty Ratio:** 12:1 **Exams:** SAT I or ACT; SAT Reasoning. **% Receiving Financial Aid:** 73 **% Residing in College-Owned, -Operated, or -Affiliated Housing:** 45 **Final Year or Final Semester Residency Requirement:** Yes **Regional Accreditation:** Southern Association of Colleges and Schools **Credit Hours For Degree:** 124 semester hours, Bachelors **Professional Accreditation:** AACN, ACBSP, APTA, ATS, CSWE, NASM. **Intercollegiate Athletics:** Baseball M; Basketball M & W; Cheerleading M & W; Cross-Country Running M & W; Football M; Golf M & W; Soccer M & W; Softball W; Tennis M & W; Track and Field M & W; Volleyball W

HILL COLLEGE

112 Lamar Dr.
Hillsboro, TX 76645
Tel: (254)582-2555
E-mail: enrollmentinfo@hillcollege.edu
Web Site: www.hillcollege.edu
President/CEO: Dr. Pam Boehm
Type: Two-Year College **Sex:** Coed **Admission Plans:** Deferred Admission; Early Admission; Open Admission **Application Deadline:** Rolling **Application Fee:** $0.00 **H.S. Requirements:** High school diploma required; GED accepted **Scholarships:** Available. **Calendar System:** Semester, Summer session available **Regional Accreditation:** Southern Association of Colleges and Schools **Credit Hours For Degree:** 62 credit hours, Associates **Intercollegiate Athletics:** Baseball M; Basketball M & W; Golf M; Soccer M & W; Softball W; Volleyball W

HOUSTON BAPTIST UNIVERSITY

7502 Fondren Rd.
Houston, TX 77074-3298
Tel: (281)649-3000; Free: 800-696-3210
Fax: (281)649-3209
E-mail: arice@hbu.edu
Web Site: www.hbu.edu
President/CEO: Dr. Robert B. Sloan, Jr.
Admissions: Amy Rice
Financial Aid: Veronica Jene Gabbard
Type: Comprehensive **Sex:** Coed **Affiliation:** Baptist. **Scores:** 99% SAT V 400+; 100% SAT M 400+; 51.2% ACT 18-23; 38.28% ACT 24-29 **% Accepted:** 33 **Admission Plans:** Early Admission **Application Deadline:** Rolling **Application Fee:** $0.00 **H.S. Requirements:** High school diploma required; GED accepted **Costs Per Year:** Application fee: $0. Comprehensive fee: $38,658 includes full-time tuition ($28,850), mandatory fees ($1950), and college room and board ($7858). College room only: $4770. Room and board charges vary according to board plan and housing facility. Part-time tuition: $1200 per credit hour. Part-time mandatory fees: $975 per term. Part-time tuition and fees vary according to course load. **Scholar-**

ships: Available. **Calendar System:** Semester, Summer session available **Enrollment:** Full-time 2,117, Graduate full-time 338, Graduate part-time 572, Part-time 133 **Faculty:** Full-time 131, Part-time 113 **Student-Faculty Ratio:** 16:1 **Exams:** ACT; ACT essay component not used; SAT I; SAT I and SAT II or ACT; SAT I or ACT; SAT II; SAT essay component used for advising; SAT essay component used for placement; SAT Reasoning; SAT Subject. **% Receiving Financial Aid:** 72 **% Residing in College-Owned, -Operated, or -Affiliated Housing:** 42 **Final Year or Final Semester Residency Requirement:** Yes **Regional Accreditation:** Southern Association of Colleges and Schools **Credit Hours For Degree:** 125 credit hours, Bachelors **ROTC:** Air Force, Army, Navy **Professional Accreditation:** ACBSP, ACEN. **Intercollegiate Athletics:** Baseball M; Basketball M & W; Cheerleading M & W; Cross-Country Running M & W; Football M; Golf M & W; Soccer M & W; Softball W; Track and Field M & W; Volleyball W

HOUSTON COMMUNITY COLLEGE

3100 Main St.
Houston, TX 77002
Tel: (713)718-2000; Free: 877-422-6111
Fax: (713)718-2111
E-mail: student.info@hccs.edu
Web Site: www.hccs.edu
President/CEO: Dr. Cesar Maldonado
Admissions: Mary Lemburg
Financial Aid: Zena Williams

Type: Two-Year College **Sex:** Coed **% Accepted:** 100 **Admission Plans:** Open Admission **Application Deadline:** Rolling **H.S. Requirements:** High school diploma required; GED accepted. For dual credit/concurrent high school enrolled, early college high school, home-schooled students: High school diploma or equivalent not required **Costs Per Year:** Area resident tuition: $1632 full-time, $411 per term part-time. State resident tuition: $3360 full-time, $843 per term part-time. Nonresident tuition: $3756 full-time, $942 per term part-time. Full-time tuition varies according to course load. Part-time tuition varies according to course load. **Scholarships:** Available. **Calendar System:** Semester, Summer session available **Enrollment:** Full-time 16,896, Part-time 39,626 **Faculty:** Full-time 759, Part-time 1,687 **Final Year or Final Semester Residency Requirement:** No **Regional Accreditation:** Southern Association of Colleges and Schools **Credit Hours For Degree:** 60 semester hours, Associates **ROTC:** Air Force, Army **Professional Accreditation:** ABET, ADA, AHIMA, AOTA, APTA, CoARC, JRCEMTP, JRCERT, JRCNMT, NAACLS.

HOWARD COLLEGE

1001 Birdwell Ln.
Big Spring, TX 79720
Tel: (915)264-5000; Free: 866-HC-HAWKS
Fax: (915)264-5082
E-mail: trichardson@howardcollege.edu
Web Site: www.howardcollege.edu
President/CEO: Dr. Cheryl T. Sparks
Admissions: TaNeal Richardson
Financial Aid: Candice Draper

Type: Two-Year College **Sex:** Coed **Affiliation:** Howard County Junior College District System. **Admission Plans:** Early Admission; Open Admission **Application Deadline:** Rolling **Application Fee:** $0.00 **H.S. Requirements:** High school diploma required; GED accepted **Scholarships:** Available. **Calendar System:** Semester, Summer session available **Enrollment:** Full-time 1,636, Part-time 2,467 **Faculty:** Full-time 144, Part-time 99 **Student-Faculty Ratio:** 14:1 **Exams:** ACT essay component used for advising; ACT essay component used for placement; SAT essay component used for advising; SAT essay component used for placement. **% Residing in College-Owned, -Operated, or -Affiliated Housing:** 8 **Regional Accreditation:** Southern Association of Colleges and Schools **Credit Hours For Degree:** 62 credit hours, Associates **Professional Accreditation:** ACEN, ADA, AHIMA. **Intercollegiate Athletics:** Baseball M; Basketball M & W; Cheerleading M & W; Softball W

HOWARD PAYNE UNIVERSITY

1000 Fisk St.
Brownwood, TX 76801-2715
Tel: (325)646-2502; Free: 800-880-4478
Fax: (325)649-8905
E-mail: enroll@hputx.edu
Web Site: www.hputx.edu

President/CEO: Dr. William N. Ellis
Admissions: P.J. Gramling
Financial Aid: Glenda Huff

Type: Comprehensive **Sex:** Coed **Affiliation:** Baptist General Convention of Texas. **Scores:** 85% SAT V 400+; 91% SAT M 400+; 56% ACT 18-23; 20% ACT 24-29 **% Accepted:** 86 **Admission Plans:** Early Admission **Application Deadline:** Rolling **Application Fee:** $0.00 **H.S. Requirements:** High school diploma required; GED accepted **Costs Per Year:** Application fee: $0. Comprehensive fee: $34,430 includes full-time tuition ($24,430), mandatory fees ($2200), and college room and board ($7800). Full-time tuition and fees vary according to course load, location, and program. Room and board charges vary according to board plan and housing facility. Part-time tuition: $790 per credit. Part-time tuition varies according to location and program. **Scholarships:** Available. **Calendar System:** Semester, Summer session available **Enrollment:** Full-time 951, Graduate full-time 27, Graduate part-time 57, Part-time 128 **Faculty:** Full-time 84, Part-time 78 **Student-Faculty Ratio:** 10:1 **Exams:** ACT essay component not used; Other; SAT I or ACT; SAT essay component not used; SAT Reasoning. **% Receiving Financial Aid:** 83 **% Residing in College-Owned, -Operated, or -Affiliated Housing:** 59 **Final Year or Final Semester Residency Requirement:** No **Regional Accreditation:** Southern Association of Colleges and Schools **Credit Hours For Degree:** 64 semester hours, Associates; 124 semester hours, Bachelors **Professional Accreditation:** CSWE, NASM. **Intercollegiate Athletics:** Baseball M; Basketball M & W; Football M; Soccer M & W; Softball W; Tennis M & W; Volleyball W

HUSTON-TILLOTSON UNIVERSITY

900 Chicon St.
Austin, TX 78702-2795
Tel: (512)505-3000
Fax: (512)505-3190
E-mail: slstinson@htu.edu
Web Site: www.htu.edu
President/CEO: Dr. Colette Pierce Burnette, EdD
Admissions: Shakitha Stinson

Type: Comprehensive **Sex:** Coed **Affiliation:** interdenominational. **Scores:** 45% SAT V 400+; 31.8% ACT 18-23; 4.5% ACT 24-29 **% Accepted:** 60 **Admission Plans:** Deferred Admission **Application Fee:** $25.00 **H.S. Requirements:** High school diploma required; GED accepted **Costs Per Year:** Application fee: $25. Comprehensive fee: $21,914 includes full-time tuition ($12,262), mandatory fees ($2084), and college room and board ($7568). College room only: $3642. Full-time tuition and fees vary according to course load. Room and board charges vary according to housing facility. Part-time tuition: $410 per credit hour. Part-time mandatory fees: $457 per term. Part-time tuition and fees vary according to course load. **Scholarships:** Available. **Calendar System:** Semester, Summer session available **Enrollment:** Full-time 923, Graduate full-time 6, Graduate part-time 49, Part-time 45 **Faculty:** Full-time 50, Part-time 46 **Student-Faculty Ratio:** 15:1 **Exams:** ACT; SAT I; SAT I and SAT II or ACT; SAT I or ACT; SAT Reasoning; SAT Subject. **% Receiving Financial Aid:** 91 **% Residing in College-Owned, -Operated, or -Affiliated Housing:** 37 **Regional Accreditation:** Southern Association of Colleges and Schools **Credit Hours For Degree:** 120 credit hours, Bachelors **ROTC:** Air Force, Army, Navy **Professional Accreditation:** ACBSP. **Intercollegiate Athletics:** Baseball M; Basketball M & W; Cross-Country Running M; Soccer M & W; Softball W; Track and Field M & W; Volleyball W

INTERACTIVE COLLEGE OF TECHNOLOGY (HOUSTON)

6200 Hillcroft Ave.
Ste. 200
Houston, TX 77081
Tel: (713)771-5336
Web Site: ict.edu

Type: Two-Year College **Sex:** Coed **H.S. Requirements:** High school diploma required; GED accepted **Calendar System:** Semester **Professional Accreditation:** COE.

INTERACTIVE COLLEGE OF TECHNOLOGY (HOUSTON)

4473 I-45 N Fwy.
Airline Plz.
Houston, TX 77022
Tel: (281)931-7717
Web Site: ict.edu

Type: Two-Year College **Sex:** Coed **Calendar System:** Semester **Professional Accreditation:** COE.

INTERACTIVE COLLEGE OF TECHNOLOGY (PASADENA)

213 W Southmore St.
Ste. 101
Pasadena, TX 77502
Tel: (713)920-1120
Web Site: ict.edu

Type: Two-Year College **Sex:** Coed **Calendar System:** Semester **Professional Accreditation:** COE.

INTERNATIONAL BUSINESS COLLEGE (EL PASO)

1155 N Zaragosa Rd.
El Paso, TX 79907
Tel: (915)859-0422
Fax: (915)859-4142
Web Site: www.ibcelpaso.edu

Type: Two-Year College **Sex:** Coed **Professional Accreditation:** ACICS.

INTERNATIONAL BUSINESS COLLEGE (EL PASO)

5700 Cromo Dr.
El Paso, TX 79912
Tel: (915)842-0422
Fax: (915)585-2584
Web Site: www.ibcelpaso.edu

Type: Two-Year College **Sex:** Coed

JACKSONVILLE COLLEGE

105 B J Albritton Dr.
Jacksonville, TX 75766-4759
Tel: (903)586-2518; Free: 800-256-8522
E-mail: admissions@jacksonville-college.org
Web Site: www.jacksonville-college.edu
President/CEO: Dr. Edwin Crank
Admissions: Danny Morris
Financial Aid: Paul Galyean

Type: Two-Year College **Sex:** Coed **Affiliation:** Baptist. **Admission Plans:** Early Admission; Open Admission **Application Deadline:** August 15 **Application Fee:** $15.00 **H.S. Requirements:** High school diploma required; GED accepted **Costs Per Year:** Application fee: $15. **Scholarships:** Available. **Calendar System:** Semester, Summer session available **Student-Faculty Ratio:** 15:1 **Exams:** ACT; Other; SAT I. **Regional Accreditation:** Southern Association of Colleges and Schools **Credit Hours For Degree:** 64 semester hours, Associates **Intercollegiate Athletics:** Basketball M & W

JARVIS CHRISTIAN COLLEGE

PR 7631 @ U S Hwy. 80 E
Hawkins, TX 75765-1470
Tel: (903)769-5700
Fax: (903)769-4842
Web Site: www.jarvis.edu
President/CEO: Dr. Lester C. Newman
Admissions: Brandon Byrd
Financial Aid: Alice Copeland

Type: Four-Year College **Sex:** Coed **Affiliation:** Christian Church (Disciples of Christ). **Scores:** 29% SAT V 400+; 30% SAT M 400+; 20% ACT 18-23; 1% ACT 24-29 **% Accepted:** 54 **Admission Plans:** Open Admission **Application Deadline:** August 1 **Application Fee:** $50.00 **H.S. Requirements:** High school diploma required; GED accepted **Costs Per Year:** Application fee: $50. Comprehensive fee: $20,160 includes full-time tuition ($10,400), mandatory fees ($1320), and college room and board ($8440). College room only: $4530. Room and board charges vary according to housing facility. Part-time tuition: $435 per semester hour. **Scholarships:** Available. **Calendar System:** Semester, Summer session available **Faculty:** Full-time 32, Part-time 5 **Student-Faculty Ratio:** 26:1 **Exams:** ACT essay component not used; SAT I or ACT; SAT essay component not used. **% Receiving Financial Aid:** 100 **% Residing in College-Owned, -Operated, or -Affiliated Housing:** 85 **Final Year or Final Semester Residency Requirement:** Yes **Regional Accreditation:** Southern Association of Colleges and Schools **Credit Hours For Degree:** 120 semester hours, Bachelors **Professional Accreditation:** ACBSP. **Intercollegiate Athletics:** Baseball M; Basketball M & W; Cheerleading W; Cross-Country Running M & W; Golf M; Soccer M & W; Softball W; Track and Field M & W; Volleyball W

KD CONSERVATORY COLLEGE OF FILM AND DRAMATIC ARTS

2600 Stemmons Fwy., No.117
Dallas, TX 75207
Tel: (214)638-0484; Free: 877-278-2283
Fax: (214)630-5140
E-mail: tataylor@kdstudio.com
Web Site: www.kdstudio.com
President/CEO: Gary Stephen Tyner, Jr.
Admissions: T. A. Taylor
Financial Aid: Linda Craft

Type: Two-Year College **Sex:** Coed **% Accepted:** 34 **Admission Plans:** Deferred Admission; Open Admission **Application Deadline:** Rolling **Application Fee:** $0.00 **H.S. Requirements:** High school diploma required; GED accepted **Costs Per Year:** Application fee: $0. Tuition: $14,025 full-time. Mandatory fees: $550 full-time. Tuition guaranteed not to increase for student's term of enrollment. **Scholarships:** Available. **Calendar System:** Semester, Summer session not available **Enrollment:** Full-time 236 **Faculty:** Full-time 28 **Student-Faculty Ratio:** 12:1 **Final Year or Final Semester Residency Requirement:** No **Credit Hours For Degree:** 70 credits, Associates **Professional Accreditation:** NAST.

KILGORE COLLEGE

1100 Broadway Blvd.
Kilgore, TX 75662-3299
Tel: (903)984-8531
Fax: (903)983-8607
E-mail: register@kilgore.cc.tx.us
Web Site: www.kilgore.edu
President/CEO: Dr. Brenda S. Kays

Type: Two-Year College **Sex:** Coed **Admission Plans:** Early Admission; Open Admission **Application Deadline:** Rolling **Application Fee:** $0.00 **H.S. Requirements:** High school diploma required; GED accepted **Costs Per Year:** Application fee: $0. Area resident tuition: $768 full-time, $32 per semester hour part-time. State resident tuition: $2424 full-time, $101 per semester hour part-time. Nonresident tuition: $3624 full-time, $151 per semester hour part-time. Mandatory fees: $696 full-time. Full-time tuition and fees vary according to course load and program. Part-time tuition varies according to course load and program. College room and board: $4640. Room and board charges vary according to board plan and housing facility. **Scholarships:** Available. **Calendar System:** Semester, Summer session available **Enrollment:** Full-time 2,245, Part-time 3,421 **Faculty:** Full-time 149, Part-time 159 **Student-Faculty Ratio:** 17:1 **% Residing in College-Owned, -Operated, or -Affiliated Housing:** 7 **Final Year or Final Semester Residency Requirement:** No **Regional Accreditation:** Southern Association of Colleges and Schools **Credit Hours For Degree:** 60 credits, Associates **Professional Accreditation:** AAMAE, ACEN, APTA, ARCST, JRCERT, NAACLS. **Intercollegiate Athletics:** Basketball M & W; Football M; Softball W

THE KING'S UNIVERSITY

2121 E Southlake Blvd.
Southlake, TX 76092
Tel: (817)552-3700; Free: 888-779-8040
E-mail: tyler.maxey@tku.edu
Web Site: www.tku.edu
President/CEO: Dr. John Spurling
Admissions: Tyler Maxey
Financial Aid: Norman V. Stoppenbrink, Jr.

Type: Comprehensive **Sex:** Coed **Affiliation:** International Church of the Foursquare Gospel. **Application Fee:** $45.00 **Scholarships:** Available. **Calendar System:** Semester **Professional Accreditation:** TRACS.

LAMAR INSTITUTE OF TECHNOLOGY

855 E Lavaca
Beaumont, TX 77705
Tel: (409)880-8321; Free: 800-950-6989
Web Site: www.lit.edu
President/CEO: Dr. Paul Szuch

Type: Two-Year College **Sex:** Coed **Scholarships:** Available. **Calendar System:** Semester **Regional Accreditation:** Southern Association of Colleges and Schools **Professional Accreditation:** ADA, AHIMA, CoARC.

LAMAR STATE COLLEGE–ORANGE

410 Front St.
Orange, TX 77630
Tel: (409)883-7750
Fax: (409)882-3374
Web Site: www.lsco.edu
President/CEO: Dr. Michael Shahan
Admissions: Kerry Olson

Type: Two-Year College **Sex:** Coed **Affiliation:** Texas State University System. **Admission Plans:** Open Admission **Application Deadline:** Rolling **Application Fee:** $0.00 **H.S. Requirements:** High school diploma required; GED accepted **Scholarships:** Available. **Calendar System:** Semester, Summer session available **Enrollment:** Full-time 992, Part-time 1,434 **Faculty:** Full-time 50, Part-time 46 **Student-Faculty Ratio:** 19:1 **Regional Accreditation:** Southern Association of Colleges and Schools **Credit Hours For Degree:** 62 credit hours, Associates **Professional Accreditation:** ADA, NAACLS.

LAMAR STATE COLLEGE–PORT ARTHUR

PO Box 310
Port Arthur, TX 77641-0310
Tel: (409)983-4921; Free: 800-477-5872
Fax: (409)984-6032
E-mail: nichoca@lamarpa.edu
Web Site: www.lamarpa.edu
President/CEO: Dr. Sam Monroe
Admissions: Connie Nicholas
Financial Aid: Diane Hargett

Type: Two-Year College **Sex:** Coed **Affiliation:** Texas State University System. **Admission Plans:** Deferred Admission; Early Admission; Open Admission **Application Deadline:** Rolling **Application Fee:** $0.00 **H.S. Requirements:** High school diploma or equivalent not required **Scholarships:** Available. **Calendar System:** Semester, Summer session available **Student-Faculty Ratio:** 18:1 **Regional Accreditation:** Southern Association of Colleges and Schools **Credit Hours For Degree:** 64 credit hours, Associates **ROTC:** Army **Professional Accreditation:** ARCST.

LAMAR UNIVERSITY

4400 Martin Luther King Pky.
Beaumont, TX 77710
Tel: (409)880-7011
Fax: (409)880-8463
E-mail: admissions@lamar.edu
Web Site: www.lamar.edu
President/CEO: Dr. Kenneth Evans
Admissions: Melissa Gallien

Type: University **Sex:** Coed **Affiliation:** Texas State University System. **Scores:** 88% SAT V 400+; 92% SAT M 400+; 53% ACT 18-23; 21% ACT 24-29 **% Accepted:** 79 **Admission Plans:** Early Admission **Application Deadline:** August 11 **Application Fee:** $25.00 **H.S. Requirements:** High school diploma required; GED accepted **Costs Per Year:** Application fee: $25. One-time mandatory fee: $10. State resident tuition: $6450 full-time, $218 per credit hour part-time. Nonresident tuition: $17,400 full-time, $580 per credit hour part-time. Mandatory fees: $2801 full-time, $382 per credit hour part-time, $784. Full-time tuition and fees vary according to course load, location, and program. Part-time tuition and fees vary according to course load, location, and program. College room and board: $8302. College room only: $5252. Room and board charges vary according to board plan. Tuition guaranteed not to increase for student's term of enrollment. **Scholarships:** Available. **Calendar System:** Semester, Summer session available **Enrollment:** Full-time 6,314, Graduate full-time 1,084, Graduate part-time 4,707, Part-time 2,860 **Faculty:** Full-time 414, Part-time 103 **Student-Faculty Ratio:** 17:1 **Exams:** ACT essay component not used; SAT I or ACT; SAT essay component not used; SAT Reasoning. **% Receiving Financial Aid:** 63 **% Residing in College-Owned, -Operated, or -Affiliated Housing:** 16 **Final Year or Final Semester Residency Requirement:** No **Regional Accreditation:** Southern Association of Colleges and Schools **Credit Hours For Degree:** 60 semester hours, Associates; 120 semester hours, Bachelors **ROTC:** Air Force **Professional Accreditation:** AACSB, AAFCS, ABET, ACEN, ACF, AND, ASHA, CSWE, JRCERT, NASM, NCATE. **Intercollegiate Athletics:** Baseball M; Basketball M & W; Cheerleading M & W; Cross-Country Running M & W; Football M; Golf M & W; Soccer W; Softball W; Tennis M & W; Track and Field M & W; Volleyball W

LAREDO COMMUNITY COLLEGE

W End Washington St.
Laredo, TX 78040-4395
Tel: (956)722-0521
Fax: (956)721-5493
Web Site: www.laredo.edu
President/CEO: Dr. Juan L. Maldonado
Admissions: Josie Soliz

Type: Two-Year College **Sex:** Coed **% Accepted:** 100 **Admission Plans:** Deferred Admission; Early Admission; Open Admission **Application Deadline:** Rolling **Application Fee:** $0.00 **Scholarships:** Available. **Calendar System:** Semester, Summer session available **Enrollment:** Full-time 3,044, Part-time 5,108 **Faculty:** Full-time 203, Part-time 140 **Student-Faculty Ratio:** 18:1 **Exams:** ACT; SAT I. **Regional Accreditation:** Southern Association of Colleges and Schools **Credit Hours For Degree:** 60 credit hours, Associates **Professional Accreditation:** ACEN, AOTA, APTA, JRCERT, NAACLS. **Intercollegiate Athletics:** Baseball M; Tennis M & W; Volleyball W

LEE COLLEGE

PO Box 818
Baytown, TX 77522-0818
Tel: (281)427-5611
Fax: (281)425-6831
E-mail: bgriffit@lee.edu
Web Site: www.lee.edu
President/CEO: Dr. Dennis Brown
Admissions: Becki Griffith

Type: Two-Year College **Sex:** Coed **Admission Plans:** Deferred Admission; Early Admission; Open Admission **Application Deadline:** Rolling **Application Fee:** $0.00 **H.S. Requirements:** High school diploma or equivalent not required **Scholarships:** Available. **Calendar System:** Semester, Summer session available **Enrollment:** Full-time 1,795, Part-time 3,552 **Faculty:** Full-time 185, Part-time 214 **Student-Faculty Ratio:** 14:1 **Regional Accreditation:** Southern Association of Colleges and Schools **Credit Hours For Degree:** 60 credit hours, Associates **ROTC:** Army **Professional Accreditation:** ACEN, AHIMA, JRCEMTP. **Intercollegiate Athletics:** Basketball M; Tennis W; Volleyball W

LETOURNEAU UNIVERSITY

PO Box 7001
Longview, TX 75607-7001
Tel: (903)233-3000; Free: 800-759-8811
Fax: (903)233-3411
Web Site: www.letu.edu
President/CEO: Dr. Dale A. Lunsford

Type: Comprehensive **Sex:** Coed **Affiliation:** nondenominational. **Scores:** 97% SAT V 400+; 97% SAT M 400+; 33.33% ACT 18-23; 38.71% ACT 24-29 **% Accepted:** 45 **Admission Plans:** Deferred Admission **Application Deadline:** Rolling **Application Fee:** $0.00 **H.S. Requirements:** High school diploma required; GED accepted **Costs Per Year:** Application fee: $0. Comprehensive fee: $37,480 includes full-time tuition ($27,380), mandatory fees ($520), and college room and board ($9580). Full-time tuition and fees vary according to course level, course load, and program. Room and board charges vary according to board plan. Part-time tuition: $1092 per credit hour. Part-time tuition varies according to course level, course load, and program. **Scholarships:** Available. **Calendar System:** Semester, Summer session available **Enrollment:** Full-time 1,262, Graduate full-time 82, Graduate part-time 428, Part-time 1,024 **Faculty:** Full-time 90, Part-time 126 **Student-Faculty Ratio:** 14:1 **Exams:** ACT essay component not used; SAT I or ACT; SAT essay component not used. **% Receiving Financial Aid:** 86 **% Residing in College-Owned, -Operated, or -Affiliated Housing:** 73 **Final Year or Final Semester Residency Requirement:** No **Regional Accreditation:** Southern Association of Colleges and Schools **Professional Accreditation:** ABET. **Intercollegiate Athletics:** Baseball M; Basketball M & W; Cross-Country Running M & W; Golf M & W; Rugby M; Soccer M & W; Softball W; Tennis M & W; Volleyball W

LINCOLN COLLEGE OF TECHNOLOGY

2915 Alouette Dr.
Grand Prairie, TX 75052
Tel: (972)660-5701
Web Site: www.lincolnedu.com
Type: Two-Year College **Sex:** Coed

LONE STAR COLLEGE–CYFAIR

9191 Barker Cypress Rd.
Cypress, TX 77433-1383
Tel: (281)290-3200
E-mail: cfc.info@lonestar.edu
Web Site: www.lonestar.edu/cyfair
President/CEO: Dr. Seelpa Keshvala

Type: Two-Year College **Sex:** Coed **Affiliation:** Lone Star College. **% Accepted:** 100 **Admission Plans:** Early Admission; Open Admission **Application Fee:** $0.00 **H.S. Requirements:** High school diploma required; GED accepted **Costs Per Year:** Application fee: $0. Area resident tuition: $1008 full-time, $42 per credit hour part-time. State resident tuition: $2688 full-time, $112 per credit hour part-time. Nonresident tuition: $3048 full-time, $127 per credit hour part-time. Mandatory fees: $496 full-time, $18 per credit hour part-time, $32. Full-time tuition and fees vary according to course load and program. Part-time tuition and fees vary according to course load and program. **Calendar System:** Semester, Summer session available **Enrollment:** Full-time 5,964, Part-time 14,546 **Faculty:** Full-time 217, Part-time 886 **Student-Faculty Ratio:** 21:1 **Final Year or Final Semester Residency Requirement:** No **Regional Accreditation:** Southern Association of Colleges and Schools **Credit Hours For Degree:** 60 credit hours, Associates **Professional Accreditation:** ACEN.

LONE STAR COLLEGE–KINGWOOD

20000 Kingwood Dr.
Kingwood, TX 77339-3801
Tel: (281)312-1600
Fax: (281)312-1477
E-mail: kingwoodadvising@lonestar.edu
Web Site: www.lonestar.edu/kingwood.htm
President/CEO: Dr. Katherine Persson
Financial Aid: Shannon Infante

Type: Two-Year College **Sex:** Coed **Affiliation:** Lone Star College. **% Accepted:** 100 **Admission Plans:** Early Admission; Open Admission **Application Deadline:** Rolling **Application Fee:** $0.00 **H.S. Requirements:** High school diploma required; GED accepted **Costs Per Year:** Application fee: $0. Area resident tuition: $1008 full-time, $42 per credit hour part-time. State resident tuition: $2688 full-time, $112 per credit hour part-time. Nonresident tuition: $3048 full-time, $127 per credit hour part-time. Mandatory fees: $496 full-time, $18 per credit hour part-time, $32 per term part-time. Full-time tuition and fees vary according to course load and program. Part-time tuition and fees vary according to course load and program. **Scholarships:** Available. **Calendar System:** Semester, Summer session available **Enrollment:** Full-time 3,852, Part-time 8,912 **Faculty:** Full-time 130, Part-time 708 **Student-Faculty Ratio:** 19:1 **Final Year or Final Semester Residency Requirement:** No **Regional Accreditation:** Southern Association of Colleges and Schools **Credit Hours For Degree:** 60 credit hours, Associates **Professional Accreditation:** ACEN, ADA, AOTA, CoARC.

LONE STAR COLLEGE–MONTGOMERY

3200 College Park Dr.
Conroe, TX 77384
Tel: (936)273-7000
Fax: (936)273-7234
E-mail: Connie.S.Garrick@lonestar.edu
Web Site: www.lonestar.edu/montgomery
President/CEO: Dr. Rebecca Riley
Admissions: Connie Garrick

Type: Two-Year College **Sex:** Coed **Affiliation:** Lone Star College. **% Accepted:** 100 **Admission Plans:** Early Admission; Open Admission **Application Deadline:** Rolling **H.S. Requirements:** High school diploma required; GED accepted **Costs Per Year:** Area resident tuition: $1008 full-time, $42 per credit hour part-time. State resident tuition: $2688 full-time, $112 per credit hour part-time. Nonresident tuition: $3048 full-time, $127 per credit hour part-time. Mandatory fees: $496 full-time, $18 per credit hour part-time, $32 per term part-time. Full-time tuition and fees vary according to course load and program. Part-time tuition and fees vary according to course load and program. **Scholarships:** Available. **Calendar System:** Semester, Summer session available **Enrollment:** Full-time 4,199, Part-time 9,627 **Faculty:** Full-time 148, Part-time 551 **Student-Faculty Ratio:** 22:1 **Regional Accreditation:** Southern Association of Colleges and Schools **Credit Hours For Degree:** 60 credit hours, Associates **Professional Accreditation:** ACEN, APTA.

LONE STAR COLLEGE–NORTH HARRIS

2700 W W Thorne Dr.
Houston, TX 77073-3499
Tel: (281)618-5400
E-mail: nhcounselor@lonestar.edu
Web Site: www.lonestar.edu/northharris
President/CEO: Dr. Gerald F. Naploes

Type: Two-Year College **Sex:** Coed **Affiliation:** Lone Star College. **% Accepted:** 100 **Admission Plans:** Early Admission; Open Admission **Application Deadline:** Rolling **Application Fee:** $0.00 **H.S. Requirements:** High school diploma required; GED accepted **Costs Per Year:** Application fee: $0. Area resident tuition: $1008 full-time, $42 per credit hour part-time. State resident tuition: $2688 full-time, $112 per credit hour part-time. Nonresident tuition: $3048 full-time, $127 per credit hour part-time. Mandatory fees: $496 full-time, $18 per credit hour part-time, $32 per term part-time. Full-time tuition and fees vary according to course load and program. Part-time tuition and fees vary according to course load and program. **Scholarships:** Available. **Calendar System:** Semester, Summer session available **Enrollment:** Full-time 4,735, Part-time 12,266 **Faculty:** Full-time 192, Part-time 908 **Student-Faculty Ratio:** 18:1 **Regional Accreditation:** Southern Association of Colleges and Schools **Credit Hours For Degree:** 60 credit hours, Associates **Professional Accreditation:** ACEN, AHIMA, MACTE.

LONE STAR COLLEGE–TOMBALL

30555 Tomball Pky.
Tomball, TX 77375-4036
Tel: (281)351-3300
Fax: (281)351-3384
E-mail: tcinfo@lonestar.edu
Web Site: www.lonestar.edu/tomball
President/CEO: Dr. Lee Ann Nutt

Type: Two-Year College **Sex:** Coed **Affiliation:** Lone Star College. **% Accepted:** 100 **Admission Plans:** Early Admission; Open Admission **Application Deadline:** Rolling **Application Fee:** $0.00 **H.S. Requirements:** High school diploma required; GED accepted **Costs Per Year:** Application fee: $0. Area resident tuition: $1008 full-time, $42 per credit hour part-time. State resident tuition: $2688 full-time, $112 per credit hour part-time. Nonresident tuition: $3048 full-time, $127 per credit hour part-time. Mandatory fees: $496 full-time, $18 per credit hour part-time, $32 per term part-time. Full-time tuition and fees vary according to course load and program. Part-time tuition and fees vary according to course load and program. **Scholarships:** Available. **Calendar System:** Semester, Summer session available **Enrollment:** Full-time 2,543, Part-time 6,337 **Faculty:** Full-time 102, Part-time 290 **Student-Faculty Ratio:** 24:1 **Regional Accreditation:** Southern Association of Colleges and Schools **Credit Hours For Degree:** 60 credit hours, Associates **Professional Accreditation:** ACEN, AOTA.

LONE STAR COLLEGE–UNIVERSITY PARK

20515 SH 249
Houston, TX 77070-2607
Tel: (281)290-2600
E-mail: Connie.S.Garrick@lonestar.edu
Web Site: www.lonestar.edu/universitypark
President/CEO: Shah Ardalan
Admissions: Connie Garrick

Type: Two-Year College **Sex:** Coed **Affiliation:** Lone Star College. **Costs Per Year:** Area resident tuition: $1008 full-time, $42 per credit hour part-time. State resident tuition: $2688 full-time, $112 per credit hour part-time. Nonresident tuition: $3048 full-time, $127 per credit hour part-time. Mandatory fees: $496 full-time, $18 per credit hour part-time, $32. Full-time tuition and fees vary according to course load and program. Part-time tuition and fees vary according to course load and program. **Enrollment:** Full-time 3,190, Part-time 7,761 **Faculty:** Full-time 69, Part-time 378 **Student-Faculty Ratio:** 30:1 **Exams:** ACT essay component used for placement; SAT essay component used for placement. **Final Year or Final Semester Residency Requirement:** No **Regional Accreditation:** Southern Association of Colleges and Schools **Credit Hours For Degree:** 62 credit hours, Associates

LUBBOCK CHRISTIAN UNIVERSITY

5601 19th St.
Lubbock, TX 79407-2099
Tel: (806)796-8800; Free: 800-933-7601
Fax: (806)796-8917
E-mail: admissions@lcu.edu

Web Site: www.lcu.edu
President/CEO: Tim Perrin
Admissions: Chris Hayes
Financial Aid: Amy Hardesty
Type: Comprehensive **Sex:** Coed **Affiliation:** Church of Christ. **Scores:** 90% SAT V 400+; 94% SAT M 400+; 49.48% ACT 18-23; 33.51% ACT 24-29 **% Accepted:** 96 **Application Deadline:** August 1 **Application Fee:** $25.00 **H.S. Requirements:** High school diploma required; GED accepted **Costs Per Year:** Application fee: $25. Comprehensive fee: $26,430 includes full-time tuition ($20,360) and college room and board ($6070). Full-time tuition varies according to degree level and program. Room and board charges vary according to board plan and housing facility. Part-time tuition: $652 per credit hour. Part-time mandatory fees: $60 per term. Part-time tuition and fees vary according to course load, degree level, and program. **Scholarships:** Available. **Calendar System:** Semester, Summer session available **Enrollment:** Full-time 1,271, Graduate full-time 45, Graduate part-time 417, Part-time 225 **Faculty:** Full-time 99, Part-time 80 **Student-Faculty Ratio:** 13:1 **Exams:** ACT essay component used for advising; ACT essay component used for placement; SAT I or ACT; SAT essay component used for advising; SAT essay component used for placement; SAT Reasoning. **% Receiving Financial Aid:** 71 **% Residing in College-Owned, -Operated, or -Affiliated Housing:** 34 **Final Year or Final Semester Residency Requirement:** Yes **Regional Accreditation:** Southern Association of Colleges and Schools **Credit Hours For Degree:** 120 semester hours, Bachelors **ROTC:** Air Force, Army **Professional Accreditation:** ACEN, ATS, CSWE. **Intercollegiate Athletics:** Baseball M; Basketball M & W; Cheerleading M & W; Cross-Country Running M & W; Golf M & W; Soccer M & W; Softball W; Track and Field M & W; Volleyball W

MCLENNAN COMMUNITY COLLEGE

1400 College Dr.
Waco, TX 76708-1499
Tel: (254)299-8622
E-mail: vjefferson@mclennan.edu
Web Site: www.mclennan.edu
President/CEO: Johnette McKown
Admissions: Dr. Vivian G. Jefferson
Type: Two-Year College **Sex:** Coed **% Accepted:** 100 **Admission Plans:** Early Admission; Open Admission **Application Deadline:** Rolling **Application Fee:** $0.00 **H.S. Requirements:** High school diploma required; GED accepted **Scholarships:** Available. **Calendar System:** Semester, Summer session available **Enrollment:** Full-time 3,467, Part-time 4,327 **Exams:** Other. **Regional Accreditation:** Southern Association of Colleges and Schools **Credit Hours For Degree:** 60 semester hours, Associates **ROTC:** Air Force **Professional Accreditation:** ACEN, AHIMA, APTA, CoARC, JRCERT, NAACLS. **Intercollegiate Athletics:** Baseball M; Basketball M & W; Golf M & W; Softball W

MCMURRY UNIVERSITY

S 14th and Sayles
Abilene, TX 79697
Tel: (325)793-3800; Free: 800-460-2392
Fax: (325)691-6599
E-mail: admissions@mcm.edu
Web Site: www.mcm.edu
President/CEO: Dr. Sandra S. Harper
Admissions: Teresa Bridwell
Financial Aid: Lori Eilene Herrick
Type: Comprehensive **Sex:** Coed **Affiliation:** United Methodist. **Scores:** 70% SAT V 400+; 83% SAT M 400+; 47% ACT 18-23; 10% ACT 24-29 **% Accepted:** 53 **Admission Plans:** Deferred Admission **Application Deadline:** August 15 **Application Fee:** $25.00 **H.S. Requirements:** High school diploma required; GED accepted **Costs Per Year:** Application fee: $25. One-time mandatory fee: $175. Comprehensive fee: $33,750 includes full-time tuition ($25,588) and college room and board ($8162). College room only: $3942. Full-time tuition varies according to course load. Room and board charges vary according to board plan and housing facility. Part-time tuition: $799 per credit hour. Part-time tuition varies according to course load. **Scholarships:** Available. **Calendar System:** Semester, Summer session available **Enrollment:** Full-time 907, Graduate full-time 2, Part-time 162 **Faculty:** Full-time 80, Part-time 32 **Student-Faculty Ratio:** 11:1 **Exams:** SAT I or ACT; SAT Reasoning. **% Receiving Financial Aid:** 85 **% Residing in College-Owned, -Operated, or -Affiliated Housing:** 51 **Final Year or Final Semester Residency Requirement:** Yes **Regional Accreditation:**

Southern Association of Colleges and Schools **Credit Hours For Degree:** 120 semester hours, Bachelors **Professional Accreditation:** AACN. **Intercollegiate Athletics:** Baseball M; Basketball M & W; Cross-Country Running M & W; Football M; Golf M & W; Soccer M & W; Swimming and Diving M & W; Tennis M & W; Track and Field M & W; Volleyball W

MEDIATECH INSTITUTE

400 E Royal Ln., Ste. 100
Irving, TX 75039
Tel: (972)869-1122
Web Site: www.mediatech.edu
Type: Two-Year College **Sex:** Coed **Professional Accreditation:** ACCSC.

MESSENGER COLLEGE

400 S Industrial Blvd., Ste. 300
Euless, TX 76040
Tel: (817)554-5950; Free: 800-385-8940
E-mail: info@messengercollege.edu
Web Site: www.messengercollege.edu
President/CEO: Charles Scott
Admissions: Ron Cannon
Financial Aid: Patricia J. Pentecost
Type: Four-Year College **Sex:** Coed **Affiliation:** Pentecostal. **Scores:** 36% ACT 18-23; 21% ACT 24-29 **% Accepted:** 77 **Application Deadline:** August 14 **Application Fee:** $35.00 **H.S. Requirements:** High school diploma required; GED accepted **Costs Per Year:** Application fee: $35. Comprehensive fee: $13,410 includes full-time tuition ($6000), mandatory fees ($1260), and college room and board ($6150). College room only: $3150. Full-time tuition and fees vary according to course load and location. Room and board charges vary according to housing facility and location. Part-time tuition: $250 per credit hour. Part-time mandatory fees: $1260 per year. Part-time tuition and fees vary according to course load and location. **Scholarships:** Available. **Calendar System:** Semester, Summer session not available **Enrollment:** Full-time 58, Part-time 12 **Faculty:** Full-time 6, Part-time 8 **Exams:** SAT I or ACT. **% Receiving Financial Aid:** 88 **Credit Hours For Degree:** 64 credits, Associates; 128 credits, Bachelors **Professional Accreditation:** TRACS.

MIDLAND COLLEGE

3600 N Garfield
Midland, TX 79705-6329
Tel: (432)685-4500
Fax: (432)685-4714
E-mail: jmartinez@midland.edu
Web Site: www.midland.edu
President/CEO: Dr. Stephen Thomas
Admissions: Jeremy Martinez
Financial Aid: Yolanda Ramos
Type: Four-Year College **Sex:** Coed **Admission Plans:** Open Admission **Application Deadline:** Rolling **Application Fee:** $0.00 **H.S. Requirements:** High school diploma required; GED accepted **Costs Per Year:** Application fee: $0. Area resident tuition: $1968 full-time. State resident tuition: $3168 full-time. Nonresident tuition: $4128 full-time. Full-time tuition varies according to class time, course level, course load, degree level, location, program, reciprocity agreements, and student level. College room and board: $4,906. Room and board charges vary according to board plan and housing facility. **Scholarships:** Available. **Calendar System:** Semester, Summer session available **Enrollment:** Full-time 1,495, Part-time 3,123 **Faculty:** Full-time 136, Part-time 119 **Student-Faculty Ratio:** 26:1 **Final Year or Final Semester Residency Requirement:** No **Regional Accreditation:** Southern Association of Colleges and Schools **Credit Hours For Degree:** 60 semester hours, Associates; 130 semester hours, Bachelors **Professional Accreditation:** ACEN, AHIMA, CoARC, JRCERT. **Intercollegiate Athletics:** Baseball M; Basketball M & W; Cheerleading M & W; Golf M; Softball W; Volleyball W

MIDWESTERN STATE UNIVERSITY

3410 Taft Blvd.
Wichita Falls, TX 76308
Tel: (940)397-4000; Free: 800-842-1922
Fax: (940)397-4302
E-mail: leah.vineyard@mwsu.edu
Web Site: www.mwsu.edu
President/CEO: Dr. Suzanne Shipley

Admissions: Leah Vineyard
Financial Aid: Kathy Pennartz
Type: Comprehensive **Sex:** Coed **Scores:** 96% SAT V 400+; 97% SAT M 400+ **% Accepted:** 76 **Application Deadline:** August 1 **Application Fee:** $25.00 **H.S. Requirements:** High school diploma required; GED accepted **Costs Per Year:** Application fee: $25. State resident tuition: $5142 full-time, $171.40 per credit hour part-time. Nonresident tuition: $7092 full-time, $236.40 per credit hour part-time. Mandatory fees: $2,862 full-time, $85.75 per credit hour part-time, $175 per term part-time. Full-time tuition and fees vary according to course load and program. Part-time tuition and fees vary according to course load and program. College room and board: $7070. Room and board charges vary according to board plan and housing facility. Tuition guaranteed not to increase for student's term of enrollment. **Scholarships:** Available. **Calendar System:** Semester, Summer session available **Enrollment:** Full-time 4,055, Graduate full-time 193, Graduate part-time 563, Part-time 1,232 **Faculty:** Full-time 236, Part-time 109 **Student-Faculty Ratio:** 18:1 **Exams:** ACT essay component not used; SAT I and SAT II or ACT; SAT I or ACT; SAT essay component not used; SAT Reasoning; SAT Subject. **% Receiving Financial Aid:** 59 **% Residing in College-Owned, -Operated, or -Affiliated Housing:** 28 **Final Year or Final Semester Residency Requirement:** No **Regional Accreditation:** Southern Association of Colleges and Schools **Credit Hours For Degree:** 120 semester hours, Bachelors **ROTC:** Air Force **Professional Accreditation:** AACN, AACSB, ABET, ADA, CSWE, CoARC, NASM. **Intercollegiate Athletics:** Basketball M & W; Cheerleading M & W; Cross-Country Running W; Fencing M & W; Football M; Golf M & W; Soccer M & W; Softball W; Tennis M & W; Volleyball W

MOUNTAIN VIEW COLLEGE

4849 W Illinois Ave.
Dallas, TX 75211-6599
Tel: (214)860-8600
Fax: (214)860-8570
E-mail: ghall@dcccd.edu
Web Site: www.mountainviewcollege.edu
President/CEO: Felix Zamora
Admissions: Glenda Hall
Type: Two-Year College **Sex:** Coed **Affiliation:** Dallas County Community College District System. **% Accepted:** 100 **Admission Plans:** Deferred Admission; Early Admission; Open Admission **Application Deadline:** Rolling **Application Fee:** $0.00 **H.S. Requirements:** High school diploma required; GED accepted **Costs Per Year:** Application fee: $0. Area resident tuition: $59 per credit hour part-time. State resident tuition: $111 per credit hour part-time. Nonresident tuition: $174 per credit hour part-time. **Scholarships:** Available. **Calendar System:** Semester, Summer session available **Enrollment:** Full-time 2,066, Part-time 7,002 **Faculty:** Full-time 86, Part-time 300 **Student-Faculty Ratio:** 28:1 **Exams:** ACT essay component used for placement; SAT essay component used for placement. **Regional Accreditation:** Southern Association of Colleges and Schools **Credit Hours For Degree:** 61 credit hours, Associates **Professional Accreditation:** AHIMA. **Intercollegiate Athletics:** Baseball M; Basketball M & W; Soccer M & W; Volleyball W

NATIONAL AMERICAN UNIVERSITY

18600 LBJ Fwy.
Mesquite, TX 75150
Tel: (972)773-8800; Free: 800-548-0605
Web Site: www.national.edu
Type: Comprehensive **Sex:** Coed **Regional Accreditation:** North Central Association of Colleges and Schools

NAVARRO COLLEGE

3200 W 7th Ave.
Corsicana, TX 75110-4899
Tel: (903)874-6501; Free: 800-628-2776
E-mail: tammy.adams@navarrocollege.edu
Web Site: www.navarrocollege.edu
President/CEO: Dr. Barbara Kavalier
Admissions: Tammy Adams
Financial Aid: Ed Ephlin
Type: Two-Year College **Sex:** Coed **Admission Plans:** Early Admission; Open Admission **H.S. Requirements:** High school diploma required; GED accepted **Costs Per Year:** Area resident tuition: $1200 full-time, $120 per credit hour part-time. State resident tuition: $1350 full-time, $135 per credit

hour part-time. Nonresident tuition: $2850 full-time, $285 per credit hour part-time. Mandatory fees: $101 per credit hour part-time. Full-time tuition varies according to course load. Part-time tuition and fees vary according to course load. College room and board: $6611. Room and board charges vary according to board plan. **Scholarships:** Available. **Calendar System:** Semester, Summer session available **Enrollment:** Full-time 3,555, Part-time 5,923 **Faculty:** Full-time 128, Part-time 405 **Student-Faculty Ratio:** 25:1 **% Residing in College-Owned, -Operated, or -Affiliated Housing:** 25 **Regional Accreditation:** Southern Association of Colleges and Schools **Credit Hours For Degree:** 60 semester hours, Associates **Professional Accreditation:** ACEN, AOTA, NAACLS. **Intercollegiate Athletics:** Baseball M; Basketball M; Football M; Soccer W; Softball W; Volleyball W

NORTH AMERICAN UNIVERSITY

3203 N Sam Houston Pky. W
Houston, TX 77038
Tel: (832)230-5555
Web Site: www.na.edu
Type: Comprehensive **Sex:** Coed **Scores:** 85% SAT V 400+; 93% SAT M 400+ **Application Deadline:** Rolling **Application Fee:** $0.00 **H.S. Requirements:** High school diploma required; GED accepted **Costs Per Year:** Application fee: $0. **Tuition:** $11,900 full-time. Full-time tuition varies according to course load, program, and reciprocity agreements. Tuition guaranteed not to increase for student's term of enrollment. **Calendar System:** Semester, Summer session available **Enrollment:** Full-time 415, Graduate full-time 24, Graduate part-time 27, Part-time 7 **Exams:** ACT essay component used for admission; SAT I or ACT; SAT essay component used for admission. **% Residing in College-Owned, -Operated, or -Affiliated Housing:** 55 **Final Year or Final Semester Residency Requirement:** No **Credit Hours For Degree:** 120 credit hour, Bachelors **Professional Accreditation:** ACICS.

NORTH CENTRAL TEXAS COLLEGE

1525 W California St.
Gainesville, TX 76240-4699
Tel: (940)668-7731
Fax: (940)668-6049
E-mail: mcarroll@nctc.edu
Web Site: www.nctc.edu
President/CEO: Dr. Brent Wallace
Admissions: Melinda Carroll
Financial Aid: Stephanie Martin
Type: Two-Year College **Sex:** Coed **% Accepted:** 100 **Admission Plans:** Early Admission; Open Admission **Application Deadline:** Rolling **H.S. Requirements:** High school diploma required; GED accepted. For some adult applicants: High school diploma or equivalent not required **Costs Per Year:** Area resident tuition: $1824 full-time, $76 per semester hour part-time. State resident tuition: $3120 full-time, $130 per semester hour part-time. Nonresident tuition: $5232 full-time, $218 per semester hour part-time. College room and board: $1964. College room only: $850. Room and board charges vary according to housing facility. **Scholarships:** Available. **Calendar System:** Semester, Summer session available **Enrollment:** Full-time 3,068, Part-time 6,550 **Faculty:** Full-time 152, Part-time 251 **Student-Faculty Ratio:** 16:1 **% Residing in College-Owned, -Operated, or -Affiliated Housing:** 1 **Regional Accreditation:** Southern Association of Colleges and Schools **Credit Hours For Degree:** 62 credit hours, Associates **ROTC:** Army **Professional Accreditation:** ACEN. **Intercollegiate Athletics:** Baseball M; Equestrian Sports M & W; Softball W; Tennis W; Volleyball W

NORTH LAKE COLLEGE

5001 N MacArthur Blvd.
Irving, TX 75038-3899
Tel: (972)273-3000
Web Site: www.northlakecollege.edu
President/CEO: Dr. Herlinda Glasscock
Type: Two-Year College **Sex:** Coed **Affiliation:** Dallas County Community College District System. **Admission Plans:** Early Admission; Open Admission **Application Deadline:** Rolling **Application Fee:** $0.00 **H.S. Requirements:** High school diploma required; GED accepted **Scholarships:** Available. **Calendar System:** Semester, Summer session available **Enrollment:** Full-time 3,171, Part-time 7,003 **Faculty:** Full-time 95, Part-time 409 **Student-Faculty Ratio:** 21:1 **Regional Accreditation:** Southern Association of Colleges and Schools **Credit Hours For Degree:** 62 semester hours,

Associates **Professional Accreditation:** ACCE. **Intercollegiate Athletics:** Baseball M; Basketball M; Cheerleading W; Swimming and Diving M & W; Volleyball W

NORTHEAST TEXAS COMMUNITY COLLEGE
PO Box 1307
Mount Pleasant, TX 75456-1307
Tel: (903)572-1911; Free: 800-870-0142
Fax: (903)572-6712
E-mail: lbond@ntcc.edu
Web Site: www.ntcc.edu
President/CEO: Dr. Brad Johnson
Admissions: Linda Bond
Financial Aid: Kim Lawrence

Type: Two-Year College **Sex:** Coed **Admission Plans:** Early Admission; Open Admission **Application Deadline:** Rolling **Application Fee:** $0.00 **H.S. Requirements:** High school diploma required; GED accepted **Costs Per Year:** Application fee: $0. Area resident tuition: $1080 full-time, $36 per credit hour part-time. State resident tuition: $2850 full-time, $95 per credit hour part-time. Nonresident tuition: $4270 full-time, $306 per credit hour part-time. Mandatory fees: $1426 full-time, $46 per credit hour part-time, $23 per term part-time. Full-time tuition and fees vary according to program. Part-time tuition and fees vary according to program. College room and board: $2900. Room and board charges vary according to housing facility. **Scholarships:** Available. **Calendar System:** Semester, Summer session available **Enrollment:** Full-time 1,104, Part-time 2,178 **Faculty:** Full-time 76, Part-time 102 **Student-Faculty Ratio:** 17:1 **Regional Accreditation:** Southern Association of Colleges and Schools **Credit Hours For Degree:** 62 credit hours, Associates **Intercollegiate Athletics:** Baseball M; Equestrian Sports M & W; Soccer M & W; Softball W

NORTHWEST VISTA COLLEGE
3535 N Ellison Dr.
San Antonio, TX 78251
Tel: (210)486-4000
E-mail: rsandberg@alamo.edu
Web Site: www.alamo.edu/nvc
President/CEO: Dr. Ric Baser
Admissions: Robin Sandberg

Type: Two-Year College **Sex:** Coed **Affiliation:** Alamo Community College District System. **Admission Plans:** Early Admission; Open Admission **Application Fee:** $0.00 **H.S. Requirements:** High school diploma required; GED accepted **Costs Per Year:** Application fee: $0. Area resident tuition: $1418 full-time. State resident tuition: $3962 full-time. Nonresident tuition: $7777 full-time. Mandatory fees: $74 full-time. Full-time tuition and fees vary according to course load, location, and program. **Calendar System:** Semester, Summer session available **Enrollment:** Full-time 4,235, Part-time 8,983 **Faculty:** Full-time 170, Part-time 706 **Student-Faculty Ratio:** 23:1 **Final Year or Final Semester Residency Requirement:** No **Regional Accreditation:** Southern Association of Colleges and Schools **Credit Hours For Degree:** 60 units, Associates **ROTC:** Army

NORTHWOOD UNIVERSITY, TEXAS CAMPUS
1114 W FM 1382
Cedar Hill, TX 75104-1204
Tel: (972)291-1541; Free: 800-927-9663
Fax: (972)291-3824
E-mail: txadmit@northwood.edu
Web Site: www.northwood.edu
President/CEO: Keith A. Pretty, JD
Admissions: Dr. Terry Silva
Financial Aid: Dawn Shestko

Type: Comprehensive **Sex:** Coed **Affiliation:** Northwood University (MI). **Admission Plans:** Deferred Admission; Early Admission **Application Deadline:** August 1 **Application Fee:** $30.00 **H.S. Requirements:** High school diploma required; GED accepted **Costs Per Year:** Application fee: $30. Tuition: $22,940 full-time. Mandatory fees: $1230 full-time. **Scholarships:** Available. **Calendar System:** Semester, Summer session available **Enrollment:** Full-time 159, Graduate full-time 7, Graduate part-time 45, Part-time 119 **Faculty:** Full-time 5, Part-time 24 **Student-Faculty Ratio:** 17:1 **Exams:** SAT I or ACT; SAT Reasoning. **% Receiving Financial Aid:** 77 **Final Year or Final Semester Residency Requirement:** No **Regional Accreditation:** North Central Association of Colleges and Schools **Credit Hours For Degree:** 60 semester hours, Associates; 123 semester hours,

Bachelors **Intercollegiate Athletics:** Baseball M; Cross-Country Running M & W; Golf M & W; Soccer M & W; Softball W; Track and Field M & W

ODESSA COLLEGE
201 W University Ave.
Odessa, TX 79764-7127
Tel: (432)335-6400
Fax: (432)335-6860
E-mail: tavery@odessa.edu
Web Site: www.odessa.edu
President/CEO: Dr. Gregory Williams
Admissions: Tracy Avery
Financial Aid: Dee Nesmith

Type: Two-Year College **Sex:** Coed **% Accepted:** 100 **Admission Plans:** Deferred Admission; Early Admission; Open Admission **Application Deadline:** Rolling **Application Fee:** $0.00 **H.S. Requirements:** High school diploma required; GED accepted. For applicants with extenuating circumstances: High school diploma required; GED not accepted **Scholarships:** Available. **Calendar System:** Semester, Summer session available **Enrollment:** Full-time 1,609, Part-time 3,487 **Faculty:** Full-time 130, Part-time 60 **Student-Faculty Ratio:** 18:1 **% Residing in College-Owned, -Operated, or -Affiliated Housing:** 5 **Regional Accreditation:** Southern Association of Colleges and Schools **Credit Hours For Degree:** 62 semester hours, Associates **Professional Accreditation:** ACEN, APTA, ARCST, CoARC, JRCERT, NAACLS, NASM. **Intercollegiate Athletics:** Baseball M; Basketball M & W; Cross-Country Running M & W; Golf M; Softball W

OUR LADY OF THE LAKE UNIVERSITY OF SAN ANTONIO
411 SW 24th St.
San Antonio, TX 78207-4689
Tel: (210)434-6711; Free: 800-436-6558
Fax: (210)436-0824
E-mail: sytijeria@lake.ollusa.edu
Web Site: www.ollusa.edu
President/CEO: Diane E. Melby, EdD
Admissions: Shannon Tijerina
Financial Aid: Esmeralda Flores

Type: Comprehensive **Sex:** Coed **Affiliation:** Roman Catholic. **Scores:** 87% SAT V 400+; 86% SAT M 400+; 70.37% ACT 18-23; 11.11% ACT 24-29 **Costs Per Year:** Comprehensive fee: $33,704 includes full-time tuition ($25,300), mandatory fees ($848), and college room and board ($7556). College room only: $4200. Full-time tuition and fees vary according to course load and location. Room and board charges vary according to board plan and housing facility. Part-time tuition: $811 per credit hour. Part-time mandatory fees: $424 per term. Part-time tuition and fees vary according to course load and location. **Scholarships:** Available. **Calendar System:** Semester, Summer session available **Enrollment:** Full-time 1,343, Graduate full-time 1,678, Graduate part-time 128, Part-time 185 **Faculty:** Full-time 101, Part-time 234 **Student-Faculty Ratio:** 13:1 **Exams:** ACT essay component not used; SAT I or ACT; SAT essay component not used. **% Receiving Financial Aid:** 87 **% Residing in College-Owned, -Operated, or -Affiliated Housing:** 41 **Final Year or Final Semester Residency Requirement:** No **Regional Accreditation:** Southern Association of Colleges and Schools **Credit Hours For Degree:** 120 credit hours, Bachelors **ROTC:** Army **Professional Accreditation:** ACBSP, APA, ASHA, CSWE. **Intercollegiate Athletics:** Baseball M; Basketball M & W; Cross-Country Running M & W; Golf M; Soccer M & W; Softball W; Tennis M & W; Track and Field M & W; Volleyball W

PALO ALTO COLLEGE
1400 W Villaret
San Antonio, TX 78224-2499
Tel: (210)921-5000
E-mail: eaguilar-villarr@alamo.edu
Web Site: www.alamo.edu/pac
President/CEO: Dr. Ruben Michael Flores
Admissions: Elizabeth Aguilar-Villarreal

Type: Two-Year College **Sex:** Coed **Affiliation:** Alamo Community College District System. **% Accepted:** 100 **Admission Plans:** Early Admission; Open Admission **Application Deadline:** Rolling **Application Fee:** $0.00 **H.S. Requirements:** High school diploma required; GED accepted **Costs Per Year:** Application fee: $0. Area resident tuition: $831 full-time, $6 per credit part-time. State resident tuition: $2216 full-time, $480 per credit part-time. Nonresident tuition: $4292 full-time, $1172 per credit part-time. **Scholarships:** Available. **Calendar System:** Semester, Summer session available **Enrollment:** Full-time 1,533, Part-time 6,843 **Faculty:** Full-time 1,423, Part-time 1,520 **Student-Faculty Ratio:** 24:1 **Regional Accreditation:** Southern Association of Colleges and Schools **Credit Hours For Degree:** 60 semester hours, Associates **Intercollegiate Athletics:** Cross-Country Running M & W; Swimming and Diving M & W; Track and Field M & W

PANOLA COLLEGE
1109 W Panola St.
Carthage, TX 75633-2397
Tel: (903)693-2000
E-mail: bsimpson@panola.edu
Web Site: www.panola.edu
President/CEO: Dr. Gregory Powell
Admissions: Jeremy Dorman
Financial Aid: Denise Welch

Type: Two-Year College **Sex:** Coed **Costs Per Year:** Area resident tuition: $750 full-time, $60 per semester hour part-time. State resident tuition: $2190 full-time, $108 per semester hour part-time. Nonresident tuition: $3120 full-time, $279 per semester hour part-time. Mandatory fees: $1440 full-time, $48 per semester hour part-time. Full-time tuition and fees vary according to course load and reciprocity agreements. Part-time tuition and fees vary according to course load and reciprocity agreements. College room and board: $4600. Room and board charges vary according to housing facility. **Scholarships:** Available. **Calendar System:** Semester, Summer session available **Enrollment:** Full-time 1,335, Part-time 1,340 **Faculty:** Full-time 69, Part-time 78 **Student-Faculty Ratio:** 18:1 **% Residing in College-Owned, -Operated, or -Affiliated Housing:** 9 **Final Year or Final Semester Residency Requirement:** No **Regional Accreditation:** Southern Association of Colleges and Schools **Credit Hours For Degree:** 60 credits, Associates **Professional Accreditation:** ACEN, AHIMA, AOTA. **Intercollegiate Athletics:** Baseball M; Basketball M & W; Equestrian Sports M & W; Volleyball W

PARIS JUNIOR COLLEGE
2400 Clarksville St.
Paris, TX 75460-6298
Tel: (903)785-7661; Free: 800-232-5804
E-mail: sreece@parisjc.edu
Web Site: www.parisjc.edu
President/CEO: Dr. Pamela Anglin
Admissions: Sheila Reece

Type: Two-Year College **Sex:** Coed **% Accepted:** 100 **Admission Plans:** Early Admission; Open Admission **Application Deadline:** Rolling **Application Fee:** $0.00 **H.S. Requirements:** High school diploma required; GED accepted **Costs Per Year:** Application fee: $0. Area resident tuition: $1500 full-time, $50 per credit hour part-time. State resident tuition: $2580 full-time, $86 per credit hour part-time. Nonresident tuition: $3990 full-time, $133 per credit hour part-time. Mandatory fees: $390 full-time. Full-time tuition and fees vary according to class time, course level, course load, degree level, location, program, and student level. Part-time tuition varies according to class time, course level, course load, degree level, location, program, and student level. College room and board: $4924. Room and board charges vary according to board plan and housing facility. **Scholarships:** Available. **Calendar System:** Semester, Summer session available **Enrollment:** Full-time 2,057, Part-time 2,942 **Faculty:** Full-time 88, Part-time 145 **Student-Faculty Ratio:** 22:1 **% Residing in College-Owned, -Operated, or -Affiliated Housing:** 4 **Final Year or Final Semester Residency Requirement:** No **Regional Accreditation:** Southern Association of Colleges and Schools **Credit Hours For Degree:** 60 semester hours, Associates **Professional Accreditation:** ACEN. **Intercollegiate Athletics:** Baseball M; Basketball M & W; Golf M; Soccer M & W; Softball W; Volleyball W

PAUL QUINN COLLEGE
3837 Simpson-Stuart Rd.
Dallas, TX 75241-4331
Tel: (214)376-1000; Free: 877-346-1063
Fax: (214)302-3559
Web Site: www.pqc.edu
President/CEO: Michael J. Sorrell
Admissions: Jessika Lara
Financial Aid: Khaleelah Ali

Type: Four-Year College **Sex:** Coed **Affiliation:** African Methodist Episcopal. **Scores:** 62% SAT V 400+; 54% SAT M 400+; 33.3% ACT 18-23 **% Accepted:** 99 **Application Deadline:** June 1 **Application Fee:** $25.00 **H.S. Requirements:** High school diploma required; GED accepted **Scholarships:** Available. **Calendar System:** Semester, Summer session available **Enrollment:** Full-time 216, Part-time 27 **Faculty:** Full-time 10, Part-time 7 **Student-Faculty Ratio:** 11:1 **Exams:** ACT essay component used as validity check; ACT essay component used for admission; ACT essay component used for advising; ACT essay component used for placement; SAT I or ACT; SAT essay component used as validity check; SAT essay component used for admission; SAT essay component used for advising; SAT essay component used for placement; SAT Reasoning; SAT Subject. **% Receiving Financial Aid:** 98 **% Residing in College-Owned, -Operated, or -Affiliated Housing:** 39 **Final Year or Final Semester Residency Requirement:** No **Credit Hours For Degree:** 120 semester hours, Bachelors **Professional Accreditation:** TRACS. **Intercollegiate Athletics:** Basketball M & W

PIMA MEDICAL INSTITUTE
10201 Katy Fwy.
Houston, TX 77024
Tel: (712)778-0778
E-mail: cluebke@pmi.edu
Web Site: www.pmi.edu
President/CEO: Philip Heine
Admissions: Christopher Luebke

Type: Two-Year College **Sex:** Coed **Exams:** Other. **Professional Accreditation:** ABHES.

PRAIRIE VIEW A&M UNIVERSITY
PO Box 519
Prairie View, TX 77446-0519
Tel: (936)857-3311
Fax: (936)857-2699
E-mail: admissions@pvamu.edu
Web Site: www.pvamu.edu
President/CEO: Dr. George C. Wright
Admissions: Lenice D. Brown
Financial Aid: Ralph Perri

Type: University **Sex:** Coed **Affiliation:** Texas A&M University System. **Scores:** 63% SAT V 400+; 70% SAT M 400+; 39.07% ACT 18-23; 6.77% ACT 24-29 **% Accepted:** 86 **Admission Plans:** Deferred Admission **Application Deadline:** June 1 **Application Fee:** $25.00 **H.S. Requirements:** High school diploma required; GED accepted **Costs Per Year:** Application fee: $25. State resident tuition: $6,052 full-time, $228 per credit hour part-time. Nonresident tuition: $18,579 full-time, $646 per credit hour part-time. Mandatory fees: $3693 full-time. Full-time tuition and fees vary according to course load, degree level, program, and reciprocity agreements. Part-time tuition varies according to course load, degree level, program, and reciprocity agreements. College room and board: $8,418. College room only: $5678. Room and board charges vary according to board plan, housing facility, and student level. Tuition guaranteed not to increase for student's term of enrollment. **Scholarships:** Available. **Calendar System:** Semester, Summer session available **Enrollment:** Full-time 6,305, Graduate full-time 541, Graduate part-time 804, Part-time 618 **Faculty:** Full-time 393, Part-time 95 **Student-Faculty Ratio:** 18:1 **Exams:** ACT essay component not used; SAT I and SAT II or ACT; SAT I or ACT; SAT II; SAT essay component not used; SAT Reasoning. **% Receiving Financial Aid:** 86 **% Residing in College-Owned, -Operated, or -Affiliated Housing:** 53 **Final Year or Final Semester Residency Requirement:** No **Regional Accreditation:** Southern Association of Colleges and Schools **Credit Hours For Degree:** 120 semester hours, Bachelors **ROTC:** Air Force, Army, Navy **Professional Accreditation:** AACN, AACSB, ABET, ACEN, AND, CSWE, NASM, NCATE. **Intercollegiate Athletics:** Baseball M; Basketball M & W; Bowling W; Cross-Country Running M & W; Football M; Golf M & W; Soccer W; Softball W; Tennis M & W; Track and Field M & W; Volleyball M & W

QUEST COLLEGE
5430 Fredericksburg Rd.
Ste. 310
San Antonio, TX 78229
Tel: (210)366-2701
Web Site: www.questcollege.edu
Type: Two-Year College **Sex:** Coed **Professional Accreditation:** COE.

RANGER COLLEGE

1100 College Cir.
Ranger, TX 76470
Tel: (254)647-3234
Web Site: www.rangercollege.edu
President/CEO: Dr. William J. Campion
Admissions: Dr. Jim Davis
Financial Aid: Don Hilton
Type: Two-Year College **Sex:** Coed **Admission Plans:** Early Admission; Open Admission **Application Deadline:** Rolling **H.S. Requirements:** High school diploma required; GED accepted **Costs Per Year:** Area resident tuition: $1200 full-time, $80 per semester hour part-time. State resident tuition: $2184 full-time, $120 per semester hour part-time. Nonresident tuition: $3072 full-time, $157 per semester hour part-time. Mandatory fees: $750 full-time, $24 per semester hour part-time, $75. Part-time tuition and fees vary according to course load. College room and board: $3805. College room only: $1450. Room and board charges vary according to location. **Scholarships:** Available. **Calendar System:** Semester, Summer session available **Faculty:** Full-time 28, Part-time 23 **% Residing in College-Owned, -Operated, or -Affiliated Housing:** 45 **Regional Accreditation:** Southern Association of Colleges and Schools **Credit Hours For Degree:** 62 semester hours, Associates **Intercollegiate Athletics:** Baseball M; Basketball M & W; Cross-Country Running M & W; Football M; Golf M; Softball W; Track and Field M & W

REMINGTON COLLEGE–DALLAS CAMPUS

1800 Eastgate Dr.
Garland, TX 75041
Tel: (972)686-7878
Fax: (972)686-5116
E-mail: shonda.wisenhunt@remingtoncollege.edu
Web Site: www.remingtoncollege.edu
President/CEO: Skip Walls
Admissions: Shonda Wisenhunt
Type: Two-Year College **Sex:** Coed **Professional Accreditation:** ACCSC.

REMINGTON COLLEGE–FORT WORTH CAMPUS

300 E Loop 820
Fort Worth, TX 76112
Tel: (817)451-0017; Free: 800-560-6192
Fax: (817)496-1257
E-mail: marcia.kline@remingtoncollege.edu
Web Site: www.remingtoncollege.edu
President/CEO: Gregg Falcon
Admissions: Marcia Kline
Type: Two-Year College **Sex:** Coed **Professional Accreditation:** ACCSC.

REMINGTON COLLEGE–HOUSTON SOUTHEAST CAMPUS

20985 Interstate 45 S
Webster, TX 77598
E-mail: lori.minor@remingtoncollege.edu
Web Site: www.remingtoncollege.edu
President/CEO: Bob Doty
Admissions: Lori Minor
Type: Two-Year College **Sex:** Coed **Professional Accreditation:** ACCSC.

REMINGTON COLLEGE–NORTH HOUSTON CAMPUS

11310 Greens Crossing Blvd.
Ste. 300
Houston, TX 77067
E-mail: edmund.flores@remingtoncollege.edu
Web Site: www.remingtoncollege.edu
President/CEO: Andrew Bossaller
Admissions: Edmund Flores
Type: Two-Year College **Sex:** Coed **Professional Accreditation:** ACCSC.

RICE UNIVERSITY

6100 Main St.
Houston, TX 77251-1892
Tel: (713)348-0000
Fax: (713)348-5323
E-mail: admi@rice.edu
Web Site: www.rice.edu
President/CEO: David W. Leebron
Financial Aid: Anne Walker
Type: University **Sex:** Coed **Scores:** 100% SAT V 400+; 100% SAT M 400+; 1.8% ACT 18-23; 8.5% ACT 24-29 **% Accepted:** 16 **Admission Plans:** Deferred Admission; Early Action **Application Deadline:** January 1 **Application Fee:** $75.00 **H.S. Requirements:** High school diploma or equivalent not required **Costs Per Year:** Application fee: $75. One-time mandatory fee: $625. Comprehensive fee: $55,903 includes full-time tuition ($41,560), mandatory fees ($693), and college room and board ($13,650). College room only: $9340. Room and board charges vary according to board plan. Part-time tuition: $1732 per credit hour. **Scholarships:** Available. **Calendar System:** Semester, Summer session available **Enrollment:** Full-time 3,863, Graduate full-time 2,609, Graduate part-time 200, Part-time 47 **Faculty:** Full-time 665, Part-time 197 **Student-Faculty Ratio:** 6:1 **Exams:** ACT essay component used for admission; SAT I and SAT II or ACT; SAT essay component used for admission; SAT Reasoning; SAT Subject. **% Receiving Financial Aid:** 37 **% Residing in College-Owned, -Operated, or -Affiliated Housing:** 72 **Regional Accreditation:** Southern Association of Colleges and Schools **Credit Hours For Degree:** 120 semester hours, Bachelors **ROTC:** Air Force, Army, Navy **Professional Accreditation:** AACSB, ABET, NAAB, TEAC. **Intercollegiate Athletics:** Badminton M & W; Baseball M; Basketball M & W; Cheerleading M & W; Crew M & W; Cross-Country Running M & W; Equestrian Sports M & W; Fencing M & W; Field Hockey W; Football M; Golf M; Lacrosse M & W; Riflery M & W; Rugby M & W; Sailing M & W; Soccer M & W; Softball W; Swimming and Diving W; Tennis M & W; Track and Field M & W; Ultimate Frisbee M & W; Volleyball M & W; Water Polo M & W

RICHLAND COLLEGE

12800 Abrams Rd.
Dallas, TX 75243-2199
Tel: (972)238-6106
Fax: (972)238-6957
Web Site: www.rlc.dcccd.edu
President/CEO: Dr. Kay Eggleston
Admissions: Carol McKinney
Type: Two-Year College **Sex:** Coed **Affiliation:** Dallas County Community College District System. **Admission Plans:** Early Admission; Open Admission **Application Deadline:** Rolling **Application Fee:** $0.00 **H.S. Requirements:** High school diploma or equivalent not required **Costs Per Year:** Application fee: $0. Area resident tuition: $1770 full-time, $59 per credit hour part-time. State resident tuition: $3330 full-time, $111 per credit hour part-time. Nonresident tuition: $5220 full-time, $174 per credit hour part-time. **Scholarships:** Available. **Calendar System:** Semester, Summer session available **Faculty:** Full-time 165, Part-time 500 **Regional Accreditation:** Southern Association of Colleges and Schools **Credit Hours For Degree:** 61 credits, Associates **Intercollegiate Athletics:** Baseball M; Basketball M; Soccer M & W; Volleyball W

RIO GRANDE BIBLE INSTITUTE

4300 S US Hwy. 281
Edinburg, TX 78539
Tel: (956)380-8100
Fax: (956)380-8256
E-mail: admisiones@riogrande.edu
Web Site: www.riogrande.edu
President/CEO: Larry Windle
Admissions: David Loyola
Type: Four-Year College **Sex:** Coed **Affiliation:** Christian. **Application Fee:** $15.00 **Professional Accreditation:** ABHE.

ST. EDWARD'S UNIVERSITY

3001 S Congress Ave.
Austin, TX 78704
Tel: (512)448-8400; Free: 800-555-0164
Fax: (512)448-8492
E-mail: seu.admit@stedwards.edu
Web Site: www.stedwards.edu
President/CEO: Dr. George E. Martin
Admissions: Kelsey McClure
Type: Comprehensive **Sex:** Coed **Affiliation:** Roman Catholic. **Scores:** 100% SAT V 400+; 100% SAT M 400+; 32% ACT 18-23; 57% ACT 24-29 **% Accepted:** 77 **Admission Plans:** Deferred Admission **Application Deadline:** May 1 **Application Fee:** $50.00 **H.S. Requirements:** High school diploma required; GED accepted **Costs Per Year:** Application fee: $50.

Comprehensive fee: $53,000 includes full-time tuition ($40,428), mandatory fees ($400), and college room and board ($12,172). College room only: $7132. Full-time tuition and fees vary according to course load and degree level. Room and board charges vary according to board plan and housing facility. Part-time tuition: $1348 per credit hour. Part-time tuition varies according to course load and degree level. **Scholarships:** Available. **Calendar System:** Semester, Summer session available **Enrollment:** Full-time 3,528, Graduate full-time 203, Graduate part-time 394, Part-time 495 **Faculty:** Full-time 191, Part-time 277 **Student-Faculty Ratio:** 14:1 **Exams:** ACT essay component not used; SAT I or ACT; SAT II; SAT essay component not used; SAT Reasoning. **% Receiving Financial Aid:** 65 **% Residing in College-Owned, -Operated, or -Affiliated Housing:** 38 **Final Year or Final Semester Residency Requirement:** No **Regional Accreditation:** Southern Association of Colleges and Schools **Credit Hours For Degree:** 120 credit hours, Bachelors **ROTC:** Air Force, Army **Professional Accreditation:** CSWE. **Intercollegiate Athletics:** Baseball M; Basketball M & W; Cheerleading M & W; Cross-Country Running M & W; Golf M & W; Soccer M & W; Softball W; Tennis M & W; Volleyball W

ST. MARY'S UNIVERSITY

1 Camino Santa Maria
San Antonio, TX 78228-8507
Tel: (210)436-3011; Free: 800-367-7868
Fax: (210)431-6742
E-mail: uadm@stmarytx.edu
Web Site: www.stmarytx.edu
President/CEO: Thomas M. Mengler, JD
Admissions: Nelson Delgado
Financial Aid: David R. Krause

Type: Comprehensive **Sex:** Coed **Affiliation:** Roman Catholic. **Scores:** 96% SAT V 400+; 97% SAT M 400+; 62.6% ACT 18-23; 29.1% ACT 24-29 **% Accepted:** 55 **Admission Plans:** Deferred Admission **Application Deadline:** Rolling **Application Fee:** $0.00 **H.S. Requirements:** High school diploma required; GED accepted **Costs Per Year:** Application fee: $0. Comprehensive fee: $36,748 includes full-time tuition ($27,160), mandatory fees ($680), and college room and board ($8908). Full-time tuition and fees vary according to course level, course load, degree level, and program. Room and board charges vary according to board plan, housing facility, and student level. Part-time tuition: $820 per credit hour. Part-time tuition varies according to course level, course load, degree level, and program. **Scholarships:** Available. **Calendar System:** Semester, Summer session available **Enrollment:** Full-time 2,196, Graduate full-time 943, Graduate part-time 373, Part-time 204 **Faculty:** Full-time 113 **Student-Faculty Ratio:** 11:1 **Exams:** SAT I or ACT; SAT Reasoning. **% Receiving Financial Aid:** 75 **% Residing in College-Owned, -Operated, or -Affiliated Housing:** 56 **Final Year or Final Semester Residency Requirement:** Yes **Regional Accreditation:** Southern Association of Colleges and Schools **Credit Hours For Degree:** 120 semester hours, Bachelors **ROTC:** Air Force, Army **Professional Accreditation:** AACSB, AALS, AAMFT, ABA, ABET, ACA, NASM. **Intercollegiate Athletics:** Baseball M; Basketball M & W; Cheerleading M & W; Golf M & W; Soccer M & W; Softball W; Tennis M & W; Volleyball W

ST. PHILIP'S COLLEGE

1801 Martin Luther King Dr.
San Antonio, TX 78203-2098
Tel: (210)486-2000
Fax: (210)531-4831
E-mail: amolina@alamo.edu
Web Site: www.alamo.edu/spc
President/CEO: Dr. Adena Williams Loston
Admissions: Angela Molina

Type: Two-Year College **Sex:** Coed **Affiliation:** Alamo Community College District System. **Admission Plans:** Early Admission; Open Admission **Application Deadline:** Rolling **Application Fee:** $0.00 **H.S. Requirements:** High school diploma required; GED accepted **Costs Per Year:** Application fee: $0. Area resident tuition: $2108 full-time. State resident tuition: $5744 full-time. Nonresident tuition: $11,194 full-time. Mandatory fees: $80 full-time. Full-time tuition and fees vary according to course load and program. **Scholarships:** Available. **Calendar System:** Semester, Summer session available **Enrollment:** Full-time 1,622, Part-time 8,892 **Faculty:** Full-time 168, Part-time 230 **Student-Faculty Ratio:** 19:1 **Regional Accreditation:** Southern Association of Colleges and Schools **Credit Hours For Degree:**

60 credits, Associates **ROTC:** Army **Professional Accreditation:** ACEN, ACF, AHIMA, AOTA, APTA, CoARC, JRCERT, NAACLS.

SAM HOUSTON STATE UNIVERSITY

Huntsville, TX 77341
Tel: (936)294-1111; Free: 866-232-7528
E-mail: robert.stephens@shsu.edu
Web Site: www.shsu.edu
President/CEO: Dr. Dana G. Hoyt
Admissions: Robert K. Stephens
Financial Aid: Lydia Hall

Type: University **Sex:** Coed **Affiliation:** Texas State University System. **Scores:** 93% SAT V 400+; 90% SAT M 400+; 63.91% ACT 18-23; 23.31% ACT 24-29 **% Accepted:** 73 **Admission Plans:** Early Admission **Application Deadline:** August 1 **Application Fee:** $45.00 **H.S. Requirements:** High school diploma required; GED accepted **Costs Per Year:** Application fee: $45. State resident tuition: $6465 full-time, $266 per credit hour part-time. Nonresident tuition: $18,165 full-time, $656 per credit hour part-time. Mandatory fees: $2872 full-time. Full-time tuition and fees vary according to course load and location. Part-time tuition varies according to course load and location. College room and board: $8676. College room only: $4896. Room and board charges vary according to board plan and housing facility. Tuition guaranteed not to increase for student's term of enrollment. **Scholarships:** Available. **Calendar System:** Semester, Summer session available **Enrollment:** Full-time 14,117, Graduate full-time 652, Graduate part-time 1,978, Part-time 3,284 **Faculty:** Full-time 531, Part-time 374 **Student-Faculty Ratio:** 25:1 **Exams:** ACT; SAT I; SAT I and SAT II or ACT; SAT I or ACT; SAT II; SAT Reasoning; SAT Subject. **% Receiving Financial Aid:** 64 **% Residing in College-Owned, -Operated, or -Affiliated Housing:** 24 **Final Year or Final Semester Residency Requirement:** No **Regional Accreditation:** Southern Association of Colleges and Schools **Credit Hours For Degree:** 120 credit hours, Bachelors **ROTC:** Army **Professional Accreditation:** AACSB, AAFCS, ABET, AND, NASM, NCATE. **Intercollegiate Athletics:** Baseball M; Basketball M & W; Bowling W; Cheerleading M & W; Cross-Country Running M & W; Equestrian Sports M & W; Football M; Golf M & W; Lacrosse M & W; Soccer W; Softball W; Tennis W; Track and Field M & W; Ultimate Frisbee M & W; Volleyball W

SAN ANTONIO COLLEGE

1300 San Pedro Ave.
San Antonio, TX 78212-4299
Tel: (210)733-2000
Fax: (210)733-2200
Web Site: www.alamo.edu/sac
President/CEO: Robert Zeigler
Admissions: J. Martin Ortega
Financial Aid: Belinda Gonzales

Type: Two-Year College **Sex:** Coed **Affiliation:** Alamo Community College District System. **Admission Plans:** Early Admission; Open Admission **Application Deadline:** Rolling **Application Fee:** $0.00 **H.S. Requirements:** High school diploma required; GED accepted **Scholarships:** Available. **Calendar System:** Semester, Summer session available **Enrollment:** Full-time 8,375, Part-time 13,425 **Faculty:** Full-time 407, Part-time 593 **Student-Faculty Ratio:** 22:1 **Exams:** Other. **Regional Accreditation:** Southern Association of Colleges and Schools **Credit Hours For Degree:** 60 credits, Associates **ROTC:** Air Force, Army **Professional Accreditation:** AAMAE, ABFSE, ACEN, ADA.

SAN JACINTO COLLEGE DISTRICT

4624 Fairmont Pky.
Pasadena, TX 77504-3323
Tel: (281)998-6150
E-mail: Wanda.Munson@sjcd.edu
Web Site: www.sanjac.edu
President/CEO: Dr. Brenda Hellyer, EdD
Admissions: Dr. Wanda Munson, EdD

Type: Two-Year College **Sex:** Coed **Scores:** 100% SAT V 400+; 100% SAT M 400+; 45% ACT 18-23; 50% ACT 24-29 **% Accepted:** 58 **Admission Plans:** Early Admission; Open Admission **Application Deadline:** Rolling **Application Fee:** $0.00 **H.S. Requirements:** High school diploma required; GED accepted **Costs Per Year:** Application fee: $0. Area resident tuition: $1408 full-time, $47 per credit hour part-time. State resident tuition: $2416 full-time, $89 per credit hour part-time. Nonresident tuition: $3856 full-time, $149 per credit hour part-time. Mandatory fees: $280 full-time. Full-time tuition and fees vary according to course load. Part-time tuition varies according to course load. **Calendar System:** Semester, Summer session available **Enrollment:** Full-time 6,613, Part-time 21,713 **Faculty:** Full-time 490, Part-time 703 **Student-Faculty Ratio:** 19:1 **Exams:** ACT essay component used for placement; SAT essay component used for placement. **Final Year or Final Semester Residency Requirement:** No **Regional Accreditation:** Southern Association of Colleges and Schools **Credit Hours For Degree:** 61 credits, Associates **ROTC:** Air Force, Army **Intercollegiate Athletics:** Baseball M; Basketball M & W; Soccer M; Softball W; Volleyball W

SCHOOL OF AUTOMOTIVE MACHINISTS
1911 Antoine Dr.
Houston, TX 77055-1803
Tel: (713)683-3817
Fax: (713)683-7077
Web Site: www.samracing.com
Type: Two-Year College **Sex:** Coed **Professional Accreditation:** ACCSC.

SCHREINER UNIVERSITY
2100 Memorial Blvd.
Kerrville, TX 78028-5697
Tel: (830)896-5411; Free: 800-343-4919
Fax: (830)792-7226
E-mail: carandall@schreiner.edu
Web Site: www.schreiner.edu
President/CEO: Dr. Tim Summerlin
Admissions: Caroline Randall
Financial Aid: Toni Bryant
Type: Comprehensive **Sex:** Coed **Affiliation:** Presbyterian. **Scores:** 91% SAT V 400+; 93% SAT M 400+; 58.87% ACT 18-23; 22.7% ACT 24-29 **% Accepted:** 90 **Admission Plans:** Deferred Admission **Application Deadline:** May 1 **Application Fee:** $25.00 **H.S. Requirements:** High school diploma required; GED accepted **Costs Per Year:** Application fee: $25. Comprehensive fee: $35,556 includes full-time tuition ($24,030), mandatory fees ($1720), and college room and board ($9806). College room only: $4994. Full-time tuition and fees vary according to course load. Room and board charges vary according to board plan and housing facility. Part-time tuition: $1028 per credit hour. Part-time mandatory fees: $800 per year. **Scholarships:** Available. **Calendar System:** Semester, Summer session available **Enrollment:** Full-time 1,081, Graduate full-time 40, Graduate part-time 8, Part-time 101 **Faculty:** Full-time 60, Part-time 49 **Student-Faculty Ratio:** 14:1 **Exams:** ACT essay component used for admission; ACT essay component used for advising; ACT essay component used for placement; SAT I or ACT; SAT essay component used for admission; SAT essay component used for advising; SAT essay component used for placement; SAT Reasoning; SAT Subject. **% Receiving Financial Aid:** 88 **% Residing in College-Owned, -Operated, or -Affiliated Housing:** 62 **Final Year or Final Semester Residency Requirement:** No **Regional Accreditation:** Southern Association of Colleges and Schools **Credit Hours For Degree:** 64 credit hours, Associates; 120 credit hours, Bachelors **Intercollegiate Athletics:** Baseball M; Basketball M & W; Cross-Country Running M & W; Golf M & W; Soccer M & W; Softball W; Tennis M & W; Volleyball W

SOUTH PLAINS COLLEGE
1401 S College Ave.
Levelland, TX 79336-6595
Tel: (806)894-9611
Fax: (806)897-3167
E-mail: arangel@southplainscollege.edu
Web Site: www.southplainscollege.edu
President/CEO: Dr. Kelvin Sharp, EdD
Admissions: Andrea Rangel
Type: Two-Year College **Sex:** Coed **% Accepted:** 100 **Admission Plans:** Early Admission; Open Admission **Application Deadline:** Rolling **Application Fee:** $0.00 **H.S. Requirements:** High school diploma required; GED accepted. For some applicants 18 or over: High school diploma required; GED not accepted **Costs Per Year:** Application fee: $0. Area resident tuition: $696 full-time, $29 per credit hour part-time. State resident tuition: $1632 full-time, $68 per credit hour part-time. Nonresident tuition: $2016 full-time, $84 per credit hour part-time. Mandatory fees: $1544 full-time, $100 per credit hour part-time. Full-time tuition and fees vary according to course load and location. Part-time tuition and fees vary according to course load and location. College room and board: $3900. Room and board charges vary

according to housing facility. **Scholarships:** Available. **Calendar System:** Semester, Summer session available **Enrollment:** Full-time 4,382, Part-time 5,062 **Faculty:** Full-time 271, Part-time 183 **Student-Faculty Ratio:** 20:1 **Exams:** ACT; SAT II. **% Residing in College-Owned, -Operated, or -Affiliated Housing:** 10 **Regional Accreditation:** Southern Association of Colleges and Schools **Credit Hours For Degree:** 62 semester hours, Associates **ROTC:** Air Force, Army **Professional Accreditation:** ACEN, AHIMA, CoARC, JRCERT. **Intercollegiate Athletics:** Basketball M & W; Cross-Country Running M & W; Equestrian Sports M & W; Track and Field M & W.

SOUTH TEXAS COLLEGE
3201 W Pecan
McAllen, TX 78501
Tel: (956)618-8323; Free: 800-742-7822
Fax: (956)928-4445
E-mail: mshebbar@southtexascollege.edu
Web Site: www.southtexascollege.edu
President/CEO: Dr. Shirley A. Reed
Admissions: Matthew Hebbard
Type: Two-Year College **Sex:** Coed **Admission Plans:** Deferred Admission; Early Admission; Open Admission **Application Deadline:** Rolling **Application Fee:** $0.00 **H.S. Requirements:** High school diploma required; GED accepted **Scholarships:** Available. **Calendar System:** Semester, Summer session available **Enrollment:** Full-time 7,027, Part-time 12,800 **Faculty:** Full-time 434, Part-time 195 **Student-Faculty Ratio:** 25:1 **Exams:** Other. **Regional Accreditation:** Southern Association of Colleges and Schools **Credit Hours For Degree:** 60 semester hours, Associates **ROTC:** Army **Professional Accreditation:** ACBSP, AHIMA, AOTA.

SOUTH UNIVERSITY
1220 W Louis Henna Blvd.
Round Rock, TX 78681
Tel: (512)516-8800; Free: 877-659-5706
Fax: (512)516-8680
Web Site: www.southuniversity.edu/austin.aspx
Type: Comprehensive **Sex:** Coed **Regional Accreditation:** Southern Association of Colleges and Schools **Professional Accreditation:** ACBSP.

SOUTHERN METHODIST UNIVERSITY
6425 Boaz Ln.
Dallas, TX 75275
Tel: (214)768-2000; Free: 800-323-0672
E-mail: ugadmission@smu.edu
Web Site: www.smu.edu
President/CEO: Dr. R. Gerald Turner
Admissions: Wes Waggoner
Financial Aid: Marc Peterson
Type: University **Sex:** Coed **Affiliation:** United Methodist Church. **Scores:** 100% SAT V 400+; 100% SAT M 400+; 3.12% ACT 18-23; 41.14% ACT 24-29 **% Accepted:** 49 **Admission Plans:** Deferred Admission; Early Action; Early Decision Plan **Application Deadline:** January 15 **Application Fee:** $60.00 **H.S. Requirements:** High school diploma required; GED not accepted **Costs Per Year:** Application fee: $60. Comprehensive fee: $66,483 includes full-time tuition ($44,694), mandatory fees ($5664), and college room and board ($16,125). Room and board charges vary according to board plan and housing facility. **Scholarships:** Available. **Calendar System:** Semester, Summer session available **Enrollment:** Full-time 6,160, Graduate full-time 2,700, Graduate part-time 2,532, Part-time 251 **Faculty:** Full-time 740, Part-time 376 **Student-Faculty Ratio:** 11:1 **Exams:** ACT essay component used as validity check; ACT essay component used for advising; SAT I or ACT; SAT II; SAT essay component used as validity check; SAT essay component used for advising; SAT Reasoning. **% Receiving Financial Aid:** 32 **% Residing in College-Owned, -Operated, or -Affiliated Housing:** 57 **Final Year or Final Semester Residency Requirement:** No **Regional Accreditation:** Southern Association of Colleges and Schools **Credit Hours For Degree:** 122 credit hours, Bachelors **ROTC:** Air Force, Army **Professional Accreditation:** AACSB, AALS, ABA, ABET, ACIPE, ATS, NASAD, NASD, NASM, NAST. **Intercollegiate Athletics:** Baseball M; Basketball M & W; Cheerleading M & W; Crew W; Cross-Country Running W; Equestrian Sports W; Fencing M & W; Football M; Golf M & W; Ice Hockey M; Lacrosse M; Rugby M & W; Soccer M & W; Swimming and Diving M & W; Tennis M & W; Track and Field W; Volleyball W; Wrestling M

SOUTHWEST TEXAS JUNIOR COLLEGE

2401 Garner Field Rd.
Uvalde, TX 78801-6297
Tel: (830)278-4401
Web Site: www.swtjc.edu
President/CEO: Dr. Hector Gonzales
Admissions: Carol LaRue
Financial Aid: Yvette Hernandez
Type: Two-Year College **Sex:** Coed **Admission Plans:** Deferred Admission; Early Admission; Open Admission; Preferred Admission **Application Deadline:** Rolling **H.S. Requirements:** High school diploma required; GED accepted **Scholarships:** Available. **Calendar System:** Semester, Summer session available **Faculty:** Full-time 114, Part-time 85 **% Residing in College-Owned, -Operated, or -Affiliated Housing:** 9 **Regional Accreditation:** Southern Association of Colleges and Schools **Credit Hours For Degree:** 62 semester hours, Associates **Intercollegiate Athletics:** Basketball M & W; Cross-Country Running M & W; Equestrian Sports M & W

SOUTHWEST UNIVERSITY AT EL PASO

1414 Geronimo Dr.
El Paso, TX 79925
Tel: (915)778-4001
Web Site: southwestuniversity.edu
Type: Four-Year College **Sex:** Coed **Professional Accreditation:** ABHES.

SOUTHWESTERN ADVENTIST UNIVERSITY

100 Hillcrest Dr.
Keene, TX 76059
Tel: (817)645-3921; Free: 800-433-2240
Fax: (817)556-4744
E-mail: rahneeka@swau.edu
Web Site: www.swau.edu
President/CEO: Dr. Kenneth Shaw
Admissions: Rahneeka Hazelton
Type: Comprehensive **Sex:** Coed **Affiliation:** Seventh-day Adventist. **Scores:** 76% SAT V 400+; 74% SAT M 400+; 47% ACT 18-23; 16% ACT 24-29 **% Accepted:** 49 **Admission Plans:** Deferred Admission **Application Deadline:** August 31 **Application Fee:** $25.00 **H.S. Requirements:** High school diploma required; GED accepted **Costs Per Year:** Application fee: $25. Comprehensive fee: $27,316 includes full-time tuition ($19,296), mandatory fees ($620), and college room and board ($7400). Full-time tuition and fees vary according to course load and program. Room and board charges vary according to board plan. Part-time tuition: $804 per semester hour. Part-time tuition varies according to course load and program. **Scholarships:** Available. **Calendar System:** Semester, Summer session available **Enrollment:** Full-time 661, Graduate full-time 5, Graduate part-time 6, Part-time 118 **Faculty:** Full-time 47, Part-time 51 **Student-Faculty Ratio:** 11:1 **Exams:** ACT essay component not used; SAT I or ACT; SAT essay component not used; SAT Reasoning. **% Residing in College-Owned, -Operated, or -Affiliated Housing:** 45 **Final Year or Final Semester Residency Requirement:** Yes **Regional Accreditation:** Southern Association of Colleges and Schools **Credit Hours For Degree:** 64 semester hours, Associates; 120 semester hours, Bachelors **Professional Accreditation:** AACN, CSWE, NCATE. **Intercollegiate Athletics:** Basketball M & W; Soccer M & W; Volleyball W

SOUTHWESTERN ASSEMBLIES OF GOD UNIVERSITY

1200 Sycamore St.
Waxahachie, TX 75165-5735
Tel: (972)937-4010; Free: 888-937-7248
E-mail: bbrooks@sagu.edu
Web Site: www.sagu.edu
President/CEO: Dr. Kermit S. Bridges
Admissions: Bryan Brooks
Type: Comprehensive **Sex:** Coed **Affiliation:** Assemblies of God. **Scores:** 85% SAT V 400+; 88% SAT M 400+; 53.9% ACT 18-23; 25.4% ACT 24-29 **% Accepted:** 33 **Admission Plans:** Deferred Admission; Early Admission **Application Deadline:** Rolling **Application Fee:** $35.00 **H.S. Requirements:** High school diploma required; GED accepted **Costs Per Year:** Application fee: $35. Comprehensive fee: $27,466 includes full-time tuition ($19,650), mandatory fees ($880), and college room and board ($6936). College room only: $3636. Room and board charges vary according to board plan and housing facility. Part-time tuition: $655 per credit hour. **Scholarships:** Available. **Calendar System:** Semester, Summer session available **Enrollment:**

Full-time 1,445, Graduate full-time 50, Graduate part-time 268, Part-time 221 **Faculty:** Full-time 75, Part-time 86 **Student-Faculty Ratio:** 15:1 **Exams:** SAT I or ACT; SAT essay component used for admission; SAT essay component used for placement; SAT Reasoning. **% Receiving Financial Aid:** 70 **% Residing in College-Owned, -Operated, or -Affiliated Housing:** 85 **Final Year or Final Semester Residency Requirement:** Yes **Regional Accreditation:** Southern Association of Colleges and Schools **Credit Hours For Degree:** 62 credit hours, Associates; 120 credit hours, Bachelors **ROTC:** Air Force **Intercollegiate Athletics:** Baseball M; Basketball M & W; Football M; Soccer M & W; Softball W; Volleyball W

SOUTHWESTERN CHRISTIAN COLLEGE

Box 10
200 Bowser St.
Terrell, TX 75160
Tel: (972)524-3341
Web Site: www.swcc.edu
President/CEO: Jack Evans
Financial Aid: Kim Smith
Type: Four-Year College **Sex:** Coed **Affiliation:** Church of Christ. **Admission Plans:** Deferred Admission; Early Admission; Open Admission **Application Deadline:** August 1 **Application Fee:** $20.00 **H.S. Requirements:** High school diploma required; GED accepted **Scholarships:** Available. **Calendar System:** Semester, Summer session not available **% Receiving Financial Aid:** 80 **% Residing in College-Owned, -Operated, or -Affiliated Housing:** 80 **Regional Accreditation:** Southern Association of Colleges and Schools **Credit Hours For Degree:** 62 credit hours, Associates; 124 credit hours, Bachelors **Intercollegiate Athletics:** Basketball M & W; Track and Field M & W

SOUTHWESTERN UNIVERSITY

1001 E University Ave.
Georgetown, TX 78626
Tel: (512)863-6511; Free: 800-252-3166
Fax: (512)863-6511
E-mail: admission@southwestern.edu
Web Site: www.southwestern.edu
President/CEO: Dr. Edward Burger
Admissions: Bob Baldwin
Financial Aid: James P. Gaeta
Type: Four-Year College **Sex:** Coed **Affiliation:** Methodist. **Scores:** 99% SAT V 400+; 100% SAT M 400+; 30% ACT 18-23; 49% ACT 24-29 **% Accepted:** 44 **Admission Plans:** Deferred Admission; Early Decision Plan **Application Deadline:** Rolling **Application Fee:** $0.00 **H.S. Requirements:** High school diploma required; GED accepted **Costs Per Year:** Application fee: $0. Comprehensive fee: $51,348 includes full-time tuition ($39,060) and college room and board ($12,288). College room only: $6140. Room and board charges vary according to board plan and housing facility. Part-time tuition: $1630 per credit hour. Part-time tuition varies according to course load. **Scholarships:** Available. **Calendar System:** Semester, Summer session available **Enrollment:** Full-time 1,499, Part-time 16 **Faculty:** Full-time 112, Part-time 52 **Student-Faculty Ratio:** 12:1 **Exams:** ACT essay component not used; SAT I or ACT; SAT essay component not used; SAT Reasoning. **% Receiving Financial Aid:** 63 **% Residing in College-Owned, -Operated, or -Affiliated Housing:** 77 **Final Year or Final Semester Residency Requirement:** Yes **Regional Accreditation:** Southern Association of Colleges and Schools **Credit Hours For Degree:** 127 semester hours, Bachelors **ROTC:** Air Force **Professional Accreditation:** JRCAT, NASM. **Intercollegiate Athletics:** Baseball M; Basketball M & W; Cross-Country Running M & W; Football M; Golf M & W; Lacrosse M & W; Soccer M & W; Softball W; Swimming and Diving M & W; Tennis M & W; Track and Field M & W; Volleyball W

STEPHEN F. AUSTIN STATE UNIVERSITY

1936 N St.
Nacogdoches, TX 75962
Tel: (936)468-2011; Free: 800-731-2902
Fax: (936)468-3849
E-mail: admissions@sfasu.edu
Web Site: www.sfasu.edu
President/CEO: Dr. Baker Pattillo
Admissions: Kevin Davis
Financial Aid: H. Rachele Garrett
Type: Comprehensive **Sex:** Coed **Scores:** 93% SAT V 400+; 95% SAT M

400+; 59.27% ACT 18-23; 26.27% ACT 24-29 **% Accepted:** 62 **Application Deadline:** Rolling **Application Fee:** $45.00 **H.S. Requirements:** High school diploma required; GED accepted **Costs Per Year:** Application fee: $45. State resident tuition: $7065 full-time, $235.50 per credit hour part-time. Nonresident tuition: $18,765 full-time, $625.50 per credit hour part-time. Mandatory fees: $2277 full-time, $157.50 per credit hour part-time. Full-time tuition and fees vary according to course load, degree level, and location. Part-time tuition and fees vary according to course load, degree level, and location. College room and board: $8868. Room and board charges vary according to board plan and housing facility. Tuition guaranteed not to increase for student's term of enrollment. **Scholarships:** Available. **Calendar System:** Semester, Summer session available **Enrollment:** Full-time 9,439, Graduate full-time 589, Graduate part-time 1,118, Part-time 1,460 **Faculty:** Full-time 517, Part-time 187 **Student-Faculty Ratio:** 19:1 **Exams:** ACT essay component not used; SAT I or ACT; SAT essay component not used. **% Receiving Financial Aid:** 67 **% Residing in College-Owned, -Operated, or -Affiliated Housing:** 44 **Final Year or Final Semester Residency Requirement:** No **Regional Accreditation:** Southern Association of Colleges and Schools **Credit Hours For Degree:** 120 semester credit hours, Bachelors **ROTC:** Army **Professional Accreditation:** AACSB, AAFCS, ABET, ACA, ACEN, AND, ASHA, CIDA, CORE, CSWE, NASAD, NASM, NAST, NCATE, SAF. **Intercollegiate Athletics:** Baseball M; Basketball M & W; Bowling W; Cheerleading M & W; Cross-Country Running M & W; Football M; Golf M & W; Lacrosse M; Rugby M; Soccer M & W; Softball W; Tennis M & W; Track and Field M & W; Volleyball W

STRAYER UNIVERSITY–CEDAR HILL CAMPUS

610 Uptown Blvd.
Ste. 3500
Cedar Hill, TX 75104
Tel: (469)454-3400
Fax: (972)293-1800
Web Site: www.strayer.edu/texas/cedar-hill
President/CEO: Brian W. Jones
Type: Comprehensive **Sex:** Coed **Regional Accreditation:** Middle States Association of Colleges and Schools

STRAYER UNIVERSITY–IRVING CAMPUS

7701 Las Colinas Ridge
Ste. 450
Irving, TX 75063
Tel: (214)429-3900
Fax: (214)910-8499
Web Site: www.strayer.edu/texas/irving
President/CEO: Brian W. Jones
Type: Comprehensive **Sex:** Coed **Regional Accreditation:** Middle States Association of Colleges and Schools

STRAYER UNIVERSITY–KATY CAMPUS

14511 Old Katy Rd.
Ste. 200
Houston, TX 77079
Tel: (281)619-9200
Fax: (281)752-4111
Web Site: www.strayer.edu/texas/katy
President/CEO: Brian W. Jones
Type: Comprehensive **Sex:** Coed **Regional Accreditation:** Middle States Association of Colleges and Schools

STRAYER UNIVERSITY–NORTH AUSTIN CAMPUS

8501 N Mopac Expy.
Ste. 100
Austin, TX 78759
Tel: (512)568-3300
Fax: (512)340-9130
Web Site: www.strayer.edu/texas/north-austin
President/CEO: Brian W. Jones
Type: Comprehensive **Sex:** Coed **Regional Accreditation:** Middle States Association of Colleges and Schools

STRAYER UNIVERSITY–NORTHWEST HOUSTON CAMPUS

10940 W Sam Houston Pky. N
Ste. 200
Houston, TX 77064
Tel: (281)949-1800
Fax: (281)469-0090
Web Site: www.strayer.edu/texas/northwest-houston
President/CEO: Brian W. Jones
Type: Comprehensive **Sex:** Coed **Regional Accreditation:** Middle States Association of Colleges and Schools

STRAYER UNIVERSITY–PLANO CAMPUS

2701 N Dallas Pky.
Ste. 300
Plano, TX 75093
Tel: (972)535-3700
Fax: (972)608-2099
Web Site: www.strayer.edu/texas/plano
President/CEO: Brian W. Jones
Type: Comprehensive **Sex:** Coed **Regional Accreditation:** Middle States Association of Colleges and Schools

SUL ROSS STATE UNIVERSITY

PO Box C - 114
Alpine, TX 79832
Tel: (432)837-8011; Free: 888-722-7778
Fax: (432)837-8334
E-mail: admissions@sulross.edu
Web Site: www.sulross.edu
President/CEO: Dr. Bill Kibler
Admissions: MaryBeth Marks
Financial Aid: Mickey Corbett
Type: Comprehensive **Sex:** Coed **Affiliation:** Texas State University System. **Scores:** 55% SAT V 400+; 72% SAT M 400+; 41.72% ACT 18-23; 5.3% ACT 24-29 **% Accepted:** 80 **Admission Plans:** Deferred Admission **Application Deadline:** Rolling **H.S. Requirements:** High school diploma or equivalent not required **Costs Per Year:** State resident tuition: $5250 full-time, $348 per credit hour part-time. Nonresident tuition: $16,950 full-time, $738 per credit hour part-time. Mandatory fees: $1960 full-time, $182 per credit hour part-time. Full-time tuition and fees vary according to location. Part-time tuition and fees vary according to location. College room and board: $7810. Room and board charges vary according to board plan and housing facility. **Scholarships:** Available. **Calendar System:** Semester, Summer session available **Enrollment:** Full-time 1,080, Graduate full-time 131, Graduate part-time 483, Part-time 279 **Faculty:** Full-time 93, Part-time 55 **Student-Faculty Ratio:** 13:1 **Exams:** SAT I or ACT. **% Receiving Financial Aid:** 88 **% Residing in College-Owned, -Operated, or -Affiliated Housing:** 48 **Final Year or Final Semester Residency Requirement:** Yes **Regional Accreditation:** Southern Association of Colleges and Schools **Credit Hours For Degree:** 120 semester credit hours, Bachelors **Intercollegiate Athletics:** Baseball M; Basketball M & W; Cheerleading M & W; Cross-Country Running W; Football M; Softball W; Tennis M & W; Track and Field M & W; Volleyball W

TARLETON STATE UNIVERSITY

Box T-0001
Tarleton Station
Stephenville, TX 76402
Tel: (254)968-9000; Free: 800-687-8236
Fax: (254)968-9920
E-mail: uadm@tarleton.edu
Web Site: www.tarleton.edu
President/CEO: Dr. F. Dominic Dottavio
Admissions: Cindy Hess
Financial Aid: Kathy Purvis
Type: Comprehensive **Sex:** Coed **Affiliation:** Texas A&M University System. **Scores:** 84% SAT V 400+; 89% SAT M 400+; 57.39% ACT 18-23; 20.1% ACT 24-29 **% Accepted:** 71 **Admission Plans:** Early Decision Plan **Application Deadline:** July 21 **Application Fee:** $45.00 **H.S. Requirements:** High school diploma required; GED accepted **Costs Per Year:** Application fee: $45. State resident tuition: $4927 full-time, $154 per credit hour part-time. Nonresident tuition: $16,628 full-time, $544 per credit hour part-time. Mandatory fees: $3466 full-time. Full-time tuition and fees vary according to course load and degree level. Part-time tuition varies according to course load and degree level. College room and board: $9045. College room only: $5400. Room and board charges vary according to board plan and housing facility. Tuition guaranteed not to increase for student's term of enrollment. **Scholarships:** Available. **Calendar System:** Semester, Summer session

available **Enrollment:** Full-time 8,309, Graduate full-time 299, Graduate part-time 1,284, Part-time 2,441 **Faculty:** Full-time 367, Part-time 299 **Student-Faculty Ratio:** 19:1 **Exams:** SAT I or ACT; SAT Reasoning. **% Receiving Financial Aid:** 63 **% Residing in College-Owned, -Operated, or -Affiliated Housing:** 35 **Final Year or Final Semester Residency Requirement:** No **Regional Accreditation:** Southern Association of Colleges and Schools **Credit Hours For Degree:** 69 credit hours, Associates; 120 semester hours, Bachelors **ROTC:** Army **Professional Accreditation:** AACN, AAFCS, ABET, ACBSP, CSWE, NAACLS, NASM. **Intercollegiate Athletics:** Baseball M; Basketball M & W; Cheerleading M & W; Cross-Country Running M & W; Football M; Golf W; Softball W; Tennis W; Track and Field M & W; Volleyball W

TARRANT COUNTY COLLEGE DISTRICT
1500 Houston St.
Fort Worth, TX 76102-6599
Tel: (817)515-5100
Fax: (817)515-5295
E-mail: nichole.mancone@tccd.edu
Web Site: www.tccd.edu
President/CEO: Angela Robinson
Admissions: Nichole Mancone
Financial Aid: Samantha Stalnaker
Type: Two-Year College **Sex:** Coed **% Accepted:** 100 **Admission Plans:** Open Admission **Application Deadline:** Rolling **Application Fee:** $0.00 **H.S. Requirements:** High school diploma or equivalent not required. For dental assisting, nursing programs: High school diploma required; GED accepted **Costs Per Year:** Application fee: $0. Area resident tuition: $1320 full-time, $55 per credit hour part-time. State resident tuition: $2064 full-time, $86 per credit hour part-time. Nonresident tuition: $4920 full-time, $205 per credit hour part-time. Full-time tuition varies according to course load and program. Part-time tuition varies according to course load and program. **Scholarships:** Available. **Calendar System:** Semester, Summer session available **Enrollment:** Full-time 15,764, Part-time 34,831 **Faculty:** Full-time 663, Part-time 1,508 **Student-Faculty Ratio:** 25:1 **Regional Accreditation:** Southern Association of Colleges and Schools **Credit Hours For Degree:** 64 semester hours, Associates **ROTC:** Air Force, Army **Professional Accreditation:** ACEN, ADA, AHIMA, APTA, CoARC, JRCERT.

TEMPLE COLLEGE
2600 S First St.
Temple, TX 76504-7435
Tel: (254)298-8282
E-mail: carey.rose@templejc.edu
Web Site: www.templejc.edu
President/CEO: Dr. Glenda O. Barron
Admissions: Toni Cuellar
Financial Aid: Peggy Watts
Type: Two-Year College **Sex:** Coed **Admission Plans:** Early Admission; Open Admission **Application Deadline:** Rolling **Application Fee:** $0.00 **H.S. Requirements:** High school diploma required; GED accepted **Scholarships:** Available. **Calendar System:** Semester, Summer session available **Faculty:** Full-time 123, Part-time 166 **Student-Faculty Ratio:** 25:1 **Final Year or Final Semester Residency Requirement:** Yes **Regional Accreditation:** Southern Association of Colleges and Schools **Credit Hours For Degree:** 64 semester hours, Associates **Professional Accreditation:** ACEN, ADA, CoARC, NAACLS. **Intercollegiate Athletics:** Baseball M; Basketball M & W; Softball W; Tennis M & W; Volleyball W

TEXARKANA COLLEGE
2500 N Robison Rd.
Texarkana, TX 75599-0001
Tel: (903)838-4541
Fax: (903)832-5030
E-mail: lee.williams@texarkanacollege.edu
Web Site: www.texarkanacollege.edu
President/CEO: James Henry Russell
Admissions: Lee Williams
Type: Two-Year College **Sex:** Coed **Admission Plans:** Deferred Admission; Early Admission; Open Admission **Application Deadline:** Rolling **Application Fee:** $0.00 **H.S. Requirements:** High school diploma required; GED accepted **Costs Per Year:** Application fee: $0. Area resident tuition: $1152 full-time, $48 per semester hour part-time. State resident tuition: $2328 full-time, $97 per semester hour part-time. Nonresident tuition: $3456 full-time,

$144 per semester hour part-time. Mandatory fees: $800 full-time, $66. College room only: $2000. **Scholarships:** Available. **Calendar System:** Semester, Summer session available **Enrollment:** Full-time 1,386, Part-time 2,779 **Faculty:** Full-time 89, Part-time 94 **Student-Faculty Ratio:** 21:1 **% Residing in College-Owned, -Operated, or -Affiliated Housing:** 1 **Regional Accreditation:** Southern Association of Colleges and Schools **Credit Hours For Degree:** 60 semester hours, Associates **Professional Accreditation:** ACEN.

TEXAS A&M INTERNATIONAL UNIVERSITY
5201 University Blvd.
Laredo, TX 78041-1900
Tel: (956)326-2001; Free: 888-489-2648
Fax: (956)326-2348
E-mail: adms@tamiu.edu
Web Site: www.tamiu.edu
President/CEO: Dr. Ray M. Keck, III
Admissions: Rosa Dickinson
Financial Aid: Laura Elizondo
Type: Comprehensive **Sex:** Coed **Affiliation:** Texas A&M University System. **Scores:** 75% SAT V 400+; 44.05% ACT 18-23; 4.18% ACT 24-29 **% Accepted:** 49 **Admission Plans:** Deferred Admission; Early Admission **Application Deadline:** July 1 **Application Fee:** $0.00 **H.S. Requirements:** High school diploma required; GED accepted **Costs Per Year:** Application fee: $0. State resident tuition: $8446 full-time. Nonresident tuition: $20,338 full-time. Full-time tuition varies according to course load. College room and board: $7882. Room and board charges vary according to board plan and housing facility. **Scholarships:** Available. **Calendar System:** Semester, Summer session available **Enrollment:** Full-time 4,586, Graduate full-time 222, Graduate part-time 594, Part-time 1,790 **Student-Faculty Ratio:** 20:1 **Exams:** ACT essay component not used; SAT I or ACT; SAT essay component not used; SAT Reasoning; SAT Subject. **% Receiving Financial Aid:** 69 **% Residing in College-Owned, -Operated, or -Affiliated Housing:** 9 **Regional Accreditation:** Southern Association of Colleges and Schools **Credit Hours For Degree:** 124 semester hours, Bachelors **ROTC:** Army **Professional Accreditation:** AACSB, ACEN. **Intercollegiate Athletics:** Baseball M; Basketball M & W; Cross-Country Running M & W; Golf M & W; Soccer M & W; Softball W; Volleyball W

TEXAS A&M UNIVERSITY
College Station, TX 77843
Tel: (979)845-3211
Web Site: www.tamu.edu
President/CEO: Michael K. Young
Type: University **Sex:** Coed **Affiliation:** Texas A&M University System. **Scores:** 98% SAT V 400+; 99% SAT M 400+; 16.24% ACT 18-23; 50.9% ACT 24-29 **% Accepted:** 66 **Admission Plans:** Preferred Admission **Application Deadline:** December 1 **Application Fee:** $75.00 **H.S. Requirements:** High school diploma required; GED accepted **Costs Per Year:** Application fee: $75. State resident tuition: $6149 full-time, $204.96 per credit hour part-time. Nonresident tuition: $24,742 full-time, $824.72 per credit hour part-time. Mandatory fees: $3279 full-time. Full-time tuition and fees vary according to program. Part-time tuition varies according to program. College room and board: $10,338. Room and board charges vary according to board plan, housing facility, and location. Tuition guaranteed not to increase for student's term of enrollment. **Scholarships:** Available. **Calendar System:** Semester, Summer session available **Enrollment:** Full-time 43,532, Graduate full-time 11,886, Graduate part-time 2,583, Part-time 5,428 **Faculty:** Full-time 2,834, Part-time 765 **Student-Faculty Ratio:** 20:1 **Exams:** ACT essay component used as validity check; SAT I or ACT; SAT essay component used as validity check; SAT Reasoning. **% Receiving Financial Aid:** 43 **% Residing in College-Owned, -Operated, or -Affiliated Housing:** 23 **Final Year or Final Semester Residency Requirement:** No **Regional Accreditation:** Southern Association of Colleges and Schools **Credit Hours For Degree:** 128 semester hours, Bachelors **ROTC:** Air Force, Army, Navy **Professional Accreditation:** AACSB, AAFCS, ABA, ABET, ACCE, ACEJMC, ACPE, ACSP, ADA, AND, APA, ASLA, AVMA, LCME/AMA, NAAB, NASPAA, NCATE, NRPA, SAF. **Intercollegiate Athletics:** Baseball M; Basketball M & W; Cross-Country Running M & W; Equestrian Sports W; Football M; Golf M & W; Soccer W; Softball W; Swimming and Diving M & W; Tennis M & W; Track and Field M & W; Volleyball W

TEXAS A&M UNIVERSITY–CENTRAL TEXAS
1001 Leadership Pl.
Killeen, TX 76549

Tel: (254)519-5400
Web Site: www.tamuct.edu
President/CEO: Dr. Marc A. Nigliazzo
Admissions: Joshua Smith
Type: Two-Year Upper Division **Sex:** Coed **Affiliation:** Texas A&M University System. **Admission Plans:** Open Admission **Costs Per Year:** State resident tuition: $19,269 full-time. Nonresident tuition: $28,023 full-time. Mandatory fees: $1610 full-time. Full-time tuition and fees vary according to course load. Tuition guaranteed not to increase for student's term of enrollment. **Calendar System:** Semester, Summer session available **Enrollment:** Full-time 579, Graduate full-time 177, Graduate part-time 385, Part-time 1,325 **Faculty:** Full-time 69, Part-time 109 **Student-Faculty Ratio:** 14:1 **Final Year or Final Semester Residency Requirement:** Yes **Regional Accreditation:** Southern Association of Colleges and Schools **Credit Hours For Degree:** 120 semester credit hours, Bachelors **ROTC:** Army

TEXAS A&M UNIVERSITY–COMMERCE

PO Box 3011
Commerce, TX 75429-3011
Tel: (903)886-5081; Free: 888-868-2682
Fax: (903)886-5888
E-mail: admissions@tamu-commerce.edu
Web Site: www.tamuc.edu
President/CEO: Dr. Dan R. Jones, PhD
Admissions: Jody Todhunter
Financial Aid: Maria Ramos
Type: University **Sex:** Coed **Affiliation:** Texas A&M University System. **Scores:** 84% SAT V 400+; 91% SAT M 400+; 54% ACT 18-23; 24% ACT 24-29 **% Accepted:** 47 **Admission Plans:** Deferred Admission **Application Fee:** $0.00 **H.S. Requirements:** High school diploma required; GED accepted **Costs Per Year:** Application fee: $0. State resident tuition: $4790 full-time, $160 per credit hour part-time. Nonresident tuition: $16,490 full-time, $550 per credit hour part-time. Mandatory fees: $2642 full-time. Full-time tuition and fees vary according to course load, location, program, and reciprocity agreements. Part-time tuition varies according to course load, location, program, and reciprocity agreements. College room and board: $8326. Room and board charges vary according to board plan and housing facility. Tuition guaranteed not to increase for student's term of enrollment. **Scholarships:** Available. **Calendar System:** Semester, Summer session available **Enrollment:** Full-time 5,445, Graduate full-time 1,521, Graduate part-time 3,139, Part-time 2,197 **Faculty:** Full-time 356, Part-time 349 **Student-Faculty Ratio:** 19:1 **Exams:** ACT essay component not used; SAT I or ACT; SAT essay component not used; SAT Reasoning. **% Receiving Financial Aid:** 76 **% Residing in College-Owned, -Operated, or -Affiliated Housing:** 30 **Final Year or Final Semester Residency Requirement:** No **Regional Accreditation:** Southern Association of Colleges and Schools **Credit Hours For Degree:** 120 semester hours, Bachelors **ROTC:** Air Force **Professional Accreditation:** AACSB, ABET, ACA, ATMAE, CSWE, NASM. **Intercollegiate Athletics:** Basketball M & W; Cheerleading M & W; Cross-Country Running M & W; Football M; Golf M & W; Soccer W; Softball W; Track and Field M & W; Volleyball W

TEXAS A&M UNIVERSITY–CORPUS CHRISTI

6300 Ocean Dr.
Corpus Christi, TX 78412-5503
Tel: (361)825-5700; Free: 800-482-6822
Fax: (361)825-5810
E-mail: monica.martinez@tamucc.edu
Web Site: www.tamucc.edu
President/CEO: Dr. Flavius Killebrew
Admissions: Monica Martinez
Financial Aid: Jeannie Gage
Type: University **Sex:** Coed **Affiliation:** Texas A&M University System. **Scores:** 87% SAT V 400+; 90% SAT M 400+; 53.5% ACT 18-23; 18.76% ACT 24-29 **% Accepted:** 84 **Application Deadline:** July 1 **Application Fee:** $40.00 **H.S. Requirements:** High school diploma required; GED accepted **Costs Per Year:** Application fee: $40. State resident tuition: $4,979 full-time, $174.27 per credit part-time. Nonresident tuition: $16,567 full-time, $560.24 per credit part-time. Mandatory fees: $3,641 full-time, $381.09 per credit part-time. Full-time tuition and fees vary according to course load, degree level, location, program, and student level. Part-time tuition and fees vary according to course load, degree level, location, program, and student level. College room and board: $9195. College room only: $5,484. Room and board charges vary according to board plan and housing facility. Tuition guaranteed not to increase for student's term of enrollment. **Scholarships:** Available. **Calendar System:** Semester, Summer session available **Enrollment:** Full-time 7,389, Graduate full-time 547, Graduate part-time 1,310, Part-time 2,415 **Faculty:** Full-time 417, Part-time 177 **Student-Faculty Ratio:** 19:1 **Exams:** ACT essay component not used; SAT I or ACT; SAT essay component not used; SAT Reasoning; SAT Subject. **% Receiving Financial Aid:** 60 **% Residing in College-Owned, -Operated, or -Affiliated Housing:** 22 **Final Year or Final Semester Residency Requirement:** No **Regional Accreditation:** Southern Association of Colleges and Schools **Credit Hours For Degree:** 124 semester hours, Bachelors **ROTC:** Army **Professional Accreditation:** AACN, AACSB, ABET, ACA, NAACLS, NASM. **Intercollegiate Athletics:** Baseball M; Basketball M & W; Cross-Country Running M & W; Golf W; Soccer W; Softball W; Tennis M & W; Track and Field M & W; Volleyball W

TEXAS A&M UNIVERSITY–KINGSVILLE

700 University Blvd.
Kingsville, TX 78363
Tel: (361)593-2111; Free: 800-687-6000
E-mail: laura.knippers@tamuk.edu
Web Site: www.tamuk.edu
President/CEO: Dr. Steven H. Tallant
Admissions: Laura Knippers
Financial Aid: Ralph Perri
Type: University **Sex:** Coed **Affiliation:** Texas A&M University System. **Scores:** 82% SAT V 400+; 93% SAT M 400+; 51.9% ACT 18-23; 17.3% ACT 24-29 **% Accepted:** 82 **Application Deadline:** August 1 **Application Fee:** $25.00 **H.S. Requirements:** High school diploma required; GED accepted **Costs Per Year:** Application fee: $25. State resident tuition: $7700 full-time, $120 per credit hour part-time. Nonresident tuition: $20,190 full-time, $440 per credit hour part-time. Full-time tuition varies according to course load and degree level. Part-time tuition varies according to course load and degree level. College room and board: $8407. College room only: $5339. Room and board charges vary according to board plan and housing facility. **Scholarships:** Available. **Calendar System:** Semester, Summer session available **Enrollment:** Full-time 5,077, Graduate full-time 1,750, Graduate part-time 852, Part-time 1,528 **Exams:** SAT I or ACT; SAT Reasoning. **% Receiving Financial Aid:** 90 **% Residing in College-Owned, -Operated, or -Affiliated Housing:** 32 **Final Year or Final Semester Residency Requirement:** Yes **Regional Accreditation:** Southern Association of Colleges and Schools **Credit Hours For Degree:** minimum 120 hours, depending on program, Bachelors **ROTC:** Army **Professional Accreditation:** ABET, ACBSP, AND, ASHA, ATMAE, CSWE, NASM. **Intercollegiate Athletics:** Baseball M; Basketball M & W; Cross-Country Running M & W; Football M; Golf W; Softball W; Tennis W; Track and Field M & W; Volleyball W

TEXAS A&M UNIVERSITY–SAN ANTONIO

One University Way
San Antonio, TX 78224
Tel: (210)784-1000
E-mail: jennifer.zamarripa@tamusa.tamus.edu
Web Site: www.tamusa.tamus.edu
President/CEO: Maria Hernandez Ferrier
Admissions: Jennifer Zamarripa
Type: Comprehensive **Sex:** Coed **Application Deadline:** August 15 **Application Fee:** $15.00 **Regional Accreditation:** Southern Association of Colleges and Schools

TEXAS A&M UNIVERSITY–TEXARKANA

PO Box 5518
Texarkana, TX 75505-5518
Tel: (903)223-3000
Fax: (903)832-8890
E-mail: admissions@tamut.edu
Web Site: www.tamut.edu
President/CEO: C.B. Rathburn
Admissions: Patricia Black
Financial Aid: Michael G. Fuller
Type: Two-Year Upper Division **Sex:** Coed **Affiliation:** Texas A&M University System. **H.S. Requirements:** High school diploma required; GED accepted **Scholarships:** Available. **Calendar System:** Semester, Summer session available **Student-Faculty Ratio:** 11:1 **Exams:** SAT I or ACT. **% Receiving Financial Aid:** 69 **Regional Accreditation:** Southern Associa-

tion of Colleges and Schools **Credit Hours For Degree:** 120 semester hours, Bachelors **Professional Accreditation:** AACN.

TEXAS CHRISTIAN UNIVERSITY

2800 S University Dr.
Fort Worth, TX 76129-0002
Tel: (817)257-7000; Free: 800-828-3764
E-mail: frogmail@tcu.edu
Web Site: www.tcu.edu
President/CEO: Dr. Victor J. Boschini, Jr.
Admissions: Heath Einstein
Financial Aid: Michael Scott

Type: University **Sex:** Coed **Affiliation:** Christian Church (Disciples of Christ). **% Accepted:** 43 **Admission Plans:** Deferred Admission; Early Action; Early Decision Plan **Application Deadline:** February 15 **Application Fee:** $40.00 **H.S. Requirements:** High school diploma required; GED not accepted **Costs Per Year:** Application fee: $40. Comprehensive fee: $52,520 includes full-time tuition ($40,630), mandatory fees ($90), and college room and board ($11,800). College room only: $7100. Room and board charges vary according to board plan and housing facility. Part-time tuition: $1715 per credit hour. Part-time mandatory fees: $45 per term. Part-time tuition and fees vary according to course load. **Scholarships:** Available. **Calendar System:** Semester, Summer session available **Enrollment:** Full-time 8,586, Graduate full-time 1,262, Graduate part-time 167, Part-time 308 **Faculty:** Full-time 623, Part-time 349 **Exams:** ACT essay component not used; SAT I or ACT; SAT essay component not used; SAT Reasoning. **% Receiving Financial Aid:** 38 **% Residing in College-Owned, -Operated, or -Affiliated Housing:** 49 **Final Year or Final Semester Residency Requirement:** Yes **Regional Accreditation:** Southern Association of Colleges and Schools **Credit Hours For Degree:** 124 semester hours, Bachelors **ROTC:** Air Force, Army **Professional Accreditation:** AACN, AACSB, AANA, ABET, ACEJMC, ACIPE, AND, ASHA, ATS, CIDA, CSWE, JRCAT, NASAD, NASD, NASM. **Intercollegiate Athletics:** Baseball M; Basketball M & W; Cross-Country Running M & W; Equestrian Sports W; Football M; Golf M & W; Gymnastics M & W; Ice Hockey M; Lacrosse M & W; Riflery W; Rock Climbing M & W; Rowing M & W; Rugby M & W; Soccer M & W; Swimming and Diving M & W; Tennis M & W; Track and Field M & W; Triathlon M & W; Ultimate Frisbee M & W; Volleyball M & W; Water Polo M & W; Wrestling M & W

TEXAS COLLEGE

2404 N Grand Ave.
Tyler, TX 75712-4500
Tel: (903)593-8311; Free: 800-306-6299
E-mail: jroberts@texascollege.edu
Web Site: www.texascollege.edu
President/CEO: Dr. Dwight J. Fennell
Admissions: John Roberts
Financial Aid: Cecelia K. Jones

Type: Four-Year College **Sex:** Coed **Affiliation:** Christian Methodist Episcopal Church. **Scores:** 30% ACT 18-23; 1% ACT 24-29 **Admission Plans:** Early Admission; Open Admission **Application Deadline:** Rolling **Application Fee:** $20.00 **H.S. Requirements:** High school diploma required; GED accepted **Scholarships:** Available. **Calendar System:** Semester, Summer session available **Enrollment:** Full-time 841, Graduate part-time 23, Part-time 19 **Student-Faculty Ratio:** 25:1 **Exams:** SAT I or ACT. **% Receiving Financial Aid:** 94 **% Residing in College-Owned, -Operated, or -Affiliated Housing:** 31 **Final Year or Final Semester Residency Requirement:** Yes **Regional Accreditation:** Southern Association of Colleges and Schools **Credit Hours For Degree:** 66 credit hours, Associates; 124 credit hours, Bachelors **Intercollegiate Athletics:** Baseball M; Basketball M & W; Cheerleading M & W; Football M; Soccer M & W; Softball W; Track and Field M & W; Volleyball W

TEXAS LUTHERAN UNIVERSITY

1000 W Ct. St.
Seguin, TX 78155-5999
Tel: (830)372-8000; Free: 800-771-8521
Fax: (830)372-8096
E-mail: toliver@tlu.edu
Web Site: www.tlu.edu
President/CEO: Dr. Stuart Dorsey
Admissions: Tom Oliver
Financial Aid: Bonnie Trevino

Type: Comprehensive **Sex:** Coed **Affiliation:** Evangelical Lutheran Church. **Scores:** 92% SAT V 400+; 97% SAT M 400+; 65.77% ACT 18-23; 19.79% ACT 24-29 **Costs Per Year:** Comprehensive fee: $37,290 includes full-time tuition ($27,600), mandatory fees ($300), and college room and board ($9390). College room only: $5400. Full-time tuition and fees vary according to course load. Room and board charges vary according to board plan and housing facility. Part-time tuition: $915 per semester hour. **Scholarships:** Available. **Calendar System:** Semester, Summer session available **Enrollment:** Full-time 1,284, Graduate full-time 7, Graduate part-time 2, Part-time 83 **Faculty:** Full-time 81, Part-time 45 **Student-Faculty Ratio:** 14:1 **Exams:** SAT I or ACT. **% Receiving Financial Aid:** 82 **% Residing in College-Owned, -Operated, or -Affiliated Housing:** 60 **Final Year or Final Semester Residency Requirement:** No **Regional Accreditation:** Southern Association of Colleges and Schools **Credit Hours For Degree:** 124 credit hours, Bachelors **ROTC:** Air Force, Army **Professional Accreditation:** ACBSP. **Intercollegiate Athletics:** Baseball M; Basketball M & W; Cross-Country Running M & W; Football M; Golf M & W; Soccer M & W; Softball W; Tennis M & W; Track and Field M & W; Volleyball W

TEXAS SOUTHERN UNIVERSITY

3100 Cleburne Ave.
Houston, TX 77004-4584
Tel: (713)313-7011
Fax: (713)527-7842
E-mail: eservices@em.tsu.edu
Web Site: www.tsu.edu
President/CEO: Dr. John M. Rudley

Type: University **Sex:** Coed **Scores:** 53% SAT V 400+; 64% SAT M 400+; 34% ACT 18-23; 2% ACT 24-29 **% Accepted:** 51 **Admission Plans:** Early Action; Early Admission; Open Admission **Application Deadline:** August 15 **Application Fee:** $42.00 **H.S. Requirements:** High school diploma required; GED accepted **Scholarships:** Available. **Calendar System:** Semester, Summer session available **Enrollment:** Full-time 5,842, Graduate full-time 1,594, Graduate part-time 724, Part-time 1,073 **Faculty:** Full-time 347, Part-time 258 **Student-Faculty Ratio:** 18:1 **Exams:** ACT essay component used for advising; SAT I or ACT; SAT essay component used for advising; SAT Reasoning; SAT Subject. **% Receiving Financial Aid:** 100 **% Residing in College-Owned, -Operated, or -Affiliated Housing:** 22 **Final Year or Final Semester Residency Requirement:** No **Regional Accreditation:** Southern Association of Colleges and Schools **Credit Hours For Degree:** 120 semester hours, Bachelors **ROTC:** Air Force, Army, Navy **Professional Accreditation:** AACSB, ABA, ABET, ACPE, ACSP, AHIMA, ATMAE, CSWE, CoARC, NAACLS, NASPAA. **Intercollegiate Athletics:** Baseball M; Basketball M & W; Bowling W; Cross-Country Running M & W; Football M; Golf M; Soccer M & W; Softball W; Tennis M & W; Track and Field M & W; Volleyball M & W

TEXAS SOUTHMOST COLLEGE

80 Fort Brown
Brownsville, TX 78520-4991
Tel: (956)882-8200; Free: 877-882-8721
Web Site: www.utb.edu

Type: Two-Year College **Sex:** Coed **Affiliation:** University of Texas System. **Admission Plans:** Open Admission **Application Deadline:** August 1 **H.S. Requirements:** High school diploma required; GED accepted **Calendar System:** Semester, Summer session available **Regional Accreditation:** Southern Association of Colleges and Schools **Credit Hours For Degree:** 62 credits, Associates **Professional Accreditation:** ABET, ACEN, CoARC, JRCERT, NAACLS, NASM. **Intercollegiate Athletics:** Baseball M; Golf M & W; Soccer M & W; Volleyball W

TEXAS STATE TECHNICAL COLLEGE

3801 Campus Dr.
Waco, TX 76705-1695
Tel: (254)799-3611; Free: 800-792-8784
E-mail: mary.daniel@tstc.edu
Web Site: www.tstc.edu
President/CEO: Elton E. Stuckly, Jr.
Admissions: Paula Arredondo
Financial Aid: Jackie Adler

Type: Two-Year College **Sex:** Coed **% Accepted:** 100 **Admission Plans:** Early Admission; Open Admission **Application Deadline:** Rolling **Application Fee:** $0.00 **H.S. Requirements:** High school diploma required; GED accepted **Costs Per Year:** Application fee: $0. State resident tuition: $4386 full-time, $142 per credit hour part-time. Nonresident tuition: $9660 full-time, $322 per credit hour part-time. Full-time tuition varies according to class time, course load, and program. Part-time tuition varies according to class time, course load, and program. College room and board: $5214. College room only: $3780. Room and board charges vary according to board plan, housing facility, and location. **Scholarships:** Available. **Calendar System:** Trimester, Summer session available **Enrollment:** Full-time 4,665, Part-time 6,024 **Faculty:** Full-time 253, Part-time 30 **Student-Faculty Ratio:** 17:1 **Exams:** Other. **Final Year or Final Semester Residency Requirement:** No **Regional Accreditation:** Southern Association of Colleges and Schools **Credit Hours For Degree:** 60 semester credits, Associates **Professional Accreditation:** ADA.

TEXAS STATE UNIVERSITY

601 University Dr.
San Marcos, TX 78666
Tel: (512)245-2111
Fax: (512)245-8044
E-mail: admissions@txstate.edu
Web Site: www.txstate.edu
President/CEO: Dr. Denise M. Trauth
Financial Aid: Chris Murr

Type: University **Sex:** Coed **Affiliation:** Texas State University System. **Scores:** 95% SAT V 400+; 98% SAT M 400+; 58.6% ACT 18-23; 35% ACT 24-29 **% Accepted:** 71 **Admission Plans:** Deferred Admission; Early Admission **Application Deadline:** May 1 **Application Fee:** $75.00 **H.S. Requirements:** High school diploma required; GED accepted **Costs Per Year:** Application fee: $75. State resident tuition: $7536 full-time, $251 per credit hour part-time. Nonresident tuition: $19,236 full-time, $641 per credit hour part-time. Mandatory fees: $2408 full-time, $56.74 per credit hour part-time, $413 per term part-time. Full-time tuition and fees vary according to course load and degree level. Part-time tuition and fees vary according to course load and degree level. College room and board: $7840. College room only: $5230. Room and board charges vary according to board plan and housing facility. Tuition guaranteed not to increase for student's term of enrollment. **Scholarships:** Available. **Calendar System:** Semester, Summer session available **Enrollment:** Full-time 27,369, Graduate full-time 2,590, Graduate part-time 1,909, Part-time 6,111 **Faculty:** Full-time 1,294, Part-time 566 **Student-Faculty Ratio:** 20:1 **Exams:** ACT essay component used as validity check; Other; SAT I or ACT; SAT essay component used as validity check; SAT Reasoning. **% Receiving Financial Aid:** 57 **% Residing in College-Owned, -Operated, or -Affiliated Housing:** 20 **Regional Accreditation:** Southern Association of Colleges and Schools **Credit Hours For Degree:** 120 semester hours, Bachelors **ROTC:** Air Force, Army **Professional Accreditation:** AACSB, AAFCS, ABET, ACA, ACEJMC, AHIMA, AND, APA, APTA, ASHA, CAHME, CIDA, CSWE, CoARC, JRCAT, JRCERT, NAACLS, NASM, NASPAA, NRPA, TEAC. **Intercollegiate Athletics:** Baseball M; Basketball M & W; Cheerleading M & W; Cross-Country Running M & W; Equestrian Sports M & W; Fencing M & W; Football M; Golf M & W; Gymnastics M & W; Lacrosse M & W; Rugby M & W; Soccer M & W; Softball M & W; Tennis M & W; Track and Field M & W; Ultimate Frisbee M & W; Volleyball W; Water Polo M & W; Weight Lifting M & W; Wrestling M & W

TEXAS TECH UNIVERSITY

Lubbock, TX 79409
Tel: (806)742-2011
Fax: (806)742-3055
E-mail: admissions@ttu.edu
Web Site: www.ttu.edu
President/CEO: Dr. M. Duane Nellis
Admissions: Dr. Ethan Logan
Financial Aid: Becky Wilson

Type: University **Sex:** Coed **Affiliation:** Texas Tech University System. **Scores:** 99% SAT V 400+; 100% SAT M 400+; 36.24% ACT 18-23; 54.32% ACT 24-29 **% Accepted:** 63 **Application Deadline:** August 1 **Application Fee:** $60.00 **H.S. Requirements:** High school diploma required; GED accepted **Costs Per Year:** Application fee: $60. State resident tuition: $7050 full-time, $235 per credit hour part-time. Nonresident tuition: $18,750 full-time, $625 per credit hour part-time. Mandatory fees: $2731 full-time. Full-time tuition and fees vary according to course level, course load, degree level, location, program, reciprocity agreements, and student level. Part-time tuition varies according to course level, course load, degree level, location, program, reciprocity agreements, and student level. College room and board: $8505. College room only: $3995. Room and board charges vary ac-

cording to board plan and housing facility. **Scholarships:** Available. **Calendar System:** Semester, Summer session available **Enrollment:** Full-time 26,121, Graduate full-time 4,250, Graduate part-time 2,372, Part-time 3,116 **Faculty:** Full-time 1,383, Part-time 248 **Student-Faculty Ratio:** 22:1 **Exams:** ACT essay component used for placement; SAT I or ACT; SAT essay component used for placement; SAT Reasoning; SAT Subject. **% Receiving Financial Aid:** 50 **% Residing in College-Owned, -Operated, or -Affiliated Housing:** 25 **Final Year or Final Semester Residency Requirement:** Yes **Regional Accreditation:** Southern Association of Colleges and Schools **Credit Hours For Degree:** 120 semester hours, Bachelors **ROTC:** Air Force, Army **Professional Accreditation:** AACSB, AAFCS, AALS, AAMFT, ABA, ABET, ACA, ACEJMC, AND, APA, ASHA, ASLA, CAHME, CIDA, CSWE, JRCEMTP, NAAB, NASAD, NASM, NASPAA, NAST, NCATE. **Intercollegiate Athletics:** Baseball M; Basketball M & W; Cross-Country Running M & W; Football M; Golf M & W; Soccer W; Softball W; Tennis M & W; Track and Field M & W; Volleyball W

TEXAS WESLEYAN UNIVERSITY

1201 Wesleyan St.
Fort Worth, TX 76105-1536
Tel: (817)531-4444; Free: 800-580-8980
Fax: (817)531-7515
E-mail: admissions@txwes.edu
Web Site: www.txwes.edu
President/CEO: Frederick G. Slabach
Admissions: Denelle Rodriguez
Financial Aid: Laurie Rosenkrantz

Type: Comprehensive **Sex:** Coed **Affiliation:** United Methodist. **Scores:** 98% SAT V 400+; 98% SAT M 400+; 73.91% ACT 18-23; 23.19% ACT 24-29 **% Accepted:** 46 **Admission Plans:** Deferred Admission **Application Deadline:** Rolling **Application Fee:** $0.00 **H.S. Requirements:** High school diploma required; GED accepted **Costs Per Year:** Application fee: $0. Comprehensive fee: $33,105 includes full-time tuition ($21,674), mandatory fees ($2780), and college room and board ($8651). College room only: $5072. Full-time tuition and fees vary according to course level, course load, degree level, program, and student level. Room and board charges vary according to housing facility. Part-time tuition: $735 per credit hour. Part-time tuition varies according to course level, course load, degree level, program, and student level. **Scholarships:** Available. **Calendar System:** Semester, Summer session available **Enrollment:** Full-time 1,549, Graduate full-time 456, Graduate part-time 212, Part-time 430 **Faculty:** Full-time 136, Part-time 97 **Student-Faculty Ratio:** 16:1 **Exams:** SAT I or ACT; SAT Reasoning; SAT Subject. **% Receiving Financial Aid:** 60 **% Residing in College-Owned, -Operated, or -Affiliated Housing:** 23 **Final Year or Final Semester Residency Requirement:** No **Regional Accreditation:** Southern Association of Colleges and Schools **Credit Hours For Degree:** 124 credit hours, Bachelors **ROTC:** Air Force, Army **Professional Accreditation:** AACSB, AANA, ABA, ACBSP, NASM. **Intercollegiate Athletics:** Baseball M; Basketball M & W; Cheerleading M & W; Cross-Country Running M & W; Golf M & W; Soccer M & W; Softball W; Table Tennis M & W; Tennis W; Track and Field M & W; Volleyball W

TEXAS WOMAN'S UNIVERSITY

304 Administration Dr.
Denton, TX 76201
Tel: (940)898-2000; Free: 866-809-6130
Fax: (940)898-3198
E-mail: admissions@twu.edu
Web Site: www.twu.edu
President/CEO: Carine M. Feyton
Admissions: Erma Nieto-Brecht
Financial Aid: Governor Jackson

Type: University **Sex:** Coed **Scores:** 81% SAT V 400+; 86% SAT M 400+; 48.18% ACT 18-23; 20.44% ACT 24-29 **% Accepted:** 75 **Admission Plans:** Deferred Admission; Early Admission; Open Admission; Preferred Admission **Application Deadline:** July 15 **Application Fee:** $50.00 **H.S. Requirements:** High school diploma required; GED accepted **Costs Per Year:** Application fee: $50. State resident tuition: $5950 full-time, $198.32 per credit hour part-time. Nonresident tuition: $17,650 full-time, $588.32 per credit hour part-time. Mandatory fees: $2616 full-time, $77.75 per credit hour part-time, $283 per term part-time. Full-time tuition and fees vary according to course level, course load, program, and reciprocity agreements. Part-time tuition and fees vary according to course level, course load, program, and reciprocity agreements. College room and board: $7443. College room only: $3700.

Room and board charges vary according to board plan and housing facility. **Scholarships:** Available. **Calendar System:** Semester, Summer session available **Enrollment:** Full-time 6,941, Graduate full-time 1,936, Graduate part-time 3,270, Part-time 3,139 **Faculty:** Full-time 483, Part-time 398 **Student-Faculty Ratio:** 19:1 **Exams:** ACT essay component not used; SAT I or ACT; SAT essay component not used; SAT Reasoning; SAT Subject. **% Receiving Financial Aid:** 71 **% Residing in College-Owned, -Operated, or -Affiliated Housing:** 24 **Final Year or Final Semester Residency Requirement:** Yes **Regional Accreditation:** Southern Association of Colleges and Schools **Credit Hours For Degree:** 120 semester hours, depending on program, Bachelors **ROTC:** Air Force, Army **Professional Accreditation:** AACN, AAFCS, ACA, ACBSP, ADA, ALA, AND, AOTA, APA, APTA, ASHA, CAHME, CSWE, NASD, NASM. **Intercollegiate Athletics:** Basketball W; Gymnastics W; Soccer W; Softball W; Volleyball W

TRINITY UNIVERSITY

One Trinity Pl.
San Antonio, TX 78212-7200
Tel: (210)999-7011; Free: 800-TRINITY
Fax: (210)999-8164
E-mail: admissions@trinity.edu
Web Site: www.trinity.edu
President/CEO: Dr. Danny J. Anderson

Type: Comprehensive **Sex:** Coed **Affiliation:** Presbyterian Church. **Scores:** 100% SAT V 400+; 100% SAT M 400+; 2.57% ACT 18-23; 50.16% ACT 24-29 **% Accepted:** 48 **Admission Plans:** Deferred Admission; Early Action; Early Decision Plan **Application Deadline:** February 1 **Application Fee:** $0.00 **H.S. Requirements:** High school diploma required; GED accepted **Costs Per Year:** Application fee: $0. Comprehensive fee: $50,218 includes full-time tuition ($37,296), mandatory fees ($560), and college room and board ($12,362). College room only: $7972. Full-time tuition and fees vary according to course load. Room and board charges vary according to board plan. Part-time tuition: $1554 per credit hour. Part-time mandatory fees: $12.50 per credit hour. Part-time tuition and fees vary according to course load. **Scholarships:** Available. **Calendar System:** Semester, Summer session available **Enrollment:** Full-time 2,228, Part-time 45 **Faculty:** Full-time 234, Part-time 77 **Student-Faculty Ratio:** 9:1 **Exams:** ACT essay component not used; SAT I or ACT; SAT essay component not used; SAT Reasoning. **% Receiving Financial Aid:** 41 **% Residing in College-Owned, -Operated, or -Affiliated Housing:** 77 **Final Year or Final Semester Residency Requirement:** Yes **Regional Accreditation:** Southern Association of Colleges and Schools **Credit Hours For Degree:** 124 semester hours, Bachelors **ROTC:** Air Force, Army **Professional Accreditation:** AACSB, ABET, CAHME, NCATE. **Intercollegiate Athletics:** Baseball M; Basketball M & W; Cross-Country Running M & W; Fencing M & W; Football M; Golf M & W; Lacrosse M & W; Riflery M & W; Soccer M & W; Softball W; Swimming and Diving M & W; Tennis M & W; Track and Field M & W; Volleyball M & W; Water Polo M & W

TRINITY VALLEY COMMUNITY COLLEGE

100 Cardinal Dr.
Athens, TX 75751-2765
Tel: (903)677-TVCC
Web Site: www.tvcc.edu
President/CEO: Dr. Glendon Forgey
Admissions: Dr. Colette Hilliard
Financial Aid: RaDonna Womack

Type: Two-Year College **Sex:** Coed **Admission Plans:** Early Admission; Open Admission **Application Deadline:** Rolling **H.S. Requirements:** High school diploma required; GED accepted **Costs Per Year:** Area resident tuition: $2340 full-time, $34 per semester hour part-time. State resident tuition: $4110 full-time, $93 per semester hour part-time. Nonresident tuition: $4680 full-time, $112 per semester hour part-time. Mandatory fees: $44 per semester hour part-time. Full-time tuition varies according to course load. Part-time tuition and fees vary according to course load. College room and board: $5580. Room and board charges vary according to board plan. **Scholarships:** Available. **Calendar System:** Semester, Summer session available **Enrollment:** Full-time 2,685, Part-time 2,487 **Faculty:** Full-time 145, Part-time 132 **Student-Faculty Ratio:** 16:1 **% Residing in College-Owned, -Operated, or -Affiliated Housing:** 14 **Regional Accreditation:** Southern Association of Colleges and Schools **Credit Hours For Degree:** 64 semester hours, Associates **Professional Accreditation:** ACEN, ARCST. **Intercollegiate Athletics:** Basketball M & W; Cheerleading M & W; Football M; Softball W; Volleyball W

TYLER JUNIOR COLLEGE

PO Box 9020
Tyler, TX 75711-9020
Tel: (903)510-2200; Free: 800-687-5680
E-mail: jcha@tjc.edu
Web Site: www.tjc.edu
President/CEO: Dr. Mike Metke
Admissions: Janna Chancey

Type: Two-Year College **Sex:** Coed **% Accepted:** 100 **Admission Plans:** Early Admission; Open Admission; Preferred Admission **Application Deadline:** Rolling **Application Fee:** $0.00 **H.S. Requirements:** High school diploma required; GED accepted. For allied health programs: High school diploma required; GED not accepted **Costs Per Year:** Application fee: $0. Area resident tuition: $900 full-time, $30 per credit hour part-time. State resident tuition: $2310 full-time, $77 per credit hour part-time. Nonresident tuition: $2910 full-time, $97 per credit hour part-time. Mandatory fees: $1602 full-time, $7 per credit hour part-time, $100 per term part-time. College room and board: $8320. College room only: $5940. Room and board charges vary according to housing facility. **Scholarships:** Available. **Calendar System:** Semester, Summer session available **Enrollment:** Full-time 6,007, Part-time 4,927 **Faculty:** Full-time 303, Part-time 250 **Student-Faculty Ratio:** 20:1 **Exams:** Other. **% Residing in College-Owned, -Operated, or -Affiliated Housing:** 10 **Regional Accreditation:** Southern Association of Colleges and Schools **Credit Hours For Degree:** 60 semester hours, Associates **Professional Accreditation:** ADA, AHIMA, ARCST, COA, CoARC, JRCEDMS, JRCERT, NAACLS. **Intercollegiate Athletics:** Baseball M; Basketball M & W; Cheerleading W; Football M; Golf M & W; Soccer M & W; Softball W; Tennis M & W; Volleyball W

UNIVERSITY OF DALLAS

1845 E Northgate Dr.
Irving, TX 75062-4736
Tel: (972)721-5000; Free: 800-628-6999
Fax: (972)721-5017
E-mail: ugadmis@udallas.edu
Web Site: www.udallas.edu
President/CEO: Thomas W. Keefe, JD
Admissions: Elizabeth Griffin-Smith
Financial Aid: Taryn Anderson

Type: University **Sex:** Coed **Affiliation:** Roman Catholic. **Scores:** 100% SAT V 400+; 100% SAT M 400+; 20.83% ACT 18-23; 47.69% ACT 24-29 **% Accepted:** 64 **Admission Plans:** Deferred Admission; Early Decision Plan **Application Deadline:** March 1 **Application Fee:** $50.00 **H.S. Requirements:** High school diploma required; GED accepted **Costs Per Year:** Application fee: $50. Comprehensive fee: $48,770 includes full-time tuition ($34,650), mandatory fees ($2580), and college room and board ($11,540). College room only: $6450. Full-time tuition and fees vary according to course load. Room and board charges vary according to board plan and housing facility. Part-time mandatory fees: $2580 per year. Part-time fees vary according to course load. **Scholarships:** Available. **Calendar System:** Semester, Summer session available **Enrollment:** Full-time 1,315, Graduate full-time 326, Graduate part-time 719, Part-time 27 **Faculty:** Full-time 143, Part-time 84 **Student-Faculty Ratio:** 10:1 **Exams:** ACT essay component used for admission; SAT I or ACT; SAT essay component used for admission; SAT Reasoning. **% Receiving Financial Aid:** 62 **% Residing in College-Owned, -Operated, or -Affiliated Housing:** 68 **Final Year or Final Semester Residency Requirement:** No **Regional Accreditation:** Southern Association of Colleges and Schools **Credit Hours For Degree:** 120 credits, Bachelors **ROTC:** Air Force, Army **Professional Accreditation:** AALE, ACBSP. **Intercollegiate Athletics:** Baseball M; Basketball M & W; Cross-Country Running M & W; Golf M; Lacrosse M & W; Soccer M & W; Softball W; Track and Field M & W; Volleyball W

UNIVERSITY OF HOUSTON

4800 Calhoun Rd.
Houston, TX 77204
Tel: (713)743-1000
Fax: (713)743-9633
E-mail: jdfuller@central.uh.edu
Web Site: www.uh.edu
President/CEO: Dr. Renu Khator
Admissions: Jeff Fuller

Type: University **Sex:** Coed **Affiliation:** University of Houston System. **Scores:** 98% SAT V 400+; 99% SAT M 400+; 31.2% ACT 18-23; 50.58%

ACT 24-29 **% Accepted:** 60 **Application Deadline:** July 1 **Application Fee:** $50.00 **H.S. Requirements:** High school diploma required; GED accepted **Costs Per Year:** Application fee: $50. State resident tuition: $9756 full-time, $325 per credit hour part-time. Nonresident tuition: $24,456 full-time, $815 per credit hour part-time. Mandatory fees: $954 full-time. Full-time tuition and fees vary according to course level, course load, degree level, program, and student level. Part-time tuition varies according to course level, course load, degree level, program, and student level. College room and board: $9849. Room and board charges vary according to board plan and housing facility. Tuition guaranteed not to increase for student's term of enrollment. **Scholarships:** Available. **Calendar System:** Semester, Summer session available **Enrollment:** Full-time 24,909, Graduate full-time 5,872, Graduate part-time 2,116, Part-time 9,807 **Faculty:** Full-time 1,501, Part-time 765 **Student-Faculty Ratio:** 21:1 **Exams:** SAT I or ACT; SAT Reasoning. **% Receiving Financial Aid:** 59 **% Residing in College-Owned, -Operated, or -Affiliated Housing:** 19 **Final Year or Final Semester Residency Requirement:** Yes **Regional Accreditation:** Southern Association of Colleges and Schools **Credit Hours For Degree:** 120 semester hours, Bachelors **ROTC:** Air Force, Army, Navy **Professional Accreditation:** AACSB, AALS, ABA, ABET, ACPE, AND, AOA, APA, ASHA, CSWE, NAAB, NASM, NCATE. **Intercollegiate Athletics:** Baseball M; Basketball M & W; Cross-Country Running M & W; Football M; Golf M & W; Soccer W; Softball W; Swimming and Diving W; Tennis W; Track and Field M & W; Volleyball W

UNIVERSITY OF HOUSTON–CLEAR LAKE

2700 Bay Area Blvd.
Houston, TX 77058-1002
Tel: (281)283-7600
Fax: (281)283-2530
E-mail: admissions@uhcl.edu
Web Site: www.uhcl.edu
President/CEO: Dr. William Staples
Admissions: Rauchelle Jones
Financial Aid: Dr. Billy Satterfield

Type: Comprehensive **Sex:** Coed **Affiliation:** University of Houston System. **Scores:** 96% SAT V 400+; 98% SAT M 400+; 66% ACT 18-23; 21% ACT 24-29 **% Accepted:** 66 **Admission Plans:** Deferred Admission; Early Admission **Application Deadline:** June 1 **Application Fee:** $45.00 **H.S. Requirements:** High school diploma required; GED accepted **Costs Per Year:** Application fee: $45. State resident tuition: $6000 full-time, $50 per credit hour part-time. Nonresident tuition: $20,460 full-time, $440 per credit hour part-time. Mandatory fees: $1278 full-time, $468 per term part-time. Full-time tuition and fees vary according to course load, degree level, and program. Part-time tuition and fees vary according to course load, degree level, and program. College room only: $9588. Room charges vary according to housing facility. **Scholarships:** Available. **Calendar System:** Semester, Summer session available **Enrollment:** Full-time 2,628, Graduate full-time 1,936, Graduate part-time 1,543, Part-time 2,799 **Faculty:** Full-time 308, Part-time 253 **Student-Faculty Ratio:** 15:1 **Exams:** SAT I or ACT; SAT Reasoning. **% Receiving Financial Aid:** 34 **% Residing in College-Owned, -Operated, or -Affiliated Housing:** 2 **Final Year or Final Semester Residency Requirement:** Yes **Regional Accreditation:** Southern Association of Colleges and Schools **Credit Hours For Degree:** NA, Associates; 120 semester hours, Bachelors **Professional Accreditation:** AACSB, AAMFT, ABET, CAHME, NCATE.

UNIVERSITY OF HOUSTON–DOWNTOWN

One Main St.
Houston, TX 77002
Tel: (713)221-8000
Fax: (713)221-8157
E-mail: uhdadmit@uhd.edu
Web Site: www.uhd.edu
President/CEO: Dr. William V. Flores
Admissions: Kecia Osbourne

Type: Comprehensive **Sex:** Coed **Affiliation:** University of Houston System. **Scores:** 74% SAT V 400+; 87% SAT M 400+; 55.88% ACT 18-23; 2.45% ACT 24-29 **% Accepted:** 78 **Application Fee:** $35.00 **H.S. Requirements:** High school diploma required; GED accepted **Costs Per Year:** Application fee: $35. State resident tuition: $5790 full-time, $193 per credit hour part-time. Nonresident tuition: $17,490 full-time, $583 per credit hour part-time. Mandatory fees: $1148 full-time. Full-time tuition and fees vary according to course load and program. Part-time tuition varies according to course load and program. **Scholarships:** Available. **Calendar System:** Semester, Sum-

mer session available **Enrollment:** Full-time 6,643, Graduate full-time 53, Graduate part-time 964, Part-time 6,602 **Faculty:** Full-time 352, Part-time 365 **Student-Faculty Ratio:** 20:1 **Exams:** ACT essay component not used; SAT I or ACT; SAT essay component not used; SAT Reasoning. **% Receiving Financial Aid:** 70 **Final Year or Final Semester Residency Requirement:** Yes **Regional Accreditation:** Southern Association of Colleges and Schools **Credit Hours For Degree:** 120 credit hours, Bachelors **ROTC:** Air Force, Army **Professional Accreditation:** AACSB, ABET.

UNIVERSITY OF HOUSTON–VICTORIA

3007 N Ben Wilson St.
Victoria, TX 77901-4450
Tel: (361)570-4848; Free: 877-970-4848
Fax: (361)572-9377
E-mail: worthamt@uhv.edu
Web Site: www.uhv.edu
President/CEO: Dr. Vic Morgan
Admissions: Trudy Wortham
Financial Aid: Carolyn Mallory

Type: Two-Year Upper Division **Sex:** Coed **Affiliation:** University of Houston System. **Scores:** 66% SAT V 400+; 72% SAT M 400+; 46% ACT 18-23; 6% ACT 24-29 **% Accepted:** 56 **Admission Plans:** Deferred Admission **Application Deadline:** Rolling **Application Fee:** $0.00 **H.S. Requirements:** High school diploma required; GED accepted **Costs Per Year:** Application fee: $0. State resident tuition: $5484 full-time, $183 per credit hour part-time. Nonresident tuition: $17,184 full-time, $573 per credit hour part-time. Mandatory fees: $1602 full-time, $77 per credit hour part-time. Full-time tuition and fees vary according to course level and course load. Part-time tuition and fees vary according to course level and course load. College room and board: $7664. Room and board charges vary according to board plan and housing facility. Tuition guaranteed not to increase for student's term of enrollment. **Scholarships:** Available. **Calendar System:** Semester **Enrollment:** Full-time 1,541, Graduate full-time 377, Graduate part-time 1,018, Part-time 1,471 **Faculty:** Full-time 136, Part-time 103 **Student-Faculty Ratio:** 18:1 **Exams:** ACT essay component not used; SAT I or ACT; SAT essay component not used. **% Receiving Financial Aid:** 72 **Final Year or Final Semester Residency Requirement:** No **Regional Accreditation:** Southern Association of Colleges and Schools **Credit Hours For Degree:** 120 semester hours, Bachelors **ROTC:** Air Force **Professional Accreditation:** AACN, AACSB, TEAC. **Intercollegiate Athletics:** Baseball M; Golf M & W; Soccer M & W; Softball W

UNIVERSITY OF THE INCARNATE WORD

4301 Broadway
San Antonio, TX 78209-6397
Tel: (210)829-6000; Free: 800-749-WORD
Fax: (210)829-3921
E-mail: jdlara@uiwtx.edu
Web Site: www.uiw.edu
President/CEO: Dr. Louis J. Agnese, Jr.
Admissions: Javier Lara
Financial Aid: Amy Carcanagues

Type: Comprehensive **Sex:** Coed **Affiliation:** Roman Catholic. **Scores:** 88% SAT V 400+; 90% SAT M 400+; 54% ACT 18-23; 20% ACT 24-29 **% Accepted:** 92 **Admission Plans:** Deferred Admission **Application Deadline:** Rolling **Application Fee:** $20.00 **H.S. Requirements:** High school diploma required; GED accepted **Costs Per Year:** Application fee: $20. Comprehensive fee: $39,598 includes full-time tuition ($25,900), mandatory fees ($1898), and college room and board ($11,800). Full-time tuition and fees vary according to course load, degree level, location, program, and reciprocity agreements. Room and board charges vary according to board plan and housing facility. Part-time tuition: $850 per credit hour. Part-time tuition varies according to course load, degree level, location, program, and reciprocity agreements. **Scholarships:** Available. **Calendar System:** Semester, Summer session available **Enrollment:** Full-time 4,286, Graduate full-time 1,076, Graduate part-time 1,145, Part-time 2,159 **Faculty:** Full-time 286, Part-time 314 **Student-Faculty Ratio:** 13:1 **Exams:** ACT essay component used for placement; SAT I or ACT; SAT essay component used for placement. **% Receiving Financial Aid:** 75 **% Residing in College-Owned, -Operated, or -Affiliated Housing:** 18 **Final Year or Final Semester Residency Requirement:** No **Regional Accreditation:** Southern Association of Colleges and Schools **Credit Hours For Degree:** 64 credit hours, Associates; 120 credit hours, Bachelors **ROTC:** Army **Professional Accreditation:** AACN, ACBSP, ACPE, AND, AOA, CAHME, JRCNMT,

NAST. **Intercollegiate Athletics:** Baseball M; Basketball M & W; Cross-Country Running M & W; Football M; Golf M & W; Soccer M & W; Softball W; Swimming and Diving M & W; Tennis M & W; Track and Field M & W; Volleyball W

UNIVERSITY OF MARY HARDIN-BAYLOR

900 College St.
Belton, TX 76513
Tel: (254)295-8642; Free: 800-727-8642
Fax: (254)295-4535
E-mail: admission@umhb.edu
Web Site: www.umhb.edu
President/CEO: Dr. Randy O'Rear
Admissions: Dr. Brent Burks
Financial Aid: David Orsag

Type: Comprehensive **Sex:** Coed **Affiliation:** Southern Baptist. **Scores:** 97% SAT V 400+; 99% SAT M 400+; 50.17% ACT 18-23; 40.34% ACT 24-29 **% Accepted:** 80 **Admission Plans:** Deferred Admission; Early Admission **Application Deadline:** Rolling **Application Fee:** $35.00 **H.S. Requirements:** High school diploma required; GED accepted **Costs Per Year:** Application fee: $35. Comprehensive fee: $32,180 includes full-time tuition ($22,680), mandatory fees ($2200), and college room and board ($7300). Full-time tuition and fees vary according to course load and degree level. Room and board charges vary according to housing facility. Part-time tuition: $810 per credit hour. Part-time tuition varies according to course load and degree level. **Scholarships:** Available. **Calendar System:** Semester, Summer session available **Enrollment:** Full-time 2,933, Graduate full-time 493, Graduate part-time 184, Part-time 288 **Faculty:** Full-time 167, Part-time 111 **Student-Faculty Ratio:** 19:1 **Exams:** ACT essay component used for advising; ACT essay component used for placement; SAT I or ACT; SAT essay component used for advising; SAT essay component used for placement. **% Receiving Financial Aid:** 78 **% Residing in College-Owned, -Operated, or -Affiliated Housing:** 55 **Final Year or Final Semester Residency Requirement:** No **Regional Accreditation:** Southern Association of Colleges and Schools **Credit Hours For Degree:** 124 semester hours, Bachelors **ROTC:** Air Force, Army **Professional Accreditation:** AACN, CSWE, NASM. **Intercollegiate Athletics:** Baseball M; Basketball M & W; Football M; Golf M & W; Soccer M & W; Softball W; Tennis M & W; Volleyball W

UNIVERSITY OF NORTH TEXAS

1155 Union Cir. No.311425
Denton, TX 76203
Tel: (940)565-2000; Free: 800-868-8211
Fax: (940)565-2408
E-mail: randall.nunn@unt.edu
Web Site: www.unt.edu
President/CEO: Dr. Neal Smatresk
Admissions: Randall Nunn
Financial Aid: Zelma DeLeon

Type: University **Sex:** Coed **Affiliation:** University of North Texas System. **Scores:** 98% SAT V 400+; 99% SAT M 400+; 47.01% ACT 18-23; 39.81% ACT 24-29 **% Accepted:** 70 **Admission Plans:** Deferred Admission; Early Admission **Application Deadline:** August 1 **Application Fee:** $75.00 **H.S. Requirements:** High school diploma required; GED accepted **Costs Per Year:** Application fee: $75. State resident tuition: $7589 full-time, $252.95 per credit hour part-time. Nonresident tuition: $19,289 full-time, $642.95 per credit hour part-time. College room and board: $8199. Room and board charges vary according to board plan and housing facility. Tuition guaranteed not to increase for student's term of enrollment. **Scholarships:** Available. **Calendar System:** Semester, Summer session available **Enrollment:** Full-time 24,957, Graduate full-time 3,101, Graduate part-time 3,571, Part-time 5,546 **Faculty:** Full-time 1,034, Part-time 455 **Student-Faculty Ratio:** 25:1 **Exams:** ACT essay component used for admission; ACT essay component used in place of application essay; SAT I and SAT II or ACT; SAT I or ACT; SAT II; SAT essay component used for admission; SAT essay component used in place of application essay; SAT Reasoning. **% Receiving Financial Aid:** 57 **% Residing in College-Owned, -Operated, or -Affiliated Housing:** 20 **Final Year or Final Semester Residency Requirement:** No **Regional Accreditation:** Southern Association of Colleges and Schools **Credit Hours For Degree:** 120 semester hours, Bachelors **ROTC:** Air Force, Army **Professional Accreditation:** AACSB, AAFCS, ABET, ACA, ACEJMC, ALA, APA, ASHA, CIDA, CORE, CSWE, NASAD, NASM, NASPAA, NCATE, NRPA. **Intercollegiate Athletics:** Archery M & W;

Badminton M & W; Baseball M; Basketball M & W; Bowling M & W; Cross-Country Running M & W; Equestrian Sports M & W; Fencing M & W; Football M; Golf M & W; Ice Hockey M & W; Lacrosse M & W; Racquetball M & W; Rugby M; Sailing M & W; Soccer M & W; Softball M & W; Swimming and Diving M & W; Table Tennis M & W; Tennis M & W; Track and Field M & W; Ultimate Frisbee M & W; Volleyball M & W; Wrestling M & W

UNIVERSITY OF NORTH TEXAS AT DALLAS

7300 University Hills Blvd.
Dallas, TX 75241
Tel: (972)780-3600
E-mail: admissions@untdallas.edu
Web Site: untdallas.edu
President/CEO: Bob Mong
Admissions: Jason Faulk

Type: Comprehensive **Sex:** Coed **Affiliation:** University of North Texas System. **Scores:** 82% SAT V 400+; 57% ACT 18-23; 5% ACT 24-29 **% Accepted:** 58 **Application Deadline:** August 10 **Application Fee:** $40.00 **H.S. Requirements:** High school diploma required; GED accepted **Costs Per Year:** Application fee: $40. State resident tuition: $7548 full-time. Nonresident tuition: $19,788 full-time. Mandatory fees: $300 full-time. College room and board: $7592. Tuition guaranteed not to increase for student's term of enrollment. **Enrollment:** Full-time 1,127, Graduate full-time 300, Graduate part-time 236, Part-time 825 **Faculty:** Full-time 94, Part-time 73 **Student-Faculty Ratio:** 15:1 **Exams:** SAT I or ACT. **Regional Accreditation:** Southern Association of Colleges and Schools **Credit Hours For Degree:** 120, Bachelors

UNIVERSITY OF PHOENIX–DALLAS CAMPUS

12400 Coit Rd.
Dallas, TX 75251
Tel: (972)385-1055; Free: 866-766-0766
Fax: (972)385-1700
Web Site: www.phoenix.edu
President/CEO: Timothy P. Slottow
Admissions: Marc Booker

Type: Comprehensive **Sex:** Coed **Admission Plans:** Deferred Admission; Open Admission **Application Deadline:** Rolling **Application Fee:** $0.00 **H.S. Requirements:** High school diploma required; GED accepted **Scholarships:** Available. **Calendar System:** Continuous, Summer session not available **Enrollment:** Full-time 1,075 **Faculty:** Full-time 15, Part-time 166 **Regional Accreditation:** North Central Association of Colleges and Schools **Credit Hours For Degree:** 60 credits, Associates; 120 credits, Bachelors **Professional Accreditation:** ACBSP.

UNIVERSITY OF PHOENIX–HOUSTON CAMPUS

11451 Katy Fwy.
Ste. 100
Houston, TX 77079-2004
Tel: (281)596-0363; Free: 866-766-0766
Fax: (281)596-0336
Web Site: www.phoenix.edu
President/CEO: Timothy P. Slottow
Admissions: Marc Booker

Type: Comprehensive **Sex:** Coed **Admission Plans:** Deferred Admission; Open Admission **Application Deadline:** Rolling **Application Fee:** $0.00 **H.S. Requirements:** High school diploma required; GED accepted **Scholarships:** Available. **Calendar System:** Continuous, Summer session not available **Enrollment:** Full-time 2,286 **Faculty:** Full-time 16, Part-time 309 **Regional Accreditation:** North Central Association of Colleges and Schools **Credit Hours For Degree:** 60 credits, Associates; 120 credits, Bachelors **Professional Accreditation:** ACBSP.

UNIVERSITY OF PHOENIX–SAN ANTONIO CAMPUS

8200 IH-10 W
San Antonio, TX 78230
Tel: (210)524-2100; Free: 866-766-0766
Web Site: www.phoenix.edu
President/CEO: Timothy P. Slottow

Type: Comprehensive **Sex:** Coed **Regional Accreditation:** North Central Association of Colleges and Schools **Professional Accreditation:** ACBSP.

UNIVERSITY OF ST. THOMAS

3800 Montrose Blvd.
Houston, TX 77006-4696
Tel: (713)522-7911; Free: 800-856-8565
Fax: (713)525-3558
E-mail: admissions@stthom.edu
Web Site: www.stthom.edu
President/CEO: Dr. Robert Ivany
Admissions: Arthur Ortiz
Financial Aid: Lynda McKendree
Type: Comprehensive **Sex:** Coed **Affiliation:** Roman Catholic. **Scores:** 98% SAT V 400+; 100% SAT M 400+; 41.27% ACT 18-23; 47.62% ACT 24-29 **% Accepted:** 79 **Admission Plans:** Deferred Admission; Early Decision Plan **Application Deadline:** May 1 **H.S. Requirements:** High school diploma required; GED accepted **Costs Per Year:** Comprehensive fee: $40,020 includes full-time tuition ($31,140), mandatory fees ($380), and college room and board ($8500). College room only: $5150. Full-time tuition and fees vary according to course load. Room and board charges vary according to board plan and housing facility. Part-time tuition: $1038 per credit hour. Part-time tuition varies according to course load. **Scholarships:** Available. **Calendar System:** Semester, Summer session available **Enrollment:** Full-time 1,362, Graduate full-time 315, Graduate part-time 1,291, Part-time 443 **Faculty:** Full-time 192, Part-time 164 **Student-Faculty Ratio:** 9:1 **Exams:** ACT essay component used for admission; ACT essay component used for placement; SAT I or ACT; SAT essay component used for admission; SAT essay component used for placement; SAT Reasoning; SAT Subject. **% Receiving Financial Aid:** 57 **% Residing in College-Owned, -Operated, or -Affiliated Housing:** 14 **Final Year or Final Semester Residency Requirement:** Yes **Regional Accreditation:** Southern Association of Colleges and Schools **Credit Hours For Degree:** 126 credit hours, Bachelors **ROTC:** Air Force, Army **Professional Accreditation:** AACSB, ACBSP, ACIPE, ATS, TEAC. **Intercollegiate Athletics:** Basketball M & W; Cheerleading M & W; Fencing M & W; Golf M & W; Soccer M & W; Tennis M & W; Track and Field M & W; Volleyball W

THE UNIVERSITY OF TEXAS AT ARLINGTON

701 S Nedderman Dr.
Arlington, TX 76019
Tel: (817)272-2011
Fax: (817)272-5656
Web Site: www.uta.edu
President/CEO: Dr. Vistasp M. Karbhari
Admissions: Dr. Hans Gatterdam
Financial Aid: Karen Krause
Type: University **Sex:** Coed **Affiliation:** University of Texas System. **Scores:** 78% SAT V 400+; 98% SAT M 400+; 45% ACT 18-23; 37% ACT 24-29 **% Accepted:** 61 **Admission Plans:** Deferred Admission **Application Deadline:** June 1 **Application Fee:** $60.00 **H.S. Requirements:** High school diploma required; GED accepted **Costs Per Year:** Application fee: $60. State resident tuition: $6758 full-time. Nonresident tuition: $21,114 full-time. Mandatory fees: $2120 full-time. Full-time tuition and fees vary according to course load, degree level, and program. College room and board: $8398. Room and board charges vary according to board plan and housing facility. Tuition guaranteed not to increase for student's term of enrollment. **Scholarships:** Available. **Calendar System:** Miscellaneous, Summer session available **Enrollment:** Full-time 15,957, Graduate full-time 3,984, Graduate part-time 5,873, Part-time 13,926 **Exams:** ACT essay component not used; ACT essay component used for admission; SAT I or ACT; SAT essay component not used; SAT essay component used for admission; SAT Reasoning. **% Receiving Financial Aid:** 70 **% Residing in College-Owned, -Operated, or -Affiliated Housing:** 13 **Final Year or Final Semester Residency Requirement:** No **Regional Accreditation:** Southern Association of Colleges and Schools **Credit Hours For Degree:** 120 semester hours, Bachelors **ROTC:** Air Force, Army **Professional Accreditation:** AACN, AACSB, ABET, ACSP, ASLA, CIDA, CSWE, NAAB, NASAD, NASM, NASPAA, NCATE. **Intercollegiate Athletics:** Baseball M; Basketball M & W; Cross-Country Running M & W; Golf M; Softball W; Tennis M & W; Track and Field M & W; Volleyball W

THE UNIVERSITY OF TEXAS AT AUSTIN

Austin, TX 78712-1111
Tel: (512)471-3434
Fax: (512)475-7475
E-mail: bencorpus@utexas.edu
Web Site: www.utexas.edu
President/CEO: Gregory L. Fenves
Admissions: Ben Corpus
Financial Aid: Dr. Tom Melecki
Type: University **Sex:** Coed **Affiliation:** University of Texas System. **Scores:** 99% SAT V 400+; 100% SAT M 400+; 9.7% ACT 18-23; 38% ACT 24-29 **Costs Per Year:** State resident tuition: $9810 full-time. Nonresident tuition: $34,806 full-time. Full-time tuition varies according to course load and program. College room and board: $11,456. Room and board charges vary according to housing facility. Tuition guaranteed not to increase for student's term of enrollment. **Scholarships:** Available. **Calendar System:** Semester, Summer session available **Enrollment:** Full-time 36,565, Graduate full-time 10,442, Graduate part-time 889, Part-time 3,054 **Faculty:** Full-time 2,729, Part-time 315 **Student-Faculty Ratio:** 18:1 **Exams:** ACT essay component used for admission; ACT essay component used for placement; SAT I or ACT; SAT essay component used for admission; SAT essay component used for placement. **% Receiving Financial Aid:** 42 **% Residing in College-Owned, -Operated, or -Affiliated Housing:** 19 **Final Year or Final Semester Residency Requirement:** Yes **Regional Accreditation:** Southern Association of Colleges and Schools **Credit Hours For Degree:** 120 semester hours, depending on program, Bachelors **ROTC:** Air Force, Army, Navy **Professional Accreditation:** AACN, AACSB, AALS, ABA, ABET, ACEJMC, ACPE, ACSP, ALA, AND, APA, ASHA, ASLA, CIDA, CORE, CSWE, NAAB, NASAD, NASD, NASM, NASPAA, NAST. **Intercollegiate Athletics:** Archery M & W; Badminton M & W; Baseball M & W; Basketball M & W; Crew M & W; Cross-Country Running M & W; Fencing M & W; Football M; Golf M & W; Gymnastics M & W; Ice Hockey M & W; Lacrosse M & W; Racquetball M & W; Rock Climbing M & W; Rugby M & W; Sailing M & W; Soccer M & W; Softball W; Swimming and Diving M & W; Table Tennis M & W; Tennis M & W; Track and Field M & W; Ultimate Frisbee M & W; Volleyball M & W; Water Polo M & W; Weight Lifting M & W; Wrestling M & W

THE UNIVERSITY OF TEXAS AT DALLAS

800 W Campbell Rd.
Richardson, TX 75080
Tel: (972)883-2111; Free: 800-889-2443
Fax: (972)883-6803
E-mail: interest@utdallas.edu
Web Site: www.utdallas.edu
President/CEO: Dr. B. Hobson Wildenthal
Financial Aid: M. Beth N. Tolan
Type: University **Sex:** Coed **Affiliation:** University of Texas System. **Scores:** 99% SAT V 400+; 100% SAT M 400+; 11% ACT 18-23; 51% ACT 24-29 **% Accepted:** 61 **Admission Plans:** Deferred Admission **Application Deadline:** July 1 **Application Fee:** $50.00 **H.S. Requirements:** High school diploma required; GED accepted **Costs Per Year:** Application fee: $50. State resident tuition: $11,806 full-time, $393.53 per credit hour part-time. Nonresident tuition: $31,328 full-time, $1,044.27 per credit hour part-time. Full-time tuition varies according to course load and degree level. Part-time tuition varies according to course load and degree level. College room and board: $9944. Room and board charges vary according to board plan and housing facility. Tuition guaranteed not to increase for student's term of enrollment. **Scholarships:** Available. **Calendar System:** Semester, Summer session available **Enrollment:** Full-time 12,754, Graduate full-time 6,143, Graduate part-time 2,836, Part-time 2,821 **Faculty:** Full-time 854, Part-time 344 **Student-Faculty Ratio:** 21:1 **Exams:** Other; SAT I or ACT; SAT Reasoning; SAT Subject. **% Receiving Financial Aid:** 53 **% Residing in College-Owned, -Operated, or -Affiliated Housing:** 27 **Final Year or Final Semester Residency Requirement:** Yes **Regional Accreditation:** Southern Association of Colleges and Schools **Credit Hours For Degree:** 120 semester hours, Bachelors **ROTC:** Air Force, Army **Professional Accreditation:** AACSB, ABET, ASHA, NASPAA. **Intercollegiate Athletics:** Baseball M; Basketball M & W; Cross-Country Running M & W; Golf M & W; Soccer M & W; Softball W; Tennis M & W; Volleyball W

THE UNIVERSITY OF TEXAS AT EL PASO

500 W University Ave.
El Paso, TX 79968-0001
Tel: (915)747-5000; Free: 877-74MINER
Fax: (915)747-5122
E-mail: futureminer@utep.edu
Web Site: www.utep.edu
President/CEO: Dr. Diana Natalicio
Admissions: Michael J. Talamantes

Financial Aid: Ron Williams

Type: University **Sex:** Coed **Affiliation:** University of Texas System. **Scores:** 74% SAT V 400+; 86% SAT M 400+; 55.34% ACT 18-23; 15.29% ACT 24-29 **% Accepted:** 100 **Admission Plans:** Deferred Admission **Application Fee:** $40.00 **H.S. Requirements:** High school diploma required; GED accepted **Costs Per Year:** Application fee: $40. State resident tuition: $5606 full-time, $187 per credit hour part-time. Nonresident tuition: $17,456 full-time, $556 per credit hour part-time. Mandatory fees: $1653 full-time. **Scholarships:** Available. **Calendar System:** Semester, Summer session available **Enrollment:** Full-time 13,079, Graduate full-time 1,281, Graduate part-time 1,896, Part-time 7,141 **Faculty:** Full-time 743, Part-time 517 **Student-Faculty Ratio:** 21:1 **Exams:** SAT I or ACT; SAT essay component not used. **% Receiving Financial Aid:** 77 **Regional Accreditation:** Southern Association of Colleges and Schools **Credit Hours For Degree:** 120 semester credit hours, Bachelors **Professional Accreditation:** AACN, AACSB, ABET, ACNM, AOTA, APTA, ASHA, CORE, CSWE, NAACLS, NASM, NASPAA. **Intercollegiate Athletics:** Basketball M & W; Cross-Country Running M & W; Football M; Golf M; Riflery M & W; Tennis W; Track and Field M & W; Volleyball W

THE UNIVERSITY OF TEXAS HEALTH SCIENCE CENTER AT HOUSTON
PO Box 20036
Houston, TX 77225-0036
Tel: (713)500-3333
Fax: (713)500-3026
E-mail: registrar@uth.tmc.edu
Web Site: www.uthouston.edu
President/CEO: Giuseppe N. Colasurdo, MD
Admissions: Robert Jenkins
Financial Aid: Araceli Alvarez

Type: Two-Year Upper Division **Sex:** Coed **Affiliation:** University of Texas System. **Admission Plans:** Preferred Admission **Application Fee:** $60.00 **H.S. Requirements:** High school diploma required; GED accepted **Costs Per Year:** Application fee: $60. State resident tuition: $5700 full-time. Nonresident tuition: $23,250 full-time. Mandatory fees: $1734 full-time. Full-time tuition and fees vary according to course load. **Scholarships:** Available. **Calendar System:** Semester, Summer session available **Enrollment:** Full-time 534, Graduate full-time 2,742, Graduate part-time 1,392, Part-time 143 **Faculty:** Full-time 84, Part-time 44 **Student-Faculty Ratio:** 9:1 **Exams:** Other. **% Receiving Financial Aid:** 96 **Regional Accreditation:** Southern Association of Colleges and Schools **Credit Hours For Degree:** 125 semester hours, Bachelors **ROTC:** Army **Professional Accreditation:** AACN, AANA, ABET, ACEN, ACIPE, ADA, AND, APA, ASC, CEPH, JRCERT, LCME/AMA, NAACLS.

THE UNIVERSITY OF TEXAS HEALTH SCIENCE CENTER AT SAN ANTONIO
7703 Floyd Curl Dr.
San Antonio, TX 78229-3900
Tel: (210)567-7000
Fax: (210)567-2685
Web Site: www.uthscsa.edu
President/CEO: William L. Henrich, MD
Financial Aid: Robert T. Lawson

Type: Two-Year Upper Division **Sex:** Coed **Affiliation:** University of Texas System. **Application Fee:** $45.00 **H.S. Requirements:** High school diploma required; GED accepted **Scholarships:** Available. **Calendar System:** Semester, Summer session available **Student-Faculty Ratio:** 3:1 **Regional Accreditation:** Southern Association of Colleges and Schools **Credit Hours For Degree:** 120 semester hours, Bachelors **ROTC:** Air Force, Army **Professional Accreditation:** AABB, AACN, ADA, AOTA, APA, APTA, CoARC, JRCEMTP, LCME/AMA, NAACLS.

THE UNIVERSITY OF TEXAS MD ANDERSON CANCER CENTER
1515 Holcombe Blvd.
Houston, TX 77030
Tel: (713)792-2121
Web Site: www.mdanderson.org/education-and-research
Type: Two-Year Upper Division **Sex:** Coed **Regional Accreditation:** Southern Association of Colleges and Schools

THE UNIVERSITY OF TEXAS MEDICAL BRANCH
301 University Blvd.
Galveston, TX 77555

Tel: (409)772-1011
Fax: (409)772-5056
E-mail: enrollment.services@utmb.edu
Web Site: www.utmb.edu
President/CEO: Dr. David L. Callender
Admissions: Vicki L. Brewer
Financial Aid: Carol A. Cromie

Type: Comprehensive **Sex:** Coed **Affiliation:** University of Texas System. **Admission Plans:** Preferred Admission **Application Fee:** $30.00 **Scholarships:** Available. **Calendar System:** Semester, Summer session available **Enrollment:** Full-time 315, Graduate full-time 1,619, Graduate part-time 319, Part-time 177 **% Receiving Financial Aid:** 68 **Regional Accreditation:** Southern Association of Colleges and Schools **Credit Hours For Degree:** 120 semester hours, Bachelors **Professional Accreditation:** AACN, ACEN, ACNM, AOTA, APA, APTA, CEPH, CoARC, LCME/AMA, NAACLS. **Intercollegiate Athletics:** Ultimate Frisbee M & W; Volleyball M & W

THE UNIVERSITY OF TEXAS OF THE PERMIAN BASIN
4901 E University Blvd.
Odessa, TX 79762-0001
Tel: (432)552-2020; Free: 866-552-UTPB
Fax: (432)552-2109
E-mail: admissions@utpb.edu
Web Site: www.utpb.edu
President/CEO: Dr. W. David Watts
Admissions: Scott Smiley
Financial Aid: Charles Edward Kerestly

Type: Comprehensive **Sex:** Coed **Affiliation:** The University of Texas System. **Scores:** 85% SAT V 400+; 94% SAT M 400+; 60% ACT 18-23; 14% ACT 24-29 **% Accepted:** 84 **Application Deadline:** August 26 **Application Fee:** $0.00 **H.S. Requirements:** High school diploma required; GED accepted **Costs Per Year:** Application fee: $0. State resident tuition: $5036 full-time, $167.88 per credit hour part-time. Nonresident tuition: $6086 full-time, $202.88 per credit hour part-time. Mandatory fees: $1422 full-time, $68.22 per credit hour part-time. Full-time tuition and fees vary according to course load, degree level, and location. Part-time tuition and fees vary according to course load, degree level, and location. College room and board: $8904. College room only: $5640. Room and board charges vary according to board plan and housing facility. Tuition guaranteed not to increase for student's term of enrollment. **Scholarships:** Available. **Calendar System:** Semester, Summer session available **Enrollment:** Full-time 2,138, Graduate full-time 188, Graduate part-time 585, Part-time 3,026 **Faculty:** Full-time 134, Part-time 117 **Student-Faculty Ratio:** 24:1 **Exams:** SAT I or ACT. **% Receiving Financial Aid:** 61 **% Residing in College-Owned, -Operated, or -Affiliated Housing:** 22 **Final Year or Final Semester Residency Requirement:** No **Regional Accreditation:** Southern Association of Colleges and Schools **Credit Hours For Degree:** 120 semester hours, Bachelors **Professional Accreditation:** AACSB, NASAD, NCATE. **Intercollegiate Athletics:** Baseball M; Basketball M & W; Cheerleading M & W; Cross-Country Running M & W; Soccer M & W; Softball W; Swimming and Diving M & W; Tennis M & W; Volleyball W

THE UNIVERSITY OF TEXAS RIO GRANDE VALLEY
1201 W University Dr.
Edinburg, TX 78539
Tel: (956)381-2011
E-mail: debbie.gilchrist@utrgv.edu
Web Site: www.utrgv.edu
President/CEO: Dr. Guy Bailey
Admissions: Dr. Debbie Gilchrist
Financial Aid: Elias Ozuna

Type: Comprehensive **Sex:** Coed **Affiliation:** University of Texas System. **Scores:** 81% SAT V 400+; 89% SAT M 400+; 58.4% ACT 18-23; 11.6% ACT 24-29 **% Accepted:** 82 **Application Deadline:** July 1 **Application Fee:** $0.00 **H.S. Requirements:** High school diploma required; GED accepted **Costs Per Year:** Application fee: $0. State resident tuition: $5824 full-time. Nonresident tuition: $15,184 full-time. Mandatory fees: $1468 full-time. Full-time tuition and fees vary according to course load, degree level, program, and student level. College room and board: $7632. College room only: $4692. Room and board charges vary according to board plan, housing facility, and location. Tuition guaranteed not to increase for student's term of enrollment. **Scholarships:** Available. **Calendar System:** Semester, Summer session available **Enrollment:** Full-time 17,642, Graduate full-time

1,173, Graduate part-time 2,474, Part-time 7,295 **Faculty:** Full-time 1,041, Part-time 217 **Exams:** SAT I or ACT; SAT Reasoning. **% Receiving Financial Aid:** 61 **% Residing in College-Owned, -Operated, or -Affiliated Housing:** 4 **Final Year or Final Semester Residency Requirement:** No **Regional Accreditation:** Southern Association of Colleges and Schools **Credit Hours For Degree:** 120 semester hours, Bachelors **ROTC:** Army **Professional Accreditation:** AACN, AACSB, ABET, AND, AOTA, ASHA, CORE, CSWE, NAACLS, NASM, NAST. **Intercollegiate Athletics:** Baseball M; Basketball M & W; Cross-Country Running M & W; Golf M & W; Tennis M & W; Track and Field M & W; Volleyball W

THE UNIVERSITY OF TEXAS AT SAN ANTONIO

One UTSA Cir.
San Antonio, TX 78249-0617
Tel: (210)458-4011; Free: 800-669-0919
E-mail: prospects@utsa.edu
Web Site: www.utsa.edu
President/CEO: Dr. Ricardo Romo
Admissions: Beverly Woodson Day
Financial Aid: Kim Canady

Type: University **Sex:** Coed **Affiliation:** University of Texas System. **Scores:** 93% SAT V 400+; 96% SAT M 400+; 53.27% ACT 18-23; 32.69% ACT 24-29 **% Accepted:** 78 **Application Deadline:** June 1 **Application Fee:** $60.00 **H.S. Requirements:** High school diploma required; GED accepted **Costs Per Year:** Application fee: $60. State resident tuition: $5982 full-time, $199.41 per credit hour part-time. Nonresident tuition: $18,135 full-time, $604.50 per credit hour part-time. Mandatory fees: $2755 full-time. Full-time tuition and fees vary according to course load and degree level. Part-time tuition varies according to course load and degree level. College room and board: $7564. College room only: $4990. Room and board charges vary according to board plan and housing facility. Tuition guaranteed not to increase for student's term of enrollment. **Scholarships:** Available. **Calendar System:** Semester, Summer session available **Enrollment:** Full-time 20,234, Graduate full-time 1,985, Graduate part-time 2,340, Part-time 4,228 **Faculty:** Full-time 908, Part-time 447 **Exams:** SAT I or ACT; SAT Reasoning. **% Receiving Financial Aid:** 65 **% Residing in College-Owned, -Operated, or -Affiliated Housing:** 14 **Final Year or Final Semester Residency Requirement:** No **Regional Accreditation:** Southern Association of Colleges and Schools **Credit Hours For Degree:** 120 semester hours, Bachelors **ROTC:** Air Force, Army **Professional Accreditation:** AACN, AACSB, ABET, ACA, CIDA, CSWE, NASAD, NASM, NASPAA. **Intercollegiate Athletics:** Badminton M & W; Baseball M; Basketball M & W; Cross-Country Running M & W; Fencing M & W; Football M; Golf M & W; Ice Hockey M; Lacrosse M & W; Racquetball M & W; Rock Climbing M & W; Rugby M & W; Soccer M & W; Softball W; Swimming and Diving M & W; Table Tennis M & W; Tennis M & W; Track and Field M & W; Ultimate Frisbee M & W; Volleyball M & W; Weight Lifting M & W

THE UNIVERSITY OF TEXAS AT TYLER

3900 University Blvd.
Tyler, TX 75799-0001
Tel: (903)566-7000; Free: 800-UTTYLER
Fax: (903)566-7068
E-mail: admissions@uttyler.edu
Web Site: www.uttyler.edu
President/CEO: Dr. Rodney H. Mabry
Admissions: Sarah Bowdin
Financial Aid: Candice A. Lindsey

Type: Comprehensive **Sex:** Coed **Affiliation:** University of Texas System. **Scores:** 98% SAT V 400+; 99% SAT M 400+; 60% ACT 18-23; 32% ACT 24-29 **% Accepted:** 64 **Admission Plans:** Deferred Admission **Application Fee:** $40.00 **H.S. Requirements:** High school diploma required; GED accepted **Costs Per Year:** Application fee: $40. State resident tuition: $5370 full-time, $50 per semester hour part-time. Nonresident tuition: $17,294 full-time, $440 per semester hour part-time. Mandatory fees: $1942 full-time. Full-time tuition and fees vary according to course load. Part-time tuition varies according to course load. College room and board: $7312. College room only: $4012. Room and board charges vary according to board plan and housing facility. **Scholarships:** Available. **Calendar System:** Semester **Enrollment:** Full-time 4,569, Graduate full-time 710, Graduate part-time 1,757, Part-time 1,749 **Exams:** SAT I or ACT; SAT essay component not used; SAT Reasoning. **% Receiving Financial Aid:** 73 **% Residing in College-Owned, -Operated, or -Affiliated Housing:** 19 **Regional Accreditation:** Southern Association of Colleges and Schools **Credit Hours**

For Degree: 120 semester hours, Bachelors **Professional Accreditation:** AACN, AACSB, ABET, ATMAE, TEAC. **Intercollegiate Athletics:** Baseball M; Basketball M & W; Cheerleading M & W; Cross-Country Running M & W; Golf M & W; Soccer M & W; Tennis M & W; Track and Field M & W; Volleyball W

VERNON COLLEGE

4400 College Dr.
Vernon, TX 76384-4092
Tel: (940)552-6291
Fax: (940)553-1753
Web Site: www.vernoncollege.edu
President/CEO: Dusty R. Johnston, EdD
Admissions: Joe Hite
Financial Aid: Melissa Elliott

Type: Two-Year College **Sex:** Coed **Admission Plans:** Early Admission; Open Admission **Application Deadline:** Rolling **Application Fee:** $10.00 **H.S. Requirements:** High school diploma required; GED accepted **Scholarships:** Available. **Calendar System:** Semester, Summer session available **Student-Faculty Ratio:** 17:1 **Regional Accreditation:** Southern Association of Colleges and Schools **Credit Hours For Degree:** 60 semester hours, Associates **Professional Accreditation:** AHIMA. **Intercollegiate Athletics:** Baseball M; Equestrian Sports M & W; Softball W; Volleyball W

VET TECH INSTITUTE OF HOUSTON

4669 SW Fwy.
Ste. 100
Houston, TX 77027
Tel: (713)629-1500; Free: 800-275-2736
Fax: (713)629-0059
Web Site: houston.vettechinstitute.edu
President/CEO: Elbert Hamilton, Jr.

Type: Two-Year College **Sex:** Coed **% Accepted:** 62 **Calendar System:** Semester **Professional Accreditation:** ACICS.

VICTORIA COLLEGE

2200 E Red River
Victoria, TX 77901-4494
Tel: (361)573-3291; Free: 877-843-4369
Fax: (361)572-3850
E-mail: registrar@victoriacollege.edu
Web Site: www.victoriacollege.edu
President/CEO: Dr. David Hinds
Admissions: Missy Klimitchek

Type: Two-Year College **Sex:** Coed **% Accepted:** 100 **Admission Plans:** Early Admission; Open Admission **Application Deadline:** Rolling **H.S. Requirements:** High school diploma required; GED accepted **Costs Per Year:** Area resident tuition: $1380 full-time, $46 per credit hour part-time. State resident tuition: $2790 full-time, $93 per credit hour part-time. Nonresident tuition: $3390 full-time, $113 per credit hour part-time. Mandatory fees: $1260 full-time, $42 per credit hour part-time. Full-time tuition and fees vary according to program. Part-time tuition and fees vary according to program. **Scholarships:** Available. **Calendar System:** Semester, Summer session available **Enrollment:** Full-time 1,144, Part-time 2,907 **Faculty:** Full-time 89, Part-time 339 **Student-Faculty Ratio:** 11:1 **Regional Accreditation:** Southern Association of Colleges and Schools **Credit Hours For Degree:** 60 semester hours, Associates **Professional Accreditation:** ACEN, CoARC, NAACLS. **Intercollegiate Athletics:** Basketball M & W; Volleyball W

VIRGINIA COLLEGE IN AUSTIN

14200 N Interstate Hwy. 35
Austin, TX 78728
Tel: (512)371-3500
Fax: (512)371-3502
Web Site: www.vc.edu
President/CEO: Harvey Giblin

Type: Two-Year College **Sex:** Coed **Application Fee:** $100.00 **Calendar System:** Quarter **Student-Faculty Ratio:** 16:1 **Professional Accreditation:** ACICS.

VIRGINIA COLLEGE IN LUBBOCK

5005 50th St.
Lubbock, TX 79414

Tel: (806)784-1900
Web Site: www.vc.edu
Type: Two-Year College **Sex:** Coed **Professional Accreditation:** ACICS.

VISTA COLLEGE
6101 Montana Ave.
El Paso, TX 79925
Tel: (915)779-8031; Free: 866-442-4197
Web Site: www.vistacollege.edu
President/CEO: Jim Tolbert
Admissions: Sarah Hernandez
Type: Two-Year College **Sex:** Coed **Admission Plans:** Open Admission **Application Fee:** $100.00 **H.S. Requirements:** High school diploma required; GED accepted **Scholarships:** Available. **Calendar System:** Miscellaneous **Credit Hours For Degree:** 68 units, Associates **Professional Accreditation:** COE.

WADE COLLEGE
INFOMart, 1950 Stemmons Fwy.
Ste. 4080, LB 562
Dallas, TX 75207
Tel: (214)637-3530; Free: 800-624-4850
Fax: (214)637-0827
E-mail: jandalman@wadecollege.edu
Web Site: www.wadecollege.edu
President/CEO: Harry Davros
Admissions: Julia Andalman
Financial Aid: Lisa Hoover
Type: Two-Year College **Sex:** Coed **Admission Plans:** Open Admission **Application Deadline:** Rolling **H.S. Requirements:** High school diploma required; GED accepted **Scholarships:** Available. **Calendar System:** Trimester, Summer session available **Faculty:** Full-time 9, Part-time 9 **Student-Faculty Ratio:** 15:1 **Final Year or Final Semester Residency Requirement:** No **Regional Accreditation:** Southern Association of Colleges and Schools **Credit Hours For Degree:** 63 credits, Associates; 123 credits, Bachelors

WAYLAND BAPTIST UNIVERSITY
1900 W Seventh St.
Plainview, TX 79072-6998
Tel: (806)291-1000; Free: 800-588-1928
Fax: (806)291-1960
E-mail: admityou@wbu.edu
Web Site: www.wbu.edu
President/CEO: Dr. Paul Armes
Admissions: Debbie Stennett
Financial Aid: Karen LaQuey
Type: Comprehensive **Sex:** Coed **Affiliation:** Baptist. **Scores:** 72% SAT V 400+; 78% SAT M 400+; 46% ACT 18-23; 21% ACT 24-29 **% Accepted:** 99 **Application Deadline:** August 1 **Application Fee:** $35.00 **H.S. Requirements:** High school diploma required; GED accepted **Costs Per Year:** Application fee: $35. Comprehensive fee: $23,520 includes full-time tuition ($15,750), mandatory fees ($1080), and college room and board ($6690). College room only: $2638. Full-time tuition and fees vary according to course load and location. Room and board charges vary according to board plan and housing facility. Part-time tuition: $525 per credit hour. Part-time tuition varies according to course load and location. **Scholarships:** Available. **Calendar System:** Semester, Summer session available **Enrollment:** Full-time 1,045, Graduate full-time 75, Graduate part-time 1,327, Part-time 2,776 **Faculty:** Full-time 154, Part-time 423 **Student-Faculty Ratio:** 10:1 **Exams:** SAT I or ACT; SAT Reasoning. **% Receiving Financial Aid:** 65 **% Residing in College-Owned, -Operated, or -Affiliated Housing:** 18 **Regional Accreditation:** Southern Association of Colleges and Schools **Credit Hours For Degree:** 60 semester hours, Associates; 124 semester hours, Bachelors **ROTC:** Air Force, Army **Professional Accreditation:** ACEN, NASM. **Intercollegiate Athletics:** Baseball M; Basketball M & W; Cheerleading M & W; Cross-Country Running M & W; Football M; Golf M & W; Soccer M & W; Track and Field M & W; Volleyball W; Wrestling M & W

WEATHERFORD COLLEGE
225 College Park Dr.
Weatherford, TX 76086
Tel: (817)594-5471; Free: 800-287-5471
Fax: (817)598-6205

E-mail: willingham@wc.edu
Web Site: www.wc.edu
President/CEO: Dr. Joe Birmingham
Admissions: Ralph Willingham
Type: Two-Year College **Sex:** Coed **Admission Plans:** Early Admission; Open Admission **Application Deadline:** Rolling **Application Fee:** $0.00 **H.S. Requirements:** High school diploma required; GED accepted. For some adult applicants: High school diploma or equivalent not required **Costs Per Year:** Application fee: $0. Area resident tuition: $1920 full-time, $80 per semester hour part-time. State resident tuition: $2976 full-time, $124 per semester hour part-time. Nonresident tuition: $4224 full-time, $176 per semester hour part-time. Full-time tuition varies according to course load and program. Part-time tuition varies according to course load and program. College room and board: $6900. College room only: $4530. Room and board charges vary according to board plan. **Scholarships:** Available. **Calendar System:** Semester, Summer session available **Faculty:** Full-time 95, Part-time 125 **Student-Faculty Ratio:** 22:1 **% Residing in College-Owned, -Operated, or -Affiliated Housing:** 7 **Regional Accreditation:** Southern Association of Colleges and Schools **Credit Hours For Degree:** 63 semester hours, Associates **ROTC:** Air Force **Professional Accreditation:** ACEN, CoARC. **Intercollegiate Athletics:** Baseball M; Basketball M & W; Cheerleading M & W; Equestrian Sports M & W; Tennis W

WEST COAST UNIVERSITY
8435 N Stemmons Fwy.
Dallas, TX 75247
Tel: (214)453-4533; Free: 866-508-2684
Web Site: www.westcoastuniversity.edu
Type: Four-Year College **Sex:** Coed **H.S. Requirements:** High school diploma required; GED accepted **Regional Accreditation:** Western Association of Colleges and Schools

WEST TEXAS A&M UNIVERSITY
2501 4th Ave.
Canyon, TX 79016-0001
Tel: (806)651-2000; Free: 800-99-WTAMU
Fax: (806)651-2126
E-mail: kmoore@mail.wtamu.edu
Web Site: www.wtamu.edu
President/CEO: Dr. Patrick O'Brien
Admissions: Kyle Moore
Financial Aid: Marian Giesecke
Type: Comprehensive **Sex:** Coed **Affiliation:** Texas A&M University System. **Scores:** 84% SAT V 400+; 89% SAT M 400+; 59.35% ACT 18-23; 20.32% ACT 24-29 **% Accepted:** 67 **Admission Plans:** Deferred Admission **Application Deadline:** Rolling **Application Fee:** $40.00 **H.S. Requirements:** High school diploma required; GED accepted **Costs Per Year:** Application fee: $40. State resident tuition: $5289 full-time. Nonresident tuition: $6279 full-time. Mandatory fees: $2392 full-time. Full-time tuition and fees vary according to course load, degree level, program, and student level. Tuition guaranteed not to increase for student's term of enrollment. **Scholarships:** Available. **Calendar System:** Semester, Summer session available **Enrollment:** Full-time 5,681, Graduate full-time 690, Graduate part-time 1,522, Part-time 1,598 **Faculty:** Full-time 317, Part-time 107 **Student-Faculty Ratio:** 21:1 **Exams:** SAT I or ACT; SAT Reasoning; SAT Subject. **% Receiving Financial Aid:** 62 **% Residing in College-Owned, -Operated, or -Affiliated Housing:** 26 **Final Year or Final Semester Residency Requirement:** No **Regional Accreditation:** Southern Association of Colleges and Schools **Credit Hours For Degree:** 120 semester hours, Bachelors **Professional Accreditation:** AACN, AACSB, ABET, ASHA, CSWE, NASM. **Intercollegiate Athletics:** Baseball M; Basketball M & W; Bowling M & W; Cross-Country Running M & W; Equestrian Sports M & W; Football M; Golf M & W; Soccer M & W; Softball W; Track and Field M & W; Volleyball W

WESTERN TECHNICAL COLLEGE (EL PASO)
9451 Diana Dr.
El Paso, TX 79930-2610
Tel: (915)566-9621; Free: 800-201-9232
E-mail: lpena@westerntech.edu
Web Site: www.westerntech.edu
President/CEO: Allan Sharpe
Admissions: Laura Pena

Type: Two-Year College **Sex:** Coed **Application Fee:** $100.00 **Scholarships:** Available. **Student-Faculty Ratio:** 12:1 **Professional Accreditation:** ACCSC.

WESTERN TECHNICAL COLLEGE (EL PASO)

9624 Plz. Cir.
El Paso, TX 79927
Tel: (915)532-3737
E-mail: bterrell@wtc-ep.edu
Web Site: www.westerntech.edu
President/CEO: Allan Sharpe
Admissions: Bill Terrell

Type: Two-Year College **Sex:** Coed **Admission Plans:** Deferred Admission; Early Admission; Open Admission **H.S. Requirements:** High school diploma required; GED accepted **Calendar System:** Continuous **Enrollment:** Full-time 600, Part-time 225 **Faculty:** Full-time 98, Part-time 32 **Student-Faculty Ratio:** 18:1 **Professional Accreditation:** ACCSC.

WESTERN TEXAS COLLEGE

6200 College Ave.
Snyder, TX 79549
Tel: (325)573-8511; Free: 888-GO-TO-WTC
E-mail: rramon@wtc.edu
Web Site: www.wtc.edu
President/CEO: Dr. Barbara Beebe
Admissions: Dr. Ralph Ramon
Financial Aid: Greg Torres, Jr.

Type: Two-Year College **Sex:** Coed **% Accepted:** 90 **Admission Plans:** Deferred Admission; Early Admission; Open Admission **Application Deadline:** Rolling **Application Fee:** $0.00 **H.S. Requirements:** High school diploma required; GED accepted **Costs Per Year:** Application fee: $0. Area resident tuition: $2370 full-time, $52 per credit hour part-time. State resident tuition: $3780 full-time, $93 per credit hour part-time. Nonresident tuition: $4890 full-time, $130 per credit hour part-time. Mandatory fees: $450 full-time, $30 per credit hour part-time. Full-time tuition and fees vary according to course load, location, and program. Part-time tuition and fees vary according to course load, location, and program. College room and board: $2550. Room and board charges vary according to housing facility. **Scholarships:** Available. **Calendar System:** Semester, Summer session available **Enrollment:** Full-time 543, Part-time 1,582 **Faculty:** Full-time 37, Part-time 60 **Student-Faculty Ratio:** 19:1 **% Residing in College-Owned, -Operated, or -Affiliated Housing:** 100 **Final Year or Final Semester Residency Requirement:** No **Regional Accreditation:** Southern Association of Colleges and Schools **Credit Hours For Degree:** 60 semester hours, Associates **Intercollegiate Athletics:** Baseball M; Basketball M & W; Cross-Country Running M & W; Golf M & W; Soccer M & W; Softball W; Track and Field M & W; Volleyball W

WHARTON COUNTY JUNIOR COLLEGE

911 Boling Hwy.
Wharton, TX 77488-3298
Tel: (979)532-4560
E-mail: albertb@wcjc.edu
Web Site: www.wcjc.edu
President/CEO: Betty McCrohan
Admissions: Albert Barnes
Financial Aid: Richard Hyde

Type: Two-Year College **Sex:** Coed **Admission Plans:** Open Admission **Application Deadline:** August 14 **Application Fee:** $10.00 **H.S. Requirements:** High school diploma required; GED accepted **Scholarships:** Available. **Calendar System:** Semester, Summer session available **Faculty:** Full-time 136, Part-time 121 **Student-Faculty Ratio:** 22:1 **% Residing in College-Owned, -Operated, or -Affiliated Housing:** 5 **Regional Accreditation:** Southern Association of Colleges and Schools **Credit Hours For Degree:** 62 semester hours, Associates **Professional Accreditation:** ADA, AHIMA, APTA, JRCERT. **Intercollegiate Athletics:** Baseball M; Volleyball W

WILEY COLLEGE

711 Wiley Ave.
Marshall, TX 75670-5199
Tel: (903)927-3300; Free: 800-658-6889
Fax: (903)938-8100
E-mail: ajones@wileyc.edu
Web Site: www.wileyc.edu
President/CEO: Dr. Haywood L. Strickland
Admissions: Alvena Jones
Financial Aid: Alan D. Jackson, Jr.

Type: Four-Year College **Sex:** Coed **Affiliation:** United Methodist Church. **Scores:** 25% SAT V 400+; 50% SAT M 400+ **% Accepted:** 40 **Admission Plans:** Deferred Admission; Early Admission; Open Admission **Application Deadline:** August 1 **Application Fee:** $10.00 **H.S. Requirements:** High school diploma required; GED accepted **Costs Per Year:** Application fee: $10. Comprehensive fee: $18,504 includes full-time tuition ($9518), mandatory fees ($2310), and college room and board ($6676). College room only: $3174. Full-time tuition and fees vary according to course load and program. Room and board charges vary according to board plan and housing facility. Part-time tuition: $318 per credit hour. Part-time tuition varies according to program. **Scholarships:** Available. **Calendar System:** Semester, Summer session available **Enrollment:** Full-time 803, Part-time 122 **Faculty:** Full-time 51, Part-time 29 **Student-Faculty Ratio:** 15:1 **Exams:** Other; SAT I or ACT. **% Receiving Financial Aid:** 88 **% Residing in College-Owned, -Operated, or -Affiliated Housing:** 51 **Regional Accreditation:** Southern Association of Colleges and Schools **Credit Hours For Degree:** 65 credit hours, Associates; 124 credit hours, Bachelors **Professional Accreditation:** ACBSP. **Intercollegiate Athletics:** Baseball M; Basketball M & W; Cheerleading M & W; Track and Field M & W; Volleyball W

AMERITECH COLLEGE
12257 S Business Park Dr.
Ste. 108
Draper, UT 84020-6545
Tel: (801)816-1444
Web Site: www.ameritech.edu
Type: Two-Year College **Sex:** Coed **Professional Accreditation:** ABHES.

ARGOSY UNIVERSITY, SALT LAKE CITY
121 Election Rd., Ste. 300
Draper, UT 84020
Tel: (801)601-5000; Free: 888-639-4756
Web Site: www.argosy.edu/locations/salt-lake-city
President/CEO: Valerie Curry
Type: University **Sex:** Coed **Regional Accreditation:** Western Association of Colleges and Schools **Professional Accreditation:** ACBSP.

BRIGHAM YOUNG UNIVERSITY
Provo, UT 84602-1001
Tel: (801)422-1211
Fax: (801)422-5278
E-mail: admissions@byu.edu
Web Site: www.byu.edu
President/CEO: Cecil O. Samuelson
Admissions: Tom Gourley
Financial Aid: Stephen E. Hill
Type: University **Sex:** Coed **Affiliation:** The Church of Jesus Christ of Latter-day Saints; Church Education System (CES) of The Church of Jesus Christ of Latter-day Saints. **Scores:** 100% SAT V 400+; 100% SAT M 400+; 7% ACT 18-23; 51.71% ACT 24-29 **% Accepted:** 48 **Admission Plans:** Deferred Admission; Early Admission **Application Fee:** $35.00 **H.S. Requirements:** High school diploma required; GED not accepted **Costs Per Year:** Application fee: $35. Comprehensive fee: $12,480 includes full-time tuition ($5150) and college room and board ($7330). Room and board charges vary according to board plan, housing facility, and location. Part-time tuition: $270 per credit hour. Part-time tuition varies according to course load. **Scholarships:** Available. **Calendar System:** Semester **Enrollment:** Full-time 27,339, Graduate full-time 2,003, Graduate part-time 1,245, Part-time 2,882 **Faculty:** Full-time 1,252, Part-time 514 **Student-Faculty Ratio:** 20:1 **Exams:** ACT essay component not used; SAT I and SAT II or ACT; SAT I or ACT; SAT II; SAT essay component not used; SAT Reasoning. **% Receiving Financial Aid:** 47 % **Residing in College-Owned, -Operated, or -Affiliated Housing:** 19 **Final Year or Final Semester Residency Requirement:** No **Credit Hours For Degree:** 120 credits, Bachelors **ROTC:** Air Force, Army **Professional Accreditation:** AACN, AACSB, AALS, AAMFT, ABA, ABET, ACA, ACCE, ACEJMC, AND, APA, ASHA, CSWE, JRCAT, NAACLS, NASAD, NASD, NASM, NASPAA, NAST, NCATE, NCCU, NRPA, TEAC. **Intercollegiate Athletics:** Baseball M; Basketball M & W; Cheerleading M & W; Cross-Country Running M & W; Football M; Golf M & W; Gymnastics W; Lacrosse M; Racquetball M & W; Rugby M; Soccer M & W; Softball W; Swimming and Diving M & W; Tennis M & W; Track and Field M & W; Volleyball M & W

BROADVIEW ENTERTAINMENT ARTS UNIVERSITY
240 E Morris Ave.
Salt Lake City, UT 84115
Tel: (801)300-4300; Free: 877-801-8889
Fax: (801)300-4301
Web Site: www.broadviewuniversity.edu
President/CEO: Mikel Gregory
Type: Four-Year College **Sex:** Coed **Affiliation:** Globe Education Network (GEN). **Admission Plans:** Open Admission **Application Deadline:** Rolling **Application Fee:** $50.00 **H.S. Requirements:** High school diploma required; GED accepted **Scholarships:** Available. **Enrollment:** Full-time 115, Part-time 36 **Faculty:** Full-time 1, Part-time 29 **Exams:** Other. **Final Year or Final Semester Residency Requirement:** No **Credit Hours For Degree:** 90 quarter credits, Associates; 180 quarter credits, Bachelors **Professional Accreditation:** ACICS.

BROADVIEW UNIVERSITY–LAYTON
869 W Hill Field Rd.
Layton, UT 84041
Tel: (801)498-6300; Free: 866-253-7744
Fax: (801)498-6301
Web Site: www.broadviewuniversity.edu
President/CEO: Michael Reeder
Type: Four-Year College **Sex:** Coed **Affiliation:** Globe Education Network (GEN). **Admission Plans:** Open Admission **Application Deadline:** Rolling **Application Fee:** $50.00 **H.S. Requirements:** High school diploma required; GED accepted **Scholarships:** Available. **Enrollment:** Full-time 104, Part-time 59 **Faculty:** Full-time 7, Part-time 21 **Exams:** Other. **Final Year or Final Semester Residency Requirement:** No **Credit Hours For Degree:** 90 quarter credits, Associates; 180 quarter credits, Bachelors **Professional Accreditation:** ACCSC, ACICS.

BROADVIEW UNIVERSITY–WEST JORDAN
1902 W 7800 S
West Jordan, UT 84088
Tel: (801)542-7600; Free: 866-304-4224
Fax: (801)542-7601
Web Site: www.broadviewuniversity.edu
President/CEO: Dee Ann Kerr
Type: Comprehensive **Sex:** Coed **Affiliation:** Globe Education Network (GEN). **Admission Plans:** Open Admission **Application Deadline:** Rolling **Application Fee:** $50.00 **H.S. Requirements:** High school diploma required; GED accepted **Scholarships:** Available. **Calendar System:** Quarter, Summer session available **Enrollment:** Full-time 142, Graduate full-time 5, Graduate part-time 3, Part-time 87 **Faculty:** Full-time 13, Part-time 20 **Exams:** Other. **Final Year or Final Semester Residency Requirement:** No **Credit Hours For Degree:** 90 quarter credits, Associates; 180 quarter credits, Bachelors **Professional Accreditation:** AAMAE, ACCSC, ACICS.

CAREERS UNLIMITED
1176 S 1480 W
Orem, UT 84058
Tel: (801)426-8234
Web Site: www.ucdh.edu
Type: Four-Year College **Sex:** Coed **Professional Accreditation:** ACCSC.

DIXIE STATE UNIVERSITY
225 S 700 E
Saint George, UT 84770-3876

Tel: (435)652-7500
Fax: (435)656-4005
E-mail: ldavenport@dixie.edu
Web Site: www.dixie.edu
President/CEO: Dr. Richard B. Williams
Admissions: Laralee Davenport
Financial Aid: J. D. Robertson
Type: Four-Year College **Sex:** Coed **Affiliation:** Utah System of Higher Education. **Scores:** 81% SAT V 400+; 80% SAT M 400+; 50.1% ACT 18-23; 22.7% ACT 24-29 **% Accepted:** 100 **Admission Plans:** Deferred Admission; Early Admission; Open Admission **Application Deadline:** August 15 **Application Fee:** $35.00 **H.S. Requirements:** High school diploma required; GED accepted **Costs Per Year:** Application fee: $35. State resident tuition: $3908 full-time, $163 per credit hour part-time. Nonresident tuition: $13,206 full-time, $520 per credit hour part-time. Mandatory fees: $712 full-time. Full-time tuition and fees vary according to course load. Part-time tuition varies according to course load. College room and board: $5615. Room and board charges vary according to board plan, housing facility, and location. **Scholarships:** Available. **Calendar System:** Semester, Summer session available **Enrollment:** Full-time 5,324, Part-time 3,179 **Faculty:** Full-time 211, Part-time 371 **Student-Faculty Ratio:** 19:1 **Exams:** SAT I or ACT. **% Receiving Financial Aid:** 64 **% Residing in College-Owned, -Operated, or -Affiliated Housing:** 4 **Final Year or Final Semester Residency Requirement:** No **Credit Hours For Degree:** 60 credits, Associates; 120 credits, Bachelors **ROTC:** Army **Professional Accreditation:** ACEN, ADA, JRCEMTP, NCCU. **Intercollegiate Athletics:** Baseball M; Basketball M & W; Cross-Country Running M & W; Football M; Golf M & W; Soccer M & W; Softball W; Tennis W; Volleyball W

EAGLE GATE COLLEGE (LAYTON)

915 N 400 W
Layton, UT 84041
Tel: (801)546-7500; Free: 866-29-EAGLE
E-mail: Aaron.escher@eaglegatecollege.edu
Web Site: eaglegatecollege.edu
President/CEO: Janet Head-Parrish
Admissions: Aaron Escher
Type: Four-Year College **Sex:** Coed **Affiliation:** Eagle Gate College Group. **Calendar System:** Quarter **Professional Accreditation:** ACICS.

EAGLE GATE COLLEGE (MURRAY)

5588 S Green St.
Murray, UT 84123
Tel: (801)333-8100; Free: 866-29-EAGLE
E-mail: lacei.torgerson@eaglegatecollege.edu
Web Site: eaglegatecollege.edu
President/CEO: Chris Nickell
Admissions: Lacei Torgerson
Type: Four-Year College **Sex:** Coed **Affiliation:** Eagle Gate College Group. **Calendar System:** Quarter **Professional Accreditation:** ACICS.

FORTIS COLLEGE

3949 S 700 E
Ste. 150
Salt Lake City, UT 84107
Tel: (801)713-0915; Free: 855-4-FORTIS
Web Site: www.fortis.edu
Type: Two-Year College **Sex:** Coed **Professional Accreditation:** ACCSC.

INDEPENDENCE UNIVERSITY

5295 S Commerce Dr.
Salt Lake City, UT 84107
Tel: (800)221-7374; Free: 800-972-5149
Fax: (801)263-0345
Web Site: www.independence.edu
President/CEO: Alan Hansen
Admissions: Deborah Hopkins
Type: Comprehensive **Sex:** Coed **Admission Plans:** Deferred Admission; Open Admission **Application Deadline:** Rolling **H.S. Requirements:** High school diploma required; GED accepted **Scholarships:** Available. **Calendar System:** Continuous, Summer session not available **% Receiving Financial Aid:** 96 **Credit Hours For Degree:** 60 semester hours, Associates; 120 semester hours, Bachelors **Professional Accreditation:** ACCSC, CoARC.

LDS BUSINESS COLLEGE

95 N 300 W
Salt Lake City, UT 84101
Tel: (801)524-8100; Free: 800-999-5767
Fax: (801)524-1900
E-mail: dfellows@ldsbc.edu
Web Site: www.ldsbc.edu
President/CEO: J. Larry Richards
Admissions: Dawn Fellows
Financial Aid: Melanie Conover
Type: Two-Year College **Sex:** Coed **Affiliation:** The Church of Jesus Christ of Latter-day Saints; Church Education System (CES) of The Church of Jesus Christ of Latter-day Saints. **% Accepted:** 93 **Admission Plans:** Deferred Admission; Open Admission **Application Deadline:** Rolling **Application Fee:** $35.00 **H.S. Requirements:** High school diploma required; GED accepted **Scholarships:** Available. **Calendar System:** Semester, Summer session available **Enrollment:** Full-time 1,589, Part-time 602 **Faculty:** Full-time 14, Part-time 128 **Student-Faculty Ratio:** 25:1 **Exams:** ACT essay component not used; SAT I or ACT; SAT essay component not used. **Final Year or Final Semester Residency Requirement:** No **Credit Hours For Degree:** 62 credit hours, Associates **ROTC:** Air Force, Army **Professional Accreditation:** AAMAE, NCCU.

MIDWIVES COLLEGE OF UTAH

1174 E 2700 S, Ste. 2
Salt Lake City, UT 84106
Tel: (801)764-9068; Free: 866-680-2756
Fax: (801)434-8704
E-mail: office@midwifery.edu
Web Site: www.midwifery.edu
President/CEO: Kristy Ridd-Young
Admissions: Kristi Ridd-Young
Type: Comprehensive **Sex:** Women **Application Deadline:** July 29 **Application Fee:** $35.00 **H.S. Requirements:** High school diploma required; GED accepted **Calendar System:** Semester **Enrollment:** Part-time 130 **Professional Accreditation:** MEAC. **Intercollegiate Athletics:** Ultimate Frisbee M & W; Volleyball M & W

NEUMONT UNIVERSITY

143 S Main St.
Salt Lake City, UT 84111
Tel: (801)302-2800; Free: 888-NEUMONT
Fax: (801)302-2880
E-mail: karick.heaton@neumont.edu
Web Site: www.neumont.edu
President/CEO: Shaun E. McAlmont
Admissions: Karick Heaton
Financial Aid: Nate Blanchard
Type: Four-Year College **Sex:** Coed **Scores:** 97% SAT V 400+; 95% SAT M 400+; 41% ACT 18-23; 42% ACT 24-29 **% Accepted:** 83 **Application Deadline:** Rolling **Application Fee:** $35.00 **H.S. Requirements:** High school diploma required; GED accepted **Costs Per Year:** Application fee: $35. Tuition: $22,950 full-time. Mandatory fees: $1500 full-time. College room only: $5670. Room charges vary according to housing facility. **Scholarships:** Available. **Calendar System:** Quarter **Enrollment:** Full-time 429 **Faculty:** Full-time 15, Part-time 27 **Student-Faculty Ratio:** 21:1 **Exams:** ACT essay component not used; SAT I or ACT; SAT essay component not used; SAT Reasoning; SAT Subject. **% Receiving Financial Aid:** 51 **% Residing in College-Owned, -Operated, or -Affiliated Housing:** 80 **Final Year or Final Semester Residency Requirement:** No **Credit Hours For Degree:** 180 units, Bachelors **Professional Accreditation:** ACICS.

NIGHTINGALE COLLEGE

4155 Harrison Blvd. No.100
Ogden, UT 84403
Tel: (801)689-2160
Web Site: www.nightingale.edu
Type: Two-Year College **Sex:** Coed **Admission Plans:** Early Admission; Open Admission **Application Fee:** $100.00 **H.S. Requirements:** High school diploma required; GED accepted **Calendar System:** Semester **Exams:** Other. **Professional Accreditation:** ABHES.

PROVO COLLEGE
1450 W 820 N
Provo, UT 84601
Tel: (801)818-8900; Free: 877-777-5886
Fax: (801)375-9728
E-mail: gordonp@provocollege.org
Web Site: www.provocollege.edu
President/CEO: Todd Smith
Admissions: Gordon Peters

Type: Two-Year College **Sex:** Coed **Application Fee:** $25.00 **Professional Accreditation:** ACCSC, ACEN, ACICS, ADA, APTA.

SALT LAKE COMMUNITY COLLEGE
PO Box 30808
Salt Lake City, UT 84130-0808
Tel: (801)957-4111
Fax: (801)957-4958
E-mail: kathy.thompson@slcc.edu
Web Site: www.slcc.edu
President/CEO: Deneece Huftalin, PhD
Admissions: Kathy Thompson

Type: Two-Year College **Sex:** Coed **Affiliation:** Utah System of Higher Education. **% Accepted:** 100 **Admission Plans:** Early Admission; Open Admission **Application Deadline:** Rolling **Application Fee:** $40.00 **H.S. Requirements:** High school diploma or equivalent not required. For health science programs: High school diploma required; GED accepted **Costs Per Year:** Application fee: $40. State resident tuition: $3130 full-time, $130 per credit hour part-time. Nonresident tuition: $10,898 full-time, $453 per credit hour part-time. Mandatory fees: $439 full-time. **Scholarships:** Available. **Calendar System:** Semester, Summer session available **Enrollment:** Full-time 7,789, Part-time 21,025 **Faculty:** Full-time 339, Part-time 1,155 **Student-Faculty Ratio:** 19:1 **Credit Hours For Degree:** 60 credits, Associates **ROTC:** Air Force, Army **Professional Accreditation:** ACBSP, ACEN, ACF, ADA, AOTA, APTA, JRCERT, NAACLS, NCCU. **Intercollegiate Athletics:** Baseball M; Basketball M & W; Cheerleading M & W; Soccer M & W; Softball W; Volleyball W

SNOW COLLEGE
150 E College Ave.
Ephraim, UT 84627-1203
Tel: (435)283-7000
Fax: (435)283-6879
E-mail: snowcollege@snow.edu
Web Site: www.snow.edu
Admissions: Lorie Parry

Type: Two-Year College **Sex:** Coed **Affiliation:** Utah System of Higher Education. **% Accepted:** 100 **Admission Plans:** Early Admission; Open Admission **Application Deadline:** June 15 **Application Fee:** $30.00 **H.S. Requirements:** High school diploma required; GED accepted **Costs Per Year:** Application fee: $30. State resident tuition: $3088 full-time. Nonresident tuition: $11,280 full-time. Mandatory fees: $396 full-time. Full-time tuition and fees vary according to course load and degree level. College room and board: $3200. College room only: $3625. Room and board charges vary according to board plan, housing facility, and location. **Scholarships:** Available. **Calendar System:** Semester, Summer session available **Enrollment:** Full-time 2,813, Part-time 1,792 **Faculty:** Full-time 116, Part-time 136 **Student-Faculty Ratio:** 21:1 **Exams:** SAT I or ACT. **% Residing in College-Owned, -Operated, or -Affiliated Housing:** 20 **Credit Hours For Degree:** 63 semester credits, Associates **Professional Accreditation:** ACBSP, NASM, NCCU. **Intercollegiate Athletics:** Basketball M & W; Football M; Softball W; Volleyball W

SOUTHERN UTAH UNIVERSITY
351 W University Blvd.
Cedar City, UT 84720-2498
Tel: (435)586-7700
Fax: (435)586-5475
E-mail: admissioninfo@suu.edu
Web Site: www.suu.edu
President/CEO: Scott Wyatt
Admissions: Brandon Wright
Financial Aid: Jan Carey-McDonald

Type: Comprehensive **Sex:** Coed **Affiliation:** Utah System of Higher Education. **Scores:** 93% SAT V 400+; 89% SAT M 400+; 42% ACT 18-23; 43%

ACT 24-29 **% Accepted:** 72 **Admission Plans:** Deferred Admission **Application Deadline:** May 1 **Application Fee:** $50.00 **H.S. Requirements:** High school diploma required; GED accepted **Costs Per Year:** Application fee: $50. State resident tuition: $5774 full-time, $271 per credit part-time. Nonresident tuition: $19,054 full-time, $897 per credit part-time. Mandatory fees: $756 full-time, $378 per term part-time. Full-time tuition and fees vary according to program. Part-time tuition and fees vary according to course load and program. College room and board: $7067. College room only: $3167. Room and board charges vary according to board plan and housing facility. **Scholarships:** Available. **Calendar System:** Semester, Summer session available **Enrollment:** Full-time 5,647, Graduate full-time 197, Graduate part-time 649, Part-time 2,388 **Faculty:** Full-time 308, Part-time 194 **Student-Faculty Ratio:** 18:1 **Exams:** ACT essay component not used; SAT I or ACT; SAT essay component not used; SAT Reasoning. **% Receiving Financial Aid:** 65 **Final Year or Final Semester Residency Requirement:** No **Credit Hours For Degree:** 60 credits, Associates; 120 credits, Bachelors **ROTC:** Army **Professional Accreditation:** AACN, AACSB, AAFCS, ABET, ACBSP, NASAD, NASD, NASM, NCCU, TEAC. **Intercollegiate Athletics:** Basketball M & W; Cross-Country Running M & W; Football M; Golf M & W; Gymnastics W; Soccer W; Softball W; Tennis M & W; Track and Field M & W; Volleyball W

STEVENS-HENAGER COLLEGE (LOGAN)
755 S Main St.
Logan, UT 84321
Tel: (435)752-0903; Free: 800-622-2640
Web Site: www.stevenshenager.edu
Type: Four-Year College **Sex:** Coed **Professional Accreditation:** ACCSC.

STEVENS-HENAGER COLLEGE (OREM)
1476 S Sandhill Rd.
Orem, UT 84058
Tel: (801)373-0285; Free: 800-622-2640
Web Site: www.stevenshenager.edu
Type: Four-Year College **Sex:** Coed **Professional Accreditation:** ACCSC.

STEVENS-HENAGER COLLEGE (SAINT GEORGE)
720 S River Rd.
Ste. C-130
Saint George, UT 84790
Tel: (435)628-9150; Free: 800-622-2640
Web Site: www.stevenshenager.edu
Type: Four-Year College **Sex:** Coed **Professional Accreditation:** ACCSC.

STEVENS-HENAGER COLLEGE (SALT LAKE CITY)
383 W Vine St.
Salt Lake City, UT 84123
Tel: (801)531-1180; Free: 800-622-2640
Web Site: www.stevenshenager.edu
Type: Comprehensive **Sex:** Coed **Professional Accreditation:** ACCSC.

STEVENS-HENAGER COLLEGE (WEST HAVEN)
1890 S 1350 W
West Haven, UT 84401
Tel: (801)392-1471; Free: 800-622-2640
Web Site: www.stevenshenager.edu
President/CEO: Vicky Dewsnup
Type: Four-Year College **Sex:** Coed **Admission Plans:** Deferred Admission; Early Admission; Open Admission **Application Deadline:** Rolling **H.S. Requirements:** High school diploma required; GED accepted **Scholarships:** Available. **Calendar System:** Quarter, Summer session not available **Student-Faculty Ratio:** 18:1 **Exams:** Other; SAT I or ACT. **Professional Accreditation:** AAMAE, ACCSC, ACEN, ARCST.

UNIVERSITY OF PHOENIX–UTAH CAMPUS
5373 S Green St.
Salt Lake City, UT 84123-4642
Tel: (801)506-4166; Free: 866-766-0766
Fax: (801)269-9766
Web Site: www.phoenix.edu
President/CEO: Timothy P. Slottow
Admissions: Marc Booker
Type: Comprehensive **Sex:** Coed **% Accepted:** 100 **Admission Plans:** Deferred Admission; Open Admission **Application Deadline:** Rolling **H.S.**

Requirements: High school diploma required; GED accepted **Scholarships:** Available. **Calendar System:** Continuous, Summer session not available **Enrollment:** Full-time 1,936 **Faculty:** Full-time 57, Part-time 349 **Regional Accreditation:** North Central Association of Colleges and Schools **Credit Hours For Degree:** 60 credits, Associates; 120 credits, Bachelors **Professional Accreditation:** ACA.

UNIVERSITY OF UTAH
201 Presidents Cir.
Salt Lake City, UT 84112-1107
Tel: (801)581-7200; Free: 800-685-8856
Fax: (801)585-3034
E-mail: mremsburg@sa.utah.edu
Web Site: www.utah.edu
President/CEO: Dr. David W. Pershing
Admissions: Mateo Remsburg
Financial Aid: Amy Capps

Type: University **Sex:** Coed **Affiliation:** Utah System of Higher Education. **Scores:** 96% SAT V 400+; 97% SAT M 400+; 36% ACT 18-23; 43% ACT 24-29 **% Accepted:** 81 **Admission Plans:** Deferred Admission; Early Admission; Early Decision Plan **Application Deadline:** April 1 **Application Fee:** $45.00 **H.S. Requirements:** High school diploma required; GED accepted **Costs Per Year:** Application fee: $45. State resident tuition: $7130 full-time, $200.29 per credit hour part-time. Nonresident tuition: $24,955 full-time, $688.62 per credit hour part-time. Mandatory fees: $1067 full-time, $416.46 per term part-time. Full-time tuition and fees vary according to course load, location, program, and student level. Part-time tuition and fees vary according to course load, location, program, and student level. College room and board: $9000. College room only: $4642. Room and board charges vary according to board plan, housing facility, and location. **Scholarships:** Available. **Calendar System:** Semester, Summer session available **Enrollment:** Full-time 16,927, Graduate full-time 6,004, Graduate part-time 1,753, Part-time 6,867 **Faculty:** Full-time 1,449, Part-time 662 **Student-Faculty Ratio:** 16:1 **Exams:** ACT essay component not used; SAT I or ACT; SAT essay component not used; SAT Reasoning; SAT Subject. **% Receiving Financial Aid:** 48 **% Residing in College-Owned, -Operated, or -Affiliated Housing:** 13 **Final Year or Final Semester Residency Requirement:** Yes **Credit Hours For Degree:** 122 credit hours, Bachelors **ROTC:** Air Force, Army, Navy **Professional Accreditation:** AACN, AACSB, AALS, ABA, ABET, ACEJMC, ACNM, ACPE, ACSP, ADA, AND, AOTA, APA, APTA, ASC, ASHA, CAHME, CEPH, CSWE, JRCAT, LCME/AMA, NAAB, NAACLS, NASD, NASM, NASPAA, NCCU, NRPA, TEAC. **Intercollegiate Athletics:** Baseball M; Basketball M & W; Cheerleading M & W; Cross-Country Running W; Fencing M & W; Football M; Golf M; Gymnastics W; Ice Hockey M; Lacrosse M & W; Racquetball M & W; Riflery M & W; Rugby M; Skiing (Cross-Country) M & W; Skiing (Downhill) M & W; Soccer M & W; Softball W; Swimming and Diving M & W; Table Tennis M & W; Tennis M & W; Track and Field W; Ultimate Frisbee M & W; Volleyball M & W; Water Polo M & W; Weight Lifting M & W; Wrestling M

UTAH STATE UNIVERSITY
Old Main Hill
Logan, UT 84322
Tel: (435)797-1000; Free: 800-488-8108
Fax: (435)797-3900
E-mail: admit@usu.edu
Web Site: www.usu.edu
President/CEO: Dr. Stan L. Albrecht
Admissions: Jeff Sorenson

Type: University **Sex:** Coed **Affiliation:** Utah System of Higher Education. **Scores:** 94% SAT V 400+; 97% SAT M 400+; 43.5% ACT 18-23; 35.6% ACT 24-29 **% Accepted:** 97 **Admission Plans:** Deferred Admission **Application Deadline:** Rolling **Application Fee:** $50.00 **H.S. Requirements:** High school diploma required; GED accepted **Costs Per Year:** Application fee: $50. State resident tuition: $5,617 full-time. Nonresident tuition: $18,087 full-time. Mandatory fees: $1,046 full-time. Full-time tuition and fees vary according to course level, course load, program, and reciprocity agreements. College room and board: $5790. College room only: $2010. Room and board charges vary according to board plan and housing facility. **Scholarships:** Available. **Calendar System:** Semester, Summer session available **Enrollment:** Full-time 17,091, Graduate full-time 1,120, Graduate part-time 2,243, Part-time 8,168 **Faculty:** Full-time 894, Part-time 262 **Student-Faculty Ratio:** 22:1 **Exams:** ACT essay component not used; SAT I or ACT; SAT essay component not used; SAT Reasoning; SAT Subject. **% Receiving**

Financial Aid: 54 **Final Year or Final Semester Residency Requirement:** No **Credit Hours For Degree:** 60 credit hours, Associates; 120 credit hours, Bachelors **ROTC:** Air Force, Army **Professional Accreditation:** AACSB, AAMFT, ABET, AND, APA, ASHA, ASLA, CIDA, CORE, CSWE, NASM, NCCU, NRPA, SAF, TEAC. **Intercollegiate Athletics:** Baseball M; Basketball M & W; Cross-Country Running M & W; Equestrian Sports M & W; Football M; Golf M; Gymnastics W; Ice Hockey M; Racquetball M & W; Rugby M & W; Soccer M & W; Softball W; Tennis M & W; Track and Field M & W; Ultimate Frisbee M & W; Volleyball M & W

UTAH VALLEY UNIVERSITY
800 W University Pky.
Orem, UT 84058-5999
Tel: (801)863-8000
Fax: (801)225-4677
E-mail: coleskr@uvu.edu
Web Site: www.uvu.edu
President/CEO: Matthew S. Holland
Admissions: Kristopher Coles
Financial Aid: Trish Howard

Type: Comprehensive **Sex:** Coed **Affiliation:** Advent Christian Church; Utah System of Higher Education. **Scores:** 47.43% ACT 18-23; 30.96% ACT 24-29 **% Accepted:** 100 **Admission Plans:** Deferred Admission; Open Admission **Application Deadline:** August 1 **Application Fee:** $35.00 **H.S. Requirements:** High school diploma required; GED accepted **Costs Per Year:** Application fee: $35. State resident tuition: $4678 full-time, $194.92 per credit part-time. Nonresident tuition: $14,494 full-time, $603.92 per credit part-time. Mandatory fees: $708 full-time, $354 per term part-time, $354 per term part-time. Full-time tuition and fees vary according to course load and degree level. Part-time tuition and fees vary according to course load and degree level. **Scholarships:** Available. **Calendar System:** Semester, Summer session available **Enrollment:** Full-time 17,173, Graduate full-time 41, Graduate part-time 144, Part-time 15,853 **Faculty:** Full-time 642, Part-time 1,204 **Student-Faculty Ratio:** 22:1 **Exams:** ACT essay component not used; Other; SAT essay component not used; SAT Reasoning; SAT Subject. **% Receiving Financial Aid:** 59 **Final Year or Final Semester Residency Requirement:** No **Credit Hours For Degree:** 60 semester hours, Associates; 120 semester hours, Bachelors **ROTC:** Air Force, Army **Professional Accreditation:** AACSB, ABET, ACEN, ADA, NCCU, TEAC. **Intercollegiate Athletics:** Baseball M; Basketball M & W; Cross-Country Running M & W; Golf M & W; Soccer W; Softball W; Track and Field M & W; Volleyball W; Wrestling M

VISTA COLLEGE
775 S 2000 E
Clearfield, UT 84015
Tel: (801)774-9900
Web Site: www.vistacollege.edu
Type: Two-Year College **Sex:** Coed **Professional Accreditation:** ACCSC.

WEBER STATE UNIVERSITY
3848 Harrison Blvd.
Ogden, UT 84408-1001
Tel: (801)626-6000; Free: 800-848-7770
Fax: (801)626-6747
E-mail: admissions@weber.edu
Web Site: www.weber.edu
President/CEO: Charles Wight
Admissions: Patrick Moody
Financial Aid: Jed Spencer

Type: Comprehensive **Sex:** Coed **Affiliation:** Utah System of Higher Education. **Scores:** 49% ACT 18-23; 24% ACT 24-29 **% Accepted:** 100 **Admission Plans:** Deferred Admission; Early Admission; Open Admission **Application Deadline:** August 31 **Application Fee:** $30.00 **H.S. Requirements:** High school diploma required; GED accepted **Costs Per Year:** Application fee: $30. State resident tuition: $4456 full-time, $2758 per year part-time. Nonresident tuition: $13,369 full-time, $7286 per year part-time. Mandatory fees: $883 full-time, $558 per year part-time. Full-time tuition and fees vary according to course level, course load, degree level, and program. Part-time tuition and fees vary according to course level, course load, degree level, and program. College room and board: $4219. Room and board charges vary according to board plan and housing facility. **Scholarships:** Available. **Calendar System:** Semester, Summer session available **Enrollment:** Full-time 10,958, Graduate full-time 285, Graduate part-time 352, Part-time 14,360 **Faculty:** Full-time 488, Part-time 810 **Student-Faculty Ratio:** 20:1 **Exams:** ACT essay component not used; Other; SAT I or ACT; SAT essay component not used; SAT Reasoning; SAT Subject. **% Receiving Financial Aid:** 54 **% Residing in College-Owned, -Operated, or -Affiliated Housing:** 4 **Final Year or Final Semester Residency Requirement:** No **Credit Hours For Degree:** 60 credit hours, Associates; 120 credit hours, Bachelors **ROTC:** Air Force, Army, Navy **Professional Accreditation:** AACSB, ABET, ACEN, ADA, AHIMA, CAHME, CSWE, CoARC, JRCEMTP, NAACLS, NASAD, NASM, NCATE, NCCU, TEAC. **Intercollegiate Athletics:** Archery M & W; Baseball M; Basketball M & W; Bowling M & W; Cheerleading M & W; Cross-Country Running M & W; Football M; Golf M & W; Ice Hockey M; Lacrosse M; Rugby M; Soccer M & W; Softball W; Swimming and Diving M & W; Tennis M & W; Track and Field M & W; Volleyball M & W; Weight Lifting M & W; Wrestling M

WESTERN GOVERNORS UNIVERSITY

4001 S 700 E, Ste. 700
Salt Lake City, UT 84107
Tel: (801)274-3280; Free: 866-225-5948
Fax: (801)274-3305
E-mail: admissions@wgu.edu
Web Site: www.wgu.edu
President/CEO: Robert Mendenhall

Type: Comprehensive **Sex:** Coed **Application Fee:** $65.00 **H.S. Requirements:** High school diploma required; GED accepted **Scholarships:** Available. **Calendar System:** Continuous, Summer session not available **Enrollment:** Full-time 44,499, Graduate full-time 13,322 **Faculty:** Full-time 1,093, Part-time 561 **Student-Faculty Ratio:** 41:1 **% Receiving Financial Aid:** 52 **Professional Accreditation:** AACN, NCATE, NCCU.

WESTMINSTER COLLEGE

1840 S 1300, E
Salt Lake City, UT 84105-3697

Tel: (801)484-7651; Free: 800-748-4753
Fax: (801)484-3252
E-mail: admission@westminstercollege.edu
Web Site: www.westminstercollege.edu
President/CEO: Steve Morgan
Admissions: Darlene Dilley
Financial Aid: Jenny Ryan

Type: Comprehensive **Sex:** Coed **Scores:** 99% SAT V 400+; 100% SAT M 400+; 36% ACT 18-23; 52% ACT 24-29 **% Accepted:** 96 **Admission Plans:** Deferred Admission **Application Deadline:** Rolling **Application Fee:** $50.00 **H.S. Requirements:** High school diploma required; GED accepted **Costs Per Year:** Application fee: $50. Comprehensive fee: $40,566 includes full-time tuition ($30,720), mandatory fees ($508), and college room and board ($9338). Full-time tuition and fees vary according to course load and program. Room and board charges vary according to board plan. Part-time tuition: $1280 per credit hour. Part-time tuition varies according to course load and program. **Scholarships:** Available. **Calendar System:** Miscellaneous, Summer session available **Enrollment:** Full-time 2,037, Graduate full-time 428, Graduate part-time 234, Part-time 122 **Faculty:** Full-time 151, Part-time 237 **Student-Faculty Ratio:** 9:1 **Exams:** ACT essay component used for admission; ACT essay component used for advising; ACT essay component used for placement; ACT essay component used in place of application essay; SAT I or ACT; SAT essay component used for admission; SAT essay component used for advising; SAT essay component used for placement; SAT essay component used in place of application essay; SAT Reasoning. **% Receiving Financial Aid:** 59 **% Residing in College-Owned, -Operated, or -Affiliated Housing:** 32 **Final Year or Final Semester Residency Requirement:** No **Credit Hours For Degree:** 124 semester hours, Bachelors **ROTC:** Air Force, Army, Navy **Professional Accreditation:** AACN, AANA, ACBSP, NCCU, TEAC. **Intercollegiate Athletics:** Basketball M & W; Cross-Country Running M & W; Golf M & W; Lacrosse M & W; Skiing (Downhill) M & W; Soccer M & W; Track and Field M & W; Volleyball W

BENNINGTON COLLEGE

One College Dr.
Bennington, VT 05201
Tel: (802)442-5401; Free: 800-833-6845
Fax: (802)447-4269
E-mail: admissions@bennington.edu
Web Site: www.bennington.edu
President/CEO: Dr. Mariko Silver
Admissions: Libby Hux
Financial Aid: Heather Clifford
Type: Comprehensive **Sex:** Coed **Scores:** 100% SAT V 400+; 99% SAT M 400+; 9% ACT 18-23; 44% ACT 24-29 **% Accepted:** 63 **Admission Plans:** Deferred Admission; Early Action; Early Admission; Early Decision Plan **Application Deadline:** January 15 **Application Fee:** $0.00 **H.S. Requirements:** High school diploma required; GED accepted **Costs Per Year:** Application fee: $0. One-time mandatory fee: $645. Comprehensive fee: $64,620 includes full-time tuition ($49,440), mandatory fees ($660), and college room and board ($14,520). College room only: $7870. Full-time tuition and fees vary according to degree level. Room and board charges vary according to board plan. Part-time tuition: $1983 per credit. **Scholarships:** Available. **Calendar System:** Semester, Summer session not available **Enrollment:** Full-time 680, Graduate full-time 96, Graduate part-time 1, Part-time 24 **Faculty:** Full-time 55, Part-time 43 **Student-Faculty Ratio:** 10:1 **Exams:** ACT; ACT essay component not used; Other; SAT I; SAT I and SAT II or ACT; SAT I or ACT; SAT II; SAT essay component not used; SAT Reasoning; SAT Subject. **% Receiving Financial Aid:** 62 **% Residing in College-Owned, -Operated, or -Affiliated Housing:** 96 **Final Year or Final Semester Residency Requirement:** No **Regional Accreditation:** New England Association of Schools and Colleges **Credit Hours For Degree:** 128 credits, Bachelors **Intercollegiate Athletics:** Basketball M & W; Fencing M & W; Soccer M & W; Ultimate Frisbee M & W; Volleyball M & W

CASTLETON UNIVERSITY

Castleton, VT 05735
Tel: (802)468-5611; Free: 800-639-8521
Fax: (802)468-1476
E-mail: info@castleton.edu
Web Site: www.castleton.edu
President/CEO: David S. Wolk
Admissions: Maurice Ouimet, Jr.
Financial Aid: Kathleen O'Meara
Type: Comprehensive **Sex:** Coed **Affiliation:** Vermont State Colleges System. **Scores:** 84% SAT V 400+; 88% SAT M 400+; 69% ACT 18-23; 13% ACT 24-29 **% Accepted:** 78 **Admission Plans:** Deferred Admission **Application Deadline:** Rolling **Application Fee:** $40.00 **H.S. Requirements:** High school diploma required; GED accepted **Scholarships:** Available. **Calendar System:** Semester, Summer session available **Enrollment:** Full-time 1,720, Graduate full-time 16, Graduate part-time 183, Part-time 265 **Faculty:** Full-time 102, Part-time 126 **Student-Faculty Ratio:** 13:1 **Exams:** ACT essay component used for advising; ACT essay component used for placement; SAT I or ACT; SAT essay component used for advising; SAT essay component used for placement; SAT Reasoning. **% Residing in College-Owned, -Operated, or -Affiliated Housing:** 54 **Final Year or Final Semester Residency Requirement:** No **Regional Accreditation:** New England Association of Schools and Colleges **Credit Hours For Degree:** 64 credits, Associates; 122 credits, Bachelors **ROTC:** Army **Professional Ac-**creditation: ACEN, CSWE, JRCAT, NCATE. **Intercollegiate Athletics:** Baseball M; Basketball M & W; Cheerleading M & W; Cross-Country Running M & W; Equestrian Sports W; Field Hockey W; Football M; Golf M; Ice Hockey M & W; Lacrosse M & W; Rugby M & W; Skiing (Downhill) M & W; Soccer M & W; Softball W; Tennis M & W; Volleyball W

CHAMPLAIN COLLEGE

PO Box 670
Burlington, VT 05402-0670
Tel: (802)860-2700; Free: 800-570-5858
Fax: (802)862-2772
E-mail: admission@champlain.edu
Web Site: www.champlain.edu
President/CEO: Donald J. Laackman
Admissions: Chris Perlongo
Financial Aid: Kristi Jovell
Type: Comprehensive **Sex:** Coed **Scores:** 100% SAT V 400+; 100% SAT M 400+; 28% ACT 18-23; 49% ACT 24-29 **% Accepted:** 66 **Admission Plans:** Deferred Admission; Early Action; Early Admission **Application Deadline:** February 1 **Application Fee:** $0.00 **H.S. Requirements:** High school diploma required; GED accepted **Costs Per Year:** Application fee: $0. Comprehensive fee: $51,586 includes full-time tuition ($37,436), mandatory fees ($100), and college room and board ($14,050). Part-time tuition: $1560 per credit hour. **Scholarships:** Available. **Calendar System:** Semester, Summer session available **Enrollment:** Full-time 2,373, Graduate full-time 547, Graduate part-time 59, Part-time 1,027 **Faculty:** Full-time 113, Part-time 370 **Student-Faculty Ratio:** 13:1 **Exams:** ACT essay component not used; SAT I or ACT; SAT II; SAT essay component not used; SAT Reasoning; SAT Subject. **% Receiving Financial Aid:** 69 **% Residing in College-Owned, -Operated, or -Affiliated Housing:** 64 **Final Year or Final Semester Residency Requirement:** No **Regional Accreditation:** New England Association of Schools and Colleges **Credit Hours For Degree:** 60 credit hours, Associates; 120 credit hours, Bachelors **ROTC:** Army **Professional Accreditation:** CoARC, JRCERT.

COLLEGE OF ST. JOSEPH

71 Clement Rd.
Rutland, VT 05701-3899
Tel: (802)773-5900; Free: 877-270-9998
E-mail: admissions@csj.edu
Web Site: www.csj.edu
President/CEO: Dr. Frank G. Miglorie, Jr.
Admissions: Alan Young
Financial Aid: Julie Rosmus
Type: Comprehensive **Sex:** Coed **Affiliation:** Roman Catholic. **Scores:** 60% SAT V 400+; 64% SAT M 400+; 40% ACT 18-23; 20% ACT 24-29 **% Accepted:** 69 **Admission Plans:** Deferred Admission; Early Admission **Application Deadline:** Rolling **Application Fee:** $25.00 **H.S. Requirements:** High school diploma required; GED accepted **Costs Per Year:** Application fee: $25. Comprehensive fee: $32,400 includes full-time tuition ($21,100), mandatory fees ($800), and college room and board ($10,500). Full-time tuition and fees vary according to course load, degree level, and program. Room and board charges vary according to housing facility. Part-time tuition: $285 per credit hour. Part-time mandatory fees: $75 per term. Part-time tuition and fees vary according to course load, degree level, and program.

Scholarships: Available. **Calendar System:** Semester, Summer session available **Enrollment:** Full-time 164, Graduate full-time 31, Graduate part-time 109, Part-time 73 **Faculty:** Full-time 12, Part-time 46 **Student-Faculty Ratio:** 10:1 **Exams:** ACT essay component used for admission; ACT essay component used for advising; ACT essay component used for placement; SAT I or ACT; SAT essay component used for admission; SAT essay component used for advising; SAT essay component used for placement. **% Receiving Financial Aid:** 94 **% Residing in College-Owned, -Operated, or -Affiliated Housing:** 33 **Final Year or Final Semester Residency Requirement:** No **Regional Accreditation:** New England Association of Schools and Colleges **Credit Hours For Degree:** 60 credits, Associates; 127 credits, Bachelors **Intercollegiate Athletics:** Basketball M & W; Bowling M & W; Cross-Country Running M & W; Soccer M & W; Softball W

COMMUNITY COLLEGE OF VERMONT

660 Elm St.
Montpelier, VT 05602
Tel: (802)828-2800
Fax: (802)828-2805
E-mail: adam.warrington@ccv.edu
Web Site: www.ccv.edu
President/CEO: Joyce Judy
Admissions: Adam G. Warrington

Type: Two-Year College **Sex:** Coed **Affiliation:** Vermont State Colleges System. **% Accepted:** 59 **Admission Plans:** Open Admission **Application Deadline:** Rolling **Application Fee:** $0.00 **H.S. Requirements:** High school diploma required; GED accepted. For non-degree students: High school diploma or equivalent not required **Costs Per Year:** Application fee: $0. State resident tuition: $7380 full-time, $246 per credit hour part-time. Nonresident tuition: $14,760 full-time, $492 per credit hour part-time. Mandatory fees: $150 full-time, $75 per term part-time. **Scholarships:** Available. **Calendar System:** Semester, Summer session available **Enrollment:** Full-time 995, Part-time 5,624 **Faculty:** Part-time 735 **Student-Faculty Ratio:** 13:1 **Exams:** ACT essay component not used; Other; SAT I or ACT; SAT essay component not used. **Regional Accreditation:** New England Association of Schools and Colleges **Credit Hours For Degree:** 60 credits, Associates

GODDARD COLLEGE

123 Pitkin Rd.
Plainfield, VT 05667-9432
Tel: (802)454-8311; Free: 800-906-8312
Fax: (802)454-1029
E-mail: kelly.allen@goddard.edu
Web Site: www.goddard.edu
President/CEO: Robert Kenny
Admissions: Kelly Allen
Financial Aid: Shannon Trainor

Type: Comprehensive **Sex:** Coed **% Accepted:** 73 **Admission Plans:** Deferred Admission **Application Deadline:** Rolling **Application Fee:** $65.00 **H.S. Requirements:** High school diploma required; GED accepted **Costs Per Year:** Application fee: $65. Comprehensive fee: $17,040 includes full-time tuition ($15,476) and college room and board ($1564). Full-time tuition varies according to location, program, and reciprocity agreements. Room and board charges vary according to housing facility and location. Part-time tuition: $5804 per term. Part-time mandatory fees: $782 per term. Part-time tuition and fees vary according to location, program, and reciprocity agreements. **Scholarships:** Available. **Calendar System:** Semester, Summer session not available **Enrollment:** Full-time 177, Graduate full-time 317, Graduate part-time 11, Part-time 7 **Faculty:** Full-time 14, Part-time 76 **% Receiving Financial Aid:** 73 **Regional Accreditation:** New England Association of Schools and Colleges **Credit Hours For Degree:** 120 credit hours, Bachelors

GREEN MOUNTAIN COLLEGE

One Brennan Cir.
Poultney, VT 05764-1199
Tel: (802)287-8000; Free: 800-776-6675
Fax: (802)287-8099
E-mail: admiss@greenmtn.edu
Web Site: www.greenmtn.edu
President/CEO: Dr. Paul J. Fonteyn, PhD
Admissions: Jeffrey Mon
Financial Aid: Wendy J. Ellis

Type: Comprehensive **Sex:** Coed **% Accepted:** 66 **Admission Plans:** Deferred Admission; Early Decision Plan **Application Deadline:** Rolling **Application Fee:** $30.00 **H.S. Requirements:** High school diploma required; GED accepted **Costs Per Year:** Application fee: $30. One-time mandatory fee: $250. Comprehensive fee: $46,832 includes full-time tuition ($33,898), mandatory fees ($1442), and college room and board ($11,492). Room and board charges vary according to location. Part-time tuition: $1130 per credit hour. Part-time mandatory fees: $25 per course, $571 per term. **Scholarships:** Available. **Calendar System:** Semester, Summer session available **Enrollment:** Full-time 571, Graduate full-time 268, Part-time 26 **Faculty:** Full-time 40, Part-time 42 **Student-Faculty Ratio:** 14:1 **Exams:** SAT I or ACT; SAT II; SAT Reasoning; SAT Subject. **% Receiving Financial Aid:** 78 **% Residing in College-Owned, -Operated, or -Affiliated Housing:** 85 **Final Year or Final Semester Residency Requirement:** Yes **Regional Accreditation:** New England Association of Schools and Colleges **Credit Hours For Degree:** 120 credits, Bachelors **Professional Accreditation:** NRPA. **Intercollegiate Athletics:** Basketball M & W; Cross-Country Running M & W; Golf M & W; Lacrosse M & W; Soccer M & W; Tennis M; Track and Field M & W; Volleyball W

JOHNSON STATE COLLEGE

337 College Hill
Johnson, VT 05656
Tel: (802)635-2356; Free: 800-635-2356
Fax: (802)635-1230
E-mail: admissions@jsc.edu
Web Site: www.jsc.edu
President/CEO: Dr. Elaine Collins
Admissions: Bethany Harrington
Financial Aid: Kimberly Goodell

Type: Comprehensive **Sex:** Coed **Affiliation:** Vermont State Colleges System. **Scores:** 86% SAT V 400+; 84% SAT M 400+ **% Accepted:** 86 **Admission Plans:** Deferred Admission; Early Admission; Early Decision Plan **Application Deadline:** Rolling **Application Fee:** $40.00 **H.S. Requirements:** High school diploma required; GED accepted **Costs Per Year:** Application fee: $40. One-time mandatory fee: $600. State resident tuition: $10,224 full-time, $426 per credit hour part-time. Nonresident tuition: $22,680 full-time, $945 per credit hour part-time. Full-time tuition varies according to reciprocity agreements and student level. Part-time tuition varies according to course load, reciprocity agreements, and student level. College room and board: $9696. College room only: $5774. Room and board charges vary according to board plan. **Scholarships:** Available. **Calendar System:** Semester, Summer session available **Enrollment:** Full-time 979, Graduate full-time 43, Graduate part-time 161, Part-time 479 **Faculty:** Full-time 44, Part-time 135 **Student-Faculty Ratio:** 14:1 **Exams:** SAT I or ACT; SAT essay component not used. **% Receiving Financial Aid:** 81 **% Residing in College-Owned, -Operated, or -Affiliated Housing:** 60 **Final Year or Final Semester Residency Requirement:** No **Regional Accreditation:** New England Association of Schools and Colleges **Credit Hours For Degree:** 60 credits, Associates; 120 credits, Bachelors **ROTC:** Army **Intercollegiate Athletics:** Basketball M & W; Cross-Country Running M & W; Golf M; Lacrosse M & W; Soccer M & W; Softball W; Tennis M & W; Track and Field M & W; Volleyball W

LANDMARK COLLEGE

River Rd. S
Putney, VT 05346
Tel: (802)387-4767
Fax: (802)387-4779
E-mail: admissions@landmark.edu
Web Site: www.landmark.edu
President/CEO: Dr. Peter Eden
Financial Aid: Cathy Mullins

Type: Two-Year College **Sex:** Coed **% Accepted:** 86 **Admission Plans:** Deferred Admission; Early Decision Plan **Application Deadline:** Rolling **Application Fee:** $75.00 **H.S. Requirements:** High school diploma required; GED accepted **Costs Per Year:** Application fee: $75. Comprehensive fee: $62,040 includes full-time tuition ($51,200), mandatory fees ($130), and college room and board ($10,710). College room only: $5530. Room and board charges vary according to board plan and housing facility. **Scholarships:** Available. **Calendar System:** Semester, Summer session available **Enrollment:** Full-time 494, Part-time 20 **Faculty:** Full-time 78 **Student-Faculty Ratio:** 6:1 **Exams:** Other. **% Residing in College-Owned, -Operated, or -Affiliated Housing:** 95 **Final Year or Final Semester Residency Require-**

ment: No **Regional Accreditation:** New England Association of Schools and Colleges **Credit Hours For Degree:** 60 credits, Associates; 121 credits, Bachelors **Intercollegiate Athletics:** Baseball M; Basketball M & W; Cross-Country Running M & W; Equestrian Sports M & W; Rock Climbing M & W; Soccer M & W; Softball W

LYNDON STATE COLLEGE

PO Box 919
Lyndonville, VT 05851-0919
Tel: (802)626-6200; Free: 800-225-1998
Fax: (802)626-6335
E-mail: admissions@lyndonstate.edu
Web Site: www.lyndonstate.edu
President/CEO: Dr. Carol A. Moore
Admissions: Cheri Goldrick

Type: Comprehensive **Sex:** Coed **Affiliation:** Vermont State Colleges System. **Scores:** 77% SAT V 400+; 74% SAT M 400+ **% Accepted:** 93 **Admission Plans:** Deferred Admission; Early Admission **Application Deadline:** Rolling **Application Fee:** $36.00 **H.S. Requirements:** High school diploma required; GED accepted **Costs Per Year:** Application fee: $36. State resident tuition: $9984 full-time, $416 per credit hour part-time. Nonresident tuition: $21,384 full-time, $891 per credit hour part-time. Mandatory fees: $262 full-time, $44 per credit hour part-time, $44. Full-time tuition and fees vary according to course load. Part-time tuition and fees vary according to course load. College room and board: $9696. College room only: $5774. Room and board charges vary according to board plan and housing facility. **Scholarships:** Available. **Calendar System:** Semester, Summer session available **Enrollment:** Full-time 1,213, Graduate full-time 4, Graduate part-time 109, Part-time 110 **Faculty:** Full-time 58, Part-time 102 **Student-Faculty Ratio:** 15:1 **Exams:** SAT I or ACT. **% Residing in College-Owned, -Operated, or -Affiliated Housing:** 51 **Regional Accreditation:** New England Association of Schools and Colleges **Credit Hours For Degree:** 62 credit hours, Associates; 122 credit hours, Bachelors **ROTC:** Air Force **Professional Accreditation:** NRPA. **Intercollegiate Athletics:** Baseball M; Basketball M & W; Cross-Country Running M & W; Lacrosse M; Soccer M & W; Softball W; Tennis M & W; Volleyball W

MARLBORO COLLEGE

PO Box A, S Rd.
Marlboro, VT 05344
Tel: (802)257-4333; Free: 800-343-0049
E-mail: blawler@marlboro.edu
Web Site: www.marlboro.edu
President/CEO: Kevin F.F. Quigley
Admissions: Brigid Lawler

Type: Comprehensive **Sex:** Coed **Scores:** 100% SAT V 400+; 100% SAT M 400+; 100% ACT 24-29 **% Accepted:** 94 **Admission Plans:** Deferred Admission; Early Action; Early Admission; Early Decision Plan **Application Deadline:** March 1 **Application Fee:** $50.00 **H.S. Requirements:** High school diploma required; GED accepted. For home-schooled applicants with curriculum documentation: High school diploma or equivalent not required **Costs Per Year:** Application fee: $50. Comprehensive fee: $50,832 includes full-time tuition ($39,086), mandatory fees ($944), and college room and board ($10,802). College room only: $5948. Full-time tuition and fees vary according to reciprocity agreements. Part-time tuition: $1305 per credit. Part-time mandatory fees: $105 per term. Part-time tuition and fees vary according to course load. **Scholarships:** Available. **Calendar System:** Semester, Summer session not available **Enrollment:** Full-time 179, Graduate full-time 23, Graduate part-time 65, Part-time 13 **Faculty:** Full-time 39, Part-time 11 **Student-Faculty Ratio:** 4:1 **Exams:** ACT essay component not used; SAT I or ACT; SAT essay component not used; SAT Reasoning. **% Receiving Financial Aid:** 83 **% Residing in College-Owned, -Operated, or -Affiliated Housing:** 78 **Final Year or Final Semester Residency Requirement:** Yes **Regional Accreditation:** New England Association of Schools and Colleges **Credit Hours For Degree:** 120 credits, Bachelors **Intercollegiate Athletics:** Soccer M & W

MIDDLEBURY COLLEGE

Middlebury, VT 05753-6002
Tel: (802)443-5000
Fax: (802)443-2056
E-mail: admissions@middlebury.edu
Web Site: www.middlebury.edu
President/CEO: Dr. Laurie L. Patton

Admissions: Greg Buckles
Financial Aid: Marguerite Corbin

Type: Comprehensive **Sex:** Coed **Scores:** 100% SAT V 400+; 100% SAT M 400+; 1.15% ACT 18-23; 24.05% ACT 24-29 **% Accepted:** 17 **Admission Plans:** Deferred Admission; Early Action; Early Admission **Application Deadline:** January 1 **Application Fee:** $65.00 **H.S. Requirements:** High school diploma or equivalent not required **Costs Per Year:** Application fee: $65. Comprehensive fee: $61,456 includes full-time tuition ($47,418), mandatory fees ($410), and college room and board ($13,628). **Scholarships:** Available. **Calendar System:** 4-1-4, Summer session available **Enrollment:** Full-time 2,516, Graduate part-time 16, Part-time 26 **Faculty:** Full-time 283, Part-time 64 **Student-Faculty Ratio:** 8:1 **Exams:** ACT essay component not used; SAT I and SAT II or ACT; SAT essay component not used; SAT Reasoning; SAT Subject. **% Receiving Financial Aid:** 45 **% Residing in College-Owned, -Operated, or -Affiliated Housing:** 95 **Final Year or Final Semester Residency Requirement:** Yes **Regional Accreditation:** New England Association of Schools and Colleges **Credit Hours For Degree:** 36 course units, Bachelors **ROTC:** Army **Intercollegiate Athletics:** Baseball M; Basketball M & W; Cross-Country Running M & W; Field Hockey W; Football M; Golf M & W; Ice Hockey M & W; Lacrosse M & W; Skiing (Cross-Country) M & W; Skiing (Downhill) M & W; Soccer M & W; Softball W; Squash M & W; Swimming and Diving M & W; Tennis M & W; Track and Field M & W; Volleyball W

NEW ENGLAND CULINARY INSTITUTE

56 College St.
Montpelier, VT 05602-9720
Tel: (802)223-6324; Free: 877-223-6324
Fax: (802)223-0634
E-mail: admissions@neci.edu
Web Site: www.neci.edu
President/CEO: Fran Voigt
Admissions: Adonica Williams

Type: Two-Year College **Sex:** Coed **% Accepted:** 37 **Admission Plans:** Deferred Admission; Early Admission **Application Deadline:** Rolling **Application Fee:** $0.00 **H.S. Requirements:** High school diploma required; GED accepted **Costs Per Year:** Application fee: $0. Comprehensive fee: $28,625 includes full-time tuition ($20,625), and college room and board ($8000). Full-time tuition varies according to course load, degree level, program, reciprocity agreements, and student level. Room and board charges vary according to housing facility. **Scholarships:** Available. **Calendar System:** Quarter, Summer session not available **Enrollment:** Full-time 338, Part-time 84 **Faculty:** Full-time 24, Part-time 15 **Student-Faculty Ratio:** 13:1 **Exams:** SAT I or ACT. **% Residing in College-Owned, -Operated, or -Affiliated Housing:** 80 **Final Year or Final Semester Residency Requirement:** No **Credit Hours For Degree:** 60 credits, Associates; 120 credits, Bachelors **Professional Accreditation:** ACCSC.

NORWICH UNIVERSITY

158 Harmon Dr.
Northfield, VT 05663
Tel: (802)485-2000; Free: 800-468-6679
Fax: (802)485-2580
E-mail: nuadm@norwich.edu
Web Site: www.norwich.edu
President/CEO: Richard Schneider
Admissions: Sherri Gilmore
Financial Aid: Jana Cox

Type: Comprehensive **Sex:** Coed **Scores:** 94% SAT V 400+; 96% SAT M 400+; 44% ACT 18-23; 42% ACT 24-29 **% Accepted:** 66 **Application Fee:** $35.00 **H.S. Requirements:** High school diploma required; GED accepted **Costs Per Year:** Application fee: $35. Comprehensive fee: $44,796 includes full-time tuition ($32,812) and college room and board ($11,984). Part-time tuition: $962 per credit hour. Part-time tuition varies according to course load. **Scholarships:** Available. **Calendar System:** Semester, Summer session available **Enrollment:** Full-time 2,271, Graduate full-time 956, Graduate part-time 67, Part-time 378 **Faculty:** Full-time 151, Part-time 181 **Student-Faculty Ratio:** 16:1 **Exams:** ACT; ACT essay component used for placement; SAT I; SAT I or ACT; SAT essay component used for placement. **% Receiving Financial Aid:** 85 **% Residing in College-Owned, -Operated, or -Affiliated Housing:** 75 **Regional Accreditation:** New England Association of Schools and Colleges **Credit Hours For Degree:** 120 credit hours, Bachelors **ROTC:** Air Force, Army, Navy **Professional Accreditation:** AACN, ABET, ACBSP, ACEN, NAAB. **Intercollegiate Athletics:** Baseball M;

Basketball M & W; Cross-Country Running M & W; Fencing M & W; Football M; Ice Hockey M & W; Lacrosse M; Riflery M & W; Rugby M & W; Sailing M & W; Skiing (Cross-Country) M & W; Skiing (Downhill) M & W; Soccer M & W; Softball W; Swimming and Diving M & W; Tennis M & W; Track and Field M & W; Volleyball M & W; Weight Lifting M & W; Wrestling M

SAINT MICHAEL'S COLLEGE

One Winooski Park
Colchester, VT 05439
Tel: (802)654-2000; Free: 800-762-8000
Fax: (802)654-2242
E-mail: admission@smcvt.edu
Web Site: www.smcvt.edu
President/CEO: Dr. John Neuhauser, PhD
Admissions: Jacqueline Murphy
Type: Comprehensive **Sex:** Coed **Affiliation:** Roman Catholic. **Scores:** 98% SAT V 400+; 99% SAT M 400+; 18% ACT 18-23; 64% ACT 24-29 **% Accepted:** 76 **Admission Plans:** Deferred Admission; Early Decision Plan **Application Deadline:** February 1 **Application Fee:** $50.00 **H.S. Requirements:** High school diploma required; GED accepted **Costs Per Year:** Application fee: $50. Comprehensive fee: $51,725 includes full-time tuition ($40,425), mandatory fees ($325), and college room and board ($10,975). Full-time tuition and fees vary according to course load. Room and board charges vary according to board plan and housing facility. Part-time tuition: $1300 per credit hour. Part-time tuition varies according to course load. **Scholarships:** Available. **Calendar System:** Semester, Summer session available **Enrollment:** Full-time 1,971, Graduate full-time 49, Graduate part-time 321, Part-time 26 **Faculty:** Full-time 148, Part-time 102 **Student-Faculty Ratio:** 11:1 **Exams:** ACT essay component used as validity check; ACT essay component used for admission; SAT essay component used as validity check; SAT essay component used for admission; SAT Reasoning. **% Receiving Financial Aid:** 64 **% Residing in College-Owned, -Operated, or -Affiliated Housing:** 95 **Final Year or Final Semester Residency Requirement:** Yes **Regional Accreditation:** New England Association of Schools and Colleges **Credit Hours For Degree:** 128 semester hours, Bachelors **ROTC:** Air Force, Army **Intercollegiate Athletics:** Baseball M; Basketball M & W; Cross-Country Running M & W; Field Hockey W; Golf M; Ice Hockey M & W; Lacrosse M & W; Rugby M & W; Skiing (Cross-Country) M & W; Skiing (Downhill) M & W; Soccer M & W; Softball W; Swimming and Diving M & W; Tennis M & W; Volleyball W

SOUTHERN VERMONT COLLEGE

982 Mansion Dr.
Bennington, VT 05201
Tel: (802)447-4000
Fax: (802)447-4695
E-mail: admissions@svc.edu
Web Site: www.svc.edu
President/CEO: Dr. David Evans
Financial Aid: Susan Rochette
Type: Four-Year College **Sex:** Coed **Scores:** 72% SAT V 400+; 75% SAT M 400+; 44% ACT 18-23; 12% ACT 24-29 **% Accepted:** 63 **Admission Plans:** Deferred Admission; Early Admission **Application Deadline:** Rolling **Application Fee:** $30.00 **H.S. Requirements:** High school diploma required; GED accepted **Costs Per Year:** Application fee: $30. Comprehensive fee: $33,960 includes full-time tuition ($22,985), mandatory fees ($275), and college room and board ($10,700). Full-time tuition and fees vary according to program. Room and board charges vary according to board plan and housing facility. Part-time tuition: $960 per credit hour. Part-time mandatory fees: $275 per year. Part-time tuition and fees vary according to course load and program. **Scholarships:** Available. **Calendar System:** Semester, Summer session available **Enrollment:** Full-time 419, Part-time 56 **Faculty:** Full-time 22, Part-time 28 **Student-Faculty Ratio:** 14:1 **Exams:** SAT I or ACT. **% Residing in College-Owned, -Operated, or -Affiliated Housing:** 67 **Final Year or Final Semester Residency Requirement:** No **Regional Accreditation:** New England Association of Schools and Colleges **Credit Hours For Degree:** 60 credits, Associates; 120 credits, Bachelors **Professional Accreditation:** ACEN. **Intercollegiate Athletics:** Baseball M; Basketball M & W; Cross-Country Running M & W; Lacrosse W; Soccer M & W; Softball W; Track and Field M & W; Volleyball M & W

STERLING COLLEGE

PO Box 72
Craftsbury Common, VT 05827-0072

Tel: (802)586-7711; Free: 800-648-3591
E-mail: tpatterson@sterlingcollege.edu
Web Site: www.sterlingcollege.edu
President/CEO: Matthew Allen Derr
Admissions: Tim Patterson
Financial Aid: Barbara Stuart
Type: Four-Year College **Sex:** Coed **Costs Per Year:** One-time mandatory fee: $285. Comprehensive fee: $41,072 includes full-time tuition ($32,592), mandatory fees ($3700), and college room and board ($4780). College room only: $4354. Full-time tuition and fees vary according to course load. Room and board charges vary according to board plan. Part-time tuition: $8148 per term. Part-time tuition varies according to course load. **Scholarships:** Available. **Calendar System:** Semester, Summer session available **Enrollment:** Full-time 119 **Faculty:** Full-time 14, Part-time 2 **Student-Faculty Ratio:** 7:1 **% Receiving Financial Aid:** 64 **% Residing in College-Owned, -Operated, or -Affiliated Housing:** 85 **Final Year or Final Semester Residency Requirement:** No **Regional Accreditation:** New England Association of Schools and Colleges **Credit Hours For Degree:** 120 credits, Bachelors **Intercollegiate Athletics:** Skiing (Cross-Country) M & W

UNIVERSITY OF VERMONT

Burlington, VT 05405
Tel: (802)656-3131
E-mail: admissions@uvm.edu
Web Site: www.uvm.edu
President/CEO: E. Thomas Sullivan, JD
Admissions: Dr. Beth A. Wiser
Type: University **Sex:** Coed **Scores:** 99% SAT V 400+; 99% SAT M 400+; 17% ACT 18-23; 55% ACT 24-29 **% Accepted:** 71 **Admission Plans:** Deferred Admission; Early Admission; Early Decision Plan; Preferred Admission **Application Deadline:** January 15 **Application Fee:** $55.00 **H.S. Requirements:** High school diploma required; GED accepted **Costs Per Year:** Application fee: $55. State resident tuition: $14,664 full-time, $611 per credit hour part-time. Nonresident tuition: $37,056 full-time, $1544 per credit hour part-time. Mandatory fees: $210,400 full-time. Part-time tuition varies according to course load. College room and board: $11,150. College room only: $7376. Room and board charges vary according to board plan and housing facility. **Scholarships:** Available. **Calendar System:** Semester, Summer session available **Enrollment:** Full-time 9,991, Graduate full-time 1,299, Graduate part-time 543, Part-time 982 **Faculty:** Full-time 609, Part-time 188 **Student-Faculty Ratio:** 17:1 **Exams:** SAT I or ACT; SAT Reasoning. **% Receiving Financial Aid:** 56 **% Residing in College-Owned, -Operated, or -Affiliated Housing:** 62 **Final Year or Final Semester Residency Requirement:** Yes **Regional Accreditation:** New England Association of Schools and Colleges **Credit Hours For Degree:** 122 credits, Bachelors **ROTC:** Army **Professional Accreditation:** AACN, AACSB, ABET, ACA, ADA, AND, APA, APTA, ASC, ASHA, CSWE, JRCAT, JRCNMT, LCME/AMA, NAACLS, NASPAA, NCATE, SAF. **Intercollegiate Athletics:** Basketball M & W; Cheerleading M & W; Crew M & W; Cross-Country Running M & W; Equestrian Sports M & W; Fencing M & W; Field Hockey W; Gymnastics M & W; Ice Hockey M & W; Lacrosse M & W; Rugby M & W; Sailing M & W; Skiing (Cross-Country) M & W; Skiing (Downhill) M & W; Soccer M & W; Swimming and Diving W; Table Tennis M & W; Track and Field M & W; Ultimate Frisbee M & W; Volleyball M & W; Water Polo M & W

VERMONT TECHNICAL COLLEGE

PO Box 500
Randolph Center, VT 05061-0500
Tel: (802)728-1000; Free: 800-442-VTC1
Fax: (802)728-1390
E-mail: admissions@vtc.edu
Web Site: www.vtc.edu
President/CEO: Dan A. Smith
Admissions: Jessica Van Deren
Financial Aid: Catherine R. McCullough
Type: Four-Year College **Sex:** Coed **Affiliation:** Vermont State Colleges System. **Scores:** 78% SAT V 400+; 88% SAT M 400+; 53% ACT 18-23; 8% ACT 24-29 **% Accepted:** 68 **Application Deadline:** Rolling **Application Fee:** $45.00 **H.S. Requirements:** High school diploma required; GED accepted **Costs Per Year:** Application fee: $45. State resident tuition: $12,456 full-time, $519 per credit hour part-time. Nonresident tuition: $23,832 full-time, $993 per credit part-time. Mandatory fees: $1394 full-time, $43 per credit hour part-time. Full-time tuition and fees vary according to course load

and program. Part-time tuition and fees vary according to program. College room and board: $9696. College room only: $5774. Room and board charges vary according to board plan. **Scholarships:** Available. **Calendar System:** Semester, Summer session available **Enrollment:** Full-time 1,068, Part-time 478 **Faculty:** Full-time 76, Part-time 82 **Student-Faculty Ratio:** 10:1 **Exams:** ACT; SAT I and SAT II or ACT; SAT I or ACT; SAT II. **% Receiv-**

ing **Financial Aid:** 77 **Final Year or Final Semester Residency Require-ment:** No **Regional Accreditation:** New England Association of Schools and Colleges **Credit Hours For Degree:** 60 credit hours, Associates; 130 credit hours, Bachelors **ROTC:** Army **Professional Accreditation:** ABET, ACEN. **Intercollegiate Athletics:** Baseball M; Basketball M & W; Golf M & W; Soccer M & W; Softball W

ADVANCED TECHNOLOGY INSTITUTE
5700 Southern Blvd.
Virginia Beach, VA 23462
Tel: (757)490-1241; Free: 888-468-1093
Web Site: www.auto.edu
President/CEO: Mark Dreyfus
Type: Two-Year College **Sex:** Coed **% Accepted:** 75 **Application Fee:** $100.00 **Student-Faculty Ratio:** 24:1 **Professional Accreditation:** ACCSC.

AMERICAN NATIONAL UNIVERSITY (CHARLOTTESVILLE)
3926 Seminole Trl.
Charlottesville, VA 22911
Tel: (434)220-7960; Free: 888-9-JOBREADY
Fax: (434)986-1344
Web Site: www.an.edu
Admissions: Kimberly Moore
Type: Comprehensive **Sex:** Coed **Affiliation:** National College of Business and Technology. **Admission Plans:** Open Admission **Application Deadline:** Rolling **H.S. Requirements:** High school diploma required; GED accepted **Scholarships:** Available. **Calendar System:** Quarter, Summer session available **Credit Hours For Degree:** 96 quarter hours, Associates **Professional Accreditation:** AAMAE, ACICS.

AMERICAN NATIONAL UNIVERSITY (DANVILLE)
336 Old Riverside Dr.
Danville, VA 24541
Tel: (434)793-6822; Free: 888-9-JOBREADY
Fax: (434)793-3634
Web Site: www.an.edu
Type: Comprehensive **Sex:** Coed **Affiliation:** National College of Business and Technology. **Admission Plans:** Open Admission **Application Deadline:** Rolling **H.S. Requirements:** High school diploma required; GED accepted **Scholarships:** Available. **Calendar System:** Quarter, Summer session available **Credit Hours For Degree:** 96 quarter hours, Associates **Professional Accreditation:** AAMAE, ACICS.

AMERICAN NATIONAL UNIVERSITY (HARRISONBURG)
1515 Country Club Rd.
Harrisonburg, VA 22802
Tel: (540)432-0943; Free: 888-9-JOBREADY
Fax: (540)986-1344
Web Site: www.an.edu
Admissions: Jack Evey
Type: Comprehensive **Sex:** Coed **Affiliation:** National College of Business and Technology. **Admission Plans:** Open Admission **Application Deadline:** Rolling **H.S. Requirements:** High school diploma required; GED accepted **Scholarships:** Available. **Calendar System:** Quarter, Summer session available **Credit Hours For Degree:** 96 credit hours, Associates **Professional Accreditation:** AAMAE, ACICS.

AMERICAN NATIONAL UNIVERSITY (LYNCHBURG)
104 Candlewood Ct.
Lynchburg, VA 24502
Tel: (434)239-3500; Free: 888-9-JOBREADY

Fax: (434)986-1344
Web Site: www.an.edu
Type: Comprehensive **Sex:** Coed **Affiliation:** National College of Business and Technology. **Admission Plans:** Open Admission **Application Deadline:** Rolling **H.S. Requirements:** High school diploma required; GED accepted **Scholarships:** Available. **Calendar System:** Quarter, Summer session available **Credit Hours For Degree:** 96 quarter hours, Associates **Professional Accreditation:** AAMAE, ACICS.

AMERICAN NATIONAL UNIVERSITY (MARTINSVILLE)
905 N Memorial Blvd.
Martinsville, VA 24112
Tel: (276)632-5621; Free: 888-9-JOBREADY
Fax: (276)986-1344
Web Site: www.an.edu
Admissions: John Scott
Type: Comprehensive **Sex:** Coed **Affiliation:** National College of Business and Technology. **Admission Plans:** Open Admission **Application Deadline:** Rolling **H.S. Requirements:** High school diploma required; GED accepted **Scholarships:** Available. **Calendar System:** Quarter, Summer session available **Credit Hours For Degree:** 96 quarter hours, Associates **Professional Accreditation:** ACICS.

AMERICAN NATIONAL UNIVERSITY (SALEM)
1813 E Main St.
Salem, VA 24153
Tel: (540)986-1800; Free: 888-9-JOBREADY
Fax: (540)986-1344
Web Site: www.an.edu
President/CEO: Frank Longaker
Type: Comprehensive **Sex:** Coed **Affiliation:** National College of Business and Technology. **Admission Plans:** Open Admission **Application Deadline:** Rolling **H.S. Requirements:** High school diploma required; GED accepted **Scholarships:** Available. **Calendar System:** Quarter, Summer session available **Credit Hours For Degree:** 96 quarter hours, Associates; 180 quarter hours, Bachelors **Professional Accreditation:** AAMAE, ACICS.

ARGOSY UNIVERSITY, WASHINGTON DC
1550 Wilson Blvd., Ste. 600
Arlington, VA 22209
Tel: (703)526-5800; Free: 866-703-2777
Fax: (703)526-5850
Web Site: www.argosy.edu/locations/washington-dc
President/CEO: David Erekson
Type: University **Sex:** Coed **Affiliation:** Argosy Education Group. **Calendar System:** Semester **Regional Accreditation:** Western Association of Colleges and Schools **Professional Accreditation:** ACBSP, APA.

THE ART INSTITUTE OF VIRGINIA BEACH, A BRANCH OF THE ART INSTITUTE OF ATLANTA
Two Columbus Ctr.
4500 Main St., Ste. 100
Virginia Beach, VA 23462
Tel: (757)493-6700; Free: 877-437-4428
Fax: (757)493-6800

Web Site: www.artinstitutes.edu/virginia-beach
President/CEO: Marilyn Burstein
Type: Four-Year College Sex: Coed Regional Accreditation: Southern Association of Colleges and Schools

THE ART INSTITUTE OF WASHINGTON, A BRANCH OF THE ART INSTITUTE OF ATLANTA
1820 N Fort Meyer Dr.
Arlington, VA 22209
Tel: (703)358-9550; Free: 877-303-3771
Fax: (703)358-9759
Web Site: www.artinstitutes.edu/arlington
President/CEO: Jim Palermo
Type: Four-Year College Sex: Coed Affiliation: Education Management Corporation. Calendar System: Quarter Regional Accreditation: Southern Association of Colleges and Schools Professional Accreditation: ACF.

AVERETT UNIVERSITY
420 W Main St.
Danville, VA 24541-3692
Tel: (434)791-5600; Free: 800-AVERETT
Fax: (434)791-5637
E-mail: joel.nester@averett.edu
Web Site: www.averett.edu
President/CEO: Dr. Tiffany M. Franks
Admissions: Joel Nester
Financial Aid: Carl Bradsher
Type: Comprehensive Sex: Coed Affiliation: Baptist General Association of Virginia. Scores: 80% SAT V 400+; 86% SAT M 400+; 46% ACT 18-23; 16% ACT 24-29 % Accepted: 61 Admission Plans: Deferred Admission Application Deadline: September 1 Application Fee: $0.00 H.S. Requirements: High school diploma required; GED accepted Costs Per Year: Application fee: $0. Comprehensive fee: $39,600 includes full-time tuition ($30,900) and college room and board ($8700). College room only: $5870. Full-time tuition varies according to class time, course load, degree level, location, and program. Room and board charges vary according to board plan and housing facility. Part-time tuition: $960 per credit. Part-time tuition varies according to class time, course load, degree level, location, and program. Scholarships: Available. Calendar System: Semester, Summer session available Enrollment: Full-time 853, Graduate full-time 3, Part-time 38 Faculty: Full-time 60, Part-time 57 Student-Faculty Ratio: 11:1 Exams: ACT; ACT essay component not used; Other; SAT I; SAT I and SAT II or ACT; SAT I or ACT; SAT II; SAT essay component not used. % Receiving Financial Aid: 86 % Residing in College-Owned, -Operated, or -Affiliated Housing: 61 Final Year or Final Semester Residency Requirement: No Regional Accreditation: Southern Association of Colleges and Schools Credit Hours For Degree: 60 credit hours, Associates; 120 credit hours, Bachelors Intercollegiate Athletics: Baseball M; Basketball M & W; Cheerleading M & W; Cross-Country Running M & W; Equestrian Sports M & W; Football M; Golf M; Soccer M & W; Softball W; Tennis M & W; Volleyball W

BETHEL COLLEGE
1705 Todds Ln.
Hampton, VA 23666
Tel: (757)826-1426
Web Site: www.bcva.edu
President/CEO: Ron DeBerry
Admissions: Nanette Bartholomew
Type: Four-Year College Sex: Coed Affiliation: Assembly of God Church. Admission Plans: Early Admission H.S. Requirements: High school diploma required; GED accepted Costs Per Year: Tuition: $250 per credit part-time. Calendar System: Semester, Summer session available Exams: SAT I or ACT. % Residing in College-Owned, -Operated, or -Affiliated Housing: 20 Professional Accreditation: ABHE.

BLUE RIDGE COMMUNITY COLLEGE
PO Box 80
Weyers Cave, VA 24486-0080
Tel: (540)234-9261; Free: 888-750-2722
E-mail: bakerb@brcc.edu
Web Site: www.brcc.edu
President/CEO: John A. Downey
Admissions: Rebecca Baker

Type: Two-Year College Sex: Coed Affiliation: Virginia Community College System. Admission Plans: Early Admission; Open Admission Application Deadline: Rolling Application Fee: $0.00 H.S. Requirements: High school diploma required; GED accepted Scholarships: Available. Calendar System: Semester, Summer session available Student-Faculty Ratio: 22:1 Exams: Other. Regional Accreditation: Southern Association of Colleges and Schools Credit Hours For Degree: 63 semester hours, Associates Professional Accreditation: ACEN.

BLUEFIELD COLLEGE
3000 College Ave.
Bluefield, VA 24605-1799
Tel: (276)326-3682; Free: 800-872-0175
Fax: (276)326-4288
E-mail: esherman@bluefield.edu
Web Site: www.bluefield.edu
President/CEO: Dr. David Olive
Admissions: Evan Sherman
Financial Aid: Carly Jean Kestner
Type: Comprehensive Sex: Coed Affiliation: Southern Baptist. Scores: 78% SAT V 400+; 80% SAT M 400+; 56% ACT 18-23; 12% ACT 24-29 Costs Per Year: Comprehensive fee: $32,528 includes full-time tuition ($23,600) and college room and board ($8928). College room only: $3878. Full-time tuition varies according to course load and program. Room and board charges vary according to housing facility. Part-time tuition: $990 per credit. Part-time tuition varies according to course load and program. Scholarships: Available. Calendar System: Semester, Summer session available Enrollment: Full-time 813, Graduate full-time 13, Graduate part-time 3, Part-time 143 Faculty: Full-time 38, Part-time 54 Student-Faculty Ratio: 15:1 Exams: ACT essay component not used; SAT I or ACT; SAT essay component not used. % Receiving Financial Aid: 84 % Residing in College-Owned, -Operated, or -Affiliated Housing: 65 Final Year or Final Semester Residency Requirement: No Regional Accreditation: Southern Association of Colleges and Schools Credit Hours For Degree: 63 semester hours, Associates; 126 semester hours, Bachelors Professional Accreditation: TEAC. Intercollegiate Athletics: Baseball M; Basketball M & W; Cross-Country Running M & W; Football M; Golf M; Soccer M & W; Softball W; Tennis M & W; Track and Field M & W; Volleyball M & W

BON SECOURS MEMORIAL COLLEGE OF NURSING
8550 Magellan Pky.
Ste. 1100
Richmond, VA 23227-1149
Tel: (804)627-5300; Free: 866-238-7414
Web Site: www.bsmcon.edu
Type: Four-Year College Sex: Coed Professional Accreditation: ACICS.

BRIDGEWATER COLLEGE
402 E College St.
Bridgewater, VA 22812-1599
Tel: (540)828-8000; Free: 800-759-8328
Fax: (540)828-5481
E-mail: admissions@bridgewater.edu
Web Site: www.bridgewater.edu
President/CEO: Dr. David W. Bushman
Admissions: Jarret L. Smith
Financial Aid: Scott Morrison
Type: Four-Year College Sex: Coed Affiliation: Church of the Brethren. Scores: 95% SAT V 400+; 95% SAT M 400+; 54.8% ACT 18-23; 32.7% ACT 24-29 % Accepted: 49 Admission Plans: Deferred Admission Application Deadline: May 1 Application Fee: $0.00 H.S. Requirements: High school diploma required; GED accepted Costs Per Year: Application fee: $0. Comprehensive fee: $44,510 includes full-time tuition ($31,890), mandatory fees ($700), and college room and board ($11,920). Room and board charges vary according to housing facility. Scholarships: Available. Calendar System: 4-1-4, Summer session available Enrollment: Full-time 1,823, Part-time 11 Faculty: Full-time 117, Part-time 37 Student-Faculty Ratio: 14:1 Exams: ACT essay component not used; SAT I or ACT; SAT essay component not used; SAT Reasoning. % Receiving Financial Aid: 80 % Residing in College-Owned, -Operated, or -Affiliated Housing: 83 Final Year or Final Semester Residency Requirement: Yes Regional Accreditation: Southern Association of Colleges and Schools Credit Hours For Degree: 123 credits, Bachelors Intercollegiate Athletics: Baseball M; Basketball M & W; Cheerleading M & W; Cross-Country Running M & W;

Equestrian Sports M & W; Field Hockey W; Football M; Golf M & W; Lacrosse M & W; Soccer M & W; Softball W; Swimming and Diving W; Tennis M & W; Track and Field M & W; Volleyball W; Wrestling M

BRYANT & STRATTON COLLEGE–HAMPTON CAMPUS
4410 E Claiborne Sq., Ste. 233
Hampton, VA 23666
Tel: (757)896-6001
Web Site: www.bryantstratton.edu
Type: Four-Year College **Sex:** Coed **Regional Accreditation:** Middle States Association of Colleges and Schools

BRYANT & STRATTON COLLEGE–RICHMOND CAMPUS
8141 Hull St. Rd.
Richmond, VA 23235
Tel: (804)745-2444
Fax: (804)499-7799
E-mail: tlawson@bryantstratton.edu
Web Site: www.bryantstratton.edu
President/CEO: Beth Murphy
Admissions: David K. Mayle
Type: Two-Year College **Sex:** Coed **Affiliation:** Bryant and Stratton Business Institute, Inc. **Admission Plans:** Deferred Admission **Application Deadline:** Rolling **H.S. Requirements:** High school diploma required; GED accepted. For applicants 19 or over who meet entrance testing requirements: High school diploma required; GED not accepted **Calendar System:** Semester, Summer session available **Enrollment:** Full-time 280, Part-time 292 **Faculty:** Full-time 14, Part-time 35 **Student-Faculty Ratio:** 10:1 **Exams:** Other; SAT I or ACT. **Regional Accreditation:** Middle States Association of Colleges and Schools **Credit Hours For Degree:** 68 per credit, Associates

BRYANT & STRATTON COLLEGE–VIRGINIA BEACH CAMPUS
301 Centre Pointe Dr.
Virginia Beach, VA 23462
Tel: (757)499-7900
Fax: (757)499-7799
E-mail: dmsoutherland@bryantstratton.edu
Web Site: www.bryantstratton.edu
President/CEO: Lee E. Hicklin
Admissions: Deana M. Southerland
Type: Two-Year College **Sex:** Coed **Affiliation:** Bryant and Stratton Business Institute, Inc. **% Accepted:** 88 **Admission Plans:** Open Admission **Application Deadline:** Rolling **Application Fee:** $35.00 **H.S. Requirements:** High school diploma required; GED accepted **Scholarships:** Available. **Calendar System:** Semester, Summer session available **Enrollment:** Full-time 267, Part-time 328 **Faculty:** Full-time 20, Part-time 40 **Student-Faculty Ratio:** 12:1 **Exams:** Other. **Final Year or Final Semester Residency Requirement:** No **Regional Accreditation:** Middle States Association of Colleges and Schools **Credit Hours For Degree:** 60 credit hours, Associates; 120 credit hours, Bachelors

CENTRA COLLEGE OF NURSING
905 Lakeside Dr., Ste. A
Lynchburg, VA 24501
Tel: (434)947-3070
Web Site: www.centrahealth.com/college-of-nursing
Type: Two-Year College **Sex:** Coed **Professional Accreditation:** ACEN.

CENTRAL VIRGINIA COMMUNITY COLLEGE
3506 Wards Rd.
Lynchburg, VA 24502-2498
Tel: (434)832-7600; Free: 800-562-3060
Fax: (434)832-7626
Web Site: www.cvcc.vccs.edu
President/CEO: Dr. John Capps
Type: Two-Year College **Sex:** Coed **Affiliation:** Virginia Community College System. **% Accepted:** 100 **Admission Plans:** Deferred Admission; Early Admission; Open Admission **Application Deadline:** Rolling **Application Fee:** $0.00 **H.S. Requirements:** High school diploma required; GED accepted **Costs Per Year:** Application fee: $0. State resident tuition: $4470 full-time, $149 per credit hour part-time. Nonresident tuition: $10,293 full-time, $343.10 per credit hour part-time. **Scholarships:** Available. **Calendar System:** Semester, Summer session available **Enrollment:** Full-time 1,464,

Part-time 2,969 **Faculty:** Full-time 62, Part-time 240 **Student-Faculty Ratio:** 18:1 **Regional Accreditation:** Southern Association of Colleges and Schools **Credit Hours For Degree:** 61 credit hours, Associates **Professional Accreditation:** JRCERT, NAACLS.

CENTURA COLLEGE (CHESAPEAKE)
932 Ventures Way
Chesapeake, VA 23320
Tel: (757)549-2121; Free: 877-575-5627
Fax: (757)548-1196
Web Site: www.centuracollege.edu
President/CEO: Ashley West
Type: Two-Year College **Sex:** Coed **Application Fee:** $25.00 **Student-Faculty Ratio:** 24:1 **Professional Accreditation:** ACCSC.

CENTURA COLLEGE (NEWPORT NEWS)
616 Denbigh Blvd.
Newport News, VA 23608
Tel: (757)874-2121; Free: 877-575-5627
Fax: (757)874-3857
E-mail: admdircpen@centura.edu
Web Site: www.centuracollege.edu
President/CEO: Paula Bowne
Admissions: Victoria Whitehead
Type: Two-Year College **Sex:** Coed **Application Fee:** $25.00 **Student-Faculty Ratio:** 8:1 **Professional Accreditation:** ACCSC.

CENTURA COLLEGE (NORFOLK)
7020 N Military Hwy.
Norfolk, VA 23518
Tel: (757)853-2121; Free: 877-575-5627
Fax: (757)852-9017
Web Site: www.centuracollege.edu
President/CEO: Chauntrell Guilford
Type: Two-Year College **Sex:** Coed **Application Fee:** $25.00 **Student-Faculty Ratio:** 17:1 **Professional Accreditation:** ACCSC.

CENTURA COLLEGE (NORTH CHESTERFIELD)
7914 Midlothian Tpke.
North Chesterfield, VA 23235-5230
Tel: (804)330-0111; Free: 877-575-5627
Fax: (804)330-3809
Web Site: www.centuracollege.edu
President/CEO: Zoe Thompson
Type: Two-Year College **Sex:** Coed **Application Fee:** $25.00 **Student-Faculty Ratio:** 10:1 **Professional Accreditation:** ACCSC.

CENTURA COLLEGE (VIRGINIA BEACH)
2697 Dean Dr.
Ste. 100
Virginia Beach, VA 23452
Tel: (757)340-2121; Free: 877-575-5627
Fax: (757)340-9704
Web Site: www.centuracollege.edu
President/CEO: Ben Clark
Type: Two-Year College **Sex:** Coed **Application Fee:** $25.00 **Student-Faculty Ratio:** 35:1 **Professional Accreditation:** ACCSC.

CHAMBERLAIN COLLEGE OF NURSING
2450 Crystal Dr.
Ste. 319
Arlington, VA 22202
Tel: (703)416-7300; Free: 877-751-5783
Fax: (703)416-7490
Web Site: www.chamberlain.edu
President/CEO: Patricia Hughes
Type: Four-Year College **Sex:** Coed **Costs Per Year:** Tuition: $17,560 full-time, $665 per credit hour part-time. Mandatory fees: $600 full-time, $300 per term part-time. Full-time tuition and fees vary according to course load. Part-time tuition and fees vary according to course load. **Calendar System:** Semester **Enrollment:** Full-time 239, Part-time 155 **Faculty:** Full-time 12, Part-time 27 **Student-Faculty Ratio:** 14:1 **Exams:** ACT essay component

used for admission; SAT I or ACT; SAT essay component used for admission. **Regional Accreditation:** North Central Association of Colleges and Schools

CHRISTENDOM COLLEGE
134 Christendom Dr.
Front Royal, VA 22630-5103
Tel: (540)636-2900; Free: 800-877-5456
Fax: (540)636-1655
E-mail: sam.phillips@christendom.edu
Web Site: www.christendom.edu
President/CEO: Dr. Timothy O'Donnell
Admissions: Samuel J. Phillips
Financial Aid: Alisa Polk

Type: Comprehensive **Sex:** Coed **Affiliation:** Roman Catholic. **Scores:** 99% SAT V 400+; 89% SAT M 400+; 30% ACT 18-23; 37% ACT 24-29 **% Accepted:** 96 **Admission Plans:** Early Admission; Early Decision Plan **Application Deadline:** March 1 **Application Fee:** $0.00 **H.S. Requirements:** High school diploma or equivalent not required **Costs Per Year:** Application fee: $0. Comprehensive fee: $34,570 includes full-time tuition ($23,990), mandatory fees ($850), and college room and board ($9730). **Scholarships:** Available. **Calendar System:** Semester, Summer session available **Enrollment:** Full-time 469, Graduate full-time 19, Graduate part-time 86 **Faculty:** Full-time 29, Part-time 20 **Student-Faculty Ratio:** 14:1 **Exams:** ACT essay component not used; SAT I or ACT; SAT essay component used for admission; SAT Reasoning. **% Receiving Financial Aid:** 58 **% Residing in College-Owned, -Operated, or -Affiliated Housing:** 90 **Final Year or Final Semester Residency Requirement:** No **Regional Accreditation:** Southern Association of Colleges and Schools **Credit Hours For Degree:** 86 credit hours, Associates; 126 credit hours, Bachelors **Intercollegiate Athletics:** Basketball M & W; Cross-Country Running M & W; Rugby M; Soccer M & W; Softball W; Volleyball W

CHRISTOPHER NEWPORT UNIVERSITY
1 Ave. of the Arts
Newport News, VA 23606-3072
Tel: (757)594-7000; Free: 800-333-4268
Fax: (757)594-7333
E-mail: admit@cnu.edu
Web Site: www.cnu.edu
President/CEO: Hon. Paul S. Trible, Jr.
Admissions: Rob J. Lange, III
Financial Aid: Christina Russell

Type: Comprehensive **Sex:** Coed **Scores:** 100% SAT V 400+; 99% SAT M 400+; 28% ACT 18-23; 62% ACT 24-29 **% Accepted:** 60 **Admission Plans:** Deferred Admission; Early Action; Early Admission; Early Decision Plan **Application Deadline:** February 1 **Application Fee:** $50.00 **H.S. Requirements:** High school diploma required; GED not accepted **Costs Per Year:** Application fee: $50. State resident tuition: $7608 full-time, $317 per credit hour part-time. Nonresident tuition: $18,510 full-time, $772 per credit hour part-time. Mandatory fees: $4918 full-time, $205 per credit hour part-time. Full-time tuition and fees vary according to course load. Part-time tuition and fees vary according to course load. College room and board: $10,614. College room only: $6664. Room and board charges vary according to board plan and housing facility. **Scholarships:** Available. **Calendar System:** Semester, Summer session available **Enrollment:** Full-time 4,961, Graduate full-time 87, Graduate part-time 34, Part-time 90 **Faculty:** Full-time 275, Part-time 180 **Student-Faculty Ratio:** 15:1 **Exams:** ACT; ACT essay component not used; SAT I; SAT I and SAT II or ACT; SAT I or ACT; SAT II; SAT essay component not used; SAT Reasoning. **% Receiving Financial Aid:** 42 **% Residing in College-Owned, -Operated, or -Affiliated Housing:** 74 **Final Year or Final Semester Residency Requirement:** Yes **Regional Accreditation:** Southern Association of Colleges and Schools **Credit Hours For Degree:** 120 semester hours, Bachelors **ROTC:** Army **Professional Accreditation:** AACSB, ABET, CSWE, NASM. **Intercollegiate Athletics:** Baseball M; Basketball M & W; Crew M & W; Cross-Country Running M & W; Equestrian Sports M & W; Field Hockey W; Football M; Golf M; Ice Hockey M; Lacrosse M & W; Rowing M & W; Rugby M; Soccer M & W; Softball W; Swimming and Diving M & W; Tennis M & W; Track and Field M & W; Ultimate Frisbee M; Volleyball M & W

THE COLLEGE OF WILLIAM AND MARY
PO Box 8795
Williamsburg, VA 23187-8795

Tel: (757)221-4000
Fax: (757)221-1242
E-mail: admission@wm.edu
Web Site: www.wm.edu
President/CEO: Taylor Reveley
Admissions: Deborah Basket
Financial Aid: Edward P. Irish

Type: University **Sex:** Coed **Scores:** 100% SAT V 400+; 100% SAT M 400+; 1.96% ACT 18-23; 34.19% ACT 24-29 **% Accepted:** 34 **Admission Plans:** Deferred Admission; Early Action; Early Admission; Preferred Admission **Application Deadline:** January 1 **Application Fee:** $70.00 **H.S. Requirements:** High school diploma or equivalent not required **Costs Per Year:** Application fee: $70. State resident tuition: $13,978 full-time, $370 per credit hour part-time. Nonresident tuition: $35,122 full-time, $1120 per credit hour part-time. Mandatory fees: $5394 full-time. College room and board: $10,978. College room only: $6792. Tuition guaranteed not to increase for student's term of enrollment. **Scholarships:** Available. **Calendar System:** Semester, Summer session available **Enrollment:** Full-time 6,217, Graduate full-time 1,675, Graduate part-time 508, Part-time 84 **Exams:** SAT I or ACT; SAT II; SAT Reasoning; SAT Subject. **% Receiving Financial Aid:** 33 **% Residing in College-Owned, -Operated, or -Affiliated Housing:** 74 **Final Year or Final Semester Residency Requirement:** Yes **Regional Accreditation:** Southern Association of Colleges and Schools **Credit Hours For Degree:** 120 credit hours, Bachelors **ROTC:** Army **Professional Accreditation:** AACSB, AALS, ABA, ACA, APA, NCATE. **Intercollegiate Athletics:** Baseball M; Basketball M & W; Cross-Country Running M & W; Field Hockey W; Football M; Golf M & W; Gymnastics M & W; Lacrosse W; Soccer M & W; Swimming and Diving M & W; Tennis M & W; Track and Field M & W; Volleyball W

COLUMBIA COLLEGE
8300 Merrifield Ave.
Fairfax, VA 22031
Tel: (703)206-0508
Web Site: www.ccdc.edu
Type: Two-Year College **Sex:** Coed **Professional Accreditation:** ACICS, COE.

CULINARY INSTITUTE OF VIRGINIA
2428 Almeda Ave., Ste. 316
Norfolk, VA 23513
Tel: (757)853-3508; Free: 866-619-CHEF
Fax: (757)857-4869
E-mail: hsadmissions@chefva.com
Web Site: www.chefva.com
President/CEO: Dorothea A. Bovani
Financial Aid: Lynn Robinson

Type: Four-Year College **Sex:** Coed **Affiliation:** ECPI College of Technology. **Application Deadline:** Rolling **Application Fee:** $100.00 **H.S. Requirements:** High school diploma required; GED accepted **Scholarships:** Available. **Faculty:** Full-time 16, Part-time 3 **% Receiving Financial Aid:** 80 **Final Year or Final Semester Residency Requirement:** No **Credit Hours For Degree:** 83 semester credits, Associates; 121 semester credits, Bachelors **Professional Accreditation:** ACF.

DABNEY S. LANCASTER COMMUNITY COLLEGE
1000 Dabney Dr.
Clifton Forge, VA 24422
Tel: (540)863-2800; Free: 877-73-DSLCC
Fax: (540)863-2915
E-mail: lwferguson@dslcc.edu
Web Site: www.dslcc.edu
President/CEO: Dr. John Rainone
Admissions: Lorrie Wilhelm Ferguson
Financial Aid: Joy F. Broyles

Type: Two-Year College **Sex:** Coed **Affiliation:** Virginia Community College System. **Costs Per Year:** State resident tuition: $3492 full-time, $134 per credit part-time. Nonresident tuition: $8,162 full-time, $310.60 per credit part-time. Mandatory fees: $276 full-time, $11.50 per credit part-time. Full-time tuition and fees vary according to reciprocity agreements. Part-time tuition and fees vary according to reciprocity agreements. **Scholarships:** Available. **Calendar System:** Semester, Summer session available **Faculty:** Full-time 23, Part-time 74 **Student-Faculty Ratio:** 16:1 **Exams:** ACT essay component used for advising; ACT essay component used for placement;

SAT I and SAT II or ACT; SAT II; SAT essay component used for advising; SAT essay component used for placement. **Final Year or Final Semester Residency Requirement:** No **Regional Accreditation:** Southern Association of Colleges and Schools **Credit Hours For Degree:** 61 semester hours, Associates **Professional Accreditation:** ACEN, ACF.

DANVILLE COMMUNITY COLLEGE

1008 S Main St.
Danville, VA 24541-4088
Tel: (434)797-2222; Free: 800-560-4291
Fax: (434)797-8541
E-mail: cpulliam@dcc.vccs.edu
Web Site: www.dcc.vccs.edu
President/CEO: B. Carlyle Ramsey
Admissions: Cathy Pulliam

Type: Two-Year College **Sex:** Coed **Affiliation:** Virginia Community College System. **Admission Plans:** Deferred Admission; Early Admission; Open Admission; Preferred Admission **Application Deadline:** Rolling **Application Fee:** $0.00 **H.S. Requirements:** High school diploma required; GED accepted **Scholarships:** Available. **Calendar System:** Semester, Summer session available **Student-Faculty Ratio:** 18:1 **Regional Accreditation:** Southern Association of Colleges and Schools **Credit Hours For Degree:** 62 semester hours, Associates

DEVRY UNIVERSITY (ARLINGTON)

2450 Crystal Dr.
Arlington, VA 22202
Tel: (703)414-4000; Free: 866-338-7941
Fax: (703)414-4040
Web Site: www.devry.edu
Financial Aid: Roberta McDevitt

Type: Comprehensive **Sex:** Coed **Affiliation:** DeVry University. **Application Fee:** $40.00 **H.S. Requirements:** High school diploma required; GED accepted **Costs Per Year:** Application fee: $40. Tuition: $17,052 full-time, $609 per credit hour part-time. Mandatory fees: $80 full-time, $40 per term part-time. **Scholarships:** Available. **Calendar System:** Semester **Enrollment:** Full-time 202, Graduate full-time 53, Graduate part-time 238, Part-time 222 **Faculty:** Full-time 14, Part-time 124 **Student-Faculty Ratio:** 7:1 **Exams:** ACT essay component used for admission; ACT essay component used for placement; SAT essay component used for admission; SAT essay component used for placement. **% Receiving Financial Aid:** 75 **Regional Accreditation:** North Central Association of Colleges and Schools **Credit Hours For Degree:** 67 credit hours, Associates; 122 credit hours, Bachelors **Professional Accreditation:** ABET, ACBSP.

DEVRY UNIVERSITY (CHESAPEAKE)

1317 Executive Blvd., Ste. 100
Chesapeake, VA 23320-3671
Tel: (757)382-5680; Free: 866-338-7941
Web Site: www.devry.edu

Type: Comprehensive **Sex:** Coed **Application Deadline:** Rolling **Costs Per Year:** Tuition: $17,052 full-time, $609 per credit hour part-time. Mandatory fees: $80 full-time, $40 per term part-time. **Regional Accreditation:** North Central Association of Colleges and Schools **Professional Accreditation:** ACBSP.

DEVRY UNIVERSITY (MANASSAS)

10432 Balls Ford Rd., Ste. 130
Manassas, VA 20109-3173
Tel: (703)396-6611; Free: 866-338-7941
Web Site: www.devry.edu

Type: Comprehensive **Sex:** Coed **Application Deadline:** Rolling **Costs Per Year:** Tuition: $17,052 full-time, $609 per credit hour part-time. Mandatory fees: $80 full-time, $40 per term part-time. **Calendar System:** Semester **Regional Accreditation:** North Central Association of Colleges and Schools **Professional Accreditation:** ACBSP.

EASTERN MENNONITE UNIVERSITY

1200 Park Rd.
Harrisonburg, VA 22802-2462
Tel: (540)432-4000; Free: 800-368-2665
Fax: (540)432-4444
E-mail: admiss@emu.edu
Web Site: www.emu.edu

President/CEO: Dr. Loren E. Swartzendruber
Admissions: Jason Good
Financial Aid: Renee Leap

Type: Comprehensive **Sex:** Coed **Affiliation:** Mennonite. **Scores:** 89% SAT V 400+; 89% SAT M 400+; 50% ACT 18-23; 20% ACT 24-29 **% Accepted:** 65 **Admission Plans:** Deferred Admission **Application Deadline:** Rolling **Application Fee:** $25.00 **H.S. Requirements:** High school diploma required; GED accepted **Scholarships:** Available. **Calendar System:** Semester, Summer session available **Enrollment:** Full-time 1,122, Graduate full-time 130, Graduate part-time 326, Part-time 62 **Faculty:** Full-time 110, Part-time 94 **Student-Faculty Ratio:** 10:1 **Exams:** SAT I or ACT. **% Receiving Financial Aid:** 72 **% Residing in College-Owned, -Operated, or -Affiliated Housing:** 58 **Final Year or Final Semester Residency Requirement:** Yes **Regional Accreditation:** Southern Association of Colleges and Schools **Credit Hours For Degree:** 64 semester hours, Associates; 128 semester hours, Bachelors **Professional Accreditation:** AACN, ACA, ACIPE, ATS, CSWE, NCATE. **Intercollegiate Athletics:** Baseball M; Basketball M & W; Cross-Country Running M & W; Field Hockey W; Golf M & W; Soccer M & W; Softball W; Track and Field M & W; Volleyball M & W

EASTERN SHORE COMMUNITY COLLEGE

29300 Lankford Hwy.
Melfa, VA 23410-3000
Tel: (757)789-1789; Free: 877-871-8455
Fax: (757)789-1739
E-mail: bsmith@es.vccs.edu
Web Site: www.es.vccs.edu
President/CEO: Dr. Linda Thomas-Glover, PhD
Admissions: P. Bryan Smith

Type: Two-Year College **Sex:** Coed **Affiliation:** Virginia Community College System. **Admission Plans:** Open Admission; Preferred Admission **Application Deadline:** Rolling **Application Fee:** $0.00 **H.S. Requirements:** High school diploma required; GED accepted **Costs Per Year:** Application fee: $0. State resident tuition: $4020 full-time, $134 per credit hour part-time. Nonresident tuition: $9320 full-time, $310 per credit hour part-time. Mandatory fees: $375 full-time, $12.50 per credit hour part-time. Full-time tuition and fees vary according to course load. Part-time tuition and fees vary according to course load. **Scholarships:** Available. **Calendar System:** Semester, Summer session available **Enrollment:** Full-time 264, Part-time 593 **Faculty:** Full-time 17, Part-time 70 **Student-Faculty Ratio:** 13:1 **Exams:** ACT essay component not used; SAT essay component not used. **Regional Accreditation:** Southern Association of Colleges and Schools **Credit Hours For Degree:** 62 semester hours, Associates

EASTERN VIRGINIA CAREER COLLEGE

10304 Spotsylvania Ave.
Ste. 400
Fredericksburg, VA 22408
Tel: (540)373-2200
Web Site: www.evcc.edu

Type: Two-Year College **Sex:** Coed **Professional Accreditation:** COE.

ECPI UNIVERSITY (GLEN ALLEN)

4305 Cox Rd.
Glen Allen, VA 23060
Tel: (804)894-9150; Free: 844-611-0688
Fax: (804)934-0054
E-mail: jpope@ecpi.edu
Web Site: www.ecpi.edu
Admissions: Jacob Pope

Type: Four-Year College **Sex:** Coed **% Accepted:** 82 **Application Deadline:** Rolling **Application Fee:** $100.00 **Calendar System:** Semester **Enrollment:** Full-time 473 **Student-Faculty Ratio:** 15:1 **Exams:** SAT I; SAT I and SAT II or ACT; SAT II. **Regional Accreditation:** Southern Association of Colleges and Schools **Professional Accreditation:** ACCSC.

ECPI UNIVERSITY (MANASSAS)

10021 Balls Ford Rd., No.100
Manassas, VA 20109
Tel: (703)348-4062; Free: 844-611-0804
Fax: (703)369-0530
Web Site: www.ecpi.edu

Type: Four-Year College **Sex:** Coed **Regional Accreditation:** Southern Association of Colleges and Schools

ECPI UNIVERSITY (NEWPORT NEWS)

1001 Omni Blvd., No.100
Newport News, VA 23606
Tel: (757)849-0548; Free: 844-611-0618
Fax: (757)827-5351
Web Site: www.ecpi.edu
Admissions: Cheryl Lokey

Type: Four-Year College **Sex:** Coed **Admission Plans:** Deferred Admission **Application Fee:** $100.00 **H.S. Requirements:** High school diploma required; GED accepted **Calendar System:** Trimester, Summer session available **Enrollment:** Full-time 556 **Faculty:** Full-time 66, Part-time 64 **Student-Faculty Ratio:** 16:1 **Exams:** SAT I; SAT I or ACT; SAT II. **Regional Accreditation:** Southern Association of Colleges and Schools **Credit Hours For Degree:** 60 semester hours, Associates

ECPI UNIVERSITY (RICHMOND)

800 Moorefield Park Dr.
Richmond, VA 23236
Tel: (804)616-3588; Free: 844-611-0694
Fax: (804)330-5577
E-mail: agerard@ecpi.edu
Web Site: www.ecpi.edu

Type: Two-Year College **Sex:** Coed **% Accepted:** 80 **Admission Plans:** Deferred Admission **Application Deadline:** Rolling **Application Fee:** $100.00 **H.S. Requirements:** High school diploma required; GED accepted **Calendar System:** Semester, Summer session available **Enrollment:** Full-time 865 **Faculty:** Full-time 20, Part-time 18 **Student-Faculty Ratio:** 18:1 **Exams:** SAT I; SAT II. **Regional Accreditation:** Southern Association of Colleges and Schools **Credit Hours For Degree:** 60 semester hours, Associates **Professional Accreditation:** ACCSC.

ECPI UNIVERSITY (VIRGINIA BEACH)

5555 Greenwich Rd.
Virginia Beach, VA 23462
Tel: (757)517-3903; Free: 844-611-0766
Fax: (757)671-8661
E-mail: rballance@ecpi.edu
Web Site: www.ecpi.edu
President/CEO: Mark Dreyfus
Admissions: Bernadette Rozman Bellas
Financial Aid: Kathi Turner

Type: Four-Year College **Sex:** Coed **% Accepted:** 80 **Admission Plans:** Deferred Admission **Application Fee:** $45.00 **H.S. Requirements:** High school diploma required; GED accepted **Scholarships:** Available. **Calendar System:** Continuous, Summer session available **Enrollment:** Full-time 13,717 **Faculty:** Full-time 563, Part-time 808 **Student-Faculty Ratio:** 17:1 **Exams:** ACT; SAT I; SAT I or ACT; SAT II. **Final Year or Final Semester Residency Requirement:** No **Regional Accreditation:** Southern Association of Colleges and Schools **Credit Hours For Degree:** 60 semester credit hours, Associates; 120 semester credit hours, Bachelors **Professional Accreditation:** ACEN.

EMORY & HENRY COLLEGE

PO Box 947
Emory, VA 24327-0947
Tel: (276)944-4121; Free: 800-848-5493
Fax: (276)944-6934
E-mail: mchrisman@ehc.edu
Web Site: www.ehc.edu
President/CEO: Jake B. Schrum
Admissions: Matt Crisman
Financial Aid: Scarlett C. Blevins

Type: Comprehensive **Sex:** Coed **Affiliation:** United Methodist. **Scores:** 87% SAT V 400+; 90% SAT M 400+; 52% ACT 18-23; 20% ACT 24-29 **% Accepted:** 76 **Admission Plans:** Early Action **Application Deadline:** Rolling **Application Fee:** $0.00 **H.S. Requirements:** High school diploma required; GED accepted **Costs Per Year:** Application fee: $0. Comprehensive fee: $44,900 includes full-time tuition ($33,500), mandatory fees ($200), and college room and board ($11,200). College room only: $6000. Full-time tuition and fees vary according to degree level, location, and student level. Room and board charges vary according to board plan and housing facility. Part-time tuition: $1250 per credit. Part-time tuition varies according to course load, degree level, location, and student level. Tuition guaranteed not to increase for student's term of enrollment. **Scholarships:** Available.

Calendar System: Semester, Summer session available **Enrollment:** Full-time 1,007, Graduate full-time 42, Graduate part-time 51, Part-time 17 **Faculty:** Full-time 85, Part-time 51 **Student-Faculty Ratio:** 11:1 **Exams:** ACT essay component used as validity check; ACT essay component used for advising; ACT essay component used for placement; ACT essay component used in place of application essay; SAT I and SAT II or ACT; SAT I or ACT; SAT II; SAT essay component used as validity check; SAT essay component used for advising; SAT essay component used for placement; SAT essay component used in place of application essay; SAT Reasoning; SAT Subject. **% Receiving Financial Aid:** 81 **% Residing in College-Owned, -Operated, or -Affiliated Housing:** 78 **Regional Accreditation:** Southern Association of Colleges and Schools **Credit Hours For Degree:** 120 hours, Bachelors **Professional Accreditation:** JRCAT. **Intercollegiate Athletics:** Baseball M; Basketball M & W; Cheerleading M & W; Cross-Country Running M & W; Equestrian Sports M & W; Football M; Soccer M & W; Softball W; Swimming and Diving W; Tennis M & W; Volleyball W

EVEREST COLLEGE

825 Greenbrier Cir.
Ste. 100
Chesapeake, VA 23320
Tel: (757)361-3900
Web Site: www.everest.edu

Type: Two-Year College **Sex:** Coed **Affiliation:** Zenith Education Group. **Professional Accreditation:** ACICS.

FERRUM COLLEGE

PO Box 1000
Ferrum, VA 24088
Tel: (540)365-2121; Free: 800-868-9797
Fax: (540)365-4266
E-mail: admissions@ferrum.edu
Web Site: www.ferrum.edu
President/CEO: Dr. Jennifer L. Braaten
Admissions: Gilda Q. Woods
Financial Aid: Heather Hollandsworth

Type: Four-Year College **Sex:** Coed **Affiliation:** United Methodist. **Scores:** 67% SAT V 400+; 66% SAT M 400+; 27.11% ACT 18-23; 23.7% ACT 24-29 **% Accepted:** 73 **Admission Plans:** Deferred Admission; Early Admission **Application Fee:** $25.00 **H.S. Requirements:** High school diploma required; GED accepted **Scholarships:** Available. **Calendar System:** Semester, Summer session available **Enrollment:** Full-time 1,432, Part-time 19 **Faculty:** Full-time 78, Part-time 38 **Student-Faculty Ratio:** 16:1 **Exams:** ACT essay component not used; SAT I or ACT; SAT essay component not used. **% Receiving Financial Aid:** 91 **% Residing in College-Owned, -Operated, or -Affiliated Housing:** 89 **Regional Accreditation:** Southern Association of Colleges and Schools **Credit Hours For Degree:** 121 credit hours, Bachelors **Professional Accreditation:** CSWE, NRPA. **Intercollegiate Athletics:** Baseball M; Basketball M & W; Cheerleading M & W; Cross-Country Running M & W; Football M; Golf M; Lacrosse M & W; Soccer M & W; Softball W; Swimming and Diving M & W; Tennis M & W; Volleyball W

FORTIS COLLEGE (NORFOLK)

6300 Ctr. Dr.
Ste. 100
Norfolk, VA 23502
Tel: (757)499-5447; Free: 855-4-FORTIS
Web Site: www.fortis.edu

Type: Two-Year College **Sex:** Coed **Professional Accreditation:** ACICS.

FORTIS COLLEGE (RICHMOND)

2000 Westmoreland St.
Ste. A
Richmond, VA 23230
Tel: (804)323-1020; Free: 855-4-FORTIS
Web Site: www.fortis.edu

Type: Two-Year College **Sex:** Coed **Professional Accreditation:** ACICS.

GEORGE MASON UNIVERSITY

4400 University Dr.
Fairfax, VA 22030
Tel: (703)993-1000; Free: 888-627-6612
E-mail: mboyce3@gmu.edu

Web Site: www.gmu.edu
President/CEO: Dr. Angel Cabrera
Admissions: Matthew Boyce
Type: University Sex: Coed Scores: 99% SAT V 400+; 100% SAT M 400+; 25% ACT 18-23; 56% ACT 24-29 Costs Per Year: State resident tuition: $7976 full-time, $332 per credit hour part-time. Nonresident tuition: $28,622 full-time, $1193 per credit hour part-time. Mandatory fees: $2976 full-time, $124 per credit hour part-time. Full-time tuition and fees vary according to course load. Part-time tuition and fees vary according to course load. College room and board: $10,510. College room only: $6240. Room and board charges vary according to board plan and housing facility. Scholarships: Available. Calendar System: Semester, Summer session available Enrollment: Full-time 18,427, Graduate full-time 4,160, Graduate part-time 6,703, Part-time 4,635 Faculty: Full-time 1,243, Part-time 1,314 Student-Faculty Ratio: 16:1 Exams: ACT essay component not used; SAT I and SAT II or ACT; SAT I or ACT; SAT II; SAT essay component not used. % Receiving Financial Aid: 53 % Residing in College-Owned, -Operated, or -Affiliated Housing: 26 Final Year or Final Semester Residency Requirement: Yes Regional Accreditation: Southern Association of Colleges and Schools Credit Hours For Degree: 120 credit hours, Bachelors ROTC: Air Force, Army Professional Accreditation: AACN, AACSB, AALS, ABA, ABET, APA, CAHME, CSWE, NASAD, NASM, NASPAA, NCATE. Intercollegiate Athletics: Baseball M; Basketball M & W; Crew W; Cross-Country Running M & W; Golf M; Lacrosse W; Soccer M & W; Softball W; Swimming and Diving M & W; Tennis M & W; Track and Field M & W; Volleyball M & W; Wrestling M

GERMANNA COMMUNITY COLLEGE

2130 Germanna Hwy.
Locust Grove, VA 22508-2102
Tel: (540)727-3000
Fax: (540)727-3207
Web Site: www.germanna.edu
President/CEO: Dr. David A. Sam
Admissions: Rita Dunston
Type: Two-Year College Sex: Coed Affiliation: Virginia Community College System. % Accepted: 100 Admission Plans: Early Admission; Open Admission Application Deadline: Rolling Application Fee: $0.00 H.S. Requirements: High school diploma or equivalent not required. For nursing program: High school diploma required; GED accepted Scholarships: Available. Calendar System: Semester, Summer session available Enrollment: Full-time 2,296, Part-time 4,739 Faculty: Full-time 69, Part-time 303 Student-Faculty Ratio: 19:1 Regional Accreditation: Southern Association of Colleges and Schools Credit Hours For Degree: 61 semester hours, Associates

GLOBAL HEALTH COLLEGE

25 S Quaker Ln., 1st Fl.
Alexandria, VA 22314
Tel: (703)212-7410
Web Site: www.global.edu
Type: Two-Year College Sex: Coed Professional Accreditation: ACICS.

HAMPDEN-SYDNEY COLLEGE

PO Box 859
Hampden-Sydney, VA 23943
Tel: (434)223-6000; Free: 800-755-0733
Fax: (434)223-6346
E-mail: hsapp@hsc.edu
Web Site: www.hsc.edu
President/CEO: Pres. Dennis G. Stevens, PhD
Admissions: Dean Anita Garland
Financial Aid: Zita Marie Barree
Type: Four-Year College Sex: Men Affiliation: Presbyterian Church (U.S. A.). Scores: 98% SAT V 400+; 98% SAT M 400+ % Accepted: 55 Admission Plans: Early Action; Early Admission; Early Decision Plan Application Deadline: March 1 Application Fee: $30.00 H.S. Requirements: High school diploma required; GED accepted Costs Per Year: Application fee: $30. Comprehensive fee: $54,790 includes full-time tuition ($39,920), mandatory fees ($1810), and college room and board ($13,060). College room only: $5652. Room and board charges vary according to board plan and housing facility. Part-time tuition: $1250 per credit hour. Scholarships: Available. Calendar System: Semester, Summer session available Enrollment: Full-time 1,085, Part-time 2 Faculty: Full-time 87, Part-time 22

Student-Faculty Ratio: 10:1 Exams: SAT I or ACT; SAT essay component not used; SAT Reasoning; SAT Subject. % Receiving Financial Aid: 64 % Residing in College-Owned, -Operated, or -Affiliated Housing: 95 Final Year or Final Semester Residency Requirement: No Regional Accreditation: Southern Association of Colleges and Schools Credit Hours For Degree: 120 semester hours, Bachelors ROTC: Army Intercollegiate Athletics: Baseball M; Basketball M; Crew M; Cross-Country Running M; Fencing M; Football M; Golf M; Lacrosse M; Riflery M; Rugby M; Soccer M; Swimming and Diving M; Tennis M; Ultimate Frisbee M; Wrestling M

HAMPTON UNIVERSITY

Hampton, VA 23668
Tel: (757)727-5000; Free: 800-624-3328
Fax: (757)727-5084
E-mail: derrick.boone@hamptonu.edu
Web Site: www.hamptonu.edu
President/CEO: Dr. William R. Harvey
Admissions: Dean Derrick Boone
Financial Aid: Martin Miles
Type: Comprehensive Sex: Coed Scores: 100% SAT V 400+; 100% SAT M 400+; 60% ACT 18-23; 19% ACT 24-29 % Accepted: 69 Admission Plans: Deferred Admission; Early Admission; Early Decision Plan Application Deadline: March 1 Application Fee: $35.00 H.S. Requirements: High school diploma required; GED accepted Costs Per Year: Application fee: $35. Comprehensive fee: $33,288 includes full-time tuition ($20,526), mandatory fees ($2586), and college room and board ($10,176). College room only: $5292. Full-time tuition and fees vary according to course load, degree level, location, program, and reciprocity agreements. Room and board charges vary according to board plan, housing facility, and location. Part-time tuition: $522 per credit. Part-time tuition varies according to class time, course load, location, and reciprocity agreements. Scholarships: Available. Calendar System: Semester, Summer session available Enrollment: Full-time 3,264, Graduate full-time 633, Graduate part-time 217, Part-time 155 Faculty: Full-time 317, Part-time 82 Student-Faculty Ratio: 8:1 Exams: ACT essay component not used; SAT I or ACT; SAT essay component not used; SAT Reasoning. % Receiving Financial Aid: 39 % Residing in College-Owned, -Operated, or -Affiliated Housing: 62 Final Year or Final Semester Residency Requirement: No Regional Accreditation: Southern Association of Colleges and Schools Credit Hours For Degree: 60 semester hours, Associates; 120 semester hours, Bachelors ROTC: Army, Navy Professional Accreditation: AABI, AACN, ABET, ACA, ACEJMC, ACEN, ACPE, APTA, ASHA, NAAB, NASM, NCATE. Intercollegiate Athletics: Basketball M & W; Bowling W; Cheerleading W; Cross-Country Running M & W; Football M; Golf M & W; Lacrosse M; Sailing M & W; Soccer W; Softball W; Tennis M & W; Track and Field M & W; Volleyball W

HOLLINS UNIVERSITY

7916 Williamson Rd.
Roanoke, VA 24020
Tel: (540)362-6000; Free: 800-456-9595
Fax: (540)362-6218
E-mail: huadm@hollins.edu
Web Site: www.hollins.edu
President/CEO: Nancy Oliver Gray
Admissions: Ashley Browning
Financial Aid: MaryJean Sullivan
Type: Comprehensive Scores: 98% SAT V 400+; 96% SAT M 400+; 41% ACT 18-23; 45% ACT 24-29 % Accepted: 61 Admission Plans: Deferred Admission; Early Action; Early Admission; Early Decision Plan Application Deadline: Rolling H.S. Requirements: High school diploma required; GED accepted Costs Per Year: Comprehensive fee: $47,935 includes full-time tuition ($35,000), mandatory fees ($635), and college room and board ($12,300). Part-time tuition: $1094 per credit hour. Part-time mandatory fees: $322.50 per year. Scholarships: Available. Calendar System: 4-1-4, Summer session not available Enrollment: Full-time 621, Graduate full-time 50, Graduate part-time 113, Part-time 18 Faculty: Full-time 68, Part-time 29 Student-Faculty Ratio: 9:1 Exams: ACT essay component not used; SAT I or ACT; SAT essay component not used; SAT Reasoning. % Receiving Financial Aid: 82 % Residing in College-Owned, -Operated, or -Affiliated Housing: 82 Final Year or Final Semester Residency Requirement: Yes Regional Accreditation: Southern Association of Colleges and Schools Credit Hours For Degree: 128 credits, Bachelors Professional Accreditation: TEAC. Intercollegiate Athletics: Basketball W; Cross-

Country Running W; Equestrian Sports W; Fencing W; Golf W; Lacrosse W; Soccer W; Swimming and Diving W; Tennis W; Volleyball W

IGLOBAL UNIVERSITY

7700 Little River Tpke.
No.600
Annandale, VA 22003
Tel: (703)941-2020
Web Site: www.iglobal.edu
Type: Comprehensive **Sex:** Coed **Professional Accreditation:** ACICS.

J. SARGEANT REYNOLDS COMMUNITY COLLEGE

PO Box 85622
Richmond, VA 23285-5622
Tel: (804)371-3000
Fax: (804)371-3650
E-mail: kpettis-walden@reynolds.edu
Web Site: www.reynolds.edu
President/CEO: Dr. Gary L. Rhodes
Admissions: Karen Pettis-Walden
Financial Aid: Kiesha Pope
Type: Two-Year College **Sex:** Coed **Affiliation:** Virginia Community College System. **Admission Plans:** Open Admission **Application Deadline:** Rolling **Application Fee:** $0.00 **H.S. Requirements:** High school diploma required; GED accepted **Costs Per Year:** Application fee: $0. State resident tuition: $3,722 full-time, $146.60 per credit part-time. Nonresident tuition: $8,393 full-time, $341.20 per credit part-time. Full-time tuition varies according to course load and program. Part-time tuition varies according to course load and program. **Scholarships:** Available. **Calendar System:** Semester, Summer session available **Enrollment:** Full-time 3,100, Part-time 7,787 **Faculty:** Full-time 140, Part-time 505 **Student-Faculty Ratio:** 18:1 **Regional Accreditation:** Southern Association of Colleges and Schools **Credit Hours For Degree:** 61 credit hours, Associates **Professional Accreditation:** ACEN, ACF, ADA, COA, CoARC, NAACLS.

JAMES MADISON UNIVERSITY

800 S Main St.
Harrisonburg, VA 22807
Tel: (540)568-6211
Fax: (540)568-3332
E-mail: admissions@jmu.edu
Web Site: www.jmu.edu
President/CEO: Jonathan R. Alger
Admissions: Michael D. Walsh
Financial Aid: Lisa L. Tumer
Type: Comprehensive **Sex:** Coed **Scores:** 99% SAT V 400+; 100% SAT M 400+; 30.56% ACT 18-23; 59.44% ACT 24-29 **% Accepted:** 73 **Admission Plans:** Deferred Admission; Early Decision Plan; Preferred Admission **Application Fee:** $70.00 **H.S. Requirements:** High school diploma required; GED accepted **Costs Per Year:** Application fee: $70. State resident tuition: $5724 full-time, $190 per credit hour part-time. Nonresident tuition: $20,848 full-time, $676 per credit hour part-time. Mandatory fees: $4294 full-time. College room and board: $9396. College room only: $4648. Room and board charges vary according to board plan. **Scholarships:** Available. **Calendar System:** Semester, Summer session available **Enrollment:** Full-time 18,433, Graduate full-time 1,113, Graduate part-time 718, Part-time 963 **Faculty:** Full-time 1,002, Part-time 457 **Student-Faculty Ratio:** 16:1 **Exams:** ACT essay component not used; SAT I or ACT; SAT II; SAT essay component not used; SAT Reasoning. **% Receiving Financial Aid:** 37 % **Residing in College-Owned, -Operated, or -Affiliated Housing:** 13 **Final Year or Final Semester Residency Requirement:** No **Regional Accreditation:** Southern Association of Colleges and Schools **Credit Hours For Degree:** 120 credit hours, Bachelors **ROTC:** Air Force, Army **Professional Accreditation:** AACN, AACSB, ABET, ACA, AND, AOTA, APA, ASHA, CIDA, CSWE, JRCAT, NASAD, NASD, NASM, NASPAA, NAST, NCATE. **Intercollegiate Athletics:** Baseball M; Basketball M & W; Cheerleading M & W; Cross-Country Running W; Field Hockey W; Football M; Golf M & W; Lacrosse W; Soccer M & W; Softball W; Swimming and Diving W; Tennis M & W; Track and Field W; Volleyball W

JEFFERSON COLLEGE OF HEALTH SCIENCES

101 Elm Ave. SE
Roanoke, VA 24013
Tel: (540)985-8483; Free: 888-985-8483

Fax: (540)985-9773
E-mail: jomckeon@jchs.edu
Web Site: www.jchs.edu
President/CEO: Nathaniel L. Bishop
Admissions: Judith McKeon
Financial Aid: Debra A. Johnson
Type: Comprehensive **Sex:** Coed **% Accepted:** 36 **Admission Plans:** Deferred Admission **Application Deadline:** Rolling **Application Fee:** $35.00 **H.S. Requirements:** High school diploma required; GED accepted **Costs Per Year:** Application fee: $35. Comprehensive fee: $32,270 includes full-time tuition ($24,000), mandatory fees ($400), and college room and board ($7870). Full-time tuition and fees vary according to course load. Part-time tuition: $695 per credit hour. Part-time tuition varies according to course load. **Scholarships:** Available. **Calendar System:** Semester, Summer session available **Enrollment:** Full-time 666, Graduate full-time 211, Graduate part-time 51, Part-time 134 **Exams:** SAT I; SAT I or ACT. **% Residing in College-Owned, -Operated, or -Affiliated Housing:** 15 **Final Year or Final Semester Residency Requirement:** No **Regional Accreditation:** Southern Association of Colleges and Schools **Credit Hours For Degree:** 60 credit hours, Associates; 120 credit hours, Bachelors **Professional Accreditation:** AACN, AOTA, APTA, CoARC, JRCEMTP. **Intercollegiate Athletics:** Basketball M; Cross-Country Running M & W; Softball M & W; Tennis M & W; Volleyball M & W

JOHN TYLER COMMUNITY COLLEGE

13101 Jefferson Davis Hwy.
Chester, VA 23831-5316
Tel: (804)796-4000; Free: 800-552-3490
Fax: (804)796-4163
E-mail: jjames@jtcc.edu
Web Site: www.jtcc.edu
President/CEO: Dr. Edward E. Raspiller
Admissions: Joy James
Financial Aid: Tony Jones
Type: Two-Year College **Sex:** Coed **Affiliation:** Virginia Community College System. **Admission Plans:** Deferred Admission; Early Admission; Open Admission; Preferred Admission **Application Deadline:** Rolling **Application Fee:** $0.00 **H.S. Requirements:** High school diploma or equivalent not required. For nursing, funeral services, emergency medical services programs; transfer students; if student has been suspended or dismissed from another college or university: High school diploma required; GED accepted **Costs Per Year:** Application fee: $0. State resident tuition: $3420 full-time, $142.50 per credit hour part-time. Nonresident tuition: $8,090 full-time, $337.10 per credit hour part-time. Mandatory fees: $70 full-time, $35 per term part-time. Full-time tuition and fees vary according to course load. Part-time tuition and fees vary according to course load. **Scholarships:** Available. **Calendar System:** Semester, Summer session available **Enrollment:** Full-time 2,558, Part-time 7,477 **Faculty:** Full-time 124, Part-time 450 **Student-Faculty Ratio:** 18:1 **Regional Accreditation:** Southern Association of Colleges and Schools **Credit Hours For Degree:** 65 semester hours, Associates **ROTC:** Army **Professional Accreditation:** ABFSE, ACEN.

LIBERTY UNIVERSITY

1971 University Blvd.
Lynchburg, VA 24515
Tel: (434)582-2000; Free: 800-543-5317
Fax: (434)582-2304
E-mail: admissions@liberty.edu
Web Site: www.liberty.edu
President/CEO: Jerry Falwell, Jr.
Admissions: Dr. Terry Elam
Financial Aid: Robert Ritz
Type: Comprehensive **Sex:** Coed **Affiliation:** nondenominational. **Scores:** 96% SAT V 400+; 95% SAT M 400+; 45.99% ACT 18-23; 35.33% ACT 24-29 **% Accepted:** 21 **Application Deadline:** Rolling **Application Fee:** $40.00 **H.S. Requirements:** High school diploma required; GED accepted. For home-schooled applicants (must provide records of academic work, grades and evaluations): High school diploma or equivalent not required **Costs Per Year:** Application fee: $40. Comprehensive fee: $32,326 includes full-time tuition ($22,000), mandatory fees ($1020), and college room and board ($9306). College room only: $5806. Full-time tuition and fees vary according to course load. Room and board charges vary according to housing facility. Part-time tuition: $917 per credit hour. Part-time tuition varies according to course load. **Scholarships:** Available. **Calendar System:** Semester, Sum-

mer session available **Enrollment:** Full-time 12,623, Graduate full-time 1,206, Graduate part-time 142, Part-time 449 **Exams:** SAT I or ACT. **% Receiving Financial Aid:** 84 **% Residing in College-Owned, -Operated, or -Affiliated Housing:** 59 **Final Year or Final Semester Residency Requirement:** No **Regional Accreditation:** Southern Association of Colleges and Schools **Credit Hours For Degree:** 60 semester hours, Associates; 120 semester hours, Bachelors **ROTC:** Air Force, Army **Professional Accreditation:** AACN, AAFCS, ABA, ACBSP, ACIPE, AOsA, NCATE. **Intercollegiate Athletics:** Baseball M; Basketball M & W; Cheerleading M & W; Crew M & W; Cross-Country Running M & W; Equestrian Sports W; Field Hockey W; Football M; Golf M; Ice Hockey M & W; Lacrosse W; Soccer M & W; Softball W; Swimming and Diving W; Tennis M & W; Track and Field M & W; Volleyball M & W

LONGWOOD UNIVERSITY

201 High St.
Farmville, VA 23909
Tel: (434)395-2000; Free: 800-281-4677
Fax: (434)395-2332
E-mail: greenjk@longwood.edu
Web Site: www.longwood.edu
President/CEO: W. Taylor Reveley, IV
Admissions: Dr. Jennifer Kingsley Green
Financial Aid: Caroline Gibbs

Type: Comprehensive **Sex:** Coed **Scores:** 94% SAT V 400+; 94% SAT M 400+; 61.56% ACT 18-23; 17.69% ACT 24-29 **% Accepted:** 79 **Admission Plans:** Deferred Admission; Early Admission; Early Decision Plan **Application Deadline:** March 1 **Application Fee:** $50.00 **H.S. Requirements:** High school diploma required; GED accepted **Costs Per Year:** Application fee: $50. State resident tuition: $7170 full-time, $239 per credit part-time. Nonresident tuition: $21,330 full-time, $688 per credit part-time. Mandatory fees: $4740 full-time, $158 per credit hour part-time. Full-time tuition and fees vary according to course load and program. Part-time tuition and fees vary according to course load and program. College room and board: $10,272. College room only: $6394. Room and board charges vary according to board plan, housing facility, and location. **Scholarships:** Available. **Calendar System:** Semester, Summer session available **Enrollment:** Full-time 4,141, Graduate full-time 161, Graduate part-time 313, Part-time 472 **Faculty:** Full-time 251, Part-time 78 **Student-Faculty Ratio:** 16:1 **Exams:** ACT essay component not used; SAT I or ACT; SAT II; SAT essay component not used. **% Receiving Financial Aid:** 53 **% Residing in College-Owned, -Operated, or -Affiliated Housing:** 69 **Final Year or Final Semester Residency Requirement:** No **Regional Accreditation:** Southern Association of Colleges and Schools **Credit Hours For Degree:** 120 credit hours, Bachelors **ROTC:** Army **Professional Accreditation:** AACSB, CSWE, JRCAT, NASM, NAST, NCATE, NRPA. **Intercollegiate Athletics:** Baseball M; Basketball M & W; Cross-Country Running M & W; Field Hockey W; Football M; Golf M & W; Lacrosse W; Soccer M & W; Softball W; Tennis M & W; Volleyball M & W

LORD FAIRFAX COMMUNITY COLLEGE

173 Skirmisher Ln.
Middletown, VA 22645
Tel: (540)868-7000; Free: 800-906-LFCC
Fax: (540)868-7100
E-mail: kbucher@lfcc.edu
Web Site: www.lfcc.edu
President/CEO: Cheryl Thompson-Stacy
Admissions: Karen Bucher
Financial Aid: Kaitlyn Lambert

Type: Two-Year College **Sex:** Coed **Affiliation:** Virginia Community College System. **Admission Plans:** Early Admission; Open Admission **Application Deadline:** Rolling **Application Fee:** $0.00 **H.S. Requirements:** High school diploma or equivalent not required **Scholarships:** Available. **Calendar System:** Semester, Summer session available **Student-Faculty Ratio:** 22:1 **Regional Accreditation:** Southern Association of Colleges and Schools **Credit Hours For Degree:** 62 semester hours, Associates

LYNCHBURG COLLEGE

1501 Lakeside Dr.
Lynchburg, VA 24501-3199
Tel: (434)544-8100; Free: 800-426-8101
Fax: (434)544-8653
E-mail: admissions@lynchburg.edu

Web Site: www.lynchburg.edu
President/CEO: Dr. Kenneth R. Garren
Admissions: Sharon Walters-Bower
Financial Aid: Michelle G. Davis

Type: Comprehensive **Sex:** Coed **Affiliation:** Christian Church (Disciples of Christ). **Scores:** 96% SAT V 400+; 97% SAT M 400+; 57% ACT 18-23; 27.9% ACT 24-29 **% Accepted:** 69 **Admission Plans:** Deferred Admission; Early Action; Early Admission **Application Deadline:** Rolling **Application Fee:** $30.00 **H.S. Requirements:** High school diploma required; GED accepted **Costs Per Year:** Application fee: $30. Comprehensive fee: $45,145 includes full-time tuition ($34,610), mandatory fees ($945), and college room and board ($9590). College room only: $4870. Room and board charges vary according to board plan and housing facility. Part-time tuition: $475 per credit hour. Part-time mandatory fees: $5.10 per credit hour. Part-time tuition and fees vary according to course load. **Scholarships:** Available. **Calendar System:** Semester, Summer session available **Enrollment:** Full-time 1,980, Graduate full-time 283, Graduate part-time 370, Part-time 161 **Faculty:** Full-time 169, Part-time 113 **Student-Faculty Ratio:** 11:1 **Exams:** ACT essay component not used; SAT I or ACT; SAT essay component not used. **% Receiving Financial Aid:** 74 **% Residing in College-Owned, -Operated, or -Affiliated Housing:** 74 **Regional Accreditation:** Southern Association of Colleges and Schools **Credit Hours For Degree:** 124 semester hours, Bachelors **Professional Accreditation:** AACN, ACA, ACBSP, NASM. **Intercollegiate Athletics:** Baseball M; Basketball M & W; Cheerleading M & W; Cross-Country Running M & W; Equestrian Sports M & W; Field Hockey W; Golf M; Lacrosse M & W; Soccer M & W; Softball W; Tennis M & W; Track and Field M & W; Volleyball W

MARY BALDWIN COLLEGE

201 E Frederick St.
Staunton, VA 24401-3610
Tel: (540)887-7000; Free: 800-468-2262
Fax: (540)886-6634
E-mail: rpalmer@mbc.edu
Web Site: www.mbc.edu
President/CEO: Dr. Pamela Fox
Admissions: Megan Speth
Financial Aid: Robin Dietrich

Type: Comprehensive **Sex:** Coed **Scores:** 92% SAT V 400+; 84% SAT M 400+; 53.2% ACT 18-23; 27.4% ACT 24-29 **% Accepted:** 50 **Admission Plans:** Deferred Admission; Early Admission **Application Deadline:** Rolling **Application Fee:** $0.00 **H.S. Requirements:** High school diploma required; GED accepted **Costs Per Year:** Application fee: $0. Comprehensive fee: $39,865 includes full-time tuition ($30,240), mandatory fees ($395), and college room and board ($9230). Full-time tuition and fees vary according to degree level. Room and board charges vary according to housing facility and student level. Part-time tuition: $455 per semester hour. Part-time mandatory fees: $58 per term. Part-time tuition and fees vary according to degree level. **Scholarships:** Available. **Calendar System:** 4-1-4, Summer session available **Enrollment:** Full-time 897, Graduate full-time 232, Graduate part-time 122, Part-time 415 **Faculty:** Full-time 95, Part-time 118 **Student-Faculty Ratio:** 11:1 **Exams:** SAT I or ACT; SAT Reasoning; SAT Subject. **% Receiving Financial Aid:** 91 **% Residing in College-Owned, -Operated, or -Affiliated Housing:** 85 **Regional Accreditation:** Southern Association of Colleges and Schools **Credit Hours For Degree:** 126 semester hours, Bachelors **ROTC:** Air Force, Army, Navy **Professional Accreditation:** TEAC. **Intercollegiate Athletics:** Basketball W; Cross-Country Running W; Soccer W; Softball W; Swimming and Diving W; Tennis W; Volleyball W

MARYMOUNT UNIVERSITY

2807 N Glebe Rd.
Arlington, VA 22207-4299
Tel: (703)522-5600; Free: 800-548-7638
Fax: (703)522-0349
E-mail: admissions@marymount.edu
Web Site: www.marymount.edu
President/CEO: Dr. Matthew D. Shank, PhD
Admissions: Heather Renault
Financial Aid: Debbie A. Raines

Type: Comprehensive **Sex:** Coed **Affiliation:** Roman Catholic Church. **Scores:** 93% SAT V 400+; 93% SAT M 400+; 57% ACT 18-23; 27% ACT 24-29 **% Accepted:** 86 **Admission Plans:** Deferred Admission **Application Deadline:** Rolling **Application Fee:** $40.00 **H.S. Requirements:** High school diploma required; GED accepted **Costs Per Year:** Application fee:

$40. One-time mandatory fee: $420. Comprehensive fee: $40,530 includes full-time tuition ($27,900), mandatory fees ($410), and college room and board ($12,220). Room and board charges vary according to housing facility. Part-time tuition: $910 per credit hour. **Scholarships:** Available. **Calendar System:** Semester, Summer session available **Enrollment:** Full-time 2,089, Graduate full-time 545, Graduate part-time 495, Part-time 234 **Faculty:** Full-time 159, Part-time 195 **Student-Faculty Ratio:** 12:1 **Exams:** SAT I or ACT; SAT Reasoning. **% Receiving Financial Aid:** 65 **% Residing in College-Owned, -Operated, or -Affiliated Housing:** 33 **Final Year or Final Semester Residency Requirement:** No **Regional Accreditation:** Southern Association of Colleges and Schools **Credit Hours For Degree:** 120 semester hours, Bachelors **ROTC:** Army **Professional Accreditation:** AACN, ACA, ACBSP, ACEN, APTA, CAHME, CIDA, NCATE. **Intercollegiate Athletics:** Baseball M; Basketball M & W; Cross-Country Running M & W; Golf M & W; Lacrosse M & W; Soccer M & W; Swimming and Diving M & W; Triathlon M & W; Volleyball M & W

MEDTECH COLLEGE

6565 Arlington Blvd.
Falls Church, VA 22042
Tel: (202)628-5800
Fax: (202)628-3680
Web Site: www.medtech.edu

Type: Two-Year College **Sex:** Coed **Professional Accreditation:** COE.

MILLER-MOTTE TECHNICAL COLLEGE (LYNCHBURG)

1011 Creekside Ln.
Lynchburg, VA 24502
Tel: (804)847-7701
Fax: (804)528-5341
E-mail: bjdierstein@miller-mott.com
Web Site: www.miller-motte.edu
Admissions: Betty J. Dierstein

Type: Two-Year College **Sex:** Coed **Professional Accreditation:** AAMAE, ACICS.

MILLER-MOTTE TECHNICAL COLLEGE (ROANOKE)

4444 Electric Rd.
Roanoke, VA 24018
Tel: (540)597-1010
Web Site: www.miller-motte.edu

Type: Two-Year College **Sex:** Coed **Professional Accreditation:** ACICS.

MOUNTAIN EMPIRE COMMUNITY COLLEGE

3441 Mountain Empire Rd.
Big Stone Gap, VA 24219
Tel: (276)523-2400
E-mail: khall@me.vccs.edu
Web Site: www.mecc.edu
President/CEO: Dr. Scott Hamilton
Admissions: Kristy Hall

Type: Two-Year College **Sex:** Coed **Affiliation:** Virginia Community College System. **Admission Plans:** Deferred Admission; Early Admission; Open Admission **Application Deadline:** Rolling **Application Fee:** $0.00 **H.S. Requirements:** High school diploma required; GED accepted **Scholarships:** Available. **Calendar System:** Semester, Summer session available **Enrollment:** Full-time 1,310, Part-time 1,614 **Faculty:** Full-time 44, Part-time 116 **Regional Accreditation:** Southern Association of Colleges and Schools **Credit Hours For Degree:** 65 credits, Associates **Professional Accreditation:** CoARC.

NEW RIVER COMMUNITY COLLEGE

5251 College Dr.
Dublin, VA 24084
Tel: (540)674-3600; Free: 866-462-6722
Fax: (540)674-3644
E-mail: tsmith@nr.edu
Web Site: www.nr.edu
President/CEO: Jack M. Lewis
Admissions: Tammy L. Smith
Financial Aid: Lori A. Nunn

Type: Two-Year College **Sex:** Coed **Affiliation:** Virginia Community College System. **Admission Plans:** Deferred Admission; Early Admission; Open Admission; Preferred Admission **Application Deadline:** Rolling **Application**

Fee: $0.00 **H.S. Requirements:** High school diploma or equivalent not required. For applicants under 18: High school diploma required; GED accepted **Costs Per Year:** Application fee: $0. State resident tuition: $145 per credit hour part-time. Nonresident tuition: $339.65 per credit hour part-time. Part-time tuition varies according to course load and program. **Scholarships:** Available. **Calendar System:** Semester, Summer session available **Enrollment:** Full-time 2,008, Part-time 2,337 **Faculty:** Full-time 51, Part-time 155 **Student-Faculty Ratio:** 22:1 **Regional Accreditation:** Southern Association of Colleges and Schools **Credit Hours For Degree:** 60 semester hours, Associates **Intercollegiate Athletics:** Baseball M

NORFOLK STATE UNIVERSITY

700 Park Ave.
Norfolk, VA 23504
Tel: (757)823-8600; Free: 800-274-1821
Fax: (757)823-9435
E-mail: admissions@nsu.edu
Web Site: www.nsu.edu
President/CEO: Dr. Carolyn W. Meyers
Admissions: Kevin M. Holmes
Financial Aid: Kevin Burns

Type: Comprehensive **Sex:** Coed **Affiliation:** State Council of Higher Education for Virginia. **Scores:** 74% SAT V 400+; 70% SAT M 400+; 13.3% ACT 18-23; 1.2% ACT 24-29 **% Accepted:** 67 **Admission Plans:** Deferred Admission **H.S. Requirements:** High school diploma required; GED accepted **Scholarships:** Available. **Calendar System:** Semester **Enrollment:** Full-time 4,416, Graduate full-time 454, Graduate part-time 217, Part-time 940 **Exams:** SAT I or ACT. **% Residing in College-Owned, -Operated, or -Affiliated Housing:** 38 **Final Year or Final Semester Residency Requirement:** No **Regional Accreditation:** Southern Association of Colleges and Schools **Credit Hours For Degree:** 60 semester hours, Associates; 120 semester hours, Bachelors **ROTC:** Army, Navy **Professional Accreditation:** AACSB, ABET, ABFSE, ACEJMC, ACEN, APA, ATMAE, CSWE, CoA-KT, NAACLS, NASM, NCATE. **Intercollegiate Athletics:** Baseball M; Basketball M & W; Bowling W; Football M; Softball W; Tennis M & W; Track and Field M & W; Volleyball W

NORTHERN VIRGINIA COMMUNITY COLLEGE

8333 Little River Tpke.
Annandale, VA 22003
Tel: (703)323-3000
Web Site: www.nvcc.edu
President/CEO: Robert G. Templin, Jr.
Admissions: Dr. Max L. Bassett

Type: Two-Year College **Sex:** Coed **Affiliation:** Virginia Community College System. **Admission Plans:** Deferred Admission; Early Admission; Open Admission **Application Deadline:** Rolling **Application Fee:** $0.00 **H.S. Requirements:** High school diploma required; GED accepted. For veterinary technology, dental hygiene, other health-related programs: High school diploma required; GED not accepted **Costs Per Year:** Application fee: $0. State resident tuition: $171.25 per credit hour part-time. Nonresident tuition: $368.50 per credit hour part-time. Part-time tuition varies according to course load. **Scholarships:** Available. **Calendar System:** Semester, Summer session available **Faculty:** Full-time 719, Part-time 1,938 **Regional Accreditation:** Southern Association of Colleges and Schools **Credit Hours For Degree:** 60 credit hours, Associates **Professional Accreditation:** ACEN, ADA, AHIMA, APTA, CoARC, JRCEMTP, NAACLS.

OLD DOMINION UNIVERSITY

5115 Hampton Blvd.
Norfolk, VA 23529
Tel: (757)683-3000; Free: 800-348-7926
Fax: (757)683-5357
E-mail: admissions@odu.edu
Web Site: www.odu.edu
President/CEO: John R. Broderick
Admissions: Shereen Williams

Type: University **Sex:** Coed **Scores:** 97% SAT V 400+; 97% SAT M 400+; 48.5% ACT 18-23; 24.6% ACT 24-29 **% Accepted:** 83 **Admission Plans:** Deferred Admission; Early Admission; Early Decision Plan **Application Deadline:** February 1 **Application Fee:** $50.00 **H.S. Requirements:** High school diploma required; GED accepted **Costs Per Year:** Application fee: $50. State resident tuition: $9480 full-time, $316 per credit hour part-time. Nonresident tuition: $26,220 full-time, $874 per credit hour part-time. Mandatory fees: $288 full-time, $64 per term part-time. College room and board: $10,404. College room only: $5860. Room and board charges vary according to board plan and housing facility. **Scholarships:** Available. **Calendar System:** Semester, Summer session available **Enrollment:** Full-time 15,358, Graduate full-time 1,604, Graduate part-time 2,967, Part-time 4,743 **Faculty:** Full-time 828, Part-time 527 **Student-Faculty Ratio:** 19:1 **Exams:** SAT I or ACT; SAT Reasoning; SAT Subject. **% Receiving Financial Aid:** 64 **% Residing in College-Owned, -Operated, or -Affiliated Housing:** 23 **Final Year or Final Semester Residency Requirement:** No **Regional Accreditation:** Southern Association of Colleges and Schools **Credit Hours For Degree:** 120 semester hours, Bachelors **ROTC:** Army, Navy **Professional Accreditation:** AACN, AACSB, AANA, ABET, ACA, ADA, APA, APTA, ASC, ASHA, CEPH, JCAHPO, JRCNMT, NAACLS, NASAD, NASM, NASPAA, NAST, NCATE, NRPA. **Intercollegiate Athletics:** Baseball M; Basketball M & W; Cheerleading M & W; Crew M & W; Cross-Country Running M & W; Equestrian Sports M & W; Fencing M & W; Field Hockey W; Football M; Golf M & W; Ice Hockey M & W; Lacrosse M & W; Rugby M & W; Sailing M & W; Soccer M & W; Softball W; Swimming and Diving M & W; Table Tennis M & W; Tennis M & W; Triathlon M & W; Ultimate Frisbee M & W; Volleyball M & W; Wrestling M

PATRICK HENRY COLLEGE

Ten Patrick Henry Cir.
Purcellville, VA 20132
Tel: (540)338-1776; Free: 888-338-1776
Fax: (540)338-8707
E-mail: admissions@phc.edu
Web Site: www.phc.edu
President/CEO: Jack W. Haye
Admissions: Stephen C. Allen
Financial Aid: William K. Kellaris
Type: Four-Year College **Sex:** Coed **Affiliation:** nondenominational. **Scores:** 100% SAT V 400+; 100% SAT M 400+; 5% ACT 18-23; 67% ACT 24-29 **% Accepted:** 95 **Admission Plans:** Deferred Admission; Early Decision Plan **Application Deadline:** June 15 **Application Fee:** $20.00 **H.S. Requirements:** High school diploma required; GED accepted **Costs Per Year:** Application fee: $20. Comprehensive fee: $38,900 includes full-time tuition ($27,922), mandatory fees ($250), and college room and board ($10,728). Full-time tuition and fees vary according to course load. Room and board charges vary according to board plan and housing facility. Part-time tuition: $1163 per credit hour. Part-time tuition varies according to course level and course load. **Scholarships:** Available. **Calendar System:** Semester, Summer session available **Enrollment:** Full-time 279, Part-time 25 **Faculty:** Full-time 19, Part-time 23 **Student-Faculty Ratio:** 11:1 **Exams:** ACT essay component not used; SAT I or ACT; SAT essay component not used; SAT Reasoning. **% Receiving Financial Aid:** 37 **% Residing in College-Owned, -Operated, or -Affiliated Housing:** 90 **Final Year or Final Semester Residency Requirement:** No **Credit Hours For Degree:** 122 semester credit hours, Bachelors **Professional Accreditation:** AALE, TRACS. **Intercollegiate Athletics:** Basketball M & W; Soccer M & W

PATRICK HENRY COMMUNITY COLLEGE

PO Box 5311
Martinsville, VA 24115-5311
Tel: (276)638-8777
Fax: (276)656-0247
Web Site: www.ph.vccs.edu
President/CEO: Dr. Angeline Godwin
Admissions: Travis Tisdale
Financial Aid: Penny Stultz
Type: Two-Year College **Sex:** Coed **Affiliation:** Virginia Community College System. **Admission Plans:** Early Admission; Open Admission; Preferred Admission **Application Deadline:** Rolling **Application Fee:** $0.00 **H.S. Requirements:** High school diploma required; GED accepted **Scholarships:** Available. **Calendar System:** Semester, Summer session available **Enrollment:** Full-time 1,486, Part-time 1,677 **Faculty:** Full-time 55, Part-time 182 **Student-Faculty Ratio:** 18:1 **Final Year or Final Semester Residency Requirement:** No **Regional Accreditation:** Southern Association of Colleges and Schools **Credit Hours For Degree:** 60 semester hours, Associates **Professional Accreditation:** ACEN. **Intercollegiate Athletics:** Baseball M; Basketball M & W; Cheerleading W; Golf M & W; Soccer M & W; Softball W

PAUL D. CAMP COMMUNITY COLLEGE

PO Box 737, 100 N College Dr.
Franklin, VA 23851-0737

Tel: (757)569-6700
E-mail: tjones@pdc.edu
Web Site: www.pdc.edu
President/CEO: Dr. Paul Conco
Admissions: Trina Jones
Type: Two-Year College **Sex:** Coed **Affiliation:** Virginia Community College System. **% Accepted:** 100 **Admission Plans:** Deferred Admission; Open Admission; Preferred Admission **Application Deadline:** Rolling **Application Fee:** $0.00 **H.S. Requirements:** High school diploma required; GED accepted **Scholarships:** Available. **Calendar System:** Semester, Summer session available **Enrollment:** Full-time 426, Part-time 1,153 **Faculty:** Full-time 18, Part-time 143 **Student-Faculty Ratio:** 16:1 **Final Year or Final Semester Residency Requirement:** No **Regional Accreditation:** Southern Association of Colleges and Schools **Credit Hours For Degree:** 61 semester hours, Associates

PIEDMONT VIRGINIA COMMUNITY COLLEGE

501 College Dr.
Charlottesville, VA 22902-7589
Tel: (434)977-3900
Fax: (434)971-8232
E-mail: mwalsh@pvcc.edu
Web Site: www.pvcc.edu
President/CEO: Dr. Frank Friedman
Admissions: Mary Lee Walsh
Type: Two-Year College **Sex:** Coed **Affiliation:** Virginia Community College System. **Admission Plans:** Deferred Admission; Early Admission; Open Admission **Application Deadline:** Rolling **Application Fee:** $0.00 **H.S. Requirements:** High school diploma or equivalent not required **Costs Per Year:** Application fee: $0. State resident tuition: $4,444 full-time, $135 per credit hour part-time. Nonresident tuition: $10,282 full-time, $311 per credit hour part-time. Mandatory fees: $394 full-time, $13.15 per credit hour part-time. Full-time tuition and fees vary according to course load. Part-time tuition and fees vary according to course load. **Scholarships:** Available. **Calendar System:** Semester, Summer session available **Enrollment:** Full-time 1,234, Part-time 4,320 **Faculty:** Full-time 75 **Student-Faculty Ratio:** 19:1 **Regional Accreditation:** Southern Association of Colleges and Schools **Credit Hours For Degree:** 61 credit hours, Associates **ROTC:** Army **Professional Accreditation:** ACEN.

RADFORD UNIVERSITY

801 E Main St.
Radford, VA 24142
Tel: (540)831-5000
Fax: (540)831-5138
E-mail: admissions@radford.edu
Web Site: www.radford.edu
President/CEO: Penelope W. Kyle
Admissions: James A. Pennix
Financial Aid: Barbara Porter
Type: Comprehensive **Sex:** Coed **Scores:** 96% SAT V 400+; 95% SAT M 400+; 61.6% ACT 18-23; 16.5% ACT 24-29 **% Accepted:** 83 **Admission Plans:** Deferred Admission; Early Admission; Early Decision Plan **Application Deadline:** February 1 **Application Fee:** $50.00 **H.S. Requirements:** High school diploma required; GED accepted **Costs Per Year:** Application fee: $50. State resident tuition: $6788 full-time, $283 per credit hour part-time. Nonresident tuition: $18,626 full-time, $776 per credit hour part-time. Mandatory fees: $3021 full-time, $127 per credit hour part-time. Part-time tuition and fees vary according to course load. College room and board: $8677. College room only: $4809. Room and board charges vary according to board plan and housing facility. **Scholarships:** Available. **Calendar System:** Semester, Summer session available **Enrollment:** Full-time 8,522, Graduate full-time 530, Graduate part-time 333, Part-time 358 **Faculty:** Full-time 455, Part-time 273 **Student-Faculty Ratio:** 17:1 **Exams:** ACT essay component used for advising; SAT I or ACT; SAT essay component used for advising; SAT Reasoning. **% Receiving Financial Aid:** 57 **% Residing in College-Owned, -Operated, or -Affiliated Housing:** 34 **Final Year or Final Semester Residency Requirement:** No **Regional Accreditation:** Southern Association of Colleges and Schools **Credit Hours For Degree:** 120 semester hours, Bachelors **ROTC:** Army **Professional Accreditation:** AACN, AACSB, ABET, ACA, AND, AOTA, ASHA, CSWE, NASM, NAST, NCATE, NRPA. **Intercollegiate Athletics:** Baseball M; Basketball M & W; Cross-Country Running M & W; Golf M & W; Lacrosse W; Soccer M & W; Softball W; Tennis M & W; Track and Field W; Volleyball W

RANDOLPH COLLEGE

2500 Rivermont Ave.
Lynchburg, VA 24503
Tel: (434)947-8000; Free: 800-745-7692
Fax: (434)947-8996
E-mail: admissions@randolphcollege.edu
Web Site: www.randolphcollege.edu
President/CEO: John E. Klein
Admissions: Margaret Blount
Financial Aid: Debi Woodall-Stevens

Type: Comprehensive **Sex:** Coed **Affiliation:** Methodist. **Scores:** 96% SAT V 400+; 92% SAT M 400+; 59% ACT 18-23; 28% ACT 24-29 **% Accepted:** 81 **Admission Plans:** Deferred Admission; Early Admission; Early Decision Plan **Application Fee:** $0.00 **H.S. Requirements:** High school diploma required; GED accepted **Costs Per Year:** Application fee: $0. Comprehensive fee: $47,507 includes full-time tuition ($34,800), mandatory fees ($601), and college room and board ($12,106). Part-time tuition: $1450 per credit hour. Part-time mandatory fees: $52.50 per term. Part-time tuition and fees vary according to course load. **Scholarships:** Available. **Calendar System:** Semester **Enrollment:** Full-time 664, Graduate full-time 12, Graduate part-time 4, Part-time 8 **Faculty:** Full-time 68, Part-time 4 **Student-Faculty Ratio:** 10:1 **Exams:** ACT essay component not used; SAT I and SAT II or ACT; SAT I or ACT; SAT II; SAT essay component not used. **% Receiving Financial Aid:** 72 **% Residing in College-Owned, -Operated, or -Affiliated Housing:** 84 **Regional Accreditation:** Southern Association of Colleges and Schools **Credit Hours For Degree:** 124 semester hours, Bachelors **Professional Accreditation:** TEAC. **Intercollegiate Athletics:** Basketball M & W; Cross-Country Running M & W; Equestrian Sports M & W; Lacrosse M & W; Soccer M & W; Softball W; Tennis M & W; Volleyball W

RANDOLPH-MACON COLLEGE

PO Box 5005
Ashland, VA 23005-5505
Tel: (804)752-7200; Free: 800-888-1762
Fax: (804)752-4707
E-mail: admissions@rmc.edu
Web Site: www.rmc.edu
President/CEO: Robert Lindgren
Admissions: Anthony Ambrogi
Financial Aid: Mary Neal

Type: Four-Year College **Sex:** Coed **Affiliation:** United Methodist. **Scores:** 99% SAT V 400+; 99% SAT M 400+; 37.17% ACT 18-23; 49.56% ACT 24-29 **% Accepted:** 60 **Admission Plans:** Deferred Admission; Early Admission; Early Decision Plan **Application Deadline:** March 1 **Application Fee:** $30.00 **H.S. Requirements:** High school diploma required; GED accepted **Costs Per Year:** Application fee: $30. Comprehensive fee: $48,480 includes full-time tuition ($36,600), mandatory fees ($1000), and college room and board ($10,880). College room only: $6050. Full-time tuition and fees vary according to reciprocity agreements. Room and board charges vary according to board plan and housing facility. Part-time tuition: $4070 per course. **Scholarships:** Available. **Calendar System:** 4-1-4, Summer session available **Enrollment:** Full-time 1,391, Part-time 27 **Faculty:** Full-time 101, Part-time 55 **Student-Faculty Ratio:** 12:1 **Exams:** ACT essay component used as validity check; ACT essay component used for admission; SAT I or ACT; SAT II; SAT essay component used as validity check; SAT essay component used for admission; SAT Reasoning; SAT Subject. **% Receiving Financial Aid:** 75 **% Residing in College-Owned, -Operated, or -Affiliated Housing:** 85 **Final Year or Final Semester Residency Requirement:** No **Regional Accreditation:** Southern Association of Colleges and Schools **Credit Hours For Degree:** 110 semester hours, Bachelors **ROTC:** Army **Intercollegiate Athletics:** Baseball M; Basketball M & W; Cheerleading W; Equestrian Sports M & W; Field Hockey W; Football M; Golf M & W; Lacrosse M & W; Soccer M & W; Softball W; Swimming and Diving M & W; Tennis M & W; Volleyball W

RAPPAHANNOCK COMMUNITY COLLEGE

12745 College Dr.
Glenns, VA 23149-2616
Tel: (804)758-6700; Free: 800-836-9381
Fax: (804)758-3852
Web Site: www.rappahannock.edu
President/CEO: Elizabeth H. Crowther
Admissions: Felicia Packett

Type: Two-Year College **Sex:** Coed **Affiliation:** Virginia Community College System. **Admission Plans:** Early Admission; Open Admission **Application Deadline:** Rolling **Application Fee:** $0.00 **H.S. Requirements:** High school diploma or equivalent not required **Costs Per Year:** Application fee: $0. State resident tuition: $4020 full-time, $134 per credit hour part-time. Nonresident tuition: $9318 full-time, $310.60 per credit hour part-time. Mandatory fees: $440 full-time. Full-time tuition and fees vary according to course load. Part-time tuition varies according to course load. **Scholarships:** Available. **Calendar System:** Semester, Summer session available **Enrollment:** Full-time 821, Part-time 2,745 **Regional Accreditation:** Southern Association of Colleges and Schools **Credit Hours For Degree:** 60 semester hours, Associates **Intercollegiate Athletics:** Softball W

REGENT UNIVERSITY

1000 Regent University Dr.
Virginia Beach, VA 23464-9800
Tel: (757)352-4127; Free: 800-373-5504
E-mail: admissions@regent.edu
Web Site: www.regent.edu
President/CEO: Dr. M.G. Robertson
Admissions: Heidi Cece
Financial Aid: Dorothy Davidson

Type: Comprehensive **Sex:** Coed **Affiliation:** Christian. **Scores:** 96% SAT V 400+; 89% SAT M 400+; 43% ACT 18-23; 36% ACT 24-29 **% Accepted:** 86 **Admission Plans:** Deferred Admission **Application Deadline:** August 1 **Application Fee:** $50.00 **H.S. Requirements:** High school diploma required; GED accepted **Costs Per Year:** Application fee: $50. Comprehensive fee: $25,180 includes full-time tuition ($15,900), mandatory fees ($800), and college room and board ($8480). College room only: $5960. Full-time tuition and fees vary according to course load. Room and board charges vary according to board plan and housing facility. Part-time tuition: $530 per credit hour. Part-time mandatory fees: $530 per credit hour, $489 per term. Part-time tuition and fees vary according to course load. **Scholarships:** Available. **Calendar System:** Trimester, Summer session available **Enrollment:** Full-time 1,777, Graduate full-time 988, Graduate part-time 3,446, Part-time 1,218 **Faculty:** Full-time 145, Part-time 507 **Student-Faculty Ratio:** 19:1 **Exams:** SAT I or ACT; SAT Reasoning. **% Receiving Financial Aid:** 76 **% Residing in College-Owned, -Operated, or -Affiliated Housing:** 20 **Final Year or Final Semester Residency Requirement:** No **Regional Accreditation:** Southern Association of Colleges and Schools **Credit Hours For Degree:** 64 credits, Associates; 120 credits, Bachelors **ROTC:** Army, Navy **Professional Accreditation:** ABA, ACA, ACBSP, ACIPE, APA, ATS, TEAC.

RICHARD BLAND COLLEGE OF THE COLLEGE OF WILLIAM AND MARY

8311 Halifax Rd.
Petersburg, VA 23805
Tel: (804)862-6100
Fax: (804)862-6189
E-mail: apply@rbc.edu
Web Site: www.rbc.edu
President/CEO: Dr. James B. McNeer

Type: Two-Year College **Sex:** Coed **Affiliation:** College of William and Mary. **Scores:** 71% SAT V 400+ **% Accepted:** 89 **Application Deadline:** August 15 **Application Fee:** $20.00 **H.S. Requirements:** High school diploma required; GED accepted **Scholarships:** Available. **Calendar System:** Semester, Summer session available **Enrollment:** Full-time 1,038, Part-time 596 **Faculty:** Full-time 33, Part-time 38 **Student-Faculty Ratio:** 25:1 **Exams:** SAT I or ACT. **Regional Accreditation:** Southern Association of Colleges and Schools **Credit Hours For Degree:** 63 semester hours, Associates **ROTC:** Army

RIVERSIDE SCHOOL OF HEALTH CAREERS

316 Main St.
Newport News, VA 23601
Tel: (757)240-2200
Web Site: www.riversideonline.com/rshc

Type: Two-Year College **Sex:** Coed **Professional Accreditation:** ABHES.

ROANOKE COLLEGE

221 College Ln.
Salem, VA 24153-3794
Tel: (540)375-2500; Free: 800-388-2276
Fax: (540)375-2267

E-mail: admissions@roanoke.edu
Web Site: www.roanoke.edu
President/CEO: Michael C. Maxey
Financial Aid: Thomas S. Blair, Jr.

Type: Four-Year College **Sex:** Coed **Affiliation:** Evangelical Lutheran Church in America. **Scores:** 98% SAT V 400+; 99% SAT M 400+; 46.48% ACT 18-23; 40.85% ACT 24-29 **% Accepted:** 72 **Admission Plans:** Deferred Admission; Early Action; Early Admission **Application Deadline:** March 15 **Application Fee:** $30.00 **H.S. Requirements:** High school diploma required; GED accepted **Costs Per Year:** Application fee: $30. One-time mandatory fee: $125. Comprehensive fee: $54,114 includes full-time tuition ($39,720), mandatory fees ($1584), and college room and board ($12,810). College room only: $5948. Full-time tuition and fees vary according to reciprocity agreements. Room and board charges vary according to board plan and housing facility. Part-time tuition: $1900 per course. Part-time mandatory fees: $60 per term. Part-time tuition and fees vary according to course load and reciprocity agreements. **Scholarships:** Available. **Calendar System:** Semester, Summer session available **Enrollment:** Full-time 1,942, Part-time 63 **Faculty:** Full-time 164, Part-time 55 **Student-Faculty Ratio:** 11:1 **Exams:** SAT I or ACT; SAT Reasoning. **% Receiving Financial Aid:** 74 **% Residing in College-Owned, -Operated, or -Affiliated Housing:** 76 **Final Year or Final Semester Residency Requirement:** Yes **Regional Accreditation:** Southern Association of Colleges and Schools **Credit Hours For Degree:** 33.5 courses, Bachelors **Professional Accreditation:** ACBSP, JRCAT. **Intercollegiate Athletics:** Baseball M; Basketball M & W; Cross-Country Running M & W; Field Hockey W; Golf M; Lacrosse M & W; Soccer M & W; Softball W; Tennis M & W; Track and Field M & W; Volleyball W

SENTARA COLLEGE OF HEALTH SCIENCES

1441 Crossways Blvd.
Crossways I, Ste. 105
Chesapeake, VA 23320
Tel: (757)388-2900
E-mail: jhowe@sentara.edu
Web Site: www.sentara.edu
President/CEO: Shelly Cohen
Admissions: Joseph Howe

Type: Four-Year College **Sex:** Coed **Affiliation:** Sentara Healthcare. **Costs Per Year:** One-time mandatory fee: $85. Tuition: $9116 full-time, $325 per credit hour part-time. Mandatory fees: $1864 full-time. Full-time tuition and fees vary according to course level, course load, degree level, and program. Part-time tuition varies according to course level, course load, degree level, and program. **Calendar System:** Semester, Summer session available **Enrollment:** Full-time 226, Part-time 226 **Faculty:** Full-time 29, Part-time 22 **Student-Faculty Ratio:** 8:1 **Exams:** Other. **Final Year or Final Semester Residency Requirement:** No **Credit Hours For Degree:** 60 credits, Associates; 120 credits, Bachelors **Professional Accreditation:** ACICS.

SHENANDOAH UNIVERSITY

1460 University Dr.
Winchester, VA 22601-5195
Tel: (540)665-4500; Free: 800-432-2266
Fax: (540)665-4627
E-mail: admit@su.edu
Web Site: www.su.edu
President/CEO: Dr. Tracy Fitzsimmons, PhD
Admissions: Kevin Zimmerman
Financial Aid: Nancy Bragg

Type: Comprehensive **Sex:** Coed **Affiliation:** United Methodist. **Scores:** 87% SAT V 400+; 87% SAT M 400+; 48% ACT 18-23; 33% ACT 24-29 **Costs Per Year:** Comprehensive fee: $41,312 includes full-time tuition ($30,132), mandatory fees ($1190), and college room and board ($9990). Full-time tuition and fees vary according to course load and program. Room and board charges vary according to board plan and housing facility. Part-time tuition: $877 per credit. Part-time mandatory fees: $515 per term. Part-time tuition and fees vary according to course load and program. **Scholarships:** Available. **Calendar System:** Semester, Summer session available **Enrollment:** Full-time 1,927, Graduate full-time 935, Graduate part-time 875, Part-time 83 **Faculty:** Full-time 250, Part-time 189 **Student-Faculty Ratio:** 10:1 **Exams:** ACT essay component not used; SAT I or ACT; SAT essay component not used. **% Receiving Financial Aid:** 75 **% Residing in College-Owned, -Operated, or -Affiliated Housing:** 46 **Final Year or Final Semester Residency Requirement:** No **Regional Accreditation:** Southern Association of Colleges and Schools **Credit Hours For Degree:** 120

semester hours, Bachelors **Professional Accreditation:** AACN, AACSB, ACNM, ACPE, AOTA, APTA, CoARC, NASM, TEAC. **Intercollegiate Athletics:** Baseball M; Basketball M & W; Cross-Country Running M & W; Field Hockey W; Football M; Golf M & W; Lacrosse M & W; Soccer M & W; Softball W; Tennis M & W; Track and Field M & W; Volleyball W

SOUTH UNIVERSITY (GLEN ALLEN)

2151 Old Brick Rd.
Glen Allen, VA 23060
Tel: (804)727-6800; Free: 888-422-5076
Fax: (804)727-6790
Web Site: www.southuniversity.edu/richmond
President/CEO: Troy Ralston

Type: Comprehensive **Sex:** Coed **Regional Accreditation:** Southern Association of Colleges and Schools **Professional Accreditation:** ACBSP.

SOUTH UNIVERSITY (VIRGINIA BEACH)

301 Bendix Rd., Ste. 100
Virginia Beach, VA 23452
Tel: (757)493-6900; Free: 877-206-1845
Fax: (757)493-6990
Web Site: www.southuniversity.edu/virginia-beach
President/CEO: Richard Kriofsky

Type: Comprehensive **Sex:** Coed **Regional Accreditation:** Southern Association of Colleges and Schools **Professional Accreditation:** ACBSP.

SOUTHERN VIRGINIA UNIVERSITY

One College Hill Dr.
Buena Vista, VA 24416
Tel: (540)261-8400; Free: 800-229-8420
Fax: (540)261-8559
E-mail: admissions@southernvirginia.edu
Web Site: www.svu.edu
President/CEO: Paul K. Sybrowsky
Admissions: Tony Caputo
Financial Aid: Darin Hassell

Type: Four-Year College **Sex:** Coed **Affiliation:** Latter-day Saints. **Scores:** 96% SAT V 400+; 95% SAT M 400+; 46.9% ACT 18-23; 39.4% ACT 24-29 **% Accepted:** 52 **Application Deadline:** July 31 **Application Fee:** $35.00 **H.S. Requirements:** High school diploma required; GED accepted **Scholarships:** Available. **Calendar System:** Semester, Summer session available **Enrollment:** Full-time 714, Part-time 35 **Faculty:** Full-time 34, Part-time 35 **Student-Faculty Ratio:** 16:1 **Exams:** SAT I or ACT. **% Receiving Financial Aid:** 81 **% Residing in College-Owned, -Operated, or -Affiliated Housing:** 65 **Regional Accreditation:** Southern Association of Colleges and Schools **Credit Hours For Degree:** 93 credits, Bachelors **ROTC:** Army **Professional Accreditation:** AALE. **Intercollegiate Athletics:** Baseball M; Basketball M & W; Cheerleading M & W; Cross-Country Running M & W; Football M; Golf M & W; Lacrosse M & W; Soccer M & W; Softball W; Tennis M & W; Track and Field M & W; Volleyball W; Wrestling M

SOUTHSIDE REGIONAL MEDICAL CENTER PROFESSIONAL SCHOOLS

430 Clairmont Ct., Ste. 200
Colonial Heights, VA 23834
Tel: (804)765-5800
Web Site: www.srmconline.com/Southside-Regional-Medical-Center/nursingeducation.aspx

Type: Two-Year College **Sex:** Coed **Costs Per Year:** Tuition: $5760 full-time, $240 per credit hour part-time. Mandatory fees: $1980 full-time, $82.50 per credit hour part-time. Full-time tuition and fees vary according to course level, course load, program, and student level. Part-time tuition and fees vary according to course level, course load, program, and student level.

SOUTHSIDE VIRGINIA COMMUNITY COLLEGE

109 Campus Dr.
Alberta, VA 23821-9719
Tel: (434)949-1000
Fax: (434)949-7863
E-mail: rhina.jones@sv.vccs.edu
Web Site: www.southside.edu
President/CEO: Dr. John Cavan
Admissions: Brent Richey

Type: Two-Year College **Sex:** Coed **Affiliation:** Virginia Community College

System. **% Accepted:** 100 **Admission Plans:** Deferred Admission; Open Admission; Preferred Admission **Application Deadline:** Rolling **Application Fee:** $0.00 **H.S. Requirements:** High school diploma required; GED accepted. For applicants 18 or over who demonstrate ability to benefit from occupational program: High school diploma required; GED not accepted **Scholarships:** Available. **Calendar System:** Semester, Summer session available **Enrollment:** Full-time 1,924, Part-time 4,429 **Faculty:** Full-time 73, Part-time 217 **Student-Faculty Ratio:** 17:1 **Regional Accreditation:** Southern Association of Colleges and Schools **Credit Hours For Degree:** 65 semester hours, Associates **ROTC:** Army

SOUTHWEST VIRGINIA COMMUNITY COLLEGE
PO Box SVCC
Richlands, VA 24641
Tel: (276)964-2555; Free: 800-822-7822
Fax: (276)964-9307
E-mail: dionne.cook@sw.edu
Web Site: www.sw.edu
President/CEO: Dr. J. Mark Estepp
Admissions: Dionne Cook

Type: Two-Year College **Sex:** Coed **Affiliation:** Virginia Community College System. **Admission Plans:** Deferred Admission; Early Admission; Open Admission; Preferred Admission **Application Deadline:** Rolling **Application Fee:** $0.00 **H.S. Requirements:** High school diploma required; GED accepted **Costs Per Year:** Application fee: $0. State resident tuition: $4335 full-time, $144.50 per credit hour part-time. Nonresident tuition: $10,173 full-time, $339.10 per credit hour part-time. Mandatory fees: $315 full-time, $10.50 per credit hour part-time. Full-time tuition and fees vary according to reciprocity agreements. Part-time tuition and fees vary according to reciprocity agreements. **Scholarships:** Available. **Calendar System:** Semester, Summer session available **Enrollment:** Full-time 1,209, Part-time 1,337 **Faculty:** Full-time 40, Part-time 89 **Student-Faculty Ratio:** 23:1 **Exams:** Other. **Final Year or Final Semester Residency Requirement:** No **Regional Accreditation:** Southern Association of Colleges and Schools **Credit Hours For Degree:** 60 semester hours, Associates **Professional Accreditation:** CoARC, JRCERT.

STANDARD HEALTHCARE SERVICES, COLLEGE OF NURSING
1073 W Broad St.
Ste. 201
Falls Church, VA 22046-4612
Tel: (703)891-1787
Web Site: www.standardcollege.edu
Type: Two-Year College **Sex:** Coed **Professional Accreditation:** ABHES.

STRATFORD UNIVERSITY (ALEXANDRIA)
2900 Eisenhower Ave.
Alexandria, VA 22314
Tel: (571)699-3200; Free: 800-444-0804
E-mail: alexandriaadmissions@stratford.edu
Web Site: www.stratford.edu
President/CEO: Dr. Richard Shurtz

Type: Comprehensive **Sex:** Coed **Admission Plans:** Open Admission **Application Deadline:** Rolling **Application Fee:** $50.00 **H.S. Requirements:** High school diploma required; GED accepted **Costs Per Year:** Application fee: $50. Tuition: $14,985 full-time, $1665 per course part-time. Full-time tuition varies according to course level, course load, degree level, and program. Part-time tuition varies according to course level, course load, degree level, and program. **Calendar System:** Quarter, Summer session available **Enrollment:** Full-time 36, Graduate full-time 18, Graduate part-time 6, Part-time 139 **Faculty:** Full-time 5, Part-time 25 **Final Year or Final Semester Residency Requirement:** No **Credit Hours For Degree:** 90 credits, Associates; 180 credits, Bachelors **Professional Accreditation:** ACICS.

STRATFORD UNIVERSITY (FALLS CHURCH)
7777 Leesburg Pke.
Ste. 100 S
Falls Church, VA 22043
Tel: (703)821-8570; Free: 800-444-0804
Fax: (703)556-9892
E-mail: fcadmissions@stratford.edu
Web Site: www.stratford.edu
President/CEO: Dr. Richard R. Shurtz, III

Financial Aid: Imane Babsiri

Type: Comprehensive **Sex:** Coed **Admission Plans:** Open Admission **Application Deadline:** Rolling **Application Fee:** $50.00 **H.S. Requirements:** High school diploma required; GED accepted **Costs Per Year:** Application fee: $50. Tuition: $14,985 full-time, $1665 per course part-time. Full-time tuition varies according to course level, degree level, and program. Part-time tuition varies according to course level, degree level, and program. **Scholarships:** Available. **Calendar System:** Quarter, Summer session available **Enrollment:** Graduate full-time 560, Graduate part-time 98 **Faculty:** Full-time 28, Part-time 136 **Final Year or Final Semester Residency Requirement:** No **Credit Hours For Degree:** 90 quarter credits, Associates; 180 quarter credits, Bachelors **Professional Accreditation:** ACF, ACICS, COE.

STRATFORD UNIVERSITY (GLEN ALLEN)
11104 W Broad St.
Glen Allen, VA 23060
Tel: (804)290-4231; Free: 877-373-5173
E-mail: gaadmissions@stratford.edu
Web Site: www.stratford.edu
President/CEO: Dr. Richard Shurtz
Financial Aid: Noshuo Rivers

Type: Comprehensive **Sex:** Coed **Costs Per Year:** Tuition: $14,985 full-time, $1665 per course part-time. Full-time tuition varies according to course level, degree level, and program. Part-time tuition varies according to course level, degree level, and program. **Scholarships:** Available. **Calendar System:** Quarter, Summer session available **Enrollment:** Full-time 25, Graduate full-time 51, Graduate part-time 32, Part-time 177 **Faculty:** Full-time 9, Part-time 53 **Final Year or Final Semester Residency Requirement:** No **Credit Hours For Degree:** 90 credits, Associates; 180 credits, Bachelors **Professional Accreditation:** ACICS.

STRATFORD UNIVERSITY (NEWPORT NEWS)
836 J. Clyde Morris Blvd.
Newport News, VA 23601
Tel: (757)873-4235; Free: 855-873-4235
E-mail: newportnewsadmissions@stratford.edu
Web Site: www.stratford.edu
President/CEO: Dr. Richard Shurtz
Financial Aid: Sheryl Kimberly

Type: Comprehensive **Sex:** Coed **Costs Per Year:** Tuition: $14,985 full-time, $1665 per course part-time. Full-time tuition varies according to course level, degree level, and program. Part-time tuition varies according to course level, degree level, and program. **Scholarships:** Available. **Calendar System:** Quarter, Summer session available **Enrollment:** Full-time 82, Graduate full-time 20, Graduate part-time 21, Part-time 242 **Faculty:** Full-time 11, Part-time 38 **Final Year or Final Semester Residency Requirement:** No **Credit Hours For Degree:** 90 credits, Associates; 180 credits, Bachelors **Professional Accreditation:** ACICS.

STRATFORD UNIVERSITY (VIRGINIA BEACH)
555 S Independence Blvd.
Virginia Beach, VA 23452
Tel: (757)497-4466; Free: 866-528-8363
E-mail: virginiabeachadmissions@stratford.edu
Web Site: www.stratford.edu
President/CEO: Dr. Richard Shurtz

Type: Comprehensive **Sex:** Coed **Admission Plans:** Open Admission **Application Deadline:** Rolling **Application Fee:** $50.00 **H.S. Requirements:** High school diploma required; GED accepted **Costs Per Year:** Application fee: $50. Tuition: $14,985 full-time, $1665 per course part-time. Full-time tuition varies according to course level, degree level, and program. Part-time tuition varies according to course level, degree level, and program. **Calendar System:** Quarter, Summer session available **Enrollment:** Full-time 79, Graduate full-time 20, Graduate part-time 12, Part-time 150 **Faculty:** Full-time 9, Part-time 38 **Final Year or Final Semester Residency Requirement:** No **Credit Hours For Degree:** 90 credits, Associates; 180 credits, Bachelors **Professional Accreditation:** ACICS.

STRATFORD UNIVERSITY (WOODBRIDGE)
14349 Gideon Dr.
Woodbridge, VA 22192
Free: 888-546-1250
E-mail: woodbridgeadmissions@stratford.edu
Web Site: www.stratford.edu

President/CEO: Dr. Richard Shurtz
Financial Aid: Sherrese Whiting
Type: Comprehensive **Sex:** Coed **Admission Plans:** Open Admission **Application Deadline:** Rolling **Application Fee:** $50.00 **H.S. Requirements:** High school diploma required; GED accepted **Costs Per Year:** Application fee: $50. Tuition: $14,985 full-time, $1665 per course part-time. Full-time tuition varies according to course level, degree level, and program. Part-time tuition varies according to course level, degree level, and program. **Scholarships:** Available. **Calendar System:** Quarter, Summer session available **Enrollment:** Full-time 113, Graduate full-time 32, Graduate part-time 13, Part-time 319 **Faculty:** Full-time 17, Part-time 51 **Final Year or Final Semester Residency Requirement:** No **Credit Hours For Degree:** 90 credits, Associates; 180 credits, Bachelors **Professional Accreditation:** ACICS.

STRAYER UNIVERSITY–ALEXANDRIA CAMPUS
2730 Eisenhower Ave.
Alexandria, VA 22314
Tel: (703)317-2626
Fax: (703)329-9602
Web Site: www.strayer.edu/virginia/alexandria
President/CEO: Brian W. Jones
Type: Comprehensive **Sex:** Coed **Regional Accreditation:** Middle States Association of Colleges and Schools

STRAYER UNIVERSITY–ARLINGTON CAMPUS
2121 15th St. N
Arlington, VA 22201
Tel: (703)892-5100
Fax: (703)769-2677
Web Site: www.strayer.edu/virginia/arlington
President/CEO: Brian W. Jones
Type: Comprehensive **Sex:** Coed **Regional Accreditation:** Middle States Association of Colleges and Schools

STRAYER UNIVERSITY–CHESAPEAKE CAMPUS
676 Independence Pky.
Ste. 300
Chesapeake, VA 23320
Tel: (757)382-9900
Fax: (757)547-6078
Web Site: www.strayer.edu/virginia/chesapeake
President/CEO: Brian W. Jones
Type: Comprehensive **Sex:** Coed **Regional Accreditation:** Middle States Association of Colleges and Schools

STRAYER UNIVERSITY–CHESTERFIELD CAMPUS
2820 Waterford Lake Dr.
Ste. 100
Midlothian, VA 23112
Tel: (804)763-6300
Fax: (804)763-6304
Web Site: www.strayer.edu/virginia/chesterfield
President/CEO: Brian W. Jones
Type: Comprehensive **Sex:** Coed **Regional Accreditation:** Middle States Association of Colleges and Schools

STRAYER UNIVERSITY–FREDERICKSBURG CAMPUS
150 Riverside Pky.
Ste. 100
Fredericksburg, VA 22406
Tel: (540)374-4300
Web Site: www.strayer.edu/virginia/fredericksburg
President/CEO: Brian W. Jones
Type: Comprehensive **Sex:** Coed **Regional Accreditation:** Middle States Association of Colleges and Schools

STRAYER UNIVERSITY–HENRICO CAMPUS
11501 Nuckols Rd.
Glen Allen, VA 23059
Tel: (804)527-1000
Fax: (804)527-6963
Web Site: www.strayer.edu/virginia/henrico
President/CEO: Brian W. Jones

Type: Comprehensive **Sex:** Coed **Regional Accreditation:** Middle States Association of Colleges and Schools

STRAYER UNIVERSITY–LOUDOUN CAMPUS
45150 Russell Branch Pky.
Ste. 200
Ashburn, VA 20147
Tel: (703)729-8800
Fax: (703)729-8820
Web Site: www.strayer.edu/virginia/loudoun
President/CEO: Brian W. Jones
Type: Comprehensive **Sex:** Coed **Regional Accreditation:** Middle States Association of Colleges and Schools

STRAYER UNIVERSITY–MANASSAS CAMPUS
9990 Battleview Pky.
Manassas, VA 20109
Tel: (703)330-8400
Fax: (703)330-8135
Web Site: www.strayer.edu/virginia/manassas
President/CEO: Brian W. Jones
Type: Comprehensive **Sex:** Coed **Regional Accreditation:** Middle States Association of Colleges and Schools

STRAYER UNIVERSITY–NEWPORT NEWS CAMPUS
99 Old Oyster Point Rd.
Unit 1
Newport News, VA 23602
Tel: (757)873-3100
Fax: (757)873-3131
Web Site: www.strayer.edu/virginia/newport-news
President/CEO: Brian W. Jones
Type: Comprehensive **Sex:** Coed **Regional Accreditation:** Middle States Association of Colleges and Schools

STRAYER UNIVERSITY–VIRGINIA BEACH CAMPUS
249 Central Park Ave., Ste. 350
Virginia Beach, VA 23462
Tel: (757)493-6000
Fax: (757)493-6030
Web Site: www.strayer.edu/virginia/virginia-beach
President/CEO: Brian W. Jones
Type: Comprehensive **Sex:** Coed **Regional Accreditation:** Middle States Association of Colleges and Schools

STRAYER UNIVERSITY–WOODBRIDGE CAMPUS
13385 Minnieville Rd.
Woodbridge, VA 22192
Tel: (703)878-2800
Fax: (703)878-2993
Web Site: www.strayer.edu/virginia/woodbridge
President/CEO: Brian W. Jones
Type: Comprehensive **Sex:** Coed **Regional Accreditation:** Middle States Association of Colleges and Schools

SWEET BRIAR COLLEGE
Sweet Briar, VA 24595
Tel: (434)381-6100; Free: 800-381-6142
Fax: (434)381-6173
E-mail: admissions@sbc.edu
Web Site: www.sbc.edu
President/CEO: Phillip C. Stone
Admissions: Steven Nape
Financial Aid: Wanda Spradley
Type: Comprehensive **Sex:** Women **Scores:** 86% SAT V 400+; 80% SAT M 400+; 44% ACT 18-23; 44% ACT 24-29 **% Accepted:** 95 **Admission Plans:** Deferred Admission; Early Decision Plan **Application Deadline:** February 1 **Application Fee:** $40.00 **H.S. Requirements:** High school diploma required; GED accepted **Costs Per Year:** Application fee: $40. Comprehensive fee: $49,060 includes full-time tuition ($35,800), mandatory fees ($625), and college room and board ($12,635). Room and board charges vary according to board plan. Part-time tuition: $1050 per credit hour. **Scholarships:** Available. **Calendar System:** Semester, Summer session available **Enrollment:** Full-time 310, Graduate full-time 2, Graduate part-time 2, Part-

time 6 **Faculty:** Full-time 49, Part-time 22 **Student-Faculty Ratio:** 5:1 **Exams:** SAT I or ACT; SAT Reasoning. **% Receiving Financial Aid:** 79 **% Residing in College-Owned, -Operated, or -Affiliated Housing:** 94 **Final Year or Final Semester Residency Requirement:** No **Regional Accreditation:** Southern Association of Colleges and Schools **Credit Hours For Degree:** 120 semester hours, Bachelors **Professional Accreditation:** ABET. **Intercollegiate Athletics:** Cross-Country Running W; Equestrian Sports W; Fencing W; Field Hockey W; Golf W; Lacrosse W; Soccer W; Softball W; Swimming and Diving W; Tennis W

THOMAS NELSON COMMUNITY COLLEGE
PO Box 9407
Hampton, VA 23670-0407
Tel: (757)825-2700
E-mail: admissions@tncc.edu
Web Site: www.tncc.edu
President/CEO: Dr. John T. Dever
Admissions: Geraldine Newson
Financial Aid: Kathryn J. Anderson
Type: Two-Year College **Sex:** Coed **Affiliation:** Virginia Community College System. **Admission Plans:** Deferred Admission; Early Admission; Open Admission **Application Deadline:** Rolling **Application Fee:** $0.00 **H.S. Requirements:** High school diploma or equivalent not required **Scholarships:** Available. **Calendar System:** Semester, Summer session available **Enrollment:** Full-time 3,689, Part-time 7,253 **Student-Faculty Ratio:** 22:1 **Regional Accreditation:** Southern Association of Colleges and Schools **Credit Hours For Degree:** 60 semester hours, Associates **Professional Accreditation:** ACEN, NAACLS.

TIDEWATER COMMUNITY COLLEGE
121 College Pl.
Norfolk, VA 23510
Tel: (757)822-1122
Fax: (757)822-1060
E-mail: centralrecords@tcc.edu
Web Site: www.tcc.edu
President/CEO: Edna V. Baehre-Kolovani
Type: Two-Year College **Sex:** Coed **Affiliation:** Virginia Community College System. **Admission Plans:** Deferred Admission; Early Admission; Open Admission **Application Deadline:** Rolling **Application Fee:** $0.00 **H.S. Requirements:** High school diploma or equivalent not required. For nursing, allied health programs: High school diploma required; GED accepted **Costs Per Year:** Application fee: $0. State resident tuition: $3354 full-time, $139.75 per credit hour part-time. Nonresident tuition: $7,592 full-time, $316.35 per credit hour part-time. Mandatory fees: $884 full-time, $36.85 per credit hour part-time. **Scholarships:** Available. **Calendar System:** Semester, Summer session available **Enrollment:** Full-time 9,499, Part-time 16,428 **Faculty:** Full-time 360, Part-time 1,060 **Student-Faculty Ratio:** 21:1 **Final Year or Final Semester Residency Requirement:** No **Regional Accreditation:** Southern Association of Colleges and Schools **Credit Hours For Degree:** 60 semester hours, Associates **Professional Accreditation:** ACEN, ACF, AHIMA, AOTA, CoARC, JRCEMTP, JRCERT, MACTE.

UNIVERSITY OF MANAGEMENT AND TECHNOLOGY
1901 N Fort Myers Dr.
Arlington, VA 22209
Tel: (703)516-0035; Free: 800-924-4883
Fax: (703)516-0985
E-mail: admissions@umtweb.edu
Web Site: www.umtweb.edu
President/CEO: Dr. Yanping Chen
Admissions: Kenny Hickey
Type: Comprehensive **Sex:** Coed **Admission Plans:** Open Admission **Application Fee:** $30.00 **H.S. Requirements:** High school diploma required; GED accepted **Scholarships:** Available. **Calendar System:** Continuous **Enrollment:** Full-time 884, Graduate full-time 238, Graduate part-time 65, Part-time 73 **Student-Faculty Ratio:** 25:1 **Exams:** ACT; SAT I; SAT I and SAT II or ACT; SAT I or ACT; SAT II. **% Receiving Financial Aid:** 94 **Professional Accreditation:** DEAC.

UNIVERSITY OF MARY WASHINGTON
1301 College Ave.
Fredericksburg, VA 22401-5358
Tel: (540)654-1000; Free: 800-468-5614

Fax: (540)654-1073
E-mail: admit@umw.edu
Web Site: www.umw.edu
President/CEO: Richard V. Hurley
Admissions: Melissa Yakabouski
Financial Aid: Heidi Hunter-Goldsworthy
Type: Comprehensive **Sex:** Coed **Scores:** 99% SAT V 400+; 99% SAT M 400+; 44% ACT 18-23; 44% ACT 24-29 **% Accepted:** 83 **Admission Plans:** Deferred Admission; Early Admission; Early Decision Plan; Preferred Admission **Application Deadline:** February 1 **Application Fee:** $50.00 **H.S. Requirements:** High school diploma required; GED accepted **Costs Per Year:** Application fee: $50. One-time mandatory fee: $60. State resident tuition: $5604 full-time, $240 per credit hour part-time. Nonresident tuition: $19,768 full-time, $828 per credit hour part-time. Mandatory fees: $5466 full-time, $155 per credit hour part-time, $30 per term part-time. Full-time tuition and fees vary according to course load, degree level, and location. Part-time tuition and fees vary according to course load, degree level, and location. College room and board: $9856. College room only: $5882. Room and board charges vary according to board plan and housing facility. **Scholarships:** Available. **Calendar System:** Semester, Summer session available **Enrollment:** Full-time 3,796, Graduate full-time 129, Graduate part-time 198, Part-time 524 **Faculty:** Full-time 245, Part-time 138 **Student-Faculty Ratio:** 16:1 **Exams:** ACT essay component not used; SAT I or ACT; SAT essay component not used; SAT Reasoning; SAT Subject. **% Receiving Financial Aid:** 39 **% Residing in College-Owned, -Operated, or -Affiliated Housing:** 57 **Final Year or Final Semester Residency Requirement:** Yes **Regional Accreditation:** Southern Association of Colleges and Schools **Credit Hours For Degree:** 122 semester hours, Bachelors **ROTC:** Army **Professional Accreditation:** NASM. **Intercollegiate Athletics:** Baseball M; Basketball M & W; Cross-Country Running M & W; Equestrian Sports M & W; Field Hockey W; Lacrosse M & W; Rugby M & W; Soccer M & W; Softball W; Swimming and Diving M & W; Tennis M & W; Track and Field M & W; Volleyball M & W

UNIVERSITY OF RICHMOND
28 Westhampton Way
University of Richmond, VA 23173
Tel: (804)289-8000; Free: 800-700-1662
Fax: (804)287-6003
E-mail: admissions@richmond.edu
Web Site: www.richmond.edu
President/CEO: Dr. Ronald A. Crutcher
Admissions: Gil Villanueva
Type: Comprehensive **Sex:** Coed **Scores:** 100% SAT V 400+; 100% SAT M 400+; 2.9% ACT 18-23; 25% ACT 24-29 **% Accepted:** 31 **Admission Plans:** Deferred Admission; Early Action **Application Deadline:** January 15 **Application Fee:** $50.00 **H.S. Requirements:** High school diploma required; GED accepted **Costs Per Year:** Application fee: $50. Comprehensive fee: $60,880 includes full-time tuition ($49,420) and college room and board ($11,460). College room only: $5260. Full-time tuition varies according to course load. Room and board charges vary according to board plan and housing facility. Part-time tuition: $2471 per credit hour. Part-time tuition varies according to course load. **Scholarships:** Available. **Calendar System:** Semester, Summer session available **Enrollment:** Full-time 2,958, Graduate full-time 496, Graduate part-time 66, Part-time 32 **Faculty:** Full-time 330, Part-time 81 **Student-Faculty Ratio:** 8:1 **Exams:** ACT essay component used for admission; SAT I or ACT; SAT II; SAT essay component used for admission; SAT Reasoning; SAT Subject. **% Receiving Financial Aid:** 40 **% Residing in College-Owned, -Operated, or -Affiliated Housing:** 90 **Final Year or Final Semester Residency Requirement:** No **Regional Accreditation:** Southern Association of Colleges and Schools **Credit Hours For Degree:** 120 semester hours, Bachelors **ROTC:** Army **Professional Accreditation:** AACSB, AALS, ABA. **Intercollegiate Athletics:** Badminton M & W; Baseball M; Basketball M & W; Crew M & W; Cross-Country Running M & W; Equestrian Sports M & W; Field Hockey W; Football M; Golf M & W; Ice Hockey M; Lacrosse M & W; Rugby M & W; Soccer W; Squash M & W; Swimming and Diving W; Tennis M & W; Track and Field W; Ultimate Frisbee M & W; Volleyball M & W; Water Polo M & W

UNIVERSITY OF VALLEY FORGE VIRGINIA CAMPUS
13909 Smoketown Rd.
Woodbridge, VA 22192
Tel: (703)580-4810; Free: 800-432-8322
Fax: (703)580-4806

Web Site: www.valleyforge.edu

Financial Aid: Christiana Bruwaa-Frimpong

Type: Four-Year College **Sex:** Coed **Affiliation:** Assemblies of God; Valley Forge Christian College. **% Accepted:** 81 **Application Deadline:** Rolling **Application Fee:** $75.00 **H.S. Requirements:** High school diploma required; GED accepted **Costs Per Year:** Application fee: $75. Tuition: $9360 full-time. Mandatory fees: $300 full-time. Full-time tuition and fees vary according to course load and location. **Scholarships:** Available. **Enrollment:** Full-time 59, Part-time 72 **Faculty:** Full-time 4, Part-time 32 **Student-Faculty Ratio:** 6:1 **Final Year or Final Semester Residency Requirement:** No **Regional Accreditation:** Middle States Association of Colleges and Schools **Credit Hours For Degree:** 60 credits, Associates; 126 credits, Bachelors

UNIVERSITY OF VIRGINIA

Charlottesville, VA 22903

Tel: (434)924-0311

Fax: (434)924-3587

E-mail: undergrad-admission@virginia.edu

Web Site: www.virginia.edu

President/CEO: Dr. Teresa A. Sullivan

Admissions: Gregory W. Roberts

Financial Aid: Scott Miller

Type: University **Sex:** Coed **Scores:** 100% SAT V 400+; 99% SAT M 400+; 3% ACT 18-23; 33% ACT 24-29 **% Accepted:** 30 **Admission Plans:** Deferred Admission; Early Decision Plan; Preferred Admission **Application Deadline:** January 1 **Application Fee:** $60.00 **H.S. Requirements:** High school diploma required; GED accepted **Costs Per Year:** Application fee: $60. State resident tuition: $11,892 full-time, $363 per credit hour part-time. Nonresident tuition: $40,506 full-time, $1350 per credit hour part-time. Mandatory fees: $2576 full-time, $2576 per year part-time. Full-time tuition and fees vary according to program and student level. College room and board: $10,400. College room only: $5680. Room and board charges vary according to board plan and housing facility. **Scholarships:** Available. **Calendar System:** Semester, Summer session available **Enrollment:** Full-time 15,816, Graduate full-time 5,867, Graduate part-time 1,280, Part-time 920 **Faculty:** Full-time 1,365, Part-time 100 **Student-Faculty Ratio:** 15:1 **Exams:** ACT essay component used for admission; ACT essay component used for advising; ACT essay component used for placement; SAT I or ACT; SAT II; SAT essay component used for admission; SAT essay component used for advising; SAT essay component used for placement; SAT Reasoning; SAT Subject. **% Receiving Financial Aid:** 33 **% Residing in College-Owned, -Operated, or -Affiliated Housing:** 40 **Final Year or Final Semester Residency Requirement:** Yes **Regional Accreditation:** Southern Association of Colleges and Schools **Credit Hours For Degree:** 120 semester hours, Bachelors **ROTC:** Air Force, Army, Navy **Professional Accreditation:** AACN, AACSB, AALS, ABA, ABET, ACA, ACSP, ACIPE, AND, APA, ASHA, ASLA, LCME/AMA, NAAB, NAST, NCATE, TEAC. **Intercollegiate Athletics:** Baseball M; Basketball M & W; Crew W; Cross-Country Running M & W; Field Hockey W; Football M; Golf M & W; Lacrosse M & W; Soccer M & W; Softball W; Swimming and Diving M & W; Tennis M & W; Track and Field M & W; Volleyball W; Wrestling M

THE UNIVERSITY OF VIRGINIA'S COLLEGE AT WISE

1 College Ave.

Wise, VA 24293

Tel: (276)328-0100; Free: 888-282-9324

Fax: (276)328-0251

E-mail: admissions@uvawise.edu

Web Site: www.uvawise.edu

President/CEO: Donna Henry

Admissions: Russell D. Necessary

Financial Aid: Rebecca Huffman

Type: Four-Year College **Sex:** Coed **Affiliation:** University of Virginia. **Scores:** 87% SAT V 400+; 87% SAT M 400+ **% Accepted:** 77 **Admission Plans:** Early Admission; Early Decision Plan **Application Deadline:** August 1 **Application Fee:** $25.00 **H.S. Requirements:** High school diploma required; GED accepted **Costs Per Year:** Application fee: $25. State resident tuition: $5190 full-time, $216 per credit hour part-time. Nonresident tuition: $20,792 full-time, $874 per credit hour part-time. Mandatory fees: $4165 full-time, $49 per credit hour part-time, $49. Part-time tuition and fees vary according to course load. College room and board: $10,256. Room and board charges vary according to board plan and housing facility. **Scholarships:** Available. **Calendar System:** Semester, Summer session available

Enrollment: Full-time 1,335, Part-time 693 **Faculty:** Full-time 103, Part-time 89 **Student-Faculty Ratio:** 12:1 **Exams:** SAT I or ACT; SAT Reasoning. **% Receiving Financial Aid:** 79 **% Residing in College-Owned, -Operated, or -Affiliated Housing:** 25 **Regional Accreditation:** Southern Association of Colleges and Schools **Credit Hours For Degree:** 120 semester hours, Bachelors **ROTC:** Army **Professional Accreditation:** AACN, ABET. **Intercollegiate Athletics:** Baseball M; Basketball M & W; Cross-Country Running M & W; Football M; Golf M & W; Lacrosse W; Softball W; Tennis M & W; Track and Field M & W; Volleyball W

VIRGINIA BAPTIST COLLEGE

4111 Plank Rd.

Fredericksburg, VA 22407

Web Site: www.vbc.edu

Type: Four-Year College **Sex:** Coed **Professional Accreditation:** TRACS.

VIRGINIA COLLEGE IN RICHMOND

7200 Midlothian Tpke.

Richmond, VA 23225

Tel: (804)977-5100

Web Site: www.vc.edu

Type: Two-Year College **Sex:** Coed **Calendar System:** Quarter **Professional Accreditation:** ACICS.

VIRGINIA COMMONWEALTH UNIVERSITY

901 W Franklin St.

Richmond, VA 23284-9005

Tel: (804)828-0100; Free: 800-841-3638

Fax: (804)828-1899

E-mail: ugrad@vcu.edu

Web Site: www.vcu.edu

President/CEO: Dr. Michael Rao

Financial Aid: Marc T . Vernon

Type: University **Sex:** Coed **Scores:** 99% SAT V 400+; 98% SAT M 400+; 41.8% ACT 18-23; 41.34% ACT 24-29 **% Accepted:** 72 **Admission Plans:** Early Admission **Application Deadline:** January 15 **Application Fee:** $50.00 **H.S. Requirements:** High school diploma required; GED accepted **Costs Per Year:** Application fee: $50. State resident tuition: $10,669 full-time, $370 per credit hour part-time. Nonresident tuition: $28,735 full-time, $993 per credit hour part-time. Mandatory fees: $2103 full-time. College room and board: $9586. Room and board charges vary according to board plan and housing facility. **Scholarships:** Available. **Calendar System:** Semester, Summer session available **Enrollment:** Full-time 20,411, Graduate full-time 5,148, Graduate part-time 2,043, Part-time 3,640 **Faculty:** Full-time 2,264, Part-time 1,015 **Student-Faculty Ratio:** 16:1 **Exams:** ACT essay component not used; SAT I or ACT; SAT essay component not used; SAT Reasoning. **% Receiving Financial Aid:** 57 **% Residing in College-Owned, -Operated, or -Affiliated Housing:** 74 **Final Year or Final Semester Residency Requirement:** No **Regional Accreditation:** Southern Association of Colleges and Schools **Credit Hours For Degree:** 120 credits (minimum), Bachelors **ROTC:** Army **Professional Accreditation:** AACSB, AANA, ABET, ACA, ACEN, ACPE, ACSP, ACIPE, ADA, AND, AOTA, APA, APTA, CAHME, CEPH, CIDA, CORE, CSWE, JRCERT, JRCNMT, LCME/AMA, NAACLS, NASAD, NASD, NASM, NASPAA, NAST, NCATE, NRPA. **Intercollegiate Athletics:** Baseball M; Basketball M & W; Cross-Country Running M & W; Field Hockey W; Golf M; Lacrosse W; Soccer M & W; Tennis M & W; Track and Field M & W; Volleyball W

VIRGINIA HIGHLANDS COMMUNITY COLLEGE

100 VHCC Dr. Abingdon

Abingdon, VA 24212

Tel: (276)739-2400; Free: 877-207-6115

Fax: (276)739-2590

E-mail: kcheers@vhcc.edu

Web Site: www.vhcc.edu

President/CEO: Dr. David Wilkin

Admissions: Karen Cheers

Type: Two-Year College **Sex:** Coed **Affiliation:** Virginia Community College System. **Admission Plans:** Deferred Admission; Early Admission; Open Admission; Preferred Admission **Application Deadline:** Rolling **H.S. Requirements:** High school diploma or equivalent not required. For nursing program: High school diploma required; GED accepted **Scholarships:** Available. **Calendar System:** Semester, Summer session available **Enrollment:** Full-time 1,001, Part-time 1,579 **Faculty:** Full-time 58, Part-time 39

Regional Accreditation: Southern Association of Colleges and Schools **Credit Hours For Degree:** 65 semester hours, Associates **Professional Accreditation:** JRCERT.

VIRGINIA INTERNATIONAL UNIVERSITY

4401 Village Dr.
Fairfax, VA 22030
Tel: (703)591-7042; Free: 800-514-6848
Fax: (703)591-7048
E-mail: admissions@viu.edu
Web Site: www.viu.edu
President/CEO: Isa Sarac, PhD
Type: Comprehensive **Sex:** Coed **Professional Accreditation:** ACICS.

VIRGINIA MILITARY INSTITUTE

Lexington, VA 24450
Tel: (540)464-7230; Free: 800-767-4207
Fax: (540)464-7746
E-mail: admissions@vmi.edu
Web Site: www.vmi.edu
President/CEO: Gen. J.H. Binford Peay, III
Admissions: Col. Tom Mortenson
Financial Aid: Lt. Col. Thomas A. Brashears
Type: Four-Year College **Sex:** Coed **Scores:** 100% SAT V 400+; 100% SAT M 400+; 35.4% ACT 18-23; 52.4% ACT 24-29 **% Accepted:** 53 **Admission Plans:** Early Action; Early Admission **Application Deadline:** February 1 **Application Fee:** $40.00 **H.S. Requirements:** High school diploma required; GED not accepted **Costs Per Year:** Application fee: $40. State resident tuition: $8136 full-time, $318 per credit hour part-time. Nonresident tuition: $31,150 full-time, $994 per credit hour part-time. Mandatory fees: $8400 full-time. College room and board: $8666. **Scholarships:** Available. **Calendar System:** Semester, Summer session available **Enrollment:** Full-time 1,717 **Faculty:** Full-time 133, Part-time 64 **Student-Faculty Ratio:** 11:1 **Exams:** ACT essay component not used; SAT I or ACT; SAT essay component not used; SAT Reasoning. **% Receiving Financial Aid:** 51 **% Residing in College-Owned, -Operated, or -Affiliated Housing:** 100 **Regional Accreditation:** Southern Association of Colleges and Schools **Credit Hours For Degree:** 136 semester hours, Bachelors **ROTC:** Air Force, Army, Navy **Professional Accreditation:** AACSB, ABET. **Intercollegiate Athletics:** Baseball M; Basketball M; Cross-Country Running M & W; Football M; Lacrosse M; Riflery M & W; Soccer M & W; Swimming and Diving M & W; Track and Field M & W; Water Polo W; Wrestling M

VIRGINIA POLYTECHNIC INSTITUTE AND STATE UNIVERSITY

Blacksburg, VA 24061
Tel: (540)231-6000
Fax: (540)231-3242
E-mail: admissions@vt.edu
Web Site: www.vt.edu
President/CEO: Dr. Timothy D. Sands
Admissions: Mildred R. Johnson
Financial Aid: Beth Armstrong
Type: University **Sex:** Coed **Scores:** 98% SAT V 400+; 100% SAT M 400+ **% Accepted:** 73 **Admission Plans:** Deferred Admission; Early Action; Early Admission **Application Deadline:** January 15 **Application Fee:** $60.00 **H.S. Requirements:** High school diploma required; GED accepted **Costs Per Year:** Application fee: $60. State resident tuition: $10,496 full-time. Nonresident tuition: $26,536 full-time. Mandatory fees: $1989 full-time. College room and board: $8266. **Scholarships:** Available. **Calendar System:** Semester, Summer session available **Enrollment:** Full-time 24,841, Graduate full-time 4,966, Graduate part-time 2,313, Part-time 543 **Faculty:** Full-time 1,731, Part-time 235 **Student-Faculty Ratio:** 14:1 **Exams:** ACT essay component not used; SAT I and SAT II or ACT; SAT I or ACT; SAT essay component not used. **% Receiving Financial Aid:** 39 **% Residing in College-Owned, -Operated, or -Affiliated Housing:** 37 **Regional Accreditation:** Southern Association of Colleges and Schools **Credit Hours For Degree:** 72 credit hours, Associates; 126 credit hours, Bachelors **ROTC:** Air Force, Army, Navy **Professional Accreditation:** AACSB, AAFCS, AAMFT, ABET, ACA, ACCE, ACSP, AND, APA, ASLA, AVMA, CIDA, NAAB, NASAD, NASM, NASPAA, NAST, NCATE, SAF. **Intercollegiate Athletics:** Baseball M; Basketball M; Cross-Country Running M & W; Football M; Golf M; Lacrosse W; Soccer M & W; Swimming and Diving M & W; Tennis M & W; Track and Field M & W; Ultimate Frisbee M & W; Volleyball W

VIRGINIA STATE UNIVERSITY

1 Hayden Dr.
Petersburg, VA 23806-0001
Tel: (804)524-5000; Free: 800-871-7611
Fax: (804)524-5055
E-mail: ilogan@vsu.edu
Web Site: www.vsu.edu
President/CEO: Dr. Makola M. Abdullah
Admissions: Irene Logan
Financial Aid: Sheila Allen
Type: Comprehensive **Sex:** Coed **Affiliation:** State Council of Higher Education for Virginia. **Scores:** 72% SAT V 400+; 67% SAT M 400+; 31% ACT 18-23; 12% ACT 24-29 **% Accepted:** 77 **Application Deadline:** May 1 **Application Fee:** $25.00 **H.S. Requirements:** High school diploma required; GED accepted **Costs Per Year:** Application fee: $25. State resident tuition: $5022 full-time, $358 per credit hour part-time. Nonresident tuition: $14,556 full-time, $793 per credit hour part-time. Mandatory fees: $3204 full-time, $10 per credit hour part-time. Full-time tuition and fees vary according to course load. Part-time tuition and fees vary according to course load. College room and board: $10,252. College room only: $5990. Room and board charges vary according to board plan and housing facility. **Scholarships:** Available. **Calendar System:** Semester, Summer session available **Enrollment:** Full-time 4,032, Graduate full-time 203, Graduate part-time 252, Part-time 209 **Faculty:** Full-time 282, Part-time 198 **Student-Faculty Ratio:** 13:1 **Exams:** SAT I or ACT; SAT Reasoning. **% Receiving Financial Aid:** 90 **Final Year or Final Semester Residency Requirement:** No **Regional Accreditation:** Southern Association of Colleges and Schools **Credit Hours For Degree:** 36 credit hours, Associates; 120 credit hours, Bachelors **ROTC:** Army **Professional Accreditation:** AACSB, ABET, AND, NASAD, NASM, NCATE. **Intercollegiate Athletics:** Baseball M; Basketball M & W; Bowling W; Cheerleading M & W; Cross-Country Running M & W; Football M; Golf M & W; Softball W; Tennis M & W; Track and Field M & W; Volleyball W

VIRGINIA UNION UNIVERSITY

1500 N Lombardy St.
Richmond, VA 23220-1170
Tel: (804)257-5600; Free: 800-368-3227
E-mail: sarandolph@vuu.edu
Web Site: www.vuu.edu
President/CEO: Dr. Claude G. Perkins
Admissions: Sharnae Randolph
Financial Aid: Antoinette House
Type: Comprehensive **Sex:** Coed **Affiliation:** Baptist. **Scores:** 42% SAT V 400+; 41% SAT M 400+; 24% ACT 18-23; 5% ACT 24-29 **% Accepted:** 49 **Admission Plans:** Deferred Admission **Application Deadline:** Rolling **Application Fee:** $25.00 **H.S. Requirements:** High school diploma required; GED accepted **Costs Per Year:** Application fee: $25. Comprehensive fee: $24,946 includes full-time tuition ($15,152), mandatory fees ($1381), and college room and board ($8413). College room only: $3875. Full-time tuition and fees vary according to course level, course load, and reciprocity agreements. Room and board charges vary according to housing facility. Part-time tuition: $470 per credit. Part-time mandatory fees: $42 per credit. Part-time tuition and fees vary according to course level, course load, and reciprocity agreements. **Scholarships:** Available. **Calendar System:** Semester, Summer session available **Enrollment:** Full-time 1,419, Graduate full-time 389, Graduate part-time 24, Part-time 90 **Faculty:** Full-time 75, Part-time 63 **Student-Faculty Ratio:** 15:1 **Exams:** SAT I or ACT; SAT Reasoning; SAT Subject. **% Receiving Financial Aid:** 95 **% Residing in College-Owned, -Operated, or -Affiliated Housing:** 70 **Final Year or Final Semester Residency Requirement:** No **Regional Accreditation:** Southern Association of Colleges and Schools **Credit Hours For Degree:** 120 semester hours, Bachelors **ROTC:** Army **Professional Accreditation:** ACBSP, ACIPE, ATS, CSWE, NCATE. **Intercollegiate Athletics:** Basketball M & W; Bowling M & W; Cross-Country Running M & W; Football M; Golf M; Softball W; Tennis M & W; Track and Field M & W; Volleyball W

VIRGINIA UNIVERSITY OF LYNCHBURG

2058 Garfield Ave.
Lynchburg, VA 24501-6417
Tel: (804)528-5276
Fax: (804)528-4257
E-mail: cglass@vul.edu
Web Site: www.vul.edu

President/CEO: Dr. Ralph Reavis
Admissions: Cheryl Glass
Financial Aid: Charlene P. Scruggs
Type: Comprehensive **Sex:** Coed **Affiliation:** Baptist. **Admission Plans:** Open Admission **Application Deadline:** Rolling **Application Fee:** $25.00 **H.S. Requirements:** High school diploma required; GED accepted **Scholarships:** Available. **Calendar System:** Semester, Summer session available **Enrollment:** Full-time 138, Graduate full-time 72, Graduate part-time 22, Part-time 95 **Faculty:** Full-time 22, Part-time 44 **Student-Faculty Ratio:** 9:1 **% Residing in College-Owned, -Operated, or -Affiliated Housing:** 14 **Final Year or Final Semester Residency Requirement:** No **Credit Hours For Degree:** 64 credits, Associates; 120 credits, Bachelors **Professional Accreditation:** TRACS. **Intercollegiate Athletics:** Basketball M & W

VIRGINIA WESLEYAN COLLEGE
1584 Wesleyan Dr.
Norfolk, VA 23502-5599
Tel: (757)455-3200; Free: 800-737-8684
Fax: (757)461-5238
E-mail: admissions@vwc.edu
Web Site: www.vwc.edu
President/CEO: Dr. Scott D. Miller
Admissions: David Waggoner
Financial Aid: Teresa Rhyne
Type: Four-Year College **Sex:** Coed **Affiliation:** United Methodist. **Scores:** 88% SAT V 400+; 90% SAT M 400+; 43% ACT 18-23; 26% ACT 24-29 **% Accepted:** 93 **Application Deadline:** Rolling **Application Fee:** $40.00 **H.S. Requirements:** High school diploma required; GED accepted **Costs Per Year:** Application fee: $40. One-time mandatory fee: $350. Comprehensive fee: $43,108 includes full-time tuition ($33,778), mandatory fees ($650), and college room and board ($8680). Full-time tuition and fees vary according to course load. Room and board charges vary according to board plan and housing facility. Part-time tuition: $1408 per credit hour. Part-time tuition varies according to course load. **Scholarships:** Available. **Calendar System:** 4-1-4, Summer session available **Enrollment:** Full-time 1,360, Part-time 81 **Faculty:** Full-time 92, Part-time 38 **Student-Faculty Ratio:** 13:1 **Exams:** ACT essay component used for placement; SAT I or ACT; SAT essay component used for placement; SAT Reasoning. **% Receiving Financial Aid:** 56 **% Residing in College-Owned, -Operated, or -Affiliated Housing:** 57 **Final Year or Final Semester Residency Requirement:** Yes **Regional Accreditation:** Southern Association of Colleges and Schools **Credit Hours For Degree:** 128 semester hours, Bachelors **ROTC:** Army **Professional Accreditation:** NRPA. **Intercollegiate Athletics:** Baseball M; Basketball M & W; Cheerleading W; Cross-Country Running M & W; Field Hockey W; Golf M; Lacrosse M & W; Soccer M & W; Softball W; Tennis M & W; Track and Field M & W; Volleyball W

VIRGINIA WESTERN COMMUNITY COLLEGE
PO Box 14007
Roanoke, VA 24038
Tel: (540)857-7311
Fax: (540)857-7204
Web Site: www.virginiawestern.edu
President/CEO: Dr. Robert H. Sandel
Type: Two-Year College **Sex:** Coed **Affiliation:** Virginia Community College System. **Admission Plans:** Deferred Admission; Early Admission; Open Admission; Preferred Admission **Application Deadline:** Rolling **Application Fee:** $0.00 **H.S. Requirements:** High school diploma required; GED accepted **Costs Per Year:** Application fee: $0. State resident tuition: $4066 full-time, $135.53 per credit hour part-time. Nonresident tuition: $9364 full-time, $312.13 per credit hour part-time. Mandatory fees: $633 full-time. **Scholarships:** Available. **Calendar System:** Semester, Summer session available **Enrollment:** Full-time 2,527, Part-time 6,105 **Student-Faculty Ratio:** 34:1 **Final Year or Final Semester Residency Requirement:** No **Regional Accreditation:** Southern Association of Colleges and Schools **Credit Hours For Degree:** 60 semester hours, Associates **Professional Accreditation:** ACBSP, ACEN, ADA, JRCERT.

WASHINGTON AND LEE UNIVERSITY
Lexington, VA 24450-0303
Tel: (540)458-8400
Fax: (540)463-8062
E-mail: admissions@wlu.edu
Web Site: www.wlu.edu
President/CEO: Dr. Kenneth P. Ruscio
Admissions: Sally S. Richmond
Financial Aid: James D. Kaster
Type: Comprehensive **Sex:** Coed **Scores:** 100% SAT V 400+; 100% SAT M 400+; 13% ACT 24-29 **% Accepted:** 24 **Admission Plans:** Deferred Admission; Early Action **Application Deadline:** January 1 **Application Fee:** $50.00 **H.S. Requirements:** High school diploma required; GED accepted **Costs Per Year:** Application fee: $50. Comprehensive fee: $57,402 includes full-time tuition ($45,460), mandatory fees ($957), and college room and board ($10,985). College room only: $4970. Full-time tuition and fees vary according to degree level. Room and board charges vary according to board plan and housing facility. Part-time tuition: $1624 per credit hour. Part-time tuition varies according to course load and degree level. **Scholarships:** Available. **Calendar System:** Miscellaneous, Summer session not available **Enrollment:** Full-time 1,851, Graduate full-time 318, Part-time 3 **Faculty:** Full-time 249, Part-time 82 **Student-Faculty Ratio:** 8:1 **Exams:** Other; SAT I or ACT; SAT II; SAT essay component used as validity check; SAT essay component used for admission; SAT Reasoning. **% Receiving Financial Aid:** 41 **% Residing in College-Owned, -Operated, or -Affiliated Housing:** 51 **Final Year or Final Semester Residency Requirement:** No **Regional Accreditation:** Southern Association of Colleges and Schools **Credit Hours For Degree:** 113 credits, Bachelors **ROTC:** Army **Professional Accreditation:** AACSB, AALS, ABA, ACEJMC. **Intercollegiate Athletics:** Baseball M; Basketball M & W; Cross-Country Running M & W; Equestrian Sports M & W; Field Hockey W; Football M; Golf M & W; Lacrosse M & W; Rugby M; Soccer M & W; Swimming and Diving M & W; Tennis M & W; Track and Field M & W; Volleyball W; Wrestling M

WYTHEVILLE COMMUNITY COLLEGE
1000 E Main St.
Wytheville, VA 24382-3308
Tel: (276)223-4700; Free: 800-468-1195
Fax: (276)223-4778
E-mail: kalexander@wcc.vccs.edu
Web Site: www.wcc.vccs.edu
President/CEO: Dr. Dean Sprinkle, PhD
Admissions: Karen Alexander
Type: Two-Year College **Sex:** Coed **Affiliation:** Virginia Community College System. **Admission Plans:** Early Admission; Open Admission; Preferred Admission **Application Deadline:** Rolling **H.S. Requirements:** High school diploma or equivalent not required. For allied health programs: High school diploma required; GED accepted **Costs Per Year:** State resident tuition: $4020 full-time, $134 per credit hour part-time. Nonresident tuition: $9318 full-time, $310.60 per credit hour part-time. Mandatory fees: $360 full-time, $12 per credit hour part-time. **Scholarships:** Available. **Calendar System:** Semester, Summer session available **Enrollment:** Full-time 1,037, Part-time 1,878 **Faculty:** Full-time 40, Part-time 97 **Student-Faculty Ratio:** 23:1 **Final Year or Final Semester Residency Requirement:** No **Regional Accreditation:** Southern Association of Colleges and Schools **Credit Hours For Degree:** 62 credit hours, Associates **Professional Accreditation:** ACEN, ADA, APTA, NAACLS. **Intercollegiate Athletics:** Volleyball W

ANTIOCH UNIVERSITY SEATTLE
2326 Sixth Ave.
Seattle, WA 98121-1814
Tel: (206)441-5352; Free: 888-268-4477
E-mail: admissions@antiochseattle.edu
Web Site: www.antiochsea.edu
President/CEO: Cassandra Manuelito-Kerkvliet
Financial Aid: Katy Stahl
Type: University **Sex:** Coed **Affiliation:** Antioch University. **Admission Plans:** Deferred Admission **Application Fee:** $75.00 **H.S. Requirements:** High school diploma required; GED accepted **Costs Per Year:** Application fee: $75. Tuition: $21,600 full-time, $600 per credit part-time. Mandatory fees: $435 full-time, $105 per term part-time. Full-time tuition and fees vary according to course load, degree level, location, and program. Part-time tuition and fees vary according to course load, degree level, location, and program. **Scholarships:** Available. **Calendar System:** Quarter, Summer session available **Enrollment:** Full-time 52, Graduate full-time 685, Graduate part-time 85, Part-time 258 **Student-Faculty Ratio:** 8:1 **% Receiving Financial Aid:** 78 **Regional Accreditation:** North Central Association of Colleges and Schools **Credit Hours For Degree:** 180 credits, Bachelors

ARGOSY UNIVERSITY, SEATTLE
2601-A Elliott Ave.
Seattle, WA 98121
Tel: (206)283-4500; Free: 866-283-2777
Fax: (206)393-3592
Web Site: www.argosy.edu/locations/seattle
President/CEO: Tom Dyer, EdD
Type: University **Sex:** Coed **Affiliation:** Education Management Corporation. **Calendar System:** Semester **Regional Accreditation:** Western Association of Colleges and Schools **Professional Accreditation:** ACBSP.

THE ART INSTITUTE OF SEATTLE
2323 Elliott Ave.
Seattle, WA 98121-1642
Tel: (206)448-6600; Free: 800-275-2471
Fax: (206)269-0275
Web Site: www.artinstitutes.edu/seattle
President/CEO: Elden Monday
Type: Four-Year College **Sex:** Coed **Affiliation:** Education Management Corporation. **Calendar System:** Quarter **Regional Accreditation:** Southern Association of Colleges and Schools **Professional Accreditation:** ACF, NCCU.

BASTYR UNIVERSITY
14500 Juanita Dr., NE
Kenmore, WA 98028-4966
Tel: (425)823-1300
Fax: (425)823-6222
E-mail: admissions@bastyr.edu
Web Site: www.bastyr.edu
President/CEO: Dr. Mac Powell
Admissions: Lauren Marani
Financial Aid: Danette Carter
Type: Two-Year Upper Division **Sex:** Coed **Admission Plans:** Deferred

Admission **Application Deadline:** April 15 **Application Fee:** $60.00 **H.S. Requirements:** High school diploma required; GED accepted **Costs Per Year:** Application fee: $60. Tuition: $23,355 full-time, $613 per credit part-time. Full-time tuition varies according to course load and program. Part-time tuition varies according to course load and program. **Scholarships:** Available. **Calendar System:** Quarter, Summer session available **Enrollment:** Full-time 217, Graduate full-time 940, Graduate part-time 39, Part-time 70 **Faculty:** Full-time 43, Part-time 256 **% Receiving Financial Aid:** 40 **% Residing in College-Owned, -Operated, or -Affiliated Housing:** 10 **Credit Hours For Degree:** 180 credits, Bachelors **Professional Accreditation:** ACAOM, AND, MEAC, NCCU.

BATES TECHNICAL COLLEGE
1101 S Yakima Ave.
Tacoma, WA 98405-4895
Tel: (253)596-1500
E-mail: registration@bates.ctc.edu
Web Site: www.bates.ctc.edu
President/CEO: Dr. David Borofsky
Type: Two-Year College **Sex:** Coed **Affiliation:** Washington State Board for Community and Technical Colleges. **Admission Plans:** Open Admission **Application Deadline:** Rolling **Application Fee:** $56.00 **Scholarships:** Available. **Calendar System:** Quarter **Professional Accreditation:** ADA, NCCU.

BELLEVUE COLLEGE
3000 Landerholm Cir., SE
Bellevue, WA 98007-6484
Tel: (425)564-1000
Fax: (425)564-2261
Web Site: www.bcc.ctc.edu
President/CEO: David Rule
Admissions: Morenika Jacobs
Type: Two-Year College **Sex:** Coed **Affiliation:** Washington State Board for Community and Technical Colleges. **Admission Plans:** Open Admission **Application Deadline:** Rolling **Application Fee:** $28.00 **H.S. Requirements:** High school diploma or equivalent not required. For applicants under 18: High school diploma required; GED accepted **Scholarships:** Available. **Calendar System:** Quarter, Summer session available **Credit Hours For Degree:** 90 quarter hours, Associates **Professional Accreditation:** ACEN, JRCEDMS, JRCERT, NCCU. **Intercollegiate Athletics:** Baseball M; Basketball M & W; Cross-Country Running M & W; Golf M; Soccer M; Softball W; Tennis W; Track and Field M & W; Volleyball W

BELLINGHAM TECHNICAL COLLEGE
3028 Lindbergh Ave.
Bellingham, WA 98225
Tel: (360)752-7000
Fax: (360)676-2798
E-mail: kbade@btc.edu
Web Site: www.btc.edu
President/CEO: Patricia McKeown
Admissions: Karen Marie Bade
Financial Aid: Brian Johnson
Type: Two-Year College **Sex:** Coed **Affiliation:** Washington State Board for

Community and Technical Colleges. **% Accepted:** 100 **Admission Plans:** Deferred Admission; Early Admission; Open Admission **Application Deadline:** Rolling **Application Fee:** $0.00 **H.S. Requirements:** High school diploma or equivalent not required. For dental assisting, dental hygiene, nursing, radiologic technology programs, students receiving financial aid: High school diploma required; GED accepted **Costs Per Year:** Application fee: $0. State resident tuition: $3,389 full-time, $102.05 per credit part-time. Nonresident tuition: $278.56 per credit part-time. Full-time tuition varies according to course load. Part-time tuition varies according to course load. **Scholarships:** Available. **Calendar System:** Quarter, Summer session available **Faculty:** Full-time 126, Part-time 63 **Student-Faculty Ratio:** 24:1 **Exams:** Other. **Final Year or Final Semester Residency Requirement:** No **Credit Hours For Degree:** 90 credits, Associates **Professional Accreditation:** ACF, ADA, NCCU.

BIG BEND COMMUNITY COLLEGE

7662 Chanute St., NE
Moses Lake, WA 98837-3299
Tel: (509)793-2222; Free: 877-745-1212
Fax: (509)762-6243
E-mail: admissions@bigbend.edu
Web Site: www.bigbend.edu
President/CEO: Dr. Terrence Leas
Admissions: Candis Lacher
Financial Aid: Jille Shankar

Type: Two-Year College **Sex:** Coed **Admission Plans:** Deferred Admission; Early Admission; Open Admission **Application Deadline:** Rolling **Application Fee:** $30.00 **H.S. Requirements:** High school diploma or equivalent not required. For aviation, nursing programs: High school diploma required; GED accepted **Costs Per Year:** Application fee: $30. State resident tuition: $3846 full-time, $102.75 per credit hour part-time. Nonresident tuition: $4254 full-time, $116 per credit hour part-time. Mandatory fees: $150 full-time, $5 per credit hour part-time. Full-time tuition and fees vary according to course load and program. Part-time tuition and fees vary according to course load and program. College room and board: $7140. **Scholarships:** Available. **Calendar System:** Quarter, Summer session available **Enrollment:** Full-time 1,458, Part-time 558 **Student-Faculty Ratio:** 22:1 **Exams:** ACT essay component used for placement; SAT essay component used for placement. **% Residing in College-Owned, -Operated, or -Affiliated Housing:** 7 **Final Year or Final Semester Residency Requirement:** No **Credit Hours For Degree:** 90 credit hours, Associates **Professional Accreditation:** ACEN, NCCU. **Intercollegiate Athletics:** Baseball M; Basketball M & W; Softball W; Volleyball W

CARRINGTON COLLEGE–SPOKANE

10102 E Knox Ave.
Ste. 200
Spokane, WA 99206
Tel: (509)532-8888
Web Site: carrington.edu
President/CEO: Peter Tenney

Type: Two-Year College **Sex:** Coed **Affiliation:** Carrington Colleges Group, Inc. **Application Fee:** $0.00 **H.S. Requirements:** High school diploma required; GED accepted **Costs Per Year:** Application fee: $0. Tuition: $15,537 full-time. Mandatory fees: $780 full-time. **Enrollment:** Full-time 413 **Faculty:** Full-time 11, Part-time 2 **Student-Faculty Ratio:** 35:1 **Professional Accreditation:** ABHES, JRCERT.

CASCADIA COLLEGE

18345 Campus Way, NE
Bothell, WA 98011
Tel: (425)352-8000
Fax: (425)398-5730
E-mail: admissions@cascadia.edu
Web Site: www.cascadia.edu
President/CEO: Dr. Eric W. Murray, PhD
Admissions: Erin Blakeney

Type: Two-Year College **Sex:** Coed **Affiliation:** Washington State Board for Community and Technical Colleges. **Admission Plans:** Open Admission **Application Deadline:** Rolling **Application Fee:** $30.00 **H.S. Requirements:** High school diploma or equivalent not required **Costs Per Year:** Application fee: $30. One-time mandatory fee: $30. State resident tuition: $3846 full-time, $102.75 per credit hour part-time. Nonresident tuition: $4,253 full-time, $115.98 per credit hour part-time. Mandatory fees: $420

full-time, $10.67 per credit hour part-time. Full-time tuition and fees vary according to course load and program. Part-time tuition and fees vary according to course load and program. **Calendar System:** Quarter, Summer session available **Enrollment:** Full-time 1,529, Part-time 1,230 **Faculty:** Full-time 31, Part-time 98 **Credit Hours For Degree:** 90 credits, Associates; 180 credits, Bachelors **Professional Accreditation:** NCCU.

CENTRAL WASHINGTON UNIVERSITY

400 E University Way
Ellensburg, WA 98926
Tel: (509)963-1111
Fax: (509)963-3022
E-mail: admissions@cwu.edu
Web Site: www.cwu.edu
President/CEO: Dr. James L. Gaudino
Admissions: Kathy Gaer-Carlton
Financial Aid: Adrian Naranjo

Type: Comprehensive **Sex:** Coed **Scores:** 89% SAT M 400+; 53.1% ACT 18-23; 24.4% ACT 24-29 **% Accepted:** 81 **Application Deadline:** March 1 **Application Fee:** $50.00 **H.S. Requirements:** High school diploma required; GED accepted **Costs Per Year:** Application fee: $50. State resident tuition: $6897 full-time, $229.90 per credit part-time. Nonresident tuition: $19,710 full-time, $657 per credit part-time. Mandatory fees: $1791 full-time. Full-time tuition and fees vary according to course load, degree level, location, and reciprocity agreements. Part-time tuition varies according to course load, degree level, location, and reciprocity agreements. College room and board: $10,175. Room and board charges vary according to board plan, housing facility, and location. **Scholarships:** Available. **Calendar System:** Quarter, Summer session available **Enrollment:** Full-time 9,069, Graduate full-time 538, Graduate part-time 476, Part-time 1,913 **Faculty:** Full-time 502, Part-time 223 **Student-Faculty Ratio:** 20:1 **Exams:** ACT essay component not used; SAT I or ACT; SAT essay component not used; SAT Reasoning. **% Receiving Financial Aid:** 64 **% Residing in College-Owned, -Operated, or -Affiliated Housing:** 30 **Final Year or Final Semester Residency Requirement:** No **Credit Hours For Degree:** 180 credits, Bachelors **ROTC:** Air Force, Army **Professional Accreditation:** AACSB, ABET, ACA, ACCE, AND, JRCEMTP, NASM, NCATE, NCCU. **Intercollegiate Athletics:** Archery M & W; Baseball M; Basketball M & W; Bowling M & W; Cheerleading M & W; Cross-Country Running M & W; Equestrian Sports M & W; Fencing M & W; Football M; Golf M & W; Ice Hockey M & W; Lacrosse M & W; Rock Climbing M & W; Rugby M & W; Soccer M & W; Softball W; Swimming and Diving M & W; Tennis M & W; Track and Field M & W; Ultimate Frisbee M & W; Volleyball W; Water Polo M & W; Wrestling M & W

CENTRALIA COLLEGE

600 Centralia College Blvd.
Centralia, WA 98531-4099
Tel: (360)736-9391
E-mail: admissions@centralia.edu
Web Site: www.centralia.edu
President/CEO: Jim Walton

Type: Two-Year College **Sex:** Coed **Affiliation:** Washington State Board for Community and Technical Colleges. **Admission Plans:** Open Admission **Application Deadline:** Rolling **Application Fee:** $0.00 **H.S. Requirements:** High school diploma required; GED accepted **Scholarships:** Available. **Calendar System:** Quarter, Summer session available **Student-Faculty Ratio:** 20:1 **Credit Hours For Degree:** 93 credits, Associates **Professional Accreditation:** NCCU. **Intercollegiate Athletics:** Baseball M; Basketball M & W; Golf W; Softball W; Volleyball W

CITY UNIVERSITY OF SEATTLE

521 Wall St.
Ste. 100
Seattle, WA 98121
Tel: (206)239-4500; Free: 800-426-5596
E-mail: info@cityu.edu
Web Site: www.cityu.edu
President/CEO: E. Lee Gorsuch, II

Type: Comprehensive **Sex:** Coed **% Accepted:** 100 **Admission Plans:** Deferred Admission; Open Admission **Application Deadline:** Rolling **Application Fee:** $50.00 **H.S. Requirements:** High school diploma required; GED accepted **Costs Per Year:** Application fee: $50. Tuition: $16,020 full-time, $398 per credit hour part-time. Full-time tuition varies according to course level, degree level, location, and program. Part-time tuition varies according to course level, degree level, location, and program. **Calendar System:** Quarter, Summer session available **Enrollment:** Full-time 532, Graduate full-time 698, Graduate part-time 332, Part-time 503 **Faculty:** Full-time 47, Part-time 285 **Student-Faculty Ratio:** 15:1 **Final Year or Final Semester Residency Requirement:** No **Credit Hours For Degree:** 90 credits, Associates; 180 credits, Bachelors **Professional Accreditation:** ACBSP, NCCU.

CLARK COLLEGE
1933 Fort Vancouver Way
Vancouver, WA 98663-3598
Tel: (360)992-2000
E-mail: admissions@clark.edu
Web Site: www.clark.edu
President/CEO: Robert K. Knight
Admissions: Sheryl Anderson
Financial Aid: Karen Driscoll

Type: Two-Year College **Sex:** Coed **Affiliation:** Washington State Board for Community and Technical Colleges. **% Accepted:** 100 **Admission Plans:** Deferred Admission; Early Admission **Application Fee:** $25.00 **H.S. Requirements:** High school diploma or equivalent not required **Costs Per Year:** Application fee: $25. Area resident tuition: $3930 full-time, $104.67 per credit hour part-time. State resident tuition: $5337 full-time, $150.56 per credit hour part-time. Nonresident tuition: $9333 full-time, $281.18 per credit hour part-time. Full-time tuition varies according to course load, degree level, program, and reciprocity agreements. Part-time tuition varies according to course load, degree level, program, and reciprocity agreements. **Scholarships:** Available. **Calendar System:** Quarter **Enrollment:** Full-time 5,035, Part-time 5,442 **Student-Faculty Ratio:** 24:1 **Final Year or Final Semester Residency Requirement:** No **ROTC:** Air Force, Army **Professional Accreditation:** AAMAE, ACEN, ADA, NCCU. **Intercollegiate Athletics:** Baseball M; Basketball M & W; Cross-Country Running M & W; Fencing M & W; Soccer M & W; Softball W; Track and Field M & W; Volleyball W

CLOVER PARK TECHNICAL COLLEGE
4500 Steilacoom Blvd., SW
Lakewood, WA 98499
Tel: (253)589-5678
Web Site: www.cptc.edu
President/CEO: Dr. Lonnie Howard
Admissions: Judy Richardson
Financial Aid: Wendy M. Joseph

Type: Two-Year College **Sex:** Coed **Affiliation:** Washington State Board for Community and Technical Colleges. **Admission Plans:** Open Admission **Application Deadline:** September 27 **Application Fee:** $41.00 **H.S. Requirements:** High school diploma required; GED accepted **Scholarships:** Available. **Professional Accreditation:** ADA, NAACLS, NCCU.

COLUMBIA BASIN COLLEGE
2600 N 20th Ave.
Pasco, WA 99301-3397
Tel: (509)547-0511
Fax: (509)546-0401
E-mail: admissions@columbiabasin.edu
Web Site: www.columbiabasin.edu
President/CEO: Richard W. Cummins

Type: Two-Year College **Sex:** Coed **Affiliation:** Washington State Board for Community and Technical Colleges. **Admission Plans:** Open Admission **Application Deadline:** Rolling **Application Fee:** $28.30 **H.S. Requirements:** High school diploma required; GED accepted **Scholarships:** Available. **Calendar System:** Quarter, Summer session available **Student-Faculty Ratio:** 22:1 **Credit Hours For Degree:** 90 quarter hours, Associates **Professional Accreditation:** ACEN, ADA, JRCEMTP, NCCU. **Intercollegiate Athletics:** Baseball M; Basketball M & W; Golf M & W; Soccer M & W; Softball W; Volleyball W

CORNISH COLLEGE OF THE ARTS
1000 Lenora St.
Seattle, WA 98121
Tel: (206)726-5151; Free: 800-726-ARTS
Fax: (206)720-1011
E-mail: admissions@cornish.edu
Web Site: www.cornish.edu

President/CEO: Dr. Nancy Uscher
Admissions: Sharron Starling
Financial Aid: Monique Theriault

Type: Four-Year College **Sex:** Coed **% Accepted:** 66 **Admission Plans:** Deferred Admission; Early Decision Plan **Application Fee:** $40.00 **H.S. Requirements:** High school diploma required; GED accepted **Costs Per Year:** Application fee: $40. Comprehensive fee: $47,920 includes full-time tuition ($36,840), mandatory fees ($400), and college room and board ($10,680). College room only: $7980. Full-time tuition and fees vary according to course load. Room and board charges vary according to board plan and housing facility. **Scholarships:** Available. **Calendar System:** Semester, Summer session available **Enrollment:** Full-time 714, Graduate full-time 4, Part-time 6 **Faculty:** Full-time 58, Part-time 131 **Student-Faculty Ratio:** 4:1 **Exams:** SAT I or ACT. **% Receiving Financial Aid:** 80 **Final Year or Final Semester Residency Requirement:** Yes **Credit Hours For Degree:** 130 credits, Bachelors **Professional Accreditation:** NASAD, NCCU.

DIGIPEN INSTITUTE OF TECHNOLOGY
9931 Willows Rd. NE
Redmond, WA 98052
Tel: (425)558-0299; Free: 866-478-5236
Fax: (425)558-0299
E-mail: admissions@digipen.edu
Web Site: www.digipen.edu
President/CEO: Claude Comair
Admissions: Danial Powers
Financial Aid: Trinity Huttner

Type: Comprehensive **Sex:** Coed **% Accepted:** 47 **Admission Plans:** Deferred Admission **Application Deadline:** Rolling **Application Fee:** $35.00 **H.S. Requirements:** High school diploma required; GED accepted **Costs Per Year:** Application fee: $35. One-time mandatory fee: $150. Tuition: $28,800 full-time, $930 per credit part-time. Mandatory fees: $200 full-time. Full-time tuition and fees vary according to course load, degree level, and program. Part-time tuition varies according to course load, degree level, and program. **Scholarships:** Available. **Calendar System:** Semester, Summer session available **Faculty:** Full-time 64, Part-time 54 **Student-Faculty Ratio:** 13:1 **Exams:** ACT essay component used for admission; SAT I or ACT; SAT essay component used for admission. **% Receiving Financial Aid:** 63 **Final Year or Final Semester Residency Requirement:** No **Credit Hours For Degree:** 131-154 Varies by degree program, Bachelors **Professional Accreditation:** ACCSC.

EASTERN WASHINGTON UNIVERSITY
526 5th St.
Cheney, WA 99004-2431
Tel: (509)359-6200
Fax: (509)359-4330
E-mail: admissions@ewu.edu
Web Site: www.ewu.edu
President/CEO: Dr. Mary Cullinan, PhD
Admissions: Catherine Sleeth
Financial Aid: Bruce DeFrates

Type: Comprehensive **Sex:** Coed **Scores:** 85% SAT V 400+; 87% SAT M 400+; 54.2% ACT 18-23; 20.6% ACT 24-29 **Costs Per Year:** State resident tuition: $235.07 per credit hour part-time. Nonresident tuition: $715.27 per credit hour part-time. Part-time tuition varies according to course level, course load, degree level, program, reciprocity agreements, and student level. **Scholarships:** Available. **Calendar System:** Quarter, Summer session available **Enrollment:** Full-time 10,163, Graduate full-time 783, Graduate part-time 278, Part-time 1,137 **Faculty:** Full-time 450, Part-time 216 **Student-Faculty Ratio:** 22:1 **Exams:** SAT I or ACT. **% Receiving Financial Aid:** 67 **% Residing in College-Owned, -Operated, or -Affiliated Housing:** 19 **Final Year or Final Semester Residency Requirement:** No **Credit Hours For Degree:** 180 quarter credits, Bachelors **ROTC:** Army **Professional Accreditation:** AACN, AACSB, ABET, ACA, ACSP, ADA, AOTA, APTA, ASHA, CSWE, NASM, NCATE, NCCU, NRPA. **Intercollegiate Athletics:** Archery M & W; Baseball M; Basketball M & W; Cheerleading W; Cross-Country Running M & W; Equestrian Sports M & W; Fencing M & W; Football M; Golf W; Ice Hockey M & W; Rugby M & W; Soccer M & W; Softball W; Tennis M & W; Track and Field M & W; Volleyball W

EDMONDS COMMUNITY COLLEGE
20000 68th Ave. W
Lynnwood, WA 98036

Tel: (425)640-1500
Fax: (425)640-1159
E-mail: nanci.froemming@edcc.edu
Web Site: www.edcc.edu
President/CEO: Dr. Jack Oharah
Admissions: Nancy Froemming

Type: Two-Year College **Sex:** Coed **Affiliation:** Washington State Board for Community and Technical Colleges. **% Accepted:** 100 **Admission Plans:** Deferred Admission; Early Admission; Open Admission **Application Deadline:** Rolling **Application Fee:** $18.00 **H.S. Requirements:** High school diploma or equivalent not required **Scholarships:** Available. **Calendar System:** Quarter, Summer session available **Enrollment:** Full-time 3,656, Part-time 4,779 **Faculty:** Full-time 145, Part-time 335 **Student-Faculty Ratio:** 21:1 **Credit Hours For Degree:** 90 credits, Associates **Professional Accreditation:** NCCU. **Intercollegiate Athletics:** Baseball M; Basketball M & W; Golf M & W; Soccer M & W; Softball W; Volleyball W

EVEREST COLLEGE
2156 Pacific Ave.
Tacoma, WA 98402
Tel: (253)207-4000
Web Site: www.everest.edu

Type: Two-Year College **Sex:** Coed **Affiliation:** Zenith Education Group. **Professional Accreditation:** ACICS.

EVERETT COMMUNITY COLLEGE
2000 Twr. St.
Everett, WA 98201-1327
Tel: (425)388-9100
Fax: (425)388-9173
E-mail: admissions@everettcc.edu
Web Site: www.everettcc.edu
President/CEO: Dr. David Beyer
Admissions: Linda Baca

Type: Two-Year College **Sex:** Coed **Affiliation:** Washington State Board for Community and Technical Colleges. **Admission Plans:** Deferred Admission; Early Admission; Open Admission **Application Deadline:** Rolling **Application Fee:** $0.00 **H.S. Requirements:** High school diploma or equivalent not required. For cosmetology, nursing, criminal justice, and fire science programs: High school diploma required; GED accepted **Scholarships:** Available. **Calendar System:** Quarter, Summer session available **Enrollment:** Full-time 3,707, Part-time 3,855 **Faculty:** Full-time 135, Part-time 234 **Student-Faculty Ratio:** 24:1 **Exams:** Other. **Credit Hours For Degree:** 90 quarter hours, Associates **Professional Accreditation:** ACEN, NCCU. **Intercollegiate Athletics:** Baseball M; Basketball M & W; Cross-Country Running M & W; Soccer M & W; Softball W; Volleyball W

THE EVERGREEN STATE COLLEGE
2700 Evergreen Pky., NW
Olympia, WA 98505
Tel: (360)867-6000
Fax: (360)867-6577
E-mail: admissions@evergreen.edu
Web Site: www.evergreen.edu
President/CEO: Dr. George Bridges
Admissions: Clarisse Leong
Financial Aid: Tracy Hall

Type: Comprehensive **Sex:** Coed **Affiliation:** Washington State Public Baccalaureate Institution. **Scores:** 95% SAT V 400+; 89% SAT M 400+; 45% ACT 18-23; 35% ACT 24-29 **% Accepted:** 98 **Admission Plans:** Deferred Admission; Preferred Admission **Application Deadline:** February 1 **Application Fee:** $50.00 **H.S. Requirements:** High school diploma required; GED accepted **Costs Per Year:** Application fee: $50. State resident tuition: $7512 full-time, $250.40 per credit hour part-time. Nonresident tuition: $21,927 full-time, $730.90 per credit hour part-time. Mandatory fees: $693 full-time, $9.25 per credit hour part-time, $5 per term part-time. Full-time tuition and fees vary according to course load, location, and program. Part-time tuition and fees vary according to course load, location, and program. College room and board: $9492. College room only: $6222. Room and board charges vary according to board plan, housing facility, location, and student level. **Scholarships:** Available. **Calendar System:** Quarter, Summer session available **Enrollment:** Full-time 3,585, Graduate full-time 209, Graduate part-time 109, Part-time 287 **Faculty:** Full-time 157, Part-time 67 **Student-Faculty Ratio:** 22:1 **Exams:** ACT essay component not used; SAT

I or ACT; SAT essay component not used; SAT Reasoning. **% Receiving Financial Aid:** 65 **% Residing in College-Owned, -Operated, or -Affiliated Housing:** 23 **Final Year or Final Semester Residency Requirement:** No **Credit Hours For Degree:** 180 quarter hours, Bachelors **Professional Accreditation:** NCCU. **Intercollegiate Athletics:** Basketball M & W; Soccer M & W; Track and Field M & W; Volleyball W

GONZAGA UNIVERSITY
502 E Boone Ave.
Spokane, WA 99258
Tel: (509)328-4220; Free: 800-322-2584
Fax: (509)324-5780
E-mail: admissions@gonzaga.edu
Web Site: www.gonzaga.edu
President/CEO: Dr. Thayne McCulloh
Admissions: Julie McCulloh
Financial Aid: James White

Type: Comprehensive **Sex:** Coed **Affiliation:** Roman Catholic. **Scores:** 100% SAT V 400+; 100% SAT M 400+; 16% ACT 18-23; 60% ACT 24-29 **% Accepted:** 73 **Admission Plans:** Deferred Admission; Early Decision Plan **Application Deadline:** February 1 **Application Fee:** $50.00 **H.S. Requirements:** High school diploma required; GED not accepted **Costs Per Year:** Application fee: $50. Comprehensive fee: $50,888 includes full-time tuition ($38,980), mandatory fees ($750), and college room and board ($11,158). College room only: $5708. Full-time tuition and fees vary according to course load, location, program, reciprocity agreements, and student level. Room and board charges vary according to board plan, housing facility, and location. Part-time tuition: $1075 per credit. Part-time mandatory fees: $180 per term. Part-time tuition and fees vary according to course load, location, program, reciprocity agreements, and student level. **Scholarships:** Available. **Calendar System:** Semester, Summer session available **Enrollment:** Full-time 4,972, Graduate full-time 1,866, Graduate part-time 584, Part-time 69 **Faculty:** Full-time 422, Part-time 291 **Student-Faculty Ratio:** 12:1 **Exams:** ACT essay component not used; SAT I or ACT; SAT essay component not used; SAT Reasoning. **% Receiving Financial Aid:** 56 **% Residing in College-Owned, -Operated, or -Affiliated Housing:** 60 **Final Year or Final Semester Residency Requirement:** Yes **Credit Hours For Degree:** 128 credit hours, Bachelors **ROTC:** Army **Professional Accreditation:** AACN, AACSB, AALS, AAMFT, AANA, ABA, ABET, ACA, ACIPE, NCATE, NCCU. **Intercollegiate Athletics:** Baseball M; Basketball M & W; Cross-Country Running M & W; Golf M & W; Ice Hockey M; Lacrosse M & W; Rowing M & W; Rugby M & W; Skiing (Downhill) M & W; Soccer M & W; Tennis M & W; Track and Field M & W; Ultimate Frisbee M & W; Volleyball M & W

GRAYS HARBOR COLLEGE
1620 Edward P Smith Dr.
Aberdeen, WA 98520-7599
Tel: (360)532-9020; Free: 800-562-4830
Fax: (360)538-4293
Web Site: www.ghc.edu
President/CEO: Dr. Edward J. Brewster
Admissions: Brenda Dell
Financial Aid: Stacey Savino

Type: Two-Year College **Sex:** Coed **Affiliation:** Washington State Board for Community and Technical Colleges. **Admission Plans:** Early Admission; Open Admission **Application Deadline:** Rolling **Application Fee:** $0.00 **H.S. Requirements:** High school diploma required; GED accepted **Scholarships:** Available. **Calendar System:** Quarter, Summer session available **Enrollment:** Full-time 1,312, Part-time 654 **Faculty:** Full-time 70, Part-time 64 **Student-Faculty Ratio:** 19:1 **Credit Hours For Degree:** 93 credits, Associates **Professional Accreditation:** ACEN, NCCU. **Intercollegiate Athletics:** Baseball M; Basketball M & W; Golf M & W; Soccer W; Softball W; Volleyball W

GREEN RIVER COLLEGE
12401 SE 320th St.
Auburn, WA 98092-3699
Tel: (253)833-9111
Fax: (253)288-3454
Web Site: www.greenriver.edu
President/CEO: Eileen Ely
Admissions: Peggy Morgan
Financial Aid: Mary Edington

Type: Two-Year College **Sex:** Coed **Affiliation:** Washington State Board for Community and Technical Colleges. **Admission Plans:** Deferred Admission; Early Admission; Open Admission **Application Deadline:** Rolling **Application Fee:** $0.00 **H.S. Requirements:** High school diploma required; GED accepted. For nursing, physical therapy, and occupational therapy programs: High school diploma required; GED not accepted **Scholarships:** Available. **Calendar System:** Quarter, Summer session available **Enrollment:** Full-time 5,056, Part-time 3,149 **Faculty:** Full-time 134, Part-time 302 **Student-Faculty Ratio:** 23:1 **Final Year or Final Semester Residency Requirement:** No **Credit Hours For Degree:** 90 quarter hours, Associates **Professional Accreditation:** AOTA, NCCU. **Intercollegiate Athletics:** Baseball M; Basketball M & W; Golf M & W; Soccer W; Softball W; Tennis M & W; Volleyball W

HERITAGE UNIVERSITY
3240 Fort Rd.
Toppenish, WA 98948-9599
Tel: (509)865-8500; Free: 888-272-6190
Fax: (509)865-4469
E-mail: admissions@heritage.edu
Web Site: www.heritage.edu
President/CEO: Dr. John Bassett
Admissions: Olivia Gutierrez
Financial Aid: Norberto Espindola
Type: Comprehensive **Sex:** Coed **Scholarships:** Available. **Calendar System:** Semester, Summer session available **Enrollment:** Full-time 724, Graduate full-time 335, Graduate part-time 45, Part-time 137 **Faculty:** Full-time 74, Part-time 111 **Student-Faculty Ratio:** 8:1 **Exams:** SAT I or ACT. **% Receiving Financial Aid:** 54 **Credit Hours For Degree:** 60 semester hours, Associates; 120 semester hours, Bachelors **Professional Accreditation:** CSWE, NCCU.

HIGHLINE COLLEGE
2400 S 240th St.
Des Moines, WA 98198-9800
Tel: (206)878-3710
Fax: (206)870-3782
Web Site: www.highline.edu
President/CEO: Dr. Jack Bermingham
Admissions: Michelle Kuwasaki
Type: Two-Year College **Sex:** Coed **Affiliation:** Washington State Board for Community and Technical Colleges. **% Accepted:** 100 **Admission Plans:** Open Admission **Application Deadline:** Rolling **Application Fee:** $26.00 **H.S. Requirements:** High school diploma or equivalent not required. For nursing, polysomnography and respiratory care: High school diploma required; GED accepted **Scholarships:** Available. **Calendar System:** Quarter, Summer session available **Enrollment:** Full-time 3,932, Part-time 2,811 **Faculty:** Full-time 144, Part-time 216 **Student-Faculty Ratio:** 19:1 **Final Year or Final Semester Residency Requirement:** No **Credit Hours For Degree:** 90 quarter hours, Associates **ROTC:** Air Force, Army **Professional Accreditation:** AAMAE, ACEN, CoARC, NCCU. **Intercollegiate Athletics:** Basketball M & W; Cross-Country Running M & W; Soccer M & W; Softball W; Track and Field M & W; Volleyball W; Wrestling M

LAKE WASHINGTON INSTITUTE OF TECHNOLOGY
11605 132nd Ave. NE
Kirkland, WA 98034-8506
Tel: (425)739-8100
E-mail: info@lwtc.edu
Web Site: www.lwtech.edu
President/CEO: Dr. Amy Morrison Goings
Admissions: Shawn Miller
Type: Two-Year College **Sex:** Coed **Affiliation:** Washington State Board for Community and Technical Colleges. **Admission Plans:** Early Admission; Open Admission **Application Deadline:** Rolling **Application Fee:** $0.00 **H.S. Requirements:** High school diploma or equivalent not required. For nursing, dental hygiene, medical assistant, dental assistant programs: High school diploma required; GED accepted **Scholarships:** Available. **Calendar System:** Quarter, Summer session available **Credit Hours For Degree:** 90 credits, Associates **Professional Accreditation:** AAMAE, ACF, ADA, NCCU.

LOWER COLUMBIA COLLEGE
1600 Maple St.
Longview, WA 98632-0310
Tel: (360)442-2311; Free: 866-900-2311
Fax: (360)442-2109
E-mail: registration@lowercolumbia.edu
Web Site: www.lowercolumbia.edu
President/CEO: Christopher Bailey
Admissions: Nichole Seroshek
Type: Two-Year College **Sex:** Coed **Affiliation:** Washington State Board for Community and Technical Colleges. **Admission Plans:** Open Admission **Application Deadline:** Rolling **Application Fee:** $30.00 **H.S. Requirements:** High school diploma or equivalent not required **Costs Per Year:** Application fee: $30. State resident tuition: $4,130 full-time, $110.80 per credit part-time. Nonresident tuition: $4644 full-time, $124.60 per credit part-time. Mandatory fees: $328 full-time, $7.30 per credit part-time. Full-time tuition and fees vary according to course load and reciprocity agreements. Part-time tuition and fees vary according to course load and reciprocity agreements. **Scholarships:** Available. **Calendar System:** Quarter, Summer session available **Enrollment:** Full-time 1,633, Part-time 1,519 **Faculty:** Full-time 67, Part-time 129 **Student-Faculty Ratio:** 15:1 **Final Year or Final Semester Residency Requirement:** No **Credit Hours For Degree:** 90 credits (varies by program), Associates **Professional Accreditation:** AAMAE, ACEN, NCCU. **Intercollegiate Athletics:** Baseball M; Basketball M & W; Soccer W; Softball W; Volleyball W

NORTH SEATTLE COLLEGE
9600 College Way N
Seattle, WA 98103-3599
Tel: (206)527-3600
Fax: (206)527-3635
E-mail: arrc@seattlecolleges.edu
Web Site: www.northseattle.edu
President/CEO: Mark Mitsui
Admissions: Betsy Abts
Type: Two-Year College **Sex:** Coed **Affiliation:** Seattle Community College District System. **% Accepted:** 100 **Admission Plans:** Deferred Admission; Early Admission; Open Admission **Application Deadline:** Rolling **Application Fee:** $0.00 **H.S. Requirements:** High school diploma or equivalent not required **Scholarships:** Available. **Calendar System:** Quarter, Summer session available **Enrollment:** Full-time 1,953, Part-time 4,350 **Faculty:** Full-time 89, Part-time 216 **Student-Faculty Ratio:** 20:1 **Credit Hours For Degree:** 90 credits, Associates **ROTC:** Army **Professional Accreditation:** AAMAE, ACEN, NCCU. **Intercollegiate Athletics:** Basketball M & W

NORTHWEST COLLEGE OF ART & DESIGN
16301 Creative Dr., NE
Poulsbo, WA 98370
Tel: (360)779-9993; Free: 800-769-ARTS
Fax: (360)779-9933
E-mail: ktonahill@nca.edu
Web Site: www.ncad.edu
President/CEO: Kim Perigard
Admissions: Kyle Tonahill
Financial Aid: Mac Fox
Type: Four-Year College **Sex:** Coed **Costs Per Year:** One-time mandatory fee: $50. Tuition: $18,200 full-time, $800 per credit part-time. Mandatory fees: $850 full-time. Part-time tuition varies according to course load. **Scholarships:** Available. **Calendar System:** Semester, Summer session available **Exams:** SAT I or ACT. **% Receiving Financial Aid:** 92 **Final Year or Final Semester Residency Requirement:** No **Credit Hours For Degree:** 134 credits, Bachelors **Professional Accreditation:** ACCSC.

NORTHWEST INDIAN COLLEGE
2522 Kwina Rd.
Bellingham, WA 98226
Tel: (360)676-2772; Free: 866-676-2772
Fax: (360)738-0136
E-mail: admissions@nwic.edu
Web Site: www.nwic.edu
President/CEO: Cheryl Crazy Bull
Type: Two-Year College **Sex:** Coed **Admission Plans:** Open Admission; Preferred Admission **Scholarships:** Available. **Calendar System:** Quarter, Summer session available **Student-Faculty Ratio:** 13:1 **Credit Hours For Degree:** 92 credits, Associates **Professional Accreditation:** NCCU.

NORTHWEST SCHOOL OF WOODEN BOATBUILDING

42 N Water St.
Port Hadlock, WA 98339
Tel: (360)385-4948
Fax: (360)385-5089
E-mail: info@nwboatschool.org
Web Site: www.nwboatschool.org
President/CEO: Betsy Davis

Type: Two-Year College **Sex:** Coed **Costs Per Year:** Tuition: $19,400 full-time. Mandatory fees: $100 full-time. Tuition guaranteed not to increase for student's term of enrollment. **Calendar System:** Quarter **Faculty:** Full-time 96, Part-time 2 **Student-Faculty Ratio:** 12:1 **Final Year or Final Semester Residency Requirement:** No **Credit Hours For Degree:** 90 quarter credits, Associates **Professional Accreditation:** ACCSC.

NORTHWEST UNIVERSITY

5520 108th Ave., NE
Kirkland, WA 98033
Tel: (425)822-8266; Free: 800-669-3781
Fax: (425)425-0148
E-mail: admissions@northwestu.edu
Web Site: www.northwestu.edu
President/CEO: Joseph Castleberry, EdD
Admissions: Andy Hall
Financial Aid: Roger Wilson

Type: Comprehensive **Sex:** Coed **Affiliation:** Assemblies of God. **Scores:** 82% SAT V 400+; 50% ACT 18-23; 23.68% ACT 24-29 **% Accepted:** 64 **Admission Plans:** Deferred Admission; Early Decision Plan **Application Deadline:** August 1 **Application Fee:** $30.00 **H.S. Requirements:** High school diploma required; GED accepted. For transfer students with 30 semester or 45 quarter credits completed at the college level can have their high school transcript requirement waived: High school diploma or equivalent not required **Costs Per Year:** Application fee: $30. Comprehensive fee: $35,876 includes full-time tuition ($27,700), mandatory fees ($386), and college room and board ($7790). College room only: $4660. Full-time tuition and fees vary according to class time, course load, location, program, and reciprocity agreements. Room and board charges vary according to housing facility and student level. Part-time tuition: $1150 per credit. Part-time mandatory fees: $95 per term. Part-time tuition and fees vary according to class time, course load, and location. **Scholarships:** Available. **Calendar System:** Semester, Summer session available **Enrollment:** Full-time 910, Graduate full-time 212, Graduate part-time 91, Part-time 25 **Faculty:** Full-time 82, Part-time 170 **Student-Faculty Ratio:** 13:1 **Exams:** SAT I or ACT; SAT Reasoning. **% Receiving Financial Aid:** 82 **% Residing in College-Owned, -Operated, or -Affiliated Housing:** 55 **Final Year or Final Semester Residency Requirement:** No **Credit Hours For Degree:** 62 credit hours, Associates; 125 credit hours, Bachelors **ROTC:** Air Force, Army **Professional Accreditation:** AACN, ACBSP, NCCU. **Intercollegiate Athletics:** Basketball M & W; Cross-Country Running M & W; Soccer M & W; Softball W; Track and Field M & W; Volleyball W

OLYMPIC COLLEGE

1600 Chester Ave.
Bremerton, WA 98337-1699
Tel: (360)792-6050; Free: 800-259-6718
Fax: (360)792-2135
E-mail: ndownard@olympic.edu
Web Site: www.olympic.edu
President/CEO: Dr. David Mitchell
Admissions: Nora Downard

Type: Two-Year College **Sex:** Coed **Affiliation:** Washington State Board for Community and Technical Colleges. **% Accepted:** 100 **Admission Plans:** Open Admission **Application Deadline:** Rolling **Application Fee:** $0.00 **H.S. Requirements:** High school diploma or equivalent not required. For nursing, medical office assistant, physical therapy assistant programs; international students: High school diploma required; GED accepted **Scholarships:** Available. **Calendar System:** Quarter, Summer session available **Faculty:** Full-time 129, Part-time 364 **% Residing in College-Owned, -Operated, or -Affiliated Housing:** 1 **Credit Hours For Degree:** 90 credits, Associates; 180 credits, Bachelors **Professional Accreditation:** AACN, ACEN, ACF, NCCU. **Intercollegiate Athletics:** Baseball M; Basketball M & W; Cross-Country Running M & W; Golf M & W; Softball W; Track and Field M & W; Volleyball W

PACIFIC LUTHERAN UNIVERSITY

Tacoma, WA 98447
Tel: (253)531-6900; Free: 800-274-6758
Fax: (253)536-5136
E-mail: admission@plu.edu
Web Site: www.plu.edu
President/CEO: Dr. Thomas W. Krise
Admissions: Melody A. Ferguson
Financial Aid: Kay W. Soltis

Type: Comprehensive **Sex:** Coed **Affiliation:** Evangelical Lutheran Church in America. **Scores:** 97% SAT V 400+; 98% SAT M 400+; 29.31% ACT 18-23; 51.63% ACT 24-29 **% Accepted:** 76 **Admission Plans:** Deferred Admission **Application Deadline:** Rolling **Application Fee:** $40.00 **H.S. Requirements:** High school diploma required; GED accepted **Costs Per Year:** Application fee: $40. Comprehensive fee: $48,280 includes full-time tuition ($37,600), mandatory fees ($350), and college room and board ($10,330). College room only: $4870. Full-time tuition and fees vary according to course load. Room and board charges vary according to board plan and housing facility. Part-time tuition: $1175 per semester hour. Part-time mandatory fees: $350 per year. Part-time tuition and fees vary according to course load. **Scholarships:** Available. **Calendar System:** 4-1-4, Summer session available **Enrollment:** Full-time 2,855, Graduate full-time 196, Graduate part-time 120, Part-time 104 **Faculty:** Full-time 216, Part-time 137 **Student-Faculty Ratio:** 12:1 **Exams:** ACT essay component not used; SAT I or ACT; SAT essay component not used; SAT Reasoning. **% Receiving Financial Aid:** 74 **% Residing in College-Owned, -Operated, or -Affiliated Housing:** 43 **Final Year or Final Semester Residency Requirement:** No **Credit Hours For Degree:** 128 semester hours, Bachelors **ROTC:** Army **Professional Accreditation:** AACN, AACSB, AAMFT, ABET, CSWE, NASM, NCATE, NCCU. **Intercollegiate Athletics:** Baseball M; Basketball M & W; Crew M & W; Cross-Country Running M & W; Football M; Golf M & W; Lacrosse M & W; Soccer M & W; Softball W; Swimming and Diving M & W; Tennis M & W; Track and Field M & W; Ultimate Frisbee M & W; Volleyball W

PENINSULA COLLEGE

1502 E Lauridsen Blvd.
Port Angeles, WA 98362-2779
Tel: (360)452-9277; Free: 877-452-9277
Fax: (360)457-8100
E-mail: admissions@pencol.edu
Web Site: www.pc.ctc.edu
President/CEO: Dr. Brinton Sprague
Admissions: Pauline Marvin

Type: Two-Year College **Sex:** Coed **Affiliation:** Washington State Board for Community and Technical Colleges. **Admission Plans:** Open Admission **Application Deadline:** Rolling **Application Fee:** $0.00 **H.S. Requirements:** High school diploma or equivalent not required **Scholarships:** Available. **Calendar System:** Quarter, Summer session available **Enrollment:** Full-time 1,705, Part-time 1,616 **Faculty:** Full-time 57, Part-time 99 **Student-Faculty Ratio:** 21:1 **Final Year or Final Semester Residency Requirement:** No **Credit Hours For Degree:** 90 credits, Associates **Professional Accreditation:** ACEN, NCCU. **Intercollegiate Athletics:** Basketball M & W; Soccer M & W

PIERCE COLLEGE AT FORT STEILACOOM

9401 Farwest Dr. SW
Lakewood, WA 98498
Tel: (253)964-6500
E-mail: admiss1@pierce.ctc.edu
Web Site: www.pierce.ctc.edu
President/CEO: Denise R. Yochum

Type: Two-Year College **Sex:** Coed **Admission Plans:** Open Admission **Application Fee:** $25.00 **Scholarships:** Available. **Calendar System:** Quarter **Student-Faculty Ratio:** 22:1 **Professional Accreditation:** NCCU.

PIERCE COLLEGE AT PUYALLUP

1601 39th Ave. SE
Puyallup, WA 98374
Tel: (253)840-8400
Fax: (253)840-8423
Web Site: www.pierce.ctc.edu
President/CEO: Marty Cavalluzzi
Admissions: Els Deming

Type: Two-Year College **Sex:** Coed **Affiliation:** Washington State Board for

Community and Technical Colleges. **Admission Plans:** Early Admission; Open Admission **Application Deadline:** Rolling **Application Fee:** $0.00 **H.S. Requirements:** High school diploma or equivalent not required. For international students, veterinary technology, dental hygiene programs: High school diploma required; GED accepted **Costs Per Year:** Application fee: $0. State resident tuition: $3388 full-time, $103 per credit hour part-time. Nonresident tuition: $8726 full-time, $279 per credit hour part-time. Mandatory fees: $303 full-time, $4.25 per credit hour part-time. Full-time tuition and fees vary according to course load and location. Part-time tuition and fees vary according to course load and location. **Scholarships:** Available. **Calendar System:** Quarter, Summer session available **Final Year or Final Semester Residency Requirement:** No **Credit Hours For Degree:** 90 quarter hours, Associates **ROTC:** Army **Professional Accreditation:** ACEN, ADA, NCCU. **Intercollegiate Athletics:** Baseball M; Basketball M & W; Soccer M; Softball W; Volleyball W

PIMA MEDICAL INSTITUTE (RENTON)
555 S Renton Village Pl.
Renton, WA 98057
Tel: (425)228-9600
E-mail: rpanerio@pmi.edu
Web Site: www.pmi.edu
President/CEO: Robert Panerio
Admissions: Robert Panerio

Type: Two-Year College **Sex:** Coed **Exams:** Other. **Professional Accreditation:** ABHES.

PIMA MEDICAL INSTITUTE (SEATTLE)
9709 Third Ave. NE
Ste. 400
Seattle, WA 98115
Tel: (206)322-6100; Free: 888-477-PIMA
Fax: (206)324-1985
Web Site: www.pmi.edu
President/CEO: Alan Clay

Type: Two-Year College **Sex:** Coed **Affiliation:** Vocational Training Institutes, Inc. **Scholarships:** Available. **Calendar System:** Miscellaneous **Exams:** Other. **Professional Accreditation:** ABHES, JRCERT.

RENTON TECHNICAL COLLEGE
3000 NE Fourth St.
Renton, WA 98056
Tel: (425)235-2352
Fax: (425)235-7832
E-mail: lbracking@rtc.edu
Web Site: www.rtc.edu
President/CEO: Steve Hanson
Admissions: Linh Bracking
Financial Aid: Debbie Solomon

Type: Two-Year College **Sex:** Coed **Affiliation:** Washington State Board for Community and Technical Colleges. **Admission Plans:** Early Admission; Preferred Admission **Application Deadline:** Rolling **Application Fee:** $30.00 **H.S. Requirements:** High school diploma or equivalent not required. For allied health programs: High school diploma required; GED accepted **Costs Per Year:** Application fee: $30. State resident tuition: $4161 full-time, $109.75 per credit hour part-time. Nonresident tuition: $4,568 full-time, $122.98 per credit hour part-time. Full-time tuition varies according to course load and program. Part-time tuition varies according to course load and program. **Scholarships:** Available. **Calendar System:** Quarter, Summer session available **Enrollment:** Full-time 1,249, Part-time 2,110 **Faculty:** Full-time 87, Part-time 157 **Student-Faculty Ratio:** 19:1 **Exams:** Other. **Final Year or Final Semester Residency Requirement:** No **Credit Hours For Degree:** 90 quarter credits, Associates; 180 quarter credits, Bachelors **Professional Accreditation:** ACF, ADA, ARCST, NCCU.

SAINT MARTIN'S UNIVERSITY
5000 Abbey Way SE
Lacey, WA 98503
Tel: (360)491-4700; Free: 800-368-8803
Fax: (360)459-4124
E-mail: admissions@stmartin.edu
Web Site: www.stmartin.edu
President/CEO: Dr. Roy F. Heynderickx
Admissions: Joselyn Barr

Financial Aid: Michael Grosso

Type: Comprehensive **Sex:** Coed **Affiliation:** Roman Catholic. **Scores:** 93% SAT V 400+; 96% SAT M 400+ **% Accepted:** 93 **Admission Plans:** Deferred Admission **Application Deadline:** July 31 **Application Fee:** $0.00 **H.S. Requirements:** High school diploma required; GED accepted **Costs Per Year:** Application fee: $0. Comprehensive fee: $43,534 includes full-time tuition ($32,800), mandatory fees ($394), and college room and board ($10,340). College room only: $5150. Full-time tuition and fees vary according to course load, degree level, location, and program. Room and board charges vary according to board plan and housing facility. Part-time tuition: $1095 per credit. Part-time tuition varies according to degree level, location, and program. **Scholarships:** Available. **Calendar System:** Semester, Summer session available **Enrollment:** Full-time 1,008, Graduate full-time 245, Graduate part-time 95, Part-time 341 **Faculty:** Full-time 76, Part-time 141 **Student-Faculty Ratio:** 11:1 **Exams:** ACT essay component not used; SAT I or ACT; SAT essay component not used; SAT Reasoning; SAT Subject. **% Receiving Financial Aid:** 85 **% Residing in College-Owned, -Operated, or -Affiliated Housing:** 30 **Final Year or Final Semester Residency Requirement:** No **Credit Hours For Degree:** 120 semester credits, Bachelors **ROTC:** Air Force, Army **Professional Accreditation:** ABET, NCCU, TEAC. **Intercollegiate Athletics:** Baseball M; Basketball M & W; Cross-Country Running M & W; Golf M & W; Soccer M & W; Softball W; Track and Field M & W; Volleyball W

SEATTLE CENTRAL COLLEGE
1701 Broadway
Seattle, WA 98122-2400
Tel: (206)587-3800
Web Site: www.seattlecentral.edu
President/CEO: Paul Killpatrick

Type: Two-Year College **Sex:** Coed **Affiliation:** Seattle Community College District System. **Admission Plans:** Open Admission **Application Deadline:** Rolling **H.S. Requirements:** High school diploma or equivalent not required. For health programs: High school diploma required; GED accepted **Scholarships:** Available. **Calendar System:** Quarter, Summer session available **Credit Hours For Degree:** 90 credits, Associates **ROTC:** Air Force, Army, Navy **Professional Accreditation:** ACEN, ACF, COA, CoARC, NCCU.

SEATTLE PACIFIC UNIVERSITY
3307 Third Ave. W
Seattle, WA 98119-1997
Tel: (206)281-2000; Free: 800-366-3344
E-mail: admissions@spu.edu
Web Site: www.spu.edu
President/CEO: Daniel Martin
Admissions: Ineliz Soto-Fuller
Financial Aid: Jordan Grant

Type: Comprehensive **Sex:** Coed **Affiliation:** Free Methodist. **Scores:** 99% SAT V 400+; 99% SAT M 400+; 29.14% ACT 18-23; 53.6% ACT 24-29 **% Accepted:** 82 **Admission Plans:** Early Admission; Early Decision Plan **Application Deadline:** February 1 **Application Fee:** $50.00 **H.S. Requirements:** High school diploma required; GED accepted **Costs Per Year:** Application fee: $50. Comprehensive fee: $47,439 includes full-time tuition ($36,684), mandatory fees ($402), and college room and board ($10,353). College room only: $5700. Room and board charges vary according to board plan and housing facility. Part-time tuition: $1019 per credit hour. Part-time tuition varies according to course load. **Scholarships:** Available. **Calendar System:** Quarter, Summer session available **Enrollment:** Full-time 3,084, Graduate full-time 381, Graduate part-time 592, Part-time 118 **Faculty:** Full-time 205, Part-time 180 **Student-Faculty Ratio:** 15:1 **Exams:** ACT essay component used as validity check; SAT I and SAT II or ACT; SAT I or ACT; SAT II; SAT essay component used as validity check; SAT Reasoning; SAT Subject. **% Receiving Financial Aid:** 71 **% Residing in College-Owned, -Operated, or -Affiliated Housing:** 52 **Final Year or Final Semester Residency Requirement:** Yes **Credit Hours For Degree:** 180 credits, Bachelors **ROTC:** Air Force, Army, Navy **Professional Accreditation:** AACN, AACSB, AAFCS, AAMFT, ABET, ATS, NASM, NCATE, NCCU. **Intercollegiate Athletics:** Basketball M & W; Crew M & W; Cross-Country Running M & W; Gymnastics W; Soccer M & W; Track and Field M & W; Volleyball W

SEATTLE UNIVERSITY
902 12th Ave.
Seattle, WA 98122-1090

Tel: (206)296-6000; Free: 800-426-7123
Fax: (206)296-5656
E-mail: admissions@seattleu.edu
Web Site: www.seattleu.edu
President/CEO: Fr. Stephen V. Sundborg
Admissions: Melore Nielsen
Financial Aid: Jeff Scofield
Type: Comprehensive **Sex:** Coed **Affiliation:** Roman Catholic. **Scores:** 99% SAT V 400+; 100% SAT M 400+; 21% ACT 18-23; 56% ACT 24-29 **% Accepted:** 73 **Admission Plans:** Deferred Admission; Early Decision Plan **Application Deadline:** Rolling **Application Fee:** $50.00 **H.S. Requirements:** High school diploma required; GED accepted **Costs Per Year:** Application fee: $50. Comprehensive fee: $50,812 includes full-time tuition ($38,970), mandatory fees ($720), and college room and board ($11,122). Full-time tuition and fees vary according to course load. Room and board charges vary according to board plan and housing facility. Part-time tuition: $866 per credit hour. Part-time tuition varies according to course load. **Scholarships:** Available. **Calendar System:** Quarter, Summer session available **Enrollment:** Full-time 4,286, Graduate full-time 1,352, Graduate part-time 1,410, Part-time 225 **Faculty:** Full-time 507, Part-time 241 **Student-Faculty Ratio:** 12:1 **Exams:** SAT I or ACT; SAT essay component used as validity check; SAT essay component used for admission; SAT Reasoning; SAT Subject. **% Receiving Financial Aid:** 57 **% Residing in College-Owned, -Operated, or -Affiliated Housing:** 47 **Credit Hours For Degree:** 180 credit hours, Bachelors **ROTC:** Air Force, Army, Navy **Professional Accreditation:** AACN, AACSB, AALS, ABA, ABET, ACA, ATS, JRCEDMS, NASPAA, NCATE, NCCU. **Intercollegiate Athletics:** Baseball M; Basketball M & W; Cheerleading M & W; Crew W; Cross-Country Running M & W; Golf M & W; Soccer M & W; Softball W; Swimming and Diving M & W; Tennis M & W; Track and Field M & W; Volleyball W

SHORELINE COMMUNITY COLLEGE
16101 Greenwood Ave. N
Shoreline, WA 98133-5696
Tel: (206)546-4101
Fax: (206)546-4599
Web Site: www.shoreline.edu
President/CEO: Cheryl Roberts
Admissions: Chris Melton
Financial Aid: Ted Haase
Type: Two-Year College **Sex:** Coed **Affiliation:** Washington State Board for Community and Technical Colleges. **Admission Plans:** Open Admission **Application Deadline:** Rolling **H.S. Requirements:** High school diploma or equivalent not required **Scholarships:** Available. **Calendar System:** Quarter, Summer session available **Faculty:** Full-time 155, Part-time 260 **Student-Faculty Ratio:** 21:1 **Exams:** Other. **Credit Hours For Degree:** 90 credits, Associates **Professional Accreditation:** ACEN, ADA, AHIMA, NAACLS, NCCU. **Intercollegiate Athletics:** Archery M & W; Baseball M; Basketball M & W; Cross-Country Running M & W; Soccer M & W; Softball W; Tennis M & W; Volleyball W

SKAGIT VALLEY COLLEGE
2405 College Way
Mount Vernon, WA 98273-5899
Tel: (360)416-7600
Fax: (360)416-7890
E-mail: karenmarie.bade@skagit.edu
Web Site: www.skagit.edu
President/CEO: Dr. Thomas Keegan
Admissions: Karen Marie Bade
Type: Two-Year College **Sex:** Coed **Affiliation:** Washington State Board for Community and Technical Colleges. **% Accepted:** 60 **Admission Plans:** Deferred Admission; Open Admission **Application Deadline:** Rolling **Application Fee:** $0.00 **H.S. Requirements:** High school diploma or equivalent not required **Scholarships:** Available. **Calendar System:** Quarter, Summer session available **Student-Faculty Ratio:** 22:1 **% Residing in College-Owned, -Operated, or -Affiliated Housing:** 1 **Credit Hours For Degree:** 90 credits, Associates **Professional Accreditation:** ACEN, ACF, NCCU. **Intercollegiate Athletics:** Baseball M; Basketball M & W; Cross-Country Running M & W; Golf M & W; Soccer M & W; Softball W; Tennis M & W; Volleyball W

SOUTH PUGET SOUND COMMUNITY COLLEGE
2011 Mottman Rd., SW
Olympia, WA 98512-6292

Tel: (360)754-7711
Fax: (360)664-9407
E-mail: hdearborn@spcc.edu
Web Site: www.spscc.edu
President/CEO: Dr. Timothy Stokes
Admissions: Heidi Dearborn
Type: Two-Year College **Sex:** Coed **Affiliation:** Washington State Board for Community and Technical Colleges. **% Accepted:** 100 **Admission Plans:** Deferred Admission; Early Admission; Open Admission **Application Deadline:** Rolling **Application Fee:** $0.00 **H.S. Requirements:** High school diploma or equivalent not required. For nursing program: High school diploma required; GED accepted **Scholarships:** Available. **Calendar System:** Quarter, Summer session available **Enrollment:** Full-time 2,693, Part-time 2,262 **Faculty:** Full-time 88, Part-time 175 **Student-Faculty Ratio:** 18:1 **Credit Hours For Degree:** 90 credits, Associates **ROTC:** Army **Professional Accreditation:** AAMAE, ACEN, ACF, ADA, NCCU. **Intercollegiate Athletics:** Basketball M & W; Soccer M; Softball W

SOUTH SEATTLE COLLEGE
6000 16th Ave., SW
Seattle, WA 98106-1499
Tel: (206)764-5300
E-mail: kimmanderb@sccd.ctc.edu
Web Site: southseattle.edu
President/CEO: Gary Oertli
Admissions: Kim Manderbach
Type: Two-Year College **Sex:** Coed **Affiliation:** Seattle Community College District System. **Admission Plans:** Early Admission; Open Admission **Application Deadline:** Rolling **Application Fee:** $0.00 **H.S. Requirements:** High school diploma or equivalent not required **Scholarships:** Available. **Calendar System:** Quarter, Summer session available **Faculty:** Full-time 75, Part-time 210 **Credit Hours For Degree:** 90 credits, Associates **Professional Accreditation:** NCCU.

SPOKANE COMMUNITY COLLEGE
1810 N Greene St.
Spokane, WA 99217-5399
Tel: (509)533-7000; Free: 800-248-5644
Fax: (509)533-8839
E-mail: mlee@ccs.spokane.edu
Web Site: www.scc.spokane.edu
President/CEO: Dr. Joe Dunlap
Admissions: Ann Hightower-Chavez
Type: Two-Year College **Sex:** Coed **Affiliation:** Washington State Board for Community and Technical Colleges. **Admission Plans:** Deferred Admission; Early Admission; Open Admission **Application Deadline:** Rolling **Application Fee:** $15.00 **H.S. Requirements:** High school diploma required; GED accepted **Scholarships:** Available. **Calendar System:** Quarter, Summer session available **Enrollment:** Full-time 4,393, Part-time 2,589 **Faculty:** Full-time 296, Part-time 213 **Student-Faculty Ratio:** 14:1 **Credit Hours For Degree:** 90 credits, Associates **ROTC:** Army **Professional Accreditation:** AAMAE, ACF, ADA, AHIMA, AOA, ARCST, CoARC, JRCECT, NCCU. **Intercollegiate Athletics:** Baseball M; Basketball M & W; Cross-Country Running M & W; Soccer M & W; Softball W; Tennis M & W; Track and Field M & W; Volleyball W

SPOKANE FALLS COMMUNITY COLLEGE
3410 W Fort George Wright Dr.
Spokane, WA 99224-5288
Tel: (509)533-3500; Free: 888-509-7944
Fax: (509)533-3433
Web Site: www.spokanefalls.edu
President/CEO: Mark Palek, EdD
Type: Two-Year College **Sex:** Coed **Affiliation:** State Board for Washington Community and Technical Colleges. **Admission Plans:** Deferred Admission; Early Admission; Open Admission **Application Deadline:** Rolling **Application Fee:** $15.00 **H.S. Requirements:** High school diploma required; GED accepted **Scholarships:** Available. **Calendar System:** Quarter, Summer session available **Enrollment:** Full-time 3,974, Part-time 1,684 **Faculty:** Full-time 164, Part-time 381 **Student-Faculty Ratio:** 27:1 **Credit Hours For Degree:** 90 credits, Associates **ROTC:** Army **Professional Accreditation:** APTA, NCCU. **Intercollegiate Athletics:** Baseball M; Basketball M & W; Cross-Country Running M & W; Soccer M & W; Softball W; Tennis M & W; Track and Field M & W; Volleyball W

TACOMA COMMUNITY COLLEGE

6501 S 19th St.
Tacoma, WA 98466
Tel: (253)566-5000
Fax: (253)566-5376
Web Site: www.tacomacc.edu
President/CEO: Dr. Pamela Transue
Type: Two-Year College **Sex:** Coed **Affiliation:** Washington State Board for Community and Technical Colleges. **Admission Plans:** Early Admission; Open Admission **Application Deadline:** Rolling **H.S. Requirements:** High school diploma or equivalent not required. For allied health, law enforcement, nursing programs: High school diploma required; GED accepted **Scholarships:** Available. **Calendar System:** Quarter, Summer session available **Student-Faculty Ratio:** 21:1 **Credit Hours For Degree:** 90 credits, Associates **ROTC:** Army **Professional Accreditation:** ACEN, AHIMA, CoARC, JRCEMTP, JRCERT, NCCU. **Intercollegiate Athletics:** Baseball M; Basketball M & W; Golf M & W; Soccer M & W; Volleyball W

UNIVERSITY OF PHOENIX–WESTERN WASHINGTON CAMPUS

7100 Fort Dent Way, Ste. 100
Tukwila, WA 98188
Tel: (206)268-5800; Free: 866-766-0766
Fax: (206)241-8848
Web Site: www.phoenix.edu
President/CEO: Timothy P. Slottow
Admissions: Marc Booker
Type: Comprehensive **Sex:** Coed **Admission Plans:** Deferred Admission; Open Admission **Application Deadline:** Rolling **Application Fee:** $0.00 **H.S. Requirements:** High school diploma required; GED accepted **Scholarships:** Available. **Calendar System:** Continuous, Summer session not available **Enrollment:** Full-time 572 **Faculty:** Full-time 14, Part-time 145 **Regional Accreditation:** North Central Association of Colleges and Schools **Credit Hours For Degree:** 60 credits, Associates; 120 credits, Bachelors

UNIVERSITY OF PUGET SOUND

1500 N Warner St.
Tacoma, WA 98416
Tel: (253)879-3100; Free: 800-396-7191
Fax: (253)879-3500
E-mail: admission@pugetsound.edu
Web Site: www.pugetsound.edu
President/CEO: Dr. Ronald R. Thomas
Admissions: Dr. Jenny Rickard
Financial Aid: Maggie A. Mittuch
Type: Comprehensive **Sex:** Coed **Scores:** 100% SAT V 400+; 100% SAT M 400+; 16.43% ACT 18-23; 53.2% ACT 24-29 **% Accepted:** 79 **Admission Plans:** Deferred Admission; Early Action; Early Admission **Application Fee:** $50.00 **H.S. Requirements:** High school diploma required; GED accepted **Costs Per Year:** Application fee: $50. Comprehensive fee: $56,456 includes full-time tuition ($44,740), mandatory fees ($236), and college room and board ($11,480). College room only: $6300. Full-time tuition and fees vary according to course load. Room and board charges vary according to board plan and housing facility. Part-time tuition: $5645 per unit. Part-time tuition varies according to course load. **Scholarships:** Available. **Calendar System:** Semester, Summer session available **Enrollment:** Full-time 2,459, Graduate full-time 228, Graduate part-time 70, Part-time 17 **Faculty:** Full-time 237, Part-time 44 **Student-Faculty Ratio:** 11:1 **Exams:** SAT I or ACT; SAT Reasoning. **% Receiving Financial Aid:** 50 **% Residing in College-Owned, -Operated, or -Affiliated Housing:** 66 **Final Year or Final Semester Residency Requirement:** Yes **Credit Hours For Degree:** 32 units, Bachelors **ROTC:** Army **Professional Accreditation:** AOTA, APTA, NASM, NCATE, NCCU. **Intercollegiate Athletics:** Baseball M; Basketball M & W; Cheerleading M & W; Crew M & W; Cross-Country Running M & W; Fencing M & W; Football M; Golf M & W; Lacrosse M & W; Rugby M & W; Sailing M & W; Skiing (Downhill) M & W; Soccer M & W; Softball W; Swimming and Diving M & W; Tennis M & W; Track and Field M & W; Ultimate Frisbee M & W; Volleyball W; Water Polo M & W

UNIVERSITY OF WASHINGTON

Seattle, WA 98195
Tel: (206)543-2100
Web Site: www.washington.edu
President/CEO: Dr. Ana Mari Cauce
Type: University **Sex:** Coed **Affiliation:** University of Washington. **Scores:**

99% SAT V 400+; 100% SAT M 400+; 12.09% ACT 18-23; 48.05% ACT 24-29 **% Accepted:** 53 **Application Deadline:** December 1 **Application Fee:** $60.00 **H.S. Requirements:** High school diploma or equivalent not required **Costs Per Year:** Application fee: $60. State resident tuition: $10,768 full-time, $359 per credit part-time. Nonresident tuition: $33,072 full-time, $1102 per credit part-time. Mandatory fees: $1071 full-time, $28 per credit part-time, $80 per term part-time. Full-time tuition and fees vary according to course load and location. Part-time tuition and fees vary according to course load and location. College room and board: $11,310. Room and board charges vary according to board plan and housing facility. **Scholarships:** Available. **Calendar System:** Quarter, Summer session available **Enrollment:** Full-time 28,377, Graduate full-time 11,706, Graduate part-time 2,639, Part-time 2,686 **Faculty:** Full-time 1,643, Part-time 1,021 **Student-Faculty Ratio:** 21:1 **Exams:** ACT essay component used for admission; SAT I or ACT; SAT essay component used for admission; SAT Reasoning. **% Receiving Financial Aid:** 41 **% Residing in College-Owned, -Operated, or -Affiliated Housing:** 25 **Final Year or Final Semester Residency Requirement:** Yes **Credit Hours For Degree:** 180 credits, Bachelors **ROTC:** Air Force, Army, Navy **Professional Accreditation:** AACN, AACSB, AALS, ABA, ABET, ACCE, ACEJMC, ACNM, ACPE, ACSP, ADA, AHIMA, ALA, AND, AOTA, APA, APTA, ASHA, ASLA, CAHME, CEPH, CSWE, LCME/AMA, NAAB, NAACLS, NASM, NASPAA, NCCU, NCOPE, SAF. **Intercollegiate Athletics:** Baseball M; Basketball M & W; Cheerleading M & W; Crew M & W; Cross-Country Running M & W; Football M; Golf M & W; Gymnastics W; Soccer M & W; Softball W; Tennis M & W; Track and Field M & W; Volleyball W

UNIVERSITY OF WASHINGTON, BOTHELL

18115 Campus Way NE
Bothell, WA 98011-8246
Tel: (425)352-5000
E-mail: freshmen@uwb.edu
Web Site: www.uwb.edu
President/CEO: Dr. Bjong Wolf Yeigh
Type: Comprehensive **Sex:** Coed **Affiliation:** University of Washington. **Scores:** 91% SAT V 400+; 94% SAT M 400+; 40.95% ACT 18-23; 37.62% ACT 24-29 **% Accepted:** 79 **Admission Plans:** Deferred Admission **Application Deadline:** January 15 **Application Fee:** $60.00 **H.S. Requirements:** High school diploma required; GED accepted **Costs Per Year:** Application fee: $60. State resident tuition: $10,768 full-time, $359 per credit part-time. Nonresident tuition: $33,072 full-time. Mandatory fees: $990 full-time, $33 per credit part-time. Full-time tuition and fees vary according to course load. Part-time tuition and fees vary according to course load. College room and board: $10,833. Room and board charges vary according to board plan, housing facility, and location. **Scholarships:** Available. **Calendar System:** Quarter, Summer session available **Enrollment:** Full-time 4,052, Graduate full-time 355, Graduate part-time 226, Part-time 644 **Faculty:** Full-time 182, Part-time 112 **Student-Faculty Ratio:** 20:1 **Exams:** ACT essay component used for admission; SAT I or ACT; SAT essay component used for admission. **% Receiving Financial Aid:** 61 **% Residing in College-Owned, -Operated, or -Affiliated Housing:** 7 **Final Year or Final Semester Residency Requirement:** Yes **Credit Hours For Degree:** 180 credits, Bachelors **ROTC:** Air Force, Army, Navy **Professional Accreditation:** AACSB, NCCU.

UNIVERSITY OF WASHINGTON, TACOMA

1900 Commerce St.
Tacoma, WA 98402-3100
Tel: (253)692-4000; Free: 800-736-7750
E-mail: megan61@u.washington.edu
Web Site: www.tacoma.washington.edu
President/CEO: Dr. Mark Pagano
Admissions: Megan Beresford
Type: Comprehensive **Sex:** Coed **Affiliation:** University of Washington. **Scores:** 83% SAT V 400+; 87% SAT M 400+; 45.59% ACT 18-23; 16.18% ACT 24-29 **% Accepted:** 83 **Admission Plans:** Deferred Admission **Application Deadline:** June 1 **Application Fee:** $60.00 **H.S. Requirements:** High school diploma or equivalent not required **Costs Per Year:** Application fee: $60. State resident tuition: $10,768 full-time, $359 per credit part-time. Nonresident tuition: $33,072 full-time, $1102 per credit part-time. Mandatory fees: $1137 full-time, $38 per credit part-time. Full-time tuition and fees vary according to course load. Part-time tuition and fees vary according to course load. College room and board: $10,833. Room and board charges vary according to housing facility and location. **Scholarships:** Available. **Calendar**

System: Quarter, Summer session available Enrollment: Full-time 3,477, Graduate full-time 406, Graduate part-time 272, Part-time 444 Faculty: Full-time 222, Part-time 68 Student-Faculty Ratio: 17:1 Exams: ACT essay component not used; SAT I or ACT; SAT II; SAT essay component not used; SAT Reasoning; SAT Subject. % Receiving Financial Aid: 71 % Residing in College-Owned, -Operated, or -Affiliated Housing: 3 Final Year or Final Semester Residency Requirement: Yes Credit Hours For Degree: 180 units, Bachelors ROTC: Air Force, Army, Navy Professional Accreditation: AACSB, ABET, NCCU.

WALLA WALLA COMMUNITY COLLEGE

500 Tausick Way
Walla Walla, WA 99362-9267
Tel: (509)522-2500; Free: 877-992-9922
Fax: (509)527-3361
Web Site: www.wwcc.edu
President/CEO: Steven L. VanAusdle
Admissions: Carlos Delgadillo

Type: Two-Year College Sex: Coed Affiliation: Washington State Board for Community and Technical Colleges. Admission Plans: Open Admission Application Deadline: Rolling H.S. Requirements: High school diploma or equivalent not required. For nursing program: High school diploma required; GED accepted Scholarships: Available. Calendar System: Quarter, Summer session available Enrollment: Full-time 2,969, Part-time 2,140 Faculty: Full-time 123, Part-time 190 Student-Faculty Ratio: 20:1 Final Year or Final Semester Residency Requirement: No Credit Hours For Degree: 90 credits, Associates Professional Accreditation: ABET, ACF, NCCU. Intercollegiate Athletics: Baseball M; Basketball M & W; Golf M & W; Soccer M & W; Softball W; Volleyball W

WALLA WALLA UNIVERSITY

204 S College Ave.
College Place, WA 99324-1198
Tel: (509)527-2615; Free: 800-541-8900
Fax: (509)527-2397
Web Site: www.wallawalla.edu
President/CEO: Dr. John McVay
Admissions: Dallas Weis
Financial Aid: Cassie Ragenovich

Type: Comprehensive Sex: Coed Affiliation: Seventh-day Adventist. Scores: 95% SAT V 400+; 95% SAT M 400+; 42.79% ACT 18-23; 40.99% ACT 24-29 % Accepted: 86 Admission Plans: Deferred Admission; Early Action Application Deadline: Rolling Application Fee: $40.00 H.S. Requirements: High school diploma required; GED accepted Scholarships: Available. Calendar System: Quarter, Summer session available Enrollment: Full-time 1,589, Graduate full-time 184, Graduate part-time 14, Part-time 100 Student-Faculty Ratio: 14:1 Exams: ACT; ACT essay component not used; SAT I or ACT; SAT essay component not used; SAT Reasoning; SAT Subject. % Receiving Financial Aid: 65 % Residing in College-Owned, -Operated, or -Affiliated Housing: 64 Credit Hours For Degree: 96 quarter hours, Associates; 192 quarter hours, Bachelors Professional Accreditation: ABET, ACBSP, ACEN, CSWE, NASM, NCCU. Intercollegiate Athletics: Basketball M & W; Soccer M; Softball W; Volleyball W

WASHINGTON STATE UNIVERSITY

Pullman, WA 99164
Tel: (509)335-3564; Free: 888-468-6978
E-mail: admissions@wsu.edu
Web Site: www.wsu.edu
President/CEO: Dr. Daniel J. Bernardo
Admissions: Wendy Peterson
Financial Aid: Brian Dixon

Type: University Sex: Coed Scores: 93% SAT V 400+; 94% SAT M 400+; 45.8% ACT 18-23; 36.1% ACT 24-29 % Accepted: 81 Application Deadline: January 31 Application Fee: $50.00 H.S. Requirements: High school diploma required; GED accepted Costs Per Year: Application fee: $50. State resident tuition: $10,356 full-time, $546 per credit hour part-time. Nonresident tuition: $23,956 full-time, $1226 per credit hour part-time. Mandatory fees: $1611 full-time. Full-time tuition and fees vary according to course load, location, and reciprocity agreements. Part-time tuition varies according to course load, location, and reciprocity agreements. College room and board: $11,356. College room only: $6858. Room and board charges vary according to board plan, housing facility, and location. Scholarships:

Available. Calendar System: Semester, Summer session available Enrollment: Full-time 16,674, Graduate full-time 2,490, Graduate part-time 224, Part-time 807 Faculty: Full-time 1,356, Part-time 530 Student-Faculty Ratio: 15:1 Exams: SAT I or ACT. % Receiving Financial Aid: 59 % Residing in College-Owned, -Operated, or -Affiliated Housing: 26 Final Year or Final Semester Residency Requirement: No Credit Hours For Degree: 120 credits, Bachelors ROTC: Air Force, Army, Navy Professional Accreditation: AACN, AACSB, ABET, ACCE, ACEN, ACPE, AND, APA, ASHA, ASLA, AVMA, CAHME, CIDA, JRCAT, NASM, NCATE, NCCU, SAF. Intercollegiate Athletics: Baseball M; Basketball M & W; Bowling M & W; Cheerleading M & W; Crew M & W; Cross-Country Running M & W; Equestrian Sports W; Fencing M & W; Football M; Golf M & W; Ice Hockey M & W; Lacrosse M & W; Rowing M & W; Rugby M & W; Skiing (Cross-Country) M & W; Skiing (Downhill) M & W; Soccer M & W; Softball W; Swimming and Diving W; Tennis M & W; Track and Field M & W; Triathlon M & W; Ultimate Frisbee M & W; Volleyball M & W; Water Polo M & W; Weight Lifting M & W; Wrestling M

WASHINGTON STATE UNIVERSITY–GLOBAL CAMPUS

Washington State University
Pullman, WA 99164-5220
Free: 800-222-4978
E-mail: admissions@wsu.edu
Web Site: www.globalcampus.wsu.edu
President/CEO: Daniel J. Bernardo
Admissions: Wendy Peterson

Type: Comprehensive Sex: Coed Scores: 100% SAT V 400+; 100% SAT M 400+; 83.3% ACT 18-23; 16.7% ACT 24-29 % Accepted: 50 Application Deadline: July 24 Application Fee: $50.00 H.S. Requirements: High school diploma required; GED accepted Costs Per Year: Application fee: $50. State resident tuition: $10,868 full-time, $543 per credit part-time. Nonresident tuition: $11,386 full-time, $570 per credit part-time. Full-time tuition varies according to course load, location, and reciprocity agreements. Part-time tuition varies according to course load, location, and reciprocity agreements. Calendar System: Semester Enrollment: Full-time 836, Graduate full-time 176, Graduate part-time 786, Part-time 1,323 Exams: SAT I or ACT. Final Year or Final Semester Residency Requirement: No Credit Hours For Degree: 120 credits, Bachelors Professional Accreditation: NCCU.

WASHINGTON STATE UNIVERSITY–SPOKANE

412 E Spokane Falls Blvd.
Spokane, WA 99210-1495
Tel: (509)358-7500
Fax: (509)358-7505
E-mail: admissions@wsu.edu
Web Site: www.spokane.wsu.edu
President/CEO: Dr. Daniel J. Bernardo
Admissions: Wendy Peterson

Type: Two-Year Upper Division Sex: Coed % Accepted: 100 Application Fee: $50.00 H.S. Requirements: High school diploma required; GED accepted Costs Per Year: Application fee: $50. State resident tuition: $10,356 full-time, $546 per credit hour part-time. Nonresident tuition: $23,956 full-time, $1226 per credit hour part-time. Mandatory fees: $733 full-time. Full-time tuition and fees vary according to course load, location, and reciprocity agreements. Part-time tuition varies according to course load, location, and reciprocity agreements. Calendar System: Semester, Summer session available Enrollment: Full-time 547, Graduate full-time 708, Graduate part-time 159, Part-time 66 Exams: SAT I or ACT. Final Year or Final Semester Residency Requirement: No Credit Hours For Degree: 120 credits, Bachelors Professional Accreditation: AND, CAHME, NCCU.

WASHINGTON STATE UNIVERSITY–TRI-CITIES

2710 Crimson Way
Richland, WA 99354
Tel: (509)372-7000
Fax: (509)372-7100
E-mail: admissions@tricity.wsu.edu
Web Site: www.tricity.wsu.edu
President/CEO: Dr. Daniel J. Bernardo
Admissions: Mariella Lora

Type: Comprehensive Sex: Coed Scores: 86% SAT V 400+; 92% SAT M 400+; 46.7% ACT 18-23; 26.7% ACT 24-29 % Accepted: 65 Application Deadline: January 31 Application Fee: $50.00 H.S. Requirements: High school diploma required; GED accepted **Costs Per Year:** Application fee: $50. State resident tuition: $10,356 full-time, $543 per credit part-time. Nonresident tuition: $23,956 full-time, $1223 per credit part-time. Mandatory fees: $512 full-time. Full-time tuition and fees vary according to course load, location, and reciprocity agreements. Part-time tuition varies according to course load, location, and reciprocity agreements. **Calendar System:** Semester, Summer session available **Enrollment:** Full-time 1,096, Graduate full-time 71, Graduate part-time 150, Part-time 276 **Exams:** SAT I or ACT. **Final Year or Final Semester Residency Requirement:** No **Credit Hours For Degree:** 120 credits, Bachelors **Professional Accreditation:** NCCU. **Intercollegiate Athletics:** Rugby M & W; Soccer M & W; Volleyball W

WASHINGTON STATE UNIVERSITY–VANCOUVER

14204 NE Salmon Creek Ave.
Vancouver, WA 98686
Tel: (360)546-9788
Fax: (360)546-9041
E-mail: van.admissions@wsu.edu
Web Site: www.vancouver.wsu.edu
President/CEO: Dr. Daniel J. Bernardo
Admissions: Kim Hiatt

Type: Comprehensive **Sex:** Coed **Scores:** 93% SAT V 400+; 91% SAT M 400+; 56.6% ACT 18-23; 35.8% ACT 24-29 **% Accepted:** 65 **Application Deadline:** January 31 **Application Fee:** $50.00 **H.S. Requirements:** High school diploma required; GED accepted **Costs Per Year:** Application fee: $50. State resident tuition: $10,356 full-time, $544 per credit part-time. Nonresident tuition: $23,956 full-time, $1224 per credit part-time. Mandatory fees: $527 full-time. Full-time tuition and fees vary according to course load, location, and reciprocity agreements. Part-time tuition varies according to course load, location, and reciprocity agreements. **Calendar System:** Semester, Summer session available **Enrollment:** Full-time 2,234, Graduate full-time 143, Graduate part-time 309, Part-time 619 **Exams:** SAT I or ACT. **Credit Hours For Degree:** 120 credits, Bachelors **ROTC:** Air Force, Army **Professional Accreditation:** ABET, NCCU.

WENATCHEE VALLEY COLLEGE

1300 Fifth St.
Wenatchee, WA 98801-1799
Tel: (509)682-6800
Fax: (509)664-2511
Web Site: www.wvc.edu
President/CEO: Dr. Jim Richardson
Admissions: Kyla O'Connor

Type: Two-Year College **Sex:** Coed **Affiliation:** Washington State Board for Community and Technical Colleges. **Admission Plans:** Deferred Admission; Early Admission; Open Admission **Application Deadline:** Rolling **H.S. Requirements:** High school diploma or equivalent not required. For allied health programs: High school diploma required; GED accepted **Costs Per Year:** State resident tuition: $3801 full-time. Nonresident tuition: $4234 full-time. Full-time tuition varies according to course load. **Scholarships:** Available. **Calendar System:** Quarter, Summer session available **Enrollment:** Full-time 2,334, Part-time 884 **Credit Hours For Degree:** 90 credits, Associates **Professional Accreditation:** ACEN, JRCERT, NAACLS, NCCU. **Intercollegiate Athletics:** Baseball M; Basketball M & W; Soccer M & W; Softball W; Volleyball W

WESTERN WASHINGTON UNIVERSITY

516 High St.
Bellingham, WA 98225-5996
Tel: (360)650-3000
E-mail: admit@wwu.edu
Web Site: www.wwu.edu
President/CEO: Dr. Bruce Shepard
Admissions: Clara Capron
Financial Aid: Barbara Luton

Type: Comprehensive **Sex:** Coed **Scores:** 97% SAT V 400+; 98% SAT M 400+; 37.1% ACT 18-23; 46.8% ACT 24-29 **% Accepted:** 85 **Admission Plans:** Deferred Admission **Application Deadline:** January 31 **Application Fee:** $55.00 **H.S. Requirements:** High school diploma required; GED accepted **Costs Per Year:** Application fee: $55. State resident tuition: $7143 full-time, $258 per credit hour part-time. Nonresident tuition: $19,495 full-time, $670 per credit hour part-time. Mandatory fees: $1,468 full-time. Full-time tuition and fees vary according to course load, location, and reciprocity agreements. Part-time tuition varies according to course load, location, and

reciprocity agreements. College room and board: $10,342. Room and board charges vary according to board plan, housing facility, and location. **Scholarships:** Available. **Calendar System:** Quarter, Summer session available **Enrollment:** Full-time 13,050, Graduate full-time 515, Graduate part-time 393, Part-time 1,102 **Faculty:** Full-time 570, Part-time 328 **Student-Faculty Ratio:** 19:1 **Exams:** ACT essay component not used; SAT I or ACT; SAT essay component not used; SAT Reasoning. **% Receiving Financial Aid:** 48 **% Residing in College-Owned, -Operated, or -Affiliated Housing:** 29 **Final Year or Final Semester Residency Requirement:** No **Credit Hours For Degree:** 180 quarter hours, Bachelors **Professional Accreditation:** AACSB, ABET, ACA, ASHA, CORE, NASAD, NASM, NCATE, NCCU, NRPA. **Intercollegiate Athletics:** Basketball M & W; Cheerleading M & W; Crew M & W; Cross-Country Running M & W; Golf M & W; Soccer M & W; Softball W; Track and Field M & W; Volleyball W

WHATCOM COMMUNITY COLLEGE

237 W Kellogg Rd.
Bellingham, WA 98226-8003
Tel: (360)383-3000
Fax: (360)676-2171
E-mail: admit@whatcom.ctc.edu
Web Site: www.whatcom.ctc.edu
President/CEO: Dr. Kathi Hiyane-Brown

Type: Two-Year College **Sex:** Coed **Affiliation:** Washington State Board for Community and Technical Colleges. **Admission Plans:** Open Admission **Application Deadline:** Rolling **Application Fee:** $0.00 **H.S. Requirements:** High school diploma or equivalent not required. For financial aid applicants, international students: High school diploma required; GED accepted **Scholarships:** Available. **Calendar System:** Quarter, Summer session available **Faculty:** Full-time 75, Part-time 150 **Credit Hours For Degree:** 90 quarter hours, Associates **Professional Accreditation:** AAMAE, ACEN, APTA, NCCU. **Intercollegiate Athletics:** Basketball M & W; Cross-Country Running M & W; Soccer M & W; Volleyball W

WHITMAN COLLEGE

345 Boyer Ave.
Walla Walla, WA 99362-2083
Tel: (509)527-5111; Free: 877-462-9448
Fax: (509)527-4967
E-mail: admission@whitman.edu
Web Site: www.whitman.edu
President/CEO: Dr. Kathleen Murray
Admissions: Tony Cabasco
Financial Aid: Tyson Harlow

Type: Four-Year College **Sex:** Coed **Scores:** 100% SAT V 400+; 100% SAT M 400+; 3.26% ACT 18-23; 39.67% ACT 24-29 **% Accepted:** 43 **Admission Plans:** Deferred Admission; Early Action **Application Deadline:** January 15 **Application Fee:** $50.00 **H.S. Requirements:** High school diploma required; GED accepted **Costs Per Year:** Application fee: $50. Comprehensive fee: $57,702 includes full-time tuition ($45,770), mandatory fees ($368), and college room and board ($11,564). College room only: $5348. Room and board charges vary according to board plan and housing facility. Part-time tuition: $1907 per credit. **Scholarships:** Available. **Calendar System:** Semester, Summer session not available **Enrollment:** Full-time 1,430, Part-time 40 **Faculty:** Full-time 170, Part-time 64 **Student-Faculty Ratio:** 8:1 **Exams:** ACT essay component used for admission; SAT I or ACT; SAT essay component used for admission; SAT Reasoning; SAT Subject. **% Receiving Financial Aid:** 46 **% Residing in College-Owned, -Operated, or -Affiliated Housing:** 64 **Final Year or Final Semester Residency Requirement:** No **Credit Hours For Degree:** 124 credits, Bachelors **Professional Accreditation:** AACN, NCCU. **Intercollegiate Athletics:** Baseball M; Basketball M & W; Cross-Country Running M & W; Golf M & W; Lacrosse M & W; Rugby M & W; Skiing (Cross-Country) M & W; Skiing (Downhill) M & W; Soccer M & W; Swimming and Diving M & W; Tennis M & W; Track and Field M & W; Ultimate Frisbee M & W; Volleyball M & W; Water Polo M & W

WHITWORTH UNIVERSITY

300 W Hawthorne Rd.
Spokane, WA 99251-0001
Tel: (509)777-1000; Free: 800-533-4668
Fax: (509)777-3773
E-mail: admission@whitworth.edu

Web Site: www.whitworth.edu

President/CEO: Dr. Beck A. Taylor

Admissions: Marianne Hansen

Financial Aid: Traci L. Stensland

Type: Comprehensive **Sex:** Coed **Affiliation:** Presbyterian. **Scores:** 98% SAT V 400+; 98% SAT M 400+; 24.5% ACT 18-23; 54.5% ACT 24-29 **% Accepted:** 62 **Admission Plans:** Deferred Admission; Early Admission; Early Decision Plan **Application Deadline:** August 1 **Application Fee:** $0.00 **H.S. Requirements:** High school diploma required; GED accepted **Costs Per Year:** Application fee: $0. Comprehensive fee: $51,732 includes full-time tuition ($39,600), mandatory fees ($962), and college room and board ($11,170). College room only: $6026. Room and board charges vary according to board plan and housing facility. Part-time tuition: $1650 per credit. Part-time mandatory fees: $421 per term. Part-time tuition and fees vary according to course load. **Scholarships:** Available. **Calendar System:** 4-1-4, Summer session available **Enrollment:** Full-time 2,303, Graduate full-time 83, Graduate part-time 223, Part-time 41 **Faculty:** Full-time 187, Part-time 142 **Student-Faculty Ratio:** 11:1 **Exams:** ACT essay component not used; SAT I or ACT; SAT II; SAT essay component not used; SAT Reasoning. **% Receiving Financial Aid:** 68 **% Residing in College-Owned, -Operated, or -Affiliated Housing:** 50 **Final Year or Final Semester Residency Requirement:** Yes **Credit Hours For Degree:** 126 credits, Bachelors **ROTC:** Army **Professional Accreditation:** JRCAT, NASM, NCATE, NCCU. **Intercollegiate Athletics:** Baseball M; Basketball M & W; Cross-Country Running M & W; Football M; Golf M & W; Soccer M & W; Softball W; Swimming and Diving M & W; Tennis M & W; Track and Field M & W; Volleyball W

YAKIMA VALLEY COMMUNITY COLLEGE
PO Box 22520
Yakima, WA 98907-2520
Tel: (509)574-4600
Fax: (509)574-6860
E-mail: admis@yvcc.edu
Web Site: www.yvcc.edu
President/CEO: Dr. Linda Kaminski
Admissions: Denise Anderson

Type: Two-Year College **Sex:** Coed **Affiliation:** Washington State Board for Community and Technical Colleges. **% Accepted:** 100 **Admission Plans:** Open Admission **Application Deadline:** August 12 **Application Fee:** $20.00 **H.S. Requirements:** High school diploma or equivalent not required. For nursing, dental hygiene, radiological technology, allied health programs: High school diploma required; GED accepted **Scholarships:** Available. **Calendar System:** Quarter, Summer session available **Enrollment:** Full-time 2,786, Part-time 1,693 **Faculty:** Full-time 106, Part-time 213 **Student-Faculty Ratio:** 20:1 **Exams:** Other. **% Residing in College-Owned, -Operated, or -Affiliated Housing:** 1 **Credit Hours For Degree:** 90 credits, Associates **Professional Accreditation:** ACEN, ADA, JRCERT, NCCU. **Intercollegiate Athletics:** Baseball M; Basketball M & W; Soccer W; Softball W; Volleyball W; Wrestling M

ALDERSON BROADDUS UNIVERSITY

101 College Hill Dr.
Philippi, WV 26416
Tel: (304)457-1700; Free: 800-263-1549
Fax: (304)457-6239
E-mail: thonel@ab.edu
Web Site: www.ab.edu
President/CEO: Dr. James T. Barry
Admissions: Erika L. Thon
Financial Aid: Amy L. King
Type: Comprehensive **Sex:** Coed **Affiliation:** American Baptist Churches in the U.S.A. **Scores:** 93% SAT V 400+; 96% SAT M 400+; 63% ACT 18-23; 23% ACT 24-29 **% Accepted:** 54 **Admission Plans:** Deferred Admission **Application Deadline:** Rolling **Application Fee:** $0.00 **H.S. Requirements:** High school diploma required; GED accepted **Costs Per Year:** Application fee: $0. Comprehensive fee: $31,746 includes full-time tuition ($23,930), mandatory fees ($210), and college room and board ($7606). Room and board charges vary according to housing facility. Part-time tuition: $798 per credit hour. Part-time mandatory fees: $52.50 per term. **Scholarships:** Available. **Calendar System:** Semester, Summer session available **Enrollment:** Full-time 1,046, Graduate full-time 69, Part-time 39 **Faculty:** Full-time 62, Part-time 35 **Student-Faculty Ratio:** 17:1 **Exams:** SAT I and SAT II or ACT; SAT Reasoning; SAT Subject. **% Receiving Financial Aid:** 84 **% Residing in College-Owned, -Operated, or -Affiliated Housing:** 81 **Final Year or Final Semester Residency Requirement:** Yes **Regional Accreditation:** North Central Association of Colleges and Schools **Credit Hours For Degree:** 64 credit hours, Associates; 120 credit hours, Bachelors **Professional Accreditation:** ACEN. **Intercollegiate Athletics:** Baseball M; Basketball M & W; Cheerleading M & W; Cross-Country Running M & W; Football M; Golf M & W; Gymnastics W; Lacrosse M & W; Soccer M & W; Softball W; Swimming and Diving M & W; Tennis W; Track and Field M & W; Volleyball M & W; Wrestling M & W

AMERICAN PUBLIC UNIVERSITY SYSTEM

111 W Congress St.
Charles Town, WV 25414
Free: 877-755-2787
E-mail: info@apus.edu
Web Site: www.apus.edu
President/CEO: Dr. Wallace Boston
Admissions: Terry Grant
Type: Comprehensive **Sex:** Coed **Affiliation:** American Military University. **Admission Plans:** Deferred Admission; Open Admission **Application Deadline:** Rolling **Application Fee:** $0.00 **H.S. Requirements:** High school diploma required; GED accepted **Costs Per Year:** Application fee: $0. Tuition: $6480 full-time, $270 per credit hour part-time. Mandatory fees: $400 full-time, $50 per course part-time. **Calendar System:** Miscellaneous, Summer session available **Enrollment:** Full-time 3,759, Graduate full-time 531, Graduate part-time 9,094, Part-time 39,129 **Faculty:** Full-time 431, Part-time 1,839 **Student-Faculty Ratio:** 18:1 **Final Year or Final Semester Residency Requirement:** No **Regional Accreditation:** North Central Association of Colleges and Schools **Credit Hours For Degree:** 61 semester hours, Associates; 121 semester hours, Bachelors **Professional Accreditation:** ACBSP.

APPALACHIAN BIBLE COLLEGE

161 College Dr.
Bradley, WV 25818
Tel: (304)877-6428; Free: 800-678-9ABC
E-mail: admissions2@abc.edu
Web Site: www.abc.edu
President/CEO: Dr. Daniel L. Anderson
Admissions: Elisabeth Anderson
Financial Aid: Deana Steinke
Type: Comprehensive **Sex:** Coed **Affiliation:** nondenominational. **Scores:** 92% SAT V 400+; 79% SAT M 400+; 46% ACT 18-23; 38% ACT 24-29 **% Accepted:** 56 **Admission Plans:** Early Admission; Open Admission **Application Deadline:** Rolling **Application Fee:** $20.00 **H.S. Requirements:** High school diploma required; GED accepted **Costs Per Year:** Application fee: $20. Comprehensive fee: $16,585 includes full-time tuition ($12,020), mandatory fees ($890), and college room and board ($3675). Full-time tuition and fees vary according to class time, course level, course load, degree level, location, program, and student level. Room and board charges vary according to housing facility. Part-time tuition: $355 per credit hour. Part-time tuition varies according to class time, course level, degree level, location, program, and student level. **Scholarships:** Available. **Calendar System:** Semester, Summer session available **Enrollment:** Full-time 209, Graduate part-time 16, Part-time 77 **Faculty:** Full-time 11, Part-time 7 **Student-Faculty Ratio:** 17:1 **Exams:** SAT I or ACT; SAT Reasoning; SAT Subject. **% Receiving Financial Aid:** 88 **% Residing in College-Owned, -Operated, or -Affiliated Housing:** 95 **Final Year or Final Semester Residency Requirement:** No **Regional Accreditation:** North Central Association of Colleges and Schools **Credit Hours For Degree:** 63 credit hours, Associates; 126 credit hours, Bachelors **Professional Accreditation:** ABHE. **Intercollegiate Athletics:** Basketball M & W; Soccer M; Volleyball W

BETHANY COLLEGE

31 E Campus Dr.
Bethany, WV 26032
Tel: (304)829-7000; Free: 800-922-7611
Fax: (304)829-7142
E-mail: enrollment@bethanywv.edu
Web Site: www.bethanywv.edu
President/CEO: Dr. Tamara Rodenberg
Admissions: Mollie Cecere
Financial Aid: Jason McClain
Type: Comprehensive **Sex:** Coed **Affiliation:** Christian Church (Disciples of Christ). **Scores:** 67% SAT V 400+; 78% SAT M 400+; 46% ACT 18-23; 14% ACT 24-29 **% Accepted:** 70 **Admission Plans:** Deferred Admission; Preferred Admission **Application Deadline:** Rolling **Application Fee:** $0.00 **H.S. Requirements:** High school diploma required; GED accepted **Costs Per Year:** Application fee: $0. Comprehensive fee: $36,300 includes full-time tuition ($25,580), mandatory fees ($920), and college room and board ($9800). College room only: $5000. Full-time tuition and fees vary according to course load. Room and board charges vary according to board plan and housing facility. Part-time tuition: $1065 per credit hour. Part-time mandatory fees: $38.25 per credit hour. Part-time tuition and fees vary according to course load. **Scholarships:** Available. **Calendar System:** Semester, Summer session available **Enrollment:** Full-time 703, Graduate full-time 23, Graduate part-time 4, Part-time 7 **Faculty:** Full-time 51, Part-time 32 **Student-Faculty Ratio:** 12:1 **Exams:** ACT essay component not used;

Other; SAT I or ACT; SAT essay component not used; SAT Reasoning. **% Receiving Financial Aid:** 88 **% Residing in College-Owned, -Operated, or -Affiliated Housing:** 98 **Final Year or Final Semester Residency Requirement:** Yes **Regional Accreditation:** North Central Association of Colleges and Schools **Credit Hours For Degree:** 128 credits, Bachelors **Professional Accreditation:** CSWE, NCATE. **Intercollegiate Athletics:** Baseball M; Basketball M & W; Cross-Country Running M & W; Field Hockey W; Football M; Golf M & W; Lacrosse M; Soccer M & W; Softball W; Swimming and Diving M & W; Tennis M & W; Track and Field M & W; Volleyball W

BLUE RIDGE COMMUNITY AND TECHNICAL COLLEGE

13650 Apple Harvest Dr.
Martinsburg, WV 25403
Tel: (304)260-4380
Fax: (304)260-4376
E-mail: bneal@blueridgectc.edu
Web Site: www.blueridgectc.edu
President/CEO: Dr. Peter G. Checkovich
Admissions: Brenda K. Neal

Type: Two-Year College **Sex:** Coed **Affiliation:** Community and Technical College System of West Virginia. **Scores:** 100% SAT V 400+ **Admission Plans:** Deferred Admission; Open Admission **Application Fee:** $25.00 **H.S. Requirements:** High school diploma required; GED accepted **Costs Per Year:** Application fee: $25. State resident tuition: $3696 full-time, $154 per credit hour part-time. Nonresident tuition: $6456 full-time, $278 per credit hour part-time. Full-time tuition varies according to class time and course load. Part-time tuition varies according to class time and course load. **Calendar System:** Semester, Summer session not available **Enrollment:** Full-time 1,093, Part-time 4,459 **Faculty:** Full-time 70, Part-time 110 **Student-Faculty Ratio:** 24:1 **Exams:** SAT I and SAT II or ACT. **Final Year or Final Semester Residency Requirement:** Yes **Regional Accreditation:** North Central Association of Colleges and Schools **Credit Hours For Degree:** 60 credits, Associates **Professional Accreditation:** ACEN.

BLUEFIELD STATE COLLEGE

219 Rock St.
Bluefield, WV 24701-2198
Tel: (304)327-4000; Free: 800-654-7798
Fax: (304)327-7747
E-mail: bscadmit@bluefieldstate.edu
Web Site: www.bluefieldstate.edu
President/CEO: Marsha V. Krotseng
Admissions: Kenneth Mandeville
Financial Aid: Tom Ilse

Type: Four-Year College **Sex:** Coed **Affiliation:** West Virginia Higher Education Policy Commission. **Scores:** 88% SAT V 400+; 91% SAT M 400+; 55.4% ACT 18-23; 14.7% ACT 24-29 **% Accepted:** 77 **Admission Plans:** Deferred Admission; Early Admission **Application Fee:** $0.00 **H.S. Requirements:** High school diploma required; GED accepted **Costs Per Year:** Application fee: $0. State resident tuition: $6120 full-time, $254 per credit hour part-time. Nonresident tuition: $11,280 full-time, $468 per credit hour part-time. **Scholarships:** Available. **Calendar System:** Semester **Enrollment:** Full-time 1,217, Part-time 269 **Faculty:** Full-time 77, Part-time 52 **Student-Faculty Ratio:** 14:1 **Exams:** SAT I or ACT. **% Receiving Financial Aid:** 71 **Regional Accreditation:** North Central Association of Colleges and Schools **Credit Hours For Degree:** 64 semester hours, Associates; 128 semester hours, Bachelors **Professional Accreditation:** AACN, ABET, ACBSP, ACEN, JRCERT, NCATE. **Intercollegiate Athletics:** Baseball M; Basketball M & W; Cheerleading W; Cross-Country Running M & W; Golf M; Softball W; Tennis M & W

BRIDGEVALLEY COMMUNITY AND TECHNICAL COLLEGE (MONTGOMERY)

619 2nd Ave.
Montgomery, WV 25136
Tel: (304)734-6600
Web Site: www.bridgevalley.edu
Admissions: Lisa Graham
Financial Aid: Bonnie Edwards

Type: Two-Year College **Sex:** Coed **Admission Plans:** Open Admission **Scholarships:** Available. **Regional Accreditation:** North Central Association of Colleges and Schools **Professional Accreditation:** ABET.

BRIDGEVALLEY COMMUNITY AND TECHNICAL COLLEGE (SOUTH CHARLESTON)

2001 Union Carbide Dr.
South Charleston, WV 25303
Tel: (304)205-6600
E-mail: castosb@wvstateu.edu
Web Site: www.bridgevalley.edu
Admissions: Bryce Casto

Type: Two-Year College **Sex:** Coed **Affiliation:** West Council for Community and Technical College Education. **% Accepted:** 63 **Enrollment:** Full-time 1,064, Part-time 653 **Faculty:** Full-time 35, Part-time 52 **Exams:** ACT. **Regional Accreditation:** North Central Association of Colleges and Schools **Professional Accreditation:** ACEN, JRCNMT.

CONCORD UNIVERSITY

Vermillion St.
Athens, WV 24712-1000
Tel: (304)384-3115; Free: 888-384-5249
Fax: (304)384-9044
E-mail: admissions@concord.edu
Web Site: www.concord.edu
President/CEO: Dr. Kendra Boggess
Admissions: Kent Gamble
Financial Aid: Debra Turner

Type: Comprehensive **Sex:** Coed **Affiliation:** State College System of West Virginia. **Scores:** 78% SAT V 400+; 82% SAT M 400+; 59% ACT 18-23; 26% ACT 24-29 **% Accepted:** 85 **Admission Plans:** Early Admission **Application Deadline:** Rolling **Application Fee:** $0.00 **H.S. Requirements:** High school diploma required; GED accepted **Costs Per Year:** Application fee: $0. State resident tuition: $7080 full-time. Nonresident tuition: $15,564 full-time. Full-time tuition varies according to course load and program. College room and board: $8350. **Scholarships:** Available. **Calendar System:** Semester, Summer session available **Enrollment:** Full-time 1,953, Graduate full-time 109, Graduate part-time 256, Part-time 189 **Faculty:** Full-time 108, Part-time 64 **Student-Faculty Ratio:** 16:1 **Exams:** SAT I or ACT; SAT essay component used for placement. **% Receiving Financial Aid:** 69 **% Residing in College-Owned, -Operated, or -Affiliated Housing:** 36 **Final Year or Final Semester Residency Requirement:** Yes **Regional Accreditation:** North Central Association of Colleges and Schools **Credit Hours For Degree:** 120 semester hours, Bachelors **Professional Accreditation:** ACBSP, CSWE, NCATE. **Intercollegiate Athletics:** Baseball M; Basketball M & W; Cheerleading M & W; Cross-Country Running M & W; Football M; Golf M & W; Soccer M & W; Softball W; Tennis M & W; Track and Field M & W; Volleyball W

DAVIS & ELKINS COLLEGE

100 Campus Dr.
Elkins, WV 26241-3996
Tel: (304)637-1900; Free: 800-624-3157
Fax: (304)637-1800
E-mail: admiss@davisandelkins.edu
Web Site: www.dewv.edu
President/CEO: Dr. G. Thomas Mann
Admissions: Reneé Heckel
Financial Aid: Susan M. George

Type: Four-Year College **Sex:** Coed **Affiliation:** Presbyterian. **Scores:** 86% SAT V 400+; 77% SAT M 400+; 48.2% ACT 18-23; 19% ACT 24-29 **% Accepted:** 75 **Admission Plans:** Deferred Admission; Early Admission **Application Deadline:** Rolling **Application Fee:** $35.00 **H.S. Requirements:** High school diploma required; GED accepted **Scholarships:** Available. **Calendar System:** 4-1-4, Summer session available **Enrollment:** Full-time 568, Part-time 72 **Faculty:** Full-time 44, Part-time 20 **Student-Faculty Ratio:** 10:1 **Exams:** SAT I or ACT. **% Receiving Financial Aid:** 77 **% Residing in College-Owned, -Operated, or -Affiliated Housing:** 49 **Regional Accreditation:** North Central Association of Colleges and Schools **Credit Hours For Degree:** 62 credit hours, Associates; 124 credit hours, Bachelors **Professional Accreditation:** ACEN, NAST. **Intercollegiate Athletics:** Baseball M; Basketball M & W; Cross-Country Running M & W; Golf M; Skiing (Downhill) M & W; Soccer M & W; Softball W; Volleyball W

EASTERN WEST VIRGINIA COMMUNITY AND TECHNICAL COLLEGE

HC 65 Box 402
Moorefield, WV 26836

Tel: (304)434-8000; Free: 877-982-2322
E-mail: askeast@eastern.wvnet.edu
Web Site: www.eastern.wvnet.edu
President/CEO: Charles Terrell
Financial Aid: Amanda J. Sites
Type: Two-Year College **Sex:** Coed **Scholarships:** Available. **Calendar System:** Semester **Student-Faculty Ratio:** 20:1 **Regional Accreditation:** North Central Association of Colleges and Schools

FAIRMONT STATE UNIVERSITY

1201 Locust Ave.
Fairmont, WV 26554
Tel: (304)367-4000; Free: 800-641-5678
Fax: (304)367-4789
E-mail: admit@fairmontstate.edu
Web Site: www.fairmontstate.edu
President/CEO: Dr. Maria Rose
Admissions: Amie Fazalare
Financial Aid: Patricia Wiemer
Type: Comprehensive **Sex:** Coed **Affiliation:** State College System of West Virginia. **Scores:** 86% SAT V 400+; 83% SAT M 400+; 60% ACT 18-23; 21% ACT 24-29 **% Accepted:** 66 **Application Deadline:** Rolling **Application Fee:** $0.00 **H.S. Requirements:** High school diploma required; GED accepted **Costs Per Year:** Application fee: $0. State resident tuition: $6620 full-time, $268 per credit hour part-time. Nonresident tuition: $13,970 full-time, $574 per credit hour part-time. Full-time tuition varies according to location. Part-time tuition varies according to course load and location. College room and board: $8766. College room only: $4878. Room and board charges vary according to board plan and housing facility. **Scholarships:** Available. **Calendar System:** Semester, Summer session available **Enrollment:** Full-time 3,259, Graduate full-time 97, Graduate part-time 137, Part-time 548 **Faculty:** Full-time 173, Part-time 152 **Student-Faculty Ratio:** 15:1 **Exams:** ACT essay component not used; SAT I or ACT; SAT essay component not used; SAT Reasoning; SAT Subject. **% Receiving Financial Aid:** 72 **% Residing in College-Owned, -Operated, or -Affiliated Housing:** 21 **Final Year or Final Semester Residency Requirement:** Yes **Regional Accreditation:** North Central Association of Colleges and Schools **Credit Hours For Degree:** 64 credits, Associates; 128 credits, Bachelors **ROTC:** Air Force, Army **Professional Accreditation:** AACN, AAFCS, ABET, ACBSP, ACEN, NCATE. **Intercollegiate Athletics:** Baseball M; Basketball M & W; Cheerleading W; Cross-Country Running M & W; Football M; Golf M & W; Softball W; Swimming and Diving M & W; Tennis M & W; Volleyball W

GLENVILLE STATE COLLEGE

200 High St.
Glenville, WV 26351-1200
Tel: (304)462-7361; Free: 800-924-2010
Fax: (304)462-8619
E-mail: ashley.weir@glenville.edu
Web Site: www.glenville.edu
President/CEO: Dr. Peter B. Barr
Admissions: Ashley Weir
Financial Aid: Karen Lay
Type: Four-Year College **Sex:** Coed **Affiliation:** West Virginia Higher Education Policy Commission. **Scores:** 70% SAT V 400+; 72% SAT M 400+; 54% ACT 18-23; 12% ACT 24-29 **% Accepted:** 72 **Admission Plans:** Deferred Admission; Open Admission; Preferred Admission **Application Deadline:** Rolling **Application Fee:** $20.00 **H.S. Requirements:** High school diploma required; GED accepted **Costs Per Year:** Application fee: $20. State resident tuition: $7032 full-time, $293 per credit hour part-time. Nonresident tuition: $15,888 full-time, $662 per credit hour part-time. Mandatory fees: $1752 full-time. Full-time tuition and fees vary according to course load. College room and board: $10,994. Room and board charges vary according to board plan and housing facility. **Scholarships:** Available. **Calendar System:** Semester, Summer session available **Enrollment:** Full-time 1,044, Part-time 688 **Faculty:** Full-time 63, Part-time 67 **Student-Faculty Ratio:** 15:1 **Exams:** ACT essay component not used; SAT I or ACT; SAT essay component not used; SAT Reasoning; SAT Subject. **% Receiving Financial Aid:** 83 **% Residing in College-Owned, -Operated, or -Affiliated Housing:** 33 **Regional Accreditation:** North Central Association of Colleges and Schools **Credit Hours For Degree:** 64 credit hours, Associates; 128 credit hours, Bachelors **ROTC:** Army **Professional Accreditation:**

NCATE. **Intercollegiate Athletics:** Basketball M & W; Cross-Country Running M & W; Football M; Golf M & W; Softball W; Track and Field M & W; Volleyball W

HUNTINGTON JUNIOR COLLEGE

900 Fifth Ave.
Huntington, WV 25701-2004
Tel: (304)697-7550; Free: 800-344-4522
Fax: (304)697-7554
Web Site: www.huntingtonjuniorcollege.com
President/CEO: Carolyn Smith
Admissions: James Garrett
Type: Two-Year College **Sex:** Coed **Admission Plans:** Open Admission **Application Deadline:** Rolling **Application Fee:** $0.00 **H.S. Requirements:** High school diploma required; GED accepted **Scholarships:** Available. **Calendar System:** Quarter, Summer session available **Regional Accreditation:** North Central Association of Colleges and Schools **Credit Hours For Degree:** 108 credits, Associates **Professional Accreditation:** AAMAE.

MARSHALL UNIVERSITY

One John Marshall Dr.
Huntington, WV 25755
Tel: (304)696-3170; Free: 800-642-3499
Fax: (304)696-3135
E-mail: admissions@marshall.edu
Web Site: www.marshall.edu
President/CEO: Dr. Jerome A. Gilbert
Admissions: Dr. Tammy Johnson
Financial Aid: Kathy Bialk
Type: University **Sex:** Coed **Affiliation:** University System of West Virginia. **Scores:** 88% SAT V 400+; 90% SAT M 400+; 55% ACT 18-23; 32% ACT 24-29 **% Accepted:** 88 **Admission Plans:** Deferred Admission **Application Deadline:** Rolling **Application Fee:** $30.00 **H.S. Requirements:** High school diploma required; GED accepted **Costs Per Year:** Application fee: $30. State resident tuition: $5724 full-time, $238.75 per credit hour part-time. Nonresident tuition: $14,512 full-time, $605 per credit hour part-time. Mandatory fees: $1090 full-time, $45.50 per credit hour part-time. Full-time tuition and fees vary according to degree level, location, program, and reciprocity agreements. Part-time tuition and fees vary according to course load, degree level, location, program, and reciprocity agreements. College room and board: $9832. College room only: $6084. Room and board charges vary according to board plan and housing facility. **Scholarships:** Available. **Calendar System:** Semester, Summer session available **Enrollment:** Full-time 8,005, Graduate full-time 2,131, Graduate part-time 1,972, Part-time 1,513 **Faculty:** Full-time 500, Part-time 216 **Student-Faculty Ratio:** 19:1 **Exams:** ACT essay component not used; SAT I or ACT; SAT essay component not used. **% Receiving Financial Aid:** 70 **Regional Accreditation:** North Central Association of Colleges and Schools **Credit Hours For Degree:** 69 semester hours, Associates; 128 semester hours, Bachelors **ROTC:** Army **Professional Accreditation:** AACSB, AAFCS, AANA, ABET, ACEJMC, ACEN, AHIMA, AND, APTA, ASHA, CSWE, JRCAT, LCME/AMA, NAACLS, NASM, NCATE, NRPA. **Intercollegiate Athletics:** Baseball M; Basketball M & W; Cross-Country Running M & W; Football M; Golf M & W; Lacrosse M; Rugby M & W; Soccer M & W; Softball W; Swimming and Diving W; Tennis W; Track and Field M & W; Volleyball W

MOUNTAIN STATE COLLEGE

1508 Spring St.
Parkersburg, WV 26101-3993
Tel: (304)485-5487; Free: 800-841-0201
Fax: (304)485-3524
E-mail: jsutton@msc.edu
Web Site: www.msc.edu
President/CEO: Judith K. Sutton
Admissions: Judith Sutton
Financial Aid: Faye Waggoner
Type: Two-Year College **Sex:** Coed **Scholarships:** Available. **Calendar System:** Quarter **Enrollment:** Full-time 174, Part-time 2 **Faculty:** Full-time 7, Part-time 4 **Student-Faculty Ratio:** 17:1 **Exams:** Other. **Final Year or Final Semester Residency Requirement:** No **Professional Accreditation:** ACICS.

MOUNTWEST COMMUNITY & TECHNICAL COLLEGE

One John Marshall Dr.
Huntington, WV 25755

Free: 866-676-5533
E-mail: admissions@marshall.edu
Web Site: www.mctc.edu
President/CEO: Dr. Keith J. Cotroneo
Admissions: Dr. Tammy Johnson
Type: Two-Year College **Sex:** Coed **Affiliation:** Community and Technical College System of West Virginia. **Scores:** 44% SAT V 400+; 22% SAT M 400+; 33% ACT 18-23; 3% ACT 24-29 **% Accepted:** 100 **Admission Plans:** Deferred Admission; Open Admission **Application Deadline:** Rolling **Application Fee:** $30.00 **H.S. Requirements:** High school diploma required; GED accepted **Calendar System:** Semester, Summer session available **Enrollment:** Full-time 1,400, Part-time 1,134 **Faculty:** Full-time 49, Part-time 107 **Student-Faculty Ratio:** 21:1 **Regional Accreditation:** North Central Association of Colleges and Schools **Credit Hours For Degree:** 64 credits, Associates **ROTC:** Army **Professional Accreditation:** AAMAE, ACBSP.

NEW RIVER COMMUNITY AND TECHNICAL COLLEGE
280 University Dr.
Beaver, WV 25813
Tel: (304)255-5821
E-mail: awithers@newriver.edu
Web Site: www.newriver.edu
President/CEO: Dr. L. Marshall Washington
Admissions: Dr. Allen B. Withers
Financial Aid: Patricia Harmon
Type: Two-Year College **Sex:** Coed **Costs Per Year:** State resident tuition: $3706 full-time, $157 per credit hour part-time. Nonresident tuition: $4834 full-time, $201 per credit hour part-time. Mandatory fees: $288 full-time. Full-time tuition and fees vary according to program. Part-time tuition varies according to course load and program. **Regional Accreditation:** North Central Association of Colleges and Schools

OHIO VALLEY UNIVERSITY
One Campus View Dr.
Vienna, WV 26105-8000
Tel: (304)865-6000; Free: 877-446-8668
Fax: (304)865-6001
E-mail: admissions@ovu.edu
Web Site: www.ovu.edu
President/CEO: Dr. Harold Shank
Admissions: Valerie Wright
Financial Aid: Lindsay Cole
Type: Comprehensive **Sex:** Coed **Affiliation:** Church of Christ. **Scores:** 66% SAT V 400+; 84% SAT M 400+; 51.16% ACT 18-23; 12.79% ACT 24-29 **% Accepted:** 47 **Application Deadline:** August 15 **H.S. Requirements:** High school diploma required; GED accepted **Costs Per Year:** Comprehensive fee: $27,910 includes full-time tuition ($20,460) and college room and board ($7450). College room only: $3720. Part-time tuition: $560 per credit hour. **Scholarships:** Available. **Calendar System:** Semester, Summer session available **Enrollment:** Full-time 396, Graduate part-time 33, Part-time 22 **Faculty:** Full-time 20, Part-time 68 **Student-Faculty Ratio:** 10:1 **Exams:** ACT essay component not used; SAT I and SAT II or ACT; SAT I or ACT; SAT II; SAT essay component not used; SAT Reasoning. **% Receiving Financial Aid:** 77 **% Residing in College-Owned, -Operated, or -Affiliated Housing:** 60 **Final Year or Final Semester Residency Requirement:** No **Regional Accreditation:** North Central Association of Colleges and Schools **Credit Hours For Degree:** 64 semester hours, Associates; 128 semester hours, Bachelors **Professional Accreditation:** NCATE, TEAC. **Intercollegiate Athletics:** Baseball M; Basketball M & W; Cross-Country Running M & W; Golf M & W; Lacrosse M; Soccer M & W; Softball W; Volleyball W; Wrestling M

PIERPONT COMMUNITY & TECHNICAL COLLEGE
1201 Locust Ave.
Fairmont, WV 26554
Tel: (304)367-4892; Free: 800-641-5678
Fax: (304)367-4692
Web Site: www.pierpont.edu
President/CEO: Blair Montgomery
Admissions: Steve Leadman
Type: Two-Year College **Sex:** Coed **Affiliation:** Fairmont State College. **% Accepted:** 92 **Admission Plans:** Deferred Admission; Open Admission **Application Deadline:** Rolling **Application Fee:** $0.00 **H.S. Requirements:**

High school diploma required; GED accepted **Calendar System:** Semester, Summer session available **Enrollment:** Full-time 1,672, Part-time 1,180 **Faculty:** Full-time 232, Part-time 263 **Student-Faculty Ratio:** 18:1 **Exams:** SAT I or ACT. **% Residing in College-Owned, -Operated, or -Affiliated Housing:** 12 **Regional Accreditation:** North Central Association of Colleges and Schools **Professional Accreditation:** ACF, AHIMA, APTA, NAACLS.

POTOMAC STATE COLLEGE OF WEST VIRGINIA UNIVERSITY
101 Fort Ave.
Keyser, WV 26726-2698
Tel: (304)788-6800; Free: 800-262-7332
Fax: (304)788-6939
E-mail: go2psc@mail.wvu.edu
Web Site: www.potomacstatecollege.edu
President/CEO: Dr. Leonard Colelli
Admissions: Beth Little
Type: Two-Year College **Sex:** Coed **Affiliation:** West Virginia Higher Education Policy Commission. **Scores:** 54% SAT V 400+; 57% SAT M 400+; 41% ACT 18-23; 18% ACT 24-29 **% Accepted:** 48 **Admission Plans:** Open Admission **Application Deadline:** Rolling **Application Fee:** $0.00 **H.S. Requirements:** High school diploma required; GED accepted **Costs Per Year:** Application fee: $0. State resident tuition: $3864 full-time, $161 per credit hour part-time. Nonresident tuition: $10,080 full-time, $420 per credit hour part-time. Full-time tuition varies according to course load and degree level. Part-time tuition varies according to course load and degree level. College room and board: $8476. College room only: $4464. Room and board charges vary according to board plan and housing facility. **Scholarships:** Available. **Calendar System:** Semester, Summer session available **Enrollment:** Full-time 1,156, Part-time 319 **Faculty:** Full-time 45, Part-time 40 **Student-Faculty Ratio:** 22:1 **Exams:** SAT I or ACT. **% Residing in College-Owned, -Operated, or -Affiliated Housing:** 52 **Final Year or Final Semester Residency Requirement:** No **Regional Accreditation:** North Central Association of Colleges and Schools **Credit Hours For Degree:** 62 credit hours, Associates; 123 credit hours, Bachelors **Intercollegiate Athletics:** Baseball M; Basketball M & W; Cross-Country Running M & W; Lacrosse M & W; Soccer M & W; Softball W; Volleyball W

SALEM INTERNATIONAL UNIVERSITY
223 W Main St.
Salem, WV 26426-0500
Tel: (304)782-5011; Free: 888-235-5024
E-mail: admissions@salemiu.edu
Web Site: www.salemu.edu
President/CEO: J. William Brooks
Admissions: Brenda Davis
Financial Aid: Pat Zinsmeister
Type: Comprehensive **Sex:** Coed **Scholarships:** Available. **Calendar System:** Miscellaneous, Summer session available **Enrollment:** Full-time 631, Graduate full-time 219 **Faculty:** Full-time 26, Part-time 34 **Student-Faculty Ratio:** 18:1 **Exams:** SAT I or ACT. **% Receiving Financial Aid:** 35 **% Residing in College-Owned, -Operated, or -Affiliated Housing:** 32 **Final Year or Final Semester Residency Requirement:** No **Regional Accreditation:** North Central Association of Colleges and Schools **Credit Hours For Degree:** 60 credit hours, Associates; 120 credit hours, Bachelors **Intercollegiate Athletics:** Baseball M; Basketball M & W; Cheerleading M & W; Soccer M & W; Softball W; Swimming and Diving M & W; Volleyball W; Water Polo M & W

SHEPHERD UNIVERSITY
PO Box 5000
Shepherdstown, WV 25443
Tel: (304)876-5000; Free: 800-344-5231
Fax: (304)876-5165
E-mail: admission@shepherd.edu
Web Site: www.shepherd.edu
President/CEO: Dr. Mary J.C. Hendrix
Admissions: Kristen Lorenz
Financial Aid: Joyce Cabral
Type: Comprehensive **Sex:** Coed **Affiliation:** West Virginia Higher Education Policy Commission. **Scores:** 93% SAT V 400+; 93% SAT M 400+; 59.3% ACT 18-23; 26.9% ACT 24-29 **% Accepted:** 90 **Admission Plans:** Deferred Admission; Early Admission; Early Decision Plan **Application Deadline:** Rolling **Application Fee:** $45.00 **H.S. Requirements:** High

school diploma required; GED accepted **Costs Per Year:** Application fee: $45. State resident tuition: $6830 full-time, $286 per credit hour part-time. Nonresident tuition: $16,628 full-time, $693 per credit hour part-time. Full-time tuition varies according to program and reciprocity agreements. Part-time tuition varies according to program. College room and board: $9682. Room and board charges vary according to board plan and housing facility. **Scholarships:** Available. **Calendar System:** Semester, Summer session available **Enrollment:** Full-time 2,935, Graduate full-time 66, Graduate part-time 151, Part-time 709 **Faculty:** Full-time 139, Part-time 228 **Student-Faculty Ratio:** 15:1 **Exams:** SAT I or ACT; SAT Reasoning. **% Receiving Financial Aid:** 63 **% Residing in College-Owned, -Operated, or -Affiliated Housing:** 34 **Final Year or Final Semester Residency Requirement:** Yes **Regional Accreditation:** North Central Association of Colleges and Schools **Credit Hours For Degree:** 120 semester hours, Bachelors **ROTC:** Air Force **Professional Accreditation:** ACEN, CSWE, NASM, NCATE. **Intercollegiate Athletics:** Baseball M; Basketball M & W; Football M; Golf M; Lacrosse W; Soccer M & W; Softball W; Tennis M & W; Volleyball W

SOUTHERN WEST VIRGINIA COMMUNITY AND TECHNICAL COLLEGE

Dempsey Branch Rd.
Mount Gay, WV 25637-2900
Tel: (304)792-7160
Fax: (304)792-7096
E-mail: admissions@southern.wvnet.edu
Web Site: southernwv.edu
President/CEO: Joanne Tomblin
Admissions: Roy Simmons

Type: Two-Year College **Sex:** Coed **Affiliation:** State College System of West Virginia. **% Accepted:** 100 **Admission Plans:** Deferred Admission; Early Admission; Open Admission **Application Deadline:** Rolling **Application Fee:** $0.00 **H.S. Requirements:** High school diploma required; GED accepted **Scholarships:** Available. **Calendar System:** Semester, Summer session available **Enrollment:** Full-time 1,192, Part-time 708 **Faculty:** Full-time 66, Part-time 105 **Student-Faculty Ratio:** 20:1 **Regional Accreditation:** North Central Association of Colleges and Schools **Credit Hours For Degree:** 63 semester hours, Associates **Professional Accreditation:** ACEN, ARCST, JRCERT, NAACLS.

STRAYER UNIVERSITY–TEAYS VALLEY CAMPUS

100 Corporate Ctr. Dr.
Scott Depot, WV 25560
Tel: (304)760-1700
Fax: (304)757-1430
Web Site: www.strayer.edu/west-virginia/teays-valley
President/CEO: Brian W. Jones

Type: Comprehensive **Sex:** Coed **Regional Accreditation:** Middle States Association of Colleges and Schools

UNIVERSITY OF CHARLESTON

2300 MacCorkle Ave., SE
Charleston, WV 25304-1099
Tel: (304)357-4800; Free: 800-995-GOUC
Fax: (304)357-4781
E-mail: admissions@ucwv.edu
Web Site: www.ucwv.edu
President/CEO: Dr. Edwin H. Welch
Admissions: Sandy Dolin
Financial Aid: Nina Morton

Type: Comprehensive **Sex:** Coed **Scores:** 87% SAT V 400+; 91% SAT M 400+; 64% ACT 18-23; 24% ACT 24-29 **% Accepted:** 52 **Admission Plans:** Deferred Admission; Early Admission **Application Deadline:** Rolling **Application Fee:** $25.00 **H.S. Requirements:** High school diploma required; GED accepted **Costs Per Year:** Application fee: $25. Comprehensive fee: $39,200 includes full-time tuition ($28,900), mandatory fees ($1200), and college room and board ($9100). College room only: $5000. Full-time tuition and fees vary according to location and program. Room and board charges vary according to board plan and housing facility. Part-time tuition: $380 per credit. Part-time tuition varies according to course load, location, and program. **Scholarships:** Available. **Calendar System:** Semester, Summer session available **Enrollment:** Full-time 1,292, Graduate full-time 581, Graduate part-time 19, Part-time 435 **Faculty:** Full-time 116, Part-time 87 **Student-Faculty Ratio:** 15:1 **Exams:** ACT essay component not used; SAT

I or ACT; SAT essay component not used. **% Receiving Financial Aid:** 84 **% Residing in College-Owned, -Operated, or -Affiliated Housing:** 47 **Regional Accreditation:** North Central Association of Colleges and Schools **Credit Hours For Degree:** 60 credit hours, Associates; 120 credit hours, Bachelors **ROTC:** Army **Professional Accreditation:** ACEN, ACPE, CoARC, JRCAT, JRCERT. **Intercollegiate Athletics:** Baseball M; Basketball M & W; Cheerleading W; Crew W; Cross-Country Running W; Football M; Golf M & W; Soccer M & W; Softball W; Swimming and Diving M & W; Tennis M & W; Track and Field M & W; Volleyball M & W

VALLEY COLLEGE

120 New River Town Ctr.
Beckley, WV 25801
Tel: (304)252-9547; Free: 888-53LEARN
Fax: (304)252-1694
Web Site: www.valley.edu
President/CEO: Gary Bettcher
Admissions: Kerri Cline

Type: Two-Year College **Sex:** Coed **% Accepted:** 100 **Student-Faculty Ratio:** 23:1 **Exams:** Other. **Professional Accreditation:** ACICS.

WEST LIBERTY UNIVERSITY

208 University Dr.
West Liberty, WV 26074
Tel: (304)336-5000; Free: 866-WESTLIB
Fax: (304)336-8285
E-mail: wladmsn1@westliberty.edu
Web Site: www.westliberty.edu
President/CEO: Robin Capehart
Admissions: Stephanie North
Financial Aid: Christ Taskalines

Type: Comprehensive **Sex:** Coed **Affiliation:** West Virginia Higher Education Policy Commission. **Scores:** 62% SAT V 400+; 76% SAT M 400+; 46. 86% ACT 18-23; 26.18% ACT 24-29 **% Accepted:** 72 **Application Fee:** $0.00 **H.S. Requirements:** High school diploma required; GED accepted **Costs Per Year:** Application fee: $0. State resident tuition: $6702 full-time, $273 per credit hour part-time. Nonresident tuition: $14,112 full-time, $581.75 per credit hour part-time. Full-time tuition varies according to course load, degree level, and program. Part-time tuition varies according to course load, degree level, and program. College room and board: $8810. College room only: $4860. Room and board charges vary according to housing facility and location. **Scholarships:** Available. **Calendar System:** Semester, Summer session available **Enrollment:** Full-time 1,847, Graduate full-time 90, Graduate part-time 84, Part-time 319 **Exams:** ACT essay component not used; SAT I or ACT; SAT essay component not used; SAT Reasoning; SAT Subject. **% Receiving Financial Aid:** 73 **% Residing in College-Owned, -Operated, or -Affiliated Housing:** 44 **Regional Accreditation:** North Central Association of Colleges and Schools **Professional Accreditation:** AACN, ACBSP, ADA, NAACLS, NASM, NCATE. **Intercollegiate Athletics:** Baseball M; Basketball M & W; Cross-Country Running M & W; Football M; Golf M & W; Softball W; Tennis M & W; Track and Field M & W; Volleyball W; Wrestling M

WEST VIRGINIA BUSINESS COLLEGE (NUTTER FORT)

116 Pennsylvania Ave.
Nutter Fort, WV 26301
Tel: (304)624-7695
Fax: (304)622-2149
E-mail: info@wvbc.edu
Web Site: www.wvbc.edu
President/CEO: Gary Gorby
Admissions: Robert Wright

Type: Two-Year College **Sex:** Coed **Application Fee:** $50.00 **Professional Accreditation:** ACICS.

WEST VIRGINIA BUSINESS COLLEGE (WHEELING)

1052 Main St.
Wheeling, WV 26003
Tel: (304)232-0361
Fax: (304)232-0363
E-mail: wvbcwheeling@stratuswave.net
Web Site: www.wvbc.edu
President/CEO: Karen D. Shaw
Admissions: Karen D. Shaw

Financial Aid: Karen D. Shaw

Type: Two-Year College **Sex:** Coed **% Accepted:** 100 **Application Fee:** $50.00 **H.S. Requirements:** High school diploma required; GED accepted **Scholarships:** Available. **Calendar System:** Quarter **Faculty:** Part-time 10 **Student-Faculty Ratio:** 6:1 **Professional Accreditation:** ACICS.

WEST VIRGINIA JUNIOR COLLEGE–BRIDGEPORT

176 Thompson Dr.
Bridgeport, WV 26330
Tel: (304)842-4007; Free: 800-470-5627
E-mail: apratt@wvjcinfo.net
Web Site: www.wvjc.edu
President/CEO: Sharron K. Stephens
Admissions: Adam Pratt

Type: Two-Year College **Sex:** Coed **Admission Plans:** Open Admission **Application Deadline:** Rolling **Application Fee:** $25.00 **H.S. Requirements:** High school diploma required; GED accepted **Scholarships:** Available. **Calendar System:** Quarter, Summer session available **Enrollment:** Full-time 389 **Faculty:** Full-time 10, Part-time 9 **Student-Faculty Ratio:** 15:1 **Exams:** ACT essay component used for advising; SAT I or ACT; SAT essay component used for advising. **Credit Hours For Degree:** 90 quarter hours, Associates **Professional Accreditation:** ACICS.

WEST VIRGINIA JUNIOR COLLEGE–CHARLESTON

1000 Virginia St. E
Charleston, WV 25301-2817
Tel: (304)345-2820; Free: 800-924-5208
Web Site: www.wvjc.edu
President/CEO: Erik Engberg

Type: Two-Year College **Sex:** Coed **Admission Plans:** Open Admission **Application Deadline:** Rolling **H.S. Requirements:** High school diploma required; GED accepted **Calendar System:** Quarter, Summer session available **Student-Faculty Ratio:** 17:1 **Credit Hours For Degree:** 90 quarter hours, Associates **Professional Accreditation:** ACICS.

WEST VIRGINIA JUNIOR COLLEGE–MORGANTOWN

148 Willey St.
Morgantown, WV 26505-5521
Tel: (304)296-8282
Web Site: www.wvjcmorgantown.edu
President/CEO: Patricia Callen

Type: Two-Year College **Sex:** Coed **Admission Plans:** Open Admission **Application Deadline:** Rolling **Application Fee:** $25.00 **H.S. Requirements:** High school diploma required; GED accepted **Calendar System:** Quarter **Student-Faculty Ratio:** 32:1 **Credit Hours For Degree:** 92 quarter hours, Associates **Professional Accreditation:** ACICS.

WEST VIRGINIA NORTHERN COMMUNITY COLLEGE

1704 Market St.
Wheeling, WV 26003-3699
Tel: (304)233-5900
Fax: (304)233-5900
E-mail: jfike@northern.wvnet.edu
Web Site: www.wvncc.edu
President/CEO: Dr. Martin J. Olshinsky
Admissions: Janet Fike
Financial Aid: Janet M. Fike

Type: Two-Year College **Sex:** Coed **% Accepted:** 100 **Admission Plans:** Deferred Admission; Early Admission; Open Admission **Application Deadline:** Rolling **Application Fee:** $0.00 **H.S. Requirements:** High school diploma required; GED accepted **Scholarships:** Available. **Calendar System:** Semester, Summer session available **Enrollment:** Full-time 1,156, Part-time 1,349 **Faculty:** Full-time 58, Part-time 132 **Exams:** Other. **Final Year or Final Semester Residency Requirement:** No **Regional Accreditation:** North Central Association of Colleges and Schools **Credit Hours For Degree:** 60 credit hours, Associates **Professional Accreditation:** ACEN, ACF, AHIMA, ARCST, CoARC, NAACLS.

WEST VIRGINIA STATE UNIVERSITY

PO Box 1000
Institute, WV 25112-1000
Tel: (304)766-3000; Free: 800-987-2112
Fax: (304)766-4158
Web Site: www.wvstateu.edu

President/CEO: Dr. Brian O. Hemphill
Admissions: Amanda Anderson
Financial Aid: JoAnn L. Ross

Type: Comprehensive **Sex:** Coed **Affiliation:** State College System of West Virginia. **Scores:** 71% SAT V 400+; 80% SAT M 400+; 61.3% ACT 18-23; 12.9% ACT 24-29 **% Accepted:** 94 **Application Deadline:** August 17 **Application Fee:** $20.00 **H.S. Requirements:** High school diploma required; GED accepted **Costs Per Year:** Application fee: $20. State resident tuition: $6662 full-time, $273 per credit hour part-time. Nonresident tuition: $15,572 full-time, $644 per credit hour part-time. Full-time tuition varies according to course load and program. Part-time tuition varies according to course load and program. College room and board: $10,806. College room only: $6768. Room and board charges vary according to board plan and housing facility. **Scholarships:** Available. **Calendar System:** Semester, Summer session available **Enrollment:** Full-time 1,860, Graduate full-time 31, Graduate part-time 28, Part-time 1,247 **Faculty:** Full-time 107, Part-time 94 **Student-Faculty Ratio:** 17:1 **Exams:** ACT essay component not used; SAT I; SAT I or ACT; SAT essay component not used; SAT Reasoning; SAT Subject. **% Residing in College-Owned, -Operated, or -Affiliated Housing:** 12 **Regional Accreditation:** North Central Association of Colleges and Schools **Credit Hours For Degree:** 120 semester hours, Bachelors **ROTC:** Army **Professional Accreditation:** ABET, ACBSP, CSWE, NCATE, NRPA. **Intercollegiate Athletics:** Baseball M; Basketball M & W; Cross-Country Running W; Football M; Golf M; Softball W; Tennis M & W; Volleyball W

WEST VIRGINIA UNIVERSITY

University Ave.
Morgantown, WV 26506
Tel: (304)293-0111; Free: 800-344-9881
Fax: (304)293-3080
E-mail: marilyn.potts@mail.wvu.edu
Web Site: www.wvu.edu
President/CEO: Dr. E. Gordon Gee
Admissions: Marilyn Potts
Financial Aid: Sandra Bennett

Type: University **Sex:** Coed **Affiliation:** West Virginia Higher Education Policy Commission. **Scores:** 93% SAT V 400+; 96% SAT M 400+ **% Accepted:** 86 **Admission Plans:** Preferred Admission **Application Deadline:** August 1 **Application Fee:** $0.00 **H.S. Requirements:** High school diploma required; GED accepted **Costs Per Year:** Application fee: $0. State resident tuition: $7632 full-time, $318 per credit hour part-time. Nonresident tuition: $21,432 full-time, $893 per credit hour part-time. Full-time tuition varies according to location, program, and reciprocity agreements. Part-time tuition varies according to course load, location, program, and reciprocity agreements. College room and board: $9872. Room and board charges vary according to board plan, housing facility, and location. **Scholarships:** Available. **Calendar System:** Semester, Summer session available **Enrollment:** Full-time 20,863, Graduate full-time 4,749, Graduate part-time 1,863, Part-time 1,700 **Faculty:** Full-time 1,132, Part-time 346 **Student-Faculty Ratio:** 21:1 **Exams:** ACT essay component not used; SAT I or ACT; SAT essay component not used; SAT Reasoning. **% Receiving Financial Aid:** 55 **% Residing in College-Owned, -Operated, or -Affiliated Housing:** 15 **Final Year or Final Semester Residency Requirement:** No **Regional Accreditation:** North Central Association of Colleges and Schools **Credit Hours For Degree:** 128 credit hours, Bachelors **ROTC:** Air Force, Army **Professional Accreditation:** AACN, AACSB, AALS, ABA, ABET, ACA, ACEJMC, ACPE, ACIPE, ADA, AND, AOTA, APA, APTA, ASHA, ASLA, CEPH, CIDA, CORE, CSWE, JRCAT, LCME/AMA, NAACLS, NASAD, NASM, NASPAA, NAST, NCATE, NRPA, SAF. **Intercollegiate Athletics:** Baseball M; Basketball M & W; Crew W; Cross-Country Running W; Football M; Golf M; Gymnastics W; Riflery M & W; Soccer M & W; Swimming and Diving M & W; Tennis W; Track and Field W; Volleyball W; Wrestling M

WEST VIRGINIA UNIVERSITY INSTITUTE OF TECHNOLOGY

405 Fayette Pke.
Montgomery, WV 25136
Tel: (304)442-3071; Free: 888-554-8324
Fax: (304)442-3097
E-mail: tech-admissions@mail.wvu.edu
Web Site: www.wvutech.edu
President/CEO: Carolyn Long
Admissions: William Allen, Jr.
Financial Aid: Michael A. White

Type: Four-Year College **Sex:** Coed **Affiliation:** West Virginia University.

Scores: 51.05% ACT 18-23; 21.05% ACT 24-29 **% Accepted:** 61 **Admission Plans:** Early Admission **Application Deadline:** Rolling **Application Fee:** $0.00 **H.S. Requirements:** High school diploma required; GED accepted **Costs Per Year:** Application fee: $0. State resident tuition: $6336 full-time, $264 per credit hour part-time. Nonresident tuition: $15,936 full-time, $664 per credit hour part-time. Full-time tuition varies according to program. Part-time tuition varies according to course load and program. College room and board: $9348. College room only: $5452. Room and board charges vary according to board plan and housing facility. **Scholarships:** Available. **Calendar System:** Semester, Summer session available **Enrollment:** Full-time 979, Part-time 284 **Faculty:** Full-time 83, Part-time 31 **Student-Faculty Ratio:** 12:1 **Exams:** ACT essay component not used; Other; SAT I or ACT; SAT essay component not used; SAT Reasoning; SAT Subject. **% Receiving Financial Aid:** 68 **% Residing in College-Owned, -Operated, or -Affiliated Housing:** 35 **Final Year or Final Semester Residency Requirement:** Yes **Regional Accreditation:** North Central Association of Colleges and Schools **Credit Hours For Degree:** 120 semester hours, Bachelors **ROTC:** Army **Professional Accreditation:** ABET, ADA, CoARC. **Intercollegiate Athletics:** Baseball M; Basketball M & W; Cross-Country Running M & W; Golf M; Soccer M & W; Softball W; Swimming and Diving M & W; Volleyball W; Wrestling M

WEST VIRGINIA UNIVERSITY AT PARKERSBURG

300 Campus Dr.
Parkersburg, WV 26104
Tel: (304)424-8000; Free: 800-WVA-WVUP
E-mail: christine.post@mail.wvu.edu
Web Site: www.wvup.edu
President/CEO: Dr. Marie Foster Gnage
Admissions: Christine Post
Financial Aid: August Kafer
Type: Two-Year College **Sex:** Coed **Affiliation:** West Virginia University. **Admission Plans:** Deferred Admission; Early Admission; Open Admission **Application Deadline:** Rolling **H.S. Requirements:** High school diploma required; GED accepted **Calendar System:** Semester, Summer session available **Student-Faculty Ratio:** 24:1 **Regional Accreditation:** North Central Association of Colleges and Schools **Credit Hours For Degree:** 64 credit hours, Associates; 128 credit hours, Bachelors **Professional Accreditation:** ACEN, NCATE.

WEST VIRGINIA WESLEYAN COLLEGE

59 College Ave.
Buckhannon, WV 26201
Tel: (304)473-8000; Free: 800-722-9933
Fax: (304)472-2571
E-mail: admission@wvwc.edu
Web Site: www.wvwc.edu
President/CEO: Dr. Pamela Balch
Admissions: John Waltz
Financial Aid: Susan George
Type: Comprehensive **Sex:** Coed **Affiliation:** United Methodist Church. **Scores:** 86% SAT V 400+; 85% SAT M 400+; 50.56% ACT 18-23; 33.33% ACT 24-29 **% Accepted:** 77 **Admission Plans:** Deferred Admission **Ap-**plication Fee: $35.00 **H.S. Requirements:** High school diploma required; GED accepted **Costs Per Year:** Application fee: $35. Comprehensive fee: $34,032 includes full-time tuition ($28,574), mandatory fees ($1378), and college room and board ($4080). College room only: $4168. Full-time tuition and fees vary according to course load and student level. Room and board charges vary according to housing facility. **Scholarships:** Available. **Calendar System:** Semester, Summer session available **Enrollment:** Full-time 1,363, Graduate full-time 115, Graduate part-time 14, Part-time 26 **Faculty:** Full-time 91, Part-time 61 **Student-Faculty Ratio:** 13:1 **Exams:** ACT essay component used for placement; SAT I or ACT; SAT II; SAT essay component used for placement; SAT Reasoning; SAT Subject. **% Receiving Financial Aid:** 78 **% Residing in College-Owned, -Operated, or -Affiliated Housing:** 81 **Regional Accreditation:** North Central Association of Colleges and Schools **Credit Hours For Degree:** 120 credit hours, Bachelors **Professional Accreditation:** AAFCS, ACBSP, ACEN, JRCAT, NASM, NCATE. **Intercollegiate Athletics:** Baseball M; Basketball M & W; Cheerleading M & W; Cross-Country Running M & W; Football M; Golf M & W; Lacrosse M & W; Skiing (Downhill) M & W; Soccer M & W; Softball W; Swimming and Diving M & W; Tennis M & W; Track and Field M & W; Volleyball W

WHEELING JESUIT UNIVERSITY

316 Washington Ave.
Wheeling, WV 26003-6295
Tel: (304)243-2000; Free: 800-624-6992
Fax: (304)243-2397
E-mail: crouhier@wju.edu
Web Site: www.wju.edu
President/CEO: Fr. James Fleming
Admissions: Christopher Rouhier
Financial Aid: Christie Tomczyk
Type: Comprehensive **Sex:** Coed **Affiliation:** Roman Catholic (Jesuit). **Scores:** 98% SAT V 400+; 98% SAT M 400+; 53.23% ACT 18-23; 38.71% ACT 24-29 **% Accepted:** 61 **Admission Plans:** Deferred Admission **Application Deadline:** Rolling **Application Fee:** $25.00 **H.S. Requirements:** High school diploma required; GED accepted **Costs Per Year:** Application fee: $25. Comprehensive fee: $35,100 includes full-time tuition ($27,000), mandatory fees ($1030), and college room and board ($7070). College room only: $3830. Room and board charges vary according to board plan, housing facility, and student level. Part-time tuition: $735 per credit hour. **Scholarships:** Available. **Calendar System:** Semester, Summer session available **Enrollment:** Full-time 858, Graduate full-time 146, Graduate part-time 196, Part-time 185 **Faculty:** Full-time 82, Part-time 84 **Student-Faculty Ratio:** 11:1 **Exams:** ACT; Other; SAT I; SAT I and SAT II or ACT; SAT I or ACT; SAT essay component used for placement; SAT Reasoning; SAT Subject. **% Receiving Financial Aid:** 74 **% Residing in College-Owned, -Operated, or -Affiliated Housing:** 64 **Final Year or Final Semester Residency Requirement:** Yes **Regional Accreditation:** North Central Association of Colleges and Schools **Credit Hours For Degree:** 120 credit hours, Bachelors **Professional Accreditation:** AACN, ACBSP, APTA, CoARC, JRCNMT. **Intercollegiate Athletics:** Baseball M; Basketball M & W; Cheerleading M & W; Cross-Country Running M & W; Golf M & W; Lacrosse M & W; Rugby M; Soccer M & W; Softball W; Swimming and Diving M & W; Track and Field M & W; Volleyball W; Wrestling M

ALVERNO COLLEGE
3400 S 43rd St.
Milwaukee, WI 53234-3922
Tel: (414)382-6000; Free: 800-933-3401
Fax: (414)382-6354
E-mail: admissions@alverno.edu
Web Site: www.alverno.edu
President/CEO: Dr. Mary Meehan
Admissions: Becky Zeman
Financial Aid: Amy Christen
Type: Comprehensive **Affiliation:** Roman Catholic. **Scores:** 50% ACT 18-23; 12.98% ACT 24-29 **% Accepted:** 77 **Admission Plans:** Deferred Admission **Application Deadline:** Rolling **Application Fee:** $0.00 **H.S. Requirements:** High school diploma required; GED accepted **Costs Per Year:** Application fee: $0. Comprehensive fee: $33,294 includes full-time tuition ($24,984), mandatory fees ($676), and college room and board ($7634). Full-time tuition and fees vary according to program. Room and board charges vary according to board plan and housing facility. Part-time tuition: $1041 per credit hour. Part-time tuition varies according to program. **Scholarships:** Available. **Calendar System:** Semester, Summer session available **Enrollment:** Full-time 1,194, Graduate full-time 406, Graduate part-time 245, Part-time 364 **Faculty:** Full-time 98, Part-time 140 **Student-Faculty Ratio:** 10:1 **Exams:** ACT essay component not used; SAT I or ACT; SAT essay component not used. **% Receiving Financial Aid:** 86 **% Residing in College-Owned, -Operated, or -Affiliated Housing:** 15 **Final Year or Final Semester Residency Requirement:** No **Regional Accreditation:** North Central Association of Colleges and Schools **Credit Hours For Degree:** 60 credits, Associates; 120 credits, Bachelors **ROTC:** Air Force, Army **Professional Accreditation:** AACN, NASM, NCATE. **Intercollegiate Athletics:** Basketball W; Cross-Country Running W; Golf W; Soccer W; Softball W; Tennis W; Volleyball W

BELLIN COLLEGE
3201 Eaton Rd.
Green Bay, WI 54305
Tel: (920)433-3560; Free: 800-236-8707
Fax: (920)433-7416
E-mail: admissio@bcon.edu
Web Site: www.bellincollege.edu
President/CEO: Dr. Connie Boerst
Admissions: Dr. Penny Croghan
Financial Aid: Lena C. Goodman
Type: Comprehensive **Sex:** Coed **Affiliation:** Bellin Health System. **Application Deadline:** Rolling **Application Fee:** $30.00 **H.S. Requirements:** High school diploma required; GED accepted **Scholarships:** Available. **Calendar System:** Semester, Summer session available **Exams:** ACT. **% Receiving Financial Aid:** 53 **Regional Accreditation:** North Central Association of Colleges and Schools **Credit Hours For Degree:** 129 credits, Bachelors **ROTC:** Army **Professional Accreditation:** AACN.

BELOIT COLLEGE
700 College St.
Beloit, WI 53511-5596
Tel: (608)363-2000; Free: 800-9-BELOIT
Fax: (608)363-2075
E-mail: admiss@beloit.edu
Web Site: www.beloit.edu
President/CEO: Dr. H. Scott Bierman
Admissions: Lindsey R. Duerr
Financial Aid: Lindsey Duerr
Type: Four-Year College **Sex:** Coed **Scores:** 96% SAT V 400+; 98% SAT M 400+; 18% ACT 18-23; 52% ACT 24-29 **Costs Per Year:** Comprehensive fee: $55,206 includes full-time tuition ($46,596), mandatory fees ($464), and college room and board ($8146). College room only: $4626. Room and board charges vary according to board plan. Part-time tuition: $1456 per credit hour. **Scholarships:** Available. **Calendar System:** Semester, Summer session available **Enrollment:** Full-time 1,296, Part-time 62 **Faculty:** Full-time 107, Part-time 41 **Student-Faculty Ratio:** 11:1 **Exams:** ACT essay component not used; SAT I or ACT; SAT essay component not used. **% Receiving Financial Aid:** 67 **% Residing in College-Owned, -Operated, or -Affiliated Housing:** 87 **Final Year or Final Semester Residency Requirement:** No **Regional Accreditation:** North Central Association of Colleges and Schools **Credit Hours For Degree:** 31 units, Bachelors **Intercollegiate Athletics:** Baseball M; Basketball M & W; Cross-Country Running M & W; Football M; Ice Hockey M & W; Lacrosse M & W; Soccer M & W; Softball W; Swimming and Diving M & W; Tennis W; Track and Field M & W; Volleyball W

BLACKHAWK TECHNICAL COLLEGE
6004 S County Rd. G
Janesville, WI 53546-9458
Tel: (608)758-6900
Fax: (608)757-9407
E-mail: erobinson@blackhawk.edu
Web Site: www.blackhawk.edu
President/CEO: Dr. Thomas C. Eckert
Admissions: Edward E. Robinson
Type: Two-Year College **Sex:** Coed **Affiliation:** Wisconsin Technical College System. **Admission Plans:** Open Admission; Preferred Admission **Application Deadline:** Rolling **Application Fee:** $30.00 **H.S. Requirements:** High school diploma required; GED accepted **Costs Per Year:** Application fee: $30. State resident tuition: $3852 full-time, $128.40 per credit hour part-time. Nonresident tuition: $5778 full-time, $192.60 per credit hour part-time. Mandatory fees: $307 full-time, $6.42 per credit hour part-time. Full-time tuition and fees vary according to course load. Part-time tuition and fees vary according to course load. **Scholarships:** Available. **Calendar System:** Semester, Summer session available **Enrollment:** Full-time 947, Part-time 1,302 **Faculty:** Full-time 96, Part-time 271 **Student-Faculty Ratio:** 8:1 **Final Year or Final Semester Residency Requirement:** No **Regional Accreditation:** North Central Association of Colleges and Schools **Credit Hours For Degree:** 64 credits, Associates **Professional Accreditation:** ACEN, ACF, ADA, APTA, JRCERT.

BRYANT & STRATTON COLLEGE–BAYSHORE CAMPUS
500 W Silver Spring Dr.
Bayshore Town Ctr., Ste. K340
Glendale, WI 53217
Tel: (414)961-9600
Web Site: www.bryantstratton.edu

Type: Two-Year College **Sex:** Coed **Regional Accreditation:** Middle States Association of Colleges and Schools

BRYANT & STRATTON COLLEGE–MILWAUKEE CAMPUS

310 W Wisconsin Ave.
Ste. 500 E
Milwaukee, WI 53203
Tel: (414)276-5200
Web Site: www.bryantstratton.edu
President/CEO: Peter J. Pavone
Admissions: Dan Basile

Type: Two-Year College **Sex:** Coed **Affiliation:** Bryant and Stratton College, Inc. **% Accepted:** 89 **Application Deadline:** Rolling **Application Fee:** $0.00 **H.S. Requirements:** High school diploma required; GED accepted **Scholarships:** Available. **Calendar System:** Semester, Summer session available **Enrollment:** Full-time 460, Part-time 368 **Faculty:** Full-time 19, Part-time 83 **Student-Faculty Ratio:** 13:1 **Exams:** Other; SAT I or ACT. **Regional Accreditation:** Middle States Association of Colleges and Schools **Credit Hours For Degree:** 60 semester hours, Associates; 120 semester hours, Bachelors **Professional Accreditation:** AAMAE.

BRYANT & STRATTON COLLEGE–WAUWATOSA CAMPUS

10950 W Potter Rd.
Wauwatosa, WI 53226
Tel: (414)302-7000
Web Site: www.bryantstratton.edu
President/CEO: Pete Pavone
Admissions: Tony Krocak

Type: Four-Year College **Sex:** Coed **Application Deadline:** Rolling **H.S. Requirements:** High school diploma required; GED accepted **Calendar System:** Semester **Enrollment:** Full-time 930, Part-time 334 **Student-Faculty Ratio:** 10:1 **Exams:** Other; SAT I or ACT. **Final Year or Final Semester Residency Requirement:** No **Regional Accreditation:** Middle States Association of Colleges and Schools **Credit Hours For Degree:** 60 credits, Associates; 120 credits, Bachelors **Professional Accreditation:** ACEN.

CARDINAL STRITCH UNIVERSITY

6801 N Yates Rd.
Milwaukee, WI 53217-3985
Tel: (414)410-4000; Free: 800-347-8822
Fax: (414)410-4239
E-mail: admityou@stritch.edu
Web Site: www.stritch.edu
President/CEO: Dr. James P. Loftus
Admissions: Sarah C. Blake

Type: University **Sex:** Coed **Affiliation:** Roman Catholic. **Scores:** 95% SAT V 400+; 95% SAT M 400+; 62% ACT 18-23; 31% ACT 24-29 **% Accepted:** 77 **Admission Plans:** Deferred Admission **Application Deadline:** Rolling **Application Fee:** $0.00 **H.S. Requirements:** High school diploma required; GED accepted **Costs Per Year:** Application fee: $0. Comprehensive fee: $35,240 includes full-time tuition ($26,890), mandatory fees ($650), and college room and board ($7700). Full-time tuition and fees vary according to degree level and program. Room and board charges vary according to board plan and housing facility. Part-time tuition: $840 per credit. Part-time mandatory fees: $325 per term. Part-time tuition and fees vary according to course load, degree level, and program. **Scholarships:** Available. **Calendar System:** Semester, Summer session available **Enrollment:** Full-time 1,756, Graduate full-time 622, Graduate part-time 580, Part-time 219 **Faculty:** Full-time 100, Part-time 181 **Student-Faculty Ratio:** 11:1 **Exams:** Other; SAT I or ACT; SAT Reasoning; SAT Subject. **% Receiving Financial Aid:** 75 % **Residing in College-Owned, -Operated, or -Affiliated Housing:** 14 **Final Year or Final Semester Residency Requirement:** Yes **Regional Accreditation:** North Central Association of Colleges and Schools **Credit Hours For Degree:** 60 credits, Associates; 120 credits, Bachelors **Professional Accreditation:** AACN, ACBSP, ACEN, NCATE. **Intercollegiate Athletics:** Basketball M & W; Cross-Country Running M & W; Golf M & W; Soccer M & W; Softball W; Tennis M & W; Track and Field M & W; Volleyball M & W

CARROLL UNIVERSITY

100 NE Ave.
Waukesha, WI 53186-5593
Tel: (262)547-1211; Free: 800-CARROLL

Fax: (262)524-7139
E-mail: info@carrollu.edu
Web Site: www.carrollu.edu
President/CEO: Dr. Douglas N. Hastad
Admissions: James Wiseman
Financial Aid: Dawn Scott

Type: Comprehensive **Sex:** Coed **Affiliation:** Presbyterian. **Scores:** 46% ACT 18-23; 45% ACT 24-29 **% Accepted:** 79 **Admission Plans:** Deferred Admission **Application Deadline:** Rolling **Application Fee:** $0.00 **H.S. Requirements:** High school diploma required; GED accepted **Costs Per Year:** Application fee: $0. One-time mandatory fee: $270. Comprehensive fee: $38,567 includes full-time tuition ($28,825), mandatory fees ($710), and college room and board ($9032). College room only: $4766. Full-time tuition and fees vary according to program. Room and board charges vary according to board plan and housing facility. Part-time tuition: $370 per credit hour. Part-time tuition varies according to course load and program. **Scholarships:** Available. **Calendar System:** Semester, Summer session available **Enrollment:** Full-time 2,675, Graduate full-time 95, Graduate part-time 151, Part-time 464 **Faculty:** Full-time 127, Part-time 203 **Student-Faculty Ratio:** 15:1 **Exams:** ACT; SAT I or ACT; SAT Reasoning; SAT Subject. **% Receiving Financial Aid:** 79 % **Residing in College-Owned, -Operated, or -Affiliated Housing:** 52 **Regional Accreditation:** North Central Association of Colleges and Schools **Credit Hours For Degree:** 128 semester hours, Bachelors **ROTC:** Air Force, Army **Professional Accreditation:** AACN, APTA. **Intercollegiate Athletics:** Baseball M; Basketball M & W; Cross-Country Running M & W; Football M; Golf M & W; Soccer M & W; Swimming and Diving M & W; Tennis M & W; Track and Field M & W; Volleyball W

CARTHAGE COLLEGE

2001 Alford Park Dr.
Kenosha, WI 53140
Tel: (262)551-8500; Free: 800-351-4058
Fax: (262)551-5762
E-mail: admissions@carthage.edu
Web Site: www.carthage.edu
President/CEO: Dr. F. Gregory Campbell
Admissions: Bradley J. Andrews
Financial Aid: Vatistas Vatistas

Type: Comprehensive **Sex:** Coed **Affiliation:** Evangelical Lutheran Church in America. **Scores:** 99% SAT V 400+; 99% SAT M 400+; 45% ACT 18-23; 44% ACT 24-29 **% Accepted:** 77 **Admission Plans:** Deferred Admission; Early Admission; Early Decision Plan **Application Deadline:** Rolling **Application Fee:** $25.00 **H.S. Requirements:** High school diploma required; GED accepted **Scholarships:** Available. **Calendar System:** 4-1-4, Summer session available **Enrollment:** Full-time 2,233, Part-time 427 **Faculty:** Full-time 137 **Student-Faculty Ratio:** 15:1 **Exams:** SAT I or ACT. **% Receiving Financial Aid:** 75 % **Residing in College-Owned, -Operated, or -Affiliated Housing:** 68 **Regional Accreditation:** North Central Association of Colleges and Schools **Credit Hours For Degree:** 138 credit hours, Bachelors **ROTC:** Air Force, Army **Professional Accreditation:** CSWE, NASM. **Intercollegiate Athletics:** Baseball M; Basketball M & W; Bowling M & W; Cross-Country Running M & W; Football M; Golf M & W; Ice Hockey M & W; Lacrosse M & W; Soccer M & W; Softball W; Swimming and Diving M & W; Tennis M & W; Track and Field M & W; Volleyball M & W; Water Polo W

CHIPPEWA VALLEY TECHNICAL COLLEGE

620 W Clairemont Ave.
Eau Claire, WI 54701-6162
Tel: (715)833-6200; Free: 800-547-2882
Fax: (715)833-6470
E-mail: infocenter@cvtc.edu
Web Site: www.cvtc.edu
President/CEO: Bruce Barker

Type: Two-Year College **Sex:** Coed **Affiliation:** Wisconsin Technical College System. **Admission Plans:** Deferred Admission; Early Admission **Application Deadline:** Rolling **Application Fee:** $30.00 **H.S. Requirements:** High school diploma required; GED accepted. For students who demonstrate the Ability to Benefit criteria as established by the Department of Education: High school diploma or equivalent not required **Costs Per Year:** Application fee: $30. State resident tuition: $3852 full-time, $128.40 per credit part-time. Nonresident tuition: $5778 full-time, $192.60 per credit part-time. Mandatory fees: $307 full-time, $307 per year part-time. Full-time tuition and fees vary according to course load and reciprocity agreements. Part-time tuition and fees vary according to course load and reciprocity agreements. **Scholar-**

ships: Available. **Calendar System:** Semester, Summer session available **Enrollment:** Full-time 2,037, Part-time 3,980 **Faculty:** Full-time 222, Part-time 212 **Exams:** ACT; ACT essay component not used; Other. **Regional Accreditation:** North Central Association of Colleges and Schools **Credit Hours For Degree:** 60-70 credits, depending on program, Associates **Professional Accreditation:** ACEN, AHIMA, JRCEDMS, JRCERT, NAACLS.

COLLEGE OF MENOMINEE NATION

PO Box 1179
Keshena, WI 54135
Tel: (715)799-5600; Free: 800-567-2344
Fax: (715)799-1308
E-mail: tjames@menominee.edu
Web Site: www.menominee.edu
President/CEO: Dr. Verna Fowler
Admissions: Tessa James

Type: Two-Year College **Sex:** Coed **Admission Plans:** Open Admission **Application Deadline:** August 14 **Application Fee:** $10.00 **H.S. Requirements:** High school diploma required; GED accepted **Scholarships:** Available. **Calendar System:** Semester **Student-Faculty Ratio:** 16:1 **Exams:** Other. **Regional Accreditation:** North Central Association of Colleges and Schools **Credit Hours For Degree:** 62 credits, Associates **Professional Accreditation:** ACEN.

COLUMBIA COLLEGE OF NURSING

4425 N Port Washington Rd.
Glendale, WI 53212
Tel: (414)326-2330
E-mail: ewade@ccon.edu
Web Site: www.ccon.edu
President/CEO: Dr. Jill Winters
Admissions: Ericka Wade
Financial Aid: Wendy Hilvo

Type: Two-Year Upper Division **Sex:** Coed **Scores:** 62% ACT 18-23; 36% ACT 24-29 **Application Fee:** $25.00 **H.S. Requirements:** High school diploma required; GED accepted **Costs Per Year:** Application fee: $25. Tuition: $26,230 full-time, $795 per credit part-time. Mandatory fees: $1100 full-time. Part-time tuition and fees vary according to program. **Scholarships:** Available. **Calendar System:** Semester, Summer session available **Enrollment:** Full-time 154, Part-time 15 **Faculty:** Full-time 18, Part-time 3 **Student-Faculty Ratio:** 9:1 **Exams:** ACT essay component used as validity check; ACT essay component used for admission; SAT I or ACT. **% Receiving Financial Aid:** 84 **Final Year or Final Semester Residency Requirement:** No **Regional Accreditation:** North Central Association of Colleges and Schools **Credit Hours For Degree:** 124 credits, Bachelors **Professional Accreditation:** ACEN.

CONCORDIA UNIVERSITY WISCONSIN

12800 N Lake Shore Dr.
Mequon, WI 53097-2402
Tel: (262)243-5700; Free: 888-628-9472
Fax: (262)243-4351
E-mail: admission@cuw.edu
Web Site: www.cuw.edu
President/CEO: Dr. Patrick T. Ferry
Admissions: Julie Schroeder
Financial Aid: Steven P. Taylor

Type: Comprehensive **Sex:** Coed **Affiliation:** Lutheran Church–Missouri Synod; Concordia University System. **Scores:** 89% SAT V 400+; 93% SAT M 400+; 53.8% ACT 18-23; 36.7% ACT 24-29 **% Accepted:** 69 **Application Deadline:** August 15 **Application Fee:** $35.00 **H.S. Requirements:** High school diploma required; GED accepted **Costs Per Year:** Application fee: $35. Comprehensive fee: $36,710 includes full-time tuition ($26,480), mandatory fees ($260), and college room and board ($9970). Full-time tuition and fees vary according to program. Room and board charges vary according to board plan. Part-time tuition: $1119 per credit hour. Part-time tuition varies according to program. **Scholarships:** Available. **Calendar System:** 4-1-4, Summer session available **Enrollment:** Full-time 3,005, Graduate full-time 1,836, Graduate part-time 2,094, Part-time 1,333 **Faculty:** Full-time 197, Part-time 385 **Student-Faculty Ratio:** 12:1 **Exams:** SAT I or ACT. **% Receiving Financial Aid:** 79 **% Residing in College-Owned, -Operated, or -Affiliated Housing:** 58 **Regional Accreditation:** North Central Association of Colleges and Schools **Credit Hours For Degree:** 126

credit hours, Bachelors **Professional Accreditation:** AACN, AOTA, APTA, CSWE. **Intercollegiate Athletics:** Baseball M; Basketball M & W; Cross-Country Running M & W; Football M; Golf M & W; Ice Hockey M & W; Soccer M & W; Softball W; Tennis M & W; Track and Field M & W; Volleyball W; Wrestling M

EDGEWOOD COLLEGE

1000 Edgewood College Dr.
Madison, WI 53711-1997
Tel: (608)663-4861; Free: 800-444-4861
Fax: (608)663-3291
E-mail: admissions@edgewood.edu
Web Site: www.edgewood.edu
President/CEO: Dr. Scott Flanagan
Admissions: Christine Benedict
Financial Aid: Kari J. Gribble

Type: Comprehensive **Sex:** Coed **Affiliation:** Roman Catholic. **Scores:** 51% ACT 18-23; 36% ACT 24-29 **% Accepted:** 77 **Admission Plans:** Deferred Admission **Application Deadline:** August 1 **Application Fee:** $30.00 **H.S. Requirements:** High school diploma required; GED accepted. For high school students in Youth Options program: High school diploma or equivalent not required **Costs Per Year:** Application fee: $30. Comprehensive fee: $35,950 includes full-time tuition ($26,550) and college room and board ($9400). Full-time tuition varies according to degree level. Room and board charges vary according to housing facility. Part-time tuition: $835 per credit. Part-time tuition varies according to course load and degree level. **Scholarships:** Available. **Calendar System:** Semester, Summer session available **Enrollment:** Full-time 1,550, Graduate full-time 216, Graduate part-time 649, Part-time 263 **Faculty:** Full-time 159, Part-time 150 **Student-Faculty Ratio:** 10:1 **Exams:** ACT essay component not used; SAT I or ACT; SAT essay component not used; SAT Reasoning. **% Receiving Financial Aid:** 77 **% Residing in College-Owned, -Operated, or -Affiliated Housing:** 30 **Final Year or Final Semester Residency Requirement:** No **Regional Accreditation:** North Central Association of Colleges and Schools **Credit Hours For Degree:** 120 credits, Bachelors **ROTC:** Air Force, Army, Navy **Professional Accreditation:** AACN, AAMFT, ACBSP, NCATE. **Intercollegiate Athletics:** Baseball M; Basketball M & W; Cross-Country Running M & W; Golf M & W; Soccer M & W; Softball W; Tennis M & W; Track and Field M & W; Volleyball W

FOX VALLEY TECHNICAL COLLEGE

1825 N Bluemound
Appleton, WI 54912-2277
Tel: (920)735-5600; Free: 800-735-3882
Fax: (920)735-2582
Web Site: www.fvtc.edu
President/CEO: Dr. Susan A. May
Financial Aid: Stacy Doran

Type: Two-Year College **Sex:** Coed **Affiliation:** Wisconsin Technical College System. **% Accepted:** 76 **Admission Plans:** Deferred Admission; Early Admission; Open Admission **Application Deadline:** Rolling **Application Fee:** $30.00 **H.S. Requirements:** High school diploma required; GED accepted **Costs Per Year:** Application fee: $30. State resident tuition: $3852 full-time, $128.40 per credit part-time. Nonresident tuition: $5778 full-time, $192.60 per credit part-time. Mandatory fees: $520 full-time, $17.35 per credit part-time. **Scholarships:** Available. **Calendar System:** Semester, Summer session available **Enrollment:** Full-time 2,545, Part-time 8,349 **Faculty:** Full-time 319, Part-time 556 **Student-Faculty Ratio:** 11:1 **Regional Accreditation:** North Central Association of Colleges and Schools **Credit Hours For Degree:** 60 credits, Associates **Professional Accreditation:** ACEN, ACF, ADA, AOTA. **Intercollegiate Athletics:** Basketball M & W

GATEWAY TECHNICAL COLLEGE

3520 30th Ave.
Kenosha, WI 53144-1690
Tel: (262)564-2200
Fax: (262)564-2201
E-mail: admissions@gtc.edu
Web Site: www.gtc.edu
President/CEO: Dr. Bryan Albrecht
Financial Aid: Janice L. Riutta

Type: Two-Year College **Sex:** Coed **Affiliation:** Wisconsin Technical College System. **% Accepted:** 98 **Admission Plans:** Deferred Admission; Early Admission; Open Admission **Application Deadline:** Rolling **Application**

Fee: $30.00 **H.S. Requirements:** High school diploma or equivalent not required. For health occupations, law enforcement/Police Academy programs: High school diploma required; GED accepted **Costs Per Year:** Application fee: $30. State resident tuition: $4002 full-time, $130.35 per credit part-time. Nonresident tuition: $5778 full-time, $195.53 per credit part-time. Mandatory fees: $338 full-time. Full-time tuition and fees vary according to course level, course load, program, and reciprocity agreements. Part-time tuition varies according to course level, course load, program, and reciprocity agreements. **Scholarships:** Available. **Calendar System:** Semester, Summer session available **Enrollment:** Full-time 1,449, Part-time 7,291 **Faculty:** Full-time 243, Part-time 476 **Student-Faculty Ratio:** 10:1 **Final Year or Final Semester Residency Requirement:** No **Regional Accreditation:** North Central Association of Colleges and Schools **Credit Hours For Degree:** 64 Credits, Associates **Professional Accreditation:** ACEN, ADA, AHIMA, APTA, ARCST.

GLOBE UNIVERSITY–APPLETON

5045 W Grande Market Dr.
Grand Chute, WI 54913
Tel: (920)384-1100
Web Site: www.globeuniversity.edu
President/CEO: Kimberly Stevens

Type: Four-Year College **Sex:** Coed **Affiliation:** Globe Education Network (GEN). **Admission Plans:** Open Admission **Application Deadline:** Rolling **Application Fee:** $50.00 **H.S. Requirements:** High school diploma required; GED accepted **Scholarships:** Available. **Enrollment:** Full-time 189, Part-time 80 **Faculty:** Full-time 5, Part-time 22 **Exams:** Other. **Final Year or Final Semester Residency Requirement:** No **Credit Hours For Degree:** 90 quarter credits, Associates; 180 quarter credits, Bachelors **Professional Accreditation:** ACICS.

GLOBE UNIVERSITY–EAU CLAIRE

4955 Bullis Farm Rd.
Eau Claire, WI 54701-5168
Tel: (715)855-6600; Free: 377-303-6060
Web Site: www.globeuniversity.edu
President/CEO: Wesley Escondo

Type: Four-Year College **Sex:** Coed **Affiliation:** Globe Education Network (GEN). **Admission Plans:** Open Admission **Application Deadline:** Rolling **Application Fee:** $50.00 **H.S. Requirements:** High school diploma required; GED accepted **Scholarships:** Available. **Enrollment:** Full-time 161, Part-time 60 **Faculty:** Full-time 12, Part-time 24 **Exams:** Other. **Final Year or Final Semester Residency Requirement:** No **Credit Hours For Degree:** 90 quarter credits, Associates; 180 quarter credits, Bachelors **Professional Accreditation:** ACICS.

GLOBE UNIVERSITY–GREEN BAY

2620 Development Dr.
Bellevue, WI 54311
Tel: (920)264-1600
Web Site: www.globeuniversity.edu
President/CEO: Jeryl Fleck

Type: Four-Year College **Sex:** Coed **Affiliation:** Globe Education Network (GEN). **Admission Plans:** Open Admission **Application Deadline:** Rolling **Application Fee:** $50.00 **H.S. Requirements:** High school diploma required; GED accepted **Scholarships:** Available. **Enrollment:** Full-time 171, Part-time 72 **Faculty:** Full-time 13, Part-time 13 **Exams:** Other. **Final Year or Final Semester Residency Requirement:** No **Credit Hours For Degree:** 90 quarter credits, Associates; 180 quarter credits, Bachelors **Professional Accreditation:** ACICS.

GLOBE UNIVERSITY–LA CROSSE

2651 Midwest Dr.
Onalaska, WI 54650
Tel: (608)779-2600
Web Site: www.globeuniversity.edu
President/CEO: Stephanie Donovan

Type: Four-Year College **Sex:** Coed **Affiliation:** Globe Education Network (GEN). **Admission Plans:** Open Admission **Application Deadline:** Rolling **Application Fee:** $50.00 **H.S. Requirements:** High school diploma required; GED accepted **Scholarships:** Available. **Enrollment:** Full-time 194, Part-time 51 **Faculty:** Full-time 4, Part-time 31 **Exams:** Other. **Final**

Year or Final Semester Residency Requirement: No **Credit Hours For Degree:** 90 quarter credits, Associates; 180 quarter credits, Bachelors **Professional Accreditation:** ACICS.

GLOBE UNIVERSITY–MADISON EAST

4901 Eastpark Blvd.
Madison, WI 53718
Tel: (608)216-9400
Web Site: www.globeuniversity.edu
President/CEO: Rocky Klitzke

Type: Four-Year College **Sex:** Coed **Affiliation:** Globe Education Network (GEN). **Admission Plans:** Open Admission **Application Deadline:** Rolling **Application Fee:** $50.00 **H.S. Requirements:** High school diploma required; GED accepted **Scholarships:** Available. **Enrollment:** Full-time 197, Part-time 69 **Faculty:** Full-time 7, Part-time 25 **Exams:** Other. **Final Year or Final Semester Residency Requirement:** No **Credit Hours For Degree:** 90 quarter credits, Associates; 180 quarter credits, Bachelors **Professional Accreditation:** ACICS.

GLOBE UNIVERSITY–MADISON WEST

1345 Deming Way
Middleton, WI 53562
Tel: (608)830-6900
Web Site: www.globeuniversity.edu
President/CEO: Jamie Buenzli

Type: Four-Year College **Sex:** Coed **Affiliation:** Globe Education Network (GEN). **Admission Plans:** Open Admission **Application Deadline:** Rolling **Application Fee:** $50.00 **H.S. Requirements:** High school diploma required; GED accepted **Scholarships:** Available. **Enrollment:** Full-time 162, Part-time 54 **Faculty:** Full-time 8, Part-time 27 **Exams:** Other. **Final Year or Final Semester Residency Requirement:** No **Credit Hours For Degree:** 90 quarter credits, Associates; 180 quarter credits, Bachelors **Professional Accreditation:** ACICS.

GLOBE UNIVERSITY–WAUSAU

1480 Country Rd. XX
Rothschild, WI 54474
Tel: (715)301-1300
Web Site: www.globeuniversity.edu
President/CEO: Dr. Mike Kranzusch

Type: Four-Year College **Sex:** Coed **Affiliation:** Globe Education Network (GEN). **Admission Plans:** Open Admission **Application Deadline:** Rolling **Application Fee:** $50.00 **H.S. Requirements:** High school diploma required; GED accepted **Scholarships:** Available. **Enrollment:** Full-time 137, Part-time 57 **Faculty:** Full-time 9, Part-time 19 **Exams:** Other. **Final Year or Final Semester Residency Requirement:** No **Credit Hours For Degree:** 90 quarter credits, Associates; 180 quarter credits, Bachelors **Professional Accreditation:** ACICS.

HERZING UNIVERSITY (BROOKFIELD)

555 S Executive Dr.
Brookfield, WI 53005
Tel: (262)649-1710; Free: 800-596-0724
Fax: (262)797-9090
Web Site: www.herzing.edu/brookfield
President/CEO: Jackie Curtis

Type: Four-Year College **Sex:** Coed **Regional Accreditation:** North Central Association of Colleges and Schools

HERZING UNIVERSITY (KENOSHA)

4006 Washington Rd.
Kenosha, WI 53144
Tel: (262)671-0675; Free: 800-596-0724
Fax: (262)653-1434
Web Site: www.herzing.edu/kenosha
President/CEO: Jennifer Paugh

Type: Four-Year College **Sex:** Coed **Regional Accreditation:** North Central Association of Colleges and Schools

HERZING UNIVERSITY (MADISON)

5218 E Ter. Dr.
Madison, WI 53718
Tel: (608)249-6611; Free: 800-596-0724
Fax: (608)249-8593

Web Site: www.herzing.edu/madison
President/CEO: William Vinson
Type: Comprehensive **Sex:** Coed **H.S. Requirements:** High school diploma required; GED accepted **Scholarships:** Available. **Calendar System:** Semester, Summer session available **Regional Accreditation:** North Central Association of Colleges and Schools **Credit Hours For Degree:** 60 credits, Associates; 123 credits, Bachelors **Professional Accreditation:** ACBSP, ACCSC, ACEN.

HERZING UNIVERSITY ONLINE

W140N8917 Lilly Rd.
Menomonee Falls, WI 53051
Free: 866-508-0748
Web Site: www.herzingonline.edu
Type: Comprehensive **Sex:** Coed **Regional Accreditation:** North Central Association of Colleges and Schools **Professional Accreditation:** AACN.

LAC COURTE OREILLES OJIBWA COMMUNITY COLLEGE

13466 W Trepania Rd.
Hayward, WI 54843-2181
Tel: (715)634-4790; Free: 888-526-6221
Web Site: www.lco.edu
President/CEO: Dan Gretz
Admissions: Annette Wiggins
Type: Two-Year College **Sex:** Coed **% Accepted:** 100 **Admission Plans:** Early Admission; Open Admission **Application Deadline:** Rolling **Application Fee:** $10.00 **H.S. Requirements:** High school diploma required; GED accepted. For senior citizens, those who demonstrate ability to benefit from program: High school diploma required; GED not accepted **Scholarships:** Available. **Calendar System:** Semester, Summer session not available **Enrollment:** Full-time 341, Part-time 220 **Faculty:** Full-time 15, Part-time 55 **Student-Faculty Ratio:** 15:1 **Exams:** Other. **Final Year or Final Semester Residency Requirement:** No **Regional Accreditation:** North Central Association of Colleges and Schools **Credit Hours For Degree:** 64 semester hours, Associates **Professional Accreditation:** AAMAE.

LAKELAND COLLEGE

PO Box 359
Sheboygan, WI 53082-0359
Tel: (920)565-1000; Free: 800-569-2166
Fax: (920)565-1206
E-mail: admissions@lakeland.edu
Web Site: www.lakeland.edu
President/CEO: Dr. Michael Grandillo
Admissions: Nick Spaeth
Financial Aid: Patty Taylor
Type: Comprehensive **Sex:** Coed **Affiliation:** United Church of Christ. **Scores:** 63% ACT 18-23; 20% ACT 24-29 **% Accepted:** 77 **Admission Plans:** Deferred Admission **Application Deadline:** Rolling **Application Fee:** $0.00 **H.S. Requirements:** High school diploma required; GED accepted **Scholarships:** Available. **Calendar System:** Miscellaneous, Summer session available **Enrollment:** Full-time 995, Graduate full-time 111, Graduate part-time 674, Part-time 1,969 **Faculty:** Full-time 57, Part-time 14 **Student-Faculty Ratio:** 15:1 **Exams:** SAT I or ACT; SAT Reasoning. **% Receiving Financial Aid:** 81 **% Residing in College-Owned, -Operated, or -Affiliated Housing:** 67 **Regional Accreditation:** North Central Association of Colleges and Schools **Credit Hours For Degree:** 120 credits, Bachelors **Professional Accreditation:** TEAC. **Intercollegiate Athletics:** Baseball M; Basketball M & W; Cross-Country Running M & W; Football M; Golf M & W; Soccer M & W; Softball W; Tennis M & W; Track and Field M & W; Volleyball M & W; Wrestling M

LAKESHORE TECHNICAL COLLEGE

1290 N Ave.
Cleveland, WI 53015-1414
Tel: (920)693-1000; Free: 888-GO TO LTC
Fax: (920)693-1363
Web Site: www.gotoltc.com
President/CEO: Dr. Michael Lanser
Type: Two-Year College **Sex:** Coed **Affiliation:** Wisconsin Technical College System. **% Accepted:** 51 **Admission Plans:** Deferred Admission; Early Admission; Open Admission **Application Deadline:** Rolling **Application Fee:** $30.00 **H.S. Requirements:** High school diploma required; GED accepted **Scholarships:** Available. **Calendar System:** Semester, Summer

session available **Enrollment:** Full-time 702, Part-time 2,087 **Faculty:** Full-time 99, Part-time 130 **Student-Faculty Ratio:** 14:1 **Exams:** Other; SAT I or ACT. **Regional Accreditation:** North Central Association of Colleges and Schools **Credit Hours For Degree:** 64 credits, Associates **Professional Accreditation:** ACEN, ADA, JRCERT.

LAWRENCE UNIVERSITY

711 E Boldt Way
Appleton, WI 54911
Tel: (920)832-7000; Free: 800-227-0982
Fax: (920)832-6606
E-mail: excel@lawrence.edu
Web Site: www.lawrence.edu
President/CEO: Dr. Jill Beck
Admissions: Ken Anselment
Financial Aid: Sara Beth Holman
Type: Four-Year College **Sex:** Coed **Scores:** 98% SAT V 400+; 99% SAT M 400+; 7% ACT 18-23; 48% ACT 24-29 **% Accepted:** 68 **Admission Plans:** Deferred Admission; Early Admission; Early Decision Plan **H.S. Requirements:** High school diploma required; GED accepted **Costs Per Year:** Comprehensive fee: $52,950 includes full-time tuition ($43,440), mandatory fees ($300), and college room and board ($9210). College room only: $4410. Room and board charges vary according to board plan. **Scholarships:** Available. **Calendar System:** Trimester, Summer session not available **Enrollment:** Full-time 1,515, Part-time 46 **Faculty:** Full-time 166, Part-time 31 **Student-Faculty Ratio:** 9:1 **Exams:** ACT essay component not used; Other; SAT essay component not used; SAT Reasoning; SAT Subject. **% Receiving Financial Aid:** 62 **% Residing in College-Owned, -Operated, or -Affiliated Housing:** 96 **Final Year or Final Semester Residency Requirement:** Yes **Regional Accreditation:** North Central Association of Colleges and Schools **Credit Hours For Degree:** 36 courses, Bachelors **Professional Accreditation:** NASM. **Intercollegiate Athletics:** Baseball M; Basketball M & W; Crew M & W; Cross-Country Running M & W; Fencing M & W; Football M; Golf M; Ice Hockey M & W; Soccer M & W; Softball W; Swimming and Diving M & W; Tennis M & W; Track and Field M & W; Ultimate Frisbee M & W; Volleyball M & W

MADISON AREA TECHNICAL COLLEGE

1701 Wright St.
Madison, WI 53704
Tel: (608)246-6100; Free: 800-322-6282
Fax: (608)246-6880
Web Site: madisoncollege.edu
President/CEO: Jack E. Daniels, III
Admissions: Maureen Menendez
Type: Two-Year College **Sex:** Coed **Affiliation:** Wisconsin Technical College System. **Admission Plans:** Early Admission; Open Admission; Preferred Admission **Application Deadline:** July 1 **Application Fee:** $25.00 **H.S. Requirements:** High school diploma or equivalent not required. For health occupations programs: High school diploma required; GED accepted **Costs Per Year:** Application fee: $25. State resident tuition: $3852 full-time. Nonresident tuition: $5778 full-time. Mandatory fees: $365 full-time. Full-time tuition and fees vary according to course load. **Scholarships:** Available. **Calendar System:** Semester, Summer session available **Faculty:** Full-time 393, Part-time 1,488 **Exams:** ACT. **Regional Accreditation:** North Central Association of Colleges and Schools **Credit Hours For Degree:** 64 credits, Associates **Professional Accreditation:** ACEN, ACF, ADA, AOA, AOTA, CoARC, JRCERT, NAACLS. **Intercollegiate Athletics:** Baseball M; Basketball M & W; Bowling M & W; Cross-Country Running M & W; Softball W; Tennis M & W; Track and Field M & W; Volleyball M & W; Wrestling M

MADISON MEDIA INSTITUTE

2702 Agriculture Dr.
Madison, WI 53718
Tel: (608)663-2000; Free: 800-236-4997
Fax: (608)442-0141
Web Site: www.mediainstitute.edu
President/CEO: Richard Denhart
Admissions: Chris K. Hutchings
Type: Two-Year College **Sex:** Coed **Application Deadline:** Rolling **Application Fee:** $30.00 **Calendar System:** Semester **Faculty:** Full-time 20, Part-time 2 **Professional Accreditation:** ACCSC.

MARANATHA BAPTIST UNIVERSITY
745 W Main St.
Watertown, WI 53094
Tel: (920)261-9300; Free: 800-622-2947
Fax: (920)261-9109
E-mail: admissions@mbbc.edu
Web Site: www.mbu.edu
President/CEO: Dr. Marty Marriott
Admissions: Dr. James Harrison
Financial Aid: Bruce Roth
Type: Comprehensive **Sex:** Coed **Affiliation:** Baptist. **Scores:** 96% SAT V 400+; 96% SAT M 400+; 49.06% ACT 18-23; 36.32% ACT 24-29 **% Accepted:** 69 **Admission Plans:** Preferred Admission **Application Fee:** $50.00 **H.S. Requirements:** High school diploma required; GED accepted **Costs Per Year:** Application fee: $50. Comprehensive fee: $20,490 includes full-time tuition ($12,780), mandatory fees ($1160), and college room and board ($6550). Full-time tuition and fees vary according to location and program. Part-time tuition: $532 per credit hour. Part-time tuition varies according to course load. **Scholarships:** Available. **Calendar System:** Semester, Summer session available **Enrollment:** Full-time 633, Graduate full-time 21, Graduate part-time 109, Part-time 272 **Faculty:** Full-time 39, Part-time 71 **Student-Faculty Ratio:** 13:1 **Exams:** SAT I and SAT II or ACT; SAT I or ACT; SAT Reasoning; SAT Subject. **% Receiving Financial Aid:** 85 **% Residing in College-Owned, -Operated, or -Affiliated Housing:** 69 **Final Year or Final Semester Residency Requirement:** Yes **Regional Accreditation:** North Central Association of Colleges and Schools **Credit Hours For Degree:** 64 semester hours, Associates; 128 semester hours, Bachelors **ROTC:** Air Force, Army **Intercollegiate Athletics:** Baseball M; Basketball M & W; Cross-Country Running M & W; Football M; Soccer M & W; Softball W; Volleyball W; Wrestling M

MARIAN UNIVERSITY
45 S National Ave.
Fond du Lac, WI 54935-4699
Tel: (920)923-7600; Free: 800-2-MARIAN
Fax: (920)923-8755
E-mail: admission@marianuniversity.edu
Web Site: www.marianuniversity.edu
President/CEO: Robert A. Fale
Admissions: Shannon LaLuzerne
Financial Aid: Pam Warren
Type: Comprehensive **Sex:** Coed **Affiliation:** Roman Catholic. **Scores:** 53. 48% ACT 18-23; 21.25% ACT 24-29 **% Accepted:** 84 **Admission Plans:** Deferred Admission **Application Deadline:** Rolling **Application Fee:** $20.00 **H.S. Requirements:** High school diploma required; GED accepted **Costs Per Year:** Application fee: $20. One-time mandatory fee: $100. Comprehensive fee: $35,280 includes full-time tuition ($27,860), mandatory fees ($420), and college room and board ($7000). College room only: $4220. Full-time tuition and fees vary according to course load and program. Room and board charges vary according to board plan. Part-time tuition: $450 per credit hour. Part-time tuition varies according to course load and program. **Scholarships:** Available. **Calendar System:** Semester, Summer session available **Enrollment:** Full-time 1,287, Graduate full-time 44, Graduate part-time 502, Part-time 266 **Faculty:** Full-time 91, Part-time 146 **Student-Faculty Ratio:** 12:1 **Exams:** ACT; SAT I or ACT. **% Receiving Financial Aid:** 92 **% Residing in College-Owned, -Operated, or -Affiliated Housing:** 34 **Final Year or Final Semester Residency Requirement:** No **Regional Accreditation:** North Central Association of Colleges and Schools **Credit Hours For Degree:** 120 credits, Bachelors **ROTC:** Army **Professional Accreditation:** AACN, CSWE, NCATE. **Intercollegiate Athletics:** Baseball M; Basketball M & W; Cross-Country Running M & W; Golf M & W; Ice Hockey M & W; Soccer M & W; Softball W; Tennis M & W; Track and Field M & W; Volleyball M & W

MARQUETTE UNIVERSITY
PO Box 1881
Milwaukee, WI 53201-1881
Tel: (414)288-7250; Free: 800-222-6544
E-mail: admissions@marquette.edu
Web Site: www.marquette.edu
President/CEO: Dr. Michael R. Lovell, PhD
Admissions: Jean Burke
Financial Aid: Susan Teerink
Type: University **Sex:** Coed **Affiliation:** Roman Catholic (Jesuit). **Scores:** 99% SAT V 400+; 100% SAT M 400+; 17.5% ACT 18-23; 56.72% ACT 24-29 **% Accepted:** 74 **Admission Plans:** Deferred Admission **Application Deadline:** December 1 **H.S. Requirements:** High school diploma required; GED accepted **Costs Per Year:** Comprehensive fee: $49,910 includes full-time tuition ($38,000), mandatory fees ($470), and college room and board ($11,440). College room only: $7420. Full-time tuition and fees vary according to course load and program. Room and board charges vary according to housing facility. Part-time tuition: $995 per credit. Part-time tuition varies according to program. **Scholarships:** Available. **Calendar System:** Semester, Summer session available **Enrollment:** Full-time 8,002, Graduate full-time 2,103, Graduate part-time 1,054, Part-time 332 **Faculty:** Full-time 630, Part-time 522 **Student-Faculty Ratio:** 15:1 **Exams:** SAT I or ACT; SAT Reasoning; SAT Subject. **% Receiving Financial Aid:** 57 **% Residing in College-Owned, -Operated, or -Affiliated Housing:** 52 **Final Year or Final Semester Residency Requirement:** Yes **Regional Accreditation:** North Central Association of Colleges and Schools **Credit Hours For Degree:** 120 credits, Bachelors **ROTC:** Air Force, Army, Navy **Professional Accreditation:** AACN, AACSB, AALS, ABA, ABET, ACEJMC, ACNM, ADA, APA, APTA, ASHA, NAACLS, NCATE. **Intercollegiate Athletics:** Basketball M & W; Cheerleading M & W; Cross-Country Running M & W; Golf M; Lacrosse M & W; Soccer M & W; Tennis M & W; Track and Field M & W; Volleyball W

MID-STATE TECHNICAL COLLEGE
500 32nd St. N
Wisconsin Rapids, WI 54494-5599
Tel: (715)422-5300
Fax: (715)422-5345
Web Site: www.mstc.edu
President/CEO: Sue Budjac
Admissions: Carole Prochnow
Type: Two-Year College **Sex:** Coed **Affiliation:** Wisconsin Technical College System. **% Accepted:** 95 **Admission Plans:** Deferred Admission; Early Admission; Open Admission **Application Deadline:** Rolling **Application Fee:** $25.00 **H.S. Requirements:** High school diploma required; GED accepted **Scholarships:** Available. **Calendar System:** Semester, Summer session available **Faculty:** Full-time 200, Part-time 100 **Regional Accreditation:** North Central Association of Colleges and Schools **Credit Hours For Degree:** 64 credits, Associates **Professional Accreditation:** ACEN, CoARC. **Intercollegiate Athletics:** Basketball M & W; Bowling M & W; Golf M; Volleyball W

MILWAUKEE AREA TECHNICAL COLLEGE
700 W State St.
Milwaukee, WI 53233-1443
Tel: (414)297-6600
Fax: (414)297-7990
E-mail: adamss4@matc.edu
Web Site: www.matc.edu
President/CEO: Dr. Michael Burke
Admissions: Sarah Adams
Type: Two-Year College **Sex:** Coed **Affiliation:** Wisconsin Technical College System. **% Accepted:** 51 **Admission Plans:** Open Admission **Application Deadline:** Rolling **Application Fee:** $30.00 **H.S. Requirements:** High school diploma required; GED accepted **Scholarships:** Available. **Calendar System:** Semester, Summer session available **Enrollment:** Full-time 7,048, Part-time 13,167 **Faculty:** Full-time 580, Part-time 771 **Student-Faculty Ratio:** 14:1 **Exams:** Other. **Final Year or Final Semester Residency Requirement:** No **Regional Accreditation:** North Central Association of Colleges and Schools **Credit Hours For Degree:** 68 credits, Associates **Professional Accreditation:** ABFSE, ACEN, ACF, ADA, AOTA, APTA, ARCST, COA, CoARC, JRCECT, JRCERT, NAACLS. **Intercollegiate Athletics:** Baseball M; Basketball M & W; Golf M & W; Soccer M; Volleyball W

MILWAUKEE CAREER COLLEGE
3077 N Mayfair Rd.
Ste. 300
Milwaukee, WI 53222
Tel: (414)257-2939
Web Site: www.mkecc.edu
Type: Two-Year College **Sex:** Coed **Professional Accreditation:** ABHES.

MILWAUKEE INSTITUTE OF ART AND DESIGN
273 E Erie St.
Milwaukee, WI 53202-6003

Tel: (414)276-7889; Free: 888-749-MIAD
Fax: (414)291-8077
E-mail: admissions@miad.edu
Web Site: www.miad.edu
President/CEO: Neil Hoffman
Admissions: David Sigman
Financial Aid: Carol Masse
Type: Four-Year College **Sex:** Coed **% Accepted:** 60 **Admission Plans:** Deferred Admission **Application Deadline:** Rolling **Application Fee:** $25.00 **H.S. Requirements:** High school diploma required; GED accepted **Costs Per Year:** Application fee: $25. Tuition: $32,190 full-time. Mandatory fees: $1600 full-time. College room only: $7550. **Scholarships:** Available. **Calendar System:** Semester, Summer session available **Student-Faculty Ratio:** 15:1 **% Receiving Financial Aid:** 86 **Regional Accreditation:** North Central Association of Colleges and Schools **Credit Hours For Degree:** 123 credits, Bachelors **Professional Accreditation:** NASAD.

MILWAUKEE SCHOOL OF ENGINEERING
1025 N Broadway
Milwaukee, WI 53202-3109
Tel: (414)277-7300; Free: 800-332-6763
Fax: (414)277-7475
Web Site: www.msoe.edu
President/CEO: Dr. Matthew Panhans
Financial Aid: Steve Midthun
Type: Comprehensive **Sex:** Coed **Scores:** 99% SAT V 400+; 100% SAT M 400+; 8% ACT 18-23; 64% ACT 24-29 **% Accepted:** 65 **Admission Plans:** Deferred Admission **Application Deadline:** January 1 **H.S. Requirements:** High school diploma required; GED accepted **Costs Per Year:** Comprehensive fee: $46,815 includes full-time tuition ($36,270), mandatory fees ($1710), and college room and board ($8835). College room only: $5550. Full-time tuition and fees vary according to course load. Room and board charges vary according to board plan and housing facility. Part-time tuition: $630 per credit. Part-time tuition varies according to course load. **Scholarships:** Available. **Calendar System:** Quarter, Summer session available **Enrollment:** Full-time 2,546, Graduate full-time 61, Graduate part-time 166, Part-time 166 **Faculty:** Full-time 134, Part-time 131 **Student-Faculty Ratio:** 16:1 **Exams:** ACT essay component not used; SAT I or ACT; SAT essay component not used; Other; SAT Reasoning; SAT Subject. **% Receiving Financial Aid:** 76 **% Residing in College-Owned, -Operated, or -Affiliated Housing:** 39 **Final Year or Final Semester Residency Requirement:** No **Regional Accreditation:** North Central Association of Colleges and Schools **ROTC:** Air Force, Army, Navy **Professional Accreditation:** AACN, ABET, ACCE, ACPeE. **Intercollegiate Athletics:** Baseball M; Basketball M & W; Cheerleading M & W; Crew M & W; Cross-Country Running M & W; Golf M; Ice Hockey M; Lacrosse M; Soccer M & W; Softball W; Tennis M & W; Track and Field M & W; Volleyball M & W; Wrestling M

MORAINE PARK TECHNICAL COLLEGE
235 N National Ave.
Fond du Lac, WI 54936-1940
Tel: (920)922-8611; Free: 800-472-4554
Fax: (920)924-2471
E-mail: kjarvis@morainepark.edu
Web Site: www.morainepark.edu
President/CEO: Bonnie Baerwald
Admissions: Karen Jarvis
Financial Aid: Julie Waldvogel-Leitner
Type: Two-Year College **Sex:** Coed **Affiliation:** Wisconsin Technical College System. **Costs Per Year:** One-time mandatory fee: $30. State resident tuition: $3947 full-time, $128.40 per credit hour part-time. Nonresident tuition: $5920 full-time, $192.60 per credit hour part-time. Mandatory fees: $316 full-time, $10.47 per credit hour part-time. Full-time tuition and fees vary according to program. Part-time tuition and fees vary according to program. **Scholarships:** Available. **Calendar System:** Semester, Summer session available **Faculty:** Full-time 145, Part-time 125 **Exams:** ACT essay component not used; Other; SAT essay component not used. **Final Year or Final Semester Residency Requirement:** No **Regional Accreditation:** North Central Association of Colleges and Schools **Credit Hours For Degree:** 60 credits, Associates **Professional Accreditation:** ACEN, ACF, AHIMA.

MOUNT MARY UNIVERSITY
2900 N Menomonee River Pky.
Milwaukee, WI 53222-4597

Tel: (414)930-3000; Free: 800-321-6265
E-mail: mmu-admiss@mtmary.edu
Web Site: www.mtmary.edu
President/CEO: Dr. Eileen Schwalbach
Admissions: Liz Saffold
Financial Aid: Debra Duff
Type: Comprehensive **Affiliation:** Roman Catholic. **Scores:** 57% ACT 18-23; 11% ACT 24-29 **% Accepted:** 53 **Admission Plans:** Deferred Admission **Application Deadline:** Rolling **Application Fee:** $0.00 **H.S. Requirements:** High school diploma required; GED accepted **Costs Per Year:** Application fee: $0. Comprehensive fee: $34,730 includes full-time tuition ($26,230), mandatory fees ($530), and college room and board ($7970). Full-time tuition and fees vary according to degree level and program. Room and board charges vary according to board plan and housing facility. Part-time tuition: $795 per credit. Part-time mandatory fees: $330 per year. Part-time tuition and fees vary according to course load, degree level, and program. **Scholarships:** Available. **Calendar System:** Semester, Summer session available **Enrollment:** Full-time 714, Graduate full-time 319, Graduate part-time 178, Part-time 102 **Faculty:** Full-time 67, Part-time 127 **Student-Faculty Ratio:** 10:1 **Exams:** ACT essay component not used; SAT I or ACT; SAT essay component not used; SAT Reasoning; SAT Subject. **% Receiving Financial Aid:** 93 **% Residing in College-Owned, -Operated, or -Affiliated Housing:** 26 **Final Year or Final Semester Residency Requirement:** Yes **Regional Accreditation:** North Central Association of Colleges and Schools **Credit Hours For Degree:** 128 credits, Bachelors **ROTC:** Air Force **Professional Accreditation:** AND, AOTA, CIDA, CSWE. **Intercollegiate Athletics:** Basketball W; Cross-Country Running W; Golf W; Soccer W; Softball W; Tennis W; Volleyball W

NICOLET AREA TECHNICAL COLLEGE
Box 518
Rhinelander, WI 54501-0518
Tel: (715)365-4410; Free: 800-544-3039
Fax: (715)365-4445
E-mail: inquire@nicoletcollege.edu
Web Site: www.nicoletcollege.edu
President/CEO: Dr. Adrian Lorbetske
Admissions: Susan Kordula
Type: Two-Year College **Sex:** Coed **Affiliation:** Wisconsin Technical College System. **Admission Plans:** Early Admission; Open Admission; Preferred Admission **Application Deadline:** Rolling **Application Fee:** $30.00 **H.S. Requirements:** High school diploma required; GED accepted **Scholarships:** Available. **Calendar System:** Semester, Summer session available **Student-Faculty Ratio:** 16:1 **Exams:** ACT; Other. **Regional Accreditation:** North Central Association of Colleges and Schools **Credit Hours For Degree:** 64 credit hours, Associates **Professional Accreditation:** ACEN. **Intercollegiate Athletics:** Golf M & W

NORTHCENTRAL TECHNICAL COLLEGE
1000 W Campus Dr.
Wausau, WI 54401-1899
Tel: (715)675-3331
Fax: (715)675-9776
Web Site: www.ntc.edu
President/CEO: Dr. Lori Weyers
Admissions: Sarah Dillon
Type: Two-Year College **Sex:** Coed **Affiliation:** Wisconsin Technical College System. **Admission Plans:** Deferred Admission; Early Admission; Open Admission; Preferred Admission **Application Deadline:** Rolling **Application Fee:** $30.00 **H.S. Requirements:** High school diploma required; GED accepted **Costs Per Year:** Application fee: $30. State resident tuition: $4233 full-time. Nonresident tuition: $6264 full-time. Full-time tuition varies according to course level, course load, and program. **Scholarships:** Available. **Calendar System:** Semester, Summer session available **Enrollment:** Full-time 1,486, Part-time 3,027 **Student-Faculty Ratio:** 23:1 **Regional Accreditation:** North Central Association of Colleges and Schools **Credit Hours For Degree:** 64 credits, Associates **Professional Accreditation:** ACEN, ADA, JRCERT.

NORTHEAST WISCONSIN TECHNICAL COLLEGE
2740 W Mason St.
Green Bay, WI 54307-9042
Tel: (920)498-5400; Free: 888-385-6982
Web Site: www.nwtc.edu

President/CEO: H. Jeffery Rafn
Admissions: Christine Lemerande
Financial Aid: Emily A. Ysebaert
Type: Two-Year College **Sex:** Coed **Affiliation:** Wisconsin Technical College System. **Admission Plans:** Early Admission; Preferred Admission **Application Deadline:** Rolling **Application Fee:** $30.00 **H.S. Requirements:** High school diploma required; GED accepted **Scholarships:** Available. **Calendar System:** Semester, Summer session available **Regional Accreditation:** North Central Association of Colleges and Schools **Credit Hours For Degree:** 64 credits, Associates **Professional Accreditation:** ABET, ACEN, ADA, AHIMA, APTA, CoARC, NAACLS.

NORTHLAND COLLEGE

1411 Ellis Ave.
Ashland, WI 54806-3925
Tel: (715)682-1699; Free: 800-753-1040
Fax: (715)682-1258
E-mail: admit@northland.edu
Web Site: www.northland.edu
President/CEO: Dr. Michael Miller
Admissions: Teege Mettille
Financial Aid: Heather Shelly
Type: Four-Year College **Sex:** Coed **Affiliation:** United Church of Christ. **Scores:** 46.49% ACT 18-23; 36.84% ACT 24-29 **% Accepted:** 57 **Admission Plans:** Deferred Admission **Application Deadline:** Rolling **Application Fee:** $0.00 **H.S. Requirements:** High school diploma required; GED accepted **Costs Per Year:** Application fee: $0. Comprehensive fee: $41,917 includes full-time tuition ($31,980), mandatory fees ($1452), and college room and board ($8485). College room only: $3875. Full-time tuition and fees vary according to course load. Room and board charges vary according to board plan and housing facility. Part-time tuition: $620 per credit. Part-time tuition varies according to course load. **Scholarships:** Available. **Calendar System:** Miscellaneous, Summer session available **Enrollment:** Full-time 513, Part-time 28 **Faculty:** Full-time 52, Part-time 12 **Student-Faculty Ratio:** 9:1 **Exams:** ACT essay component not used; SAT I or ACT; SAT essay component not used; SAT Reasoning; SAT Subject. **% Receiving Financial Aid:** 85 **% Residing in College-Owned, -Operated, or -Affiliated Housing:** 74 **Regional Accreditation:** North Central Association of Colleges and Schools **Credit Hours For Degree:** 124 credits, Bachelors **Intercollegiate Athletics:** Baseball M; Basketball M & W; Cross-Country Running M & W; Golf M & W; Ice Hockey M & W; Lacrosse M & W; Soccer M & W; Softball W; Volleyball W

RASMUSSEN COLLEGE APPLETON

3500 E Destination Dr.
Appleton, WI 54915
Tel: (920)750-5900; Free: 888-549-6755
E-mail: susan.hammerstrom@rasmussen.edu
Web Site: www.rasmussen.edu
President/CEO: Kristi Waite
Admissions: Susan Hammerstrom
Type: Four-Year College **Sex:** Coed **Affiliation:** Rasmussen College System. **Admission Plans:** Deferred Admission; Early Admission **Application Deadline:** Rolling **Application Fee:** $0.00 **H.S. Requirements:** High school diploma required; GED accepted **Costs Per Year:** Application fee: $0. Tuition: $13,455 full-time. Mandatory fees: $1800 full-time. Full-time tuition and fees vary according to course level, course load, degree level, location, and program. Tuition guaranteed not to increase for student's term of enrollment. **Calendar System:** Quarter, Summer session available **Enrollment:** Full-time 162, Part-time 305 **Faculty:** Full-time 3, Part-time 33 **Student-Faculty Ratio:** 22:1 **Exams:** ACT essay component not used; Other; SAT essay component not used. **Final Year or Final Semester Residency Requirement:** No **Credit Hours For Degree:** 90 credits, Associates; 180 credits, Bachelors **Professional Accreditation:** ACBSP.

RASMUSSEN COLLEGE GREEN BAY

904 S Taylor St.
Ste. 100
Green Bay, WI 54303
Tel: (920)593-8400; Free: 888-549-6755
E-mail: susan.hammerstrom@rasmussen.edu
Web Site: www.rasmussen.edu
President/CEO: Kristi Waite
Admissions: Susan Hammerstrom

Type: Four-Year College **Sex:** Coed **Affiliation:** Rasmussen College System. **Admission Plans:** Deferred Admission; Early Admission **Application Deadline:** Rolling **Application Fee:** $0.00 **H.S. Requirements:** High school diploma required; GED accepted **Costs Per Year:** Application fee: $0. Tuition: $13,455 full-time. Mandatory fees: $1800 full-time. Full-time tuition and fees vary according to course level, course load, degree level, location, and program. Tuition guaranteed not to increase for student's term of enrollment. **Calendar System:** Quarter, Summer session available **Enrollment:** Full-time 190, Part-time 353 **Faculty:** Full-time 12, Part-time 41 **Student-Faculty Ratio:** 22:1 **Exams:** ACT essay component not used; Other; SAT essay component not used. **Final Year or Final Semester Residency Requirement:** No **Regional Accreditation:** North Central Association of Colleges and Schools **Credit Hours For Degree:** 90 credits, Associates; 180 credits, Bachelors **Professional Accreditation:** ACBSP.

RASMUSSEN COLLEGE WAUSAU

1101 Westwood Dr.
Wausau, WI 54401
Tel: (715)841-8000; Free: 888-549-6755
E-mail: susan.hammerstrom@rasmussen.edu
Web Site: www.rasmussen.edu
President/CEO: Kristi Waite
Admissions: Susan Hammerstrom
Type: Four-Year College **Sex:** Coed **Affiliation:** Rasmussen College System. **Admission Plans:** Deferred Admission; Early Admission **Application Deadline:** Rolling **Application Fee:** $0.00 **H.S. Requirements:** High school diploma required; GED accepted **Costs Per Year:** Application fee: $0. Tuition: $13,455 full-time. Mandatory fees: $1800 full-time. Full-time tuition and fees vary according to course level, course load, degree level, location, and program. Tuition guaranteed not to increase for student's term of enrollment. **Calendar System:** Quarter, Summer session available **Enrollment:** Full-time 158, Part-time 284 **Faculty:** Full-time 8, Part-time 40 **Student-Faculty Ratio:** 22:1 **Exams:** ACT essay component not used; Other; SAT essay component not used. **Final Year or Final Semester Residency Requirement:** No **Credit Hours For Degree:** 90 credits, Associates; 180 credits, Bachelors **Professional Accreditation:** ACBSP.

RIPON COLLEGE

300 Seward St.
Ripon, WI 54971
Tel: (920)748-8115; Free: 800-947-4766
Fax: (920)748-7243
E-mail: adminfo@ripon.edu
Web Site: www.ripon.edu
President/CEO: Dr. Zach Messitte
Financial Aid: Leigh D. Mlodzik
Type: Four-Year College **Sex:** Coed **Scores:** 99% SAT V 400+; 100% SAT M 400+; 38% ACT 18-23; 41% ACT 24-29 **% Accepted:** 66 **Admission Plans:** Deferred Admission **Application Deadline:** Rolling **Application Fee:** $30.00 **H.S. Requirements:** High school diploma required; GED accepted **Costs Per Year:** Application fee: $30. Comprehensive fee: $46,502 includes full-time tuition ($38,025), mandatory fees ($300), and college room and board ($8177). Part-time tuition: $1200 per credit. **Scholarships:** Available. **Calendar System:** Semester, Summer session not available **Enrollment:** Full-time 785, Part-time 9 **Faculty:** Full-time 64, Part-time 19 **Student-Faculty Ratio:** 11:1 **Exams:** ACT essay component not used; SAT I or ACT; SAT essay component not used. **% Receiving Financial Aid:** 81 **% Residing in College-Owned, -Operated, or -Affiliated Housing:** 89 **Final Year or Final Semester Residency Requirement:** No **Regional Accreditation:** North Central Association of Colleges and Schools **Credit Hours For Degree:** 124 credits, Bachelors **ROTC:** Army **Intercollegiate Athletics:** Baseball M; Basketball M & W; Cheerleading M & W; Cross-Country Running M & W; Football M; Rugby M & W; Soccer M & W; Softball W; Swimming and Diving M & W; Tennis M & W; Track and Field M & W; Volleyball W

ST. NORBERT COLLEGE

100 Grant St.
De Pere, WI 54115-2099
Tel: (920)337-3181; Free: 800-236-4878
Fax: (920)403-4088
E-mail: admit@snc.edu
Web Site: www.snc.edu
President/CEO: Thomas J. Kunkel
Admissions: Mark Selin

Financial Aid: Jessica Rafeld
Type: Comprehensive **Sex:** Coed **Affiliation:** Roman Catholic. **Scores:** 39% ACT 18-23; 48% ACT 24-29 **% Accepted:** 78 **Admission Plans:** Deferred Admission; Preferred Admission **Application Deadline:** Rolling **Application Fee:** $10.00 **H.S. Requirements:** High school diploma required; GED accepted **Costs Per Year:** Application fee: $10. Comprehensive fee: $43,031 includes full-time tuition ($33,622), mandatory fees ($615), and college room and board ($8794). College room only: $4695. Full-time tuition and fees vary according to course load. Room and board charges vary according to board plan and housing facility. Part-time tuition: $1051 per credit. Part-time tuition varies according to course load. **Scholarships:** Available. **Calendar System:** Semester, Summer session available **Enrollment:** Full-time 2,040, Graduate full-time 24, Graduate part-time 60, Part-time 56 **Faculty:** Full-time 136, Part-time 63 **Student-Faculty Ratio:** 14:1 **Exams:** ACT essay component used as validity check; ACT essay component used for admission; SAT I or ACT; SAT Reasoning; SAT Subject. **% Receiving Financial Aid:** 74 **% Residing in College-Owned, -Operated, or -Affiliated Housing:** 84 **Final Year or Final Semester Residency Requirement:** Yes **Regional Accreditation:** North Central Association of Colleges and Schools **Credit Hours For Degree:** 32 courses, Bachelors **ROTC:** Army **Intercollegiate Athletics:** Baseball M; Basketball M & W; Cross-Country Running M & W; Football M; Golf M & W; Ice Hockey M & W; Soccer M & W; Softball W; Tennis M & W; Track and Field M & W; Volleyball W

SILVER LAKE COLLEGE OF THE HOLY FAMILY
2406 S Alverno Rd.
Manitowoc, WI 54220-9319
Tel: (920)684-6691; Free: 800-236-4752
Fax: (920)684-7082
E-mail: jamie.grant@sl.edu
Web Site: www.sl.edu
President/CEO: Dr. Chris Domes
Admissions: Jamie Grant
Financial Aid: Michelle Leider
Type: Comprehensive **Sex:** Coed **Affiliation:** Roman Catholic. **Scores:** 23% ACT 18-23; 14% ACT 24-29 **% Accepted:** 83 **Admission Plans:** Deferred Admission **Application Deadline:** September 1 **Application Fee:** $50.00 **H.S. Requirements:** High school diploma required; GED accepted **Costs Per Year:** Application fee: $50. Comprehensive fee: $34,565 includes full-time tuition ($24,800), mandatory fees ($520), and college room and board ($9245). College room only: $5825. Full-time tuition and fees vary according to program. Room and board charges vary according to board plan and housing facility. Part-time tuition: $500 per credit. Part-time tuition and fees vary according to course load and program. **Scholarships:** Available. **Calendar System:** Semester, Summer session available **Enrollment:** Full-time 218, Graduate full-time 11, Graduate part-time 182, Part-time 218 **Faculty:** Full-time 42, Part-time 46 **Student-Faculty Ratio:** 6:1 **Exams:** ACT essay component used for advising; ACT essay component used for placement; SAT I or ACT; SAT Reasoning. **% Receiving Financial Aid:** 84 **% Residing in College-Owned, -Operated, or -Affiliated Housing:** 24 **Final Year or Final Semester Residency Requirement:** No **Regional Accreditation:** North Central Association of Colleges and Schools **Credit Hours For Degree:** 120 credits, Bachelors **Professional Accreditation:** AACN, NASM. **Intercollegiate Athletics:** Basketball M & W; Cross-Country Running M & W; Golf M & W; Soccer M & W; Volleyball W

SOUTHWEST WISCONSIN TECHNICAL COLLEGE
1800 Bronson Blvd.
Fennimore, WI 53809-9778
Tel: (608)822-3262; Free: 800-362-3322
Fax: (608)822-6019
E-mail: student-services@swtc.edu
Web Site: www.swtc.edu
President/CEO: Dr. Karen R. Knox
Type: Two-Year College **Sex:** Coed **Affiliation:** Wisconsin Technical College System. **% Accepted:** 100 **Admission Plans:** Early Admission; Open Admission; Preferred Admission **Application Deadline:** Rolling **Application Fee:** $30.00 **H.S. Requirements:** High school diploma or equivalent not required **Scholarships:** Available. **Calendar System:** Semester, Summer session available **Enrollment:** Full-time 852, Part-time 2,557 **Faculty:** Full-time 94, Part-time 18 **Student-Faculty Ratio:** 18:1 **Exams:** Other. **% Residing in College-Owned, -Operated, or -Affiliated Housing:** 3 **Final Year or Final Semester Residency Requirement:** No **Regional Accreditation:**

North Central Association of Colleges and Schools **Credit Hours For Degree:** 64 credits, Associates **Professional Accreditation:** ACEN. **Intercollegiate Athletics:** Golf M & W

UNIVERSITY OF WISCONSIN–BARABOO/SAUK COUNTY
1006 Connie Rd.
Baraboo, WI 53913-1015
Tel: (608)356-8351
Fax: (608)356-4074
E-mail: booinfo@uwc.edu
Web Site: www.baraboo.uwc.edu
Admissions: Jan Gerlach
Financial Aid: Kristin Fillhouer
Type: Two-Year College **Sex:** Coed **Affiliation:** University of Wisconsin System. **Admission Plans:** Deferred Admission; Early Admission; Preferred Admission **Application Deadline:** Rolling **Application Fee:** $35.00 **H.S. Requirements:** High school diploma required; GED accepted **Scholarships:** Available. **Calendar System:** Semester, Summer session available **Enrollment:** Full-time 354, Part-time 199 **Faculty:** Full-time 15, Part-time 27 **Student-Faculty Ratio:** 13:1 **Exams:** ACT; SAT I or ACT. **Regional Accreditation:** North Central Association of Colleges and Schools **Credit Hours For Degree:** 60 credits, Associates **Intercollegiate Athletics:** Basketball M; Golf M & W; Soccer M & W; Tennis M & W; Volleyball W

UNIVERSITY OF WISCONSIN–BARRON COUNTY
1800 College Dr.
Rice Lake, WI 54868-2497
Tel: (715)234-8176
Web Site: www.barron.uwc.edu
Financial Aid: Brittany Lueth
Type: Two-Year College **Sex:** Coed **Affiliation:** University of Wisconsin System. **Admission Plans:** Deferred Admission **Application Deadline:** September 15 **Application Fee:** $44.00 **H.S. Requirements:** High school diploma required; GED accepted **Scholarships:** Available. **Calendar System:** Semester, Summer session available **Exams:** ACT. **Regional Accreditation:** North Central Association of Colleges and Schools **Credit Hours For Degree:** 60 credits, Associates

UNIVERSITY OF WISCONSIN–EAU CLAIRE
PO Box 4004
Eau Claire, WI 54702-4004
Tel: (715)836-2637
Fax: (715)836-2380
E-mail: admissions@uwec.edu
Web Site: www.uwec.edu
President/CEO: Dr. James Schmidt
Admissions: Heather Kretz
Financial Aid: Kathleen Sahlhoff
Type: Comprehensive **Sex:** Coed **Affiliation:** University of Wisconsin System. **Scores:** 96% SAT V 400+; 96% SAT M 400+; 45.1% ACT 18-23; 46.6% ACT 24-29 **% Accepted:** 85 **Admission Plans:** Early Admission **Application Deadline:** August 25 **Application Fee:** $44.00 **H.S. Requirements:** High school diploma required; GED accepted **Costs Per Year:** Application fee: $44. State resident tuition: $7361 full-time, $307 per credit part-time. Nonresident tuition: $14,934 full-time, $622 per credit part-time. Mandatory fees: $1461 full-time, $61 per credit part-time. Full-time tuition and fees vary according to reciprocity agreements. Part-time tuition and fees vary according to reciprocity agreements. College room and board: $7322. College room only: $3910. Room and board charges vary according to board plan and housing facility. **Scholarships:** Available. **Calendar System:** Semester, Summer session available **Enrollment:** Full-time 9,165, Graduate full-time 94, Graduate part-time 472, Part-time 729 **Faculty:** Full-time 446, Part-time 79 **Student-Faculty Ratio:** 21:1 **Exams:** ACT essay component not used; SAT I or ACT; SAT essay component not used; SAT Reasoning; SAT Subject. **% Receiving Financial Aid:** 54 **% Residing in College-Owned, -Operated, or -Affiliated Housing:** 41 **Final Year or Final Semester Residency Requirement:** Yes **Regional Accreditation:** North Central Association of Colleges and Schools **Credit Hours For Degree:** 60 credits, Associates; 120 credits, Bachelors **ROTC:** Army **Professional Accreditation:** AACN, AACSB, ABET, ACEJMC, ASHA, CSWE, NASM. **Intercollegiate Athletics:** Basketball M & W; Cross-Country Running M & W; Football M; Golf M & W; Gymnastics W; Ice Hockey M & W; Soccer W; Softball W; Swimming and Diving M & W; Tennis M & W; Track and Field M & W; Volleyball W; Wrestling M

UNIVERSITY OF WISCONSIN–FOND DU LAC

400 University Dr.
Fond du Lac, WI 54935
Tel: (920)929-1100
E-mail: tom.martin@uwc.edu
Web Site: www.fdl.uwc.edu
President/CEO: Dr. Judy Goldsmith
Admissions: Tom Martin
Financial Aid: Carla Rabe

Type: Two-Year College **Sex:** Coed **Affiliation:** University of Wisconsin System. **Scores:** 73% ACT 18-23; 19% ACT 24-29 **% Accepted:** 85 **Application Deadline:** Rolling **Application Fee:** $0.00 **H.S. Requirements:** High school diploma required; GED accepted **Costs Per Year:** Application fee: $0. One-time mandatory fee: $135. State resident tuition: $5200 full-time. Nonresident tuition: $11,734 full-time. Mandatory fees: $221 full-time. Full-time tuition and fees vary according to course load and reciprocity agreements. **Scholarships:** Available. **Calendar System:** Semester, Summer session available **Faculty:** Full-time 16, Part-time 11 **Student-Faculty Ratio:** 18:1 **Exams:** SAT I or ACT. **Final Year or Final Semester Residency Requirement:** Yes **Regional Accreditation:** North Central Association of Colleges and Schools **Credit Hours For Degree:** 60 credits, Associates **Intercollegiate Athletics:** Basketball M & W; Golf M & W; Soccer M & W; Tennis M & W; Volleyball W

UNIVERSITY OF WISCONSIN–FOX VALLEY

1478 Midway Rd.
Menasha, WI 54952
Tel: (920)832-2600
Fax: (920)832-2674
E-mail: foxinfo@uwc.edu
Web Site: www.uwfox.uwc.edu
President/CEO: Dr. Martin Rudd
Admissions: Carla Rabe
Financial Aid: Carla Rabe

Type: Two-Year College **Sex:** Coed **Affiliation:** University of Wisconsin System. **Costs Per Year:** State resident tuition: $5019 full-time. Nonresident tuition: $12,002 full-time. Full-time tuition varies according to course load. **Scholarships:** Available. **Calendar System:** Semester, Summer session available **Enrollment:** Full-time 1,037, Part-time 760 **Faculty:** Full-time 31, Part-time 60 **Student-Faculty Ratio:** 20:1 **Exams:** ACT. **Final Year or Final Semester Residency Requirement:** No **Regional Accreditation:** North Central Association of Colleges and Schools **Credit Hours For Degree:** 60 credit hours, Associates **Intercollegiate Athletics:** Basketball M & W; Golf M & W; Soccer M & W; Tennis M & W; Volleyball M & W

UNIVERSITY OF WISCONSIN–GREEN BAY

2420 Nicolet Dr.
Green Bay, WI 54311-7001
Tel: (920)465-2000
Fax: (920)465-2032
E-mail: uwgb@uwgb.edu
Web Site: www.uwgb.edu
President/CEO: Dr. Gary L. Miller
Admissions: Jen Jones
Financial Aid: James Rohan

Type: Comprehensive **Sex:** Coed **Affiliation:** University of Wisconsin System. **Scores:** 54% ACT 18-23; 38% ACT 24-29 **% Accepted:** 85 **Admission Plans:** Deferred Admission **Application Deadline:** Rolling **Application Fee:** $44.00 **H.S. Requirements:** High school diploma required; GED accepted **Costs Per Year:** Application fee: $44. One-time mandatory fee: $212. State resident tuition: $6298 full-time, $262 per credit part-time. Nonresident tuition: $13,871 full-time, $578 per credit part-time. Mandatory fees: $1526 full-time, $57 per credit part-time. Full-time tuition and fees vary according to course load and reciprocity agreements. Part-time tuition and fees vary according to reciprocity agreements. College room and board: $7270. College room only: $4138. Room and board charges vary according to board plan and housing facility. **Scholarships:** Available. **Calendar System:** Semester, Summer session available **Enrollment:** Full-time 4,007, Graduate full-time 58, Graduate part-time 193, Part-time 2,521 **Faculty:** Full-time 187, Part-time 134 **Student-Faculty Ratio:** 21:1 **Exams:** SAT I or ACT. **% Receiving Financial Aid:** 63 **% Residing in College-Owned, -Operated, or -Affiliated Housing:** 33 **Final Year or Final Semester Residency Requirement:** No **Regional Accreditation:** North Central Association of Colleges and Schools **Credit Hours For Degree:** 60 credits, Associates;

120 credits, Bachelors **ROTC:** Army **Professional Accreditation:** AACN, AND, CSWE, NASM. **Intercollegiate Athletics:** Basketball M & W; Cross-Country Running M & W; Golf M & W; Skiing (Cross-Country) M & W; Soccer M & W; Softball W; Swimming and Diving M & W; Tennis M & W; Volleyball W

UNIVERSITY OF WISCONSIN–LA CROSSE

1725 State St.
La Crosse, WI 54601-3742
Tel: (608)785-8000
Fax: (608)785-6695
E-mail: admissions@uwlax.edu
Web Site: www.uwlax.edu
President/CEO: Dr. Joe Gow
Admissions: Corey Sjoquist
Financial Aid: Louise Janke

Type: Comprehensive **Sex:** Coed **Affiliation:** University of Wisconsin System. **Scores:** 100% SAT V 400+; 100% SAT M 400+; 36% ACT 18-23; 58% ACT 24-29 **% Accepted:** 80 **Application Deadline:** Rolling **Application Fee:** $44.00 **H.S. Requirements:** High school diploma required; GED accepted **Costs Per Year:** Application fee: $44. State resident tuition: $7,585 full-time. Nonresident tuition: $15,536 full-time. Mandatory fees: $1247 full-time. College room and board: $5850. College room only: $3500. Room and board charges vary according to board plan and housing facility. **Scholarships:** Available. **Calendar System:** Semester, Summer session available **Enrollment:** Full-time 9,163, Graduate full-time 437, Graduate part-time 321, Part-time 466 **Faculty:** Full-time 522, Part-time 94 **Student-Faculty Ratio:** 18:1 **Exams:** ACT essay component not used; SAT I or ACT; SAT essay component not used. **% Receiving Financial Aid:** 51 **% Residing in College-Owned, -Operated, or -Affiliated Housing:** 37 **Final Year or Final Semester Residency Requirement:** Yes **Regional Accreditation:** North Central Association of Colleges and Schools **Credit Hours For Degree:** 60 credits, Associates; 120 credits, Bachelors **ROTC:** Army **Professional Accreditation:** AACSB, AANA, AOTA, APTA, CEPH, JRCAT, JRCERT, NAACLS, NASM, NCATE, NRPA. **Intercollegiate Athletics:** Baseball M; Basketball M & W; Cross-Country Running M & W; Football M; Gymnastics W; Soccer W; Softball W; Swimming and Diving M & W; Tennis M & W; Track and Field M & W; Volleyball W; Wrestling M

UNIVERSITY OF WISCONSIN–MADISON

500 Lincoln Dr.
Madison, WI 53706-1380
Tel: (608)262-1234
Fax: (608)262-1429
E-mail: onwisconsin@admissions.wisc.edu
Web Site: www.wisc.edu
President/CEO: Dr. Rebecca M. Blank

Type: University **Sex:** Coed **Affiliation:** University of Wisconsin System. **Scores:** 100% SAT V 400+; 100% SAT M 400+; 5% ACT 18-23; 53.5% ACT 24-29 **% Accepted:** 49 **Admission Plans:** Deferred Admission **Application Deadline:** February 1 **Application Fee:** $50.00 **H.S. Requirements:** High school diploma required; GED accepted **Costs Per Year:** Application fee: $50. State resident tuition: $9,273 full-time, $386.39 per credit hour part-time. Nonresident tuition: $28,523 full-time, $1,188.46 per credit hour part-time. Mandatory fees: $1,142 full-time, $94.35 per credit hour part-time. Full-time tuition and fees vary according to program and reciprocity agreements. Part-time tuition and fees vary according to course load, program, and reciprocity agreements. College room and board: $8804. Room and board charges vary according to board plan and housing facility. **Scholarships:** Available. **Calendar System:** Semester, Summer session available **Enrollment:** Full-time 28,569, Graduate full-time 9,775, Graduate part-time 1,952, Part-time 3,093 **Faculty:** Full-time 2,443, Part-time 453 **Student-Faculty Ratio:** 17:1 **Exams:** ACT essay component used for admission; SAT I or ACT; SAT essay component used for admission; SAT Reasoning; SAT Subject. **% Receiving Financial Aid:** 36 **% Residing in College-Owned, -Operated, or -Affiliated Housing:** 25 **Final Year or Final Semester Residency Requirement:** Yes **Regional Accreditation:** North Central Association of Colleges and Schools **Credit Hours For Degree:** 120 semester hours, Bachelors **ROTC:** Air Force, Army, Navy **Professional Accreditation:** AACN, AACSB, AAFCS, AALS, ABA, ABET, ACPE, ACSP, ALA, AND, AOTA, APA, APTA, ASC, ASHA, ASLA, AVMA, CAHME, CIDA, CORE, CSWE, JRCAT, LCME/AMA, NAACLS, NASAD, NASM, NAST, SAF. **Intercollegiate Athletics:** Basketball M & W; Cheerleading M & W; Crew M & W; Cross-Country Running M & W; Fencing M & W; Football M; Golf M &

W; Ice Hockey M & W; Lacrosse M & W; Racquetball M & W; Rugby M & W; Sailing M & W; Soccer M & W; Softball W; Swimming and Diving M & W; Tennis M & W; Track and Field M & W; Ultimate Frisbee M & W; Volleyball M & W; Water Polo M & W; Wrestling M

UNIVERSITY OF WISCONSIN–MANITOWOC
705 Viebahn St.
Manitowoc, WI 54220-6699
Tel: (920)683-4700
Fax: (920)683-4776
E-mail: christopher.lewis@uwc.edu
Web Site: www.manitowoc.uwc.edu
President/CEO: Dr. Daniel Campagna
Admissions: Dr. Christopher Lewis
Financial Aid: Carla Rabe
Type: Two-Year College **Sex:** Coed **Affiliation:** University of Wisconsin System. **% Accepted:** 100 **Admission Plans:** Deferred Admission; Early Admission **Application Deadline:** September 1 **Application Fee:** $35.00 **H.S. Requirements:** High school diploma required; GED accepted **Scholarships:** Available. **Calendar System:** Semester **Enrollment:** Full-time 596 **Faculty:** Full-time 22, Part-time 18 **Student-Faculty Ratio:** 24:1 **Exams:** SAT I or ACT. **Regional Accreditation:** North Central Association of Colleges and Schools **Credit Hours For Degree:** 60 credits, Associates **Intercollegiate Athletics:** Basketball M & W; Golf M & W; Tennis M & W; Volleyball W

UNIVERSITY OF WISCONSIN–MARATHON COUNTY
518 S Seventh Ave.
Wausau, WI 54401-5396
Tel: (715)261-6100; Free: 888-367-8962
Fax: (715)261-6333
Web Site: www.uwmc.uwc.edu
Admissions: Dr. Nolan Beck
Financial Aid: Cindy Bailey
Type: Two-Year College **Sex:** Coed **Affiliation:** University of Wisconsin System. **Admission Plans:** Deferred Admission; Early Admission **Application Fee:** $44.00 **H.S. Requirements:** High school diploma required; GED accepted **Scholarships:** Available. **Calendar System:** Semester, Summer session available **Exams:** ACT. **Regional Accreditation:** North Central Association of Colleges and Schools **Credit Hours For Degree:** 60 credits, Associates **ROTC:** Army

UNIVERSITY OF WISCONSIN–MARINETTE
750 W Bay Shore
Marinette, WI 54143-4299
Tel: (715)735-4300
E-mail: cynthia.bailey@uwc.edu
Web Site: www.marinette.uwc.edu
Admissions: Cynthia M. Bailey
Financial Aid: Cindy Bailey
Type: Two-Year College **Sex:** Coed **Affiliation:** University of Wisconsin System. **Admission Plans:** Open Admission **Application Deadline:** Rolling **Application Fee:** $35.00 **H.S. Requirements:** High school diploma required; GED accepted **Scholarships:** Available. **Calendar System:** Semester, Summer session available **Enrollment:** Full-time 462 **Faculty:** Full-time 18, Part-time 13 **Student-Faculty Ratio:** 15:1 **Exams:** SAT I or ACT. **Regional Accreditation:** North Central Association of Colleges and Schools **Credit Hours For Degree:** 60 credits, Associates **Intercollegiate Athletics:** Basketball M & W; Volleyball W

UNIVERSITY OF WISCONSIN–MARSHFIELD/WOOD COUNTY
2000 W 5th St.
Marshfield, WI 54449
Tel: (715)389-6500
Web Site: marshfield.uwc.edu
Admissions: Brittany Lueth
Financial Aid: Brittany Lueth
Type: Two-Year College **Sex:** Coed **Affiliation:** University of Wisconsin System. **Scores:** 75% ACT 18-23; 15% ACT 24-29 **% Accepted:** 93 **Admission Plans:** Deferred Admission; Early Admission **Application Deadline:** Rolling **Application Fee:** $35.00 **H.S. Requirements:** High school diploma required; GED accepted **Costs Per Year:** Application fee: $35. State resident tuition: $2,571 full-time, $197.93 per credit part-time. Nonresident tuition: $6,063 full-time, $488.92 per credit part-time. Mandatory fees: $196

full-time, $5.22 per credit part-time, $5.22. Full-time tuition and fees vary according to degree level and reciprocity agreements. Part-time tuition and fees vary according to course load and degree level. College room only: $4800. **Scholarships:** Available. **Calendar System:** Semester, Summer session available **Faculty:** Full-time 13, Part-time 23 **Student-Faculty Ratio:** 17:1 **Exams:** SAT I or ACT. **Regional Accreditation:** North Central Association of Colleges and Schools **Credit Hours For Degree:** 60 credits, Associates **ROTC:** Army **Intercollegiate Athletics:** Basketball M & W; Golf M & W; Tennis M & W; Volleyball W

UNIVERSITY OF WISCONSIN–MILWAUKEE
PO Box 413
Milwaukee, WI 53201-0413
Tel: (414)229-1122
Fax: (414)229-6940
E-mail: uwmlook@uwm.edu
Web Site: www.uwm.edu
President/CEO: Dr. Mark Mone
Admissions: Brian Troyer
Financial Aid: Tim Opgenorth
Type: University **Sex:** Coed **Affiliation:** University of Wisconsin System. **Scores:** 54.9% ACT 18-23; 31.2% ACT 24-29 **% Accepted:** 73 **Admission Plans:** Deferred Admission **Application Deadline:** Rolling **H.S. Requirements:** High school diploma required; GED accepted **Costs Per Year:** State resident tuition: $8091 full-time, $337.13 per credit part-time. Nonresident tuition: $18,265 full-time, $761.04 per credit part-time. Mandatory fees: $1337 full-time, $1337 per year part-time. Full-time tuition and fees vary according to course load, degree level, location, program, and reciprocity agreements. Part-time tuition and fees vary according to course load, degree level, location, program, and reciprocity agreements. College room and board: $10,030. College room only: $6290. Room and board charges vary according to board plan, housing facility, and location. **Scholarships:** Available. **Calendar System:** Semester, Summer session available **Enrollment:** Full-time 18,284, Graduate full-time 2,638, Graduate part-time 2,187, Part-time 4,000 **Faculty:** Full-time 1,062, Part-time 476 **Student-Faculty Ratio:** 19:1 **Exams:** ACT essay component not used; Other; SAT I or ACT; SAT essay component not used; SAT Reasoning. **% Receiving Financial Aid:** 67 **% Residing in College-Owned, -Operated, or -Affiliated Housing:** 19 **Final Year or Final Semester Residency Requirement:** No **Regional Accreditation:** North Central Association of Colleges and Schools **Credit Hours For Degree:** 120 credit hours, Bachelors **ROTC:** Air Force, Army, Navy **Professional Accreditation:** AACN, AACSB, ABET, ACSP, AHIMA, ALA, AOTA, APA, APTA, ASHA, CSWE, NAAB, NAACLS, NASD, NASM. **Intercollegiate Athletics:** Baseball M; Basketball M & W; Bowling M & W; Cross-Country Running M & W; Equestrian Sports M & W; Football M & W; Ice Hockey M & W; Lacrosse M & W; Rugby M & W; Sailing M & W; Soccer M & W; Swimming and Diving M & W; Tennis W; Track and Field M & W; Ultimate Frisbee M & W; Volleyball M & W

UNIVERSITY OF WISCONSIN–OSHKOSH
800 Algoma Blvd.
Oshkosh, WI 54901
Tel: (920)424-1234
Fax: (920)424-1098
E-mail: oshadmuw@uwosh.edu
Web Site: www.uwosh.edu
President/CEO: Dr. Andrew Leavitt
Financial Aid: Stacy Drews
Type: Comprehensive **Sex:** Coed **Affiliation:** University of Wisconsin System. **Scores:** 62.1% ACT 18-23; 30.6% ACT 24-29 **% Accepted:** 68 **Admission Plans:** Deferred Admission **Application Fee:** $44.00 **H.S. Requirements:** High school diploma required; GED accepted **Scholarships:** Available. **Calendar System:** Semester, Summer session available **Enrollment:** Full-time 9,020, Graduate full-time 186, Graduate part-time 1,031, Part-time 4,174 **Faculty:** Full-time 431, Part-time 197 **Student-Faculty Ratio:** 22:1 **Exams:** ACT; ACT essay component not used; SAT essay component not used; SAT Reasoning. **% Receiving Financial Aid:** 54 **% Residing in College-Owned, -Operated, or -Affiliated Housing:** 32 **Regional Accreditation:** North Central Association of Colleges and Schools **Credit Hours For Degree:** 60 credits, Associates; 120 credits, Bachelors **ROTC:** Army **Professional Accreditation:** AACN, AACSB, ABET, ACA, ACEJMC, CSWE, NASM. **Intercollegiate Athletics:** Baseball M; Basketball M & W; Cross-Country Running M & W; Football M; Golf W; Gymnastics W;

Riflery M & W; Soccer M & W; Softball W; Swimming and Diving M & W; Tennis M & W; Track and Field M & W; Volleyball W; Wrestling M

UNIVERSITY OF WISCONSIN–PARKSIDE

900 Wood Rd., Box 2000
Kenosha, WI 53141-2000
Tel: (262)595-2345
Fax: (262)595-2630
E-mail: moldenht@uwp.edu
Web Site: www.uwp.edu
President/CEO: Dr. Deborah Ford
Admissions: Troy Moldenhauer
Financial Aid: Kristina Klemens
Type: Comprehensive **Sex:** Coed **Affiliation:** University of Wisconsin System. **Scores:** 59.87% ACT 18-23; 21.41% ACT 24-29 **% Accepted:** 75 **Application Deadline:** August 1 **Application Fee:** $44.00 **H.S. Requirements:** High school diploma required; GED accepted **Costs Per Year:** Application fee: $44. One-time mandatory fee: $140. State resident tuition: $6298 full-time, $262.43 per credit part-time. Nonresident tuition: $14,287 full-time, $595.31 per credit part-time. Mandatory fees: $1183 full-time. Full-time tuition and fees vary according to course load, degree level, program, and reciprocity agreements. Part-time tuition varies according to course load, degree level, program, and reciprocity agreements. College room and board: $7712. College room only: $4494. Room and board charges vary according to board plan and housing facility. **Scholarships:** Available. **Calendar System:** Semester, Summer session available **Enrollment:** Full-time 3,272, Graduate full-time 27, Graduate part-time 115, Part-time 1,028 **Faculty:** Full-time 169, Part-time 53 **Student-Faculty Ratio:** 20:1 **Exams:** ACT essay component not used; SAT I or ACT; SAT essay component not used. **% Receiving Financial Aid:** 67 **% Residing in College-Owned, -Operated, or -Affiliated Housing:** 18 **Final Year or Final Semester Residency Requirement:** No **Regional Accreditation:** North Central Association of Colleges and Schools **Credit Hours For Degree:** 120 credits, Bachelors **ROTC:** Air Force, Army **Professional Accreditation:** AACSB. **Intercollegiate Athletics:** Baseball M; Basketball M & W; Cross-Country Running M & W; Golf M; Soccer M & W; Softball W; Track and Field M & W; Volleyball W; Wrestling M

UNIVERSITY OF WISCONSIN–PLATTEVILLE

1 University Plz.
Platteville, WI 53818-3099
Tel: (608)342-1491; Free: 800-362-5515
E-mail: rulea@uwplatt.edu
Web Site: www.uwplatt.edu
President/CEO: Dr. Dennis J. Shields
Admissions: Angela Udelhofen
Financial Aid: Elizabeth Tucker
Type: Comprehensive **Sex:** Coed **Affiliation:** University of Wisconsin System. **Scores:** 49.11% ACT 18-23; 41.52% ACT 24-29 **Costs Per Year:** State resident tuition: $6298 full-time, $267 per credit hour part-time. Nonresident tuition: $14,149 full-time, $595 per credit hour part-time. Mandatory fees: $1190 full-time, $49.58 per credit hour part-time. Full-time tuition and fees vary according to course load, degree level, and reciprocity agreements. Part-time tuition and fees vary according to course load, degree level, and reciprocity agreements. College room and board: $7160. College room only: $3970. Room and board charges vary according to board plan and housing facility. **Scholarships:** Available. **Calendar System:** Semester, Summer session available **Enrollment:** Full-time 7,109, Graduate full-time 87, Graduate part-time 880, Part-time 869 **Faculty:** Full-time 347, Part-time 79 **Student-Faculty Ratio:** 21:1 **Exams:** ACT essay component not used; SAT I or ACT; SAT essay component not used. **% Receiving Financial Aid:** 51 **% Residing in College-Owned, -Operated, or -Affiliated Housing:** 47 **Regional Accreditation:** North Central Association of Colleges and Schools **Credit Hours For Degree:** 64 credits, Associates; 120 credits, Bachelors **ROTC:** Army **Professional Accreditation:** ABET, ATMAE, NASM, NCATE. **Intercollegiate Athletics:** Baseball M; Basketball M & W; Bowling M & W; Cheerleading M & W; Cross-Country Running M & W; Football M; Golf W; Ice Hockey M & W; Lacrosse M & W; Rugby M & W; Soccer M & W; Softball W; Track and Field M & W; Ultimate Frisbee M & W; Volleyball M & W; Wrestling M

UNIVERSITY OF WISCONSIN–RICHLAND

1200 Hwy. 14 W
Richland Center, WI 53581

Tel: (608)647-6186
Fax: (608)647-6225
E-mail: john.poole@uwc.edu
Web Site: richland.uwc.edu
President/CEO: Dr. Patrick Glen Hagen
Admissions: John D. Poole
Financial Aid: Kristin Fillhouer
Type: Two-Year College **Sex:** Coed **Affiliation:** University of Wisconsin System. **Application Deadline:** Rolling **Application Fee:** $44.00 **H.S. Requirements:** High school diploma required; GED accepted **Scholarships:** Available. **Calendar System:** Semester, Summer session available **Enrollment:** Full-time 291, Part-time 228 **Faculty:** Full-time 13, Part-time 18 **Student-Faculty Ratio:** 17:1 **Exams:** ACT; SAT I or ACT. **Regional Accreditation:** North Central Association of Colleges and Schools **Credit Hours For Degree:** 60 credits, Associates **Intercollegiate Athletics:** Basketball M & W; Volleyball W

UNIVERSITY OF WISCONSIN–RIVER FALLS

410 S Third St.
River Falls, WI 54022
Tel: (715)425-3911
Fax: (715)425-0678
E-mail: admit@uwrf.edu
Web Site: www.uwrf.edu
President/CEO: Dean Van Galen
Admissions: Sarah Egerstrom
Financial Aid: Robert Bode
Type: Comprehensive **Sex:** Coed **Affiliation:** University of Wisconsin System. **Scores:** 80% SAT V 400+; 90% SAT M 400+; 57.03% ACT 18-23; 32.84% ACT 24-29 **% Accepted:** 90 **Admission Plans:** Deferred Admission **Application Fee:** $44.00 **H.S. Requirements:** High school diploma required; GED accepted **Costs Per Year:** Application fee: $44. State resident tuition: $6428 full-time, $267.85 per credit hour part-time. Nonresident tuition: $14,001 full-time, $583.39 per credit hour part-time. Mandatory fees: $1509 full-time, $160.53 per credit hour part-time. Full-time tuition and fees vary according to course load, degree level, and reciprocity agreements. Part-time tuition and fees vary according to course load, degree level, and reciprocity agreements. College room and board: $7674. Room and board charges vary according to board plan and housing facility. **Scholarships:** Available. **Calendar System:** Semester, Summer session available **Enrollment:** Full-time 4,917, Graduate full-time 164, Graduate part-time 287, Part-time 590 **Faculty:** Full-time 199, Part-time 94 **Student-Faculty Ratio:** 23:1 **Exams:** ACT; ACT essay component not used; SAT I or ACT; SAT essay component not used; SAT Reasoning. **% Receiving Financial Aid:** 61 **% Residing in College-Owned, -Operated, or -Affiliated Housing:** 42 **Final Year or Final Semester Residency Requirement:** No **Regional Accreditation:** North Central Association of Colleges and Schools **Credit Hours For Degree:** 120 semester credits, Bachelors **ROTC:** Army **Professional Accreditation:** AACSB, ACEJMC, ASHA, CSWE, NASM, NCATE. **Intercollegiate Athletics:** Badminton M & W; Baseball M; Basketball M & W; Cross-Country Running M & W; Equestrian Sports M & W; Football M; Golf W; Ice Hockey M & W; Lacrosse M & W; Racquetball M & W; Rock Climbing M & W; Rugby M & W; Skiing (Cross-Country) M & W; Soccer W; Softball W; Tennis W; Track and Field M & W; Volleyball M & W; Wrestling M

UNIVERSITY OF WISCONSIN–ROCK COUNTY

2909 Kellogg Ave.
Janesville, WI 53546-5699
Tel: (608)758-6565; Free: 888-INFO-UWC
Fax: (608)758-6564
Web Site: rock.uwc.edu
Financial Aid: Kristin Fillhouer
Type: Two-Year College **Sex:** Coed **Affiliation:** University of Wisconsin System. **Admission Plans:** Deferred Admission **Application Deadline:** Rolling **Application Fee:** $44.00 **H.S. Requirements:** High school diploma required; GED accepted **Scholarships:** Available. **Calendar System:** Semester, Summer session available **Exams:** ACT. **Regional Accreditation:** North Central Association of Colleges and Schools **Credit Hours For Degree:** 60 credits, Associates

UNIVERSITY OF WISCONSIN–SHEBOYGAN

One University Dr.
Sheboygan, WI 53081-4789

Tel: (920)459-6600
Fax: (920)459-6602
E-mail: elisa.carr@uwc.edu
Web Site: www.sheboygan.uwc.edu
Admissions: Elisa Carr
Financial Aid: Courtney O'Connell

Type: Two-Year College **Sex:** Coed **Affiliation:** University of Wisconsin System. **% Accepted:** 100 **Admission Plans:** Open Admission **Application Deadline:** Rolling **Application Fee:** $44.00 **H.S. Requirements:** High school diploma required; GED accepted **Costs Per Year:** Application fee: $44. State resident tuition: $4,750 full-time, $197.93 per credit part-time. Nonresident tuition: $11,737 full-time, $488.92 per credit part-time. Mandatory fees: $354 full-time, $14.75 per credit part-time. Full-time tuition and fees vary according to course load. Part-time tuition and fees vary according to course load. **Scholarships:** Available. **Calendar System:** Semester, Summer session available **Enrollment:** Full-time 305, Part-time 464 **Faculty:** Full-time 17 **Student-Faculty Ratio:** 16:1 **Exams:** ACT essay component not used; SAT I or ACT; SAT essay component not used. **Regional Accreditation:** North Central Association of Colleges and Schools **Credit Hours For Degree:** 60 credit hours, Associates **Intercollegiate Athletics:** Basketball M; Golf M & W; Soccer M & W; Tennis M & W; Volleyball W

UNIVERSITY OF WISCONSIN–STEVENS POINT

2100 Main St.
Stevens Point, WI 54481-3897
Tel: (715)346-0123
Fax: (715)346-2561
E-mail: bjordan@uwsp.edu
Web Site: www.uwsp.edu
President/CEO: Dr. Bernie Patterson
Admissions: William Jordan
Financial Aid: Mandy Slowinski

Type: Comprehensive **Sex:** Coed **Affiliation:** University of Wisconsin System. **Scores:** 76% SAT V 400+; 83% SAT M 400+; 60% ACT 18-23; 32% ACT 24-29 **% Accepted:** 74 **Admission Plans:** Deferred Admission **Application Deadline:** Rolling **Application Fee:** $44.00 **H.S. Requirements:** High school diploma required; GED accepted **Costs Per Year:** Application fee: $44. State resident tuition: $7674 full-time, $378.79 per credit part-time. Nonresident tuition: $15,940 full-time, $723.23 per credit part-time. Full-time tuition varies according to course load, program, and reciprocity agreements. Part-time tuition varies according to course load, program, and reciprocity agreements. College room and board: $6828. College room only: $4098. Room and board charges vary according to board plan and housing facility. **Scholarships:** Available. **Calendar System:** Semester, Summer session available **Enrollment:** Full-time 8,172, Graduate full-time 69, Graduate part-time 323, Part-time 667 **Faculty:** Full-time 369 **Student-Faculty Ratio:** 21:1 **Exams:** ACT essay component not used; SAT I or ACT; SAT essay component not used. **% Receiving Financial Aid:** 60 **% Residing in College-Owned, -Operated, or -Affiliated Housing:** 26 **Final Year or Final Semester Residency Requirement:** No **Regional Accreditation:** North Central Association of Colleges and Schools **Credit Hours For Degree:** 60 credits, Associates; 120 credits, Bachelors **ROTC:** Army **Professional Accreditation:** ABET, ASHA, CIDA, NAACLS, NASAD, NASD, NASM, NAST, SAF. **Intercollegiate Athletics:** Baseball M; Basketball M & W; Cross-Country Running M & W; Football M; Golf W; Ice Hockey M & W; Soccer W; Softball W; Swimming and Diving M & W; Tennis W; Track and Field M & W; Volleyball W; Wrestling M

UNIVERSITY OF WISCONSIN–STOUT

Menomonie, WI 54751
Tel: (715)232-1122; Free: 800-HI-STOUT
Fax: (715)232-1667
E-mail: admissions@uwstout.edu
Web Site: www.uwstout.edu
President/CEO: Dr. Charles W. Sorensen
Admissions: Dr. Pamela Holsinger-Fuchs
Financial Aid: Beth Boisen

Type: Comprehensive **Sex:** Coed **Affiliation:** University of Wisconsin System. **Scores:** 58.6% ACT 18-23; 29.2% ACT 24-29 **% Accepted:** 84 **Application Deadline:** Rolling **Application Fee:** $44.00 **H.S. Requirements:** High school diploma required; GED accepted **Costs Per Year:** Application fee: $44. State resident tuition: $7014 full-time, $234 per credit hour part-time. Nonresident tuition: $14,760 full-time, $492 per credit hour part-time.

Mandatory fees: $2189 full-time. Full-time tuition and fees vary according to degree level and reciprocity agreements. Part-time tuition varies according to degree level and reciprocity agreements. College room and board: $6504. College room only: $3960. Room and board charges vary according to board plan and housing facility. **Scholarships:** Available. **Calendar System:** 4-1-4, Summer session available **Enrollment:** Full-time 6,841, Graduate full-time 288, Graduate part-time 859, Part-time 1,547 **Faculty:** Full-time 392, Part-time 93 **Student-Faculty Ratio:** 18:1 **Exams:** ACT essay component not used; SAT I or ACT; SAT essay component not used. **% Receiving Financial Aid:** 55 **% Residing in College-Owned, -Operated, or -Affiliated Housing:** 40 **Regional Accreditation:** North Central Association of Colleges and Schools **Credit Hours For Degree:** 124 credits, Bachelors **ROTC:** Air Force, Army **Professional Accreditation:** AAMFT, ABET, ACA, ACBSP, ACCE, AND, ATMAE, CIDA, CORE, NASAD, NCATE. **Intercollegiate Athletics:** Baseball M; Basketball M & W; Cross-Country Running M & W; Football M; Gymnastics W; Ice Hockey M & W; Soccer M & W; Softball W; Tennis W; Track and Field M & W; Volleyball M & W

UNIVERSITY OF WISCONSIN–SUPERIOR

Belknap and Catlin
Superior, WI 54880-4500
Tel: (715)394-8101
Fax: (715)394-8407
E-mail: admissions@uwsuper.edu
Web Site: www.uwsuper.edu
President/CEO: Dr. Renee Wachter
Financial Aid: Tammi Reijo

Type: Comprehensive **Sex:** Coed **Affiliation:** University of Wisconsin System. **Scores:** 64.46% ACT 18-23; 20.21% ACT 24-29 **% Accepted:** 72 **Admission Plans:** Deferred Admission; Early Admission **Application Deadline:** August 1 **Application Fee:** $44.00 **H.S. Requirements:** High school diploma required; GED accepted **Costs Per Year:** Application fee: $44. State resident tuition: $6,535 full-time, $272.31 per credit hour part-time. Nonresident tuition: $14,108 full-time, $587.85 per credit hour part-time. Mandatory fees: $1501 full-time. Full-time tuition and fees vary according to course load and reciprocity agreements. Part-time tuition varies according to course load and reciprocity agreements. College room and board: $6410. College room only: $3490. Room and board charges vary according to board plan and housing facility. **Scholarships:** Available. **Calendar System:** Semester, Summer session available **Enrollment:** Full-time 1,869, Graduate full-time 53, Graduate part-time 74, Part-time 493 **Faculty:** Full-time 123, Part-time 78 **Student-Faculty Ratio:** 14:1 **Exams:** ACT essay component not used; SAT I or ACT; SAT essay component not used; SAT Reasoning; SAT Subject. **% Receiving Financial Aid:** 64 **% Residing in College-Owned, -Operated, or -Affiliated Housing:** 33 **Final Year or Final Semester Residency Requirement:** No **Regional Accreditation:** North Central Association of Colleges and Schools **Credit Hours For Degree:** 60 credits, Associates; 120 credits, Bachelors **ROTC:** Air Force **Professional Accreditation:** ACA, CSWE, NASM. **Intercollegiate Athletics:** Baseball M; Basketball M & W; Cross-Country Running M & W; Ice Hockey M & W; Soccer M & W; Softball W; Track and Field M & W; Volleyball W

UNIVERSITY OF WISCONSIN–WASHINGTON COUNTY

400 University Dr.
West Bend, WI 53095-3699
Tel: (262)335-5200
Fax: (262)335-5257
E-mail: dan.cibrario@uwc.edu
Web Site: www.washington.uwc.edu
Admissions: Dan Cebrario
Financial Aid: Courtney O'Connell

Type: Two-Year College **Sex:** Coed **Affiliation:** University of Wisconsin System. **% Accepted:** 67 **Admission Plans:** Deferred Admission **Application Deadline:** Rolling **Application Fee:** $35.00 **H.S. Requirements:** High school diploma required; GED accepted **Scholarships:** Available. **Calendar System:** Semester, Summer session available **Enrollment:** Full-time 663, Part-time 288 **Faculty:** Full-time 29, Part-time 23 **Student-Faculty Ratio:** 21:1 **Exams:** ACT. **Regional Accreditation:** North Central Association of Colleges and Schools **Credit Hours For Degree:** 60 credits, Associates **Intercollegiate Athletics:** Basketball M & W; Golf M & W; Soccer M & W; Tennis M & W; Volleyball W

UNIVERSITY OF WISCONSIN–WAUKESHA

1500 N University Dr.
Waukesha, WI 53188-2799

Tel: (262)521-5200
Fax: (414)521-5491
E-mail: deborah.kusick@uwc.edu
Web Site: www.waukesha.uwc.edu
President/CEO: Dean Harry Muir
Admissions: Deb Kusick
Financial Aid: Courtney O'Connell
Type: Two-Year College **Sex:** Coed **Affiliation:** University of Wisconsin System. **Admission Plans:** Deferred Admission; Early Admission **Application Deadline:** Rolling **Application Fee:** $44.00 **H.S. Requirements:** High school diploma required; GED accepted **Costs Per Year:** Application fee: $44. State resident tuition: $5091 full-time, $215 per credit part-time. Nonresident tuition: $12,072 full-time, $506 per credit part-time. Mandatory fees: $230 full-time. Full-time tuition and fees vary according to course load. Part-time tuition varies according to course load. **Scholarships:** Available. **Calendar System:** Semester, Summer session available **Enrollment:** Full-time 1,069, Part-time 1,170 **Faculty:** Full-time 64, Part-time 29 **Student-Faculty Ratio:** 24:1 **Exams:** ACT essay component used for admission; SAT I or ACT; SAT essay component used for admission; SAT Reasoning; SAT Subject. **Final Year or Final Semester Residency Requirement:** No **Regional Accreditation:** North Central Association of Colleges and Schools **Credit Hours For Degree:** 60 credits, Associates; 120 credits, Bachelors **Intercollegiate Athletics:** Basketball M & W; Golf M & W; Soccer M & W; Tennis M & W; Volleyball W

UNIVERSITY OF WISCONSIN–WHITEWATER

800 W Main St.
Whitewater, WI 53190-1790
Tel: (262)472-1234
Fax: (262)472-1515
E-mail: registrar@uww.edu
Web Site: www.uww.edu
President/CEO: Dr. Beverly Kopper, PhD
Admissions: Jodi Hare
Financial Aid: Carol Miller
Type: Comprehensive **Sex:** Coed **Affiliation:** University of Wisconsin System. **Scores:** 88% SAT V 400+; 55.23% ACT 18-23; 35.64% ACT 24-29 **% Accepted:** 68 **Admission Plans:** Deferred Admission **Application Deadline:** May 1 **Application Fee:** $44.00 **H.S. Requirements:** High school diploma required; GED accepted **Costs Per Year:** Application fee: $44. State resident tuition: $6519 full-time, $262 per credit hour part-time. Nonresident tuition: $14,092 full-time, $578 per credit hour part-time. Mandatory fees: $1081 full-time. Full-time tuition and fees vary according to course load, degree level, and reciprocity agreements. College room and board: $7082. Room and board charges vary according to board plan and housing facility. **Scholarships:** Available. **Calendar System:** Semester, Summer session available **Enrollment:** Full-time 9,963, Graduate full-time 404, Graduate part-time 805, Part-time 1,179 **Faculty:** Full-time 473, Part-time 118 **Student-Faculty Ratio:** 22:1 **Exams:** ACT essay component not used; SAT I or ACT; SAT essay component not used; SAT Reasoning; SAT Subject. **% Receiving Financial Aid:** 51 **% Residing in College-Owned, -Operated, or -Affiliated Housing:** 40 **Final Year or Final Semester Residency Requirement:** No **Regional Accreditation:** North Central Association of Colleges and Schools **Credit Hours For Degree:** 60 credits, Associates; 120 credits, Bachelors **ROTC:** Air Force, Army **Professional Accreditation:** AACSB, ACA, ASHA, CSWE, NASAD, NASM, NAST, NCATE. **Intercollegiate Athletics:** Archery M & W; Baseball M; Basketball M & W; Bowling M & W; Cheerleading M & W; Cross-Country Running M & W; Football M; Golf M & W; Gymnastics M & W; Ice Hockey M & W; Lacrosse M; Rugby M & W; Soccer M & W; Softball W; Swimming and Diving M & W; Tennis M & W; Track and Field M & W; Volleyball M & W; Water Polo M & W; Weight Lifting M & W; Wrestling M

VITERBO UNIVERSITY

900 Viterbo Dr.
La Crosse, WI 54601-4797
Tel: (608)796-3000; Free: 800-VITERBO
Fax: (608)796-3050
E-mail: admission@viterbo.edu
Web Site: www.viterbo.edu
President/CEO: Dr. Richard Artman
Admissions: Eric Schmidt
Financial Aid: Terry Norman
Type: Comprehensive **Sex:** Coed **Affiliation:** Roman Catholic. **Scores:**

54% ACT 18-23; 39% ACT 24-29 **% Accepted:** 66 **Admission Plans:** Deferred Admission **Application Deadline:** August 15 **Application Fee:** $25.00 **H.S. Requirements:** High school diploma required; GED accepted **Costs Per Year:** Application fee: $25. Comprehensive fee: $34,660 includes full-time tuition ($25,460), mandatory fees ($690), and college room and board ($8510). College room only: $3760. Full-time tuition and fees vary according to program. Room and board charges vary according to board plan and housing facility. **Scholarships:** Available. **Calendar System:** Semester **Enrollment:** Full-time 1,465, Graduate full-time 402, Graduate part-time 484, Part-time 405 **Faculty:** Full-time 122, Part-time 198 **Student-Faculty Ratio:** 12:1 **Exams:** ACT essay component used for admission; ACT essay component used for advising; ACT essay component used for placement; SAT I or ACT; SAT essay component used for admission; SAT essay component used for advising; SAT essay component used for placement. **% Receiving Financial Aid:** 80 **% Residing in College-Owned, -Operated, or -Affiliated Housing:** 24 **Regional Accreditation:** North Central Association of Colleges and Schools **Credit Hours For Degree:** 128 credits, Bachelors **ROTC:** Army **Professional Accreditation:** AACN, ACA, ACBSP, AND, NASM, NCATE. **Intercollegiate Athletics:** Baseball M; Basketball M & W; Bowling M & W; Cross-Country Running M & W; Golf M & W; Soccer M & W; Softball W; Track and Field M & W; Volleyball W

WAUKESHA COUNTY TECHNICAL COLLEGE

800 Main St.
Pewaukee, WI 53072-4601
Tel: (262)691-5566
Fax: (262)691-5693
E-mail: kkazda@wctc.edu
Web Site: www.wctc.edu
President/CEO: Kaylen Betzig
Admissions: Kathleen Kazda
Financial Aid: Timothy K. Jacobson
Type: Two-Year College **Sex:** Coed **Affiliation:** Wisconsin Technical College System. **Admission Plans:** Open Admission **Application Deadline:** Rolling **Application Fee:** $30.00 **H.S. Requirements:** High school diploma or equivalent not required **Costs Per Year:** Application fee: $30. State resident tuition: $3852 full-time, $128.40 per credit hour part-time. Nonresident tuition: $5778 full-time, $192.60 per credit hour part-time. Mandatory fees: $231 full-time, $7.70 per credit hour part-time. Full-time tuition and fees vary according to program. Part-time tuition and fees vary according to program. **Scholarships:** Available. **Calendar System:** Semester, Summer session available **Enrollment:** Full-time 1,679, Part-time 6,249 **Faculty:** Full-time 196, Part-time 668 **Student-Faculty Ratio:** 18:1 **Regional Accreditation:** North Central Association of Colleges and Schools **Credit Hours For Degree:** 66 credits, Associates **Professional Accreditation:** ABET, ACEN, ACF, ADA, ARCST.

WESTERN TECHNICAL COLLEGE

304 6th St. N
La Crosse, WI 54602-0908
Tel: (608)785-9200; Free: 800-322-9982
Fax: (608)785-9205
E-mail: mildes@wwtc.edu
Web Site: www.westerntc.edu
President/CEO: J. Lee Rasch, EdD
Admissions: Jane Wells
Type: Two-Year College **Sex:** Coed **Affiliation:** Wisconsin Technical College System. **% Accepted:** 35 **Admission Plans:** Early Admission; Open Admission **Application Deadline:** Rolling **Application Fee:** $30.00 **H.S. Requirements:** High school diploma required; GED accepted **Scholarships:** Available. **Calendar System:** Semester, Summer session available **Enrollment:** Full-time 1,910, Part-time 2,855 **Faculty:** Full-time 203, Part-time 685 **Student-Faculty Ratio:** 7:1 **Exams:** ACT; Other. **% Residing in College-Owned, -Operated, or -Affiliated Housing:** 2 **Regional Accreditation:** North Central Association of Colleges and Schools **Credit Hours For Degree:** 68 credit hours, Associates **Professional Accreditation:** ACEN, ADA, AHIMA, AOTA, APTA, CoARC, JRCEND, JRCERT, NAACLS. **Intercollegiate Athletics:** Baseball M; Basketball M & W; Volleyball W

WISCONSIN INDIANHEAD TECHNICAL COLLEGE

505 Pine Ridge Dr.
Shell Lake, WI 54871
Tel: (715)468-2815; Free: 800-243-9482
Fax: (715)468-2819

E-mail: steve.bitzer@witc.edu
Web Site: www.witc.edu
President/CEO: John Will
Admissions: Steve Bitzer
Type: Two-Year College **Sex:** Coed **Affiliation:** Wisconsin Technical College System. **Admission Plans:** Open Admission **Application Deadline:** Rolling **Application Fee:** $30.00 **Costs Per Year:** Application fee: $30. State resident tuition: $3852 full-time, $128.40 per credit part-time. Nonresident tuition: $5778 full-time, $192.60 per credit part-time. Mandatory fees: $408 full-time. Full-time tuition and fees vary according to course load, program, and reciprocity agreements. Part-time tuition varies according to course load, program, and reciprocity agreements. **Calendar System:** Semester **Enrollment:** Full-time 1,142, Part-time 1,752 **Faculty:** Full-time 178, Part-time 195 **Student-Faculty Ratio:** 17:1 **Final Year or Final Semester Residency Requirement:** No **Regional Accreditation:** North Central Association of Colleges and Schools **Professional Accreditation:** ACEN, AOTA.

WISCONSIN LUTHERAN COLLEGE
8800 W Bluemound Rd.
Milwaukee, WI 53226-9942
Tel: (414)443-8800

Fax: (414)443-8514
E-mail: cameron.teske@wlc.edu
Web Site: www.wlc.edu
President/CEO: Dr. Daniel W. Johnson
Admissions: Cameron Teske
Financial Aid: Linda Loeffel
Type: Comprehensive **Sex:** Coed **Affiliation:** Wisconsin Evangelical Lutheran Synod. **Scores:** 45% ACT 18-23; 43% ACT 24-29 **% Accepted:** 64 **Admission Plans:** Deferred Admission **Application Fee:** $0.00 **H.S. Requirements:** High school diploma required; GED accepted **Scholarships:** Available. **Calendar System:** Semester, Summer session available **Enrollment:** Full-time 1,002, Graduate full-time 9, Graduate part-time 99, Part-time 68 **Faculty:** Full-time 65, Part-time 86 **Student-Faculty Ratio:** 11:1 **Exams:** ACT essay component not used; SAT I or ACT; SAT essay component not used. **% Receiving Financial Aid:** 80 **% Residing in College-Owned, -Operated, or -Affiliated Housing:** 60 **Final Year or Final Semester Residency Requirement:** No **Regional Accreditation:** North Central Association of Colleges and Schools **Credit Hours For Degree:** 128 credits, Bachelors **ROTC:** Air Force **Intercollegiate Athletics:** Baseball M; Basketball M & W; Cross-Country Running M & W; Football M; Golf M & W; Soccer M & W; Softball W; Tennis M & W; Track and Field M & W; Volleyball W

CASPER COLLEGE

125 College Dr.
Casper, WY 82601-4699
Tel: (307)268-2110; Free: 800-442-2963
Fax: (307)268-2682
E-mail: kfoltz@caspercollege.edu
Web Site: www.caspercollege.edu
President/CEO: Dr. Darren Divine
Admissions: Kyla Foltz

Type: Two-Year College **Sex:** Coed **Scores:** 58% ACT 18-23; 17% ACT 24-29 **% Accepted:** 100 **Admission Plans:** Early Admission; Open Admission **Application Deadline:** August 15 **Application Fee:** $0.00 **H.S. Requirements:** High school diploma required; GED accepted **Costs Per Year:** Application fee: $0. State resident tuition: $1992 full-time, $83 per credit part-time. Nonresident tuition: $5976 full-time, $249 per credit part-time. Mandatory fees: $648 full-time, $27 per credit part-time. Part-time tuition and fees vary according to course load. College room and board: $6294. Room and board charges vary according to board plan and housing facility. **Scholarships:** Available. **Calendar System:** Semester, Summer session available **Enrollment:** Full-time 1,719, Part-time 1,961 **Faculty:** Full-time 148, Part-time 110 **Student-Faculty Ratio:** 13:1 **% Residing in College-Owned, -Operated, or -Affiliated Housing:** 10 **Final Year or Final Semester Residency Requirement:** Yes **Regional Accreditation:** North Central Association of Colleges and Schools **Credit Hours For Degree:** 64 credit hours, Associates **Professional Accreditation:** ACBSP, ACEN, AOTA, JRCERT, NASAD, NASM, NAST. **Intercollegiate Athletics:** Basketball M & W; Equestrian Sports M & W; Volleyball W

CENTRAL WYOMING COLLEGE

2660 Peck Ave.
Riverton, WY 82501-2273
Tel: (307)855-2000; Free: 800-735-8418
Fax: (307)855-2092
E-mail: admit@cwc.edu
Web Site: www.cwc.edu
President/CEO: Dr. Cristobal Valdez
Admissions: Deborah Graham
Financial Aid: Scott McFarland

Type: Two-Year College **Sex:** Coed **Affiliation:** Wyoming Community College Commission. **Scores:** 79% SAT V 400+; 79% SAT M 400+; 53% ACT 18-23; 17% ACT 24-29 **% Accepted:** 100 **Admission Plans:** Deferred Admission; Early Admission; Open Admission **Application Deadline:** Rolling **Application Fee:** $0.00 **H.S. Requirements:** High school diploma or equivalent not required **Costs Per Year:** Application fee: $0. State resident tuition: $1992 full-time, $83 per credit part-time. Nonresident tuition: $5976 full-time, $249 per credit part-time. Mandatory fees: $720 full-time, $30 per credit part-time. Full-time tuition and fees vary according to course load, program, and reciprocity agreements. Part-time tuition and fees vary according to course load, program, and reciprocity agreements. College room and board: $5130. College room only: $2530. Room and board charges vary according to board plan and housing facility. **Scholarships:** Available. **Calendar System:** Semester, Summer session available **Enrollment:** Full-time 727, Part-time 1,459 **Faculty:** Full-time 58, Part-time 140 **Student-Faculty Ratio:** 12:1 **% Residing in College-Owned, -Operated, or -Affiliated Housing:** 10 **Final Year or Final Semester Residency Requirement:** No **Regional Accreditation:** North Central Association of Colleges

and Schools **Credit Hours For Degree:** 64 credits, Associates **Professional Accreditation:** ACEN, ARCST. **Intercollegiate Athletics:** Basketball M & W; Cross-Country Running M & W; Equestrian Sports M & W; Golf M & W; Volleyball W

COLLEGEAMERICA–CHEYENNE

6101 Yellowstone Rd.
Cheyenne, WY 82009
Tel: (307)632-7048
Web Site: www.collegeamerica.edu
Type: Four-Year College **Sex:** Coed **Professional Accreditation:** ACCSC.

EASTERN WYOMING COLLEGE

3200 W C St.
Torrington, WY 82240-1699
Tel: (307)532-8200; Free: 866-327-8996
Fax: (307)532-8222
E-mail: rex.cogdill@ewc.wy.edu
Web Site: www.ewc.wy.edu
President/CEO: Dr. Richard L. Patterson
Admissions: Dr. Rex Cogdill
Financial Aid: Susan N. Stephenson

Type: Two-Year College **Sex:** Coed **Affiliation:** Wyoming Community College Commission. **Costs Per Year:** State resident tuition: $1992 full-time, $83 per credit part-time. Nonresident tuition: $5976 full-time, $249 per credit part-time. Mandatory fees: $648 full-time, $27 per credit part-time. Full-time tuition and fees vary according to course load, location, and program. Part-time tuition and fees vary according to course load, location, and program. College room and board: $6136. College room only: $3292. Room and board charges vary according to housing facility. **Scholarships:** Available. **Calendar System:** Semester, Summer session available **Enrollment:** Full-time 571, Part-time 1,144 **Faculty:** Full-time 40, Part-time 28 **Student-Faculty Ratio:** 21:1 **Exams:** ACT. **Regional Accreditation:** North Central Association of Colleges and Schools **Credit Hours For Degree:** 60 credit hours, Associates **Intercollegiate Athletics:** Basketball M & W; Equestrian Sports M & W; Golf M; Volleyball W

LARAMIE COUNTY COMMUNITY COLLEGE

1400 E College Dr.
Cheyenne, WY 82007-3299
Tel: (307)778-5222; Free: 800-522-2993
Fax: (307)778-1399
E-mail: learnmore@lccc.wy.edu
Web Site: www.lccc.wy.edu
President/CEO: Dr. Joseph Schaffer
Admissions: Holly Bruegman
Financial Aid: Julie Wilson

Type: Two-Year College **Sex:** Coed **Affiliation:** Wyoming Community College Commission. **Scores:** 54.89% ACT 18-23; 19.15% ACT 24-29 **% Accepted:** 100 **Admission Plans:** Deferred Admission; Open Admission **Application Fee:** $0.00 **H.S. Requirements:** High school diploma required; GED accepted **Costs Per Year:** Application fee: $0. State resident tuition: $1992 full-time, $83 per credit hour part-time. Nonresident tuition: $5976 full-time, $249 per credit hour part-time. Mandatory fees: $1152 full-time. Part-time tuition varies according to course load. College room and board: $7988.

Room and board charges vary according to housing facility. **Scholarships:** Available. **Calendar System:** Semester, Summer session available **Enrollment:** Full-time 1,800, Part-time 2,348 **Faculty:** Full-time 110, Part-time 196 **Student-Faculty Ratio:** 14:1 **Exams:** ACT essay component not used; SAT essay component not used. **% Residing in College-Owned, -Operated, or -Affiliated Housing:** 13 **Regional Accreditation:** North Central Association of Colleges and Schools **Credit Hours For Degree:** 64 credit hours, Associates **ROTC:** Air Force, Army **Professional Accreditation:** ACEN, ADA, JRCERT. **Intercollegiate Athletics:** Basketball M; Cheerleading M & W; Equestrian Sports M & W; Soccer M & W; Volleyball W

NORTHWEST COLLEGE
231 W 6th St.
Powell, WY 82435-1898
Tel: (307)754-6000; Free: 800-560-4692
Fax: (307)754-6700
E-mail: west.hernandez@nwc.edu
Web Site: www.nwc.edu
President/CEO: Dr. Stefani Hicswa
Admissions: West Hernandez
Financial Aid: Marianne Harrison

Type: Two-Year College **Sex:** Coed **Affiliation:** Wyoming Community College System. **Admission Plans:** Open Admission **Application Deadline:** Rolling **Application Fee:** $0.00 **H.S. Requirements:** High school diploma required; GED accepted **Costs Per Year:** Application fee: $0. State resident tuition: $1992 full-time, $83 per credit hour part-time. Nonresident tuition: $5976 full-time, $249 per credit hour part-time. Mandatory fees: $797 full-time, $26 per credit hour part-time. Full-time tuition and fees vary according to course load, location, and program. Part-time tuition and fees vary according to course load, location, and program. College room and board: $5198. Room and board charges vary according to board plan and housing facility. **Scholarships:** Available. **Calendar System:** Semester, Summer session available **Enrollment:** Full-time 976, Part-time 721 **Faculty:** Full-time 77, Part-time 69 **Student-Faculty Ratio:** 12:1 **Exams:** ACT essay component not used; Other; SAT I or ACT; SAT essay component not used. **Final Year or Final Semester Residency Requirement:** No **Regional Accreditation:** North Central Association of Colleges and Schools **Credit Hours For Degree:** 64 credits, Associates **Professional Accreditation:** ACEN, NASM. **Intercollegiate Athletics:** Basketball M & W; Equestrian Sports M & W; Soccer M & W; Volleyball W; Wrestling M

SHERIDAN COLLEGE
3059 Coffeen Ave.
Sheridan, WY 82801-1500
Tel: (307)674-6446; Free: 800-913-9139
Fax: (307)674-7205
E-mail: madams@sheridan.edu
Web Site: www.sheridan.edu
President/CEO: Dr. Paul Young
Admissions: Matt Adams
Financial Aid: Randy Thompson

Type: Two-Year College **Sex:** Coed **Affiliation:** Wyoming Community College Commission. **Admission Plans:** Deferred Admission; Early Admission; Open Admission **Application Deadline:** Rolling **Application Fee:** $0.00 **H.S. Requirements:** High school diploma or equivalent not required **Costs Per Year:** Application fee: $0. State resident tuition: $1992 full-time, $83 per credit part-time. Nonresident tuition: $5976 full-time, $249 per credit part-time. Mandatory fees: $960 full-time, $32 per hour part-time. Full-time tuition and fees vary according to course load, location, and reciprocity agreements. Part-time tuition and fees vary according to location and reciprocity agreements. College room and board: $6170. Room and board charges vary according to board plan, housing facility, and location. **Scholarships:** Available. **Calendar System:** Semester, Summer session available **Enrollment:** Full-time 1,398, Part-time 2,909 **Faculty:** Full-time 99, Part-time 118 **Student-Faculty Ratio:** 17:1 **Exams:** ACT essay component not used; SAT essay component not used. **% Residing in College-Owned, -Operated, or -Affiliated Housing:** 10 **Final Year or Final Semester Residency Requirement:** No **Regional Accreditation:** North Central Association of Colleges and Schools **Credit Hours For Degree:** 60 credit hours, Associates **Professional Accreditation:** ACEN, ADA. **Intercollegiate Athletics:** Basketball M & W; Cross-Country Running M & W; Equestrian Sports M & W; Soccer M & W; Volleyball W

UNIVERSITY OF WYOMING
1000 E University Ave.
Laramie, WY 82071
Tel: (307)766-1121; Free: 800-342-5996
Fax: (307)766-2271
E-mail: admissions@uwyo.edu
Web Site: www.uwyo.edu
President/CEO: Dr. Richard McGinity, CD
Admissions: Ryan Goeken
Financial Aid: Kathy Bobbitt

Type: University **Sex:** Coed **Scores:** 93% SAT V 400+; 96% SAT M 400+; 35.8% ACT 18-23; 48.9% ACT 24-29 **% Accepted:** 96 **Admission Plans:** Deferred Admission **Application Deadline:** August 10 **Application Fee:** $40.00 **H.S. Requirements:** High school diploma required; GED accepted **Costs Per Year:** Application fee: $40. One-time mandatory fee: $40. State resident tuition: $3570 full-time, $119 per credit hour part-time. Nonresident tuition: $14,310 full-time, $477 per credit hour part-time. Mandatory fees: $1,322 full-time, $317.56 per term part-time. Full-time tuition and fees vary according to course load, location, and reciprocity agreements. Part-time tuition and fees vary according to course load, location, and reciprocity agreements. College room and board: $10,037. College room only: $4310. Room and board charges vary according to board plan and housing facility. **Scholarships:** Available. **Calendar System:** Semester, Summer session available **Enrollment:** Full-time 8,394, Graduate full-time 1,555, Graduate part-time 1,048, Part-time 1,651 **Faculty:** Full-time 754, Part-time 65 **Student-Faculty Ratio:** 14:1 **Exams:** ACT essay component not used; SAT I or ACT; SAT essay component not used; SAT Reasoning. **% Receiving Financial Aid:** 45 **% Residing in College-Owned, -Operated, or -Affiliated Housing:** 24 **Final Year or Final Semester Residency Requirement:** No **Regional Accreditation:** North Central Association of Colleges and Schools **Credit Hours For Degree:** 120 semester hours, Bachelors **ROTC:** Air Force, Army **Professional Accreditation:** AACN, AACSB, AAFCS, AALS, ABA, ABET, ACA, ACPE, APA, ASHA, CSWE, NASM, NCATE. **Intercollegiate Athletics:** Badminton M & W; Baseball M; Basketball M & W; Cross-Country Running M & W; Equestrian Sports M & W; Fencing M & W; Football M; Golf M & W; Ice Hockey M & W; Lacrosse M & W; Racquetball M & W; Riflery M & W; Rugby M & W; Skiing (Cross-Country) M & W; Skiing (Downhill) M & W; Soccer M & W; Softball W; Swimming and Diving M & W; Tennis M & W; Track and Field M & W; Ultimate Frisbee M & W; Volleyball W; Water Polo M; Wrestling M

WESTERN WYOMING COMMUNITY COLLEGE
PO Box 428
Rock Springs, WY 82902-0428
Tel: (307)382-1600; Free: 800-226-1181
Fax: (307)382-1636
E-mail: admissions@wwcc.wy.edu
Web Site: www.wwcc.wy.edu
President/CEO: Dr. Karla Leach
Admissions: Erin M. Grey

Type: Two-Year College **Sex:** Coed **Admission Plans:** Deferred Admission; Early Admission; Open Admission **Application Deadline:** Rolling **Application Fee:** $0.00 **H.S. Requirements:** High school diploma required; GED accepted **Costs Per Year:** Application fee: $0. State resident tuition: $996 full-time, $83 per credit hour part-time. Nonresident tuition: $2988 full-time, $249 per credit hour part-time. Mandatory fees: $204 full-time, $18 per credit hour part-time, $18. **Scholarships:** Available. **Calendar System:** Semester, Summer session available **Enrollment:** Full-time 1,154, Part-time 2,139 **Faculty:** Full-time 79, Part-time 234 **Student-Faculty Ratio:** 16:1 **Exams:** SAT I or ACT. **% Residing in College-Owned, -Operated, or -Affiliated Housing:** 41 **Final Year or Final Semester Residency Requirement:** No **Regional Accreditation:** North Central Association of Colleges and Schools **Credit Hours For Degree:** 64 credit hours, Associates **Professional Accreditation:** ACEN, CoARC. **Intercollegiate Athletics:** Basketball M & W; Cheerleading M & W; Soccer M & W; Volleyball W; Wrestling M

WYOTECH LARAMIE
4373 N Third St.
Laramie, WY 82072-9519
Tel: (307)742-3776; Free: 888-577-7559
Web Site: www.wyotech.edu
President/CEO: W. Guy Warpness

Type: Two-Year College **Sex:** Coed **Affiliation:** Zenith Education Group. **Admission Plans:** Open Admission **Application Deadline:** Rolling **Application Fee:** $100.00 **H.S. Requirements:** High school diploma required; GED accepted **Scholarships:** Available. **Calendar System:** Miscellaneous **Student-Faculty Ratio:** 13:1 **Credit Hours For Degree:** 1500 hours, Associates **Professional Accreditation:** ACCSC.

American Samoa

AMERICAN SAMOA COMMUNITY COLLEGE

PO Box 2609
Pago Pago, AS 96799-2609
Tel: (684)699-9155
Fax: (684)699-6259
Web Site: www.amsamoa.edu
President/CEO: Dr. Seth Galea'i
Admissions: Elizabeth Leuma
Financial Aid: Peteru Kitiona Lam Yuen
Type: Two-Year College **Sex:** Coed **Scores:** 47% SAT V 400+; 59% SAT M 400+ **% Accepted:** 100 **Admission Plans:** Deferred Admission; Early Admission; Open Admission **Application Deadline:** Rolling **Application Fee:** $0.00 **H.S. Requirements:** High school diploma required; GED accepted **Costs Per Year:** Application fee: $0. Territory resident tuition: $3300 full-time, $110 per credit part-time. Nonresident tuition: $3600 full-time, $120 per credit part-time. Mandatory fees: $250 full-time, $120 per term part-time. Full-time tuition and fees vary according to course load. Part-time tuition and fees vary according to course load. **Scholarships:** Available. **Calendar System:** Semester, Summer session available **Enrollment:** Full-time 705, Part-time 580 **Faculty:** Full-time 64, Part-time 18 **Student-Faculty Ratio:** 20:1 **Exams:** ACT; ACT essay component used for placement; SAT I; SAT I and SAT II or ACT; SAT I or ACT; SAT II; SAT essay component used for placement; SAT Reasoning; SAT Subject. **Final Year or Final Semester Residency Requirement:** No **Regional Accreditation:** Western Association of Colleges and Schools **Credit Hours For Degree:** 60 credits, Associates; 127 credits, Bachelors **ROTC:** Army

Guam

GUAM COMMUNITY COLLEGE

1 Sesame St.
Mangilao, GU 96913
Tel: (671)735-5531
Fax: (671)734-5238
E-mail: patrick.clymer@guamcc.edu
Web Site: www.guamcc.edu
President/CEO: Dr. Mary A.Y. Okada
Admissions: Patrick L. Clymer
Type: Two-Year College **Sex:** Coed **% Accepted:** 100 **Admission Plans:** Early Admission; Open Admission **Application Deadline:** Rolling **Application Fee:** $0.00 **H.S. Requirements:** High school diploma required; GED accepted. For Some adult applicants: High school diploma or equivalent not required **Costs Per Year:** Application fee: $0. Territory resident tuition: $3120 full-time, $130 per credit hour part-time. Nonresident tuition: $3720 full-time, $155 per credit hour part-time. Mandatory fees: $294 full-time, $147 per term part-time. **Scholarships:** Available. **Calendar System:** Semester, Summer session available **Enrollment:** Full-time 989, Part-time 1,469 **Faculty:** Full-time 115, Part-time 79 **Student-Faculty Ratio:** 15:1 **Final Year or Final Semester Residency Requirement:** No **Regional Accreditation:** Western Association of Colleges and Schools **Credit Hours For Degree:** 60 semester hours, Associates **ROTC:** Army **Professional Accreditation:** AAMAE.

PACIFIC ISLANDS UNIVERSITY

172 Kinney's Rd.
Mangilao, GU 96913
Tel: (671)734-1812
Fax: (671)734-1813
E-mail: guamcampus@pibc.edu
Web Site: www.piu.edu
President/CEO: Dr. David Owen
Admissions: Ethel Laco
Type: Four-Year College **Sex:** Coed **Affiliation:** interdenominational. **Application Deadline:** August 25 **Application Fee:** $25.00 **Calendar System:** Semester **Enrollment:** Full-time 132, Part-time 56 **Faculty:** Full-time 12, Part-time 10 **Student-Faculty Ratio:** 7:1 **Exams:** Other. **Professional Accreditation:** TRACS.

UNIVERSITY OF GUAM

303 University Dr.
UOG Station
Mangilao, GU 96923
Fax: (671)734-6005
E-mail: admitme@uguam.uog.edu
Web Site: www.uog.edu
President/CEO: Dr. Robert A. Underwood, EdD
Admissions: Angelica Anthonio
Type: Comprehensive **Sex:** Coed **% Accepted:** 96 **Admission Plans:** Deferred Admission; Open Admission **Application Deadline:** June 1 **Application Fee:** $49.00 **H.S. Requirements:** High school diploma required; GED accepted **Costs Per Year:** Application fee: $49. Territory resident tuition: $4800 full-time, $200 per credit part-time. Nonresident tuition: $11,520 full-time, $480 per credit part-time. Mandatory fees: $538 full-time, $269 per term part-time. Part-time tuition and fees vary according to course load. College room only: $1910. Room charges vary according to housing facility. **Scholarships:** Available. **Calendar System:** Semester, Summer session available **Enrollment:** Full-time 2,801, Graduate full-time 118, Graduate part-time 180, Part-time 859 **% Residing in College-Owned, -Operated, or -Affiliated Housing:** 5 **Final Year or Final Semester Residency Requirement:** Yes **Regional Accreditation:** Western Association of Colleges and Schools **Credit Hours For Degree:** 92 credits, Associates; 124 credits, Bachelors **ROTC:** Army **Professional Accreditation:** ACEN, CSWE, NCATE.

Northern Mariana Islands

NORTHERN MARIANAS COLLEGE

Box 501250
Saipan, MP 96950-1250
Tel: (670)234-3690
Fax: (670)234-0759
E-mail: leilanib@nmcnet.edu
Web Site: www.marianas.edu
President/CEO: Dr. Sharon Y. Hart
Admissions: Leilani M. Basa-Alam
Type: Two-Year College **Sex:** Coed **Admission Plans:** Deferred Admission; Early Admission; Open Admission **Application Deadline:** Rolling **Applica-

tion Fee: $25.00 H.S. Requirements: High school diploma or equivalent not required Calendar System: Semester, Summer session available Enrollment: Full-time 783, Part-time 516 Faculty: Full-time 49, Part-time 50 Regional Accreditation: Western Association of Colleges and Schools Credit Hours For Degree: 61 credits, Associates; 141 credits, Bachelors

Puerto Rico

AMERICAN UNIVERSITY OF PUERTO RICO (BAYAMON)
PO Box 2037
Bayamon, PR 00960-2037
Tel: (787)620-2040
Fax: (787)785-7377
E-mail: kllanos@aupr.edu
Web Site: www.aupr.edu
President/CEO: Juan C. Nazario-Torres
Admissions: Keren Llanos Figueroa
Financial Aid: Yahaira Melendez
Type: Comprehensive Sex: Coed % Accepted: 83 Admission Plans: Deferred Admission; Open Admission Application Fee: $25.00 H.S. Requirements: High school diploma required; GED accepted Scholarships: Available. Calendar System: Semester, Summer session available Enrollment: Full-time 2,123, Graduate full-time 98, Graduate part-time 46, Part-time 201 Faculty: Full-time 41, Part-time 121 Exams: SAT I; SAT I and SAT II or ACT; SAT II. % Receiving Financial Aid: 99 Regional Accreditation: Middle States Association of Colleges and Schools Credit Hours For Degree: 60 credits, Associates; 133 credits, Bachelors ROTC: Army Intercollegiate Athletics: Basketball M & W; Swimming and Diving M & W; Track and Field M & W; Volleyball M & W

AMERICAN UNIVERSITY OF PUERTO RICO (MANATI)
Carretera Estatal No.2 Km. 48.7
Manati, PR 00674-1082
Tel: (787)621-2835
Web Site: www.aupr.edu
Type: Comprehensive Sex: Coed Regional Accreditation: Middle States Association of Colleges and Schools

ATENAS COLLEGE
Paseo de La Atenas No.101 Altos
Manati, PR 00674
Tel: (787)884-3838
Web Site: www.atenascollege.edu
Type: Four-Year College Sex: Coed Professional Accreditation: ACCSC.

ATLANTIC UNIVERSITY COLLEGE
PO Box 3918
Guaynabo, PR 00970
Tel: (787)720-1022
Fax: (787)720-1092
E-mail: admisiones@atlanticcollege.edu
Web Site: www.atlanticu.edu
President/CEO: Teresa de Dios-Unanue
Admissions: Zaida Perez
Financial Aid: Velma Aponte
Type: Comprehensive Sex: Coed Admission Plans: Open Admission Application Fee: $30.00 H.S. Requirements: High school diploma required; GED accepted Scholarships: Available. Calendar System: Semester, Summer session not available % Receiving Financial Aid: 86 Credit Hours For Degree: 78 credits, Associates; 138 credits, Bachelors Professional Accreditation: ACICS.

BAYAMÓN CENTRAL UNIVERSITY
PO Box 1725
Bayamón, PR 00960-1725
Tel: (787)786-3030
E-mail: chernandez@ucb.edu.pr
Web Site: www.ucb.edu.pr
President/CEO: Dr. LILLIAM NEGRON
Admissions: Christine M. Hernandez
Type: Comprehensive Sex: Coed Affiliation: Roman Catholic. % Accepted: 38 Application Fee: $25.00 H.S. Requirements: High school diploma required; GED accepted Scholarships: Available. Calendar

System: Semester, Summer session available Enrollment: Full-time 857, Graduate full-time 153, Graduate part-time 111, Part-time 81 Faculty: Full-time 39, Part-time 114 Exams: Other. Regional Accreditation: Middle States Association of Colleges and Schools Credit Hours For Degree: 72 credits, Associates; 131 credits, Bachelors ROTC: Air Force, Army Professional Accreditation: TEAC. Intercollegiate Athletics: Basketball M; Bowling M & W; Cross-Country Running M & W; Swimming and Diving M & W; Track and Field M & W; Volleyball M & W; Weight Lifting M & W

CARIBBEAN UNIVERSITY
Box 493
Bayamón, PR 00960-0493
Tel: (787)780-0070
Fax: (787)785-0101
Web Site: www.caribbean.edu
President/CEO: Dr. Ana E. Cucurella-Adorno
Admissions: M. Sgt. Rosalie Morales
Type: Comprehensive Sex: Coed % Accepted: 52 Admission Plans: Deferred Admission; Open Admission Application Deadline: Rolling Application Fee: $30.00 H.S. Requirements: High school diploma required; GED accepted Costs Per Year: Application fee: $30. Tuition: $5400 full-time. Mandatory fees: $780 full-time. Full-time tuition and fees vary according to class time, degree level, location, and program. Scholarships: Available. Calendar System: Semester, Summer session available Enrollment: Full-time 2,558, Graduate full-time 275, Graduate part-time 452, Part-time 890 Faculty: Full-time 90, Part-time 314 Student-Faculty Ratio: 14:1 Exams: Other. Regional Accreditation: Middle States Association of Colleges and Schools Credit Hours For Degree: 69 credit hours, Associates; 122 credit hours, Bachelors ROTC: Army Intercollegiate Athletics: Baseball M; Basketball M & W; Cheerleading M & W; Cross-Country Running M & W; Soccer M & W; Softball W; Table Tennis M; Track and Field M & W; Volleyball M & W; Wrestling M & W

CARIBBEAN UNIVERSITY–CAROLINA
Calle Ignacio Arzuaga No.208
Carolina, PR 00985
Tel: (787)769-0007
Web Site: www.caribbean.edu
Type: Comprehensive Sex: Coed Regional Accreditation: Middle States Association of Colleges and Schools

CARIBBEAN UNIVERSITY–PONCE
Ave. Ednita Nazario No.1015
Ponce, PR 00716-7733
Tel: (787)840-2955
Web Site: www.caribbean.edu
Type: Comprehensive Sex: Coed Regional Accreditation: Middle States Association of Colleges and Schools

CARIBBEAN UNIVERSITY–VEGA BAJA
Carr 671 K.M. 5, Sector El Criollo, Bo. Algarrobo
Vega Baja, PR 00964
Tel: (787)858-3668
Web Site: www.caribbean.edu
Type: Comprehensive Sex: Coed Regional Accreditation: Middle States Association of Colleges and Schools

CARLOS ALBIZU UNIVERSITY
151 Tanca St.
San Juan, PR 00901
Tel: (787)725-6500
Fax: (787)721-7187
E-mail: crodriguez@albizu.edu
Web Site: www.albizu.edu
President/CEO: Dr. Ileana Rodriguez
Admissions: Carlos Rodriguez
Financial Aid: Doris J. Quero
Type: University Sex: Coed % Accepted: 84 Admission Plans: Deferred Admission; Early Admission Application Deadline: July 16 Application Fee: $75.00 H.S. Requirements: High school diploma required; GED accepted Scholarships: Available. Calendar System: Semester, Summer session not available Enrollment: Full-time 78, Graduate full-time 695, Graduate part-time 82, Part-time 64 Faculty: Full-time 1, Part-time 13 Student-Faculty Ratio: 10:1 Exams: Other; SAT Reasoning; SAT Subject.

% Receiving Financial Aid: 100 **Final Year or Final Semester Residency Requirement:** No **Regional Accreditation:** Middle States Association of Colleges and Schools **Credit Hours For Degree:** 126 credits, Bachelors **Professional Accreditation:** APA.

THE CENTER OF CINEMATOGRAPHY, ARTS AND TELEVISION
51 Dr. Veve St., Degetau St. Corner
Bayamon, PR 00960
Tel: (787)779-2500
Web Site: ccatmiami.com
Type: Two-Year College **Sex:** Coed **Professional Accreditation:** ACCSC.

CENTRO DE ESTUDIOS MULTIDISCIPLINARIOS (BAYAMON)
Calle Degetau No.25
Bayamon, PR 00961
Tel: (787)780-8900
Web Site: www.cempr.edu
Type: Four-Year College **Sex:** Coed **Professional Accreditation:** ACCSC.

CENTRO DE ESTUDIOS MULTIDISCIPLINARIOS (HUMACAO)
Calle Dr. Vidal No.8 y No.53
Humacao, PR 00791
Tel: (809)852-5505
E-mail: oortiz@cempr.edu
Web Site: www.cempr.edu
President/CEO: Hector Davila
Admissions: Orlando Ortiz
Type: Four-Year College **Sex:** Coed **Costs Per Year:** Comprehensive fee: $9149 includes full-time tuition ($5271), mandatory fees ($1145), and college room and board ($2733). Full-time tuition and fees vary according to course load, degree level, and program. **Calendar System:** Quarter **Enrollment:** Full-time 151 **Faculty:** Full-time 5, Part-time 23 **Student-Faculty Ratio:** 5:1 **Exams:** ACT; ACT essay component not used; Other; SAT I; SAT I and SAT II or ACT; SAT I or ACT; SAT II; SAT essay component not used. **Credit Hours For Degree:** 79, Associates; 131, Bachelors **Professional Accreditation:** ACCSC.

CENTRO DE ESTUDIOS MULTIDISCIPLINARIOS (MAYAGUEZ)
Calle Cristy No.56
Mayaguez, PR 00680
Tel: (787)986-7440
Web Site: www.cempr.edu
Type: Two-Year College **Sex:** Coed **Professional Accreditation:** ACCSC.

CENTRO DE ESTUDIOS MULTIDISCIPLINARIOS (RIO PIEDRAS)
Calle 13 No.1206
Ext. San Agustin
Rio Piedras, PR 00926
Tel: (787)765-4210; Free: 877-779-CDEM
Web Site: www.cempr.edu
President/CEO: Juan J. Pagani Soto
Type: Two-Year College **Sex:** Coed **% Accepted:** 95 **Application Fee:** $30.00 **Professional Accreditation:** ACCSC.

COLEGIO UNIVERSITARIO DE SAN JUAN
180 Jose R Oliver St.
Tres Monjitas Industrial Park
San Juan, PR 00918
Tel: (787)480-2400
Fax: (787)250-7395
Web Site: www.cunisanjuan.edu
President/CEO: Haydee Zayas Hernandez
Financial Aid: Ken Lira
Type: Four-Year College **Sex:** Coed **% Accepted:** 100 **Application Fee:** $15.00 **H.S. Requirements:** High school diploma required; GED accepted **Scholarships:** Available. **Calendar System:** Semester, Summer session available **Student-Faculty Ratio:** 16:1 **Exams:** SAT I. **Regional Accreditation:** Middle States Association of Colleges and Schools **Credit Hours For Degree:** 69 credits, Associates **Professional Accreditation:** ACEN.

COLUMBIA CENTRO UNIVERSITARIO (CAGUAS)
PO Box 8517
Caguas, PR 00726
Tel: (787)743-4041

Fax: (787)744-7931
E-mail: lmiletti@columbiaco.edu
Web Site: www.columbiacentral.edu
President/CEO: Dr. Gladys Serrano, EdD
Admissions: Linette J. Miletti
Type: Comprehensive **Sex:** Coed **% Accepted:** 54 **Application Deadline:** Rolling **Application Fee:** $50.00 **H.S. Requirements:** High school diploma required; GED accepted **Costs Per Year:** Application fee: $50. Tuition: $9630 full-time, $1605 per semester hour part-time. Mandatory fees: $100 full-time, $267 per credit hour part-time. Full-time tuition and fees vary according to class time, degree level, and program. Part-time tuition and fees vary according to class time, degree level, and program. **Scholarships:** Available. **Calendar System:** Semester, Summer session not available **Enrollment:** Full-time 743, Graduate full-time 43, Graduate part-time 71, Part-time 1,007 **Faculty:** Full-time 19, Part-time 126 **Student-Faculty Ratio:** 19:1 **% Receiving Financial Aid:** 84 **Final Year or Final Semester Residency Requirement:** No **Regional Accreditation:** Middle States Association of Colleges and Schools **Credit Hours For Degree:** 60 credits, Associates; 120 credits, Bachelors **Professional Accreditation:** ACICS.

COLUMBIA CENTRO UNIVERSITARIO (YAUCO)
Calle Betances No.3
Box 3062
Yauco, PR 00698
Tel: (787)856-0945
Fax: (787)267-2335
E-mail: cipabon@columbiaco.edu
Web Site: www.columbiacentral.edu
President/CEO: Jorge A. Negron
Admissions: Carmen Ivette Pabon, MSC
Type: Four-Year College **Sex:** Coed **Affiliation:** Columbia Centro Universitario, Recinto Caguas. **Admission Plans:** Open Admission **Application Deadline:** Rolling **Application Fee:** $50.00 **H.S. Requirements:** High school diploma required; GED accepted **Costs Per Year:** Application fee: $50. Tuition: $9630 full-time. Mandatory fees: $100 full-time. Full-time tuition and fees vary according to course load and program. **Calendar System:** Trimester, Summer session not available **Enrollment:** Full-time 212, Part-time 195 **Faculty:** Full-time 7, Part-time 30 **Student-Faculty Ratio:** 11:1 **Final Year or Final Semester Residency Requirement:** No **Credit Hours For Degree:** 71 credits, Associates; 120 credits, Bachelors **Professional Accreditation:** ACICS.

CONSERVATORIO DE MUSICA DE PUERTO RICO
951 Ave. Ponce de León
Parada 15, Miramar
San Juan, PR 00907
Tel: (787)751-0160
E-mail: aarraiza2@cmpr.gobierno.pr
Web Site: www.cmpr.edu
President/CEO: Prof. Luis Hernandez-Mergal
Admissions: Ana Marta Arraiza
Financial Aid: Michael Rajaballey
Type: Comprehensive **Sex:** Coed **% Accepted:** 74 **Application Deadline:** December 15 **Application Fee:** $75.00 **H.S. Requirements:** High school diploma required; GED accepted **Costs Per Year:** Application fee: $75. Commonwealth resident tuition: $2520 full-time, $105 per credit part-time. Nonresident tuition: $2520 full-time, $105 per credit part-time. Mandatory fees: $850 full-time, $850 per term part-time, $850 per term part-time. Full-time tuition and fees vary according to program. Part-time tuition and fees vary according to program. **Scholarships:** Available. **Calendar System:** Semester, Summer session available **Enrollment:** Full-time 281, Graduate full-time 37, Graduate part-time 8, Part-time 142 **Faculty:** Full-time 53, Part-time 36 **Student-Faculty Ratio:** 6:1 **Final Year or Final Semester Residency Requirement:** No **Regional Accreditation:** Middle States Association of Colleges and Schools **Credit Hours For Degree:** 132 credits, Bachelors **Professional Accreditation:** NASM.

DEWEY UNIVERSITY–ARROYO
Carr. No.3, Km.129.7, Barrio Palmas
Arroyo, PR 00910
Tel: (787)271-1515
Web Site: www.dewey.edu
Type: Two-Year College **Sex:** Coed **Professional Accreditation:** ACICS.

DEWEY UNIVERSITY–BAYAMÓN

Carr. No.2, Km. 15.9, Parque Industrial Corujo, Hato Tejas
Bayamón, PR 00959
Tel: (787)778-1200
Web Site: www.dewey.edu
Type: Two-Year College Sex: Coed Professional Accreditation: ACICS.

DEWEY UNIVERSITY–CAROLINA

Carr. No.3, Km. 11, Parque Industrial de Carolina, Lote 7
Carolina, PR 00986
Tel: (787)769-1515
Web Site: www.dewey.edu
Type: Two-Year College Sex: Coed Professional Accreditation: ACICS.

DEWEY UNIVERSITY–FAJARDO

267 Calle General Valero
Fajardo, PR 00910
Tel: (787)860-1212
Web Site: www.dewey.edu
Type: Two-Year College Sex: Coed Professional Accreditation: ACICS.

DEWEY UNIVERSITY–HATILLO

Carr. No.2 Km. 86.9 Barrio Pueblo
Hatillo, PR 00659
Tel: (787)544-1515
Web Site: www.dewey.edu
Type: Two-Year College Sex: Coed Regional Accreditation: Middle States
Association of Colleges and Schools

DEWEY UNIVERSITY–HATO REY

427 Avenida Barbosa
Hato Rey, PR 00923
Tel: (787)753-0039
Web Site: www.dewey.edu
Type: Two-Year College Sex: Coed Professional Accreditation: ACICS.

DEWEY UNIVERSITY–JUANA DIAZ

Carr. 149, Km. 55.9, Parque Industrial Lomas
Juana Diaz, PR 00910
Tel: (787)260-1023
Web Site: www.dewey.edu
Type: Two-Year College Sex: Coed Professional Accreditation: ACICS.

DEWEY UNIVERSITY–MANATI

Carr. 604, Km. 49.1 Barrio Tierras Nuevas, Salientes
Manati, PR 00674
Tel: (787)854-3800; Free: 866-773-3939
Fax: (787)854-1899
Web Site: www.dewey.edu
Type: Two-Year College Sex: Coed Professional Accreditation: ACICS.

DEWEY UNIVERSITY–MAYAGUEZ

Carr. No.64 Km 6.6 Barrio Algarrobo
Mayaguez, PR 00682
Tel: (787)652-1212
Web Site: dewey.edu
Type: Two-Year College Sex: Coed Professional Accreditation: ACICS.

EDIC COLLEGE

Ave. Rafael Cordero Calle Génova Urb. Caguas Norte
Caguas, PR 00726
Tel: (787)744-8519
Fax: (787)743-0855
Web Site: www.ediccollege.edu
Type: Two-Year College Sex: Coed Professional Accreditation: ACICS.

EDP UNIVERSITY OF PUERTO RICO

560 Ave. Ponce de Leon
Hato Rey, PR 00918
Tel: (787)765-3560
E-mail: oscarmorales@edpuniversity.edu
Web Site: www.edpuniversity.edu
President/CEO: Gladys Nieves Vazquez
Admissions: Oscar Morales
Financial Aid: Yaitzaenid Gonzalez
Type: Comprehensive Sex: Coed % Accepted: 61 Admission Plans:
Deferred Admission; Early Action; Early Admission Application Deadline:
Rolling Application Fee: $15.00 H.S. Requirements: High school diploma
required; GED accepted Costs Per Year: Application fee: $15. Tuition:
$5100 full-time, $170 per credit part-time. Mandatory fees: $840 full-time,
$420 per term part-time. Full-time tuition and fees vary according to course
load and program. Part-time tuition and fees vary according to course load
and program. Scholarships: Available. Calendar System: Semester, Summer session available Enrollment: Full-time 1,048, Graduate full-time 112,
Graduate part-time 13, Part-time 543 Faculty: Full-time 36, Part-time 140
Student-Faculty Ratio: 15:1 Exams: Other. % Receiving Financial Aid:
90 Final Year or Final Semester Residency Requirement: No Regional
Accreditation: Middle States Association of Colleges and Schools Credit
Hours For Degree: 64 credits, depending on program, Associates; 110
credits, depending on program, Bachelors Professional Accreditation:
ACICS.

EDP UNIVERSITY OF PUERTO RICO–SAN SEBASTIAN

Ave. Betances No.49
San Sebastian, PR 00685
Tel: (787)896-2137
Fax: (787)896-0066
E-mail: dvarela@edpuniversity.edu
Web Site: www.edpuniversity.edu
President/CEO: Dr. Melba G. Rivera Delgado
Admissions: Dr. Damarys Varela Velez
Financial Aid: Yaitzaenid Gonzalez
Type: Comprehensive Sex: Coed % Accepted: 88 Admission Plans: Open
Admission Application Deadline: Rolling Application Fee: $15.00 H.S.
Requirements: High school diploma required; GED accepted Costs Per
Year: Application fee: $15. Tuition: $5100 full-time. Mandatory fees: $840
full-time, $170 per credit hour part-time, $420 per term part-time. Full-time
tuition and fees vary according to course load and program. Part-time fees
vary according to course load and program. Scholarships: Available.
Calendar System: Semester, Summer session available Enrollment: Full-
time 766, Graduate full-time 33, Graduate part-time 7, Part-time 312
Faculty: Full-time 24, Part-time 100 Student-Faculty Ratio: 15:1 Exams:
Other. % Receiving Financial Aid: 91 Final Year or Final Semester
Residency Requirement: No Credit Hours For Degree: 64 credit hours,
Associates; 110 credit hours, Bachelors Professional Accreditation:
ACICS.

ESCUELA DE ARTES PLASTICAS Y DISEÑO DE PUERTO RICO

PO Box 9021112
San Juan, PR 00902-1112
Tel: (787)725-8120
E-mail: nmelendez@eap.edu
Web Site: www.eap.edu
President/CEO: Carlos E. Rivera-Perez
Admissions: Nitza Melendez
Financial Aid: Alfred Diaz Melendez
Type: Four-Year College Sex: Coed % Accepted: 85 Application
Deadline: March 18 Application Fee: $25.00 H.S. Requirements: High
school diploma required; GED accepted Costs Per Year: Application fee:
$25. Commonwealth resident tuition: $2997 full-time, $90 per credit part-
time. Nonresident tuition: $5157 full-time, $180 per credit part-time. Manda-
tory fees: $251 full-time, $251 per year part-time. Scholarships: Available.
Calendar System: Semester, Summer session available Enrollment: Full-
time 420, Part-time 153 Faculty: Full-time 15, Part-time 62 Student-Faculty
Ratio: 13:1 Exams: SAT I; SAT essay component not used; SAT Reasoning;
SAT Subject. % Receiving Financial Aid: 83 Final Year or Final Semester
Residency Requirement: No Regional Accreditation: Middle States Association of Colleges and Schools Credit Hours For Degree: 132 credit
hours, Bachelors Professional Accreditation: NASAD.

HUERTAS JUNIOR COLLEGE

PO Box 8429
Caguas, PR 00726
Tel: (787)743-2156
E-mail: huertas@huertas.org
Web Site: www.huertas.edu
President/CEO: Maria del Mar Lopez

Admissions: Barbara Hassim López
Type: Two-Year College **Sex:** Coed **Admission Plans:** Deferred Admission; Open Admission **Application Deadline:** Rolling **Application Fee:** $25.00 **H.S. Requirements:** High school diploma required; GED accepted **Scholarships:** Available. **Calendar System:** Trimester, Summer session not available **Regional Accreditation:** Middle States Association of Colleges and Schools **Credit Hours For Degree:** 76 credits, Associates **Professional Accreditation:** ACICS, AHIMA.

HUMACAO COMMUNITY COLLEGE
PO Box 9139
Humacao, PR 00792
Tel: (787)852-1430
Fax: (787)850-1760
E-mail: lquinones@hccpr.edu
Web Site: www.hccpr.edu
President/CEO: Jorge E. Mojica
Admissions: Loalis Quinones

Type: Two-Year College **Sex:** Coed **% Accepted:** 89 **Admission Plans:** Open Admission **Application Fee:** $15.00 **H.S. Requirements:** High school diploma required; GED accepted **Costs Per Year:** Application fee: $15. One-time mandatory fee: $140. Tuition: $4932 full-time, $2340 per year part-time. Mandatory fees: $450 full-time. Full-time tuition and fees vary according to degree level. Part-time tuition varies according to degree level. **Scholarships:** Available. **Calendar System:** Trimester, Summer session not available **Enrollment:** Full-time 435, Part-time 119 **Faculty:** Full-time 13, Part-time 14 **Student-Faculty Ratio:** 30:1 **Exams:** ACT; Other; SAT I; SAT I and SAT II or ACT; SAT I or ACT; SAT II. **Final Year or Final Semester Residency Requirement:** No **Credit Hours For Degree:** 66 credits, Associates; 127 credits, Bachelors **Professional Accreditation:** ACICS.

ICPR JUNIOR COLLEGE–HATO REY CAMPUS
558 Munoz Rivera Ave.
Hato Rey, PR 00919-0304
Tel: (787)753-6000
Fax: (787)763-7249
Web Site: www.icprjc.edu
President/CEO: Olga Rivera

Type: Two-Year College **Sex:** Coed **Admission Plans:** Early Admission **Application Fee:** $25.00 **H.S. Requirements:** High school diploma required; GED accepted **Scholarships:** Available. **Calendar System:** Trimester, Summer session not available **Faculty:** Full-time 34, Part-time 55 **Student-Faculty Ratio:** 17:1 **Regional Accreditation:** Middle States Association of Colleges and Schools **Credit Hours For Degree:** 73 credits, Associates **ROTC:** Army

INTER AMERICAN UNIVERSITY OF PUERTO RICO, AGUADILLA CAMPUS
Call Box 20000
Aguadilla, PR 00605
Tel: (787)891-0925
Web Site: www.aguadilla.inter.edu
President/CEO: Dr. Elie Agesilas
Admissions: Daisy Irizarry
Financial Aid: Juan Gonzalez

Type: Comprehensive **Sex:** Coed **Affiliation:** Inter American University of Puerto Rico. **% Accepted:** 53 **Application Deadline:** Rolling **Application Fee:** $0.00 **H.S. Requirements:** High school diploma required; GED accepted **Costs Per Year:** Application fee: $0. Tuition: $4392 full-time, $183 per semester hour part-time. Mandatory fees: $652 full-time. Full-time tuition and fees vary according to course load and program. Part-time tuition varies according to course load and program. **Calendar System:** Semester, Summer session available **Enrollment:** Full-time 3,676, Graduate full-time 242, Graduate part-time 47, Part-time 616 **Faculty:** Full-time 79, Part-time 178 **Student-Faculty Ratio:** 29:1 **Exams:** ACT essay component used for admission; Other; SAT I or ACT; SAT essay component used for admission. **Final Year or Final Semester Residency Requirement:** No **Regional Accreditation:** Middle States Association of Colleges and Schools **Credit Hours For Degree:** 55 semester hours, depending on program, Associates; 129 semester hours, depending on program, Bachelors **ROTC:** Air Force, Army **Intercollegiate Athletics:** Baseball M; Basketball M & W; Cheerleading M & W; Cross-Country Running M & W; Soccer M & W; Softball M & W; Swimming and Diving M & W; Table Tennis M & W; Tennis M & W; Track and Field M & W; Volleyball M & W; Weight Lifting M & W; Wrestling M

INTER AMERICAN UNIVERSITY OF PUERTO RICO, ARECIBO CAMPUS
PO Box 4050
Arecibo, PR 00614-4050
Tel: (787)878-5475
Fax: (787)880-1624
E-mail: pmontalvo@arecibo.inter.edu
Web Site: www.arecibo.inter.edu
President/CEO: Dr. Rafael Ramirez
Admissions: Provi Montalvo
Financial Aid: Ramón O. de Jesús

Type: Comprehensive **Sex:** Coed **Affiliation:** Inter American University of Puerto Rico. **Admission Plans:** Deferred Admission; Early Admission **Application Deadline:** Rolling **Application Fee:** $0.00 **H.S. Requirements:** High school diploma required; GED accepted **Costs Per Year:** Application fee: $0. Tuition: $4272 full-time, $178 per credit part-time. Mandatory fees: $690 full-time, $281 per term part-time. Full-time tuition and fees vary according to course load and program. Part-time tuition and fees vary according to course load and program. **Scholarships:** Available. **Calendar System:** Semester, Summer session available **Enrollment:** Full-time 3,789, Graduate full-time 267, Graduate part-time 64, Part-time 758 **Faculty:** Full-time 88, Part-time 210 **Student-Faculty Ratio:** 24:1 **Exams:** Other. **% Receiving Financial Aid:** 85 **Regional Accreditation:** Middle States Association of Colleges and Schools **Credit Hours For Degree:** 60 credit hours, Associates; 124 credit hours, Bachelors **ROTC:** Army **Professional Accreditation:** AANA, ACEN, CSWE, TEAC. **Intercollegiate Athletics:** Baseball M; Basketball M & W; Cheerleading M & W; Track and Field M & W; Volleyball M & W

INTER AMERICAN UNIVERSITY OF PUERTO RICO, BARRANQUITAS CAMPUS
PO Box 517
Barranquitas, PR 00794
Tel: (787)857-3600
Fax: (787)857-2284
E-mail: acartagena@br.inter.edu
Web Site: www.br.inter.edu
President/CEO: Dr. Irene Fernandez
Admissions: Aramilda Cartagena
Financial Aid: Eduardo Fontanez Colon

Type: Comprehensive **Sex:** Coed **Affiliation:** Inter American University of Puerto Rico. **Costs Per Year:** Tuition: $5340 full-time. Mandatory fees: $451 full-time. **Scholarships:** Available. **Calendar System:** Semester, Summer session available **Enrollment:** Full-time 1,925, Graduate part-time 9, Part-time 182 **Faculty:** Full-time 31, Part-time 112 **Student-Faculty Ratio:** 29:1 **Exams:** Other; SAT I or ACT. **Regional Accreditation:** Middle States Association of Colleges and Schools **Credit Hours For Degree:** 65 credits, Associates; 125 credits, Bachelors **ROTC:** Army **Professional Accreditation:** TEAC. **Intercollegiate Athletics:** Baseball M; Basketball M & W; Cross-Country Running M & W; Softball M & W; Table Tennis M & W; Tennis M & W; Track and Field M & W; Volleyball M & W; Weight Lifting M & W; Wrestling M & W

INTER AMERICAN UNIVERSITY OF PUERTO RICO, BAYAMÓN CAMPUS
Dr. John Will Harris 500
Bayamón, PR 00957
Tel: (787)279-1912
Fax: (787)279-2205
E-mail: abaez@bayamon.inter.edu
Web Site: bayamon.inter.edu
President/CEO: Juan F. Martinez
Admissions: Aurelis Baez
Financial Aid: Aurelis Baez

Type: Comprehensive **Sex:** Coed **Affiliation:** Inter American University of Puerto Rico. **% Accepted:** 54 **Application Deadline:** July 30 **Application Fee:** $0.00 **H.S. Requirements:** High school diploma required; GED accepted **Costs Per Year:** Application fee: $0. Tuition: $5490 full-time, $305 per semester hour part-time. Mandatory fees: $690 full-time. Full-time tuition and fees vary according to class time, course load, and program. Part-time tuition varies according to class time, course load, and program. **Scholarships:** Available. **Calendar System:** Semester, Summer session available **Enrollment:** Full-time 3,965, Graduate full-time 104, Graduate part-time 19, Part-time 542 **Faculty:** Full-time 92, Part-time 194 **Student-Faculty Ratio:**

25:1 **Exams:** Other; SAT I. **% Receiving Financial Aid:** 93 **Regional Accreditation:** Middle States Association of Colleges and Schools **Credit Hours For Degree:** 70 semester hours, Associates; 120 semester hours, Bachelors **ROTC:** Army **Professional Accreditation:** ABET. **Intercollegiate Athletics:** Baseball M; Basketball M & W; Cross-Country Running M & W; Softball M & W; Swimming and Diving M & W; Table Tennis M & W; Track and Field M & W; Volleyball M & W; Weight Lifting M

INTER AMERICAN UNIVERSITY OF PUERTO RICO, FAJARDO CAMPUS
Call Box 70003
Fajardo, PR 00738-7003
Tel: (787)863-2390
E-mail: ghisita.garcia@fajardo.inter.edu
Web Site: www.fajardo.inter.edu
President/CEO: Dr. Ismael Suarez
Admissions: Ghisita M. Garcia

Type: Comprehensive **Sex:** Coed **Affiliation:** Inter American University of Puerto Rico. **% Accepted:** 88 **Admission Plans:** Deferred Admission; Early Admission **Application Deadline:** May 15 **Application Fee:** $0.00 **H.S. Requirements:** High school diploma required; GED accepted **Costs Per Year:** Application fee: $0. Tuition: $4272 full-time, $178 per credit part-time. Full-time tuition varies according to class time, course level, course load, degree level, location, program, and student level. Part-time tuition varies according to class time, course level, course load, degree level, location, program, and student level. **Calendar System:** Semester, Summer session available **Enrollment:** Full-time 1,774, Graduate part-time 62, Part-time 235 **Faculty:** Full-time 40, Part-time 68 **Student-Faculty Ratio:** 11:1 **Exams:** Other. **Final Year or Final Semester Residency Requirement:** No **Regional Accreditation:** Middle States Association of Colleges and Schools **Credit Hours For Degree:** 60 semester hours, Associates; 124 semester hours, Bachelors **ROTC:** Army **Intercollegiate Athletics:** Baseball M; Basketball M & W; Bowling M; Cheerleading W; Softball W; Table Tennis M & W; Tennis M & W; Track and Field M & W; Volleyball M & W

INTER AMERICAN UNIVERSITY OF PUERTO RICO, GUAYAMA CAMPUS
Call Box 10004
Guayama, PR 00785
Tel: (787)864-2222
E-mail: laura.ferrer@guayama.inter.edu
Web Site: www.guayama.inter.edu
President/CEO: Prof. Carlos E. Colon
Admissions: Laura E. Ferrer
Financial Aid: Jose A. Vechini

Type: Comprehensive **Sex:** Coed **Affiliation:** Inter American University of Puerto Rico. **% Accepted:** 48 **Application Deadline:** August 1 **Application Fee:** $0.00 **H.S. Requirements:** High school diploma required; GED accepted **Costs Per Year:** Application fee: $0. One-time mandatory fee: $55. Tuition: $5490 full-time. Mandatory fees: $677 full-time. **Scholarships:** Available. **Calendar System:** Semester, Summer session available **Enrollment:** Full-time 1,610, Graduate full-time 83, Graduate part-time 27, Part-time 407 **Faculty:** Full-time 41, Part-time 140 **Student-Faculty Ratio:** 12:1 **Exams:** Other; SAT I. **% Receiving Financial Aid:** 47 **Regional Accreditation:** Middle States Association of Colleges and Schools **Credit Hours For Degree:** 52 academic credits, Associates; 110 academic credits, Bachelors **ROTC:** Army **Professional Accreditation:** ACBSP. **Intercollegiate Athletics:** Baseball M; Basketball M & W; Cross-Country Running M & W; Swimming and Diving M

INTER AMERICAN UNIVERSITY OF PUERTO RICO, METROPOLITAN CAMPUS
PO Box 191293
San Juan, PR 00919-1293
Tel: (787)250-1912
E-mail: jolivieri@metro.inter.edu
Web Site: metro.inter.edu
President/CEO: Prof. Marilina Wayland
Admissions: Janies Olivieri
Financial Aid: Luz M. Medina

Type: Comprehensive **Sex:** Coed **Affiliation:** Inter American University of Puerto Rico. **% Accepted:** 36 **Application Deadline:** May 15 **Application Fee:** $0.00 **H.S. Requirements:** High school diploma required; GED accepted **Costs Per Year:** Application fee: $0. Tuition: $6408 full-time, $178

per credit part-time. Mandatory fees: $714 full-time. **Scholarships:** Available. **Calendar System:** Semester, Summer session available **Enrollment:** Full-time 5,320, Graduate full-time 1,880, Graduate part-time 652, Part-time 1,242 **Faculty:** Full-time 200, Part-time 394 **Exams:** Other; SAT I. **% Receiving Financial Aid:** 80 **Regional Accreditation:** Middle States Association of Colleges and Schools **Credit Hours For Degree:** 60 credits, Associates; 130 credits, Bachelors **ROTC:** Air Force, Army, Navy **Professional Accreditation:** ABA, ACEN, CSWE, NAACLS, TEAC. **Intercollegiate Athletics:** Baseball M; Basketball M; Soccer M; Table Tennis M & W; Tennis M & W; Volleyball W

INTER AMERICAN UNIVERSITY OF PUERTO RICO, PONCE CAMPUS
104 Industrial Park Turpò Rd. 1
Mercedita, PR 00715-1602
Tel: (787)284-1912
E-mail: fidiaz@ponce.inter.edu
Web Site: www.ponce.inter.edu
President/CEO: Dr. Vilma E. Colon
Admissions: Franco Diaz
Financial Aid: Debra Martinez

Type: Comprehensive **Sex:** Coed **Affiliation:** Inter American University of Puerto Rico. **% Accepted:** 66 **Admission Plans:** Deferred Admission **Application Deadline:** May 15 **Application Fee:** $0.00 **H.S. Requirements:** High school diploma required; GED accepted **Costs Per Year:** Application fee: $0. Tuition: $4272 full-time, $178 per credit part-time. Mandatory fees: $690 full-time. Full-time tuition and fees vary according to course load and program. Part-time tuition varies according to course load and program. **Scholarships:** Available. **Calendar System:** Semester, Summer session available **Enrollment:** Full-time 4,632, Graduate full-time 262, Graduate part-time 111, Part-time 729 **Faculty:** Full-time 99, Part-time 196 **Student-Faculty Ratio:** 32:1 **Exams:** Other; SAT I. **% Receiving Financial Aid:** 71 **Regional Accreditation:** Middle States Association of Colleges and Schools **Credit Hours For Degree:** 60 semester hours, Associates; 124 semester hours, Bachelors **Professional Accreditation:** ACBSP. **Intercollegiate Athletics:** Baseball M; Cross-Country Running M & W; Soccer M & W; Softball M & W; Swimming and Diving M & W; Table Tennis M & W; Track and Field M & W; Volleyball M & W; Weight Lifting M & W; Wrestling M

INTER AMERICAN UNIVERSITY OF PUERTO RICO, SAN GERMÁN CAMPUS
PO Box 5100
San Germán, PR 00683-5008
Tel: (787)264-1912
Fax: (787)892-6350
E-mail: milcama@intersg.edu
Web Site: www.sg.inter.edu
President/CEO: Prof. Agnes Mojica
Admissions: Prof. Mildred Camacho
Financial Aid: Maria I. Lugo

Type: University **Sex:** Coed **Affiliation:** Inter American University of Puerto Rico. **% Accepted:** 64 **Admission Plans:** Early Admission **Application Deadline:** May 15 **Application Fee:** $0.00 **H.S. Requirements:** High school diploma required; GED accepted **Costs Per Year:** Application fee: $0. Comprehensive fee: $8880 includes full-time tuition ($5490), mandatory fees ($690), and college room and board ($2700). College room only: $1200. Full-time tuition and fees vary according to degree level. Room and board charges vary according to board plan and housing facility. Part-time tuition: $183 per credit. Part-time mandatory fees: $183 per credit. Part-time tuition and fees vary according to degree level. **Scholarships:** Available. **Calendar System:** Semester, Summer session available **Enrollment:** Full-time 3,838, Graduate full-time 497, Graduate part-time 213, Part-time 451 **Faculty:** Full-time 109, Part-time 182 **Student-Faculty Ratio:** 21:1 **Exams:** Other; SAT I or ACT; SAT Reasoning. **% Receiving Financial Aid:** 79 **% Residing in College-Owned, -Operated, or -Affiliated Housing:** 5 **Final Year or Final Semester Residency Requirement:** No **Regional Accreditation:** Middle States Association of Colleges and Schools **Credit Hours For Degree:** 60 credits, Associates; 124 credits, Bachelors **ROTC:** Air Force, Army, Navy **Professional Accreditation:** AHIMA, NAACLS, TEAC. **Intercollegiate Athletics:** Baseball M; Basketball M & W; Cross-Country Running M & W; Soccer M; Softball M & W; Swimming and Diving M & W; Table Tennis M & W; Tennis M & W; Track and Field M & W; Volleyball M & W; Weight Lifting M

NATIONAL UNIVERSITY COLLEGE (BAYAMÓN)
National College Plz. Bldg.
Bayamón, PR 00960

Tel: (787)780-5134; Free: 800-780-5134
Fax: (787)740-7360
Web Site: www.nuc.edu
President/CEO: Carmen Zoraida Claudio
Financial Aid: Elizabeth Cruz
Type: Comprehensive **Sex:** Coed **Affiliation:** EDUK Services Center. **Costs Per Year:** One-time mandatory fee: $25. Tuition: $6120 full-time, $170 per credit part-time. Mandatory fees: $390 full-time, $130 per term part-time. Full-time tuition and fees vary according to course load and location. Part-time tuition and fees vary according to course load and location. **Scholarships:** Available. **Calendar System:** Trimester, Summer session not available **Faculty:** Full-time 82, Part-time 382 **Student-Faculty Ratio:** 17:1 **Exams:** Other; SAT II. **% Receiving Financial Aid:** 96 **Final Year or Final Semester Residency Requirement:** No **Regional Accreditation:** Middle States Association of Colleges and Schools **Credit Hours For Degree:** 70 credits, Associates; 120 credits, Bachelors **Professional Accreditation:** ACICS.

NATIONAL UNIVERSITY COLLEGE (CAGUAS)
190 Avenida Gautier Benitez Esquina Avenida Federico Degatau
Caguas, PR 00725
Tel: (787)653-4733; Free: 800-780-5134
Web Site: www.nuc.edu
Type: Four-Year College **Sex:** Coed **Regional Accreditation:** Middle States Association of Colleges and Schools

NATIONAL UNIVERSITY COLLEGE (PONCE)
PO Box 801243
Ponce, PR 00716
Tel: (787)840-4474
Web Site: www.nuc.edu
Type: Comprehensive **Sex:** Coed **Regional Accreditation:** Middle States Association of Colleges and Schools

NATIONAL UNIVERSITY COLLEGE (RIO GRANDE)
Carretera No.3 Km. 22.1
Bo. Ciénaga Baja
Rio Grande, PR 00745
Tel: (787)809-5100; Free: 800-981-0812
Fax: (787)888-8280
Web Site: www.nuc.edu
Type: Comprehensive **Sex:** Coed **Regional Accreditation:** Middle States Association of Colleges and Schools

POLYTECHNIC UNIVERSITY OF PUERTO RICO
377 Ponce de Leon Ave.
Hato Rey, PR 00919
Tel: (787)754-8000
E-mail: tcardona@pupr.edu
Web Site: www.pupr.edu
President/CEO: Prof. Ernesto Vazquez-Barquet
Admissions: Teresa Cardona
Financial Aid: Sergio E. Villoldo
Type: Comprehensive **Sex:** Coed **Scores:** 100% SAT M 400+ **% Accepted:** 87 **Application Deadline:** August 15 **Application Fee:** $30.00 **H.S. Requirements:** High school diploma required; GED accepted **Costs Per Year:** Application fee: $30. Tuition: $7200 full-time, $200 per credit part-time. Mandatory fees: $840 full-time, $280 per term part-time. Full-time tuition and fees vary according to course level, course load, degree level, and program. Part-time tuition and fees vary according to course level, course load, degree level, and program. **Scholarships:** Available. **Calendar System:** Trimester, Summer session available **Enrollment:** Full-time 1,592, Graduate full-time 537, Graduate part-time 261, Part-time 1,901 **Faculty:** Full-time 133, Part-time 93 **Student-Faculty Ratio:** 21:1 **Exams:** ACT essay component not used; SAT I; SAT essay component not used; SAT Reasoning; SAT Subject. **% Receiving Financial Aid:** 81 **Regional Accreditation:** Middle States Association of Colleges and Schools **Credit Hours For Degree:** 132 credit hours, Bachelors **ROTC:** Army **Intercollegiate Athletics:** Basketball M; Table Tennis W; Track and Field M & W; Volleyball M & W; Weight Lifting M & W

PONCE PARAMEDICAL COLLEGE
L-15 Acacia St. Villa Flores Urbanizacion
Ponce, PR 00731

Tel: (787)848-1589
Fax: (787)259-0169
Web Site: www.popac.edu
Type: Two-Year College **Sex:** Coed **Professional Accreditation:** ACCSC.

PONTIFICAL CATHOLIC UNIVERSITY OF PUERTO RICO
2250 Las Americas Ave., Ste. 564
Ponce, PR 00717-0777
Tel: (787)841-2000; Free: 800-961-7696
Fax: (787)840-4295
E-mail: admissions@email.pucpr.edu
Web Site: www.pucpr.edu
President/CEO: Dr. Jorge I. Velez
Admissions: Sra. Ana O. Bonilla
Financial Aid: Rosalia Martinez
Type: University **Sex:** Coed **Affiliation:** Roman Catholic Church. **% Accepted:** 83 **Admission Plans:** Deferred Admission; Early Admission **Application Fee:** $15.00 **H.S. Requirements:** High school diploma required; GED accepted **Costs Per Year:** Application fee: $15. Comprehensive fee: $9688 includes full-time tuition ($4560), mandatory fees ($570), and college room and board ($4558). College room only: $1390. Full-time tuition and fees vary according to location. Part-time tuition: $190 per credit hour. Part-time mandatory fees: $217 per term. Part-time tuition and fees vary according to location. **Scholarships:** Available. **Calendar System:** Semester, Summer session available **Enrollment:** Full-time 4,857, Graduate full-time 1,608, Graduate part-time 703, Part-time 514 **Faculty:** Full-time 191, Part-time 194 **Student-Faculty Ratio:** 23:1 **Exams:** Other; SAT I. **% Receiving Financial Aid:** 88 **Regional Accreditation:** Middle States Association of Colleges and Schools **Credit Hours For Degree:** 67 credits, Associates; 130 credits, Bachelors **ROTC:** Air Force, Army **Professional Accreditation:** ABA, ACEN, CORE, CSWE, NAACLS, TEAC. **Intercollegiate Athletics:** Basketball M; Cross-Country Running M & W; Swimming and Diving M & W; Table Tennis M & W; Tennis M & W; Track and Field M & W; Volleyball M & W; Weight Lifting M & W; Wrestling M

PONTIFICAL CATHOLIC UNIVERSITY OF PUERTO RICO–ARECIBO CAMPUS
PO Box 144045
Arecibo, PR 00614-4045
Tel: (787)881-1212
Web Site: www.pucpr.edu/arecibo
Type: Comprehensive **Sex:** Coed **Affiliation:** Roman Catholic Church. **Regional Accreditation:** Middle States Association of Colleges and Schools

PONTIFICAL CATHOLIC UNIVERSITY OF PUERTO RICO–MAYAGUEZ CAMPUS
482 Sur Calle Ramon Emerito Betances
Mayaguez, PR 00680
Web Site: www.pucpr.edu/mayaguez
Type: Comprehensive **Sex:** Coed **Affiliation:** Roman Catholic Church. **Regional Accreditation:** Middle States Association of Colleges and Schools

THEOLOGICAL UNIVERSITY OF THE CARIBBEAN
PO Box 901
Saint Just, PR 00978-0901
Tel: (787)761-0640
E-mail: admisiones1@utcpr.edu
Web Site: www.utcpr.edu
President/CEO: Rev. Francisco Ortiz
Admissions: Raul McClin
Financial Aid: Claudia M. Rodriguez
Type: Comprehensive **Sex:** Coed **Affiliation:** Pentecostal. **% Accepted:** 100 **Admission Plans:** Early Admission; Open Admission **Application Fee:** $25.00 **H.S. Requirements:** High school diploma required; GED accepted **Costs Per Year:** Application fee: $25. One-time mandatory fee: $13. Comprehensive fee: $6848 includes full-time tuition ($3784), mandatory fees ($664), and college room and board ($2400). College room only: $1200. Full-time tuition and fees vary according to course load. Room and board charges vary according to board plan. **Scholarships:** Available. **Calendar System:** Semester, Summer session available **Enrollment:** Full-time 148, Graduate part-time 52, Part-time 94 **Faculty:** Full-time 6, Part-time 37 **Student-Faculty Ratio:** 6:1 **% Receiving Financial Aid:** 100 **Final Year or**

Final Semester Residency Requirement: No **Credit Hours For Degree:** 60 credits, Associates; 133 credits, Bachelors **Professional Accreditation:** ABHE.

UNIVERSIDAD ADVENTISTA DE LAS ANTILLAS

PO Box 118
Mayagüez, PR 00681-0118
Tel: (787)834-9595
Fax: (787)834-9597
E-mail: admissions@uaa.edu
Web Site: www.uaa.edu
President/CEO: Dr. Obed Jimenez, PhD
Admissions: Yolanda Ferrer
Financial Aid: Awilda Matos

Type: Comprehensive **Sex:** Coed **Affiliation:** Seventh-day Adventist. **% Accepted:** 97 **Admission Plans:** Early Admission **Application Deadline:** July 15 **Application Fee:** $20.00 **H.S. Requirements:** High school diploma required; GED accepted **Costs Per Year:** Application fee: $20. One-time mandatory fee: $20. Comprehensive fee: $12,050 includes full-time tuition ($5750), mandatory fees ($1100), and college room and board ($5200). College room only: $1600. Full-time tuition and fees vary according to course load and program. Room and board charges vary according to board plan and housing facility. Part-time tuition: $175 per credit hour. Part-time mandatory fees: $1100 per term. Part-time tuition and fees vary according to course load and program. **Scholarships:** Available. **Calendar System:** Semester, Summer session available **Enrollment:** Full-time 1,220, Graduate full-time 53, Graduate part-time 27, Part-time 118 **Faculty:** Full-time 42, Part-time 42 **Student-Faculty Ratio:** 20:1 **Exams:** ACT essay component not used; Other; SAT I or ACT; SAT essay component not used. **% Receiving Financial Aid:** 90 **% Residing in College-Owned, -Operated, or -Affiliated Housing:** 26 **Final Year or Final Semester Residency Requirement:** Yes **Regional Accreditation:** Middle States Association of Colleges and Schools **Credit Hours For Degree:** 60 credits, Associates; 120 credits, Bachelors **Professional Accreditation:** ACEN, AHIMA, CoARC.

UNIVERSIDAD CENTRAL DEL CARIBE

PO Box 60-327
Bayamón, PR 00960-6032
Tel: (787)798-3001
Web Site: www.uccaribe.edu
President/CEO: Dr. José Ginel Rodríguez

Type: Comprehensive **Sex:** Coed **Application Fee:** $25.00 **Calendar System:** Semester **Student-Faculty Ratio:** 22:1 **Regional Accreditation:** Middle States Association of Colleges and Schools **Professional Accreditation:** JRCERT, LCME/AMA.

UNIVERSIDAD DEL ESTE

PO Box 2010
Carolina, PR 00984
Tel: (787)257-7373
Fax: (787)257-7373
E-mail: ue_csantiago@suagm.edu
Web Site: www.suagm.edu/une
President/CEO: Alberto Maldonado Ruiz
Admissions: Clotilde Santiago
Financial Aid: Eigna De Jess Molinari

Type: Comprehensive **Sex:** Coed **Affiliation:** Ana G. Mendez University System. **% Accepted:** 43 **Admission Plans:** Deferred Admission **Application Fee:** $15.00 **H.S. Requirements:** High school diploma required; GED accepted **Costs Per Year:** Application fee: $15. Tuition: $4920 full-time. Mandatory fees: $900 full-time. **Calendar System:** Semester, Summer session available **Enrollment:** Full-time 8,539, Graduate full-time 537, Graduate part-time 696, Part-time 3,286 **Student-Faculty Ratio:** 21:1 **Exams:** Other. **Regional Accreditation:** Middle States Association of Colleges and Schools **Credit Hours For Degree:** 62 credits, Associates **Professional Accreditation:** ACBSP, ACF, AHIMA. **Intercollegiate Athletics:** Baseball M; Basketball M & W; Cheerleading M & W; Cross-Country Running M & W; Softball W; Track and Field M & W; Volleyball M & W; Weight Lifting M

UNIVERSIDAD METROPOLITANA

Apartado 21150
San Juan, PR 00928-1150
Tel: (787)766-1717; Free: 800-747-8362
Fax: (787)759-7663

E-mail: yrivera@suagm.edu
Web Site: www.suagm.edu/umet
President/CEO: Dr. Carlos M. Padin, PhD
Admissions: Yadira Rivera Lugo

Type: Comprehensive **Sex:** Coed **Affiliation:** Ana G. Mendez University System. **% Accepted:** 65 **Admission Plans:** Early Admission **Application Deadline:** August 15 **Application Fee:** $15.00 **Costs Per Year:** Application fee: $15. Tuition: $4920 full-time, $205 per credit hour part-time. Mandatory fees: $900 full-time, $450 per term part-time. Full-time tuition and fees vary according to degree level, location, and program. Part-time tuition and fees vary according to degree level, location, and program. **Calendar System:** Semester, Summer session available **Enrollment:** Full-time 9,073, Graduate full-time 1,161, Graduate part-time 1,169, Part-time 2,516 **Faculty:** Full-time 179, Part-time 1,071 **Student-Faculty Ratio:** 22:1 **Exams:** Other; SAT I. **Final Year or Final Semester Residency Requirement:** No **Regional Accreditation:** Middle States Association of Colleges and Schools **Credit Hours For Degree:** 72 credits, Associates; 128 credits, Bachelors **Professional Accreditation:** ACBSP, ACEN. **Intercollegiate Athletics:** Baseball M; Basketball M & W; Cheerleading M & W; Cross-Country Running M & W; Soccer M & W; Softball W; Table Tennis M & W; Tennis M & W; Track and Field M & W; Volleyball M & W; Weight Lifting M & W

UNIVERSIDAD PENTECOSTAL MIZPA

Bo Caimito Rd. 199
Apartado 20966
San Juan, PR 00928-0966
Tel: (787)720-4476
Fax: (787)720-2012
Web Site: www.mizpa.edu
President/CEO: Rev. Abner Rivera Angel Rivera
Admissions: Omar Alicea
Financial Aid: Myriam Juarbe

Type: Four-Year College **Sex:** Coed **Affiliation:** Pentecostal Church. **Admission Plans:** Open Admission **Application Fee:** $40.00 **Scholarships:** Available. **Calendar System:** Semester **Student-Faculty Ratio:** 13:1 **Professional Accreditation:** ABHE.

UNIVERSIDAD DEL TURABO

PO Box 3030
Gurabo, PR 00778-3030
Tel: (787)743-7979
E-mail: msanchez@suagm.edu
Web Site: www.suagm.edu/ut
President/CEO: Dennis Alicea, PhD
Admissions: Melba Sanchez
Financial Aid: Carmen J. Rivera Lopez

Type: University **Sex:** Coed **Affiliation:** Ana G. Mendez University System. **% Accepted:** 52 **Application Deadline:** Rolling **Application Fee:** $15.00 **H.S. Requirements:** High school diploma required; GED accepted **Costs Per Year:** Application fee: $15. Tuition: $4920 full-time, $205 per credit hour part-time. Mandatory fees: $900 full-time, $450 per term part-time. Full-time tuition and fees vary according to degree level and program. Part-time tuition and fees vary according to degree level and program. **Scholarships:** Available. **Calendar System:** Semester, Summer session available **Enrollment:** Full-time 10,696, Graduate full-time 1,411, Graduate part-time 1,402, Part-time 4,000 **Faculty:** Full-time 237, Part-time 934 **Student-Faculty Ratio:** 22:1 **Exams:** Other; SAT I. **Final Year or Final Semester Residency Requirement:** No **Regional Accreditation:** Middle States Association of Colleges and Schools **Credit Hours For Degree:** 64 credits, Associates; 120 credits, Bachelors **ROTC:** Air Force, Army **Professional Accreditation:** AACN, TEAC. **Intercollegiate Athletics:** Baseball M; Basketball M & W; Cross-Country Running M & W; Soccer M; Softball M & W; Swimming and Diving M & W; Tennis M & W; Track and Field M & W; Volleyball M & W; Weight Lifting M & W

UNIVERSITY OF PUERTO RICO IN AGUADILLA

PO Box 6150
Aguadilla, PR 00604
Tel: (787)890-2681
Web Site: www.uprag.edu
President/CEO: Dr. Nelson A. Vera Hernandez
Admissions: Melba Serrano Lugo

Type: Four-Year College **Sex:** Coed **Affiliation:** University of Puerto Rico System. **% Accepted:** 89 **Admission Plans:** Deferred Admission; Early

Admission **Application Fee:** $20.00 **H.S. Requirements:** High school diploma required; GED accepted **Costs Per Year:** Application fee: $20. Commonwealth resident tuition: $1870 full-time, $55 per credit hour part-time. Nonresident tuition: $3892 full-time. Mandatory fees: $149 full-time, $149 per unit part-time, $149. Full-time tuition and fees vary according to class time. Part-time tuition and fees vary according to class time. **Calendar System:** Semester, Summer session available **Exams:** Other; SAT I; SAT II. **Regional Accreditation:** Middle States Association of Colleges and Schools **Credit Hours For Degree:** 66 credits, Associates; 129 credits, Bachelors **ROTC:** Army **Professional Accreditation:** ACBSP, NCATE. **Intercollegiate Athletics:** Baseball M; Basketball M; Cross-Country Running M & W; Softball W; Swimming and Diving M & W; Table Tennis M; Tennis W; Track and Field M & W; Weight Lifting M & W

UNIVERSITY OF PUERTO RICO IN ARECIBO

Carretera 653 Km. 0.8, Sector Las Dunas
Arecibo, PR 00614
Tel: (787)878-2830
E-mail: dbarrios@upra.edu
Web Site: www.upra.edu
President/CEO: Otilio Gonzalez
Admissions: Delma Barrios Colon
Financial Aid: Myrta F. Salcedo-Ortiz
Type: Four-Year College **Sex:** Coed **Affiliation:** University of Puerto Rico System. **% Accepted:** 47 **Application Fee:** $20.00 **H.S. Requirements:** High school diploma required; GED accepted **Costs Per Year:** Application fee: $20. One-time mandatory fee: $35. Commonwealth resident tuition: $1870 full-time, $550 per year part-time. Nonresident tuition: $3891 full-time, $2518 per year part-time. Mandatory fees: $55 per term part-time. Full-time tuition varies according to course load and program. Part-time tuition and fees vary according to course load and program. Tuition guaranteed not to increase for student's term of enrollment. **Scholarships:** Available. **Calendar System:** Semester, Summer session available **Exams:** Other; SAT II. **Regional Accreditation:** Middle States Association of Colleges and Schools **Credit Hours For Degree:** 68 credits, Associates; 132 credits, Bachelors **ROTC:** Army **Professional Accreditation:** ABET, ACBSP, ACEN, NCATE. **Intercollegiate Athletics:** Baseball M; Basketball M & W; Cross-Country Running M & W; Softball W; Swimming and Diving M & W; Tennis M & W; Track and Field M & W; Volleyball M & W; Weight Lifting M & W; Wrestling M

UNIVERSITY OF PUERTO RICO IN BAYAMÓN

Industrial Minillas 170 Carr 174
Bayamón, PR 00959
Tel: (787)993-0000
E-mail: carmen.montes1@upr.edu
Web Site: www.uprb.edu
President/CEO: Margarita Fernandez Zavala
Admissions: Carmen I. Montes Burgos
Financial Aid: Marcos Cesar De Jesus Rosado
Type: Four-Year College **Sex:** Coed **Affiliation:** University of Puerto Rico System. **% Accepted:** 22 **Application Deadline:** January 6 **Application Fee:** $30.00 **H.S. Requirements:** High school diploma required; GED accepted **Costs Per Year:** Application fee: $30. Commonwealth resident tuition: $1870 full-time, $55 per credit part-time. Nonresident tuition: $3892 full-time, $114 per credit part-time. Mandatory fees: $144 full-time. Full-time tuition and fees vary according to class time, course load, and program. Part-time tuition varies according to class time, course load, and program. Tuition guaranteed not to increase for student's term of enrollment. **Scholarships:** Available. **Calendar System:** Semester, Summer session available **Enrollment:** Full-time 4,290, Part-time 675 **Faculty:** Full-time 199, Part-time 55 **Student-Faculty Ratio:** 20:1 **Exams:** Other. **Final Year or Final Semester Residency Requirement:** No **Regional Accreditation:** Middle States Association of Colleges and Schools **Credit Hours For Degree:** 72 credits, Associates; 130 credits, Bachelors **Professional Accreditation:** ABET, ACBSP, NCATE. **Intercollegiate Athletics:** Basketball M & W; Cross-Country Running M & W; Tennis M & W; Track and Field M & W; Volleyball M & W

UNIVERSITY OF PUERTO RICO IN CAROLINA

PO Box 4800
Carolina, PR 00984-4800
Tel: (787)257-0000
Web Site: www.uprc.edu

President/CEO: Dr. Moises Orengo-Aviles
Admissions: Celia Mendez
Type: Four-Year College **Sex:** Coed **Affiliation:** University of Puerto Rico System. **% Accepted:** 76 **Application Fee:** $20.00 **H.S. Requirements:** High school diploma required; GED accepted **Costs Per Year:** Application fee: $20. One-time mandatory fee: $868. Commonwealth resident tuition: $2805 full-time, $825 per year part-time. Nonresident tuition: $5,837 full-time. Mandatory fees: $251 full-time, $221 per year part-time, $72 per term part-time. Full-time tuition and fees vary according to class time, course load, program, and student level. Part-time tuition and fees vary according to class time, course load, program, and student level. **Calendar System:** Quarter, Summer session not available **Student-Faculty Ratio:** 22:1 **Exams:** ACT; Other; SAT I; SAT II. **Regional Accreditation:** Middle States Association of Colleges and Schools **Credit Hours For Degree:** 68 credits, Associates; 137 credits, Bachelors **ROTC:** Air Force, Army **Professional Accreditation:** ACBSP. **Intercollegiate Athletics:** Basketball M & W; Cross-Country Running M & W; Tennis M & W; Track and Field M & W; Volleyball M & W

UNIVERSITY OF PUERTO RICO IN CAYEY

205 Ave. Antonio R. Barcelo
Cayey, PR 00736
Tel: (787)738-2161
E-mail: wilfredo.lopez3@upr.edu
Web Site: www.cayey.upr.edu
President/CEO: Dr. Raul Castro
Admissions: Wilfredo Lopez
Financial Aid: Hector Maldonado Otero
Type: Four-Year College **Sex:** Coed **Affiliation:** University of Puerto Rico System. **% Accepted:** 78 **Admission Plans:** Early Action; Early Admission **Application Fee:** $20.00 **H.S. Requirements:** High school diploma required; GED accepted **Scholarships:** Available. **Calendar System:** Semester, Summer session available **Enrollment:** Full-time 3,458, Part-time 372 **Student-Faculty Ratio:** 21:1 **Exams:** Other; SAT I. **% Receiving Financial Aid:** 76 **Regional Accreditation:** Middle States Association of Colleges and Schools **Credit Hours For Degree:** 72 credits, Associates; 128 credits, Bachelors **ROTC:** Army **Professional Accreditation:** ACBSP, NCATE. **Intercollegiate Athletics:** Basketball M & W; Cross-Country Running M & W; Soccer M; Softball M & W; Swimming and Diving M & W; Table Tennis M; Tennis M & W; Track and Field M & W; Volleyball M & W; Weight Lifting M & W; Wrestling M

UNIVERSITY OF PUERTO RICO IN HUMACAO

HUC Station 100, Rd. 908
Humacao, PR 00791
Tel: (787)850-0000
Fax: (787)852-4638
E-mail: elizabeth.gerena@upr.edu
Web Site: www.uprh.edu
President/CEO: Dr. Carmen J. Hernandez
Admissions: Elizabeth Gerena
Financial Aid: Alfredo Aponte Serrano
Type: Four-Year College **Sex:** Coed **Affiliation:** University of Puerto Rico System. **Scores:** 98% SAT V 400+; 98% SAT M 400+ **% Accepted:** 40 **Admission Plans:** Deferred Admission **Application Deadline:** January 31 **Application Fee:** $20.00 **H.S. Requirements:** High school diploma required; GED accepted **Costs Per Year:** Application fee: $20. Commonwealth resident tuition: $1870 full-time, $55 per credit hour part-time. Nonresident tuition: $3892 full-time, $114.46 per credit hour part-time. Mandatory fees: $179 full-time. Full-time tuition and fees vary according to class time, course load, and student level. Part-time tuition varies according to class time, course load, and student level. College room and board: $8751. College room only: $3151. Tuition guaranteed not to increase for student's term of enrollment. **Scholarships:** Available. **Calendar System:** Semester, Summer session available **Enrollment:** Full-time 3,473, Part-time 301 **Faculty:** Full-time 219, Part-time 38 **Student-Faculty Ratio:** 16:1 **Exams:** ACT essay component not used; Other; SAT I or ACT; SAT II; SAT essay component not used; SAT Reasoning; SAT Subject. **% Receiving Financial Aid:** 82 **Regional Accreditation:** Middle States Association of Colleges and Schools **Credit Hours For Degree:** 65 credits, Associates; 128 credits, Bachelors **Professional Accreditation:** ACBSP, ACEN, AOTA, APTA, CSWE, NCATE. **Intercollegiate Athletics:** Baseball M; Basketball M & W; Cheerleading M & W; Cross-Country Running M & W; Softball W;

Swimming and Diving M & W; Table Tennis M & W; Tennis W; Track and Field M & W; Volleyball M & W; Weight Lifting M & W; Wrestling M

UNIVERSITY OF PUERTO RICO, MAYAGÜEZ CAMPUS

PO Box 9000
Mayagüez, PR 00681-9000
Tel: (787)832-4040
E-mail: smarty@uprm.edu
Web Site: www.uprm.edu
President/CEO: Jorge Velez-Arocho
Admissions: Sheila Marty-Rodriquez
Financial Aid: Miriam Barreto
Type: University **Sex:** Coed **Affiliation:** University of Puerto Rico System. **% Accepted:** 77 **Admission Plans:** Early Decision Plan **Application Fee:** $20.00 **H.S. Requirements:** High school diploma required; GED accepted **Scholarships:** Available. **Calendar System:** Semester, Summer session available **Student-Faculty Ratio:** 16:1 **Exams:** Other; SAT II. **% Receiving Financial Aid:** 67 **Regional Accreditation:** Middle States Association of Colleges and Schools **Credit Hours For Degree:** 134 credits, Bachelors **ROTC:** Air Force, Army **Professional Accreditation:** ACEN, NCATE. **Intercollegiate Athletics:** Baseball M; Basketball M & W; Cross-Country Running M & W; Soccer M; Softball W; Swimming and Diving M & W; Tennis M & W; Track and Field M & W; Volleyball M & W; Water Polo M; Wrestling M

UNIVERSITY OF PUERTO RICO, MEDICAL SCIENCES CAMPUS

PO Box 365067
San Juan, PR 00936-5067
Tel: (787)758-2525
Fax: (787)754-0474
E-mail: margarita.rivera4@upr.edu
Web Site: www.rcm.upr.edu
President/CEO: Dr. Noel Aymat
Admissions: Margarita Rivera Rosario
Financial Aid: Zoraida Figueroa
Type: University **Sex:** Coed **Affiliation:** University of Puerto Rico System. **Admission Plans:** Preferred Admission **Application Fee:** $20.00 **Scholarships:** Available. **Calendar System:** Semester, Summer session available **% Receiving Financial Aid:** 69 **Regional Accreditation:** Middle States Association of Colleges and Schools **Credit Hours For Degree:** 91 credits, Bachelors **Professional Accreditation:** AACN, AANA, ACNM, ACPE, ADA, AHIMA, AND, AOTA, APTA, ASHA, CAHME, CEPH, JRCERT, JRCNMT, LCME/AMA, NAACLS.

UNIVERSITY OF PUERTO RICO IN PONCE

PO Box 7186
Ponce, PR 00732-7186
Tel: (787)844-8181
Fax: (787)844-8679
E-mail: avelazquez@uprp.edu
Web Site: www.uprp.edu
President/CEO: Dr. Leonardo Morales-Tomassini
Admissions: Emily Matos-Cortes
Financial Aid: Carmelo Vega Montes
Type: Four-Year College **Sex:** Coed **Affiliation:** University of Puerto Rico System. **% Accepted:** 74 **Admission Plans:** Early Admission **Application Deadline:** November 15 **Application Fee:** $20.00 **H.S. Requirements:** High school diploma required; GED accepted **Scholarships:** Available. **Calendar System:** Semester, Summer session available **Enrollment:** Full-time 3,028, Part-time 201 **Faculty:** Full-time 134, Part-time 54 **Student-Faculty Ratio:** 17:1 **Exams:** Other. **% Receiving Financial Aid:** 75 **Final Year or Final Semester Residency Requirement:** No **Regional Accreditation:** Middle States Association of Colleges and Schools **Credit Hours For Degree:** 73 credits, Associates; 136 credits, Bachelors **ROTC:** Army **Professional Accreditation:** ACBSP, APTA, NCATE. **Intercollegiate Athletics:** Baseball M; Basketball M & W; Cross-Country Running M & W; Table Tennis M & W; Tennis M; Track and Field M & W; Volleyball M & W; Weight Lifting M & W

UNIVERSITY OF PUERTO RICO, RÍO PIEDRAS CAMPUS

PO Box 23300
San Juan, PR 00931-3300
Tel: (787)764-0000
Web Site: www.uprrp.edu
President/CEO: Ana Guadalupe, PhD

Admissions: Cruz B. Valentìn
Financial Aid: Efraim Williams
Type: University **Sex:** Coed **Affiliation:** University of Puerto Rico System. **% Accepted:** 36 **Application Deadline:** December 15 **Application Fee:** $20.00 **H.S. Requirements:** High school diploma required; GED accepted **Scholarships:** Available. **Calendar System:** Semester, Summer session available **Enrollment:** Graduate full-time 2,714, Graduate part-time 896 **Faculty:** Full-time 749, Part-time 335 **Student-Faculty Ratio:** 16:1 **Exams:** Other; SAT I. **Regional Accreditation:** Middle States Association of Colleges and Schools **Credit Hours For Degree:** 120 credits, Bachelors **ROTC:** Air Force, Army **Professional Accreditation:** AACN, AALS, ABA, ABET, ACBSP, ACSP, ALA, CORE, CSWE, NAAB, NCATE. **Intercollegiate Athletics:** Baseball M; Basketball M & W; Cross-Country Running M & W; Soccer M; Softball M & W; Swimming and Diving M & W; Table Tennis M & W; Tennis M & W; Track and Field M & W; Volleyball M & W; Water Polo M & W; Weight Lifting M & W; Wrestling M & W

UNIVERSITY OF PUERTO RICO IN UTUADO

PO Box 2500
Utuado, PR 00641-2500
Tel: (787)894-2828
Web Site: www.uprutuado.edu
President/CEO: Cesar Cordero Montalvo
Admissions: Maria Robles Serrano
Financial Aid: Edgar Salvá
Type: Four-Year College **Sex:** Coed **Affiliation:** University of Puerto Rico System. **% Accepted:** 45 **Admission Plans:** Deferred Admission; Early Admission **Application Deadline:** Rolling **Application Fee:** $20.00 **H.S. Requirements:** High school diploma required; GED accepted **Costs Per Year:** Application fee: $20. One-time mandatory fee: $35. Commonwealth resident tuition: $1870 full-time, $550 per year part-time. Nonresident tuition: $3892 full-time. Mandatory fees: $144 full-time, $55 per credit hour part-time. Full-time tuition and fees vary according to course load and program. Part-time tuition and fees vary according to course load and program. Tuition guaranteed not to increase for student's term of enrollment. **Scholarships:** Available. **Calendar System:** Semester, Summer session available **Enrollment:** Full-time 1,448, Part-time 175 **Faculty:** Full-time 74, Part-time 33 **Student-Faculty Ratio:** 18:1 **Exams:** Other; SAT II. **Regional Accreditation:** Middle States Association of Colleges and Schools **Credit Hours For Degree:** 60 credits, Associates; 137 credits, Bachelors **Professional Accreditation:** ACBSP, NCATE. **Intercollegiate Athletics:** Basketball M & W; Cross-Country Running M & W; Softball M & W; Table Tennis M & W; Track and Field M & W; Volleyball M & W; Weight Lifting M & W

UNIVERSITY OF THE SACRED HEART

PO Box 12383
San Juan, PR 00914-0383
Tel: (787)728-1515
Web Site: www.sagrado.edu
President/CEO: Dr. Jose J. Rivera
Admissions: Luis Heviquez
Financial Aid: Maria Torres
Type: Comprehensive **Sex:** Coed **Affiliation:** Roman Catholic. **% Accepted:** 35 **Admission Plans:** Early Admission **Application Deadline:** June 30 **Application Fee:** $15.00 **H.S. Requirements:** High school diploma required; GED accepted **Scholarships:** Available. **Calendar System:** Semester, Summer session available **Enrollment:** Full-time 3,765, Part-time 870 **Faculty:** Full-time 122, Part-time 245 **Student-Faculty Ratio:** 20:1 **Regional Accreditation:** Middle States Association of Colleges and Schools **Credit Hours For Degree:** 67 credits, Associates; 133 credits, Bachelors **Professional Accreditation:** ACBSP, ACEN, CSWE, NAACLS. **Intercollegiate Athletics:** Basketball M & W; Swimming and Diving M & W; Tennis M & W; Track and Field M & W; Ultimate Frisbee M & W; Volleyball M & W; Weight Lifting M & W

United States Virgin Islands

UNIVERSITY OF THE VIRGIN ISLANDS

2 John Brewers Bay
Saint Thomas, VI 00802-9990
Tel: (340)776-9200
E-mail: xallen@uvi.edu
Web Site: www.uvi.edu

President/CEO: Dr. David Hall
Admissions: Dr. Xuri Maurice Allen
Financial Aid: Mavis M. Gilchrist
Type: Comprehensive **Sex:** Coed **Scores:** 56% SAT V 400+; 44% SAT M 400+; 35% ACT 18-23; 13% ACT 24-29 **% Accepted:** 95 **Admission Plans:** Deferred Admission; Early Admission **Application Deadline:** April 30 **Application Fee:** $25.00 **H.S. Requirements:** High school diploma required; GED accepted **Costs Per Year:** Application fee: $25. Territory resident tuition: $4631 full-time, $154 per credit part-time. Nonresident tuition: $13,892 full-time, $463 per credit part-time. Mandatory fees: $604 full-time, $254 per term part-time. Full-time tuition and fees vary according to reciprocity agreements. Part-time tuition and fees vary according to course load and reciprocity agreements. College room and board: $9900. College room only: $4120. Room and board charges vary according to board plan and housing facility. **Scholarships:** Available. **Calendar System:** Semester, Summer session available **Enrollment:** Full-time 1,487, Graduate full-time 66, Graduate part-time 117, Part-time 651 **Faculty:** Full-time 109, Part-time 148 **Student-Faculty Ratio:** 12:1 **Exams:** ACT essay component used for placement; SAT I or ACT; SAT essay component used for placement; SAT Reasoning; SAT Subject. **% Receiving Financial Aid:** 83 **Final Year or Final Semester Residency Requirement:** Yes **Regional Accreditation:** Middle States Association of Colleges and Schools **Credit Hours For Degree:** 62 credits, Associates; 120 credits, Bachelors **ROTC:** Army **Professional Accreditation:** ACBSP, ACEN. **Intercollegiate Athletics:** Basketball M & W; Cheerleading W; Cross-Country Running M & W; Soccer M; Track and Field M & W

ALBERTA COLLEGE OF ART & DESIGN

1407 14 Ave. NW
Calgary, AB, Canada T2N 4R3
Tel: (403)284-7600; Free: 800-251-8290
E-mail: admissions@acad.ca
Web Site: www.acad.ca
President/CEO: Dr. Daniel Doz
Admissions: Katie Potapoff
Type: Four-Year College **Sex:** Coed **% Accepted:** 37 **Admission Plans:** Early Action **Application Deadline:** February 1 **Application Fee:** $85.00 **H.S. Requirements:** High school diploma required; GED accepted. For mature applicants who are Canadian citizens/permanent residents; applicants to the Artstream program: High school diploma or equivalent not required **Scholarships:** Available. **Calendar System:** Semester, Summer session available **Enrollment:** Full-time 1,043, Part-time 107 **Faculty:** Full-time 40, Part-time 82 **Student-Faculty Ratio:** 16:1 **% Residing in College-Owned, -Operated, or -Affiliated Housing:** 9 **Final Year or Final Semester Residency Requirement:** Yes **Credit Hours For Degree:** 120 credits, Bachelors

AMBROSE UNIVERSITY

150 Ambrose Cir. SW
Calgary, AB, Canada T3H 0L5
Tel: (403)410-2000; Free: 800-461-1222
E-mail: enrolment@ambrose.edu
Web Site: www.ambrose.edu
President/CEO: Dr. Gordon T. Smith
Admissions: Kalie Eeles
Financial Aid: Hannah Temple
Type: Comprehensive **Sex:** Coed **Affiliation:** The Christian and Missionary Alliance. **Costs Per Year:** Tuition, fee, and room and board charges are reported in Canadian dollars. Comprehensive fee: $17,608 includes full-time tuition ($10,500), mandatory fees ($908), and college room and board ($6200). College room only: $3400. Full-time tuition and fees vary according to course load, degree level, and program. Room and board charges vary according to board plan and housing facility. Part-time tuition: $350 per credit hour. Part-time mandatory fees: $30.25 per credit hour. Part-time tuition and fees vary according to course load, degree level, and program. **Scholarships:** Available. **Calendar System:** Semester, Summer session available **Enrollment:** Full-time 644, Graduate full-time 62, Graduate part-time 145, Part-time 69 **Faculty:** Full-time 44, Part-time 40 **Student-Faculty Ratio:** 13:1 **Exams:** SAT I or ACT. **% Residing in College-Owned, -Operated, or -Affiliated Housing:** 29 **Final Year or Final Semester Residency Requirement:** No **Credit Hours For Degree:** 90 credits, Bachelors **Professional Accreditation:** ABHE, ATS. **Intercollegiate Athletics:** Basketball M & W; Soccer M & W; Volleyball M & W

ATHABASCA UNIVERSITY

1 University Dr.
Athabasca, AB, Canada T9S 3A3
Tel: (780)675-6100; Free: 800-788-9041
Fax: (780)675-6437
Web Site: www.athabascau.ca
President/CEO: Dr. Frits Pannekoek
Financial Aid: Becky Jonasson
Type: Comprehensive **Sex:** Coed **Admission Plans:** Open Admission **Application Deadline:** Rolling **Application Fee:** $60.00 **H.S. Requirements:** High school diploma or equivalent not required **Scholarships:** Available. **Calendar System:** Continuous, Summer session available **Enrollment:** Graduate part-time 3,791, Part-time 35,071 **Final Year or Final Semester Residency Requirement:** No **Regional Accreditation:** Middle States Association of Colleges and Schools **Credit Hours For Degree:** 120 credits, Bachelors

CONCORDIA UNIVERSITY OF EDMONTON

7128 Ada Blvd., NW
Edmonton, AB, Canada T5B 4E4
Tel: (780)479-8481; Free: 866-479-5200
Fax: (780)474-1933
E-mail: admits@concordia.ab.ca
Web Site: www.concordia.ab.ca
President/CEO: Rev. Gerald S. Krispin
Financial Aid: Margie Schoepp
Type: Comprehensive **Sex:** Coed **Affiliation:** Lutheran. **% Accepted:** 65 **Admission Plans:** Early Admission; Open Admission **Application Deadline:** June 30 **Application Fee:** $0.00 **H.S. Requirements:** High school diploma required; GED not accepted **Scholarships:** Available. **Calendar System:** Semester, Summer session available **Faculty:** Full-time 59, Part-time 94 **Student-Faculty Ratio:** 18:1 **% Residing in College-Owned, -Operated, or -Affiliated Housing:** 3 **Credit Hours For Degree:** 120 credits, Bachelors **Intercollegiate Athletics:** Badminton M & W; Basketball M & W; Cross-Country Running M & W; Golf M & W; Ice Hockey M; Soccer M & W; Swimming and Diving M & W

THE KING'S UNIVERSITY

9125 50th St.
Edmonton, AB, Canada T6B 2H3
Tel: (780)465-3500; Free: 800-661-8582
Fax: (780)465-3534
E-mail: admissions@kingsu.ca
Web Site: www.kingsu.ca
President/CEO: Melanie Humphreys
Admissions: Hilda Buisman
Financial Aid: Lesley Huska
Type: Four-Year College **Sex:** Coed **Affiliation:** interdenominational. **% Accepted:** 85 **Application Deadline:** Rolling **Application Fee:** $70.00 **H.S. Requirements:** High school diploma required; GED not accepted **Costs Per Year:** Application fee: $70. Comprehensive fee: $19,197 includes full-time tuition ($11,780), mandatory fees ($857), and college room and board ($6560). College room only: $3560. Full-time tuition and fees vary according to course load. Room and board charges vary according to board plan and housing facility. Part-time tuition: $380 per credit. Part-time tuition varies according to course load. **Scholarships:** Available. **Calendar System:** Miscellaneous, Summer session available **Enrollment:** Full-time 644, Graduate full-time 69, Graduate part-time 4, Part-time 68 **Faculty:** Full-time 50, Part-time 70 **Student-Faculty Ratio:** 11:1 **Exams:** ACT essay component not used; SAT essay component not used. **% Residing in College-Owned, -Operated, or -Affiliated Housing:** 29 **Credit Hours For Degree:** 93 credits, Bachelors **Intercollegiate Athletics:** Badminton M & W; Basketball M & W; Soccer M & W; Volleyball M & W

MOUNT ROYAL UNIVERSITY

4825 Mount Royal Gate SW
Calgary, AB, Canada T3E 6K6
Tel: (403)440-6111; Free: 877-440-5001
Fax: (403)440-5938
Web Site: www.mtroyal.ca
President/CEO: David Marshall, PhD
Type: Four-Year College **Sex:** Coed **Application Fee:** $70.00

PRAIRIE BIBLE INSTITUTE

330 Sixth Ave. N
Three Hills, AB, Canada T0M 2N0
Tel: (403)443-5511; Free: 800-661-2425
Fax: (403)443-5540
E-mail: admissions@prairie.edu
Web Site: www.prairie.edu
Admissions: Kevin Kirk
Financial Aid: Doug Johnson
Type: Four-Year College **Sex:** Coed **Affiliation:** interdenominational. **Application Deadline:** August 15 **Application Fee:** $35.00 **H.S. Requirements:** High school diploma required; GED accepted **Scholarships:** Available. **Calendar System:** Semester, Summer session not available **Credit Hours For Degree:** 129 credits, Bachelors **Professional Accreditation:** ABHE.

ROCKY MOUNTAIN COLLEGE

4039 Brentwood Rd., NW
Calgary, AB, Canada T2L 1L1
Tel: (403)284-5100; Free: 877-YOUnRMC
E-mail: enrolment@rockymountaincollege.ca
Web Site: www.rockymountaincollege.ca
Admissions: Robert Harris
Financial Aid: Duane Erion
Type: Four-Year College **Sex:** Coed **Affiliation:** Missionary Church. **Admission Plans:** Deferred Admission; Early Action; Open Admission **Application Fee:** $50.00 **H.S. Requirements:** High school diploma required; GED accepted **Scholarships:** Available. **Calendar System:** Semester, Summer session available **Credit Hours For Degree:** 128 semester hours, Bachelors **Professional Accreditation:** ABHE.

SOUTHERN ALBERTA INSTITUTE OF TECHNOLOGY

1301 16th Ave. NW
Calgary, AB, Canada T2M 0L4
Tel: (403)284-8110; Free: 877-284-SAIT
Fax: (403)284-7112
Web Site: www.sait.ca
President/CEO: Irene Lewis
Admissions: Jennifer Bennett
Type: Two-Year College **Sex:** Coed **Admission Plans:** Early Action; Early Admission **Application Deadline:** Rolling **Application Fee:** $50.00 **H.S. Requirements:** High school diploma required; GED accepted **Calendar System:** Trimester **Enrollment:** Full-time 6,954, Part-time 718 **Credit Hours For Degree:** 120 credits, Bachelors **Intercollegiate Athletics:** Basketball M & W; Cross-Country Running M & W; Ice Hockey M & W; Soccer M & W; Volleyball M & W

UNIVERSITY OF ALBERTA

Edmonton, AB, Canada T6G 2E1
Tel: (780)492-3111; Free: 855-492-3113
Fax: (780)492-7172
Web Site: www.ualberta.ca
President/CEO: Dr. Indira Samarasekera, PhD
Admissions: Melissa Padfield
Financial Aid: Jane Lee
Type: University **Sex:** Coed **Admission Plans:** Early Action; Early Decision Plan; Preferred Admission **Application Deadline:** May 1 **Application Fee:** $125.00 **H.S. Requirements:** High school diploma required; GED not accepted. For students taking Canadian curricula: High school diploma or equivalent not required **Scholarships:** Available. **Calendar System:** Miscellaneous, Summer session available **Enrollment:** Full-time 29,098, Graduate full-time 6,004, Graduate part-time 1,568, Part-time 2,063 **Student-Faculty Ratio:** 20:1 **Exams:** ACT; Other; SAT I; SAT I and SAT II or ACT; SAT I or ACT; SAT II; SAT Reasoning; SAT Subject. **Final Year or Final Semester Residency Requirement:** No **Credit Hours For Degree:** 120 credits,

Bachelors **Professional Accreditation:** AACSB, ADA, ALA, LCME/AMA. **Intercollegiate Athletics:** Basketball M & W; Cross-Country Running M & W; Football M; Golf M & W; Ice Hockey M & W; Rugby W; Soccer M & W; Swimming and Diving M & W; Tennis M & W; Track and Field M & W; Volleyball M & W; Wrestling M & W

UNIVERSITY OF CALGARY

2500 University Dr., NW
Calgary, AB, Canada T2N 1N4
Tel: (403)220-5110
E-mail: future.students@ucalgary.ca
Web Site: www.ucalgary.ca
President/CEO: Dr. Elizabeth M. Cannon
Admissions: Kaili Xu
Type: University **Sex:** Coed **Scores:** 24% ACT 24-29 **% Accepted:** 47 **Admission Plans:** Early Admission **Application Deadline:** March 1 **Application Fee:** $145.00 **H.S. Requirements:** High school diploma required; GED not accepted **Costs Per Year:** Application fee: $145. Province resident tuition: $5,386 full-time. Canadian resident tuition: $5,386 full-time. Mandatory fees: $1,204 full-time. Full-time tuition and fees vary according to course load and program. International student tuition: $18,338 full-time. **Calendar System:** Semester, Summer session available **Enrollment:** Full-time 22,491, Graduate full-time 5,311, Graduate part-time 493, Part-time 1,906 **Faculty:** Full-time 1,780, Part-time 52 **Student-Faculty Ratio:** 21:1 **Exams:** ACT essay component used for admission; SAT I or ACT; SAT essay component used for admission. **Credit Hours For Degree:** 120 credit hours, Bachelors **Professional Accreditation:** AACSB, LCME/AMA. **Intercollegiate Athletics:** Baseball M & W; Basketball M & W; Cross-Country Running M & W; Field Hockey W; Football M; Golf M & W; Ice Hockey M & W; Rowing M & W; Rugby M & W; Skiing (Cross-Country) M & W; Soccer M & W; Swimming and Diving M & W; Tennis M & W; Track and Field M & W; Volleyball M & W; Wrestling M & W

UNIVERSITY OF LETHBRIDGE

4401 University Dr.
Lethbridge, AB, Canada T1K 3M4
Tel: (403)329-2111
E-mail: regoffice@uleth.ca
Web Site: www.uleth.ca
President/CEO: Dr. Mike Mahon
Type: University **Sex:** Coed **% Accepted:** 84 **Admission Plans:** Deferred Admission **Application Deadline:** June 30 **Application Fee:** $100.00 **H.S. Requirements:** High school diploma required; GED not accepted **Costs Per Year:** Application fee: $100. Province resident tuition: $4974 full-time. Canadian resident tuition: $4974 full-time. Mandatory fees: $1,015 full-time. Full-time tuition and fees vary according to course load. College room and board: $6268. College room only: $2568. Room and board charges vary according to board plan and housing facility. International student tuition: $15,251 full-time. **Scholarships:** Available. **Calendar System:** Semester, Summer session available **Enrollment:** Full-time 6,958, Graduate full-time 439, Graduate part-time 119, Part-time 779 **% Residing in College-Owned, -Operated, or -Affiliated Housing:** 12 **Final Year or Final Semester Residency Requirement:** No **Credit Hours For Degree:** 40 semester courses, Bachelors **Intercollegiate Athletics:** Basketball M & W; Ice Hockey M & W; Rugby W; Soccer M & W; Swimming and Diving M & W; Track and Field M & W

VANGUARD COLLEGE

12140 103rd St.
Edmonton, AB, Canada T5G 2J9
Tel: (780)452-0808
Fax: (780)452-5803
E-mail: admissions@vanguardcollege.com
Web Site: www.vanguardcollege.com
Type: Four-Year College **Sex:** Coed **Affiliation:** Pentecostal Assemblies of Canada; Pentecostal Assemblies of Canada (PAOC). **Admission Plans:** Early Action **Application Deadline:** August 19 **Application Fee:** $75.00 **H.S. Requirements:** High school diploma required; GED accepted **Costs Per Year:** Application fee: $75 Canadian dollars. Tuition, fee, and room and board charges are reported in Canadian dollars. Comprehensive fee: $13,215 includes full-time tuition ($7500), mandatory fees ($1315), and college room and board ($4400). College room only: $3800. Full-time tuition and fees vary according to course load, degree level, program, and student level. Room and board charges vary according to housing facility. Part-time

tuition: $218 per credit hour. Part-time tuition varies according to course load, degree level, program, and student level. **Scholarships:** Available. **Calendar System:** Semester, Summer session available **Student-Faculty** **Ratio:** 11:1 **% Residing in College-Owned, -Operated, or -Affiliated Housing:** 6 **Credit Hours For Degree:** 133 credits, Bachelors **Professional Accreditation:** ABHE.

THE ART INSTITUTE OF VANCOUVER

2665 Renfrew St.
Vancouver, BC, Canada V5M 0A7
Tel: (604)683-9200; Free: 866-717-8080
Fax: (604)684-8839
Web Site: www.artinstitutes.edu/vancouver
Type: Four-Year College **Sex:** Coed **Regional Accreditation:** Southern Association of Colleges and Schools **Professional Accreditation:** ACICS.

BRITISH COLUMBIA INSTITUTE OF TECHNOLOGY

3700 Willingdon Ave.
Burnaby, BC, Canada V5G 3H2
Tel: (604)434-5734; Free: 866-434-1610
Fax: (604)278-5363
Web Site: www.bcit.ca
President/CEO: Dr. Don Wright
Admissions: Anna Dosen
Type: Four-Year College **Sex:** Coed **% Accepted:** 44 **Application Fee:** $60.00 **H.S. Requirements:** High school diploma required; GED accepted **Calendar System:** Quarter **Enrollment:** Full-time 7,120, Part-time 15,387 **Faculty:** Full-time 735, Part-time 624 **Professional Accreditation:** ACBSP.

CAPILANO UNIVERSITY

2055 Purcell Way
North Vancouver, BC, Canada V7J 3H5
Tel: (604)986-1911
Fax: (604)984-4985
Web Site: www.capilanou.ca
President/CEO: Dr. Kris Bulcroft, PhD
Type: Four-Year College **Sex:** Coed **% Accepted:** 31 **Costs Per Year:** Tuition and fee charges are reported in Canadian dollars. Province resident tuition: $3756 full-time, $125.21 per credit part-time. Canadian resident tuition: $3756 full-time, $125.21 per credit part-time. Mandatory fees: $12.24 per credit part-time, $27.57 per term part-time. Full-time tuition varies according to degree level and program. Part-time tuition and fees vary according to degree level and program. **Calendar System:** Semester, Summer session available **Enrollment:** Full-time 4,898, Part-time 1,937 **Faculty:** Full-time 161, Part-time 479 **Student-Faculty Ratio:** 11:1 **Professional Accreditation:** ACBSP, NCCU.

COLUMBIA BIBLE COLLEGE

2940 Clearbrook Rd.
Abbotsford, BC, Canada V2T 2Z8
Tel: (604)853-3358; Free: 800-283-0881
Fax: (604)853-3063
E-mail: nathan.martin@columbiabc.edu
Web Site: www.columbiabc.edu
President/CEO: Dr. Bryan Born
Admissions: Nathan Martin
Financial Aid: Laura Abraham
Type: Four-Year College **Sex:** Coed **Affiliation:** Mennonite Brethren. **% Accepted:** 79 **Admission Plans:** Deferred Admission; Early Action; Early Admission; Open Admission; Preferred Admission **Application Deadline:** August 15 **Application Fee:** $50.00 **H.S. Requirements:** High school diploma required; GED accepted **Costs Per Year:** Application fee: $50

Canadian dollars. Tuition and fee charges are reported in Canadian dollars. Tuition: $9951 full-time, $321 per credit part-time. Full-time tuition varies according to course load. Part-time tuition varies according to course load. **Scholarships:** Available. **Calendar System:** Semester, Summer session not available **Faculty:** Full-time 14, Part-time 27 **Student-Faculty Ratio:** 21:1 **% Residing in College-Owned, -Operated, or -Affiliated Housing:** 45 **Final Year or Final Semester Residency Requirement:** No **Credit Hours For Degree:** 126 credit hours, Bachelors **Professional Accreditation:** ABHE. **Intercollegiate Athletics:** Basketball M & W; Volleyball M & W

EMILY CARR UNIVERSITY OF ART + DESIGN

1399 Johnston St.
Vancouver, BC, Canada V6H 3R9
Tel: (604)844-3800; Free: 800-832-7788
Fax: (604)844-3801
E-mail: admissions@ecuad.ca
Web Site: www.ecuad.ca
President/CEO: John C. Kerr
Type: Comprehensive **Sex:** Coed **Application Deadline:** January 15 **Application Fee:** $70.00 **H.S. Requirements:** High school diploma required; GED not accepted **Costs Per Year:** Application fee: $70 Canadian dollars. Tuition and fee charges are reported in Canadian dollars. Province resident tuition: $3864 full-time. Mandatory fees: $418 full-time. Full-time tuition and fees vary according to course load. International student tuition: $14,061 full-time. **Faculty:** Full-time 56, Part-time 164 **Student-Faculty Ratio:** 18:1 **Final Year or Final Semester Residency Requirement:** Yes **Credit Hours For Degree:** 43 courses/129.0 credits, Bachelors

OKANAGAN COLLEGE

1000 KLO Rd.
Kelowna, BC, Canada V1Y 4X8
Tel: (250)762-5445; Free: 877-755-2266
E-mail: ahickey@okanagan.bc.ca
Web Site: www.okanagan.bc.ca
President/CEO: Jim Hamilton
Admissions: Allan Hickey
Financial Aid: Joelle Ebner
Type: Four-Year College **Sex:** Coed **Affiliation:** Ministry of Advanced Education, Industry Training Authority. **Enrollment:** Full-time 1,942, Part-time 1,241 **Faculty:** Full-time 190, Part-time 78 **Student-Faculty Ratio:** 12:1 **Final Year or Final Semester Residency Requirement:** No **Credit Hours For Degree:** 60 credits, Associates; 120 credits, Bachelors **Professional Accreditation:** ACBSP. **Intercollegiate Athletics:** Baseball M

ROYAL ROADS UNIVERSITY

2005 Sooke Rd.
Victoria, BC, Canada V9B 5Y2
Tel: (250)391-2511; Free: 800-788-8028
Fax: (250)391-2522
E-mail: learn.more@royalroads.ca
Web Site: www.royalroads.ca
President/CEO: Allan Cahoon
Type: Two-Year Upper Division **Sex:** Coed **Application Fee:** $110.00 **H.S. Requirements:** High school diploma or equivalent not required **Calendar**

System: Continuous, Summer session available **Faculty:** Full-time 50 **Credit Hours For Degree:** 120 credits, Bachelors

SIMON FRASER UNIVERSITY

8888 University Dr.
Burnaby, BC, Canada V5A 1S6
Tel: (778)782-3111
E-mail: undergraduate-admissions@sfu.ca
Web Site: www.sfu.ca
President/CEO: Prof. Andrew Petter
Admissions: Louise Legris
Financial Aid: Manoj Bhakthan

Type: University **Sex:** Coed **% Accepted:** 63 **Admission Plans:** Deferred Admission; Early Admission; Early Decision Plan **Application Deadline:** February 28 **Application Fee:** $75.00 **H.S. Requirements:** High school diploma required; GED not accepted **Costs Per Year:** Application fee: $75 Canadian dollars. Tuition, fee, and room and board charges are reported in Canadian dollars. Province resident tuition: $5321 full-time, $177.39 per credit hour part-time. Canadian resident tuition: $5321 full-time, $177.39 per credit hour part-time. Mandatory fees: $709 full-time. Full-time tuition and fees vary according to course level and program. Part-time tuition varies according to course level and program. College room and board: $9136. College room only: $5616. Room and board charges vary according to housing facility. International student tuition: $21,613 full-time. **Scholarships:** Available. **Calendar System:** Trimester, Summer session available **Enrollment:** Full-time 13,160, Graduate full-time 3,611, Graduate part-time 719, Part-time 12,161 **Faculty:** Full-time 961, Part-time 8 **Student-Faculty Ratio:** 22:1 **Exams:** ACT essay component not used; SAT I or ACT; SAT essay component not used; SAT Reasoning. **% Residing in College-Owned, -Operated, or -Affiliated Housing: 9 Final Year or Final Semester Residency Requirement:** No **Credit Hours For Degree:** 120 credit hours, Bachelors **Professional Accreditation:** AACSB, APA, NCCU. **Intercollegiate Athletics:** Basketball M & W; Cross-Country Running M & W; Football M; Golf M & W; Gymnastics M; Soccer M & W; Softball W; Swimming and Diving M & W; Track and Field M & W; Volleyball W; Wrestling M & W

SUMMIT PACIFIC COLLEGE

Box 1700
Abbotsford, BC, Canada V2S 7E7
Tel: (604)853-7491; Free: 800-976-8388
Fax: (604)853-8951
E-mail: registrar@summitpacific.ca
Web Site: www.summitpacific.ca
Admissions: Melody Deeley

Type: Four-Year College **Sex:** Coed **Affiliation:** Pentecostal Assemblies of Canada. **Admission Plans:** Deferred Admission **Application Deadline:** Rolling **Application Fee:** $50.00 **H.S. Requirements:** High school diploma required; GED accepted **Calendar System:** Semester, Summer session available **Credit Hours For Degree:** 120 credits, Bachelors **Professional Accreditation:** ABHE.

THOMPSON RIVERS UNIVERSITY

900 McGill Rd.
Kamloops, BC, Canada V2C 0C8
Tel: (250)828-5000
Fax: (250)828-5086
E-mail: jkeller@tru.ca
Web Site: www.tru.ca
President/CEO: Dr. Alan Shaver
Admissions: Josh Keller
Financial Aid: Gordon Down

Type: Comprehensive **Sex:** Coed **Affiliation:** Ministry of Advanced Education, Province of British Columbia. **% Accepted:** 82 **Admission Plans:** Deferred Admission; Early Action; Early Admission; Open Admission **Application Deadline:** April 30 **Application Fee:** $25.50 **H.S. Requirements:** High school diploma required; GED accepted. For mature students: High school diploma or equivalent not required **Scholarships:** Available. **Calendar System:** Semester, Summer session available **Enrollment:** Full-time 6,360, Graduate full-time 375, Graduate part-time 123, Part-time 791 **% Residing in College-Owned, -Operated, or -Affiliated Housing:** 14 **Final Year or Final Semester Residency Requirement:** No **Credit Hours For Degree:** 60 credits, Associates; 120 credits, Bachelors **Intercollegiate**

Athletics: Badminton M & W; Baseball M; Basketball M & W; Cross-Country Running M & W; Golf M; Ice Hockey M; Soccer M & W; Volleyball M & W

TRINITY WESTERN UNIVERSITY

7600 Glover Rd.
Langley, BC, Canada V2Y 1Y1
Tel: (604)888-7511; Free: 888-468-6898
Fax: (604)513-2061
Web Site: www.twu.ca
Financial Aid: Corwin Koch

Type: Comprehensive **Sex:** Coed **Affiliation:** Evangelical Free Church of America. **Admission Plans:** Deferred Admission **Application Deadline:** June 15 **H.S. Requirements:** High school diploma required; GED accepted **Scholarships:** Available. **Calendar System:** Semester, Summer session available **Professional Accreditation:** ACA, ATS. **Intercollegiate Athletics:** Basketball M & W; Rugby M; Soccer M & W; Volleyball M & W

THE UNIVERSITY OF BRITISH COLUMBIA

2075 Wesbrook Mall
Vancouver, BC, Canada V6T 1Z1
Tel: (604)822-2211
Fax: (604)822-3599
E-mail: registrar.admissions@ubc.ca
Web Site: www.ubc.ca
President/CEO: Prof. Arvind Gupta
Admissions: Andrew Arida

Type: University **Sex:** Coed **% Accepted:** 70 **Admission Plans:** Deferred Admission **Application Deadline:** January 31 **Application Fee:** $108.00 **H.S. Requirements:** High school diploma required; GED not accepted **Costs Per Year:** Application fee: $108 Canadian dollars. Tuition, fee, and room and board charges are reported in Canadian dollars. Province resident tuition: $5037 full-time, $168 per credit part-time. Canadian resident tuition: $5037 full-time, $168 per credit part-time. Mandatory fees: $935 full-time. Full-time tuition and fees vary according to course level, course load, program, and student level. Part-time tuition varies according to course level, course load, and program. College room and board: $9625. Room and board charges vary according to board plan, housing facility, and location. International student tuition: $26,399 full-time. **Scholarships:** Available. **Calendar System:** Miscellaneous, Summer session available **Enrollment:** Full-time 24,322, Graduate full-time 12,352, Graduate part-time 3,877, Part-time 11,022 **Faculty:** Full-time 2,783, Part-time 564 **Student-Faculty Ratio:** 15:1 **Exams:** ACT essay component not used; Other; SAT I or ACT; SAT essay component not used. **% Receiving Financial Aid:** 23 **% Residing in College-Owned, -Operated, or -Affiliated Housing:** 25 **Final Year or Final Semester Residency Requirement:** No **Credit Hours For Degree:** 120 credits, Bachelors **Professional Accreditation:** AACSB, ACA, ACSP, ADA, ALA, APA, ASLA, LCME/AMA, NCATE. **Intercollegiate Athletics:** Baseball M; Basketball M & W; Cheerleading W; Crew M & W; Cross-Country Running M & W; Equestrian Sports M & W; Field Hockey M & W; Football M; Golf M & W; Ice Hockey M & W; Rugby M & W; Skiing (Downhill) M & W; Soccer M & W; Softball M & W; Swimming and Diving M & W; Track and Field M & W; Volleyball M & W

THE UNIVERSITY OF BRITISH COLUMBIA–OKANAGAN CAMPUS

3333 University Way
Kelowna, BC, Canada V1V 1V7
Tel: (250)807-8521
Fax: (250)807-8522
Web Site: www.ubc.ca/okanagan/welcome.html
President/CEO: Dr. Deborah Buszard

Type: University **Sex:** Coed **Affiliation:** University of British Columbia. **% Accepted:** 85 **Admission Plans:** Deferred Admission **Application Deadline:** January 31 **Application Fee:** $108.00 **H.S. Requirements:** High school diploma required; GED not accepted **Costs Per Year:** Application fee: $108 Canadian dollars. Tuition, fee, and room and board charges are reported in Canadian dollars. Province resident tuition: $5061 full-time, $169 per credit part-time. Canadian resident tuition: $5061 full-time, $880 per credit part-time. Mandatory fees: $665 full-time. Full-time tuition and fees vary according to course load and program. Part-time tuition varies according to course load and program. College room and board: $10,760. Room and board charges vary according to board plan and housing facility. International student tuition: $26,399 full-time. **Calendar System:** Semester, Summer session available **Enrollment:** Full-time 5,524, Graduate full-time 814, Graduate part-time 95, Part-time 1,784 **Faculty:** Full-time 374, Part-time 38 **Student-Faculty Ratio:** 18:1 **Exams:** ACT essay component used for admission; SAT I or ACT; SAT Reasoning. **% Residing in College-Owned, -Operated, or -Affiliated Housing:** 31 **Final Year or Final Semester Residency Requirement:** No **Credit Hours For Degree:** 120 credits, Bachelors **Intercollegiate Athletics:** Basketball M & W; Cross-Country Running M & W; Golf M & W; Rugby M & W; Soccer M & W; Volleyball M & W

UNIVERSITY OF THE FRASER VALLEY
33844 King Rd.
Abbotsford, BC, Canada V2S 7M8
Tel: (604)504-7441
Fax: (604)855-7614
E-mail: jjulie.croft@ufv.ca
Web Site: www.ufv.ca
President/CEO: Dr. Mark Evered, PhD
Admissions: Julie Croft
Financial Aid: Lorraine Bingert
Type: Comprehensive **Sex:** Coed **Admission Plans:** Deferred Admission; Open Admission **Application Deadline:** Rolling **Application Fee:** $45.00 **H.S. Requirements:** High school diploma required; GED accepted **Costs Per Year:** Application fee: $45. Province resident tuition: $4700 full-time, $150.35 per credit hour part-time. Canadian resident tuition: $4700 full-time, $150.35 per credit hour part-time. Mandatory fees: $455 full-time, $154.31 per term part-time. Full-time tuition and fees vary according to course load. Part-time tuition and fees vary according to course load. College room and board: $7571. College room only: $5571. Room and board charges vary according to board plan. International student tuition: $15,600 full-time. **Scholarships:** Available. **Calendar System:** Semester, Summer session available **Enrollment:** Full-time 3,750, Graduate full-time 19, Part-time 4,654 **Faculty:** Full-time 332, Part-time 364 **Final Year or Final Semester Residency Requirement:** No **Credit Hours For Degree:** 60 credits, Associates; 120 credits, Bachelors **Intercollegiate Athletics:** Basketball M & W; Soccer M & W

UNIVERSITY OF NORTHERN BRITISH COLUMBIA
3333 University Way
Prince George, BC, Canada V2N 4Z9
Tel: (250)960-5555
Fax: (250)960-5791
E-mail: registrar-info@unbc.ca
Web Site: www.unbc.ca
President/CEO: Charles Jago
Admissions: Pamela Flagel
Financial Aid: Linda Roa
Type: University **Sex:** Coed **% Accepted:** 76 **Admission Plans:** Early Ac-

tion; Early Admission **Application Deadline:** March 1 **Application Fee:** $25.00 **H.S. Requirements:** High school diploma required; GED accepted **Costs Per Year:** Application fee: $25 Canadian dollars. Tuition, fee, and room and board charges are reported in Canadian dollars. Province resident tuition: $5,011 full-time, $167.03 per credit part-time. Canadian resident tuition: $5,011 full-time, $167.03 per credit part-time. Mandatory fees: $678 full-time, $5 per credit part-time, $264.07 per term part-time. Full-time tuition and fees vary according to course load, degree level, location, and program. Part-time tuition and fees vary according to course load, degree level, location, and program. College room and board: $8,824. Room and board charges vary according to housing facility. International student tuition: $17,538 full-time. **Scholarships:** Available. **Calendar System:** Semester, Summer session available **Faculty:** Full-time 178, Part-time 204 **Student-Faculty Ratio:** 10:1 **% Residing in College-Owned, -Operated, or -Affiliated Housing:** 16 **Credit Hours For Degree:** 120 credits, Bachelors **Intercollegiate Athletics:** Basketball M & W; Skiing (Cross-Country) M & W

UNIVERSITY OF VICTORIA
PO Box 1700 STN CSC
Victoria, BC, Canada V8W 2Y2
Tel: (250)721-7211
Fax: (250)721-6225
E-mail: admit@uvic.ca
Web Site: www.uvic.ca
Admissions: Bruno Rocca
Type: University **Sex:** Coed **% Accepted:** 75 **Admission Plans:** Deferred Admission; Early Admission; Early Decision Plan **Application Deadline:** April 30 **Application Fee:** $100.00 **H.S. Requirements:** High school diploma required; GED accepted **Scholarships:** Available. **Calendar System:** Miscellaneous, Summer session available **Enrollment:** Full-time 10,716, Part-time 5,866 **Faculty:** Full-time 721, Part-time 39 **Student-Faculty Ratio:** 27:1 **Credit Hours For Degree:** 60 units, Bachelors **Professional Accreditation:** AACSB, APA. **Intercollegiate Athletics:** Basketball M & W; Crew M & W; Cross-Country Running M & W; Field Hockey W; Golf M & W; Rugby M & W; Soccer M & W; Swimming and Diving M & W

VANCOUVER ISLAND UNIVERSITY
900 Fifth St.
Nanaimo, BC, Canada V9R 5S5
Tel: (250)753-3245
Web Site: www.viu.ca
Admissions: Andrew Amour
Financial Aid: Karen Stant
Type: Comprehensive **Sex:** Coed **Application Fee:** $30.00 **Scholarships:** Available. **Calendar System:** Semester **Professional Accreditation:** ACBSP.

BOOTH UNIVERSITY COLLEGE

447 Webb Pl.
Winnipeg, MB, Canada R3B 2P2
Tel: (204)947-6701; Free: 877-942-6684
Fax: (204)942-3856
E-mail: cburt@boothcollege.ca
Web Site: www.boothuc.ca
Admissions: Chantel Burt
Type: Four-Year College **Sex:** Coed **Affiliation:** Salvation Army. **% Accepted:** 71 **Application Deadline:** July 31 **Application Fee:** $0.00 **H.S. Requirements:** High school diploma required; GED accepted **Calendar System:** Semester, Summer session available **Faculty:** Full-time 9, Part-time 19 **Student-Faculty Ratio:** 9:1 **% Residing in College-Owned, -Operated, or -Affiliated Housing:** 10 **Credit Hours For Degree:** 98 credit hours, Bachelors **Intercollegiate Athletics:** Volleyball M & W

BRANDON UNIVERSITY

270 18th St.
Brandon, MB, Canada R7A 6A9
Tel: (204)728-9520
E-mail: kerr@brandonu.ca
Web Site: www.brandonu.ca
Admissions: Murray Kerr
Type: Comprehensive **Sex:** Coed **% Accepted:** 70 **Admission Plans:** Deferred Admission; Open Admission **Application Deadline:** Rolling **Application Fee:** $60.00 **H.S. Requirements:** High school diploma required; GED accepted **Scholarships:** Available. **Calendar System:** Miscellaneous, Summer session available **Enrollment:** Full-time 2,306, Part-time 1,095 **Faculty:** Full-time 215, Part-time 13 **Student-Faculty Ratio:** 11:1 **% Residing in College-Owned, -Operated, or -Affiliated Housing:** 9 **Credit Hours For Degree:** 90 credit hours, Bachelors **Intercollegiate Athletics:** Basketball M & W; Volleyball M & W

PROVIDENCE UNIVERSITY COLLEGE & THEOLOGICAL SEMINARY

10 College Crescent
Otterburne, MB, Canada R0A 1G0
Tel: (204)433-7488; Free: 800-668-7768
E-mail: info@prov.ca
Web Site: www.providenceuc.ca
President/CEO: David Johnson
Admissions: Adrian Enns
Type: Comprehensive **Sex:** Coed **Affiliation:** interdenominational. **% Accepted:** 100 **Admission Plans:** Deferred Admission; Open Admission **Application Deadline:** Rolling **Application Fee:** $50.00 **H.S. Requirements:** High school diploma required; GED accepted **Calendar System:** Semester, Summer session not available **Enrollment:** Full-time 236, Graduate full-time 185, Part-time 49 **Faculty:** Full-time 18, Part-time 32 **Student-Faculty Ratio:** 19:1 **% Residing in College-Owned, -Operated, or -Affiliated Housing:** 65 **Credit Hours For Degree:** 96 semester hours, Bachelors **Professional Accreditation:** ABHE, ATS. **Intercollegiate Athletics:** Basketball M & W; Soccer M & W; Volleyball M & W

STEINBACH BIBLE COLLEGE

50 PTH 12N
Steinbach, MB, Canada R5G 1T4
Tel: (204)326-6451; Free: 800-230-8478
E-mail: info@sbcollege.ca
Web Site: www.sbcollege.ca
President/CEO: Pres. Rob Reimer
Admissions: Kaylene Buhler
Financial Aid: Patrick Martens
Type: Four-Year College **Sex:** Coed **Affiliation:** Mennonite. **% Accepted:** 81 **Application Fee:** $50.00 **H.S. Requirements:** High school diploma required; GED accepted **Costs Per Year:** Application fee: $50 Canadian dollars. Tuition, fee, and room and board charges are reported in Canadian dollars. Comprehensive fee: $13,979 includes full-time tuition ($7200), mandatory fees ($929), and college room and board ($5850). College room only: $2250. Room and board charges vary according to housing facility. Part-time tuition: $225 per credit hour. Part-time mandatory fees: $22 per credit hour. **Scholarships:** Available. **Calendar System:** Semester **Enrollment:** Full-time 94, Part-time 54 **Faculty:** Full-time 4, Part-time 10 **Student-Faculty Ratio:** 18:1 **Professional Accreditation:** ABHE.

UNIVERSITÉ DE SAINT-BONIFACE

200 Ave. de la Cathèdrale
Saint-Boniface, MB, Canada R2H 0H7
Tel: (204)233-0210
Fax: (204)237-3240
Web Site: www.ustboniface.mb.ca
Type: Comprehensive **Sex:** Coed **Affiliation:** Roman Catholic.

UNIVERSITY OF MANITOBA

Winnipeg, MB, Canada R3T 2N2
Tel: (204)474-8880
Web Site: www.umanitoba.ca
Admissions: Peter Dueck
Type: University **Sex:** Coed **Admission Plans:** Early Admission **Application Fee:** $65.00 **H.S. Requirements:** High school diploma required; GED not accepted. For students 21 or over: High school diploma or equivalent not required **Costs Per Year:** Application fee: $65 Canadian dollars. Tuition and fee charges are reported in Canadian dollars. Province resident tuition: $4000 full-time. Canadian resident tuition: $13,600 full-time. Full-time tuition varies according to course load, program, and reciprocity agreements. **Scholarships:** Available. **Calendar System:** Miscellaneous, Summer session available **Enrollment:** Full-time 19,522, Graduate full-time 3,049, Graduate part-time 773, Part-time 4,407 **% Receiving Financial Aid:** 10 **Credit Hours For Degree:** 90 credits, Bachelors **Professional Accreditation:** AACSB, ADA, APA, ASLA, CIDA, LCME/AMA. **Intercollegiate Athletics:** Basketball M & W; Cross-Country Running M & W; Field Hockey M & W; Football M & W; Gymnastics M & W; Ice Hockey M & W; Swimming and Diving M & W; Track and Field M & W; Volleyball M & W

THE UNIVERSITY OF WINNIPEG

515 Portage Ave.
Winnipeg, MB, Canada R3B 2E9
Tel: (204)786-7811
E-mail: admissions@uwinnipeg.ca
Web Site: www.uwinnipeg.ca
President/CEO: Dr. Lloyd Axworthy
Admissions: Colin Russell

Financial Aid: Kam Holland

Type: Comprehensive **Sex:** Coed **% Accepted:** 75 **Admission Plans:** Deferred Admission; Early Admission **Application Deadline:** August 9 **Application Fee:** $60.00 **H.S. Requirements:** High school diploma required; GED not accepted. For applicants 21 or over: High school diploma required; GED accepted **Scholarships:** Available. **Calendar System:** Miscellaneous,

Summer session available **Enrollment:** Full-time 6,231, Part-time 2,775 **Faculty:** Full-time 270, Part-time 51 **Student-Faculty Ratio:** 35:1 **% Residing in College-Owned, -Operated, or -Affiliated Housing:** 3 **Credit Hours For Degree:** 15 full-year courses, Bachelors **Professional Accreditation:** AAMFT, ATS. **Intercollegiate Athletics:** Basketball M & W; Volleyball M & W

New Brunswick

CRANDALL UNIVERSITY

Box 6004
Moncton, NB, Canada E1C 9L7
Tel: (506)858-8970; Free: 888-968-6228
Fax: (506)858-9694
E-mail: admissions@crandallu.ca
Web Site: www.crandallu.ca
President/CEO: Dr. Bruce Fawcett
Admissions: Lorrie Weir

Type: Comprehensive **Sex:** Coed **Affiliation:** Baptist. **% Accepted:** 70 **Admission Plans:** Deferred Admission; Early Action; Early Admission **Application Deadline:** Rolling **Application Fee:** $35.00 **H.S. Requirements:** High school diploma required; GED accepted **Costs Per Year:** Application fee: $35. One-time mandatory fee: $50. Comprehensive fee: $16,840 includes full-time tuition ($7880), mandatory fees ($1000), and college room and board ($7960). College room only: $3970. Full-time tuition and fees vary according to course load, degree level, and program. Room and board charges vary according to board plan and housing facility. Part-time tuition: $788 per course. Part-time mandatory fees: $100 per course. Part-time tuition and fees vary according to course load, degree level, and program. **Scholarships:** Available. **Calendar System:** Trimester, Summer session available **Enrollment:** Full-time 481, Graduate part-time 97, Part-time 74 **Faculty:** Full-time 28, Part-time 34 **Student-Faculty Ratio:** 13:1 **% Residing in College-Owned, -Operated, or -Affiliated Housing:** 27 **Final Year or Final Semester Residency Requirement:** No **Credit Hours For Degree:** 60 credits hours for an Education degree; 120 credit hours for an Arts, Business, or Science degree, Bachelors **Intercollegiate Athletics:** Baseball M; Basketball M & W; Cross-Country Running M & W; Soccer M & W

KINGSWOOD UNIVERSITY

26 Western St.
Sussex, NB, Canada E4E 5L2
Tel: (506)432-4400; Free: 888-432-4422
Fax: (506)432-4425
E-mail: vails@kingswood.edu
Web Site: www.kingswood.edu
President/CEO: Dr. Mark L. Gorveatte
Admissions: Shelley Vail
Financial Aid: Ruth Muscroft

Type: Comprehensive **Sex:** Coed **Affiliation:** Wesleyan Church. **Scores:** 86% SAT V 400+; 100% SAT M 400+ **% Accepted:** 40 **Admission Plans:** Deferred Admission; Early Admission **Application Deadline:** Rolling **Application Fee:** $20.00 **H.S. Requirements:** High school diploma required; GED accepted. For Early Enrolment Program for grade 12 only: High school diploma or equivalent not required **Costs Per Year:** Application fee: $20 Canadian dollars. Tuition, fee, and room and board charges are reported in Canadian dollars. Comprehensive fee: $16,850 includes full-time tuition ($10,100), mandatory fees ($650), and college room and board ($6100). College room only: $2650. Full-time tuition and fees vary according to program. Room and board charges vary according to board plan and housing facility. Part-time tuition: $325 per contact hour. Part-time tuition varies according to program. **Scholarships:** Available. **Calendar System:**

Semester, Summer session available **Enrollment:** Full-time 172, Graduate full-time 6, Graduate part-time 7, Part-time 14 **Faculty:** Full-time 11, Part-time 5 **Student-Faculty Ratio:** 14:1 **Exams:** SAT I or ACT. **% Residing in College-Owned, -Operated, or -Affiliated Housing:** 69 **Final Year or Final Semester Residency Requirement:** No **Credit Hours For Degree:** 62 hours, Associates; 120 hours, Bachelors **Professional Accreditation:** ABHE. **Intercollegiate Athletics:** Basketball M

MOUNT ALLISON UNIVERSITY

65 York St.
Sackville, NB, Canada E4L 1E4
Tel: (506)364-2269
Fax: (506)364-2272
E-mail: admissions@mta.ca
Web Site: www.mta.ca
President/CEO: Dr. Robert M. Campbell
Admissions: Curtis Michaelis
Financial Aid: Margaret Ann Esparza-Lee

Type: Comprehensive **Sex:** Coed **% Accepted:** 90 **Admission Plans:** Deferred Admission **Application Deadline:** Rolling **Application Fee:** $50.00 **H.S. Requirements:** High school diploma required; GED accepted **Costs Per Year:** Application fee: $50 Canadian dollars. Tuition, fee, and room and board charges are reported in Canadian dollars. Province resident tuition: $7465 full-time, $1642 per course part-time. Canadian resident tuition: $7465 full-time, $1642 per course part-time. Mandatory fees: $956 full-time, $194 per year part-time. Full-time tuition and fees vary according to course load and degree level. Part-time tuition and fees vary according to course load and degree level. College room and board: $9002. College room only: $4493. Room and board charges vary according to board plan and housing facility. International student tuition: $16,420 full-time. **Scholarships:** Available. **Calendar System:** Miscellaneous, Summer session available **Enrollment:** Full-time 2,411, Graduate full-time 15, Part-time 106 **Faculty:** Full-time 132, Part-time 55 **Student-Faculty Ratio:** 16:1 **% Residing in College-Owned, -Operated, or -Affiliated Housing:** 50 **Credit Hours For Degree:** 120 credits, Bachelors **Intercollegiate Athletics:** Basketball M & W; Football M; Ice Hockey W; Rugby M & W; Soccer M & W; Swimming and Diving M & W

ST. THOMAS UNIVERSITY

51 Dineen Dr.
Fredericton, NB, Canada E3B 5G3
Tel: (506)452-0640
Fax: (506)450-9615
E-mail: admissions@stu.ca
Web Site: www.stu.ca
President/CEO: Prof. Dawn Russell
Admissions: Kathryn Monti

Type: Four-Year College **Sex:** Coed **Affiliation:** Roman Catholic. **% Accepted:** 93 **Admission Plans:** Early Decision Plan **Application Deadline:** August 31 **Application Fee:** $55.00 **H.S. Requirements:** High school diploma required; GED not accepted. For adult learners: High school diploma or equivalent not required **Costs Per Year:** Application fee: $55. Comprehensive fee: $14,694 includes full-time tuition ($5914), mandatory fees ($500), and college room and board ($8280). Full-time tuition and fees vary according to course load, degree level, and program. Room and board charges vary according to board plan, housing facility, and location. Part-time mandatory fees: $41 per course. Part-time fees vary according to course load. International student tuition: $13,385 full-time. **Calendar System:** Semester, Summer session available **Enrollment:** Full-time 1,792, Graduate full-time 181, Part-time 122 **Faculty:** Full-time 106, Part-time 82 **Student-Faculty Ratio:** 16:1 **Exams:** SAT I. **% Residing in College-Owned, -Operated, or -Affiliated Housing:** 26 **Credit Hours For Degree:** 120 credit hours, Bachelors **Intercollegiate Athletics:** Basketball M & W; Cross-Country Running M & W; Golf M & W; Ice Hockey M & W; Soccer M & W; Volleyball M & W

UNIVERSITÉ DE MONCTON

Moncton, NB, Canada E1A 3E9
Tel: (506)858-4000
Fax: (506)858-4544
E-mail: gallanrm@umoncton.ca
Web Site: www.umoncton.ca
Admissions: Nicole Savois
Financial Aid: Sylvette Dionne-Cormier

Type: Comprehensive **Sex:** Coed **% Accepted:** 86 **Admission Plans:** Deferred Admission **Application Deadline:** June 1 **Application Fee:** $30.00 **H.S. Requirements:** High school diploma required; GED accepted. For education, science, engineering, nutrition, nursing, forestry programs: High school diploma required; GED not accepted **Scholarships:** Available. **Calendar System:** Semester, Summer session available **Enrollment:** Full-time 4,540, Part-time 980 **Faculty:** Full-time 374, Part-time 113 **Student-Faculty Ratio:** 12:1 **% Receiving Financial Aid:** 42 **% Residing in College-Owned, -Operated, or -Affiliated Housing:** 15 **Credit Hours For Degree:** 126 credits, Bachelors **Intercollegiate Athletics:** Cross-Country Running M & W; Gymnastics W; Ice Hockey M & W; Soccer M & W; Track and Field M & W; Volleyball W

UNIVERSITY OF NEW BRUNSWICK FREDERICTON

PO Box 4400
Fredericton, NB, Canada E3B 5A3
Tel: (506)453-4666
Fax: (506)453-5016
E-mail: admissions@unb.ca
Web Site: www.unb.ca
President/CEO: Dr. Eddy Campbell
Financial Aid: Shelley Clayton

Type: University **Sex:** Coed **Affiliation:** Province of New Brunswick. **Costs Per Year:** Tuition, fee, and room and board charges are reported in Canadian dollars. Province resident tuition: $6187 full-time, $619 per course part-time. Mandatory fees: $588 full-time, $35.25 per course part-time. Full-time tuition and fees vary according to course load, location, and program. Part-time tuition and fees vary according to course load, location, and program. College room and board: $9170. Room and board charges vary according to board plan and location. International student tuition: $13,905 full-time. **Scholarships:** Available. **Calendar System:** Miscellaneous, Summer session available **Enrollment:** Full-time 5,666, Graduate full-time 842, Graduate part-time 592, Part-time 567 **Faculty:** Full-time 532 **Student-Faculty Ratio:** 15:1 **Exams:** SAT I. **% Residing in College-Owned, -Operated, or -Affiliated Housing:** 21 **Final Year or Final Semester Residency Requirement:** No **Credit Hours For Degree:** 120 credit hours, Bachelors **Professional Accreditation:** APA. **Intercollegiate Athletics:** Basketball M & W; Cross-Country Running M & W; Ice Hockey M; Soccer M & W; Swimming and Diving W; Track and Field M & W; Volleyball M & W; Wrestling M & W

UNIVERSITY OF NEW BRUNSWICK SAINT JOHN

PO Box 5050
Saint John, NB, Canada E2L 4L5
Tel: (506)648-5500
Web Site: www.unb.ca
Financial Aid: Renea Sleep

Type: Comprehensive **Sex:** Coed **Admission Plans:** Deferred Admission; Early Admission **Application Deadline:** Rolling **Application Fee:** $55.00 **H.S. Requirements:** High school diploma required; GED not accepted. For adult students: High school diploma or equivalent not required **Costs Per Year:** Application fee: $55 Canadian dollars. Tuition, fee, and room and board charges are reported in Canadian dollars. Province resident tuition: $6187 full-time, $619 per course part-time. Mandatory fees: $470 full-time, $40.25 per course part-time. Full-time tuition and fees vary according to

course load, location, and program. Part-time tuition and fees vary according to course load, location, and program. College room and board: $6994. Room and board charges vary according to board plan, housing facility, and location. International student tuition: $13,905 full-time. **Scholarships:** Available. **Calendar System:** Miscellaneous, Summer session available **Exams:** SAT I. **% Residing in College-Owned, -Operated, or -Affiliated Housing:** 5 **Credit Hours For Degree:** 120 credits, Bachelors **Intercollegiate Athletics:** Badminton M & W; Basketball M & W; Crew M & W; Cross-Country Running M & W; Fencing M & W; Ice Hockey M & W; Rugby M & W; Soccer M & W; Volleyball M & W

Nova Scotia

ACADIA UNIVERSITY

Wolfville, NS, Canada B4P 2R6
Tel: (902)542-2201; Free: 877-585-1121
Fax: (902)585-1081
E-mail: admissions@acadiau.ca
Web Site: www.acadiau.ca
President/CEO: Raymond Ivany
Admissions: Anne Scott
Financial Aid: Judy Noel-Walsh

Type: Comprehensive **Sex:** Coed **% Accepted:** 31 **Admission Plans:** Deferred Admission **Application Deadline:** July 1 **Application Fee:** $40.00 **H.S. Requirements:** High school diploma required; GED not accepted. For adult students: High school diploma or equivalent not required **Costs Per Year:** Application fee: $40 Canadian dollars. Tuition, fee, and room and board charges are reported in Canadian dollars. One-time mandatory fee: $397.17. Province resident tuition: $7245 full-time, $903.70 per course part-time. Canadian resident tuition: $8528 full-time, $1032 per course part-time. Mandatory fees: $265 full-time, $10.30 per course part-time. Full-time tuition and fees vary according to course level, course load, degree level, and program. Part-time tuition and fees vary according to course level, course load, degree level, and program. College room and board: $9613. College room only: $5400. Room and board charges vary according to board plan and housing facility. International student tuition: $16,255 full-time. **Scholarships:** Available. **Calendar System:** Miscellaneous, Summer session available **Enrollment:** Full-time 3,287, Graduate full-time 99, Graduate part-time 292, Part-time 147 **Student-Faculty Ratio:** 15:1 **Final Year or Final Semester Residency Requirement:** No **Credit Hours For Degree:** 120 credit hours, Bachelors **Professional Accreditation:** ATS. **Intercollegiate Athletics:** Basketball M & W; Cross-Country Running W; Football M; Ice Hockey M; Rugby W; Soccer M & W; Swimming and Diving M & W; Track and Field W; Volleyball W

CAPE BRETON UNIVERSITY

Box 5300
1250 Grand Lake Rd.
Sydney, NS, Canada B1P 6L2
Tel: (902)539-5300; Free: 888-959-9995
Fax: (902)562-0119
E-mail: jennifer_billard@cbu.ca
Web Site: www.cbu.ca
President/CEO: Pres. David Wheeler, PhD
Admissions: Jennifer Billard
Financial Aid: John Mayich

Type: Comprehensive **Sex:** Coed **% Accepted:** 75 **Admission Plans:** Deferred Admission; Early Admission **Application Deadline:** Rolling **Application Fee:** $36.00 **H.S. Requirements:** High school diploma required; GED accepted **Costs Per Year:** Application fee: $36. Province resident tuition: $5287 full-time, $528.70 per course part-time. Canadian resident tuition: $6570 full-time, $657 per course part-time. Mandatory fees: $432 full-time, $37 per course part-time, $62 per year part-time. Full-time tuition and fees vary according to course load, degree level, and program. Part-time tuition and fees vary according to course load, degree level, and program. College room and board: $8780. College room only: $4120. Room and board charges vary according to board plan and housing facility. International student tuition: $13,260 full-time. **Calendar System:** Semester **Enrollment:** Full-time 2,207, Graduate full-time 147, Graduate part-time 206, Part-time 357 **Faculty:** Full-time 168 **% Receiving Financial Aid:** 100 **% Residing in College-Owned, -Operated, or -Affiliated Housing:** 24 **Intercollegiate Athletics:** Basketball M & W; Ice Hockey W; Rugby M; Soccer M & W

DALHOUSIE UNIVERSITY

Halifax, NS, Canada B3H 4R2
Tel: (902)494-2211
Fax: (902)494-1630
E-mail: admissions@dal.ca
Web Site: www.dal.ca
President/CEO: Dr. Tom Traves
Admissions: Katie Sparks

Type: University **Sex:** Coed **% Accepted:** 59 **Admission Plans:** Deferred Admission; Early Admission **Application Deadline:** June 1 **Application Fee:** $65.00 **H.S. Requirements:** High school diploma required; GED not accepted **Scholarships:** Available. **Calendar System:** Semester, Summer session available **Enrollment:** Full-time 13,304, Graduate full-time 3,135, Graduate part-time 698, Part-time 1,594 **Student-Faculty Ratio:** 14:1 **Exams:** SAT I or ACT; SAT Reasoning. **Final Year or Final Semester Residency Requirement:** No **Credit Hours For Degree:** 15 courses (90 credit hours), Bachelors **Professional Accreditation:** AACSB, ADA, ALA, APA, CAHME, LCME/AMA. **Intercollegiate Athletics:** Basketball M & W; Cross-Country Running M & W; Field Hockey W; Ice Hockey M & W; Soccer M & W; Swimming and Diving M & W; Track and Field M & W; Volleyball M & W

MOUNT SAINT VINCENT UNIVERSITY

166 Bedford Hwy.
Halifax, NS, Canada B3M 2J6
Tel: (902)457-6788; Free: 877-733-6788
Fax: (902)457-6455
E-mail: admissions@msvu.ca
Web Site: www.msvu.ca
Admissions: Heidi Tattrie
Financial Aid: Frances C. Cody

Type: Comprehensive **Sex:** Coed **% Accepted:** 60 **Admission Plans:** Deferred Admission **Application Deadline:** March 15 **Application Fee:** $30.00 **H.S. Requirements:** High school diploma or equivalent not required. For students out of high school 3 years or more: High school diploma required; GED accepted **Costs Per Year:** Application fee: $30 Canadian dollars. Tuition, fee, and room and board charges are reported in Canadian dollars. Province resident tuition: $34,350 full-time. Mandatory fees: $800 full-time. Full-time tuition and fees vary according to course level, course load, degree level, location, program, reciprocity agreements, and student level. College room and board: $8720. Room and board charges vary according to board plan and housing facility. **Scholarships:** Available. **Calendar System:** Miscellaneous, Summer session available **Faculty:** Full-time 149, Part-time 227 **Student-Faculty Ratio:** 13:1 **% Receiving Financial Aid:** 21 **Credit Hours For Degree:** 15 full-year courses, Bachelors **Intercollegiate Athletics:** Badminton M & W; Basketball M & W; Soccer M & W; Volleyball W

NSCAD UNIVERSITY

5163 Duke St.
Halifax, NS, Canada B3J 3J6
Tel: (902)422-7381; Free: 888-444-5989
Fax: (902)425-2420
E-mail: admissions@nscad.ca
Web Site: www.nscad.ca
President/CEO: Prof. David B. Smith
Admissions: Terry Bailey
Financial Aid: Bernadette Kehoe

Type: Comprehensive **Sex:** Coed **% Accepted:** 75 **Admission Plans:** Deferred Admission **Application Deadline:** May 15 **Application Fee:** $35.00 **H.S. Requirements:** High school diploma required; GED accepted **Costs Per Year:** Application fee: $35 Canadian dollars. Tuition and fee charges are reported in Canadian dollars. Province resident tuition: $6154 full-time. Canadian resident tuition: $7438 full-time. Full-time tuition varies according to course load and reciprocity agreements. International student tuition: $15,996 full-time. **Scholarships:** Available. **Calendar System:** Semester, Summer session available **Faculty:** Full-time 46, Part-time 68 **Student-Faculty Ratio:** 9:1 **% Residing in College-Owned, -Operated, or -Affiliated Housing:** 10 **Credit Hours For Degree:** 120 credits, Bachelors

ST. FRANCIS XAVIER UNIVERSITY

Box 5000
Antigonish, NS, Canada B2G 2W5
Tel: (902)863-3300; Free: 877-867-STFX
Fax: (902)867-2329

E-mail: mbarry@stfx.ca
Web Site: www.stfx.ca
President/CEO: Dr. Sean E. Riley
Admissions: Sarah Murray
Financial Aid: Heidi Steinitz

Type: Comprehensive **Sex:** Coed **Affiliation:** Roman Catholic. **% Accepted:** 65 **Admission Plans:** Deferred Admission; Early Action; Early Admission **Application Deadline:** Rolling **Application Fee:** $40.00 **H.S. Requirements:** High school diploma required; GED accepted **Scholarships:** Available. **Calendar System:** Miscellaneous, Summer session available **Enrollment:** Full-time 2,209, Graduate full-time 129, Graduate part-time 413, Part-time 2,046 **Faculty:** Full-time 251, Part-time 67 **Student-Faculty Ratio:** 12:1 **Exams:** ACT essay component not used; SAT I or ACT; SAT II; SAT essay component not used; SAT Reasoning; SAT Subject. **% Residing in College-Owned, -Operated, or -Affiliated Housing:** 45 **Credit Hours For Degree:** 120 credits, Bachelors **Intercollegiate Athletics:** Baseball M; Basketball M & W; Cheerleading W; Crew M & W; Cross-Country Running M & W; Equestrian Sports W; Field Hockey W; Football M; Ice Hockey M & W; Lacrosse M; Rugby M & W; Soccer M & W; Track and Field M & W; Volleyball W

SAINT MARY'S UNIVERSITY

Halifax, NS, Canada B3H 3C3
Tel: (902)420-5400
Fax: (902)496-8100
E-mail: greg.ferguson@smu.ca
Web Site: www.smu.ca
Admissions: Greg Ferguson
Financial Aid: Michelle Fougere

Type: Comprehensive **Sex:** Coed **Admission Plans:** Early Decision Plan **Application Deadline:** July 1 **Application Fee:** $40.00 **H.S. Requirements:** High school diploma required; GED accepted **Scholarships:** Available. **Calendar System:** Semester, Summer session available **Credit Hours For Degree:** 15 courses, Bachelors **Professional Accreditation:** AACSB. **Intercollegiate Athletics:** Basketball M & W; Cross-Country Running M & W; Field Hockey W; Football M; Ice Hockey M & W; Rugby W; Soccer M & W; Track and Field M & W; Volleyball W

UNIVERSITÉ SAINTE-ANNE

Church Point, NS, Canada B0W 1M0
Tel: (902)769-2114
Fax: (902)769-2930
E-mail: admission@usainteanne.ca
Web Site: www.usainteanne.ca
President/CEO: Allister Surette
Admissions: Blanche Theriault
Financial Aid: Arlene Comeau

Type: Comprehensive **Sex:** Coed **Calendar System:** Semester, Summer session not available **Enrollment:** Graduate part-time 20 **Faculty:** Full-time 33, Part-time 8 **% Residing in College-Owned, -Operated, or -Affiliated Housing:** 60 **Final Year or Final Semester Residency Requirement:** No **Credit Hours For Degree:** 90 credits, Bachelors **Intercollegiate Athletics:** Badminton M & W; Volleyball M & W

UNIVERSITY OF KING'S COLLEGE

6350 Coburg Rd.
Halifax, NS, Canada B3H 2A1
Tel: (902)422-1271
Fax: (902)423-3357
E-mail: admissions@ukings.ns.ca
Web Site: www.ukings.ca
President/CEO: Dr. George Cooper
Admissions: Tara Wigglesworth-Hines
Financial Aid: Christina M. Warren

Type: Comprehensive **Sex:** Coed **Affiliation:** Dalhousie University. **% Accepted:** 80 **Admission Plans:** Deferred Admission; Early Action; Early Admission **Application Deadline:** March 1 **Application Fee:** $65.00 **H.S. Requirements:** High school diploma or equivalent not required **Calendar System:** Miscellaneous, Summer session available **Enrollment:** Full-time 925, Graduate full-time 47, Part-time 34 **Faculty:** Full-time 45 **Student-Faculty Ratio:** 21:1 **Exams:** SAT I. **% Residing in College-Owned, -Operated, or -Affiliated Housing:** 23 **Credit Hours For Degree:** 15 courses, Bachelors **Intercollegiate Athletics:** Badminton M & W; Basketball M & W; Rugby M & W; Soccer M & W; Volleyball M

Prince Edward Island

UNIVERSITY OF PRINCE EDWARD ISLAND

550 University Ave.
Charlottetown, PE, Canada C1A 4P3
Tel: (902)566-0439
Fax: (902)566-0795
E-mail: dmccardle@upei.ca
Web Site: home.upei.ca
President/CEO: H. Wade MacLauchlan
Admissions: Darcy McCardle
Financial Aid: Belinda Rogers

Type: Comprehensive **Sex:** Coed **% Accepted:** 61 **Admission Plans:** Early Admission **Application Deadline:** August 1 **Application Fee:** $50.00 **H.S. Requirements:** High school diploma required; GED not accepted. For students 22 or over and out of high school at least 2 years can be accepted as mature students: High school diploma or equivalent not required **Scholarships:** Available. **Calendar System:** Miscellaneous, Summer session available **Enrollment:** Full-time 2,904, Part-time 561 **Faculty:** Full-time 240, Part-time 190 **Student-Faculty Ratio:** 12:1 **Exams:** SAT I or ACT. **% Residing in College-Owned, -Operated, or -Affiliated Housing:** 14 **Credit Hours For Degree:** 120 semester hours, Bachelors **Professional Accreditation:** AVMA. **Intercollegiate Athletics:** Basketball M & W; Field Hockey W; Golf M; Ice Hockey M & W; Rugby M & W; Soccer M & W; Volleyball W

MEMORIAL UNIVERSITY OF NEWFOUNDLAND

Elizabeth Ave.
Saint John's, NL, Canada A1C 5S7
Tel: (709)864-8000
Fax: (709)864-4569
E-mail: sturecru@morgan.ucs.mun.ca
Web Site: www.mun.ca
President/CEO: Dr. C. Loomis
Admissions: Marian Abbott

Type: University **Sex:** Coed **Affiliation:** Marine Institute, Sir Wilfred Grenfell College, WRSON, CNS. **Admission Plans:** Deferred Admission; Early Action; Early Admission **Application Deadline:** Rolling **Application Fee:** $40.00 **H.S. Requirements:** High school diploma required; GED not accepted. For mature students (over 21 years), senior citizens: High school diploma or equivalent not required **Calendar System:** Trimester, Summer session available **Enrollment:** Full-time 12,382, Graduate full-time 1,567, Graduate part-time 1,106, Part-time 2,323 **Faculty:** Full-time 1,233, Part-time 36 **Student-Faculty Ratio:** 12:1 **% Residing in College-Owned, -Operated, or -Affiliated Housing:** 10 **Credit Hours For Degree:** 120 credit hours, Bachelors **Professional Accreditation:** AACSB, LCME/AMA. **Intercollegiate Athletics:** Basketball M & W; Cross-Country Running M & W; Soccer M & W; Swimming and Diving M & W; Volleyball M & W; Wrestling M & W

BROCK UNIVERSITY

500 Glenridge Ave.
Saint Catharines, ON, Canada L2S 3A1
Tel: (905)688-5550
Fax: (905)988-5488
E-mail: admissns@brocku.ca
Web Site: www.brocku.ca
President/CEO: Dr. Jack N. Lightstone
Admissions: Lynn Thompson-Dovi
Financial Aid: Rico Natale
Type: University **Sex:** Coed **Application Fee:** $0.00 **H.S. Requirements:** High school diploma required; GED not accepted **Scholarships:** Available. **Calendar System:** Miscellaneous, Summer session available **Enrollment:** Full-time 16,341, Graduate full-time 1,536 **Faculty:** Full-time 578 **Student-Faculty Ratio:** 30:1 **Exams:** SAT I or ACT. **% Residing in College-Owned, -Operated, or -Affiliated Housing:** 14 **Credit Hours For Degree:** 15 courses, Bachelors **Professional Accreditation:** AACSB, ATS. **Intercollegiate Athletics:** Baseball M; Basketball M & W; Cheerleading M & W; Crew M & W; Cross-Country Running M & W; Fencing M & W; Field Hockey W; Ice Hockey M & W; Lacrosse M; Rugby M & W; Soccer M & W; Swimming and Diving M & W; Volleyball W; Wrestling M & W

CARLETON UNIVERSITY

1125 Colonel By Dr.
Ottawa, ON, Canada K1S 5B6
Tel: (613)520-7400
Fax: (613)520-7455
E-mail: liaison@admissions.carleton.ca
Web Site: www.carleton.ca
Admissions: Jean Mullan
Type: University **Sex:** Coed **% Accepted:** 73 **Admission Plans:** Deferred Admission **Application Deadline:** June 1 **Application Fee:** $85.00 **H.S. Requirements:** High school diploma required; GED not accepted **Calendar System:** Miscellaneous, Summer session available **Enrollment:** Full-time 16,509, Part-time 4,237 **Faculty:** Full-time 783, Part-time 8 **Student-Faculty Ratio:** 26:1 **Exams:** SAT I; SAT I and SAT II or ACT. **% Residing in College-Owned, -Operated, or -Affiliated Housing:** 15 **Credit Hours For Degree:** 15 full-year courses, Bachelors **Intercollegiate Athletics:** Basketball M & W; Crew M & W; Fencing M & W; Field Hockey W; Football M; Golf M; Ice Hockey M & W; Lacrosse M; Rugby M & W; Skiing (Cross-Country) M & W; Soccer M & W; Swimming and Diving M & W; Volleyball W; Water Polo M & W

CENTENNIAL COLLEGE

PO Box 631, Station 'A'
Scarborough, ON, Canada M1K 5E9
Tel: (416)698-4192
Fax: (416)694-9263
E-mail: success@centennialcollege.ca
Web Site: www.centennialcollege.ca
President/CEO: Ann Buller
Type: Four-Year College **Sex:** Coed **Affiliation:** Ontario College Application System. **Application Fee:** $95.00 **Costs Per Year:** Application fee: $95. One-time mandatory fee: $55. Area resident tuition: $7267 full-time, $11.08 per contact hour part-time. Canadian resident tuition: $31.80 per contact hour part-time. Mandatory fees: $1333 full-time, $.89 per contact hour part-time, $17.20. Full-time tuition and fees vary according to course level, course load, degree level, program, reciprocity agreements, and student level. Part-time tuition and fees vary according to class time, course level, course load, degree level, reciprocity agreements, and student level. College room only: $5480. Room charges vary according to housing facility. International student tuition: $16,175 full-time. **Calendar System:** Semester, Summer session available **Enrollment:** Full-time 14,718, Part-time 1,680 **Professional Accreditation:** ACBSP.

EMMANUEL BIBLE COLLEGE

100 Fergus Ave.
Kitchener, ON, Canada N2A 2H2
Tel: (519)894-8900
Fax: (519)894-9430
E-mail: smahon@ebcollege.on.ca
Web Site: www.emmanuelbiblecollege.ca
Admissions: Sherry Mahon
Financial Aid: Robert Tees
Type: Four-Year College **Sex:** Coed **Affiliation:** Missionary Church. **Admission Plans:** Deferred Admission **Application Deadline:** Rolling **Application Fee:** $100.00 **H.S. Requirements:** High school diploma required; GED accepted **Scholarships:** Available. **Calendar System:** Semester, Summer session available **Credit Hours For Degree:** 96 semester hours, Bachelors **Professional Accreditation:** ABHE.

HERITAGE COLLEGE AND SEMINARY

175 Holiday Inn Dr.
Cambridge, ON, Canada N3C 3T2
Tel: (519)651-2869; Free: 800-465-1961
E-mail: mwalther@heritagecollege.net
Web Site: www.heritagecambridge.com
President/CEO: Rev. Marvin R. Brubacher
Admissions: Mark Walther
Type: Comprehensive **Sex:** Coed **Affiliation:** Baptist. **% Accepted:** 100 **Admission Plans:** Deferred Admission; Open Admission **Application Deadline:** September 1 **Application Fee:** $50.00 **H.S. Requirements:** High school diploma required; GED accepted **Scholarships:** Available. **Calendar System:** Miscellaneous, Summer session available **Enrollment:** Full-time 154, Graduate full-time 18, Graduate part-time 65, Part-time 37 **Faculty:** Full-time 8, Part-time 28 **Student-Faculty Ratio:** 11:1 **Final Year or Final Semester Residency Requirement:** No **Credit Hours For Degree:** 65 credit hours, Associates; 97 credit hours, Bachelors **Professional Accreditation:** ABHE, ATS. **Intercollegiate Athletics:** Basketball M & W; Volleyball M & W

LAKEHEAD UNIVERSITY

955 Oliver Rd.
Thunder Bay, ON, Canada P7B 5E1
Tel: (807)343-8110; Free: 800-465-3959
Fax: (807)343-8156
E-mail: admissions@lakeheadu.ca
Web Site: www.lakeheadu.ca
President/CEO: Dr. Brian Stevenson
Admissions: Nicholas Chamut

Type: Comprehensive **Sex:** Coed **% Accepted:** 84 **Admission Plans:** Deferred Admission; Early Admission **Application Deadline:** September 12 **Application Fee:** $125.00 **H.S. Requirements:** High school diploma required; GED not accepted **Costs Per Year:** Application fee: $125 Canadian dollars. Tuition, fee, and room and board charges are reported in Canadian dollars. Province resident tuition: $6,056 full-time, $1,211.21 per course part-time. Canadian resident tuition: $6,056 full-time, $1,211.21 per course part-time. Mandatory fees: $944 full-time, $106.23 per year part-time. Full-time tuition and fees vary according to course level, degree level, location, program, and student level. Part-time tuition and fees vary according to course level, course load, degree level, location, program, and student level. College room and board: $9670. College room only: $6,702. Room and board charges vary according to board plan, housing facility, and location. International student tuition: $19,313 full-time. **Scholarships:** Available. **Calendar System:** Miscellaneous, Summer session available **Enrollment:** Full-time 6,364, Graduate full-time 678, Graduate part-time 27, Part-time 1,611 **Faculty:** Full-time 319 **Exams:** ACT essay component not used; SAT I or ACT; SAT essay component not used; SAT Reasoning; SAT Subject. **% Residing in College-Owned, -Operated, or -Affiliated Housing:** 20 **Credit Hours For Degree:** 15 courses, Bachelors **Professional Accreditation:** LCME/AMA. **Intercollegiate Athletics:** Baseball M; Basketball M & W; Cross-Country Running M & W; Equestrian Sports M & W; Golf M; Ice Hockey M; Skiing (Cross-Country) M & W; Skiing (Downhill) M & W; Soccer M & W; Track and Field M & W; Volleyball W; Wrestling M & W

LAKEHEAD UNIVERSITY–ORILLIA
500 University Ave.
Orillia, ON, Canada L3V 0B9
Tel: (705)330-4008
Web Site: orillia.lakeheadu.ca
Type: Comprehensive **Sex:** Coed

LAURENTIAN UNIVERSITY
935 Ramsey Lake Rd.
Sudbury, ON, Canada P3E 2C6
Tel: (705)675-1151; Free: 800-263-4188
Fax: (705)675-4840
E-mail: explore@laurentian.ca
Web Site: www.laurentian.ca
President/CEO: Dominic Giroux
Financial Aid: Diane Bleauparlant
Type: Comprehensive **Sex:** Coed **Costs Per Year:** Tuition, fee, and room and board charges are reported in Canadian dollars. Province resident tuition: $6,102 full-time, $1,220 per course part-time. Mandatory fees: $800 full-time, $41.10 per course part-time. Full-time tuition and fees vary according to degree level and program. Part-time tuition and fees vary according to course load and degree level. College room and board: $9835. College room only: $5760. Room and board charges vary according to board plan and housing facility. International student tuition: $19,407 full-time. **Scholarships:** Available. **Calendar System:** Miscellaneous, Summer session available **Faculty:** Full-time 403 **Student-Faculty Ratio:** 18:1 **Final Year or Final Semester Residency Requirement:** No **Credit Hours For Degree:** 90 credits, Bachelors **Professional Accreditation:** LCME/AMA. **Intercollegiate Athletics:** Basketball M & W; Cross-Country Running M & W; Golf M & W; Ice Hockey M & W; Lacrosse M; Rowing M & W; Skiing (Downhill) M & W; Soccer M & W; Swimming and Diving M & W; Track and Field M & W; Volleyball M; Wrestling M & W

MASTER'S COLLEGE AND SEMINARY
780 Argyle St.
Peterborough, ON, Canada K9H 5T2
Tel: (705)749-0725; Free: 800-295-6368
Fax: (705)749-0417
E-mail: flora.anthony@mcs.edu
Web Site: www.mcs.edu
President/CEO: Rev. Richard Janes
Admissions: Flora Anthony
Financial Aid: Heather Boudreau
Type: Four-Year College **Sex:** Coed **Affiliation:** Pentecostal. **% Accepted:** 98 **Admission Plans:** Deferred Admission **Application Deadline:** August 31 **Application Fee:** $75.00 **H.S. Requirements:** High school diploma required; GED accepted **Costs Per Year:** Application fee: $75 Canadian dollars. Tuition, fee, and room and board charges are reported in Canadian dollars. One-time mandatory fee: $280. Comprehensive fee: $14,862 includes

full-time tuition ($7480), mandatory fees ($782), and college room and board ($6600). Full-time tuition and fees vary according to course load, location, and program. Part-time tuition: $197 per credit hour. Part-time mandatory fees: $23 per credit hour. Part-time tuition and fees vary according to course load, location, and program. **Scholarships:** Available. **Calendar System:** Semester, Summer session available **Faculty:** Full-time 5, Part-time 21 **Student-Faculty Ratio:** 15:1 **% Residing in College-Owned, -Operated, or -Affiliated Housing:** 65 **Final Year or Final Semester Residency Requirement:** No **Credit Hours For Degree:** 126 credit hours, Bachelors **Professional Accreditation:** ABHE.

MCMASTER UNIVERSITY
1280 Main St. W
Hamilton, ON, Canada L8S 4M2
Tel: (905)525-9140
Fax: (905)527-1105
E-mail: admitmac@mcmaster.ca
Web Site: www.mcmaster.ca
President/CEO: Dr. Peter George
Admissions: Olivia Demerling
Financial Aid: Kim Finlay
Type: University **Sex:** Coed **% Accepted:** 68 **Admission Plans:** Deferred Admission **Application Deadline:** June 1 **Application Fee:** $95.00 **H.S. Requirements:** High school diploma required; GED accepted **Calendar System:** Miscellaneous, Summer session available **Faculty:** Full-time 894 **Student-Faculty Ratio:** 25:1 **Exams:** SAT I or ACT. **% Residing in College-Owned, -Operated, or -Affiliated Housing:** 20 **Credit Hours For Degree:** 90 units, Bachelors **Professional Accreditation:** AACSB, ATS, LCME/AMA, NCATE. **Intercollegiate Athletics:** Badminton M & W; Baseball M; Basketball M & W; Cross-Country Running M & W; Fencing M & W; Football M; Golf M & W; Lacrosse M & W; Rugby M & W; Soccer M & W; Squash M & W; Swimming and Diving M & W; Tennis M & W; Track and Field M & W; Volleyball M & W; Water Polo M & W; Wrestling M & W

NER ISRAEL YESHIVA COLLEGE OF TORONTO
8950 Bathurst St.
Thornhill, ON, Canada L4J 8A7
Tel: (905)731-1224
Admissions: Rabbi Y. Kravetz
Type: Comprehensive **Sex:** Men **Affiliation:** Jewish. **Application Deadline:** August 15 **Calendar System:** Miscellaneous, Summer session available **Professional Accreditation:** AARTS.

NIPISSING UNIVERSITY
100 College Dr., Box 5002
North Bay, ON, Canada P1B 8L7
Tel: (705)474-3461
Fax: (705)474-1947
E-mail: liaison@nipissingu.ca
Web Site: www.nipissingu.ca
Admissions: Lori-Ann Beckford
Type: Comprehensive **Sex:** Coed **Affiliation:** Ontario Ministry of Training, Colleges and Universities. **Admission Plans:** Early Action; Early Admission **H.S. Requirements:** High school diploma required; GED not accepted **Calendar System:** Semester, Summer session available **Exams:** SAT I and SAT II or ACT. **Credit Hours For Degree:** 90 credits, Bachelors **Intercollegiate Athletics:** Cross-Country Running M & W; Ice Hockey M; Skiing (Cross-Country) M & W; Soccer M & W; Volleyball M & W

QUEEN'S UNIVERSITY AT KINGSTON
Kingston, ON, Canada K7L 3N6
Tel: (613)533-2000
Fax: (613)533-6300
E-mail: admission@queensu.ca
Web Site: www.queensu.ca
President/CEO: Dr. Daniel Woolfe
Admissions: Iveta Reinikovaite
Financial Aid: Teresa Alm
Type: University **Sex:** Coed **Admission Plans:** Deferred Admission **Application Deadline:** February 1 **Application Fee:** $230.00 **H.S. Requirements:** High school diploma required; GED not accepted **Scholarships:** Available. **Calendar System:** Miscellaneous, Summer session available **Enrollment:** Full-time 16,339, Part-time 1,063 **Faculty:** Full-time 1,087, Part-time 438 **Student-Faculty Ratio:** 15:1 **Exams:** ACT essay component

not used; SAT I or ACT; SAT essay component not used; SAT Reasoning. **% Receiving Financial Aid:** 58 **% Residing in College-Owned, -Operated, or -Affiliated Housing:** 32 **Final Year or Final Semester Residency Requirement:** No **Credit Hours For Degree:** 90 units, Bachelors **Professional Accreditation:** AACSB, APA, ATS, LCME/AMA. **Intercollegiate Athletics:** Baseball M; Basketball M & W; Cheerleading M & W; Crew M & W; Cross-Country Running M & W; Fencing M & W; Field Hockey W; Football M; Golf M; Gymnastics M & W; Ice Hockey M & W; Lacrosse M & W; Rugby M & W; Sailing M & W; Skiing (Cross-Country) M & W; Skiing (Downhill) M & W; Soccer M & W; Squash M & W; Swimming and Diving M & W; Track and Field M & W; Ultimate Frisbee M; Volleyball M & W; Water Polo M & W; Wrestling M & W

REDEEMER UNIVERSITY COLLEGE

777 Garner Rd. E
Ancaster, ON, Canada L9K 1J4
Tel: (905)648-2131; Free: 800-263-6467
Fax: (905)648-2134
E-mail: recruitment@redeemer.ca
Web Site: www.redeemer.ca
President/CEO: Dr. Hubert Krygsman
Financial Aid: Jeannette Lodewyks
Type: Four-Year College **Sex:** Coed **Affiliation:** interdenominational. **Scores:** 36% ACT 18-23; 64% ACT 24-29 **% Accepted:** 96 **Admission Plans:** Deferred Admission; Preferred Admission **Application Deadline:** May 31 **Application Fee:** $40.00 **H.S. Requirements:** High school diploma required; GED accepted. For adult students: High school diploma or equivalent not required **Costs Per Year:** Application fee: $40. Comprehensive fee: $23,136 includes full-time tuition ($15,616), mandatory fees ($508), and college room and board ($7012). College room only: $4800. Full-time tuition and fees vary according to course load. Room and board charges vary according to board plan and housing facility. Part-time tuition: $1566 per course. Part-time mandatory fees: $38.19 per course. Part-time tuition and fees vary according to course load. **Scholarships:** Available. **Calendar System:** Semester, Summer session available **Enrollment:** Full-time 638, Part-time 78 **Faculty:** Full-time 46, Part-time 66 **Student-Faculty Ratio:** 11:1 **Exams:** SAT I or ACT. **% Receiving Financial Aid:** 69 **% Residing in College-Owned, -Operated, or -Affiliated Housing:** 52 **Final Year or Final Semester Residency Requirement:** Yes **Credit Hours For Degree:** 40 courses, Bachelors **Intercollegiate Athletics:** Badminton M & W; Basketball M & W; Cross-Country Running M & W; Soccer M & W; Volleyball M & W

ROYAL MILITARY COLLEGE OF CANADA

PO Box 17000, Station Forces
Kingston, ON, Canada K7K 7B4
Tel: (613)541-6000
Fax: (613)542-3565
E-mail: liaison@rmc.ca
Web Site: www.rmc.ca
President/CEO: Brig. Gen. Sean Friday
Admissions: Karl Michaud
Financial Aid: Mme. Sophie Pepin
Type: University **Sex:** Coed **Affiliation:** Council of Ontario Universities. **Scholarships:** Available. **Calendar System:** Miscellaneous, Summer session not available **Faculty:** Full-time 233, Part-time 284 **Student-Faculty Ratio:** 5:1 **% Residing in College-Owned, -Operated, or -Affiliated Housing:** 97 **Credit Hours For Degree:** 40 credits, Bachelors **Intercollegiate Athletics:** Basketball M & W; Cross-Country Running M & W; Fencing M & W; Ice Hockey M; Rock Climbing M; Rugby M; Soccer M & W; Volleyball M & W

RYERSON UNIVERSITY

350 Victoria St.
Toronto, ON, Canada M5B 2K3
Tel: (416)979-5000
E-mail: inquire@ryerson.ca
Web Site: www.ryerson.ca
Admissions: Michelle Beaton
Financial Aid: Carole Scrase
Type: Comprehensive **Sex:** Coed **Application Deadline:** February 1 **Application Fee:** $80.00 **H.S. Requirements:** High school diploma required; GED not accepted **Scholarships:** Available. **Calendar System:** Miscellaneous, Summer session available **Faculty:** Full-time 744, Part-time 211 **% Residing in College-Owned, -Operated, or -Affiliated Housing:** 3 **Profes-**

sional **Accreditation:** CIDA. **Intercollegiate Athletics:** Badminton M & W; Basketball M & W; Crew M & W; Fencing M & W; Ice Hockey M & W; Soccer M & W; Volleyball M & W

SAINT PAUL UNIVERSITY

223 Main St.
Ottawa, ON, Canada K1S 1C4
Tel: (613)236-1393; Free: 800-637-6859
Fax: (613)782-3033
E-mail: admission@ustpaul.ca
Web Site: www.ustpaul.ca
Type: University **Sex:** Coed **Affiliation:** University of Ottawa. **Admission Plans:** Deferred Admission **Application Fee:** $35.00 **H.S. Requirements:** High school diploma required; GED not accepted **Calendar System:** Miscellaneous, Summer session available **Student-Faculty Ratio:** 12:1 **Exams:** SAT I. **Credit Hours For Degree:** 90 credits, Bachelors **Professional Accreditation:** ATS.

TRENT UNIVERSITY

1600 W Bank Dr.
Peterborough, ON, Canada K9J 7B8
Tel: (705)748-1011
Fax: (705)748-1629
E-mail: admissions@trentu.ca
Web Site: www.trentu.ca
President/CEO: Dr. Leo Groarke
Admissions: Kevin Whitmore
Financial Aid: Alice Pelkman
Type: University **Sex:** Coed **% Accepted:** 23 **Admission Plans:** Deferred Admission **Application Deadline:** June 1 **Application Fee:** $150.00 **H.S. Requirements:** High school diploma required; GED accepted **Costs Per Year:** Application fee: $150 Canadian dollars. Tuition, fee, and room and board charges are reported in Canadian dollars. Province resident tuition: $6,221 full-time, $1,244.28 per credit part-time. Canadian resident tuition: $3,554.52 per credit part-time. Mandatory fees: $1,580 full-time, $121.81 per credit part-time. Full-time tuition and fees vary according to course load, location, program, and student level. Part-time tuition and fees vary according to course load, location, program, and student level. College room and board: $9357. Room and board charges vary according to board plan, housing facility, and location. International student tuition: $18,283.28 full-time. **Calendar System:** Miscellaneous, Summer session available **Enrollment:** Full-time 6,569, Graduate full-time 504, Graduate part-time 110, Part-time 1,022 **Faculty:** Full-time 300, Part-time 200 **Student-Faculty Ratio:** 19:1 **% Residing in College-Owned, -Operated, or -Affiliated Housing:** 17 **Final Year or Final Semester Residency Requirement:** No **Credit Hours For Degree:** 15 credits, Bachelors **Intercollegiate Athletics:** Crew M & W; Cross-Country Running M & W; Golf M; Lacrosse M & W; Rugby M & W; Soccer M & W; Track and Field M & W; Volleyball M & W

TYNDALE UNIVERSITY COLLEGE & SEMINARY

25 Ballyconnor Ct.
Toronto, ON, Canada M2M 4B3
Tel: (416)226-6380
Fax: (416)226-4210
E-mail: admissions@tydale.ca
Web Site: www.tyndale.ca
President/CEO: Dr. Brian C. Stiller
Admissions: Tricia McKenley
Financial Aid: Janis Ruff
Type: Comprehensive **Sex:** Coed **Affiliation:** interdenominational. **% Accepted:** 53 **Admission Plans:** Deferred Admission **Application Deadline:** August 15 **Application Fee:** $50.00 **H.S. Requirements:** High school diploma required; GED accepted. For mature student category: High school diploma or equivalent not required **Scholarships:** Available. **Calendar System:** Semester, Summer session available **Enrollment:** Full-time 348, Part-time 131 **Faculty:** Full-time 54 **Student-Faculty Ratio:** 23:1 **% Residing in College-Owned, -Operated, or -Affiliated Housing:** 30 **Credit Hours For Degree:** 90 credit hours, Bachelors **Professional Accreditation:** ABHE, ATS. **Intercollegiate Athletics:** Basketball M & W; Ice Hockey M; Ultimate Frisbee M & W; Volleyball M & W

UNIVERSITY OF GUELPH

Guelph, ON, Canada N1G 2W1
Tel: (519)824-4120

E-mail: jhogan@registrar.uoguelph.ca
Web Site: www.uoguelph.ca
President/CEO: Dr. Franco Vaccarino
Admissions: Janette Hogan

Type: University **Sex:** Coed **% Accepted:** 66 **Admission Plans:** Deferred Admission; Early Admission **Application Deadline:** March 1 **Application Fee:** $135.00 **H.S. Requirements:** High school diploma required; GED not accepted **Costs Per Year:** Application fee: $135 Canadian dollars. Tuition, fee, and room and board charges are reported in Canadian dollars. Province resident tuition: $6200 full-time, $619.25 per course part-time. Mandatory fees: $22.23 per course part-time, $466.52 per term part-time. Full-time tuition varies according to degree level and program. Part-time tuition and fees vary according to course load, degree level, and program. College room and board: $11,152. College room only: $6346. Room and board charges vary according to board plan, housing facility, and location. International student tuition: $19,309 full-time. Tuition guaranteed not to increase for student's term of enrollment. **Scholarships:** Available. **Calendar System:** Trimester, Summer session available **Enrollment:** Full-time 17,979, Graduate full-time 2,910, Graduate part-time 225, Part-time 2,226 **Faculty:** Full-time 760, Part-time 80 **Student-Faculty Ratio:** 23:1 **Exams:** ACT essay component not used; SAT I or ACT; SAT essay component not used; SAT Reasoning; SAT Subject. **% Residing in College-Owned, -Operated, or -Affiliated Housing:** 28 **Final Year or Final Semester Residency Requirement:** No **Credit Hours For Degree:** 30 courses, Bachelors **Professional Accreditation:** AAMFT, ASLA, AVMA. **Intercollegiate Athletics:** Baseball M; Basketball M & W; Crew M & W; Cross-Country Running M & W; Field Hockey W; Football M; Golf M & W; Ice Hockey M & W; Lacrosse M & W; Rugby M & W; Skiing (Cross-Country) M & W; Soccer M & W; Swimming and Diving M & W; Track and Field M & W; Volleyball M & W; Wrestling M & W

UNIVERSITY OF OTTAWA
550 Cumberland St.
Ottawa, ON, Canada K1N 6N5
Tel: (613)562-5700
E-mail: hdore@uOttawa.ca
Web Site: www.uottawa.ca
President/CEO: Allan Rock
Admissions: Mme. Helene Dore-Lavigne
Financial Aid: Normand Seguin

Type: University **Sex:** Coed **Affiliation:** Saint-Paul University (Ottawa, Ontario). **% Accepted:** 55 **Admission Plans:** Deferred Admission; Early Admission **Application Fee:** $167.00 **H.S. Requirements:** High school diploma required; GED not accepted. For adult applicants to arts and social science programs: High school diploma or equivalent not required **Costs Per Year:** Application fee: $167 Canadian dollars. Tuition, fee, and room and board charges are reported in Canadian dollars. Province resident tuition: $6191 full-time, $245.36 per credit part-time. Canadian resident tuition: $245.36 per credit part-time. Mandatory fees: $522 full-time, $130.69 per term part-time. Full-time tuition and fees vary according to course load, degree level, program, and student level. Part-time tuition and fees vary according to course load, degree level, program, and student level. College room and board: $8767. College room only: $5267. Room and board charges vary according to board plan, housing facility, and location. International student tuition: $23,882 full-time. **Scholarships:** Available. **Calendar System:** Semester, Summer session available **Enrollment:** Full-time 26,563, Graduate full-time 8,799, Graduate part-time 2,118, Part-time 5,095 **Faculty:** Full-time 1,262, Part-time 984 **Student-Faculty Ratio:** 26:1 **Exams:** Other. **% Residing in College-Owned, -Operated, or -Affiliated Housing:** 9 **Credit Hours For Degree:** 90 credits, Bachelors **Professional Accreditation:** AACSB, APA, CAHME, LCME/AMA, NRPA. **Intercollegiate Athletics:** Badminton M & W; Baseball M & W; Basketball M & W; Cheerleading M & W; Crew M & W; Cross-Country Running M & W; Equestrian Sports M & W; Fencing M & W; Football M; Golf M & W; Ice Hockey W; Rugby W; Soccer M & W; Swimming and Diving M & W; Track and Field M & W; Ultimate Frisbee M & W; Volleyball M & W; Water Polo M & W

UNIVERSITY OF TORONTO
27 King's College Cir.
Toronto, ON, Canada M5S 1A1
Tel: (416)978-2011
Web Site: www.utoronto.ca
Type: University **Sex:** Coed **% Accepted:** 21 **Admission Plans:** Deferred

Admission; Preferred Admission **Application Deadline:** March 1 **Application Fee:** $255.00 **H.S. Requirements:** High school diploma or equivalent not required **Costs Per Year:** Application fee: $255. Province resident tuition: $5786 full-time. Canadian resident tuition: $5786 full-time. Mandatory fees: $1500 full-time. Full-time tuition and fees vary according to course level, course load, program, and student level. College room and board: $10,000. College room only: $6000. Room and board charges vary according to board plan, housing facility, location, and student level. International student tuition: $30,710 full-time. **Calendar System:** Miscellaneous, Summer session available **Enrollment:** Full-time 64,001, Graduate full-time 15,809, Graduate part-time 1,534, Part-time 6,591 **Faculty:** Full-time 2,811, Part-time 364 **Student-Faculty Ratio:** 24:1 **Exams:** SAT I and SAT II or ACT. **% Residing in College-Owned, -Operated, or -Affiliated Housing:** 15 **Final Year or Final Semester Residency Requirement:** No **Credit Hours For Degree:** 20 courses, Bachelors **Professional Accreditation:** AACSB, ADA, ALA, APA, APTA, ARCMI, ASLA, ATS, CAHME, LCME/AMA. **Intercollegiate Athletics:** Archery M & W; Badminton M & W; Basketball M & W; Crew M; Cross-Country Running M & W; Fencing M & W; Field Hockey W; Football W; Golf M; Gymnastics M & W; Ice Hockey M & W; Rugby M; Skiing (Cross-Country) M & W; Skiing (Downhill) M & W; Soccer M & W; Squash M & W; Swimming and Diving M & W; Tennis M & W; Track and Field M & W; Volleyball M & W; Wrestling M

UNIVERSITY OF WATERLOO
200 University Ave. W
Waterloo, ON, Canada N2L 3G1
Tel: (519)888-4567
Fax: (519)746-2882
E-mail: myapplication@uwaterloo.ca
Web Site: www.uwaterloo.ca
President/CEO: Feridun Hamdullahpur
Financial Aid: Maureen Jones

Type: University **Sex:** Coed **Admission Plans:** Deferred Admission; Early Admission; Open Admission **Application Deadline:** March 31 **Application Fee:** $140.00 **H.S. Requirements:** High school diploma required; GED not accepted **Costs Per Year:** Application fee: $140 Canadian dollars. Tuition, fee, and room and board charges are reported in Canadian dollars. Province resident tuition: $9000 full-time, $700 per course part-time. Mandatory fees: $500 full-time, $60 per term part-time. Full-time tuition and fees vary according to course load, degree level, program, and student level. Part-time tuition and fees vary according to course load, degree level, program, and student level. College room and board: $9500. College room only: $5968. Room and board charges vary according to board plan, housing facility, and location. International student tuition: $25,000 full-time. **Scholarships:** Available. **Calendar System:** Trimester, Summer session not available **Enrollment:** Full-time 29,307, Graduate full-time 4,128, Graduate part-time 1,163, Part-time 866 **Student-Faculty Ratio:** 25:1 **Final Year or Final Semester Residency Requirement:** No **Credit Hours For Degree:** 40 courses, Bachelors **Professional Accreditation:** AOA, APA. **Intercollegiate Athletics:** Badminton M & W; Baseball M; Basketball M & W; Cheerleading M & W; Cross-Country Running M & W; Field Hockey W; Football M; Golf M & W; Ice Hockey M & W; Rugby M & W; Skiing (Cross-Country) M & W; Soccer M & W; Squash M & W; Swimming and Diving M & W; Tennis M & W; Track and Field M & W; Volleyball M & W

THE UNIVERSITY OF WESTERN ONTARIO
London, ON, Canada N6A 5B8
Tel: (519)661-2111
E-mail: reg-admissions@uwo.ca
Web Site: www.uwo.ca
President/CEO: Dr. Amit Chakma
Financial Aid: Dorathy Cochrane

Type: University **Sex:** Coed **% Accepted:** 58 **Admission Plans:** Deferred Admission **Application Deadline:** June 1 **Application Fee:** $155.00 **H.S. Requirements:** High school diploma required; GED not accepted **Costs Per Year:** Application fee: $155 Canadian dollars. Tuition, fee, and room and board charges are reported in Canadian dollars. Province resident tuition: $6154 full-time, $1,231 per course part-time. Mandatory fees: $1,373 full-time, $163.64 per course part-time. Full-time tuition and fees vary according to course level and program. Part-time tuition and fees vary according to course load, location, and program. College room and board: $11,220. College room only: $7640. Room and board charges vary according to board plan, housing facility, and location. International student tuition: $22,817 full-time. **Scholarships:** Available. **Calendar System:** Miscellaneous, Summer session available **Enrollment:** Full-time 28,888, Graduate full-time 5,436, Graduate part-time 386, Part-time 2,647 **Faculty:** Full-time 1,391 **Exams:** SAT I or ACT. **% Residing in College-Owned, -Operated, or -Affiliated Housing:** 20 **Final Year or Final Semester Residency Requirement:** No **Credit Hours For Degree:** 15 credits (Note: At Western, 1 full credit = 1 full course), Bachelors **Professional Accreditation:** ADA, ALA, APA, APTA, ATS, LCME/AMA. **Intercollegiate Athletics:** Badminton M & W; Baseball M; Basketball M & W; Cheerleading M & W; Crew M & W; Cross-Country Running M & W; Equestrian Sports W; Fencing M & W; Field Hockey W; Football M; Golf M & W; Ice Hockey M & W; Lacrosse M & W; Rugby M & W; Soccer M & W; Softball W; Squash M & W; Swimming and Diving M & W; Table Tennis M & W; Tennis M & W; Track and Field M & W; Ultimate Frisbee M & W; Volleyball M & W; Water Polo M; Wrestling M & W

UNIVERSITY OF WINDSOR

401 Sunset Ave.
Windsor, ON, Canada N9B 3P4
Tel: (519)253-3000
Fax: (519)973-7050
E-mail: registrar@uwindsor.ca
Web Site: www.uwindsor.ca
President/CEO: Dr. Alan Wildeman
Admissions: Charlene Yates
Financial Aid: Gillian Baxter

Type: University **Sex:** Coed **Costs Per Year:** Tuition, fee, and room and board charges are reported in Canadian dollars. Area resident tuition: $6930 full-time. Mandatory fees: $7044 full-time. Full-time tuition and fees vary according to course load, degree level, program, and student level. College room and board: $11,312. College room only: $6482. Room and board charges vary according to board plan and housing facility. International student tuition: $22,829 full-time. **Scholarships:** Available. **Calendar System:** Semester, Summer session available **Enrollment:** Full-time 10,023, Graduate full-time 3,537, Graduate part-time 126, Part-time 1,888 **Faculty:** Full-time 598, Part-time 284 **Student-Faculty Ratio:** 21:1 **Exams:** SAT I and SAT II or ACT; SAT I or ACT; SAT II. **% Residing in College-Owned, -Operated, or -Affiliated Housing:** 45 **Final Year or Final Semester Residency Requirement:** No **Credit Hours For Degree:** 30 courses, Bachelors **Professional Accreditation:** APA. **Intercollegiate Athletics:** Basketball M & W; Cross-Country Running M & W; Football M; Golf M & W; Ice Hockey M & W; Soccer M & W; Track and Field M & W; Volleyball M & W

WILFRID LAURIER UNIVERSITY

75 University Ave. W
Waterloo, ON, Canada N2L 3C5
Tel: (519)884-1970
Fax: (519)884-8826

E-mail: admissions@wlu.ca
Web Site: www.wlu.ca
President/CEO: Dr. Max Blouw
Admissions: Lois Wood
Financial Aid: Ruth MacNeil

Type: Comprehensive **Sex:** Coed **% Accepted:** 70 **Admission Plans:** Deferred Admission; Early Action; Early Admission **Application Deadline:** May 1 **Application Fee:** $120.00 **H.S. Requirements:** High school diploma required; GED not accepted **Scholarships:** Available. **Calendar System:** Miscellaneous, Summer session available **Enrollment:** Full-time 13,954, Graduate full-time 866, Graduate part-time 620, Part-time 1,942 **Faculty:** Full-time 516 **Student-Faculty Ratio:** 25:1 **Exams:** SAT I or ACT. **% Residing in College-Owned, -Operated, or -Affiliated Housing:** 25 **Credit Hours For Degree:** 15 courses, Bachelors **Professional Accreditation:** AACSB, ATS. **Intercollegiate Athletics:** Baseball M; Basketball M & W; Cheerleading M & W; Cross-Country Running M & W; Football M; Golf M; Ice Hockey M & W; Lacrosse W; Rugby M & W; Soccer M & W; Swimming and Diving M & W; Volleyball M & W

YORK UNIVERSITY

4700 Keele St.
Toronto, ON, Canada M3J 1P3
Tel: (416)736-2100
Fax: (416)736-5741
E-mail: intlenq@yorku.ca
Web Site: www.yorku.ca
President/CEO: Mamdouh Shoukri

Type: University **Sex:** Coed **Admission Plans:** Deferred Admission; Preferred Admission **Application Deadline:** February 1 **Application Fee:** $210.00 **H.S. Requirements:** High school diploma required; GED not accepted. For mature applicants: High school diploma or equivalent not required **Costs Per Year:** Application fee: $210 Canadian dollars. Tuition, fee, and room and board charges are reported in Canadian dollars. Province resident tuition: $7102 full-time, $236.73 per credit part-time. Canadian resident tuition: $7102 full-time, $236.73 per credit part-time. Full-time tuition varies according to program. Part-time tuition varies according to program. College room and board: $7791. College room only: $5166. Room and board charges vary according to board plan and housing facility. International student tuition: $21,419 full-time. **Scholarships:** Available. **Calendar System:** Semester, Summer session available **Enrollment:** Full-time 41,247, Graduate full-time 3,917, Graduate part-time 2,042, Part-time 7,384 **Exams:** SAT I or ACT. **% Receiving Financial Aid:** 48 **Credit Hours For Degree:** 15 courses, Bachelors **Professional Accreditation:** APA. **Intercollegiate Athletics:** Badminton M & W; Basketball M & W; Cross-Country Running M & W; Field Hockey W; Football M; Ice Hockey M & W; Rugby W; Soccer M & W; Swimming and Diving M & W; Tennis M & W; Track and Field M & W; Volleyball M & W; Water Polo M & W

BISHOP'S UNIVERSITY

2600 College St.
Sherbrooke, QC, Canada J1M 0C8
Tel: (819)822-9600; Free: 877-822-8200
Fax: (819)822-9661
E-mail: recruitment@ubishops.ca
Web Site: www.ubishops.ca
President/CEO: Michael Goldbloom
Admissions: Jacqueline Belleau
Type: Comprehensive **Sex:** Coed **Affiliation:** Association of Universities and Colleges of Canada (AUCC). **Admission Plans:** Deferred Admission; Early Admission **Application Deadline:** March 1 **Application Fee:** $60.00 **H.S. Requirements:** High school diploma required; GED not accepted **Costs Per Year:** Application fee: $60 Canadian dollars. Tuition, fee, and room and board charges are reported in Canadian dollars. Province resident tuition: $2,294 full-time, $76.45 per credit part-time. Canadian resident tuition: $7,030 full-time, $234.35 per credit part-time. Mandatory fees: $1,284 full-time, $29.61 per credit part-time, $345 per term part-time. Full-time tuition and fees vary according to course load, degree level, program, and reciprocity agreements. Part-time tuition and fees vary according to course load, degree level, and program. College room and board: $8900. College room only: $4400. Room and board charges vary according to board plan and housing facility. International student tuition: $15,707 full-time. **Scholarships:** Available. **Calendar System:** Semester **Student-Faculty Ratio:** 15:1 **Exams:** SAT I or ACT; SAT Reasoning. **Intercollegiate Athletics:** Basketball M & W; Field Hockey W; Football M; Golf M; Ice Hockey W; Lacrosse M & W; Rock Climbing M & W; Skiing (Downhill) M & W; Soccer W; Volleyball W

CONCORDIA UNIVERSITY

1455 de Maisonneuve Blvd. W
Montréal, QC, Canada H3G 1M8
Tel: (514)848-2424
Fax: (514)848-2621
E-mail: matthew.stiegemeyer@concordia.ca
Web Site: www.concordia.ca
President/CEO: Dr. Alan Shepard
Admissions: Dr. Matthew Stiegemeyer
Type: University **Sex:** Coed **Affiliation:** Quebec University Network. **% Accepted:** 72 **Admission Plans:** Deferred Admission **Application Deadline:** March 1 **Application Fee:** $100.00 **H.S. Requirements:** High school diploma required; GED not accepted **Costs Per Year:** Application fee: $100 Canadian dollars. Tuition, fee, and room and board charges are reported in Canadian dollars. Province resident tuition: $2,294 full-time, $76.44 per credit part-time. Canadian resident tuition: $7,030 full-time, $234.35 per credit part-time. Mandatory fees: $1,432 full-time, $56.01 per credit part-time. Full-time tuition and fees vary according to course load. Part-time tuition and fees vary according to course load. College room and board: $9590. College room only: $5600. Room and board charges vary according to housing facility and location. International student tuition: $17,545 full-time. **Scholarships:** Available. **Calendar System:** Semester, Summer session available **Enrollment:** Full-time 20,021, Graduate full-time 4,871, Graduate part-time 2,031, Part-time 10,333 **Faculty:** Full-time 1,029, Part-time 955 **Student-Faculty Ratio:** 22:1 **% Residing in College-Owned, -Operated, or -Affiliated Housing:** 2 **Final Year or Final Semester Residency Requirement:** Yes **Credit Hours For Degree:** 90 credits,

Bachelors **Professional Accreditation:** AACSB, APA. **Intercollegiate Athletics:** Baseball M; Basketball M & W; Cross-Country Running M & W; Football M; Golf M & W; Ice Hockey M & W; Rugby M & W; Skiing (Downhill) M & W; Soccer M & W; Wrestling M & W

ÉCOLE POLYTECHNIQUE DE MONTRÉAL

CP 6079, Succursale Centre-Ville
Montréal, QC, Canada H3C 3A7
Tel: (514)340-4943
Web Site: www.polymtl.ca
Type: University **Sex:** Coed **Calendar System:** Trimester

HEC MONTREAL

3000, chemin de la Côte-Sainte-Catherine
Montréal, QC, Canada H3T 2A7
Tel: (514)340-6000
Fax: (514)340-5640
E-mail: admission.info@hec.ca
Web Site: www.hec.ca
President/CEO: Michel Patry
Admissions: Virginie Lefebvre
Financial Aid: Joanne Diwan
Type: Comprehensive **Sex:** Coed **Affiliation:** Universite de Montreal. **% Accepted:** 76 **Admission Plans:** Deferred Admission **Application Deadline:** March 1 **Application Fee:** $85.07 **H.S. Requirements:** High school diploma or equivalent not required **Costs Per Year:** Application fee: $85.07. Province resident tuition: $2,294 full-time, $76.45 per credit part-time. Canadian resident tuition: $7,030 full-time, $234.35 per credit part-time. Mandatory fees: $1,415 full-time, $42.07 per credit part-time, $81.66. Full-time tuition and fees vary according to program. Part-time tuition and fees vary according to program. College room and board: $3820. Room and board charges vary according to board plan and housing facility. International student tuition: $21,000 full-time. **Scholarships:** Available. **Calendar System:** Trimester, Summer session available **Enrollment:** Full-time 5,113, Graduate full-time 1,646, Graduate part-time 1,660, Part-time 5,286 **Student-Faculty Ratio:** 21:1 **% Receiving Financial Aid:** 47 **Final Year or Final Semester Residency Requirement:** No **Credit Hours For Degree:** 90 credits, Bachelors **Professional Accreditation:** AACSB.

MCGILL UNIVERSITY

845 Sherbrooke St. W
Montréal, QC, Canada H3A 2T5
Tel: (514)398-4455
Fax: (514)398-4193
E-mail: admissions@mcgill.ca
Web Site: www.mcgill.ca
President/CEO: Heather Munroe-Blum
Financial Aid: Judy Stymest
Type: University **Sex:** Coed **Scores:** 100% SAT V 400+; 100% SAT M 400+; 1.26% ACT 18-23; 38.66% ACT 24-29 **% Accepted:** 54 **Admission Plans:** Deferred Admission **Application Deadline:** January 15 **Application Fee:** $85.00 **H.S. Requirements:** High school diploma required; GED not accepted **Scholarships:** Available. **Calendar System:** Semester, Summer session available **Enrollment:** Full-time 18,722, Part-time 3,801 **Faculty:** Full-time 1,689, Part-time 867 **Student-Faculty Ratio:** 16:1 **Exams:** SAT I

and SAT II or ACT. **% Residing in College-Owned, -Operated, or -Affiliated Housing:** 12 **Credit Hours For Degree:** 120 credits, Bachelors **Professional Accreditation:** ADA, ALA, APA, ATS, LCME/AMA. **Intercollegiate Athletics:** Badminton M & W; Baseball M; Basketball M & W; Cheerleading M & W; Crew M & W; Cross-Country Running M & W; Fencing M & W; Field Hockey W; Football M; Golf M & W; Ice Hockey M & W; Lacrosse M & W; Rugby M & W; Sailing M & W; Skiing (Cross-Country) M & W; Skiing (Downhill) M & W; Soccer M & W; Squash M & W; Swimming and Diving M & W; Tennis M & W; Track and Field M & W; Ultimate Frisbee M & W; Volleyball M & W; Wrestling M & W

TÉLÉ-UNIVERSITÉ

455, rue de l'Église
C.P. 4800, succ. Terminus
Québec, QC, Canada G1K 9H5
Tel: (418)657-2262
Fax: (418)657-2094
Web Site: www.teluq.uquebec.ca
Admissions: Louise Bertrand

Type: Comprehensive **Sex:** Coed **Affiliation:** Université du Québec. **% Accepted:** 100 **Admission Plans:** Open Admission **Application Deadline:** Rolling **Application Fee:** $30.00 **H.S. Requirements:** High school diploma required; GED not accepted **Calendar System:** Trimester, Summer session available **Faculty:** Full-time 36 **Credit Hours For Degree:** 90 credits, Bachelors

UNIVERSITÉ LAVAL

C.P. 2208, succursale Terminus
Québec, QC, Canada G1K 7P4
Tel: (418)656-3333; Free: 877-785-2825
Fax: (418)656-2809
E-mail: info@dap.ulaval.ca
Web Site: www.ulaval.ca

Type: University **Sex:** Coed **% Accepted:** 63 **Application Deadline:** March 1 **Application Fee:** $30.00 **H.S. Requirements:** High school diploma required; GED accepted **Calendar System:** Trimester, Summer session available **Enrollment:** Full-time 19,938, Part-time 7,971 **Faculty:** Full-time 1,380, Part-time 76 **Student-Faculty Ratio:** 7:1 **% Residing in College-Owned, -Operated, or -Affiliated Housing:** 7 **Credit Hours For Degree:** 90 credits, Bachelors **Professional Accreditation:** AACSB, ADA, LCME/AMA. **Intercollegiate Athletics:** Badminton M & W; Baseball M; Basketball M & W; Cross-Country Running M & W; Football M; Golf M & W; Gymnastics M & W; Skiing (Downhill) M & W; Soccer M & W; Swimming and Diving M & W; Track and Field M & W; Volleyball M & W

UNIVERSITÉ DE MONTRÉAL

CP 6128, Succursale Centre-ville
Montréal, QC, Canada H3C 3J7
Tel: (514)343-6111
Fax: (514)343-5788
E-mail: marie-claude.binette@umontreal.ca
Web Site: www.umontreal.ca
President/CEO: Guy BRETON, MD
Admissions: Mme. Marie-Claude Binette
Financial Aid: Sylvianne Latour

Type: University **Sex:** Coed **Affiliation:** L'Ecole Polytechnique de Montreal, HEC Montreal. **Costs Per Year:** One-time mandatory fee: $53.06. Province resident tuition: $3071 full-time, $161 per credit part-time. Canadian resident tuition: $7808 full-time, $320 per credit part-time. Mandatory fees: $291 full-time, $291 per year part-time. International student tuition: $21,491 full-time. **Scholarships:** Available. **Calendar System:** Trimester, Summer session available **Enrollment:** Full-time 27,641, Graduate full-time 8,941, Graduate part-time 3,009, Part-time 9,203 **Faculty:** Full-time 1,500, Part-time 4,200 **Final Year or Final Semester Residency Requirement:** No **Credit Hours For Degree:** No associate degrees, Associates; 90 credits, Bachelors **Professional Accreditation:** ACSP, ADA, ALA, AOA, ASLA, AVMA, CAHME, LCME/AMA. **Intercollegiate Athletics:** Badminton M & W; Baseball M & W; Cheerleading M & W; Cross-Country Running M & W; Football M; Golf M & W; Ice Hockey M & W; Rowing M & W; Rugby M & W; Skiing (Downhill) M & W; Soccer M & W; Swimming and Diving M & W; Tennis M & W; Track and Field M & W; Triathlon M & W; Ultimate Frisbee M & W; Volleyball M & W

UNIVERSITÉ DU QUÉBEC EN ABITIBI-TÉMISCAMINGUE

445 Blvd. de l'Université
Rouyn-Noranda, QC, Canada J9X 5E4
Tel: (819)762-0971
Fax: (819)797-4727
E-mail: micheline.chevalier@uqat.uquebec.ca
Web Site: www.uqat.ca
Admissions: Monique Fay

Type: Comprehensive **Sex:** Coed **Affiliation:** Université du Québec. **Admission Plans:** Open Admission **Application Deadline:** Rolling **Application Fee:** $30.00 **H.S. Requirements:** High school diploma required; GED not accepted **Calendar System:** Trimester, Summer session available **Faculty:** Full-time 71, Part-time 88 **Credit Hours For Degree:** 90 credits, Bachelors

UNIVERSITÉ DU QUÉBEC À CHICOUTIMI

555, Blvd. de L'Université
Chicoutimi, QC, Canada G7H 2B1
Tel: (418)545-5011
Fax: (418)545-5012
E-mail: czoccast@uqac.uquebec.ca
Web Site: www.uqac.ca
Admissions: Jean Wauthier
Financial Aid: Mme. Marie-Claude Bergeron

Type: University **Sex:** Coed **Affiliation:** Université du Québec. **Admission Plans:** Open Admission **Application Deadline:** March 1 **H.S. Requirements:** High school diploma required; GED not accepted **Scholarships:** Available. **Calendar System:** Trimester, Summer session available **Faculty:** Full-time 221, Part-time 173 **Credit Hours For Degree:** 90 credits, Bachelors **Intercollegiate Athletics:** Badminton M & W; Cross-Country Running M & W; Soccer W; Volleyball M & W

UNIVERSITÉ DU QUÉBEC, ÉCOLE DE TECHNOLOGIE SUPÉRIEURE

1100, rue Notre Dame Ouest
Montréal, QC, Canada H3C 1K3
Tel: (514)396-8800
Fax: (514)289-8950
E-mail: admission@ets.mtl.ca
Web Site: www.etsmtl.ca
Admissions: Mme. Francine Gamache

Type: Comprehensive **Sex:** Coed **Affiliation:** Université du Québec. **% Accepted:** 88 **Admission Plans:** Open Admission **Application Deadline:** March 1 **Application Fee:** $30.00 **H.S. Requirements:** High school diploma required; GED not accepted **Scholarships:** Available. **Calendar System:** Trimester, Summer session available **Enrollment:** Full-time 2,763, Part-time 1,091 **Faculty:** Full-time 119, Part-time 162 **Credit Hours For Degree:** 114 credits, Bachelors **Intercollegiate Athletics:** Rugby M

UNIVERSITÉ DU QUÉBEC À MONTRÉAL

CP 8888, Succursale Centre-ville
Montréal, QC, Canada H3C 3P8
Tel: (514)987-3000
Fax: (514)987-7728
E-mail: admission@uqam.ca
Web Site: www.uqam.ca
Admissions: Lucille Boisselle-Roy

Type: University **Sex:** Coed **Affiliation:** Université du Québec. **Admission Plans:** Open Admission **Application Deadline:** March 1 **H.S. Requirements:** High school diploma required; GED not accepted **Calendar System:** Trimester, Summer session available **Faculty:** Full-time 993, Part-time 2,011 **Credit Hours For Degree:** 90 credits, Bachelors

UNIVERSITÉ DU QUÉBEC EN OUTAOUAIS

Case Postale 1250, Succursale Hull
Gatineau, QC, Canada J8X 3X7
Tel: (819)595-3900; Free: 800-567-1283
E-mail: registraire@uqo.ca
Web Site: www.uqo.ca
President/CEO: Denis Harrisson

Type: University **Sex:** Coed **Affiliation:** Université du Québec. **Admission Plans:** Open Admission **Application Fee:** $60.00 **H.S. Requirements:** High school diploma or equivalent not required **Costs Per Year:** Application fee: $60 Canadian dollars. Tuition and fee charges are reported in Canadian dollars. Area resident tuition: $508.96 per course part-time. Province resident tuition: $982.66 per course part-time. Canadian resident tuition: $1,800.12

per course part-time. Part-time tuition varies according to class time, course load, degree level, and program. **Calendar System:** Trimester, Summer session available **Credit Hours For Degree:** 90 credits, Bachelors **Intercollegiate Athletics:** Cheerleading M & W; Golf M & W; Soccer M & W; Swimming and Diving M & W; Volleyball W

UNIVERSITÉ DU QUÉBEC À RIMOUSKI
300, Allee des Ursulines, CP 3300
Rimouski, QC, Canada G5L 3A1
Tel: (418)723-1986
Fax: (418)724-1525
E-mail: philippe_horth@uqar.uquebec.ca
Web Site: www.uqar.ca
Admissions: Marie Saint-Laurent
Type: Comprehensive **Sex:** Coed **Affiliation:** Université du Québec. **% Accepted:** 99 **Admission Plans:** Open Admission **Application Deadline:** March 1 **H.S. Requirements:** High school diploma required; GED not accepted **Calendar System:** Trimester, Summer session available **Faculty:** Full-time 168, Part-time 156 **Credit Hours For Degree:** 90 credits, Bachelors **Intercollegiate Athletics:** Badminton M & W; Cross-Country Running M & W; Skiing (Downhill) M & W

UNIVERSITÉ DU QUÉBEC À TROIS-RIVIÈRES
3351 Blvd. des Forges, Case post 500
Trois-Rivières, QC, Canada G9A 5H7
Tel: (819)376-5011; Free: 800-365-0922
Fax: (819)376-5210
E-mail: registraire@uqtr.ca
Web Site: www.uqtr.ca
Admissions: Jean Bois
Type: University **Sex:** Coed **Affiliation:** Université du Québec. **Admission Plans:** Open Admission **Application Deadline:** March 1 **Application Fee:** $30.00 **H.S. Requirements:** High school diploma required; GED not accepted **Calendar System:** Trimester, Summer session available **Faculty:** Full-time 317, Part-time 413 **Credit Hours For Degree:** 90 credits, Bachelors **Intercollegiate Athletics:** Badminton M & W; Cross-Country Running M; Ice Hockey M & W; Soccer M & W; Swimming and Diving M & W; Track and Field M & W

UNIVERSITÉ DE SHERBROOKE
Sherbrooke, QC, Canada J1K 2R1
Tel: (819)821-8000
Fax: (819)821-7966
Web Site: www.usherbrooke.ca
Admissions: Mme. Lisa Bedard
Financial Aid: Gilles Godin
Type: University **Sex:** Coed **% Accepted:** 56 **Admission Plans:** Early Admission; Preferred Admission **Application Deadline:** March 1 **Application Fee:** $70.00 **H.S. Requirements:** High school diploma required; GED not accepted **Costs Per Year:** Application fee: $70 Canadian dollars. Tuition, fee, and room only charges are reported in Canadian dollars. Province resident tuition: $2,294 full-time, $76.45 per credit part-time. Canadian resident tuition: $7,030 full-time, $234.35 per credit part-time. Mandatory fees: $619 full-time, $15.49 per credit part-time, $102.34 per term part-time. Full-time tuition and fees vary according to course load and location. Part-time tuition and fees vary according to course load and location. College room only: $3360. Room charges vary according to location. International student tuition: $17,545 full-time. **Scholarships:** Available. **Calendar System:** Miscellaneous, Summer session available **Enrollment:** Full-time 11,392, Graduate full-time 4,682, Graduate part-time 5,511, Part-time 2,884 **Faculty:** Full-time 1,131, Part-time 1,833 **Credit Hours For Degree:** 90 credits, Bachelors **Professional Accreditation:** LCME/AMA. **Intercollegiate Athletics:** Badminton M & W; Cheerleading M & W; Golf M & W; Rugby M & W

BRIERCREST COLLEGE

510 College Dr.

Caronport, SK, Canada S0H 0S0

Tel: (306)756-3200; Free: 800-667-5199

Fax: (306)756-5500

E-mail: admissions@briercrest.ca

Web Site: www.briercrest.ca

President/CEO: Dr. Dwayne Uglem

Admissions: Ralph Troshke

Financial Aid: Joan Ballantyne

Type: Four-Year College **Sex:** Coed **Affiliation:** interdenominational; Briercrest College and Seminary. **% Accepted:** 57 **Admission Plans:** Deferred Admission; Open Admission **Application Deadline:** August 15 **Application Fee:** $50.00 **H.S. Requirements:** High school diploma required; GED accepted **Costs Per Year:** Application fee: $50 Canadian dollars. Tuition, fee, and room and board charges are reported in Canadian dollars. One-time mandatory fee: $50. Comprehensive fee: $13,288 includes full-time tuition ($6420), mandatory fees ($400), and college room and board ($6468). College room only: $4008. Full-time tuition and fees vary according to course load and program. Room and board charges vary according to board plan and housing facility. Part-time tuition: $12 per credit hour. Part-time mandatory fees: $321 per credit hour, $400 per term. Part-time tuition and fees vary according to course load and program. **Scholarships:** Available. **Calendar System:** Semester, Summer session available **Exams:** SAT I or ACT. **% Residing in College-Owned, -Operated, or -Affiliated Housing:** 15 **Final Year or Final Semester Residency Requirement:** No **Credit Hours For Degree:** 60 semester hours, Associates; 126 semester hours, Bachelors **Professional Accreditation:** ABHE, ATS. **Intercollegiate Athletics:** Basketball M & W; Ice Hockey M; Volleyball M & W

ESTON COLLEGE

730 1st St. E

Box 579

Eston, SK, Canada S0L 1A0

Tel: (306)962-3621; Free: 888-440-3424

Fax: (306)962-3810

E-mail: admissions@estoncollege.ca

Web Site: www.estoncollege.ca

President/CEO: Brian Fuller

Type: Four-Year College **Sex:** Coed **Affiliation:** Apostolic Church of Pentecost. **Application Fee:** $50.00 **Costs Per Year:** Application fee: $50 Canadian dollars. Tuition, fee, and room and board charges are reported in Canadian dollars. One-time mandatory fee: $150. Comprehensive fee: $12,363 includes full-time tuition ($6368), mandatory fees ($305), and college room and board ($5690). Full-time tuition and fees vary according to class time, course level, course load, degree level, location, program, reciprocity agreements, and student level. Part-time tuition: $199.99 per credit hour. Part-time mandatory fees: $50 per term. Part-time tuition and fees vary according to class time, course level, course load, degree level, location, program, reciprocity agreements, and student level. Tuition guaranteed not to increase for student's term of enrollment. **Professional Accreditation:** ABHE.

HORIZON COLLEGE & SEMINARY

1303 Jackson Ave.

Saskatoon, SK, Canada S7H 2M9

Tel: (306)374-6655; Free: 877-374-6655

Fax: (306)373-6968

E-mail: admissions@horizon.edu

Web Site: www.horizon.edu

President/CEO: Dr. Jeromey Martini

Admissions: Jenn Lundy

Financial Aid: Jan Andreae

Type: Four-Year College **Sex:** Coed **Affiliation:** Pentecostal Assemblies of Canada; University of Saskatchewan. **Admission Plans:** Deferred Admission **Application Deadline:** December 15 **Application Fee:** $50.00 **H.S. Requirements:** High school diploma required; GED accepted **Scholarships:** Available. **Calendar System:** Semester, Summer session not available **Enrollment:** Full-time 39, Part-time 13 **Faculty:** Full-time 1, Part-time 11 **Student-Faculty Ratio:** 11:1 **% Residing in College-Owned, -Operated, or -Affiliated Housing:** 72 **Final Year or Final Semester Residency Requirement:** No **Credit Hours For Degree:** 64 credit hours, Associates; 128 credit hours, Bachelors **Professional Accreditation:** ABHE.

UNIVERSITY OF REGINA

3737 Wascana Pky.

Regina, SK, Canada S4S 0A2

Tel: (306)585-4111; Free: 800-644-4756

Fax: (306)585-5203

E-mail: enrolment.services@uregina.ca

Web Site: www.uregina.ca

President/CEO: Dr. Vianne Timmons

Admissions: Christine McBain

Financial Aid: Cherie Mutschler

Type: University **Sex:** Coed **Affiliation:** intentionally left blank. **% Accepted:** 68 **Admission Plans:** Deferred Admission; Early Admission; Early Decision Plan; Preferred Admission **Application Deadline:** August 15 **Application Fee:** $100.00 **H.S. Requirements:** High school diploma required; GED accepted. For High school diploma is not required for Mature Students (21 years of age or older) and for University transfer students who have completed a minimum of 15 credit hours at an accredited secondary institution: High school diploma required; GED not accepted **Costs Per Year:** Application fee: $100 Canadian dollars. Tuition, fee, and room and board charges are reported in Canadian dollars. Province resident tuition: $5970 full-time, $199 per credit hour part-time. Mandatory fees: $613 full-time. Full-time tuition and fees vary according to course load and program. Part-time tuition varies according to course load and program. College room and board: $7380. College room only: $5046. Room and board charges vary according to board plan and housing facility. International student tuition: $17,910 full-time. **Scholarships:** Available. **Calendar System:** Semester, Summer session available **Enrollment:** Full-time 10,478, Graduate full-time 827, Graduate part-time 921, Part-time 2,134 **Faculty:** Full-time 425 **Student-Faculty Ratio:** 21:1 **Exams:** ACT essay component not used; SAT I or ACT; SAT essay component not used; SAT Reasoning; SAT Subject. **% Residing in College-Owned, -Operated, or -Affiliated Housing:** 10 **Final Year or Final Semester Residency Requirement:** No **Credit Hours For Degree:** 120 credit hours, Bachelors **Intercollegiate Athletics:** Basketball M & W; Cross-Country Running M & W; Football M; Ice Hockey M & W; Soccer W; Swimming and Diving M & W; Track and Field M & W; Volleyball M & W; Wrestling M & W

UNIVERSITY OF SASKATCHEWAN

105 Administration Pl.
Saskatoon, SK, Canada S7N 5A2
Tel: (306)966-4343
Fax: (306)966-7026
E-mail: admissions@usask.ca
Web Site: www.usask.ca
President/CEO: Peter Stoicheff
Type: University **Sex:** Coed **% Accepted:** 62 **Admission Plans:** Early Admission **Application Deadline:** May 1 **Application Fee:** $90.00 **H.S. Requirements:** High school diploma required; GED not accepted. For special (mature) admission, transition program (special cases): High school diploma or equivalent not required **Costs Per Year:** Application fee: $90. Province resident tuition: $5954 full-time. Canadian resident tuition: $5954 full-time. Mandatory fees: $413 full-time. Full-time tuition and fees vary according to course load and program. International student tuition: $15,480 full-time. **Scholarships:** Available. **Calendar System:** Miscellaneous, Summer session available **% Residing in College-Owned, -Operated, or -Affiliated Housing:** 12 **Final Year or Final Semester Residency Requirement:** No **Credit Hours For Degree:** 90 credit units, Bachelors **Professional Accreditation:** ADA, APA, AVMA, LCME/AMA. **Intercollegiate Athletics:** Basketball M & W; Cross-Country Running M & W; Football M; Ice Hockey M & W; Soccer M & W; Track and Field M & W; Volleyball M & W; Wrestling M & W

Archery

Appalachian State University *North Carolina* M & W
Atlantic Cape Community College *New Jersey* M & W
Barnard College *New York* W
California State University, Fullerton *California* M & W
California State University, Long Beach *California* M & W
Central Washington University *Washington* M & W
Claremont McKenna College *California* M & W
Columbia University *New York* M & W
Columbia University, School of General Studies *New York* W
Diné College *Arizona* M & W
Eastern Washington University *Washington* M & W
Emmanuel College *Georgia* M & W
Kentucky Christian University *Kentucky* M & W
Lake Forest College *Illinois* M & W
Michigan Technological University *Michigan* M & W
Mount Marty College *South Dakota* M & W
Oberlin College *Ohio* M & W
Pennsylvania College of Technology *Pennsylvania* M & W
Rensselaer Polytechnic Institute *New York* M & W
Shoreline Community College *Washington* M & W
Stanford University *California* M & W
United States Air Force Academy *Colorado* M & W
University of California, Irvine *California* M & W
University of the Cumberlands *Kentucky* M & W
University of New Hampshire *New Hampshire* M & W
University of North Carolina at Asheville *North Carolina* M & W
University of North Texas *Texas* M & W
University of Rio Grande *Ohio* M
University of Rochester *New York* M & W
University of Southern California *California* M & W
The University of Texas at Austin *Texas* M & W
University of Toronto *Ontario (Canada)* M & W
University of Wisconsin - Whitewater *Wisconsin* M & W
Weber State University *Utah* M & W
Yale University *Connecticut* M & W

Badminton

Albright College *Pennsylvania* W
Boston University *Massachusetts* M & W
Bryn Mawr College *Pennsylvania* W
California State University, Long Beach *California* M & W
Carleton College *Minnesota* M & W
City College of San Francisco *California* W
Colgate University *New York* M & W
Columbia University *New York* M & W
Columbia University, School of General Studies *New York* M & W
Concordia University of Edmonton *Alberta (Canada)* M & W
Dartmouth College *New Hampshire* M & W
Dickinson State University *North Dakota* M & W

Duke University *North Carolina* M & W
Eastern Illinois University *Illinois* M & W
Emory University *Georgia* M & W
Fresno City College *California* W
Fullerton College *California* W
Grossmont College *California* W
Haverford College *Pennsylvania* W
Illinois Institute of Technology *Illinois* M & W
The King's University *Alberta (Canada)* M & W
Lycoming College *Pennsylvania* M & W
McGill University *Quebec (Canada)* M & W
McMaster University *Ontario (Canada)* M & W
Michigan Technological University *Michigan* M & W
Mission College *California* M & W
Mount Saint Vincent University *Nova Scotia (Canada)* M & W
Mt. San Antonio College *California* W
North Dakota State University *North Dakota* M & W
Oberlin College *Ohio* M & W
Pasadena City College *California* M & W
Redeemer University College *Ontario (Canada)* M & W
Rensselaer Polytechnic Institute *New York* M & W
Rhodes College *Tennessee* M & W
Rice University *Texas* M & W
Ryerson University *Ontario (Canada)* M & W
Saint Louis University *Missouri* M & W
St. Mary's College of Maryland *Maryland* M & W
Stanford University *California* M & W
State University of New York College at Geneseo *New York* M & W
Swarthmore College *Pennsylvania* M & W
Syracuse University *New York* M & W
Thompson Rivers University *British Columbia (Canada)* M & W
Université Laval *Quebec (Canada)* M & W
Université de Montréal *Quebec (Canada)* M & W
Université du Québec à Chicoutimi *Quebec (Canada)* M & W
Université du Québec à Rimouski *Quebec (Canada)* M & W
Université du Québec à Trois-Rivières *Quebec (Canada)* M & W
Université Sainte-Anne *Nova Scotia (Canada)* M & W
Université de Sherbrooke *Quebec (Canada)* M & W
The University of Alabama *Alabama* M & W
The University of Arizona *Arizona* M & W
University of California, Irvine *California* M & W
University of California, Santa Cruz *California* M & W
University of Georgia *Georgia* M & W
University of Hartford *Connecticut* M & W
University of King's College *Nova Scotia (Canada)* M & W
University of Maryland, Baltimore County *Maryland* M & W
University of Minnesota, Duluth *Minnesota* M & W
University of Mississippi *Mississippi* M & W
University of New Brunswick Saint John *New Brunswick (Canada)* M & W

The University of North Carolina at Chapel Hill *North Carolina* M & W
University of North Texas *Texas* M & W
University of Ottawa *Ontario (Canada)* M & W
University of Richmond *Virginia* M & W
University of Rochester *New York* M & W
University of South Florida *Florida* M & W
University of Southern California *California* M & W
The University of Texas at Austin *Texas* M & W
The University of Texas at San Antonio *Texas* M & W
University of Toronto *Ontario (Canada)* M & W
University of Waterloo *Ontario (Canada)* M & W
The University of Western Ontario *Ontario (Canada)* M & W
University of Wisconsin - River Falls *Wisconsin* M & W
University of Wyoming *Wyoming* M & W
Yale University *Connecticut* M & W
York University *Ontario (Canada)* M & W

Baseball

Abilene Christian University *Texas* M
Abraham Baldwin Agricultural College *Georgia* M
Academy of Art University *California* M
Adams State University *Colorado* M
Adelphi University *New York* M
Adirondack Community College *New York* M
Adrian College *Michigan* M
Alabama Agricultural and Mechanical University *Alabama* M
Alabama Southern Community College *Alabama* M
Alabama State University *Alabama* M
Albany State University *Georgia* M
Albertus Magnus College *Connecticut* M
Albion College *Michigan* M
Albright College *Pennsylvania* M
Alcorn State University *Mississippi* M
Alderson Broaddus University *West Virginia* M
Alice Lloyd College *Kentucky* M
Allan Hancock College *California* M
Allegany College of Maryland *Maryland* M
Allegheny College *Pennsylvania* M
Allen Community College *Kansas* M
Alma College *Michigan* M
Alvernia University *Pennsylvania* M
Alvin Community College *Texas* M
American International College *Massachusetts* M
American River College *California* M
Amherst College *Massachusetts* M
Ancilla College *Indiana* M
Anderson University *Indiana* M
Anderson University *South Carolina* M
Andrew College *Georgia* M
Angelina College *Texas* M
Angelo State University *Texas* M
Anna Maria College *Massachusetts* M
Anne Arundel Community College *Maryland* M
Anoka-Ramsey Community College *Minnesota* M
Antelope Valley College *California* M
Appalachian State University *North Carolina* M
Aquinas College *Michigan* M

M = Men; W = Women

Arcadia University *Pennsylvania* M
Arizona Christian University *Arizona* M
Arizona State University at the Downtown Phoenix campus *Arizona* M
Arizona State University at the Polytechnic campus *Arizona* M
Arizona State University at the Tempe campus *Arizona* M
Arizona State University at the West campus *Arizona* M
Arizona Western College *Arizona* M
Arkansas Baptist College *Arkansas* M
Arkansas State University *Arkansas* M
Arkansas Tech University *Arkansas* M
Arlington Baptist College *Texas* M
Armstrong State University *Georgia* M
ASA College *New York* M
Asbury University *Kentucky* M
Ashford University *California* M
Ashland University *Ohio* M
Assumption College *Massachusetts* M
Auburn University *Alabama* M
Auburn University at Montgomery *Alabama* M
Augsburg College *Minnesota* M
Augusta University *Georgia* M
Augustana College *Illinois* M
Augustana University *South Dakota* M
Aurora University *Illinois* M
Austin College *Texas* M
Austin Peay State University *Tennessee* M
Ave Maria University *Florida* M
Averett University *Virginia* M
Avila University *Missouri* M
Azusa Pacific University *California* M
Babson College *Massachusetts* M
Baker University *Kansas* M
Bakersfield College *California* M
Baldwin Wallace University *Ohio* M
Ball State University *Indiana* M & W
Baltimore City Community College *Maryland* M
Bard College *New York* M
Barry University *Florida* M
Barstow Community College *California* M
Barton College *North Carolina* M
Barton County Community College *Kansas* M
Baruch College of the City University of New York *New York* M
Bates College *Maine* M
Baton Rouge Community College *Louisiana* M
Baylor University *Texas* M
Becker College *Massachusetts* M
Belhaven University *Mississippi* M
Bellarmine University *Kentucky* M
Bellevue College *Washington* M
Belmont Abbey College *North Carolina* M
Belmont University *Tennessee* M
Beloit College *Wisconsin* M
Bemidji State University *Minnesota* M
Benedict College *South Carolina* M
Benedictine College *Kansas* M
Benedictine University *Illinois* M
Bentley University *Massachusetts* M
Berea College *Kentucky* M
Bergen Community College *New Jersey* M
Berry College *Georgia* M
Bethany College *Kansas* M
Bethany College *West Virginia* M
Bethany Lutheran College *Minnesota* M
Bethel College *Indiana* M
Bethel University *Minnesota* M
Bethel University *Tennessee* M
Bethune-Cookman University *Florida* M
Big Bend Community College *Washington* M
Binghamton University, State University of New York *New York* M
Biola University *California* M
Birmingham-Southern College *Alabama* M
Bishop State Community College *Alabama* M & W
Bismarck State College *North Dakota* M
Black Hawk College *Illinois* M
Blackburn College *Illinois* M
Blessing-Rieman College of Nursing *Illinois* M & W
Blinn College *Texas* M
Bloomfield College *New Jersey* M

Bloomsburg University of Pennsylvania *Pennsylvania* M
Blue Mountain College *Mississippi* M
Blue Mountain Community College *Oregon* M
Blue Ridge Community College *North Carolina* M
Bluefield College *Virginia* M
Bluefield State College *West Virginia* M
Bluffton University *Ohio* M
Bossier Parish Community College *Louisiana* M
Boston College *Massachusetts* M
Boston University *Massachusetts* M
Bowdoin College *Maine* M
Bowling Green State University *Ohio* M
Bradley University *Illinois* M
Brandeis University *Massachusetts* M
Brescia University *Kentucky* M
Brevard College *North Carolina* M
Brewton-Parker College *Georgia* M
Briar Cliff University *Iowa* M
Bridgewater College *Virginia* M
Bridgewater State University *Massachusetts* M
Brigham Young University *Utah* M
Brock University *Ontario (Canada)* M
Bronx Community College of the City University of New York *New York* M
Brookdale Community College *New Jersey* M
Brookhaven College *Texas* M
Broome Community College *New York* M
Broward College *Florida* M
Brown University *Rhode Island* M
Brunswick Community College *North Carolina* M
Bryan College *Tennessee* M
Bryant University *Rhode Island* M
Bucknell University *Pennsylvania* M
Bucks County Community College *Pennsylvania* M
Buena Vista University *Iowa* M
Buffalo State College, State University of New York *New York* M
Bunker Hill Community College *Massachusetts* M
Butler Community College *Kansas* M
Butler County Community College *Pennsylvania* M
Butler University *Indiana* M
Butte College *California* M
Cabrillo College *California* M
Cabrini University *Pennsylvania* M
Cairn University *Pennsylvania* M
Caldwell University *New Jersey* M
Calhoun Community College *Alabama* M
California Baptist University *California* M
California Institute of Technology *California* M
California Lutheran University *California* M
California Polytechnic State University, San Luis Obispo *California* M
California State Polytechnic University, Pomona *California* M
California State University, Chico *California* M
California State University, Dominguez Hills *California* M
California State University, East Bay *California* M
California State University, Fresno *California* M
California State University, Fullerton *California* M
California State University, Los Angeles *California* M
California State University, Monterey Bay *California* M
California State University, Northridge *California* M
California State University, Sacramento *California* M
California State University, San Bernardino *California* M
California State University, San Marcos *California* M
California State University, Stanislaus *California* M
California University of Pennsylvania *Pennsylvania* M
Calumet College of Saint Joseph *Indiana* M
Calvin College *Michigan* M
Camden County College *New Jersey* M
Cameron University *Oklahoma* M
Campbell University *North Carolina* M
Campbellsville University *Kentucky* M
Cañada College *California* M
Canisius College *New York* M
Capital University *Ohio* M

Caribbean University *Puerto Rico* M
Carl Albert State College *Oklahoma* M
Carl Sandburg College *Illinois* M
Carleton College *Minnesota* M
Carnegie Mellon University *Pennsylvania* M
Carroll University *Wisconsin* M
Carson-Newman University *Tennessee* M
Carthage College *Wisconsin* M
Case Western Reserve University *Ohio* M
Castleton University *Vermont* M
Catawba College *North Carolina* M
Catawba Valley Community College *North Carolina* M
The Catholic University of America *District of Columbia* M
Cazenovia College *New York* M
Cecil College *Maryland* M
Cedar Valley College *Texas* M
Cedarville University *Ohio* M
Centenary College *New Jersey* M
Centenary College of Louisiana *Louisiana* M
Central Alabama Community College *Alabama* M
Central Arizona College *Arizona* M
Central Baptist College *Arkansas* M
Central Christian College of Kansas *Kansas* M
Central College *Iowa* M
Central Connecticut State University *Connecticut* M
Central Lakes College *Minnesota* M
Central Maine Community College *Maine* M
Central Methodist University *Missouri* M
Central Michigan University *Michigan* M
Central Penn College *Pennsylvania* M
Central Washington University *Washington* M
Centralia College *Washington* M
Centre College *Kentucky* M
Century College *Minnesota* M
Cerritos College *California* M
Cerro Coso Community College *California* M
Chabot College *California* M
Chaffey College *California* M
Chandler-Gilbert Community College *Arizona* M
Chapman University *California* M
Charleston Southern University *South Carolina* M
Chatham University *Pennsylvania* M
Chattahoochee Valley Community College *Alabama* M
Chattanooga State Community College *Tennessee* M
Chemeketa Community College *Oregon* M
Chesapeake College *Maryland* M
Chestnut Hill College *Pennsylvania* M
Chicago State University *Illinois* M
Chipola College *Florida* M
Chowan University *North Carolina* M
Christian Brothers University *Tennessee* M
Christopher Newport University *Virginia* M
Cisco College *Texas* M
The Citadel, The Military College of South Carolina *South Carolina* M
Citrus College *California* M
City College of the City University of New York *New York* M
City College of San Francisco *California* M
City Colleges of Chicago, Olive-Harvey College *Illinois* M
Clackamas Community College *Oregon* M
Claflin University *South Carolina* M
Claremont McKenna College *California* M
Clarendon College *Texas* M
Clarion University of Pennsylvania *Pennsylvania* M
Clark Atlanta University *Georgia* M
Clark College *Washington* M
Clark State Community College *Ohio* M
Clark University *Massachusetts* M
Clarke University *Iowa* M
Clarkson University *New York* M
Clemson University *South Carolina* M
Cleveland State Community College *Tennessee* M
Clinton Community College *New York* M
Cloud County Community College *Kansas* M
Coahoma Community College *Mississippi* M
Coastal Carolina University *South Carolina* M
Cochise County Community College District *Arizona* M

M = Men; W = Women

Coe College *Iowa* M
Coffeyville Community College *Kansas* M
Coker College *South Carolina* M
Colby College *Maine* M
Colby Community College *Kansas* M
Colby-Sawyer College *New Hampshire* M
Colgate University *New York* M
The College at Brockport, State University of New York *New York* M
College of the Canyons *California* M
College of Central Florida *Florida* M
College of Charleston *South Carolina* M
College of the Desert *California* M
College of DuPage *Illinois* M
College of the Holy Cross *Massachusetts* M
The College of Idaho *Idaho* M
College of Lake County *Illinois* M
College of Marin *California* M
College of Mount Saint Vincent *New York* M
The College of New Jersey *New Jersey* M
College of the Ozarks *Missouri* M
College of the Redwoods *California* M
The College of Saint Rose *New York* M
The College of St. Scholastica *Minnesota* M
College of San Mateo *California* M
College of the Sequoias *California* M
College of the Siskiyous *California* M
College of Southern Idaho *Idaho* M
College of Southern Maryland *Maryland* M
College of Staten Island of the City University of New York *New York* M
The College of William and Mary *Virginia* M
The College of Wooster *Ohio* M
Colorado Christian University *Colorado* M
The Colorado College *Colorado* M
Colorado Mesa University *Colorado* M
Colorado Northwestern Community College *Colorado* M
Colorado School of Mines *Colorado* M
Colorado State University *Colorado* M
Colorado State University - Pueblo *Colorado* M
Columbia Basin College *Washington* M
Columbia College *Missouri* M
Columbia College Chicago *Illinois* M
Columbia-Greene Community College *New York* M & W
Columbia State Community College *Tennessee* M
Columbia University *New York* M
Columbia University, School of General Studies *New York* M
Columbus State University *Georgia* M
Community College of Allegheny County *Pennsylvania* M
Community College of Baltimore County *Maryland* M
Community College of Rhode Island *Rhode Island* M
Concord University *West Virginia* M
Concordia College *Minnesota* M
Concordia College Alabama *Alabama* M
Concordia College - New York *New York* M
Concordia University *Oregon* M
Concordia University *Quebec (Canada)* M
Concordia University Ann Arbor *Michigan* M
Concordia University Chicago *Illinois* M
Concordia University Irvine *California* M
Concordia University, Nebraska *Nebraska* M
Concordia University, St. Paul *Minnesota* M
Concordia University Texas *Texas* M
Concordia University Wisconsin *Wisconsin* M
Connecticut College *Connecticut* M
Connors State College *Oklahoma* M
Contra Costa College *California* M
Copiah-Lincoln Community College *Mississippi* M
Coppin State University *Maryland* M
Corban University *Oregon* M
Cornell College *Iowa* M
Cornell University *New York* M
Cornerstone University *Michigan* M
Corning Community College *New York* M
County College of Morris *New Jersey* M
Covenant College *Georgia* M
Cowley County Community College and Area Vocational - Technical School *Kansas* M

Crandall University *New Brunswick (Canada)* M
Creighton University *Nebraska* M
Crowder College *Missouri* M
Crown College *Minnesota* M
Cuesta College *California* M
Culver-Stockton College *Missouri* M
Cumberland County College *New Jersey* M
Cumberland University *Tennessee* M
Curry College *Massachusetts* M
Cuyahoga Community College *Ohio* M
Cypress College *California* M
Dakota College at Bottineau *North Dakota* M
Dakota County Technical College *Minnesota* M
Dakota State University *South Dakota* M
Dakota Wesleyan University *South Dakota* M
Dallas Baptist University *Texas* M
Dallas Christian College *Texas* M
Daniel Webster College *New Hampshire* M
Danville Area Community College *Illinois* M
Dartmouth College *New Hampshire* M
Darton State College *Georgia* M
Davenport University *Michigan* M
Davidson College *North Carolina* M
Davis & Elkins College *West Virginia* M
Dawson Community College *Montana* M
Daytona State College *Florida* M
De Anza College *California* M
Dean College *Massachusetts* M
Defiance College *Ohio* M
Delaware County Community College *Pennsylvania* M
Delaware State University *Delaware* M
Delaware Technical & Community College, Jack F. Owens Campus *Delaware* M
Delaware Valley University *Pennsylvania* M
Delgado Community College *Louisiana* M
Delta College *Michigan* M
Delta State University *Mississippi* M
Denison University *Ohio* M
DePauw University *Indiana* M
Des Moines Area Community College *Iowa* M
DeSales University *Pennsylvania* M
Dickinson College *Pennsylvania* M
Dickinson State University *North Dakota* M
Dixie State University *Utah* M
Doane University *Nebraska* M
Dodge City Community College *Kansas* M
Dominican College *New York* M
Dominican University *Illinois* M
Dordt College *Iowa* M
Drew University *New Jersey* M
Drury University *Missouri* M
Duke University *North Carolina* M
Dutchess Community College *New York* M
Dyersburg State Community College *Tennessee* M
D'Youville College *New York* M
Earlham College *Indiana* M
East Carolina University *North Carolina* M
East Central Community College *Mississippi* M
East Central University *Oklahoma* M
East Los Angeles College *California* M
East Mississippi Community College *Mississippi* M
East Stroudsburg University of Pennsylvania *Pennsylvania* M
East Tennessee State University *Tennessee* M
East Texas Baptist University *Texas* M
Eastern Arizona College *Arizona* M
Eastern Connecticut State University *Connecticut* M
Eastern Florida State College *Florida* M
Eastern Illinois University *Illinois* M
Eastern Kentucky University *Kentucky* M
Eastern Mennonite University *Virginia* M
Eastern Michigan University *Michigan* M
Eastern Nazarene College *Massachusetts* M
Eastern New Mexico University *New Mexico* M
Eastern Oklahoma State College *Oklahoma* M
Eastern University *Pennsylvania* M
Eastern Washington University *Washington* M
Eastfield College *Texas* M
Ecclesia College *Arkansas* M
Eckerd College *Florida* M
Edgewood College *Wisconsin* M
Edison Community College *Ohio* M

Edmonds Community College *Washington* M
El Camino College *California* M
El Paso Community College *Texas* M
Elgin Community College *Illinois* M
Elizabeth City State University *North Carolina* M
Elizabethtown College *Pennsylvania* M
Ellsworth Community College *Iowa* M
Elmhurst College *Illinois* M
Elmira College *New York* M
Elms College *Massachusetts* M
Elon University *North Carolina* M
Embry-Riddle Aeronautical University - Daytona *Florida* M
Emerson College *Massachusetts* M
Emmanuel College *Georgia* M
Emory & Henry College *Virginia* M
Emory University *Georgia* M
Emporia State University *Kansas* M
Endicott College *Massachusetts* M
Enterprise State Community College *Alabama* M
Erie Community College *New York* M
Erie Community College, North Campus *New York* M
Erie Community College, South Campus *New York* M
Erskine College *South Carolina* M
Eureka College *Illinois* M
Evangel University *Missouri* M
Everett Community College *Washington* M
Fairfield University *Connecticut* M
Fairleigh Dickinson University, College at Florham *New Jersey* M
Fairleigh Dickinson University, Metropolitan Campus *New Jersey* M
Fairmont State University *West Virginia* M
Farmingdale State College *New York* M
Faulkner University *Alabama* M
Feather River College *California* M
Felician University *New Jersey* M
Ferrum College *Virginia* M
Finger Lakes Community College *New York* M
Finlandia University *Michigan* M
Fisher College *Massachusetts* M
Fitchburg State University *Massachusetts* M
Flagler College *Florida* M
Florida Agricultural and Mechanical University *Florida* M
Florida Atlantic University *Florida* M
Florida Gulf Coast University *Florida* M
Florida Institute of Technology *Florida* M
Florida International University *Florida* M
Florida Memorial University *Florida* M
Florida Southern College *Florida* M
Florida SouthWestern State College *Florida* M
Florida State College at Jacksonville *Florida* M
Florida State University *Florida* M
Fontbonne University *Missouri* M
Fordham University *New York* M
Fort Lewis College *Colorado* M
Fort Scott Community College *Kansas* M
Framingham State University *Massachusetts* M
Francis Marion University *South Carolina* M
Frank Phillips College *Texas* M
Franklin College *Indiana* M
Franklin & Marshall College *Pennsylvania* M
Franklin Pierce University *New Hampshire* M
Frederick Community College *Maryland* M
Freed-Hardeman University *Tennessee* M
Fresno City College *California* M
Fresno Pacific University *California* M
Friends University *Kansas* M
Frostburg State University *Maryland* M
Fullerton College *California* M
Fulton-Montgomery Community College *New York* M
Furman University *South Carolina* M
Gallaudet University *District of Columbia* M
Galveston College *Texas* M
Gannon University *Pennsylvania* M
Garden City Community College *Kansas* M
Gardner-Webb University *North Carolina* M
Garrett College *Maryland* M
GateWay Community College *Arizona* M
Gateway Community College *Connecticut* M

M = Men; W = Women

Gavilan College *California* M
Genesee Community College *New York* M
Geneva College *Pennsylvania* M
George C. Wallace Community College *Alabama* M
George Corley Wallace State Community College *Alabama* M
George Fox University *Oregon* M
George Mason University *Virginia* M
The George Washington University *District of Columbia* M
Georgetown College *Kentucky* M
Georgetown University *District of Columbia* M
Georgia College & State University *Georgia* M
Georgia Gwinnett College *Georgia* M
Georgia Highlands College *Georgia* M & W
Georgia Institute of Technology *Georgia* M
Georgia Southern University *Georgia* M
Georgia Southwestern State University *Georgia* M
Georgia State University *Georgia* M
Gettysburg College *Pennsylvania* M
Glen Oaks Community College *Michigan* M
Glendale Community College *Arizona* M
Glendale Community College *California* M
Globe Institute of Technology *New York* M
Golden West College *California* M
Gonzaga University *Washington* M
Gordon College *Massachusetts* M
Gordon State College *Georgia* M
Goshen College *Indiana* M
Grace College *Indiana* M
Graceland University *Iowa* M
Grambling State University *Louisiana* M
Grand Canyon University *Arizona* M
Grand Rapids Community College *Michigan* M
Grand Valley State University *Michigan* M
Grand View University *Iowa* M
Grays Harbor College *Washington* M
Grayson College *Texas* M
Green River College *Washington* M
Greensboro College *North Carolina* M
Greenville College *Illinois* M
Grinnell College *Iowa* M
Grossmont College *California* M
Grove City College *Pennsylvania* M
Guilford College *North Carolina* M
Guilford Technical Community College *North Carolina* M
Gulf Coast State College *Florida* M
Gustavus Adolphus College *Minnesota* M
Gwynedd Mercy University *Pennsylvania* M
Hagerstown Community College *Maryland* M
Hamilton College *New York* M
Hamline University *Minnesota* M
Hampden-Sydney College *Virginia* M
Hannibal-LaGrange University *Missouri* M
Hanover College *Indiana* M
Hardin-Simmons University *Texas* M
Harding University *Arkansas* M
Harford Community College *Maryland* M
Harper College *Illinois* M
Harris-Stowe State University *Missouri* M
Harvard University *Massachusetts* M
Harvey Mudd College *California* M
Hastings College *Nebraska* M
Haverford College *Pennsylvania* M
Hawai'i Pacific University *Hawaii* M
Heartland Community College *Illinois* M
Heidelberg University *Ohio* M
Henderson State University *Arkansas* M
Hendrix College *Arkansas* M
Herkimer County Community College *New York* M
Hesston College *Kansas* M
Hibbing Community College *Minnesota* M
High Point University *North Carolina* M
Highland Community College *Illinois* M
Highland Community College *Kansas* M
Hilbert College *New York* M
Hill College *Texas* M
Hillsborough Community College *Florida* M
Hillsdale College *Michigan* M
Hillsdale Free Will Baptist College *Oklahoma* M
Hinds Community College *Mississippi* M
Hiram College *Ohio* M
Hiwassee College *Tennessee* M

Hofstra University *New York* M
Holmes Community College *Mississippi* M
Holy Names University *California* M
Holyoke Community College *Massachusetts* M
Hood College *Maryland* M
Hope College *Michigan* M
Houghton College *New York* M
Houston Baptist University *Texas* M
Howard College *Texas* M
Howard Payne University *Texas* M
Hudson Valley Community College *New York* M
Huntingdon College *Alabama* M
Huntington University *Indiana* M
Husson University *Maine* M
Huston-Tillotson University *Texas* M
Hutchinson Community College *Kansas* M
Illinois Central College *Illinois* M
Illinois College *Illinois* M
Illinois Eastern Community Colleges, Lincoln Trail College *Illinois* M
Illinois Eastern Community Colleges, Olney Central College *Illinois* M
Illinois Eastern Community Colleges, Wabash Valley College *Illinois* M
Illinois Institute of Technology *Illinois* M
Illinois State University *Illinois* M
Illinois Valley Community College *Illinois* M
Illinois Wesleyan University *Illinois* M
Imperial Valley College *California* M
Independence Community College *Kansas* M
Indian Hills Community College *Iowa* M
Indian River State College *Florida* M
Indiana State University *Indiana* M
Indiana Tech *Indiana* M
Indiana University Bloomington *Indiana* M
Indiana University of Pennsylvania *Pennsylvania* M
Indiana University - Purdue University Fort Wayne *Indiana* M
Indiana University South Bend *Indiana* M
Indiana University Southeast *Indiana* M
Indiana Wesleyan University *Indiana* M
Inter American University of Puerto Rico, Aguadilla Campus *Puerto Rico* M
Inter American University of Puerto Rico, Arecibo Campus *Puerto Rico* M
Inter American University of Puerto Rico, Barranquitas Campus *Puerto Rico* M
Inter American University of Puerto Rico, Bayamón Campus *Puerto Rico* M
Inter American University of Puerto Rico, Fajardo Campus *Puerto Rico* M
Inter American University of Puerto Rico, Guayama Campus *Puerto Rico* M
Inter American University of Puerto Rico, Metropolitan Campus *Puerto Rico* M
Inter American University of Puerto Rico, Ponce Campus *Puerto Rico* M
Inter American University of Puerto Rico, San Germán Campus *Puerto Rico* M
Iona College *New York* M
Iowa Central Community College *Iowa* M
Iowa Lakes Community College *Iowa* M
Iowa Wesleyan University *Iowa* M
Iowa Western Community College *Iowa* M
Itasca Community College *Minnesota* M
Ithaca College *New York* M
Jackson College *Michigan* M
Jackson State Community College *Tennessee* M
Jackson State University *Mississippi* M
Jacksonville State University *Alabama* M
Jacksonville University *Florida* M
James A. Rhodes State College *Ohio* M
James H. Faulkner State Community College *Alabama* M
James Madison University *Virginia* M
Jamestown Community College *New York* M
Jarvis Christian College *Texas* M
Jefferson College *Missouri* M
Jefferson Community College *New York* M
Jefferson Davis Community College *Alabama* M
John A. Logan College *Illinois* M
John Carroll University *Ohio* M
John Jay College of Criminal Justice of the City University of New York *New York* M

John Wood Community College *Illinois* M
Johns Hopkins University *Maryland* M
Johnson County Community College *Kansas* M
Johnson University *Tennessee* M
Johnson University Florida *Florida* M
Johnson & Wales University *Colorado* M
Johnson & Wales University *Rhode Island* M
Joliet Junior College *Illinois* M
Jones County Junior College *Mississippi* M
Judson University *Illinois* M
Juniata College *Pennsylvania* M
Kalamazoo College *Michigan* M
Kalamazoo Valley Community College *Michigan* M
Kankakee Community College *Illinois* M
Kansas City Kansas Community College *Kansas* M
Kansas State University *Kansas* M
Kansas Wesleyan University *Kansas* M
Kaskaskia College *Illinois* M
Kean University *New Jersey* M
Keene State College *New Hampshire* M
Kellogg Community College *Michigan* M
Kennesaw State University *Georgia* M
Kent State University *Ohio* M
Kentucky State University *Kentucky* M
Kentucky Wesleyan College *Kentucky* M
Kenyon College *Ohio* M
Keuka College *New York* M
Keystone College *Pennsylvania* M
King University *Tennessee* M
The King's College *New York* M
King's College *Pennsylvania* M
Kingsborough Community College of the City University of New York *New York* M
Kirkwood Community College *Iowa* M
Kishwaukee College *Illinois* M
Knox College *Illinois* M
Kutztown University of Pennsylvania *Pennsylvania* M
La Roche College *Pennsylvania* M
La Salle University *Pennsylvania* M
Labette Community College *Kansas* M
Lackawanna College *Pennsylvania* M
Lafayette College *Pennsylvania* M
LaGrange College *Georgia* M
Lake Erie College *Ohio* M
Lake Forest College *Illinois* M
Lake Land College *Illinois* M
Lake Michigan College *Michigan* M
Lake Region State College *North Dakota* M
Lake-Sumter State College *Florida* M
Lakehead University *Ontario (Canada)* M
Lakeland College *Wisconsin* M
Lakeland Community College *Ohio* M
Lamar Community College *Colorado* M
Lamar University *Texas* M
Lancaster Bible College *Pennsylvania* M
Lander University *South Carolina* M
Landmark College *Vermont* M
Lane College *Tennessee* M
Lane Community College *Oregon* M
Laney College *California* M
Lansing Community College *Michigan* M
Laredo Community College *Texas* M
Lasell College *Massachusetts* M
Lawrence University *Wisconsin* M
Lawson State Community College *Alabama* M
Le Moyne College *New York* M
Lebanon Valley College *Pennsylvania* M
Lee University *Tennessee* M
Lehigh Carbon Community College *Pennsylvania* M
Lehigh University *Pennsylvania* M
Lehman College of the City University of New York *New York* M
LeMoyne-Owen College *Tennessee* M
Lenoir Community College *North Carolina* M
Lenoir-Rhyne University *North Carolina* M
Lesley University *Massachusetts* M
LeTourneau University *Texas* M
Lewis & Clark College *Oregon* M
Lewis and Clark Community College *Illinois* M
Lewis-Clark State College *Idaho* M
Lewis University *Illinois* M
Liberty University *Virginia* M
Limestone College *South Carolina* M

M = Men; W = Women

Lincoln Christian University *Illinois* M
Lincoln Land Community College *Illinois* M
Lincoln Memorial University *Tennessee* M
Lincoln University *Missouri* M
Lincoln University *Pennsylvania* M
Lindenwood University *Missouri* M
Lindsey Wilson College *Kentucky* M
Linfield College *Oregon* M
Lipscomb University *Tennessee* M
Lock Haven University of Pennsylvania *Pennsylvania* M
Long Beach City College *California* M
Long Island University - LIU Brooklyn *New York* M
Long Island University - LIU Post *New York* M
Longwood University *Virginia* M
Loras College *Iowa* M
Los Angeles Harbor College *California* M
Los Angeles Pierce College *California* M
Los Angeles Valley College *California* M
Los Medanos College *California* M
Louisburg College *North Carolina* M
Louisiana College *Louisiana* M
Louisiana State University and Agricultural & Mechanical College *Louisiana* M
Louisiana State University at Alexandria *Louisiana* M
Louisiana State University at Eunice *Louisiana* M
Louisiana State University in Shreveport *Louisiana* M
Louisiana Tech University *Louisiana* M
Lourdes University *Ohio* M
Lower Columbia College *Washington* M
Loyola Marymount University *California* M
Loyola University New Orleans *Louisiana* M
Lubbock Christian University *Texas* M
Lurleen B. Wallace Community College *Alabama* M
Luther College *Iowa* M
Luzerne County Community College *Pennsylvania* M
Lynchburg College *Virginia* M
Lyndon State College *Vermont* M
Lynn University *Florida* M
Lyon College *Arkansas* M
Macalester College *Minnesota* M
MacMurray College *Illinois* M
Macomb Community College *Michigan* M
Madison Area Technical College *Wisconsin* M
Madonna University *Michigan* M
Malone University *Ohio* M
Manchester Community College *Connecticut* M
Manchester University *Indiana* M
Manhattan Christian College *Kansas* M
Manhattan College *New York* M
Manhattanville College *New York* M
Mansfield University of Pennsylvania *Pennsylvania* M
Maranatha Baptist University *Wisconsin* M
Marian University *Indiana* M
Marian University *Wisconsin* M
Marietta College *Ohio* M
Marion Military Institute *Alabama* M
Marist College *New York* M
Mars Hill University *North Carolina* M
Marshall University *West Virginia* M
Marshalltown Community College *Iowa* M
Martin Luther College *Minnesota* M
Martin Methodist College *Tennessee* M
Marymount California University *California* M
Marymount University *Virginia* M
Maryville College *Tennessee* M
Maryville University of Saint Louis *Missouri* M
Marywood University *Pennsylvania* M
Massachusetts Bay Community College *Massachusetts* M
Massachusetts College of Liberal Arts *Massachusetts* M
Massachusetts Institute of Technology *Massachusetts* M
Massachusetts Maritime Academy *Massachusetts* M
Massasoit Community College *Massachusetts* M
The Master's College and Seminary *California* M
Mayville State University *North Dakota* M
McDaniel College *Maryland* M

McGill University *Quebec (Canada)* M
McHenry County College *Illinois* M
McKendree University *Illinois* M
McLennan Community College *Texas* M
McMaster University *Ontario (Canada)* M
McMurry University *Texas* M
McNeese State University *Louisiana* M
Medaille College *New York* M
Mendocino College *California* M
Merced College *California* M
Mercer County Community College *New Jersey* M
Mercer University *Georgia* M
Mercy College *New York* M
Mercyhurst North East *Pennsylvania* M
Mercyhurst University *Pennsylvania* M
Meridian Community College *Mississippi* M
Merrimack College *Massachusetts* M
Mesa Community College *Arizona* M
Mesabi Range College *Minnesota* M
Messiah College *Pennsylvania* M
Methodist University *North Carolina* M
Metropolitan Community College - Kansas City *Missouri* M
Metropolitan State University of Denver *Colorado* M
Miami Dade College *Florida* M
Miami University *Ohio* M & W
Miami University Hamilton *Ohio* M
Miami University Middletown *Ohio* M
Michigan State University *Michigan* M
Michigan Technological University *Michigan* M
Mid-America Christian University *Oklahoma* M
Mid-Plains Community College *Nebraska* M
MidAmerica Nazarene University *Kansas* M
Middle Georgia State University *Georgia* M
Middle Tennessee State University *Tennessee* M
Middlebury College *Vermont* M
Middlesex County College *New Jersey* M
Midland College *Texas* M
Midland University *Nebraska* M
Miles College *Alabama* M
Miles Community College *Montana* M
Millersville University of Pennsylvania *Pennsylvania* M
Milligan College *Tennessee* M
Millikin University *Illinois* M
Millsaps College *Mississippi* M
Milwaukee Area Technical College *Wisconsin* M
Milwaukee School of Engineering *Wisconsin* M
Mineral Area College *Missouri* M
Minnesota State Community and Technical College *Minnesota* M
Minnesota State University Mankato *Minnesota* M
Minnesota West Community and Technical College *Minnesota* M
Minot State University *North Dakota* M
Misericordia University *Pennsylvania* M
Mission College *California* M
Mississippi College *Mississippi* M
Mississippi Delta Community College *Mississippi* M
Mississippi Gulf Coast Community College *Mississippi* M
Mississippi State University *Mississippi* M
Mississippi Valley State University *Mississippi* M
Missouri Baptist University *Missouri* M
Missouri Southern State University *Missouri* M
Missouri State University *Missouri* M
Missouri University of Science and Technology *Missouri* M
Missouri Valley College *Missouri* M
Missouri Western State University *Missouri* M
Mitchell College *Connecticut* M
Modesto Junior College *California* M
Mohawk Valley Community College *New York* M
Molloy College *New York* M
Monmouth College *Illinois* M
Monmouth University *New Jersey* M
Monroe College *New York* M
Monroe Community College *New York* M
Montana State University Billings *Montana* M
Montclair State University *New Jersey* M
Monterey Peninsula College *California* M
Montgomery College *Maryland* M
Montgomery County Community College *Pennsylvania* M

Montreat College *North Carolina* M
Moorpark College *California* M
Moraine Valley Community College *Illinois* M
Moravian College *Pennsylvania* M
Morehead State University *Kentucky* M
Morehouse College *Georgia* M
Morningside College *Iowa* M
Morris College *South Carolina* M
Morton College *Illinois* M
Motlow State Community College *Tennessee* M
Mott Community College *Michigan* M
Mount Aloysius College *Pennsylvania* M
Mt. Hood Community College *Oregon* M
Mount Ida College *Massachusetts* M
Mount Marty College *South Dakota* M
Mount Mercy University *Iowa* M
Mount St. Joseph University *Ohio* M
Mount Saint Mary College *New York* M
Mount St. Mary's University *Maryland* M
Mt. San Antonio College *California* M
Mt. San Jacinto College *California* M
Mount Vernon Nazarene University *Ohio* M
Mountain View College *Texas* M
Muhlenberg College *Pennsylvania* M
Murray State College *Oklahoma* M
Murray State University *Kentucky* M
Muscatine Community College *Iowa* M
Muskegon Community College *Michigan* M
Muskingum University *Ohio* M
Napa Valley College *California* M
Nassau Community College *New York* M
Navarro College *Texas* M
Nebraska Wesleyan University *Nebraska* M
Neosho County Community College *Kansas* M
Neumann University *Pennsylvania* M
New England College *New Hampshire* M
New Jersey City University *New Jersey* M
New Jersey Institute of Technology *New Jersey* M
New Mexico Highlands University *New Mexico* M
New Mexico Junior College *New Mexico* M
New Mexico Military Institute *New Mexico* M
New Mexico State University *New Mexico* M
New River Community College *Virginia* M
New York Institute of Technology *New York* M
New York University *New York* M
Newberry College *South Carolina* M
Newbury College *Massachusetts* M
Newman University *Kansas* M & W
NHTI, Concord's Community College *New Hampshire* M
Niagara County Community College *New York* M
Niagara University *New York* M
Nicholls State University *Louisiana* M
Nichols College *Massachusetts* M
Norfolk State University *Virginia* M
North Arkansas College *Arkansas* M
North Carolina Agricultural and Technical State University *North Carolina* M
North Carolina Central University *North Carolina* M
North Carolina State University *North Carolina* M
North Carolina Wesleyan College *North Carolina* M
North Central College *Illinois* M
North Central Missouri College *Missouri* M
North Central Texas College *Texas* M
North Central University *Minnesota* M
North Dakota State University *North Dakota* M
North Greenville University *South Carolina* M
North Iowa Area Community College *Iowa* M
North Lake College *Texas* M
North Park University *Illinois* M
Northampton Community College *Pennsylvania* M
Northeast Mississippi Community College *Mississippi* M
Northeast Texas Community College *Texas* M
Northeastern Junior College *Colorado* M
Northeastern Oklahoma Agricultural and Mechanical College *Oklahoma* M
Northeastern State University *Oklahoma* M
Northeastern University *Massachusetts* M
Northern Essex Community College *Massachusetts* M
Northern Illinois University *Illinois* M
Northern Kentucky University *Kentucky* M
Northern Michigan University *Michigan* M

M = Men; W = Women

Northern Oklahoma College *Oklahoma* M
Northern State University *South Dakota* M
Northland College *Wisconsin* M
Northland Community and Technical College *Minnesota* M
Northwest Florida State College *Florida* M
Northwest Mississippi Community College *Mississippi* M
Northwest Missouri State University *Missouri* M
Northwest Nazarene University *Idaho* M
Northwestern College *Iowa* M
Northwestern Oklahoma State University *Oklahoma* M
Northwestern State University of Louisiana *Louisiana* M
Northwood University, Michigan Campus *Michigan* M
Northwood University, Texas Campus *Texas* M
Norwich University *Vermont* M
Notre Dame College *Ohio* M
Nova Southeastern University *Florida* M
Nyack College *New York* M
Oakland City University *Indiana* M
Oakland University *Michigan* M
Oakton Community College *Illinois* M
Oberlin College *Ohio* M
Occidental College *California* M
Ocean County College *New Jersey* M
Odessa College *Texas* M
Oglethorpe University *Georgia* M
Ohio Christian University *Ohio* M
Ohio Dominican University *Ohio* M
Ohio Northern University *Ohio* M
The Ohio State University *Ohio* M
Ohio University *Ohio* M
Ohio University - Zanesville *Ohio* M
Ohio Valley University *West Virginia* M
Ohio Wesleyan University *Ohio* M
Ohlone College *California* M
Okanagan College *British Columbia (Canada)* M
Oklahoma Baptist University *Oklahoma* M
Oklahoma Christian University *Oklahoma* M
Oklahoma City University *Oklahoma* M
Oklahoma Panhandle State University *Oklahoma* M
Oklahoma State University *Oklahoma* M
Oklahoma Wesleyan University *Oklahoma* M
Old Dominion University *Virginia* M
Olivet College *Michigan* M
Olivet Nazarene University *Illinois* M
Olympic College *Washington* M
Onondaga Community College *New York* M
Oral Roberts University *Oklahoma* M
Orange Coast College *California* M
Orange County Community College *New York* M
Oregon Institute of Technology *Oregon* M
Oregon State University *Oregon* M
Otero Junior College *Colorado* M
Ottawa University *Kansas* M
Otterbein University *Ohio* M
Ouachita Baptist University *Arkansas* M
Our Lady of the Lake University of San Antonio *Texas* M
Owens Community College *Ohio* M
Oxnard College *California* M
Pace University *New York* M
Pace University, Pleasantville Campus *New York* M
Pacific Lutheran University *Washington* M
Pacific University *Oregon* M
Paine College *Georgia* M
Palm Beach Atlantic University *Florida* M
Palm Beach State College *Florida* M
Palomar College *California* M
Panola College *Texas* M
Paradise Valley Community College *Arizona* M
Paris Junior College *Texas* M
Park University *Missouri* M
Parkland College *Illinois* M
Pasadena City College *California* M
Pasco-Hernando State College *Florida* M
Patrick Henry Community College *Virginia* M
Patten University *California* M
Pearl River Community College *Mississippi* M
Penn State Abington *Pennsylvania* M
Penn State Altoona *Pennsylvania* M

Penn State Beaver *Pennsylvania* M
Penn State Berks *Pennsylvania* M
Penn State Brandywine *Pennsylvania* M
Penn State Erie, The Behrend College *Pennsylvania* M
Penn State Fayette, The Eberly Campus *Pennsylvania* M
Penn State Greater Allegheny *Pennsylvania* M
Penn State Harrisburg *Pennsylvania* M
Penn State Hazleton *Pennsylvania* M
Penn State Lehigh Valley *Pennsylvania* M
Penn State New Kensington *Pennsylvania* M
Penn State University Park *Pennsylvania* M
Penn State Wilkes-Barre *Pennsylvania* M
Penn State Worthington Scranton *Pennsylvania* M
Pennsylvania College of Technology *Pennsylvania* M
Pensacola State College *Florida* M
Pepperdine University *California* M
Peru State College *Nebraska* M
Pfeiffer University *North Carolina* M
Philadelphia University *Pennsylvania* M
Phoenix College *Arizona* M
Piedmont College *Georgia* M
Pierce College at Puyallup *Washington* M
Pitt Community College *North Carolina* M
Pittsburg State University *Kansas* M
Pitzer College *California* M
Plymouth State University *New Hampshire* M
Point Loma Nazarene University *California* M
Point Park University *Pennsylvania* M
Point University *Georgia* M
Polk State College *Florida* M
Pomona College *California* M
Porterville College *California* M
Post University *Connecticut* M
Potomac State College of West Virginia University *West Virginia* M
Prairie State College *Illinois* M
Prairie View A&M University *Texas* M
Pratt Community College *Kansas* M
Presbyterian College *South Carolina* M
Presentation College *South Dakota* M
Prince George's Community College *Maryland* M
Princeton University *New Jersey* M
Principia College *Illinois* M
Purchase College, State University of New York *New York* M
Purdue University *Indiana* M
Purdue University Northwest *Hammond, Indiana* M
Queens College of the City University of New York *New York* M
Queen's University at Kingston *Ontario (Canada)* M
Queensborough Community College of the City University of New York *New York* M
Quincy University *Illinois* M
Quinnipiac University *Connecticut* M
Quinsigamond Community College *Massachusetts* M
Radford University *Virginia* M
Ramapo College of New Jersey *New Jersey* M
Randolph-Macon College *Virginia* M
Ranger College *Texas* M
Raritan Valley Community College *New Jersey* M
Redlands Community College *Oklahoma* M
Reedley College *California* M
Regis University *Colorado* M
Reinhardt University *Georgia* M
Rend Lake College *Illinois* M
Rensselaer Polytechnic Institute *New York* M & W
Research College of Nursing *Missouri* M
Rhode Island College *Rhode Island* M
Rhodes College *Tennessee* M
Rice University *Texas* M
Richland College *Texas* M
Rider University *New Jersey* M
Ridgewater College *Minnesota* M
Rio Hondo College *California* M
Ripon College *Wisconsin* M
Riverland Community College *Minnesota* M
Rivier University *New Hampshire* M
Roane State Community College *Tennessee* M
Roanoke College *Virginia* M
Robert Morris University Illinois *Illinois* M

Rochester College *Michigan* M
Rochester Community and Technical College *Minnesota* M
Rochester Institute of Technology *New York* M
Rock Valley College *Illinois* M
Rockford University *Illinois* M
Rockhurst University *Missouri* M
Rockingham Community College *North Carolina* M
Rockland Community College *New York* M
Roger Williams University *Rhode Island* M
Rogers State University *Oklahoma* M
Rollins College *Florida* M
Roosevelt University *Illinois* M
Rose-Hulman Institute of Technology *Indiana* M
Rose State College *Oklahoma* M
Rowan College at Burlington County *New Jersey* M
Rowan College at Gloucester County *New Jersey* M
Rowan University *New Jersey* M
Roxbury Community College *Massachusetts* M
Rust College *Mississippi* M
Rutgers University - Camden *New Jersey* M
Rutgers University - New Brunswick *New Jersey* M
Rutgers University - Newark *New Jersey* M
Sacramento City College *California* M
Sacred Heart University *Connecticut* M
Saddleback College *California* M
Saginaw Valley State University *Michigan* M
St. Ambrose University *Iowa* M
St. Andrews University *North Carolina* M
Saint Anselm College *New Hampshire* M
Saint Augustine's University *North Carolina* M
St. Bonaventure University *New York* M
St. Charles Community College *Missouri* M
St. Clair County Community College *Michigan* M
St. Cloud State University *Minnesota* M
St. Cloud Technical & Community College *Minnesota* M
St. Edward's University *Texas* M
St. Francis Xavier University *Nova Scotia (Canada)* M
St. Gregory's University *Oklahoma* M
St. John Fisher College *New York* M
St. Johns River State College *Florida* M
Saint John's University *Minnesota* M
St. John's University *New York* M
Saint Joseph's College *Indiana* M
St. Joseph's College, Long Island Campus *New York* M
Saint Joseph's College of Maine *Maine* M
St. Joseph's College, New York *New York* M
Saint Joseph's University *Pennsylvania* M
Saint Katherine College *California* M
St. Lawrence University *New York* M
Saint Leo University *Florida* M
Saint Louis Christian College *Missouri* M
St. Louis Community College *Missouri* M
Saint Louis University *Missouri* M
Saint Martin's University *Washington* M
Saint Mary's College of California *California* M
St. Mary's College of Maryland *Maryland* M
St. Mary's University *Texas* M
Saint Mary's University of Minnesota *Minnesota* M
Saint Michael's College *Vermont* M
St. Norbert College *Wisconsin* M
St. Olaf College *Minnesota* M
Saint Peter's University *New Jersey* M
St. Petersburg College *Florida* M
St. Thomas Aquinas College *New York* M
St. Thomas University *Florida* M
Saint Vincent College *Pennsylvania* M
Saint Xavier University *Illinois* M
Salem International University *West Virginia* M
Salem State University *Massachusetts* M
Salisbury University *Maryland* M
Salt Lake Community College *Utah* M
Salve Regina University *Rhode Island* M
Sam Houston State University *Texas* M
Samford University *Alabama* M
San Diego Christian College *California* M
San Diego City College *California* M
San Diego Mesa College *California* M
San Diego State University *California* M
San Francisco State University *California* M

M = Men; W = Women

San Jacinto College District *Texas* M
San Joaquin Delta College *California* M
San Jose City College *California* M
San Jose State University *California* M
Santa Ana College *California* M
Santa Barbara City College *California* M
Santa Clara University *California* M
Santa Fe College *Florida* M
Santa Rosa Junior College *California* M
Sauk Valley Community College *Illinois* M
Savannah State University *Georgia* M
Schenectady County Community College *New York* M
Schoolcraft College *Michigan* M
Schreiner University *Texas* M
Scottsdale Community College *Arizona* M
Seattle University *Washington* M
Selma University *Alabama* M
Seminole State College *Oklahoma* M
Seminole State College of Florida *Florida* M
Seton Hall University *New Jersey* M
Seton Hill University *Pennsylvania* M
Sewanee: The University of the South *Tennessee* M
Seward County Community College and Area Technical School *Kansas* M
Shasta College *California* M
Shawnee Community College *Illinois* M
Shawnee State University *Ohio* M
Shelton State Community College *Alabama* M
Shenandoah University *Virginia* M
Shepherd University *West Virginia* M
Shippensburg University of Pennsylvania *Pennsylvania* M
Shoreline Community College *Washington* M
Shorter University *Georgia* M
Siena College *New York* M
Siena Heights University *Michigan* M
Sierra College *California* M
Simpson College *Iowa* M
Simpson University *California* M
Sinclair Community College *Ohio* M
Skagit Valley College *Washington* M
Skidmore College *New York* M
Skyline College *California* M
Slippery Rock University of Pennsylvania *Pennsylvania* M
Snead State Community College *Alabama* M
Solano Community College *California* M
Sonoma State University *California* M
South Dakota State University *South Dakota* M
South Florida State College *Florida* M
South Georgia State College *Georgia* M
South Mountain Community College *Arizona* M
South Suburban College *Illinois* M
Southeast Community College, Lincoln Campus *Nebraska* M
Southeast Community College, Milford Campus *Nebraska* M
Southeast Missouri State University *Missouri* M
Southeastern Community College *Iowa* M
Southeastern Community College *North Carolina* M
Southeastern Illinois College *Illinois* M
Southeastern Louisiana University *Louisiana* M
Southeastern Oklahoma State University *Oklahoma* M
Southeastern University *Florida* M
Southern Arkansas University - Magnolia *Arkansas* M
Southern Connecticut State University *Connecticut* M
Southern Illinois University Carbondale *Illinois* M
Southern Illinois University Edwardsville *Illinois* M
Southern Maine Community College *Maine* M
Southern Methodist University *Texas* M
Southern Nazarene University *Oklahoma* M
Southern New Hampshire University *New Hampshire* M
Southern University and Agricultural and Mechanical College *Louisiana* M
Southern Vermont College *Vermont* M
Southern Virginia University *Virginia* M
Southern Wesleyan University *South Carolina* M
Southwest Baptist University *Missouri* M

Southwest Minnesota State University *Minnesota* M
Southwest Mississippi Community College *Mississippi* M
Southwestern Assemblies of God University *Texas* M
Southwestern College *California* M
Southwestern Community College *Iowa* M
Southwestern Illinois College *Illinois* M
Southwestern Oklahoma State University *Oklahoma* M
Southwestern Oregon Community College *Oregon* M
Southwestern University *Texas* M
Spalding University *Kentucky* M
Spartanburg Methodist College *South Carolina* M
Spokane Community College *Washington* M
Spokane Falls Community College *Washington* M
Spoon River College *Illinois* M
Spring Arbor University *Michigan* M
Spring Hill College *Alabama* M
Springfield College *Massachusetts* M
Stanford University *California* M
Stanly Community College *North Carolina* M
State College of Florida Manatee-Sarasota *Florida* M
State University of New York College at Cortland *New York* M
State University of New York College at Geneseo *New York* M & W
State University of New York College at Old Westbury *New York* M
State University of New York College at Oneonta *New York* M
State University of New York College of Technology at Alfred *New York* M
State University of New York College of Technology at Canton *New York* M
State University of New York at Fredonia *New York* M
State University of New York Maritime College *New York* M
State University of New York at New Paltz *New York* M
State University of New York at Oswego *New York* M
State University of New York at Plattsburgh *New York* M
State University of New York Polytechnic Institute *New York* M
Stephen F. Austin State University *Texas* M
Sterling College *Kansas* M
Stetson University *Florida* M
Stevens Institute of Technology *New Jersey* M
Stevenson University *Maryland* M
Stillman College *Alabama* M
Stockton University *New Jersey* M
Stonehill College *Massachusetts* M
Stony Brook University, State University of New York *New York* M
Suffolk County Community College *New York* M
Suffolk University *Massachusetts* M
Sul Ross State University *Texas* M
Sullivan County Community College *New York* M
Summit University *Pennsylvania* M
Surry Community College *North Carolina* M
Susquehanna University *Pennsylvania* M
Sussex County Community College *New Jersey* M
Swarthmore College *Pennsylvania* M
Syracuse University *New York* M
Tabor College *Kansas* M
Tacoma Community College *Washington* M
Taft College *California* M
Talladega College *Alabama* M
Tallahassee Community College *Florida* M
Tarleton State University *Texas* M
Taylor University *Indiana* M
Temple College *Texas* M
Tennessee Technological University *Tennessee* M
Tennessee Wesleyan College *Tennessee* M
Texas A&M International University *Texas* M
Texas A&M University *Texas* M
Texas A&M University - Corpus Christi *Texas* M
Texas A&M University - Kingsville *Texas* M
Texas Christian University *Texas* M

Texas College *Texas* M
Texas Lutheran University *Texas* M
Texas Southern University *Texas* M
Texas Southmost College *Texas* M
Texas State University *Texas* M
Texas Tech University *Texas* M
Texas Wesleyan University *Texas* M
Thiel College *Pennsylvania* M
Thomas College *Maine* M
Thomas More College *Kentucky* M
Thomas University *Georgia* M
Thompson Rivers University *British Columbia (Canada)* M
Three Rivers Community College *Missouri* M
Tiffin University *Ohio* M
Toccoa Falls College *Georgia* M
Tompkins Cortland Community College *New York* M
Tougaloo College *Mississippi* M
Towson University *Maryland* M
Transylvania University *Kentucky* M
Treasure Valley Community College *Oregon* M
Trevecca Nazarene University *Tennessee* M
Trine University *Indiana* M
Trinidad State Junior College *Colorado* M
Trinity Bible College *North Dakota* M
Trinity Christian College *Illinois* M
Trinity College *Connecticut* M
Trinity International University *Illinois* M
Trinity University *Texas* M
Triton College *Illinois* M
Troy University *Alabama* M
Truett-McConnell College *Georgia* M
Truman State University *Missouri* M
Tufts University *Massachusetts* M
Tulane University *Louisiana* M
Tusculum College *Tennessee* M
Tuskegee University *Alabama* M
Tyler Junior College *Texas* M
Ulster County Community College *New York* M
Union College *Kentucky* M
Union College *New York* M
Union County College *New Jersey* M
Union University *Tennessee* M
United States Air Force Academy *Colorado* M
United States Coast Guard Academy *Connecticut* M
United States Merchant Marine Academy *New York* M
United States Military Academy *New York* M
United States Naval Academy *Maryland* M
Universidad del Este *Puerto Rico* M
Universidad Metropolitana *Puerto Rico* M
Universidad del Turabo *Puerto Rico* M
Université Laval *Quebec (Canada)* M
Université de Montréal *Quebec (Canada)* M & W
The University of Alabama *Alabama* M
The University of Alabama at Birmingham *Alabama* M
The University of Alabama in Huntsville *Alabama* M
University at Albany, State University of New York *New York* M
The University of Arizona *Arizona* M
University of Arkansas *Arkansas* M
University of Arkansas - Fort Smith *Arkansas* M
University of Arkansas at Little Rock *Arkansas* M
University of Arkansas at Monticello *Arkansas* M
University of Arkansas at Pine Bluff *Arkansas* M
University of Bridgeport *Connecticut* M
The University of British Columbia *British Columbia (Canada)* M
University at Buffalo, the State University of New York *New York* M
University of Calgary *Alberta (Canada)* M & W
University of California, Berkeley *California* M
University of California, Davis *California* M
University of California, Irvine *California* M
University of California, Los Angeles *California* M
University of California, Riverside *California* M
University of California, San Diego *California* M
University of California, Santa Barbara *California* M
University of California, Santa Cruz *California* M & W
University of Central Arkansas *Arkansas* M

M = Men; W = Women

University of Central Florida *Florida* M
University of Central Missouri *Missouri* M
University of Central Oklahoma *Oklahoma* M
University of Charleston *West Virginia* M
University of Chicago *Illinois* M
University of Cincinnati *Ohio* M
University of Cincinnati Clermont College *Ohio* M
University of Colorado Boulder *Colorado* M
University of Colorado Colorado Springs *Colorado* M
University of Connecticut *Connecticut* M
University of the Cumberlands *Kentucky* M
University of Dallas *Texas* M
University of Dayton *Ohio* M
University of Delaware *Delaware* M
University of Denver *Colorado* M
University of Dubuque *Iowa* M
University of Evansville *Indiana* M
The University of Findlay *Ohio* M
University of Florida *Florida* M
University of Georgia *Georgia* M
University of Guelph *Ontario (Canada)* M
University of Hartford *Connecticut* M
University of Hawaii at Hilo *Hawaii* M
University of Hawaii at Manoa *Hawaii* M
University of Houston *Texas* M
University of Houston - Victoria *Texas* M
University of Illinois at Chicago *Illinois* M
University of Illinois at Springfield *Illinois* M
University of Illinois at Urbana - Champaign *Illinois* M
University of the Incarnate Word *Texas* M
University of Indianapolis *Indiana* M
The University of Iowa *Iowa* M
University of Jamestown *North Dakota* M
The University of Kansas *Kansas* M
University of Kentucky *Kentucky* M
University of La Verne *California* M
University of Louisiana at Lafayette *Louisiana* M
University of Louisiana at Monroe *Louisiana* M
University of Louisville *Kentucky* M
University of Maine *Maine* M
University of Maine at Farmington *Maine* M
University of Maine at Presque Isle *Maine* M
University of Mary *North Dakota* M
University of Mary Hardin-Baylor *Texas* M
University of Mary Washington *Virginia* M
University of Maryland, Baltimore County *Maryland* M
University of Maryland, College Park *Maryland* M
University of Maryland Eastern Shore *Maryland* M
University of Massachusetts Amherst *Massachusetts* M
University of Massachusetts Boston *Massachusetts* M
University of Massachusetts Dartmouth *Massachusetts* M
University of Massachusetts Lowell *Massachusetts* M
University of Memphis *Tennessee* M
University of Miami *Florida* M
University of Michigan *Michigan* M
University of Minnesota, Crookston *Minnesota* M
University of Minnesota, Duluth *Minnesota* M
University of Minnesota, Morris *Minnesota* M
University of Minnesota, Twin Cities Campus *Minnesota* M
University of Mississippi *Mississippi* M
University of Missouri *Missouri* M
University of Missouri - St. Louis *Missouri* M
University of Mobile *Alabama* M
University of Montana *Montana* M
University of Montevallo *Alabama* M
University of Mount Olive *North Carolina* M
University of Mount Union *Ohio* M
University of Nebraska at Kearney *Nebraska* M
University of Nebraska - Lincoln *Nebraska* M
University of Nebraska at Omaha *Nebraska* M
University of Nevada, Las Vegas *Nevada* M
University of Nevada, Reno *Nevada* M
University of New Hampshire *New Hampshire* M
University of New Haven *Connecticut* M
University of New Mexico *New Mexico* M
University of New Orleans *Louisiana* M

University of North Alabama *Alabama* M
University of North Carolina at Asheville *North Carolina* M
The University of North Carolina at Chapel Hill *North Carolina* M
The University of North Carolina at Charlotte *North Carolina* M
The University of North Carolina at Greensboro *North Carolina* M
The University of North Carolina at Pembroke *North Carolina* M
The University of North Carolina Wilmington *North Carolina* M
University of North Dakota *North Dakota* M
University of North Florida *Florida* M
University of North Georgia *Georgia* M
University of North Texas *Texas* M
University of Northern Colorado *Colorado* M
University of Northwestern - St. Paul *Minnesota* M
University of Notre Dame *Indiana* M
University of Oklahoma *Oklahoma* M
University of Oregon *Oregon* M
University of Ottawa *Ontario (Canada)* M & W
University of the Pacific *California* M
University of Pennsylvania *Pennsylvania* M
University of Pikeville *Kentucky* M
University of Pittsburgh *Pennsylvania* M
University of Pittsburgh at Bradford *Pennsylvania* M
University of Pittsburgh at Greensburg *Pennsylvania* M
University of Pittsburgh at Johnstown *Pennsylvania* M
University of Portland *Oregon* M
University of Puerto Rico in Aguadilla *Puerto Rico* M
University of Puerto Rico in Arecibo *Puerto Rico* M
University of Puerto Rico in Humacao *Puerto Rico* M
University of Puerto Rico, Mayagüez Campus *Puerto Rico* M
University of Puerto Rico in Ponce *Puerto Rico* M
University of Puerto Rico, Río Piedras Campus *Puerto Rico* M
University of Puget Sound *Washington* M
University of Redlands *California* M
University of Rhode Island *Rhode Island* M
University of Richmond *Virginia* M
University of Rio Grande *Ohio* M
University of Rochester *New York* M
University of St. Francis *Illinois* M
University of Saint Francis *Indiana* M
University of Saint Mary *Kansas* M
University of St. Thomas *Minnesota* M
University of San Diego *California* M
University of San Francisco *California* M
University of Science and Arts of Oklahoma *Oklahoma* M
University of the Sciences *Pennsylvania* M
The University of Scranton *Pennsylvania* M
University of Sioux Falls *South Dakota* M
University of South Alabama *Alabama* M
University of South Carolina *South Carolina* M
University of South Carolina Aiken *South Carolina* M
University of South Carolina Beaufort *South Carolina* M
University of South Carolina Lancaster *South Carolina* M
University of South Carolina Salkehatchie *South Carolina* M
University of South Carolina Upstate *South Carolina* M
University of South Florida *Florida* M
University of South Florida, St. Petersburg *Florida* M
University of Southern California *California* M
University of Southern Indiana *Indiana* M
University of Southern Maine *Maine* M
University of Southern Mississippi *Mississippi* M
University of the Southwest *New Mexico* M
The University of Tampa *Florida* M
The University of Tennessee *Tennessee* M
The University of Tennessee at Martin *Tennessee* M

The University of Texas at Arlington *Texas* M
The University of Texas at Austin *Texas* M & W
The University of Texas at Dallas *Texas* M
The University of Texas of the Permian Basin *Texas* M
The University of Texas Rio Grande Valley *Texas* M
The University of Texas at San Antonio *Texas* M
The University of Texas at Tyler *Texas* M
The University of Toledo *Ohio* M
University of Utah *Utah* M
University of Valley Forge *Pennsylvania* M
University of Virginia *Virginia* M
The University of Virginia's College at Wise *Virginia* M
University of Washington *Washington* M
University of Waterloo *Ontario (Canada)* M
The University of West Alabama *Alabama* M
University of West Florida *Florida* M
University of West Georgia *Georgia* M
The University of Western Ontario *Ontario (Canada)* M
University of Wisconsin - La Crosse *Wisconsin* M
University of Wisconsin - Milwaukee *Wisconsin* M
University of Wisconsin - Oshkosh *Wisconsin* M
University of Wisconsin - Parkside *Wisconsin* M
University of Wisconsin - Platteville *Wisconsin* M
University of Wisconsin - River Falls *Wisconsin* M
University of Wisconsin - Stevens Point *Wisconsin* M
University of Wisconsin - Stout *Wisconsin* M
University of Wisconsin - Superior *Wisconsin* M
University of Wisconsin - Whitewater *Wisconsin* M
University of Wyoming *Wyoming* M
Upper Iowa University *Iowa* M
Urbana University *Ohio* M
Ursinus College *Pennsylvania* M
Utah State University *Utah* M
Utah Valley University *Utah* M
Utica College *New York* M
Valdosta State University *Georgia* M
Valley City State University *North Dakota* M
Valparaiso University *Indiana* M
Vanderbilt University *Tennessee* M
Vanguard University of Southern California *California* M
Vassar College *New York* M
Ventura College *California* M
Vermilion Community College *Minnesota* M
Vermont Technical College *Vermont* M
Vernon College *Texas* M
Victor Valley College *California* M
Villanova University *Pennsylvania* M
Vincennes University *Indiana* M
Virginia Commonwealth University *Virginia* M
Virginia Military Institute *Virginia* M
Virginia Polytechnic Institute and State University *Virginia* M
Virginia State University *Virginia* M
Virginia Wesleyan College *Virginia* M
Viterbo University *Wisconsin* M
Volunteer State Community College *Tennessee* M
Voorhees College *South Carolina* M
Wabash College *Indiana* M
Wagner College *New York* M
Wake Forest University *North Carolina* M
Waldorf College *Iowa* M
Walla Walla Community College *Washington* M
Wallace State Community College *Alabama* M
Walsh University *Ohio* M
Walters State Community College *Tennessee* M
Warner University *Florida* M
Wartburg College *Iowa* M
Washburn University *Kansas* M
Washington Adventist University *Maryland* M
Washington College *Maryland* M
Washington & Jefferson College *Pennsylvania* M
Washington and Lee University *Virginia* M
Washington State University *Washington* M
Washington University in St. Louis *Missouri* M
Waubonsee Community College *Illinois* M
Wayland Baptist University *Texas* M
Wayne State College *Nebraska* M
Wayne State University *Michigan* M
Waynesburg University *Pennsylvania* M

M = Men; W = Women

Weatherford College *Texas* M
Webber International University *Florida* M
Weber State University *Utah* M
Webster University *Missouri* M
Wells College *New York* M
Wenatchee Valley College *Washington* M
Wentworth Institute of Technology *Massachusetts* M
Wesley College *Delaware* M
Wesleyan University *Connecticut* M
West Chester University of Pennsylvania *Pennsylvania* M
West Hills Community College *California* M
West Liberty University *West Virginia* M
West Texas A&M University *Texas* M
West Virginia State University *West Virginia* M
West Virginia University *West Virginia* M
West Virginia University Institute of Technology *West Virginia* M
West Virginia Wesleyan College *West Virginia* M
Westchester Community College *New York* M
Western Carolina University *North Carolina* M
Western Connecticut State University *Connecticut* M
Western Illinois University *Illinois* M
Western Kentucky University *Kentucky* M
Western Michigan University *Michigan* M
Western Nebraska Community College *Nebraska* M
Western Nevada College *Nevada* M
Western New England University *Massachusetts* M
Western Oklahoma State College *Oklahoma* M
Western Oregon University *Oregon* M
Western State Colorado University *Colorado* M
Western Technical College *Wisconsin* M
Western Texas College *Texas* M
Westfield State University *Massachusetts* M
Westminster College *Missouri* M
Westminster College *Pennsylvania* M
Westmont College *California* M
Westmoreland County Community College *Pennsylvania* M
Wharton County Junior College *Texas* M
Wheaton College *Illinois* M
Wheaton College *Massachusetts* M
Wheeling Jesuit University *West Virginia* M
Whitman College *Washington* M
Whittier College *California* M
Whitworth University *Washington* M
Wichita State University *Kansas* M
Widener University *Pennsylvania* M
Wiley College *Texas* M
Wilfrid Laurier University *Ontario (Canada)* M
Wilkes Community College *North Carolina* M
Wilkes University *Pennsylvania* M
Willamette University *Oregon* M
William Carey University *Mississippi* M
William Jessup University *California* M
William Jewell College *Missouri* M
William Paterson University of New Jersey *New Jersey* M
William Peace University *North Carolina* M
William Penn University *Iowa* M
William Woods University *Missouri* M
Williams Baptist College *Arkansas* M
Williams College *Massachusetts* M
Williamson College of the Trades *Pennsylvania* M
Williston State College *North Dakota* M
Wilmington College *Ohio* M
Wilmington University *Delaware* M
Wingate University *North Carolina* M
Winona State University *Minnesota* M
Winthrop University *South Carolina* M
Wisconsin Lutheran College *Wisconsin* M
Wittenberg University *Ohio* M
Wofford College *South Carolina* M
Worcester Polytechnic Institute *Massachusetts* M
Worcester State University *Massachusetts* M
Wright State University *Ohio* M
Wright State University - Lake Campus *Ohio* M
Xavier University *Ohio* M
Yakima Valley Community College *Washington* M
Yale University *Connecticut* M
Yavapai College *Arizona* M
Yeshiva University *New York* M

M = Men; W = Women

York College *Nebraska* M
York College of the City University of New York *New York* M & W
York College of Pennsylvania *Pennsylvania* M
Young Harris College *Georgia* M
Youngstown State University *Ohio* M
Yuba College *California* M
Zane State College *Ohio* M

Basketball

Abilene Christian University *Texas* M & W
Academy of Art University *California* M & W
Acadia University *Nova Scotia (Canada)* M & W
Adams State University *Colorado* M & W
Adelphi University *New York* M & W
Adirondack Community College *New York* M & W
Adrian College *Michigan* M & W
Agnes Scott College *Georgia* W
Alabama Agricultural and Mechanical University *Alabama* M & W
Alabama Southern Community College *Alabama* M & W
Alabama State University *Alabama* M & W
Albany College of Pharmacy and Health Sciences *New York* M & W
Albany State University *Georgia* M & W
Albertus Magnus College *Connecticut* M & W
Albion College *Michigan* M & W
Albright College *Pennsylvania* M & W
Alcorn State University *Mississippi* M & W
Alderson Broaddus University *West Virginia* M & W
Alfred University *New York* M & W
Alice Lloyd College *Kentucky* M & W
Allan Hancock College *California* M & W
Allegany College of Maryland *Maryland* M & W
Allegheny College *Pennsylvania* M & W
Allen Community College *Kansas* M & W
Allen University *South Carolina* M & W
Alma College *Michigan* M & W
Alpena Community College *Michigan* M & W
Alvernia University *Pennsylvania* M & W
Alverno College *Wisconsin* W
Ambrose University *Alberta (Canada)* M & W
American International College *Massachusetts* M & W
American River College *California* M & W
American University *District of Columbia* M & W
American University of Puerto Rico *Bayamon, Puerto Rico* M & W
Amherst College *Massachusetts* M & W
Ancilla College *Indiana* M & W
Anderson University *Indiana* M & W
Anderson University *South Carolina* M & W
Andrew College *Georgia* W
Angelina College *Texas* M & W
Angelo State University *Texas* M & W
Anna Maria College *Massachusetts* M & W
Anne Arundel Community College *Maryland* M & W
Anoka-Ramsey Community College *Minnesota* M & W
Antelope Valley College *California* M & W
Appalachian Bible College *West Virginia* M & W
Appalachian State University *North Carolina* M & W
Aquinas College *Michigan* M & W
Arcadia University *Pennsylvania* M & W
Arizona Christian University *Arizona* M & W
Arizona State University at the Downtown Phoenix campus *Arizona* M & W
Arizona State University at the Polytechnic campus *Arizona* M & W
Arizona State University at the Tempe campus *Arizona* M & W
Arizona State University at the West campus *Arizona* M & W
Arizona Western College *Arizona* M & W
Arkansas Baptist College *Arkansas* M & W
Arkansas State University *Arkansas* M & W
Arkansas Tech University *Arkansas* M & W
Arlington Baptist College *Texas* M & W
Armstrong State University *Georgia* M & W
ASA College *New York* M & W
Asbury University *Kentucky* M & W
Ashford University *California* M & W
Ashland University *Ohio* M & W

Assumption College *Massachusetts* M & W
Atlanta Metropolitan State College *Georgia* M & W
Atlantic Cape Community College *New Jersey* M & W
Auburn University *Alabama* M & W
Auburn University at Montgomery *Alabama* M & W
Augsburg College *Minnesota* M & W
Augusta University *Georgia* M & W
Augustana College *Illinois* M & W
Augustana University *South Dakota* M & W
Aurora University *Illinois* M & W
Austin College *Texas* M & W
Austin Peay State University *Tennessee* M & W
Ave Maria University *Florida* M & W
Averett University *Virginia* M & W
Avila University *Missouri* M & W
Azusa Pacific University *California* M & W
Babson College *Massachusetts* M & W
Baker University *Kansas* M & W
Bakersfield College *California* M & W
Baldwin Wallace University *Ohio* M & W
Ball State University *Indiana* M & W
Baltimore City Community College *Maryland* M & W
Baptist Bible College *Missouri* M & W
Barclay College *Kansas* M & W
Bard College *New York* M & W
Bard College at Simon's Rock *Massachusetts* M & W
Barnard College *New York* W
Barry University *Florida* M & W
Barstow Community College *California* M & W
Barton College *North Carolina* M & W
Barton County Community College *Kansas* M & W
Baruch College of the City University of New York *New York* M & W
Bates College *Maine* M & W
Bay Path University *Massachusetts* W
Bayamón Central University *Puerto Rico* M
Baylor University *Texas* M & W
Becker College *Massachusetts* M & W
Belhaven University *Mississippi* M & W
Bellarmine University *Kentucky* M & W
Bellevue College *Washington* M & W
Belmont Abbey College *North Carolina* M & W
Belmont University *Tennessee* M & W
Beloit College *Wisconsin* M & W
Bemidji State University *Minnesota* M & W
Benedict College *South Carolina* M & W
Benedictine College *Kansas* M & W
Benedictine University *Illinois* M & W
Bennington College *Vermont* M & W
Bentley University *Massachusetts* M & W
Berea College *Kentucky* M & W
Bergen Community College *New Jersey* M & W
Berkeley College - New York City Campus *New York* M & W
Berkeley College - White Plains Campus *New York* M & W
Berry College *Georgia* M & W
Bethany College *Kansas* M & W
Bethany College *West Virginia* M & W
Bethany Lutheran College *Minnesota* M & W
Bethel College *Indiana* M & W
Bethel College *Kansas* M & W
Bethel University *Minnesota* M & W
Bethel University *Tennessee* M & W
Bethune-Cookman University *Florida* M & W
Big Bend Community College *Washington* M & W
Binghamton University, State University of New York *New York* M & W
Biola University *California* M & W
Birmingham-Southern College *Alabama* M & W
Bishop State Community College *Alabama* M & W
Bishop's University *Quebec (Canada)* M & W
Bismarck State College *North Dakota* M & W
Black Hawk College *Illinois* M & W
Black Hills State University *South Dakota* M & W
Blackburn College *Illinois* M & W
Blessing-Rieman College of Nursing *Illinois* M & W
Blinn College *Texas* M & W
Bloomfield College *New Jersey* M & W
Bloomsburg University of Pennsylvania *Pennsylvania* M & W

Blue Mountain College *Mississippi* M & W
Blue Mountain Community College *Oregon* M & W
Bluefield College *Virginia* M & W
Bluefield State College *West Virginia* M & W
Bluffton University *Ohio* M & W
Bob Jones University *South Carolina* M & W
Boise State University *Idaho* M & W
Borough of Manhattan Community College of the City University of New York *New York* M & W
Bossier Parish Community College *Louisiana* M
Boston Baptist College *Massachusetts* M
Boston College *Massachusetts* M & W
Boston University *Massachusetts* M & W
Bowdoin College *Maine* M & W
Bowie State University *Maryland* M & W
Bowling Green State University *Ohio* M & W
Bradley University *Illinois* M & W
Brandeis University *Massachusetts* M & W
Brandon University *Manitoba (Canada)* M & W
Brenau University *Georgia* W
Brescia University *Kentucky* M & W
Brevard College *North Carolina* M & W
Brewton-Parker College *Georgia* M & W
Briar Cliff University *Iowa* M & W
Bridgewater College *Virginia* M & W
Bridgewater State University *Massachusetts* M & W
Briercrest College *Saskatchewan (Canada)* M & W
Brigham Young University *Utah* M & W
Brigham Young University - Hawaii *Hawaii* M & W
Brock University *Ontario (Canada)* M & W
Bronx Community College of the City University of New York *New York* M
Brookdale Community College *New Jersey* M & W
Brookhaven College *Texas* M
Brooklyn College of the City University of New York *New York* M & W
Broome Community College *New York* M & W
Broward College *Florida* M & W
Brown University *Rhode Island* M & W
Brunswick Community College *North Carolina* M & W
Bryan College *Tennessee* M & W
Bryant University *Rhode Island* M & W
Bryn Athyn College of the New Church *Pennsylvania* M & W
Bryn Mawr College *Pennsylvania* W
Bucknell University *Pennsylvania* M & W
Bucks County Community College *Pennsylvania* M
Buena Vista University *Iowa* M & W
Buffalo State College, State University of New York *New York* M & W
Bunker Hill Community College *Massachusetts* M & W
Butler Community College *Kansas* M & W
Butler County Community College *Pennsylvania* M
Butler University *Indiana* M & W
Butte College *California* M & W
Cabrillo College *California* M & W
Cabrini University *Pennsylvania* M & W
Cairn University *Pennsylvania* M & W
Caldwell Community College and Technical Institute *North Carolina* M & W
Caldwell University *New Jersey* M & W
California Baptist University *California* M & W
California Institute of Technology *California* M & W
California Lutheran University *California* M & W
California Maritime Academy *California* M & W
California Polytechnic State University, San Luis Obispo *California* M & W
California State Polytechnic University, Pomona *California* M & W
California State University, Bakersfield *California* M
California State University, Chico *California* M & W
California State University, Dominguez Hills *California* M & W
California State University, East Bay *California* M & W
California State University, Fresno *California* M & W
California State University, Fullerton *California* M & W
California State University, Long Beach *California* M & W

California State University, Los Angeles *California* M & W
California State University, Monterey Bay *California* M & W
California State University, Northridge *California* M & W
California State University, Sacramento *California* M & W
California State University, San Bernardino *California* M & W
California State University, San Marcos *California* M & W
California State University, Stanislaus *California* M & W
California University of Pennsylvania *Pennsylvania* M & W
Calumet College of Saint Joseph *Indiana* M & W
Calvary Bible College and Theological Seminary *Missouri* M & W
Calvin College *Michigan* M & W
Camden County College *New Jersey* M & W
Cameron University *Oklahoma* M & W
Campbell University *North Carolina* M & W
Campbellsville University *Kentucky* M & W
Cañada College *California* M
Canisius College *New York* M & W
Cape Breton University *Nova Scotia (Canada)* M & W
Cape Fear Community College *North Carolina* M & W
Capital University *Ohio* M & W
Cardinal Stritch University *Wisconsin* M & W
Caribbean University *Puerto Rico* M & W
Carl Albert State College *Oklahoma* M & W
Carl Sandburg College *Illinois* M & W
Carleton College *Minnesota* M & W
Carleton University *Ontario (Canada)* M & W
Carlow University *Pennsylvania* M & W
Carnegie Mellon University *Pennsylvania* M & W
Carroll College *Montana* M & W
Carroll University *Wisconsin* M & W
Carson-Newman University *Tennessee* M & W
Carthage College *Wisconsin* M & W
Carver College *Georgia* M & W
Case Western Reserve University *Ohio* M & W
Casper College *Wyoming* M & W
Castleton University *Vermont* M & W
Catawba College *North Carolina* M & W
Catawba Valley Community College *North Carolina* M & W
The Catholic University of America *District of Columbia* M & W
Cayuga County Community College *New York* M & W
Cazenovia College *New York* M & W
Cecil College *Maryland* M & W
Cedar Crest College *Pennsylvania* W
Cedar Valley College *Texas* M
Cedarville University *Ohio* M & W
Centenary College *New Jersey* M & W
Centenary College of Louisiana *Louisiana* M & W
Central Arizona College *Arizona* M & W
Central Baptist College *Arkansas* M & W
Central Carolina Community College *North Carolina* M & W
Central Christian College of the Bible *Missouri* M & W
Central Christian College of Kansas *Kansas* M & W
Central College *Iowa* M & W
Central Community College - Columbus Campus *Nebraska* M
Central Connecticut State University *Connecticut* M & W
Central Lakes College *Minnesota* M & W
Central Maine Community College *Maine* M & W
Central Methodist University *Missouri* M & W
Central Michigan University *Michigan* M & W
Central Penn College *Pennsylvania* M & W
Central State University *Ohio* M & W
Central Washington University *Washington* M & W
Central Wyoming College *Wyoming* M & W
Centralia College *Washington* M & W
Centre College *Kentucky* M & W
Cerritos College *California* M & W

Cerro Coso Community College *California* W
Chabot College *California* M & W
Chadron State College *Nebraska* M & W
Chaffey College *California* M & W
Chaminade University of Honolulu *Hawaii* M & W
Chandler-Gilbert Community College *Arizona* M & W
Chapman University *California* M & W
Charleston Southern University *South Carolina* M & W
Chatham University *Pennsylvania* M & W
Chattahoochee Valley Community College *Alabama* M & W
Chattanooga State Community College *Tennessee* M & W
Chemeketa Community College *Oregon* M & W
Chesapeake College *Maryland* M & W
Chestnut Hill College *Pennsylvania* M & W
Cheyney University of Pennsylvania *Pennsylvania* M & W
Chicago State University *Illinois* M & W
Chipola College *Florida* M & W
Chowan University *North Carolina* M & W
Christendom College *Virginia* M & W
Christian Brothers University *Tennessee* M & W
Christopher Newport University *Virginia* M & W
Cincinnati Christian University *Ohio* M & W
Cincinnati State Technical and Community College *Ohio* M & W
Cisco College *Texas* W
The Citadel, The Military College of South Carolina *South Carolina* M
Citrus College *California* M & W
City College of the City University of New York *New York* M & W
City College of San Francisco *California* M & W
City Colleges of Chicago, Harry S. Truman College *Illinois* M
City Colleges of Chicago, Kennedy-King College *Illinois* M & W
City Colleges of Chicago, Malcolm X College *Illinois* M & W
City Colleges of Chicago, Olive-Harvey College *Illinois* M & W
City Colleges of Chicago, Richard J. Daley College *Illinois* M & W
City Colleges of Chicago, Wilbur Wright College *Illinois* M & W
Clackamas Community College *Oregon* M & W
Claflin University *South Carolina* M & W
Claremont McKenna College *California* M & W
Clarendon College *Texas* M & W
Clarion University of Pennsylvania *Pennsylvania* M & W
Clark Atlanta University *Georgia* M & W
Clark College *Washington* M & W
Clark State Community College *Ohio* M & W
Clark University *Massachusetts* M & W
Clarke University *Iowa* M & W
Clarkson University *New York* M & W
Clayton State University *Georgia* M & W
Clemson University *South Carolina* M & W
Cleveland State Community College *Tennessee* M & W
Cleveland State University *Ohio* M & W
Clinton College *South Carolina* M & W
Clinton Community College *Iowa* M
Clinton Community College *New York* M & W
Cloud County Community College *Kansas* M & W
Coahoma Community College *Mississippi* M & W
Coastal Bend College *Texas* M
Coastal Carolina University *South Carolina* M & W
Cochise County Community College District *Arizona* M & W
Coe College *Iowa* M & W
Coffeyville Community College *Kansas* M & W
Coker College *South Carolina* M & W
Colby College *Maine* M & W
Colby Community College *Kansas* M & W
Colby-Sawyer College *New Hampshire* M & W
Colgate University *New York* M & W
College of Alameda *California* M
The College at Brockport, State University of New York *New York* M & W

M = Men; W = Women

College of the Canyons *California* M & W
College of Central Florida *Florida* M & W
College of Charleston *South Carolina* M & W
College of Coastal Georgia *Georgia* M & W
College of the Desert *California* M & W
College of DuPage *Illinois* M & W
College of the Holy Cross *Massachusetts* M & W
The College of Idaho *Idaho* M & W
College of Lake County *Illinois* M & W
College of the Mainland *Texas* M
College of Marin *California* M & W
College of Mount Saint Vincent *New York* M & W
The College of New Jersey *New Jersey* M & W
The College of New Rochelle *New York* W
College of the Ozarks *Missouri* M & W
College of the Redwoods *California* M & W
College of Saint Benedict *Minnesota* W
College of Saint Elizabeth *New Jersey* W
College of St. Joseph *Vermont* M & W
College of Saint Mary *Nebraska* W
The College of Saint Rose *New York* M & W
The College of St. Scholastica *Minnesota* M & W
College of San Mateo *California* W
College of the Sequoias *California* M & W
College of the Siskiyous *California* M & W
College of Southern Idaho *Idaho* M & W
College of Southern Maryland *Maryland* M & W
College of Staten Island of the City University of
    New York *New York* M & W
The College of William and Mary *Virginia* M & W
The College of Wooster *Ohio* M & W
Collin County Community College District
    Texas M & W
Colorado Christian University *Colorado* M & W
The Colorado College *Colorado* M & W
Colorado Mesa University *Colorado* M & W
Colorado Northwestern Community College *Colo-
    rado* M & W
Colorado School of Mines *Colorado* M & W
Colorado State University *Colorado* M & W
Colorado State University - Pueblo *Colo-
    rado* M & W
Columbia Basin College *Washington* M & W
Columbia Bible College *British Columbia
    (Canada)* M & W
Columbia College *California* M
Columbia College *Missouri* M & W
Columbia College *South Carolina* W
Columbia College Chicago *Illinois* M
Columbia-Greene Community College *New York* M
Columbia International University *South Caro-
    lina* M & W
Columbia State Community College *Tennes-
    see* M & W
Columbia University *New York* M & W
Columbia University, School of General Studies
    New York M & W
Columbus State Community College *Ohio* M & W
Columbus State University *Georgia* M & W
Community College of Allegheny County *Pennsylva-
    nia* M & W
Community College of Baltimore County *Mary-
    land* M & W
Community College of Philadelphia *Pennsylva-
    nia* M & W
Community College of Rhode Island *Rhode Is-
    land* M & W
Concord University *West Virginia* M & W
Concordia College *Minnesota* M & W
Concordia College Alabama *Alabama* M & W
Concordia College - New York *New York* M & W
Concordia University *Oregon* M & W
Concordia University *Quebec (Canada)* M & W
Concordia University Ann Arbor *Michigan* M & W
Concordia University Chicago *Illinois* M & W
Concordia University of Edmonton *Alberta
    (Canada)* M & W
Concordia University Irvine *California* M & W
Concordia University, Nebraska *Nebraska* M & W
Concordia University, St. Paul *Minnesota* M & W
Concordia University Texas *Texas* M & W
Concordia University Wisconsin *Wisconsin* M & W
Connecticut College *Connecticut* M & W
Connors State College *Oklahoma* M & W

Contra Costa College *California* M & W
Converse College *South Carolina* W
Cooper Union for the Advancement of Science and
    Art *New York* M & W
Copiah-Lincoln Community College *Missis-
    sippi* M & W
Coppin State University *Maryland* M & W
Corban University *Oregon* M & W
Cornell College *Iowa* M & W
Cornell University *New York* M & W
Cornerstone University *Michigan* M & W
Corning Community College *New York* M & W
Cottey College *Missouri* W
County College of Morris *New Jersey* M & W
Covenant College *Georgia* M & W
Cowley County Community College and Area Voca-
    tional - Technical School *Kansas* M & W
Crandall University *New Brunswick
    (Canada)* M & W
Creighton University *Nebraska* M & W
Crossroads College *Minnesota* M & W
Crowder College *Missouri*. W
Crown College *Minnesota* M & W
Cuesta College *California* M & W
The Culinary Institute of America *New York* M & W
Culver-Stockton College *Missouri* M & W
Cumberland County College *New Jersey* M & W
Cumberland University *Tennessee* M & W
Curry College *Massachusetts* M & W
Cuyahoga Community College *Ohio* M
Cuyamaca College *California* M & W
Cypress College *California* M & W
Daemen College *New York* M & W
Dakota College at Bottineau *North Dakota* M & W
Dakota County Technical College *Minnesota* M
Dakota State University *South Dakota* M & W
Dakota Wesleyan University *South Dakota* M & W
Dalhousie University *Nova Scotia (Canada)* M & W
Dallas Baptist University *Texas* M
Dallas Christian College *Texas* M & W
Dalton State College *Georgia* M & W
Daniel Webster College *New Hampshire* M & W
Danville Area Community College *Illinois* M & W
Dartmouth College *New Hampshire* M & W
Darton State College *Georgia* W
Davenport University *Michigan* M & W
Davidson College *North Carolina* M & W
Davidson County Community College *North Caro-
    lina* M
Davis College *New York* M & W
Davis & Elkins College *West Virginia* M & W
Dawson Community College *Montana* M & W
Daytona State College *Florida* M & W
De Anza College *California* M & W
Dean College *Massachusetts* M & W
Defiance College *Ohio* M & W
Delaware County Community College *Pennsylva-
    nia* M & W
Delaware State University *Delaware* M & W
Delaware Technical & Community College,
    Stanton/Wilmington Campus *Delaware* M & W
Delaware Valley University *Pennsylvania* M & W
Delgado Community College *Louisiana* M & W
Delta College *Michigan* M & W
Delta State University *Mississippi* M & W
Denison University *Ohio* M & W
Denmark Technical College *South Carolina* M & W
DePaul University *Illinois* M & W
DePauw University *Indiana* M & W
Des Moines Area Community College *Iowa* M & W
DeSales University *Pennsylvania* M & W
Diablo Valley College *California* M & W
Dickinson College *Pennsylvania* M & W
Dickinson State University *North Dakota* M & W
Dillard University *Louisiana* M & W
Dixie State University *Utah* M & W
Doane University *Nebraska* M & W
Dodge City Community College *Kansas* M & W
Dominican College *New York* M & W
Dominican University *Illinois* M & W
Dominican University of California *California* M & W
Dordt College *Iowa* M & W
Drake University *Iowa* M & W
Drew University *New Jersey* M & W

Drexel University *Pennsylvania* M & W
Drury University *Missouri* M & W
Duke University *North Carolina* M & W
Duquesne University *Pennsylvania* M & W
Dutchess Community College *New York* M & W
Dyersburg State Community College *Tennes-
    see* M & W
D'Youville College *New York* M & W
Earlham College *Indiana* M & W
East Carolina University *North Carolina* M & W
East Central Community College *Missis-
    sippi* M & W
East Central University *Oklahoma* M & W
East Los Angeles College *California* M & W
East Mississippi Community College *Missis-
    sippi* M & W
East Stroudsburg University of Pennsylvania *Penn-
    sylvania* M & W
East Tennessee State University *Tennessee* M & W
East Texas Baptist University *Texas* M & W
East-West University *Illinois* M
Eastern Arizona College *Arizona* M & W
Eastern Connecticut State University *Connecti-
    cut* M & W
Eastern Florida State College *Florida* M & W
Eastern Illinois University *Illinois* M & W
Eastern Kentucky University *Kentucky* M & W
Eastern Maine Community College *Maine* M & W
Eastern Mennonite University *Virginia* M & W
Eastern Michigan University *Michigan* M & W
Eastern Nazarene College *Massachusetts* M & W
Eastern New Mexico University *New
    Mexico* M & W
Eastern Oklahoma State College *Oklahoma* M & W
Eastern Oregon University *Oregon* M & W
Eastern University *Pennsylvania* M & W
Eastern Washington University *Washington* M & W
Eastern Wyoming College *Wyoming* M & W
Eastfield College *Texas* M
Ecclesia College *Arkansas* M & W
Eckerd College *Florida* M & W
Edgewood College *Wisconsin* M & W
Edinboro University of Pennsylvania *Pennsylva-
    nia* M & W
Edison Community College *Ohio* M & W
Edmonds Community College *Washington* M & W
Edward Waters College *Florida* M & W
El Camino College *California* M & W
Elgin Community College *Illinois* M & W
Elizabeth City State University *North Caro-
    lina* M & W
Elizabethtown College *Pennsylvania* M & W
Ellsworth Community College *Iowa* M & W
Elmhurst College *Illinois* M & W
Elmira College *New York* M & W
Elms College *Massachusetts* M & W
Elon University *North Carolina* M & W
Embry-Riddle Aeronautical University - Daytona
    Florida M & W
Embry-Riddle Aeronautical University - Prescott *Ari-
    zona* M & W
Emerson College *Massachusetts* M & W
Emmanuel College *Georgia* M & W
Emmanuel College *Massachusetts* M & W
Emmaus Bible College *Iowa* M & W
Emory & Henry College *Virginia* M & W
Emory University *Georgia* M & W
Emory University, Oxford College *Georgia* M
Emporia State University *Kansas* M & W
Endicott College *Massachusetts* M & W
Enterprise State Community College *Ala-
    bama* M & W
Erie Community College *New York* M & W
Erie Community College, North Campus *New
    York* M & W
Erie Community College, South Campus *New
    York* M & W
Erskine College *South Carolina* M & W
Essex County College *New Jersey* M & W
Eugenio María de Hostos Community College of the
    City University of New York *New York* M & W
Eureka College *Illinois* M & W
Evangel University *Missouri* M & W
Everett Community College *Washington* M & W

M = Men; W = Women

The Evergreen State College *Washington* M & W
Fairfield University *Connecticut* M & W
Fairleigh Dickinson University, College at Florham *New Jersey* M & W
Fairleigh Dickinson University, Metropolitan Campus *New Jersey* M & W
Fairmont State University *West Virginia* M & W
Faith Baptist Bible College and Theological Seminary *Iowa* M & W
Farmingdale State College *New York* M & W
Faulkner University *Alabama* M & W
Fayetteville State University *North Carolina* M & W
Feather River College *California* M & W
Felician University *New Jersey* M & W
Ferris State University *Michigan* M & W
Ferrum College *Virginia* M & W
Finger Lakes Community College *New York* M & W
Finlandia University *Michigan* M & W
Fiorello H. LaGuardia Community College of the City University of New York *New York* M & W
Fisher College *Massachusetts* M & W
Fisk University *Tennessee* M & W
Fitchburg State University *Massachusetts* M & W
Flagler College *Florida* M & W
Florida Agricultural and Mechanical University *Florida* M & W
Florida Atlantic University *Florida* M & W
Florida College *Florida* M & W
Florida Gulf Coast University *Florida* M & W
Florida Institute of Technology *Florida* M & W
Florida International University *Florida* M & W
Florida Memorial University *Florida* M & W
Florida National University *Florida* M
Florida Southern College *Florida* M & W
Florida State College at Jacksonville *Florida* M & W
Florida State University *Florida* M & W
Fond du Lac Tribal and Community College *Minnesota* M & W
Fontbonne University *Missouri* M & W
Foothill College *California* M & W
Fordham University *New York* M & W
Fort Lewis College *Colorado* M & W
Fort Scott Community College *Kansas* M & W
Fort Valley State University *Georgia* M & W
Fox Valley Technical College *Wisconsin* M & W
Framingham State University *Massachusetts* M & W
Francis Marion University *South Carolina* M & W
Franciscan University of Steubenville *Ohio* M & W
Frank Phillips College *Texas* M & W
Franklin College *Indiana* M & W
Franklin & Marshall College *Pennsylvania* M & W
Franklin Pierce University *New Hampshire* M & W
Frederick Community College *Maryland* M & W
Freed-Hardeman University *Tennessee* M & W
Fresno City College *California* M & W
Fresno Pacific University *California* M & W
Friends University *Kansas* M & W
Frostburg State University *Maryland* M & W
Fullerton College *California* M & W
Fulton-Montgomery Community College *New York* M & W
Furman University *South Carolina* M & W
Gadsden State Community College *Alabama* M & W
Gallaudet University *District of Columbia* M & W
Gannon University *Pennsylvania* M & W
Garden City Community College *Kansas* M & W
Gardner-Webb University *North Carolina* M & W
Garrett College *Maryland* M & W
Gateway Community College *Connecticut* M & W
Gavilan College *California* M
Genesee Community College *New York* M & W
Geneva College *Pennsylvania* M & W
George Corley Wallace State Community College *Alabama* M
George Fox University *Oregon* M & W
George Mason University *Virginia* M & W
The George Washington University *District of Columbia* M & W
Georgetown College *Kentucky* M & W
Georgetown University *District of Columbia* M & W
Georgia College & State University *Georgia* M & W
Georgia Highlands College *Georgia* M & W

Georgia Institute of Technology *Georgia* M & W
Georgia Southern University *Georgia* M & W
Georgia Southwestern State University *Georgia* M & W
Georgia State University *Georgia* M & W
Georgian Court University *New Jersey* M & W
Gettysburg College *Pennsylvania* M & W
Glen Oaks Community College *Michigan* M & W
Glendale Community College *Arizona* M & W
Glendale Community College *California* M & W
Glenville State College *West Virginia* M & W
Globe Institute of Technology *New York* M & W
Gogebic Community College *Michigan* M & W
Goldey-Beacom College *Delaware* M & W
Gonzaga University *Washington* M & W
Gordon College *Massachusetts* M & W
Gordon State College *Georgia* M
Goshen College *Indiana* M & W
Goucher College *Maryland* M & W
Governors State University *Illinois* M & W
Grace Bible College *Michigan* M & W
Grace College *Indiana* M & W
Grace University *Nebraska* M & W
Graceland University *Iowa* M & W
Grambling State University *Louisiana* M & W
Grand Canyon University *Arizona* M & W
Grand Rapids Community College *Michigan* M & W
Grand Valley State University *Michigan* M & W
Grand View University *Iowa* M & W
Grays Harbor College *Washington* M & W
Great Lakes Christian College *Michigan* M & W
Green Mountain College *Vermont* M & W
Green River College *Washington* M & W
Greensboro College *North Carolina* M & W
Greenville College *Illinois* M & W
Grinnell College *Iowa* M & W
Grossmont College *California* M & W
Grove City College *Pennsylvania* M & W
Guilford College *North Carolina* M & W
Guilford Technical Community College *North Carolina* M & W
Gulf Coast State College *Florida* M & W
Gustavus Adolphus College *Minnesota* M & W
Gwynedd Mercy University *Pennsylvania* M & W
Hagerstown Community College *Maryland* M & W
Hamilton College *New York* M & W
Hamline University *Minnesota* M & W
Hampden-Sydney College *Virginia* M
Hampshire College *Massachusetts* M & W
Hampton University *Virginia* M & W
Hannibal-LaGrange University *Missouri* M & W
Hanover College *Indiana* M & W
Harcum College *Pennsylvania* M & W
Hardin-Simmons University *Texas* M & W
Harding University *Arkansas* M & W
Harford Community College *Maryland* M & W
Harper College *Illinois* M & W
Harris-Stowe State University *Missouri* M & W
Harrisburg Area Community College *Pennsylvania* M & W
Hartwick College *New York* M & W
Harvard University *Massachusetts* M & W
Harvey Mudd College *California* M & W
Haskell Indian Nations University *Kansas* M & W
Hastings College *Nebraska* M & W
Haverford College *Pennsylvania* M & W
Hawai'i Pacific University *Hawaii* M & W
Heidelberg University *Ohio* M & W
Henderson State University *Arkansas* M & W
Hendrix College *Arkansas* M & W
Henry Ford College *Michigan* M & W
Heritage College and Seminary *Ontario (Canada)* M & W
Herkimer County Community College *New York* M & W
Hesston College *Kansas* M & W
Hibbing Community College *Minnesota* M & W
High Point University *North Carolina* M & W
Highland Community College *Illinois* M & W
Highland Community College *Kansas* M & W
Highline College *Washington* M & W
Hilbert College *New York* M & W
Hill College *Texas* M & W
Hillsborough Community College *Florida* M & W

Hillsdale College *Michigan* M & W
Hillsdale Free Will Baptist College *Oklahoma* M & W
Hinds Community College *Mississippi* M & W
Hiram College *Ohio* M & W
Hiwassee College *Tennessee* M & W
Hobart and William Smith Colleges *New York* M & W
Hofstra University *New York* M & W
Hollins University *Virginia* W
Holmes Community College *Mississippi* M & W
Holy Cross College *Indiana* M & W
Holy Family University *Pennsylvania* M & W
Holy Names University *California* M & W
Holyoke Community College *Massachusetts* M & W
Hood College *Maryland* M & W
Hope College *Michigan* M & W
Hope International University *California* M & W
Houghton College *New York* M & W
Houston Baptist University *Texas* M & W
Howard College *Texas* M & W
Howard Community College *Maryland* M & W
Howard Payne University *Texas* M & W
Howard University *District of Columbia* M & W
Hudson Valley Community College *New York* M & W
Humboldt State University *California* M & W
Hunter College of the City University of New York *New York* M & W
Huntingdon College *Alabama* M & W
Huntington University *Indiana* M & W
Husson University *Maine* M & W
Huston-Tillotson University *Texas* M & W
Hutchinson Community College *Kansas* M & W
Idaho State University *Idaho* M & W
Illinois Central College *Illinois* M & W
Illinois Eastern Community Colleges, Lincoln Trail College *Illinois* M & W
Illinois Eastern Community Colleges, Olney Central College *Illinois* M & W
Illinois Eastern Community Colleges, Wabash Valley College *Illinois* M & W
Illinois Institute of Technology *Illinois* M & W
Illinois State University *Illinois* M & W
Illinois Valley Community College *Illinois* M & W
Illinois Wesleyan University *Illinois* M & W
Immaculata University *Pennsylvania* W
Imperial Valley College *California* M & W
Independence Community College *Kansas* M & W
Indian Hills Community College *Iowa* M
Indian River State College *Florida* M & W
Indiana State University *Indiana* M & W
Indiana Tech *Indiana* M & W
Indiana University Bloomington *Indiana* M & W
Indiana University East *Indiana* M & W
Indiana University Kokomo *Indiana* M & W
Indiana University Northwest *Indiana* M & W
Indiana University of Pennsylvania *Pennsylvania* M & W
Indiana University - Purdue University Fort Wayne *Indiana* M & W
Indiana University - Purdue University Indianapolis *Indiana* M & W
Indiana University South Bend *Indiana* M & W
Indiana University Southeast *Indiana* M & W
Indiana Wesleyan University *Indiana* M & W
Inter American University of Puerto Rico, Aguadilla Campus *Puerto Rico* M & W
Inter American University of Puerto Rico, Arecibo Campus *Puerto Rico* M & W
Inter American University of Puerto Rico, Barranquitas Campus *Puerto Rico* M & W
Inter American University of Puerto Rico, Bayamón Campus *Puerto Rico* M & W
Inter American University of Puerto Rico, Fajardo Campus *Puerto Rico* M & W
Inter American University of Puerto Rico, Guayama Campus *Puerto Rico* M & W
Inter American University of Puerto Rico, Metropolitan Campus *Puerto Rico* M & W
Inter American University of Puerto Rico, San Germán Campus *Puerto Rico* M & W
Iona College *New York* M & W
Iowa Central Community College *Iowa* M & W

M = Men; W = Women

Iowa Lakes Community College *Iowa* M & W
Iowa State University of Science and Technology *Iowa* M & W
Iowa Wesleyan University *Iowa* M & W
Iowa Western Community College *Iowa* M & W
Irvine Valley College *California* M & W
Itasca Community College *Minnesota* M & W
Itawamba Community College *Mississippi* M & W
Ithaca College *New York* M & W
Jackson College *Michigan* M & W
Jackson State Community College *Tennessee* M & W
Jackson State University *Mississippi* M & W
Jacksonville College *Texas* M & W
Jacksonville State University *Alabama* M & W
Jacksonville University *Florida* M & W
James A. Rhodes State College *Ohio* M & W
James H. Faulkner State Community College *Alabama* M & W
James Madison University *Virginia* M & W
Jamestown Community College *New York* M & W
Jarvis Christian College *Texas* M & W
Jefferson College *Missouri* W
Jefferson College of Health Sciences *Virginia* M
Jefferson Community College *New York* M & W
Jefferson Davis Community College *Alabama* M
John A. Logan College *Illinois* M & W
John Brown University *Arkansas* M & W
John Carroll University *Ohio* M & W
John Jay College of Criminal Justice of the City University of New York *New York* M & W
John Wood Community College *Illinois* M & W
Johns Hopkins University *Maryland* M & W
Johnson C. Smith University *North Carolina* M & W
Johnson College *Pennsylvania* M & W
Johnson County Community College *Kansas* M & W
Johnson State College *Vermont* M & W
Johnson University *Tennessee* M & W
Johnson University Florida *Florida* M & W
Johnson & Wales University *Colorado* M & W
Johnson & Wales University *Rhode Island* M & W
Joliet Junior College *Illinois* M & W
Jones County Junior College *Mississippi* M & W
Judson College *Alabama* W
Judson University *Illinois* M & W
Juniata College *Pennsylvania* M & W
Kalamazoo College *Michigan* M & W
Kalamazoo Valley Community College *Michigan* M & W
Kankakee Community College *Illinois* M & W
Kansas City Kansas Community College *Kansas* M & W
Kansas State University *Kansas* M & W
Kansas Wesleyan University *Kansas* M & W
Kaskaskia College *Illinois* M & W
Kean University *New Jersey* M & W
Keene State College *New Hampshire* M & W
Kellogg Community College *Michigan* M & W
Kennesaw State University *Georgia* M & W
Kent State University *Ohio* M & W
Kentucky Christian University *Kentucky* M & W
Kentucky State University *Kentucky* M & W
Kentucky Wesleyan College *Kentucky* M & W
Kenyon College *Ohio* M & W
Keuka College *New York* M & W
Keystone College *Pennsylvania* M & W
Kilgore College *Texas* M & W
King University *Tennessee* M & W
The King's College *New York* M & W
King's College *Pennsylvania* M & W
The King's University *Alberta (Canada)* M & W
Kingsborough Community College of the City University of New York *New York* M & W
Kingswood University *New Brunswick (Canada)* M
Kirkwood Community College *Iowa* M & W
Kishwaukee College *Illinois* M & W
Knox College *Illinois* M & W
Kutztown University of Pennsylvania *Pennsylvania* M & W
La Roche College *Pennsylvania* M & W
La Salle University *Pennsylvania* M & W
La Sierra University *California* M & W
Labette Community College *Kansas* M & W

Lackawanna College *Pennsylvania* M & W
Lafayette College *Pennsylvania* M & W
LaGrange College *Georgia* M & W
Lake Erie College *Ohio* M & W
Lake Forest College *Illinois* M & W
Lake Land College *Illinois* M & W
Lake Michigan College *Michigan* M & W
Lake Region State College *North Dakota* M & W
Lake Superior State University *Michigan* M & W
Lakehead University *Ontario (Canada)* M & W
Lakeland College *Wisconsin* M & W
Lakeland Community College *Ohio* M & W
Lamar Community College *Colorado* M & W
Lamar University *Texas* M & W
Lancaster Bible College *Pennsylvania* M & W
Lander University *South Carolina* M & W
Landmark College *Vermont* M & W
Lane College *Tennessee* M & W
Lane Community College *Oregon* M & W
Langston University *Oklahoma* M & W
Lansing Community College *Michigan* M & W
Laramie County Community College *Wyoming* M
Lasell College *Massachusetts* M & W
Lassen Community College District *California* M & W
Laurentian University *Ontario (Canada)* M & W
Lawrence Technological University *Michigan* M & W
Lawrence University *Wisconsin* M & W
Lawson State Community College *Alabama* M & W
Le Moyne College *New York* M & W
Lebanon Valley College *Pennsylvania* M & W
Lee College *Texas* M
Lee University *Tennessee* M & W
Lees-McRae College *North Carolina* M & W
Lehigh Carbon Community College *Pennsylvania* M & W
Lehigh University *Pennsylvania* M & W
Lehman College of the City University of New York *New York* M & W
LeMoyne-Owen College *Tennessee* M & W
Lenoir Community College *North Carolina* M & W
Lenoir-Rhyne University *North Carolina* M & W
Lesley University *Massachusetts* M & W
LeTourneau University *Texas* M & W
Lewis & Clark College *Oregon* M & W
Lewis and Clark Community College *Illinois* M & W
Lewis-Clark State College *Idaho* M & W
Lewis University *Illinois* M & W
Liberty University *Virginia* M & W
Limestone College *South Carolina* M & W
Lincoln Christian University *Illinois* M & W
Lincoln Land Community College *Illinois* M & W
Lincoln Memorial University *Tennessee* M & W
Lincoln University *Missouri* M & W
Lincoln University *Pennsylvania* M & W
Lindenwood University *Missouri* M & W
Lindsey Wilson College *Kentucky* M & W
Linfield College *Oregon* M & W
Linn-Benton Community College *Oregon* M
Lipscomb University *Tennessee* M & W
Little Big Horn College *Montana* M & W
Livingstone College *North Carolina* M & W
Lock Haven University of Pennsylvania *Pennsylvania* M & W
Logan University *Missouri* M & W
Long Beach City College *California* M & W
Long Island University - LIU Brooklyn *New York* M & W
Long Island University - LIU Post *New York* M & W
Longwood University *Virginia* M & W
Loras College *Iowa* M & W
Los Angeles City College *California* M
Los Angeles Harbor College *California* M
Los Angeles Pierce College *California* W
Los Angeles Southwest College *California* M & W
Los Angeles Trade-Technical College *California* M & W
Los Angeles Valley College *California* M & W
Los Medanos College *California* M & W
Louisburg College *North Carolina* M & W
Louisiana College *Louisiana* M & W
Louisiana State University and Agricultural & Mechanical College *Louisiana* M & W

Louisiana State University at Alexandria *Louisiana* M & W
Louisiana State University at Eunice *Louisiana* W
Louisiana State University in Shreveport *Louisiana* M & W
Louisiana Tech University *Louisiana* M & W
Lourdes University *Ohio* M & W
Lower Columbia College *Washington* M & W
Loyola Marymount University *California* M & W
Loyola University Chicago *Illinois* M & W
Loyola University Maryland *Maryland* M & W
Loyola University New Orleans *Louisiana* M & W
Lubbock Christian University *Texas* M & W
Lurleen B. Wallace Community College *Alabama* M & W
Luther College *Iowa* M & W
Luzerne County Community College *Pennsylvania* M & W
Lycoming College *Pennsylvania* M & W
Lynchburg College *Virginia* M & W
Lyndon State College *Vermont* M & W
Lynn University *Florida* M & W
Lyon College *Arkansas* M & W
Macalester College *Minnesota* M & W
MacMurray College *Illinois* M & W
Macomb Community College *Michigan* M
Madison Area Technical College *Wisconsin* M & W
Madonna University *Michigan* M & W
Maine Maritime Academy *Maine* M & W
Malone University *Ohio* M & W
Manchester Community College *Connecticut* M & W
Manchester Community College *New Hampshire* M
Manchester University *Indiana* M & W
Manhattan Christian College *Kansas* M & W
Manhattan College *New York* M & W
Manhattanville College *New York* M & W
Manor College *Pennsylvania* M & W
Mansfield University of Pennsylvania *Pennsylvania* M & W
Maranatha Baptist University *Wisconsin* M & W
Marian University *Indiana* M & W
Marian University *Wisconsin* M & W
Marietta College *Ohio* M & W
Marion Military Institute *Alabama* M
Marion Technical College *Ohio* M & W
Marist College *New York* M & W
Marquette University *Wisconsin* M & W
Mars Hill University *North Carolina* M & W
Marshall University *West Virginia* M & W
Marshalltown Community College *Iowa* M & W
Martin Luther College *Minnesota* M & W
Martin Methodist College *Tennessee* M & W
Mary Baldwin College *Virginia* W
Marygrove College *Michigan* M & W
Marymount University *Virginia* M & W
Maryville College *Tennessee* M & W
Maryville University of Saint Louis *Missouri* M & W
Marywood University *Pennsylvania* M & W
Massachusetts Bay Community College *Massachusetts* M & W
Massachusetts College of Liberal Arts *Massachusetts* M & W
Massachusetts Institute of Technology *Massachusetts* M & W
Massasoit Community College *Massachusetts* M & W
The Master's College and Seminary *California* M & W
Mayland Community College *North Carolina* M
Mayville State University *North Dakota* M & W
McDaniel College *Maryland* M & W
McGill University *Quebec (Canada)* M & W
McHenry County College *Illinois* M & W
McKendree University *Illinois* M & W
McLennan Community College *Texas* M & W
McMaster University *Ontario (Canada)* M & W
McMurry University *Texas* M & W
McNeese State University *Louisiana* M & W
McPherson College *Kansas* M & W
Medaille College *New York* M & W
Medgar Evers College of the City University of New York *New York* M & W

M = Men; W = Women

Memorial University of Newfoundland *Newfoundland and Labrador (Canada)* M & W
Mendocino College *California* M & W
Menlo College *California* M & W
Merced College *California* M & W
Mercer County Community College *New Jersey* M & W
Mercer University *Georgia* M & W
Mercy College *New York* M & W
Mercyhurst North East *Pennsylvania* M & W
Mercyhurst University *Pennsylvania* M & W
Meredith College *North Carolina* W
Meridian Community College *Mississippi* M & W
Merrimack College *Massachusetts* M & W
Merritt College *California* M & W
Mesa Community College *Arizona* M & W
Mesabi Range College *Minnesota* M & W
Messiah College *Pennsylvania* M & W
Methodist University *North Carolina* M & W
Metropolitan Community College - Kansas City *Missouri* M & W
Metropolitan State University of Denver *Colorado* M & W
Miami Dade College *Florida* M & W
Miami University *Ohio* M & W
Miami University Hamilton *Ohio* M & W
Miami University Middletown *Ohio* M & W
Michigan State University *Michigan* M & W
Michigan Technological University *Michigan* M & W
Mid-America Christian University *Oklahoma* M & W
Mid-Atlantic Christian University *North Carolina* M & W
Mid Michigan Community College *Michigan* M & W
Mid-Plains Community College *Nebraska* M & W
Mid-State Technical College *Wisconsin* M & W
MidAmerica Nazarene University *Kansas* M & W
Middle Georgia State University *Georgia* M & W
Middle Tennessee State University *Tennessee* M & W
Middlebury College *Vermont* M & W
Middlesex County College *New Jersey* M & W
Midland College *Texas* M & W
Midland University *Nebraska* M & W
Midway University *Kentucky* W
Midwestern State University *Texas* M & W
Miles College *Alabama* M & W
Miles Community College *Montana* M & W
Millersville University of Pennsylvania *Pennsylvania* M & W
Milligan College *Tennessee* M & W
Millikin University *Illinois* M & W
Millsaps College *Mississippi* M & W
Milwaukee Area Technical College *Wisconsin* M & W
Milwaukee School of Engineering *Wisconsin* M & W
Mineral Area College *Missouri* M & W
Minnesota State Community and Technical College *Minnesota* M & W
Minnesota State University Mankato *Minnesota* M & W
Minnesota State University Moorhead *Minnesota* M & W
Minnesota West Community and Technical College *Minnesota* M & W
Minot State University *North Dakota* M & W
MiraCosta College *California* M & W
Misericordia University *Pennsylvania* M & W
Mission College *California* W
Mississippi College *Mississippi* M & W
Mississippi Delta Community College *Mississippi* M & W
Mississippi Gulf Coast Community College *Mississippi* M & W
Mississippi State University *Mississippi* M & W
Mississippi Valley State University *Mississippi* M & W
Missouri Baptist University *Missouri* M & W
Missouri Southern State University *Missouri* M & W
Missouri State University *Missouri* M & W
Missouri State University - West Plains *Missouri* M
Missouri University of Science and Technology *Missouri* M & W
Missouri Valley College *Missouri* M & W

Missouri Western State University *Missouri* M & W
Mitchell College *Connecticut* M & W
Moberly Area Community College *Missouri* M & W
Modesto Junior College *California* M & W
Mohawk Valley Community College *New York* M & W
Molloy College *New York* M & W
Monmouth College *Illinois* M & W
Monmouth University *New Jersey* M & W
Monroe College *New York* M & W
Monroe Community College *New York* M & W
Montana State University *Montana* M & W
Montana State University Billings *Montana* M & W
Montana State University - Northern *Montana* M & W
Montana Tech of The University of Montana *Montana* M & W
Montclair State University *New Jersey* M & W
Monterey Peninsula College *California* M
Montgomery College *Maryland* M & W
Montgomery County Community College *Pennsylvania* M & W
Montreat College *North Carolina* M & W
Moody Bible Institute *Illinois* M & W
Moorpark College *California* M & W
Moraine Valley Community College *Illinois* M & W
Moravian College *Pennsylvania* M & W
Morehead State University *Kentucky* M & W
Morehouse College *Georgia* M
Morgan State University *Maryland* M & W
Morningside College *Iowa* M & W
Morris College *South Carolina* M & W
Morrisville State College *New York* M & W
Morton College *Illinois* M & W
Motlow State Community College *Tennessee* M & W
Mott Community College *Michigan* M & W
Mount Allison University *New Brunswick (Canada)* M & W
Mount Aloysius College *Pennsylvania* M & W
Mount Holyoke College *Massachusetts* W
Mt. Hood Community College *Oregon* M & W
Mount Ida College *Massachusetts* M & W
Mount Marty College *South Dakota* M & W
Mount Mary University *Wisconsin* W
Mount Mercy University *Iowa* M & W
Mount St. Joseph University *Ohio* M & W
Mount Saint Mary College *New York* M & W
Mount St. Mary's University *Maryland* M & W
Mount Saint Vincent University *Nova Scotia (Canada)* M & W
Mt. San Antonio College *California* M & W
Mt. San Jacinto College *California* M & W
Mount Vernon Nazarene University *Ohio* M & W
Mountain View College *Texas* M & W
Muhlenberg College *Pennsylvania* M & W
Multnomah University *Oregon* M & W
Murray State College *Oklahoma* M & W
Murray State University *Kentucky* M & W
Muskegon Community College *Michigan* M & W
Muskingum University *Ohio* M & W
Napa Valley College *California* M & W
Nassau Community College *New York* M & W
Navarro College *Texas* M
Nazareth College of Rochester *New York* M & W
Nebraska Christian College *Nebraska* M
Nebraska College of Technical Agriculture *Nebraska* M & W
Nebraska Wesleyan University *Nebraska* M & W
Neosho County Community College *Kansas* M & W
Neumann University *Pennsylvania* M & W
New England College *New Hampshire* M & W
New Hope Christian College *Oregon* M
New Jersey City University *New Jersey* M & W
New Jersey Institute of Technology *New Jersey* M & W
New Mexico Highlands University *New Mexico* M & W
New Mexico Junior College *New Mexico* M & W
New Mexico Military Institute *New Mexico* M
New Mexico State University *New Mexico* M & W
New York Institute of Technology *New York* M & W
New York University *New York* M & W
Newberry College *South Carolina* M & W

Newbury College *Massachusetts* M & W
Newman University *Kansas* M & W
NHTI, Concord's Community College *New Hampshire* M & W
Niagara County Community College *New York* M & W
Niagara University *New York* M & W
Nicholls State University *Louisiana* M & W
Nichols College *Massachusetts* M & W
Norfolk State University *Virginia* M & W
North Arkansas College *Arkansas* M & W
North Carolina Agricultural and Technical State University *North Carolina* M & W
North Carolina Central University *North Carolina* M & W
North Carolina State University *North Carolina* M & W
North Carolina Wesleyan College *North Carolina* M & W
North Central College *Illinois* M & W
North Central Missouri College *Missouri* M & W
North Central University *Minnesota* M & W
North Country Community College *New York* M & W
North Dakota State College of Science *North Dakota* M & W
North Dakota State University *North Dakota* M & W
North Greenville University *South Carolina* M & W
North Idaho College *Idaho* M & W
North Iowa Area Community College *Iowa* M & W
North Lake College *Texas* M
North Park University *Illinois* M & W
North Seattle College *Washington* M & W
Northampton Community College *Pennsylvania* M & W
Northeast Community College *Nebraska* M & W
Northeast Mississippi Community College *Mississippi* M & W
Northeastern Junior College *Colorado* M & W
Northeastern Oklahoma Agricultural and Mechanical College *Oklahoma* M & W
Northeastern State University *Oklahoma* M & W
Northeastern University *Massachusetts* M & W
Northern Arizona University *Arizona* M & W
Northern Essex Community College *Massachusetts* M & W
Northern Illinois University *Illinois* M & W
Northern Kentucky University *Kentucky* M & W
Northern Michigan University *Michigan* M & W
Northern Oklahoma College *Oklahoma* M & W
Northern State University *South Dakota* M & W
Northland College *Wisconsin* M & W
Northland Community and Technical College *Minnesota* M & W
Northwest Christian University *Oregon* M & W
Northwest College *Wyoming* M & W
Northwest Florida State College *Florida* M & W
Northwest Mississippi Community College *Mississippi* M & W
Northwest Missouri State University *Missouri* M & W
Northwest Nazarene University *Idaho* M & W
Northwest University *Washington* M & W
Northwestern College *Iowa* M & W
Northwestern Oklahoma State University *Oklahoma* M & W
Northwestern State University of Louisiana *Louisiana* M & W
Northwood University, Michigan Campus *Michigan* M & W
Norwich University *Vermont* M & W
Notre Dame College *Ohio* M & W
Notre Dame of Maryland University *Maryland* W
Notre Dame de Namur University *California* M & W
Nova Southeastern University *Florida* M & W
Nyack College *New York* M & W
Oak Hills Christian College *Minnesota* M
Oakland City University *Indiana* M & W
Oakland Community College *Michigan* M & W
Oakland University *Michigan* M & W
Oakton Community College *Illinois* M & W
Oakwood University *Alabama* M & W
Oberlin College *Ohio* M & W
Occidental College *California* M & W

M = Men; W = Women

Ocean County College *New Jersey* M & W
Odessa College *Texas* M & W
Oglethorpe University *Georgia* M & W
Ohio Christian University *Ohio* M & W
Ohio Dominican University *Ohio* M & W
Ohio Northern University *Ohio* M & W
The Ohio State University *Ohio* M & W
The Ohio State University at Marion *Ohio* M
Ohio University *Ohio* M & W
Ohio University - Eastern *Ohio* M & W
Ohio University - Zanesville *Ohio* M & W
Ohio Valley University *West Virginia* M & W
Ohio Wesleyan University *Ohio* M & W
Ohlone College *California* M & W
Oklahoma Baptist University *Oklahoma* M & W
Oklahoma Christian University *Oklahoma* M & W
Oklahoma City University *Oklahoma* M & W
Oklahoma Panhandle State University *Oklahoma* M & W
Oklahoma State University *Oklahoma* M & W
Oklahoma Wesleyan University *Oklahoma* M & W
Old Dominion University *Virginia* M & W
Olivet College *Michigan* M & W
Olivet Nazarene University *Illinois* M & W
Olympic College *Washington* M & W
Onondaga Community College *New York* M & W
Oral Roberts University *Oklahoma* M & W
Orange Coast College *California* M & W
Orange County Community College *New York* M & W
Oregon Institute of Technology *Oregon* M & W
Oregon State University *Oregon* M & W
Otero Junior College *Colorado* M & W
Ottawa University *Kansas* M & W
Otterbein University *Ohio* M & W
Ouachita Baptist University *Arkansas* M & W
Our Lady of the Lake University of San Antonio *Texas* M & W
Owens Community College *Ohio* M & W
Oxnard College *California* M & W
Ozark Christian College *Missouri* M & W
Pace University *New York* M & W
Pace University, Pleasantville Campus *New York* M & W
Pacific Lutheran University *Washington* M & W
Pacific Union College *California* M & W
Pacific University *Oregon* M & W
Paine College *Georgia* M & W
Palm Beach Atlantic University *Florida* M & W
Palm Beach State College *Florida* M & W
Palomar College *California* M & W
Panola College *Texas* M & W
Paris Junior College *Texas* M & W
Park University *Missouri* M & W
Parkland College *Illinois* M & W
Pasadena City College *California* M & W
Pasco-Hernando State College *Florida* M
Passaic County Community College *New Jersey* M & W
Patrick Henry College *Virginia* M & W
Patrick Henry Community College *Virginia* M & W
Paul Quinn College *Texas* M & W
Paul Smith's College *New York* M & W
Pearl River Community College *Mississippi* M & W
Peninsula College *Washington* M & W
Penn State Abington *Pennsylvania* M & W
Penn State Altoona *Pennsylvania* M & W
Penn State Beaver *Pennsylvania* M
Penn State Berks *Pennsylvania* M & W
Penn State Brandywine *Pennsylvania* M & W
Penn State DuBois *Pennsylvania* M
Penn State Erie, The Behrend College *Pennsylvania* M & W
Penn State Fayette, The Eberly Campus *Pennsylvania* M
Penn State Greater Allegheny *Pennsylvania* M
Penn State Harrisburg *Pennsylvania* M & W
Penn State Hazleton *Pennsylvania* M & W
Penn State Lehigh Valley *Pennsylvania* M & W
Penn State Mont Alto *Pennsylvania* M & W
Penn State New Kensington *Pennsylvania* M & W
Penn State Schuylkill *Pennsylvania* M
Penn State University Park *Pennsylvania* M & W
Penn State Wilkes-Barre *Pennsylvania* M

Penn State Worthington Scranton *Pennsylvania* M & W
Pennsylvania College of Technology *Pennsylvania* M & W
Pennsylvania Highlands Community College *Pennsylvania* M
Pensacola State College *Florida* M & W
Pepperdine University *California* M & W
Peru State College *Nebraska* M & W
Pfeiffer University *North Carolina* M & W
Philadelphia University *Pennsylvania* M & W
Philander Smith College *Arkansas* M & W
Phoenix College *Arizona* M & W
Piedmont College *Georgia* M & W
Piedmont International University *North Carolina* M
Pierce College at Puyallup *Washington* M & W
Pine Manor College *Massachusetts* M & W
Pitt Community College *North Carolina* M
Pittsburg State University *Kansas* M & W
Pitzer College *California* M & W
Plymouth State University *New Hampshire* M & W
Point Loma Nazarene University *California* M & W
Point Park University *Pennsylvania* M & W
Point University *Georgia* M & W
Polk State College *Florida* M
Polytechnic University of Puerto Rico *Puerto Rico* M
Pomona College *California* M & W
Pontifical Catholic University of Puerto Rico *Puerto Rico* M
Porterville College *California* M & W
Portland Community College *Oregon* M & W
Portland State University *Oregon* M & W
Post University *Connecticut* M & W
Potomac State College of West Virginia University *West Virginia* M & W
Prairie State College *Illinois* M & W
Prairie View A&M University *Texas* M & W
Pratt Community College *Kansas* M & W
Pratt Institute *New York* M
Presbyterian College *South Carolina* M & W
Presentation College *South Dakota* M & W
Prince George's Community College *Maryland* M & W
Princeton University *New Jersey* M & W
Principia College *Illinois* M & W
Providence College *Rhode Island* M & W
Providence University College & Theological Seminary *Manitoba (Canada)* M & W
Purchase College, State University of New York *New York* M & W
Purdue University *Indiana* M & W
Purdue University Northwest *Hammond, Indiana* M & W
Queens College of the City University of New York *New York* M & W
Queens University of Charlotte *North Carolina* M & W
Queen's University at Kingston *Ontario (Canada)* M & W
Queensborough Community College of the City University of New York *New York* M & W
Quincy University *Illinois* M & W
Quinnipiac University *Connecticut* M & W
Quinsigamond Community College *Massachusetts* M & W
Radford University *Virginia* M & W
Rainy River Community College *Minnesota* M & W
Ramapo College of New Jersey *New Jersey* M & W
Randolph College *Virginia* M & W
Randolph-Macon College *Virginia* M & W
Ranger College *Texas* M & W
Raritan Valley Community College *New Jersey* M & W
Redeemer University College *Ontario (Canada)* M & W
Redlands Community College *Oklahoma* M & W
Reedley College *California* M & W
Regis College *Massachusetts* M & W
Regis University *Colorado* M & W
Reinhardt University *Georgia* M & W
Rend Lake College *Illinois* M & W
Rensselaer Polytechnic Institute *New York* M & W

Research College of Nursing *Missouri* M & W
Rhode Island College *Rhode Island* M & W
Rhodes College *Tennessee* M & W
Rice University *Texas* M & W
Richland College *Texas* M
Rider University *New Jersey* M & W
Ridgewater College *Minnesota* M & W
Rio Hondo College *California* M & W
Ripon College *Wisconsin* M & W
Riverland Community College *Minnesota* M & W
Rivier University *New Hampshire* M & W
Roane State Community College *Tennessee* M & W
Roanoke College *Virginia* M & W
Robert Morris University *Pennsylvania* M & W
Robert Morris University Illinois *Illinois* M & W
Roberts Wesleyan College *New York* M & W
Rochester College *Michigan* M & W
Rochester Community and Technical College *Minnesota* M & W
Rochester Institute of Technology *New York* M & W
Rock Valley College *Illinois* M & W
Rockford University *Illinois* M & W
Rockhurst University *Missouri* M & W
Rockland Community College *New York* M & W
Rocky Mountain College *Montana* M & W
Roger Williams University *Rhode Island* M & W
Rogers State University *Oklahoma* M & W
Rollins College *Florida* M & W
Roosevelt University *Illinois* M & W
Rose-Hulman Institute of Technology *Indiana* M & W
Rose State College *Oklahoma* M & W
Rosemont College *Pennsylvania* M & W
Rowan College at Burlington County *New Jersey* M & W
Rowan College at Gloucester County *New Jersey* M & W
Rowan University *New Jersey* M & W
Roxbury Community College *Massachusetts* M & W
Royal Military College of Canada *Ontario (Canada)* M & W
Rust College *Mississippi* M & W
Rutgers University - Camden *New Jersey* M & W
Rutgers University - New Brunswick *New Jersey* M & W
Rutgers University - Newark *New Jersey* M & W
Ryerson University *Ontario (Canada)* M & W
Sacramento City College *California* M & W
Sacred Heart University *Connecticut* M & W
Saddleback College *California* M & W
The Sage Colleges *New York* M & W
Saginaw Valley State University *Michigan* M & W
St. Ambrose University *Iowa* M & W
St. Andrews University *North Carolina* M & W
Saint Anselm College *New Hampshire* M & W
Saint Augustine's University *North Carolina* M & W
St. Bonaventure University *New York* M & W
St. Catherine University *Minnesota* W
St. Clair County Community College *Michigan* M & W
St. Cloud State University *Minnesota* M & W
St. Cloud Technical & Community College *Minnesota* M & W
St. Edward's University *Texas* M & W
St. Francis College *New York* M & W
Saint Francis University *Pennsylvania* M & W
St. Francis Xavier University *Nova Scotia (Canada)* M & W
St. Gregory's University *Oklahoma* M & W
St. John Fisher College *New York* M & W
St. Johns River State College *Florida* M
Saint John's University *Minnesota* M
St. John's University *New York* M & W
Saint Joseph's College *Indiana* M & W
St. Joseph's College, Long Island Campus *New York* M & W
Saint Joseph's College of Maine *Maine* M & W
St. Joseph's College, New York *New York* M & W
Saint Joseph's University *Pennsylvania* M & W
Saint Katherine College *California* W
St. Lawrence University *New York* M & W
Saint Leo University *Florida* M & W

M = Men; W = Women

Saint Louis Christian College *Missouri* M & W
St. Louis College of Pharmacy *Missouri* M & W
St. Louis Community College *Missouri* M & W
Saint Louis University *Missouri* M & W
Saint Martin's University *Washington* M & W
Saint Mary-of-the-Woods College *Indiana* W
Saint Mary's College *Indiana* W
Saint Mary's College of California *California* M & W
St. Mary's College of Maryland *Maryland* M & W
Saint Mary's University *Nova Scotia* (Canada) M & W
St. Mary's University *Texas* M & W
Saint Mary's University of Minnesota *Minnesota* M & W
Saint Michael's College *Vermont* M & W
St. Norbert College *Wisconsin* M & W
St. Olaf College *Minnesota* M & W
Saint Peter's University *New Jersey* M & W
St. Petersburg College *Florida* M & W
St. Thomas Aquinas College *New York* M & W
St. Thomas University *Florida* M & W
St. Thomas University *New Brunswick* (Canada) M & W
Saint Vincent College *Pennsylvania* M & W
Saint Xavier University *Illinois* M & W
Salem College *North Carolina* W
Salem International University *West Virginia* M & W
Salem State University *Massachusetts* M & W
Salisbury University *Maryland* M & W
Salt Lake Community College *Utah* M & W
Salve Regina University *Rhode Island* M & W
Sam Houston State University *Texas* M & W
Samford University *Alabama* M & W
San Bernardino Valley College *California* M & W
San Diego Christian College *California* M & W
San Diego City College *California* M & W
San Diego Mesa College *California* M & W
San Diego Miramar College *California* M
San Diego State University *California* M & W
San Francisco State University *California* M & W
San Jacinto College District *Texas* M & W
San Joaquin Delta College *California* M & W
San Jose City College *California* M & W
San Jose State University *California* M & W
Sandhills Community College *North Carolina* M
Santa Ana College *California* M & W
Santa Barbara City College *California* M & W
Santa Clara University *California* M & W
Santa Fe College *Florida* M & W
Santa Monica College *California* M & W
Santa Rosa Junior College *California* M & W
Sarah Lawrence College *New York* M & W
Sauk Valley Community College *Illinois* M & W
Savannah State University *Georgia* M & W
Schenectady County Community College *New York* M & W
Schoolcraft College *Michigan* M & W
Schreiner University *Texas* M & W
Scottsdale Community College *Arizona* M & W
Scripps College *California* W
Seattle Pacific University *Washington* M & W
Seattle University *Washington* M & W
Selma University *Alabama* M & W
Seminole State College *Oklahoma* M & W
Seton Hall University *New Jersey* M & W
Seton Hill University *Pennsylvania* M & W
Sewanee: The University of the South *Tennessee* M & W
Seward County Community College and Area Technical School *Kansas* M & W
Shasta College *California* M & W
Shaw University *North Carolina* M & W
Shawnee Community College *Illinois* M & W
Shawnee State University *Ohio* M & W
Shelton State Community College *Alabama* M & W
Shenandoah University *Virginia* M & W
Shepherd University *West Virginia* M & W
Sheridan College *Wyoming* M & W
Shippensburg University of Pennsylvania *Pennsylvania* M & W
Shoreline Community College *Washington* M & W
Shorter College *Arkansas* M & W
Shorter University *Georgia* M & W
Siena College *New York* M & W

Siena Heights University *Michigan* M & W
Sierra College *California* M & W
Silver Lake College of the Holy Family *Wisconsin* M & W
Simmons College *Massachusetts* W
Simon Fraser University *British Columbia* (Canada) M & W
Simpson College *Iowa* M & W
Simpson University *California* M & W
Sinclair Community College *Ohio* M & W
Sitting Bull College *North Dakota* M & W
Skagit Valley College *Washington* M & W
Skidmore College *New York* M & W
Skyline College *California* M
Slippery Rock University of Pennsylvania *Pennsylvania* M & W
Smith College *Massachusetts* W
Snead State Community College *Alabama* M & W
Snow College *Utah* M & W
Solano Community College *California* M & W
Sonoma State University *California* M & W
South Carolina State University *South Carolina* M & W
South Dakota School of Mines and Technology *South Dakota* M & W
South Dakota State University *South Dakota* M & W
South Georgia State College *Georgia* M
South Mountain Community College *Arizona* M & W
South Plains College *Texas* M & W
South Puget Sound Community College *Washington* M & W
South Suburban College *Illinois* M & W
Southeast Community College, Beatrice Campus *Nebraska* M & W
Southeast Community College, Lincoln Campus *Nebraska* M & W
Southeast Community College, Milford Campus *Nebraska* M & W
Southeast Missouri State University *Missouri* M & W
Southeastern Community College *Iowa* M
Southeastern Illinois College *Illinois* M & W
Southeastern Louisiana University *Louisiana* M & W
Southeastern Oklahoma State University *Oklahoma* M & W
Southeastern University *Florida* M & W
Southern Alberta Institute of Technology *Alberta* (Canada) M & W
Southern Arkansas University - Magnolia *Arkansas* M & W
The Southern Baptist Theological Seminary *Kentucky* M
Southern Connecticut State University *Connecticut* M & W
Southern Illinois University Carbondale *Illinois* M & W
Southern Illinois University Edwardsville *Illinois* M & W
Southern Maine Community College *Maine* M & W
Southern Methodist University *Texas* M & W
Southern Nazarene University *Oklahoma* M & W
Southern New Hampshire University *New Hampshire* M & W
Southern Oregon University *Oregon* M & W
Southern State Community College *Ohio* M & W
Southern University and Agricultural and Mechanical College *Louisiana* M & W
Southern University at New Orleans *Louisiana* M & W
Southern University at Shreveport *Louisiana* M & W
Southern Utah University *Utah* M & W
Southern Vermont College *Vermont* M & W
Southern Virginia University *Virginia* M & W
Southern Wesleyan University *South Carolina* M & W
Southwest Baptist University *Missouri* M & W
Southwest Minnesota State University *Minnesota* M & W
Southwest Mississippi Community College *Mississippi* M & W

Southwest Texas Junior College *Texas* M & W
Southwestern Adventist University *Texas* M & W
Southwestern Assemblies of God University *Texas* M & W
Southwestern Christian College *Texas* M & W
Southwestern Christian University *Oklahoma* M & W
Southwestern College *California* M & W
Southwestern College *Kansas* M & W
Southwestern Community College *Iowa* M & W
Southwestern Illinois College *Illinois* M & W
Southwestern Oklahoma State University *Oklahoma* M & W
Southwestern Oregon Community College *Oregon* M & W
Southwestern University *Texas* M & W
Spalding University *Kentucky* M & W
Spartanburg Methodist College *South Carolina* M & W
Spokane Community College *Washington* M & W
Spokane Falls Community College *Washington* M & W
Spring Arbor University *Michigan* M & W
Spring Hill College *Alabama* M & W
Springfield College *Massachusetts* M & W
Springfield Technical Community College *Massachusetts* M & W
Stanford University *California* M & W
State College of Florida Manatee-Sarasota *Florida* M
State Fair Community College *Missouri* M & W
State University of New York College of Agriculture and Technology at Cobleskill *New York* M & W
State University of New York College at Cortland *New York* M & W
State University of New York College of Environmental Science and Forestry *New York* M
State University of New York College at Geneseo *New York* M & W
State University of New York College at Old Westbury *New York* M & W
State University of New York College at Oneonta *New York* M & W
State University of New York College at Potsdam *New York* M & W
State University of New York College of Technology at Alfred *New York* M & W
State University of New York College of Technology at Canton *New York* M & W
State University of New York College of Technology at Delhi *New York* M & W
State University of New York at Fredonia *New York* M & W
State University of New York Maritime College *New York* M
State University of New York at New Paltz *New York* M & W
State University of New York at Oswego *New York* M & W
State University of New York at Plattsburgh *New York* M & W
State University of New York Polytechnic Institute *New York* M & W
Stephen F. Austin State University *Texas* M & W
Stephens College *Missouri* W
Sterling College *Kansas* M & W
Stetson University *Florida* M & W
Stevens Institute of Technology *New Jersey* M & W
Stevenson University *Maryland* M & W
Stillman College *Alabama* M & W
Stockton University *New Jersey* M & W
Stonehill College *Massachusetts* M & W
Stony Brook University, State University of New York *New York* M & W
Suffolk County Community College *New York* M & W
Suffolk University *Massachusetts* M & W
Sul Ross State University *Texas* M & W
Sullivan County Community College *New York* M & W
Summit University *Pennsylvania* M & W
Surry Community College *North Carolina* M
Susquehanna University *Pennsylvania* M & W

M = Men; W = Women

Sussex County Community College *New Jersey* M & W
Swarthmore College *Pennsylvania* M & W
Syracuse University *New York* M & W
Tabor College *Kansas* M & W
Tacoma Community College *Washington* M & W
Taft College *California* W
Talladega College *Alabama* M
Tallahassee Community College *Florida* M & W
Tarleton State University *Texas* M & W
Taylor University *Indiana* M & W
Temple College *Texas* M & W
Temple University *Pennsylvania* M & W
Tennessee State University *Tennessee* M & W
Tennessee Technological University *Tennessee* M & W
Tennessee Wesleyan College *Tennessee* M & W
Texas A&M International University *Texas* M & W
Texas A&M University *Texas* M & W
Texas A&M University - Commerce *Texas* M & W
Texas A&M University - Corpus Christi *Texas* M & W
Texas A&M University - Kingsville *Texas* M & W
Texas Christian University *Texas* M & W
Texas College *Texas* M & W
Texas Lutheran University *Texas* M & W
Texas Southern University *Texas* M & W
Texas State University *Texas* M & W
Texas Tech University *Texas* M & W
Texas Wesleyan University *Texas* M & W
Texas Woman's University *Texas* W
Thaddeus Stevens College of Technology *Pennsylvania* M
Thiel College *Pennsylvania* M & W
Thomas College *Maine* M & W
Thomas More College *Kentucky* M & W
Thompson Rivers University *British Columbia (Canada)* M & W
Three Rivers Community College *Missouri* M & W
Tiffin University *Ohio* M & W
Toccoa Falls College *Georgia* M & W
Tohono O'odham Community College *Arizona* M
Tompkins Cortland Community College *New York* M & W
Tougaloo College *Mississippi* M & W
Towson University *Maryland* M & W
Transylvania University *Kentucky* M & W
Treasure Valley Community College *Oregon* M & W
Trevecca Nazarene University *Tennessee* M & W
Trine University *Indiana* M & W
Trinidad State Junior College *Colorado* M
Trinity Baptist College *Florida* M & W
Trinity Bible College *North Dakota* M & W
Trinity Christian College *Illinois* M & W
Trinity College *Connecticut* M & W
Trinity College of Florida *Florida* M & W
Trinity International University *Illinois* M & W
Trinity University *Texas* M & W
Trinity Valley Community College *Texas* M & W
Trinity Washington University *District of Columbia* W
Trinity Western University *British Columbia (Canada)* M & W
Triton College *Illinois* M & W
Troy University *Alabama* M & W
Truett-McConnell College *Georgia* M & W
Truman State University *Missouri* M & W
Tufts University *Massachusetts* M & W
Tulane University *Louisiana* M & W
Tusculum College *Tennessee* M & W
Tuskegee University *Alabama* M & W
Tyler Junior College *Texas* M & W
Tyndale University College & Seminary *Ontario (Canada)* M & W
Ulster County Community College *New York* M & W
Umpqua Community College *Oregon* M & W
Union College *Kentucky* M & W
Union College *Nebraska* M & W
Union College *New York* M & W
Union County College *New Jersey* M & W
Union University *Tennessee* M & W
United States Air Force Academy *Colorado* M & W

United States Coast Guard Academy *Connecticut* M & W
United States Merchant Marine Academy *New York* M & W
United States Military Academy *New York* M & W
United States Naval Academy *Maryland* M & W
United Tribes Technical College *North Dakota* M
Unity College *Maine* M & W
Universidad del Este *Puerto Rico* M & W
Universidad Metropolitana *Puerto Rico* M & W
Universidad del Turabo *Puerto Rico* M & W
Université Laval *Quebec (Canada)* M & W
The University of Akron *Ohio* M & W
The University of Akron Wayne College *Ohio* M & W
The University of Alabama *Alabama* M & W
The University of Alabama at Birmingham *Alabama* M & W
The University of Alabama in Huntsville *Alabama* M & W
University of Alaska Anchorage *Alaska* M & W
University of Alaska Fairbanks *Alaska* M & W
University at Albany, State University of New York *New York* M & W
University of Alberta *Alberta (Canada)* M & W
The University of Arizona *Arizona* M & W
University of Arkansas *Arkansas* M & W
University of Arkansas - Fort Smith *Arkansas* M & W
University of Arkansas at Little Rock *Arkansas* M & W
University of Arkansas at Monticello *Arkansas* M & W
University of Arkansas at Pine Bluff *Arkansas* M & W
University of Bridgeport *Connecticut* M & W
The University of British Columbia *British Columbia (Canada)* M & W
The University of British Columbia - Okanagan Campus *British Columbia (Canada)* M & W
University at Buffalo, the State University of New York *New York* M & W
University of Calgary *Alberta (Canada)* M & W
University of California, Berkeley *California* M & W
University of California, Davis *California* M & W
University of California, Irvine *California* M & W
University of California, Los Angeles *California* M & W
University of California, Merced *California* M & W
University of California, Riverside *California* M & W
University of California, San Diego *California* M & W
University of California, Santa Barbara *California* M & W
University of California, Santa Cruz *California* M & W
University of Central Arkansas *Arkansas* M & W
University of Central Florida *Florida* M & W
University of Central Missouri *Missouri* M & W
University of Central Oklahoma *Oklahoma* M & W
University of Charleston *West Virginia* M & W
University of Chicago *Illinois* M & W
University of Cincinnati *Ohio* M & W
University of Cincinnati Clermont College *Ohio* M & W
University of Colorado Boulder *Colorado* M & W
University of Colorado Colorado Springs *Colorado* M & W
University of Colorado Denver *Colorado* M & W
University of Connecticut *Connecticut* M & W
University of the Cumberlands *Kentucky* M & W
University of Dallas *Texas* M & W
University of Dayton *Ohio* M & W
University of Delaware *Delaware* M & W
University of Denver *Colorado* M & W
University of Detroit Mercy *Michigan* M & W
University of the District of Columbia *District of Columbia* M & W
University of Dubuque *Iowa* M & W
University of Evansville *Indiana* M & W
The University of Findlay *Ohio* M & W
University of Florida *Florida* M & W
University of the Fraser Valley *British Columbia (Canada)* M & W

University of Georgia *Georgia* M & W
University of Great Falls *Montana* M & W
University of Guelph *Ontario (Canada)* M & W
University of Hartford *Connecticut* M & W
University of Hawaii at Hilo *Hawaii* M & W
University of Hawaii at Manoa *Hawaii* M & W
University of Houston *Texas* M & W
University of Idaho *Idaho* M & W
University of Illinois at Chicago *Illinois* M & W
University of Illinois at Springfield *Illinois* M & W
University of Illinois at Urbana - Champaign *Illinois* M & W
University of the Incarnate Word *Texas* M & W
University of Indianapolis *Indiana* M & W
The University of Iowa *Iowa* M & W
University of Jamestown *North Dakota* M & W
The University of Kansas *Kansas* M & W
University of Kentucky *Kentucky* M & W
University of King's College *Nova Scotia (Canada)* M & W
University of La Verne *California* M & W
University of Lethbridge *Alberta (Canada)* M & W
University of Louisiana at Lafayette *Louisiana* M & W
University of Louisiana at Monroe *Louisiana* M & W
University of Louisville *Kentucky* M & W
University of Maine *Maine* M & W
University of Maine at Augusta *Maine* M & W
University of Maine at Farmington *Maine* M & W
University of Maine at Fort Kent *Maine* M & W
University of Maine at Machias *Maine* M & W
University of Maine at Presque Isle *Maine* M & W
University of Manitoba *Manitoba (Canada)* M & W
University of Mary *North Dakota* M & W
University of Mary Hardin-Baylor *Texas* M & W
University of Mary Washington *Virginia* M & W
University of Maryland, Baltimore County *Maryland* M & W
University of Maryland, College Park *Maryland* M & W
University of Maryland Eastern Shore *Maryland* M & W
University of Massachusetts Amherst *Massachusetts* M & W
University of Massachusetts Boston *Massachusetts* M & W
University of Massachusetts Dartmouth *Massachusetts* M & W
University of Massachusetts Lowell *Massachusetts* M & W
University of Memphis *Tennessee* M & W
University of Miami *Florida* M & W
University of Michigan *Michigan* M & W
University of Michigan - Dearborn *Michigan* M & W
University of Minnesota, Crookston *Minnesota* M & W
University of Minnesota, Duluth *Minnesota* M & W
University of Minnesota, Morris *Minnesota* M & W
University of Minnesota, Twin Cities Campus *Minnesota* M & W
University of Mississippi *Mississippi* M & W
University of Missouri *Missouri* M & W
University of Missouri - Kansas City *Missouri* M & W
University of Missouri - St. Louis *Missouri* M & W
University of Mobile *Alabama* M & W
University of Montana *Montana* M & W
The University of Montana Western *Montana* M & W
University of Montevallo *Alabama* M & W
University of Mount Olive *North Carolina* M & W
University of Mount Union *Ohio* M & W
University of Nebraska at Kearney *Nebraska* M & W
University of Nebraska - Lincoln *Nebraska* M & W
University of Nebraska at Omaha *Nebraska* M & W
University of Nevada, Las Vegas *Nevada* M & W
University of Nevada, Reno *Nevada* M & W
University of New Brunswick Fredericton *New Brunswick (Canada)* M & W
University of New Brunswick Saint John *New Brunswick (Canada)* M & W
University of New England *Maine* M & W

M = Men; W = Women

University of New Hampshire *New Hampshire* M & W
University of New Haven *Connecticut* M & W
University of New Mexico *New Mexico* M & W
University of New Orleans *Louisiana* M & W
University of North Alabama *Alabama* M & W
University of North Carolina at Asheville *North Carolina* M & W
The University of North Carolina at Chapel Hill *North Carolina* M & W
The University of North Carolina at Charlotte *North Carolina* M & W
The University of North Carolina at Greensboro *North Carolina* M & W
The University of North Carolina at Pembroke *North Carolina* M & W
The University of North Carolina Wilmington *North Carolina* M & W
University of North Dakota *North Dakota* M & W
University of North Florida *Florida* M & W
University of North Georgia *Georgia* M & W
University of North Texas *Texas* M & W
University of Northern British Columbia *British Columbia (Canada)* M & W
University of Northern Colorado *Colorado* M & W
University of Northern Iowa *Iowa* M & W
University of Northwestern - St. Paul *Minnesota* M & W
University of Notre Dame *Indiana* M & W
University of Oklahoma *Oklahoma* M & W
University of Oregon *Oregon* M & W
University of Ottawa *Ontario (Canada)* M & W
University of the Pacific *California* M & W
University of Pennsylvania *Pennsylvania* M & W
University of Pikeville *Kentucky* M & W
University of Pittsburgh *Pennsylvania* M & W
University of Pittsburgh at Bradford *Pennsylvania* M & W
University of Pittsburgh at Greensburg *Pennsylvania* M & W
University of Pittsburgh at Johnstown *Pennsylvania* M & W
University of Pittsburgh at Titusville *Pennsylvania* M & W
University of Portland *Oregon* M & W
University of Prince Edward Island *Prince Edward Island (Canada)* M & W
University of Puerto Rico in Aguadilla *Puerto Rico* M
University of Puerto Rico in Arecibo *Puerto Rico* M & W
University of Puerto Rico in Bayamón *Puerto Rico* M & W
University of Puerto Rico in Carolina *Puerto Rico* M & W
University of Puerto Rico in Cayey *Puerto Rico* M & W
University of Puerto Rico in Humacao *Puerto Rico* M & W
University of Puerto Rico, Mayagüez Campus *Puerto Rico* M & W
University of Puerto Rico in Ponce *Puerto Rico* M & W
University of Puerto Rico, Río Piedras Campus *Puerto Rico* M & W
University of Puerto Rico in Utuado *Puerto Rico* M & W
University of Puget Sound *Washington* M & W
University of Redlands *California* M & W
University of Regina *Saskatchewan (Canada)* M & W
University of Rhode Island *Rhode Island* M
University of Richmond *Virginia* M & W
University of Rio Grande *Ohio* M & W
University of Rochester *New York* M & W
University of the Sacred Heart *Puerto Rico* M & W
University of St. Francis *Illinois* M & W
University of Saint Francis *Indiana* M & W
University of Saint Joseph *Connecticut* W
University of Saint Mary *Kansas* M & W
University of St. Thomas *Minnesota* M & W
University of St. Thomas *Texas* M & W
University of San Diego *California* M & W
University of San Francisco *California* M & W

University of Saskatchewan *Saskatchewan (Canada)* M & W
University of Science and Arts of Oklahoma *Oklahoma* M & W
University of the Sciences *Pennsylvania* M & W
The University of Scranton *Pennsylvania* M & W
University of Sioux Falls *South Dakota* M & W
University of South Alabama *Alabama* M & W
University of South Carolina *South Carolina* M & W
University of South Carolina Aiken *South Carolina* M & W
University of South Carolina Salkehatchie *South Carolina* M
University of South Carolina Upstate *South Carolina* M & W
The University of South Dakota *South Dakota* M & W
University of South Florida *Florida* W
University of Southern California *California* M & W
University of Southern Indiana *Indiana* M & W
University of Southern Maine *Maine* M & W
University of Southern Mississippi *Mississippi* M & W
University of the Southwest *New Mexico* M & W
The University of Tampa *Florida* M & W
The University of Tennessee *Tennessee* M & W
The University of Tennessee at Chattanooga *Tennessee* M & W
The University of Tennessee at Martin *Tennessee* M & W
The University of Texas at Arlington *Texas* M & W
The University of Texas at Austin *Texas* M & W
The University of Texas at Dallas *Texas* M & W
The University of Texas at El Paso *Texas* M & W
The University of Texas of the Permian Basin *Texas* M & W
The University of Texas Rio Grande Valley *Texas* M & W
The University of Texas at San Antonio *Texas* M & W
The University of Texas at Tyler *Texas* M & W
The University of Toledo *Ohio* M & W
University of Toronto *Ontario (Canada)* M & W
The University of Tulsa *Oklahoma* M & W
University of Utah *Utah* M & W
University of Valley Forge *Pennsylvania* M & W
University of Vermont *Vermont* M & W
University of Victoria *British Columbia (Canada)* M & W
University of the Virgin Islands *United States Virgin Islands* M & W
University of Virginia *Virginia* M & W
The University of Virginia's College at Wise *Virginia* M & W
University of Washington *Washington* M & W
University of Waterloo *Ontario (Canada)* M & W
The University of West Alabama *Alabama* M & W
University of West Florida *Florida* M & W
University of West Georgia *Georgia* M & W
The University of Western Ontario *Ontario (Canada)* M & W
University of Windsor *Ontario (Canada)* M & W
The University of Winnipeg *Manitoba (Canada)* M & W
University of Wisconsin - Baraboo/Sauk County *Wisconsin* M
University of Wisconsin - Eau Claire *Wisconsin* M & W
University of Wisconsin - Fond du Lac *Wisconsin* M & W
University of Wisconsin - Fox Valley *Wisconsin* M & W
University of Wisconsin - Green Bay *Wisconsin* M & W
University of Wisconsin - La Crosse *Wisconsin* M & W
University of Wisconsin - Madison *Wisconsin* M & W
University of Wisconsin - Manitowoc *Wisconsin* M & W
University of Wisconsin - Marinette *Wisconsin* M & W
University of Wisconsin - Marshfield/Wood County *Wisconsin* M & W

University of Wisconsin - Milwaukee *Wisconsin* M & W
University of Wisconsin - Oshkosh *Wisconsin* M & W
University of Wisconsin - Parkside *Wisconsin* M & W
University of Wisconsin - Platteville *Wisconsin* M & W
University of Wisconsin - Richland *Wisconsin* M & W
University of Wisconsin - River Falls *Wisconsin* M & W
University of Wisconsin - Sheboygan *Wisconsin* M
University of Wisconsin - Stevens Point *Wisconsin* M & W
University of Wisconsin - Stout *Wisconsin* M & W
University of Wisconsin - Superior *Wisconsin* M & W
University of Wisconsin - Washington County *Wisconsin* M & W
University of Wisconsin - Waukesha *Wisconsin* M & W
University of Wisconsin - Whitewater *Wisconsin* M & W
University of Wyoming *Wyoming* M & W
Upper Iowa University *Iowa* M & W
Urbana University *Ohio* M & W
Ursinus College *Pennsylvania* M & W
Ursuline College *Ohio* W
Utah State University *Utah* M & W
Utah Valley University *Utah* M & W
Utica College *New York* M & W
Valdosta State University *Georgia* M & W
Valley City State University *North Dakota* M & W
Valley Forge Military College *Pennsylvania* M
Valparaiso University *Indiana* M & W
Vanderbilt University *Tennessee* M & W
Vanguard University of Southern California *California* M & W
Vassar College *New York* M & W
Vaughn College of Aeronautics and Technology *New York* M & W
Ventura College *California* M & W
Vermilion Community College *Minnesota* M & W
Vermont Technical College *Vermont* M & W
Victor Valley College *California* M & W
Victoria College *Texas* M & W
Villa Maria College *New York* M & W
Villanova University *Pennsylvania* M & W
Vincennes University *Indiana* M & W
Virginia Commonwealth University *Virginia* M & W
Virginia Military Institute *Virginia* M
Virginia Polytechnic Institute and State University *Virginia* M
Virginia State University *Virginia* M & W
Virginia Union University *Virginia* M & W
Virginia University of Lynchburg *Virginia* M & W
Virginia Wesleyan College *Virginia* M & W
Viterbo University *Wisconsin* M & W
Volunteer State Community College *Tennessee* M & W
Voorhees College *South Carolina* M & W
Wabash College *Indiana* M
Wagner College *New York* M & W
Wake Forest University *North Carolina* M & W
Waldorf College *Iowa* M & W
Walla Walla Community College *Washington* M & W
Walla Walla University *Washington* M & W
Wallace State Community College *Alabama* M & W
Walsh University *Ohio* M & W
Walters State Community College *Tennessee* M & W
Warner Pacific College *Oregon* M & W
Warner University *Florida* M & W
Warren Wilson College *North Carolina* M & W
Wartburg College *Iowa* M & W
Washburn University *Kansas* M & W
Washington Adventist University *Maryland* M & W
Washington College *Maryland* M & W
Washington & Jefferson College *Pennsylvania* M & W
Washington and Lee University *Virginia* M & W
Washington State University *Washington* M & W

M = Men; W = Women

Washington University in St. Louis *Missouri* M & W
Waubonsee Community College *Illinois* M & W
Wayland Baptist University *Texas* M & W
Wayne County Community College District *Michigan* M & W
Wayne State College *Nebraska* M & W
Wayne State University *Michigan* M & W
Waynesburg University *Pennsylvania* M & W
Weatherford College *Texas* M & W
Webb Institute *New York* M & W
Webber International University *Florida* M & W
Weber State University *Utah* M & W
Webster University *Missouri* M & W
Welch College *Tennessee* M & W
Wellesley College *Massachusetts* W
Wells College *New York* M & W
Wenatchee Valley College *Washington* M & W
Wentworth Institute of Technology *Massachusetts* M & W
Wentworth Military Academy and College *Missouri* M
Wesley College *Delaware* M & W
Wesleyan College *Georgia* W
Wesleyan University *Connecticut* M & W
West Chester University of Pennsylvania *Pennsylvania* M & W
West Hills Community College *California* M
West Liberty University *West Virginia* M & W
West Los Angeles College *California* M
West Texas A&M University *Texas* M & W
West Valley College *California* M & W
West Virginia State University *West Virginia* M & W
West Virginia University *West Virginia* M & W
West Virginia University Institute of Technology *West Virginia* M & W
West Virginia Wesleyan College *West Virginia* M & W
Westchester Community College *New York* M & W
Western Carolina University *North Carolina* M & W
Western Connecticut State University *Connecticut* M & W
Western Illinois University *Illinois* M & W
Western Kentucky University *Kentucky* M & W
Western Michigan University *Michigan* M & W
Western Nebraska Community College *Nebraska* M & W
Western New England University *Massachusetts* M & W
Western New Mexico University *New Mexico* M & W
Western Oklahoma State College *Oklahoma* M & W
Western Oregon University *Oregon* M & W
Western State Colorado University *Colorado* M & W
Western Technical College *Wisconsin* M & W
Western Texas College *Texas* M & W
Western Washington University *Washington* M & W
Western Wyoming Community College *Wyoming* M & W
Westfield State University *Massachusetts* M & W
Westminster College *Missouri* M & W
Westminster College *Pennsylvania* M & W
Westminster College *Utah* M & W
Westmont College *California* M & W
Westmoreland County Community College *Pennsylvania* M & W
Whatcom Community College *Washington* M & W
Wheaton College *Illinois* M & W
Wheaton College *Massachusetts* M & W
Wheeling Jesuit University *West Virginia* M & W
Wheelock College *Massachusetts* M & W
Whitman College *Washington* M & W
Whittier College *California* M & W
Whitworth University *Washington* M & W
Wichita State University *Kansas* M & W
Widener University *Pennsylvania* M & W
Wilberforce University *Ohio* M & W
Wiley College *Texas* M & W
Wilfrid Laurier University *Ontario (Canada)* M & W
Wilkes Community College *North Carolina* M & W
Wilkes University *Pennsylvania* M & W
Willamette University *Oregon* M & W
William Carey University *Mississippi* M & W

William Jessup University *California* M & W
William Jewell College *Missouri* M & W
William Paterson University of New Jersey *New Jersey* M & W
William Peace University *North Carolina* M & W
William Penn University *Iowa* M & W
William Woods University *Missouri* M & W
Williams Baptist College *Arkansas* M & W
Williams College *Massachusetts* M & W
Williamson College of the Trades *Pennsylvania* M
Williston State College *North Dakota* M & W
Wilmington College *Ohio* M & W
Wilmington University *Delaware* M & W
Wilson College *Pennsylvania* M & W
Wingate University *North Carolina* M & W
Winona State University *Minnesota* M & W
Winston-Salem State University *North Carolina* M & W
Winthrop University *South Carolina* M & W
Wisconsin Lutheran College *Wisconsin* M & W
Wittenberg University *Ohio* M & W
Wofford College *South Carolina* M & W
Worcester Polytechnic Institute *Massachusetts* M & W
Worcester State University *Massachusetts* M & W
Wright State University *Ohio* M & W
Wright State University - Lake Campus *Ohio* M & W
Xavier University *Ohio* M & W
Xavier University of Louisiana *Louisiana* M & W
Yakima Valley Community College *Washington* M & W
Yale University *Connecticut* M & W
Yeshiva University *New York* M & W
York College *Nebraska* M & W
York College of the City University of New York *New York* M & W
York College of Pennsylvania *Pennsylvania* M & W
York University *Ontario (Canada)* M & W
Young Harris College *Georgia* M & W
Youngstown State University *Ohio* M & W
Yuba College *California* M & W
Zane State College *Ohio* M & W

Bowling

Adelphi University *New York* W
Adirondack Community College *New York* M & W
Adrian College *Michigan* W
Alabama State University *Alabama* W
Alma College *Michigan* W
Ancilla College *Indiana* M & W
Aquinas College *Michigan* M & W
Arkansas State University *Arkansas* W
Aurora University *Illinois* W
Baker University *Kansas* W
Ball State University *Indiana* M & W
Bayamón Central University *Puerto Rico* M & W
Bethel University *Tennessee* M & W
Bethune-Cookman University *Florida* W
Bowie State University *Maryland* W
Bryant University *Rhode Island* M & W
Buffalo State College, State University of New York *New York* M & W
Caldwell University *New Jersey* W
California State University, Fullerton *California* M & W
California State University, Long Beach *California* M & W
California State University, Sacramento *California* M & W
Calumet College of Saint Joseph *Indiana* M & W
Campbellsville University *Kentucky* M & W
Carthage College *Wisconsin* M & W
Cayuga County Community College *New York* M & W
Central Washington University *Washington* M & W
Chestnut Hill College *Pennsylvania* W
Cheyney University of Pennsylvania *Pennsylvania* W
Chowan University *North Carolina* W
Clarke University *Iowa* M & W
Clemson University *South Carolina* M & W
Coastal Carolina University *South Carolina* M & W
College of St. Joseph *Vermont* M & W

Colorado School of Mines *Colorado* M & W
Colorado State University - Pueblo *Colorado* M & W
Community College of Allegheny County *Pennsylvania* M & W
Concordia University Ann Arbor *Michigan* M & W
Coppin State University *Maryland* W
Cornerstone University *Michigan* M & W
Corning Community College *New York* M & W
Culver-Stockton College *Missouri* M & W
Cumberland University *Tennessee* M & W
Davenport University *Michigan* M & W
Delaware State University *Delaware* W
Duquesne University *Pennsylvania* M & W
Elizabeth City State University *North Carolina* W
Elmhurst College *Illinois* W
Emmanuel College *Georgia* M & W
Erie Community College *New York* M & W
Erie Community College, North Campus *New York* M & W
Erie Community College, South Campus *New York* M & W
Fairleigh Dickinson University, Metropolitan Campus *New Jersey* W
Fayetteville State University *North Carolina* W
Felician University *New Jersey* W
Florida Agricultural and Mechanical University *Florida* W
Florida State University *Florida* M & W
Fontbonne University *Missouri* W
Graceland University *Iowa* M & W
Grambling State University *Louisiana* W
Grand View University *Iowa* M & W
Hampton University *Virginia* W
Hastings College *Nebraska* M & W
Highland Community College *Illinois* M & W
Howard University *District of Columbia* W
Hudson Valley Community College *New York* M & W
Huntington University *Indiana* M & W
Illinois Institute of Technology *Illinois* M & W
Indiana Tech *Indiana* M & W
Inter American University of Puerto Rico, Fajardo Campus *Puerto Rico* M
Iowa Central Community College *Iowa* M & W
Jackson State University *Mississippi* W
Johnson C. Smith University *North Carolina* W
Johnson College *Pennsylvania* M & W
Judson University *Illinois* M & W
Kansas Wesleyan University *Kansas* M & W
Kentucky Wesleyan College *Kentucky* W
Kirtland Community College *Michigan* M & W
Kutztown University of Pennsylvania *Pennsylvania* W
Lawrence Technological University *Michigan* M & W
Lincoln University *Missouri* W
Lindenwood University *Missouri* M & W
Lindsey Wilson College *Kentucky* M & W
Livingstone College *North Carolina* W
Long Island University - LIU Brooklyn *New York* M & W
Long Island University - LIU Post *New York* W
Madison Area Technical College *Wisconsin* M & W
Madonna University *Michigan* M & W
Marian University *Indiana* M & W
Marist College *New York* M & W
Martin Methodist College *Tennessee* M & W
Maryville University of Saint Louis *Missouri* W
McKendree University *Illinois* M & W
Medaille College *New York* W
Merced College *California* M & W
Mid-State Technical College *Wisconsin* M & W
Minnesota State University Mankato *Minnesota* W
Mississippi Valley State University *Mississippi* W
Missouri Baptist University *Missouri* W
Missouri State University *Missouri* M & W
Mohawk Valley Community College *New York* M & W
Molloy College *New York* W
Monmouth University *New Jersey* W
Moravian College *Pennsylvania* M
Morehead State University *Kentucky* M & W
Morgan State University *Maryland* W
Morningside College *Iowa* M & W
Mount Mercy University *Iowa* M & W

M = Men; W = Women

Nassau Community College New York M & W
New Jersey City University New Jersey W
New Jersey Institute of Technology New Jersey M
Newman University Kansas M & W
Norfolk State University Virginia W
North Carolina Agricultural and Technical State University North Carolina W
North Carolina Central University North Carolina W
North Carolina State University North Carolina M & W
North Dakota State University North Dakota M & W
Oberlin College Ohio M & W
Orange Coast College California M & W
Penn State Lehigh Valley Pennsylvania M & W
Pennsylvania College of Technology Pennsylvania M & W
Pennsylvania Highlands Community College Pennsylvania M & W
Prairie View A&M University Texas W
Prince George's Community College Maryland M & W
Robert Morris University Illinois Illinois M & W
Rochester Institute of Technology New York M & W
Rockland Community College New York M & W
Sacred Heart University Connecticut W
Saginaw Valley State University Michigan M & W
St. Ambrose University Iowa M & W
Saint Augustine's University North Carolina W
St. Cloud State University Minnesota M & W
Saint Francis University Pennsylvania M & W
Saint Louis University Missouri M & W
Saint Peter's University New Jersey M & W
Sam Houston State University Texas W
Schenectady County Community College New York M & W
Schoolcraft College Michigan M & W
Shaw University North Carolina W
Siena Heights University Michigan M & W
South Dakota State University South Dakota M & W
Southern University and Agricultural and Mechanical College Louisiana W
Southwestern Christian University Oklahoma M & W
Spalding University Kentucky W
Stephen F. Austin State University Texas W
Stonehill College Massachusetts M & W
Suffolk County Community College New York M & W
Syracuse University New York M & W
Tabor College Kansas W
Tennessee Wesleyan College Tennessee M & W
Texas Southern University Texas W
Thiel College Pennsylvania W
Thomas More College Kentucky M & W
Truman State University Missouri M & W
Union College Kentucky M & W
University of California, Santa Barbara California M & W
University of Central Missouri Missouri M & W
University of the Cumberlands Kentucky M & W
University of Delaware Delaware M & W
University of Florida Florida M & W
University of Maine at Augusta Maine M & W
University of Maryland, Baltimore County Maryland M & W
University of Michigan - Dearborn Michigan M & W
University of Nebraska - Lincoln Nebraska W
University of North Texas Texas M & W
University of Pikeville Kentucky M & W
University of Rochester New York M & W
University of St. Francis Illinois M & W
University of South Florida Florida M & W
University of Wisconsin - Milwaukee Wisconsin M & W
University of Wisconsin - Platteville Wisconsin M & W
University of Wisconsin - Whitewater Wisconsin M & W
Ursuline College Ohio W
Valparaiso University Indiana W
Vanderbilt University Tennessee W
Villa Maria College New York W
Vincennes University Indiana M

Virginia State University Virginia W
Virginia Union University Virginia M & W
Viterbo University Wisconsin W
Waldorf College Iowa M & W
Washington State University Washington M & W
Wayne County Community College District Michigan M & W
Webber International University Florida M & W
Weber State University Utah M & W
West Chester University of Pennsylvania Pennsylvania M & W
West Texas A&M University Texas M & W
Westchester Community College New York M & W
Westmoreland County Community College Pennsylvania M & W
Wichita State University Kansas M & W
William Penn University Iowa M & W
Winston-Salem State University North Carolina M & W
Youngstown State University Ohio W

Cheerleading

Alabama State University Alabama M & W
Albany State University Georgia M & W
Albright College Pennsylvania M & W
Alderson Broaddus University West Virginia M & W
Alice Lloyd College Kentucky W
Allegheny College Pennsylvania M & W
Allen Community College Kansas M & W
Alma College Michigan M & W
Alvernia University Pennsylvania M & W
Amherst College Massachusetts W
Ancilla College Indiana M & W
Anderson University South Carolina W
Aquinas College Michigan W
Arkansas Baptist College Arkansas W
Arkansas Tech University Arkansas M & W
Assumption College Massachusetts W
Auburn University at Montgomery Alabama M & W
Augustana College Illinois M & W
Augustana University South Dakota M & W
Austin College Texas M & W
Austin Peay State University Tennessee M & W
Ave Maria University Florida W
Averett University Virginia M & W
Avila University Missouri W
Babson College Massachusetts W
Baker University Kansas M & W
Ball State University Indiana M & W
Barclay College Kansas M & W
Barton County Community College Kansas M & W
Baruch College of the City University of New York New York M & W
Baylor University Texas M & W
Becker College Massachusetts M & W
Bellarmine University Kentucky M & W
Belmont Abbey College North Carolina W
Benedict College South Carolina W
Benedictine College Kansas W
Bethany College Kansas W
Bethel College Indiana M & W
Bethel University Tennessee M & W
Bethune-Cookman University Florida W
Birmingham-Southern College Alabama M & W
Bishop State Community College Alabama W
Blinn College Texas M & W
Bluefield State College West Virginia W
Boston College Massachusetts M & W
Boston University Massachusetts M & W
Bradley University Illinois M & W
Brenau University Georgia W
Brevard College North Carolina W
Brewton-Parker College Georgia M & W
Briar Cliff University Iowa W
Bridgewater College Virginia M & W
Brigham Young University Utah M & W
Brock University Ontario (Canada) M & W
Bryant University Rhode Island W
Bucknell University Pennsylvania M & W
Buffalo State College, State University of New York New York W
California Baptist University California W
California Lutheran University California M & W

California State University, Sacramento California M & W
Campbell University North Carolina W
Campbellsville University Kentucky M & W
Cape Fear Community College North Carolina M & W
Caribbean University Puerto Rico M & W
Carroll College Montana M & W
Castleton University Vermont M & W
Catawba College North Carolina M & W
Catawba Valley Community College North Carolina M & W
Cazenovia College New York M & W
Cecil College Maryland W
Cedarville University Ohio M & W
Centenary College New Jersey W
Central Christian College of Kansas Kansas M & W
Central State University Ohio M & W
Central Washington University Washington M & W
Centre College Kentucky W
Chapman University California W
Charleston Southern University South Carolina M & W
Chowan University North Carolina M & W
Cisco College Texas M & W
Claflin University South Carolina M & W
Claremont McKenna College California M & W
Clarendon College Texas M & W
Clarke University Iowa W
Clayton State University Georgia W
Clemson University South Carolina M & W
Cleveland State University Ohio M & W
Clinton Community College Iowa M & W
Coahoma Community College Mississippi W
Coastal Carolina University South Carolina M & W
Colby Community College Kansas M & W
Colgate University New York M & W
College of Charleston South Carolina M & W
College of Mount Saint Vincent New York W
College of the Ozarks Missouri M & W
College of Southern Idaho Idaho M & W
College of Staten Island of the City University of New York New York M & W
The College of Wooster Ohio W
Colorado State University - Pueblo Colorado M & W
Columbus State University Georgia M & W
Community College of Philadelphia Pennsylvania M & W
Concord University West Virginia M & W
Concordia College Minnesota M & W
Concordia College Alabama Alabama M
Concordia University Ann Arbor Michigan W
Concordia University Chicago Illinois M & W
Concordia University, Nebraska Nebraska W
Cornell College Iowa M & W
Cornerstone University Michigan W
Culver-Stockton College Missouri M & W
Cumberland University Tennessee M & W
Dakota State University South Dakota M & W
Dakota Wesleyan University South Dakota M & W
Dallas Baptist University Texas W
Danville Area Community College Illinois W
Dartmouth College New Hampshire M & W
Davenport University Michigan W
Delaware State University Delaware W
Delaware Valley University Pennsylvania W
Delta State University Mississippi M & W
Denmark Technical College South Carolina W
DePauw University Indiana M & W
Dickinson College Pennsylvania M & W
Dickinson State University North Dakota M & W
Dodge City Community College Kansas M & W
Drake University Iowa M & W
Drury University Missouri M & W
Dyersburg State Community College Tennessee M & W
D'Youville College New York W
Earlham College Indiana W
East Los Angeles College California W
East Mississippi Community College Mississippi W
East Stroudsburg University of Pennsylvania Pennsylvania M & W

M = Men; W = Women

Eastern Connecticut State University *Connecticut* M & W
Eastern Kentucky University *Kentucky* M & W
Eastern Washington University *Washington* W
Elizabeth City State University *North Carolina* W
Elmira College *New York* W
Elon University *North Carolina* M & W
Embry-Riddle Aeronautical University - Daytona *Florida* M & W
Emory & Henry College *Virginia* M & W
Emporia State University *Kansas* M & W
Endicott College *Massachusetts* W
Enterprise State Community College *Alabama* M & W
Erie Community College *New York* W
Erie Community College, North Campus *New York* W
Erie Community College, South Campus *New York* W
Fairmont State University *West Virginia* W
Faulkner University *Alabama* M & W
Ferrum College *Virginia* M & W
Flagler College *Florida* M & W
Florida Agricultural and Mechanical University *Florida* M & W
Florida Atlantic University *Florida* M & W
Florida College *Florida* W
Florida Gulf Coast University *Florida* W
Florida Southern College *Florida* W
Florida State University *Florida* M & W
Fontbonne University *Missouri* W
Fordham University *New York* W
Fort Lewis College *Colorado* M & W
Francis Marion University *South Carolina* W
Franklin College *Indiana* W
Freed-Hardeman University *Tennessee* W
Fresno Pacific University *California* W
Friends University *Kansas* M & W
Furman University *South Carolina* M & W
Gallaudet University *District of Columbia* M & W
Gannon University *Pennsylvania* W
Garden City Community College *Kansas* M & W
Gardner-Webb University *North Carolina* M & W
Genesee Community College *New York* M & W
Georgetown College *Kentucky* W
Georgia College & State University *Georgia* M & W
Georgia Southern University *Georgia* M & W
Gettysburg College *Pennsylvania* M & W
Grace College *Indiana* M & W
Graceland University *Iowa* M & W
Grand Valley State University *Michigan* M & W
Grand View University *Iowa* M & W
Greensboro College *North Carolina* M & W
Guilford Technical Community College *North Carolina* M & W
Gwynedd Mercy University *Pennsylvania* W
Hamline University *Minnesota* W
Hampton University *Virginia* W
Hannibal-LaGrange University *Missouri* M & W
Hardin-Simmons University *Texas* M & W
Harding University *Arkansas* W
Harris-Stowe State University *Missouri* M & W
Hartwick College *New York* W
Haskell Indian Nations University *Kansas* M & W
Hastings College *Nebraska* W
Heidelberg University *Ohio* M & W
High Point University *North Carolina* W
Hillsdale College *Michigan* W
Hinds Community College *Mississippi* M & W
Hope College *Michigan* M & W
Hope International University *California* M & W
Houston Baptist University *Texas* M & W
Howard College *Texas* M & W
Humboldt State University *California* W
Huntington University *Indiana* M & W
Hutchinson Community College *Kansas* M & W
Illinois College *Illinois* W
Illinois Wesleyan University *Illinois* M & W
Indiana Tech *Indiana* M & W
Indiana Wesleyan University *Indiana* M & W
Inter American University of Puerto Rico, Aguadilla Campus *Puerto Rico* M & W
Inter American University of Puerto Rico, Arecibo Campus *Puerto Rico* M & W

Inter American University of Puerto Rico, Fajardo Campus *Puerto Rico* W
Iowa Central Community College *Iowa* M & W
Iowa Lakes Community College *Iowa* W
James Madison University *Virginia* M & W
Jarvis Christian College *Texas* W
Jefferson College *Missouri* M & W
John Brown University *Arkansas* M & W
John Carroll University *Ohio* W
Johnson C. Smith University *North Carolina* W
Johnson University *Tennessee* M & W
Johnson & Wales University *Colorado* M & W
Judson University *Illinois* W
Kansas Wesleyan University *Kansas* M & W
Kaskaskia College *Illinois* M & W
Keene State College *New Hampshire* W
Kent State University *Ohio* W
Kentucky Christian University *Kentucky* M & W
Kentucky Wesleyan College *Kentucky* M & W
Keuka College *New York* M & W
King University *Tennessee* W
Kutztown University of Pennsylvania *Pennsylvania* W
La Salle University *Pennsylvania* M & W
Labette Community College *Kansas* W
Lackawanna College *Pennsylvania* W
LaGrange College *Georgia* W
Lake Forest College *Illinois* M & W
Lake Land College *Illinois* W
Lamar University *Texas* M & W
Lane College *Tennessee* W
Langston University *Oklahoma* W
Laramie County Community College *Wyoming* M & W
Lawrence Technological University *Michigan* W
Lenoir-Rhyne University *North Carolina* M & W
Lewis University *Illinois* W
Liberty University *Virginia* M & W
Limestone College *South Carolina* M & W
Lincoln University *Missouri* W
Lindenwood University *Missouri* M & W
Lindsey Wilson College *Kentucky* M & W
Long Island University - LIU Post *New York* M & W
Loras College *Iowa* M & W
Louisiana College *Louisiana* M & W
Louisiana State University and Agricultural & Mechanical College *Louisiana* M & W
Lourdes University *Ohio* M & W
Loyola Marymount University *California* M & W
Loyola University New Orleans *Louisiana* M & W
Lubbock Christian University *Texas* M & W
Lycoming College *Pennsylvania* M & W
Lynchburg College *Virginia* M & W
Malone University *Ohio* M & W
Manchester University *Indiana* W
Manhattan College *New York* W
Marian University *Indiana* M & W
Marietta College *Ohio* M & W
Marist College *New York* M & W
Marquette University *Wisconsin* M & W
Mars Hill University *North Carolina* M & W
Marshalltown Community College *Iowa* M & W
Martin Methodist College *Tennessee* W
Maryville College *Tennessee* M & W
McGill University *Quebec (Canada)* M & W
McKendree University *Illinois* M & W
McPherson College *Kansas* M & W
Methodist University *North Carolina* M & W
Miami University Hamilton *Ohio* W
Michigan State University *Michigan* M & W
Michigan Technological University *Michigan* M & W
MidAmerica Nazarene University *Kansas* M & W
Middle Tennessee State University *Tennessee* M & W
Midland College *Texas* M & W
Midwestern State University *Texas* M & W
Miles College *Alabama* W
Millikin University *Illinois* M & W
Milwaukee School of Engineering *Wisconsin* M & W
Minnesota State University Mankato *Minnesota* M & W
Minnesota State University Moorhead *Minnesota* M & W

Minnesota West Community and Technical College *Minnesota* W
Minot State University *North Dakota* W
Mississippi State University *Mississippi* M & W
Missouri Baptist University *Missouri* M & W
Missouri Valley College *Missouri* M & W
Moberly Area Community College *Missouri* M & W
Monmouth University *New Jersey* M & W
Montana State University *Montana* W
Moravian College *Pennsylvania* W
Morehead State University *Kentucky* M & W
Morgan State University *Maryland* W
Morris College *South Carolina* M & W
Mount Ida College *Massachusetts* W
Mount St. Joseph University *Ohio* W
Mount Saint Mary College *New York* W
Mount St. Mary's University *Maryland* W
Mt. San Antonio College *California* M & W
Muhlenberg College *Pennsylvania* M & W
Murray State College *Oklahoma* M & W
Murray State University *Kentucky* W
Nassau Community College *New York* M & W
Nebraska Wesleyan University *Nebraska* W
Newberry College *South Carolina* M & W
North Carolina State University *North Carolina* M & W
North Central College *Illinois* W
North Greenville University *South Carolina* M & W
North Idaho College *Idaho* M & W
North Lake College *Texas* W
Northeastern Oklahoma Agricultural and Mechanical College *Oklahoma* M & W
Northeastern University *Massachusetts* M & W
Northern Kentucky University *Kentucky* M & W
Northwest Florida State College *Florida* M & W
Northwest Missouri State University *Missouri* M & W
Northwest Nazarene University *Idaho* W
Northwestern College *Iowa* M & W
Northwestern Oklahoma State University *Oklahoma* M & W
Northwood University, Michigan Campus *Michigan* M & W
Nova Southeastern University *Florida* W
Oakland City University *Indiana* W
The Ohio State University *Ohio* M & W
Ohio University *Ohio* M & W
Oklahoma City University *Oklahoma* M & W
Oklahoma Panhandle State University *Oklahoma* W
Oklahoma State University *Oklahoma* M & W
Old Dominion University *Virginia* M & W
Olivet Nazarene University *Illinois* M & W
Otterbein University *Ohio* M & W
Ouachita Baptist University *Arkansas* M & W
Ozark Christian College *Missouri* M & W
Palm Beach Atlantic University *Florida* M & W
Pasadena City College *California* W
Patrick Henry Community College *Virginia* W
Penn State Berks *Pennsylvania* M & W
Penn State Erie, The Behrend College *Pennsylvania* M & W
Penn State Hazleton *Pennsylvania* M & W
Penn State Lehigh Valley *Pennsylvania* M & W
Penn State Mont Alto *Pennsylvania* M & W
Penn State New Kensington *Pennsylvania* M & W
Penn State Worthington Scranton *Pennsylvania* W
Peru State College *Nebraska* W
Pfeiffer University *North Carolina* M & W
Pittsburg State University *Kansas* M & W
Point University *Georgia* W
Polk State College *Florida* W
Pratt Community College *Kansas* W
Presbyterian College *South Carolina* M & W
Purdue University Northwest *Westville, Indiana* M & W
Queen's University at Kingston *Ontario (Canada)* M & W
Quincy University *Illinois* M & W
Randolph-Macon College *Virginia* W
Rhodes College *Tennessee* W
Rice University *Texas* M & W
Rider University *New Jersey* M & W

M = Men; W = Women

Ripon College *Wisconsin* M & W
Robert Morris University Illinois *Illinois* M & W
Roberts Wesleyan College *New York* M & W
Rochester Institute of Technology *New York* M & W
Rocky Mountain College *Montana* M & W
Roger Williams University *Rhode Island* M & W
Rogers State University *Oklahoma* M & W
Rust College *Mississippi* M & W
Sacred Heart University *Connecticut* W
Saginaw Valley State University *Michigan* M & W
St. Ambrose University *Iowa* M & W
Saint Augustine's University *North Carolina* W
St. Cloud State University *Minnesota* M & W
St. Edward's University *Texas* M & W
St. Francis Xavier University *Nova Scotia (Canada)* W
St. Gregory's University *Oklahoma* M & W
Saint Joseph's College *Indiana* M & W
Saint Joseph's College of Maine *Maine* M & W
Saint Joseph's University *Pennsylvania* M & W
Saint Mary's College of California *California* W
St. Mary's College of Maryland *Maryland* M & W
St. Mary's University *Texas* M & W
St. Thomas University *Florida* W
Saint Vincent College *Pennsylvania* W
Salem International University *West Virginia* M & W
Salt Lake Community College *Utah* M & W
Sam Houston State University *Texas* M & W
Savannah State University *Georgia* M & W
Seattle University *Washington* M & W
Seminole State College *Oklahoma* W
Sewanee: The University of the South *Tennessee* W
Shelton State Community College *Alabama* M & W
Shorter University *Georgia* M & W
Siena College *New York* W
Siena Heights University *Michigan* M & W
Simpson College *Iowa* M & W
Slippery Rock University of Pennsylvania *Pennsylvania* M & W
South Dakota State University *South Dakota* M & W
Southeast Missouri State University *Missouri* M & W
Southeastern University *Florida* M & W
Southern Arkansas University - Magnolia *Arkansas* M & W
Southern Connecticut State University *Connecticut* M & W
Southern Illinois University Carbondale *Illinois* M & W
Southern Illinois University Edwardsville *Illinois* M & W
Southern Methodist University *Texas* M & W
Southern Nazarene University *Oklahoma* M & W
Southern New Hampshire University *New Hampshire* M & W
Southern Oregon University *Oregon* W
Southern Virginia University *Virginia* M & W
Southern Wesleyan University *South Carolina* M & W
Southwest Baptist University *Missouri* M & W
Southwestern Christian University *Oklahoma* W
Southwestern Oklahoma State University *Oklahoma* M & W
Southwestern Oregon Community College *Oregon* M & W
Stanford University *California* M & W
State University of New York College of Agriculture and Technology at Cobleskill *New York* M & W
State University of New York College at Geneseo *New York* M & W
State University of New York College at Oneonta *New York* W
State University of New York at Fredonia *New York* M & W
Stephen F. Austin State University *Texas* M & W
Stevenson University *Maryland* M & W
Stockton University *New Jersey* M & W
Stonehill College *Massachusetts* M & W
Sul Ross State University *Texas* M & W
Summit University *Pennsylvania* W
Susquehanna University *Pennsylvania* M & W
Syracuse University *New York* M & W

Tabor College *Kansas* M & W
Tarleton State University *Texas* M & W
Tennessee Technological University *Tennessee* M & W
Tennessee Wesleyan College *Tennessee* M & W
Texas A&M University - Commerce *Texas* M & W
Texas College *Texas* M & W
Texas State University *Texas* M & W
Texas Wesleyan University *Texas* M & W
Thiel College *Pennsylvania* M & W
Three Rivers Community College *Missouri* M & W
Transylvania University *Kentucky* M & W
Trinity Baptist College *Florida* W
Trinity Valley Community College *Texas* M & W
Truman State University *Missouri* M & W
Tusculum College *Tennessee* W
Tyler Junior College *Texas* W
Union College *Kentucky* M & W
Union College *New York* M & W
Union University *Tennessee* W
United States Air Force Academy *Colorado* M & W
United States Coast Guard Academy *Connecticut* M & W
United States Military Academy *New York* M & W
United States Naval Academy *Maryland* M & W
Universidad del Este *Puerto Rico* M & W
Universidad Metropolitana *Puerto Rico* M & W
Université de Montréal *Quebec (Canada)* M & W
Université du Québec en Outaouais *Quebec (Canada)* M & W
Université de Sherbrooke *Quebec (Canada)* M & W
The University of Akron *Ohio* M & W
The University of Akron Wayne College *Ohio* W
The University of Alabama *Alabama* M & W
The University of Alabama in Huntsville *Alabama* M & W
The University of Arizona *Arizona* M & W
The University of British Columbia *British Columbia (Canada)* W
University of California, Santa Cruz *California* M & W
University of Central Arkansas *Arkansas* M & W
University of Charleston *West Virginia* W
University of Cincinnati *Ohio* M & W
University of Cincinnati Clermont College *Ohio* W
University of Colorado Boulder *Colorado* M & W
University of the Cumberlands *Kentucky* M & W
University of Dayton *Ohio* M & W
University of Delaware *Delaware* M & W
University of Florida *Florida* M & W
University of Georgia *Georgia* M & W
University of Great Falls *Montana* M & W
University of Hawaii at Manoa *Hawaii* M & W
University of Illinois at Springfield *Illinois* M & W
University of Illinois at Urbana - Champaign *Illinois* M & W
The University of Iowa *Iowa* M & W
University of Louisville *Kentucky* M & W
University of Maine *Maine* M & W
University of Maryland Eastern Shore *Maryland* M & W
University of Memphis *Tennessee* M & W
University of Miami *Florida* M & W
University of Michigan *Michigan* M & W
University of Michigan - Dearborn *Michigan* M & W
University of Minnesota, Duluth *Minnesota* W
University of Mississippi *Mississippi* M & W
University of Missouri *Missouri* M & W
University of Missouri - St. Louis *Missouri* W
University of Mobile *Alabama* W
The University of Montana Western *Montana* W
University of Montevallo *Alabama* W
University of Mount Olive *North Carolina* W
University of Mount Union *Ohio* W
University of Nevada, Las Vegas *Nevada* M & W
University of Nevada, Reno *Nevada* M & W
University of North Alabama *Alabama* M & W
The University of North Carolina at Chapel Hill *North Carolina* W
The University of North Carolina at Charlotte *North Carolina* M & W
The University of North Carolina at Pembroke *North Carolina* M & W

The University of North Carolina Wilmington *North Carolina* M & W
University of North Georgia *Georgia* M & W
University of Oklahoma *Oklahoma* M & W
University of Ottawa *Ontario (Canada)* M & W
University of Pikeville *Kentucky* M & W
University of Pittsburgh at Johnstown *Pennsylvania* W
University of Pittsburgh at Titusville *Pennsylvania* M & W
University of Puerto Rico in Humacao *Puerto Rico* M & W
University of Puget Sound *Washington* M & W
University of Redlands *California* M & W
University of Rochester *New York* M & W
University of St. Francis *Illinois* M & W
University of Saint Francis *Indiana* W
University of Saint Mary *Kansas* M & W
University of St. Thomas *Texas* M & W
University of Science and Arts of Oklahoma *Oklahoma* M & W
University of Sioux Falls *South Dakota* M & W
University of South Carolina Upstate *South Carolina* M & W
University of Southern California *California* M & W
University of Southern Mississippi *Mississippi* M & W
The University of Tennessee at Martin *Tennessee* M & W
The University of Texas of the Permian Basin *Texas* M & W
The University of Texas at Tyler *Texas* M & W
The University of Tulsa *Oklahoma* M & W
University of Utah *Utah* M & W
University of Vermont *Vermont* M & W
University of the Virgin Islands *United States Virgin Islands* W
University of Washington *Washington* M & W
University of Waterloo *Ontario (Canada)* M & W
University of West Georgia *Georgia* W
The University of Western Ontario *Ontario (Canada)* M & W
University of Wisconsin - Madison *Wisconsin* M & W
University of Wisconsin - Platteville *Wisconsin* M & W
University of Wisconsin - Whitewater *Wisconsin* M & W
Valdosta State University *Georgia* M & W
Ventura College *California* M & W
Villanova University *Pennsylvania* M & W
Virginia State University *Virginia* M & W
Virginia Wesleyan College *Virginia* W
Voorhees College *South Carolina* W
Wagner College *New York* W
Waldorf College *Iowa* W
Walsh University *Ohio* W
Warner University *Florida* M & W
Wartburg College *Iowa* W
Washburn University *Kansas* M & W
Washington College *Maryland* W
Washington & Jefferson College *Pennsylvania* M & W
Washington State University *Washington* M & W
Waubonsee Community College *Illinois* M & W
Wayland Baptist University *Texas* M & W
Wayne State College *Nebraska* M & W
Wayne State University *Michigan* M & W
Weatherford College *Texas* M & W
Webber International University *Florida* M & W
Weber State University *Utah* W
West Chester University of Pennsylvania *Pennsylvania* W
West Virginia Wesleyan College *West Virginia* W
Western Carolina University *North Carolina* M & W
Western Connecticut State University *Connecticut* W
Western New Mexico University *New Mexico* M & W
Western State Colorado University *Colorado* M & W
Western Washington University *Washington* M & W

M = Men; W = Women

Western Wyoming Community College *Wyoming* M & W
Westfield State University *Massachusetts* W
Wheaton College *Illinois* W
Wheeling Jesuit University *West Virginia* M & W
Wichita State University *Kansas* M & W
Widener University *Pennsylvania* W
Wiley College *Texas* M & W
Wilfrid Laurier University *Ontario (Canada)* M & W
William Carey University *Mississippi* M & W
William Jewell College *Missouri* M & W
William Penn University *Iowa* M & W
William Woods University *Missouri* W
Winston-Salem State University *North Carolina* M
Winthrop University *South Carolina* M & W
Wofford College *South Carolina* W
Wright State University *Ohio* M & W
Xavier University *Ohio* M & W
Yale University *Connecticut* M & W
York College of Pennsylvania *Pennsylvania* M & W
Young Harris College *Georgia* M & W

Crew

Allegheny College *Pennsylvania* M & W
Amherst College *Massachusetts* M & W
Augustana College *Illinois* M & W
Barnard College *New York* W
Barry University *Florida* W
Bates College *Maine* M & W
Baylor University *Texas* M & W
Boston College *Massachusetts* W
Boston University *Massachusetts* M & W
Bowdoin College *Maine* M & W
Brenau University *Georgia* W
Brock University *Ontario (Canada)* M & W
Brown University *Rhode Island* M & W
Bryant University *Rhode Island* W
Bryn Mawr College *Pennsylvania* W
Bucknell University *Pennsylvania* M & W
Butler University *Indiana* M & W
California Maritime Academy *California* M & W
California State University, Long Beach *California* M & W
California State University, Sacramento *California* M & W
Carleton University *Ontario (Canada)* M & W
Carnegie Mellon University *Pennsylvania* M & W
Cazenovia College *New York* M & W
Chapman University *California* M & W
Christopher Newport University *Virginia* M & W
Clark University *Massachusetts* M & W
Clemson University *South Carolina* M & W
Colby College *Maine* M & W
Colgate University *New York* M & W
College of the Holy Cross *Massachusetts* M & W
College of Saint Benedict *Minnesota* W
Colorado State University *Colorado* M & W
Columbia University *New York* M & W
Columbia University, School of General Studies *New York* M & W
Connecticut College *Connecticut* M & W
Cornell University *New York* M & W
Creighton University *Nebraska* W
Dartmouth College *New Hampshire* M & W
Davidson College *North Carolina* M & W
Denison University *Ohio* M
DePauw University *Indiana* M & W
Drake University *Iowa* W
Drexel University *Pennsylvania* M & W
Duke University *North Carolina* M & W
Duquesne University *Pennsylvania* W
Eastern Michigan University *Michigan* W
Emory University *Georgia* M & W
Endicott College *Massachusetts* M & W
Fairfield University *Connecticut* M & W
Florida Institute of Technology *Florida* M & W
Fordham University *New York* W
Franklin & Marshall College *Pennsylvania* M & W
Franklin Pierce University *New Hampshire* M & W
Furman University *South Carolina* M & W
George Mason University *Virginia* W
The George Washington University *District of Columbia* M & W
Georgetown University *District of Columbia* M & W

Georgia State University *Georgia* M & W
Grand Valley State University *Michigan* M & W
Hamilton College *New York* M & W
Hampden-Sydney College *Virginia* M
Harvard University *Massachusetts* M & W
Haverford College *Pennsylvania* M & W
Hillsdale College *Michigan* M & W
Hobart and William Smith Colleges *New York* M & W
Humboldt State University *California* M & W
Indiana University Bloomington *Indiana* W
Ithaca College *New York* M & W
Jacksonville University *Florida* M & W
John Carroll University *Ohio* M & W
Kansas State University *Kansas* W
La Salle University *Pennsylvania* M & W
Lafayette College *Pennsylvania* M & W
Lawrence University *Wisconsin* M & W
Lehigh University *Pennsylvania* M & W
Lewis & Clark College *Oregon* M & W
Liberty University *Virginia* M & W
Long Island University - LIU Post *New York* M & W
Loyola Marymount University *California* M & W
Loyola University Maryland *Maryland* M & W
Lycoming College *Pennsylvania* M & W
Macalester College *Minnesota* M & W
Manhattan College *New York* M & W
Marietta College *Ohio* M & W
Marist College *New York* M & W
Massachusetts Institute of Technology *Massachusetts* M & W
Massachusetts Maritime Academy *Massachusetts* M & W
McGill University *Quebec (Canada)* M & W
Mercyhurst University *Pennsylvania* M & W
Merrimack College *Massachusetts* W
Michigan State University *Michigan* M & W
Michigan Technological University *Michigan* M & W
Mills College *California* W
Milwaukee School of Engineering *Wisconsin* M & W
Mount Holyoke College *Massachusetts* W
Murray State University *Kentucky* M & W
North Carolina State University *North Carolina* M & W
North Park University *Illinois* M & W
Northeastern University *Massachusetts* M & W
Northern Michigan University *Michigan* M & W
Nova Southeastern University *Florida* W
Oklahoma City University *Oklahoma* M & W
Old Dominion University *Virginia* M & W
Orange Coast College *California* M & W
Oregon State University *Oregon* M & W
Pacific Lutheran University *Washington* M & W
Palm Beach Atlantic University *Florida* M & W
Princeton University *New Jersey* M & W
Queen's University at Kingston *Ontario (Canada)* M & W
Rensselaer Polytechnic Institute *New York* M & W
Rhodes College *Tennessee* M & W
Rice University *Texas* M & W
Robert Morris University *Pennsylvania*
Rochester Institute of Technology *New York* M & W
Roger Williams University *Rhode Island* M & W
Rollins College *Florida* M & W
Rutgers University - Camden *New Jersey* M & W
Rutgers University - New Brunswick *New Jersey* M & W
Ryerson University *Ontario (Canada)* M & W
Sacred Heart University *Connecticut* W
St. Cloud State University *Minnesota* M & W
St. Francis Xavier University *Nova Scotia (Canada)* M & W
St. John Fisher College *New York* W
St. John's College *Maryland* M & W
Saint John's University *Minnesota* M
Saint Joseph's University *Pennsylvania* M & W
Saint Louis University *Missouri* M & W
Saint Mary's College of California *California* M & W
St. Mary's College of Maryland *Maryland* M & W
Sarah Lawrence College *New York* W
Seattle Pacific University *Washington* M & W
Seattle University *Washington* W

Sewanee: The University of the South *Tennessee* M & W
Simmons College *Massachusetts* W
Skidmore College *New York* M & W
Smith College *Massachusetts* W
Southern Methodist University *Texas* W
Southwestern Christian University *Oklahoma* M & W
Stanford University *California* M & W
State University of New York College at Geneseo *New York* M & W
State University of New York Maritime College *New York* M & W
State University of New York at Oswego *New York* M & W
Stetson University *Florida* M & W
Stockton University *New Jersey* W
Susquehanna University *Pennsylvania* M & W
Syracuse University *New York* M & W
Temple University *Pennsylvania* M & W
Trent University *Ontario (Canada)* M & W
Trinity College *Connecticut* M & W
Tufts University *Massachusetts* M & W
Tulane University *Louisiana* W
Union College *New York* M & W
United States Coast Guard Academy *Connecticut* M & W
United States Merchant Marine Academy *New York* M & W
United States Military Academy *New York* M & W
United States Naval Academy *Maryland* M & W
The University of Alabama *Alabama* M & W
The University of Alabama in Huntsville *Alabama* M & W
University at Albany, State University of New York *New York* M & W
The University of British Columbia *British Columbia (Canada)* M & W
University at Buffalo, the State University of New York *New York* W
University of California, Berkeley *California* M & W
University of California, Irvine *California* M & W
University of California, Los Angeles *California* W
University of California, San Diego *California* M & W
University of California, Santa Barbara *California* M & W
University of Central Florida *Florida* W
University of Charleston *West Virginia* W
University of Colorado Boulder *Colorado* M & W
University of Connecticut *Connecticut* W
University of Dayton *Ohio* W
University of Delaware *Delaware* M & W
University of Georgia *Georgia* W
University of Guelph *Ontario (Canada)* M & W
The University of Iowa *Iowa* M & W
The University of Kansas *Kansas* W
University of Louisville *Kentucky* W
University of Maryland, Baltimore County *Maryland* M & W
University of Massachusetts Amherst *Massachusetts* W
University of Miami *Florida* W
University of Michigan *Michigan* M & W
University of Minnesota, Duluth *Minnesota* M & W
University of Montana *Montana* W
University of New Brunswick Saint John *New Brunswick (Canada)* M & W
University of New Hampshire *New Hampshire* M & W
The University of North Carolina at Chapel Hill *North Carolina* M & W
University of Notre Dame *Indiana* W
University of Oklahoma *Oklahoma* W
University of Ottawa *Ontario (Canada)* M & W
University of Pennsylvania *Pennsylvania* M & W
University of Portland *Oregon* W
University of Puget Sound *Washington* M & W
University of Rhode Island *Rhode Island* M
University of Richmond *Virginia* M & W
University of Rochester *New York* M & W
University of San Diego *California* M & W
The University of Scranton *Pennsylvania* M & W
University of South Florida *Florida* M & W

M = Men; W = Women

University of Southern California *California* M & W
The University of Tampa *Florida* W
The University of Tennessee *Tennessee* W
The University of Texas at Austin *Texas* M & W
University of Toronto *Ontario (Canada)* M
The University of Tulsa *Oklahoma* W
University of Vermont *Vermont* M & W
University of Victoria *British Columbia (Canada)* M & W
University of Virginia *Virginia* W
University of Washington *Washington* M & W
The University of Western Ontario *Ontario (Canada)* M & W
University of Wisconsin - Madison *Wisconsin* M & W
Vassar College *New York* M & W
Villanova University *Pennsylvania* M & W
Washington College *Maryland* M & W
Washington State University *Washington* M & W
Washington University in St. Louis *Missouri* M & W
Wellesley College *Massachusetts* W
Wentworth Institute of Technology *Massachusetts* M
Wesleyan University *Connecticut* M & W
West Virginia University *West Virginia* W
Western Washington University *Washington* M & W
Wheaton College *Illinois* M & W
Willamette University *Oregon* M & W
Williams College *Massachusetts* M & W
Wittenberg University *Ohio* M & W
Worcester Polytechnic Institute *Massachusetts* M & W
Xavier University *Ohio* M & W
Yale University *Connecticut* M & W

Cross-Country Running

Abilene Christian University *Texas* M & W
Academy of Art University *California* M & W
Acadia University *Nova Scotia (Canada)* W
Adams State University *Colorado* M & W
Adelphi University *New York* M & W
Adrian College *Michigan* M & W
Agnes Scott College *Georgia* W
Alabama Agricultural and Mechanical University *Alabama* M & W
Alabama State University *Alabama* M & W
Albany College of Pharmacy and Health Sciences *New York* M & W
Albany State University *Georgia* M & W
Albion College *Michigan* M & W
Albright College *Pennsylvania* M & W
Alcorn State University *Mississippi* M & W
Alderson Broaddus University *West Virginia* M & W
Alfred University *New York* M & W
Alice Lloyd College *Kentucky* M & W
Allan Hancock College *California* M & W
Allegheny College *Pennsylvania* M & W
Allen Community College *Kansas* M & W
Allen University *South Carolina* M & W
Alpena Community College *Michigan* M
Alvernia University *Pennsylvania* M & W
Alverno College *Wisconsin* W
American International College *Massachusetts* M & W
American River College *California* M & W
American University *District of Columbia* M & W
Amherst College *Massachusetts* M & W
Ancilla College *Indiana* M & W
Anderson University *Indiana* M & W
Anderson University *South Carolina* M & W
Andrew College *Georgia* M & W
Angelo State University *Texas* M & W
Anna Maria College *Massachusetts* M & W
Anne Arundel Community College *Maryland* M & W
Antelope Valley College *California* M & W
Appalachian State University *North Carolina* M & W
Aquinas College *Michigan* M & W
Arizona Christian University *Arizona* M & W
Arizona State University at the Downtown Phoenix campus *Arizona* M & W
Arizona State University at the Polytechnic campus *Arizona* M & W
Arizona State University at the Tempe campus *Arizona* M & W

Arizona State University at the West campus *Arizona* M & W
Arkansas State University *Arkansas* M & W
Arkansas Tech University *Arkansas* W
Arlington Baptist College *Texas* M & W
Armstrong State University *Georgia* M & W
Asbury University *Kentucky* M & W
Ashford University *California* M & W
Ashland University *Ohio* M & W
Assumption College *Massachusetts* M & W
Auburn University *Alabama* M & W
Auburn University at Montgomery *Alabama* M & W
Augsburg College *Minnesota* M & W
Augusta University *Georgia* M & W
Augustana College *Illinois* M & W
Augustana University *South Dakota* M & W
Aurora University *Illinois* M & W
Austin College *Texas* M & W
Austin Peay State University *Tennessee* M & W
Ave Maria University *Florida* M & W
Averett University *Virginia* M & W
Avila University *Missouri* M & W
Azusa Pacific University *California* M & W
Babson College *Massachusetts* M & W
Baker University *Kansas* M & W
Bakersfield College *California* M & W
Baldwin Wallace University *Ohio* M & W
Ball State University *Indiana* W
Bard College *New York* M & W
Barnard College *New York* W
Barstow Community College *California* M & W
Barton College *North Carolina* M & W
Barton County Community College *Kansas* M & W
Baruch College of the City University of New York *New York* M & W
Bates College *Maine* M & W
Bay Path University *Massachusetts* W
Bayamón Central University *Puerto Rico* M & W
Baylor University *Texas* M & W
Belhaven University *Mississippi* M & W
Bellarmine University *Kentucky* M & W
Bellevue College *Washington* M & W
Belmont Abbey College *North Carolina* M & W
Belmont University *Tennessee* M & W
Beloit College *Wisconsin* M & W
Bemidji State University *Minnesota* W
Benedictine College *Kansas* M & W
Benedictine University *Illinois* M & W
Bentley University *Massachusetts* M & W
Berea College *Kentucky* M & W
Bergen Community College *New Jersey* M & W
Berkeley College - New York City Campus *New York* M & W
Berkeley College - White Plains Campus *New York* M & W
Berkeley College - Woodland Park Campus *New Jersey* M & W
Berry College *Georgia* M & W
Bethany College *Kansas* M & W
Bethany College *West Virginia* M & W
Bethany Lutheran College *Minnesota* M & W
Bethel College *Indiana* M & W
Bethel College *Kansas* M & W
Bethel University *Minnesota* M & W
Bethel University *Tennessee* M & W
Bethune-Cookman University *Florida* M & W
Binghamton University, State University of New York *New York* M & W
Biola University *California* M & W
Birmingham-Southern College *Alabama* M & W
Black Hills State University *South Dakota* M & W
Blackburn College *Illinois* M & W
Bloomfield College *New Jersey* M & W
Bloomsburg University of Pennsylvania *Pennsylvania* M & W
Blue Mountain College *Mississippi* M & W
Bluefield College *Virginia* M & W
Bluefield State College *West Virginia* M & W
Bluffton University *Ohio* M & W
Bob Jones University *South Carolina* M & W
Boise State University *Idaho* M & W
Boston College *Massachusetts* M & W
Boston University *Massachusetts* M & W
Bowdoin College *Maine* M & W

Bowie State University *Maryland* M & W
Bowling Green State University *Ohio* M & W
Bradley University *Illinois* M & W
Brandeis University *Massachusetts* M & W
Brenau University *Georgia* W
Brescia University *Kentucky* M & W
Brevard College *North Carolina* M & W
Brewton-Parker College *Georgia* M & W
Briar Cliff University *Iowa* M & W
Bridgewater College *Virginia* M & W
Bridgewater State University *Massachusetts* M & W
Brigham Young University *Utah* M & W
Brigham Young University - Hawaii *Hawaii* M & W
Brock University *Ontario (Canada)* M & W
Bronx Community College of the City University of New York *New York* M & W
Brooklyn College of the City University of New York *New York* M & W
Broome Community College *New York* M & W
Brown University *Rhode Island* M & W
Bryan College *Tennessee* M & W
Bryant University *Rhode Island* M & W
Bryn Athyn College of the New Church *Pennsylvania* M & W
Bryn Mawr College *Pennsylvania* W
Bucknell University *Pennsylvania* M & W
Buena Vista University *Iowa* M & W
Buffalo State College, State University of New York *New York* M & W
Butler Community College *Kansas* M & W
Butler University *Indiana* M & W
Butte College *California* M & W
Cabrini University *Pennsylvania* M & W
Cairn University *Pennsylvania* M & W
Caldwell University *New Jersey* M & W
California Baptist University *California* M & W
California Institute of Technology *California* M & W
California Lutheran University *California* M & W
California Polytechnic State University, San Luis Obispo *California* M & W
California State Polytechnic University, Pomona *California* M & W
California State University, Chico *California* M & W
California State University, East Bay *California* M & W
California State University, Fresno *California* M & W
California State University, Fullerton *California* M & W
California State University, Long Beach *California* M & W
California State University, Los Angeles *California* W
California State University, Monterey Bay *California* M & W
California State University, Northridge *California* M & W
California State University, Sacramento *California* M & W
California State University, San Bernardino *California* W
California State University, San Marcos *California* M & W
California State University, Stanislaus *California* M & W
California University of Pennsylvania *Pennsylvania* M & W
Calumet College of Saint Joseph *Indiana* M & W
Calvin College *Michigan* M & W
Cameron University *Oklahoma* M
Campbell University *North Carolina* M & W
Campbellsville University *Kentucky* M & W
Canisius College *New York* M & W
Capital University *Ohio* M & W
Cardinal Stritch University *Wisconsin* M & W
Caribbean University *Puerto Rico* M & W
Carleton College *Minnesota* M & W
Carlow University *Pennsylvania* M & W
Carnegie Mellon University *Pennsylvania* M & W
Carroll College *Montana* M & W
Carroll University *Wisconsin* M & W
Carson-Newman University *Tennessee* M & W
Carthage College *Wisconsin* M & W
Case Western Reserve University *Ohio* M & W

M = Men; W = Women

Castleton University *Vermont* M & W
Catawba College *North Carolina* M & W
The Catholic University of America *District of Columbia* M & W
Cazenovia College *New York* M & W
Cedar Crest College *Pennsylvania* W
Cedarville University *Ohio* M & W
Centenary College *New Jersey* M & W
Centenary College of Louisiana *Louisiana* M & W
Central Arizona College *Arizona* M & W
Central College *Iowa* M & W
Central Connecticut State University *Connecticut* M & W
Central Methodist University *Missouri* M & W
Central Michigan University *Michigan* M & W
Central Penn College *Pennsylvania* M & W
Central State University *Ohio* M & W
Central Washington University *Washington* M & W
Central Wyoming College *Wyoming* M & W
Centre College *Kentucky* M & W
Cerritos College *California* M & W
Chabot College *California* M & W
Chaminade University of Honolulu *Hawaii* M & W
Chapman University *California* M & W
Charleston Southern University *South Carolina* M & W
Chatham University *Pennsylvania* M & W
Chestnut Hill College *Pennsylvania* M & W
Cheyney University of Pennsylvania *Pennsylvania* M & W
Chicago State University *Illinois* M & W
Chowan University *North Carolina* M & W
Christendom College *Virginia* M & W
Christian Brothers University *Tennessee* M & W
Christopher Newport University *Virginia* M & W
Cincinnati Christian University *Ohio* M & W
The Citadel, The Military College of South Carolina *South Carolina* M & W
Citrus College *California* M & W
City College of the City University of New York *New York* M & W
City Colleges of Chicago, Malcolm X College *Illinois* M
Clackamas Community College *Oregon* M & W
Claflin University *South Carolina* M & W
Claremont McKenna College *California* M & W
Clarendon College *Texas* M & W
Clarion University of Pennsylvania *Pennsylvania* W
Clark Atlanta University *Georgia* M & W
Clark College *Washington* M & W
Clark University *Massachusetts* M & W
Clarke University *Iowa* M & W
Clarkson University *New York* M & W
Clayton State University *Georgia* M & W
Cleary University *Michigan* M & W
Clemson University *South Carolina* M & W
Cleveland State University *Ohio* W
Cloud County Community College *Kansas* M & W
Coastal Carolina University *South Carolina* M & W
Coe College *Iowa* M & W
Coffeyville Community College *Kansas* M & W
Coker College *South Carolina* M & W
Colby College *Maine* M & W
Colby Community College *Kansas* M & W
Colby-Sawyer College *New Hampshire* M & W
Colgate University *New York* M & W
The College at Brockport, State University of New York *New York* M & W
College of the Canyons *California* M & W
College of Charleston *South Carolina* M & W
College of the Desert *California* M & W
College of the Holy Cross *Massachusetts* M & W
The College of Idaho *Idaho* M & W
College of Lake County *Illinois* M & W
College of Mount Saint Vincent *New York* M & W
The College of New Jersey *New Jersey* M & W
The College of New Rochelle *New York* W
College of the Ozarks *Missouri* M & W
College of Saint Benedict *Minnesota* W
College of St. Joseph *Vermont* M & W
College of Saint Mary *Nebraska* W
The College of Saint Rose *New York* M & W
The College of St. Scholastica *Minnesota* M & W
College of San Mateo *California* M & W

College of the Sequoias *California* M & W
College of Staten Island of the City University of New York *New York* M & W
The College of William and Mary *Virginia* M & W
The College of Wooster *Ohio* M & W
Colorado Christian University *Colorado* M & W
The Colorado College *Colorado* M & W
Colorado Mesa University *Colorado* M & W
Colorado School of Mines *Colorado* M & W
Colorado State University *Colorado* M & W
Colorado State University - Pueblo *Colorado* M & W
Columbia College *Missouri* M & W
Columbia College *South Carolina* W
Columbia-Greene Community College *New York* M & W
Columbia International University *South Carolina* M & W
Columbia University *New York* M & W
Columbia University, School of General Studies *New York* M & W
Columbus State Community College *Ohio* M & W
Columbus State University *Georgia* M & W
Community College of Baltimore County *Maryland* W
Community College of Philadelphia *Pennsylvania* M & W
Concord University *West Virginia* M & W
Concordia College *Minnesota* M & W
Concordia College - New York *New York* M & W
Concordia University *Oregon* M & W
Concordia University *Quebec (Canada)* M & W
Concordia University Ann Arbor *Michigan* M & W
Concordia University Chicago *Illinois* M & W
Concordia University of Edmonton *Alberta (Canada)* M & W
Concordia University Irvine *California* M & W
Concordia University, Nebraska *Nebraska* M & W
Concordia University, St. Paul *Minnesota* M & W
Concordia University Texas *Texas* M & W
Concordia University Wisconsin *Wisconsin* M & W
Connecticut College *Connecticut* M & W
Converse College *South Carolina* W
Cooper Union for the Advancement of Science and Art *New York* M & W
Coppin State University *Maryland* M & W
Corban University *Oregon* M & W
Cornell College *Iowa* M & W
Cornell University *New York* M & W
Cornerstone University *Michigan* M & W
Cottey College *Missouri* W
Covenant College *Georgia* M & W
Cowley County Community College and Area Vocational - Technical School *Kansas* M & W
Crandall University *New Brunswick (Canada)* M & W
Creighton University *Nebraska* M & W
Crown College *Minnesota* M & W
Cuesta College *California* M & W
The Culinary Institute of America *New York* M & W
Culver-Stockton College *Missouri* M & W
Cumberland County College *New Jersey* M & W
Cumberland University *Tennessee* M & W
Curry College *Massachusetts* W
Cuyahoga Community College *Ohio* M & W
Cuyamaca College *California* M & W
Daemen College *New York* M & W
Dakota State University *South Dakota* M & W
Dakota Wesleyan University *South Dakota* M & W
Dalhousie University *Nova Scotia (Canada)* M & W
Dallas Baptist University *Texas* M & W
Daniel Webster College *New Hampshire* M & W
Danville Area Community College *Illinois* M & W
Dartmouth College *New Hampshire* M & W
Darton State College *Georgia* M & W
Davenport University *Michigan* M & W
Davidson College *North Carolina* M & W
Davis & Elkins College *West Virginia* M & W
De Anza College *California* M & W
Defiance College *Ohio* M & W
Delaware State University *Delaware* M & W
Delaware Valley University *Pennsylvania* M & W
Delta State University *Mississippi* W
Denison University *Ohio* M & W

DePaul University *Illinois* M & W
DePauw University *Indiana* M & W
Des Moines Area Community College *Iowa* W
DeSales University *Pennsylvania* M & W
Diablo Valley College *California* M & W
Dickinson College *Pennsylvania* M & W
Dickinson State University *North Dakota* M & W
Dillard University *Louisiana* M & W
Diné College *Arizona* M & W
Dixie State University *Utah* M & W
Doane University *Nebraska* M & W
Dodge City Community College *Kansas* M & W
Dominican College *New York* M & W
Dominican University *Illinois* M & W
Dominican University of California *California* M & W
Dordt College *Iowa* M & W
Drake University *Iowa* M & W
Drew University *New Jersey* M & W
Drury University *Missouri* M & W
Duke University *North Carolina* M & W
Duquesne University *Pennsylvania* M & W
Dutchess Community College *New York* M & W
D'Youville College *New York* M & W
Earlham College *Indiana* M & W
East Carolina University *North Carolina* M & W
East Central University *Oklahoma* M & W
East Los Angeles College *California* M & W
East Stroudsburg University of Pennsylvania *Pennsylvania* M & W
East Tennessee State University *Tennessee* M & W
East Texas Baptist University *Texas* M & W
Eastern Connecticut State University *Connecticut* M & W
Eastern Illinois University *Illinois* M & W
Eastern Kentucky University *Kentucky* M & W
Eastern Mennonite University *Virginia* M & W
Eastern Michigan University *Michigan* M & W
Eastern Nazarene College *Massachusetts* M & W
Eastern New Mexico University *New Mexico* M & W
Eastern Oregon University *Oregon* M & W
Eastern University *Pennsylvania* M & W
Eastern Washington University *Washington* M & W
Edgewood College *Wisconsin* M & W
Edinboro University of Pennsylvania *Pennsylvania* M & W
El Camino College *California* M & W
Elgin Community College *Illinois* M & W
Elizabeth City State University *North Carolina* M & W
Elizabethtown College *Pennsylvania* M & W
Elmhurst College *Illinois* M & W
Elmira College *New York* M & W
Elms College *Massachusetts* M & W
Elon University *North Carolina* M & W
Embry-Riddle Aeronautical University - Daytona *Florida* M & W
Embry-Riddle Aeronautical University - Prescott *Arizona* M & W
Emerson College *Massachusetts* M & W
Emmanuel College *Georgia* M & W
Emmanuel College *Massachusetts* M & W
Emory & Henry College *Virginia* M & W
Emory University *Georgia* M & W
Emporia State University *Kansas* M & W
Endicott College *Massachusetts* M & W
Erskine College *South Carolina* M & W
Essex County College *New Jersey* M & W
Estrella Mountain Community College *Arizona* M & W
Eureka College *Illinois* M & W
Evangel University *Missouri* M & W
Everett Community College *Washington* M & W
Fairfield University *Connecticut* M & W
Fairleigh Dickinson University, College at Florham *New Jersey* M & W
Fairleigh Dickinson University, Metropolitan Campus *New Jersey* M & W
Fairmont State University *West Virginia* M & W
Faith Baptist Bible College and Theological Seminary *Iowa* M & W
Farmingdale State College *New York* M & W
Fashion Institute of Technology *New York* M & W
Fayetteville State University *North Carolina* M & W

M = Men; W = Women

Feather River College *California* W
Felician University *New Jersey* M & W
Ferris State University *Michigan* M & W
Ferrum College *Virginia* M & W
Finger Lakes Community College *New York* M & W
Finlandia University *Michigan* M & W
Fisk University *Tennessee* M & W
Fitchburg State University *Massachusetts* M & W
Flagler College *Florida* M & W
Florida Agricultural and Mechanical University *Florida* M & W
Florida Atlantic University *Florida* M & W
Florida College *Florida* M & W
Florida Gulf Coast University *Florida* M & W
Florida Institute of Technology *Florida* M & W
Florida International University *Florida* M & W
Florida Memorial University *Florida* M & W
Florida Southern College *Florida* M & W
Florida State University *Florida* M & W
Fontbonne University *Missouri* M & W
Fordham University *New York* M & W
Fort Lewis College *Colorado* M & W
Framingham State University *Massachusetts* M & W
Francis Marion University *South Carolina* M & W
Franciscan University of Steubenville *Ohio* M & W
Franklin College *Indiana* M & W
Franklin & Marshall College *Pennsylvania* M & W
Franklin Pierce University *New Hampshire* M & W
Freed-Hardeman University *Tennessee* M & W
Fresno City College *California* M & W
Fresno Pacific University *California* M & W
Friends University *Kansas* M & W
Frostburg State University *Maryland* M & W
Fullerton College *California* M & W
Furman University *South Carolina* M & W
Gallaudet University *District of Columbia* M & W
Gannon University *Pennsylvania* M & W
Garden City Community College *Kansas* M & W
Gardner-Webb University *North Carolina* M & W
GateWay Community College *Arizona* M & W
Geneva College *Pennsylvania* M & W
George Fox University *Oregon* M & W
George Mason University *Virginia* M & W
The George Washington University *District of Columbia* M & W
Georgetown College *Kentucky* M & W
Georgetown University *District of Columbia* M & W
Georgia College & State University *Georgia* M & W
Georgia Institute of Technology *Georgia* M & W
Georgia Military College *Georgia* M & W
Georgia Southern University *Georgia* W
Georgia Southwestern State University *Georgia* W
Georgia State University *Georgia* W
Georgian Court University *New Jersey* W
Gettysburg College *Pennsylvania* M & W
Glendale Community College *Arizona* M & W
Glendale Community College *California* M & W
Glenville State College *West Virginia* M & W
Globe Institute of Technology *New York* M & W
Gogebic Community College *Michigan* M & W
Golden West College *California* M & W
Goldey-Beacom College *Delaware* M & W
Gonzaga University *Washington* M & W
Gordon College *Massachusetts* M & W
Goshen College *Indiana* M & W
Goucher College *Maryland* M & W
Governors State University *Illinois* M & W
Grace Bible College *Michigan* M & W
Grace College *Indiana* M & W
Graceland University *Iowa* M & W
Grambling State University *Louisiana* M & W
Grand Canyon University *Arizona* M & W
Grand Rapids Community College *Michigan* M & W
Grand Valley State University *Michigan* M & W
Grand View University *Iowa* M & W
Green Mountain College *Vermont* M & W
Greenville College *Illinois* M & W
Grinnell College *Iowa* M & W
Grossmont College *California* M
Grove City College *Pennsylvania* M & W
Guilford College *North Carolina* M & W
Gustavus Adolphus College *Minnesota* M & W
Gwynedd Mercy University *Pennsylvania* M & W

Hagerstown Community College *Maryland* M & W
Hamilton College *New York* M & W
Hamline University *Minnesota* M & W
Hampden-Sydney College *Virginia* M
Hampshire College *Massachusetts* M & W
Hampton University *Virginia* M & W
Hannibal-LaGrange University *Missouri* M & W
Hanover College *Indiana* M & W
Hardin-Simmons University *Texas* M & W
Harding University *Arkansas* M & W
Harford Community College *Maryland* M & W
Harper College *Illinois* M & W
Hartwick College *New York* M & W
Harvard University *Massachusetts* M & W
Harvey Mudd College *California* M & W
Haskell Indian Nations University *Kansas* M & W
Hastings College *Nebraska* M & W
Haverford College *Pennsylvania* M & W
Hawai'i Pacific University *Hawaii* M & W
Heidelberg University *Ohio* M & W
Henderson State University *Arkansas* W
Hendrix College *Arkansas* M & W
Herkimer County Community College *New York* M & W
Hesston College *Kansas* M & W
High Point University *North Carolina* M & W
Highland Community College *Kansas* M & W
Highline College *Washington* M & W
Hilbert College *New York* M & W
Hillsdale College *Michigan* M & W
Hillsdale Free Will Baptist College *Oklahoma* M & W
Hiwassee College *Tennessee* M & W
Hobart and William Smith Colleges *New York* M & W
Hofstra University *New York* M & W
Hollins University *Virginia* W
Holy Family University *Pennsylvania* M & W
Holy Names University *California* M & W
Holyoke Community College *Massachusetts* M & W
Hood College *Maryland* M & W
Hope College *Michigan* M & W
Hope International University *California* M & W
Houghton College *New York* M & W
Houston Baptist University *Texas* M & W
Howard Community College *Maryland* M & W
Howard University *District of Columbia* M & W
Hudson Valley Community College *New York* W
Humboldt State University *California* M & W
Hunter College of the City University of New York *New York* M & W
Huntington University *Indiana* M & W
Husson University *Maine* M & W
Huston-Tillotson University *Texas* M
Hutchinson Community College *Kansas* M & W
Idaho State University *Idaho* M & W
Illinois Central College *Illinois* M & W
Illinois College *Illinois* M & W
Illinois Institute of Technology *Illinois* M & W
Illinois State University *Illinois* M & W
Illinois Wesleyan University *Illinois* M & W
Immaculata University *Pennsylvania* W
Indiana State University *Indiana* M & W
Indiana Tech *Indiana* M & W
Indiana University Bloomington *Indiana* M & W
Indiana University East *Indiana* M & W
Indiana University Kokomo *Indiana* M & W
Indiana University Northwest *Indiana* M & W
Indiana University of Pennsylvania *Pennsylvania* M & W
Indiana University - Purdue University Fort Wayne *Indiana* M & W
Indiana University - Purdue University Indianapolis *Indiana* M & W
Indiana University South Bend *Indiana* M & W
Indiana Wesleyan University *Indiana* M & W
Inter American University of Puerto Rico, Aguadilla Campus *Puerto Rico* M & W
Inter American University of Puerto Rico, Barranquitas Campus *Puerto Rico* M & W
Inter American University of Puerto Rico, Bayamón Campus *Puerto Rico* M & W
Inter American University of Puerto Rico, Guayama Campus *Puerto Rico* M & W

Inter American University of Puerto Rico, Ponce Campus *Puerto Rico* M & W
Inter American University of Puerto Rico, San Germán Campus *Puerto Rico* M & W
Iona College *New York* M & W
Iowa Central Community College *Iowa* M & W
Iowa Lakes Community College *Iowa* M & W
Iowa State University of Science and Technology *Iowa* M & W
Irvine Valley College *California* M & W
Ithaca College *New York* M & W
Jackson College *Michigan* M & W
Jackson State University *Mississippi* M & W
Jacksonville State University *Alabama* M & W
Jacksonville University *Florida* M & W
James Madison University *Virginia* W
Jarvis Christian College *Texas* M & W
Jefferson College of Health Sciences *Virginia* M & W
John Brown University *Arkansas* M & W
John Carroll University *Ohio* M & W
John Jay College of Criminal Justice of the City University of New York *New York* M & W
Johns Hopkins University *Maryland* M & W
Johnson C. Smith University *North Carolina* M & W
Johnson College *Pennsylvania* M & W
Johnson County Community College *Kansas* M & W
Johnson State College *Vermont* M & W
Johnson University *Tennessee* M & W
Johnson University Florida *Florida* M & W
Johnson & Wales University *Rhode Island* M & W
Judson University *Illinois* M & W
Juniata College *Pennsylvania* M & W
Kalamazoo College *Michigan* M & W
Kansas City Kansas Community College *Kansas* M & W
Kansas State University *Kansas* M & W
Kansas Wesleyan University *Kansas* M & W
Kaskaskia College *Illinois* M & W
Keene State College *New Hampshire* M & W
Kennesaw State University *Georgia* M & W
Kent State University *Ohio* M & W
Kentucky State University *Kentucky* M & W
Kentucky Wesleyan College *Kentucky* M & W
Kenyon College *Ohio* M & W
Keuka College *New York* M & W
Keystone College *Pennsylvania* M & W
King University *Tennessee* M & W
King's College *Pennsylvania* M & W
Kirtland Community College *Michigan* M & W
Knox College *Illinois* M & W
Kutztown University of Pennsylvania *Pennsylvania* M & W
La Roche College *Pennsylvania* M & W
La Salle University *Pennsylvania* M & W
Lackawanna College *Pennsylvania* M & W
Lafayette College *Pennsylvania* M & W
LaGrange College *Georgia* M & W
Lake Erie College *Ohio* M & W
Lake Forest College *Illinois* M & W
Lake Superior State University *Michigan* M & W
Lakehead University *Ontario (Canada)* M & W
Lakeland College *Wisconsin* M & W
Lamar University *Texas* M & W
Landmark College *Vermont* M & W
Lane College *Tennessee* M & W
Lane Community College *Oregon* M & W
Langston University *Oklahoma* M & W
Lansing Community College *Michigan* M & W
Las Positas College *California* M & W
Lasell College *Massachusetts* M & W
Lassen Community College District *California* M & W
Laurentian University *Ontario (Canada)* M & W
Lawrence Technological University *Michigan* M & W
Lawrence University *Wisconsin* M & W
Le Moyne College *New York* M & W
Lebanon Valley College *Pennsylvania* M & W
Lee University *Tennessee* M & W
Lees-McRae College *North Carolina* M & W
Lehigh University *Pennsylvania* M & W
Lehman College of the City University of New York *New York* M & W

M = Men; W = Women

LeMoyne-Owen College *Tennessee* M & W
Lenoir-Rhyne University *North Carolina* M & W
Lesley University *Massachusetts* M & W
LeTourneau University *Texas* M & W
Lewis & Clark College *Oregon* M & W
Lewis-Clark State College *Idaho* M & W
Lewis University *Illinois* M & W
Liberty University *Virginia* M & W
Life University *Georgia* W
Limestone College *South Carolina* M & W
Lincoln Memorial University *Tennessee* M & W
Lincoln University *Missouri* W
Lincoln University *Pennsylvania* M & W
Lindenwood University *Missouri* M & W
Lindsey Wilson College *Kentucky* M & W
Linfield College *Oregon* M & W
Lipscomb University *Tennessee* M & W
Livingstone College *North Carolina* M & W
Lock Haven University of Pennsylvania *Pennsylvania* M & W
Long Island University - LIU Brooklyn *New York* M & W
Long Island University - LIU Post *New York* M & W
Longwood University *Virginia* M & W
Loras College *Iowa* M & W
Los Angeles City College *California* M
Los Angeles Southwest College *California* M & W
Los Angeles Valley College *California* M & W
Louisiana College *Louisiana* M & W
Louisiana State University and Agricultural & Mechanical College *Louisiana* M & W
Louisiana State University in Shreveport *Louisiana* M & W
Louisiana Tech University *Louisiana* M & W
Lourdes University *Ohio* M & W
Loyola Marymount University *California* M & W
Loyola University Chicago *Illinois* M & W
Loyola University Maryland *Maryland* M & W
Loyola University New Orleans *Louisiana* M & W
Lubbock Christian University *Texas* M & W
Luther College *Iowa* M & W
Luzerne County Community College *Pennsylvania* M & W
Lycoming College *Pennsylvania* M & W
Lynchburg College *Virginia* M & W
Lyndon State College *Vermont* M & W
Lynn University *Florida* W
Lyon College *Arkansas* M & W
Macalester College *Minnesota* M & W
Macomb Community College *Michigan* M & W
Madison Area Technical College *Wisconsin* M & W
Madonna University *Michigan* M & W
Maine Maritime Academy *Maine* M & W
Malone University *Ohio* M & W
Manchester University *Indiana* M & W
Manhattan Christian College *Kansas* M & W
Manhattan College *New York* M & W
Manhattanville College *New York* M & W
Mansfield University of Pennsylvania *Pennsylvania* M & W
Maranatha Baptist University *Wisconsin* M & W
Marian University *Indiana* M & W
Marian University *Wisconsin* M & W
Marietta College *Ohio* M & W
Marist College *New York* M & W
Marquette University *Wisconsin* M & W
Mars Hill University *North Carolina* M & W
Marshall University *West Virginia* M & W
Martin Luther College *Minnesota* M & W
Mary Baldwin College *Virginia* W
Marymount University *Virginia* M & W
Maryville College *Tennessee* M & W
Maryville University of Saint Louis *Missouri* M & W
Marywood University *Pennsylvania* M & W
Massachusetts Bay Community College *Massachusetts* M & W
Massachusetts College of Liberal Arts *Massachusetts* M & W
Massachusetts Institute of Technology *Massachusetts* M & W
Massachusetts Maritime Academy *Massachusetts* M & W
The Master's College and Seminary *California* M & W

McDaniel College *Maryland* M & W
McGill University *Quebec (Canada)* M & W
McKendree University *Illinois* M & W
McMaster University *Ontario (Canada)* M & W
McMurry University *Texas* M & W
McNeese State University *Louisiana* M & W
McPherson College *Kansas* M & W
Medaille College *New York* M & W
Medgar Evers College of the City University of New York *New York* M & W
Memorial University of Newfoundland *Newfoundland and Labrador (Canada)* M & W
Menlo College *California* M & W
Merced College *California* M
Mercer University *Georgia* M & W
Mercyhurst University *Pennsylvania* M & W
Meredith College *North Carolina* W
Meridian Community College *Mississippi* M & W
Merrimack College *Massachusetts* M & W
Merritt College *California* M & W
Mesa Community College *Arizona* M
Messiah College *Pennsylvania* M & W
Methodist University *North Carolina* M & W
Metropolitan Community College - Kansas City *Missouri* M
Metropolitan State University of Denver *Colorado* M & W
Miami University *Ohio* M & W
Michigan State University *Michigan* M & W
Michigan Technological University *Michigan* M & W
Middle Georgia State University *Georgia* W
Middle Tennessee State University *Tennessee* M & W
Middlebury College *Vermont* M & W
Middlesex County College *New Jersey* M & W
Midland University *Nebraska* M & W
Midwestern State University *Texas* W
Miles College *Alabama* M
Millersville University of Pennsylvania *Pennsylvania* M & W
Milligan College *Tennessee* M & W
Millikin University *Illinois* M & W
Mills College *California* W
Millsaps College *Mississippi* M & W
Milwaukee School of Engineering *Wisconsin* M & W
Minnesota State University Mankato *Minnesota* M & W
Minnesota State University Moorhead *Minnesota* M & W
Minot State University *North Dakota* M & W
Misericordia University *Pennsylvania* M & W
Mississippi College *Mississippi* M & W
Mississippi State University *Mississippi* M & W
Mississippi Valley State University *Mississippi* M & W
Missouri Baptist University *Missouri* M & W
Missouri Southern State University *Missouri* M & W
Missouri State University *Missouri* W
Missouri University of Science and Technology *Missouri* M & W
Missouri Valley College *Missouri* M & W
Mitchell College *Connecticut* M & W
Modesto Junior College *California* M & W
Mohawk Valley Community College *New York* M & W
Molloy College *New York* M & W
Monmouth College *Illinois* M & W
Monmouth University *New Jersey* M & W
Monroe College *New York* M & W
Montana State University *Montana* M & W
Montana State University Billings *Montana* M & W
Monterey Peninsula College *California* M & W
Montreat College *North Carolina* M & W
Moorpark College *California* M & W
Moraine Valley Community College *Illinois* M & W
Moravian College *Pennsylvania* M & W
Morehead State University *Kentucky* M & W
Morehouse College *Georgia* M
Morgan State University *Maryland* M & W
Morningside College *Iowa* M & W
Morris College *South Carolina* M & W
Morrisville State College *New York* M & W
Morton College *Illinois* M & W

Mott Community College *Michigan* M & W
Mount Aloysius College *Pennsylvania* M & W
Mount Holyoke College *Massachusetts* W
Mt. Hood Community College *Oregon* M & W
Mount Ida College *Massachusetts* M & W
Mount Marty College *South Dakota* M & W
Mount Mary University *Wisconsin* W
Mount Mercy University *Iowa* M & W
Mount St. Joseph University *Ohio* M & W
Mount Saint Mary College *New York* M & W
Mount St. Mary's University *Maryland* M & W
Mt. San Antonio College *California* M & W
Mount Vernon Nazarene University *Ohio* M & W
Muhlenberg College *Pennsylvania* M & W
Multnomah University *Oregon* M & W
Murray State University *Kentucky* M & W
Muskingum University *Ohio* M & W
Napa Valley College *California* M & W
Nassau Community College *New York* M & W
Nazareth College of Rochester *New York* M & W
Nebraska Wesleyan University *Nebraska* M & W
Neosho County Community College *Kansas* M & W
Neumann University *Pennsylvania* M & W
New England College *New Hampshire* M & W
New Jersey City University *New Jersey* M & W
New Jersey Institute of Technology *New Jersey* M & W
New Mexico Highlands University *New Mexico* M & W
New Mexico State University *New Mexico* M & W
New York Institute of Technology *New York* M & W
New York University *New York* M & W
Newberry College *South Carolina* M & W
Newbury College *Massachusetts* M & W
Newman University *Kansas* M & W
Niagara University *New York* M & W
Nicholls State University *Louisiana* M & W
Nipissing University *Ontario (Canada)* M & W
North Carolina Agricultural and Technical State University *North Carolina* M & W
North Carolina Central University *North Carolina* M & W
North Carolina State University *North Carolina* M & W
North Carolina Wesleyan College *North Carolina* W
North Central College *Illinois* M & W
North Central University *Minnesota* M & W
North Dakota State University *North Dakota* M & W
North Greenville University *South Carolina* M & W
North Iowa Area Community College *Iowa* M & W
North Park University *Illinois* M & W
Northampton Community College *Pennsylvania* M & W
Northeastern University *Massachusetts* M & W
Northern Arizona University *Arizona* M & W
Northern Illinois University *Illinois* W
Northern Kentucky University *Kentucky* M & W
Northern Michigan University *Michigan* W
Northern State University *South Dakota* M & W
Northland College *Wisconsin* M & W
Northwest Christian University *Oregon* M & W
Northwest Missouri State University *Missouri* M & W
Northwest Nazarene University *Idaho* M & W
Northwest University *Washington* M & W
Northwestern College *Iowa* M & W
Northwestern Oklahoma State University *Oklahoma* M & W
Northwestern State University of Louisiana *Louisiana* M & W
Northwood University, Michigan Campus *Michigan* M & W
Northwood University, Texas Campus *Texas* M & W
Norwich University *Vermont* M & W
Notre Dame College *Ohio* M & W
Notre Dame de Namur University *California* M & W
Nova Southeastern University *Florida* M & W
Nyack College *New York* M & W
Oakland City University *Indiana* M & W
Oakland Community College *Michigan* M & W
Oakland University *Michigan* M & W
Oakton Community College *Illinois* M & W
Oberlin College *Ohio* M & W
Occidental College *California* M & W

M = Men; W = Women

Ocean County College *New Jersey* M & W
Odessa College *Texas* M & W
Oglethorpe University *Georgia* M & W
Ohio Dominican University *Ohio* M & W
Ohio Northern University *Ohio* M & W
The Ohio State University *Ohio* M & W
Ohio University *Ohio* M & W
Ohio Valley University *West Virginia* M & W
Ohio Wesleyan University *Ohio* M & W
Oklahoma Baptist University *Oklahoma* M & W
Oklahoma Christian University *Oklahoma* M & W
Oklahoma Panhandle State University *Oklahoma* M & W
Oklahoma State University *Oklahoma* M & W
Oklahoma Wesleyan University *Oklahoma* M & W
Old Dominion University *Virginia* M & W
Olivet College *Michigan* M & W
Olivet Nazarene University *Illinois* M & W
Olympic College *Washington* M & W
Onondaga Community College *New York* M & W
Oral Roberts University *Oklahoma* M & W
Orange Coast College *California* M & W
Oregon Institute of Technology *Oregon* M & W
Oregon State University *Oregon* W
Ottawa University *Kansas* M & W
Otterbein University *Ohio* M & W
Ouachita Baptist University *Arkansas* W
Our Lady of the Lake University of San Antonio *Texas* M & W
Oxnard College *California* M & W
Pace University *New York* M & W
Pace University, Pleasantville Campus *New York* M & W
Pacific Lutheran University *Washington* M & W
Pacific Union College *California* M & W
Pacific University *Oregon* M & W
Paine College *Georgia* M & W
Palm Beach Atlantic University *Florida* W
Palo Alto College *Texas* M & W
Paradise Valley Community College *Arizona* M & W
Park University *Missouri* M & W
Pasadena City College *California* M & W
Pasco-Hernando State College *Florida* W
Paul Smith's College *New York* M & W
Penn State Altoona *Pennsylvania* M & W
Penn State Berks *Pennsylvania* M & W
Penn State DuBois *Pennsylvania* M & W
Penn State Erie, The Behrend College *Pennsylvania* M & W
Penn State Harrisburg *Pennsylvania* M & W
Penn State Lehigh Valley *Pennsylvania* M & W
Penn State Mont Alto *Pennsylvania* M & W
Penn State Schuylkill *Pennsylvania* M & W
Penn State University Park *Pennsylvania* M & W
Penn State Wilkes-Barre *Pennsylvania* M & W
Penn State Worthington Scranton *Pennsylvania* M & W
Pennsylvania College of Technology *Pennsylvania* M & W
Pennsylvania Highlands Community College *Pennsylvania* M & W
Pepperdine University *California* M & W
Peru State College *Nebraska* W
Pfeiffer University *North Carolina* M & W
Philadelphia University *Pennsylvania* M & W
Piedmont College *Georgia* M & W
Pine Manor College *Massachusetts* M & W
Pittsburg State University *Kansas* M & W
Pitzer College *California* M & W
Plymouth State University *New Hampshire* M & W
Point Loma Nazarene University *California* W
Point Park University *Pennsylvania* M & W
Point University *Georgia* M & W
Pomona College *California* M & W
Pontifical Catholic University of Puerto Rico *Puerto Rico* M & W
Portland State University *Oregon* M & W
Post University *Connecticut* M & W
Potomac State College of West Virginia University *West Virginia* M & W
Prairie View A&M University *Texas* M & W
Pratt Community College *Kansas* M & W
Pratt Institute *New York* M & W
Presbyterian College *South Carolina* M & W

Princeton University *New Jersey* M & W
Principia College *Illinois* M & W
Providence College *Rhode Island* M & W
Purchase College, State University of New York *New York* M & W
Purdue University *Indiana* M & W
Purdue University Northwest *Hammond, Indiana* M & W
Queens College of the City University of New York *New York* M & W
Queens University of Charlotte *North Carolina* M & W
Queen's University at Kingston *Ontario (Canada)* M & W
Queensborough Community College of the City University of New York *New York* M & W
Quincy University *Illinois* M & W
Quinnipiac University *Connecticut* M & W
Radford University *Virginia* M & W
Ramapo College of New Jersey *New Jersey* M & W
Randolph College *Virginia* M & W
Ranger College *Texas* M & W
Redeemer University College *Ontario (Canada)* M & W
Regis University *Colorado* M & W
Reinhardt University *Georgia* M & W
Rensselaer Polytechnic Institute *New York* M & W
Rhode Island College *Rhode Island* M & W
Rhodes College *Tennessee* M & W
Rice University *Texas* M & W
Rider University *New Jersey* M & W
Rio Hondo College *California* M & W
Ripon College *Wisconsin* M & W
Rivier University *New Hampshire* M & W
Roanoke College *Virginia* M & W
Robert Morris University *Pennsylvania* W
Robert Morris University Illinois *Illinois* M & W
Roberts Wesleyan College *New York* M & W
Rochester Institute of Technology *New York* M & W
Rockford University *Illinois* M & W
Rockhurst University *Missouri* W
Rocky Mountain College *Montana* M & W
Roger Williams University *Rhode Island* M & W
Rogers State University *Oklahoma* M & W
Rollins College *Florida* M & W
Roosevelt University *Illinois* M & W
Rose-Hulman Institute of Technology *Indiana* M & W
Rosemont College *Pennsylvania* M & W
Rowan College at Gloucester County *New Jersey* M & W
Rowan University *New Jersey* M & W
Royal Military College of Canada *Ontario (Canada)* M & W
Rust College *Mississippi* M & W
Rutgers University - Camden *New Jersey* W
Rutgers University - New Brunswick *New Jersey* M & W
Rutgers University - Newark *New Jersey* M & W
Sacramento City College *California* M & W
Sacred Heart University *Connecticut* M & W
Saddleback College *California* M & W
The Sage Colleges *New York* M & W
Saginaw Valley State University *Michigan* M & W
St. Ambrose University *Iowa* M & W
St. Andrews University *North Carolina* M & W
Saint Anselm College *New Hampshire* M & W
Saint Augustine's University *North Carolina* M & W
St. Bonaventure University *New York* M & W
St. Catherine University *Minnesota* W
St. Cloud State University *Minnesota* M & W
St. Edward's University *Texas* M & W
St. Francis College *New York* M & W
Saint Francis University *Pennsylvania* M & W
St. Francis Xavier University *Nova Scotia (Canada)* M & W
St. John Fisher College *New York* M & W
Saint John's University *Minnesota* M
St. John's University *New York* W
Saint Joseph's College *Indiana* M & W
St. Joseph's College, Long Island Campus *New York* M & W
Saint Joseph's College of Maine *Maine* M & W

St. Joseph's College, New York *New York* M & W
Saint Joseph's University *Pennsylvania* M & W
Saint Katherine College *California* M & W
St. Lawrence University *New York* M & W
Saint Leo University *Florida* M & W
Saint Louis Christian College *Missouri* W
St. Louis College of Pharmacy *Missouri* M & W
Saint Louis University *Missouri* M & W
Saint Martin's University *Washington* M & W
Saint Mary-of-the-Woods College *Indiana* W
Saint Mary's College *Indiana* W
Saint Mary's College of California *California* M & W
St. Mary's College of Maryland *Maryland* M & W
Saint Mary's University *Nova Scotia (Canada)* M & W
Saint Mary's University of Minnesota *Minnesota* M & W
Saint Michael's College *Vermont* M & W
St. Norbert College *Wisconsin* M & W
St. Olaf College *Minnesota* M & W
Saint Peter's University *New Jersey* M & W
St. Thomas Aquinas College *New York* M & W
St. Thomas University *Florida* M & W
St. Thomas University *New Brunswick (Canada)* M & W
Saint Vincent College *Pennsylvania* M & W
Saint Xavier University *Illinois* W
Salem College *North Carolina* W
Salem State University *Massachusetts* M & W
Salisbury University *Maryland* M & W
Salve Regina University *Rhode Island* M & W
Sam Houston State University *Texas* M & W
Samford University *Alabama* M & W
San Bernardino Valley College *California* M & W
San Diego Christian College *California* M & W
San Diego City College *California* M & W
San Diego Mesa College *California* M & W
San Diego State University *California* W
San Francisco State University *California* M & W
San Joaquin Delta College *California* M & W
San Jose City College *California* M & W
San Jose State University *California* M & W
Santa Ana College *California* M & W
Santa Barbara City College *California* M & W
Santa Clara University *California* M & W
Santa Monica College *California* M & W
Santa Rosa Junior College *California* M & W
Sarah Lawrence College *New York* M & W
Sauk Valley Community College *Illinois* M & W
Savannah College of Art and Design *Georgia* M & W
Savannah State University *Georgia* M & W
Schoolcraft College *Michigan* M & W
Schreiner University *Texas* M & W
Scottsdale Community College *Arizona* M & W
Scripps College *California* W
Seattle Pacific University *Washington* M & W
Seattle University *Washington* M & W
Seton Hall University *New Jersey* M & W
Seton Hill University *Pennsylvania* M & W
Sewanee: The University of the South *Tennessee* M & W
Shasta College *California* M & W
Shaw University *North Carolina* M & W
Shawnee State University *Ohio* M & W
Shenandoah University *Virginia* M & W
Sheridan College *Wyoming* M & W
Shippensburg University of Pennsylvania *Pennsylvania* M & W
Shoreline Community College *Washington* M & W
Shorter University *Georgia* M & W
Siena College *New York* M & W
Siena Heights University *Michigan* M & W
Sierra Nevada College *Nevada* M & W
Silver Lake College of the Holy Family *Wisconsin* M & W
Simmons College *Massachusetts* W
Simon Fraser University *British Columbia (Canada)* M & W
Simpson College *Iowa* M & W
Simpson University *California* M & W
Skagit Valley College *Washington* M & W
Skyline College *California* M & W

M = Men; W = Women

Slippery Rock University of Pennsylvania *Pennsylvania* M & W
Smith College *Massachusetts* W
Soka University of America *California* M & W
Sonoma State University *California* W
South Carolina State University *South Carolina* M & W
South Dakota School of Mines and Technology *South Dakota* M & W
South Dakota State University *South Dakota* M & W
South Florida State College *Florida* W
South Georgia State College *Georgia* M & W
South Plains College *Texas* M & W
Southeast Missouri State University *Missouri* M & W
Southeastern Louisiana University *Louisiana* M & W
Southeastern Oklahoma State University *Oklahoma* W
Southeastern University *Florida* M & W
Southern Alberta Institute of Technology *Alberta (Canada)* M & W
Southern Arkansas University - Magnolia *Arkansas* M & W
Southern Connecticut State University *Connecticut* M & W
Southern Illinois University Carbondale *Illinois* M & W
Southern Illinois University Edwardsville *Illinois* M & W
Southern Methodist University *Texas* W
Southern Nazarene University *Oklahoma* M & W
Southern New Hampshire University *New Hampshire* M & W
Southern University and Agricultural and Mechanical College *Louisiana* M
Southern University at New Orleans *Louisiana* M & W
Southern Utah University *Utah* M & W
Southern Vermont College *Vermont* M & W
Southern Virginia University *Virginia* M & W
Southern Wesleyan University *South Carolina* M & W
Southwest Baptist University *Missouri* M & W
Southwest Texas Junior College *Texas* M & W
Southwestern Christian University *Oklahoma* W
Southwestern College *California* M & W
Southwestern College *Kansas* M & W
Southwestern Oklahoma State University *Oklahoma* W
Southwestern Oregon Community College *Oregon* M & W
Southwestern University *Texas* M & W
Spalding University *Kentucky* M & W
Spartanburg Methodist College *South Carolina* M & W
Spokane Community College *Washington* M & W
Spokane Falls Community College *Washington* M & W
Spoon River College *Illinois* M & W
Spring Arbor University *Michigan* M & W
Spring Hill College *Alabama* M & W
Springfield College *Massachusetts* M & W
Stanford University *California* M & W
State University of New York College of Agriculture and Technology at Cobleskill *New York* M & W
State University of New York College at Cortland *New York* M & W
State University of New York College of Environmental Science and Forestry *New York* M & W
State University of New York College at Geneseo *New York* M & W
State University of New York College at Old Westbury *New York* M & W
State University of New York College at Oneonta *New York* M & W
State University of New York College at Potsdam *New York* M & W
State University of New York College of Technology at Alfred *New York* M & W
State University of New York College of Technology at Canton *New York* M & W

State University of New York College of Technology at Delhi *New York* M & W
State University of New York at Fredonia *New York* M & W
State University of New York Maritime College *New York* M & W
State University of New York at New Paltz *New York* M & W
State University of New York at Oswego *New York* M & W
State University of New York at Plattsburgh *New York* M & W
State University of New York Polytechnic Institute *New York* M & W
Stephen F. Austin State University *Texas* M & W
Stephens College *Missouri* W
Sterling College *Kansas* M & W
Stetson University *Florida* M & W
Stevens Institute of Technology *New Jersey* M & W
Stevenson University *Maryland* M & W
Stillman College *Alabama* M & W
Stockton University *New Jersey* M & W
Stonehill College *Massachusetts* M & W
Stony Brook University, State University of New York *New York* M & W
Suffolk County Community College *New York* M & W
Suffolk University *Massachusetts* M & W
Sul Ross State University *Texas* W
Sullivan County Community College *New York* M & W
Summit University *Pennsylvania* M & W
Susquehanna University *Pennsylvania* M & W
Swarthmore College *Pennsylvania* M & W
Sweet Briar College *Virginia* W
Syracuse University *New York* M & W
Tabor College *Kansas* M & W
Tarleton State University *Texas* M & W
Taylor University *Indiana* M & W
Temple University *Pennsylvania* M & W
Tennessee State University *Tennessee* M & W
Tennessee Technological University *Tennessee* M & W
Tennessee Wesleyan College *Tennessee* M & W
Texas A&M International University *Texas* M & W
Texas A&M University *Texas* M & W
Texas A&M University - Commerce *Texas* M & W
Texas A&M University - Corpus Christi *Texas* M & W
Texas A&M University - Kingsville *Texas* M & W
Texas Christian University *Texas* M & W
Texas Lutheran University *Texas* M & W
Texas Southern University *Texas* M & W
Texas State University *Texas* M & W
Texas Tech University *Texas* M & W
Texas Wesleyan University *Texas* M & W
Thaddeus Stevens College of Technology *Pennsylvania* M
Thiel College *Pennsylvania* M & W
Thomas College *Maine* M & W
Thomas More College *Kentucky* M & W
Thompson Rivers University *British Columbia (Canada)* M & W
Tiffin University *Ohio* M & W
Toccoa Falls College *Georgia* M & W
Tougaloo College *Mississippi* M & W
Towson University *Maryland* W
Transylvania University *Kentucky* M & W
Treasure Valley Community College *Oregon* M & W
Trent University *Ontario (Canada)* M & W
Trevecca Nazarene University *Tennessee* M & W
Trine University *Indiana* M & W
Trinity Christian College *Illinois* M & W
Trinity College *Connecticut* M & W
Trinity University *Texas* M & W
Troy University *Alabama* M & W
Truett-McConnell College *Georgia* M & W
Truman State University *Missouri* M & W
Tufts University *Massachusetts* M & W
Tulane University *Louisiana* M & W
Tusculum College *Tennessee* M & W
Tuskegee University *Alabama* M & W
Union College *Kentucky* M & W
Union College *New York* M & W

Union University *Tennessee* M & W
United States Air Force Academy *Colorado* M & W
United States Coast Guard Academy *Connecticut* M & W
United States Merchant Marine Academy *New York* M & W
United States Military Academy *New York* M & W
United States Naval Academy *Maryland* M & W
United Tribes Technical College *North Dakota* M & W
Unity College *Maine* M & W
Universidad del Este *Puerto Rico* M & W
Universidad Metropolitana *Puerto Rico* M & W
Universidad del Turabo *Puerto Rico* M & W
Université Laval *Quebec (Canada)* M & W
Université de Moncton *New Brunswick (Canada)* M & W
Université de Montréal *Quebec (Canada)* M & W
Université du Québec à Chicoutimi *Quebec (Canada)* M & W
Université du Québec à Rimouski *Quebec (Canada)* M & W
Université du Québec à Trois-Rivières *Quebec (Canada)* M
The University of Akron *Ohio* M & W
The University of Alabama *Alabama* M & W
The University of Alabama at Birmingham *Alabama* W
The University of Alabama in Huntsville *Alabama* M & W
University of Alaska Anchorage *Alaska* M & W
University of Alaska Fairbanks *Alaska* M & W
University at Albany, State University of New York *New York* M & W
University of Alberta *Alberta (Canada)* M & W
The University of Arizona *Arizona* M & W
University of Arkansas *Arkansas* M & W
University of Arkansas - Fort Smith *Arkansas* M & W
University of Arkansas at Little Rock *Arkansas* M & W
University of Arkansas at Monticello *Arkansas* W
University of Arkansas at Pine Bluff *Arkansas* M & W
University of Bridgeport *Connecticut* M & W
The University of British Columbia *British Columbia (Canada)* M & W
The University of British Columbia - Okanagan Campus *British Columbia (Canada)* M & W
University at Buffalo, the State University of New York *New York* M & W
University of Calgary *Alberta (Canada)* M & W
University of California, Berkeley *California* M & W
University of California, Davis *California* M & W
University of California, Irvine *California* M & W
University of California, Los Angeles *California* M & W
University of California, Merced *California* M & W
University of California, Riverside *California* M & W
University of California, San Diego *California* M & W
University of California, Santa Barbara *California* M & W
University of California, Santa Cruz *California* M & W
University of Central Arkansas *Arkansas* M & W
University of Central Florida *Florida* W
University of Central Missouri *Missouri* M & W
University of Central Oklahoma *Oklahoma* W
University of Charleston *West Virginia* W
University of Chicago *Illinois* M & W
University of Cincinnati *Ohio* M & W
University of Colorado Boulder *Colorado* M & W
University of Colorado Colorado Springs *Colorado* M & W
University of Connecticut *Connecticut* M & W
University of the Cumberlands *Kentucky* M & W
University of Dallas *Texas* M & W
University of Dayton *Ohio* M & W
University of Delaware *Delaware* M & W
University of Denver *Colorado* M & W
University of Detroit Mercy *Michigan* M & W
University of the District of Columbia *District of Columbia* W

M = Men; W = Women

University of Dubuque *Iowa* M & W
University of Evansville *Indiana* M & W
The University of Findlay *Ohio* M & W
University of Florida *Florida* M & W
University of Georgia *Georgia* M & W
University of Great Falls *Montana* M & W
University of Guelph *Ontario (Canada)* M & W
University of Hartford *Connecticut* M & W
University of Hawaii at Hilo *Hawaii* M & W
University of Hawaii at Manoa *Hawaii* W
University of Houston *Texas* M & W
University of Idaho *Idaho* M & W
University of Illinois at Chicago *Illinois* M & W
University of Illinois at Springfield *Illinois* M & W
University of Illinois at Urbana - Champaign *Illinois* M & W
University of the Incarnate Word *Texas* M & W
University of Indianapolis *Indiana* M & W
The University of Iowa *Iowa* M & W
University of Jamestown *North Dakota* M & W
The University of Kansas *Kansas* M & W
University of Kentucky *Kentucky* M & W
University of La Verne *California* M & W
University of Louisiana at Lafayette *Louisiana* M & W
University of Louisiana at Monroe *Louisiana* M & W
University of Louisville *Kentucky* M & W
University of Maine *Maine* M & W
University of Maine at Augusta *Maine* M & W
University of Maine at Farmington *Maine* M & W
University of Maine at Machias *Maine* M & W
University of Maine at Presque Isle *Maine* M & W
University of Manitoba *Manitoba (Canada)* M & W
University of Mary *North Dakota* M & W
University of Mary Washington *Virginia* M & W
University of Maryland, Baltimore County *Maryland* M & W
University of Maryland, College Park *Maryland* W
University of Maryland Eastern Shore *Maryland* M & W
University of Massachusetts Amherst *Massachusetts* M & W
University of Massachusetts Boston *Massachusetts* M & W
University of Massachusetts Dartmouth *Massachusetts* M & W
University of Massachusetts Lowell *Massachusetts* M & W
University of Memphis *Tennessee* M & W
University of Miami *Florida* M & W
University of Michigan *Michigan* M & W
University of Michigan - Dearborn *Michigan* M & W
University of Minnesota, Duluth *Minnesota* M & W
University of Minnesota, Morris *Minnesota* M & W
University of Minnesota, Twin Cities Campus *Minnesota* M & W
University of Mississippi *Mississippi* M & W
University of Missouri *Missouri* M & W
University of Missouri - Kansas City *Missouri* M & W
University of Mobile *Alabama* M & W
University of Montana *Montana* M & W
The University of Montana Western *Montana* M & W
University of Montevallo *Alabama* M & W
University of Mount Olive *North Carolina* M & W
University of Mount Union *Ohio* M & W
University of Nebraska at Kearney *Nebraska* M & W
University of Nebraska - Lincoln *Nebraska* M & W
University of Nevada, Las Vegas *Nevada* W
University of Nevada, Reno *Nevada* W
University of New Brunswick Fredericton *New Brunswick (Canada)* M & W
University of New Brunswick Saint John *New Brunswick (Canada)* M & W
University of New England *Maine* M & W
University of New Hampshire *New Hampshire* M & W
University of New Haven *Connecticut* M & W
University of New Mexico *New Mexico* M & W
University of New Orleans *Louisiana* M & W
University of North Alabama *Alabama* M & W

University of North Carolina at Asheville *North Carolina* M & W
The University of North Carolina at Chapel Hill *North Carolina* M & W
The University of North Carolina at Charlotte *North Carolina* M & W
The University of North Carolina at Greensboro *North Carolina* M & W
The University of North Carolina at Pembroke *North Carolina* M & W
The University of North Carolina Wilmington *North Carolina* M & W
University of North Dakota *North Dakota* M & W
University of North Florida *Florida* M & W
University of North Georgia *Georgia* M & W
University of North Texas *Texas* M & W
University of Northern Colorado *Colorado* W
University of Northern Iowa *Iowa* M & W
University of Northwestern - St. Paul *Minnesota* M & W
University of Notre Dame *Indiana* M & W
University of Oklahoma *Oklahoma* M & W
University of Oregon *Oregon* M & W
University of Ottawa *Ontario (Canada)* M & W
University of the Pacific *California* W
University of Pennsylvania *Pennsylvania* M & W
University of Pikeville *Kentucky* M & W
University of Pittsburgh *Pennsylvania* M & W
University of Pittsburgh at Bradford *Pennsylvania* M & W
University of Pittsburgh at Greensburg *Pennsylvania* M & W
University of Pittsburgh at Johnstown *Pennsylvania* W
University of Portland *Oregon* M & W
University of Puerto Rico in Aguadilla *Puerto Rico* M & W
University of Puerto Rico in Arecibo *Puerto Rico* M & W
University of Puerto Rico in Bayamón *Puerto Rico* M & W
University of Puerto Rico in Carolina *Puerto Rico* M & W
University of Puerto Rico in Cayey *Puerto Rico* M & W
University of Puerto Rico in Humacao *Puerto Rico* M & W
University of Puerto Rico, Mayagüez Campus *Puerto Rico* M & W
University of Puerto Rico in Ponce *Puerto Rico* M & W
University of Puerto Rico, Río Piedras Campus *Puerto Rico* M & W
University of Puerto Rico in Utuado *Puerto Rico* M & W
University of Puget Sound *Washington* M & W
University of Redlands *California* M & W
University of Regina *Saskatchewan (Canada)* M & W
University of Rhode Island *Rhode Island* M & W
University of Richmond *Virginia* M & W
University of Rio Grande *Ohio* M & W
University of Rochester *New York* M & W
University of St. Francis *Illinois* M & W
University of Saint Francis *Indiana* M & W
University of Saint Joseph *Connecticut* W
University of Saint Mary *Kansas* M & W
University of St. Thomas *Minnesota* M & W
University of San Diego *California* M & W
University of San Francisco *California* M & W
University of Saskatchewan *Saskatchewan (Canada)* M & W
University of Science and Arts of Oklahoma *Oklahoma* M & W
University of the Sciences *Pennsylvania* M & W
The University of Scranton *Pennsylvania* M & W
University of Sioux Falls *South Dakota* M & W
University of South Alabama *Alabama* M & W
University of South Carolina *South Carolina* M & W
University of South Carolina Aiken *South Carolina* W
University of South Carolina Beaufort *South Carolina* M & W

University of South Carolina Upstate *South Carolina* M & W
The University of South Dakota *South Dakota* M & W
University of South Florida *Florida* M & W
University of Southern California *California* M & W
University of Southern Indiana *Indiana* M & W
University of Southern Maine *Maine* M & W
University of Southern Mississippi *Mississippi* W
University of the Southwest *New Mexico* M & W
The University of Tampa *Florida* M & W
The University of Tennessee *Tennessee* M & W
The University of Tennessee at Chattanooga *Tennessee* M & W
The University of Tennessee at Martin *Tennessee* M & W
The University of Texas at Arlington *Texas* M & W
The University of Texas at Austin *Texas* M & W
The University of Texas at Dallas *Texas* M & W
The University of Texas at El Paso *Texas* M & W
The University of Texas of the Permian Basin *Texas* M & W
The University of Texas Rio Grande Valley *Texas* M & W
The University of Texas at San Antonio *Texas* M & W
The University of Texas at Tyler *Texas* M & W
The University of Toledo *Ohio* M & W
University of Toronto *Ontario (Canada)* M & W
The University of Tulsa *Oklahoma* M & W
University of Utah *Utah* M & W
University of Valley Forge *Pennsylvania* M & W
University of Vermont *Vermont* M & W
University of Victoria *British Columbia (Canada)* M & W
University of the Virgin Islands *United States Virgin Islands* M & W
University of Virginia *Virginia* M & W
The University of Virginia's College at Wise *Virginia* M & W
University of Washington *Washington* M & W
University of Waterloo *Ontario (Canada)* M & W
The University of West Alabama *Alabama* M & W
University of West Florida *Florida* M & W
University of West Georgia *Georgia* M & W
The University of Western Ontario *Ontario (Canada)* M & W
University of Windsor *Ontario (Canada)* M & W
University of Wisconsin - Eau Claire *Wisconsin* M & W
University of Wisconsin - Green Bay *Wisconsin* M & W
University of Wisconsin - La Crosse *Wisconsin* M & W
University of Wisconsin - Madison *Wisconsin* M & W
University of Wisconsin - Milwaukee *Wisconsin* M & W
University of Wisconsin - Oshkosh *Wisconsin* M & W
University of Wisconsin - Parkside *Wisconsin* M & W
University of Wisconsin - Platteville *Wisconsin* M & W
University of Wisconsin - River Falls *Wisconsin* M & W
University of Wisconsin - Stevens Point *Wisconsin* M & W
University of Wisconsin - Stout *Wisconsin* M & W
University of Wisconsin - Superior *Wisconsin* M & W
University of Wisconsin - Whitewater *Wisconsin* M & W
University of Wyoming *Wyoming* M & W
Upper Iowa University *Iowa* M & W
Ursinus College *Pennsylvania* M & W
Ursuline College *Ohio* W
Utah State University *Utah* M & W
Utah Valley University *Utah* M & W
Utica College *New York* M & W
Valdosta State University *Georgia* M & W
Valley City State University *North Dakota* M & W
Valley Forge Military College *Pennsylvania* M
Valparaiso University *Indiana* M & W

M = Men; W = Women

Vanderbilt University *Tennessee* M & W
Vanguard University of Southern California *California* M & W
Vassar College *New York* M & W
Vaughn College of Aeronautics and Technology *New York* M & W
Victor Valley College *California* M & W
Villa Maria College *New York* M & W
Villanova University *Pennsylvania* M & W
Vincennes University *Indiana* M & W
Virginia Commonwealth University *Virginia* M & W
Virginia Military Institute *Virginia* M & W
Virginia Polytechnic Institute and State University *Virginia* M & W
Virginia State University *Virginia* M & W
Virginia Union University *Virginia* M & W
Virginia Wesleyan College *Virginia* M & W
Viterbo University *Wisconsin* M & W
Voorhees College *South Carolina* M & W
Wabash College *Indiana* M
Wagner College *New York* M & W
Wake Forest University *North Carolina* M & W
Waldorf College *Iowa* M & W
Wallace State Community College *Alabama* M & W
Walsh University *Ohio* M & W
Warner Pacific College *Oregon* M & W
Warner University *Florida* M & W
Warren Wilson College *North Carolina* M & W
Wartburg College *Iowa* M & W
Washington Adventist University *Maryland* M & W
Washington & Jefferson College *Pennsylvania* M & W
Washington and Lee University *Virginia* M & W
Washington State University *Washington* M & W
Washington University in St. Louis *Missouri* M & W
Waubonsee Community College *Illinois* M & W
Wayland Baptist University *Texas* M & W
Wayne County Community College District *Michigan* M & W
Wayne State College *Nebraska* M & W
Wayne State University *Michigan* M & W
Waynesburg University *Pennsylvania* M & W
Webb Institute *New York* M & W
Webber International University *Florida* M & W
Weber State University *Utah* M & W
Webster University *Missouri* M & W
Wellesley College *Massachusetts* W
Wells College *New York* M & W
Wentworth Institute of Technology *Massachusetts* M
Wentworth Military Academy and College *Missouri* M & W
Wesleyan College *Georgia* W
Wesleyan University *Connecticut* M & W
West Chester University of Pennsylvania *Pennsylvania* M & W
West Liberty University *West Virginia* M & W
West Texas A&M University *Texas* M & W
West Valley College *California* M & W
West Virginia State University *West Virginia* W
West Virginia University *West Virginia* W
West Virginia University Institute of Technology *West Virginia* M & W
West Virginia Wesleyan College *West Virginia* M & W
Western Carolina University *North Carolina* M & W
Western Illinois University *Illinois* M & W
Western Kentucky University *Kentucky* M & W
Western Michigan University *Michigan* W
Western New England University *Massachusetts* M & W
Western New Mexico University *New Mexico* M & W
Western Oregon University *Oregon* M & W
Western State Colorado University *Colorado* M & W
Western Texas College *Texas* M & W
Western Washington University *Washington* M & W
Westfield State University *Massachusetts* M & W
Westminster College *Missouri* M & W
Westminster College *Pennsylvania* M & W
Westminster College *Utah* M & W
Westmont College *California* M & W

Westmoreland County Community College *Pennsylvania* M & W
Whatcom Community College *Washington* M & W
Wheaton College *Illinois* M & W
Wheaton College *Massachusetts* M & W
Wheeling Jesuit University *West Virginia* M & W
Wheelock College *Massachusetts* M & W
Whitman College *Washington* M & W
Whittier College *California* M & W
Whitworth University *Washington* M & W
Wichita State University *Kansas* M & W
Widener University *Pennsylvania* M & W
Wilfrid Laurier University *Ontario (Canada)* M & W
Wilkes University *Pennsylvania* M & W
Willamette University *Oregon* M & W
William Jessup University *California* M & W
William Jewell College *Missouri* M & W
William Peace University *North Carolina* W
William Penn University *Iowa* M & W
William Woods University *Missouri* M & W
Williams Baptist College *Arkansas* M & W
Williams College *Massachusetts* M & W
Williamson College of the Trades *Pennsylvania* M
Wilmington College *Ohio* M & W
Wilmington University *Delaware* M & W
Wilson College *Pennsylvania* M & W
Wingate University *North Carolina* M & W
Winona State University *Minnesota* M & W
Winston-Salem State University *North Carolina* M & W
Winthrop University *South Carolina* M & W
Wisconsin Lutheran College *Wisconsin* M & W
Wittenberg University *Ohio* M & W
Wofford College *South Carolina* M & W
Worcester Polytechnic Institute *Massachusetts* M & W
Worcester State University *Massachusetts* M & W
Wright State University *Ohio* M & W
Xavier University *Ohio* M & W
Xavier University of Louisiana *Louisiana* M & W
Yale University *Connecticut* M & W
Yeshiva University *New York* M & W
York College *Nebraska* M & W
York College of the City University of New York *New York* M & W
York College of Pennsylvania *Pennsylvania* M & W
York University *Ontario (Canada)* M & W
Young Harris College *Georgia* M & W
Youngstown State University *Ohio* M & W
Yuba College *California* M & W

Equestrian Sports

Adrian College *Michigan* W
Albion College *Michigan* M & W
Alfred University *New York* M & W
Allegheny College *Pennsylvania* M & W
Alma College *Michigan* W
Amherst College *Massachusetts* M & W
Appalachian State University *North Carolina* W
Arcadia University *Pennsylvania* M & W
Auburn University *Alabama* W
Augustana College *Illinois* M & W
Averett University *Virginia* M & W
Ball State University *Indiana* M & W
Barnard College *New York* W
Bates College *Maine* M & W
Baylor University *Texas* W
Becker College *Massachusetts* M & W
Berry College *Georgia* W
Bethany Lutheran College *Minnesota* M & W
Boston University *Massachusetts* M & W
Bowdoin College *Maine* M & W
Bridgewater College *Virginia* M & W
Brown University *Rhode Island* W
Bucknell University *Pennsylvania* M & W
Bucks County Community College *Pennsylvania* M & W
Butler University *Indiana* W
California State University, Fresno *California* W
California State University, Fullerton *California* M & W
Calvin College *Michigan* M & W
Canisius College *New York* W
Carleton College *Minnesota* M & W

Casper College *Wyoming* M & W
Castleton University *Vermont* W
Cazenovia College *New York* M & W
Cedar Crest College *Pennsylvania* W
Centenary College *New Jersey* M & W
Central Arizona College *Arizona* W
Central Washington University *Washington* M & W
Central Wyoming College *Wyoming* M & W
Christopher Newport University *Virginia* M & W
Claremont McKenna College *California* M & W
Clemson University *South Carolina* M & W
Coastal Carolina University *South Carolina* M & W
Colby Community College *Kansas* M & W
Colby-Sawyer College *New Hampshire* M & W
Colgate University *New York* M & W
College of Charleston *South Carolina* W
College of Southern Idaho *Idaho* M & W
The College of Wooster *Ohio* M & W
The Colorado College *Colorado* M & W
Columbia University, School of General Studies *New York* M & W
Connecticut College *Connecticut* M & W
Converse College *South Carolina* W
Cornell University *New York* W
Curry College *Massachusetts* M & W
Dartmouth College *New Hampshire* M & W
Dawson Community College *Montana* M & W
Delaware State University *Delaware* W
Denison University *Ohio* M & W
Dickinson College *Pennsylvania* M & W
Drew University *New Jersey* W
Duke University *North Carolina* M & W
Earlham College *Indiana* W
East Stroudsburg University of Pennsylvania *Pennsylvania* M & W
Eastern Illinois University *Illinois* M & W
Eastern Oklahoma State College *Oklahoma* M & W
Eastern Washington University *Washington* M & W
Eastern Wyoming College *Wyoming* M & W
Elon University *North Carolina* M & W
Emory & Henry College *Virginia* M & W
Emory University *Georgia* M & W
Endicott College *Massachusetts* M & W
Erskine College *South Carolina* W
Feather River College *California* W
Florida Southern College *Florida* W
Franklin & Marshall College *Pennsylvania* W
Furman University *South Carolina* W
Georgia State University *Georgia* M & W
Gettysburg College *Pennsylvania* M & W
Goucher College *Maryland* M & W
Hamilton College *New York* M & W
Hampshire College *Massachusetts* M & W
Hartwick College *New York* W
Hillsdale College *Michigan* M & W
Hobart and William Smith Colleges *New York* M & W
Hollins University *Virginia* W
Hood College *Maryland* M & W
Johnson & Wales University *Rhode Island* M & W
Judson College *Alabama* W
Kenyon College *Ohio* M & W
Keuka College *New York* M & W
Kutztown University of Pennsylvania *Pennsylvania* M & W
Lafayette College *Pennsylvania* M & W
Lake Forest College *Illinois* M & W
Lakehead University *Ontario (Canada)* M & W
Lamar Community College *Colorado* M & W
Landmark College *Vermont* M & W
Laramie County Community College *Wyoming* M & W
Lehigh University *Pennsylvania* M & W
Liberty University *Virginia* W
Long Island University - LIU Post *New York* M & W
Lycoming College *Pennsylvania* M & W
Lynchburg College *Virginia* M & W
Manchester University *Indiana* W
Marist College *New York* M & W
Maryville College *Tennessee* M & W
Merced College *California* M & W
Miami University *Ohio* M & W
Michigan State University *Michigan* M & W

M = Men; W = Women

Middle Tennessee State University *Tennessee* M & W
Midway University *Kentucky* W
Missouri State University *Missouri* M & W
Mitchell Technical Institute *South Dakota* M & W
Moravian College *Pennsylvania* M & W
Morehead State University *Kentucky* M & W
Morrisville State College *New York* M & W
Mount Holyoke College *Massachusetts* W
Mount Ida College *Massachusetts* W
Mount St. Mary's University *Maryland* M & W
Murray State University *Kentucky* M & W
National American University *Rapid City, South Dakota* M & W
Nazareth College of Rochester *New York* M & W
New Mexico State University *New Mexico* W
North Carolina State University *North Carolina* M & W
North Central Texas College *Texas* M & W
North Dakota State University *North Dakota* W
Northeast Texas Community College *Texas* M & W
Northeastern Junior College *Colorado* M & W
Northwest College *Wyoming* W
Northwest Mississippi Community College *Mississippi* M & W
Oberlin College *Ohio* M & W
Ohio Wesleyan University *Ohio* M & W
Oklahoma Panhandle State University *Oklahoma* W
Oklahoma State University *Oklahoma* W
Old Dominion University *Virginia* M & W
Otterbein University *Ohio* M & W
Panola College *Texas* M & W
Post University *Connecticut* M & W
Randolph College *Virginia* M & W
Randolph-Macon College *Virginia* M & W
Rensselaer Polytechnic Institute *New York* M & W
Rice University *Texas* M & W
Rochester Institute of Technology *New York* M & W
Rocky Mountain College *Montana* M & W
Roger Williams University *Rhode Island* M & W
Sacred Heart University *Connecticut* W
Saginaw Valley State University *Michigan* M & W
St. Andrews University *North Carolina* M & W
St. Cloud State University *Minnesota* M & W
St. Francis Xavier University *Nova Scotia (Canada)* W
St. Joseph's College, Long Island Campus *New York* W
St. Lawrence University *New York* W
Saint Louis University *Missouri* M & W
Saint Mary-of-the-Woods College *Indiana* W
St. Mary's College of Maryland *Maryland* M & W
Saint Vincent College *Pennsylvania* M & W
Sam Houston State University *Texas* M & W
Santa Clara University *California* M & W
Sarah Lawrence College *New York* M & W
Savannah College of Art and Design *Georgia* M & W
Scripps College *California* W
Seton Hill University *Pennsylvania* W
Sewanee: The University of the South *Tennessee* W
Sheridan College *Wyoming* M & W
Siena College *New York* M & W
Skidmore College *New York* W
Slippery Rock University of Pennsylvania *Pennsylvania* M & W
Smith College *Massachusetts* W
South Dakota State University *South Dakota* M & W
South Plains College *Texas* M & W
Southern Methodist University *Texas* W
Southern Nazarene University *Oklahoma* M & W
Southwest Texas Junior College *Texas* M & W
Southwestern Oklahoma State University *Oklahoma* M & W
Stanford University *California* M & W
State University of New York College at Geneseo *New York* W
Stevens Institute of Technology *New Jersey* W
Stonehill College *Massachusetts* W
Susquehanna University *Pennsylvania* M & W
Sweet Briar College *Virginia* W
Syracuse University *New York* M & W

M = Men; W = Women

Texas A&M University *Texas* W
Texas Christian University *Texas* W
Texas State University *Texas* M & W
Transylvania University *Kentucky* M & W
Trinity College *Connecticut* M & W
Truman State University *Missouri* M & W
Tufts University *Massachusetts* M & W
Union College *New York* W
United States Air Force Academy *Colorado* M & W
United States Military Academy *New York* M & W
The University of Alabama *Alabama* M & W
The University of British Columbia *British Columbia (Canada)* M & W
University of California, Santa Barbara *California* M & W
University of California, Santa Cruz *California* M & W
University of Colorado Boulder *Colorado* M & W
University of Delaware *Delaware* M & W
University of Denver *Colorado* M & W
The University of Findlay *Ohio* W
University of Georgia *Georgia* W
University of Great Falls *Montana* M & W
University of Mary Washington *Virginia* M & W
University of Massachusetts Dartmouth *Massachusetts* W
University of Minnesota, Crookston *Minnesota* W
University of Mississippi *Mississippi* M & W
University of Montana *Montana* W
University of North Carolina at Asheville *North Carolina* M & W
The University of North Carolina at Chapel Hill *North Carolina* M & W
University of North Georgia *Georgia* W
University of North Texas *Texas* M & W
University of Ottawa *Ontario (Canada)* M & W
University of Richmond *Virginia* M & W
University of Rochester *New York* M & W
University of San Diego *California* M & W
The University of Scranton *Pennsylvania* M & W
University of South Carolina *South Carolina* W
University of Southern California *California* W
The University of Tennessee at Martin *Tennessee* W
University of Vermont *Vermont* M & W
The University of Western Ontario *Ontario (Canada)* W
University of Wisconsin - Milwaukee *Wisconsin* M & W
University of Wisconsin - River Falls *Wisconsin* M & W
University of Wyoming *Wyoming* M & W
Utah State University *Utah* M & W
Valley Forge Military College *Pennsylvania* M
Vernon College *Texas* M & W
Villanova University *Pennsylvania* M & W
Washington College *Maryland* M & W
Washington & Jefferson College *Pennsylvania* M & W
Washington and Lee University *Virginia* M & W
Washington State University *Washington* W
Washington University in St. Louis *Missouri* M & W
Weatherford College *Texas* M & W
Wesleyan College *Georgia* W
Wesleyan University *Connecticut* M & W
West Chester University of Pennsylvania *Pennsylvania* M & W
West Hills Community College *California* M & W
West Texas A&M University *Texas* M & W
Western Carolina University *North Carolina* M & W
Western Michigan University *Michigan* W
Western Oklahoma State College *Oklahoma* M & W
Westminster College *Pennsylvania* M & W
Westmont College *California* W
Williams College *Massachusetts* M & W
Xavier University *Ohio* M & W
Yale University *Connecticut* M & W

Fencing

Allegheny College *Pennsylvania* M & W
Amherst College *Massachusetts* M & W
Appalachian State University *North Carolina* M & W
Augustana College *Illinois* M & W

Ball State University *Indiana* M & W
Barnard College *New York* W
Bates College *Maine* M & W
Baylor University *Texas* M & W
Bennington College *Vermont* M & W
Boston College *Massachusetts* M & W
Boston University *Massachusetts* M & W
Bowdoin College *Maine* M & W
Brandeis University *Massachusetts* M & W
Brock University *Ontario (Canada)* M & W
Brown University *Rhode Island* M & W
Buffalo State College, State University of New York *New York* M
California Institute of Technology *California* M & W
California State University, Long Beach *California* M & W
Carleton College *Minnesota* M & W
Carleton University *Ontario (Canada)* M & W
Carnegie Mellon University *Pennsylvania* M & W
Central Washington University *Washington* M & W
City College of the City University of New York *New York* W
Claremont McKenna College *California* M & W
Clark College *Washington* M & W
Clemson University *South Carolina* M & W
Cleveland State University *Ohio* M & W
Colby College *Maine* M & W
Colgate University *New York* M & W
College of the Desert *California* M & W
Columbia University *New York* M & W
Columbia University, School of General Studies *New York* M & W
Cornell University *New York* W
Dartmouth College *New Hampshire* M & W
Davidson College *North Carolina* M & W
Dickinson College *Pennsylvania* M & W
Drew University *New Jersey* M & W
Duke University *North Carolina* M & W
Eastern Connecticut State University *Connecticut* M & W
Eastern Washington University *Washington* M & W
Emory University *Georgia* M & W
Fairleigh Dickinson University, Metropolitan Campus *New Jersey* W
Fort Lewis College *Colorado* M & W
Furman University *South Carolina* M & W
Grove City College *Pennsylvania* M & W
Hamilton College *New York* M & W
Hampden-Sydney College *Virginia* M
Hampshire College *Massachusetts* M & W
Harvard University *Massachusetts* M & W
Haverford College *Pennsylvania* M & W
Hollins University *Virginia* W
Hunter College of the City University of New York *New York* M & W
Johns Hopkins University *Maryland* M & W
Kutztown University of Pennsylvania *Pennsylvania* M & W
Lafayette College *Pennsylvania* M & W
Lake Forest College *Illinois* M & W
Lawrence University *Wisconsin* M & W
Lehigh University *Pennsylvania* M & W
Long Island University - LIU Post *New York* W
Lycoming College *Pennsylvania* M & W
Marist College *New York* M & W
Massachusetts Institute of Technology *Massachusetts* M & W
McGill University *Quebec (Canada)* M & W
McKendree University *Illinois* M & W
McMaster University *Ontario (Canada)* M & W
Miami University *Ohio* M & W
Michigan State University *Michigan* M & W
Michigan Technological University *Michigan* M & W
Midwestern State University *Texas* M & W
New Jersey Institute of Technology *New Jersey* M & W
New Mexico Military Institute *New Mexico* M & W
New York University *New York* M & W
North Carolina State University *North Carolina* M & W
Norwich University *Vermont* M & W
Oberlin College *Ohio* M & W
The Ohio State University *Ohio* M & W
Old Dominion University *Virginia* M & W

Penn State University Park *Pennsylvania* M & W
Princeton University *New Jersey* M & W
Queens College of the City University of New York *New York* W
Queen's University at Kingston *Ontario (Canada)* M & W
Rensselaer Polytechnic Institute *New York* M & W
Rhodes College *Tennessee* M & W
Rice University *Texas* M & W
Rochester Institute of Technology *New York* M & W
Royal Military College of Canada *Ontario (Canada)* M & W
Rutgers University - New Brunswick *New Jersey* M & W
Ryerson University *Ontario (Canada)* M & W
Sacred Heart University *Connecticut* M & W
St. John's College *Maryland* M & W
St. John's College *New Mexico* M & W
St. John's University *New York* M & W
Saint Louis University *Missouri* M & W
St. Mary's College of Maryland *Maryland* M & W
Saint Vincent College *Pennsylvania* M & W
San Joaquin Delta College *California* M & W
Scripps College *California* W
Sewanee: The University of the South *Tennessee* M & W
Southern Methodist University *Texas* M & W
Stanford University *California* M & W
State University of New York College at Geneseo *New York* M & W
State University of New York College at Oneonta *New York* M & W
Stevens Institute of Technology *New Jersey* M & W
Swarthmore College *Pennsylvania* M & W
Sweet Briar College *Virginia* W
Syracuse University *New York* M & W
Temple University *Pennsylvania* W
Texas State University *Texas* M & W
Trinity College *Connecticut* M & W
Trinity University *Texas* M & W
Tufts University *Massachusetts* W
United States Air Force Academy *Colorado* M & W
United States Military Academy *New York* M & W
United States Naval Academy *Maryland* M & W
University of California, Irvine *California* M & W
University of California, San Diego *California* M & W
University of California, Santa Barbara *California* M & W
University of California, Santa Cruz *California* M & W
University of Colorado Boulder *Colorado* M & W
University of Detroit Mercy *Michigan* M & W
University of Georgia *Georgia* M & W
University of Maryland, Baltimore County *Maryland* M & W
University of Michigan *Michigan* M & W
University of Mississippi *Mississippi* M & W
University of Montana *Montana* M & W
University of New Brunswick Saint John *New Brunswick (Canada)* M & W
University of New Hampshire *New Hampshire* M & W
University of North Carolina at Asheville *North Carolina* M & W
The University of North Carolina at Chapel Hill *North Carolina* M & W
University of North Texas *Texas* M & W
University of Notre Dame *Indiana* M & W
University of Ottawa *Ontario (Canada)* M & W
University of Pennsylvania *Pennsylvania* M & W
University of Puget Sound *Washington* M & W
University of Rochester *New York* M & W
University of St. Thomas *Texas* M & W
The University of Scranton *Pennsylvania* M & W
University of South Florida *Florida* M & W
University of Southern California *California* W
University of Southern Maine *Maine* M & W
The University of Texas at Austin *Texas* M & W
The University of Texas at San Antonio *Texas* M & W
University of Toronto *Ontario (Canada)* M & W
University of Utah *Utah* M & W
University of Vermont *Vermont* M & W

The University of Western Ontario *Ontario (Canada)* M & W
University of Wisconsin - Madison *Wisconsin* M & W
University of Wyoming *Wyoming* M & W
Vassar College *New York* M & W
Wagner College *New York* W
Washington State University *Washington* M & W
Washington University in St. Louis *Missouri* M & W
Wayne State University *Michigan* M & W
Wellesley College *Massachusetts* W
West Chester University of Pennsylvania *Pennsylvania* M & W
Western Carolina University *North Carolina* M & W
Winthrop University *South Carolina* M & W
Xavier University *Ohio* M & W
Yale University *Connecticut* M & W
Yeshiva University *New York* M & W

Field Hockey

Adelphi University *New York* W
Albright College *Pennsylvania* W
Alvernia University *Pennsylvania* W
American International College *Massachusetts* W
American University *District of Columbia* W
Amherst College *Massachusetts* W
Anna Maria College *Massachusetts* W
Appalachian State University *North Carolina* W
Arcadia University *Pennsylvania* W
Assumption College *Massachusetts* W
Babson College *Massachusetts* W
Ball State University *Indiana* W
Barnard College *New York* W
Bates College *Maine* W
Bay Path University *Massachusetts* W
Becker College *Massachusetts* W
Bellarmine University *Kentucky* W
Bentley University *Massachusetts* W
Bethany College *West Virginia* W
Bishop's University *Quebec (Canada)* W
Bloomsburg University of Pennsylvania *Pennsylvania* W
Boston College *Massachusetts* W
Boston University *Massachusetts* W
Bowdoin College *Maine* W
Bridgewater College *Virginia* W
Bridgewater State University *Massachusetts* W
Brock University *Ontario (Canada)* W
Brown University *Rhode Island* W
Bryant University *Rhode Island* W
Bryn Mawr College *Pennsylvania* W
Bucknell University *Pennsylvania* W
Cabrini University *Pennsylvania* W
Carleton College *Minnesota* W
Carleton University *Ontario (Canada)* W
Castleton University *Vermont* W
The Catholic University of America *District of Columbia* W
Cedar Crest College *Pennsylvania* W
Central Michigan University *Michigan* W
Centre College *Kentucky* W
Christopher Newport University *Virginia* W
Claremont McKenna College *California* M & W
Clark University *Massachusetts* W
Clemson University *South Carolina* M & W
Coastal Carolina University *South Carolina* M & W
Colby College *Maine* W
Colby-Sawyer College *New Hampshire* W
Colgate University *New York* W
The College at Brockport, State University of New York *New York* W
College of the Holy Cross *Massachusetts* W
The College of New Jersey *New Jersey* W
The College of William and Mary *Virginia* W
The College of Wooster *Ohio* W
Colorado State University *Colorado* M & W
Columbia University *New York* W
Columbia University, School of General Studies *New York* W
Connecticut College *Connecticut* W
Cornell University *New York* W
Dalhousie University *Nova Scotia (Canada)* W
Daniel Webster College *New Hampshire* W
Dartmouth College *New Hampshire* W

Davidson College *North Carolina* W
Delaware Valley University *Pennsylvania* W
Denison University *Ohio* W
DePauw University *Indiana* W
DeSales University *Pennsylvania* W
Dickinson College *Pennsylvania* W
Drew University *New Jersey* W
Drexel University *Pennsylvania* W
Duke University *North Carolina* M & W
Earlham College *Indiana* W
East Stroudsburg University of Pennsylvania *Pennsylvania* W
Eastern Connecticut State University *Connecticut* W
Eastern Mennonite University *Virginia* W
Eastern University *Pennsylvania* W
Elizabethtown College *Pennsylvania* W
Elmira College *New York* W
Elms College *Massachusetts* W
Elon University *North Carolina* W
Emory University *Georgia* M & W
Endicott College *Massachusetts* W
Fairfield University *Connecticut* W
Fairleigh Dickinson University, College at Florham *New Jersey* W
Fitchburg State University *Massachusetts* W
Fontbonne University *Missouri* W
Framingham State University *Massachusetts* W
Franklin & Marshall College *Pennsylvania* W
Franklin Pierce University *New Hampshire* W
Frostburg State University *Maryland* W
Georgetown University *District of Columbia* W
Gettysburg College *Pennsylvania* W
Gordon College *Massachusetts* W
Goucher College *Maryland* W
Gwynedd Mercy University *Pennsylvania* W
Hamilton College *New York* W
Hartwick College *New York* W
Harvard University *Massachusetts* W
Haverford College *Pennsylvania* W
Hendrix College *Arkansas* W
Herkimer County Community College *New York* W
Hobart and William Smith Colleges *New York* W
Hofstra University *New York* W
Hood College *Maryland* W
Houghton College *New York* W
Husson University *Maine* W
Immaculata University *Pennsylvania* W
Indiana University Bloomington *Indiana* W
Indiana University of Pennsylvania *Pennsylvania* W
Ithaca College *New York* W
James Madison University *Virginia* W
John Carroll University *Ohio* W
Johns Hopkins University *Maryland* W
Juniata College *Pennsylvania* W
Kean University *New Jersey* W
Keene State College *New Hampshire* W
Kent State University *Ohio* W
Kenyon College *Ohio* W
Keuka College *New York* W
Keystone College *Pennsylvania* W
King's College *Pennsylvania* W
Kutztown University of Pennsylvania *Pennsylvania* W
La Salle University *Pennsylvania* W
Lafayette College *Pennsylvania* W
Lasell College *Massachusetts* W
Lebanon Valley College *Pennsylvania* W
Lehigh University *Pennsylvania* W
Liberty University *Virginia* W
Limestone College *South Carolina* W
Lindenwood University *Missouri* W
Lock Haven University of Pennsylvania *Pennsylvania* W
Long Island University - LIU Brooklyn *New York* W
Long Island University - LIU Post *New York* W
Longwood University *Virginia* W
Lynchburg College *Virginia* W
Manhattanville College *New York* W
Mansfield University of Pennsylvania *Pennsylvania* W
Marywood University *Pennsylvania* W
Massachusetts Institute of Technology *Massachusetts* W

M = Men; W = Women

McDaniel College *Maryland* W
McGill University *Quebec (Canada)* W
Mercy College *New York* W
Mercyhurst University *Pennsylvania* W
Merrimack College *Massachusetts* W
Messiah College *Pennsylvania* W
Miami University *Ohio* M & W
Michigan State University *Michigan* W
Middlebury College *Vermont* W
Millersville University of Pennsylvania *Pennsylvania* W
Misericordia University *Pennsylvania* W
Missouri State University *Missouri* W
Monmouth University *New Jersey* W
Montclair State University *New Jersey* W
Moravian College *Pennsylvania* W
Morrisville State College *New York* W
Mount Holyoke College *Massachusetts* W
Muhlenberg College *Pennsylvania* W
Nazareth College of Rochester *New York* W
Neumann University *Pennsylvania* W
New England College *New Hampshire* W
Newberry College *South Carolina* W
Nichols College *Massachusetts* W
North Carolina State University *North Carolina* M & W
Northeastern University *Massachusetts* W
Notre Dame College *Ohio* W
Notre Dame of Maryland University *Maryland* W
Oberlin College *Ohio* W
The Ohio State University *Ohio* W
Ohio University *Ohio* W
Ohio Wesleyan University *Ohio* W
Old Dominion University *Virginia* W
Pace University *New York* W
Pace University, Pleasantville Campus *New York* W
Penn State University Park *Pennsylvania* W
Plymouth State University *New Hampshire* W
Princeton University *New Jersey* W
Providence College *Rhode Island* W
Queen's University at Kingston *Ontario (Canada)* W
Quinnipiac University *Connecticut* W
Ramapo College of New Jersey *New Jersey* W
Randolph-Macon College *Virginia* W
Regis College *Massachusetts* W
Rensselaer Polytechnic Institute *New York* W
Rhodes College *Tennessee* W
Rice University *Texas* W
Rider University *New Jersey* W
Rivier University *New Hampshire* W
Roanoke College *Virginia* W
Rochester Institute of Technology *New York* W
Roger Williams University *Rhode Island* W
Rowan University *New Jersey* W
Sacred Heart University *Connecticut* W
Saint Anselm College *New Hampshire* W
St. Bonaventure University *New York* W
Saint Francis University *Pennsylvania* W
St. Francis Xavier University *Nova Scotia (Canada)* W
St. John Fisher College *New York* W
Saint Joseph's College of Maine *Maine* W
Saint Joseph's University *Pennsylvania* W
St. Lawrence University *New York* W
Saint Louis University *Missouri* W
St. Mary's College of Maryland *Maryland* W
Saint Mary's University *Nova Scotia (Canada)* W
Saint Michael's College *Vermont* W
Salem College *North Carolina* W
Salem State University *Massachusetts* W
Salisbury University *Maryland* W
Salve Regina University *Rhode Island* W
Seton Hill University *Pennsylvania* W
Sewanee: The University of the South *Tennessee* W
Shenandoah University *Virginia* W
Shippensburg University of Pennsylvania *Pennsylvania* W
Siena College *New York* W
Simmons College *Massachusetts* W
Skidmore College *New York* W
Slippery Rock University of Pennsylvania *Pennsylvania* W

Smith College *Massachusetts* W
Southern Connecticut State University *Connecticut* W
Southern New Hampshire University *New Hampshire* W
Springfield College *Massachusetts* W
Stanford University *California* W
State University of New York College at Cortland *New York* W
State University of New York College at Geneseo *New York* W
State University of New York College at Oneonta *New York* W
State University of New York at Fredonia *New York* M & W
State University of New York at New Paltz *New York* W
State University of New York at Oswego *New York* W
Stevens Institute of Technology *New Jersey* W
Stevenson University *Maryland* W
Stockton University *New Jersey* W
Stonehill College *Massachusetts* W
Susquehanna University *Pennsylvania* W
Swarthmore College *Pennsylvania* W
Sweet Briar College *Virginia* W
Syracuse University *New York* W
Temple University *Pennsylvania* W
Thomas College *Maine* W
Towson University *Maryland* W
Transylvania University *Kentucky* W
Trine University *Indiana* W
Trinity Washington University *District of Columbia* W
Tufts University *Massachusetts* W
Union College *New York* W
United States Naval Academy *Maryland* W
The University of Alabama *Alabama* W
University at Albany, State University of New York *New York* W
The University of British Columbia *British Columbia (Canada)* M & W
University of Calgary *Alberta (Canada)* W
University of California, Berkeley *California* W
University of California, Davis *California* W
University of California, Santa Barbara *California* W
University of Colorado Boulder *Colorado* M & W
University of Connecticut *Connecticut* W
University of Delaware *Delaware* W
University of Guelph *Ontario (Canada)* W
The University of Iowa *Iowa* W
University of Louisville *Kentucky* W
University of Maine *Maine* W
University of Maine at Farmington *Maine* W
University of Manitoba *Manitoba (Canada)* M & W
University of Mary Washington *Virginia* W
University of Maryland, Baltimore County *Maryland* W
University of Maryland, College Park *Maryland* W
University of Massachusetts Amherst *Massachusetts* W
University of Massachusetts Dartmouth *Massachusetts* W
University of Massachusetts Lowell *Massachusetts* W
University of Michigan *Michigan* W
University of Montana *Montana* W
University of New England *Maine* W
University of New Hampshire *New Hampshire* W
University of New Haven *Connecticut* W
The University of North Carolina at Chapel Hill *North Carolina* M & W
University of the Pacific *California* W
University of Pennsylvania *Pennsylvania* W
University of Prince Edward Island *Prince Edward Island (Canada)* W
University of Richmond *Virginia* W
University of Rochester *New York* W
The University of Scranton *Pennsylvania* W
University of Southern California *California* W
University of Southern Maine *Maine* W
University of Toronto *Ontario (Canada)* W
University of Vermont *Vermont* W
University of Victoria *British Columbia (Canada)* W

University of Virginia *Virginia* W
University of Waterloo *Ontario (Canada)* W
The University of Western Ontario *Ontario (Canada)* W
Ursinus College *Pennsylvania* W
Utica College *New York* W
Vassar College *New York* W
Villanova University *Pennsylvania* W
Virginia Commonwealth University *Virginia* W
Virginia Wesleyan College *Virginia* W
Wake Forest University *North Carolina* W
Washington College *Maryland* W
Washington & Jefferson College *Pennsylvania* W
Washington and Lee University *Virginia* W
Washington University in St. Louis *Missouri* W
Wellesley College *Massachusetts* W
Wells College *New York* W
Wesley College *Delaware* W
Wesleyan University *Connecticut* W
West Chester University of Pennsylvania *Pennsylvania* W
Western Connecticut State University *Connecticut* W
Western New England University *Massachusetts* W
Westfield State University *Massachusetts* W
Wheaton College *Massachusetts* W
Wheelock College *Massachusetts* W
Widener University *Pennsylvania* W
Wilkes University *Pennsylvania* W
William Paterson University of New Jersey *New Jersey* W
Williams College *Massachusetts* W
Wilson College *Pennsylvania* W
Wittenberg University *Ohio* W
Worcester Polytechnic Institute *Massachusetts* W
Worcester State University *Massachusetts* W
Yale University *Connecticut* W
York College of Pennsylvania *Pennsylvania* W
York University *Ontario (Canada)* W

Football

Abilene Christian University *Texas* M
Acadia University *Nova Scotia (Canada)* M
Adams State University *Colorado* M
Adrian College *Michigan* M
Alabama Agricultural and Mechanical University *Alabama* M
Alabama State University *Alabama* M
Albany State University *Georgia* M
Albion College *Michigan* M
Albright College *Pennsylvania* M
Alcorn State University *Mississippi* M
Alderson Broaddus University *West Virginia* M
Alfred University *New York* M
Allan Hancock College *California* M
Allegheny College *Pennsylvania* M
Alma College *Michigan* M
American International College *Massachusetts* M
American River College *California* M
Amherst College *Massachusetts* M
Anderson University *Indiana* M
Angelo State University *Texas* M
Anna Maria College *Massachusetts* M
Antelope Valley College *California* M
Appalachian State University *North Carolina* M
Arizona Christian University *Arizona* M
Arizona State University at the Downtown Phoenix campus *Arizona* M
Arizona State University at the Polytechnic campus *Arizona* M
Arizona State University at the Tempe campus *Arizona* M
Arizona State University at the West campus *Arizona* M
Arizona Western College *Arizona* M
Arkansas Baptist College *Arkansas* M
Arkansas State University *Arkansas* M
Arkansas Tech University *Arkansas* M
ASA College *New York* M
Ashland University *Ohio* M
Assumption College *Massachusetts* M
Auburn University *Alabama* M
Augsburg College *Minnesota* M
Augustana College *Illinois* M

M = Men; W = Women

Augustana University *South Dakota* M
Aurora University *Illinois* M
Austin College *Texas* M
Austin Peay State University *Tennessee* M
Ave Maria University *Florida* M
Averett University *Virginia* M
Avila University *Missouri* M
Azusa Pacific University *California* M
Baker University *Kansas* M
Bakersfield College *California* M
Baldwin Wallace University *Ohio* M
Ball State University *Indiana* M
Bates College *Maine* M
Baylor University *Texas* M
Becker College *Massachusetts* M
Belhaven University *Mississippi* M
Beloit College *Wisconsin* M
Bemidji State University *Minnesota* M
Benedict College *South Carolina* M
Benedictine College *Kansas* M
Benedictine University *Illinois* M
Bentley University *Massachusetts* M
Berry College *Georgia* M
Bethany College *Kansas* M
Bethany College *West Virginia* M
Bethel College *Kansas* M
Bethel University *Minnesota* M
Bethel University *Tennessee* M
Bethune-Cookman University *Florida* M
Birmingham-Southern College *Alabama* M
Bishop's University *Quebec (Canada)* M
Black Hills State University *South Dakota* M
Blessing-Rieman College of Nursing *Illinois* M
Blinn College *Texas* M
Bloomsburg University of Pennsylvania *Pennsylvania* M
Bluefield College *Virginia* M
Bluffton University *Ohio* M
Boise State University *Idaho* M
Boston College *Massachusetts* M
Bowdoin College *Maine* M
Bowie State University *Maryland* M
Bowling Green State University *Ohio* M
Brevard College *North Carolina* M
Briar Cliff University *Iowa* M
Bridgewater College *Virginia* M
Bridgewater State University *Massachusetts* M
Brigham Young University *Utah* M
Brown University *Rhode Island* M
Bryant University *Rhode Island* M
Bucknell University *Pennsylvania* M
Buena Vista University *Iowa* M
Buffalo State College, State University of New York *New York* M
Butler Community College *Kansas* M
Butler University *Indiana* M
Butte College *California* M
Cabrillo College *California* M
California Lutheran University *California* M
California Polytechnic State University, San Luis Obispo *California* M
California State University, Fresno *California* M
California State University, Northridge *California* M
California State University, Sacramento *California* M
California University of Pennsylvania *Pennsylvania* M
Campbellsville University *Kentucky* M
Capital University *Ohio* M
Carleton College *Minnesota* M
Carleton University *Ontario (Canada)* M
Carnegie Mellon University *Pennsylvania* M
Carroll College *Montana* M
Carroll University *Wisconsin* M
Carson-Newman University *Tennessee* M
Carthage College *Wisconsin* M
Case Western Reserve University *Ohio* M
Castleton University *Vermont* M
Catawba College *North Carolina* M
The Catholic University of America *District of Columbia* M
Central College *Iowa* M
Central Connecticut State University *Connecticut* M
Central Lakes College *Minnesota* M

Central Methodist University *Missouri* M
Central Michigan University *Michigan* M
Central Washington University *Washington* M
Centre College *Kentucky* M
Cerritos College *California* M
Chabot College *California* M
Chadron State College *Nebraska* M
Chaffey College *California* M
Chapman University *California* M
Charleston Southern University *South Carolina* M
Chestnut Hill College *Pennsylvania* M
Cheyney University of Pennsylvania *Pennsylvania* M
Chowan University *North Carolina* M
Christopher Newport University *Virginia* M
Cisco College *Texas* M
The Citadel, The Military College of South Carolina *South Carolina* M
Citrus College *California* M
City College of San Francisco *California* M
Claremont McKenna College *California* M
Clarion University of Pennsylvania *Pennsylvania* M
Clark Atlanta University *Georgia* M
Clemson University *South Carolina* M
Coahoma Community College *Mississippi* M
Coastal Carolina University *South Carolina* M
Coe College *Iowa* M
Coffeyville Community College *Kansas* M
Colby College *Maine* M
Colgate University *New York* M
The College at Brockport, State University of New York *New York* M
College of the Canyons *California* M
College of the Desert *California* M
College of the Holy Cross *Massachusetts* M
The College of New Jersey *New Jersey* M
College of the Redwoods *California* M
The College of St. Scholastica *Minnesota* M
College of San Mateo *California* M
College of the Sequoias *California* M
College of the Siskiyous *California* M
The College of William and Mary *Virginia* M
The College of Wooster *Ohio* M
Colorado Mesa University *Colorado* M
Colorado School of Mines *Colorado* M
Colorado State University *Colorado* M
Colorado State University - Pueblo *Colorado* M
Columbia University *New York* M
Columbia University, School of General Studies *New York* M
Concord University *West Virginia* M
Concordia College *Minnesota* M
Concordia College Alabama *Alabama* M
Concordia University *Quebec (Canada)* M
Concordia University Ann Arbor *Michigan* M
Concordia University Chicago *Illinois* M
Concordia University, Nebraska *Nebraska* M
Concordia University, St. Paul *Minnesota* M
Concordia University Wisconsin *Wisconsin* M
Contra Costa College *California* M
Copiah-Lincoln Community College *Mississippi* M
Cornell College *Iowa* M
Cornell University *New York* M
Crown College *Minnesota* M
Culver-Stockton College *Missouri* M
Cumberland University *Tennessee* M
Curry College *Massachusetts* M
Dakota College at Bottineau *North Dakota* M
Dakota State University *South Dakota* M
Dakota Wesleyan University *South Dakota* M
Dartmouth College *New Hampshire* M
Davenport University *Michigan* M
Davidson College *North Carolina* M
De Anza College *California* M
Dean College *Massachusetts* M
Defiance College *Ohio* M
Delaware State University *Delaware* M
Delaware Valley University *Pennsylvania* M
Delta State University *Mississippi* M
Denison University *Ohio* M
DePauw University *Indiana* M
Diablo Valley College *California* M
Dickinson College *Pennsylvania* M
Dickinson State University *North Dakota* M

Dixie State University *Utah* M
Doane University *Nebraska* M
Dodge City Community College *Kansas* M
Dordt College *Iowa* M
Drake University *Iowa* M
Duke University *North Carolina* M & W
Duquesne University *Pennsylvania* M
Earlham College *Indiana* M
East Carolina University *North Carolina* M
East Central Community College *Mississippi* M
East Central University *Oklahoma* M
East Los Angeles College *California* M
East Mississippi Community College *Mississippi* M
East Stroudsburg University of Pennsylvania *Pennsylvania* M
East Tennessee State University *Tennessee* M
East Texas Baptist University *Texas* M
Eastern Arizona College *Arizona* M
Eastern Connecticut State University *Connecticut* M & W
Eastern Illinois University *Illinois* M
Eastern Kentucky University *Kentucky* M
Eastern Michigan University *Michigan* M
Eastern New Mexico University *New Mexico* M
Eastern Oregon University *Oregon* M
Eastern Washington University *Washington* M
Edinboro University of Pennsylvania *Pennsylvania* M
El Camino College *California* M
Elizabeth City State University *North Carolina* M
Ellsworth Community College *Iowa* M
Elmhurst College *Illinois* M
Elon University *North Carolina* M
Emory & Henry College *Virginia* M
Emporia State University *Kansas* M
Endicott College *Massachusetts* M
Erie Community College *New York* M
Erie Community College, North Campus *New York* M
Erie Community College, South Campus *New York* M
Eureka College *Illinois* M
Evangel University *Missouri* M
Fairleigh Dickinson University, College at Florham *New Jersey* M
Fairmont State University *West Virginia* M
Faulkner University *Alabama* M
Fayetteville State University *North Carolina* M
Feather River College *California* M
Ferris State University *Michigan* M
Ferrum College *Virginia* M
Fitchburg State University *Massachusetts* M
Florida Agricultural and Mechanical University *Florida* M
Florida Atlantic University *Florida* M
Florida Institute of Technology *Florida* M
Florida International University *Florida* M
Florida State University *Florida* M
Fond du Lac Tribal and Community College *Minnesota* M
Foothill College *California* M
Fordham University *New York* M
Fort Lewis College *Colorado* M
Fort Scott Community College *Kansas* M
Fort Valley State University *Georgia* M
Framingham State University *Massachusetts* M
Franklin College *Indiana* M
Franklin & Marshall College *Pennsylvania* M
Fresno City College *California* M
Friends University *Kansas* M
Frostburg State University *Maryland* M
Fullerton College *California* M
Furman University *South Carolina* M
Gallaudet University *District of Columbia* M
Gannon University *Pennsylvania* M
Garden City Community College *Kansas* M
Gardner-Webb University *North Carolina* M
Gavilan College *California* M
Geneva College *Pennsylvania* M
George Fox University *Oregon* M
Georgetown College *Kentucky* M
Georgetown University *District of Columbia* M
Georgia Institute of Technology *Georgia* M
Georgia Military College *Georgia* M

M = Men; W = Women

Georgia Southern University *Georgia* M
Georgia State University *Georgia* M
Gettysburg College *Pennsylvania* M
Glendale Community College *Arizona* M
Glendale Community College *California* M
Glenville State College *West Virginia* M
Golden West College *California* M
Graceland University *Iowa* M
Grambling State University *Louisiana* M
Grand Valley State University *Michigan* M
Grand View University *Iowa* M
Greensboro College *North Carolina* M
Greenville College *Illinois* M
Grinnell College *Iowa* M
Grossmont College *California* M
Grove City College *Pennsylvania* M
Guilford College *North Carolina* M
Gustavus Adolphus College *Minnesota* M
Hamilton College *New York* M
Hamline University *Minnesota* M
Hampden-Sydney College *Virginia* M
Hampton University *Virginia* M
Hanover College *Indiana* M
Hardin-Simmons University *Texas* M
Harding University *Arkansas* M
Hartwick College *New York* M
Harvard University *Massachusetts* M
Harvey Mudd College *California* M
Haskell Indian Nations University *Kansas* M
Hastings College *Nebraska* M
Heidelberg University *Ohio* M
Henderson State University *Arkansas* M
Hendrix College *Arkansas* M
Highland Community College *Kansas* M
Hillsdale College *Michigan* M
Hinds Community College *Mississippi* M
Hiram College *Ohio* M
Hobart and William Smith Colleges *New York* M
Holmes Community College *Mississippi* M
Hope College *Michigan* M
Houston Baptist University *Texas* M
Howard Payne University *Texas* M
Howard University *District of Columbia* M
Hudson Valley Community College *New York* M
Humboldt State University *California* M
Huntingdon College *Alabama* M
Husson University *Maine* M
Hutchinson Community College *Kansas* M
Idaho State University *Idaho* M
Illinois College *Illinois* M
Illinois State University *Illinois* M
Illinois Wesleyan University *Illinois* M
Independence Community College *Kansas* M
Indiana State University *Indiana* M
Indiana University Bloomington *Indiana* M
Indiana University of Pennsylvania *Pennsylvania* M
Iowa Central Community College *Iowa* M
Iowa State University of Science and Technology *Iowa* M
Iowa Wesleyan University *Iowa* M
Itasca Community College *Minnesota* M
Itawamba Community College *Mississippi* M
Ithaca College *New York* M
Jackson State University *Mississippi* M
Jacksonville State University *Alabama* M
Jacksonville University *Florida* M
James Madison University *Virginia* M
John Carroll University *Ohio* M
Johns Hopkins University *Maryland* M
Johnson C. Smith University *North Carolina* M
Joliet Junior College *Illinois* M
Jones County Junior College *Mississippi* M
Juniata College *Pennsylvania* M
Kalamazoo College *Michigan* M
Kansas State University *Kansas* M
Kansas Wesleyan University *Kansas* M
Kean University *New Jersey* M
Kennesaw State University *Georgia* M
Kent State University *Ohio* M
Kentucky Christian University *Kentucky* M
Kentucky State University *Kentucky* M
Kentucky Wesleyan College *Kentucky* M
Kenyon College *Ohio* M
Kilgore College *Texas* M

King's College *Pennsylvania* M
Knox College *Illinois* M
Kutztown University of Pennsylvania *Pennsylvania* M
Lackawanna College *Pennsylvania* M
Lafayette College *Pennsylvania* M
LaGrange College *Georgia* M
Lake Erie College *Ohio* M
Lake Forest College *Illinois* M
Lakeland College *Wisconsin* M
Lamar University *Texas* M
Lane College *Tennessee* M
Laney College *California* M
Langston University *Oklahoma* M
Lawrence University *Wisconsin* M
Lebanon Valley College *Pennsylvania* M
Lehigh University *Pennsylvania* M
Lenoir-Rhyne University *North Carolina* M
Lewis & Clark College *Oregon* M
Liberty University *Virginia* M
Limestone College *South Carolina* M
Lincoln University *Missouri* M
Lincoln University *Pennsylvania* M
Lindenwood University *Missouri* M
Lindsey Wilson College *Kentucky* M & W
Linfield College *Oregon* M
Livingstone College *North Carolina* M
Lock Haven University of Pennsylvania *Pennsylvania* M
Long Beach City College *California* M
Long Island University - LIU Post *New York* M
Longwood University *Virginia* M
Loras College *Iowa* M
Los Angeles City College *California* M
Los Angeles Harbor College *California* M
Los Angeles Pierce College *California* M
Los Angeles Southwest College *California* M
Los Angeles Valley College *California* M
Los Medanos College *California* M
Louisiana College *Louisiana* M
Louisiana State University and Agricultural & Mechanical College *Louisiana* M
Louisiana Tech University *Louisiana* M
Luther College *Iowa* M
Lycoming College *Pennsylvania* M
Lyon College *Arkansas* M
Macalester College *Minnesota* M
MacMurray College *Illinois* M
Maine Maritime Academy *Maine* M
Malone University *Ohio* M
Manchester University *Indiana* M
Mansfield University of Pennsylvania *Pennsylvania* M
Maranatha Baptist University *Wisconsin* M
Marian University *Indiana* M
Marietta College *Ohio* M
Marist College *New York* M
Mars Hill University *North Carolina* M
Marshall University *West Virginia* M
Martin Luther College *Minnesota* M
Maryville College *Tennessee* M
Massachusetts Institute of Technology *Massachusetts* M
Massachusetts Maritime Academy *Massachusetts* M
Mayville State University *North Dakota* M
McDaniel College *Maryland* M
McGill University *Quebec (Canada)* M
McKendree University *Illinois* M
McMaster University *Ontario (Canada)* M
McMurry University *Texas* M
McNeese State University *Louisiana* M
McPherson College *Kansas* M
Mendocino College *California* M
Merced College *California* M
Mercer University *Georgia* M
Mercyhurst University *Pennsylvania* M
Merrimack College *Massachusetts* M
Mesa Community College *Arizona* M
Mesabi Range College *Minnesota* M
Methodist University *North Carolina* M
Miami University *Ohio* M
Michigan State University *Michigan* M
Michigan Technological University *Michigan* M

MidAmerica Nazarene University *Kansas* M
Middle Tennessee State University *Tennessee* M
Middlebury College *Vermont* M
Midland University *Nebraska* M
Midwestern State University *Texas* M
Miles College *Alabama* M
Millersville University of Pennsylvania *Pennsylvania* M
Millikin University *Illinois* M
Millsaps College *Mississippi* M
Minnesota State Community and Technical College *Minnesota* M
Minnesota State University Mankato *Minnesota* M
Minnesota State University Moorhead *Minnesota* M
Minnesota West Community and Technical College *Minnesota* M
Minot State University *North Dakota* M
Misericordia University *Pennsylvania* M
Mississippi College *Mississippi* M
Mississippi Delta Community College *Mississippi* M
Mississippi Gulf Coast Community College *Mississippi* M
Mississippi State University *Mississippi* M
Mississippi Valley State University *Mississippi* M
Missouri Baptist University *Missouri* M
Missouri Southern State University *Missouri* M
Missouri State University *Missouri* M
Missouri University of Science and Technology *Missouri* M
Missouri Valley College *Missouri* M
Missouri Western State University *Missouri* M
Modesto Junior College *California* M
Monmouth College *Illinois* M
Monmouth University *New Jersey* M
Monroe College *New York* M
Montana State University *Montana* M
Montana State University - Northern *Montana* M
Montana Tech of The University of Montana *Montana* M
Montclair State University *New Jersey* M
Monterey Peninsula College *California* M
Moorpark College *California* M
Moravian College *Pennsylvania* M
Morehead State University *Kentucky* M
Morehouse College *Georgia* M
Morgan State University *Maryland* M
Morningside College *Iowa* M
Morrisville State College *New York* M
Mount Allison University *New Brunswick (Canada)* M
Mount Ida College *Massachusetts* M
Mount St. Joseph University *Ohio* M
Mt. San Antonio College *California* M
Mt. San Jacinto College *California* M
Muhlenberg College *Pennsylvania* M
Murray State University *Kentucky* M
Muskingum University *Ohio* M
Nassau Community College *New York* M
Navarro College *Texas* M
Nebraska Wesleyan University *Nebraska* M
New Mexico Highlands University *New Mexico* M
New Mexico Military Institute *New Mexico* M
New Mexico State University *New Mexico* M
Newberry College *South Carolina* M
Nicholls State University *Louisiana* M
Nichols College *Massachusetts* M
Norfolk State University *Virginia* M
North Carolina Agricultural and Technical State University *North Carolina* M
North Carolina Central University *North Carolina* M
North Carolina State University *North Carolina* M
North Carolina Wesleyan College *North Carolina* M
North Central College *Illinois* M
North Dakota State College of Science *North Dakota* M
North Dakota State University *North Dakota* M
North Greenville University *South Carolina* M
North Park University *Illinois* M
Northeast Mississippi Community College *Mississippi* M
Northeastern Oklahoma Agricultural and Mechanical College *Oklahoma* M
Northeastern State University *Oklahoma* M
Northern Arizona University *Arizona* M

M = Men; W = Women

Northern Illinois University *Illinois* M
Northern Michigan University *Michigan* M
Northern State University *South Dakota* M
Northland Community and Technical College *Minnesota* M
Northwest Mississippi Community College *Mississippi* M
Northwest Missouri State University *Missouri* M
Northwestern College *Iowa* M
Northwestern Oklahoma State University *Oklahoma* M
Northwestern State University of Louisiana *Louisiana* M
Northwood University, Michigan Campus *Michigan* M
Norwich University *Vermont* M
Oberlin College *Ohio* M
Occidental College *California* M
Ohio Dominican University *Ohio* M
Ohio Northern University *Ohio* M
The Ohio State University *Ohio* M
Ohio University *Ohio* M
Ohio Wesleyan University *Ohio* M
Oklahoma Baptist University *Oklahoma* M
Oklahoma Panhandle State University *Oklahoma* M
Oklahoma State University *Oklahoma* M
Old Dominion University *Virginia* M
Olivet College *Michigan* M
Olivet Nazarene University *Illinois* M
Orange Coast College *California* M
Oregon State University *Oregon* M
Ottawa University *Kansas* M
Otterbein University *Ohio* M
Ouachita Baptist University *Arkansas* M
Pace University *New York* M
Pace University, Pleasantville Campus *New York* M
Pacific Lutheran University *Washington* M
Pacific University *Oregon* M
Palomar College *California* M
Pasadena City College *California* M
Pearl River Community College *Mississippi* M
Penn State Lehigh Valley *Pennsylvania* M
Penn State University Park *Pennsylvania* M
Peru State College *Nebraska* M
Phoenix College *Arizona* M
Pittsburg State University *Kansas* M
Pitzer College *California* M
Plymouth State University *New Hampshire* M
Point University *Georgia* M
Pomona College *California* M
Portland State University *Oregon* M
Post University *Connecticut* M
Prairie View A&M University *Texas* M
Presbyterian College *South Carolina* M
Presentation College *South Dakota* M
Princeton University *New Jersey* M
Purdue University *Indiana* M
Queen's University at Kingston *Ontario (Canada)* M
Quincy University *Illinois* M
Randolph-Macon College *Virginia* M
Ranger College *Texas* M
Reedley College *California* M
Reinhardt University *Georgia* M
Rensselaer Polytechnic Institute *New York* M
Rhodes College *Tennessee* M
Rice University *Texas* M
Ridgewater College *Minnesota* M
Ripon College *Wisconsin* M
Robert Morris University *Pennsylvania* M
Robert Morris University Illinois *Illinois* M
Rochester Community and Technical College *Minnesota* M
Rockford University *Illinois* M
Rocky Mountain College *Montana* M
Rose-Hulman Institute of Technology *Indiana* M
Rowan University *New Jersey* M
Rutgers University - New Brunswick *New Jersey* M
Sacramento City College *California* M
Sacred Heart University *Connecticut* M
Saddleback College *California* M
Saginaw Valley State University *Michigan* M
St. Ambrose University *Iowa* M
Saint Anselm College *New Hampshire* M
Saint Augustine's University *North Carolina* M

St. Cloud State University *Minnesota* M
Saint Francis University *Pennsylvania* M
St. Francis Xavier University *Nova Scotia (Canada)* M
St. John Fisher College *New York* M
Saint John's University *Minnesota* M
Saint Joseph's College *Indiana* M
St. Lawrence University *New York* M
Saint Mary's University *Nova Scotia (Canada)* M
St. Norbert College *Wisconsin* M
St. Olaf College *Minnesota* M
Saint Vincent College *Pennsylvania* M
Saint Xavier University *Illinois* M
Salisbury University *Maryland* M
Salve Regina University *Rhode Island* M
Sam Houston State University *Texas* M
Samford University *Alabama* M
San Bernardino Valley College *California* M
San Diego City College *California* M
San Diego Mesa College *California* M
San Diego State University *California* M
San Joaquin Delta College *California* M
San Jose City College *California* M
San Jose State University *California* M
Santa Ana College *California* M
Santa Barbara City College *California* M
Santa Monica College *California* M
Santa Rosa Junior College *California* M
Savannah State University *Georgia* M
Scottsdale Community College *Arizona* M
Seton Hill University *Pennsylvania* M
Sewanee: The University of the South *Tennessee* M
Shasta College *California* M
Shaw University *North Carolina* M
Shenandoah University *Virginia* M
Shepherd University *West Virginia* M
Shippensburg University of Pennsylvania *Pennsylvania* M
Shorter University *Georgia* M
Siena Heights University *Michigan* M
Sierra College *California* M
Simon Fraser University *British Columbia (Canada)* M
Simpson College *Iowa* M
Slippery Rock University of Pennsylvania *Pennsylvania* M
Snow College *Utah* M
Solano Community College *California* M
South Carolina State University *South Carolina* M
South Dakota School of Mines and Technology *South Dakota* M
South Dakota State University *South Dakota* M
Southeast Missouri State University *Missouri* M
Southeastern Louisiana University *Louisiana* M
Southeastern Oklahoma State University *Oklahoma* M
Southeastern University *Florida* M
Southern Arkansas University - Magnolia *Arkansas* M
Southern Connecticut State University *Connecticut* M
Southern Illinois University Carbondale *Illinois* M
Southern Methodist University *Texas* M
Southern Nazarene University *Oklahoma* M
Southern Oregon University *Oregon* M
Southern University and Agricultural and Mechanical College *Louisiana* M
Southern Utah University *Utah* M
Southern Virginia University *Virginia* M
Southwest Baptist University *Missouri* M
Southwest Minnesota State University *Minnesota* M
Southwest Mississippi Community College *Mississippi* M
Southwestern Assemblies of God University *Texas* M
Southwestern College *California* M
Southwestern College *Kansas* M
Southwestern Oklahoma State University *Oklahoma* M
Southwestern University *Texas* M
Springfield College *Massachusetts* M
Stanford University *California* M

State University of New York College at Cortland *New York* M & W
State University of New York College of Technology at Alfred *New York* M
State University of New York Maritime College *New York* M
Stephen F. Austin State University *Texas* M
Sterling College *Kansas* M
Stetson University *Florida* M
Stevenson University *Maryland* M
Stillman College *Alabama* M
Stonehill College *Massachusetts* M
Stony Brook University, State University of New York *New York* M
Sul Ross State University *Texas* M
Susquehanna University *Pennsylvania* M
Syracuse University *New York* M
Tabor College *Kansas* M
Tarleton State University *Texas* M
Taylor University *Indiana* M
Temple University *Pennsylvania* M
Tennessee State University *Tennessee* M
Tennessee Technological University *Tennessee* M
Texas A&M University *Texas* M
Texas A&M University - Commerce *Texas* M
Texas A&M University - Kingsville *Texas* M
Texas Christian University *Texas* M
Texas College *Texas* M
Texas Lutheran University *Texas* M
Texas Southern University *Texas* M
Texas State University *Texas* M
Texas Tech University *Texas* M
Thaddeus Stevens College of Technology *Pennsylvania* M
Thiel College *Pennsylvania* M
Thomas More College *Kentucky* M
Tiffin University *Ohio* M
Towson University *Maryland* M
Trine University *Indiana* M
Trinity Bible College *North Dakota* M
Trinity College *Connecticut* M
Trinity International University *Illinois* M
Trinity University *Texas* M
Trinity Valley Community College *Texas* M
Troy University *Alabama* M
Truman State University *Missouri* M
Tufts University *Massachusetts* M
Tulane University *Louisiana* M
Tusculum College *Tennessee* M
Tuskegee University *Alabama* M
Tyler Junior College *Texas* M
Union College *Kentucky* M
Union College *New York* M
United States Air Force Academy *Colorado* M
United States Coast Guard Academy *Connecticut* M
United States Merchant Marine Academy *New York* M
United States Military Academy *New York* M
United States Naval Academy *Maryland* M
Université Laval *Quebec (Canada)* M
Université de Montréal *Quebec (Canada)* M
The University of Akron *Ohio* M
The University of Alabama *Alabama* M
University at Albany, State University of New York *New York* M
University of Alberta *Alberta (Canada)* M
The University of Arizona *Arizona* M
University of Arkansas *Arkansas* M
University of Arkansas at Monticello *Arkansas* M
University of Arkansas at Pine Bluff *Arkansas* M
The University of British Columbia *British Columbia (Canada)* M
University at Buffalo, the State University of New York *New York* M
University of Calgary *Alberta (Canada)* M
University of California, Berkeley *California* M
University of California, Davis *California* M
University of California, Los Angeles *California* M
University of Central Arkansas *Arkansas* M
University of Central Florida *Florida* M
University of Central Missouri *Missouri* M
University of Central Oklahoma *Oklahoma* M
University of Charleston *West Virginia* M

M = Men; W = Women

University of Chicago *Illinois* M
University of Cincinnati *Ohio* M
University of Colorado Boulder *Colorado* M
University of Connecticut *Connecticut* M
University of the Cumberlands *Kentucky* M
University of Dayton *Ohio* M
University of Delaware *Delaware* M
University of Dubuque *Iowa* M
The University of Findlay *Ohio* M
University of Florida *Florida* M
University of Georgia *Georgia* M
University of Guelph *Ontario (Canada)* M
University of Hawaii at Manoa *Hawaii* M
University of Houston *Texas* M
University of Idaho *Idaho* M
University of Illinois at Urbana - Champaign *Illinois* M
University of the Incarnate Word *Texas* M
University of Indianapolis *Indiana* M
The University of Iowa *Iowa* M
University of Jamestown *North Dakota* M
The University of Kansas *Kansas* M
University of Kentucky *Kentucky* M
University of La Verne *California* M
University of Louisiana at Lafayette *Louisiana* M
University of Louisiana at Monroe *Louisiana* M
University of Louisville *Kentucky* M
University of Maine *Maine* M
University of Manitoba *Manitoba (Canada)* M & W
University of Mary *North Dakota* M
University of Mary Hardin-Baylor *Texas* M
University of Maryland, College Park *Maryland* M
University of Massachusetts Amherst *Massachusetts* M
University of Massachusetts Dartmouth *Massachusetts* M
University of Memphis *Tennessee* M
University of Miami *Florida* M
University of Michigan *Michigan* M
University of Minnesota, Crookston *Minnesota* M
University of Minnesota, Duluth *Minnesota* M
University of Minnesota, Morris *Minnesota* M
University of Minnesota, Twin Cities Campus *Minnesota* M
University of Mississippi *Mississippi* M
University of Missouri *Missouri* M
University of Montana *Montana* M
The University of Montana Western *Montana* M
University of Mount Union *Ohio* M
University of Nebraska at Kearney *Nebraska* M
University of Nebraska - Lincoln *Nebraska* M
University of Nevada, Las Vegas *Nevada* M
University of Nevada, Reno *Nevada* M
University of New Hampshire *New Hampshire* M
University of New Haven *Connecticut* M
University of New Mexico *New Mexico* M
University of North Alabama *Alabama* M
The University of North Carolina at Chapel Hill *North Carolina* M
The University of North Carolina at Charlotte *North Carolina* M
The University of North Carolina at Pembroke *North Carolina* M
University of North Dakota *North Dakota* M
University of North Texas *Texas* M
University of Northern Colorado *Colorado* M
University of Northern Iowa *Iowa* M
University of Northwestern - St. Paul *Minnesota* M
University of Notre Dame *Indiana* M
University of Oklahoma *Oklahoma* M
University of Oregon *Oregon* M
University of Ottawa *Ontario (Canada)* M
University of Pennsylvania *Pennsylvania* M
University of Pikeville *Kentucky* M
University of Pittsburgh *Pennsylvania* M
University of Puget Sound *Washington* M
University of Redlands *California* M
University of Regina *Saskatchewan (Canada)* M
University of Rhode Island *Rhode Island* M
University of Richmond *Virginia* M
University of Rochester *New York* M
University of St. Francis *Illinois* M
University of Saint Francis *Indiana* M
University of Saint Mary *Kansas* M

University of St. Thomas *Minnesota* M
University of San Diego *California* M
University of Saskatchewan *Saskatchewan (Canada)* M
University of Sioux Falls *South Dakota* M
University of South Alabama *Alabama* M
University of South Carolina *South Carolina* M
The University of South Dakota *South Dakota* M
University of South Florida *Florida* M
University of Southern California *California* M
University of Southern Mississippi *Mississippi* M
The University of Tennessee *Tennessee* M
The University of Tennessee at Chattanooga *Tennessee* M
The University of Tennessee at Martin *Tennessee* M
The University of Texas at Austin *Texas* M
The University of Texas at El Paso *Texas* M
The University of Texas at San Antonio *Texas* M
The University of Toledo *Ohio* M
University of Toronto *Ontario (Canada)* M
The University of Tulsa *Oklahoma* M
University of Utah *Utah* M
University of Virginia *Virginia* M
The University of Virginia's College at Wise *Virginia* M
University of Washington *Washington* M
University of Waterloo *Ontario (Canada)* M
The University of West Alabama *Alabama* M
University of West Georgia *Georgia* M
The University of Western Ontario *Ontario (Canada)* M
University of Windsor *Ontario (Canada)* M
University of Wisconsin - Eau Claire *Wisconsin* M
University of Wisconsin - La Crosse *Wisconsin* M
University of Wisconsin - Madison *Wisconsin* M
University of Wisconsin - Milwaukee *Wisconsin* M & W
University of Wisconsin - Oshkosh *Wisconsin* M
University of Wisconsin - Platteville *Wisconsin* M
University of Wisconsin - River Falls *Wisconsin* M
University of Wisconsin - Stevens Point *Wisconsin* M
University of Wisconsin - Stout *Wisconsin* M
University of Wisconsin - Whitewater *Wisconsin* M
University of Wyoming *Wyoming* M
Upper Iowa University *Iowa* M
Urbana University *Ohio* M
Ursinus College *Pennsylvania* M
Utah State University *Utah* M
Utica College *New York* M
Valdosta State University *Georgia* M
Valley City State University *North Dakota* M
Valley Forge Military College *Pennsylvania* M
Valparaiso University *Indiana* M
Vanderbilt University *Tennessee* M
Ventura College *California* M
Vermilion Community College *Minnesota* M
Victor Valley College *California* M
Villanova University *Pennsylvania* M
Virginia Military Institute *Virginia* M
Virginia Polytechnic Institute and State University *Virginia* M
Virginia State University *Virginia* M
Virginia Union University *Virginia* M
Wabash College *Indiana* M
Wagner College *New York* M
Wake Forest University *North Carolina* M
Waldorf College *Iowa* M
Walsh University *Ohio* M
Wartburg College *Iowa* M
Washburn University *Kansas* M
Washington & Jefferson College *Pennsylvania* M
Washington and Lee University *Virginia* M
Washington State University *Washington* M
Washington University in St. Louis *Missouri* M
Wayland Baptist University *Texas* M
Wayne State College *Nebraska* M
Wayne State University *Michigan* M
Waynesburg University *Pennsylvania* M
Webber International University *Florida* M
Weber State University *Utah* M
Wesley College *Delaware* M
Wesleyan University *Connecticut* M

West Chester University of Pennsylvania *Pennsylvania* M
West Hills Community College *California* M
West Liberty University *West Virginia* M
West Los Angeles College *California* M
West Texas A&M University *Texas* M
West Valley College *California* M
West Virginia State University *West Virginia* M
West Virginia University *West Virginia* M
West Virginia Wesleyan College *West Virginia* M
Western Carolina University *North Carolina* M
Western Connecticut State University *Connecticut* M
Western Illinois University *Illinois* M
Western Kentucky University *Kentucky* M
Western Michigan University *Michigan* M
Western New England University *Massachusetts* M
Western New Mexico University *New Mexico* M
Western Oregon University *Oregon* M
Western State Colorado University *Colorado* M
Westfield State University *Massachusetts* M
Westminster College *Missouri* M
Westminster College *Pennsylvania* M
Wheaton College *Illinois* M
Whittier College *California* M
Whitworth University *Washington* M
Widener University *Pennsylvania* M
Wilfrid Laurier University *Ontario (Canada)* M
Wilkes University *Pennsylvania* M
Willamette University *Oregon* M
William Jewell College *Missouri* M
William Paterson University of New Jersey *New Jersey* M
William Penn University *Iowa* M
Williams College *Massachusetts* M
Williamson College of the Trades *Pennsylvania* M
Wilmington College *Ohio* M
Wingate University *North Carolina* M
Winona State University *Minnesota* M
Winston-Salem State University *North Carolina* M
Wisconsin Lutheran College *Wisconsin* M
Wittenberg University *Ohio* M
Wofford College *South Carolina* M
Worcester Polytechnic Institute *Massachusetts* M
Worcester State University *Massachusetts* M
Yale University *Connecticut* M
York University *Ontario (Canada)* M
Youngstown State University *Ohio* M
Yuba College *California* M

Golf

Abilene Christian University *Texas* M
Abraham Baldwin Agricultural College *Georgia* M
Academy of Art University *California* M & W
Adams State University *Colorado* M & W
Adelphi University *New York* M & W
Adirondack Community College *New York* M & W
Adrian College *Michigan* M & W
Alabama Agricultural and Mechanical University *Alabama* M
Alabama State University *Alabama* M & W
Albertus Magnus College *Connecticut* M & W
Albion College *Michigan* M & W
Albright College *Pennsylvania* M & W
Alcorn State University *Mississippi* M & W
Alderson Broaddus University *West Virginia* M & W
Alice Lloyd College *Kentucky* M & W
Allan Hancock College *California* M
Allegheny College *Pennsylvania* M & W
Allen Community College *Kansas* M
Allen University *South Carolina* M & W
Alma College *Michigan* M & W
Alvernia University *Pennsylvania* M & W
Alverno College *Wisconsin* W
American International College *Massachusetts* M & W
American River College *California* M & W
Amherst College *Massachusetts* M & W
Ancilla College *Indiana* M & W
Anderson University *Indiana* M & W
Anderson University *South Carolina* M & W
Andrew College *Georgia* M & W
Angelo State University *Texas* W
Anna Maria College *Massachusetts* M

M = Men; W = Women

Anne Arundel Community College *Maryland* M
Antelope Valley College *California* M
Appalachian State University *North Carolina* M & W
Aquinas College *Michigan* M & W
Arcadia University *Pennsylvania* M & W
Arizona Christian University *Arizona* M & W
Arizona State University at the Downtown Phoenix campus *Arizona* M & W
Arizona State University at the Polytechnic campus *Arizona* M & W
Arizona State University at the Tempe campus *Arizona* M & W
Arizona State University at the West campus *Arizona* M & W
Arkansas State University *Arkansas* M & W
Arkansas Tech University *Arkansas* M & W
Armstrong State University *Georgia* M & W
Asbury University *Kentucky* M & W
Ashford University *California* M & W
Ashland University *Ohio* M & W
Assumption College *Massachusetts* M
Auburn University *Alabama* M & W
Augsburg College *Minnesota* M & W
Augusta University *Georgia* M & W
Augustana College *Illinois* M & W
Augustana University *South Dakota* M & W
Aurora University *Illinois* M & W
Austin Peay State University *Tennessee* M & W
Ave Maria University *Florida* M
Averett University *Virginia* M
Avila University *Missouri* M & W
Babson College *Massachusetts* M
Baker University *Kansas* M & W
Bakersfield College *California* M
Baldwin Wallace University *Ohio* M & W
Ball State University *Indiana* M & W
Barnard College *New York* W
Barry University *Florida* M & W
Barton College *North Carolina* M & W
Barton County Community College *Kansas* M & W
Bates College *Maine* M & W
Baylor University *Texas* M & W
Becker College *Massachusetts* M
Belhaven University *Mississippi* M & W
Bellarmine University *Kentucky* M & W
Bellevue College *Washington* M
Belmont Abbey College *North Carolina* M & W
Belmont University *Tennessee* M & W
Bemidji State University *Minnesota* M & W
Benedict College *South Carolina* M
Benedictine University *Illinois* M & W
Bentley University *Massachusetts* M
Berea College *Kentucky* M
Bergen Community College *New Jersey* M
Berry College *Georgia* M & W
Bethany College *Kansas* M & W
Bethany College *West Virginia* M & W
Bethany Lutheran College *Minnesota* M & W
Bethel College *Indiana* M & W
Bethel College *Kansas* M & W
Bethel University *Minnesota* M & W
Bethel University *Tennessee* M & W
Bethune-Cookman University *Florida* M & W
Binghamton University, State University of New York *New York* M
Biola University *California* M & W
Birmingham-Southern College *Alabama* M & W
Bishop's University *Quebec (Canada)* M
Bismarck State College *North Dakota* M & W
Black Hawk College *Illinois* M
Black Hills State University *South Dakota* W
Blackburn College *Illinois* M
Blue Mountain College *Mississippi* M
Bluefield College *Virginia* M
Bluefield State College *West Virginia* M
Bob Jones University *South Carolina* M & W
Boise State University *Idaho* M & W
Boston College *Massachusetts* M & W
Boston University *Massachusetts* M & W
Bowdoin College *Maine* M & W
Bowling Green State University *Ohio* M & W
Bradley University *Illinois* M & W
Brescia University *Kentucky* M & W
Brevard College *North Carolina* M & W

Briar Cliff University *Iowa* M & W
Bridgewater College *Virginia* M & W
Brigham Young University *Utah* M & W
Brigham Young University - Hawaii *Hawaii* M
Brookdale Community College *New Jersey* M
Broome Community College *New York* M
Brown University *Rhode Island* M & W
Bryan College *Tennessee* M & W
Bryant University *Rhode Island* M & W
Bryn Athyn College of the New Church *Pennsylvania* M
Bucknell University *Pennsylvania* M & W
Bucks County Community College *Pennsylvania* M
Buena Vista University *Iowa* M & W
Butler County Community College *Pennsylvania* M & W
Butler University *Indiana* M & W
Butte College *California* M & W
Cabrillo College *California* M
Cabrini University *Pennsylvania* M
Cairn University *Pennsylvania* M
Caldwell Community College and Technical Institute *North Carolina* M
California Baptist University *California* M & W
California Lutheran University *California* M & W
California Maritime Academy *California* M & W
California Polytechnic State University, San Luis Obispo *California* M & W
California State University, Bakersfield *California* M
California State University, Chico *California* M & W
California State University, Dominguez Hills *California* M
California State University, Fresno *California* M & W
California State University, Fullerton *California* M & W
California State University, Long Beach *California* M & W
California State University, Monterey Bay *California* M & W
California State University, Northridge *California* M
California State University, Sacramento *California* M & W
California State University, San Bernardino *California* M
California State University, San Marcos *California* M & W
California State University, Stanislaus *California* M
California University of Pennsylvania *Pennsylvania* M & W
Calumet College of Saint Joseph *Indiana* M & W
Calvin College *Michigan* M & W
Camden County College *New Jersey* M
Cameron University *Oklahoma* M & W
Campbell University *North Carolina* M & W
Campbellsville University *Kentucky* M & W
Cañada College *California* W
Canisius College *New York* M
Cape Fear Community College *North Carolina* M
Capital University *Ohio* M & W
Cardinal Stritch University *Wisconsin* M & W
Carleton College *Minnesota* M & W
Carleton University *Ontario (Canada)* M
Carnegie Mellon University *Pennsylvania* M & W
Carroll College *Montana* M & W
Carroll University *Wisconsin* M & W
Carson-Newman University *Tennessee* M & W
Carthage College *Wisconsin* M & W
Castleton University *Vermont* M
Catawba College *North Carolina* M & W
Cayuga County Community College *New York* M & W
Cazenovia College *New York* M
Cedarville University *Ohio* M
Centenary College *New Jersey* M
Centenary College of Louisiana *Louisiana* M & W
Central Alabama Community College *Alabama* M
Central Baptist College *Arkansas* M & W
Central Carolina Community College *North Carolina* M
Central Christian College of Kansas *Kansas* M & W
Central College *Iowa* M & W
Central Community College - Columbus Campus *Nebraska* M

Central Connecticut State University *Connecticut* M & W
Central Lakes College *Minnesota* M & W
Central Maine Community College *Maine* M & W
Central Michigan University *Michigan* W
Central Oregon Community College *Oregon* M & W
Central State University *Ohio* M & W
Central Washington University *Washington* M & W
Central Wyoming College *Wyoming* M & W
Centralia College *Washington* M
Centre College *Kentucky* M & W
Cerritos College *California* M
Chabot College *California* M
Chadron State College *Nebraska* W
Chaminade University of Honolulu *Hawaii* M
Chandler-Gilbert Community College *Arizona* M & W
Chapman University *California* M
Charleston Southern University *South Carolina* M & W
Chestnut Hill College *Pennsylvania* M & W
Chicago State University *Illinois* M & W
Chowan University *North Carolina* M & W
Christian Brothers University *Tennessee* M & W
Christopher Newport University *Virginia* M & W
Cincinnati Christian University *Ohio* M
Cincinnati State Technical and Community College *Ohio* M & W
The Citadel, The Military College of South Carolina *South Carolina* M
Citrus College *California* M & W
Claremont McKenna College *California* M & W
Clarion University of Pennsylvania *Pennsylvania* M & W
Clarke University *Iowa* M & W
Clarkson University *New York* M
Clayton State University *Georgia* M
Cleary University *Michigan* M & W
Clemson University *South Carolina* M
Cleveland State University *Ohio* M & W
Coastal Carolina University *South Carolina* M & W
Coe College *Iowa* M & W
Coffeyville Community College *Kansas* M & W
Coker College *South Carolina* M & W
Colby College *Maine* M & W
Colby Community College *Kansas* M & W
Colby-Sawyer College *New Hampshire* M & W
Colgate University *New York* M & W
College of the Canyons *California* M & W
College of Charleston *South Carolina* M & W
College of Coastal Georgia *Georgia* M & W
College of the Desert *California* M & W
College of DuPage *Illinois* M
College of the Holy Cross *Massachusetts* M & W
The College of Idaho *Idaho* M & W
College of Lake County *Illinois* M
College of Saint Benedict *Minnesota* W
College of Saint Mary *Nebraska* W
The College of Saint Rose *New York* M & W
The College of St. Scholastica *Minnesota* M & W
College of the Sequoias *California* M
College of Southern Maryland *Maryland* M & W
The College of William and Mary *Virginia* M & W
The College of Wooster *Ohio* M & W
Colorado Christian University *Colorado* M & W
Colorado Mesa University *Colorado* M & W
Colorado School of Mines *Colorado* M
Colorado State University *Colorado* M & W
Colorado State University - Pueblo *Colorado* M & W
Columbia Basin College *Washington* M & W
Columbia College *Missouri* M & W
Columbia College *South Carolina* W
Columbia-Greene Community College *New York* M & W
Columbia International University *South Carolina* M
Columbia University *New York* M
Columbia University, School of General Studies *New York* M & W
Columbus State Community College *Ohio* M & W
Columbus State University *Georgia* M & W
Community College of Allegheny County *Pennsylvania* M & W

M = Men; W = Women

Community College of Rhode Island *Rhode Island* M & W
Concord University *West Virginia* M & W
Concordia College *Minnesota* M & W
Concordia College - New York *New York* M
Concordia University *Oregon* M & W
Concordia University *Quebec (Canada)* M & W
Concordia University Ann Arbor *Michigan* M & W
Concordia University Chicago *Illinois* M
Concordia University of Edmonton *Alberta (Canada)* M & W
Concordia University, Nebraska *Nebraska* M & W
Concordia University, St. Paul *Minnesota* M & W
Concordia University Texas *Texas* M & W
Concordia University Wisconsin *Wisconsin* M & W
Converse College *South Carolina* W
Copiah-Lincoln Community College *Mississippi* M & W
Corban University *Oregon* M & W
Cornell University *New York* M
Cornerstone University *Michigan* M & W
County College of Morris *New Jersey* M
Covenant College *Georgia* M & W
Creighton University *Nebraska* M & W
Crossroads College *Minnesota* M & W
Crown College *Minnesota* M
Culver-Stockton College *Missouri* M & W
Cumberland University *Tennessee* M & W
Cuyamaca College *California* M
Cypress College *California* M
Daemen College *New York* M
Dakota Wesleyan University *South Dakota* M & W
Dallas Baptist University *Texas* M & W
Dalton State College *Georgia* W
Daniel Webster College *New Hampshire* M
Dartmouth College *New Hampshire* M & W
Darton State College *Georgia* M
Davenport University *Michigan* M & W
Davidson College *North Carolina* M
Davis & Elkins College *West Virginia* M & W
Daytona State College *Florida* W
De Anza College *California* M & W
Dean College *Massachusetts* M
Defiance College *Ohio* M & W
Delaware County Community College *Pennsylvania* M & W
Delaware Technical & Community College, Jack F. Owens Campus *Delaware* M
Delaware Valley University *Pennsylvania* M & W
Delta College *Michigan* M
Delta State University *Mississippi* M
Denison University *Ohio* M
DePaul University *Illinois* M
DePauw University *Indiana* M
Des Moines Area Community College *Iowa* M & W
DeSales University *Pennsylvania* M
Dickinson College *Pennsylvania* M & W
Dickinson State University *North Dakota* M & W
Dixie State University *Utah* M & W
Doane University *Nebraska* M & W
Dodge City Community College *Kansas* M & W
Dominican College *New York* M
Dominican University *Illinois* M
Dominican University of California *California* M & W
Dordt College *Iowa* M & W
Drake University *Iowa* M & W
Drexel University *Pennsylvania* M
Drury University *Missouri* M & W
Duke University *North Carolina* M & W
D'Youville College *New York* M & W
Earlham College *Indiana* M & W
East Carolina University *North Carolina* M & W
East Central Community College *Mississippi* M & W
East Central University *Oklahoma* M & W
East Mississippi Community College *Mississippi* M
East Stroudsburg University of Pennsylvania *Pennsylvania* M & W
East Tennessee State University *Tennessee* M & W
Eastern Arizona College *Arizona* M & W
Eastern Florida State College *Florida* M
Eastern Illinois University *Illinois* M & W
Eastern Kentucky University *Kentucky* M & W
Eastern Maine Community College *Maine* M

Eastern Mennonite University *Virginia* M & W
Eastern Michigan University *Michigan* M & W
Eastern Nazarene College *Massachusetts* M & W
Eastern University *Pennsylvania* M & W
Eastern Washington University *Washington* W
Eastern Wyoming College *Wyoming* M
Eastfield College *Texas* M
Eckerd College *Florida* M & W
Edgewood College *Wisconsin* M & W
Edmonds Community College *Washington* M & W
El Camino College *California* M
Elgin Community College *Illinois* M
Elizabeth City State University *North Carolina* M
Elizabethtown College *Pennsylvania* M
Ellsworth Community College *Iowa* M & W
Elmhurst College *Illinois* M & W
Elmira College *New York* M & W
Elms College *Massachusetts* M
Elon University *North Carolina* M & W
Embry-Riddle Aeronautical University - Daytona *Florida* M & W
Embry-Riddle Aeronautical University - Prescott *Arizona* M & W
Emerson College *Massachusetts* M & W
Emmanuel College *Georgia* M & W
Emmanuel College *Massachusetts* M
Emory University *Georgia* M & W
Endicott College *Massachusetts* M
Erskine College *South Carolina* M & W
Estrella Mountain Community College *Arizona* M & W
Eureka College *Illinois* M
Evangel University *Missouri* M & W
Fairfield University *Connecticut* M & W
Fairleigh Dickinson University, College at Florham *New Jersey* M & W
Fairleigh Dickinson University, Metropolitan Campus *New Jersey* M & W
Fairmont State University *West Virginia* M & W
Farmingdale State College *New York* M
Faulkner University *Alabama* M & W
Fayetteville State University *North Carolina* M & W
Felician University *New Jersey* M
Ferris State University *Michigan* M & W
Ferrum College *Virginia* M
Flagler College *Florida* M & W
Florida Agricultural and Mechanical University *Florida* M & W
Florida Atlantic University *Florida* M & W
Florida Gulf Coast University *Florida* M & W
Florida Institute of Technology *Florida* M & W
Florida International University *Florida* W
Florida Southern College *Florida* M & W
Florida State University *Florida* M & W
Fontbonne University *Missouri* M & W
Fordham University *New York* M
Fort Lewis College *Colorado* M
Fort Valley State University *Georgia* M
Francis Marion University *South Carolina* M
Franklin College *Indiana* M
Franklin & Marshall College *Pennsylvania* M & W
Franklin Pierce University *New Hampshire* M
Frederick Community College *Maryland* M & W
Freed-Hardeman University *Tennessee* M & W
Fresno City College *California* M & W
Friends University *Kansas* M
Fullerton College *California* W
Furman University *South Carolina* M & W
Gannon University *Pennsylvania* M & W
Garden City Community College *Kansas* M
Gardner-Webb University *North Carolina* M & W
Garrett College *Maryland* M
GateWay Community College *Arizona* M & W
Genesee Community College *New York* M & W
Geneva College *Pennsylvania* M & W
George Fox University *Oregon* M & W
George Mason University *Virginia* M
The George Washington University *District of Columbia* M
Georgetown College *Kentucky* M & W
Georgetown University *District of Columbia* M & W
Georgia College & State University *Georgia* M
Georgia Institute of Technology *Georgia* M
Georgia Military College *Georgia* M & W

Georgia Southern University *Georgia* M
Georgia Southwestern State University *Georgia* M
Georgia State University *Georgia* M
Gettysburg College *Pennsylvania* M & W
Glen Oaks Community College *Michigan* M
Glendale Community College *Arizona* M
Glendale Community College *California* M & W
Glenville State College *West Virginia* M & W
Goldey-Beacom College *Delaware* M & W
Gonzaga University *Washington* M & W
Governors State University *Illinois* M & W
Grace College *Indiana* M & W
Graceland University *Iowa* M & W
Grand Canyon University *Arizona* M & W
Grand Rapids Community College *Michigan* M & W
Grand Valley State University *Michigan* M & W
Grand View University *Iowa* M & W
Grays Harbor College *Washington* M & W
Green Mountain College *Vermont* M & W
Green River College *Washington* M & W
Greensboro College *North Carolina* M & W
Grinnell College *Iowa* M & W
Grove City College *Pennsylvania* M & W
Guilford College *North Carolina* M
Gustavus Adolphus College *Minnesota* M & W
Gwynedd Mercy University *Pennsylvania* M
Hagerstown Community College *Maryland* M & W
Hamilton College *New York* M & W
Hampden-Sydney College *Virginia* M
Hampton University *Virginia* M & W
Hannibal-LaGrange University *Missouri* M & W
Hanover College *Indiana* M & W
Hardin-Simmons University *Texas* M & W
Harding University *Arkansas* M & W
Harford Community College *Maryland* M
Harvard University *Massachusetts* M & W
Harvey Mudd College *California* M & W
Haskell Indian Nations University *Kansas* M
Hastings College *Nebraska* M & W
Haverford College *Pennsylvania* M & W
Hawai'i Pacific University *Hawaii* M & W
Heidelberg University *Ohio* M & W
Henderson State University *Arkansas* M & W
Hendrix College *Arkansas* M & W
Henry Ford College *Michigan* M
Hesston College *Kansas* M
Hibbing Community College *Minnesota* M & W
High Point University *North Carolina* M & W
Highland Community College *Illinois* M & W
Hilbert College *New York* M
Hill College *Texas* M
Hillsdale College *Michigan* M
Hinds Community College *Mississippi* M
Hiram College *Ohio* M & W
Hiwassee College *Tennessee* M & W
Hobart and William Smith Colleges *New York* M & W
Hofstra University *New York* M & W
Hollins University *Virginia* W
Holmes Community College *Mississippi* M
Holy Cross College *Indiana* M & W
Holy Names University *California* M & W
Holyoke Community College *Massachusetts* M & W
Hood College *Maryland* M & W
Hope College *Michigan* M & W
Hope International University *California* M & W
Houston Baptist University *Texas* M & W
Huntingdon College *Alabama* M & W
Huntington University *Indiana* M
Husson University *Maine* M & W
Hutchinson Community College *Kansas* M
Idaho State University *Idaho* W
Illinois Central College *Illinois* M
Illinois College *Illinois* M & W
Illinois Eastern Community Colleges, Frontier Community College *Illinois* M & W
Illinois State University *Illinois* M & W
Illinois Valley Community College *Illinois* M
Illinois Wesleyan University *Illinois* M & W
Indian Hills Community College *Iowa* M & W
Indiana State University *Indiana* W
Indiana Tech *Indiana* M & W
Indiana University Bloomington *Indiana* M & W
Indiana University East *Indiana* M & W

M = Men; W = Women

Indiana University Kokomo *Indiana* M & W
Indiana University Northwest *Indiana* M & W
Indiana University of Pennsylvania *Pennsylvania* M
Indiana University - Purdue University Fort Wayne *Indiana* M & W
Indiana University - Purdue University Indianapolis *Indiana* M & W
Indiana University South Bend *Indiana* M
Indiana Wesleyan University *Indiana* M & W
Iona College *New York* M
Iowa Central Community College *Iowa* M & W
Iowa Lakes Community College *Iowa* M & W
Iowa State University of Science and Technology *Iowa* M & W
Iowa Wesleyan University *Iowa* M & W
Iowa Western Community College *Iowa* M & W
Itawamba Community College *Mississippi* M
Ithaca College *New York* W
Jackson College *Michigan* M & W
Jackson State University *Mississippi* M & W
Jacksonville State University *Alabama* M & W
Jacksonville University *Florida* M & W
James A. Rhodes State College *Ohio* M
James H. Faulkner State Community College *Alabama* M
James Madison University *Virginia* M & W
Jamestown Community College *New York* M & W
Jarvis Christian College *Texas* M & W
John A. Logan College *Illinois* M & W
John Brown University *Arkansas* M
John Carroll University *Ohio* M & W
Johnson C. Smith University *North Carolina* M
Johnson College *Pennsylvania* M & W
Johnson County Community College *Kansas* M
Johnson State College *Vermont* M
Johnson & Wales University *Colorado* M & W
Johnson & Wales University *Rhode Island* M & W
Johnston Community College *North Carolina* M & W
Jones County Junior College *Mississippi* M
Judson University *Illinois* M & W
Kalamazoo College *Michigan* M & W
Kalamazoo Valley Community College *Michigan* M
Kansas City Kansas Community College *Kansas* M
Kansas State University *Kansas* M & W
Kansas Wesleyan University *Kansas* M & W
Kaskaskia College *Illinois* M & W
Kennesaw State University *Georgia* M & W
Kent State University *Ohio* M & W
Kentucky State University *Kentucky* M
Kentucky Wesleyan University *Kentucky* M & W
Kenyon College *Ohio* M
Keuka College *New York* M & W
Keystone College *Pennsylvania* M
King University *Tennessee* M & W
The King's College *New York* M & W
King's College *Pennsylvania* M
Kirkwood Community College *Iowa* M & W
Kirtland Community College *Michigan* M & W
Knox College *Illinois* M & W
Kutztown University of Pennsylvania *Pennsylvania* W
La Roche College *Pennsylvania* M
La Salle University *Pennsylvania* M & W
La Sierra University *California* M
Lackawanna College *Pennsylvania* M & W
Lafayette College *Pennsylvania* M
LaGrange College *Georgia* M
Lake Erie College *Ohio* M & W
Lake Forest College *Illinois* M & W
Lake Region State College *North Dakota* M & W
Lake Superior State University *Michigan* M & W
Lakehead University *Ontario (Canada)* M
Lakeland College *Wisconsin* M & W
Lakeland Community College *Ohio* M
Lamar Community College *Colorado* M
Lamar University *Texas* M & W
Lander University *South Carolina* M & W
Laney College *California* M
Lassen Community College District *California* M & W
Laurentian University *Ontario (Canada)* M & W
Lawrence Technological University *Michigan* M & W
Lawrence University *Wisconsin* M

Le Moyne College *New York* M & W
Lebanon Valley College *Pennsylvania* M & W
Lee University *Tennessee* M & W
Lehigh Carbon Community College *Pennsylvania* M & W
Lehigh University *Pennsylvania* M & W
LeMoyne-Owen College *Tennessee* M & W
Lenoir-Rhyne University *North Carolina* M & W
LeTourneau University *Texas* M & W
Lewis & Clark College *Oregon* M & W
Lewis and Clark Community College *Illinois* M
Lewis-Clark State College *Idaho* M & W
Lewis University *Illinois* M & W
Liberty University *Virginia* M
Limestone College *South Carolina* M & W
Lincoln Memorial University *Tennessee* M & W
Lincoln University *Missouri* M & W
Lindenwood University *Missouri* M & W
Lindsey Wilson College *Kentucky* M & W
Linfield College *Oregon* M & W
Lipscomb University *Tennessee* M & W
Logan University *Missouri* M
Long Beach City College *California* M & W
Long Island University - LIU Brooklyn *New York* M & W
Long Island University - LIU Post *New York* W
Longwood University *Virginia* M & W
Loras College *Iowa* M & W
Louisburg College *North Carolina* M & W
Louisiana College *Louisiana* M & W
Louisiana State University and Agricultural & Mechanical College *Louisiana* M & W
Louisiana State University at Alexandria *Louisiana* M & W
Louisiana Tech University *Louisiana* M
Lourdes University *Ohio* M & W
Loyola Marymount University *California* M
Loyola University Chicago *Illinois* M & W
Loyola University Maryland *Maryland* M
Loyola University New Orleans *Louisiana* M & W
Lubbock Christian University *Texas* M & W
Luther College *Iowa* M & W
Luzerne County Community College *Pennsylvania* M & W
Lycoming College *Pennsylvania* M & W
Lynchburg College *Virginia* M
Lynn University *Florida* M & W
Lyon College *Arkansas* M & W
Macalester College *Minnesota* M & W
MacMurray College *Illinois* M
Madonna University *Michigan* M & W
Malone University *Ohio* M & W
Manchester University *Indiana* M & W
Manhattan College *New York* M
Manhattanville College *New York* M & W
Marian University *Indiana* M & W
Marian University *Wisconsin* M & W
Marion Technical College *Ohio* M & W
Marquette University *Wisconsin* M
Mars Hill University *North Carolina* M & W
Marshall University *West Virginia* M & W
Marshalltown Community College *Iowa* M & W
Martin Luther College *Minnesota* M
Martin Methodist College *Tennessee* M & W
Marymount California University *California* M & W
Marymount University *Virginia* M & W
Maryville College *Tennessee* M & W
Maryville University of Saint Louis *Missouri* M & W
Marywood University *Pennsylvania* M
Massachusetts Bay Community College *Massachusetts* M & W
Massachusetts College of Liberal Arts *Massachusetts* M
The Master's College and Seminary *California* M
McDaniel College *Maryland* M & W
McGill University *Quebec (Canada)* M & W
McKendree University *Illinois* M & W
McLennan Community College *Texas* M & W
McMaster University *Ontario (Canada)* M & W
McMurry University *Texas* M & W
McNeese State University *Louisiana* M & W
Medaille College *New York* M
Menlo College *California* M & W
Merced College *California* M & W

Mercer County Community College *New Jersey* M & W
Mercer University *Georgia* M & W
Mercyhurst University *Pennsylvania* M & W
Meridian Community College *Mississippi* M
Merrimack College *Massachusetts* W
Mesa Community College *Arizona* M & W
Mesabi Range College *Minnesota* M & W
Messiah College *Pennsylvania* M
Methodist University *North Carolina* M & W
Miami University *Ohio* M
Miami University Hamilton *Ohio* M
Miami University Middletown *Ohio* M & W
Michigan State University *Michigan* M & W
Michigan Technological University *Michigan* M & W
Mid-America Christian University *Oklahoma* M
Mid-Atlantic Christian University *North Carolina* M
Mid-Plains Community College *Nebraska* M
Mid-State Technical College *Wisconsin* M
Middle Tennessee State University *Tennessee* M
Middlebury College *Vermont* M & W
Midland College *Texas* M
Midland University *Nebraska* M & W
Midwestern State University *Texas* M & W
Miles Community College *Montana* M & W
Millersville University of Pennsylvania *Pennsylvania* M & W
Milligan College *Tennessee* M & W
Millikin University *Illinois* M & W
Millsaps College *Mississippi* M & W
Milwaukee Area Technical College *Wisconsin* M
Milwaukee School of Engineering *Wisconsin* M
Mineral Area College *Missouri* M
Minnesota State Community and Technical College *Minnesota* M & W
Minnesota State University Mankato *Minnesota* M & W
Minnesota State University Moorhead *Minnesota* W
Minot State University *North Dakota* M & W
Misericordia University *Pennsylvania* M & W
Mississippi College *Mississippi* M
Mississippi Gulf Coast Community College *Mississippi* M
Mississippi State University *Mississippi* M & W
Mississippi Valley State University *Mississippi* M
Missouri Baptist University *Missouri* M & W
Missouri Southern State University *Missouri* M
Missouri State University *Missouri* M & W
Missouri Valley College *Missouri* M & W
Missouri Western State University *Missouri* M & W
Mitchell College *Connecticut* M
Modesto Junior College *California* M
Mohawk Valley Community College *New York* M
Monmouth College *Illinois* M & W
Monmouth University *New Jersey* M & W
Monroe Community College *New York* M
Montana State University *Montana* W
Montana State University Billings *Montana* M & W
Montana State University - Northern *Montana* W
Montana Tech of The University of Montana *Montana* M
Monterey Peninsula College *California* M & W
Montreat College *North Carolina* M
Moorpark College *California* M & W
Moraine Valley Community College *Illinois* M
Moravian College *Pennsylvania* M & W
Morehead State University *Kentucky* M & W
Morehouse College *Georgia* M
Morningside College *Iowa* M & W
Morrisville State College *New York* M
Mott Community College *Michigan* M
Mount Aloysius College *Pennsylvania* M & W
Mount Holyoke College *Massachusetts* W
Mount Marty College *South Dakota* M & W
Mount Mary University *Wisconsin* W
Mount Mercy University *Iowa* M & W
Mount St. Joseph University *Ohio* M & W
Mount Saint Mary College *New York* M
Mt. San Antonio College *California* M & W
Mt. San Jacinto College *California* M
Mount Vernon Nazarene University *Ohio* M & W

M = Men; W = Women

Muhlenberg College *Pennsylvania* M & W
Multnomah University *Oregon* M & W
Murray State College *Oklahoma* M & W
Murray State University *Kentucky* M & W
Muskegon Community College *Michigan* M & W
Muskingum University *Ohio* M & W
Nassau Community College *New York* M & W
Nazareth College of Rochester *New York* M & W
Nebraska College of Technical Agriculture *Nebraska* M
Nebraska Wesleyan University *Nebraska* M & W
Neumann University *Pennsylvania* M & W
New Jersey City University *New Jersey* M
New Mexico Institute of Mining and Technology *New Mexico* M & W
New Mexico Junior College *New Mexico* M
New Mexico Military Institute *New Mexico* M
New Mexico State University *New Mexico* M & W
New York University *New York* M & W
Newberry College *South Carolina* M & W
Newman University *Kansas* M & W
Niagara County Community College *New York* M & W
Niagara University *New York* M & W
Nicholls State University *Louisiana* M
Nichols College *Massachusetts* M
Nicolet Area Technical College *Wisconsin* M & W
North Carolina Central University *North Carolina* M
North Carolina State University *North Carolina* M & W
North Carolina Wesleyan College *North Carolina* M
North Central College *Illinois* M & W
North Central University *Minnesota* M
North Dakota State University *North Dakota* M & W
North Greenville University *South Carolina* M & W
North Iowa Area Community College *Iowa* M & W
North Park University *Illinois* M & W
Northampton Community College *Pennsylvania* M
Northeast Community College *Nebraska* M
Northeast Mississippi Community College *Mississippi* M
Northeastern Junior College *Colorado* M & W
Northeastern Oklahoma Agricultural and Mechanical College *Oklahoma* M
Northeastern State University *Oklahoma* M & W
Northeastern University *Massachusetts* M & W
Northern Arizona University *Arizona* W
Northern Illinois University *Illinois* M & W
Northern Kentucky University *Kentucky* M & W
Northern Maine Community College *Maine* M & W
Northern Michigan University *Michigan* M & W
Northland College *Wisconsin* M & W
Northwest Christian University *Oregon* M & W
Northwest Mississippi Community College *Mississippi* M
Northwest Missouri State University *Missouri* W
Northwest Nazarene University *Idaho* M & W
Northwestern College *Iowa* M & W
Northwestern Oklahoma State University *Oklahoma* M & W
Northwood University, Michigan Campus *Michigan* M & W
Northwood University, Texas Campus *Texas* M & W
Notre Dame College *Ohio* M & W
Notre Dame de Namur University *California* M
Nova Southeastern University *Florida* M & W
Nyack College *New York* M
Oakland City University *Indiana* M & W
Oakland Community College *Michigan* M
Oakland University *Michigan* M & W
Oberlin College *Ohio* M & W
Occidental College *California* M & W
Ocean County College *New Jersey* M
Odessa College *Texas* M
Oglethorpe University *Georgia* M & W
Ohio Christian University *Ohio* M
Ohio Dominican University *Ohio* M & W
Ohio Northern University *Ohio* M & W
The Ohio State University *Ohio* M & W
The Ohio State University at Marion *Ohio* M
Ohio University *Ohio* M & W
Ohio University - Zanesville *Ohio* M & W
Ohio Valley University *West Virginia* M & W
Ohio Wesleyan University *Ohio* M

Oklahoma Baptist University *Oklahoma* M & W
Oklahoma Christian University *Oklahoma* M & W
Oklahoma City University *Oklahoma* M & W
Oklahoma Panhandle State University *Oklahoma* M & W
Oklahoma State University *Oklahoma* M & W
Oklahoma Wesleyan University *Oklahoma* M & W
Old Dominion University *Virginia* M & W
Olivet College *Michigan* M & W
Olivet Nazarene University *Illinois* M & W
Olympic College *Washington* M & W
Oral Roberts University *Oklahoma* M & W
Orange Coast College *California* M & W
Orange County Community College *New York* M
Oregon State University *Oregon* M & W
Otero Junior College *Colorado* M & W
Ottawa University *Kansas* M
Otterbein University *Ohio* M & W
Our Lady of the Lake University of San Antonio *Texas* M
Owens Community College *Ohio* M & W
Pacific Lutheran University *Washington* M & W
Pacific University *Oregon* M & W
Paine College *Georgia* M
Palm Beach Atlantic University *Florida* M & W
Palomar College *California* M
Paradise Valley Community College *Arizona* M & W
Paris Junior College *Texas* M
Park University *Missouri* W
Parkland College *Illinois* M
Patrick Henry Community College *Virginia* M & W
Pearl River Community College *Mississippi* M & W
Penn State Abington *Pennsylvania* M
Penn State Altoona *Pennsylvania* M & W
Penn State Berks *Pennsylvania* M
Penn State DuBois *Pennsylvania* M
Penn State Erie, The Behrend College *Pennsylvania* M & W
Penn State Harrisburg *Pennsylvania* M & W
Penn State Lehigh Valley *Pennsylvania* M & W
Penn State Mont Alto *Pennsylvania* M & W
Penn State New Kensington *Pennsylvania* M & W
Penn State Schuylkill *Pennsylvania* M
Penn State University Park *Pennsylvania* M & W
Penn State Wilkes-Barre *Pennsylvania* M & W
Pennsylvania College of Technology *Pennsylvania* M & W
Pepperdine University *California* M & W
Peru State College *Nebraska* W
Pfeiffer University *North Carolina* M & W
Philadelphia University *Pennsylvania* M
Piedmont College *Georgia* M & W
Pitt Community College *North Carolina* M
Pittsburg State University *Kansas* M
Pitzer College *California* M
Point Loma Nazarene University *California* W
Point Park University *Pennsylvania* M & W
Point University *Georgia* M & W
Pomona College *California* M & W
Portland State University *Oregon* W
Post University *Connecticut* M & W
Prairie State College *Illinois* M
Prairie View A&M University *Texas* M & W
Presbyterian College *South Carolina* M & W
Presentation College *South Dakota* M & W
Prince George's Community College *Maryland* M
Princeton University *New Jersey* M & W
Purchase College, State University of New York *New York* M
Purdue University *Indiana* M & W
Purdue University Northwest *Hammond, Indiana* M
Queens University of Charlotte *North Carolina* M & W
Queen's University at Kingston *Ontario (Canada)* M
Quincy University *Illinois* M & W
Quinnipiac University *Connecticut* W
Radford University *Virginia* M & W
Randolph-Macon College *Virginia* M & W
Ranger College *Texas* M
Reedley College *California* M
Regis University *Colorado* M
Reinhardt University *Georgia* M
Rend Lake College *Illinois* M & W
Rensselaer Polytechnic Institute *New York* M

Research College of Nursing *Missouri* M & W
Rhode Island College *Rhode Island* M & W
Rhodes College *Tennessee* M & W
Rice University *Texas* M
Rider University *New Jersey* M
Riverland Community College *Minnesota* M & W
Roanoke College *Virginia* M
Robert Morris University *Pennsylvania* M
Robert Morris University Illinois *Illinois* M & W
Roberts Wesleyan College *New York* M
Rochester College *Michigan* M
Rochester Community and Technical College *Minnesota* M
Rock Valley College *Illinois* M
Rockford University *Illinois* M
Rockhurst University *Missouri* M & W
Rockland Community College *New York* M
Rocky Mountain College *Montana* M & W
Roger Williams University *Rhode Island* M
Rogers State University *Oklahoma* M & W
Rollins College *Florida* M & W
Roosevelt University *Illinois* M
Rose-Hulman Institute of Technology *Indiana* M & W
Rosemont College *Pennsylvania* M
Rowan College at Burlington County *New Jersey* M & W
Rutgers University - Camden *New Jersey* M
Rutgers University - New Brunswick *New Jersey* M & W
Sacramento City College *California* M & W
Sacred Heart University *Connecticut* M & W
Saddleback College *California* M
The Sage Colleges *New York* M
Saginaw Valley State University *Michigan* M
St. Ambrose University *Iowa* M & W
St. Andrews University *North Carolina* M & W
Saint Anselm College *New Hampshire* M
Saint Augustine's University *North Carolina* M
St. Bonaventure University *New York* M
St. Clair County Community College *Michigan* M
St. Cloud State University *Minnesota* M & W
St. Edward's University *Texas* M & W
St. Francis College *New York* M & W
Saint Francis University *Pennsylvania* M & W
St. John Fisher College *New York* M & W
Saint John's University *Minnesota* M
St. John's University *New York* M & W
Saint Joseph's College *Indiana* M & W
St. Joseph's College, Long Island Campus *New York* M
Saint Joseph's College of Maine *Maine* M
Saint Joseph's University *Pennsylvania* M
St. Lawrence University *New York* M & W
Saint Leo University *Florida* M & W
Saint Louis University *Missouri* M & W
Saint Martin's University *Washington* M & W
Saint Mary-of-the-Woods College *Indiana* W
Saint Mary's University *Indiana* M
Saint Mary's College of California *California* M
St. Mary's University *Texas* M & W
Saint Mary's University of Minnesota *Minnesota* M & W
Saint Michael's College *Vermont* M
St. Norbert College *Wisconsin* M & W
St. Olaf College *Minnesota* M & W
Saint Peter's University *New Jersey* M
St. Thomas Aquinas College *New York* M & W
St. Thomas University *Florida* M & W
St. Thomas University *New Brunswick (Canada)* M & W
Saint Vincent College *Pennsylvania* M & W
Saint Xavier University *Illinois* M
Salem State University *Massachusetts* M
Sam Houston State University *Texas* M & W
Samford University *Alabama* M & W
San Bernardino Valley College *California* M
San Diego City College *California* M & W
San Diego State University *California* M & W
San Joaquin Delta College *California* M & W
San Jose City College *California* M
San Jose State University *California* M & W
Sandhills Community College *North Carolina* M & W

M = Men; W = Women

Santa Ana College *California* M
Santa Barbara City College *California* M & W
Santa Clara University *California* M & W
Santa Rosa Junior College *California* M
Savannah College of Art and Design *Georgia* M & W
Savannah State University *Georgia* M & W
Schoolcraft College *Michigan* M
Schreiner University *Texas* M & W
Scott Community College *Iowa* M & W
Scottsdale Community College *Arizona* M & W
Scripps College *California* W
Seattle University *Washington* M & W
Seminole State College *Oklahoma* M & W
Seminole State College of Florida *Florida* W
Seton Hall University *New Jersey* M & W
Seton Hill University *Pennsylvania* W
Sewanee: The University of the South *Tennessee* M & W
Shasta College *California* M & W
Shawnee State University *Ohio* M
Shenandoah University *Virginia* M & W
Shepherd University *West Virginia* M
Shorter University *Georgia* M & W
Siena College *New York* M & W
Siena Heights University *Michigan* M & W
Sierra College *California* M & W
Sierra Nevada College *Nevada* M & W
Silver Lake College of the Holy Family *Wisconsin* M & W
Simon Fraser University *British Columbia (Canada)* M & W
Simpson College *Iowa* M & W
Simpson University *California* M & W
Sinclair Community College *Ohio* M
Skagit Valley College *Washington* M & W
Skidmore College *New York* M
Soka University of America *California* W
Sonoma State University *California* M & W
South Dakota School of Mines and Technology *South Dakota* M & W
South Dakota State University *South Dakota* M & W
South Mountain Community College *Arizona* M
Southeast Community College, Beatrice Campus *Nebraska* M
Southeast Community College, Lincoln Campus *Nebraska* M
Southeast Community College, Milford Campus *Nebraska* M
Southeastern Louisiana University *Louisiana* M
Southeastern Oklahoma State University *Oklahoma* M
Southeastern University *Florida* M & W
Southern Arkansas University - Magnolia *Arkansas* M & W
Southern Illinois University Carbondale *Illinois* M & W
Southern Illinois University Edwardsville *Illinois* M & W
Southern Maine Community College *Maine* M & W
Southern Methodist University *Texas* M & W
Southern Nazarene University *Oklahoma* M & W
Southern New Hampshire University *New Hampshire* M & W
Southern University and Agricultural and Mechanical College *Louisiana* M & W
Southern Utah University *Utah* M & W
Southern Virginia University *Virginia* M & W
Southern Wesleyan University *South Carolina* M
Southwest Baptist University *Missouri* M
Southwest Minnesota State University *Minnesota* W
Southwest Wisconsin Technical College *Wisconsin* M & W
Southwestern Christian University *Oklahoma* M & W
Southwestern College *Kansas* M & W
Southwestern Oklahoma State University *Oklahoma* M & W
Southwestern Oregon Community College *Oregon* M & W
Southwestern University *Texas* M & W

Spalding University *Kentucky* M & W
Spartanburg Methodist College *South Carolina* M & W
Spring Arbor University *Michigan* M & W
Spring Hill College *Alabama* M & W
Springfield College *Massachusetts* M
Springfield Technical Community College *Massachusetts* M
Stanford University *California* M & W
State University of New York College of Agriculture and Technology at Cobleskill *New York* M & W
State University of New York College at Cortland *New York* W
State University of New York College of Environmental Science and Forestry *New York* M & W
State University of New York College at Old Westbury *New York* M
State University of New York College at Potsdam *New York* M
State University of New York College of Technology at Canton *New York* M
State University of New York College of Technology at Delhi *New York* M & W
State University of New York at Oswego *New York* M
Stephen F. Austin State University *Texas* M & W
Stephens College *Missouri* W
Sterling College *Kansas* M & W
Stetson University *Florida* M & W
Stevens Institute of Technology *New Jersey* M
Stevenson University *Maryland* M & W
Stonehill College *Massachusetts* M & W
Suffolk County Community College *New York* M & W
Suffolk University *Massachusetts* M
Summit University *Pennsylvania* M
Susquehanna University *Pennsylvania* M & W
Swarthmore College *Pennsylvania* M
Sweet Briar College *Virginia* W
Tacoma Community College *Washington* M & W
Talladega College *Alabama* M & W
Tarleton State University *Texas* W
Taylor University *Indiana* M & W
Temple University *Pennsylvania* M
Tennessee State University *Tennessee* M
Tennessee Technological University *Tennessee* M & W
Tennessee Wesleyan College *Tennessee* M & W
Texas A&M International University *Texas* M & W
Texas A&M University *Texas* M & W
Texas A&M University - Commerce *Texas* M & W
Texas A&M University - Corpus Christi *Texas* W
Texas A&M University - Kingsville *Texas* W
Texas Christian University *Texas* M & W
Texas Lutheran University *Texas* M & W
Texas Southern University *Texas* M
Texas Southmost College *Texas* M & W
Texas State University *Texas* M & W
Texas Tech University *Texas* M & W
Texas Wesleyan University *Texas* M & W
Thiel College *Pennsylvania* M & W
Thomas College *Maine* M
Thomas More College *Kentucky* M & W
Thomas University *Georgia* M & W
Thompson Rivers University *British Columbia (Canada)* M
Tiffin University *Ohio* M & W
Tompkins Cortland Community College *New York* M & W
Tougaloo College *Mississippi* M
Towson University *Maryland* M & W
Transylvania University *Kentucky* M & W
Trent University *Ontario (Canada)* M
Trevecca Nazarene University *Tennessee* M & W
Tri-County Technical College *South Carolina* M
Trine University *Indiana* M & W
Trinidad State Junior College *Colorado* M
Trinity Bible College *North Dakota* M
Trinity Christian College *Illinois* M & W
Trinity College *Connecticut* M
Trinity University *Texas* M & W
Troy University *Alabama* M & W
Truett-McConnell College *Georgia* M & W
Truman State University *Missouri* W

Tufts University *Massachusetts* M
Tulane University *Louisiana* W
Tusculum College *Tennessee* M & W
Tuskegee University *Alabama* M
Tyler Junior College *Texas* M & W
Ulster County Community College *New York* M
Union College *Kentucky* M & W
Union College *Nebraska* M
Union College *New York* W
Union County College *New Jersey* M & W
Union University *Tennessee* M
United States Air Force Academy *Colorado* M & W
United States Military Academy *New York* M
United States Naval Academy *Maryland* M & W
Université Laval *Quebec (Canada)* M & W
Université de Montréal *Quebec (Canada)* M & W
Université du Québec en Outaouais *Quebec (Canada)* M & W
Université de Sherbrooke *Quebec (Canada)* M & W
The University of Akron *Ohio* M & W
The University of Akron Wayne College *Ohio* M
The University of Alabama *Alabama* M & W
The University of Alabama at Birmingham *Alabama* M & W
University at Albany, State University of New York *New York* M
University of Alberta *Alberta (Canada)* M & W
The University of Arizona *Arizona* M & W
University of Arkansas *Arkansas* M & W
University of Arkansas - Fort Smith *Arkansas* M & W
University of Arkansas at Little Rock *Arkansas* M & W
University of Arkansas at Monticello *Arkansas* M
University of Arkansas at Pine Bluff *Arkansas* M
The University of British Columbia *British Columbia (Canada)* M & W
The University of British Columbia - Okanagan Campus *British Columbia (Canada)* M & W
University of Calgary *Alberta (Canada)* M & W
University of California, Berkeley *California* M & W
University of California, Davis *California* M & W
University of California, Irvine *California* M & W
University of California, Los Angeles *California* M & W
University of California, Merced *California* M & W
University of California, Riverside *California* M
University of California, San Diego *California* M
University of California, Santa Barbara *California* M
University of California, Santa Cruz *California* W
University of Central Arkansas *Arkansas* M & W
University of Central Florida *Florida* M & W
University of Central Missouri *Missouri* M
University of Central Oklahoma *Oklahoma* M & W
University of Charleston *West Virginia* M & W
University of Cincinnati *Ohio* M & W
University of Cincinnati Clermont College *Ohio* M
University of Colorado Boulder *Colorado* M & W
University of Colorado Colorado Springs *Colorado* M & W
University of Connecticut *Connecticut* M
University of the Cumberlands *Kentucky* M & W
University of Dallas *Texas* M
University of Dayton *Ohio* M & W
University of Delaware *Delaware* M & W
University of Denver *Colorado* M & W
University of Detroit Mercy *Michigan* M & W
University of Dubuque *Iowa* M & W
University of Evansville *Indiana* M & W
The University of Findlay *Ohio* M & W
University of Florida *Florida* M & W
University of Georgia *Georgia* M & W
University of Great Falls *Montana* M & W
University of Guelph *Ontario (Canada)* M & W
University of Hartford *Connecticut* M & W
University of Hawaii at Hilo *Hawaii* M & W
University of Hawaii at Manoa *Hawaii* M & W
University of Houston *Texas* M & W
University of Houston - Victoria *Texas* M & W
University of Idaho *Idaho* M & W
University of Illinois at Springfield *Illinois* M & W
University of Illinois at Urbana - Champaign *Illinois* M & W
University of the Incarnate Word *Texas* M & W

M = Men; W = Women

University of Indianapolis *Indiana* M & W
The University of Iowa *Iowa* M & W
University of Jamestown *North Dakota* M & W
The University of Kansas *Kansas* M & W
University of Kentucky *Kentucky* M & W
University of La Verne *California* M
University of Louisiana at Lafayette *Louisiana* M
University of Louisiana at Monroe *Louisiana* M & W
University of Louisville *Kentucky* M & W
University of Maine at Augusta *Maine* M & W
University of Maine at Farmington *Maine* M
University of Maine at Presque Isle *Maine* M
University of Mary *North Dakota* M & W
University of Mary Hardin-Baylor *Texas* M & W
University of Maryland, College Park *Maryland* M & W
University of Massachusetts Dartmouth *Massachusetts* M
University of Massachusetts Lowell *Massachusetts* M
University of Memphis *Tennessee* M & W
University of Miami *Florida* W
University of Michigan *Michigan* M & W
University of Minnesota, Crookston *Minnesota* M & W
University of Minnesota, Morris *Minnesota* M & W
University of Minnesota, Twin Cities Campus *Minnesota* M & W
University of Mississippi *Mississippi* M & W
University of Missouri *Missouri* M & W
University of Missouri - Kansas City *Missouri* M & W
University of Missouri - St. Louis *Missouri* M & W
University of Mobile *Alabama* M & W
University of Montana *Montana* W
University of Montevallo *Alabama* M & W
University of Mount Olive *North Carolina* M & W
University of Mount Union *Ohio* M & W
University of Nebraska at Kearney *Nebraska* M & W
University of Nebraska - Lincoln *Nebraska* M & W
University of Nebraska at Omaha *Nebraska* M & W
University of Nevada, Las Vegas *Nevada* M
University of Nevada, Reno *Nevada* M & W
University of New England *Maine* M
University of New Hampshire *New Hampshire* M & W
University of New Mexico *New Mexico* M & W
University of New Orleans *Louisiana* M
University of North Alabama *Alabama* M
University of North Carolina at Asheville *North Carolina* W
The University of North Carolina at Chapel Hill *North Carolina* M & W
The University of North Carolina at Charlotte *North Carolina* M & W
The University of North Carolina at Greensboro *North Carolina* M & W
The University of North Carolina at Pembroke *North Carolina* W
The University of North Carolina Wilmington *North Carolina* M & W
University of North Dakota *North Dakota* M & W
University of North Florida *Florida* M & W
University of North Georgia *Georgia* M & W
University of North Texas *Texas* M & W
University of Northern Colorado *Colorado* M & W
University of Northern Iowa *Iowa* M & W
University of Northwestern - St. Paul *Minnesota* M & W
University of Notre Dame *Indiana* M & W
University of Oklahoma *Oklahoma* M & W
University of Oregon *Oregon* M & W
University of Ottawa *Ontario (Canada)* M & W
University of the Pacific *California* M
University of Pennsylvania *Pennsylvania* M & W
University of Pikeville *Kentucky* M & W
University of Pittsburgh at Bradford *Pennsylvania* M
University of Pittsburgh at Greensburg *Pennsylvania* M
University of Pittsburgh at Johnstown *Pennsylvania* M & W
University of Prince Edward Island *Prince Edward Island (Canada)* M

University of Puget Sound *Washington* M & W
University of Redlands *California* M & W
University of Rhode Island *Rhode Island* M
University of Richmond *Virginia* M & W
University of Rochester *New York* M
University of St. Francis *Illinois* M
University of Saint Francis *Indiana* M & W
University of St. Thomas *Minnesota* M & W
University of St. Thomas *Texas* M & W
University of San Diego *California* M
University of San Francisco *California* M & W
University of the Sciences *Pennsylvania* M & W
The University of Scranton *Pennsylvania* M
University of Sioux Falls *South Dakota* M & W
University of South Alabama *Alabama* M & W
University of South Carolina *South Carolina* M & W
University of South Carolina Aiken *South Carolina* M
University of South Carolina Beaufort *South Carolina* M & W
University of South Carolina Lancaster *South Carolina* M
University of South Carolina Upstate *South Carolina* M & W
The University of South Dakota *South Dakota* M & W
University of South Florida *Florida* M & W
University of Southern California *California* M & W
University of Southern Indiana *Indiana* M & W
University of Southern Maine *Maine* M & W
University of Southern Mississippi *Mississippi* M & W
University of the Southwest *New Mexico* M & W
The University of Tampa *Florida* M & W
The University of Tennessee *Tennessee* M & W
The University of Tennessee at Chattanooga *Tennessee* M & W
The University of Tennessee at Martin *Tennessee* M
The University of Texas at Arlington *Texas* M
The University of Texas at Austin *Texas* M & W
The University of Texas at Dallas *Texas* M & W
The University of Texas at El Paso *Texas* M
The University of Texas Rio Grande Valley *Texas* M & W
The University of Texas at San Antonio *Texas* M & W
The University of Texas at Tyler *Texas* M & W
The University of Toledo *Ohio* M & W
University of Toronto *Ontario (Canada)* M
The University of Tulsa *Oklahoma* M & W
University of Utah *Utah* M
University of Valley Forge *Pennsylvania* M
University of Victoria *British Columbia (Canada)* M & W
University of Virginia *Virginia* M & W
The University of Virginia's College at Wise *Virginia* M & W
University of Washington *Washington* M & W
University of Waterloo *Ontario (Canada)* M & W
The University of West Alabama *Alabama* M & W
University of West Florida *Florida* M & W
University of West Georgia *Georgia* M & W
The University of Western Ontario *Ontario (Canada)* M & W
University of Windsor *Ontario (Canada)* M & W
University of Wisconsin - Baraboo/Sauk County *Wisconsin* M & W
University of Wisconsin - Eau Claire *Wisconsin* M & W
University of Wisconsin - Fond du Lac *Wisconsin* M & W
University of Wisconsin - Fox Valley *Wisconsin* M & W
University of Wisconsin - Green Bay *Wisconsin* M & W
University of Wisconsin - Madison *Wisconsin* M & W
University of Wisconsin - Manitowoc *Wisconsin* M & W
University of Wisconsin - Marshfield/Wood County *Wisconsin* M & W
University of Wisconsin - Oshkosh *Wisconsin* W
University of Wisconsin - Parkside *Wisconsin* M

University of Wisconsin - Platteville *Wisconsin* W
University of Wisconsin - River Falls *Wisconsin* W
University of Wisconsin - Sheboygan *Wisconsin* M & W
University of Wisconsin - Stevens Point *Wisconsin* W
University of Wisconsin - Washington County *Wisconsin* M & W
University of Wisconsin - Waukesha *Wisconsin* M & W
University of Wisconsin - Whitewater *Wisconsin* M & W
University of Wyoming *Wyoming* M & W
Upper Iowa University *Iowa* M & W
Urbana University *Ohio* M & W
Ursinus College *Pennsylvania* M & W
Ursuline College *Ohio* W
Utah State University *Utah* M
Utah Valley University *Utah* M & W
Utica College *New York* M & W
Valdosta State University *Georgia* M
Valley City State University *North Dakota* M & W
Valley Forge Military College *Pennsylvania* M
Valparaiso University *Indiana* M & W
Vanderbilt University *Tennessee* M & W
Vassar College *New York* W
Ventura College *California* M
Vermont Technical College *Vermont* M & W
Victor Valley College *California* M
Villa Maria College *New York* M
Villanova University *Pennsylvania* M
Vincennes University *Indiana* M
Virginia Commonwealth University *Virginia* M
Virginia Polytechnic Institute and State University *Virginia* M
Virginia State University *Virginia* M & W
Virginia Union University *Virginia* M
Virginia Wesleyan College *Virginia* M
Viterbo University *Wisconsin* M & W
Wabash College *Indiana* M
Wagner College *New York* M & W
Wake Forest University *North Carolina* M & W
Waldorf College *Iowa* M & W
Walla Walla Community College *Washington* M & W
Wallace State Community College *Alabama* M
Walsh University *Ohio* M & W
Walters State Community College *Tennessee* M
Warner Pacific College *Oregon* M & W
Warner University *Florida* M & W
Wartburg College *Iowa* M & W
Washburn University *Kansas* M
Washington & Jefferson College *Pennsylvania* M & W
Washington and Lee University *Virginia* M & W
Washington State University *Washington* M
Washington University in St. Louis *Missouri* M & W
Waubonsee Community College *Illinois* M
Wayland Baptist University *Texas* M & W
Wayne County Community College District *Michigan* M
Wayne State University *Michigan* M & W
Waynesburg University *Pennsylvania* M & W
Webber International University *Florida* M & W
Weber State University *Utah* M & W
Webster University *Missouri* M
Welch College *Tennessee* M & W
Wellesley College *Massachusetts* W
Wentworth Institute of Technology *Massachusetts* M
Wesley College *Delaware* M & W
Wesleyan University *Connecticut* M
West Chester University of Pennsylvania *Pennsylvania* M & W
West Liberty University *West Virginia* M & W
West Los Angeles College *California* M
West Texas A&M University *Texas* M & W
West Valley College *California* M
West Virginia State University *West Virginia* M
West Virginia University *West Virginia* M
West Virginia University Institute of Technology *West Virginia* M
West Virginia Wesleyan College *West Virginia* M & W

M = Men; W = Women

Westchester Community College *New York* M
Western Carolina University *North Carolina* M & W
Western Illinois University *Illinois* M & W
Western Kentucky University *Kentucky* M & W
Western Michigan University *Michigan* M & W
Western New England University *Massachusetts* M
Western New Mexico University *New Mexico* M & W
Western Texas College *Texas* M & W
Western Washington University *Washington* M & W
Westfield State University *Massachusetts* M & W
Westminster College *Missouri* M & W
Westminster College *Pennsylvania* M & W
Westminster College *Utah* M & W
Westmoreland County Community College *Pennsylvania* M & W
Wheaton College *Illinois* M & W
Wheeling Jesuit University *West Virginia* M & W
Whitman College *Washington* M & W
Whittier College *California* M & W
Whitworth University *Washington* M & W
Wichita State University *Kansas* M & W
Widener University *Pennsylvania* M
Wilfrid Laurier University *Ontario (Canada)* M
Wilkes University *Pennsylvania* M & W
Willamette University *Oregon* M & W
William Carey University *Mississippi* M
William Jessup University *California* M
William Jewell College *Missouri* M & W
William Paterson University of New Jersey *New Jersey* M
William Peace University *North Carolina* M
William Penn University *Iowa* M & W
William Woods University *Missouri* M & W
Williams Baptist College *Arkansas* M
Williams College *Massachusetts* M & W
Wilmington College *Ohio* M & W
Wilson College *Pennsylvania* M
Wingate University *North Carolina* M & W
Winona State University *Minnesota* M & W
Winston-Salem State University *North Carolina* M
Winthrop University *South Carolina* M & W
Wisconsin Lutheran College *Wisconsin* M & W
Wittenberg University *Ohio* M & W
Wofford College *South Carolina* M & W
Worcester State University *Massachusetts* M
Wright State University *Ohio* M
Xavier University *Ohio* M & W
Yale University *Connecticut* M & W
Yeshiva University *New York* M
York College of Pennsylvania *Pennsylvania* M
Young Harris College *Georgia* M & W
Youngstown State University *Ohio* M & W
Zane State College *Ohio* M & W

Gymnastics

Adrian College *Michigan* W
Alderson Broaddus University *West Virginia* W
Arizona State University at the Downtown Phoenix campus *Arizona* W
Arizona State University at the Polytechnic campus *Arizona* W
Arizona State University at the Tempe campus *Arizona* M & W
Arizona State University at the West campus *Arizona* W
Auburn University *Alabama* W
Azusa Pacific University *California* W
Ball State University *Indiana* W
Baylor University *Texas* M & W
Boise State University *Idaho* W
Boston University *Massachusetts* M & W
Bowling Green State University *Ohio* W
Brigham Young University *Utah* W
Brown University *Rhode Island* W
California State University, Sacramento *California* W
Centenary College of Louisiana *Louisiana* W
Central Michigan University *Michigan* W
The College at Brockport, State University of New York *New York* W
The College of William and Mary *Virginia* M & W
Cornell University *New York* W
Dartmouth College *New Hampshire* M & W

Eastern Michigan University *Michigan* W
El Camino College *California* W
Emory University *Georgia* W
Gannon University *Pennsylvania* W
The George Washington University *District of Columbia* W
Gustavus Adolphus College *Minnesota* W
Hamline University *Minnesota* W
Hawai'i Pacific University *Hawaii* W
Hunter College of the City University of New York *New York* W
Illinois State University *Illinois* W
Iowa State University of Science and Technology *Iowa* W
Ithaca College *New York* W
Kent State University *Ohio* W
Lindenwood University *Missouri* W
Los Angeles City College *California* M
Louisiana State University and Agricultural & Mechanical College *Louisiana* W
Miami University *Ohio* M & W
Michigan State University *Michigan* W
Michigan Technological University *Michigan* M & W
Modesto Junior College *California* W
NHTI, Concord's Community College *New Hampshire* M
North Carolina State University *North Carolina* M & W
Northern Illinois University *Illinois* W
The Ohio State University *Ohio* M & W
Oregon State University *Oregon* W
Penn State University Park *Pennsylvania* M & W
Queen's University at Kingston *Ontario (Canada)* M & W
Quinnipiac University *Connecticut* W
Redlands Community College *Oklahoma* W
Rhode Island College *Rhode Island* W
Rutgers University - New Brunswick *New Jersey* W
Saginaw Valley State University *Michigan* M & W
St. Bonaventure University *New York* W
San Jose State University *California* W
Seattle Pacific University *Washington* W
Simon Fraser University *British Columbia (Canada)* W
Southeast Missouri State University *Missouri* W
Southern Connecticut State University *Connecticut* W
Southern Utah University *Utah* W
Springfield College *Massachusetts* M & W
Stanford University *California* M & W
State University of New York College at Cortland *New York* W
Syracuse University *New York* M & W
Temple University *Pennsylvania* W
Texas Christian University *Texas* M & W
Texas State University *Texas* W
Texas Woman's University *Texas* W
Towson University *Maryland* W
Tulane University *Louisiana* M & W
United States Air Force Academy *Colorado* M & W
United States Military Academy *New York* M
United States Naval Academy *Maryland* M & W
Université Laval *Quebec (Canada)* M & W
Université de Moncton *New Brunswick (Canada)* W
The University of Alabama *Alabama* W
University of Alaska Anchorage *Alaska* W
The University of Arizona *Arizona* W
University of Arkansas *Arkansas* W
University of Bridgeport *Connecticut* W
University of California, Berkeley *California* M & W
University of California, Davis *California* W
University of California, Los Angeles *California* W
University of California, Santa Barbara *California* M & W
University of Denver *Colorado* W
University of Florida *Florida* W
University of Georgia *Georgia* W
University of Illinois at Chicago *Illinois* M & W
University of Illinois at Urbana - Champaign *Illinois* M & W
The University of Iowa *Iowa* M & W
University of Kentucky *Kentucky* W
University of Manitoba *Manitoba (Canada)* M & W
University of Maryland, College Park *Maryland* W

University of Michigan *Michigan* M & W
University of Minnesota, Twin Cities Campus *Minnesota* M & W
University of Missouri *Missouri* W
University of Montana *Montana* W
University of Nebraska - Lincoln *Nebraska* M & W
University of New Hampshire *New Hampshire* W
The University of North Carolina at Chapel Hill *North Carolina* M & W
University of Oklahoma *Oklahoma* M & W
University of Pennsylvania *Pennsylvania* W
University of Pittsburgh *Pennsylvania* W
University of South Florida *Florida* W
University of Southern California *California* W
The University of Texas at Austin *Texas* M & W
University of Toronto *Ontario (Canada)* M & W
University of Utah *Utah* W
University of Vermont *Vermont* M & W
University of Washington *Washington* W
University of Wisconsin - Eau Claire *Wisconsin* W
University of Wisconsin - La Crosse *Wisconsin* W
University of Wisconsin - Oshkosh *Wisconsin* W
University of Wisconsin - Stout *Wisconsin* W
University of Wisconsin - Whitewater *Wisconsin* W
Ursinus College *Pennsylvania* W
Utah State University *Utah* W
Washington University in St. Louis *Missouri* M & W
West Chester University of Pennsylvania *Pennsylvania* W
West Virginia University *West Virginia* W
Western Michigan University *Michigan* W
Winona State University *Minnesota* W
Xavier University *Ohio* M & W
Yale University *Connecticut* W

Ice Hockey

Acadia University *Nova Scotia (Canada)* M
Adrian College *Michigan* M & W
Allegheny College *Pennsylvania* M
Alvernia University *Pennsylvania* M
American International College *Massachusetts* M
Amherst College *Massachusetts* M & W
Appalachian State University *North Carolina* M & W
Aquinas College *Michigan* M
Arizona State University at the Downtown Phoenix campus *Arizona* M
Arizona State University at the Polytechnic campus *Arizona* M
Arizona State University at the Tempe campus *Arizona* M
Arizona State University at the West campus *Arizona* M
Assumption College *Massachusetts* M
Augsburg College *Minnesota* M & W
Augustana College *Illinois* M
Aurora University *Illinois* M
Babson College *Massachusetts* M & W
Barnard College *New York* W
Bates College *Maine* M & W
Baylor University *Texas* M
Becker College *Massachusetts* M & W
Beloit College *Wisconsin* M & W
Bemidji State University *Minnesota* M & W
Bentley University *Massachusetts* M
Bethel University *Minnesota* M & W
Bishop's University *Quebec (Canada)* W
Boston College *Massachusetts* M & W
Boston University *Massachusetts* M & W
Bowdoin College *Maine* M & W
Bowling Green State University *Ohio* M
Briercrest College *Saskatchewan (Canada)* M
Brock University *Ontario (Canada)* M & W
Broome Community College *New York* M
Brown University *Rhode Island* M & W
Bryant University *Rhode Island* M
Bryn Athyn College of the New Church *Pennsylvania* M
Bucknell University *Pennsylvania* M
Buffalo State College, State University of New York *New York* M & W
Butler University *Indiana* M
California State University, Fullerton *California* M & W

M = Men; W = Women

California State University, Sacramento *California* M
Calvin College *Michigan* M
Canisius College *New York* M
Cape Breton University *Nova Scotia (Canada)* W
Carleton College *Minnesota* M & W
Carleton University *Ontario (Canada)* M & W
Carnegie Mellon University *Pennsylvania* M & W
Carthage College *Wisconsin* M & W
Castleton University *Vermont* M & W
Central Washington University *Washington* M & W
Chapman University *California* M
Chatham University *Pennsylvania* W
Christopher Newport University *Virginia* M
The Citadel, The Military College of South Carolina
    South Carolina M
Clarkson University *New York* M & W
Clemson University *South Carolina* M & W
Colby College *Maine* M & W
Colby-Sawyer College *New Hampshire* M & W
Colgate University *New York* M & W
The College at Brockport, State University of New
    York *New York* M
College of the Canyons *California* M
College of the Holy Cross *Massachusetts* M & W
College of Saint Benedict *Minnesota* W
The College of St. Scholastica *Minnesota* M & W
The Colorado College *Colorado* M & W
Colorado School of Mines *Colorado* M & W
Colorado State University *Colorado* M & W
Colorado State University - Pueblo *Colorado* M
Columbia University *New York* M
Columbia University, School of General Studies
    New York M & W
Community College of Allegheny County *Pennsylvania* M
Concordia College *Minnesota* M & W
Concordia University *Quebec (Canada)* M & W
Concordia University of Edmonton *Alberta
    (Canada)* M
Concordia University Wisconsin *Wisconsin* M & W
Connecticut College *Connecticut* M & W
Cornell University *New York* M & W
Curry College *Massachusetts* M & W
Dakota College at Bottineau *North Dakota* M
Dalhousie University *Nova Scotia (Canada)* M & W
Dallas Baptist University *Texas* M
Daniel Webster College *New Hampshire* M & W
Dartmouth College *New Hampshire* M & W
Davenport University *Michigan* M & W
Denison University *Ohio* M
Dickinson College *Pennsylvania* M & W
Dordt College *Iowa* M
Duke University *North Carolina* M & W
East Stroudsburg University of Pennsylvania *Pennsylvania* M & W
Eastern Connecticut State University *Connecticut* M & W
Eastern Illinois University *Illinois* M
Eastern Washington University *Washington* M & W
Elmira College *New York* M & W
Elon University *North Carolina* M
Endicott College *Massachusetts* M & W
Erie Community College *New York* M
Erie Community College, North Campus *New
    York* M
Erie Community College, South Campus *New
    York* M
Farmingdale State College *New York* M
Ferris State University *Michigan* M
Finlandia University *Michigan* M & W
Fitchburg State University *Massachusetts* M
Fordham University *New York* M
Fort Lewis College *Colorado* M & W
Framingham State University *Massachusetts* M
Franklin & Marshall College *Pennsylvania* M
Franklin Pierce University *New Hampshire* M
Furman University *South Carolina* M
Gannon University *Pennsylvania* M
Georgetown University *District of Columbia* M
Georgia State University *Georgia* M
Gettysburg College *Pennsylvania* M
Gonzaga University *Washington* M
Grand Valley State University *Michigan* M

Gustavus Adolphus College *Minnesota* M & W
Hamilton College *New York* M & W
Hamline University *Minnesota* M & W
Harvard University *Massachusetts* M & W
Hobart and William Smith Colleges *New
    York* M & W
Holy Cross College *Indiana* M
Hope College *Michigan* M
Hudson Valley Community College *New York* M
John Carroll University *Ohio* M
Johnson & Wales University *Rhode Island* M
Keene State College *New Hampshire* M & W
Kennebec Valley Community College *Maine* M & W
Kutztown University of Pennsylvania *Pennsylvania* M
Lafayette College *Pennsylvania* M
Lake Forest College *Illinois* M & W
Lake Superior State University *Michigan* M & W
Lakehead University *Ontario (Canada)* M
Laurentian University *Ontario (Canada)* M & W
Lawrence Technological University *Michigan* M
Lawrence University *Wisconsin* M & W
Lebanon Valley College *Pennsylvania* M & W
Lehigh University *Pennsylvania* M
Lewis University *Illinois* M
Liberty University *Virginia* M & W
Life University *Georgia* M
Lindenwood University *Missouri* M & W
Long Island University - LIU Post *New York* M
Loras College *Iowa* M
Macalester College *Minnesota* M & W
Manhattanville College *New York* M & W
Marian University *Wisconsin* M & W
Marist College *New York* M
McGill University *Quebec (Canada)* M & W
McKendree University *Illinois* M & W
Mercyhurst University *Pennsylvania* M & W
Merrimack College *Massachusetts* M & W
Messiah College *Pennsylvania* M
Methodist University *North Carolina* M
Miami University *Ohio* M & W
Michigan State University *Michigan* M & W
Michigan Technological University *Michigan* M & W
Mid Michigan Community College *Michigan* M
Middlebury College *Vermont* M & W
Milwaukee School of Engineering *Wisconsin* M
Minnesota State University Mankato *Minnesota* M & W
Minot State University *North Dakota* M
Missouri State University *Missouri* M
Mohawk Valley Community College *New York* M
Monmouth University *New Jersey* M
Monroe Community College *New York* M
Moravian College *Pennsylvania* M & W
Morrisville State College *New York* M & W
Mount Allison University *New Brunswick
    (Canada)* W
Mount St. Mary's University *Maryland* M & W
Nazareth College of Rochester *New York* M
Neumann University *Pennsylvania* M & W
New England College *New Hampshire* M & W
New Jersey Institute of Technology *New Jersey* M
Niagara University *New York* M
Nichols College *Massachusetts* M & W
Nipissing University *Ontario (Canada)* M
North Carolina State University *North Carolina* M
North Country Community College *New York* M
North Dakota State University *North Dakota* M & W
Northeastern University *Massachusetts* M & W
Northern Michigan University *Michigan* M & W
Northland College *Wisconsin* M & W
Norwich University *Vermont* M & W
Oberlin College *Ohio* M & W
The Ohio State University *Ohio* M & W
Ohio University *Ohio* M
Ohio Wesleyan University *Ohio* M & W
Old Dominion University *Virginia* M & W
Penn State Erie, The Behrend College *Pennsylvania* M
Penn State Lehigh Valley *Pennsylvania* M & W
Penn State University Park *Pennsylvania* M & W
Plymouth State University *New Hampshire* M & W
Post University *Connecticut* M & W
Princeton University *New Jersey* M & W

Providence College *Rhode Island* M & W
Queen's University at Kingston *Ontario
    (Canada)* M & W
Quinnipiac University *Connecticut* M & W
Rainy River Community College *Minnesota* W
Rensselaer Polytechnic Institute *New York* M & W
Robert Morris University *Pennsylvania* M & W
Robert Morris University Illinois *Illinois* M & W
Rochester Institute of Technology *New York* M & W
Royal Military College of Canada *Ontario
    (Canada)* M
Ryerson University *Ontario (Canada)* M & W
Sacred Heart University *Connecticut* M & W
Saginaw Valley State University *Michigan* M & W
Saint Anselm College *New Hampshire* M & W
St. Bonaventure University *New York* M
St. Catherine University *Minnesota* W
St. Cloud State University *Minnesota* M & W
St. Francis Xavier University *Nova Scotia
    (Canada)* M & W
Saint John's University *Minnesota* M
Saint Joseph's College of Maine *Maine* M & W
St. Lawrence University *New York* M & W
Saint Louis University *Missouri* M
Saint Mary's University *Nova Scotia
    (Canada)* M & W
Saint Mary's University of Minnesota *Minnesota* M & W
Saint Michael's College *Vermont* M & W
St. Norbert College *Wisconsin* M & W
St. Olaf College *Minnesota* M & W
St. Thomas University *New Brunswick
    (Canada)* M & W
Saint Vincent College *Pennsylvania* M
Salem State University *Massachusetts* M & W
Salve Regina University *Rhode Island* M & W
Santa Clara University *California* M
Santa Rosa Junior College *California* M
Seton Hall University *New Jersey* M
Sewanee: The University of the South *Tennessee* M & W
Siena College *New York* M
Skidmore College *New York* M
Slippery Rock University of Pennsylvania *Pennsylvania* M
South Dakota State University *South Dakota* M & W
Southern Alberta Institute of Technology *Alberta
    (Canada)* M & W
Southern Methodist University *Texas* M
Southern New Hampshire University *New Hampshire* M
Stanford University *California* M
State University of New York College at Cortland
    New York M & W
State University of New York College at Geneseo
    New York M & W
State University of New York College at Oneonta
    New York M
State University of New York College at Potsdam
    New York M & W
State University of New York College of Technology
    at Canton *New York* M & W
State University of New York at Fredonia *New
    York* M
State University of New York Maritime College *New
    York* M
State University of New York at Oswego *New
    York* M & W
State University of New York at Plattsburgh *New
    York* M & W
Stevenson University *Maryland* W
Stonehill College *Massachusetts* M & W
Suffolk University *Massachusetts* M
Swarthmore College *Pennsylvania* M & W
Syracuse University *New York* M & W
Texas Christian University *Texas* M
Thomas College *Maine* M
Thompson Rivers University *British Columbia
    (Canada)* M
Trinity College *Connecticut* M & W
Tufts University *Massachusetts* M
Tulane University *Louisiana* M & W

M = Men; W = Women

Tyndale University College & Seminary *Ontario (Canada)* M
Union College *New York* M & W
United States Air Force Academy *Colorado* M
United States Coast Guard Academy *Connecticut* M & W
United States Military Academy *New York* M
United States Naval Academy *Maryland* M & W
Université de Moncton *New Brunswick (Canada)* M & W
Université de Montréal *Quebec (Canada)* W
Université du Québec à Trois-Rivières *Quebec (Canada)* M & W
The University of Alabama *Alabama* M
The University of Alabama in Huntsville *Alabama* M
University of Alaska Anchorage *Alaska* M
University of Alaska Fairbanks *Alaska* M
University of Alberta *Alberta (Canada)* M & W
The University of Arizona *Arizona* M
The University of British Columbia *British Columbia (Canada)* M & W
University of Calgary *Alberta (Canada)* M & W
University of Colorado Boulder *Colorado* M & W
University of Colorado Denver *Colorado* M
University of Connecticut *Connecticut* M & W
University of Delaware *Delaware* M & W
University of Denver *Colorado* M & W
University of Georgia *Georgia* W
University of Guelph *Ontario (Canada)* M & W
The University of Iowa *Iowa* M & W
University of Jamestown *North Dakota* M
University of Lethbridge *Alberta (Canada)* M & W
University of Maine *Maine* M & W
University of Manitoba *Manitoba (Canada)* M & W
University of Maryland, Baltimore County *Maryland* M
University of Massachusetts Amherst *Massachusetts* M
University of Massachusetts Boston *Massachusetts* M & W
University of Massachusetts Dartmouth *Massachusetts* M
University of Massachusetts Lowell *Massachusetts* M
University of Michigan *Michigan* M
University of Michigan - Dearborn *Michigan* M
University of Minnesota, Duluth *Minnesota* M & W
University of Minnesota, Twin Cities Campus *Minnesota* M & W
University of Mississippi *Mississippi* M
University of Missouri - St. Louis *Missouri* M
University of Montana *Montana* M & W
University of Nebraska at Omaha *Nebraska* M
University of New Brunswick Fredericton *New Brunswick (Canada)* M
University of New Brunswick Saint John *New Brunswick (Canada)* M & W
University of New England *Maine* M & W
University of New Hampshire *New Hampshire* M & W
University of New Haven *Connecticut* M
The University of North Carolina at Chapel Hill *North Carolina* M
University of North Dakota *North Dakota* M & W
University of North Texas *Texas* M & W
University of Northern Colorado *Colorado* M
University of Northwestern - St. Paul *Minnesota* M
University of Notre Dame *Indiana* M
University of Ottawa *Ontario (Canada)* W
University of Prince Edward Island *Prince Edward Island (Canada)* M & W
University of Regina *Saskatchewan (Canada)* M & W
University of Richmond *Virginia* M
University of Rochester *New York* M & W
University of St. Thomas *Minnesota* M & W
University of Saskatchewan *Saskatchewan (Canada)* M & W
The University of Scranton *Pennsylvania* M
University of Southern California *California* M & W
University of Southern Maine *Maine* M & W
The University of Texas at Austin *Texas* M & W
The University of Texas at San Antonio *Texas* M
University of Toronto *Ontario (Canada)* M & W

University of Utah *Utah* M
University of Vermont *Vermont* M & W
University of Waterloo *Ontario (Canada)* M & W
The University of Western Ontario *Ontario (Canada)* M & W
University of Windsor *Ontario (Canada)* M & W
University of Wisconsin - Eau Claire *Wisconsin* M & W
University of Wisconsin - Madison *Wisconsin* M & W
University of Wisconsin - Milwaukee *Wisconsin* M & W
University of Wisconsin - Platteville *Wisconsin* M & W
University of Wisconsin - River Falls *Wisconsin* M & W
University of Wisconsin - Stevens Point *Wisconsin* M & W
University of Wisconsin - Stout *Wisconsin* M & W
University of Wisconsin - Superior *Wisconsin* M & W
University of Wisconsin - Whitewater *Wisconsin* M & W
University of Wyoming *Wyoming* M & W
Utah State University *Utah* M
Utica College *New York* M & W
Villanova University *Pennsylvania* M & W
Wagner College *New York* M
Waldorf College *Iowa* M
Washington College *Maryland* M
Washington & Jefferson College *Pennsylvania* M
Washington State University *Washington* M
Washington University in St. Louis *Missouri* M
Weber State University *Utah* M
Wentworth Institute of Technology *Massachusetts* M
Wesleyan University *Connecticut* M & W
West Chester University of Pennsylvania *Pennsylvania* M & W
Western Michigan University *Michigan* M
Western New England University *Massachusetts* M
Western State Colorado University *Colorado* M
Westfield State University *Massachusetts* M
Westminster College *Pennsylvania* M
Wheaton College *Illinois* M
Wilfrid Laurier University *Ontario (Canada)* M & W
Williams College *Massachusetts* M & W
Williston State College *North Dakota* M
Worcester State University *Massachusetts* M
Xavier University *Ohio* M & W
Yale University *Connecticut* M & W
York University *Ontario (Canada)* M & W

Lacrosse

Adams State University *Colorado* M & W
Adelphi University *New York* M & W
Adrian College *Michigan* M & W
Albertus Magnus College *Connecticut* M & W
Albion College *Michigan* M & W
Albright College *Pennsylvania* M & W
Alderson Broaddus University *West Virginia* M & W
Alfred University *New York* M & W
Allegheny College *Pennsylvania* M & W
Alma College *Michigan* M & W
Alvernia University *Pennsylvania* M & W
American International College *Massachusetts* M & W
American University *District of Columbia* W
Amherst College *Massachusetts* M & W
Ancilla College *Indiana* W
Anna Maria College *Massachusetts* M & W
Anne Arundel Community College *Maryland* M & W
Appalachian State University *North Carolina* M & W
Aquinas College *Michigan* M & W
Arcadia University *Pennsylvania* M & W
Arizona State University at the Downtown Phoenix campus *Arizona* W
Arizona State University at the Polytechnic campus *Arizona* W
Arizona State University at the Tempe campus *Arizona* W
Arizona State University at the West campus *Arizona* W
Asbury University *Kentucky* M & W

Assumption College *Massachusetts* M & W
Augsburg College *Minnesota* W
Augustana College *Illinois* M & W
Aurora University *Illinois* M & W
Ave Maria University *Florida* W
Babson College *Massachusetts* M & W
Baldwin Wallace University *Ohio* M & W
Ball State University *Indiana* M & W
Bard College *New York* M & W
Barnard College *New York* W
Bates College *Maine* M & W
Bay Path University *Massachusetts* W
Baylor University *Texas* W
Becker College *Massachusetts* M & W
Bellarmine University *Kentucky* M
Belmont Abbey College *North Carolina* M & W
Beloit College *Wisconsin* M & W
Benedictine College *Kansas* M & W
Benedictine University *Illinois* M & W
Bentley University *Massachusetts* M & W
Berry College *Georgia* M & W
Bethany College *West Virginia* M
Bethel College *Indiana* W
Binghamton University, State University of New York *New York* M & W
Birmingham-Southern College *Alabama* M & W
Bishop's University *Quebec (Canada)* M & W
Bloomsburg University of Pennsylvania *Pennsylvania* M & W
Boston College *Massachusetts* W
Boston University *Massachusetts* M & W
Bowdoin College *Maine* M & W
Brevard College *North Carolina* M & W
Bridgewater College *Virginia* M & W
Bridgewater State University *Massachusetts* W
Brigham Young University *Utah* M
Brock University *Ontario (Canada)* M
Broome Community College *New York* M
Brown University *Rhode Island* M & W
Bryant University *Rhode Island* M & W
Bryn Athyn College of the New Church *Pennsylvania* M & W
Bryn Mawr College *Pennsylvania* W
Bucknell University *Pennsylvania* M & W
Buffalo State College, State University of New York *New York* M & W
Butler University *Indiana* M & W
Cabrini University *Pennsylvania* M & W
Caldwell University *New Jersey* W
California State University, Fresno *California* W
California State University, Fullerton *California* M & W
California State University, Sacramento *California* M & W
Calvin College *Michigan* M & W
Canisius College *New York* M & W
Capital University *Ohio* M & W
Carleton College *Minnesota* W
Carleton University *Ontario (Canada)* M
Carnegie Mellon University *Pennsylvania* M & W
Carthage College *Wisconsin* M & W
Castleton University *Vermont* M & W
Catawba College *North Carolina* M & W
The Catholic University of America *District of Columbia* M & W
Cazenovia College *New York* M & W
Cecil College *Maryland* M
Cedar Crest College *Pennsylvania* W
Centenary College *New Jersey* M & W
Centenary College of Louisiana *Louisiana* M
Central Connecticut State University *Connecticut* W
Central Michigan University *Michigan* W
Central Washington University *Washington* M & W
Centre College *Kentucky* M & W
Chapman University *California* M & W
Chatham University *Pennsylvania* M & W
Chestnut Hill College *Pennsylvania* M & W
Chowan University *North Carolina* M & W
Christopher Newport University *Virginia* M & W
The Citadel, The Military College of South Carolina *South Carolina* M
City College of the City University of New York *New York* M
Claremont McKenna College *California* M & W

M = Men; W = Women

Clark University *Massachusetts* M
Clarke University *Iowa* M & W
Clarkson University *New York* M & W
Clemson University *South Carolina* M & W
Coastal Carolina University *South Carolina* M & W
Coker College *South Carolina* M & W
Colby College *Maine* M & W
Colby-Sawyer College *New Hampshire* W
Colgate University *New York* M & W
The College at Brockport, State University of New York *New York* M & W
College of the Holy Cross *Massachusetts* M & W
The College of Idaho *Idaho* M
College of Mount Saint Vincent *New York* M & W
The College of New Jersey *New Jersey* W
College of Saint Benedict *Minnesota* W
College of Saint Elizabeth *New Jersey* W
The College of Saint Rose *New York* M
College of Southern Maryland *Maryland* M & W
The College of William and Mary *Virginia* W
The College of Wooster *Ohio* M & W
The Colorado College *Colorado* M & W
Colorado Mesa University *Colorado* M & W
Colorado School of Mines *Colorado* M & W
Colorado State University *Colorado* M & W
Colorado State University - Pueblo *Colorado* M & W
Columbia College *South Carolina* W
Columbia College Chicago *Illinois* M
Columbia University *New York* M & W
Columbia University, School of General Studies *New York* M & W
Community College of Baltimore County *Maryland* M & W
Concordia University Irvine *California* M & W
Concordia University, St. Paul *Minnesota* W
Connecticut College *Connecticut* M & W
Converse College *South Carolina* W
Cornell College *Iowa* M & W
Cornell University *New York* M & W
County College of Morris *New Jersey* M
Curry College *Massachusetts* M & W
Dallas Baptist University *Texas* M
Daniel Webster College *New Hampshire* M & W
Dartmouth College *New Hampshire* M & W
Davenport University *Michigan* M & W
Davidson College *North Carolina* W
Dean College *Massachusetts* M & W
Defiance College *Ohio* M
Delaware Technical & Community College, Terry Campus *Delaware* M
Delaware Valley University *Pennsylvania* M & W
Denison University *Ohio* M & W
DeSales University *Pennsylvania* M
Dickinson College *Pennsylvania* M & W
Dominican College *New York* M & W
Dominican University of California *California* M
Dordt College *Iowa* M
Drew University *New Jersey* M & W
Drexel University *Pennsylvania* M & W
Duke University *North Carolina* M & W
Duquesne University *Pennsylvania* W
Earlham College *Indiana* M & W
East Stroudsburg University of Pennsylvania *Pennsylvania* M & W
Eastern Connecticut State University *Connecticut* M & W
Eastern University *Pennsylvania* M & W
Edinboro University of Pennsylvania *Pennsylvania* W
Elizabethtown College *Pennsylvania* M & W
Elmhurst College *Illinois* M & W
Elmira College *New York* M & W
Elms College *Massachusetts* W
Elon University *North Carolina* M & W
Embry-Riddle Aeronautical University - Daytona *Florida* M & W
Emerson College *Massachusetts* M & W
Emmanuel College *Georgia* M & W
Emmanuel College *Massachusetts* M & W
Emory University *Georgia* M & W
Endicott College *Massachusetts* M & W
Erie Community College *New York* W

Erie Community College, North Campus *New York* W
Erie Community College, South Campus *New York* W
Erskine College *South Carolina* W
Fairfield University *Connecticut* M & W
Fairleigh Dickinson University, College at Florham *New Jersey* M & W
Farmingdale State College *New York* M & W
Ferrum College *Virginia* M & W
Finger Lakes Community College *New York* M
Fitchburg State University *Massachusetts* W
Florida Institute of Technology *Florida* M & W
Florida Southern College *Florida* W
Fontbonne University *Missouri* M & W
Fort Lewis College *Colorado* M & W
Framingham State University *Massachusetts* W
Franciscan University of Steubenville *Ohio* M & W
Franklin College *Indiana* W
Franklin & Marshall College *Pennsylvania* M & W
Franklin Pierce University *New Hampshire* M & W
Frederick Community College *Maryland* M & W
Frostburg State University *Maryland* M & W
Furman University *South Carolina* M & W
Gannon University *Pennsylvania* W
Genesee Community College *New York* M & W
George Fox University *Oregon* W
George Mason University *Virginia* W
Georgetown College *Kentucky* W
Georgetown University *District of Columbia* M & W
Georgia State University *Georgia* M
Georgian Court University *New Jersey* M & W
Gettysburg College *Pennsylvania* M & W
Gonzaga University *Washington* M & W
Gordon College *Massachusetts* M & W
Goucher College *Maryland* M & W
Grand Canyon University *Arizona* M
Grand Valley State University *Michigan* M & W
Green Mountain College *Vermont* M & W
Greensboro College *North Carolina* M & W
Grove City College *Pennsylvania* M & W
Guilford College *North Carolina* M & W
Gustavus Adolphus College *Minnesota* W
Gwynedd Mercy University *Pennsylvania* M & W
Hamilton College *New York* M & W
Hamline University *Minnesota* W
Hampden-Sydney College *Virginia* M
Hampton University *Virginia* M
Hanover College *Indiana* M & W
Harding University *Arkansas* M
Harford Community College *Maryland* M & W
Hartwick College *New York* M & W
Harvard University *Massachusetts* M & W
Harvey Mudd College *California* W
Haverford College *Pennsylvania* M & W
Heidelberg University *Ohio* M & W
Hendrix College *Arkansas* M & W
Herkimer County Community College *New York* M & W
High Point University *North Carolina* M & W
Hilbert College *New York* M & W
Hiram College *Ohio* M & W
Hobart and William Smith Colleges *New York* M & W
Hofstra University *New York* M & W
Hollins University *Virginia* W
Holy Cross College *Indiana* M
Holy Family University *Pennsylvania* W
Hood College *Maryland* M & W
Hope College *Michigan* M & W
Houghton College *New York* M & W
Howard Community College *Maryland* M & W
Howard University *District of Columbia* W
Hudson Valley Community College *New York* M
Humboldt State University *California* M
Huntingdon College *Alabama* M & W
Husson University *Maine* M & W
Illinois Institute of Technology *Illinois* M & W
Illinois Wesleyan University *Illinois* M & W
Immaculata University *Pennsylvania* W
Indiana Tech *Indiana* M & W
Indiana University of Pennsylvania *Pennsylvania* W
Iona College *New York* W
Ithaca College *New York* M & W

Jacksonville University *Florida* M & W
James Madison University *Virginia* W
Jefferson Community College *New York* M & W
John Carroll University *Ohio* M & W
Johns Hopkins University *Maryland* M & W
Johnson State College *Vermont* M & W
Judson University *Illinois* M
Juniata College *Pennsylvania* M
Kalamazoo College *Michigan* M & W
Kean University *New Jersey* M & W
Keene State College *New Hampshire* M & W
Kennesaw State University *Georgia* W
Kenyon College *Ohio* M & W
Keuka College *New York* M & W
Keystone College *Pennsylvania* M & W
King's College *Pennsylvania* M & W
Kutztown University of Pennsylvania *Pennsylvania* M & W
La Roche College *Pennsylvania* M & W
La Salle University *Pennsylvania* W
Lafayette College *Pennsylvania* M & W
LaGrange College *Georgia* W
Lake Erie College *Ohio* M & W
Lake Forest College *Illinois* M & W
Lancaster Bible College *Pennsylvania* W
Lasell College *Massachusetts* M & W
Laurentian University *Ontario (Canada)* M
Lawrence Technological University *Michigan* M & W
Le Moyne College *New York* M & W
Lebanon Valley College *Pennsylvania* M & W
Lees-McRae College *North Carolina* M & W
Lehigh University *Pennsylvania* M & W
Lenoir-Rhyne University *North Carolina* M & W
Lewis & Clark College *Oregon* W
Lewis University *Illinois* M & W
Liberty University *Virginia* W
Limestone College *South Carolina* M & W
Lincoln Memorial University *Tennessee* M & W
Lindenwood University *Missouri* M & W
Linfield College *Oregon* W
Lock Haven University of Pennsylvania *Pennsylvania* W
Long Island University - LIU Brooklyn *New York* W
Long Island University - LIU Post *New York* M & W
Longwood University *Virginia* W
Loras College *Iowa* W
Lourdes University *Ohio* M & W
Loyola University Maryland *Maryland* M & W
Lycoming College *Pennsylvania* M & W
Lynchburg College *Virginia* M & W
Lyndon State College *Vermont* M
Lynn University *Florida* W
Macalester College *Minnesota* W
Madonna University *Michigan* M & W
Maine Maritime Academy *Maine* M
Manhattan College *New York* M & W
Manhattanville College *New York* M & W
Marian University *Indiana* W
Marist College *New York* M & W
Marquette University *Wisconsin* M & W
Mars Hill University *North Carolina* M
Marshall University *West Virginia* W
Marymount California University *California* M & W
Marymount University *Virginia* M & W
Maryville University of Saint Louis *Missouri* M
Marywood University *Pennsylvania* M & W
Massachusetts College of Liberal Arts *Massachusetts* W
Massachusetts Institute of Technology *Massachusetts* M & W
Massachusetts Maritime Academy *Massachusetts* M & W
McDaniel College *Maryland* M & W
McGill University *Quebec (Canada)* M & W
McKendree University *Illinois* W
McMaster University *Ontario (Canada)* M & W
Medaille College *New York* M & W
Mercer University *Georgia* W
Mercy College *New York* M & W
Mercyhurst North East *Pennsylvania* M
Mercyhurst University *Pennsylvania* M & W
Meredith College *North Carolina* W
Merrimack College *Massachusetts* M & W
Messiah College *Pennsylvania* M & W

M = Men; W = Women

Methodist University *North Carolina* M & W
Miami University *Ohio* M & W
Michigan State University *Michigan* M & W
Michigan Technological University *Michigan* M & W
Middlebury College *Vermont* M & W
Millersville University of Pennsylvania *Pennsylvania* W
Millsaps College *Mississippi* M & W
Milwaukee School of Engineering *Wisconsin* W
Misericordia University *Pennsylvania* M & W
Missouri Baptist University *Missouri* M & W
Missouri State University *Missouri* M
Missouri Valley College *Missouri* M & W
Mitchell College *Connecticut* M
Mohawk Valley Community College *New York* M & W
Molloy College *New York* M & W
Monmouth College *Illinois* M & W
Monmouth University *New Jersey* M & W
Monroe Community College *New York* M
Montclair State University *New Jersey* M & W
Moravian College *Pennsylvania* M & W
Morrisville State College *New York* M & W
Mount Holyoke College *Massachusetts* W
Mount Ida College *Massachusetts* M & W
Mount St. Joseph University *Ohio* M & W
Mount Saint Mary College *New York* M & W
Mount St. Mary's University *Maryland* M & W
Muhlenberg College *Pennsylvania* M & W
Nassau Community College *New York* M & W
Nazareth College of Rochester *New York* M & W
Neumann University *Pennsylvania* M & W
New England College *New Hampshire* M & W
New York Institute of Technology *New York* M
Newberry College *South Carolina* W
Newbury College *Massachusetts* W
Niagara University *New York* W
Nichols College *Massachusetts* M & W
North Carolina State University *North Carolina* W
North Central College *Illinois* M & W
North Dakota State University *North Dakota* M & W
North Greenville University *South Carolina* W
Northampton Community College *Pennsylvania* M
Northeastern University *Massachusetts* M & W
Northern Michigan University *Michigan* M & W
Northland College *Wisconsin* M & W
Norwich University *Vermont* M
Notre Dame of Maryland University *Maryland* W
Notre Dame de Namur University *California* M
Nyack College *New York* W
Oberlin College *Ohio* M & W
Occidental College *California* M & W
Ocean County College *New Jersey* M
Oglethorpe University *Georgia* M & W
Ohio Northern University *Ohio* M & W
The Ohio State University *Ohio* M & W
Ohio Valley University *West Virginia* M
Ohio Wesleyan University *Ohio* M & W
Oklahoma Baptist University *Oklahoma* W
Old Dominion University *Virginia* M & W
Olivet College *Michigan* M & W
Onondaga Community College *New York* M & W
Otterbein University *Ohio* M & W
Pace University *New York* M & W
Pace University, Pleasantville Campus *New York* M & W
Pacific Lutheran University *Washington* M & W
Pacific University *Oregon* W
Palm Beach Atlantic University *Florida* M & W
Penn State Erie, The Behrend College *Pennsylvania* M
Penn State University Park *Pennsylvania* M & W
Pepperdine University *California* W
Pfeiffer University *North Carolina* M & W
Philadelphia University *Pennsylvania* W
Piedmont College *Georgia* M & W
Pitzer College *California* W
Plymouth State University *New Hampshire* M & W
Point University *Georgia* M & W
Pomona College *California* W
Post University *Connecticut* M & W
Potomac State College of West Virginia University *West Virginia* M & W

Presbyterian College *South Carolina* W
Princeton University *New Jersey* M & W
Principia College *Illinois* W
Providence College *Rhode Island* M
Purchase College, State University of New York *New York* W
Queens College of the City University of New York *New York* W
Queens University of Charlotte *North Carolina* M & W
Queen's University at Kingston *Ontario (Canada)* M & W
Quinnipiac University *Connecticut* M & W
Radford University *Virginia* W
Ramapo College of New Jersey *New Jersey* W
Randolph College *Virginia* M & W
Randolph-Macon College *Virginia* M & W
Regis College *Massachusetts* M & W
Regis University *Colorado* W
Reinhardt University *Georgia* M & W
Rensselaer Polytechnic Institute *New York* M & W
Rhode Island College *Rhode Island* W
Rhodes College *Tennessee* M & W
Rice University *Texas* W
Rivier University *New Hampshire* M & W
Roanoke College *Virginia* M & W
Robert Morris University *Pennsylvania* M & W
Robert Morris University Illinois *Illinois* M & W
Roberts Wesleyan College *New York* M & W
Rochester Institute of Technology *New York* M & W
Rockhurst University *Missouri* M & W
Roger Williams University *Rhode Island* M & W
Rollins College *Florida* M & W
Rosemont College *Pennsylvania* M & W
Rowan University *New Jersey* W
Rutgers University - Camden *New Jersey* W
Rutgers University - New Brunswick *New Jersey* M & W
Sacred Heart University *Connecticut* M & W
The Sage Colleges *New York* W
Saginaw Valley State University *Michigan* M & W
St. Ambrose University *Iowa* M
St. Andrews University *North Carolina* M & W
Saint Anselm College *New Hampshire* M & W
St. Bonaventure University *New York* M & W
Saint Francis University *Pennsylvania* W
St. Francis Xavier University *Nova Scotia (Canada)* M
St. Gregory's University *Oklahoma* M
St. John Fisher College *New York* M & W
Saint John's University *Minnesota* M
St. John's University *New York* M
St. Joseph's College, Long Island Campus *New York* M & W
Saint Joseph's College of Maine *Maine* M & W
Saint Joseph's University *Pennsylvania* M & W
St. Lawrence University *New York* M & W
Saint Leo University *Florida* M & W
Saint Louis University *Missouri* M & W
Saint Mary's College *Indiana* W
Saint Mary's College of California *California* M & W
St. Mary's College of Maryland *Maryland* M & W
Saint Michael's College *Vermont* M & W
St. Thomas Aquinas College *New York* W
Saint Vincent College *Pennsylvania* M & W
Salem State University *Massachusetts* M & W
Salisbury University *Maryland* M & W
Salve Regina University *Rhode Island* M & W
Sam Houston State University *Texas* M & W
San Diego State University *California* W
Santa Clara University *California* M & W
Savannah College of Art and Design *Georgia* M & W
Scripps College *California* W
Seton Hill University *Pennsylvania* M & W
Sewanee: The University of the South *Tennessee* M & W
Shenandoah University *Virginia* M & W
Shepherd University *West Virginia* W
Shippensburg University of Pennsylvania *Pennsylvania* W
Siena College *New York* M & W
Siena Heights University *Michigan* M & W
Sierra Nevada College *Nevada* M & W

Simmons College *Massachusetts* W
Skidmore College *New York* M & W
Slippery Rock University of Pennsylvania *Pennsylvania* M & W
Smith College *Massachusetts* W
Southern Connecticut State University *Connecticut* W
Southern Methodist University *Texas* M
Southern New Hampshire University *New Hampshire* M & W
Southern Oregon University *Oregon* M
Southern Vermont College *Vermont* W
Southern Virginia University *Virginia* M & W
Southwestern University *Texas* M & W
Springfield College *Massachusetts* M & W
Stanford University *California* M & W
State University of New York College of Agriculture and Technology at Cobleskill *New York* M
State University of New York College at Cortland *New York* M & W
State University of New York College at Geneseo *New York* M & W
State University of New York College at Old Westbury *New York* W
State University of New York College at Oneonta *New York* M & W
State University of New York College at Potsdam *New York* M & W
State University of New York College of Technology at Alfred *New York* M
State University of New York College of Technology at Canton *New York* M & W
State University of New York College of Technology at Delhi *New York* M
State University of New York at Fredonia *New York* M & W
State University of New York Maritime College *New York* M & W
State University of New York at New Paltz *New York* W
State University of New York at Oswego *New York* M & W
State University of New York at Plattsburgh *New York* M
State University of New York Polytechnic Institute *New York* M & W
Stephen F. Austin State University *Texas* M
Stetson University *Florida* W
Stevens Institute of Technology *New Jersey* M & W
Stevenson University *Maryland* M & W
Stockton University *New Jersey* M
Stonehill College *Massachusetts* M & W
Stony Brook University, State University of New York *New York* M & W
Suffolk County Community College *New York* M
Susquehanna University *Pennsylvania* M & W
Swarthmore College *Pennsylvania* M & W
Sweet Briar College *Virginia* W
Syracuse University *New York* M & W
Temple University *Pennsylvania* W
Tennessee Wesleyan College *Tennessee* M & W
Texas Christian University *Texas* M & W
Texas State University *Texas* M & W
Thiel College *Pennsylvania* M & W
Thomas College *Maine* M & W
Thomas More College *Kentucky* W
Tiffin University *Ohio* W
Tompkins Cortland Community College *New York* M
Towson University *Maryland* M & W
Transylvania University *Kentucky* M & W
Trent University *Ontario (Canada)* M & W
Trine University *Indiana* M & W
Trinity College *Connecticut* M & W
Trinity University *Texas* M & W
Trinity Washington University *District of Columbia* W
Truett-McConnell College *Georgia* W
Truman State University *Missouri* W
Tufts University *Massachusetts* M & W
Tulane University *Louisiana* M & W
Tusculum College *Tennessee* M & W
Union College *New York* M & W
United States Air Force Academy *Colorado* M & W

M = Men; W = Women

United States Coast Guard Academy *Connecticut* M & W
United States Merchant Marine Academy *New York* M & W
United States Military Academy *New York* M & W
United States Naval Academy *Maryland* M & W
The University of Alabama *Alabama* M & W
The University of Alabama in Huntsville *Alabama* M & W
University at Albany, State University of New York *New York* M & W
The University of Arizona *Arizona* M & W
University of Bridgeport *Connecticut* W
University of California, Berkeley *California* M & W
University of California, Davis *California* W
University of California, Irvine *California* M & W
University of California, Santa Barbara *California* M & W
University of California, Santa Cruz *California* M & W
University of Cincinnati *Ohio* W
University of Colorado Boulder *Colorado* M & W
University of Colorado Colorado Springs *Colorado* W
University of Colorado Denver *Colorado* M & W
University of Connecticut *Connecticut* W
University of the Cumberlands *Kentucky* M & W
University of Dallas *Texas* M & W
University of Delaware *Delaware* M & W
University of Denver *Colorado* M & W
University of Detroit Mercy *Michigan* M & W
University of the District of Columbia *District of Columbia* M & W
The University of Findlay *Ohio* W
University of Florida *Florida* W
University of Georgia *Georgia* M & W
University of Guelph *Ontario (Canada)* M & W
University of Hartford *Connecticut* M
University of Indianapolis *Indiana* M & W
The University of Iowa *Iowa* M & W
University of Louisville *Kentucky* W
University of Maine at Farmington *Maine* M & W
University of Maine at Machias *Maine* M & W
University of Mary Washington *Virginia* M & W
University of Maryland, Baltimore County *Maryland* M & W
University of Maryland, College Park *Maryland* M & W
University of Massachusetts Amherst *Massachusetts* M & W
University of Massachusetts Boston *Massachusetts* M
University of Massachusetts Dartmouth *Massachusetts* M & W
University of Massachusetts Lowell *Massachusetts* M & W
University of Michigan *Michigan* M & W
University of Michigan - Dearborn *Michigan* M
University of Minnesota, Duluth *Minnesota* M & W
University of Mississippi *Mississippi* M & W
University of Montana *Montana* M & W
University of Montevallo *Alabama* W
University of Mount Union *Ohio* M & W
University of New England *Maine* M & W
University of New Hampshire *New Hampshire* M & W
University of New Haven *Connecticut* M & W
The University of North Carolina at Chapel Hill *North Carolina* M & W
University of North Georgia *Georgia* M & W
University of North Texas *Texas* M & W
University of Northern Colorado *Colorado* M
University of Northwestern - St. Paul *Minnesota* W
University of Notre Dame *Indiana* M & W
University of Oregon *Oregon* W
University of Pennsylvania *Pennsylvania* M & W
University of Pikeville *Kentucky* W
University of Puget Sound *Washington* M & W
University of Redlands *California* W
University of Richmond *Virginia* M & W
University of Rochester *New York* M & W
University of Saint Joseph *Connecticut* W
University of St. Thomas *Minnesota* W
University of San Diego *California* M & W

The University of Scranton *Pennsylvania* M & W
University of Southern California *California* M & W
University of Southern Maine *Maine* M & W
The University of Tampa *Florida* M
The University of Texas at Austin *Texas* M & W
The University of Texas at San Antonio *Texas* M & W
University of Utah *Utah* M & W
University of Vermont *Vermont* M & W
University of Virginia *Virginia* M & W
The University of Virginia's College at Wise *Virginia* W
The University of Western Ontario *Ontario (Canada)* M & W
University of Wisconsin - Madison *Wisconsin* M & W
University of Wisconsin - Milwaukee *Wisconsin* M & W
University of Wisconsin - Platteville *Wisconsin* M & W
University of Wisconsin - River Falls *Wisconsin* M & W
University of Wisconsin - Whitewater *Wisconsin* M
University of Wyoming *Wyoming* M & W
Ursinus College *Pennsylvania* M & W
Ursuline College *Ohio* W
Utica College *New York* M & W
Valley Forge Military College *Pennsylvania* M
Vanderbilt University *Tennessee* W
Vassar College *New York* M & W
Villanova University *Pennsylvania* M & W
Virginia Commonwealth University *Virginia* W
Virginia Military Institute *Virginia* M
Virginia Polytechnic Institute and State University *Virginia* M & W
Virginia Wesleyan College *Virginia* M & W
Wabash College *Indiana* M
Wagner College *New York* M & W
Walsh University *Ohio* M & W
Wartburg College *Iowa* W
Washington College *Maryland* M & W
Washington & Jefferson College *Pennsylvania* M & W
Washington and Lee University *Virginia* M & W
Washington State University *Washington* M & W
Washington University in St. Louis *Missouri* M & W
Wayne State University *Michigan* M
Waynesburg University *Pennsylvania* W
Weber State University *Utah* M
Wellesley College *Massachusetts* W
Wells College *New York* M & W
Wentworth Institute of Technology *Massachusetts* M & W
Wesley College *Delaware* M & W
Wesleyan University *Connecticut* M & W
West Chester University of Pennsylvania *Pennsylvania* M & W
West Virginia Wesleyan College *West Virginia* M & W
Western Connecticut State University *Connecticut* M & W
Western Michigan University *Michigan* M & W
Western New England University *Massachusetts* M & W
Western State Colorado University *Colorado* M & W
Westfield State University *Massachusetts* W
Westminster College *Pennsylvania* M
Westminster College *Utah* M & W
Wheaton College *Illinois* M & W
Wheaton College *Massachusetts* M & W
Wheeling Jesuit University *West Virginia* M & W
Wheelock College *Massachusetts* M & W
Whitman College *Washington* M & W
Whittier College *California* M & W
Widener University *Pennsylvania* M & W
Wilfrid Laurier University *Ontario (Canada)* W
Wilkes University *Pennsylvania* M & W
Willamette University *Oregon* M
Williams College *Massachusetts* M & W
Williamson College of the Trades *Pennsylvania* M
Wilson College *Pennsylvania* W
Wingate University *North Carolina* M & W
Winthrop University *South Carolina* M & W

Wittenberg University *Ohio* M & W
Worcester State University *Massachusetts* W
Xavier University *Ohio* M & W
Yale University *Connecticut* M & W
York College of Pennsylvania *Pennsylvania* M & W
Young Harris College *Georgia* M & W

Racquetball

Ball State University *Indiana* M & W
Bard College at Simon's Rock *Massachusetts* M & W
Brigham Young University *Utah* M & W
Bryant University *Rhode Island* M & W
California State University, Sacramento *California* M & W
Columbia University *New York* M & W
Columbia University, School of General Studies *New York* M & W
Crossroads College *Minnesota* M & W
Duke University *North Carolina* M & W
Kutztown University of Pennsylvania *Pennsylvania* M & W
Lehman College of the City University of New York *New York* M & W
Michigan Technological University *Michigan* M & W
Missouri State University *Missouri* M & W
North Carolina State University *North Carolina* M & W
Rensselaer Polytechnic Institute *New York* M & W
Saint Louis University *Missouri* M & W
Stanford University *California* M & W
State University of New York College at Cortland *New York* M & W
United States Air Force Academy *Colorado* M & W
The University of Alabama *Alabama* M & W
The University of Arizona *Arizona* M & W
University of California, Santa Cruz *California* M & W
University of Colorado Boulder *Colorado* M & W
University of Denver *Colorado* M & W
University of Florida *Florida* M & W
University of Georgia *Georgia* M & W
University of Hartford *Connecticut* M & W
University of Memphis *Tennessee* M & W
The University of North Carolina at Chapel Hill *North Carolina* M & W
University of North Texas *Texas* M & W
University of Southern California *California* M & W
The University of Texas at Austin *Texas* M & W
The University of Texas at San Antonio *Texas* M & W
University of Utah *Utah* M & W
University of Wisconsin - Madison *Wisconsin* M & W
University of Wisconsin - River Falls *Wisconsin* M & W
University of Wyoming *Wyoming* M & W
Utah State University *Utah* M & W

Riflery

Bethel University *Tennessee* M & W
The Citadel, The Military College of South Carolina *South Carolina* M & W
Clemson University *South Carolina* M & W
Columbia University *New York* M & W
Columbus State University *Georgia* M & W
Denison University *Ohio* M & W
Emmanuel College *Georgia* M & W
Georgia Military College *Georgia* M & W
Georgia Southern University *Georgia* M & W
Hampden-Sydney College *Virginia* M
Hastings College *Nebraska* M & W
Hillsdale College *Michigan* M & W
Jacksonville State University *Alabama* M & W
Lassen Community College District *California* M & W
Lindenwood University *Missouri* M & W
Massachusetts Institute of Technology *Massachusetts* M & W
Michigan Technological University *Michigan* M & W
Morehead State University *Kentucky* M & W
Mount Marty College *South Dakota* M & W
Murray State University *Kentucky* M & W
New Mexico Military Institute *New Mexico* M & W

M = Men; W = Women

North Carolina State University *North Carolina* M & W
North Dakota State University *North Dakota* M & W
Northeastern University *Massachusetts* M & W
Norwich University *Vermont* M & W
The Ohio State University *Ohio* M & W
Rensselaer Polytechnic Institute *New York* M & W
Rice University *Texas* M & W
Rose-Hulman Institute of Technology *Indiana* M & W
Saint John's University *Minnesota* M
State University of New York Maritime College *New York* M & W
Texas Christian University *Texas* W
Trinity University *Texas* M & W
Truman State University *Missouri* M & W
Tuskegee University *Alabama* M & W
United States Air Force Academy *Colorado* M & W
United States Coast Guard Academy *Connecticut* M & W
United States Military Academy *New York* M & W
United States Naval Academy *Maryland* M & W
The University of Akron *Ohio* M & W
University of Alaska Fairbanks *Alaska* M & W
University of Alaska Southeast *Alaska* M & W
University of Kentucky *Kentucky* M & W
University of Memphis *Tennessee* M & W
University of Michigan *Michigan* M & W
University of Mississippi *Mississippi* W
University of Nebraska - Lincoln *Nebraska* W
University of Nevada, Reno *Nevada* M & W
University of New Hampshire *New Hampshire* M & W
University of North Georgia *Georgia* M & W
University of the Sciences *Pennsylvania* M & W
The University of Tennessee at Martin *Tennessee* M & W
The University of Texas at El Paso *Texas* M & W
University of Utah *Utah* M & W
University of Wisconsin - Oshkosh *Wisconsin* M & W
University of Wyoming *Wyoming* M & W
Valley Forge Military College *Pennsylvania* M & W
Virginia Military Institute *Virginia* M & W
West Virginia University *West Virginia* M & W
Wofford College *South Carolina* M & W
Yale University *Connecticut* M & W

Rock Climbing

Appalachian State University *North Carolina* M & W
Ball State University *Indiana* M & W
Baylor University *Texas* M & W
Bishop's University *Quebec (Canada)* M & W
Bucknell University *Pennsylvania* M & W
Central Washington University *Washington* M & W
Elon University *North Carolina* M & W
Emory University *Georgia* M & W
Fort Lewis College *Colorado* M & W
Hobart and William Smith Colleges *New York* M & W
Landmark College *Vermont* M & W
Royal Military College of Canada *Ontario (Canada)* M
St. Cloud State University *Minnesota* M & W
St. Mary's College of Maryland *Maryland* M & W
Sierra Nevada College *Nevada* M & W
Stanford University *California* M & W
Texas Christian University *Texas* M & W
Truman State University *Missouri* M & W
United States Air Force Academy *Colorado* M & W
University at Albany, State University of New York *New York* M & W
University of Central Missouri *Missouri* M & W
University of New Hampshire *New Hampshire* M & W
University of San Diego *California* M & W
University of Southern California *California* M & W
The University of Texas at Austin *Texas* M & W
The University of Texas at San Antonio *Texas* M & W
University of Wisconsin - River Falls *Wisconsin* M & W
Western Carolina University *North Carolina* M & W

Western New Mexico University *New Mexico* M & W
Western State Colorado University *Colorado* M & W
Westminster College *Pennsylvania* M & W
Yale University *Connecticut* M & W

Rowing

Assumption College *Massachusetts* W
Bryant University *Rhode Island* W
Cabrini University *Pennsylvania* W
Carnegie Mellon University *Pennsylvania* M & W
Christopher Newport University *Virginia* M & W
Dartmouth College *New Hampshire* M & W
Embry-Riddle Aeronautical University - Daytona *Florida* M & W
Endicott College *Massachusetts* M & W
Gonzaga University *Washington* M & W
Iona College *New York* M & W
Laurentian University *Ontario (Canada)* M & W
Massachusetts Institute of Technology *Massachusetts* M & W
Murray State University *Kentucky* M & W
St. Lawrence University *New York* M & W
San Diego State University *California* W
Santa Clara University *California* M & W
Stanford University *California* M & W
Texas Christian University *Texas* M & W
Université de Montréal *Quebec (Canada)* M & W
University of Calgary *Alberta (Canada)* M & W
University of California, Santa Cruz *California* M & W
University of Central Oklahoma *Oklahoma* W
University of Oklahoma *Oklahoma* W
Washington State University *Washington* M & W

Rugby

Acadia University *Nova Scotia (Canada)* W
Albright College *Pennsylvania* M & W
Allegheny College *Pennsylvania* M & W
American International College *Massachusetts* M & W
Amherst College *Massachusetts* M & W
Appalachian State University *North Carolina* M & W
Augustana University *South Dakota* M & W
Ball State University *Indiana* M & W
Barnard College *New York* W
Bates College *Maine* M & W
Baylor University *Texas* M
Bethel College *Indiana* M
Boston University *Massachusetts* M & W
Bowdoin College *Maine* M & W
Brigham Young University *Utah* M
Brock University *Ontario (Canada)* M & W
Brown University *Rhode Island* M & W
Bryant University *Rhode Island* M & W
Bucknell University *Pennsylvania* M & W
Buffalo State College, State University of New York *New York* M & W
Butler University *Indiana* M
California Maritime Academy *California* M
California State University, Fullerton *California* M & W
California State University, Long Beach *California* M
California State University, Sacramento *California* M
Calvin College *Michigan* M & W
Canisius College *New York* M & W
Cape Breton University *Nova Scotia (Canada)* M
Carleton College *Minnesota* M & W
Carleton University *Ontario (Canada)* M & W
Carnegie Mellon University *Pennsylvania* M & W
Castleton University *Vermont* M & W
Central Washington University *Washington* M & W
Christendom College *Virginia* M
Christopher Newport University *Virginia* M
The Citadel, The Military College of South Carolina *South Carolina* M & W
Claremont McKenna College *California* M & W
Clemson University *South Carolina* M & W
Coastal Carolina University *South Carolina* M & W
Colby College *Maine* M & W

Colby-Sawyer College *New Hampshire* M & W
Colgate University *New York* M & W
College of Saint Benedict *Minnesota* W
The College of Wooster *Ohio* M & W
The Colorado College *Colorado* M & W
Colorado Mesa University *Colorado* M & W
Colorado School of Mines *Colorado* M & W
Colorado State University *Colorado* M & W
Columbia University *New York* M & W
Columbia University, School of General Studies *New York* M & W
Concordia University *Quebec (Canada)* M & W
Connecticut College *Connecticut* W
Coppin State University *Maryland* M
Curry College *Massachusetts* M
Dartmouth College *New Hampshire* M & W
Davenport University *Michigan* M & W
Davidson College *North Carolina* M
Denison University *Ohio* M & W
DePauw University *Indiana* M
Drew University *New Jersey* M & W
Duke University *North Carolina* M & W
Earlham College *Indiana* M & W
East Stroudsburg University of Pennsylvania *Pennsylvania* M & W
Eastern Connecticut State University *Connecticut* M
Eastern Washington University *Washington* M & W
Elon University *North Carolina* M & W
Emory University *Georgia* M
Endicott College *Massachusetts* M & W
Florida State University *Florida* M & W
Fort Lewis College *Colorado* M & W
Franciscan University of Steubenville *Ohio* M
Franklin & Marshall College *Pennsylvania* M & W
Freed-Hardeman University *Tennessee* M
Furman University *South Carolina* M & W
Gannon University *Pennsylvania* M
Georgetown University *District of Columbia* M & W
Georgia State University *Georgia* M
Gettysburg College *Pennsylvania* M & W
Gonzaga University *Washington* M & W
Grand Valley State University *Michigan* M & W
Grove City College *Pennsylvania* M & W
Gustavus Adolphus College *Minnesota* M & W
Hamilton College *New York* M & W
Hampden-Sydney College *Virginia* M
Harding University *Arkansas* M
Harvard University *Massachusetts* W
Haverford College *Pennsylvania* M
Hillsdale College *Michigan* M
Hobart and William Smith Colleges *New York* M & W
Illinois Institute of Technology *Illinois* M & W
Iowa Central Community College *Iowa* M
John Carroll University *Ohio* M & W
Juniata College *Pennsylvania* M & W
Keene State College *New Hampshire* M & W
Kenyon College *Ohio* M & W
Kutztown University of Pennsylvania *Pennsylvania* M & W
Lafayette College *Pennsylvania* M & W
Lake Forest College *Illinois* M & W
Lehigh University *Pennsylvania* M & W
LeTourneau University *Texas* M
Lewis & Clark College *Oregon* M & W
Lewis University *Illinois* M
Life University *Georgia* M & W
Lindenwood University *Missouri* M & W
Long Island University - LIU Post *New York* W
Loras College *Iowa* M
Louisiana State University at Alexandria *Louisiana* M
Lycoming College *Pennsylvania* M
Macalester College *Minnesota* M & W
Manhattan College *New York* M
Marion Technical College *Ohio* M
Marist College *New York* M & W
Marshall University *West Virginia* M & W
McGill University *Quebec (Canada)* M & W
McMaster University *Ontario (Canada)* M & W
Miami University *Ohio* M & W
Michigan State University *Michigan* M & W
Michigan Technological University *Michigan* M & W

M = Men; W = Women

Moravian College *Pennsylvania* M & W
Mount Allison University *New Brunswick (Canada)* M & W
Mount St. Mary's University *Maryland* M & W
Neumann University *Pennsylvania* M & W
New Mexico Institute of Mining and Technology *New Mexico* M & W
North Carolina State University *North Carolina* M & W
North Dakota State University *North Dakota* M & W
Northeastern University *Massachusetts* M & W
Northern Michigan University *Michigan* M & W
Norwich University *Vermont* M & W
Oberlin College *Ohio* M & W
Occidental College *California* M & W
Ohio Wesleyan University *Ohio* M & W
Old Dominion University *Virginia* M & W
Palmer College of Chiropractic *Iowa* M & W
Pepperdine University *California* M
Principia College *Illinois* M
Queen's University at Kingston *Ontario (Canada)* M & W
Quinnipiac University *Connecticut* W
Rensselaer Polytechnic Institute *New York* M & W
Rhodes College *Tennessee* M
Rice University *Texas* M & W
Ripon College *Wisconsin* M & W
Roger Williams University *Rhode Island* M & W
Royal Military College of Canada *Ontario (Canada)* M
Saginaw Valley State University *Michigan* M & W
St. Bonaventure University *New York* M & W
St. Francis Xavier University *Nova Scotia (Canada)* M & W
Saint John's University *Minnesota* M
Saint Louis University *Missouri* M & W
Saint Mary's College of California *California* M
St. Mary's College of Maryland *Maryland* M & W
Saint Mary's University *Nova Scotia (Canada)* W
Saint Michael's College *Vermont* M & W
Salve Regina University *Rhode Island* M & W
Santa Clara University *California* M & W
Santa Rosa Junior College *California* M
Scripps College *California* W
Seton Hall University *New Jersey* M
Sewanee: The University of the South *Tennessee* M & W
Siena College *New York* M & W
Slippery Rock University of Pennsylvania *Pennsylvania* M & W
Southern Connecticut State University *Connecticut* M & W
Southern Methodist University *Texas* M & W
Southern Oregon University *Oregon* M & W
Stanford University *California* M & W
State University of New York College at Cortland *New York* M & W
State University of New York College at Geneseo *New York* M & W
State University of New York College at Oneonta *New York* W
State University of New York College at Potsdam *New York* M
State University of New York at Fredonia *New York* M & W
Stephen F. Austin State University *Texas* M
Stonehill College *Massachusetts* M & W
Susquehanna University *Pennsylvania* M & W
Swarthmore College *Pennsylvania* M & W
Syracuse University *New York* M & W
Texas Christian University *Texas* M & W
Texas State University *Texas* M & W
Thomas Jefferson University *Pennsylvania* M
Trent University *Ontario (Canada)* M & W
Trinity College *Connecticut* M & W
Trinity Western University *British Columbia (Canada)* M
Truman State University *Missouri* M & W
Tufts University *Massachusetts* M & W
Tulane University *Louisiana* M
Union College *New York* M & W
United States Coast Guard Academy *Connecticut* M & W
United States Military Academy *New York* M & W

United States Naval Academy *Maryland* M & W
Université de Montréal *Quebec (Canada)* M & W
Université du Québec, École de technologie supérieure *Quebec (Canada)* M
Université de Sherbrooke *Quebec (Canada)* M & W
The University of Alabama *Alabama* M & W
University of Alberta *Alberta (Canada)* W
The University of Arizona *Arizona* M & W
The University of British Columbia *British Columbia (Canada)* M & W
The University of British Columbia - Okanagan Campus *British Columbia (Canada)* M & W
University of Calgary *Alberta (Canada)* M & W
University of California, Berkeley *California* M
University of California, Irvine *California* M & W
University of California, Santa Barbara *California* M
University of California, Santa Cruz *California* M & W
University of Colorado Boulder *Colorado* M & W
University of Delaware *Delaware* M & W
University of Georgia *Georgia* M & W
University of Guelph *Ontario (Canada)* M & W
University of Hartford *Connecticut* M & W
The University of Iowa *Iowa* M & W
The University of Kansas *Kansas* M
University of King's College *Nova Scotia (Canada)* M & W
University of Lethbridge *Alberta (Canada)* W
University of Mary Washington *Virginia* M & W
University of Maryland, Baltimore County *Maryland* M & W
University of Michigan *Michigan* M & W
University of Michigan - Dearborn *Michigan* M
University of Minnesota, Duluth *Minnesota* M & W
University of Mississippi *Mississippi* M
University of Montana *Montana* M & W
University of New Brunswick Saint John *New Brunswick (Canada)* M & W
University of New England *Maine* W
University of New Hampshire *New Hampshire* M & W
University of New Haven *Connecticut* M
University of North Carolina at Asheville *North Carolina* M & W
The University of North Carolina at Chapel Hill *North Carolina* M & W
University of North Texas *Texas* M & W
University of Northern Colorado *Colorado* M & W
University of Ottawa *Ontario (Canada)* W
University of Portland *Oregon* M
University of Prince Edward Island *Prince Edward Island (Canada)* M & W
University of Puget Sound *Washington* M & W
University of Richmond *Virginia* M & W
University of Rochester *New York* M & W
University of San Diego *California* M
The University of Scranton *Pennsylvania* M & W
University of South Florida *Florida* M & W
University of Southern California *California* M & W
University of Southern Indiana *Indiana* M & W
The University of Texas at Austin *Texas* M & W
The University of Texas at San Antonio *Texas* M & W
University of Toronto *Ontario (Canada)* M
University of Utah *Utah* M
University of Vermont *Vermont* M & W
University of Victoria *British Columbia (Canada)* M & W
University of Waterloo *Ontario (Canada)* M & W
The University of Western Ontario *Ontario (Canada)* M & W
University of Wisconsin - Madison *Wisconsin* M & W
University of Wisconsin - Milwaukee *Wisconsin* M & W
University of Wisconsin - Platteville *Wisconsin* M & W
University of Wisconsin - River Falls *Wisconsin* M & W
University of Wisconsin - Whitewater *Wisconsin* M & W
University of Wyoming *Wyoming* M & W
Utah State University *Utah* M & W
Vassar College *New York* M & W

Wabash College *Indiana* M
Washington College *Maryland* M & W
Washington & Jefferson College *Pennsylvania* M & W
Washington and Lee University *Virginia* M
Washington State University *Washington* M & W
Washington State University - Tri-Cities *Washington* M & W
Washington University in St. Louis *Missouri* M & W
Wayne State College *Nebraska* M & W
Weber State University *Utah* M
Wellesley College *Massachusetts* W
Wentworth Institute of Technology *Massachusetts* M & W
Wesleyan University *Connecticut* M & W
West Chester University of Pennsylvania *Pennsylvania* M & W
Western Carolina University *North Carolina* M
Western Michigan University *Michigan* M & W
Western State Colorado University *Colorado* M & W
Westmont College *California* M
Wheeling Jesuit University *West Virginia* M
Whitman College *Washington* M
Wilfrid Laurier University *Ontario (Canada)* M & W
Williams College *Massachusetts* M & W
Winthrop University *South Carolina* M
Wittenberg University *Ohio* M & W
Xavier University *Ohio* M
Yale University *Connecticut* M & W
York University *Ontario (Canada)* W

Sailing

Amherst College *Massachusetts* M & W
Barnard College *New York* W
Bates College *Maine* M & W
Baylor University *Texas* M & W
Boston College *Massachusetts* M & W
Boston University *Massachusetts* M & W
Bowdoin College *Maine* M & W
Brown University *Rhode Island* M & W
Bucknell University *Pennsylvania* M & W
California Maritime Academy *California* M & W
California State University, Fullerton *California* M & W
California State University, Long Beach *California* M & W
California State University, Monterey Bay *California* M & W
Carleton College *Minnesota* M & W
Claremont McKenna College *California* M & W
Clemson University *South Carolina* M & W
Colby College *Maine* M & W
Colgate University *New York* M & W
College of Charleston *South Carolina* M & W
Columbia University, School of General Studies *New York* M & W
Connecticut College *Connecticut* M & W
Cornell University *New York* W
Dartmouth College *New Hampshire* M & W
Davidson College *North Carolina* M & W
Denison University *Ohio* M & W
Duke University *North Carolina* M & W
Eckerd College *Florida* M & W
Emory University *Georgia* M & W
Endicott College *Massachusetts* M & W
Fordham University *New York* M & W
Georgetown University *District of Columbia* M & W
Grand Valley State University *Michigan* M & W
Hamilton College *New York* M & W
Hampton University *Virginia* M & W
Harvard University *Massachusetts* M & W
Hobart and William Smith Colleges *New York* M & W
Hope College *Michigan* M & W
John Carroll University *Ohio* M & W
Johnson & Wales University *Rhode Island* M & W
Lake Forest College *Illinois* M & W
Maine Maritime Academy *Maine* M & W
Massachusetts Institute of Technology *Massachusetts* M & W
Massachusetts Maritime Academy *Massachusetts* M & W
McGill University *Quebec (Canada)* M & W

M = Men; W = Women

Miami University *Ohio* M & W
Michigan State University *Michigan* M & W
Michigan Technological University *Michigan* M & W
Mitchell College *Connecticut* M & W
Monmouth University *New Jersey* M & W
New College of Florida *Florida* M & W
North Carolina State University *North Carolina* M & W
Northeastern University *Massachusetts* M & W
Northern Michigan University *Michigan* M & W
Norwich University *Vermont* M & W
Ohio Wesleyan University *Ohio* M & W
Oklahoma City University *Oklahoma* M & W
Old Dominion University *Virginia* M & W
Queen's University at Kingston *Ontario (Canada)* M & W
Rensselaer Polytechnic Institute *New York* M & W
Rice University *Texas* M & W
Roger Williams University *Rhode Island* M & W
Rollins College *Florida* M & W
St. John's College *Maryland* M & W
St. Mary's College of Maryland *Maryland* M & W
Salve Regina University *Rhode Island* M & W
Santa Clara University *California* M & W
Stanford University *California* M & W
State University of New York Maritime College *New York* M & W
Syracuse University *New York* M & W
Trinity College *Connecticut* M & W
Tufts University *Massachusetts* M & W
Tulane University *Louisiana* M & W
United States Coast Guard Academy *Connecticut* M & W
United States Merchant Marine Academy *New York* M & W
United States Naval Academy *Maryland* M & W
University of California, Irvine *California* M & W
University of California, Santa Barbara *California* M & W
University of California, Santa Cruz *California* M & W
University of Delaware *Delaware* M & W
University of Georgia *Georgia* M & W
University of Hawaii at Manoa *Hawaii* M & W
The University of Iowa *Iowa* M & W
University of Maryland, Baltimore County *Maryland* M & W
University of Massachusetts Dartmouth *Massachusetts* W
University of Michigan *Michigan* M & W
University of New Hampshire *New Hampshire* M & W
The University of North Carolina at Chapel Hill *North Carolina* M & W
University of North Texas *Texas* M & W
University of Puget Sound *Washington* M & W
University of Rochester *New York* M & W
University of South Florida, St. Petersburg *Florida* W
University of Southern California *California* W
University of Southern Maine *Maine* M & W
The University of Texas at Austin *Texas* M & W
University of Vermont *Vermont* M & W
University of Wisconsin - Madison *Wisconsin* M & W
University of Wisconsin - Milwaukee *Wisconsin* M & W
Villanova University *Pennsylvania* M & W
Washington College *Maryland* M & W
Washington University in St. Louis *Missouri* M & W
Webb Institute *New York* M & W
Wellesley College *Massachusetts* W
Wesleyan University *Connecticut* M & W
Western Michigan University *Michigan* M & W
Williams College *Massachusetts* M & W
Yale University *Connecticut* M & W

Skiing (Cross-Country)

Bates College *Maine* M & W
Bowdoin College *Maine* M & W
Buffalo State College, State University of New York *New York* M & W
Carleton College *Minnesota* M & W
Carleton University *Ontario (Canada)* M & W

M = Men; W = Women

Clarkson University *New York* M & W
Colby College *Maine* M & W
College of Saint Benedict *Minnesota* W
The College of St. Scholastica *Minnesota* M & W
Colorado Mesa University *Colorado* M & W
Columbia University *New York* M & W
Connecticut College *Connecticut* M & W
Dartmouth College *New Hampshire* M & W
Duke University *North Carolina* M & W
Fort Lewis College *Colorado* M & W
Gogebic Community College *Michigan* M & W
Gustavus Adolphus College *Minnesota* M & W
Hamilton College *New York* M & W
Harvard University *Massachusetts* M & W
John Carroll University *Ohio* M & W
Lakehead University *Ontario (Canada)* M & W
Macalester College *Minnesota* M & W
McGill University *Quebec (Canada)* M & W
Michigan Technological University *Michigan* M & W
Middlebury College *Vermont* M & W
Montana State University *Montana* M & W
Nipissing University *Ontario (Canada)* M & W
Northern Michigan University *Michigan* M & W
Norwich University *Vermont* M & W
Paul Smith's College *New York* M & W
Queen's University at Kingston *Ontario (Canada)* M & W
Rensselaer Polytechnic Institute *New York* M & W
St. Cloud State University *Minnesota* M & W
Saint John's University *Minnesota* M
Saint Michael's College *Vermont* M & W
St. Olaf College *Minnesota* M & W
Sterling College *Vermont* M & W
United States Air Force Academy *Colorado* M & W
United States Military Academy *New York* M & W
University of Alaska Anchorage *Alaska* M & W
University of Alaska Fairbanks *Alaska* M & W
University of Calgary *Alberta (Canada)* M & W
University of Colorado Boulder *Colorado* M & W
University of Denver *Colorado* M & W
University of Guelph *Ontario (Canada)* M & W
University of Maine at Farmington *Maine* M & W
University of Maine at Presque Isle *Maine* M & W
University of New Hampshire *New Hampshire* M & W
University of New Mexico *New Mexico* M & W
University of Northern British Columbia *British Columbia (Canada)* M & W
University of Toronto *Ontario (Canada)* M & W
University of Utah *Utah* M & W
University of Vermont *Vermont* M & W
University of Waterloo *Ontario (Canada)* M & W
University of Wisconsin - Green Bay *Wisconsin* M & W
University of Wisconsin - River Falls *Wisconsin* M & W
University of Wyoming *Wyoming* M & W
Washington State University *Washington* M & W
Wesleyan University *Connecticut* M & W
Western State Colorado University *Colorado* M & W
Whitman College *Washington* M & W
Williams College *Massachusetts* M & W
Yale University *Connecticut* M & W

Skiing (Downhill)

Alfred University *New York* M & W
Amherst College *Massachusetts* M & W
Appalachian State University *North Carolina* M & W
Babson College *Massachusetts* M & W
Barnard College *New York* W
Bates College *Maine* M & W
Baylor University *Texas* M & W
Bishop's University *Quebec (Canada)* M & W
Boston College *Massachusetts* M & W
Boston University *Massachusetts* M & W
Brown University *Rhode Island* M & W
Bucknell University *Pennsylvania* M & W
Bucks County Community College *Pennsylvania* M & W
Buffalo State College, State University of New York *New York* M & W
California State University, Fullerton *California* M & W

California State University, Long Beach *California* M & W
California State University, Sacramento *California* M & W
Carleton College *Minnesota* M & W
Carnegie Mellon University *Pennsylvania* M & W
Castleton University *Vermont* M & W
Claremont McKenna College *California* M & W
Clarkson University *New York* M & W
Colby College *Maine* M & W
Colby-Sawyer College *New Hampshire* M & W
Colgate University *New York* M & W
The College of Idaho *Idaho* M & W
The Colorado College *Colorado* M & W
Colorado Mesa University *Colorado* M & W
Colorado Mountain College Glenwood Springs, *Colorado* M & W
Colorado Mountain College Leadville, *Colorado* M & W
Colorado Mountain College Steamboat Springs, *Colorado* M & W
Colorado State University *Colorado* M & W
Columbia University *New York* M & W
Columbia University, School of General Studies *New York* M & W
Concordia University *Quebec (Canada)* M & W
Connecticut College *Connecticut* M & W
Dartmouth College *New Hampshire* M & W
Davis & Elkins College *West Virginia* M & W
Denison University *Ohio* M & W
Dickinson College *Pennsylvania* M & W
Duke University *North Carolina* M & W
Eastern Nazarene College *Massachusetts* M
Fort Lewis College *Colorado* M & W
Gonzaga University *Washington* M & W
Grand Valley State University *Michigan* M & W
Hamilton College *New York* M & W
Harvard University *Massachusetts* M & W
Hobart and William Smith Colleges *New York* M & W
John Carroll University *Ohio* M & W
Lafayette College *Pennsylvania* M & W
Lakehead University *Ontario (Canada)* M & W
Laurentian University *Ontario (Canada)* M & W
Lehigh University *Pennsylvania* M & W
Lewis University *Illinois* M & W
Manchester Community College *New Hampshire* M & W
Marist College *New York* M & W
McGill University *Quebec (Canada)* M & W
Michigan State University *Michigan* M & W
Michigan Technological University *Michigan* M & W
Middlebury College *Vermont* M & W
Montana State University *Montana* M & W
North Carolina State University *North Carolina* M & W
Northern Michigan University *Michigan* M & W
Norwich University *Vermont* M & W
Penn State Erie, The Behrend College *Pennsylvania* M & W
Penn State Lehigh Valley *Pennsylvania* M & W
Plymouth State University *New Hampshire* M & W
Queen's University at Kingston *Ontario (Canada)* M & W
Rochester Institute of Technology *New York* M & W
Rocky Mountain College *Montana* M & W
Rollins College *Florida* M & W
Saint Anselm College *New Hampshire* M & W
St. Cloud State University *Minnesota* M & W
St. Lawrence University *New York* M & W
Saint Michael's College *Vermont* M & W
St. Olaf College *Minnesota* M & W
Scripps College *California* W
Sierra Nevada College *Nevada* M & W
Stanford University *California* M & W
State University of New York College at Geneseo *New York* M & W
Syracuse University *New York* M & W
Trinity College *Connecticut* M & W
United States Air Force Academy *Colorado* M & W
United States Military Academy *New York* M & W
United States Naval Academy *Maryland* M & W
Université Laval *Quebec (Canada)* M & W
Université de Montréal *Quebec (Canada)* M & W

Université du Québec à Rimouski *Quebec (Canada)* M & W
University of Alaska Anchorage *Alaska* M & W
The University of British Columbia *British Columbia (Canada)* M & W
University of California, Santa Barbara *California* M & W
University of Colorado Boulder *Colorado* M & W
University of Denver *Colorado* M & W
University of Maine at Farmington *Maine* M & W
University of Maryland, Baltimore County *Maryland* M & W
University of Minnesota, Duluth *Minnesota* M & W
University of Montana *Montana* M & W
University of New Hampshire *New Hampshire* M & W
University of New Mexico *New Mexico* M & W
The University of North Carolina at Chapel Hill *North Carolina* M & W
University of Puget Sound *Washington* M & W
University of Rochester *New York* M & W
University of Southern California *California* M & W
University of Toronto *Ontario (Canada)* M & W
University of Utah *Utah* M & W
University of Vermont *Vermont* M & W
University of Wyoming *Wyoming* M & W
Villanova University *Pennsylvania* M & W
Washington State University *Washington* M & W
Wellesley College *Massachusetts* W
Wesleyan University *Connecticut* M & W
West Chester University of Pennsylvania *Pennsylvania* M & W
West Virginia Wesleyan College *West Virginia* M & W
Western Michigan University *Michigan* M & W
Western State Colorado University *Colorado* M & W
Westminster College *Pennsylvania* M & W
Westminster College *Utah* M & W
Whitman College *Washington* M & W
Williams College *Massachusetts* M & W
Yale University *Connecticut* M & W

Soccer

Abilene Christian University *Texas* W
Abraham Baldwin Agricultural College *Georgia* W
Academy of Art University *California* M & W
Acadia University *Nova Scotia (Canada)* M & W
Adams State University *Colorado* M & W
Adelphi University *New York* M & W
Adirondack Community College *New York* M
Adrian College *Michigan* M & W
Agnes Scott College *Georgia* W
Alabama Agricultural and Mechanical University *Alabama* M
Alabama State University *Alabama* W
Albany College of Pharmacy and Health Sciences *New York* M & W
Albertus Magnus College *Connecticut* M & W
Albion College *Michigan* M & W
Albright College *Pennsylvania* M & W
Alcorn State University *Mississippi* W
Alderson Broaddus University *West Virginia* M & W
Alfred University *New York* M & W
Allan Hancock College *California* M & W
Allegany College of Maryland *Maryland* M & W
Allegheny College *Pennsylvania* M & W
Allen Community College *Kansas* M & W
Alma College *Michigan* M & W
Alvernia University *Pennsylvania* M & W
Alverno College *Wisconsin* W
Ambrose University *Alberta (Canada)* M & W
American International College *Massachusetts* M & W
American River College *California* M & W
American University *District of Columbia* M & W
Amherst College *Massachusetts* M & W
Ancilla College *Indiana* M & W
Anderson University *Indiana* M & W
Anderson University *South Carolina* M & W
Andrew College *Georgia* M & W
Angelo State University *Texas* W
Anna Maria College *Massachusetts* M & W
Anne Arundel Community College *Maryland* M & W

Anoka-Ramsey Community College *Minnesota* M & W
Antelope Valley College *California* W
Appalachian Bible College *West Virginia* M
Appalachian State University *North Carolina* M & W
Aquinas College *Michigan* M & W
Arcadia University *Pennsylvania* M & W
Arizona Christian University *Arizona* M & W
Arizona State University at the Downtown Phoenix campus *Arizona* W
Arizona State University at the Polytechnic campus *Arizona* W
Arizona State University at the Tempe campus *Arizona* W
Arizona State University at the West campus *Arizona* W
Arizona Western College *Arizona* M & W
Arkansas State University *Arkansas* W
Armstrong State University *Georgia* W
ASA College *New York* M
Asbury University *Kentucky* M & W
Ashford University *California* M & W
Ashland University *Ohio* M & W
Assumption College *Massachusetts* M & W
Auburn University *Alabama* W
Auburn University at Montgomery *Alabama* M & W
Augsburg College *Minnesota* M & W
Augustana College *Illinois* M & W
Augustana University *South Dakota* M & W
Aurora University *Illinois* M & W
Austin College *Texas* M & W
Austin Peay State University *Tennessee* W
Ave Maria University *Florida* M & W
Averett University *Virginia* M & W
Avila University *Missouri* M & W
Azusa Pacific University *California* M & W
Babson College *Massachusetts* M & W
Baker University *Kansas* M & W
Bakersfield College *California* W
Baldwin Wallace University *Ohio* M & W
Ball State University *Indiana* M & W
Baptist Bible College *Missouri* M
Barclay College *Kansas* M
Bard College *New York* M & W
Bard College at Simon's Rock *Massachusetts* M & W
Barnard College *New York* W
Barry University *Florida* M & W
Barton College *North Carolina* M & W
Barton County Community College *Kansas* M & W
Baruch College of the City University of New York *New York* M
Bates College *Maine* M & W
Bay Path University *Massachusetts* W
Baylor University *Texas* W
Becker College *Massachusetts* M & W
Belhaven University *Mississippi* M & W
Bellarmine University *Kentucky* M & W
Bellevue College *Washington* M
Belmont Abbey College *North Carolina* M & W
Belmont University *Tennessee* M & W
Beloit College *Wisconsin* M & W
Bemidji State University *Minnesota* W
Benedictine College *Kansas* M & W
Benedictine University *Illinois* M & W
Benjamin Franklin Institute of Technology *Massachusetts* M
Bennington College *Vermont* M & W
Bentley University *Massachusetts* M & W
Berea College *Kentucky* M & W
Bergen Community College *New Jersey* M & W
Berkeley College - New York City Campus *New York* M & W
Berkeley College - White Plains Campus *New York* M & W
Berkeley College - Woodland Park Campus *New Jersey* M
Berry College *Georgia* M & W
Bethany College *Kansas* M & W
Bethany College *West Virginia* M & W
Bethany Lutheran College *Minnesota* M & W
Bethel College *Indiana* M & W
Bethel College *Kansas* M & W
Bethel University *Minnesota* M & W

Bethel University *Tennessee* M & W
Binghamton University, State University of New York *New York* M & W
Biola University *California* M & W
Birmingham-Southern College *Alabama* M & W
Bishop's University *Quebec (Canada)* W
Bismarck State College *North Dakota* M
Blackburn College *Illinois* M & W
Blessing-Rieman College of Nursing *Illinois* M & W
Bloomfield College *New Jersey* M & W
Bloomsburg University of Pennsylvania *Pennsylvania* M & W
Bluefield College *Virginia* M & W
Bluffton University *Ohio* M & W
Bob Jones University *South Carolina* M & W
Boise State University *Idaho* W
Borough of Manhattan Community College of the City University of New York *New York* M & W
Bossier Parish Community College *Louisiana* W
Boston College *Massachusetts* M & W
Boston University *Massachusetts* M & W
Bowdoin College *Maine* M & W
Bowling Green State University *Ohio* M & W
Bradley University *Illinois* W
Brandeis University *Massachusetts* M & W
Brenau University *Georgia* W
Brescia University *Kentucky* M & W
Brevard College *North Carolina* M & W
Brewton-Parker College *Georgia* M & W
Briar Cliff University *Iowa* M & W
Bridgewater College *Virginia* M & W
Bridgewater State University *Massachusetts* M & W
Brigham Young University *Utah* M & W
Brigham Young University - Hawaii *Hawaii* M & W
Brock University *Ontario (Canada)* M & W
Bronx Community College of the City University of New York *New York* M
Brookdale Community College *New Jersey* M & W
Brookhaven College *Texas* W
Brooklyn College of the City University of New York *New York* M
Broome Community College *New York* M & W
Brown University *Rhode Island* M & W
Bryan College *Tennessee* M & W
Bryant & Stratton College - Syracuse Campus *New York* M & W
Bryant University *Rhode Island* M & W
Bryn Athyn College of the New Church *Pennsylvania* M & W
Bryn Mawr College *Pennsylvania* W
Bucknell University *Pennsylvania* M & W
Bucks County Community College *Pennsylvania* M & W
Buena Vista University *Iowa* M & W
Buffalo State College, State University of New York *New York* M & W
Bunker Hill Community College *Massachusetts* M
Butler Community College *Kansas* W
Butler University *Indiana* M & W
Butte College *California* M & W
Cabrillo College *California* M & W
Cabrini University *Pennsylvania* M & W
Cairn University *Pennsylvania* M & W
Caldwell University *New Jersey* M & W
California Baptist University *California* M & W
California Institute of Technology *California* M & W
California Lutheran University *California* M & W
California Maritime Academy *California* M
California Polytechnic State University, San Luis Obispo *California* M & W
California State Polytechnic University, Pomona *California* M & W
California State University, Bakersfield *California* M
California State University, Chico *California* M & W
California State University, Dominguez Hills *California* M & W
California State University, East Bay *California* M & W
California State University, Fresno *California* W
California State University, Fullerton *California* M & W
California State University, Long Beach *California* M & W

M = Men; W = Women

California State University, Los Angeles *California* M & W
California State University, Monterey Bay *California* M & W
California State University, Northridge *California* M
California State University, Sacramento *California* M & W
California State University, San Bernardino *California* M & W
California State University, San Marcos *California* M & W
California State University, Stanislaus *California* M & W
California University of Pennsylvania *Pennsylvania* M & W
Calumet College of Saint Joseph *Indiana* M & W
Calvary Bible College and Theological Seminary *Missouri* M
Calvin College *Michigan* M & W
Camden County College *New Jersey* M & W
Campbell University *North Carolina* M & W
Campbellsville University *Kentucky* M & W
Cañada College *California* M & W
Canisius College *New York* M & W
Cape Breton University *Nova Scotia (Canada)* M & W
Cape Fear Community College *North Carolina* M & W
Capital University *Ohio* M & W
Cardinal Stritch University *Wisconsin* M & W
Caribbean University *Puerto Rico* M & W
Carleton College *Minnesota* M & W
Carleton University *Ontario (Canada)* M & W
Carlow University *Pennsylvania* W
Carnegie Mellon University *Pennsylvania* M & W
Carroll College *Montana* M & W
Carroll University *Wisconsin* M & W
Carson-Newman University *Tennessee* M & W
Carthage College *Wisconsin* M & W
Case Western Reserve University *Ohio* M & W
Castleton University *Vermont* M & W
Catawba College *North Carolina* M & W
The Catholic University of America *District of Columbia* M & W
Cayuga County Community College *New York* M & W
Cazenovia College *New York* M & W
Cecil College *Maryland* M & W
Cedar Crest College *Pennsylvania* W
Cedar Valley College *Texas* W
Cedarville University *Ohio* M & W
Centenary College *New Jersey* M & W
Centenary College of Louisiana *Louisiana* M & W
Central Baptist College *Arkansas* M & W
Central Christian College of the Bible *Missouri* M
Central Christian College of Kansas *Kansas* M & W
Central College *Iowa* M & W
Central Connecticut State University *Connecticut* M & W
Central Maine Community College *Maine* M & W
Central Methodist University *Missouri* M & W
Central Michigan University *Michigan* W
Central Penn College *Pennsylvania* M & W
Central Washington University *Washington* M & W
Centre College *Kentucky* M & W
Century College *Minnesota* M & W
Cerritos College *California* M & W
Chabot College *California* M & W
Chaffey College *California* M & W
Chaminade University of Honolulu *Hawaii* M & W
Chandler-Gilbert Community College *Arizona* M & W
Chapman University *California* M & W
Charleston Southern University *South Carolina* W
Chatham University *Pennsylvania* W
Chesapeake College *Maryland* M
Chestnut Hill College *Pennsylvania* M & W
Chowan University *North Carolina* M & W
Christendom College *Virginia* M & W
Christian Brothers University *Tennessee* M & W
Christopher Newport University *Virginia* M & W
Cincinnati Christian University *Ohio* M & W
Cincinnati State Technical and Community College *Ohio* M & W

Cisco College *Texas* M
The Citadel, The Military College of South Carolina *South Carolina* M & W
Citrus College *California* M & W
City College of the City University of New York *New York* M & W
City College of San Francisco *California* M & W
City Colleges of Chicago, Kennedy-King College *Illinois* M
City Colleges of Chicago, Richard J. Daley College *Illinois* M & W
Clackamas Community College *Oregon* W
Claremont McKenna College *California* M & W
Clarion University of Pennsylvania *Pennsylvania* W
Clark College *Washington* M & W
Clark University *Massachusetts* M & W
Clarke University *Iowa* M & W
Clarkson University *New York* M & W
Clayton State University *Georgia* M & W
Cleary University *Michigan* M & W
Clemson University *South Carolina* M & W
Cleveland State University *Ohio* M & W
Clinton Community College *Iowa* M & W
Clinton Community College *New York* M & W
Cloud County Community College *Kansas* M
Coastal Carolina University *South Carolina* M & W
Cochise County Community College District *Arizona* M
Coe College *Iowa* M & W
Coffeyville Community College *Kansas* M & W
Coker College *South Carolina* M & W
Colby College *Maine* M & W
Colby-Sawyer College *New Hampshire* M & W
Colgate University *New York* M & W
The College at Brockport, State University of New York *New York* M & W
College of the Canyons *California* M & W
College of Charleston *South Carolina* M & W
College of the Desert *California* M & W
College of DuPage *Illinois* M & W
College of the Holy Cross *Massachusetts* M & W
The College of Idaho *Idaho* M & W
College of Lake County *Illinois* M & W
College of the Mainland *Texas* M
College of Marin *California* M & W
College of Mount Saint Vincent *New York* M & W
The College of New Jersey *New Jersey* M & W
College of the Redwoods *California* W
College of Saint Benedict *Minnesota* W
College of Saint Elizabeth *New Jersey* W
College of St. Joseph *Vermont* M & W
College of Saint Mary *Nebraska* W
The College of Saint Rose *New York* M & W
The College of St. Scholastica *Minnesota* M & W
College of the Sequoias *California* M
College of Southern Maryland *Maryland* M & W
College of Staten Island of the City University of New York *New York* M & W
College of The Albemarle *North Carolina* M
The College of William and Mary *Virginia* M & W
The College of Wooster *Ohio* M & W
Colorado Christian University *Colorado* M & W
The Colorado College *Colorado* M & W
Colorado Mesa University *Colorado* M & W
Colorado School of Mines *Colorado* M & W
Colorado State University *Colorado* M & W
Colorado State University - Pueblo *Colorado* M & W
Columbia Basin College *Washington* M & W
Columbia College *Missouri* M & W
Columbia College *South Carolina* W
Columbia International University *South Carolina* M & W
Columbia University *New York* M & W
Columbia University, School of General Studies *New York* M & W
Columbus State University *Georgia* W
Community College of Baltimore County *Maryland* M & W
Community College of Rhode Island *Rhode Island* M & W
Concord University *West Virginia* M & W
Concordia College *Minnesota* M & W
Concordia College Alabama *Alabama* M

Concordia College - New York *New York* M & W
Concordia University *Oregon* M & W
Concordia University *Quebec (Canada)* M & W
Concordia University Ann Arbor *Michigan* M & W
Concordia University Chicago *Illinois* M & W
Concordia University of Edmonton *Alberta (Canada)* M & W
Concordia University Irvine *California* M & W
Concordia University, Nebraska *Nebraska* M & W
Concordia University, St. Paul *Minnesota* W
Concordia University Texas *Texas* M & W
Concordia University Wisconsin *Wisconsin* M & W
Connecticut College *Connecticut* M & W
Contra Costa College *California* M & W
Converse College *South Carolina* W
Cooper Union for the Advancement of Science and Art *New York* M & W
Corban University *Oregon* M & W
Cornell College *Iowa* M & W
Cornell University *New York* M & W
Cornerstone University *Michigan* M & W
Corning Community College *New York* M & W
Cossatot Community College of the University of Arkansas *Arkansas* M & W
County College of Morris *New Jersey* M & W
Covenant College *Georgia* M & W
Cowley County Community College and Area Vocational - Technical School *Kansas* M & W
Crandall University *New Brunswick (Canada)* M & W
Creighton University *Nebraska* M & W
Crossroads College *Minnesota* M & W
Crowder College *Missouri* M
Crown College *Minnesota* M & W
Cuesta College *California* M & W
The Culinary Institute of America *New York* M & W
Culver-Stockton College *Missouri* M & W
Cumberland University *Tennessee* M & W
Curry College *Massachusetts* M & W
Cuyahoga Community College *Ohio* M
Cuyamaca College *California* M & W
Cypress College *California* M & W
Daemen College *New York* M & W
Dakota County Technical College *Minnesota* M & W
Dalhousie University *Nova Scotia (Canada)* M & W
Dallas Baptist University *Texas* M & W
Dallas Christian College *Texas* M & W
Daniel Webster College *New Hampshire* M & W
Dartmouth College *New Hampshire* M & W
Darton State College *Georgia* M & W
Davenport University *Michigan* M & W
Davidson College *North Carolina* M & W
Davis College *New York* W
Davis & Elkins College *West Virginia* M & W
De Anza College *California* M & W
Dean College *Massachusetts* M & W
Defiance College *Ohio* M & W
Delaware County Community College *Pennsylvania* M
Delaware State University *Delaware* W
Delaware Technical & Community College, Stanton/Wilmington Campus *Delaware* M
Delaware Technical & Community College, Terry Campus *Delaware* M & W
Delaware Valley University *Pennsylvania* M & W
Delta College *Michigan* W
Delta State University *Mississippi* M & W
Denison University *Ohio* M & W
DePaul University *Illinois* M & W
DePauw University *Indiana* M & W
DeSales University *Pennsylvania* M & W
Diablo Valley College *California* W
Dickinson College *Pennsylvania* M & W
Dixie State University *Utah* M & W
Doane University *Nebraska* M & W
Dodge City Community College *Kansas* M & W
Dominican College *New York* M & W
Dominican University *Illinois* M & W
Dominican University of California *California* M & W
Dordt College *Iowa* M & W
Drake University *Iowa* M & W
Drew University *New Jersey* M & W
Drexel University *Pennsylvania* M & W

M = Men; W = Women

Drury University *Missouri* M & W
Duke University *North Carolina* M & W
Duquesne University *Pennsylvania* M & W
Dutchess Community College *New York* M
D'Youville College *New York* M & W
Earlham College *Indiana* M & W
East Carolina University *North Carolina* W
East Central College *Missouri* M
East Central Community College *Mississippi* M & W
East Central University *Oklahoma* W
East Los Angeles College *California* M & W
East Mississippi Community College *Mississippi* M & W
East Stroudsburg University of Pennsylvania *Pennsylvania* M & W
East Tennessee State University *Tennessee* M & W
East Texas Baptist University *Texas* M & W
Eastern Connecticut State University *Connecticut* M & W
Eastern Illinois University *Illinois* M & W
Eastern Mennonite University *Virginia* M & W
Eastern Michigan University *Michigan* W
Eastern Nazarene College *Massachusetts* M & W
Eastern New Mexico University *New Mexico* M & W
Eastern Oregon University *Oregon* M & W
Eastern University *Pennsylvania* M & W
Eastern Washington University *Washington* M & W
Eastfield College *Texas* W
Eckerd College *Florida* M & W
Edgewood College *Wisconsin* M & W
Edinboro University of Pennsylvania *Pennsylvania* W
Edmonds Community College *Washington* M & W
El Camino College *California* M
Elgin Community College *Illinois* M & W
Elizabethtown College *Pennsylvania* M & W
Elmhurst College *Illinois* M & W
Elmira College *New York* M & W
Elms College *Massachusetts* M & W
Elon University *North Carolina* M & W
Embry-Riddle Aeronautical University - Daytona *Florida* M & W
Embry-Riddle Aeronautical University - Prescott *Arizona* M & W
Emerson College *Massachusetts* M & W
Emmanuel College *Georgia* M & W
Emmanuel College *Massachusetts* M & W
Emmaus Bible College *Iowa* M
Emory & Henry College *Virginia* M & W
Emory University *Georgia* M & W
Emory University, Oxford College *Georgia* W
Emporia State University *Kansas* W
Endicott College *Massachusetts* M & W
Erie Community College *New York* M & W
Erie Community College, North Campus *New York* M & W
Erie Community College, South Campus *New York* M & W
Erskine College *South Carolina* M & W
Essex County College *New York* M
Eugenio María de Hostos Community College of the City University of New York *New York* M
Eureka College *Illinois* M & W
Everett Community College *Washington* M & W
The Evergreen State College *Washington* M & W
Evergreen Valley College *California* M & W
Fairfield University *Connecticut* M & W
Fairleigh Dickinson University, College at Florham *New Jersey* M & W
Fairleigh Dickinson University, Metropolitan Campus *New Jersey* M & W
Faith Baptist Bible College and Theological Seminary *Iowa* M & W
Farmingdale State College *New York* M & W
Fashion Institute of Technology *New York* W
Faulkner University *Alabama* M & W
Feather River College *California* M & W
Felician University *New Jersey* M & W
Ferris State University *Michigan* W
Ferrum College *Virginia* M & W
Finger Lakes Community College *New York* M & W
Finlandia University *Michigan* M & W

Fisher College *Massachusetts* M & W
Fitchburg State University *Massachusetts* M & W
Flagler College *Florida* M & W
Florida Atlantic University *Florida* M & W
Florida College *Florida* M & W
Florida Gulf Coast University *Florida* M & W
Florida Institute of Technology *Florida* M & W
Florida International University *Florida* M & W
Florida National University *Florida* M
Florida Southern College *Florida* M & W
Florida State University *Florida* M & W
Fontbonne University *Missouri* M & W
Foothill College *California* M & W
Fordham University *New York* M & W
Fort Hays State University *Kansas* M & W
Fort Lewis College *Colorado* M & W
Framingham State University *Massachusetts* M & W
Francis Marion University *South Carolina* M & W
Franciscan University of Steubenville *Ohio* M & W
Franklin College *Indiana* M & W
Franklin & Marshall College *Pennsylvania* M & W
Franklin Pierce University *New Hampshire* M & W
Franklin W. Olin College of Engineering *Massachusetts* M & W
Frederick Community College *Maryland* M & W
Freed-Hardeman University *Tennessee* M & W
Fresno City College *California* M & W
Fresno Pacific University *California* M & W
Friends University *Kansas* M & W
Frostburg State University *Maryland* M & W
Fullerton College *California* M & W
Fulton-Montgomery Community College *New York* M & W
Furman University *South Carolina* M & W
Gallaudet University *District of Columbia* M & W
Gannon University *Pennsylvania* M & W
Garden City Community College *Kansas* W
Gardner-Webb University *North Carolina* M & W
GateWay Community College *Arizona* M & W
Gateway Community College *Connecticut* M
Gavilan College *California* M
Genesee Community College *New York* M & W
Geneva College *Pennsylvania* M & W
George Fox University *Oregon* M & W
George Mason University *Virginia* M & W
The George Washington University *District of Columbia* M & W
Georgetown College *Kentucky* M & W
Georgetown University *District of Columbia* M & W
Georgia College & State University *Georgia* W
Georgia Gwinnett College *Georgia* M & W
Georgia Military College *Georgia* M & W
Georgia Southern University *Georgia* M & W
Georgia Southwestern State University *Georgia* M & W
Georgia State University *Georgia* M & W
Georgian Court University *New Jersey* M & W
Gettysburg College *Pennsylvania* M & W
Glendale Community College *Arizona* M & W
Glendale Community College *California* M & W
Globe Institute of Technology *New York* M
Golden West College *California* M & W
Goldey-Beacom College *Delaware* M & W
Gonzaga University *Washington* M & W
Gordon College *Massachusetts* M & W
Gordon State College *Georgia* M & W
Goshen College *Indiana* M & W
Goucher College *Maryland* M & W
Grace Bible College *Michigan* M & W
Grace College *Indiana* M & W
Grace University *Nebraska* M
Graceland University *Iowa* M & W
Grambling State University *Louisiana* W
Grand Canyon University *Arizona* M & W
Grand Valley State University *Michigan* M & W
Grand View University *Iowa* M & W
Grays Harbor College *Washington* W
Great Lakes Christian College *Michigan* M
Green Mountain College *Vermont* M & W
Green River College *Washington* W
Greensboro College *North Carolina* M & W
Greenville College *Illinois* M & W
Grinnell College *Iowa* M & W

Grossmont College *California* W
Grove City College *Pennsylvania* M & W
Guilford College *North Carolina* M & W
Gustavus Adolphus College *Minnesota* M & W
Gwynedd Mercy University *Pennsylvania* M & W
Hagerstown Community College *Maryland* M & W
Hamilton College *New York* M & W
Hamline University *Minnesota* M & W
Hampden-Sydney College *Virginia* M
Hampshire College *Massachusetts* M & W
Hampton University *Virginia* W
Hannibal-LaGrange University *Missouri* M & W
Hanover College *Indiana* M & W
Hardin-Simmons University *Texas* M & W
Harding University *Arkansas* M & W
Harford Community College *Maryland* M & W
Harper College *Illinois* M & W
Harris-Stowe State University *Missouri* M & W
Harrisburg Area Community College *Pennsylvania* M
Hartwick College *New York* M & W
Harvard University *Massachusetts* M & W
Harvey Mudd College *California* M & W
Hastings College *Nebraska* M & W
Haverford College *Pennsylvania* M & W
Hawai'i Pacific University *Hawaii* M & W
Heartland Community College *Illinois* M & W
Heidelberg University *Ohio* M & W
Hendrix College *Arkansas* M & W
Herkimer County Community College *New York* M & W
Hesston College *Kansas* M & W
High Point University *North Carolina* M & W
Highline College *Washington* M & W
Hilbert College *New York* M & W
Hill College *Texas* M & W
Hillsdale College *Michigan* M & W
Hillsdale Free Will Baptist College *Oklahoma* M
Hinds Community College *Mississippi* M & W
Hiram College *Ohio* M & W
Hiwassee College *Tennessee* M & W
Hobart and William Smith Colleges *New York* M & W
Hofstra University *New York* M & W
Hollins University *Virginia* W
Holmes Community College *Mississippi* M
Holy Cross College *Indiana* M & W
Holy Family University *Pennsylvania* M & W
Holy Names University *California* M & W
Holyoke Community College *Massachusetts* M & W
Hood College *Maryland* M & W
Hope College *Michigan* M & W
Hope International University *California* M & W
Houghton College *New York* M & W
Houston Baptist University *Texas* M & W
Howard Community College *Maryland* M & W
Howard Payne University *Texas* M & W
Howard University *District of Columbia* M & W
Hudson Valley Community College *New York* M & W
Humboldt State University *California* M & W
Hunter College of the City University of New York *New York* M
Huntingdon College *Alabama* M & W
Huntington University *Indiana* M & W
Husson University *Maine* M & W
Huston-Tillotson University *Texas* M & W
Hutchinson Community College *Kansas* W
Idaho State University *Idaho* W
Illinois Central College *Illinois* M & W
Illinois College *Illinois* M & W
Illinois Institute of Technology *Illinois* M & W
Illinois State University *Illinois* W
Illinois Wesleyan University *Illinois* M & W
Immaculata University *Pennsylvania* W
Imperial Valley College *California* M & W
Indiana State University *Indiana* W
Indiana Tech *Indiana* M & W
Indiana University Bloomington *Indiana* M & W
Indiana University of Pennsylvania *Pennsylvania* W
Indiana University - Purdue University Fort Wayne *Indiana* M & W
Indiana University - Purdue University Indianapolis *Indiana* M & W

M = Men; W = Women

Indiana Wesleyan University *Indiana* M & W
Inter American University of Puerto Rico, Aguadilla Campus *Puerto Rico* M & W
Inter American University of Puerto Rico, Metropolitan Campus *Puerto Rico* M
Inter American University of Puerto Rico, Ponce Campus *Puerto Rico* M & W
Inter American University of Puerto Rico, San Germán Campus *Puerto Rico* M
Iona College *New York* M & W
Iowa Central Community College *Iowa* M & W
Iowa Lakes Community College *Iowa* M & W
Iowa State University of Science and Technology *Iowa* W
Iowa Wesleyan University *Iowa* M & W
Irvine Valley College *California* M & W
Ithaca College *New York* M & W
Jackson College *Michigan* M & W
Jackson State University *Mississippi* W
Jacksonville State University *Alabama* W
Jacksonville University *Florida* M & W
James Madison University *Virginia* M & W
Jamestown Community College *New York* M & W
Jarvis Christian College *Texas* M & W
Jefferson College *Missouri* M & W
Jefferson Community College *New York* M & W
John Brown University *Arkansas* M & W
John Carroll University *Ohio* M & W
John Jay College of Criminal Justice of the City University of New York *New York* M & W
John Wesley University *North Carolina* M & W
Johns Hopkins University *Maryland* M & W
Johnson County Community College *Kansas* M & W
Johnson State College *Vermont* M & W
Johnson University *Tennessee* M & W
Johnson University Florida *Florida* W
Johnson & Wales University *Colorado* M
Johnson & Wales University *Rhode Island* M & W
Joliet Junior College *Illinois* M & W
Jones County Junior College *Mississippi* M & W
Judson College *Alabama* W
Judson University *Illinois* M & W
Juniata College *Pennsylvania* M & W
Kalamazoo College *Michigan* M & W
Kankakee Community College *Illinois* M
Kansas City Kansas Community College *Kansas* M
Kansas State University *Kansas* W
Kansas Wesleyan University *Kansas* M & W
Kaskaskia College *Illinois* W
Kean University *New Jersey* M & W
Keene State College *New Hampshire* M & W
Kellogg Community College *Michigan* W
Kennesaw State University *Georgia* W
Kent State University *Ohio* W
Kentucky Christian University *Kentucky* M & W
Kentucky Wesleyan College *Kentucky* M & W
Kenyon College *Ohio* M & W
Keuka College *New York* M & W
Keystone College *Pennsylvania* M & W
King University *Tennessee* M & W
The King's College *New York* M & W
King's College *Pennsylvania* M & W
The King's University *Alberta (Canada)* M & W
Kingsborough Community College of the City University of New York *New York* M
Kirkwood Community College *Iowa* M & W
Knox College *Illinois* M & W
Kutztown University of Pennsylvania *Pennsylvania* M & W
La Roche College *Pennsylvania* M & W
La Salle University *Pennsylvania* M & W
La Sierra University *California* M
Lackawanna College *Pennsylvania* W
Lafayette College *Pennsylvania* M & W
LaGrange College *Georgia* M & W
Lake Erie College *Ohio* M & W
Lake Forest College *Illinois* M & W
Lake Superior State University *Michigan* M & W
Lake Tahoe Community College *California* M & W
Lakehead University *Ontario (Canada)* M & W
Lakeland College *Wisconsin* M & W
Lakeland Community College *Ohio* M
Lamar Community College *Colorado* M

Lamar University *Texas* W
Lancaster Bible College *Pennsylvania* M & W
Lander University *South Carolina* M & W
Landmark College *Vermont* M & W
Lane Community College *Oregon* W
Laramie County Community College *Wyoming* M & W
Las Positas College *California* M & W
Lasell College *Massachusetts* M & W
Laurentian University *Ontario (Canada)* M & W
Lawrence Technological University *Michigan* M & W
Lawrence University *Wisconsin* M & W
Le Moyne College *New York* M & W
Lebanon Valley College *Pennsylvania* M & W
Lee University *Tennessee* M & W
Lees-McRae College *North Carolina* M & W
Lehigh Carbon Community College *Pennsylvania* M
Lehigh University *Pennsylvania* M & W
Lehman College of the City University of New York *New York* M & W
Lenoir-Rhyne University *North Carolina* M & W
Lesley University *Massachusetts* M & W
LeTourneau University *Texas* M & W
Lewis & Clark College *Oregon* M & W
Lewis and Clark Community College *Illinois* M & W
Lewis University *Illinois* M & W
Liberty University *Virginia* M & W
Limestone College *South Carolina* M & W
Lincoln Christian University *Illinois* M & W
Lincoln Land Community College *Illinois* M
Lincoln Memorial University *Tennessee* M & W
Lincoln University *Pennsylvania* W
Lindenwood University *Missouri* M & W
Lindsey Wilson College *Kentucky* M & W
Linfield College *Oregon* M & W
Lipscomb University *Tennessee* M & W
Lock Haven University of Pennsylvania *Pennsylvania* M & W
Logan University *Missouri* M
Long Beach City College *California* M & W
Long Island University - LIU Brooklyn *New York* M & W
Long Island University - LIU Post *New York* M & W
Longwood University *Virginia* M & W
Loras College *Iowa* M & W
Los Angeles Harbor College *California* M & W
Los Angeles Valley College *California* W
Los Medanos College *California* M
Louisburg College *North Carolina* M & W
Louisiana State University and Agricultural & Mechanical College *Louisiana* M & W
Louisiana State University at Alexandria *Louisiana* M & W
Louisiana State University in Shreveport *Louisiana* W
Lourdes University *Ohio* M & W
Lower Columbia College *Washington* W
Loyola Marymount University *California* M & W
Loyola University Chicago *Illinois* M & W
Loyola University Maryland *Maryland* M & W
Lubbock Christian University *Texas* M & W
Luther College *Iowa* M & W
Luzerne County Community College *Pennsylvania* M & W
Lycoming College *Pennsylvania* M & W
Lynchburg College *Virginia* M & W
Lyndon State College *Vermont* M & W
Lynn University *Florida* M & W
Lyon College *Arkansas* M & W
Macalester College *Minnesota* M & W
MacMurray College *Illinois* M & W
Macomb Community College *Michigan* M
Madonna University *Michigan* M & W
Maharishi University of Management *Iowa* M & W
Maine Maritime Academy *Maine* M & W
Malone University *Ohio* M & W
Manchester Community College *Connecticut* M & W
Manchester Community College *New Hampshire* M & W
Manchester University *Indiana* M & W
Manhattan Christian College *Kansas* M & W
Manhattan College *New York* M & W

Manhattanville College *New York* M & W
Manor College *Pennsylvania* M & W
Mansfield University of Pennsylvania *Pennsylvania* W
Maranatha Baptist University *Wisconsin* M & W
Marian University *Indiana* M & W
Marian University *Wisconsin* M & W
Marietta College *Ohio* M & W
Marist College *New York* M & W
Marlboro College *Vermont* M & W
Marquette University *Wisconsin* M & W
Mars Hill University *North Carolina* M & W
Marshall University *West Virginia* M & W
Marshalltown Community College *Iowa* M & W
Martin Luther College *Minnesota* M & W
Martin Methodist College *Tennessee* M & W
Mary Baldwin University *Virginia* W
Marymount California University *California* M & W
Marymount University *Virginia* M & W
Maryville College *Tennessee* M & W
Maryville University of Saint Louis *Missouri* M & W
Marywood University *Pennsylvania* M & W
Massachusetts Bay Community College *Massachusetts* M & W
Massachusetts College of Liberal Arts *Massachusetts* M & W
Massachusetts Institute of Technology *Massachusetts* M & W
Massachusetts Maritime Academy *Massachusetts* M & W
Massasoit Community College *Massachusetts* M & W
The Master's College and Seminary *California* M & W
McDaniel College *Maryland* M & W
McGill University *Quebec (Canada)* M & W
McHenry County College *Illinois* M
McKendree University *Illinois* M & W
McMaster University *Ontario (Canada)* M & W
McMurry University *Texas* M & W
McNeese State University *Louisiana* W
McPherson College *Kansas* M & W
Medaille College *New York* M & W
Medgar Evers College of the City University of New York *New York* M & W
Memorial University of Newfoundland *Newfoundland and Labrador (Canada)* M & W
Mendocino College *California* M & W
Menlo College *California* M & W
Merced College *California* M
Mercer County Community College *New Jersey* M & W
Mercer University *Georgia* M & W
Mercy College *New York* M & W
Mercyhurst North East *Pennsylvania* M & W
Mercyhurst University *Pennsylvania* M & W
Meredith College *North Carolina* W
Meridian Community College *Mississippi* M & W
Merrimack College *Massachusetts* M & W
Mesa Community College *Arizona* M & W
Messiah College *Pennsylvania* M & W
Methodist University *North Carolina* M & W
Metropolitan Community College - Kansas City *Missouri* M & W
Metropolitan State University of Denver *Colorado* M & W
Miami University *Ohio* M & W
Michigan State University *Michigan* M & W
Michigan Technological University *Michigan* M & W
Mid-America Christian University *Oklahoma* M & W
Mid-Atlantic Christian University *North Carolina* M
Mid Michigan Community College *Michigan* M & W
MidAmerica Nazarene University *Kansas* M & W
Middle Georgia State University *Georgia* M & W
Middle Tennessee State University *Tennessee* W
Middlebury College *Vermont* M & W
Middlesex County College *New Jersey* M & W
Midland University *Nebraska* M & W
Midway University *Kentucky* W
Midwestern State University *Texas* M & W
Millersville University of Pennsylvania *Pennsylvania* M & W
Milligan College *Tennessee* M & W
Millikin University *Illinois* M & W

M = Men; W = Women

Mills College *California* W
Millsaps College *Mississippi* M & W
Milwaukee Area Technical College *Wisconsin* M
Milwaukee School of Engineering *Wisconsin* M & W
Minnesota State University Mankato *Minnesota* W
Minnesota State University Moorhead *Minnesota* W
Minot State University *North Dakota* W
MiraCosta College *California* M & W
Misericordia University *Pennsylvania* M & W
Mission College *California* M & W
Mississippi College *Mississippi* M & W
Mississippi Gulf Coast Community College *Mississippi* M & W
Mississippi State University *Mississippi* W
Missouri Baptist University *Missouri* M & W
Missouri Southern State University *Missouri* M & W
Missouri State University *Missouri* W
Missouri University of Science and Technology *Missouri* M & W
Missouri Valley College *Missouri* M & W
Missouri Western State University *Missouri* W
Mitchell College *Connecticut* M & W
Modesto Junior College *California* M & W
Mohawk Valley Community College *New York* M & W
Molloy College *New York* M & W
Monmouth College *Illinois* M & W
Monmouth University *New Jersey* M & W
Monroe College *New York* M & W
Monroe Community College *New York* M & W
Montana State University Billings *Montana* M & W
Montclair State University *New Jersey* M & W
Montgomery College *Maryland* M & W
Montgomery County Community College *Pennsylvania* M & W
Montreat College *North Carolina* M & W
Moody Bible Institute *Illinois* M
Moorpark College *California* M & W
Moraine Valley Community College *Illinois* M & W
Moravian College *Pennsylvania* M & W
Morehead State University *Kentucky* W
Morningside College *Iowa* M & W
Morrisville State College *New York* M & W
Morton College *Illinois* M & W
Mount Allison University *New Brunswick (Canada)* M & W
Mount Aloysius College *Pennsylvania* M & W
Mount Holyoke College *Massachusetts* W
Mount Ida College *Massachusetts* M & W
Mount Marty College *South Dakota* M & W
Mount Mary University *Wisconsin* W
Mount Mercy University *Iowa* M & W
Mount St. Joseph University *Ohio* M & W
Mount Saint Mary College *New York* M & W
Mount St. Mary's University *Maryland* W
Mount Saint Vincent University *Nova Scotia (Canada)* M & W
Mt. San Antonio College *California* M & W
Mt. San Jacinto College *California* W
Mount Vernon Nazarene University *Ohio* M & W
Mountain View College *Texas* M & W
Muhlenberg College *Pennsylvania* M & W
Multnomah University *Oregon* M
Murray State University *Kentucky* W
Muskingum University *Ohio* M & W
Napa Valley College *California* M
Nashua Community College *New Hampshire* M & W
Nassau Community College *New York* M & W
Navarro College *Texas* W
Nazareth College of Rochester *New York* M & W
Nebraska Wesleyan University *Nebraska* M & W
Neumann University *Pennsylvania* M & W
New England College *New Hampshire* M & W
New Hope Christian College *Oregon* M & W
New Jersey City University *New Jersey* M & W
New Jersey Institute of Technology *New Jersey* M & W
New Mexico Highlands University *New Mexico* W
New Mexico Institute of Mining and Technology *New Mexico* M & W
New Mexico State University *New Mexico* W
New York Institute of Technology *New York* M & W

New York University *New York* M & W
Newberry College *South Carolina* M & W
Newbury College *Massachusetts* M & W
Newman University *Kansas* M & W
NHTI, Concord's Community College *New Hampshire* M & W
Niagara County Community College *New York* M & W
Niagara University *New York* M & W
Nicholls State University *Louisiana* W
Nichols College *Massachusetts* M & W
Nipissing University *Ontario (Canada)* M & W
North Carolina State University *North Carolina* M & W
North Carolina Wesleyan College *North Carolina* M & W
North Central College *Illinois* M & W
North Central University *Minnesota* M & W
North Country Community College *New York* M & W
North Dakota State University *North Dakota* M & W
North Greenville University *South Carolina* M & W
North Idaho College *Idaho* M & W
North Iowa Area Community College *Iowa* M
North Park University *Illinois* M & W
Northampton Community College *Pennsylvania* M & W
Northeast Texas Community College *Texas* M & W
Northeastern Junior College *Colorado* M & W
Northeastern Oklahoma Agricultural and Mechanical College *Oklahoma* M & W
Northeastern State University *Oklahoma* M & W
Northeastern University *Massachusetts* M & W
Northern Arizona University *Arizona* W
Northern Illinois University *Illinois* W
Northern Kentucky University *Kentucky* M & W
Northern Maine Community College *Maine* M & W
Northern Michigan University *Michigan* M & W
Northern Oklahoma College *Oklahoma* M & W
Northern State University *South Dakota* W
Northland College *Wisconsin* M & W
Northwest Christian University *Oregon* M & W
Northwest College *Wyoming* M & W
Northwest Missouri State University *Missouri* M & W
Northwest Nazarene University *Idaho* M & W
Northwest University *Washington* M & W
Northwestern College *Iowa* M & W
Northwestern Oklahoma State University *Oklahoma* M & W
Northwestern State University of Louisiana *Louisiana* W
Northwood University, Michigan Campus *Michigan* M & W
Northwood University, Texas Campus *Texas* M & W
Norwich University *Vermont* M & W
Notre Dame College *Ohio* M & W
Notre Dame of Maryland University *Maryland* W
Notre Dame de Namur University *California* M & W
Nova Southeastern University *Florida* M & W
Nyack College *New York* M & W
Oakland City University *Indiana* M & W
Oakland University *Michigan* M & W
Oakton Community College *Illinois* M & W
Oberlin College *Ohio* M & W
Occidental College *California* M & W
Ocean County College *New Jersey* M & W
Oglethorpe University *Georgia* M & W
Ohio Christian University *Ohio* M
Ohio Dominican University *Ohio* M & W
Ohio Northern University *Ohio* M & W
The Ohio State University *Ohio* M & W
Ohio University *Ohio* W
Ohio Valley University *West Virginia* M & W
Ohio Wesleyan University *Ohio* M & W
Ohlone College *California* M & W
Oklahoma Baptist University *Oklahoma* M & W
Oklahoma Christian University *Oklahoma* M & W
Oklahoma City University *Oklahoma* M & W
Oklahoma Panhandle State University *Oklahoma* M & W
Oklahoma State University *Oklahoma* W
Oklahoma Wesleyan University *Oklahoma* M & W
Old Dominion University *Virginia* M & W
Olivet College *Michigan* M & W

Olivet Nazarene University *Illinois* M & W
Onondaga Community College *New York* M & W
Oral Roberts University *Oklahoma* M & W
Orange Coast College *California* M & W
Orange County Community College *New York* M
Oregon Institute of Technology *Oregon* W
Oregon State University *Oregon* W
Otero Junior College *Colorado* M & W
Ottawa University *Kansas* M & W
Otterbein University *Ohio* M & W
Ouachita Baptist University *Arkansas* M & W
Our Lady of the Lake University of San Antonio *Texas* M & W
Owens Community College *Ohio* M & W
Oxnard College *California* M & W
Ozark Christian College *Missouri* M
Pace University *New York* W
Pace University, Pleasantville Campus *New York* W
Pacific Lutheran University *Washington* M & W
Pacific Union College *California* M
Pacific University *Oregon* M & W
Palm Beach Atlantic University *Florida* M & W
Palomar College *California* M & W
Paradise Valley Community College *Arizona* M & W
Paris Junior College *Texas* M & W
Park University *Missouri* M & W
Parkland College *Illinois* M & W
Pasadena City College *California* M & W
Passaic County Community College *New Jersey* M
Patrick Henry College *Virginia* M & W
Patrick Henry Community College *Virginia* M & W
Paul Smith's College *New York* M & W
Pearl River Community College *Mississippi* M & W
Peninsula College *Washington* M & W
Penn State Abington *Pennsylvania* M & W
Penn State Altoona *Pennsylvania* M & W
Penn State Berks *Pennsylvania* M & W
Penn State Brandywine *Pennsylvania* M & W
Penn State Erie, The Behrend College *Pennsylvania* M & W
Penn State Harrisburg *Pennsylvania* M & W
Penn State Hazleton *Pennsylvania* M
Penn State Lehigh Valley *Pennsylvania* M & W
Penn State Mont Alto *Pennsylvania* M & W
Penn State Schuylkill *Pennsylvania* M
Penn State University Park *Pennsylvania* M & W
Penn State Wilkes-Barre *Pennsylvania* M & W
Penn State Worthington Scranton *Pennsylvania* M
Pennsylvania College of Technology *Pennsylvania* M & W
Pepperdine University *California* M & W
Pfeiffer University *North Carolina* M & W
Philadelphia University *Pennsylvania* M & W
Phoenix College *Arizona* M & W
Piedmont College *Georgia* M & W
Pierce College at Puyallup *Washington* M
Pine Manor College *Massachusetts* M & W
Pitzer College *California* M & W
Plymouth State University *New Hampshire* M & W
Point Loma Nazarene University *California* M & W
Point Park University *Pennsylvania* M & W
Point University *Georgia* M & W
Polk State College *Florida* W
Pomona College *California* M & W
Porterville College *California* M & W
Portland State University *Oregon* W
Post University *Connecticut* M & W
Potomac State College of West Virginia University *West Virginia* M & W
Prairie State College *Illinois* M
Prairie View A&M University *Texas* W
Pratt Community College *Kansas* M & W
Pratt Institute *New York* M & W
Presbyterian College *South Carolina* M & W
Presentation College *South Dakota* M & W
Prince George's Community College *Maryland* M & W
Princeton University *New Jersey* M & W
Principia College *Illinois* M & W
Providence College *Rhode Island* M & W
Providence University College & Theological Seminary *Manitoba (Canada)* M & W
Purchase College, State University of New York *New York* M & W

M = Men; W = Women

Purdue University *Indiana* W

Purdue University Northwest *Hammond, Indiana* M & W

Queens College of the City University of New York *New York* M & W

Queens University of Charlotte *North Carolina* M & W

Queen's University at Kingston *Ontario (Canada)* M & W

Queensborough Community College of the City University of New York *New York* M

Quincy University *Illinois* M & W

Quinnipiac University *Connecticut* M & W

Radford University *Virginia* M & W

Ramapo College of New Jersey *New Jersey* M & W

Randolph College *Virginia* M & W

Randolph-Macon College *Virginia* M & W

Raritan Valley Community College *New Jersey* M & W

Redeemer University College *Ontario (Canada)* M & W

Regis College *Massachusetts* M & W

Regis University *Colorado* M & W

Reinhardt University *Georgia* M & W

Rensselaer Polytechnic Institute *New York* M & W

Research College of Nursing *Missouri* M & W

Rhode Island College *Rhode Island* M & W

Rhodes College *Tennessee* M & W

Rice University *Texas* M & W

Richland College *Texas* M & W

Rider University *New Jersey* M & W

Ridgewater College *Minnesota* M

Rio Hondo College *California* M & W

Ripon College *Wisconsin* M & W

Rivier University *New Hampshire* M & W

Roanoke College *Virginia* M & W

Robert Morris University *Pennsylvania* M & W

Robert Morris University Illinois *Illinois* M & W

Roberts Wesleyan College *New York* M & W

Rochester College *Michigan* M & W

Rochester Community and Technical College *Minnesota* W

Rochester Institute of Technology *New York* M & W

Rock Valley College *Illinois* M & W

Rockford University *Illinois* M & W

Rockhurst University *Missouri* M & W

Rockland Community College *New York* M & W

Rocky Mountain College *Montana* M & W

Roger Williams University *Rhode Island* M & W

Rogers State University *Oklahoma* M & W

Rogue Community College *Oregon* M & W

Rollins College *Florida* M & W

Roosevelt University *Illinois* M & W

Rose-Hulman Institute of Technology *Indiana* M & W

Rose State College *Oklahoma* W

Rosemont College *Pennsylvania* M & W

Rowan College at Burlington County *New Jersey* M & W

Rowan College at Gloucester County *New Jersey* M & W

Rowan University *New Jersey* M & W

Roxbury Community College *Massachusetts* M & W

Royal Military College of Canada *Ontario (Canada)* M & W

Rutgers University - Camden *New Jersey* M & W

Rutgers University - New Brunswick *New Jersey* M & W

Rutgers University - Newark *New Jersey* M & W

Ryerson University *Ontario (Canada)* M & W

Sacramento City College *California* W

Sacred Heart University *Connecticut* M & W

The Sage Colleges *New York* M & W

Saginaw Valley State University *Michigan* M & W

St. Ambrose University *Iowa* M & W

St. Andrews University *North Carolina* M & W

Saint Anselm College *New Hampshire* M & W

St. Bonaventure University *New York* M & W

St. Catherine University *Minnesota* W

St. Charles Community College *Missouri* M & W

St. Cloud State University *Minnesota* M & W

St. Edward's University *Texas* M & W

St. Francis College *New York* M

Saint Francis University *Pennsylvania* M & W

St. Francis Xavier University *Nova Scotia (Canada)* M & W

St. Gregory's University *Oklahoma* M & W

St. John Fisher College *New York* M & W

Saint John's University *Minnesota* M

St. John's University *New York* M & W

Saint Joseph's College *Indiana* M & W

St. Joseph's College, Long Island Campus *New York* M & W

Saint Joseph's College of Maine *Maine* M & W

St. Joseph's College, New York *New York* M & W

Saint Joseph's University *Pennsylvania* M & W

Saint Katherine College *California* M & W

St. Lawrence University *New York* M & W

Saint Leo University *Florida* M & W

St. Louis College of Pharmacy *Missouri* M & W

St. Louis Community College *Missouri* M & W

Saint Louis University *Missouri* M & W

Saint Martin's University *Washington* M & W

Saint Mary-of-the-Woods College *Indiana* W

Saint Mary's College *Indiana* W

Saint Mary's College of California *California* M & W

St. Mary's College of Maryland *Maryland* M & W

Saint Mary's University *Nova Scotia (Canada)* M & W

St. Mary's University *Texas* M & W

Saint Mary's University of Minnesota *Minnesota* M & W

Saint Michael's College *Vermont* M & W

St. Norbert College *Wisconsin* M & W

St. Olaf College *Minnesota* M & W

Saint Peter's University *New Jersey* M & W

St. Thomas Aquinas College *New York* M & W

St. Thomas University *Florida* M & W

St. Thomas University *New Brunswick (Canada)* M & W

Saint Vincent College *Pennsylvania* M & W

Saint Xavier University *Illinois* M & W

Salem College *North Carolina* W

Salem International University *West Virginia* M & W

Salem State University *Massachusetts* M & W

Salisbury University *Maryland* M & W

Salt Lake Community College *Utah* M & W

Salve Regina University *Rhode Island* M & W

Sam Houston State University *Texas* W

Samford University *Alabama* W

San Bernardino Valley College *California* M & W

San Diego Christian College *California* M & W

San Diego City College *California* M & W

San Diego Mesa College *California* M & W

San Diego State University *California* M & W

San Francisco State University *California* M & W

San Jacinto College District *Texas* M

San Joaquin Delta College *California* M & W

San Jose State University *California* M & W

Santa Ana College *California* M

Santa Barbara City College *California* M & W

Santa Clara University *California* M & W

Santa Monica College *California* W

Santa Rosa Junior College *California* M & W

Sarah Lawrence College *New York* M & W

Savannah College of Art and Design *Georgia* M & W

Schoolcraft College *Michigan* M & W

Schreiner University *Texas* M & W

Scott Community College *Iowa* M & W

Scottsdale Community College *Arizona* M & W

Scripps College *California* W

Seattle Pacific University *Washington* M & W

Seattle University *Washington* M & W

Seton Hall University *New Jersey* M & W

Seton Hill University *Pennsylvania* M & W

Sewanee: The University of the South *Tennessee* M & W

Shasta College *California* M & W

Shawnee State University *Ohio* M & W

Shenandoah University *Virginia* M & W

Shepherd University *West Virginia* M & W

Sheridan College *Wyoming* M & W

Shippensburg University of Pennsylvania *Pennsylvania* M & W

Shoreline Community College *Washington* M & W

Shorter University *Georgia* M & W

Siena College *New York* M & W

Siena Heights University *Michigan* M & W

Sierra College *California* W

Sierra Nevada College *Nevada* M & W

Silver Lake College of the Holy Family *Wisconsin* M & W

Simmons College *Massachusetts* W

Simon Fraser University *British Columbia (Canada)* M & W

Simpson College *Iowa* M & W

Simpson University *California* M & W

Skagit Valley College *Washington* M & W

Skidmore College *New York* M & W

Skyline College *California* M

Slippery Rock University of Pennsylvania *Pennsylvania* M & W

Smith College *Massachusetts* W

Soka University of America *California* M & W

Sonoma State University *California* M & W

South Carolina State University *South Carolina* W

South Dakota School of Mines and Technology *South Dakota* M

South Dakota State University *South Dakota* W

South Georgia State College *Georgia* W

South Mountain Community College *Arizona* M

South Puget Sound Community College *Washington* M

South Suburban College *Illinois* M & W

Southeast Missouri State University *Missouri* W

Southeastern Louisiana University *Louisiana* W

Southeastern University *Florida* M & W

Southern Alberta Institute of Technology *Alberta (Canada)* M & W

Southern Connecticut State University *Connecticut* M & W

Southern Illinois University Edwardsville *Illinois* M & W

Southern Maine Community College *Maine* M & W

Southern Methodist University *Texas* M & W

Southern Nazarene University *Oklahoma* M & W

Southern New Hampshire University *New Hampshire* M & W

Southern Oregon University *Oregon* M & W

Southern State Community College *Ohio* M

Southern Utah University *Utah* W

Southern Vermont College *Vermont* M & W

Southern Virginia University *Virginia* M & W

Southern Wesleyan University *South Carolina* M & W

Southwest Baptist University *Missouri* M & W

Southwest Minnesota State University *Minnesota* W

Southwest Mississippi Community College *Mississippi* M

Southwestern Adventist University *Texas* M & W

Southwestern Assemblies of God University *Texas* M & W

Southwestern Christian University *Oklahoma* M & W

Southwestern College *California* M & W

Southwestern College *Kansas* M & W

Southwestern Illinois College *Illinois* M & W

Southwestern Oklahoma State University *Oklahoma* W

Southwestern Oregon Community College *Oregon* M & W

Southwestern University *Texas* M & W

Spalding University *Kentucky* M & W

Spartanburg Methodist College *South Carolina* M & W

Spokane Community College *Washington* M & W

Spokane Falls Community College *Washington* M & W

Spring Arbor University *Michigan* M & W

Spring Hill College *Alabama* M & W

Springfield College *Massachusetts* M & W

Springfield Technical Community College *Massachusetts* M & W

Stanford University *California* M & W

State University of New York College of Agriculture and Technology at Cobleskill *New York* M & W

State University of New York College at Cortland *New York* M & W

M = Men; W = Women

State University of New York College of Environmental Science and Forestry *New York* M & W
State University of New York College at Geneseo *New York* M & W
State University of New York College at Old Westbury *New York* M & W
State University of New York College at Oneonta *New York* M & W
State University of New York College at Potsdam *New York* M & W
State University of New York College of Technology at Alfred *New York* M & W
State University of New York College of Technology at Canton *New York* M & W
State University of New York College of Technology at Delhi *New York* M & W
State University of New York at Fredonia *New York* M & W
State University of New York Maritime College *New York* M & W
State University of New York at New Paltz *New York* M & W
State University of New York at Oswego *New York* M & W
State University of New York at Plattsburgh *New York* M & W
State University of New York Polytechnic Institute *New York* M & W
Stephen F. Austin State University *Texas* M & W
Stephens College *Missouri* W
Sterling College *Kansas* M & W
Stetson University *Florida* M & W
Stevens Institute of Technology *New Jersey* M & W
Stevenson University *Maryland* M & W
Stockton University *New Jersey* M & W
Stonehill College *Massachusetts* M & W
Stony Brook University, State University of New York *New York* M & W
Suffolk County Community College *New York* M
Suffolk University *Massachusetts* M
Summit University *Pennsylvania* M & W
Susquehanna University *Pennsylvania* M & W
Sussex County Community College *New Jersey* M & W
Swarthmore College *Pennsylvania* M & W
Sweet Briar College *Virginia* W
Syracuse University *New York* W
Tabor College *Kansas* M & W
Tacoma Community College *Washington* M & W
Taft College *California* M
Talladega College *Alabama* M & W
Taylor University *Indiana* M & W
Temple University *Pennsylvania* M & W
Tennessee Technological University *Tennessee* W
Tennessee Wesleyan College *Tennessee* M & W
Texas A&M International University *Texas* M & W
Texas A&M University *Texas* W
Texas A&M University - Commerce *Texas* W
Texas A&M University - Corpus Christi *Texas* W
Texas Christian University *Texas* M & W
Texas College *Texas* M & W
Texas Lutheran University *Texas* M & W
Texas Southern University *Texas* M & W
Texas Southmost College *Texas* M & W
Texas State University *Texas* M & W
Texas Tech University *Texas* W
Texas Wesleyan University *Texas* M & W
Texas Woman's University *Texas* W
Thiel College *Pennsylvania* M & W
Thomas College *Maine* M & W
Thomas More College *Kentucky* M & W
Thomas University *Georgia* M & W
Thompson Rivers University *British Columbia (Canada)* M & W
Tiffin University *Ohio* M & W
Toccoa Falls College *Georgia* M & W
Tompkins Cortland Community College *New York* M & W
Towson University *Maryland* W
Transylvania University *Kentucky* M & W
Treasure Valley Community College *Oregon* M & W
Trent University *Ontario (Canada)* M & W
Trevecca Nazarene University *Tennessee* M & W
Tri-County Technical College *South Carolina* M

Trine University *Indiana* M & W
Trinidad State Junior College *Colorado* M & W
Trinity Baptist College *Florida* M
Trinity Christian College *Illinois* M & W
Trinity College *Connecticut* M & W
Trinity College of Florida *Florida* M
Trinity International University *Illinois* M & W
Trinity University *Texas* M & W
Trinity Washington University *District of Columbia* W
Trinity Western University *British Columbia (Canada)* M & W
Triton College *Illinois* M
Troy University *Alabama* W
Truett-McConnell College *Georgia* M & W
Truman State University *Missouri* M & W
Tufts University *Massachusetts* M & W
Tulane University *Louisiana* M & W
Tusculum College *Tennessee* M & W
Tuskegee University *Alabama* M
Tyler Junior College *Texas* M & W
Ulster County Community College *New York* M
Union College *Kentucky* M & W
Union College *New York* M & W
Union County College *New Jersey* M & W
Union University *Tennessee* M & W
United States Air Force Academy *Colorado* M & W
United States Coast Guard Academy *Connecticut* M & W
United States Merchant Marine Academy *New York* M
United States Military Academy *New York* M & W
United States Naval Academy *Maryland* M & W
Unity College *Maine* M & W
Universidad Metropolitana *Puerto Rico* M & W
Universidad del Turabo *Puerto Rico* M
Université Laval *Quebec (Canada)* M & W
Université de Moncton *New Brunswick (Canada)* M & W
Université de Montréal *Quebec (Canada)* M & W
Université du Québec à Chicoutimi *Quebec (Canada)* M & W
Université du Québec en Outaouais *Quebec (Canada)* M & W
Université du Québec à Trois-Rivières *Quebec (Canada)* M & W
The University of Akron *Ohio* M & W
The University of Alabama *Alabama* M & W
The University of Alabama at Birmingham *Alabama* M & W
The University of Alabama in Huntsville *Alabama* M & W
University at Albany, State University of New York *New York* M & W
University of Alberta *Alberta (Canada)* M & W
The University of Arizona *Arizona* M & W
University of Arkansas *Arkansas* W
University of Arkansas at Little Rock *Arkansas* M & W
University of Bridgeport *Connecticut* M & W
The University of British Columbia *British Columbia (Canada)* M & W
The University of British Columbia - Okanagan Campus *British Columbia (Canada)* M & W
University at Buffalo, the State University of New York *New York* M & W
University of Calgary *Alberta (Canada)* M & W
University of California, Berkeley *California* M & W
University of California, Davis *California* M & W
University of California, Irvine *California* M & W
University of California, Los Angeles *California* M & W
University of California, Merced *California* M & W
University of California, Riverside *California* M & W
University of California, San Diego *California* M & W
University of California, Santa Barbara *California* M & W
University of California, Santa Cruz *California* M & W
University of Central Arkansas *Arkansas* M & W
University of Central Florida *Florida* M & W
University of Central Missouri *Missouri* M & W
University of Central Oklahoma *Oklahoma* W

University of Charleston *West Virginia* M & W
University of Chicago *Illinois* M & W
University of Cincinnati *Ohio* M & W
University of Cincinnati Clermont College *Ohio* M & W
University of Colorado Boulder *Colorado* M & W
University of Colorado Colorado Springs *Colorado* M & W
University of Colorado Denver *Colorado* M & W
University of Connecticut *Connecticut* M & W
University of the Cumberlands *Kentucky* M & W
University of Dallas *Texas* M & W
University of Dayton *Ohio* M & W
University of Delaware *Delaware* M & W
University of Denver *Colorado* M & W
University of Detroit Mercy *Michigan* M & W
University of the District of Columbia *District of Columbia* M
University of Dubuque *Iowa* M & W
University of Evansville *Indiana* M & W
The University of Findlay *Ohio* M & W
University of Florida *Florida* M & W
University of the Fraser Valley *British Columbia (Canada)* M & W
University of Georgia *Georgia* W
University of Great Falls *Montana* M & W
University of Guelph *Ontario (Canada)* M & W
University of Hartford *Connecticut* M & W
University of Hawaii at Hilo *Hawaii* M & W
University of Hawaii at Manoa *Hawaii* W
University of Houston *Texas* W
University of Houston - Victoria *Texas* M & W
University of Idaho *Idaho* W
University of Illinois at Chicago *Illinois* M
University of Illinois at Springfield *Illinois* M & W
University of Illinois at Urbana - Champaign *Illinois* W
University of the Incarnate Word *Texas* M & W
University of Indianapolis *Indiana* M & W
The University of Iowa *Iowa* M & W
University of Jamestown *North Dakota* M & W
The University of Kansas *Kansas* W
University of Kentucky *Kentucky* M & W
University of King's College *Nova Scotia (Canada)* M & W
University of La Verne *California* M & W
University of Lethbridge *Alberta (Canada)* M & W
University of Louisiana at Lafayette *Louisiana* W
University of Louisiana at Monroe *Louisiana* W
University of Louisville *Kentucky* M & W
University of Maine *Maine* W
University of Maine at Farmington *Maine* M & W
University of Maine at Fort Kent *Maine* M & W
University of Maine at Machias *Maine* M & W
University of Maine at Presque Isle *Maine* M & W
University of Mary *North Dakota* M & W
University of Mary Hardin-Baylor *Texas* M & W
University of Mary Washington *Virginia* M & W
University of Maryland, Baltimore County *Maryland* M & W
University of Maryland, College Park *Maryland* M & W
University of Massachusetts Amherst *Massachusetts* M & W
University of Massachusetts Boston *Massachusetts* M & W
University of Massachusetts Dartmouth *Massachusetts* M & W
University of Massachusetts Lowell *Massachusetts* M & W
University of Memphis *Tennessee* M & W
University of Miami *Florida* W
University of Michigan *Michigan* M & W
University of Michigan - Dearborn *Michigan* M & W
University of Minnesota, Crookston *Minnesota* W
University of Minnesota, Duluth *Minnesota* M & W
University of Minnesota, Morris *Minnesota* M & W
University of Minnesota, Twin Cities Campus *Minnesota* W
University of Mississippi *Mississippi* M & W
University of Missouri *Missouri* W
University of Missouri - Kansas City *Missouri* M & W
University of Missouri - St. Louis *Missouri* M & W

M = Men; W = Women

University of Mobile *Alabama* M & W
University of Montana *Montana* W
University of Montevallo *Alabama* M & W
University of Mount Olive *North Carolina* M & W
University of Mount Union *Ohio* M & W
University of Nebraska at Kearney *Nebraska* W
University of Nebraska - Lincoln *Nebraska* W
University of Nebraska at Omaha *Nebraska* M & W
University of Nevada, Las Vegas *Nevada* M & W
University of Nevada, Reno *Nevada* W
University of New Brunswick Fredericton *New Brunswick (Canada)* M & W
University of New Brunswick Saint John *New Brunswick (Canada)* M & W
University of New England *Maine* M & W
University of New Hampshire *New Hampshire* M & W
University of New Haven *Connecticut* M & W
University of New Mexico *New Mexico* M & W
University of North Alabama *Alabama* W
University of North Carolina at Asheville *North Carolina* M & W
The University of North Carolina at Chapel Hill *North Carolina* M & W
The University of North Carolina at Charlotte *North Carolina* M & W
The University of North Carolina at Greensboro *North Carolina* M & W
The University of North Carolina at Pembroke *North Carolina* M & W
The University of North Carolina Wilmington *North Carolina* M & W
University of North Dakota *North Dakota* W
University of North Florida *Florida* M & W
University of North Georgia *Georgia* M & W
University of North Texas *Texas* M & W
University of Northern Colorado *Colorado* M & W
University of Northern Iowa *Iowa* W
University of Northwestern - St. Paul *Minnesota* M & W
University of Notre Dame *Indiana* M & W
University of Oklahoma *Oklahoma* W
University of Oregon *Oregon* W
University of Ottawa *Ontario (Canada)* M & W
University of the Pacific *California* W
University of Pennsylvania *Pennsylvania* M & W
University of Pikeville *Kentucky* M & W
University of Pittsburgh *Pennsylvania* M & W
University of Pittsburgh at Bradford *Pennsylvania* M & W
University of Pittsburgh at Greensburg *Pennsylvania* M & W
University of Pittsburgh at Johnstown *Pennsylvania* M & W
University of Portland *Oregon* M & W
University of Prince Edward Island *Prince Edward Island (Canada)* M & W
University of Puerto Rico in Cayey *Puerto Rico* M
University of Puerto Rico, Mayagüez Campus *Puerto Rico* M
University of Puerto Rico, Río Piedras Campus *Puerto Rico* M
University of Puget Sound *Washington* M & W
University of Redlands *California* M & W
University of Regina *Saskatchewan (Canada)* W
University of Rhode Island *Rhode Island* M & W
University of Richmond *Virginia* W
University of Rio Grande *Ohio* M & W
University of Rochester *New York* M & W
University of St. Francis *Illinois* M & W
University of Saint Francis *Indiana* M & W
University of Saint Joseph *Connecticut* W
University of Saint Mary *Kansas* M & W
University of St. Thomas *Minnesota* M & W
University of St. Thomas *Texas* M & W
University of San Diego *California* M & W
University of San Francisco *California* M & W
University of Saskatchewan *Saskatchewan (Canada)* W
University of Science and Arts of Oklahoma *Oklahoma* M & W
The University of Scranton *Pennsylvania* M & W
University of Sioux Falls *South Dakota* M & W
University of South Alabama *Alabama* W

University of South Carolina *South Carolina* M & W
University of South Carolina Aiken *South Carolina* M & W
University of South Carolina Beaufort *South Carolina* W
University of South Carolina Lancaster *South Carolina* W
University of South Carolina Salkehatchie *South Carolina* M & W
University of South Carolina Upstate *South Carolina* M & W
The University of South Dakota *South Dakota* W
University of South Florida *Florida* M & W
University of Southern California *California* M & W
University of Southern Indiana *Indiana* M & W
University of Southern Maine *Maine* M & W
University of Southern Mississippi *Mississippi* W
University of the Southwest *New Mexico* M & W
The University of Tampa *Florida* M & W
The University of Tennessee *Tennessee* W
The University of Tennessee at Chattanooga *Tennessee* W
The University of Tennessee at Martin *Tennessee* W
The University of Texas at Austin *Texas* M & W
The University of Texas at Dallas *Texas* M & W
The University of Texas of the Permian Basin *Texas* M & W
The University of Texas at San Antonio *Texas* M & W
The University of Texas at Tyler *Texas* M & W
The University of Toledo *Ohio* W
University of Toronto *Ontario (Canada)* M & W
The University of Tulsa *Oklahoma* M & W
University of Utah *Utah* M & W
University of Valley Forge *Pennsylvania* M & W
University of Vermont *Vermont* M & W
University of Victoria *British Columbia (Canada)* M & W
University of the Virgin Islands *United States Virgin Islands* M
University of Virginia *Virginia* M & W
University of Washington *Washington* M & W
University of Waterloo *Ontario (Canada)* M & W
The University of West Alabama *Alabama* M & W
University of West Florida *Florida* M & W
University of West Georgia *Georgia* W
The University of Western Ontario *Ontario (Canada)* M & W
University of Windsor *Ontario (Canada)* M & W
University of Wisconsin - Baraboo/Sauk County *Wisconsin* M & W
University of Wisconsin - Eau Claire *Wisconsin* W
University of Wisconsin - Fond du Lac *Wisconsin* M & W
University of Wisconsin - Fox Valley *Wisconsin* M & W
University of Wisconsin - Green Bay *Wisconsin* W
University of Wisconsin - La Crosse *Wisconsin* W
University of Wisconsin - Madison *Wisconsin* W
University of Wisconsin - Milwaukee *Wisconsin* M & W
University of Wisconsin - Oshkosh *Wisconsin* M & W
University of Wisconsin - Parkside *Wisconsin* M & W
University of Wisconsin - Platteville *Wisconsin* M & W
University of Wisconsin - River Falls *Wisconsin* W
University of Wisconsin - Sheboygan *Wisconsin* M & W
University of Wisconsin - Stevens Point *Wisconsin* W
University of Wisconsin - Stout *Wisconsin* M & W
University of Wisconsin - Superior *Wisconsin* M & W
University of Wisconsin - Washington County *Wisconsin* M & W
University of Wisconsin - Waukesha *Wisconsin* M & W
University of Wisconsin - Whitewater *Wisconsin* M & W

University of Wyoming *Wyoming* M & W
Upper Iowa University *Iowa* M & W
Urbana University *Ohio* M & W
Ursinus College *Pennsylvania* M & W
Ursuline College *Ohio* W
Utah State University *Utah* M & W
Utah Valley University *Utah* W
Utica College *New York* M & W
Valdosta State University *Georgia* W
Valley Forge Military College *Pennsylvania* M
Valparaiso University *Indiana* M & W
Vanderbilt University *Tennessee* W
Vanguard University of Southern California *California* M & W
Vassar College *New York* M & W
Vaughn College of Aeronautics and Technology *New York* M
Ventura College *California* W
Vermont Technical College *Vermont* M & W
Victor Valley College *California* M & W
Villa Maria College *New York* M & W
Villanova University *Pennsylvania* M & W
Virginia Commonwealth University *Virginia* M & W
Virginia Military Institute *Virginia* M & W
Virginia Polytechnic Institute and State University *Virginia* M & W
Virginia Wesleyan College *Virginia* M & W
Viterbo University *Wisconsin* M & W
Wabash College *Indiana* M
Wagner College *New York* W
Wake Forest University *North Carolina* M & W
Waldorf College *Iowa* M & W
Walla Walla Community College *Washington* M & W
Walla Walla University *Washington* M
Wallace State Community College *Alabama* M & W
Walsh University *Ohio* M & W
Warner Pacific College *Oregon* M & W
Warner University *Florida* M & W
Warren Wilson College *North Carolina* M & W
Wartburg College *Iowa* M & W
Washburn University *Kansas* W
Washington Adventist University *Maryland* M & W
Washington College *Maryland* M & W
Washington & Jefferson College *Pennsylvania* M & W
Washington and Lee University *Virginia* M & W
Washington State University *Washington* M & W
Washington State University - Tri-Cities *Washington* M & W
Washington University in St. Louis *Missouri* M & W
Waubonsee Community College *Illinois* M & W
Wayland Baptist University *Texas* M & W
Wayne State College *Nebraska* M & W
Wayne State University *Michigan* M & W
Waynesburg University *Pennsylvania* M & W
Webb Institute *New York* M & W
Webber International University *Florida* M & W
Weber State University *Utah* M & W
Webster University *Missouri* M & W
Wellesley College *Massachusetts* W
Wells College *New York* M & W
Wenatchee Valley College *Washington* M & W
Wentworth Institute of Technology *Massachusetts* M & W
Wentworth Military Academy and College *Missouri* M
Wesley College *Delaware* M & W
Wesleyan College *Georgia* W
Wesleyan University *Connecticut* M & W
West Chester University of Pennsylvania *Pennsylvania* M & W
West Texas A&M University *Texas* M & W
West Valley College *California* M
West Virginia University *West Virginia* M & W
West Virginia University Institute of Technology *West Virginia* M & W
West Virginia Wesleyan College *West Virginia* M & W
Westchester Community College *New York* M
Western Carolina University *North Carolina* W
Western Connecticut State University *Connecticut* M & W
Western Illinois University *Illinois* M & W

M = Men; W = Women

Western Kentucky University *Kentucky* W
Western Michigan University *Michigan* M & W
Western Nebraska Community College *Nebraska* M & W
Western New England University *Massachusetts* M & W
Western Oregon University *Oregon* W
Western State Colorado University *Colorado* M & W
Western Texas College *Texas* M & W
Western Washington University *Washington* M & W
Western Wyoming Community College *Wyoming* M & W
Westfield State University *Massachusetts* M & W
Westminster College *Missouri* M & W
Westminster College *Pennsylvania* M & W
Westminster College *Utah* M & W
Westmont College *California* M & W
Westmoreland County Community College *Pennsylvania* M & W
Whatcom Community College *Washington* W
Wheaton College *Illinois* M & W
Wheaton College *Massachusetts* M & W
Wheeling Jesuit University *West Virginia* M & W
Wheelock College *Massachusetts* M & W
Whitman College *Washington* M & W
Whittier College *California* M & W
Whitworth University *Washington* M & W
Widener University *Pennsylvania* M & W
Wilfrid Laurier University *Ontario (Canada)* M & W
Wilkes University *Pennsylvania* M & W
Willamette University *Oregon* M & W
William Carey University *Mississippi* M & W
William Jessup University *California* M & W
William Jewell College *Missouri* M & W
William Paterson University of New Jersey *New Jersey* M & W
William Peace University *North Carolina* M & W
William Penn University *Iowa* M & W
William Woods University *Missouri* M & W
Williams Baptist College *Arkansas* M & W
Williams College *Massachusetts* M & W
Williamson College of the Trades *Pennsylvania* M
Wilmington College *Ohio* M & W
Wilson College *Pennsylvania* M & W
Wingate University *North Carolina* M & W
Winona State University *Minnesota* W
Winthrop University *South Carolina* M & W
Wisconsin Lutheran College *Wisconsin* M & W
Wittenberg University *Ohio* M & W
Wofford College *South Carolina* M & W
Worcester Polytechnic Institute *Massachusetts* M & W
Worcester State University *Massachusetts* M & W
Wright State University *Ohio* M & W
Xavier University *Ohio* M & W
Yakima Valley Community College *Washington* W
Yale University *Connecticut* M & W
Yavapai College *Arizona* M
Yeshiva University *New York* M & W
York College *Nebraska* M & W
York College of the City University of New York *New York* M
York College of Pennsylvania *Pennsylvania* M & W
York University *Ontario (Canada)* M & W
Young Harris College *Georgia* M & W
Youngstown State University *Ohio* W
Yuba College *California* M & W

Softball

Abilene Christian University *Texas* W
Abraham Baldwin Agricultural College *Georgia* W
Academy of Art University *California* W
Adams State University *Colorado* W
Adelphi University *New York* W
Adirondack Community College *New York* W
Adrian College *Michigan* W
Agnes Scott College *Georgia* W
Alabama Southern Community College *Alabama* W
Alabama State University *Alabama* W
Albany State University *Georgia* W
Albertus Magnus College *Connecticut* W
Albion College *Michigan* W
Albright College *Pennsylvania* W

Alcorn State University *Mississippi* W
Alderson Broaddus University *West Virginia* W
Alfred University *New York* W
Alice Lloyd College *Kentucky* W
Allan Hancock College *California* W
Allegany College of Maryland *Maryland* W
Allegheny College *Pennsylvania* W
Allen Community College *Kansas* W
Alma College *Michigan* W
Alpena Community College *Michigan* W
Alvernia University *Pennsylvania* W
Alverno College *Wisconsin* W
Alvin Community College *Texas* W
American International College *Massachusetts* W
American River College *California* W
Amherst College *Massachusetts* W
Ancilla College *Indiana* W
Anderson University *Indiana* W
Anderson University *South Carolina* W
Andrew College *Georgia* W
Angelina College *Texas* W
Angelo State University *Texas* W
Anna Maria College *Massachusetts* W
Anne Arundel Community College *Maryland* W
Anoka-Ramsey Community College *Minnesota* W
Antelope Valley College *California* W
Appalachian State University *North Carolina* W
Aquinas College *Michigan* W
Arcadia University *Pennsylvania* W
Arizona Christian University *Arizona* W
Arizona State University at the Downtown Phoenix campus *Arizona* W
Arizona State University at the Polytechnic campus *Arizona* W
Arizona State University at the Tempe campus *Arizona* W
Arizona State University at the West campus *Arizona* W
Arizona Western College *Arizona* W
Arkansas Tech University *Arkansas* W
Armstrong State University *Georgia* W
Asbury University *Kentucky* W
Ashford University *California* W
Ashland University *Ohio* W
Assumption College *Massachusetts* W
Auburn University *Alabama* W
Auburn University at Montgomery *Alabama* W
Augsburg College *Minnesota* W
Augusta University *Georgia* W
Augustana College *Illinois* W
Augustana University *South Dakota* W
Aurora University *Illinois* W
Austin College *Texas* W
Austin Peay State University *Tennessee* W
Ave Maria University *Florida* W
Averett University *Virginia* W
Avila University *Missouri* W
Azusa Pacific University *California* W
Babson College *Massachusetts* W
Baker University *Kansas* W
Bakersfield College *California* W
Baldwin Wallace University *Ohio* W
Ball State University *Indiana* W
Barnard College *New York* W
Barry University *Florida* W
Barton College *North Carolina* W
Barton County Community College *Kansas* W
Baruch College of the City University of New York *New York* W
Bates College *Maine* W
Bay Path University *Massachusetts* W
Baylor University *Texas* W
Becker College *Massachusetts* W
Belhaven University *Mississippi* W
Bellarmine University *Kentucky* W
Bellevue College *Washington* W
Belmont Abbey College *North Carolina* W
Belmont University *Tennessee* W
Beloit College *Wisconsin* W
Bemidji State University *Minnesota* W
Benedict College *South Carolina* W
Benedictine College *Kansas* W
Benedictine University *Illinois* W
Bentley University *Massachusetts* W

Berea College *Kentucky* W
Bergen Community College *New Jersey* W
Berry College *Georgia* W
Bethany College *Kansas* W
Bethany College *West Virginia* W
Bethany Lutheran College *Minnesota* W
Bethel College *Indiana* W
Bethel University *Minnesota* W
Bethel University *Tennessee* W
Bethune-Cookman University *Florida* W
Big Bend Community College *Washington* W
Binghamton University, State University of New York *New York* W
Biola University *California* W
Birmingham-Southern College *Alabama* W
Bishop State Community College *Alabama* W
Bismarck State College *North Dakota* W
Black Hawk College *Illinois* W
Blackburn College *Illinois* W
Blinn College *Texas* W
Bloomfield College *New Jersey* W
Bloomsburg University of Pennsylvania *Pennsylvania* W
Blue Mountain College *Mississippi* W
Blue Mountain Community College *Oregon* W
Bluefield College *Virginia* W
Bluefield State College *West Virginia* W
Bluffton University *Ohio* W
Boise State University *Idaho* W
Bossier Parish Community College *Louisiana* W
Boston College *Massachusetts* W
Boston University *Massachusetts* W
Bowdoin College *Maine* W
Bowie State University *Maryland* W
Bowling Green State University *Ohio* W
Bradley University *Illinois* W
Brandeis University *Massachusetts* W
Brenau University *Georgia* W
Brescia University *Kentucky* W
Brevard College *North Carolina* W
Brewton-Parker College *Georgia* W
Briar Cliff University *Iowa* W
Bridgewater College *Virginia* W
Bridgewater State University *Massachusetts* W
Brigham Young University *Utah* W
Brigham Young University - Hawaii *Hawaii* W
Brookdale Community College *New Jersey* W
Brooklyn College of the City University of New York *New York* W
Broome Community College *New York* W
Broward College *Florida* W
Brown University *Rhode Island* W
Bryan College *Tennessee* W
Bryant University *Rhode Island* W
Bucknell University *Pennsylvania* W
Buena Vista University *Iowa* W
Buffalo State College, State University of New York *New York* W
Butler Community College *Kansas* W
Butler County Community College *Pennsylvania* W
Butler University *Indiana* W
Butte College *California* W
Cabrillo College *California* W
Cabrini University *Pennsylvania* W
Cairn University *Pennsylvania* W
Caldwell University *New Jersey* W
Calhoun Community College *Alabama* W
California Baptist University *California* W
California Lutheran University *California* W
California Polytechnic State University, San Luis Obispo *California* W
California State University, Bakersfield *California* W
California State University, Chico *California* W
California State University, Dominguez Hills *California* W
California State University, East Bay *California* W
California State University, Fresno *California* W
California State University, Fullerton *California* W
California State University, Long Beach *California* W
California State University, Monterey Bay *California* W
California State University, Northridge *California* W

M = Men; W = Women

California State University, Sacramento *California* W
California State University, San Bernardino *California* W
California State University, San Marcos *California* W
California State University, Stanislaus *California* W
California University of Pennsylvania *Pennsylvania* W
Calumet College of Saint Joseph *Indiana* W
Calvin College *Michigan* W
Camden County College *New Jersey* W
Cameron University *Oklahoma* W
Campbell University *North Carolina* W
Campbellsville University *Kentucky* W
Canisius College *New York* W
Capital University *Ohio* W
Cardinal Stritch University *Wisconsin* W
Caribbean University *Puerto Rico* W
Carl Albert State College *Oklahoma* M
Carleton College *Minnesota* W
Carlow University *Pennsylvania* W
Carroll College *Montana* W
Carson-Newman University *Tennessee* W
Carthage College *Wisconsin* W
Case Western Reserve University *Ohio* W
Castleton University *Vermont* W
Catawba College *North Carolina* W
The Catholic University of America *District of Columbia* W
Cayuga County Community College *New York* W
Cazenovia College *New York* W
Cecil College *Maryland* W
Cedar Crest College *Pennsylvania* W
Cedarville University *Ohio* W
Centenary College *New Jersey* W
Centenary College of Louisiana *Louisiana* W
Central Alabama Community College *Alabama* W
Central Arizona College *Arizona* W
Central Baptist College *Arkansas* W
Central Christian College of Kansas *Kansas* W
Central College *Iowa* W
Central Community College - Columbus Campus *Nebraska* W
Central Connecticut State University *Connecticut* W
Central Lakes College *Minnesota* W
Central Maine Community College *Maine* W
Central Methodist University *Missouri* W
Central Michigan University *Michigan* W
Central Washington University *Washington* W
Centralia College *Washington* W
Centre College *Kentucky* W
Century College *Minnesota* W
Cerritos College *California* W
Chabot College *California* W
Chadron State College *Nebraska* W
Chaffey College *California* W
Chaminade University of Honolulu *Hawaii* W
Chandler-Gilbert Community College *Arizona* W
Chapman University *California* W
Charleston Southern University *South Carolina* W
Chatham University *Pennsylvania* W
Chattahoochee Valley Community College *Alabama* W
Chattanooga State Community College *Tennessee* W
Chemeketa Community College *Oregon* W
Chesapeake College *Maryland* W
Chestnut Hill College *Pennsylvania* W
Chipola College *Florida* W
Chowan University *North Carolina* W
Christendom College *Virginia* W
Christian Brothers University *Tennessee* W
Christopher Newport University *Virginia* W
Cisco College *Texas* W
Citrus College *California* W
City College of the City University of New York *New York* W
City College of San Francisco *California* W
Clackamas Community College *Oregon* W
Claflin University *South Carolina* W
Claremont McKenna College *California* W
Clarendon College *Texas* W
Clarion University of Pennsylvania *Pennsylvania* W

Clark Atlanta University *Georgia* W
Clark College *Washington* W
Clark State Community College *Ohio* W
Clark University *Massachusetts* W
Clarke University *Iowa* W
Clarkson University *New York* W
Cleary University *Michigan* W
Clemson University *South Carolina* W
Cleveland State Community College *Tennessee* W
Cleveland State University *Ohio* W
Clinton Community College *Iowa* W
Cloud County Community College *Kansas* W
Coahoma Community College *Mississippi* W
Coastal Carolina University *South Carolina* W
Coe College *Iowa* W
Coffeyville Community College *Kansas* W
Coker College *South Carolina* W
Colby College *Maine* W
Colby Community College *Kansas* W
Colby-Sawyer College *New Hampshire* W
Colgate University *New York* W
The College at Brockport, State University of New York *New York* W
College of the Canyons *California* W
College of Central Florida *Florida* W
College of Charleston *South Carolina* W
College of Coastal Georgia *Georgia* W
College of the Desert *California* W
College of DuPage *Illinois* M & W
College of the Holy Cross *Massachusetts* W
The College of Idaho *Idaho* W
College of Lake County *Illinois* W
College of Marin *California* W
College of Mount Saint Vincent *New York* W
The College of New Jersey *New Jersey* W
The College of New Rochelle *New York* W
College of the Redwoods *California* W
College of Saint Benedict *Minnesota* W
College of Saint Elizabeth *New Jersey* W
College of St. Joseph *Vermont* W
College of Saint Mary *Nebraska* W
The College of Saint Rose *New York* W
The College of St. Scholastica *Minnesota* W
College of San Mateo *California* W
College of the Sequoias *California* W
College of the Siskiyous *California* W
College of Southern Idaho *Idaho* W
College of Southern Maryland *Maryland* W
College of Staten Island of the City University of New York *New York* W
The College of Wooster *Ohio* W
Colorado Christian University *Colorado* W
The Colorado College *Colorado* W
Colorado Mesa University *Colorado* W
Colorado Northwestern Community College *Colorado* W
Colorado School of Mines *Colorado* W
Colorado State University *Colorado* W
Colorado State University - Pueblo *Colorado* W
Columbia Basin College *Washington* W
Columbia College *Missouri* W
Columbia College *South Carolina* W
Columbia-Greene Community College *New York* W
Columbia State Community College *Tennessee* W
Columbia University *New York* W
Columbia University, School of General Studies *New York* W
Columbus State University *Georgia* W
Community College of Allegheny County *Pennsylvania* W
Community College of Baltimore County *Maryland* W
Community College of Rhode Island *Rhode Island* W
Concord University *West Virginia* W
Concordia College *Minnesota* W
Concordia College Alabama *Alabama* W
Concordia College - New York *New York* W
Concordia University *Oregon* W
Concordia University Ann Arbor *Michigan* W
Concordia University Chicago *Illinois* W
Concordia University Irvine *California* W
Concordia University, Nebraska *Nebraska* W
Concordia University, St. Paul *Minnesota* W

Concordia University Texas *Texas* W
Concordia University Wisconsin *Wisconsin* W
Connors State College *Oklahoma* W
Contra Costa College *California* W
Copiah-Lincoln Community College *Mississippi* W
Coppin State University *Maryland* W
Corban University *Oregon* W
Cornell College *Iowa* W
Cornell University *New York* W
Cornerstone University *Michigan* W
Corning Community College *New York* W
Cottey College *Missouri* W
County College of Morris *New Jersey* W
Covenant College *Georgia* W
Cowley County Community College and Area Vocational - Technical School *Kansas* W
Creighton University *Nebraska* W
Crown College *Minnesota* W
Cuesta College *California* W
Culver-Stockton College *Missouri* W
Cumberland County College *New Jersey* W
Cumberland University *Tennessee* W
Curry College *Massachusetts* W
Cuyahoga Community College *Ohio* W
Cypress College *California* W
Dakota College at Bottineau *North Dakota* W
Dakota County Technical College *Minnesota* W
Dakota State University *South Dakota* W
Dakota Wesleyan University *South Dakota* W
Dalton State College *Georgia* M & W
Daniel Webster College *New Hampshire* W
Danville Area Community College *Illinois* W
Dartmouth College *New Hampshire* W
Darton State College *Georgia* W
Davenport University *Michigan* M & W
Davis & Elkins College *West Virginia* W
Dawson Community College *Montana* W
Daytona State College *Florida* W
De Anza College *California* W
Dean College *Massachusetts* W
Defiance College *Ohio* W
Delaware County Community College *Pennsylvania* W
Delaware State University *Delaware* W
Delaware Technical & Community College, Jack F. Owens Campus *Delaware* W
Delaware Technical & Community College, Stanton/Wilmington Campus *Delaware* W
Delaware Technical & Community College, Terry Campus *Delaware* W
Delaware Valley University *Pennsylvania* W
Delta College *Michigan* W
Delta State University *Mississippi* W
Denison University *Ohio* W
DePaul University *Illinois* W
DePauw University *Indiana* W
DeSales University *Pennsylvania* W
Diablo Valley College *California* W
Dickinson College *Pennsylvania* W
Dickinson State University *North Dakota* W
Dixie State University *Utah* W
Doane University *Nebraska* W
Dodge City Community College *Kansas* W
Dominican College *New York* W
Dominican University *Illinois* W
Dominican University of California *California* W
Dordt College *Iowa* W
Drake University *Iowa* W
Drew University *New Jersey* W
Drexel University *Pennsylvania* W
Drury University *Missouri* W
Duke University *North Carolina* M & W
Dutchess Community College *New York* W
Dyersburg State Community College *Tennessee* W
D'Youville College *New York* W
East Carolina University *North Carolina* W
East Central College *Missouri* W
East Central Community College *Mississippi* W
East Central University *Oklahoma* W
East Los Angeles College *California* W
East Mississippi Community College *Mississippi* W
East Stroudsburg University of Pennsylvania *Pennsylvania* W
East Tennessee State University *Tennessee* W

M = Men; W = Women

East Texas Baptist University *Texas* W
Eastern Arizona College *Arizona* W
Eastern Connecticut State University *Connecticut* W
Eastern Florida State College *Florida* W
Eastern Illinois University *Illinois* W
Eastern Kentucky University *Kentucky* W
Eastern Mennonite University *Virginia* W
Eastern Michigan University *Michigan* W
Eastern Nazarene College *Massachusetts* W
Eastern New Mexico University *New Mexico* W
Eastern Oklahoma State College *Oklahoma* W
Eastern Oregon University *Oregon* W
Eastern University *Pennsylvania* W
Eastern Washington University *Washington* W
Eckerd College *Florida* W
Edgewood College *Wisconsin* W
Edinboro University of Pennsylvania *Pennsylvania* W
Edmonds Community College *Washington* W
El Paso Community College *Texas* W
Elgin Community College *Illinois* W
Elizabeth City State University *North Carolina* W
Elizabethtown College *Pennsylvania* W
Ellsworth Community College *Iowa* W
Elmhurst College *Illinois* W
Elmira College *New York* W
Elms College *Massachusetts* W
Elon University *North Carolina* W
Embry-Riddle Aeronautical University - Daytona *Florida* W
Embry-Riddle Aeronautical University - Prescott *Arizona* W
Emerson College *Massachusetts* W
Emmanuel College *Georgia* W
Emmanuel College *Massachusetts* W
Emory & Henry College *Virginia* W
Emory University *Georgia* W
Emporia State University *Kansas* W
Endicott College *Massachusetts* W
Enterprise State Community College *Alabama* W
Erie Community College *New York* W
Erie Community College, North Campus *New York* W
Erie Community College, South Campus *New York* W
Erskine College *South Carolina* W
Eureka College *Illinois* W
Evangel University *Missouri* W
Everett Community College *Washington* W
Fairfield University *Connecticut* W
Fairleigh Dickinson University, College at Florham *New Jersey* W
Fairleigh Dickinson University, Metropolitan Campus *New Jersey* W
Fairmont State University *West Virginia* W
Farmingdale State College *New York* W
Faulkner University *Alabama* W
Fayetteville State University *North Carolina* W
Feather River College *California* W
Felician University *New Jersey* W
Ferris State University *Michigan* W
Ferrum College *Virginia* W
Finger Lakes Community College *New York* W
Finlandia University *Michigan* W
Fisher College *Massachusetts* W
Fisk University *Tennessee* W
Fitchburg State University *Massachusetts* W
Flagler College *Florida* W
Florida Agricultural and Mechanical University *Florida* W
Florida Atlantic University *Florida* W
Florida Gulf Coast University *Florida* W
Florida Institute of Technology *Florida* W
Florida International University *Florida* W
Florida Southern College *Florida* W
Florida SouthWestern State College *Florida* W
Florida State College at Jacksonville *Florida* W
Florida State University *Florida* W
Fond du Lac Tribal and Community College *Minnesota* W
Fontbonne University *Missouri* W
Foothill College *California* W
Fordham University *New York* W

Fort Lewis College *Colorado* W
Fort Scott Community College *Kansas* W
Framingham State University *Massachusetts* W
Francis Marion University *South Carolina* W
Franciscan University of Steubenville *Ohio* W
Frank Phillips College *Texas* W
Franklin College *Indiana* W
Franklin & Marshall College *Pennsylvania* W
Franklin Pierce University *New Hampshire* W
Frederick Community College *Maryland* W
Freed-Hardeman University *Tennessee* W
Fresno City College *California* W
Friends University *Kansas* W
Frostburg State University *Maryland* W
Fullerton College *California* W
Fulton-Montgomery Community College *New York* W
Furman University *South Carolina* W
Gadsden State Community College *Alabama* W
Gallaudet University *District of Columbia* W
Galveston College *Texas* W
Gannon University *Pennsylvania* W
Garden City Community College *Kansas* W
Gardner-Webb University *North Carolina* W
Garrett College *Maryland* W
GateWay Community College *Arizona* W
Gateway Community College *Connecticut* W
Gavilan College *California* W
Genesee Community College *New York* W
Geneva College *Pennsylvania* W
George C. Wallace Community College *Alabama* W
George Fox University *Oregon* W
George Mason University *Virginia* W
Georgetown College *Kentucky* W
Georgetown University *District of Columbia* W
Georgia College & State University *Georgia* W
Georgia Gwinnett College *Georgia* W
Georgia Highlands College *Georgia* M & W
Georgia Institute of Technology *Georgia* W
Georgia Military College *Georgia* W
Georgia Southern University *Georgia* W
Georgia Southwestern State University *Georgia* W
Georgia State University *Georgia* W
Georgian Court University *New Jersey* W
Gettysburg College *Pennsylvania* W
Glen Oaks Community College *Michigan* W
Glendale Community College *Arizona* W
Glendale Community College *California* W
Glenville State College *West Virginia* W
Golden West College *California* W
Goldey-Beacom College *Delaware* W
Gordon College *Massachusetts* W
Gordon State College *Georgia* W
Goshen College *Indiana* W
Grace College *Indiana* W
Graceland University *Iowa* W
Grambling State University *Louisiana* W
Grand Canyon University *Arizona* W
Grand Rapids Community College *Michigan* W
Grand Valley State University *Michigan* W
Grand View University *Iowa* W
Grays Harbor College *Washington* W
Grayson College *Texas* W
Green River College *Washington* W
Greensboro College *North Carolina* W
Greenville College *Illinois* W
Grinnell College *Iowa* W
Grossmont College *California* W
Grove City College *Pennsylvania* W
Guilford College *North Carolina* W
Gulf Coast State College *Florida* W
Gustavus Adolphus College *Minnesota* W
Gwynedd Mercy University *Pennsylvania* W
Hagerstown Community College *Maryland* W
Hamilton College *New York* W
Hamline University *Minnesota* W
Hampton University *Virginia* W
Hannibal-LaGrange University *Missouri* W
Hanover College *Indiana* W
Hardin-Simmons University *Texas* W
Harford Community College *Maryland* W
Harper College *Illinois* W
Harris-Stowe State University *Missouri* W
Harvard University *Massachusetts* W

Harvey Mudd College *California* W
Haskell Indian Nations University *Kansas* W
Hastings College *Nebraska* W
Haverford College *Pennsylvania* W
Hawai'i Pacific University *Hawaii* W
Heartland Community College *Illinois* W
Heidelberg University *Ohio* W
Henderson State University *Arkansas* W
Hendrix College *Arkansas* W
Henry Ford College *Michigan* W
Herkimer County Community College *New York* W
Hesston College *Kansas* W
Hibbing Community College *Minnesota* W
Highland Community College *Illinois* W
Highland Community College *Kansas* W
Highline College *Washington* W
Hilbert College *New York* W
Hill College *Texas* W
Hillsborough Community College *Florida* W
Hillsdale College *Michigan* W
Hillsdale Free Will Baptist College *Oklahoma* W
Hinds Community College *Mississippi* W
Hiram College *Ohio* W
Hiwassee College *Tennessee* W
Hofstra University *New York* W
Holmes Community College *Mississippi* W
Holy Family University *Pennsylvania* W
Holy Names University *California* W
Holyoke Community College *Massachusetts* W
Hood College *Maryland* W
Hope College *Michigan* W
Hope International University *California* W
Houghton College *New York* W
Houston Baptist University *Texas* W
Howard College *Texas* W
Howard Payne University *Texas* W
Howard University *District of Columbia* W
Hudson Valley Community College *New York* W
Humboldt State University *California* W
Huntingdon College *Alabama* W
Huntington University *Indiana* W
Husson University *Maine* W
Huston-Tillotson University *Texas* W
Hutchinson Community College *Kansas* W
Idaho State University *Idaho* W
Illinois Central College *Illinois* W
Illinois College *Illinois* W
Illinois Eastern Community Colleges, Lincoln Trail College *Illinois* W
Illinois Eastern Community Colleges, Olney Central College *Illinois* W
Illinois Eastern Community Colleges, Wabash Valley College *Illinois* W
Illinois State University *Illinois* W
Illinois Valley Community College *Illinois* W
Illinois Wesleyan University *Illinois* W
Immaculata University *Pennsylvania* W
Imperial Valley College *California* W
Indian Hills Community College *Iowa* W
Indian River State College *Florida* W
Indiana State University *Indiana* W
Indiana Tech *Indiana* W
Indiana University Bloomington *Indiana* W
Indiana University of Pennsylvania *Pennsylvania* W
Indiana University - Purdue University Fort Wayne *Indiana* W
Indiana University - Purdue University Indianapolis *Indiana* W
Indiana University Southeast *Indiana* W
Indiana Wesleyan University *Indiana* W
Inter American University of Puerto Rico, Aguadilla Campus *Puerto Rico* M & W
Inter American University of Puerto Rico, Barranquitas Campus *Puerto Rico* M & W
Inter American University of Puerto Rico, Bayamón Campus *Puerto Rico* M & W
Inter American University of Puerto Rico, Fajardo Campus *Puerto Rico* W
Inter American University of Puerto Rico, Ponce Campus *Puerto Rico* M & W
Inter American University of Puerto Rico, San Germán Campus *Puerto Rico* M & W
Iona College *New York* W
Iowa Central Community College *Iowa* W

M = Men; W = Women

Iowa Lakes Community College *Iowa* W
Iowa State University of Science and Technology *Iowa* W
Iowa Wesleyan University *Iowa* W
Iowa Western Community College *Iowa* W
Itasca Community College *Minnesota* W
Ithaca College *New York* W
Jackson College *Michigan* W
Jackson State Community College *Tennessee* W
Jackson State University *Mississippi* W
Jacksonville State University *Alabama* W
Jacksonville University *Florida* W
James H. Faulkner State Community College *Alabama* W
James Madison University *Virginia* W
Jamestown Community College *New York* W
Jarvis Christian College *Texas* W
Jefferson College *Missouri* W
Jefferson College of Health Sciences *Virginia* M & W
Jefferson Community College *New York* W
Jefferson Davis Community College *Alabama* W
John A. Logan College *Illinois* W
John Carroll University *Ohio* W
John Jay College of Criminal Justice of the City University of New York *New York* W
John Wesley University *North Carolina* W
John Wood Community College *Illinois* W
Johnson C. Smith University *North Carolina* W
Johnson County Community College *Kansas* W
Johnson State College *Vermont* W
Johnson & Wales University *Rhode Island* W
Joliet Junior College *Illinois* W
Jones County Junior College *Mississippi* W
Judson College *Alabama* W
Judson University *Illinois* W
Juniata College *Pennsylvania* W
Kalamazoo College *Michigan* W
Kalamazoo Valley Community College *Michigan* W
Kankakee Community College *Illinois* W
Kansas City Kansas Community College *Kansas* W
Kansas Wesleyan University *Kansas* W
Kaskaskia College *Illinois* W
Kean University *New Jersey* W
Keene State College *New Hampshire* W
Kellogg Community College *Michigan* W
Kennesaw State University *Georgia* W
Kent State University *Ohio* W
Kentucky Christian University *Kentucky* W
Kentucky State University *Kentucky* W
Kentucky Wesleyan College *Kentucky* W
Kenyon College *Ohio* W
Keuka College *New York* W
Keystone College *Pennsylvania* W
Kilgore College *Texas* W
King University *Tennessee* W
King's College *Pennsylvania* W
Kingsborough Community College of the City University of New York *New York* W
Kirkwood Community College *Iowa* W
Kishwaukee College *Illinois* W
Knox College *Illinois* W
Kutztown University of Pennsylvania *Pennsylvania* W
La Roche College *Pennsylvania* W
La Salle University *Pennsylvania* W
La Sierra University *California* W
Labette Community College *Kansas* W
Lackawanna College *Pennsylvania* W
Lafayette College *Pennsylvania* W
LaGrange College *Georgia* W
Lake Erie College *Ohio* W
Lake Forest College *Illinois* W
Lake Land College *Illinois* W
Lake Michigan College *Michigan* W
Lake Region State College *North Dakota* W
Lake-Sumter State College *Florida* W
Lake Superior State University *Michigan* W
Lakeland College *Wisconsin* W
Lakeland Community College *Ohio* W
Lamar Community College *Colorado* W
Lamar University *Texas* W
Lander University *South Carolina* W
Landmark College *Vermont* W

Lane College *Tennessee* W
Laney College *California* W
Langston University *Oklahoma* W
Lansing Community College *Michigan* W
Lasell College *Massachusetts* W
Lassen Community College District *California* W
Lawrence University *Wisconsin* W
Le Moyne College *New York* W
Lebanon Valley College *Pennsylvania* W
Lee University *Tennessee* W
Lees-McRae College *North Carolina* W
Lehigh Carbon Community College *Pennsylvania* W
Lehigh University *Pennsylvania* W
Lehman College of the City University of New York *New York* M & W
LeMoyne-Owen College *Tennessee* W
Lenoir-Rhyne University *North Carolina* W
Lesley University *Massachusetts* W
LeTourneau University *Texas* W
Lewis & Clark College *Oregon* W
Lewis and Clark Community College *Illinois* W
Lewis University *Illinois* W
Liberty University *Virginia* W
Limestone College *South Carolina* W
Lincoln Land Community College *Illinois* W
Lincoln Memorial University *Tennessee* W
Lincoln University *Missouri* W
Lincoln University *Pennsylvania* W
Lindenwood University *Missouri* W
Lindsey Wilson College *Kentucky* W
Linfield College *Oregon* W
Lipscomb University *Tennessee* W
Livingstone College *North Carolina* W
Lock Haven University of Pennsylvania *Pennsylvania* W
Long Beach City College *California* W
Long Island University - LIU Brooklyn *New York* W
Long Island University - LIU Post *New York* W
Longwood University *Virginia* W
Loras College *Iowa* W
Los Angeles Harbor College *California* W
Los Angeles Pierce College *California* W
Los Angeles Valley College *California* W
Los Medanos College *California* W
Louisburg College *North Carolina* W
Louisiana College *Louisiana* W
Louisiana State University and Agricultural & Mechanical College *Louisiana* W
Louisiana State University at Alexandria *Louisiana* W
Louisiana Tech University *Louisiana* W
Lourdes University *Ohio* W
Lower Columbia College *Washington* W
Loyola Marymount University *California* W
Loyola University Chicago *Illinois* W
Lubbock Christian University *Texas* W
Lurleen B. Wallace Community College *Alabama* W
Luther College *Iowa* W
Luzerne County Community College *Pennsylvania* W
Lycoming College *Pennsylvania* W
Lynchburg College *Virginia* W
Lyndon State College *Vermont* W
Lynn University *Florida* W
Lyon College *Arkansas* W
Macalester College *Minnesota* W
MacMurray College *Illinois* W
Macomb Community College *Michigan* W
Madison Area Technical College *Wisconsin* W
Madonna University *Michigan* W
Maine Maritime Academy *Maine* W
Malone University *Ohio* W
Manchester Community College *Connecticut* W
Manchester University *Indiana* W
Manhattan College *New York* W
Manhattanville College *New York* W
Mansfield University of Pennsylvania *Pennsylvania* W
Maranatha Baptist University *Wisconsin* W
Marian University *Indiana* W
Marian University *Wisconsin* W
Marietta College *Ohio* W
Marion Military Institute *Alabama* W

Marion Technical College *Ohio* W
Marist College *New York* W
Mars Hill University *North Carolina* W
Marshall University *West Virginia* W
Marshalltown Community College *Iowa* W
Martin Luther College *Minnesota* W
Martin Methodist College *Tennessee* W
Mary Baldwin College *Virginia* W
Maryville College *Tennessee* W
Maryville University of Saint Louis *Missouri* W
Marywood University *Pennsylvania* W
Massachusetts Bay Community College *Massachusetts* W
Massachusetts College of Liberal Arts *Massachusetts* W
Massachusetts Institute of Technology *Massachusetts* W
Massachusetts Maritime Academy *Massachusetts* W
Massasoit Community College *Massachusetts* W
Mayville State University *North Dakota* W
McDaniel College *Maryland* W
McHenry County College *Illinois* W
McKendree University *Illinois* W
McLennan Community College *Texas* W
McNeese State University *Louisiana* W
McPherson College *Kansas* W
Medaille College *New York* W
Mendocino College *California* W
Menlo College *California* W
Merced College *California* W
Mercer County Community College *New Jersey* W
Mercer University *Georgia* W
Mercy College *New York* W
Mercyhurst North East *Pennsylvania* W
Mercyhurst University *Pennsylvania* W
Meredith College *North Carolina* W
Meridian Community College *Mississippi* W
Merrimack College *Massachusetts* W
Mesa Community College *Arizona* W
Mesabi Range College *Minnesota* W
Messiah College *Pennsylvania* W
Methodist University *North Carolina* W
Metropolitan Community College - Kansas City *Missouri* W
Metropolitan State University of Denver *Colorado* W
Miami Dade College *Florida* W
Miami University *Ohio* M & W
Miami University Hamilton *Ohio* W
Miami University Middletown *Ohio* W
Michigan State University *Michigan* W
Michigan Technological University *Michigan* W
Mid-America Christian University *Oklahoma* W
Mid-America College of Funeral Service *Indiana* M & W
Mid-Plains Community College *Nebraska* W
MidAmerica Nazarene University *Kansas* W
Middle Georgia State University *Georgia* W
Middle Tennessee State University *Tennessee* W
Middlebury College *Vermont* W
Middlesex County College *New Jersey* W
Midland College *Texas* W
Midland University *Nebraska* W
Midway University *Kentucky* W
Midwestern State University *Texas* W
Miles College *Alabama* W
Millersville University of Pennsylvania *Pennsylvania* W
Milligan College *Tennessee* W
Millikin University *Illinois* W
Millsaps College *Mississippi* W
Milwaukee School of Engineering *Wisconsin* W
Mineral Area College *Missouri* W
Minnesota State Community and Technical College *Minnesota* W
Minnesota State University Mankato *Minnesota* W
Minnesota State University Moorhead *Minnesota* W
Minnesota West Community and Technical College *Minnesota* W
Minot State University *North Dakota* W
Misericordia University *Pennsylvania* W
Mission College *California* W
Mississippi College *Mississippi* W

M = Men; W = Women

Mississippi Delta Community College *Mississippi* W
Mississippi Gulf Coast Community College *Mississippi* W
Mississippi State University *Mississippi* W
Mississippi Valley State University *Mississippi* W
Missouri Baptist University *Missouri* W
Missouri Southern State University *Missouri* W
Missouri State University *Missouri* W
Missouri University of Science and Technology *Missouri* W
Missouri Valley College *Missouri* W
Missouri Western State University *Missouri* W
Mitchell College *Connecticut* W
Modesto Junior College *California* W
Mohawk Valley Community College *New York* W
Molloy College *New York* W
Monmouth College *Illinois* W
Monmouth University *New Jersey* W
Monroe College *New York* W
Monroe Community College *New York* W
Montana State University Billings *Montana* W
Montclair State University *New Jersey* W
Monterey Peninsula College *California* W
Montgomery College *Maryland* W
Montgomery County Community College *Pennsylvania* W
Montreat College *North Carolina* W
Moorpark College *California* W
Moraine Valley Community College *Illinois* W
Moravian College *Pennsylvania* W
Morehead State University *Kentucky* W
Morgan State University *Maryland* W
Morningside College *Iowa* W
Morris College *South Carolina* W
Morrisville State College *New York* W
Morton College *Illinois* W
Motlow State Community College *Tennessee* W
Mott Community College *Michigan* W
Mount Aloysius College *Pennsylvania* W
Mt. Hood Community College *Oregon* W
Mount Ida College *Massachusetts* W
Mount Marty College *South Dakota* W
Mount Mary University *Wisconsin* W
Mount Mercy University *Iowa* W
Mount St. Joseph University *Ohio* W
Mount Saint Mary College *New York* W
Mount St. Mary's University *Maryland* W
Mt. San Antonio College *California* W
Mt. San Jacinto College *California* W
Mount Vernon Nazarene University *Ohio* W
Muhlenberg College *Pennsylvania* W
Murray State College *Oklahoma* W
Murray State University *Kentucky* W
Muscatine Community College *Iowa* W
Muskegon Community College *Michigan* W
Muskingum University *Ohio* W
Napa Valley College *California* W
Nassau Community College *New York* W
Navarro College *Texas* W
Nazareth College of Rochester *New York* W
Nebraska Wesleyan University *Nebraska* W
Neosho County Community College *Kansas* W
Neumann University *Pennsylvania* W
New England College *New Hampshire* W
New Jersey City University *New Jersey* W
New Mexico Highlands University *New Mexico* W
New Mexico State University *New Mexico* W
New York Institute of Technology *New York* W
New York University *New York* W
Newberry College *South Carolina* W
Newbury College *Massachusetts* W
Newman University *Kansas* W
NHTI, Concord's Community College *New Hampshire* W
Niagara County Community College *New York* W
Niagara University *New York* W
Nicholls State University *Louisiana* W
Nichols College *Massachusetts* W
Norfolk State University *Virginia* W
North Arkansas College *Arkansas* W
North Carolina Agricultural and Technical State University *North Carolina* W
North Carolina Central University *North Carolina* W
North Carolina State University *North Carolina* W

North Carolina Wesleyan College *North Carolina* W
North Central College *Illinois* W
North Central Missouri College *Missouri* W
North Central Texas College *Texas* W
North Central University *Minnesota* W
North Country Community College *New York* W
North Dakota State College of Science *North Dakota* W
North Dakota State University *North Dakota* W
North Greenville University *South Carolina* W
North Idaho College *Idaho* W
North Iowa Area Community College *Iowa* W
North Park University *Illinois* W
Northampton Community College *Pennsylvania* W
Northeast Mississippi Community College *Mississippi* W
Northeast Texas Community College *Texas* W
Northeastern Junior College *Colorado* W
Northeastern Oklahoma Agricultural and Mechanical College *Oklahoma* W
Northeastern State University *Oklahoma* W
Northeastern University *Massachusetts* M & W
Northern Essex Community College *Massachusetts* W
Northern Illinois University *Illinois* W
Northern Kentucky University *Kentucky* W
Northern Oklahoma College *Oklahoma* W
Northern State University *South Dakota* W
Northland College *Wisconsin* W
Northland Community and Technical College *Minnesota* W
Northwest Christian University *Oregon* W
Northwest Florida State College *Florida* W
Northwest Mississippi Community College *Mississippi* W
Northwest Missouri State University *Missouri* W
Northwest Nazarene University *Idaho* W
Northwest University *Washington* W
Northwestern College *Iowa* W
Northwestern Oklahoma State University *Oklahoma* W
Northwestern State University of Louisiana *Louisiana* W
Northwood University, Michigan Campus *Michigan* W
Northwood University, Texas Campus *Texas* W
Norwich University *Vermont* W
Notre Dame College *Ohio* W
Notre Dame of Maryland University *Maryland* W
Notre Dame de Namur University *California* W
Nova Southeastern University *Florida* W
Nyack College *New York* W
Oakland City University *Indiana* W
Oakland Community College *Michigan* W
Oakland University *Michigan* W
Oakton Community College *Illinois* W
Oberlin College *Ohio* W
Occidental College *California* W
Ocean County College *New Jersey* W
Odessa College *Texas* W
Ohio Christian University *Ohio* W
Ohio Dominican University *Ohio* W
Ohio Northern University *Ohio* W
The Ohio State University *Ohio* W
Ohio University *Ohio* W
Ohio University - Zanesville *Ohio* W
Ohio Valley University *West Virginia* W
Ohio Wesleyan University *Ohio* W
Ohlone College *California* W
Oklahoma Baptist University *Oklahoma* W
Oklahoma Christian University *Oklahoma* W
Oklahoma City University *Oklahoma* W
Oklahoma Panhandle State University *Oklahoma* W
Oklahoma State University *Oklahoma* W
Oklahoma Wesleyan University *Oklahoma* W
Old Dominion University *Virginia* W
Olivet College *Michigan* W
Olivet Nazarene University *Illinois* W
Olympic College *Washington* W
Onondaga Community College *New York* W
Orange Coast College *California* W
Orange County Community College *New York* W
Oregon Institute of Technology *Oregon* W

Oregon State University *Oregon* W
Otero Junior College *Colorado* W
Ottawa University *Kansas* W
Otterbein University *Ohio* W
Ouachita Baptist University *Arkansas* W
Our Lady of the Lake University of San Antonio *Texas* W
Owens Community College *Ohio* W
Oxnard College *California* W
Pace University *New York* W
Pace University, Pleasantville Campus *New York* W
Pacific Lutheran University *Washington* W
Pacific University *Oregon* W
Paine College *Georgia* W
Palm Beach Atlantic University *Florida* W
Palm Beach State College *Florida* W
Palomar College *California* W
Paradise Valley Community College *Arizona* W
Paris Junior College *Texas* W
Park University *Missouri* W
Parkland College *Illinois* W
Pasadena City College *California* W
Pasco-Hernando State College *Florida* W
Patrick Henry Community College *Virginia* W
Patten University *California* W
Pearl River Community College *Mississippi* W
Penn State Abington *Pennsylvania* W
Penn State Altoona *Pennsylvania* W
Penn State Beaver *Pennsylvania* M & W
Penn State Berks *Pennsylvania* W
Penn State Erie, The Behrend College *Pennsylvania* W
Penn State Fayette, The Eberly Campus *Pennsylvania* W
Penn State Greater Allegheny *Pennsylvania* W
Penn State Harrisburg *Pennsylvania* W
Penn State Hazleton *Pennsylvania* W
Penn State Mont Alto *Pennsylvania* W
Penn State New Kensington *Pennsylvania* W
Penn State Schuylkill *Pennsylvania* W
Penn State University Park *Pennsylvania* W
Penn State Worthington Scranton *Pennsylvania* W
Pennsylvania College of Technology *Pennsylvania* W
Pensacola State College *Florida* W
Peru State College *Nebraska* W
Pfeiffer University *North Carolina* W
Philadelphia University *Pennsylvania* W
Phoenix College *Arizona* W
Piedmont College *Georgia* W
Pierce College at Puyallup *Washington* W
Pine Manor College *Massachusetts* W
Pitt Community College *North Carolina* W
Pittsburg State University *Kansas* W
Pitzer College *California* W
Plymouth State University *New Hampshire* W
Point Park University *Pennsylvania* W
Point University *Georgia* W
Polk State College *Florida* W
Pomona College *California* W
Porterville College *California* W
Portland State University *Oregon* W
Post University *Connecticut* W
Potomac State College of West Virginia University *West Virginia* W
Prairie State College *Illinois* W
Prairie View A&M University *Texas* W
Pratt Community College *Kansas* W
Presbyterian College *South Carolina* W
Presentation College *South Dakota* W
Prince George's Community College *Maryland* W
Princeton University *New Jersey* W
Principia College *Illinois* W
Providence College *Rhode Island* W
Purchase College, State University of New York *New York* W
Purdue University *Indiana* W
Purdue University Northwest *Hammond, Indiana* W
Queens College of the City University of New York *New York* W
Queens University of Charlotte *North Carolina* W
Queensborough Community College of the City University of New York *New York* W
Quincy University *Illinois* W

M = Men; W = Women

Quinnipiac University *Connecticut* W
Quinsigamond Community College *Massachusetts* W
Radford University *Virginia* W
Rainy River Community College *Minnesota* W
Ramapo College of New Jersey *New Jersey* W
Randolph College *Virginia* W
Randolph-Macon College *Virginia* W
Ranger College *Texas* W
Rappahannock Community College *Virginia* W
Raritan Valley Community College *New Jersey* W
Reedley College *California* W
Regis College *Massachusetts* W
Regis University *Colorado* W
Reinhardt University *Georgia* W
Rend Lake College *Illinois* W
Rensselaer Polytechnic Institute *New York* W
Research College of Nursing *Missouri* W
Rhode Island College *Rhode Island* W
Rhodes College *Tennessee* W
Rice University *Texas* W
Rider University *New Jersey* W
Ridgewater College *Minnesota* W
Rio Hondo College *California* W
Ripon College *Wisconsin* W
Riverland Community College *Minnesota* W
Rivier University *New Hampshire* W
Roane State Community College *Tennessee* W
Roanoke College *Virginia* W
Robert Morris University *Pennsylvania* W
Robert Morris University Illinois *Illinois* W
Rochester College *Michigan* W
Rochester Community and Technical College *Minnesota* W
Rochester Institute of Technology *New York* W
Rock Valley College *Illinois* W
Rockford University *Illinois* W
Rockhurst University *Missouri* W
Rockland Community College *New York* W
Roger Williams University *Rhode Island* W
Rogers State University *Oklahoma* W
Rollins College *Florida* W
Roosevelt University *Illinois* W
Rose-Hulman Institute of Technology *Indiana* W
Rosemont College *Pennsylvania* W
Rowan College at Burlington County *New Jersey* W
Rowan College at Gloucester County *New Jersey* W
Rowan University *New Jersey* W
Rust College *Mississippi* W
Rutgers University - Camden *New Jersey* W
Rutgers University - New Brunswick *New Jersey* W
Sacramento City College *California* W
Sacred Heart University *Connecticut* W
Saddleback College *California* W
The Sage Colleges *New York* W
Saginaw Valley State University *Michigan* W
St. Ambrose University *Iowa* W
St. Andrews University *North Carolina* W
Saint Anselm College *New Hampshire* W
Saint Augustine's University *North Carolina* W
St. Bonaventure University *New York* W
St. Catherine University *Minnesota* W
St. Charles Community College *Missouri* W
St. Clair County Community College *Michigan* W
St. Cloud State University *Minnesota* W
St. Cloud Technical & Community College *Minnesota* W
St. Edward's University *Texas* W
Saint Francis University *Pennsylvania* W
St. Gregory's University *Oklahoma* W
St. John Fisher College *New York* W
St. Johns River State College *Florida* W
St. John's University *New York* W
Saint Joseph's College *Indiana* W
St. Joseph's College, Long Island Campus *New York* W
Saint Joseph's College of Maine *Maine* W
St. Joseph's College, New York *New York* W
Saint Joseph's University *Pennsylvania* W
Saint Katherine College *California* W
St. Lawrence University *New York* W
Saint Leo University *Florida* W

St. Louis College of Pharmacy *Missouri* W
St. Louis Community College *Missouri* W
Saint Louis University *Missouri* W
Saint Martin's University *Washington* W
Saint Mary-of-the-Woods College *Indiana* W
Saint Mary's College *Indiana* W
Saint Mary's College of California *California* W
St. Mary's University *Texas* W
Saint Mary's University of Minnesota *Minnesota* W
Saint Michael's College *Vermont* W
St. Norbert College *Wisconsin* W
St. Olaf College *Minnesota* W
Saint Peter's University *New Jersey* W
St. Petersburg College *Florida* W
St. Thomas Aquinas College *New York* W
St. Thomas University *Florida* W
Saint Vincent College *Pennsylvania* W
Saint Xavier University *Illinois* W
Salem International University *West Virginia* W
Salem State University *Massachusetts* W
Salisbury University *Maryland* W
Salt Lake Community College *Utah* W
Salve Regina University *Rhode Island* W
Sam Houston State University *Texas* W
Samford University *Alabama* W
San Diego Christian College *California* W
San Diego City College *California* W
San Diego Mesa College *California* W
San Diego State University *California* W
San Francisco State University *California* W
San Jacinto College District *Texas* W
San Joaquin Delta College *California* W
San Jose City College *California* W
San Jose State University *California* W
Santa Ana College *California* W
Santa Barbara City College *California* W
Santa Clara University *California* W
Santa Fe College *Florida* W
Santa Monica College *California* W
Santa Rosa Junior College *California* W
Sarah Lawrence College *New York* W
Sauk Valley Community College *Illinois* W
Savannah State University *Georgia* W
Schenectady County Community College *New York* W
Schoolcraft College *Michigan* W
Schreiner University *Texas* W
Scottsdale Community College *Arizona* W
Scripps College *California* W
Seattle University *Washington* W
Seminole State College *Oklahoma* W
Seminole State College of Florida *Florida* W
Seton Hall University *New Jersey* W
Seton Hill University *Pennsylvania* W
Sewanee: The University of the South *Tennessee* W
Seward County Community College and Area Technical School *Kansas* W
Shasta College *California* W
Shaw University *North Carolina* W
Shawnee Community College *Illinois* W
Shawnee State University *Ohio* W
Shelton State Community College *Alabama* W
Shenandoah University *Virginia* W
Shepherd University *West Virginia* W
Shippensburg University of Pennsylvania *Pennsylvania* W
Shoreline Community College *Washington* W
Shorter University *Georgia* W
Siena College *New York* W
Siena Heights University *Michigan* W
Sierra College *California* W
Simmons College *Massachusetts* W
Simon Fraser University *British Columbia (Canada)* W
Simpson College *Iowa* W
Simpson University *California* W
Skagit Valley College *Washington* W
Skidmore College *New York* W
Skyline College *California* W
Slippery Rock University of Pennsylvania *Pennsylvania* W
Smith College *Massachusetts* W
Snead State Community College *Alabama* W

Snow College *Utah* W
Solano Community College *California* W
Sonoma State University *California* W
South Carolina State University *South Carolina* W
South Dakota State University *South Dakota* W
South Florida State College *Florida* W
South Georgia State College *Georgia* W
South Mountain Community College *Arizona* W
South Puget Sound Community College *Washington* W
South Suburban College *Illinois* W
Southeast Community College, Lincoln Campus *Nebraska* W
Southeast Community College, Milford Campus *Nebraska* W
Southeast Missouri State University *Missouri* W
Southeastern Community College *Iowa* W
Southeastern Community College *North Carolina* W
Southeastern Illinois College *Illinois* W
Southeastern Louisiana University *Louisiana* W
Southeastern Oklahoma State University *Oklahoma* W
Southeastern University *Florida* W
Southern Arkansas University - Magnolia *Arkansas* W
Southern Connecticut State University *Connecticut* W
Southern Illinois University Carbondale *Illinois* W
Southern Illinois University Edwardsville *Illinois* W
Southern Maine Community College *Maine* W
Southern Nazarene University *Oklahoma* W
Southern New Hampshire University *New Hampshire* W
Southern Oregon University *Oregon* W
Southern State Community College *Ohio* W
Southern University and Agricultural and Mechanical College *Louisiana* W
Southern Utah University *Utah* W
Southern Vermont College *Vermont* W
Southern Virginia University *Virginia* W
Southern Wesleyan University *South Carolina* W
Southwest Baptist University *Missouri* W
Southwest Minnesota State University *Minnesota* W
Southwest Mississippi Community College *Mississippi* W
Southwestern Assemblies of God University *Texas* W
Southwestern Christian University *Oklahoma* W
Southwestern College *California* W
Southwestern College *Kansas* W
Southwestern Illinois College *Illinois* W
Southwestern Oklahoma State University *Oklahoma* W
Southwestern Oregon Community College *Oregon* W
Southwestern University *Texas* W
Spalding University *Kentucky* W
Spartanburg Methodist College *South Carolina* W
Spokane Community College *Washington* W
Spokane Falls Community College *Washington* W
Spoon River College *Illinois* W
Spring Arbor University *Michigan* W
Spring Hill College *Alabama* W
Springfield College *Massachusetts* W
Stanford University *California* W
Stanly Community College *North Carolina* W
State College of Florida Manatee-Sarasota *Florida* W
State University of New York College of Agriculture and Technology at Cobleskill *New York* W
State University of New York College at Cortland *New York* W
State University of New York College at Geneseo *New York* W
State University of New York College at Old Westbury *New York* W
State University of New York College at Oneonta *New York* W
State University of New York College at Potsdam *New York* W
State University of New York College of Technology at Alfred *New York* W

M = Men; W = Women

State University of New York College of Technology at Canton *New York* W
State University of New York College of Technology at Delhi *New York* W
State University of New York at Fredonia *New York* W
State University of New York at Oswego *New York* W
State University of New York at Plattsburgh *New York* W
State University of New York Polytechnic Institute *New York* W
Stephen F. Austin State University *Texas* W
Stephens College *Missouri* W
Sterling College *Kansas* W
Stetson University *Florida* W
Stevens Institute of Technology *New Jersey* W
Stevenson University *Maryland* W
Stillman College *Alabama* W
Stockton University *New Jersey* W
Stonehill College *Massachusetts* W
Stony Brook University, State University of New York *New York* W
Suffolk County Community College *New York* W
Suffolk University *Massachusetts* W
Sul Ross State University *Texas* W
Sullivan County Community College *New York* W
Summit University *Pennsylvania* W
Susquehanna University *Pennsylvania* W
Sussex County Community College *New Jersey* W
Swarthmore College *Pennsylvania* W
Sweet Briar College *Virginia* W
Syracuse University *New York* W
Tabor College *Kansas* W
Taft College *California* W
Talladega College *Alabama* W
Tallahassee Community College *Florida* W
Tarleton State University *Texas* W
Taylor University *Indiana* W
Temple College *Texas* W
Tennessee State University *Tennessee* W
Tennessee Technological University *Tennessee* W
Tennessee Wesleyan College *Tennessee* W
Texas A&M International University *Texas* W
Texas A&M University *Texas* W
Texas A&M University - Commerce *Texas* W
Texas A&M University - Corpus Christi *Texas* W
Texas A&M University - Kingsville *Texas* W
Texas College *Texas* W
Texas Lutheran University *Texas* W
Texas Southern University *Texas* W
Texas State University *Texas* M & W
Texas Tech University *Texas* W
Texas Wesleyan University *Texas* W
Texas Woman's University *Texas* W
Thiel College *Pennsylvania* W
Thomas College *Maine* W
Thomas More College *Kentucky* W
Thomas University *Georgia* W
Three Rivers Community College *Missouri* W
Tiffin University *Ohio* W
Tompkins Cortland Community College *New York* W
Towson University *Maryland* W
Transylvania University *Kentucky* W
Treasure Valley Community College *Oregon* W
Trevecca Nazarene University *Tennessee* W
Trine University *Indiana* W
Trinidad State Junior College *Colorado* W
Trinity Christian College *Illinois* W
Trinity College *Connecticut* W
Trinity International University *Illinois* W
Trinity University *Texas* W
Trinity Valley Community College *Texas* W
Trinity Washington University *District of Columbia* W
Triton College *Illinois* W
Troy University *Alabama* W
Truett-McConnell College *Georgia* W
Truman State University *Missouri* W
Tufts University *Massachusetts* W
Tusculum College *Tennessee* W
Tyler Junior College *Texas* W
Ulster County Community College *New York* W

Union College *Kentucky* W
Union College *New York* W
Union University *Tennessee* W
United States Air Force Academy *Colorado* W
United States Coast Guard Academy *Connecticut* W
United States Military Academy *New York* W
United States Naval Academy *Maryland* W
Universidad del Este *Puerto Rico* W
Universidad Metropolitana *Puerto Rico* W
Universidad del Turabo *Puerto Rico* M & W
The University of Akron *Ohio* W
The University of Alabama *Alabama* W
The University of Alabama at Birmingham *Alabama* W
The University of Alabama in Huntsville *Alabama* W
University at Albany, State University of New York *New York* W
The University of Arizona *Arizona* W
University of Arkansas *Arkansas* W
University of Arkansas at Monticello *Arkansas* W
University of Bridgeport *Connecticut* W
The University of British Columbia *British Columbia (Canada)* M & W
University at Buffalo, the State University of New York *New York* W
University of California, Berkeley *California* W
University of California, Davis *California* W
University of California, Los Angeles *California* W
University of California, Riverside *California* W
University of California, San Diego *California* W
University of California, Santa Barbara *California* W
University of California, Santa Cruz *California* W
University of Central Arkansas *Arkansas* W
University of Central Florida *Florida* W
University of Central Missouri *Missouri* W
University of Central Oklahoma *Oklahoma* W
University of Charleston *West Virginia* W
University of Chicago *Illinois* W
University of Cincinnati Clermont College *Ohio* W
University of Colorado Boulder *Colorado* W
University of Colorado Colorado Springs *Colorado* W
University of Connecticut *Connecticut* W
University of the Cumberlands *Kentucky* W
University of Dallas *Texas* W
University of Dayton *Ohio* W
University of Delaware *Delaware* W
University of Denver *Colorado* W
University of Detroit Mercy *Michigan* W
University of Dubuque *Iowa* W
University of Evansville *Indiana* W
The University of Findlay *Ohio* W
University of Florida *Florida* W
University of Georgia *Georgia* W
University of Great Falls *Montana* W
University of Hartford *Connecticut* W
University of Hawaii at Hilo *Hawaii* W
University of Hawaii at Manoa *Hawaii* W
University of Houston *Texas* W
University of Houston - Victoria *Texas* W
University of Illinois at Chicago *Illinois* W
University of Illinois at Springfield *Illinois* W
University of Illinois at Urbana - Champaign *Illinois* W
University of the Incarnate Word *Texas* W
University of Indianapolis *Indiana* W
The University of Iowa *Iowa* W
University of Jamestown *North Dakota* W
The University of Kansas *Kansas* W
University of Kentucky *Kentucky* W
University of La Verne *California* W
University of Louisiana at Lafayette *Louisiana* W
University of Louisiana at Monroe *Louisiana* W
University of Louisville *Kentucky* W
University of Maine *Maine* W
University of Maine at Farmington *Maine* W
University of Maine at Presque Isle *Maine* W
University of Mary *North Dakota* W
University of Mary Hardin-Baylor *Texas* W
University of Mary Washington *Virginia* W
University of Maryland, Baltimore County *Maryland* W
University of Maryland, College Park *Maryland* W

University of Maryland Eastern Shore *Maryland* W
University of Massachusetts Amherst *Massachusetts* W
University of Massachusetts Boston *Massachusetts* W
University of Massachusetts Dartmouth *Massachusetts* W
University of Massachusetts Lowell *Massachusetts* W
University of Memphis *Tennessee* W
University of Michigan *Michigan* W
University of Michigan - Dearborn *Michigan* W
University of Minnesota, Crookston *Minnesota* W
University of Minnesota, Duluth *Minnesota* W
University of Minnesota, Morris *Minnesota* W
University of Minnesota, Twin Cities Campus *Minnesota* W
University of Mississippi *Mississippi* W
University of Missouri *Missouri* W
University of Missouri - Kansas City *Missouri* W
University of Missouri - St. Louis *Missouri* W
University of Mobile *Alabama* W
University of Montana *Montana* W
University of Montevallo *Alabama* W
University of Mount Olive *North Carolina* W
University of Mount Union *Ohio* W
University of Nebraska at Kearney *Nebraska* W
University of Nebraska - Lincoln *Nebraska* W
University of Nebraska at Omaha *Nebraska* W
University of Nevada, Las Vegas *Nevada* W
University of Nevada, Reno *Nevada* W
University of New England *Maine* W
University of New Hampshire *New Hampshire* W
University of New Haven *Connecticut* W
University of New Mexico *New Mexico* W
University of North Alabama *Alabama* W
The University of North Carolina at Chapel Hill *North Carolina* W
The University of North Carolina at Charlotte *North Carolina* W
The University of North Carolina at Greensboro *North Carolina* W
The University of North Carolina at Pembroke *North Carolina* W
The University of North Carolina Wilmington *North Carolina* W
University of North Dakota *North Dakota* W
University of North Florida *Florida* W
University of North Georgia *Georgia* W
University of North Texas *Texas* M & W
University of Northern Colorado *Colorado* W
University of Northern Iowa *Iowa* W
University of Northwestern - St. Paul *Minnesota* W
University of Notre Dame *Indiana* W
University of Oklahoma *Oklahoma* W
University of Oregon *Oregon* W
University of the Pacific *California* W
University of Pennsylvania *Pennsylvania* W
University of Pikeville *Kentucky* W
University of Pittsburgh *Pennsylvania* W
University of Pittsburgh at Bradford *Pennsylvania* W
University of Pittsburgh at Greensburg *Pennsylvania* W
University of Puerto Rico in Aguadilla *Puerto Rico* W
University of Puerto Rico in Arecibo *Puerto Rico* W
University of Puerto Rico in Cayey *Puerto Rico* M & W
University of Puerto Rico in Humacao *Puerto Rico* W
University of Puerto Rico, Mayagüez Campus *Puerto Rico* W
University of Puerto Rico, Río Piedras Campus *Puerto Rico* M & W
University of Puerto Rico in Utuado *Puerto Rico* M & W
University of Puget Sound *Washington* W
University of Redlands *California* W
University of Rhode Island *Rhode Island* W
University of Rio Grande *Ohio* W
University of Rochester *New York* W
University of St. Francis *Illinois* W
University of Saint Francis *Indiana* W

M = Men; W = Women

University of Saint Joseph *Connecticut* W
University of Saint Mary *Kansas* W
University of St. Thomas *Minnesota* W
University of San Diego *California* W
University of San Francisco *California* M & W
University of Science and Arts of Oklahoma *Oklahoma* W
University of the Sciences *Pennsylvania* W
The University of Scranton *Pennsylvania* W
University of Sioux Falls *South Dakota* W
University of South Alabama *Alabama* W
University of South Carolina *South Carolina* W
University of South Carolina Aiken *South Carolina* W
University of South Carolina Beaufort *South Carolina* W
University of South Carolina Salkehatchie *South Carolina* W
University of South Carolina Upstate *South Carolina* W
The University of South Dakota *South Dakota* W
University of South Florida *Florida* W
University of Southern California *California* W
University of Southern Indiana *Indiana* W
University of Southern Maine *Maine* W
University of Southern Mississippi *Mississippi* W
University of the Southwest *New Mexico* W
The University of Tampa *Florida* W
The University of Tennessee *Tennessee* W
The University of Tennessee at Chattanooga *Tennessee* W
The University of Tennessee at Martin *Tennessee* W
The University of Texas at Arlington *Texas* W
The University of Texas at Austin *Texas* W
The University of Texas at Dallas *Texas* W
The University of Texas of the Permian Basin *Texas* W
The University of Texas at San Antonio *Texas* W
The University of Toledo *Ohio* W
The University of Tulsa *Oklahoma* W
University of Utah *Utah* W
University of Valley Forge *Pennsylvania* W
University of Virginia *Virginia* W
The University of Virginia's College at Wise *Virginia* W
University of Washington *Washington* W
The University of West Alabama *Alabama* W
University of West Florida *Florida* W
University of West Georgia *Georgia* W
The University of Western Ontario *Ontario (Canada)* W
University of Wisconsin - Eau Claire *Wisconsin* W
University of Wisconsin - Green Bay *Wisconsin* W
University of Wisconsin - La Crosse *Wisconsin* W
University of Wisconsin - Madison *Wisconsin* W
University of Wisconsin - Oshkosh *Wisconsin* W
University of Wisconsin - Parkside *Wisconsin* W
University of Wisconsin - Platteville *Wisconsin* W
University of Wisconsin - River Falls *Wisconsin* W
University of Wisconsin - Stevens Point *Wisconsin* W
University of Wisconsin - Stout *Wisconsin* W
University of Wisconsin - Superior *Wisconsin* W
University of Wisconsin - Whitewater *Wisconsin* W
University of Wyoming *Wyoming* W
Upper Iowa University *Iowa* W
Urbana University *Ohio* W
Ursinus College *Pennsylvania* W
Ursuline College *Ohio* W
Utah State University *Utah* W
Utah Valley University *Utah* W
Utica College *New York* W
Valdosta State University *Georgia* W
Valley City State University *North Dakota* W
Valparaiso University *Indiana* W
Vanguard University of Southern California *California* W
Ventura College *California* W
Vermilion Community College *Minnesota* W
Vermont Technical College *Vermont* W
Vernon College *Texas* W
Victor Valley College *California* W
Villanova University *Pennsylvania* W

Virginia State University *Virginia* W
Virginia Union University *Virginia* W
Virginia Wesleyan College *Virginia* W
Viterbo University *Wisconsin* W
Volunteer State Community College *Tennessee* W
Voorhees College *South Carolina* W
Wagner College *New York* W
Waldorf College *Iowa* W
Walla Walla Community College *Washington* W
Walla Walla University *Washington* W
Wallace State Community College *Alabama* W
Walsh University *Ohio* W
Walters State Community College *Tennessee* W
Warner University *Florida* W
Wartburg College *Iowa* W
Washburn University *Kansas* W
Washington Adventist University *Maryland* W
Washington College *Maryland* W
Washington & Jefferson College *Pennsylvania* W
Washington State University *Washington* W
Washington University in St. Louis *Missouri* W
Waubonsee Community College *Illinois* W
Wayne State College *Nebraska* W
Wayne State University *Michigan* W
Waynesburg University *Pennsylvania* W
Webber International University *Florida* W
Weber State University *Utah* W
Webster University *Missouri* W
Wellesley College *Massachusetts* W
Wells College *New York* W
Wenatchee Valley College *Washington* W
Wentworth Institute of Technology *Massachusetts* W
Wesley College *Delaware* W
Wesleyan College *Georgia* W
Wesleyan University *Connecticut* W
West Chester University of Pennsylvania *Pennsylvania* W
West Hills Community College *California* W
West Liberty University *West Virginia* W
West Texas A&M University *Texas* W
West Virginia State University *West Virginia* W
West Virginia University Institute of Technology *West Virginia* W
West Virginia Wesleyan College *West Virginia* W
Westchester Community College *New York* W
Western Carolina University *North Carolina* W
Western Connecticut State University *Connecticut* W
Western Illinois University *Illinois* W
Western Kentucky University *Kentucky* W
Western Michigan University *Michigan* W
Western Nebraska Community College *Nebraska* W
Western Nevada College *Nevada* W
Western New England University *Massachusetts* W
Western New Mexico University *New Mexico* W
Western Oklahoma State College *Oklahoma* W
Western Oregon University *Oregon* W
Western Texas College *Texas* W
Western Washington University *Washington* W
Westfield State University *Massachusetts* W
Westminster College *Missouri* M & W
Westminster College *Pennsylvania* W
Westmoreland County Community College *Pennsylvania* W
Wheaton College *Illinois* W
Wheaton College *Massachusetts* W
Wheeling Jesuit University *West Virginia* W
Wheelock College *Massachusetts* W
Whittier College *California* W
Whitworth University *Washington* W
Wichita State University *Kansas* W
Widener University *Pennsylvania* W
Wilkes University *Pennsylvania* W
Willamette University *Oregon* W
William Carey University *Mississippi* W
William Jessup University *California* W
William Jewell College *Missouri* W
William Paterson University of New Jersey *New Jersey* W
William Peace University *North Carolina* W
William Penn University *Iowa* W
William Woods University *Missouri* W

Williams Baptist College *Arkansas* W
Williams College *Massachusetts* W
Williston State College *North Dakota* W
Wilmington College *Ohio* W
Wilmington University *Delaware* W
Wilson College *Pennsylvania* W
Wingate University *North Carolina* W
Winona State University *Minnesota* W
Winston-Salem State University *North Carolina* M & W
Winthrop University *South Carolina* W
Wisconsin Lutheran College *Wisconsin* W
Wittenberg University *Ohio* W
Worcester Polytechnic Institute *Massachusetts* W
Worcester State University *Massachusetts* W
Wright State University *Ohio* W
Xavier University *Ohio* W
Yakima Valley Community College *Washington* W
Yale University *Connecticut* W
Yavapai College *Arizona* W
York College *Nebraska* W
York College of the City University of New York *New York* W
York College of Pennsylvania *Pennsylvania* W
Young Harris College *Georgia* W
Youngstown State University *Ohio* W
Yuba College *California* W

Squash

Amherst College *Massachusetts* M & W
Bard College *New York* M
Barnard College *New York* W
Bates College *Maine* M & W
Boston University *Massachusetts* M & W
Bowdoin College *Maine* M & W
Brown University *Rhode Island* M & W
Bryant University *Rhode Island* M & W
Bucknell University *Pennsylvania* M & W
Colby College *Maine* M & W
Colgate University *New York* M & W
Columbia University *New York* M & W
Columbia University, School of General Studies *New York* M & W
Connecticut College *Connecticut* M & W
Cornell University *New York* M & W
Dartmouth College *New Hampshire* M & W
Denison University *Ohio* M & W
Dickinson College *Pennsylvania* M & W
Drexel University *Pennsylvania* M & W
Duke University *North Carolina* M & W
Emory University *Georgia* M & W
Fordham University *New York* M
Franklin & Marshall College *Pennsylvania* M & W
Georgia State University *Georgia* M & W
Hamilton College *New York* M & W
Harvard University *Massachusetts* M & W
Haverford College *Pennsylvania* M & W
Hobart and William Smith Colleges *New York* M & W
Illinois Eastern Community Colleges, Frontier Community College *Illinois* W
Kenyon College *Ohio* M & W
Lafayette College *Pennsylvania* M
Lehigh University *Pennsylvania* M & W
Massachusetts Institute of Technology *Massachusetts* M
McGill University *Quebec (Canada)* M & W
McMaster University *Ontario (Canada)* M & W
Middlebury College *Vermont* M & W
Mount Holyoke College *Massachusetts* W
Northeastern University *Massachusetts* M & W
Princeton University *New Jersey* M & W
Queen's University at Kingston *Ontario (Canada)* M & W
Rensselaer Polytechnic Institute *New York* M & W
Rock Valley College *Illinois* W
St. Lawrence University *New York* M & W
Sewanee: The University of the South *Tennessee* M & W
Siena College *New York* M & W
Smith College *Massachusetts* W
Southeastern Community College *North Carolina* W
Stanford University *California* M & W
Swarthmore College *Pennsylvania* M & W

M = Men; W = Women

Trinity College *Connecticut* M & W
Tufts University *Massachusetts* M & W
United States Naval Academy *Maryland* M
University of Hartford *Connecticut* M & W
University of Mississippi *Mississippi* M & W
University of Pennsylvania *Pennsylvania* M & W
University of Richmond *Virginia* M & W
University of Rochester *New York* M
University of Southern California *California* M & W
University of Toronto *Ontario (Canada)* M & W
University of Waterloo *Ontario (Canada)* M & W
The University of Western Ontario *Ontario (Canada)* M & W
Vassar College *New York* M & W
Wellesley College *Massachusetts* W
Wesleyan University *Connecticut* M & W
Williams College *Massachusetts* M & W
Yale University *Connecticut* M & W

Swimming and Diving

Acadia University *Nova Scotia (Canada)* M & W
Adams State University *Colorado* M & W
Adelphi University *New York* M & W
Albion College *Michigan* M & W
Albright College *Pennsylvania* M & W
Alderson Broaddus University *West Virginia* M & W
Alfred University *New York* M & W
Allegheny College *Pennsylvania* M & W
Alma College *Michigan* M & W
American River College *California* M & W
American University *District of Columbia* M & W
American University of Puerto Rico *Bayamon, Puerto Rico* M & W
Amherst College *Massachusetts* M & W
Appalachian State University *North Carolina* M & W
Arcadia University *Pennsylvania* M & W
Arizona State University at the Downtown Phoenix campus *Arizona* M & W
Arizona State University at the Polytechnic campus *Arizona* M & W
Arizona State University at the Tempe campus *Arizona* M & W
Arizona State University at the West campus *Arizona* M & W
Asbury University *Kentucky* M & W
Ashland University *Ohio* M & W
Assumption College *Massachusetts* W
Auburn University *Alabama* M & W
Augsburg College *Minnesota* W
Augustana College *Illinois* M & W
Augustana University *South Dakota* W
Austin College *Texas* M & W
Azusa Pacific University *California* W
Babson College *Massachusetts* M & W
Baldwin Wallace University *Ohio* M & W
Ball State University *Indiana* M & W
Bard College *New York* M & W
Bard College at Simon's Rock *Massachusetts* M & W
Barnard College *New York* W
Baruch College of the City University of New York *New York* M & W
Bates College *Maine* M & W
Bayamón Central University *Puerto Rico* M & W
Bellarmine University *Kentucky* M & W
Beloit College *Wisconsin* M & W
Bentley University *Massachusetts* M & W
Berry College *Georgia* M & W
Bethany College *West Virginia* M & W
Binghamton University, State University of New York *New York* M & W
Biola University *California* M & W
Birmingham-Southern College *Alabama* M & W
Bloomsburg University of Pennsylvania *Pennsylvania* M & W
Boise State University *Idaho* W
Boston College *Massachusetts* M & W
Boston University *Massachusetts* M & W
Bowdoin College *Maine* M & W
Bowling Green State University *Ohio* W
Brandeis University *Massachusetts* M & W
Brenau University *Georgia* W
Bridgewater College *Virginia* M & W
Bridgewater State University *Massachusetts* M & W

Brigham Young University *Utah* M & W
Brock University *Ontario (Canada)* M & W
Brooklyn College of the City University of New York *New York* M & W
Brown University *Rhode Island* M & W
Bryant University *Rhode Island* M & W
Bryn Mawr College *Pennsylvania* W
Bucknell University *Pennsylvania* M & W
Buffalo State College, State University of New York *New York* M & W
Butler University *Indiana* M & W
Cabrillo College *California* M & W
Cabrini University *Pennsylvania* M & W
California Baptist University *California* M & W
California Institute of Technology *California* M & W
California Lutheran University *California* M & W
California Polytechnic State University, San Luis Obispo *California* M & W
California State University, Bakersfield *California* M & W
California State University, East Bay *California* W
California State University, Fresno *California* W
California State University, Northridge *California* M & W
California University of Pennsylvania *Pennsylvania* W
Calvin College *Michigan* M & W
Campbell University *North Carolina* W
Campbellsville University *Kentucky* M & W
Canisius College *New York* M & W
Carleton College *Minnesota* M & W
Carleton University *Ontario (Canada)* M & W
Carnegie Mellon University *Pennsylvania* M & W
Carroll University *Wisconsin* M & W
Carson-Newman University *Tennessee* M & W
Carthage College *Wisconsin* M & W
Case Western Reserve University *Ohio* M & W
Catawba College *North Carolina* M & W
The Catholic University of America *District of Columbia* M & W
Cazenovia College *New York* M & W
Cedar Crest College *Pennsylvania* W
Centenary College of Louisiana *Louisiana* M & W
Central Connecticut State University *Connecticut* W
Central Washington University *Washington* M & W
Centre College *Kentucky* M & W
Cerritos College *California* M & W
Chabot College *California* M & W
Chaffey College *California* M & W
Chapman University *California* M & W
Chatham University *Pennsylvania* M & W
Chowan University *North Carolina* M & W
Christopher Newport University *Virginia* M & W
Citrus College *California* W
Claremont McKenna College *California* M & W
Clarion University of Pennsylvania *Pennsylvania* M & W
Clark University *Massachusetts* M & W
Clarkson University *New York* M & W
Cleveland State University *Ohio* M & W
Coastal Carolina University *South Carolina* M & W
Coe College *Iowa* M & W
Colby College *Maine* M & W
Colby-Sawyer College *New Hampshire* M & W
Colgate University *New York* M & W
The College at Brockport, State University of New York *New York* M & W
College of the Canyons *California* M & W
College of the Holy Cross *Massachusetts* M & W
The College of Idaho *Idaho* M & W
College of Marin *California* M & W
College of Mount Saint Vincent *New York* M & W
The College of New Jersey *New Jersey* M & W
The College of New Rochelle *New York* W
College of Saint Benedict *Minnesota* W
College of Saint Mary *Nebraska* W
The College of Saint Rose *New York* M & W
College of San Mateo *California* M & W
College of the Sequoias *California* M & W
College of Staten Island of the City University of New York *New York* M & W
The College of William and Mary *Virginia* M & W
The College of Wooster *Ohio* M & W
The Colorado College *Colorado* M & W

Colorado Mesa University *Colorado* M & W
Colorado School of Mines *Colorado* M & W
Colorado State University *Colorado* M & W
Colorado State University - Pueblo *Colorado* W
Columbia College *South Carolina* W
Columbia University *New York* M & W
Columbia University, School of General Studies *New York* M & W
Concordia College *Minnesota* W
Concordia University of Edmonton *Alberta (Canada)* M & W
Concordia University Irvine *California* M & W
Connecticut College *Connecticut* M & W
Converse College *South Carolina* W
Cornell University *New York* M & W
Cuesta College *California* M & W
Cypress College *California* M & W
Dalhousie University *Nova Scotia (Canada)* M & W
Dartmouth College *New Hampshire* M & W
Darton State College *Georgia* M & W
Davidson College *North Carolina* M & W
De Anza College *California* M & W
Delta State University *Mississippi* M & W
Denison University *Ohio* M & W
DePauw University *Indiana* M & W
Diablo Valley College *California* M & W
Dickinson College *Pennsylvania* M & W
Drew University *New Jersey* M & W
Drexel University *Pennsylvania* M & W
Drury University *Missouri* M & W
Duke University *North Carolina* M & W
Duquesne University *Pennsylvania* W
East Carolina University *North Carolina* M & W
East Stroudsburg University of Pennsylvania *Pennsylvania* W
Eastern Connecticut State University *Connecticut* W
Eastern Illinois University *Illinois* M & W
Eastern Michigan University *Michigan* M & W
Edinboro University of Pennsylvania *Pennsylvania* M & W
El Camino College *California* M & W
Elizabethtown College *Pennsylvania* M & W
Elms College *Massachusetts* M & W
Elon University *North Carolina* M & W
Emmanuel College *Georgia* M & W
Emory & Henry College *Virginia* W
Emory University *Georgia* M & W
Eureka College *Illinois* M & W
Fairfield University *Connecticut* M & W
Fairleigh Dickinson University, College at Florham *New Jersey* M & W
Fairmont State University *West Virginia* M & W
Fashion Institute of Technology *New York* M & W
Ferrum College *Virginia* M & W
Florida Agricultural and Mechanical University *Florida* W
Florida Atlantic University *Florida* M & W
Florida Gulf Coast University *Florida* W
Florida Institute of Technology *Florida* M & W
Florida International University *Florida* W
Florida Southern College *Florida* M & W
Florida State University *Florida* M & W
Foothill College *California* M & W
Fordham University *New York* M & W
Franciscan University of Steubenville *Ohio* W
Franklin College *Indiana* M & W
Franklin & Marshall College *Pennsylvania* M & W
Fresno Pacific University *California* M & W
Frostburg State University *Maryland* M & W
Fullerton College *California* M & W
Furman University *South Carolina* M & W
Gallaudet University *District of Columbia* M & W
Gannon University *Pennsylvania* M & W
Gardner-Webb University *North Carolina* M & W
Genesee Community College *New York* M & W
George Mason University *Virginia* M & W
The George Washington University *District of Columbia* M & W
Georgetown University *District of Columbia* M & W
Georgia Institute of Technology *Georgia* M & W
Georgia Southern University *Georgia* W
Georgia State University *Georgia* M & W
Gettysburg College *Pennsylvania* M & W

M = Men; W = Women

Golden West College *California* M & W
Gordon College *Massachusetts* M & W
Goucher College *Maryland* M & W
Grand Canyon University *Arizona* M & W
Grand Valley State University *Michigan* M & W
Greensboro College *North Carolina* M & W
Grinnell College *Iowa* M & W
Grossmont College *California* M & W
Grove City College *Pennsylvania* M & W
Guilford College *North Carolina* M & W
Gustavus Adolphus College *Minnesota* M & W
Hamilton College *New York* M & W
Hamline University *Minnesota* M & W
Hampden-Sydney College *Virginia* M
Hartwick College *New York* M & W
Harvard University *Massachusetts* M & W
Harvey Mudd College *California* M & W
Henderson State University *Arkansas* M & W
Hendrix College *Arkansas* M & W
Herkimer County Community College *New York* M & W
Hillsdale College *Michigan* M & W
Hiram College *Ohio* M & W
Hobart and William Smith Colleges *New York* W
Hollins University *Virginia* W
Hood College *Maryland* M & W
Hope College *Michigan* M & W
Howard University *District of Columbia* M & W
Hunter College of the City University of New York *New York* W
Husson University *Maine* M & W
Illinois College *Illinois* M & W
Illinois Institute of Technology *Illinois* M & W
Illinois State University *Illinois* W
Illinois Wesleyan University *Illinois* M & W
Indian River State College *Florida* M & W
Indiana State University *Indiana* W
Indiana University Bloomington *Indiana* M & W
Indiana University of Pennsylvania *Pennsylvania* M & W
Indiana University - Purdue University Indianapolis *Indiana* M & W
Indiana Wesleyan University *Indiana* W
Inter American University of Puerto Rico, Aguadilla Campus *Puerto Rico* M & W
Inter American University of Puerto Rico, Bayamón Campus *Puerto Rico* M & W
Inter American University of Puerto Rico, Guayama Campus *Puerto Rico* M
Inter American University of Puerto Rico, Ponce Campus *Puerto Rico* M & W
Inter American University of Puerto Rico, San Germán Campus *Puerto Rico* M & W
Iona College *New York* M & W
Iowa Central Community College *Iowa* M & W
Iowa Lakes Community College *Iowa* M & W
Iowa State University of Science and Technology *Iowa* M & W
Ithaca College *New York* M & W
James Madison University *Virginia* W
Jamestown Community College *New York* M & W
John Carroll University *Ohio* M & W
John Jay College of Criminal Justice of the City University of New York *New York* W
Johns Hopkins University *Maryland* M & W
Juniata College *Pennsylvania* W
Kalamazoo College *Michigan* M & W
Keene State College *New Hampshire* M & W
Kenyon College *Ohio* M & W
King University *Tennessee* M & W
King's College *Pennsylvania* M & W
Knox College *Illinois* M & W
Kutztown University of Pennsylvania *Pennsylvania* W
La Salle University *Pennsylvania* M & W
Lafayette College *Pennsylvania* M & W
LaGrange College *Georgia* M & W
Lake Forest College *Illinois* M & W
Laurentian University *Ontario (Canada)* M & W
Lawrence University *Wisconsin* M & W
Le Moyne College *New York* M & W
Lebanon Valley College *Pennsylvania* M & W
Lehigh University *Pennsylvania* M & W

Lehman College of the City University of New York *New York* M & W
Lenoir-Rhyne University *North Carolina* M & W
Lewis & Clark College *Oregon* M & W
Lewis University *Illinois* M & W
Liberty University *Virginia* W
Life University *Georgia* W
Limestone College *South Carolina* M & W
Lindenwood University *Missouri* M & W
Lindsey Wilson College *Kentucky* M & W
Linfield College *Oregon* M & W
Lock Haven University of Pennsylvania *Pennsylvania* W
Long Beach City College *California* M & W
Long Island University - LIU Brooklyn *New York* W
Long Island University - LIU Post *New York* W
Loras College *Iowa* M & W
Los Angeles Pierce College *California* M & W
Los Angeles Trade-Technical College *California* M & W
Los Angeles Valley College *California* M & W
Louisiana State University and Agricultural & Mechanical College *Louisiana* M & W
Loyola Marymount University *California* W
Loyola University Maryland *Maryland* M & W
Loyola University New Orleans *Louisiana* M & W
Luther College *Iowa* M & W
Lycoming College *Pennsylvania* M & W
Lynn University *Florida* W
Macalester College *Minnesota* M & W
Malone University *Ohio* M & W
Manchester University *Indiana* M & W
Manhattan College *New York* M & W
Mansfield University of Pennsylvania *Pennsylvania* W
Marist College *New York* M & W
Mars Hill University *North Carolina* M & W
Marshall University *West Virginia* W
Mary Baldwin College *Virginia* W
Marymount University *Virginia* M & W
Maryville College *Tennessee* M & W
Maryville University of Saint Louis *Missouri* M & W
Marywood University *Pennsylvania* M & W
Massachusetts Institute of Technology *Massachusetts* M & W
McDaniel College *Maryland* M & W
McGill University *Quebec (Canada)* M & W
McKendree University *Illinois* M & W
McMaster University *Ontario (Canada)* M & W
McMurry University *Texas* M & W
Memorial University of Newfoundland *Newfoundland and Labrador (Canada)* M & W
Merced College *California* M & W
Merrimack College *Massachusetts* W
Messiah College *Pennsylvania* M & W
Miami University *Ohio* M & W
Michigan State University *Michigan* M & W
Michigan Technological University *Michigan* M & W
Middlebury College *Vermont* M & W
Millersville University of Pennsylvania *Pennsylvania* W
Milligan College *Tennessee* M & W
Millikin University *Illinois* M & W
Mills College *California* W
Minnesota State University Mankato *Minnesota* W
Minnesota State University Moorhead *Minnesota* W
Misericordia University *Pennsylvania* M & W
Missouri State University *Missouri* M & W
Missouri University of Science and Technology *Missouri* M
Modesto Junior College *California* M & W
Monmouth College *Illinois* M & W
Monroe Community College *New York* M & W
Montclair State University *New Jersey* M & W
Monterey Peninsula College *California* M & W
Morningside College *Iowa* M & W
Mount Allison University *New Brunswick (Canada)* M & W
Mount Holyoke College *Massachusetts* W
Mount Saint Mary College *New York* M & W
Mount St. Mary's University *Maryland* W
Mt. San Antonio College *California* M & W
Napa Valley College *California* M & W
Nazareth College of Rochester *New York* M & W

Nebraska Wesleyan University *Nebraska* M & W
New Jersey Institute of Technology *New Jersey* M & W
New Mexico State University *New Mexico* W
New York University *New York* M & W
Niagara University *New York* M & W
North Carolina Agricultural and Technical State University *North Carolina* W
North Carolina State University *North Carolina* M & W
North Central College *Illinois* M & W
North Lake College *Texas* M & W
Northeastern University *Massachusetts* W
Northern Arizona University *Arizona* W
Northern Illinois University *Illinois* M & W
Northern Michigan University *Michigan* M & W
Northern State University *South Dakota* W
Norwich University *Vermont* M & W
Notre Dame of Maryland University *Maryland* W
Nova Southeastern University *Florida* M & W
Oakland University *Michigan* M & W
Oberlin College *Ohio* M & W
Occidental College *California* M & W
Ohio Northern University *Ohio* M & W
The Ohio State University *Ohio* M & W
Ohio University *Ohio* W
Ohio Wesleyan University *Ohio* M & W
Ohlone College *California* M & W
Oklahoma Baptist University *Oklahoma* M & W
Old Dominion University *Virginia* M & W
Olivet College *Michigan* M & W
Orange Coast College *California* M & W
Oregon State University *Oregon* W
Ouachita Baptist University *Arkansas* M & W
Pace University *New York* M & W
Pace University, Pleasantville Campus *New York* M & W
Pacific Lutheran University *Washington* M & W
Pacific University *Oregon* M & W
Palo Alto College *Texas* M & W
Palomar College *California* M & W
Pasadena City College *California* M & W
Penn State Altoona *Pennsylvania* M & W
Penn State Erie, The Behrend College *Pennsylvania* M & W
Penn State University Park *Pennsylvania* M & W
Pepperdine University *California* W
Pfeiffer University *North Carolina* M & W
Pitzer College *California* M & W
Plymouth State University *New Hampshire* W
Point University *Georgia* M & W
Pomona College *California* M & W
Pontifical Catholic University of Puerto Rico *Puerto Rico* M & W
Princeton University *New Jersey* M & W
Principia College *Illinois* M & W
Providence College *Rhode Island* M & W
Purchase College, State University of New York *New York* M & W
Purdue University *Indiana* M & W
Queens College of the City University of New York *New York* M & W
Queens University of Charlotte *North Carolina* M & W
Queen's University at Kingston *Ontario (Canada)* M & W
Queensborough Community College of the City University of New York *New York* M & W
Quincy University *Illinois* W
Ramapo College of New Jersey *New Jersey* M & W
Randolph-Macon College *Virginia* M & W
Regis College *Massachusetts* M & W
Rensselaer Polytechnic Institute *New York* M & W
Rhode Island College *Rhode Island* W
Rhodes College *Tennessee* M & W
Rice University *Texas* W
Rider University *New Jersey* M & W
Rio Hondo College *California* M & W
Ripon College *Wisconsin* M & W
Rochester Institute of Technology *New York* M & W
Roger Williams University *Rhode Island* M & W
Rollins College *Florida* M & W

M = Men; W = Women

Rose-Hulman Institute of Technology *Indiana* M & W
Rowan University *New Jersey* M & W
Rutgers University - New Brunswick *New Jersey* M & W
Sacramento City College *California* M & W
Sacred Heart University *Connecticut* W
Saddleback College *California* M & W
Saginaw Valley State University *Michigan* M & W
St. Bonaventure University *New York* M & W
St. Catherine University *Minnesota* W
St. Cloud State University *Minnesota* M & W
St. Francis College *New York* M & W
Saint Francis University *Pennsylvania* M & W
Saint John's University *Minnesota* M
St. Joseph's College, Long Island Campus *New York* W
Saint Joseph's College of Maine *Maine* M & W
St. Joseph's College, New York *New York* W
St. Lawrence University *New York* M & W
Saint Leo University *Florida* W
Saint Louis University *Missouri* M & W
St. Mary's College of Maryland *Maryland* M & W
Saint Mary's University of Minnesota *Minnesota* M & W
Saint Michael's College *Vermont* M & W
St. Olaf College *Minnesota* M & W
Saint Peter's University *New Jersey* M & W
Saint Vincent College *Pennsylvania* M & W
Salem College *North Carolina* W
Salem International University *West Virginia* M & W
Salisbury University *Maryland* M & W
San Diego Mesa College *California* M & W
San Diego State University *California* W
San Joaquin Delta College *California* M & W
San Jose State University *California* W
Santa Ana College *California* M
Santa Clara University *California* M & W
Santa Monica College *California* M & W
Santa Rosa Junior College *California* M & W
Sarah Lawrence College *New York* M & W
Savannah College of Art and Design *Georgia* M & W
Scripps College *California* W
Seattle University *Washington* M & W
Seton Hall University *New Jersey* M & W
Sewanee: The University of the South *Tennessee* M & W
Shasta College *California* M & W
Shippensburg University of Pennsylvania *Pennsylvania* M & W
Siena College *New York* W
Sierra College *California* M & W
Simmons College *Massachusetts* W
Simon Fraser University *British Columbia (Canada)* M & W
Simpson College *Iowa* M & W
Skidmore College *New York* M & W
Smith College *Massachusetts* W
Soka University of America *California* M & W
Solano Community College *California* M & W
South Dakota State University *South Dakota* M & W
South Georgia State College *Georgia* M & W
Southern Connecticut State University *Connecticut* M & W
Southern Illinois University Carbondale *Illinois* M & W
Southern Methodist University *Texas* M & W
Southwestern College *California* M & W
Southwestern Oregon Community College *Oregon* M & W
Southwestern University *Texas* M & W
Springfield College *Massachusetts* M & W
Stanford University *California* M & W
State University of New York College of Agriculture and Technology at Cobleskill *New York* M & W
State University of New York College at Cortland *New York* M & W
State University of New York College at Geneseo *New York* M & W
State University of New York College at Old Westbury *New York* M & W

State University of New York College at Oneonta *New York* M & W
State University of New York College at Potsdam *New York* M & W
State University of New York College of Technology at Alfred *New York* M & W
State University of New York College of Technology at Delhi *New York* M & W
State University of New York at Fredonia *New York* M & W
State University of New York Maritime College *New York* M & W
State University of New York at New Paltz *New York* M & W
State University of New York at Oswego *New York* M & W
Stevens Institute of Technology *New Jersey* M & W
Stony Brook University, State University of New York *New York* M & W
Suffolk County Community College *New York* M & W
Susquehanna University *Pennsylvania* M & W
Swarthmore College *Pennsylvania* M & W
Sweet Briar College *Virginia* W
Tabor College *Kansas* M & W
Texas A&M University *Texas* M & W
Texas Christian University *Texas* M & W
Tiffin University *Ohio* M & W
Towson University *Maryland* M & W
Transylvania University *Kentucky* M & W
Trinity College *Connecticut* M & W
Trinity University *Texas* M & W
Trinity Washington University *District of Columbia* W
Truman State University *Missouri* M & W
Tufts University *Massachusetts* M & W
Tulane University *Louisiana* M & W
Union College *Kentucky* M & W
Union College *New York* M & W
United States Air Force Academy *Colorado* M & W
United States Coast Guard Academy *Connecticut* M & W
United States Merchant Marine Academy *New York* M & W
United States Military Academy *New York* M & W
United States Naval Academy *Maryland* M & W
Universidad del Turabo *Puerto Rico* M & W
Université Laval *Quebec (Canada)* M & W
Université de Montréal *Quebec (Canada)* M & W
Université du Québec en Outaouais *Quebec (Canada)* M & W
Université du Québec à Trois-Rivières *Quebec (Canada)* M & W
The University of Akron *Ohio* W
The University of Alabama *Alabama* M & W
University of Alaska Fairbanks *Alaska* W
University of Alberta *Alberta (Canada)* M & W
The University of Arizona *Arizona* M & W
University of Arkansas *Arkansas* W
University of Arkansas at Little Rock *Arkansas* W
University of Bridgeport *Connecticut* M & W
The University of British Columbia *British Columbia (Canada)* M & W
University at Buffalo, the State University of New York *New York* M & W
University of Calgary *Alberta (Canada)* M & W
University of California, Berkeley *California* M & W
University of California, Davis *California* W
University of California, Los Angeles *California* W
University of California, San Diego *California* M & W
University of California, Santa Barbara *California* M & W
University of California, Santa Cruz *California* M & W
University of Charleston *West Virginia* M & W
University of Chicago *Illinois* M & W
University of Cincinnati *Ohio* M & W
University of Colorado Boulder *Colorado* M & W
University of Connecticut *Connecticut* M & W
University of the Cumberlands *Kentucky* M & W
University of Delaware *Delaware* M & W
University of Denver *Colorado* M & W
University of Evansville *Indiana* M & W

The University of Findlay *Ohio* M & W
University of Florida *Florida* M & W
University of Georgia *Georgia* M & W
University of Guelph *Ontario (Canada)* M & W
University of Hawaii at Manoa *Hawaii* M & W
University of Houston *Texas* W
University of Idaho *Idaho* W
University of Illinois at Chicago *Illinois* M & W
University of Illinois at Urbana - Champaign *Illinois* W
University of the Incarnate Word *Texas* M & W
University of Indianapolis *Indiana* M & W
The University of Iowa *Iowa* M & W
The University of Kansas *Kansas* W
University of Kentucky *Kentucky* M & W
University of La Verne *California* M & W
University of Lethbridge *Alberta (Canada)* M & W
University of Louisville *Kentucky* M & W
University of Maine *Maine* M & W
University of Manitoba *Manitoba (Canada)* M & W
University of Mary Washington *Virginia* M & W
University of Maryland, Baltimore County *Maryland* M & W
University of Maryland, College Park *Maryland* M & W
University of Massachusetts Amherst *Massachusetts* M & W
University of Massachusetts Dartmouth *Massachusetts* M & W
University of Memphis *Tennessee* M & W
University of Miami *Florida* M & W
University of Michigan *Michigan* M & W
University of Minnesota, Duluth *Minnesota* M & W
University of Minnesota, Morris *Minnesota* W
University of Minnesota, Twin Cities Campus *Minnesota* M & W
University of Mississippi *Mississippi* M & W
University of Missouri *Missouri* M & W
University of Missouri - St. Louis *Missouri* M & W
University of Mount Union *Ohio* M & W
University of Nebraska at Kearney *Nebraska* W
University of Nebraska - Lincoln *Nebraska* W
University of Nebraska at Omaha *Nebraska* W
University of Nevada, Las Vegas *Nevada* M & W
University of Nevada, Reno *Nevada* W
University of New Brunswick Fredericton *New Brunswick (Canada)* W
University of New England *Maine* W
University of New Hampshire *New Hampshire* W
University of New Mexico *New Mexico* M & W
University of North Carolina at Asheville *North Carolina* W
The University of North Carolina at Chapel Hill *North Carolina* M & W
The University of North Carolina Wilmington *North Carolina* M & W
University of North Dakota *North Dakota* M & W
University of North Florida *Florida* W
University of North Texas *Texas* W
University of Northern Colorado *Colorado* W
University of Northern Iowa *Iowa* W
University of Notre Dame *Indiana* M & W
University of Ottawa *Ontario (Canada)* M & W
University of the Pacific *California* W
University of Pennsylvania *Pennsylvania* M & W
University of Pittsburgh *Pennsylvania* M & W
University of Pittsburgh at Bradford *Pennsylvania* M & W
University of Puerto Rico in Aguadilla *Puerto Rico* M & W
University of Puerto Rico in Arecibo *Puerto Rico* M & W
University of Puerto Rico in Cayey *Puerto Rico* M & W
University of Puerto Rico in Humacao *Puerto Rico* M & W
University of Puerto Rico, Mayagüez Campus *Puerto Rico* M & W
University of Puerto Rico, Río Piedras Campus *Puerto Rico* M & W
University of Puget Sound *Washington* M & W
University of Redlands *California* M & W
University of Regina *Saskatchewan (Canada)* M & W

M = Men; W = Women

University of Rhode Island *Rhode Island* W
University of Richmond *Virginia* W
University of Rochester *New York* M & W
University of the Sacred Heart *Puerto Rico* M & W
University of Saint Joseph *Connecticut* W
University of St. Thomas *Minnesota* M & W
University of San Diego *California* W
The University of Scranton *Pennsylvania* M & W
University of South Carolina *South Carolina* M & W
The University of South Dakota *South Dakota* M & W
University of Southern California *California* M & W
The University of Tampa *Florida* W
The University of Tennessee *Tennessee* M & W
The University of Texas at Austin *Texas* M & W
The University of Texas of the Permian Basin *Texas* M & W
The University of Texas at San Antonio *Texas* M & W
The University of Toledo *Ohio* W
University of Toronto *Ontario (Canada)* M & W
University of Utah *Utah* M & W
University of Vermont *Vermont* W
University of Victoria *British Columbia (Canada)* M & W
University of Virginia *Virginia* M & W
University of Waterloo *Ontario (Canada)* M & W
University of West Florida *Florida* W
The University of Western Ontario *Ontario (Canada)* M & W
University of Wisconsin - Eau Claire *Wisconsin* M & W
University of Wisconsin - Green Bay *Wisconsin* M & W
University of Wisconsin - La Crosse *Wisconsin* M & W
University of Wisconsin - Madison *Wisconsin* M & W
University of Wisconsin - Milwaukee *Wisconsin* M & W
University of Wisconsin - Oshkosh *Wisconsin* M & W
University of Wisconsin - Stevens Point *Wisconsin* M & W
University of Wisconsin - Whitewater *Wisconsin* M & W
University of Wyoming *Wyoming* M & W
Ursinus College *Pennsylvania* M & W
Ursuline College *Ohio* W
Utica College *New York* M & W
Valparaiso University *Indiana* M & W
Vanderbilt University *Tennessee* W
Vassar College *New York* M & W
Ventura College *California* M & W
Villa Maria College *New York* M & W
Villanova University *Pennsylvania* M & W
Virginia Military Institute *Virginia* M & W
Virginia Polytechnic Institute and State University *Virginia* M & W
Wabash College *Indiana* M
Wagner College *New York* W
Warren Wilson College *North Carolina* M & W
Washington College *Maryland* M & W
Washington & Jefferson College *Pennsylvania* M & W
Washington and Lee University *Virginia* M & W
Washington State University *Washington* W
Washington University in St. Louis *Missouri* M & W
Wayne State University *Michigan* M & W
Weber State University *Utah* M & W
Wellesley College *Massachusetts* W
Wells College *New York* M & W
Wesleyan University *Connecticut* M & W
West Chester University of Pennsylvania *Pennsylvania* M & W
West Valley College *California* M & W
West Virginia University *West Virginia* M & W
West Virginia University Institute of Technology *West Virginia* M & W
West Virginia Wesleyan College *West Virginia* M & W
Western Carolina University *North Carolina* M & W
Western Connecticut State University *Connecticut* W

Western Illinois University *Illinois* M & W
Western Michigan University *Michigan* M & W
Western New England University *Massachusetts* W
Western State Colorado University *Colorado* W
Westfield State University *Massachusetts* W
Westminster College *Pennsylvania* M & W
Wheaton College *Illinois* M & W
Wheaton College *Massachusetts* M & W
Wheeling Jesuit University *West Virginia* M & W
Whitman College *Washington* M & W
Whittier College *California* M & W
Whitworth University *Washington* M & W
Widener University *Pennsylvania* M & W
Wilfrid Laurier University *Ontario (Canada)* M & W
Wilkes University *Pennsylvania* M & W
Willamette University *Oregon* M & W
William Jewell College *Missouri* M & W
William Paterson University of New Jersey *New Jersey* M & W
Williams College *Massachusetts* M & W
Wilmington College *Ohio* M & W
Wingate University *North Carolina* M & W
Wittenberg University *Ohio* M & W
Worcester Polytechnic Institute *Massachusetts* M & W
Wright State University *Ohio* M & W
Xavier University *Ohio* M & W
Yale University *Connecticut* M & W
York College of the City University of New York *New York* M & W
York College of Pennsylvania *Pennsylvania* M & W
York University *Ontario (Canada)* M & W
Youngstown State University *Ohio* W

Table Tennis

Boston University *Massachusetts* M & W
California State University, Long Beach *California* M
Caribbean University *Puerto Rico* M
Carleton College *Minnesota* M & W
Colgate University *New York* M & W
Columbia University *New York* M & W
Columbia University, School of General Studies *New York* M & W
Community College of Allegheny County *Pennsylvania* M & W
Dalton State College *Georgia* M & W
Dartmouth College *New Hampshire* M & W
Duke University *North Carolina* M & W
Fashion Institute of Technology *New York* M & W
Florida State University *Florida* M & W
Georgia State University *Georgia* M & W
Inter American University of Puerto Rico, Aguadilla Campus *Puerto Rico* M & W
Inter American University of Puerto Rico, Barranquitas Campus *Puerto Rico* M & W
Inter American University of Puerto Rico, Bayamón Campus *Puerto Rico* M & W
Inter American University of Puerto Rico, Fajardo Campus *Puerto Rico* M & W
Inter American University of Puerto Rico, Metropolitan Campus *Puerto Rico* M & W
Inter American University of Puerto Rico, Ponce Campus *Puerto Rico* M & W
Inter American University of Puerto Rico, San Germán Campus *Puerto Rico* M & W
Lehman College of the City University of New York *New York* M & W
Lindenwood University *Missouri* M & W
Loyola University New Orleans *Louisiana* M & W
Michigan State University *Michigan* M & W
North Carolina State University *North Carolina* M & W
Northeastern University *Massachusetts* M & W
Northwestern Polytechnic University *California* M
Old Dominion University *Virginia* M & W
Polytechnic University of Puerto Rico *Puerto Rico* W
Pontifical Catholic University of Puerto Rico *Puerto Rico* M & W
Rensselaer Polytechnic Institute *New York* M & W
Saint Louis University *Missouri* M & W
San Jose State University *California* W
Texas Wesleyan University *Texas* M & W

Universidad Metropolitana *Puerto Rico* M & W
The University of Alabama *Alabama* W
University of California, Irvine *California* M & W
University of California, Santa Cruz *California* M & W
University of Florida *Florida* M & W
The University of Iowa *Iowa* M & W
University of Michigan *Michigan* M & W
University of Minnesota, Duluth *Minnesota* M & W
University of Missouri - St. Louis *Missouri* M & W
University of North Texas *Texas* M & W
University of Puerto Rico in Aguadilla *Puerto Rico* M
University of Puerto Rico in Cayey *Puerto Rico* M
University of Puerto Rico in Humacao *Puerto Rico* M & W
University of Puerto Rico in Ponce *Puerto Rico* M & W
University of Puerto Rico, Río Piedras Campus *Puerto Rico* M & W
University of Puerto Rico in Utuado *Puerto Rico* M & W
The University of Texas at Austin *Texas* M & W
The University of Texas at San Antonio *Texas* M & W
University of Utah *Utah* M & W
University of Vermont *Vermont* M & W
The University of Western Ontario *Ontario (Canada)* M & W
Washington University in St. Louis *Missouri* M & W
Yale University *Connecticut* M & W

Tennis

Abilene Christian University *Texas* M & W
Abraham Baldwin Agricultural College *Georgia* M & W
Academy of Art University *California* W
Adelphi University *New York* M & W
Adirondack Community College *New York* M & W
Adrian College *Michigan* M & W
Agnes Scott College *Georgia* W
Alabama Agricultural and Mechanical University *Alabama* M & W
Alabama State University *Alabama* M & W
Albany State University *Georgia* W
Albertus Magnus College *Connecticut* M & W
Albion College *Michigan* M & W
Albright College *Pennsylvania* M & W
Alcorn State University *Mississippi* M & W
Alderson Broaddus University *West Virginia* W
Alfred University *New York* M & W
Alice Lloyd College *Kentucky* M & W
Allan Hancock College *California* M & W
Allegany College of Maryland *Maryland* M & W
Allegheny College *Pennsylvania* M & W
Alma College *Michigan* M & W
Alvernia University *Pennsylvania* M & W
Alverno College *Wisconsin* W
American International College *Massachusetts* M & W
American River College *California* M & W
Amherst College *Massachusetts* M & W
Ancilla College *Indiana* M & W
Anderson University *Indiana* M & W
Anderson University *South Carolina* M & W
Anna Maria College *Massachusetts* M & W
Antelope Valley College *California* W
Appalachian State University *North Carolina* M & W
Aquinas College *Michigan* M & W
Arcadia University *Pennsylvania* M & W
Arizona Christian University *Arizona* M & W
Arizona State University at the Downtown Phoenix campus *Arizona* W
Arizona State University at the Polytechnic campus *Arizona* W
Arizona State University at the Tempe campus *Arizona* W
Arizona State University at the West campus *Arizona* W
Arkansas State University *Arkansas* W
Arkansas Tech University *Arkansas* W
Armstrong State University *Georgia* M & W
ASA College *New York* M & W
Asbury University *Kentucky* M & W

M = Men; W = Women

Ashland University *Ohio* W
Assumption College *Massachusetts* M & W
Auburn University *Alabama* M & W
Auburn University at Montgomery *Alabama* M & W
Augusta University *Georgia* M & W
Augustana College *Illinois* M & W
Augustana University *South Dakota* M & W
Aurora University *Illinois* M & W
Austin College *Texas* M & W
Austin Peay State University *Tennessee* M & W
Ave Maria University *Florida* M & W
Averett University *Virginia* M & W
Azusa Pacific University *California* M & W
Babson College *Massachusetts* M & W
Baker University *Kansas* M & W
Bakersfield College *California* M & W
Baldwin Wallace University *Ohio* M & W
Ball State University *Indiana* M & W
Barclay College *Kansas* M & W
Bard College *New York* M & W
Barnard College *New York* W
Barry University *Florida* M & W
Barton College *North Carolina* M & W
Barton County Community College *Kansas* M & W
Baruch College of the City University of New York
   New York M & W
Bates College *Maine* M & W
Bay Path University *Massachusetts* W
Baylor University *Texas* M & W
Becker College *Massachusetts* M & W
Belhaven University *Mississippi* M & W
Bellarmine University *Kentucky* M & W
Bellevue College *Washington* W
Belmont Abbey College *North Carolina* M & W
Belmont University *Tennessee* M & W
Beloit College *Wisconsin* W
Bemidji State University *Minnesota* W
Benedict College *South Carolina* M
Benedictine University *Illinois* W
Bentley University *Massachusetts* M & W
Berea College *Kentucky* M & W
Bergen Community College *New Jersey* M
Berkeley College - White Plains Campus *New
   York* M & W
Berry College *Georgia* M & W
Bethany College *Kansas* M & W
Bethany College *West Virginia* M & W
Bethany Lutheran College *Minnesota* M & W
Bethel College *Indiana* M & W
Bethel College *Kansas* M & W
Bethel University *Minnesota* M & W
Bethel University *Tennessee* M & W
Bethune-Cookman University *Florida* M & W
Binghamton University, State University of New York
   New York M & W
Biola University *California* M & W
Birmingham-Southern College *Alabama* M & W
Blackburn College *Illinois* W
Bloomfield College *New Jersey* M
Bloomsburg University of Pennsylvania *Pennsylva-
   nia* M & W
Bluefield College *Virginia* M & W
Bluefield State College *West Virginia* M & W
Boise State University *Idaho* M & W
Boston College *Massachusetts* M & W
Boston University *Massachusetts* M & W
Bowdoin College *Maine* M & W
Bowie State University *Maryland* W
Bowling Green State University *Ohio* W
Bradley University *Illinois* W
Brandeis University *Massachusetts* M & W
Brenau University *Georgia* W
Brevard College *North Carolina* M & W
Briar Cliff University *Iowa* M & W
Bridgewater College *Virginia* M & W
Bridgewater State University *Massachusetts* M & W
Brigham Young University *Utah* M & W
Brigham Young University - Hawaii *Hawaii* M & W
Brookdale Community College *New Jersey* M & W
Brooklyn College of the City University of New York
   New York M & W
Broome Community College *New York* M & W
Broward College *Florida* W
Brown University *Rhode Island* M & W

Bryant University *Rhode Island* M & W
Bryn Athyn College of the New Church *Pennsylva-
   nia* M & W
Bryn Mawr College *Pennsylvania* W
Bucknell University *Pennsylvania* M & W
Bucks County Community College *Pennsylva-
   nia* M & W
Buena Vista University *Iowa* M & W
Buffalo State College, State University of New York
   New York W
Butler Community College *Kansas* M & W
Butler University *Indiana* M & W
Cabrillo College *California* M & W
Cabrini University *Pennsylvania* M & W
Cairn University *Pennsylvania* W
Caldwell University *New Jersey* M & W
California Institute of Technology *California* M & W
California Lutheran University *California* M & W
California Polytechnic State University, San Luis
   Obispo *California* M & W
California State University, Bakersfield *California* W
California State University, Fresno *Califor-
   nia* M & W
California State University, Fullerton *California* W
California State University, Long Beach *Califor-
   nia* W
California State University, Los Angeles *Califor-
   nia* W
California State University, Northridge *California* W
California State University, Sacramento *Califor-
   nia* M & W
California State University, Stanislaus *California* W
California University of Pennsylvania *Pennsylva-
   nia* W
Calumet College of Saint Joseph *Indiana* M & W
Calvin College *Michigan* M & W
Cameron University *Oklahoma* M & W
Campbell University *North Carolina* M & W
Campbellsville University *Kentucky* M & W
Cañada College *California* W
Capital University *Ohio* M & W
Cardinal Stritch University *Wisconsin* M & W
Carleton College *Minnesota* M & W
Carlow University *Pennsylvania* M & W
Carnegie Mellon University *Pennsylvania* M & W
Carroll University *Wisconsin* M & W
Carson-Newman University *Tennessee* M & W
Carthage College *Wisconsin* M & W
Case Western Reserve University *Ohio* M & W
Castleton University *Vermont* M & W
Catawba College *North Carolina* M & W
The Catholic University of America *District of Co-
   lumbia* M & W
Cazenovia College *New York* M & W
Cecil College *Maryland* W
Cedar Crest College *Pennsylvania* W
Cedarville University *Ohio* M & W
Centenary College of Louisiana *Louisiana* M & W
Central Alabama Community College *Ala-
   bama* M & W
Central Christian College of Kansas *Kansas* M & W
Central College *Iowa* M & W
Central State University *Ohio* M & W
Central Washington University *Washington* M & W
Centre College *Kentucky* M & W
Cerritos College *California* M & W
Chabot College *California* M & W
Chaminade University of Honolulu *Hawaii* W
Chapman University *California* M & W
Charleston Southern University *South Carolina* W
Chestnut Hill College *Pennsylvania* M & W
Chicago State University *Illinois* M & W
Chowan University *North Carolina* M & W
Christian Brothers University *Tennessee* M & W
Christopher Newport University *Virginia* M & W
The Citadel, The Military College of South Carolina
   South Carolina M
City College of the City University of New York *New
   York* M & W
City College of San Francisco *California* W
Claremont McKenna College *California* M & W
Clarion University of Pennsylvania *Pennsylvania* W
Clark Atlanta University *Georgia* W
Clark University *Massachusetts* M & W

Clayton State University *Georgia* W
Clemson University *South Carolina* M & W
Cleveland State University *Ohio* M & W
Cloud County Community College *Kansas* M & W
Coastal Carolina University *South Carolina* M & W
Coe College *Iowa* M & W
Coker College *South Carolina* M & W
Colby College *Maine* M & W
Colby-Sawyer College *New Hampshire* M & W
Colgate University *New York* M & W
The College at Brockport, State University of New
   York *New York* W
College of Charleston *South Carolina* M & W
College of Coastal Georgia *Georgia* M & W
College of the Desert *California* M & W
College of the Holy Cross *Massachusetts* M & W
The College of Idaho *Idaho* W
College of Lake County *Illinois* M & W
College of Mount Saint Vincent *New York* M & W
The College of New Jersey *New Jersey* M & W
The College of New Rochelle *New York* W
College of Saint Benedict *Minnesota* W
College of Saint Elizabeth *New Jersey* W
College of Saint Mary *Nebraska* W
The College of Saint Rose *New York* W
The College of St. Scholastica *Minnesota* M & W
College of the Sequoias *California* M & W
College of Staten Island of the City University of
   New York *New York* M & W
The College of William and Mary *Virginia* M & W
The College of Wooster *Ohio* M & W
Collin County Community College District
   Texas M & W
Colorado Christian University *Colorado* M & W
The Colorado College *Colorado* M & W
Colorado Mesa University *Colorado* M & W
Colorado State University *Colorado* W
Colorado State University - Pueblo *Colo-
   rado* M & W
Columbia College *South Carolina* W
Columbia University *New York* M & W
Columbia University, School of General Studies
   New York M & W
Columbus State University *Georgia* M & W
Community College of Allegheny County *Pennsylva-
   nia* M & W
Community College of Philadelphia *Pennsylva-
   nia* M & W
Community College of Rhode Island *Rhode Is-
   land* M & W
Concord University *West Virginia* M & W
Concordia College *Minnesota* M & W
Concordia College - New York *New York* M & W
Concordia University Chicago *Illinois* M & W
Concordia University Irvine *California* M & W
Concordia University, Nebraska *Nebraska* M & W
Concordia University Wisconsin *Wisconsin* M & W
Connecticut College *Connecticut* M & W
Converse College *South Carolina* W
Cooper Union for the Advancement of Science and
   Art *New York* M & W
Copiah-Lincoln Community College *Missis-
   sippi* M & W
Coppin State University *Maryland* M & W
Cornell College *Iowa* M & W
Cornell University *New York* M & W
Covenant College *Georgia* M & W
Cowley County Community College and Area Voca-
   tional - Technical School *Kansas* M & W
Creighton University *Nebraska* M & W
Crossroads College *Minnesota* M & W
Cuesta College *California* W
The Culinary Institute of America *New York* M & W
Cumberland University *Tennessee* M & W
Curry College *Massachusetts* M & W
Cuyamaca College *California* W
Cypress College *California* M & W
Daemen College *New York* M & W
Dallas Baptist University *Texas* M & W
Dalton State College *Georgia* M & W
Dartmouth College *New Hampshire* M & W
Davenport University *Michigan* M & W
Davidson College *North Carolina* M & W
De Anza College *California* M & W

M = Men; W = Women

Defiance College *Ohio* M & W
Delaware County Community College *Pennsylvania* M & W
Delaware State University *Delaware* W
Delaware Valley University *Pennsylvania* M & W
Delta State University *Mississippi* M & W
Denison University *Ohio* M & W
DePaul University *Illinois* M & W
DePauw University *Indiana* M & W
Diablo Valley College *California* M & W
Dickinson College *Pennsylvania* M & W
Dixie State University *Utah* W
Doane University *Nebraska* M & W
Dominican University *Illinois* M & W
Dominican University of California *California* W
Drake University *Iowa* M & W
Drew University *New Jersey* M & W
Drexel University *Pennsylvania* M & W
Drury University *Missouri* M & W
Duke University *North Carolina* M & W
Duquesne University *Pennsylvania* M & W
D'Youville College *New York* M & W
Earlham College *Indiana* M & W
East Carolina University *North Carolina* M & W
East Central Community College *Mississippi* M & W
East Central University *Oklahoma* M & W
East Stroudsburg University of Pennsylvania *Pennsylvania* M & W
East Tennessee State University *Tennessee* M & W
East Texas Baptist University *Texas* M & W
Eastern Illinois University *Illinois* M & W
Eastern Kentucky University *Kentucky* M & W
Eastern Michigan University *Michigan* W
Eastern Nazarene College *Massachusetts* M & W
Eastern University *Pennsylvania* M & W
Eastern Washington University *Washington* M & W
Eastfield College *Texas* M & W
Eckerd College *Florida* M & W
Edgewood College *Wisconsin* M & W
Edinboro University of Pennsylvania *Pennsylvania* M & W
Edward Waters College *Florida* M & W
El Camino College *California* M & W
Elgin Community College *Illinois* M & W
Elizabeth City State University *North Carolina* W
Elizabethtown College *Pennsylvania* M & W
Elmhurst College *Illinois* M & W
Elmira College *New York* M & W
Elon University *North Carolina* M & W
Embry-Riddle Aeronautical University - Daytona *Florida* M & W
Emerson College *Massachusetts* M & W
Emmanuel College *Georgia* M & W
Emory & Henry College *Virginia* M & W
Emory University *Georgia* M & W
Emory University, Oxford College *Georgia* M & W
Emporia State University *Kansas* M & W
Endicott College *Massachusetts* M & W
Erskine College *South Carolina* M & W
Evangel University *Missouri* M & W
Fairfield University *Connecticut* M & W
Fairleigh Dickinson University, College at Florham *New Jersey* M & W
Fairleigh Dickinson University, Metropolitan Campus *New Jersey* M & W
Fairmont State University *West Virginia* M & W
Farmingdale State College *New York* M & W
Fashion Institute of Technology *New York* M & W
Fayetteville State University *North Carolina* M & W
Ferris State University *Michigan* M & W
Ferrum College *Virginia* M & W
Fisk University *Tennessee* M & W
Flagler College *Florida* M & W
Florida Agricultural and Mechanical University *Florida* M & W
Florida Atlantic University *Florida* M & W
Florida Gulf Coast University *Florida* M & W
Florida Institute of Technology *Florida* M & W
Florida International University *Florida* W
Florida Southern College *Florida* M & W
Florida State College at Jacksonville *Florida* W
Florida State University *Florida* M & W
Fontbonne University *Missouri* M & W

Foothill College *California* M & W
Fordham University *New York* M & W
Fort Valley State University *Georgia* M & W
Francis Marion University *South Carolina* M & W
Franciscan University of Steubenville *Ohio* M & W
Franklin College *Indiana* M & W
Franklin & Marshall College *Pennsylvania* M & W
Franklin Pierce University *New Hampshire* M & W
Fresno City College *California* M & W
Fresno Pacific University *California* M & W
Friends University *Kansas* M & W
Frostburg State University *Maryland* M & W
Fullerton College *California* M & W
Furman University *South Carolina* M & W
Gadsden State Community College *Alabama* M
Gardner-Webb University *North Carolina* M & W
Geneva College *Pennsylvania* M & W
George Fox University *Oregon* M & W
George Mason University *Virginia* M & W
The George Washington University *District of Columbia* M & W
Georgetown College *Kentucky* M & W
Georgetown University *District of Columbia* M & W
Georgia College & State University *Georgia* M & W
Georgia Gwinnett College *Georgia* M & W
Georgia Institute of Technology *Georgia* M & W
Georgia Southern University *Georgia* M & W
Georgia Southwestern State University *Georgia* M & W
Georgia State University *Georgia* M & W
Georgian Court University *New Jersey* W
Gettysburg College *Pennsylvania* M & W
Glendale Community College *Arizona* M & W
Glendale Community College *California* M & W
Goldey-Beacom College *Delaware* W
Gonzaga University *Washington* M & W
Gordon College *Massachusetts* M & W
Goshen College *Indiana* M & W
Goucher College *Maryland* M & W
Grace Bible College *Michigan* M & W
Grace College *Indiana* M & W
Graceland University *Iowa* M & W
Grambling State University *Louisiana* W
Grand Canyon University *Arizona* M & W
Grand Valley State University *Michigan* M & W
Grand View University *Iowa* M & W
Green Mountain College *Vermont* M
Green River Community College *Washington* M & W
Greensboro College *North Carolina* M & W
Greenville College *Illinois* M & W
Grinnell College *Iowa* M & W
Grossmont College *California* M & W
Grove City College *Pennsylvania* M & W
Guilford College *North Carolina* M & W
Gustavus Adolphus College *Minnesota* M & W
Gwynedd Mercy University *Pennsylvania* M & W
Hamilton College *New York* M & W
Hamline University *Minnesota* M & W
Hampden-Sydney College *Virginia* M
Hampton University *Virginia* M & W
Hanover College *Indiana* M & W
Hardin-Simmons University *Texas* M & W
Harding University *Arkansas* M & W
Harford Community College *Maryland* M & W
Harrisburg Area Community College *Pennsylvania* M & W
Hartwick College *New York* M & W
Harvard University *Massachusetts* M & W
Harvey Mudd College *California* M & W
Hastings College *Nebraska* M & W
Haverford College *Pennsylvania* M & W
Hawai'i Pacific University *Hawaii* M & W
Heidelberg University *Ohio* M & W
Henderson State University *Arkansas* W
Hendrix College *Arkansas* M & W
Herkimer County Community College *New York* M & W
Hesston College *Kansas* M & W
Hillsborough Community College *Florida* M & W
Hillsdale College *Michigan* M & W
Hinds Community College *Mississippi* M & W
Hobart and William Smith Colleges *New York* M & W
Hofstra University *New York* M & W

Hollins University *Virginia* W
Holmes Community College *Mississippi* W
Holy Family University *Pennsylvania* W
Holy Names University *California* M & W
Hood College *Maryland* M & W
Hope College *Michigan* M & W
Hope International University *California* M & W
Houghton College *New York* M & W
Howard Payne University *Texas* M & W
Howard University *District of Columbia* M & W
Hudson Valley Community College *New York* W
Hunter College of the City University of New York *New York* M & W
Huntingdon College *Alabama* M & W
Huntington University *Indiana* M & W
Husson University *Maine* M
Idaho State University *Idaho* M & W
Illinois College *Illinois* M & W
Illinois State University *Illinois* M & W
Illinois Valley Community College *Illinois* M & W
Illinois Wesleyan University *Illinois* M & W
Immaculata University *Pennsylvania* W
Imperial Valley College *California* M & W
Indiana Tech *Indiana* M & W
Indiana University Bloomington *Indiana* M & W
Indiana University East *Indiana* M & W
Indiana University of Pennsylvania *Pennsylvania* W
Indiana University - Purdue University Fort Wayne *Indiana* M & W
Indiana University - Purdue University Indianapolis *Indiana* M & W
Indiana University Southeast *Indiana* M & W
Indiana Wesleyan University *Indiana* M & W
Inter American University of Puerto Rico, Aguadilla Campus *Puerto Rico* M & W
Inter American University of Puerto Rico, Barranquitas Campus *Puerto Rico* M & W
Inter American University of Puerto Rico, Fajardo Campus *Puerto Rico* M & W
Inter American University of Puerto Rico, Metropolitan Campus *Puerto Rico* M & W
Inter American University of Puerto Rico, San Germán Campus *Puerto Rico* M & W
Iowa Central Community College *Iowa* M & W
Iowa State University of Science and Technology *Iowa* W
Irvine Valley College *California* M & W
Itawamba Community College *Mississippi* M & W
Ithaca College *New York* M & W
Jackson State University *Mississippi* M & W
Jacksonville State University *Alabama* M & W
James H. Faulkner State Community College *Alabama* M & W
James Madison University *Virginia* M & W
Jefferson College of Health Sciences *Virginia* M & W
John Brown University *Arkansas* M & W
John Carroll University *Ohio* M & W
John Jay College of Criminal Justice of the City University of New York *New York* M & W
Johns Hopkins University *Maryland* M & W
Johnson C. Smith University *North Carolina* M & W
Johnson County Community College *Kansas* M & W
Johnson State College *Vermont* M & W
Johnson & Wales University *Colorado* M & W
Johnson & Wales University *Rhode Island* M & W
Jones County Junior College *Mississippi* M & W
Judson College *Alabama* W
Judson University *Illinois* M & W
Juniata College *Pennsylvania* M & W
Kalamazoo College *Michigan* M & W
Kalamazoo Valley Community College *Michigan* W
Kansas State University *Kansas* W
Kansas Wesleyan University *Kansas* M & W
Kaskaskia College *Illinois* M
Kean University *New Jersey* W
Kennesaw State University *Georgia* M & W
Kentucky Wesleyan College *Kentucky* W
Kenyon College *Ohio* M & W
Keuka College *New York* M & W
Keystone College *Pennsylvania* M & W
King University *Tennessee* M & W
King's College *Pennsylvania* M & W

M = Men; W = Women

Kingsborough Community College of the City University of New York *New York* M & W
Knox College *Illinois* M & W
Kutztown University of Pennsylvania *Pennsylvania* M & W
La Roche College *Pennsylvania* W
La Salle University *Pennsylvania* M & W
Labette Community College *Kansas* W
Lafayette College *Pennsylvania* M & W
LaGrange College *Georgia* M & W
Lake Forest College *Illinois* M & W
Lake Land College *Illinois* M & W
Lake Superior State University *Michigan* M & W
Lakeland University *Wisconsin* M & W
Lamar University *Texas* M & W
Lander University *South Carolina* M & W
Lane College *Tennessee* W
Laredo Community College *Texas* M & W
Lawrence Technological University *Michigan* M & W
Lawrence University *Wisconsin* M & W
Le Moyne College *New York* M & W
Lebanon Valley College *Pennsylvania* M & W
Lee College *Texas* W
Lee University *Tennessee* M & W
Lees-McRae College *North Carolina* M & W
Lehigh University *Pennsylvania* M & W
Lehman College of the City University of New York *New York* M & W
LeMoyne-Owen College *Tennessee* M & W
Lenoir-Rhyne University *North Carolina* M & W
LeTourneau University *Texas* M & W
Lewis & Clark College *Oregon* M & W
Lewis and Clark Community College *Illinois* M & W
Lewis-Clark State College *Idaho* M & W
Lewis University *Illinois* M & W
Liberty University *Virginia* M & W
Limestone College *South Carolina* M & W
Lincoln Memorial University *Tennessee* M & W
Lincoln University *Missouri* W
Lindenwood University *Missouri* M & W
Lindsey Wilson College *Kentucky* M & W
Linfield College *Oregon* M & W
Lipscomb University *Tennessee* M & W
Livingstone College *North Carolina* W
Logan University *Missouri* M
Long Beach City College *California* M & W
Long Island University - LIU Brooklyn *New York* W
Long Island University - LIU Post *New York* W
Longwood University *Virginia* M & W
Loras College *Iowa* M & W
Los Angeles Pierce College *California* M & W
Louisiana College *Louisiana* M & W
Louisiana State University and Agricultural & Mechanical College *Louisiana* M & W
Louisiana State University at Alexandria *Louisiana* W
Louisiana State University in Shreveport *Louisiana* W
Louisiana Tech University *Louisiana* W
Loyola Marymount University *California* M & W
Loyola University Maryland *Maryland* M & W
Loyola University New Orleans *Louisiana* M & W
Luther College *Iowa* M & W
Lycoming College *Pennsylvania* M & W
Lynchburg College *Virginia* M & W
Lyndon State College *Vermont* M & W
Lynn University *Florida* M & W
Macalester College *Minnesota* M & W
Madison Area Technical College *Wisconsin* M & W
Manchester University *Indiana* M & W
Manhattan College *New York* M & W
Marian University *Indiana* M & W
Marian University *Wisconsin* M & W
Marietta College *Ohio* M & W
Marion Military Institute *Alabama* M & W
Marist College *New York* M & W
Marquette University *Wisconsin* M & W
Mars Hill University *North Carolina* M & W
Marshall University *West Virginia* M & W
Martin Luther College *Minnesota* M & W
Martin Methodist College *Tennessee* M & W
Mary Baldwin College *Virginia* W
Maryville College *Tennessee* M & W
Maryville University of Saint Louis *Missouri* W

Marywood University *Pennsylvania* M & W
Massachusetts Bay Community College *Massachusetts* M & W
Massachusetts College of Liberal Arts *Massachusetts* M & W
Massachusetts Institute of Technology *Massachusetts* M & W
McDaniel College *Maryland* M & W
McDowell Technical Community College *North Carolina* M
McGill University *Quebec (Canada)* M & W
McHenry County College *Illinois* M & W
McKendree University *Illinois* M & W
McMaster University *Ontario (Canada)* M & W
McMurry University *Texas* M & W
McNeese State University *Louisiana* W
McPherson College *Kansas* M & W
Medgar Evers College of the City University of New York *New York* W
Merced College *California* M & W
Mercer County Community College *New Jersey* M & W
Mercer University *Georgia* M & W
Mercyhurst University *Pennsylvania* M & W
Meredith College *North Carolina* W
Meridian Community College *Mississippi* M & W
Merrimack College *Massachusetts* M & W
Mesa Community College *Arizona* M & W
Messiah College *Pennsylvania* M & W
Methodist University *North Carolina* M & W
Metropolitan State University of Denver *Colorado* M & W
Miami University *Ohio* M & W
Miami University Hamilton *Ohio* M & W
Miami University Middletown *Ohio* M & W
Michigan State University *Michigan* M & W
Michigan Technological University *Michigan* M & W
Middle Georgia State University *Georgia* M & W
Middle Tennessee State University *Tennessee* M & W
Middlebury College *Vermont* M & W
Midland University *Nebraska* M & W
Midway University *Kentucky* W
Midwestern State University *Texas* M & W
Millersville University of Pennsylvania *Pennsylvania* M & W
Milligan College *Tennessee* M & W
Millikin University *Illinois* W
Mills College *California* W
Millsaps College *Mississippi* M & W
Milwaukee School of Engineering *Wisconsin* M & W
Minnesota State University Mankato *Minnesota* M & W
Minnesota State University Moorhead *Minnesota* W
Misericordia University *Pennsylvania* M & W
Mission College *California* M & W
Mississippi College *Mississippi* M & W
Mississippi Gulf Coast Community College *Mississippi* M & W
Mississippi State University *Mississippi* M & W
Mississippi Valley State University *Mississippi* M & W
Missouri Baptist University *Missouri* M & W
Missouri Southern State University *Missouri* W
Missouri Valley College *Missouri* M & W
Missouri Western State University *Missouri* W
Mitchell College *Connecticut* M & W
Modesto Junior College *California* M & W
Mohawk Valley Community College *New York* M & W
Molloy College *New York* W
Monmouth College *Illinois* M & W
Monmouth University *New Jersey* M & W
Monroe Community College *New York* M & W
Montana State University *Montana* M & W
Monterey Peninsula College *California* M & W
Montgomery College *Maryland* M & W
Montreat College *North Carolina* M & W
Moraine Valley Community College *Illinois* M & W
Moravian College *Pennsylvania* M & W
Morehead State University *Kentucky* M & W
Morehouse College *Georgia* M
Morgan State University *Maryland* M & W

Morningside College *Iowa* M & W
Mount Aloysius College *Pennsylvania* M & W
Mount Holyoke College *Massachusetts* W
Mount Ida College *Massachusetts* W
Mount Marty College *South Dakota* W
Mount Mary University *Wisconsin* W
Mount St. Joseph University *Ohio* M & W
Mount Saint Mary College *New York* M & W
Mount St. Mary's University *Maryland* M & W
Mt. San Antonio College *California* M & W
Mt. San Jacinto College *California* M & W
Muhlenberg College *Pennsylvania* M & W
Murray State University *Kentucky* M & W
Muskegon Community College *Michigan* M & W
Muskingum University *Ohio* M & W
Napa Valley College *California* M & W
Nassau Community College *New York* M & W
Nazareth College of Rochester *New York* M & W
Nebraska Wesleyan University *Nebraska* M & W
Neumann University *Pennsylvania* M & W
New Jersey Institute of Technology *New Jersey* M & W
New Mexico Military Institute *New Mexico* M & W
New Mexico State University *New Mexico* M & W
New York Institute of Technology *New York* M & W
New York University *New York* M & W
Newberry College *South Carolina* M & W
Newman University *Kansas* M & W
Niagara University *New York* M & W
Nicholls State University *Louisiana* M & W
Nichols College *Massachusetts* M & W
Norfolk State University *Virginia* M & W
North Carolina Agricultural and Technical State University *North Carolina* W
North Carolina Central University *North Carolina* M & W
North Carolina State University *North Carolina* M & W
North Carolina Wesleyan College *North Carolina* M & W
North Central College *Illinois* M & W
North Central Texas College *Texas* W
North Central University *Minnesota* M & W
North Greenville University *South Carolina* M & W
North Park University *Illinois* W
Northampton Community College *Pennsylvania* W
Northeast Mississippi Community College *Mississippi* M & W
Northeastern State University *Oklahoma* W
Northeastern University *Massachusetts* M & W
Northern Arizona University *Arizona* W
Northern Illinois University *Illinois* M & W
Northern Kentucky University *Kentucky* M & W
Northwest Mississippi Community College *Mississippi* M & W
Northwest Missouri State University *Missouri* M & W
Northwestern College *Iowa* W
Northwestern State University of Louisiana *Louisiana* W
Northwood University, Michigan Campus *Michigan* M & W
Norwich University *Vermont* M & W
Notre Dame College *Ohio* M
Notre Dame of Maryland University *Maryland* W
Notre Dame de Namur University *California* W
Nova Southeastern University *Florida* W
Oakland City University *Indiana* M & W
Oakland University *Michigan* W
Oakton Community College *Illinois* M & W
Oberlin College *Ohio* M & W
Occidental College *California* M & W
Ocean County College *New Jersey* M & W
Oglethorpe University *Georgia* M & W
Ohio Northern University *Ohio* M & W
The Ohio State University *Ohio* M & W
Ohio Wesleyan University *Ohio* M & W
Ohlone College *California* M & W
Oklahoma Baptist University *Oklahoma* M & W
Oklahoma State University *Oklahoma* M & W
Oklahoma Wesleyan University *Oklahoma* M & W
Old Dominion University *Virginia* M & W
Olivet College *Michigan* W
Olivet Nazarene University *Illinois* M & W

M = Men; W = Women

Onondaga Community College *New York* M & W
Oral Roberts University *Oklahoma* M & W
Orange Coast College *California* M & W
Orange County Community College *New York* M & W
Otterbein University *Ohio* M & W
Ouachita Baptist University *Arkansas* M & W
Our Lady of the Lake University of San Antonio *Texas* M & W
Pacific Lutheran University *Washington* M & W
Pacific University *Oregon* M & W
Palm Beach Atlantic University *Florida* M & W
Palomar College *California* M & W
Paradise Valley Community College *Arizona* M & W
Pasadena City College *California* M & W
Pearl River Community College *Mississippi* M & W
Penn State Abington *Pennsylvania* M & W
Penn State Altoona *Pennsylvania* M & W
Penn State Berks *Pennsylvania* M & W
Penn State Brandywine *Pennsylvania* M & W
Penn State Erie, The Behrend College *Pennsylvania* M & W
Penn State Harrisburg *Pennsylvania* M & W
Penn State Hazleton *Pennsylvania* M & W
Penn State Lehigh Valley *Pennsylvania* M & W
Penn State Mont Alto *Pennsylvania* M & W
Penn State University Park *Pennsylvania* M & W
Pennsylvania College of Technology *Pennsylvania* M & W
Pepperdine University *California* M & W
Pfeiffer University *North Carolina* M & W
Philadelphia University *Pennsylvania* M & W
Piedmont College *Georgia* M & W
Pitzer College *California* M & W
Plymouth State University *New Hampshire* W
Point Loma Nazarene University *California* M & W
Point University *Georgia* M & W
Pomona College *California* M & W
Pontifical Catholic University of Puerto Rico *Puerto Rico* M & W
Porterville College *California* M & W
Portland State University *Oregon* M & W
Post University *Connecticut* M & W
Prairie View A&M University *Texas* M & W
Pratt Institute *New York* M & W
Presbyterian College *South Carolina* M & W
Prince George's Community College *Maryland* M & W
Princeton University *New Jersey* M & W
Principia College *Illinois* M & W
Providence College *Rhode Island* W
Purchase College, State University of New York *New York* M & W
Purdue University *Indiana* M & W
Purdue University Northwest *Hammond, Indiana* M & W
Queens College of the City University of New York *New York* M & W
Queens University of Charlotte *North Carolina* M & W
Quincy University *Illinois* M & W
Quinnipiac University *Connecticut* M & W
Radford University *Virginia* M & W
Ramapo College of New Jersey *New Jersey* M & W
Randolph College *Virginia* M & W
Randolph-Macon College *Virginia* M & W
Reedley College *California* M & W
Regis College *Massachusetts* M & W
Reinhardt University *Georgia* M & W
Rend Lake College *Illinois* W
Rensselaer Polytechnic Institute *New York* M & W
Research College of Nursing *Missouri* M & W
Rhode Island College *Rhode Island* M & W
Rhodes College *Tennessee* M & W
Rice University *Texas* M & W
Rider University *New Jersey* M & W
Rio Hondo College *California* M & W
Ripon College *Wisconsin* M & W
Roanoke College *Virginia* M & W
Robert Morris University Illinois *Illinois* W
Roberts Wesleyan College *New York* M & W
Rochester Institute of Technology *New York* M & W
Rock Valley College *Illinois* M & W

Rockhurst University *Missouri* M & W
Rockland Community College *New York* M & W
Roger Williams University *Rhode Island* M & W
Rollins College *Florida* M & W
Roosevelt University *Illinois* M & W
Rose-Hulman Institute of Technology *Indiana* M & W
Rosemont College *Pennsylvania* M & W
Rowan College at Gloucester County *New Jersey* M & W
Roxbury Community College *Massachusetts* M & W
Rust College *Mississippi* M & W
Rutgers University - New Brunswick *New Jersey* M & W
Rutgers University - Newark *New Jersey* M & W
Sacramento City College *California* M & W
Sacred Heart University *Connecticut* M & W
Saddleback College *California* M & W
The Sage Colleges *New York* M & W
Saginaw Valley State University *Michigan* M & W
St. Ambrose University *Iowa* M & W
Saint Anselm College *New Hampshire* M & W
St. Bonaventure University *New York* M & W
St. Catherine University *Minnesota* W
St. Cloud State University *Minnesota* M & W
St. Edward's University *Texas* M & W
St. Francis College *New York* M & W
Saint Francis University *Pennsylvania* M & W
St. John Fisher College *New York* M & W
Saint John's University *Minnesota* M
St. John's University *New York* M & W
Saint Joseph's College *Indiana* M & W
St. Joseph's College, Long Island Campus *New York* M & W
St. Joseph's College, New York *New York* M & W
Saint Joseph's University *Pennsylvania* M & W
St. Lawrence University *New York* M & W
Saint Leo University *Florida* M & W
St. Louis College of Pharmacy *Missouri* M & W
Saint Louis University *Missouri* M & W
Saint Mary's College *Indiana* W
Saint Mary's College of California *California* M & W
St. Mary's College of Maryland *Maryland* M & W
St. Mary's University *Texas* M & W
Saint Mary's University of Minnesota *Minnesota* M & W
Saint Michael's College *Vermont* M & W
St. Norbert College *Wisconsin* M & W
St. Olaf College *Minnesota* M & W
Saint Peter's University *New Jersey* M & W
St. Petersburg College *Florida* W
St. Thomas Aquinas College *New York* M & W
St. Thomas University *Florida* M & W
Saint Vincent College *Pennsylvania* M & W
Salem College *North Carolina* W
Salem State University *Massachusetts* M & W
Salisbury University *Maryland* M & W
Salve Regina University *Rhode Island* M & W
Sam Houston State University *Texas* W
Samford University *Alabama* M & W
San Bernardino Valley College *California* W
San Diego Christian College *California* M & W
San Diego City College *California* M & W
San Diego Mesa College *California* M & W
San Diego State University *California* M & W
San Joaquin Delta College *California* M & W
San Jose State University *California* W
Santa Ana College *California* M & W
Santa Barbara City College *California* M & W
Santa Clara University *California* M & W
Santa Monica College *California* W
Santa Rosa Junior College *California* M & W
Sarah Lawrence College *New York* M & W
Sauk Valley Community College *Illinois* M & W
Savannah College of Art and Design *Georgia* M & W
Savannah State University *Georgia* W
Schreiner University *Texas* M & W
Scripps College *California* W
Seattle University *Washington* M & W
Seminole State College *Oklahoma* M & W
Seton Hall University *New Jersey* W
Seton Hill University *Pennsylvania* W

Sewanee: The University of the South *Tennessee* M & W
Seward County Community College and Area Technical School *Kansas* M & W
Shasta College *California* M & W
Shaw University *North Carolina* M & W
Shawnee State University *Ohio* W
Shenandoah University *Virginia* M & W
Shepherd University *West Virginia* M & W
Shippensburg University of Pennsylvania *Pennsylvania* W
Shoreline Community College *Washington* M & W
Shorter University *Georgia* M & W
Siena College *New York* M & W
Sierra College *California* M & W
Simmons College *Massachusetts* W
Simpson College *Iowa* M & W
Sinclair Community College *Ohio* M & W
Skagit Valley College *Washington* M & W
Skidmore College *New York* M & W
Slippery Rock University of Pennsylvania *Pennsylvania* M & W
Smith College *Massachusetts* W
Snead State Community College *Alabama* W
Sonoma State University *California* M & W
South Carolina State University *South Carolina* M & W
South Dakota State University *South Dakota* M & W
Southeast Missouri State University *Missouri* W
Southeastern Louisiana University *Louisiana* W
Southeastern Oklahoma State University *Oklahoma* M & W
Southeastern University *Florida* M & W
Southern Arkansas University - Magnolia *Arkansas* W
Southern Illinois University Carbondale *Illinois* M & W
Southern Illinois University Edwardsville *Illinois* M & W
Southern Methodist University *Texas* M & W
Southern Nazarene University *Oklahoma* M & W
Southern New Hampshire University *New Hampshire* M & W
Southern Oregon University *Oregon* M & W
Southern University and Agricultural and Mechanical College *Louisiana* M & W
Southern Utah University *Utah* M & W
Southern Virginia University *Virginia* M & W
Southwest Baptist University *Missouri* M & W
Southwest Minnesota State University *Minnesota* W
Southwestern Christian University *Oklahoma* M & W
Southwestern College *California* M & W
Southwestern College *Kansas* M & W
Southwestern University *Texas* M & W
Spartanburg Methodist College *South Carolina* M & W
Spokane Community College *Washington* M & W
Spokane Falls Community College *Washington* M & W
Spring Arbor University *Michigan* M & W
Spring Hill College *Alabama* M & W
Springfield College *Massachusetts* M & W
Stanford University *California* M & W
State University of New York College of Agriculture and Technology at Cobleskill *New York* M & W
State University of New York College at Cortland *New York* W
State University of New York College at Geneseo *New York* M & W
State University of New York College at Oneonta *New York* M & W
State University of New York College of Technology at Delhi *New York* M & W
State University of New York at Fredonia *New York* M & W
State University of New York at New Paltz *New York* M & W
State University of New York at Oswego *New York* M & W
State University of New York at Plattsburgh *New York* W

M = Men; W = Women

Stephen F. Austin State University *Texas* M & W
Stephens College *Missouri* W
Stetson University *Florida* M & W
Stevens Institute of Technology *New Jersey* M & W
Stevenson University *Maryland* M & W
Stillman College *Alabama* M & W
Stockton University *New Jersey* W
Stonehill College *Massachusetts* M & W
Stony Brook University, State University of New York *New York* M & W
Suffolk County Community College *New York* M & W
Suffolk University *Massachusetts* M & W
Sul Ross State University *Texas* M & W
Summit University *Pennsylvania* W
Susquehanna University *Pennsylvania* M & W
Swarthmore College *Pennsylvania* M & W
Sweet Briar College *Virginia* W
Syracuse University *New York* M & W
Tabor College *Kansas* M & W
Talladega College *Alabama* W
Tarleton State University *Texas* W
Taylor University *Indiana* M & W
Temple College *Texas* M & W
Temple University *Pennsylvania* M & W
Tennessee State University *Tennessee* M & W
Tennessee Technological University *Tennessee* M
Tennessee Wesleyan College *Tennessee* M & W
Texas A&M University *Texas* M & W
Texas A&M University - Corpus Christi *Texas* M & W
Texas A&M University - Kingsville *Texas* W
Texas Christian University *Texas* M & W
Texas Lutheran University *Texas* M & W
Texas Southern University *Texas* M & W
Texas State University *Texas* M & W
Texas Tech University *Texas* M & W
Texas Wesleyan University *Texas* W
Thiel College *Pennsylvania* M & W
Thomas College *Maine* M & W
Thomas More College *Kentucky* M & W
Tiffin University *Ohio* M & W
Tougaloo College *Mississippi* M & W
Towson University *Maryland* M & W
Transylvania University *Kentucky* M & W
Treasure Valley Community College *Oregon* M & W
Trine University *Indiana* M & W
Trinity College *Connecticut* M & W
Trinity University *Texas* M & W
Trinity Washington University *District of Columbia* W
Troy University *Alabama* M & W
Truman State University *Missouri* M & W
Tufts University *Massachusetts* M & W
Tulane University *Louisiana* W
Tusculum College *Tennessee* M & W
Tuskegee University *Alabama* M & W
Tyler Junior College *Texas* W
Ulster County Community College *New York* M
Union College *Kentucky* M & W
Union College *New York* M & W
United States Air Force Academy *Colorado* M & W
United States Coast Guard Academy *Connecticut* M
United States Merchant Marine Academy *New York* M
United States Military Academy *New York* M & W
United States Naval Academy *Maryland* M & W
Universidad Metropolitana *Puerto Rico* M & W
Universidad del Turabo *Puerto Rico* M & W
Université de Montréal *Quebec (Canada)* M & W
The University of Akron *Ohio* W
The University of Alabama *Alabama* M & W
The University of Alabama at Birmingham *Alabama* M & W
The University of Alabama in Huntsville *Alabama* M & W
University at Albany, State University of New York *New York* W
University of Alberta *Alberta (Canada)* M & W
The University of Arizona *Arizona* M & W
University of Arkansas *Arkansas* M & W
University of Arkansas - Fort Smith *Arkansas* M & W

University of Arkansas at Monticello *Arkansas* W
University at Buffalo, the State University of New York *New York* M & W
University of Calgary *Alberta (Canada)* M & W
University of California, Berkeley *California* M & W
University of California, Davis *California* M & W
University of California, Irvine *California* M & W
University of California, Los Angeles *California* M & W
University of California, Riverside *California* M & W
University of California, San Diego *California* M & W
University of California, Santa Barbara *California* M & W
University of California, Santa Cruz *California* M & W
University of Central Arkansas *Arkansas* W
University of Central Florida *Florida* M & W
University of Central Oklahoma *Oklahoma* W
University of Charleston *West Virginia* M & W
University of Chicago *Illinois* M & W
University of Cincinnati *Ohio* W
University of Colorado Boulder *Colorado* M & W
University of Connecticut *Connecticut* M & W
University of the Cumberlands *Kentucky* M & W
University of Dayton *Ohio* M & W
University of Delaware *Delaware* M & W
University of Denver *Colorado* M & W
University of Detroit Mercy *Michigan* M & W
University of the District of Columbia *District of Columbia* M & W
University of Dubuque *Iowa* M & W
University of Evansville *Indiana* W
The University of Findlay *Ohio* M & W
University of Florida *Florida* M & W
University of Georgia *Georgia* M & W
University of Hartford *Connecticut* M & W
University of Hawaii at Hilo *Hawaii* M & W
University of Hawaii at Manoa *Hawaii* M & W
University of Houston *Texas* W
University of Idaho *Idaho* M & W
University of Illinois at Chicago *Illinois* M & W
University of Illinois at Springfield *Illinois* M & W
University of Illinois at Urbana - Champaign *Illinois* M & W
University of the Incarnate Word *Texas* M & W
University of Indianapolis *Indiana* M & W
The University of Iowa *Iowa* M & W
The University of Kansas *Kansas* W
University of Kentucky *Kentucky* M & W
University of La Verne *California* M & W
University of Louisiana at Lafayette *Louisiana* M & W
University of Louisiana at Monroe *Louisiana* W
University of Louisville *Kentucky* M & W
University of Maine at Farmington *Maine* M & W
University of Mary *North Dakota* M & W
University of Mary Hardin-Baylor *Texas* M & W
University of Mary Washington *Virginia* M & W
University of Maryland, Baltimore County *Maryland* M & W
University of Maryland, College Park *Maryland* M & W
University of Maryland Eastern Shore *Maryland* M & W
University of Massachusetts Amherst *Massachusetts* W
University of Massachusetts Boston *Massachusetts* M & W
University of Massachusetts Dartmouth *Massachusetts* M & W
University of Memphis *Tennessee* M & W
University of Miami *Florida* M & W
University of Michigan *Michigan* M & W
University of Michigan - Dearborn *Michigan* M & W
University of Minnesota, Crookston *Minnesota* W
University of Minnesota, Duluth *Minnesota* W
University of Minnesota, Morris *Minnesota* M & W
University of Minnesota, Twin Cities Campus *Minnesota* M & W
University of Mississippi *Mississippi* M & W
University of Missouri *Missouri* W
University of Missouri - Kansas City *Missouri* M & W

University of Missouri - St. Louis *Missouri* M & W
University of Mobile *Alabama* M & W
University of Montana *Montana* M & W
University of Montevallo *Alabama* W
University of Mount Olive *North Carolina* M & W
University of Mount Union *Ohio* M & W
University of Nebraska at Kearney *Nebraska* M & W
University of Nebraska - Lincoln *Nebraska* M & W
University of Nebraska at Omaha *Nebraska* M & W
University of Nevada, Las Vegas *Nevada* M & W
University of Nevada, Reno *Nevada* M & W
University of New Hampshire *New Hampshire* M & W
University of New Haven *Connecticut* W
University of New Mexico *New Mexico* M & W
University of New Orleans *Louisiana* M & W
University of North Alabama *Alabama* M & W
University of North Carolina at Asheville *North Carolina* M & W
The University of North Carolina at Chapel Hill *North Carolina* M & W
The University of North Carolina at Charlotte *North Carolina* M & W
The University of North Carolina at Greensboro *North Carolina* M & W
The University of North Carolina Wilmington *North Carolina* M & W
University of North Dakota *North Dakota* W
University of North Florida *Florida* M & W
University of North Georgia *Georgia* M & W
University of North Texas *Texas* M & W
University of Northern Colorado *Colorado* M & W
University of Northern Iowa *Iowa* W
University of Northwestern - St. Paul *Minnesota* M & W
University of Notre Dame *Indiana* M & W
University of Oklahoma *Oklahoma* M & W
University of Oregon *Oregon* M & W
University of the Pacific *California* M & W
University of Pennsylvania *Pennsylvania* M & W
University of Pikeville *Kentucky* M & W
University of Pittsburgh *Pennsylvania* W
University of Pittsburgh at Bradford *Pennsylvania* M & W
University of Pittsburgh at Greensburg *Pennsylvania* M & W
University of Portland *Oregon* M & W
University of Puerto Rico in Aguadilla *Puerto Rico* W
University of Puerto Rico in Arecibo *Puerto Rico* M & W
University of Puerto Rico in Bayamón *Puerto Rico* M & W
University of Puerto Rico in Carolina *Puerto Rico* M & W
University of Puerto Rico in Cayey *Puerto Rico* M & W
University of Puerto Rico in Humacao *Puerto Rico* W
University of Puerto Rico, Mayagüez Campus *Puerto Rico* M & W
University of Puerto Rico in Ponce *Puerto Rico* M
University of Puerto Rico, Río Piedras Campus *Puerto Rico* M & W
University of Puget Sound *Washington* M & W
University of Redlands *California* M & W
University of Rhode Island *Rhode Island* W
University of Richmond *Virginia* W
University of Rochester *New York* M & W
University of the Sacred Heart *Puerto Rico* M & W
University of St. Francis *Illinois* M & W
University of Saint Francis *Indiana* M & W
University of Saint Joseph *Connecticut* W
University of St. Thomas *Minnesota* M & W
University of St. Thomas *Texas* M & W
University of San Diego *California* M & W
University of San Francisco *California* M & W
University of the Sciences *Pennsylvania* M & W
The University of Scranton *Pennsylvania* M & W
University of Sioux Falls *South Dakota* M & W
University of South Alabama *Alabama* M & W
University of South Carolina *South Carolina* M & W

M = Men; W = Women

University of South Carolina Aiken *South Carolina* M & W
University of South Carolina Lancaster *South Carolina* M & W
University of South Carolina Upstate *South Carolina* M & W
The University of South Dakota *South Dakota* W
University of South Florida *Florida* M & W
University of Southern California *California* M & W
University of Southern Indiana *Indiana* M & W
University of Southern Maine *Maine* M & W
University of Southern Mississippi *Mississippi* M & W
University of the Southwest *New Mexico* M & W
The University of Tampa *Florida* W
The University of Tennessee *Tennessee* M & W
The University of Tennessee at Chattanooga *Tennessee* M & W
The University of Tennessee at Martin *Tennessee* W
The University of Texas at Arlington *Texas* M & W
The University of Texas at Austin *Texas* M & W
The University of Texas at Dallas *Texas* M & W
The University of Texas at El Paso *Texas* W
The University of Texas of the Permian Basin *Texas* M & W
The University of Texas Rio Grande Valley *Texas* M & W
The University of Texas at San Antonio *Texas* M & W
The University of Texas at Tyler *Texas* M & W
The University of Toledo *Ohio* M & W
University of Toronto *Ontario (Canada)* M & W
The University of Tulsa *Oklahoma* M & W
University of Utah *Utah* M & W
University of Virginia *Virginia* M & W
The University of Virginia's College at Wise *Virginia* M & W
University of Washington *Washington* M & W
University of Waterloo *Ontario (Canada)* M & W
The University of West Alabama *Alabama* M & W
University of West Florida *Florida* M & W
University of West Georgia *Georgia* W
The University of Western Ontario *Ontario (Canada)* M & W
University of Wisconsin - Baraboo/Sauk County *Wisconsin* M & W
University of Wisconsin - Eau Claire *Wisconsin* M & W
University of Wisconsin - Fond du Lac *Wisconsin* M & W
University of Wisconsin - Fox Valley *Wisconsin* M & W
University of Wisconsin - Green Bay *Wisconsin* M & W
University of Wisconsin - La Crosse *Wisconsin* M & W
University of Wisconsin - Madison *Wisconsin* M & W
University of Wisconsin - Manitowoc *Wisconsin* M & W
University of Wisconsin - Marshfield/Wood County *Wisconsin* M & W
University of Wisconsin - Milwaukee *Wisconsin* W
University of Wisconsin - Oshkosh *Wisconsin* M & W
University of Wisconsin - River Falls *Wisconsin* M & W
University of Wisconsin - Sheboygan *Wisconsin* M & W
University of Wisconsin - Stevens Point *Wisconsin* W
University of Wisconsin - Stout *Wisconsin* W
University of Wisconsin - Washington County *Wisconsin* M & W
University of Wisconsin - Waukesha *Wisconsin* M & W
University of Wisconsin - Whitewater *Wisconsin* M & W
University of Wyoming *Wyoming* M & W
Upper Iowa University *Iowa* W
Ursinus College *Pennsylvania* M & W
Ursuline College *Ohio* W
Utah State University *Utah* M & W
Utica College *New York* M & W

Valdosta State University *Georgia* M & W
Valley City State University *North Dakota* M & W
Valley Forge Military College *Pennsylvania* M
Valparaiso University *Indiana* M & W
Vanderbilt University *Tennessee* M & W
Vassar College *New York* M & W
Vaughn College of Aeronautics and Technology *New York* M & W
Ventura College *California* M & W
Victor Valley College *California* M & W
Villanova University *Pennsylvania* M & W
Virginia Commonwealth University *Virginia* M & W
Virginia Polytechnic Institute and State University *Virginia* M & W
Virginia State University *Virginia* M & W
Virginia Union University *Virginia* M & W
Virginia Wesleyan College *Virginia* M & W
Wabash College *Indiana* M
Wagner College *New York* M & W
Wake Forest University *North Carolina* M & W
Wallace State Community College *Alabama* M & W
Walsh University *Ohio* M & W
Warner University *Florida* M & W
Wartburg College *Iowa* M & W
Washburn University *Kansas* M & W
Washington College *Maryland* M & W
Washington & Jefferson College *Pennsylvania* M & W
Washington and Lee University *Virginia* M & W
Washington State University *Washington* M & W
Washington University in St. Louis *Missouri* M & W
Waubonsee Community College *Illinois* M & W
Wayne State University *Michigan* M & W
Waynesburg University *Pennsylvania* M & W
Weatherford College *Texas* W
Webb Institute *New York* M & W
Webber International University *Florida* M & W
Weber State University *Utah* M & W
Webster University *Missouri* M & W
Wellesley College *Massachusetts* W
Wells College *New York* W
Wentworth Institute of Technology *Massachusetts* M & W
Wesley College *Delaware* M & W
Wesleyan College *Georgia* W
Wesleyan University *Connecticut* M & W
West Chester University of Pennsylvania *Pennsylvania* M & W
West Hills Community College *California* W
West Liberty University *West Virginia* M & W
West Valley College *California* W
West Virginia State University *West Virginia* M & W
West Virginia University *West Virginia* W
West Virginia Wesleyan College *West Virginia* M & W
Western Carolina University *North Carolina* M & W
Western Connecticut State University *Connecticut* M & W
Western Illinois University *Illinois* M & W
Western Kentucky University *Kentucky* M & W
Western Michigan University *Michigan* M & W
Western New England University *Massachusetts* M & W
Western New Mexico University *New Mexico* M & W
Westminster College *Missouri* M & W
Westminster College *Pennsylvania* M & W
Westmont College *California* M & W
Wheaton College *Illinois* M & W
Wheaton College *Massachusetts* M & W
Wheelock College *Massachusetts* M
Whitman College *Washington* M & W
Whittier College *California* M & W
Whitworth University *Washington* M & W
Wichita State University *Kansas* M & W
Wilkes University *Pennsylvania* M & W
Willamette University *Oregon* M & W
William Jewell College *Missouri* M & W
William Paterson University of New Jersey *New Jersey* W
William Peace University *North Carolina* M & W
Williams College *Massachusetts* M & W
Williamson College of the Trades *Pennsylvania* M
Wilmington College *Ohio* M & W

Wingate University *North Carolina* M & W
Winona State University *Minnesota* W
Winston-Salem State University *North Carolina* M & W
Winthrop University *South Carolina* M & W
Wisconsin Lutheran College *Wisconsin* M & W
Wittenberg University *Ohio* M & W
Wofford College *South Carolina* M & W
Worcester State University *Massachusetts* W
Wright State University *Ohio* M & W
Xavier University *Ohio* M & W
Xavier University of Louisiana *Louisiana* M & W
Yale University *Connecticut* M & W
Yeshiva University *New York* M & W
York College of the City University of New York *New York* M
York College of Pennsylvania *Pennsylvania* M & W
York University *Ontario (Canada)* M & W
Young Harris College *Georgia* M & W
Youngstown State University *Ohio* M & W
Yuba College *California* M & W

Track and Field

Abilene Christian University *Texas* M & W
Academy of Art University *California* M & W
Acadia University *Nova Scotia (Canada)* W
Adams State University *Colorado* M & W
Adelphi University *New York* M & W
Adrian College *Michigan* M & W
Alabama Agricultural and Mechanical University *Alabama* M & W
Alabama State University *Alabama* M & W
Albany College of Pharmacy and Health Sciences *New York* M & W
Albany State University *Georgia* M & W
Albion College *Michigan* M & W
Albright College *Pennsylvania* M & W
Alcorn State University *Mississippi* M & W
Alderson Broaddus University *West Virginia* M & W
Alfred University *New York* M & W
Alice Lloyd College *Kentucky* M & W
Allan Hancock College *California* M & W
Allegheny College *Pennsylvania* M & W
Allen Community College *Kansas* M & W
Allen University *South Carolina* M & W
Alma College *Michigan* M & W
Alvernia University *Pennsylvania* M & W
American International College *Massachusetts* M & W
American River College *California* M & W
American University *District of Columbia* M & W
American University of Puerto Rico *Bayamon, Puerto Rico* M & W
Amherst College *Massachusetts* M & W
Anderson University *Indiana* M & W
Anderson University *South Carolina* M & W
Angelo State University *Texas* M & W
Antelope Valley College *California* M & W
Appalachian State University *North Carolina* M & W
Aquinas College *Michigan* M & W
Arizona Christian University *Arizona* M & W
Arizona State University at the Downtown Phoenix campus *Arizona* M & W
Arizona State University at the Polytechnic campus *Arizona* M & W
Arizona State University at the Tempe campus *Arizona* M & W
Arizona State University at the West campus *Arizona* M & W
Arkansas State University *Arkansas* M & W
Ashford University *California* M & W
Ashland University *Ohio* M & W
Assumption College *Massachusetts* M & W
Auburn University *Alabama* M & W
Augsburg College *Minnesota* M & W
Augusta University *Georgia* M & W
Augustana College *Illinois* M & W
Augustana University *South Dakota* M & W
Aurora University *Illinois* M & W
Austin Peay State University *Tennessee* W
Avila University *Missouri* M & W
Azusa Pacific University *California* M & W
Babson College *Massachusetts* M & W
Baker University *Kansas* M & W

M = Men; W = Women

Bakersfield College *California* M & W
Baldwin Wallace University *Ohio* M & W
Ball State University *Indiana* W
Bard College *New York* M & W
Barnard College *New York* W
Barton College *North Carolina* M & W
Barton County Community College *Kansas* M & W
Bates College *Maine* M & W
Bayamón Central University *Puerto Rico* M & W
Baylor University *Texas* M & W
Bellarmine University *Kentucky* M & W
Bellevue College *Washington* M & W
Belmont Abbey College *North Carolina* M & W
Belmont University *Tennessee* M & W
Beloit College *Wisconsin* M & W
Bemidji State University *Minnesota* W
Benedict College *South Carolina* M
Benedictine College *Kansas* M & W
Benedictine University *Illinois* M & W
Bentley University *Massachusetts* M & W
Berea College *Kentucky* M & W
Bergen Community College *New Jersey* M & W
Berkeley College - New York City Campus *New York* M & W
Berry College *Georgia* M & W
Bethany College *Kansas* M & W
Bethany College *West Virginia* M & W
Bethany Lutheran College *Minnesota* M & W
Bethel College *Indiana* M & W
Bethel College *Kansas* M & W
Bethel University *Minnesota* W
Bethel University *Tennessee* M & W
Bethune-Cookman University *Florida* M & W
Binghamton University, State University of New York *New York* M & W
Biola University *California* M & W
Birmingham-Southern College *Alabama* M & W
Black Hills State University *South Dakota* M & W
Bloomsburg University of Pennsylvania *Pennsylvania* M & W
Bluefield College *Virginia* M & W
Bluffton University *Ohio* M & W
Boise State University *Idaho* M & W
Boston College *Massachusetts* M & W
Boston University *Massachusetts* M & W
Bowdoin College *Maine* M & W
Bowie State University *Maryland* M & W
Bowling Green State University *Ohio* W
Bradley University *Illinois* M & W
Brandeis University *Massachusetts* M & W
Brescia University *Kentucky* M & W
Brevard College *North Carolina* M & W
Briar Cliff University *Iowa* M & W
Bridgewater College *Virginia* M & W
Bridgewater State University *Massachusetts* M & W
Brigham Young University *Utah* M & W
Bronx Community College of the City University of New York *New York* M & W
Brooklyn College of the City University of New York *New York* M & W
Brown University *Rhode Island* M & W
Bryan College *Tennessee* M & W
Bryant University *Rhode Island* M & W
Bryn Mawr College *Pennsylvania* W
Bucknell University *Pennsylvania* M & W
Buena Vista University *Iowa* M & W
Buffalo State College, State University of New York *New York* M & W
Butler Community College *Kansas* M & W
Butler University *Indiana* M & W
Butte College *California* M & W
Caldwell University *New Jersey* M & W
California Baptist University *California* M & W
California Institute of Technology *California* M & W
California Lutheran University *California* M & W
California Polytechnic State University, San Luis Obispo *California* M & W
California State Polytechnic University, Pomona *California* M & W
California State University, Bakersfield *California* M & W
California State University, Chico *California* M & W
California State University, Dominguez Hills *California* W

California State University, Fresno *California* M & W
California State University, Fullerton *California* M & W
California State University, Long Beach *California* M & W
California State University, Los Angeles *California* M & W
California State University, Northridge *California* M & W
California State University, Sacramento *California* M & W
California State University, San Bernardino *California* W
California State University, San Marcos *California* M & W
California State University, Stanislaus *California* M & W
California University of Pennsylvania *Pennsylvania* M & W
Calumet College of Saint Joseph *Indiana* M & W
Calvin College *Michigan* M & W
Campbell University *North Carolina* M & W
Campbellsville University *Kentucky* M & W
Capital University *Ohio* M & W
Cardinal Stritch University *Wisconsin* M & W
Caribbean University *Puerto Rico* M & W
Carleton College *Minnesota* M & W
Carnegie Mellon University *Pennsylvania* M & W
Carroll College *Montana* M & W
Carroll University *Wisconsin* M & W
Carson-Newman University *Tennessee* M & W
Carthage College *Wisconsin* M & W
Case Western Reserve University *Ohio* M & W
The Catholic University of America *District of Columbia* M & W
Cedar Crest College *Pennsylvania* W
Cedarville University *Ohio* M & W
Central Arizona College *Arizona* M & W
Central College *Iowa* M & W
Central Connecticut State University *Connecticut* M & W
Central Methodist University *Missouri* M & W
Central Michigan University *Michigan* M & W
Central State University *Ohio* M & W
Central Washington University *Washington* M & W
Centre College *Kentucky* M & W
Cerritos College *California* M & W
Chabot College *California* M & W
Chadron State College *Nebraska* M & W
Chaffey College *California* M & W
Chapman University *California* M & W
Charleston Southern University *South Carolina* M & W
Chatham University *Pennsylvania* M & W
Chestnut Hill College *Pennsylvania* M & W
Cheyney University of Pennsylvania *Pennsylvania* M & W
Chicago State University *Illinois* M & W
Christian Brothers University *Tennessee* M & W
Christopher Newport University *Virginia* M & W
The Citadel, The Military College of South Carolina *South Carolina* M & W
City College of the City University of New York *New York* M & W
City College of San Francisco *California* M & W
Clackamas Community College *Oregon* M & W
Claflin University *South Carolina* M & W
Claremont McKenna College *California* M & W
Clarion University of Pennsylvania *Pennsylvania* W
Clark Atlanta University *Georgia* M & W
Clark College *Washington* M & W
Clarke University *Iowa* M & W
Clayton State University *Georgia* M & W
Clemson University *South Carolina* M & W
Cleveland State University *Ohio* W
Cloud County Community College *Kansas* M & W
Coastal Carolina University *South Carolina* M & W
Coe College *Iowa* M & W
Coffeyville Community College *Kansas* M & W
Coker College *South Carolina* M & W
Colby College *Maine* M & W
Colby Community College *Kansas* M & W
Colby-Sawyer College *New Hampshire* M & W

Colgate University *New York* M & W
The College at Brockport, State University of New York *New York* M & W
College of the Canyons *California* M & W
College of the Desert *California* M & W
College of the Holy Cross *Massachusetts* M & W
The College of Idaho *Idaho* M & W
College of Marin *California* M & W
College of Mount Saint Vincent *New York* M & W
The College of New Jersey *New Jersey* M & W
College of Saint Benedict *Minnesota* W
The College of Saint Rose *New York* M & W
The College of St. Scholastica *Minnesota* M & W
College of San Mateo *California* M & W
College of the Sequoias *California* M & W
College of the Siskiyous *California* M & W
College of Staten Island of the City University of New York *New York* M & W
The College of William and Mary *Virginia* M & W
The College of Wooster *Ohio* M & W
Colorado Christian University *Colorado* M & W
The Colorado College *Colorado* M & W
Colorado Mesa University *Colorado* M & W
Colorado School of Mines *Colorado* M & W
Colorado State University *Colorado* M & W
Colorado State University - Pueblo *Colorado* M & W
Columbia College *South Carolina* W
Columbia-Greene Community College *New York* M & W
Columbia University *New York* M & W
Columbia University, School of General Studies *New York* M & W
Columbus State Community College *Ohio* M & W
Community College of Baltimore County *Maryland* W
Community College of Philadelphia *Pennsylvania* M & W
Community College of Rhode Island *Rhode Island* M & W
Concord University *West Virginia* M & W
Concordia College *Minnesota* M & W
Concordia College Alabama *Alabama* M & W
Concordia University *Oregon* M & W
Concordia University Ann Arbor *Michigan* M & W
Concordia University Chicago *Illinois* M & W
Concordia University Irvine *California* M & W
Concordia University, Nebraska *Nebraska* M & W
Concordia University, St. Paul *Minnesota* M & W
Concordia University Texas *Texas* M & W
Concordia University Wisconsin *Wisconsin* M & W
Connecticut College *Connecticut* M & W
Converse College *South Carolina* W
Copiah-Lincoln Community College *Mississippi* M
Coppin State University *Maryland* M & W
Corban University *Oregon* M & W
Cornell College *Iowa* M & W
Cornell University *New York* M & W
Cornerstone University *Michigan* M & W
Cowley County Community College and Area Vocational - Technical School *Kansas* M & W
Cuesta College *California* M & W
Culver-Stockton College *Missouri* M & W
Cumberland County College *New Jersey* M
Cuyamaca College *California* M & W
Daemen College *New York* M & W
Dakota State University *South Dakota* M & W
Dakota Wesleyan University *South Dakota* M & W
Dalhousie University *Nova Scotia (Canada)* M & W
Dallas Baptist University *Texas* M & W
Dartmouth College *New Hampshire* M & W
Davenport University *Michigan* M & W
Davidson College *North Carolina* M & W
De Anza College *California* M & W
Defiance College *Ohio* M & W
Delaware State University *Delaware* M & W
Delaware Valley University *Pennsylvania* M & W
Delgado Community College *Louisiana* W
Denison University *Ohio* M & W
DePaul University *Illinois* M & W
DePauw University *Indiana* M & W
DeSales University *Pennsylvania* M & W
Diablo Valley College *California* M & W
Dickinson College *Pennsylvania* M & W

M = Men; W = Women

Dickinson State University *North Dakota* M & W
Dillard University *Louisiana* M & W
Doane University *Nebraska* M & W
Dodge City Community College *Kansas* M & W
Dominican College *New York* M & W
Dordt College *Iowa* M & W
Drake University *Iowa* M & W
Drew University *New Jersey* M & W
Drury University *Missouri* M & W
Duke University *North Carolina* M & W
Duquesne University *Pennsylvania* M & W
Earlham College *Indiana* M & W
East Carolina University *North Carolina* M & W
East Central University *Oklahoma* M & W
East Los Angeles College *California* M & W
East Stroudsburg University of Pennsylvania *Pennsylvania* M & W
East Tennessee State University *Tennessee* M & W
East Texas Baptist University *Texas* M & W
Eastern Connecticut State University *Connecticut* M & W
Eastern Illinois University *Illinois* M & W
Eastern Kentucky University *Kentucky* M & W
Eastern Mennonite University *Virginia* M & W
Eastern Michigan University *Michigan* M & W
Eastern New Mexico University *New Mexico* M & W
Eastern Oregon University *Oregon* M & W
Eastern Washington University *Washington* M & W
Edgewood College *Wisconsin* M & W
Edinboro University of Pennsylvania *Pennsylvania* M & W
Edward Waters College *Florida* M & W
El Camino College *California* M & W
El Paso Community College *Texas* M & W
Elizabethtown College *Pennsylvania* M & W
Ellsworth Community College *Iowa* M & W
Elmhurst College *Illinois* M & W
Elon University *North Carolina* W
Embry-Riddle Aeronautical University - Daytona *Florida* M & W
Embry-Riddle Aeronautical University - Prescott *Arizona* M & W
Emerson College *Massachusetts* W
Emmanuel College *Georgia* M & W
Emmanuel College *Massachusetts* M & W
Emory University *Georgia* M & W
Emporia State University *Kansas* M & W
Essex County College *New Jersey* M & W
Eureka College *Illinois* M & W
Evangel University *Missouri* M & W
The Evergreen State College *Washington* M & W
Fairleigh Dickinson University, Metropolitan Campus *New Jersey* M & W
Faith Baptist Bible College and Theological Seminary *Iowa* M & W
Farmingdale State College *New York* M & W
Fashion Institute of Technology *New York* M & W
Fayetteville State University *North Carolina* M & W
Feather River College *California* M & W
Ferris State University *Michigan* M & W
Finger Lakes Community College *New York* M & W
Fisk University *Tennessee* M & W
Fitchburg State University *Massachusetts* M & W
Florida Agricultural and Mechanical University *Florida* M & W
Florida Atlantic University *Florida* M & W
Florida Institute of Technology *Florida* M & W
Florida International University *Florida* M & W
Florida Memorial University *Florida* M & W
Florida Southern College *Florida* M & W
Florida State University *Florida* M & W
Fontbonne University *Missouri* M & W
Fordham University *New York* M & W
Fort Scott Community College *Kansas* M & W
Fort Valley State University *Georgia* M & W
Francis Marion University *South Carolina* M & W
Franciscan University of Steubenville *Ohio* M & W
Franklin College *Indiana* M & W
Franklin & Marshall College *Pennsylvania* M & W
Fresno City College *California* M & W
Fresno Pacific University *California* M & W
Friends University *Kansas* M & W
Frostburg State University *Maryland* M & W

Fullerton College *California* M & W
Furman University *South Carolina* M & W
Gallaudet University *District of Columbia* M & W
Garden City Community College *Kansas* M & W
Gardner-Webb University *North Carolina* M & W
Geneva College *Pennsylvania* M & W
George Fox University *Oregon* M & W
George Mason University *Virginia* M & W
Georgetown College *Kentucky* M & W
Georgetown University *District of Columbia* M & W
Georgia Institute of Technology *Georgia* M & W
Georgia Southern University *Georgia* W
Georgia State University *Georgia* W
Georgian Court University *New Jersey* W
Gettysburg College *Pennsylvania* M & W
Glen Oaks Community College *Michigan* M & W
Glendale Community College *Arizona* M & W
Glendale Community College *California* M & W
Glenville State College *West Virginia* M & W
Globe Institute of Technology *New York* M & W
Golden West College *California* M & W
Gonzaga University *Washington* M & W
Gordon College *Massachusetts* M & W
Goshen College *Indiana* M & W
Goucher College *Maryland* M & W
Grace College *Indiana* M & W
Graceland University *Iowa* M & W
Grambling State University *Louisiana* M & W
Grand Canyon University *Arizona* M & W
Grand Valley State University *Michigan* M & W
Grand View University *Iowa* M & W
Green Mountain College *Vermont* M & W
Greenville College *Illinois* M & W
Grinnell College *Iowa* M & W
Grossmont College *California* M
Grove City College *Pennsylvania* M & W
Gustavus Adolphus College *Minnesota* M & W
Gwynedd Mercy University *Pennsylvania* M & W
Hagerstown Community College *Maryland* M & W
Hamilton College *New York* M & W
Hamline University *Minnesota* M & W
Hampton University *Virginia* M & W
Hannibal-LaGrange University *Missouri* M & W
Hanover College *Indiana* M & W
Harcum College *Pennsylvania* M & W
Hardin-Simmons University *Texas* M & W
Harding University *Arkansas* M & W
Harper College *Illinois* M & W
Harvard University *Massachusetts* M & W
Harvey Mudd College *California* M & W
Haskell Indian Nations University *Kansas* M & W
Hastings College *Nebraska* M & W
Haverford College *Pennsylvania* M & W
Heidelberg University *Ohio* M & W
Hendrix College *Arkansas* M & W
Herkimer County Community College *New York* M & W
High Point University *North Carolina* M & W
Highland Community College *Kansas* M & W
Highline College *Washington* M & W
Hillsdale College *Michigan* M & W
Hinds Community College *Mississippi* M & W
Holy Family University *Pennsylvania* M & W
Holyoke Community College *Massachusetts* M & W
Hood College *Maryland* M & W
Hope College *Michigan* M & W
Hope International University *California* M & W
Houghton College *New York* M & W
Houston Baptist University *Texas* M & W
Howard Community College *Maryland* M & W
Howard University *District of Columbia* M & W
Humboldt State University *California* M & W
Hunter College of the City University of New York *New York* M & W
Huntington University *Indiana* M & W
Husson University *Maine* M & W
Huston-Tillotson University *Texas* M & W
Hutchinson Community College *Kansas* M & W
Idaho State University *Idaho* M & W
Illinois College *Illinois* M & W
Illinois Institute of Technology *Illinois* M & W
Illinois State University *Illinois* M & W
Illinois Wesleyan University *Illinois* M & W
Indiana State University *Indiana* M & W

Indiana Tech *Indiana* M & W
Indiana University Bloomington *Indiana* M & W
Indiana University East *Indiana* M & W
Indiana University of Pennsylvania *Pennsylvania* M & W
Indiana University - Purdue University Fort Wayne *Indiana* W
Indiana University - Purdue University Indianapolis *Indiana* M & W
Indiana Wesleyan University *Indiana* M & W
Inter American University of Puerto Rico, Aguadilla Campus *Puerto Rico* M & W
Inter American University of Puerto Rico, Arecibo Campus *Puerto Rico* M & W
Inter American University of Puerto Rico, Barranquitas Campus *Puerto Rico* M & W
Inter American University of Puerto Rico, Bayamón Campus *Puerto Rico* M & W
Inter American University of Puerto Rico, Fajardo Campus *Puerto Rico* M & W
Inter American University of Puerto Rico, Ponce Campus *Puerto Rico* M & W
Inter American University of Puerto Rico, San Germán Campus *Puerto Rico* M & W
Iona College *New York* M & W
Iowa State University of Science and Technology *Iowa* M & W
Iowa Western Community College *Iowa* M & W
Itawamba Community College *Mississippi* M
Ithaca College *New York* M & W
Jackson State University *Mississippi* M & W
Jacksonville University *Florida* W
James Madison University *Virginia* W
Jarvis Christian College *Texas* M & W
John Carroll University *Ohio* M & W
Johns Hopkins University *Maryland* M & W
Johnson C. Smith University *North Carolina* M & W
Johnson County Community College *Kansas* M & W
Johnson State College *Vermont* M & W
Joliet Junior College *Illinois* M & W
Jones County Junior College *Mississippi* M
Judson University *Illinois* M & W
Juniata College *Pennsylvania* M & W
Kansas City Kansas Community College *Kansas* M & W
Kansas State University *Kansas* M & W
Kansas Wesleyan University *Kansas* M & W
Keene State College *New Hampshire* M & W
Kennesaw State University *Georgia* M & W
Kent State University *Ohio* M & W
Kentucky State University *Kentucky* M & W
Kentucky Wesleyan College *Kentucky* M & W
Kenyon College *Ohio* M & W
Keystone College *Pennsylvania* M & W
King University *Tennessee* M & W
King's College *Pennsylvania* M & W
Kingsborough Community College of the City University of New York *New York* M & W
Knox College *Illinois* M & W
Kutztown University of Pennsylvania *Pennsylvania* M & W
La Salle University *Pennsylvania* M & W
Lafayette College *Pennsylvania* M & W
Lake Erie College *Ohio* M & W
Lake Forest College *Illinois* M & W
Lake Superior State University *Michigan* M & W
Lakehead University *Ontario (Canada)* M & W
Lakeland College *Wisconsin* M & W
Lamar University *Texas* M & W
Lane College *Tennessee* M & W
Lane Community College *Oregon* M & W
Langston University *Oklahoma* M & W
Lansing Community College *Michigan* M & W
Lasell College *Massachusetts* M & W
Lassen Community College District *California* M & W
Laurentian University *Ontario (Canada)* M & W
Lawrence University *Wisconsin* M & W
Le Moyne College *New York* M & W
Lebanon Valley College *Pennsylvania* M & W
Lee University *Tennessee* M & W
Lees-McRae College *North Carolina* M & W
Lehigh University *Pennsylvania* M & W

M = Men; W = Women

Lehman College of the City University of New York *New York* M & W
Lenoir-Rhyne University *North Carolina* M & W
Lewis & Clark College *Oregon* M & W
Lewis University *Illinois* M & W
Liberty University *Virginia* M & W
Life University *Georgia* W
Limestone College *South Carolina* M & W
Lincoln University *Missouri* M & W
Lincoln University *Pennsylvania* M & W
Lindenwood University *Missouri* M & W
Lindsey Wilson College *Kentucky* M & W
Linfield College *Oregon* M & W
Lipscomb University *Tennessee* M & W
Livingstone College *North Carolina* M & W
Lock Haven University of Pennsylvania *Pennsylvania* M & W
Long Beach City College *California* M & W
Long Island University - LIU Brooklyn *New York* M & W
Long Island University - LIU Post *New York* M & W
Loras College *Iowa* M & W
Los Angeles City College *California* M & W
Los Angeles Southwest College *California* M & W
Los Angeles Valley College *California* M & W
Louisiana State University and Agricultural & Mechanical College *Louisiana* M & W
Louisiana Tech University *Louisiana* M & W
Lourdes University *Ohio* M & W
Loyola Marymount University *California* M & W
Loyola University Chicago *Illinois* M & W
Loyola University Maryland *Maryland* W
Loyola University New Orleans *Louisiana* M & W
Lubbock Christian University *Texas* M & W
Luther College *Iowa* M & W
Lynchburg College *Virginia* M & W
Macalester College *Minnesota* M & W
Macomb Community College *Michigan* M & W
Madison Area Technical College *Wisconsin* M & W
Madonna University *Michigan* M & W
Malone University *Ohio* M & W
Manchester University *Indiana* M & W
Manhattan College *New York* M & W
Manhattanville College *New York* M & W
Mansfield University of Pennsylvania *Pennsylvania* M & W
Marian University *Indiana* M & W
Marian University *Wisconsin* M & W
Marietta College *Ohio* M & W
Marist College *New York* M & W
Marquette University *Wisconsin* M & W
Mars Hill University *North Carolina* M & W
Marshall University *West Virginia* M & W
Martin Luther College *Minnesota* M & W
Marymount California University *California* M
Maryville University of Saint Louis *Missouri* M & W
Marywood University *Pennsylvania* M & W
Massachusetts Institute of Technology *Massachusetts* M & W
Massachusetts Maritime Academy *Massachusetts* M & W
The Master's College and Seminary *California* M & W
McDaniel College *Maryland* M & W
McGill University *Quebec (Canada)* M & W
McKendree University *Illinois* M & W
McMaster University *Ontario (Canada)* M & W
McMurry University *Texas* M & W
McNeese State University *Louisiana* M & W
McPherson College *Kansas* M & W
Medgar Evers College of the City University of New York *New York* M & W
Menlo College *California* M & W
Merced College *California* M & W
Mercer County Community College *New Jersey* M & W
Mercer University *Georgia* W
Meredith College *North Carolina* W
Meridian Community College *Mississippi* M & W
Merrimack College *Massachusetts* M & W
Merritt College *California* M & W
Mesa Community College *Arizona* M & W
Messiah College *Pennsylvania* M & W
Methodist University *North Carolina* M & W

Metropolitan State University of Denver *Colorado* M & W
Miami University *Ohio* M & W
Michigan State University *Michigan* M & W
Michigan Technological University *Michigan* M & W
MidAmerica Nazarene University *Kansas* M & W
Middle Tennessee State University *Tennessee* M & W
Middlebury College *Vermont* M & W
Middlesex County College *New Jersey* M & W
Midland University *Nebraska* M & W
Midway University *Kentucky* W
Miles College *Alabama* M
Millersville University of Pennsylvania *Pennsylvania* W
Milligan College *Tennessee* M & W
Millikin University *Illinois* M & W
Millsaps College *Mississippi* M & W
Milwaukee School of Engineering *Wisconsin* M & W
Minnesota State University Mankato *Minnesota* M & W
Minnesota State University Moorhead *Minnesota* M & W
Minot State University *North Dakota* M & W
Misericordia University *Pennsylvania* M & W
Mississippi College *Mississippi* M & W
Mississippi Gulf Coast Community College *Mississippi* M
Mississippi State University *Mississippi* M & W
Mississippi Valley State University *Mississippi* M & W
Missouri Baptist University *Missouri* M & W
Missouri Southern State University *Missouri* M & W
Missouri State University *Missouri* W
Missouri University of Science and Technology *Missouri* M & W
Missouri Valley College *Missouri* M & W
Modesto Junior College *California* M & W
Mohawk Valley Community College *New York* M & W
Molloy College *New York* M & W
Monmouth College *Illinois* M & W
Monmouth University *New Jersey* M & W
Monroe College *New York* M & W
Montana State University *Montana* M & W
Montclair State University *New Jersey* M & W
Monterey Peninsula College *California* M & W
Montgomery College *Maryland* M & W
Montreat College *North Carolina* M & W
Moorpark College *California* M & W
Moravian College *Pennsylvania* M & W
Morehead State University *Kentucky* M & W
Morehouse College *Georgia* M
Morgan State University *Maryland* M & W
Morningside College *Iowa* M & W
Morris College *South Carolina* M & W
Mount Holyoke College *Massachusetts* W
Mt. Hood Community College *Oregon* M & W
Mount Marty College *South Dakota* M & W
Mount Mercy University *Iowa* M & W
Mount St. Joseph University *Ohio* M & W
Mount Saint Mary College *New York* M & W
Mount St. Mary's University *Maryland* M & W
Mt. San Antonio College *California* M & W
Mount Vernon Nazarene University *Ohio* M & W
Muhlenberg College *Pennsylvania* M & W
Murray State University *Kentucky* W
Muskingum University *Ohio* M & W
Nassau Community College *New York* M & W
Nazareth College of Rochester *New York* M & W
Nebraska Wesleyan University *Nebraska* M & W
Neosho County Community College *Kansas* M
Neumann University *Pennsylvania* M & W
New Jersey Institute of Technology *New Jersey* M & W
New Mexico Highlands University *New Mexico* M & W
New Mexico Military Institute *New Mexico* M
New Mexico State University *New Mexico* W
New York University *New York* M & W
Newbury College *Massachusetts* M & W
Niagara University *New York* W
Nicholls State University *Louisiana* W

Nichols College *Massachusetts* M & W
Norfolk State University *Virginia* M & W
North Carolina Agricultural and Technical State University *North Carolina* M & W
North Carolina Central University *North Carolina* M & W
North Carolina State University *North Carolina* M & W
North Central College *Illinois* M & W
North Central University *Minnesota* M & W
North Dakota State University *North Dakota* M & W
North Greenville University *South Carolina* M & W
North Iowa Area Community College *Iowa* M & W
North Park University *Illinois* M & W
Northeastern University *Massachusetts* M & W
Northern Arizona University *Arizona* M & W
Northern Kentucky University *Kentucky* M & W
Northern Michigan University *Michigan* M & W
Northern State University *South Dakota* M & W
Northwest Christian University *Oregon* M & W
Northwest Missouri State University *Missouri* M & W
Northwest Nazarene University *Idaho* M & W
Northwest University *Washington* M & W
Northwestern College *Iowa* M & W
Northwestern State University of Louisiana *Louisiana* M & W
Northwood University, Michigan Campus *Michigan* M & W
Northwood University, Texas Campus *Texas* M & W
Norwich University *Vermont* M & W
Notre Dame College *Ohio* M & W
Nova Southeastern University *Florida* M & W
Oakland University *Michigan* M & W
Oakton Community College *Illinois* M & W
Oberlin College *Ohio* M & W
Occidental College *California* M & W
Oglethorpe University *Georgia* M & W
Ohio Dominican University *Ohio* M & W
Ohio Northern University *Ohio* M & W
The Ohio State University *Ohio* M & W
Ohio University *Ohio* W
Ohio Wesleyan University *Ohio* M & W
Oklahoma Baptist University *Oklahoma* M & W
Oklahoma Christian University *Oklahoma* M & W
Oklahoma City University *Oklahoma* M & W
Oklahoma State University *Oklahoma* M & W
Oklahoma Wesleyan University *Oklahoma* M & W
Olivet College *Michigan* M & W
Olivet Nazarene University *Illinois* M & W
Olympic College *Washington* M & W
Oral Roberts University *Oklahoma* M & W
Orange Coast College *California* M & W
Oregon Institute of Technology *Oregon* M & W
Oregon State University *Oregon* W
Ottawa University *Kansas* M & W
Otterbein University *Ohio* M & W
Our Lady of the Lake University of San Antonio *Texas* M & W
Pacific Lutheran University *Washington* M & W
Pacific University *Oregon* M & W
Paine College *Georgia* M & W
Palo Alto College *Texas* M & W
Palomar College *California* M & W
Paradise Valley Community College *Arizona* M & W
Park University *Missouri* M & W
Pasadena City College *California* M & W
Penn State Erie, The Behrend College *Pennsylvania* M & W
Penn State University Park *Pennsylvania* M & W
Pepperdine University *California* W
Philander Smith College *Arkansas* M & W
Piedmont College *Georgia* M & W
Pittsburg State University *Kansas* M & W
Pitzer College *California* M & W
Plymouth State University *New Hampshire* M & W
Point Loma Nazarene University *California* W
Polytechnic University of Puerto Rico *Puerto Rico* M & W
Pomona College *California* M & W
Pontifical Catholic University of Puerto Rico *Puerto Rico* M & W
Portland State University *Oregon* M & W
Post University *Connecticut* M & W

M = Men; W = Women

Prairie State College *Illinois* M & W
Prairie View A&M University *Texas* M & W
Pratt Community College *Kansas* M & W
Pratt Institute *New York* M & W
Presentation College *South Dakota* M
Princeton University *New Jersey* M & W
Principia College *Illinois* M & W
Providence College *Rhode Island* M & W
Purdue University *Indiana* M & W
Queens College of the City University of New York *New York* M & W
Queens University of Charlotte *North Carolina* M & W
Queen's University at Kingston *Ontario (Canada)* M & W
Queensborough Community College of the City University of New York *New York* M & W
Quinnipiac University *Connecticut* W
Radford University *Virginia* W
Ramapo College of New Jersey *New Jersey* M & W
Ranger College *Texas* M & W
Reedley College *California* M & W
Regis College *Massachusetts* M & W
Rensselaer Polytechnic Institute *New York* M & W
Rhode Island College *Rhode Island* M & W
Rhodes College *Tennessee* M & W
Rice University *Texas* M & W
Rider University *New Jersey* M & W
Rio Hondo College *California* M & W
Ripon College *Wisconsin* M & W
Roanoke College *Virginia* M & W
Robert Morris University *Pennsylvania* W
Robert Morris University Illinois *Illinois* M & W
Roberts Wesleyan College *New York* M & W
Rochester Institute of Technology *New York* M & W
Rockford University *Illinois* M & W
Rocky Mountain College *Montana* M & W
Roger Williams University *Rhode Island* M & W
Rogers State University *Oklahoma* M & W
Rose-Hulman Institute of Technology *Indiana* M & W
Rowan College at Gloucester County *New Jersey* M & W
Rowan University *New Jersey* M & W
Rust College *Mississippi* M & W
Rutgers University - Camden *New Jersey* M & W
Rutgers University - New Brunswick *New Jersey* M & W
Rutgers University - Newark *New Jersey* M
Sacramento City College *California* M & W
Sacred Heart University *Connecticut* M & W
Saddleback College *California* M & W
The Sage Colleges *New York* M & W
Saginaw Valley State University *Michigan* M & W
St. Ambrose University *Iowa* M & W
Saint Augustine's University *North Carolina* M & W
St. Catherine University *Minnesota* W
St. Cloud State University *Minnesota* M & W
St. Francis College *New York* M
Saint Francis University *Pennsylvania* M & W
St. Francis Xavier University *Nova Scotia (Canada)* M & W
St. Gregory's University *Oklahoma* M & W
St. John Fisher College *New York* M & W
Saint John's University *Minnesota* M
St. John's University *New York* W
Saint Joseph's College *Indiana* M & W
St. Joseph's College, Long Island Campus *New York* M & W
Saint Joseph's University *Pennsylvania* M & W
St. Lawrence University *New York* M & W
Saint Leo University *Florida* M & W
St. Louis College of Pharmacy *Missouri* M & W
Saint Louis University *Missouri* M & W
Saint Martin's University *Washington* M & W
Saint Mary's College of California *California* M & W
Saint Mary's University *Nova Scotia (Canada)* M & W
Saint Mary's University of Minnesota *Minnesota* M & W
St. Norbert College *Wisconsin* M & W
St. Olaf College *Minnesota* M & W
Saint Peter's University *New Jersey* M & W

Saint Vincent College *Pennsylvania* M & W
Salisbury University *Maryland* M & W
Salve Regina University *Rhode Island* W
Sam Houston State University *Texas* M & W
Samford University *Alabama* M & W
San Bernardino Valley College *California* M & W
San Diego City College *California* M & W
San Diego Mesa College *California* M & W
San Diego State University *California* W
San Francisco State University *California* W
San Joaquin Delta College *California* M & W
San Jose City College *California* M & W
San Jose State University *California* W
Santa Ana College *California* M & W
Santa Barbara City College *California* M & W
Santa Clara University *California* M & W
Santa Monica College *California* M & W
Santa Rosa Junior College *California* M & W
Savannah College of Art and Design *Georgia* M & W
Savannah State University *Georgia* M & W
Scripps College *California* W
Seattle Pacific University *Washington* M & W
Seattle University *Washington* M & W
Seton Hill University *Pennsylvania* M & W
Sewanee: The University of the South *Tennessee* M & W
Shasta College *California* M & W
Shaw University *North Carolina* M & W
Shenandoah University *Virginia* M & W
Shippensburg University of Pennsylvania *Pennsylvania* M & W
Shorter University *Georgia* M & W
Siena Heights University *Michigan* M & W
Simon Fraser University *British Columbia (Canada)* M & W
Simpson College *Iowa* M & W
Skyline College *California* M & W
Slippery Rock University of Pennsylvania *Pennsylvania* M & W
Smith College *Massachusetts* W
Soka University of America *California* M & W
Sonoma State University *California* W
South Carolina State University *South Carolina* M & W
South Dakota School of Mines and Technology *South Dakota* M & W
South Dakota State University *South Dakota* M & W
South Plains College *Texas* M & W
Southeast Missouri State University *Missouri* M & W
Southeastern Louisiana University *Louisiana* M & W
Southern Arkansas University - Magnolia *Arkansas* M & W
Southern Connecticut State University *Connecticut* M & W
Southern Illinois University Carbondale *Illinois* M & W
Southern Illinois University Edwardsville *Illinois* M & W
Southern Methodist University *Texas* W
Southern Nazarene University *Oklahoma* M & W
Southern New Hampshire University *New Hampshire* W
Southern Oregon University *Oregon* M & W
Southern University and Agricultural and Mechanical College *Louisiana* M & W
Southern University at New Orleans *Louisiana* M & W
Southern Utah University *Utah* M & W
Southern Vermont College *Vermont* M & W
Southern Virginia University *Virginia* M & W
Southwest Baptist University *Missouri* M & W
Southwestern Christian College *Texas* M & W
Southwestern Christian University *Oklahoma* M & W
Southwestern College *California* M & W
Southwestern College *Kansas* M & W
Southwestern Oregon Community College *Oregon* M & W
Southwestern University *Texas* M & W
Spalding University *Kentucky* M & W

Spokane Community College *Washington* M & W
Spokane Falls Community College *Washington* M & W
Spoon River College *Illinois* M & W
Spring Arbor University *Michigan* M & W
Spring Hill College *Alabama* M & W
Springfield College *Massachusetts* M & W
Stanford University *California* M & W
State University of New York College of Agriculture and Technology at Cobleskill *New York* M & W
State University of New York College at Cortland *New York* M & W
State University of New York College of Environmental Science and Forestry *New York* M & W
State University of New York College at Geneseo *New York* M & W
State University of New York College at Oneonta *New York* M & W
State University of New York College of Technology at Alfred *New York* M & W
State University of New York College of Technology at Delhi *New York* M & W
State University of New York at Fredonia *New York* M & W
State University of New York at Oswego *New York* M & W
State University of New York at Plattsburgh *New York* M & W
Stephen F. Austin State University *Texas* M & W
Sterling College *Kansas* M & W
Stevens Institute of Technology *New Jersey* M & W
Stevenson University *Maryland* M & W
Stillman College *Alabama* M & W
Stockton University *New Jersey* M & W
Stonehill College *Massachusetts* M & W
Stony Brook University, State University of New York *New York* M & W
Suffolk County Community College *New York* M & W
Sul Ross State University *Texas* M & W
Summit University *Pennsylvania* M & W
Susquehanna University *Pennsylvania* M & W
Swarthmore College *Pennsylvania* M & W
Syracuse University *New York* M & W
Tabor College *Kansas* M & W
Talladega College *Alabama* M & W
Tarleton State University *Texas* M & W
Taylor University *Indiana* M & W
Temple University *Pennsylvania* W
Tennessee State University *Tennessee* M & W
Tennessee Technological University *Tennessee* W
Tennessee Wesleyan College *Tennessee* M & W
Texas A&M University *Texas* M & W
Texas A&M University - Commerce *Texas* M & W
Texas A&M University - Corpus Christi *Texas* M & W
Texas A&M University - Kingsville *Texas* M & W
Texas Christian University *Texas* M & W
Texas College *Texas* M & W
Texas Lutheran University *Texas* M & W
Texas Southern University *Texas* M & W
Texas State University *Texas* M & W
Texas Tech University *Texas* M & W
Texas Wesleyan University *Texas* M & W
Thaddeus Stevens College of Technology *Pennsylvania* M & W
Thiel College *Pennsylvania* M & W
Thomas College *Maine* M & W
Thomas More College *Kentucky* M & W
Tiffin University *Ohio* M & W
Towson University *Maryland* W
Transylvania University *Kentucky* M & W
Treasure Valley Community College *Oregon* M & W
Trent University *Ontario (Canada)* M & W
Trevecca Nazarene University *Tennessee* M & W
Trine University *Indiana* M & W
Trinity Bible College *North Dakota* M & W
Trinity Christian College *Illinois* M & W
Trinity College *Connecticut* M & W
Trinity International University *Illinois* M & W
Trinity University *Texas* M & W
Troy University *Alabama* M & W
Truman State University *Missouri* M & W
Tufts University *Massachusetts* M & W

M = Men; W = Women

Tulane University *Louisiana* M & W
Tuskegee University *Alabama* M & W
Union College *Kentucky* M & W
Union College *New York* M & W
Union University *Tennessee* M & W
United States Air Force Academy *Colorado* M & W
United States Coast Guard Academy *Connecticut* M & W
United States Merchant Marine Academy *New York* M & W
United States Military Academy *New York* M & W
United States Naval Academy *Maryland* M & W
Universidad del Este *Puerto Rico* M & W
Universidad Metropolitana *Puerto Rico* M & W
Universidad del Turabo *Puerto Rico* M & W
Université Laval *Quebec (Canada)* M & W
Université de Moncton *New Brunswick (Canada)* M & W
Université de Montréal *Quebec (Canada)* M & W
Université du Québec à Trois-Rivières *Quebec (Canada)* M & W
The University of Akron *Ohio* M & W
The University of Alabama *Alabama* M & W
The University of Alabama at Birmingham *Alabama* W
The University of Alabama in Huntsville *Alabama* M & W
University of Alaska Anchorage *Alaska* M & W
University at Albany, State University of New York *New York* M & W
University of Alberta *Alberta (Canada)* M & W
The University of Arizona *Arizona* M & W
University of Arkansas *Arkansas* M & W
University of Arkansas at Little Rock *Arkansas* M & W
University of Arkansas at Pine Bluff *Arkansas* M & W
The University of British Columbia *British Columbia (Canada)* M & W
University at Buffalo, the State University of New York *New York* M & W
University of Calgary *Alberta (Canada)* M & W
University of California, Berkeley *California* M & W
University of California, Davis *California* M & W
University of California, Irvine *California* M & W
University of California, Los Angeles *California* M & W
University of California, San Diego *California* M & W
University of California, Santa Barbara *California* M & W
University of California, Santa Cruz *California* M & W
University of Central Arkansas *Arkansas* M & W
University of Central Florida *Florida* M & W
University of Central Missouri *Missouri* M & W
University of Charleston *West Virginia* M & W
University of Chicago *Illinois* M & W
University of Cincinnati *Ohio* M & W
University of Colorado Boulder *Colorado* M & W
University of Colorado Colorado Springs *Colorado* M & W
University of Connecticut *Connecticut* M & W
University of the Cumberlands *Kentucky* M & W
University of Dallas *Texas* M & W
University of Dayton *Ohio* W
University of Delaware *Delaware* M & W
University of Detroit Mercy *Michigan* M & W
University of the District of Columbia *District of Columbia* W
University of Dubuque *Iowa* M & W
The University of Findlay *Ohio* M & W
University of Florida *Florida* M & W
University of Georgia *Georgia* M & W
University of Great Falls *Montana* M & W
University of Guelph *Ontario (Canada)* M & W
University of Hartford *Connecticut* M & W
University of Hawaii at Manoa *Hawaii* W
University of Houston *Texas* M & W
University of Idaho *Idaho* M & W
University of Illinois at Chicago *Illinois* M & W
University of Illinois at Springfield *Illinois* W
University of Illinois at Urbana - Champaign *Illinois* M & W

University of the Incarnate Word *Texas* M & W
University of Indianapolis *Indiana* M & W
The University of Iowa *Iowa* M & W
University of Jamestown *North Dakota* M & W
The University of Kansas *Kansas* M & W
University of Kentucky *Kentucky* M & W
University of La Verne *California* M & W
University of Lethbridge *Alberta (Canada)* M & W
University of Louisiana at Lafayette *Louisiana* M & W
University of Louisiana at Monroe *Louisiana* M & W
University of Louisville *Kentucky* M & W
University of Maine *Maine* M & W
University of Maine at Farmington *Maine* M & W
University of Manitoba *Manitoba (Canada)* M & W
University of Mary *North Dakota* M & W
University of Mary Washington *Virginia* M & W
University of Maryland, Baltimore County *Maryland* M & W
University of Maryland, College Park *Maryland* M & W
University of Maryland Eastern Shore *Maryland* M & W
University of Massachusetts Amherst *Massachusetts* M & W
University of Massachusetts Boston *Massachusetts* M & W
University of Massachusetts Dartmouth *Massachusetts* M & W
University of Massachusetts Lowell *Massachusetts* M & W
University of Memphis *Tennessee* M & W
University of Miami *Florida* M & W
University of Michigan *Michigan* M & W
University of Minnesota, Duluth *Minnesota* M & W
University of Minnesota, Morris *Minnesota* M & W
University of Minnesota, Twin Cities Campus *Minnesota* M & W
University of Mississippi *Mississippi* M & W
University of Missouri *Missouri* M & W
University of Missouri - Kansas City *Missouri* M & W
University of Mobile *Alabama* M & W
University of Montana *Montana* M & W
University of Montevallo *Alabama* M & W
University of Mount Union *Ohio* M & W
University of Nebraska at Kearney *Nebraska* M & W
University of Nebraska - Lincoln *Nebraska* M & W
University of Nebraska at Omaha *Nebraska* W
University of Nevada, Las Vegas *Nevada* W
University of Nevada, Reno *Nevada* M & W
University of New Brunswick Fredericton *New Brunswick (Canada)* M & W
University of New Hampshire *New Hampshire* M & W
University of New Haven *Connecticut* M & W
University of New Mexico *New Mexico* M & W
University of New Orleans *Louisiana* M & W
University of North Carolina at Asheville *North Carolina* M & W
The University of North Carolina at Chapel Hill *North Carolina* M & W
The University of North Carolina at Charlotte *North Carolina* M & W
The University of North Carolina at Greensboro *North Carolina* M & W
The University of North Carolina at Pembroke *North Carolina* M & W
The University of North Carolina Wilmington *North Carolina* M & W
University of North Dakota *North Dakota* M & W
University of North Florida *Florida* M & W
University of North Texas *Texas* M & W
University of Northern Colorado *Colorado* M & W
University of Northern Iowa *Iowa* M & W
University of Northwestern - St. Paul *Minnesota* M & W
University of Notre Dame *Indiana* M & W
University of Oklahoma *Oklahoma* M & W
University of Oregon *Oregon* M & W
University of Ottawa *Ontario (Canada)* M & W
University of Pennsylvania *Pennsylvania* M & W
University of Pikeville *Kentucky* M & W

University of Pittsburgh *Pennsylvania* M & W
University of Pittsburgh at Johnstown *Pennsylvania* W
University of Portland *Oregon* M & W
University of Puerto Rico in Aguadilla *Puerto Rico* M & W
University of Puerto Rico in Arecibo *Puerto Rico* M & W
University of Puerto Rico in Bayamón *Puerto Rico* M & W
University of Puerto Rico in Carolina *Puerto Rico* M & W
University of Puerto Rico in Cayey *Puerto Rico* M & W
University of Puerto Rico in Humacao *Puerto Rico* M & W
University of Puerto Rico, Mayagüez Campus *Puerto Rico* M & W
University of Puerto Rico in Ponce *Puerto Rico* M & W
University of Puerto Rico, Río Piedras Campus *Puerto Rico* M & W
University of Puerto Rico in Utuado *Puerto Rico* M & W
University of Puget Sound *Washington* M & W
University of Redlands *California* M & W
University of Regina *Saskatchewan (Canada)* M & W
University of Rhode Island *Rhode Island* M & W
University of Richmond *Virginia* W
University of Rio Grande *Ohio* M & W
University of Rochester *New York* M & W
University of the Sacred Heart *Puerto Rico* M & W
University of St. Francis *Illinois* M & W
University of Saint Francis *Indiana* M & W
University of Saint Mary *Kansas* M & W
University of St. Thomas *Texas* M & W
University of San Diego *California* W
University of San Francisco *California* M & W
University of Saskatchewan *Saskatchewan (Canada)* M & W
University of Sioux Falls *South Dakota* M & W
University of South Alabama *Alabama* M & W
University of South Carolina *South Carolina* M & W
University of South Carolina Beaufort *South Carolina* M & W
University of South Carolina Upstate *South Carolina* M & W
The University of South Dakota *South Dakota* M & W
University of South Florida *Florida* M & W
University of Southern California *California* M & W
University of Southern Indiana *Indiana* M & W
University of Southern Maine *Maine* M & W
University of Southern Mississippi *Mississippi* M & W
University of the Southwest *New Mexico* M & W
The University of Tennessee *Tennessee* M & W
The University of Tennessee at Chattanooga *Tennessee* M & W
The University of Texas at Arlington *Texas* M & W
The University of Texas at Austin *Texas* M & W
The University of Texas at El Paso *Texas* M & W
The University of Texas Rio Grande Valley *Texas* M & W
The University of Texas at San Antonio *Texas* M & W
The University of Texas at Tyler *Texas* M & W
The University of Toledo *Ohio* W
University of Toronto *Ontario (Canada)* M & W
The University of Tulsa *Oklahoma* M & W
University of Utah *Utah* W
University of Vermont *Vermont* M & W
University of the Virgin Islands *United States Virgin Islands* M & W
University of Virginia *Virginia* M & W
The University of Virginia's College at Wise *Virginia* M & W
University of Washington *Washington* M & W
University of Waterloo *Ontario (Canada)* M & W
The University of West Alabama *Alabama* M & W
University of West Georgia *Georgia* W
The University of Western Ontario *Ontario (Canada)* M & W

M = Men; W = Women

University of Windsor *Ontario (Canada)* M & W
University of Wisconsin - Eau Claire *Wisconsin* M & W
University of Wisconsin - La Crosse *Wisconsin* M & W
University of Wisconsin - Madison *Wisconsin* M & W
University of Wisconsin - Milwaukee *Wisconsin* M & W
University of Wisconsin - Oshkosh *Wisconsin* M & W
University of Wisconsin - Parkside *Wisconsin* M & W
University of Wisconsin - Platteville *Wisconsin* M & W
University of Wisconsin - River Falls *Wisconsin* M & W
University of Wisconsin - Stevens Point *Wisconsin* M & W
University of Wisconsin - Stout *Wisconsin* M & W
University of Wisconsin - Superior *Wisconsin* M & W
University of Wisconsin - Whitewater *Wisconsin* M & W
University of Wyoming *Wyoming* M & W
Upper Iowa University *Iowa* W
Ursinus College *Pennsylvania* M & W
Ursuline College *Ohio* W
Utah State University *Utah* M & W
Utah Valley University *Utah* M & W
Utica College *New York* M & W
Valley City State University *North Dakota* M & W
Valparaiso University *Indiana* M & W
Vanderbilt University *Tennessee* W
Vanguard University of Southern California *California* M & W
Vassar College *New York* M & W
Ventura College *California* M & W
Victor Valley College *California* M & W
Villanova University *Pennsylvania* M & W
Vincennes University *Indiana* M & W
Virginia Commonwealth University *Virginia* M & W
Virginia Military Institute *Virginia* M & W
Virginia Polytechnic Institute and State University *Virginia* M & W
Virginia State University *Virginia* M & W
Virginia Union University *Virginia* M & W
Virginia Wesleyan College *Virginia* M & W
Viterbo University *Wisconsin* M & W
Voorhees College *South Carolina* M & W
Wabash College *Indiana* M
Wagner College *New York* M & W
Wake Forest University *North Carolina* M & W
Wallace State Community College *Alabama* M & W
Walsh University *Ohio* M & W
Warner Pacific College *Oregon* M & W
Warner University *Florida* M & W
Wartburg College *Iowa* M & W
Washington Adventist University *Maryland* M & W
Washington & Jefferson College *Pennsylvania* M & W
Washington and Lee University *Virginia* M & W
Washington State University *Washington* M & W
Washington University in St. Louis *Missouri* M & W
Wayland Baptist University *Texas* M & W
Wayne State College *Nebraska* M & W
Wayne State University *Michigan* W
Waynesburg University *Pennsylvania* M & W
Webber International University *Florida* M & W
Weber State University *Utah* M & W
Webster University *Missouri* M & W
Wellesley College *Massachusetts* W
Wentworth Military Academy and College *Missouri* M & W
Wesleyan University *Connecticut* M & W
West Chester University of Pennsylvania *Pennsylvania* M & W
West Liberty University *West Virginia* M & W
West Los Angeles College *California* M & W
West Texas A&M University *Texas* M & W
West Valley College *California* M
West Virginia University *West Virginia* W
West Virginia Wesleyan College *West Virginia* M & W

Western Carolina University *North Carolina* M & W
Western Illinois University *Illinois* M & W
Western Kentucky University *Kentucky* M & W
Western Michigan University *Michigan* W
Western Oregon University *Oregon* M & W
Western State Colorado University *Colorado* M & W
Western Texas College *Texas* M & W
Western Washington University *Washington* M & W
Westfield State University *Massachusetts* M & W
Westminster College *Missouri* M & W
Westminster College *Pennsylvania* M & W
Westminster College *Utah* M & W
Westmont College *California* M & W
Wheaton College *Illinois* M & W
Wheaton College *Massachusetts* M & W
Wheeling Jesuit University *West Virginia* M & W
Whitman College *Washington* M & W
Whittier College *California* M & W
Whitworth University *Washington* M & W
Wichita State University *Kansas* M & W
Widener University *Pennsylvania* M & W
Wiley College *Texas* M & W
Willamette University *Oregon* M & W
William Jessup University *California* M & W
William Jewell College *Missouri* M & W
William Penn University *Iowa* M & W
William Woods University *Missouri* M & W
Williams Baptist College *Arkansas* M & W
Williams College *Massachusetts* M & W
Wilmington College *Ohio* M & W
Wingate University *North Carolina* M & W
Winona State University *Minnesota* W
Winthrop University *South Carolina* M & W
Wisconsin Lutheran College *Wisconsin* M & W
Wittenberg University *Ohio* M & W
Wofford College *South Carolina* M & W
Worcester Polytechnic Institute *Massachusetts* M & W
Worcester State University *Massachusetts* M & W
Wright State University *Ohio* W
Xavier University *Ohio* M & W
Yale University *Connecticut* M & W
York College *Nebraska* M & W
York College of the City University of New York *New York* M & W
York College of Pennsylvania *Pennsylvania* M & W
York University *Ontario (Canada)* M & W
Youngstown State University *Ohio* M & W
Yuba College *California* M & W

Triathlon

Arizona State University at the Downtown Phoenix campus *Arizona* W
Arizona State University at the Polytechnic campus *Arizona* W
Arizona State University at the Tempe campus *Arizona* W
Arizona State University at the West campus *Arizona* W
Ball State University *Indiana* M & W
Colorado State University *Colorado* M & W
Elon University *North Carolina* M & W
Marymount University *Virginia* M & W
North Central College *Illinois* W
Old Dominion University *Virginia* M & W
Pepperdine University *California* M & W
Santa Clara University *California* M & W
Stanford University *California* M & W
Texas Christian University *Texas* M & W
Université de Montréal *Quebec (Canada)* M & W
The University of Alabama *Alabama* M & W
University of California, Santa Cruz *California* M & W
University of Colorado Boulder *Colorado* M & W
The University of North Carolina at Chapel Hill *North Carolina* M & W
The University of West Alabama *Alabama* W
Washington State University *Washington* M & W

Ultimate Frisbee

Albright College *Pennsylvania* M & W
Allegheny College *Pennsylvania* M & W
Amherst College *Massachusetts* M & W

Appalachian State University *North Carolina* M & W
Augustana College *Illinois* M & W
Augustana University *South Dakota* M & W
Ball State University *Indiana* M & W
Bates College *Maine* M & W
Baylor University *Texas* M
Bennington College *Vermont* M & W
Boston University *Massachusetts* M & W
Bowdoin College *Maine* M & W
Bryant University *Rhode Island* M & W
Bucknell University *Pennsylvania* M & W
Butler University *Indiana* M & W
California State University, Fullerton *California* M & W
Calvin College *Michigan* M & W
Carleton College *Minnesota* M & W
Carnegie Mellon University *Pennsylvania* M & W
Central Washington University *Washington* M & W
Christopher Newport University *Virginia* M
Clemson University *South Carolina* M & W
Colby College *Maine* M & W
College of Saint Benedict *Minnesota* W
The College of Wooster *Ohio* M & W
The Colorado College *Colorado* M & W
Colorado State University *Colorado* M & W
Columbia University *New York* M & W
Columbia University, School of General Studies *New York* M & W
Connecticut College *Connecticut* M & W
Cornell College *Iowa* M & W
Cornell University *New York* M & W
Dartmouth College *New Hampshire* M & W
Davidson College *North Carolina* M & W
Dickinson College *Pennsylvania* M & W
Duke University *North Carolina* M & W
Earlham College *Indiana* M & W
East Stroudsburg University of Pennsylvania *Pennsylvania* M & W
Eastern Illinois University *Illinois* M & W
Elon University *North Carolina* M & W
Emory University *Georgia* M & W
Fort Lewis College *Colorado* M & W
Franklin & Marshall College *Pennsylvania* M & W
Franklin W. Olin College of Engineering *Massachusetts* M & W
Furman University *South Carolina* M & W
Georgetown University *District of Columbia* M & W
Georgia State University *Georgia* M & W
Gettysburg College *Pennsylvania* M & W
Gonzaga University *Washington* M & W
Grove City College *Pennsylvania* M & W
Gustavus Adolphus College *Minnesota* M & W
Hamilton College *New York* M & W
Hampden-Sydney College *Virginia* M
Hampshire College *Massachusetts* M & W
Harding University *Arkansas* M & W
Haverford College *Pennsylvania* M & W
Hobart and William Smith Colleges *New York* M & W
Huntington University *Indiana* M
Illinois Institute of Technology *Illinois* M & W
Illinois Wesleyan University *Illinois* M & W
John Carroll University *Ohio* M
Juniata College *Pennsylvania* M & W
Keene State College *New Hampshire* M & W
Kenyon College *Ohio* M & W
Kutztown University of Pennsylvania *Pennsylvania* M & W
Lake Forest College *Illinois* M & W
Lawrence University *Wisconsin* M & W
Lehigh University *Pennsylvania* M & W
Lewis & Clark College *Oregon* M & W
Lewis University *Illinois* M & W
Loras College *Iowa* M & W
Luther College *Iowa* M & W
Lycoming College *Pennsylvania* M & W
Macalester College *Minnesota* M & W
Maharishi University of Management *Iowa* M & W
Maryville College *Tennessee* M & W
McGill University *Quebec (Canada)* M & W
Messiah College *Pennsylvania* M & W
Miami University *Ohio* M & W
Michigan Technological University *Michigan* M & W
Midwives College of Utah *Utah* M & W

M = Men; W = Women

Missouri State University *Missouri* M & W
Moravian College *Pennsylvania* W
National American University *Rapid City, South Dakota* M & W
North Carolina State University *North Carolina* M & W
North Park University *Illinois* M & W
Northeastern University *Massachusetts* M & W
Northern Michigan University *Michigan* M & W
Oberlin College *Ohio* M & W
Occidental College *California* M & W
Ohio Wesleyan University *Ohio* M & W
Old Dominion University *Virginia* M & W
Pacific Lutheran University *Washington* M & W
Pepperdine University *California* M & W
Pomona College *California* M & W
Queen's University at Kingston *Ontario (Canada)* M
Rabbinical College of America *New Jersey* M
Rensselaer Polytechnic Institute *New York* M & W
Rhodes College *Tennessee* M & W
Rice University *Texas* M & W
Rochester Institute of Technology *New York* M & W
St. Cloud State University *Minnesota* M & W
Saint John's University *Minnesota* M
Saint Louis University *Missouri* M & W
Saint Luke's College of Health Sciences *Missouri* M & W
St. Mary's College of Maryland *Maryland* M & W
Sam Houston State University *Texas* M & W
Santa Clara University *California* M & W
Scripps College *California* W
Siena College *New York* M & W
Southern Connecticut State University *Connecticut* M & W
Southern University at New Orleans *Louisiana* M & W
Stanford University *California* M & W
State University of New York College at Geneseo *New York* M & W
Stonehill College *Massachusetts* M & W
Swarthmore College *Pennsylvania* M & W
Texas Christian University *Texas* M & W
Texas State University *Texas* M & W
Towson University *Maryland* M & W
Truman State University *Missouri* M & W
Tufts University *Massachusetts* M & W
Tyndale University College & Seminary *Ontario (Canada)* M & W
Union College *New York* M & W
United States Air Force Academy *Colorado* M & W
Université de Montréal *Quebec (Canada)* M & W
The University of Alabama *Alabama* M & W
The University of Arizona *Arizona* M & W
University of Arkansas for Medical Sciences *Arkansas* M & W
University of California, Irvine *California* M & W
University of California, Santa Barbara *California* M & W
University of California, Santa Cruz *California* M & W
University of Colorado Boulder *Colorado* M & W
University of Florida *Florida* M & W
University of Georgia *Georgia* M & W
The University of Iowa *Iowa* M & W
University of Maryland, Baltimore County *Maryland* M & W
University of Michigan *Michigan* M & W
University of Michigan - Dearborn *Michigan* M
University of Minnesota, Duluth *Minnesota* M & W
University of Mississippi *Mississippi* M & W
University of Montana *Montana* M & W
University of New Hampshire *New Hampshire* M & W
University of New Haven *Connecticut* M & W
The University of North Carolina at Chapel Hill *North Carolina* M & W
University of North Texas *Texas* M & W
University of Ottawa *Ontario (Canada)* M & W
University of Puget Sound *Washington* M & W
University of Richmond *Virginia* M & W
University of Rochester *New York* M & W
University of the Sacred Heart *Puerto Rico* M & W
University of San Diego *California* M & W

The University of Scranton *Pennsylvania* M & W
University of Southern California *California* M & W
University of Southern Indiana *Indiana* M & W
The University of Texas at Austin *Texas* M & W
The University of Texas Medical Branch *Texas* M & W
The University of Texas at San Antonio *Texas* M & W
University of Utah *Utah* M & W
University of Vermont *Vermont* M & W
The University of Western Ontario *Ontario (Canada)* M & W
University of Wisconsin - Madison *Wisconsin* M & W
University of Wisconsin - Milwaukee *Wisconsin* M & W
University of Wisconsin - Platteville *Wisconsin* M & W
University of Wyoming *Wyoming* M & W
Utah State University *Utah* M & W
Virginia Polytechnic Institute and State University *Virginia* M & W
Wabash College *Indiana* M
Washington & Jefferson College *Pennsylvania* M & W
Washington State University *Washington* M & W
Washington University in St. Louis *Missouri* M & W
Wellesley College *Massachusetts* W
Wentworth Institute of Technology *Massachusetts* M & W
West Chester University of Pennsylvania *Pennsylvania* M
Western Carolina University *North Carolina* M & W
Western Michigan University *Michigan* M
Westminster College *Pennsylvania* M & W
Whitman College *Washington* M & W
Williams College *Massachusetts* M & W
Xavier University *Ohio* M
Yale University *Connecticut* M & W

Volleyball

Abilene Christian University *Texas* W
Academy of Art University *California* W
Acadia University *Nova Scotia (Canada)* W
Adams State University *Colorado* W
Adelphi University *New York* W
Adirondack Community College *New York* W
Adrian College *Michigan* W
Agnes Scott College *Georgia* W
Alabama Agricultural and Mechanical University *Alabama* W
Alabama State University *Alabama* W
Albany State University *Georgia* W
Albertus Magnus College *Connecticut* M & W
Albion College *Michigan* W
Albright College *Pennsylvania* W
Alcorn State University *Mississippi* W
Alderson Broaddus University *West Virginia* M & W
Alfred University *New York* W
Alice Lloyd College *Kentucky* W
Allan Hancock College *California* W
Allegany College of Maryland *Maryland* W
Allegheny College *Pennsylvania* M & W
Allen Community College *Kansas* W
Allen University *South Carolina* W
Alma College *Michigan* W
Alpena Community College *Michigan* W
Alvernia University *Pennsylvania* W
Alverno College *Wisconsin* W
Ambrose University *Alberta (Canada)* M & W
American International College *Massachusetts* W
American River College *California* W
American University *District of Columbia* W
American University of Puerto Rico *Bayamon, Puerto Rico* M & W
Amherst College *Massachusetts* M & W
Ancilla College *Indiana* W
Anderson University *Indiana* W
Anderson University *South Carolina* W
Angelo State University *Texas* W
Anna Maria College *Massachusetts* W
Anne Arundel Community College *Maryland* W
Anoka-Ramsey Community College *Minnesota* W
Antelope Valley College *California* W

Appalachian Bible College *West Virginia* W
Appalachian State University *North Carolina* W
Aquinas College *Michigan* W
Arcadia University *Pennsylvania* W
Arizona Christian University *Arizona* W
Arizona State University at the Downtown Phoenix campus *Arizona* W
Arizona State University at the Polytechnic campus *Arizona* W
Arizona State University at the Tempe campus *Arizona* W
Arizona State University at the West campus *Arizona* W
Arizona Western College *Arizona* W
Arkansas State University *Arkansas* W
Arkansas Tech University *Arkansas* W
Arlington Baptist College *Texas* W
Armstrong State University *Georgia* W
Asbury University *Kentucky* W
Ashford University *California* W
Ashland University *Ohio* W
Assumption College *Massachusetts* M & W
Auburn University *Alabama* W
Augsburg College *Minnesota* W
Augustana College *Illinois* W
Augustana University *South Dakota* W
Aurora University *Illinois* W
Austin College *Texas* W
Austin Peay State University *Tennessee* W
Ave Maria University *Florida* W
Averett University *Virginia* W
Avila University *Missouri* W
Azusa Pacific University *California* W
Babson College *Massachusetts* W
Baker University *Kansas* W
Bakersfield College *California* W
Baldwin Wallace University *Ohio* W
Ball State University *Indiana* M & W
Baltimore City Community College *Maryland* W
Baptist Bible College *Missouri* W
Barclay College *Kansas* W
Bard College *New York* M & W
Barnard College *New York* W
Barry University *Florida* W
Barton College *North Carolina* M & W
Barton County Community College *Kansas* W
Baruch College of the City University of New York *New York* M & W
Bates College *Maine* M & W
Bay Path University *Massachusetts* W
Bayamón Central University *Puerto Rico* M & W
Baylor University *Texas* M & W
Becker College *Massachusetts* W
Belhaven University *Mississippi* W
Bellarmine University *Kentucky* W
Bellevue College *Washington* W
Belmont Abbey College *North Carolina* M & W
Belmont University *Tennessee* W
Beloit College *Wisconsin* W
Bemidji State University *Minnesota* W
Benedict College *South Carolina* W
Benedictine College *Kansas* W
Benedictine University *Illinois* W
Bennington College *Vermont* M & W
Bentley University *Massachusetts* W
Berea College *Kentucky* W
Bergen Community College *New Jersey* W
Berry College *Georgia* W
Bethany College *Kansas* W
Bethany College *West Virginia* W
Bethany Lutheran College *Minnesota* W
Bethel College *Indiana* W
Bethel College *Kansas* W
Bethel University *Minnesota* M & W
Bethel University *Tennessee* W
Bethune-Cookman University *Florida* W
Big Bend Community College *Washington* W
Binghamton University, State University of New York *New York* W
Biola University *California* W
Birmingham-Southern College *Alabama* W
Bishop's University *Quebec (Canada)* W
Bismarck State College *North Dakota* W
Black Hawk College *Illinois* W

M = Men; W = Women

Black Hills State University *South Dakota* W
Blackburn College *Illinois* W
Blessing-Rieman College of Nursing *Illinois* M & W
Blinn College *Texas* W
Bloomfield College *New Jersey* W
Blue Mountain Community College *Oregon* W
Blue Ridge Community College *North Carolina* W
Bluefield College *Virginia* M & W
Bluffton University *Ohio* W
Boise State University *Idaho* W
Booth University College *Manitoba (Canada)* M & W
Borough of Manhattan Community College of the City University of New York *New York* W
Boston College *Massachusetts* W
Boston University *Massachusetts* M & W
Bowdoin College *Maine* M & W
Bowie State University *Maryland* W
Bowling Green State University *Ohio* W
Bradley University *Illinois* W
Brandeis University *Massachusetts* W
Brandon University *Manitoba (Canada)* M & W
Brenau University *Georgia* W
Brescia University *Kentucky* W
Brevard College *North Carolina* W
Brewton-Parker College *Georgia* W
Briar Cliff University *Iowa* W
Bridgewater College *Virginia* W
Bridgewater State University *Massachusetts* W
Briercrest College *Saskatchewan (Canada)* M & W
Brigham Young University *Utah* M & W
Brigham Young University - Hawaii *Hawaii* W
Brock University *Ontario (Canada)* M & W
Bronx Community College of the City University of New York *New York* W
Brookhaven College *Texas* W
Brooklyn College of the City University of New York *New York* M & W
Broome Community College *New York* W
Broward College *Florida* W
Brown University *Rhode Island* M & W
Brunswick Community College *North Carolina* W
Bryan College *Tennessee* M & W
Bryant University *Rhode Island* M & W
Bryn Athyn College of the New Church *Pennsylvania* W
Bryn Mawr College *Pennsylvania* W
Bucknell University *Pennsylvania* M & W
Bucks County Community College *Pennsylvania* W
Buena Vista University *Iowa* W
Buffalo State College, State University of New York *New York* M & W
Bunker Hill Community College *Massachusetts* W
Butler Community College *Kansas* W
Butler County Community College *Pennsylvania* W
Butler University *Indiana* M & W
Butte College *California* W
Cabrillo College *California* W
Cabrini University *Pennsylvania* W
Cairn University *Pennsylvania* M & W
Caldwell Community College and Technical Institute *North Carolina* W
Caldwell University *New Jersey* W
California Baptist University *California* M & W
California Institute of Technology *California* M & W
California Lutheran University *California* M & W
California Maritime Academy *California* W
California Polytechnic State University, San Luis Obispo *California* W
California State Polytechnic University, Pomona *California* W
California State University, Bakersfield *California* W
California State University, Chico *California* W
California State University, Dominguez Hills *California* W
California State University, East Bay *California* W
California State University, Fresno *California* W
California State University, Fullerton *California* M & W
California State University, Long Beach *California* M & W
California State University, Los Angeles *California* W

California State University, Monterey Bay *California* W
California State University, Northridge *California* M & W
California State University, Sacramento *California* M & W
California State University, San Bernardino *California* W
California State University, San Marcos *California* W
California State University, Stanislaus *California* W
California University of Pennsylvania *Pennsylvania* W
Calumet College of Saint Joseph *Indiana* M & W
Calvary Bible College and Theological Seminary *Missouri* W
Calvin College *Michigan* M & W
Cameron University *Oklahoma* W
Campbell University *North Carolina* W
Campbellsville University *Kentucky* W
Canisius College *New York* M & W
Cape Fear Community College *North Carolina* W
Capital University *Ohio* W
Cardinal Stritch University *Wisconsin* M & W
Caribbean University *Puerto Rico* M & W
Carl Sandburg College *Illinois* W
Carleton College *Minnesota* M & W
Carleton University *Ontario (Canada)* W
Carlow University *Pennsylvania* W
Carnegie Mellon University *Pennsylvania* M & W
Carroll College *Montana* W
Carroll University *Wisconsin* W
Carson-Newman University *Tennessee* W
Carthage College *Wisconsin* M & W
Case Western Reserve University *Ohio* W
Casper College *Wyoming* W
Castleton University *Vermont* W
Catawba College *North Carolina* W
Catawba Valley Community College *North Carolina* W
The Catholic University of America *District of Columbia* W
Cayuga County Community College *New York* W
Cazenovia College *New York* M & W
Cecil College *Maryland* W
Cedar Crest College *Pennsylvania* W
Cedar Valley College *Texas* W
Cedarville University *Ohio* W
Centenary College *New Jersey* W
Centenary College of Louisiana *Louisiana* W
Central Alabama Community College *Alabama* W
Central Baptist College *Arkansas* W
Central Carolina Community College *North Carolina* W
Central Christian College of the Bible *Missouri* W
Central Christian College of Kansas *Kansas* W
Central College *Iowa* W
Central Community College - Columbus Campus *Nebraska* W
Central Connecticut State University *Connecticut* W
Central Lakes College *Minnesota* W
Central Methodist University *Missouri* W
Central Michigan University *Michigan* W
Central Penn College *Pennsylvania* W
Central State University *Ohio* W
Central Washington University *Washington* W
Central Wyoming College *Wyoming* W
Centralia College *Washington* W
Centre College *Kentucky* W
Cerritos College *California* W
Chabot College *California* W
Chadron State College *Nebraska* W
Chaffey College *California* W
Chaminade University of Honolulu *Hawaii* W
Chandler-Gilbert Community College *Arizona* W
Chapman University *California* M & W
Charleston Southern University *South Carolina* W
Chatham University *Pennsylvania* W
Chemeketa Community College *Oregon* W
Chesapeake College *Maryland* W
Chestnut Hill College *Pennsylvania* W
Cheyney University of Pennsylvania *Pennsylvania* W
Chicago State University *Illinois* W

Chowan University *North Carolina* W
Christendom College *Virginia* W
Christian Brothers University *Tennessee* W
Christopher Newport University *Virginia* M & W
Cincinnati Christian University *Ohio* M & W
Cincinnati State Technical and Community College *Ohio* W
Cisco College *Texas* W
The Citadel, The Military College of South Carolina *South Carolina* W
Citrus College *California* W
City College of the City University of New York *New York* W
City College of San Francisco *California* W
City Colleges of Chicago, Olive-Harvey College *Illinois* W
Clackamas Community College *Oregon* W
Claflin University *South Carolina* W
Claremont McKenna College *California* M & W
Clarendon College *Texas* W
Clarion University of Pennsylvania *Pennsylvania* W
Clark Atlanta University *Georgia* W
Clark College *Washington* W
Clark State Community College *Ohio* W
Clark University *Massachusetts* W
Clarke University *Iowa* M & W
Clarkson University *New York* W
Clemson University *South Carolina* M & W
Cleveland State University *Ohio* W
Clinton Community College *Iowa* W
Cloud County Community College *Kansas* W
Coastal Bend College *Texas* W
Coastal Carolina University *South Carolina* M & W
Coe College *Iowa* W
Coffeyville Community College *Kansas* W
Coker College *South Carolina* M & W
Colby College *Maine* M & W
Colby Community College *Kansas* W
Colby-Sawyer College *New Hampshire* W
Colgate University *New York* M & W
College of Alameda *California* W
The College at Brockport, State University of New York *New York* W
College of the Canyons *California* W
College of Central Florida *Florida* W
College of Charleston *South Carolina* W
College of Coastal Georgia *Georgia* W
College of the Desert *California* W
College of the Holy Cross *Massachusetts* W
The College of Idaho *Idaho* W
College of Lake County *Illinois* W
College of the Mainland *Texas* W
College of Marin *California* W
College of Mount Saint Vincent *New York* M & W
The College of New Rochelle *New York* W
College of the Ozarks *Missouri* W
College of the Redwoods *California* W
College of Saint Benedict *Minnesota* W
College of Saint Elizabeth *New Jersey* W
College of Saint Mary *Nebraska* W
The College of Saint Rose *New York* W
The College of St. Scholastica *Minnesota* W
College of the Sequoias *California* W
College of the Siskiyous *California* W
College of Southern Idaho *Idaho* M & W
College of Southern Maryland *Maryland* W
College of Staten Island of the City University of New York *New York* M & W
The College of William and Mary *Virginia* W
The College of Wooster *Ohio* M & W
Colorado Christian University *Colorado* W
The Colorado College *Colorado* W
Colorado Mesa University *Colorado* W
Colorado Northwestern Community College *Colorado* W
Colorado School of Mines *Colorado* W
Colorado State University *Colorado* M & W
Colorado State University - Pueblo *Colorado* W
Columbia Basin College *Washington* W
Columbia Bible College *British Columbia (Canada)* M & W
Columbia College *California* W
Columbia College *Missouri* W
Columbia College *South Carolina* W

M = Men; W = Women

Columbia-Greene Community College *New York* W
Columbia University *New York* M & W
Columbia University, School of General Studies *New York* W
Columbus State Community College *Ohio* W
Columbus State University *Georgia* W
Community College of Allegheny County *Pennsylvania* W
Community College of Baltimore County *Maryland* W
Community College of Philadelphia *Pennsylvania* W
Community College of Rhode Island *Rhode Island* W
Concord University *West Virginia* W
Concordia College *Minnesota* M & W
Concordia College Alabama *Alabama* M & W
Concordia College - New York *New York* W
Concordia University *Oregon* W
Concordia University Ann Arbor *Michigan* W
Concordia University Chicago *Illinois* W
Concordia University Irvine *California* M & W
Concordia University, Nebraska *Nebraska* W
Concordia University, St. Paul *Minnesota* W
Concordia University Texas *Texas* W
Concordia University Wisconsin *Wisconsin* W
Connecticut College *Connecticut* M & W
Contra Costa College *California* W
Converse College *South Carolina* W
Cooper Union for the Advancement of Science and Art *New York* M & W
Coppin State University *Maryland* W
Corban University *Oregon* W
Cornell College *Iowa* M & W
Cornell University *New York* M & W
Cornerstone University *Michigan* W
Corning Community College *New York* W
Cottey College *Missouri* W
County College of Morris *New Jersey* W
Covenant College *Georgia* W
Cowley County Community College and Area Vocational - Technical School *Kansas* W
Creighton University *Nebraska* W
Crossroads College *Minnesota* W
Crown College *Minnesota* W
Cuesta College *California* W
The Culinary Institute of America *New York* M & W
Culver-Stockton College *Missouri* M & W
Cumberland University *Tennessee* W
Curry College *Massachusetts* W
Cuyamaca College *California* W
Cypress College *California* W
Daemen College *New York* W
Dakota College at Bottineau *North Dakota* W
Dakota County Technical College *Minnesota* W
Dakota State University *South Dakota* W
Dakota Wesleyan University *South Dakota* W
Dalhousie University *Nova Scotia (Canada)* M & W
Dallas Baptist University *Texas* W
Dallas Christian College *Texas* W
Dalton State College *Georgia* M & W
Daniel Webster College *New Hampshire* M & W
Dartmouth College *New Hampshire* M & W
Davenport University *Michigan* W
Davidson College *North Carolina* W
Davidson County Community College *North Carolina* W
Davis College *New York* W
Davis & Elkins College *West Virginia* W
Daytona State College *Florida* W
De Anza College *California* M & W
Dean College *Massachusetts* W
Defiance College *Ohio* W
Delaware County Community College *Pennsylvania* W
Delaware State University *Delaware* W
Delaware Valley University *Pennsylvania* W
Denison University *Ohio* W
DePaul University *Illinois* W
DePauw University *Indiana* W
Des Moines Area Community College *Iowa* W
DeSales University *Pennsylvania* W
Diablo Valley College *California* W
Dickinson College *Pennsylvania* M & W

Dickinson State University *North Dakota* W
Dillard University *Louisiana* W
Dixie State University *Utah* W
Doane University *Nebraska* W
Dodge City Community College *Kansas* W
Dominican College *New York* W
Dominican University *Illinois* M & W
Dominican University of California *California* W
Dordt College *Iowa* W
Drake University *Iowa* W
Drury University *Missouri* W
Duke University *North Carolina* M & W
Duquesne University *Pennsylvania* W
Dutchess Community College *New York* W
D'Youville College *New York* M & W
Earlham College *Indiana* M & W
East Carolina University *North Carolina* W
East Central College *Missouri* W
East Central University *Oklahoma* W
East Los Angeles College *California* W
East Stroudsburg University of Pennsylvania *Pennsylvania* M & W
East Tennessee State University *Tennessee* W
East Texas Baptist University *Texas* W
Eastern Arizona College *Arizona* W
Eastern Connecticut State University *Connecticut* W
Eastern Florida State College *Florida* W
Eastern Illinois University *Illinois* W
Eastern Kentucky University *Kentucky* W
Eastern Mennonite University *Virginia* M & W
Eastern Michigan University *Michigan* W
Eastern Nazarene College *Massachusetts* M & W
Eastern New Mexico University *New Mexico* W
Eastern Oregon University *Oregon* W
Eastern University *Pennsylvania* W
Eastern Washington University *Washington* W
Eastern Wyoming College *Wyoming* W
Eastfield College *Texas* M & W
Eckerd College *Florida* W
Edgewood College *Wisconsin* W
Edinboro University of Pennsylvania *Pennsylvania* W
Edison Community College *Ohio* W
Edmonds Community College *Washington* W
El Camino College *California* M & W
Elgin Community College *Illinois* W
Elizabeth City State University *North Carolina* W
Elizabethtown College *Pennsylvania* W
Ellsworth Community College *Iowa* W
Elmhurst College *Illinois* W
Elmira College *New York* M & W
Elms College *Massachusetts* M & W
Elon University *North Carolina* M & W
Embry-Riddle Aeronautical University - Daytona *Florida* W
Embry-Riddle Aeronautical University - Prescott *Arizona* W
Emerson College *Massachusetts* M & W
Emmanuel College *Georgia* M & W
Emmanuel College *Massachusetts* M & W
Emmaus Bible College *Iowa* W
Emory & Henry College *Virginia* W
Emory University *Georgia* M & W
Emporia State University *Kansas* W
Endicott College *Massachusetts* M & W
Erie Community College *New York* W
Erie Community College, North Campus *New York* W
Erie Community College, South Campus *New York* W
Erskine College *South Carolina* W
Eugenio María de Hostos Community College of the City University of New York *New York* W
Eureka College *Illinois* W
Evangel University *Missouri* W
Everett Community College *Washington* W
The Evergreen State College *Washington* W
Fairfield University *Connecticut* W
Fairleigh Dickinson University, College at Florham *New Jersey* W
Fairleigh Dickinson University, Metropolitan Campus *New Jersey* W
Fairmont State University *West Virginia* W

Faith Baptist Bible College and Theological Seminary *Iowa* W
Farmingdale State College *New York* W
Fashion Institute of Technology *New York* W
Faulkner University *Alabama* W
Fayetteville State University *North Carolina* W
Feather River College *California* W
Felician University *New Jersey* W
Ferris State University *Michigan* W
Ferrum College *Virginia* W
Finger Lakes Community College *New York* W
Finlandia University *Michigan* W
Fisk University *Tennessee* W
Flagler College *Florida* W
Florida Agricultural and Mechanical University *Florida* W
Florida Atlantic University *Florida* W
Florida College *Florida* W
Florida Gulf Coast University *Florida* W
Florida Institute of Technology *Florida* W
Florida International University *Florida* W
Florida Memorial University *Florida* M & W
Florida National University *Florida* W
Florida Southern College *Florida* W
Florida State College at Jacksonville *Florida* W
Florida State University *Florida* M & W
Fontbonne University *Missouri* M & W
Foothill College *California* W
Fordham University *New York* W
Fort Lewis College *Colorado* W
Fort Scott Community College *Kansas* W
Fort Valley State University *Georgia* W
Framingham State University *Massachusetts* W
Francis Marion University *South Carolina* W
Franciscan University of Steubenville *Ohio* W
Frank Phillips College *Texas* W
Franklin College *Indiana* W
Franklin & Marshall College *Pennsylvania* M & W
Franklin Pierce University *New Hampshire* W
Frederick Community College *Maryland* W
Freed-Hardeman University *Tennessee* W
Fresno City College *California* W
Fresno Pacific University *California* M & W
Friends University *Kansas* W
Frostburg State University *Maryland* W
Fullerton College *California* W
Fulton-Montgomery Community College *New York* W
Furman University *South Carolina* W
Gadsden State Community College *Alabama* W
Gallaudet University *District of Columbia* W
Gannon University *Pennsylvania* W
Garden City Community College *Kansas* W
Gardner-Webb University *North Carolina* W
Garrett College *Maryland* W
Gavilan College *California* W
Genesee Community College *New York* W
Geneva College *Pennsylvania* M & W
George Fox University *Oregon* W
George Mason University *Virginia* M & W
The George Washington University *District of Columbia* W
Georgetown College *Kentucky* W
Georgetown University *District of Columbia* M & W
Georgia College & State University *Georgia* W
Georgia Institute of Technology *Georgia* W
Georgia Southern University *Georgia* W
Georgia State University *Georgia* W
Georgian Court University *New Jersey* W
Gettysburg College *Pennsylvania* W
Glendale Community College *Arizona* W
Glendale Community College *California* W
Glenville State College *West Virginia* W
Globe Institute of Technology *New York* W
Gogebic Community College *Michigan* W
Golden West College *California* M & W
Goldey-Beacom College *Delaware* W
Gonzaga University *Washington* M & W
Gordon College *Massachusetts* W
Goshen College *Indiana* W
Goucher College *Maryland* W
Governors State University *Illinois* W
Grace Bible College *Michigan* W
Grace College *Indiana* W

M = Men; W = Women

Grace University *Nebraska* W
Graceland University *Iowa* M & W
Grambling State University *Louisiana* W
Grand Canyon University *Arizona* M & W
Grand Rapids Community College *Michigan* W
Grand Valley State University *Michigan* M & W
Grand View University *Iowa* M & W
Grays Harbor College *Washington* W
Great Lakes Christian College *Michigan* W
Green Mountain College *Vermont* W
Green River College *Washington* W
Greensboro College *North Carolina* W
Greenville College *Illinois* M & W
Grinnell College *Iowa* W
Grossmont College *California* M & W
Grove City College *Pennsylvania* M & W
Guilford College *North Carolina* W
Guilford Technical Community College *North Carolina* W
Gulf Coast State College *Florida* W
Gustavus Adolphus College *Minnesota* M & W
Gwynedd Mercy University *Pennsylvania* W
Hagerstown Community College *Maryland* W
Hamilton College *New York* M & W
Hamline University *Minnesota* W
Hampton University *Virginia* W
Hannibal-LaGrange University *Missouri* M & W
Hanover College *Indiana* W
Harcum College *Pennsylvania* W
Hardin-Simmons University *Texas* W
Harding University *Arkansas* W
Harford Community College *Maryland* W
Harper College *Illinois* W
Harris-Stowe State University *Missouri* W
Hartwick College *New York* W
Harvard University *Massachusetts* M & W
Harvey Mudd College *California* W
Haskell Indian Nations University *Kansas* W
Hastings College *Nebraska* W
Haverford College *Pennsylvania* M & W
Hawai'i Pacific University *Hawaii* W
Heidelberg University *Ohio* M & W
Henderson State University *Arkansas* W
Hendrix College *Arkansas* W
Henry Ford College *Michigan* W
Heritage College and Seminary *Ontario (Canada)* M & W
Herkimer County Community College *New York* W
Hesston College *Kansas* W
Hibbing Community College *Minnesota* W
High Point University *North Carolina* W
Highland Community College *Illinois* W
Highland Community College *Kansas* W
Highline College *Washington* W
Hilbert College *New York* M & W
Hill College *Texas* W
Hillsborough Community College *Florida* W
Hillsdale College *Michigan* M & W
Hillsdale Free Will Baptist College *Oklahoma* W
Hiram College *Ohio* W
Hofstra University *New York* W
Hollins University *Virginia* W
Holy Family University *Pennsylvania* W
Holy Names University *California* M & W
Holyoke Community College *Massachusetts* W
Hood College *Maryland* W
Hope College *Michigan* W
Hope International University *California* M & W
Houghton College *New York* W
Houston Baptist University *Texas* W
Howard Community College *Maryland* W
Howard Payne University *Texas* W
Howard University *District of Columbia* W
Hudson Valley Community College *New York* W
Humboldt State University *California* W
Hunter College of the City University of New York *New York* M & W
Huntingdon College *Alabama* W
Huntington University *Indiana* W
Husson University *Maine* W
Huston-Tillotson University *Texas* W
Hutchinson Community College *Kansas* W
Idaho State University *Idaho* W
Illinois Central College *Illinois* W

Illinois College *Illinois* W
Illinois Eastern Community Colleges, Frontier Community College *Illinois* W
Illinois Institute of Technology *Illinois* M & W
Illinois State University *Illinois* W
Illinois Wesleyan University *Illinois* M & W
Immaculata University *Pennsylvania* W
Independence Community College *Kansas* W
Indian Hills Community College *Iowa* W
Indian River State College *Florida* W
Indiana State University *Indiana* W
Indiana Tech *Indiana* W
Indiana University Bloomington *Indiana* W
Indiana University East *Indiana* W
Indiana University Kokomo *Indiana* W
Indiana University Northwest *Indiana* W
Indiana University of Pennsylvania *Pennsylvania* W
Indiana University - Purdue University Fort Wayne *Indiana* M & W
Indiana University - Purdue University Indianapolis *Indiana* W
Indiana University South Bend *Indiana* W
Indiana University Southeast *Indiana* W
Indiana Wesleyan University *Indiana* W
Inter American University of Puerto Rico, Aguadilla Campus *Puerto Rico* M & W
Inter American University of Puerto Rico, Arecibo Campus *Puerto Rico* M & W
Inter American University of Puerto Rico, Barranquitas Campus *Puerto Rico* M & W
Inter American University of Puerto Rico, Bayamón Campus *Puerto Rico* M & W
Inter American University of Puerto Rico, Fajardo Campus *Puerto Rico* M & W
Inter American University of Puerto Rico, Metropolitan Campus *Puerto Rico* W
Inter American University of Puerto Rico, Ponce Campus *Puerto Rico* M & W
Inter American University of Puerto Rico, San Germán Campus *Puerto Rico* M & W
Iona College *New York* W
Iowa Central Community College *Iowa* W
Iowa Lakes Community College *Iowa* W
Iowa State University of Science and Technology *Iowa* W
Iowa Wesleyan University *Iowa* W
Iowa Western Community College *Iowa* W
Irvine Valley College *California* W
Itasca Community College *Minnesota* W
Ithaca College *New York* W
Jackson College *Michigan* W
Jackson State University *Mississippi* W
Jacksonville State University *Alabama* W
Jacksonville University *Florida* W
James H. Faulkner State Community College *Alabama* W
James Madison University *Virginia* W
Jamestown Community College *New York* W
Jarvis Christian College *Texas* W
Jefferson College *Missouri* W
Jefferson College of Health Sciences *Virginia* M & W
Jefferson Community College *New York* W
Jefferson Davis Community College *Alabama* W
John A. Logan College *Illinois* W
John Brown University *Arkansas* W
John Carroll University *Ohio* M & W
John Jay College of Criminal Justice of the City University of New York *New York* W
John Wesley University *North Carolina* W
Johns Hopkins University *Maryland* W
Johnson C. Smith University *North Carolina* W
Johnson County Community College *Kansas* W
Johnson State College *Vermont* W
Johnson University *Tennessee* W
Johnson University Florida *Florida* W
Johnson & Wales University *Rhode Island* M & W
Joliet Junior College *Illinois* W
Judson College *Alabama* W
Judson University *Illinois* W
Juniata College *Pennsylvania* M & W
Kalamazoo College *Michigan* W
Kalamazoo Valley Community College *Michigan* W
Kankakee Community College *Illinois* W

Kansas City Kansas Community College *Kansas* W
Kansas State University *Kansas* W
Kansas Wesleyan University *Kansas* W
Kaskaskia College *Illinois* W
Kean University *New Jersey* M & W
Keene State College *New Hampshire* W
Kellogg Community College *Michigan* W
Kennesaw State University *Georgia* W
Kent State University *Ohio* W
Kentucky Christian University *Kentucky* W
Kentucky State University *Kentucky* W
Kentucky Wesleyan College *Kentucky* W
Kenyon College *Ohio* W
Keuka College *New York* M & W
Keystone College *Pennsylvania* W
King University *Tennessee* M & W
The King's College *New York* W
King's College *Pennsylvania* W
The King's University *Alberta (Canada)* M & W
Kingsborough Community College of the City University of New York *New York* W
Kirkwood Community College *Iowa* W
Kishwaukee College *Illinois* W
Knox College *Illinois* W
Kutztown University of Pennsylvania *Pennsylvania* M & W
La Roche College *Pennsylvania* W
La Salle University *Pennsylvania* W
La Sierra University *California* W
Labette Community College *Kansas* W
Lackawanna College *Pennsylvania* W
Lafayette College *Pennsylvania* W
LaGrange College *Georgia* W
Lake Erie College *Ohio* W
Lake Forest College *Illinois* M & W
Lake Land College *Illinois* W
Lake Michigan College *Michigan* W
Lake Region State College *North Dakota* W
Lake-Sumter State College *Florida* W
Lake Superior State University *Michigan* W
Lakehead University *Ontario (Canada)* W
Lakeland College *Wisconsin* M & W
Lakeland Community College *Ohio* W
Lamar Community College *Colorado* W
Lamar University *Texas* W
Lancaster Bible College *Pennsylvania* M & W
Lander University *South Carolina* W
Lane College *Tennessee* W
Laney College *California* W
Langston University *Oklahoma* W
Lansing Community College *Michigan* W
Laramie County Community College *Wyoming* W
Laredo Community College *Texas* W
Lasell College *Massachusetts* M & W
Lassen Community College District *California* W
Laurentian University *Ontario (Canada)* W
Lawrence Technological University *Michigan* M & W
Lawrence University *Wisconsin* M & W
Lawson State Community College *Alabama* W
Le Moyne College *New York* W
Lebanon Valley College *Pennsylvania* W
Lee College *Texas* W
Lee University *Tennessee* W
Lees-McRae College *North Carolina* M & W
Lehigh Carbon Community College *Pennsylvania* W
Lehigh University *Pennsylvania* M & W
Lehman College of the City University of New York *New York* M & W
LeMoyne-Owen College *Tennessee* W
Lenoir Community College *North Carolina* W
Lenoir-Rhyne University *North Carolina* W
Lesley University *Massachusetts* M & W
LeTourneau University *Texas* W
Lewis & Clark College *Oregon* W
Lewis and Clark Community College *Illinois* W
Lewis-Clark State College *Idaho* W
Lewis University *Illinois* M & W
Liberty University *Virginia* M & W
Limestone College *South Carolina* M & W
Lincoln Christian University *Illinois* W
Lincoln Land Community College *Illinois* W
Lincoln Memorial University *Tennessee* W
Lincoln University *Pennsylvania* W

M = Men; W = Women

Lindenwood University *Missouri* M & W
Lindsey Wilson College *Kentucky* W
Linfield College *Oregon* W
Linn-Benton Community College *Oregon* W
Lipscomb University *Tennessee* W
Livingstone College *North Carolina* W
Lock Haven University of Pennsylvania *Pennsylvania* W
Long Beach City College *California* M & W
Long Island University - LIU Brooklyn *New York* W
Long Island University - LIU Post *New York* W
Longwood University *Virginia* M & W
Loras College *Iowa* M & W
Los Angeles City College *California* M & W
Los Angeles Harbor College *California* W
Los Angeles Pierce College *California* M & W
Los Angeles Trade-Technical College *California* M & W
Los Angeles Valley College *California* M & W
Los Medanos College *California* W
Louisburg College *North Carolina* M & W
Louisiana State University and Agricultural & Mechanical College *Louisiana* W
Louisiana Tech University *Louisiana* W
Lourdes University *Ohio* M & W
Lower Columbia College *Washington* W
Loyola Marymount University *California* W
Loyola University Chicago *Illinois* M & W
Loyola University Maryland *Maryland* W
Loyola University New Orleans *Louisiana* W
Lubbock Christian University *Texas* W
Luther College *Iowa* W
Luzerne County Community College *Pennsylvania* W
Lycoming College *Pennsylvania* W
Lynchburg College *Virginia* W
Lyndon State College *Vermont* W
Lynn University *Florida* W
Lyon College *Arkansas* W
Macalester College *Minnesota* M & W
MacMurray College *Illinois* W
Macomb Community College *Michigan* W
Madison Area Technical College *Wisconsin* M & W
Madonna University *Michigan* W
Maharishi University of Management *Iowa* M & W
Maine Maritime Academy *Maine* W
Malone University *Ohio* W
Manchester Community College *New Hampshire* M & W
Manchester University *Indiana* W
Manhattan Christian College *Kansas* W
Manhattan College *New York* W
Manhattanville College *New York* W
Maranatha Baptist University *Wisconsin* W
Marian University *Indiana* W
Marian University *Wisconsin* M & W
Marietta College *Ohio* W
Marion Technical College *Ohio* W
Marist College *New York* M & W
Marquette University *Wisconsin* W
Mars Hill University *North Carolina* W
Marshall University *West Virginia* W
Marshalltown Community College *Iowa* W
Martin Luther College *Minnesota* W
Martin Methodist College *Tennessee* W
Mary Baldwin College *Virginia* W
Marymount University *Virginia* M & W
Maryville College *Tennessee* W
Maryville University of Saint Louis *Missouri* W
Marywood University *Pennsylvania* W
Massachusetts Bay Community College *Massachusetts* W
Massachusetts College of Liberal Arts *Massachusetts* W
Massachusetts Institute of Technology *Massachusetts* M & W
Massachusetts Maritime Academy *Massachusetts* W
The Master's College and Seminary *California* W
Mayland Community College *North Carolina* W
Mayville State University *North Dakota* W
McDaniel College *Maryland* W
McGill University *Quebec (Canada)* M & W
McHenry County College *Illinois* W

McKendree University *Illinois* M & W
McMaster University *Ontario (Canada)* M & W
McMurry University *Texas* W
McNeese State University *Louisiana* W
McPherson College *Kansas* W
Medaille College *New York* W
Medgar Evers College of the City University of New York *New York* M & W
Memorial University of Newfoundland *Newfoundland and Labrador (Canada)* M & W
Mendocino College *California* W
Menlo College *California* W
Merced College *California* W
Mercer University *Georgia* W
Mercy College *New York* W
Mercyhurst North East *Pennsylvania* W
Mercyhurst University *Pennsylvania* W
Meredith College *North Carolina* W
Merrimack College *Massachusetts* W
Mesa Community College *Arizona* W
Mesabi Range College *Minnesota* W
Messiah College *Pennsylvania* W
Methodist University *North Carolina* W
Metropolitan Community College - Kansas City *Missouri* W
Metropolitan State University of Denver *Colorado* W
Miami Dade College *Florida* W
Miami University *Ohio* M & W
Miami University Hamilton *Ohio* W
Miami University Middletown *Ohio* W
Michigan State University *Michigan* M & W
Michigan Technological University *Michigan* M & W
Mid-America Christian University *Oklahoma* W
Mid-Atlantic Christian University *North Carolina* W
Mid-Plains Community College *Nebraska* W
Mid-State Technical College *Wisconsin* W
MidAmerica Nazarene University *Kansas* W
Middle Tennessee State University *Tennessee* W
Middlebury College *Vermont* W
Midland College *Texas* W
Midland University *Nebraska* W
Midway University *Kentucky* W
Midwestern State University *Texas* W
Midwives College of Utah *Utah* M & W
Millersville University of Pennsylvania *Pennsylvania* W
Milligan College *Tennessee* W
Millikin University *Illinois* W
Mills College *California* W
Millsaps College *Mississippi* W
Milwaukee Area Technical College *Wisconsin* W
Milwaukee School of Engineering *Wisconsin* M & W
Mineral Area College *Missouri* W
Minnesota State Community and Technical College *Minnesota* W
Minnesota State University Mankato *Minnesota* W
Minnesota State University Moorhead *Minnesota* W
Minnesota West Community and Technical College *Minnesota* W
Minot State University *North Dakota* W
Misericordia University *Pennsylvania* W
Mississippi College *Mississippi* W
Mississippi State University *Mississippi* W
Missouri Baptist University *Missouri* M & W
Missouri Southern State University *Missouri* W
Missouri State University *Missouri* M & W
Missouri State University - West Plains *Missouri* W
Missouri University of Science and Technology *Missouri* W
Missouri Valley College *Missouri* M & W
Missouri Western State University *Missouri* W
Mitchell College *Connecticut* W
Modesto Junior College *California* W
Mohawk Valley Community College *New York* W
Molloy College *New York* W
Monmouth College *Illinois* W
Monroe College *New York* W
Monroe Community College *New York* W
Montana State University *Montana* W
Montana State University Billings *Montana* W
Montana State University - Northern *Montana* W

Montana Tech of The University of Montana *Montana* W
Montclair State University *New Jersey* W
Monterey Peninsula College *California* W
Montgomery College *Maryland* W
Montgomery County Community College *Pennsylvania* W
Montreat College *North Carolina* W
Moody Bible Institute *Illinois* M & W
Moorpark College *California* W
Moraine Valley Community College *Illinois* W
Moravian College *Pennsylvania* W
Morehead State University *Kentucky* W
Morgan State University *Maryland* W
Morningside College *Iowa* W
Morris College *South Carolina* W
Morrisville State College *New York* W
Morton College *Illinois* W
Mott Community College *Michigan* W
Mount Aloysius College *Pennsylvania* W
Mount Holyoke College *Massachusetts* W
Mt. Hood Community College *Oregon* W
Mount Ida College *Massachusetts* M & W
Mount Marty College *South Dakota* W
Mount Mary University *Wisconsin* W
Mount Mercy University *Iowa* W
Mount St. Joseph University *Ohio* M & W
Mount Saint Mary College *New York* W
Mount Saint Vincent University *Nova Scotia (Canada)* W
Mt. San Antonio College *California* M & W
Mt. San Jacinto College *California* W
Mount Vernon Nazarene University *Ohio* W
Mountain View College *Texas* W
Muhlenberg College *Pennsylvania* W
Multnomah University *Oregon* W
Murray State University *Kentucky* W
Muskegon Community College *Michigan* W
Muskingum University *Ohio* W
Napa Valley College *California* W
Nassau Community College *New York* W
National American University *Rapid City, South Dakota* M & W
Navarro College *Texas* W
Nazareth College of Rochester *New York* M & W
Nebraska Wesleyan University *Nebraska* W
Neosho County Community College *Kansas* W
Neumann University *Pennsylvania* W
New Hope Christian College *Oregon* M & W
New Jersey City University *New Jersey* M & W
New Jersey Institute of Technology *New Jersey* M & W
New Mexico Highlands University *New Mexico* W
New Mexico Military Institute *New Mexico* W
New Mexico State University *New Mexico* W
New York Institute of Technology *New York* W
New York University *New York* M & W
Newberry College *South Carolina* W
Newbury College *Massachusetts* M & W
Newman University *Kansas* W
NHTI, Concord's Community College *New Hampshire* M & W
Niagara County Community College *New York* W
Niagara University *New York* W
Nicholls State University *Louisiana* W
Nichols College *Massachusetts* W
Nipissing University *Ontario (Canada)* M & W
Norfolk State University *Virginia* W
North Carolina Agricultural and Technical State University *North Carolina* W
North Carolina Central University *North Carolina* W
North Carolina State University *North Carolina* M & W
North Carolina Wesleyan College *North Carolina* W
North Central College *Illinois* M & W
North Central Texas College *Texas* W
North Central University *Minnesota* W
North Country Community College *New York* W
North Dakota State College of Science *North Dakota* W
North Dakota State University *North Dakota* M & W
North Greenville University *South Carolina* M & W
North Idaho College *Idaho* W
North Iowa Area Community College *Iowa* W

M = Men; W = Women

North Lake College *Texas* W
North Park University *Illinois* W
Northampton Community College *Pennsylvania* W
Northeast Community College *Nebraska* W
Northeastern Junior College *Colorado* W
Northeastern Oklahoma Agricultural and Mechanical College *Oklahoma* W
Northeastern University *Massachusetts* W
Northern Arizona University *Arizona* W
Northern Essex Community College *Massachusetts* M & W
Northern Illinois University *Illinois* W
Northern Kentucky University *Kentucky* W
Northern Michigan University *Michigan* W
Northern Oklahoma College *Oklahoma* M & W
Northern State University *South Dakota* W
Northland College *Wisconsin* W
Northland Community and Technical College *Minnesota* W
Northwest Christian University *Oregon* W
Northwest College *Wyoming* W
Northwest Missouri State University *Missouri* W
Northwest Nazarene University *Idaho* W
Northwest University *Washington* W
Northwestern College *Iowa* W
Northwestern Oklahoma State University *Oklahoma* W
Northwestern State University of Louisiana *Louisiana* W
Northwood University, Michigan Campus *Michigan* W
Norwich University *Vermont* M & W
Notre Dame College *Ohio* W
Notre Dame of Maryland University *Maryland* W
Notre Dame de Namur University *California* W
Nova Southeastern University *Florida* W
Nyack College *New York* W
Oak Hills Christian College *Minnesota* W
Oakland City University *Indiana* W
Oakland Community College *Michigan* W
Oakland University *Michigan* W
Oakton Community College *Illinois* W
Oberlin College *Ohio* M & W
Occidental College *California* W
Ocean County College *New Jersey* W
Oglethorpe University *Georgia* W
Ohio Christian University *Ohio* W
Ohio Dominican University *Ohio* W
Ohio Northern University *Ohio* M & W
The Ohio State University *Ohio* M & W
The Ohio State University at Marion *Ohio* W
Ohio University *Ohio* W
Ohio University - Eastern *Ohio* W
Ohio University - Zanesville *Ohio* W
Ohio Valley University *West Virginia* W
Ohio Wesleyan University *Ohio* M & W
Ohlone College *California* M & W
Oklahoma Baptist University *Oklahoma* W
Oklahoma City University *Oklahoma* W
Oklahoma Panhandle State University *Oklahoma* W
Oklahoma Wesleyan University *Oklahoma* W
Old Dominion University *Virginia* M & W
Olivet College *Michigan* W
Olivet Nazarene University *Illinois* W
Olympic College *Washington* W
Onondaga Community College *New York* W
Oral Roberts University *Oklahoma* W
Orange Coast College *California* W
Orange County Community College *New York* W
Oregon Institute of Technology *Oregon* W
Oregon State University *Oregon* W
Otero Junior College *Colorado* W
Ottawa University *Kansas* W
Otterbein University *Ohio* W
Ouachita Baptist University *Arkansas* W
Our Lady of the Lake University of San Antonio *Texas* W
Owens Community College *Ohio* W
Ozark Christian College *Missouri* W
Pace University *New York* W
Pace University, Pleasantville Campus *New York* W
Pacific Lutheran University *Washington* W
Pacific Union College *California* W

Pacific University *Oregon* W
Paine College *Georgia* W
Palm Beach Atlantic University *Florida* W
Palm Beach State College *Florida* W
Palomar College *California* M & W
Panola College *Texas* W
Paris Junior College *Texas* W
Park University *Missouri* M & W
Parkland College *Illinois* W
Pasadena City College *California* W
Pasco-Hernando State College *Florida* W
Passaic County Community College *New Jersey* W
Paul Smith's College *New York* W
Penn State Abington *Pennsylvania* W
Penn State Beaver *Pennsylvania* W
Penn State Berks *Pennsylvania* W
Penn State Brandywine *Pennsylvania* W
Penn State DuBois *Pennsylvania* W
Penn State Erie, The Behrend College *Pennsylvania* M & W
Penn State Fayette, The Eberly Campus *Pennsylvania* W
Penn State Greater Allegheny *Pennsylvania* W
Penn State Harrisburg *Pennsylvania* W
Penn State Hazleton *Pennsylvania* M & W
Penn State Lehigh Valley *Pennsylvania* M & W
Penn State Mont Alto *Pennsylvania* W
Penn State New Kensington *Pennsylvania* W
Penn State Schuylkill *Pennsylvania* W
Penn State University Park *Pennsylvania* M & W
Penn State Wilkes-Barre *Pennsylvania* W
Penn State Worthington Scranton *Pennsylvania* W
Pennsylvania College of Technology *Pennsylvania* M & W
Pennsylvania Highlands Community College *Pennsylvania* W
Pensacola State College *Florida* W
Pepperdine University *California* M & W
Peru State College *Nebraska* W
Pfeiffer University *North Carolina* W
Philadelphia University *Pennsylvania* W
Philander Smith College *Arkansas* W
Phoenix College *Arizona* W
Piedmont College *Georgia* W
Piedmont International University *North Carolina* W
Pierce College at Puyallup *Washington* W
Pine Manor College *Massachusetts* W
Pitt Community College *North Carolina* W
Pittsburg State University *Kansas* W
Pitzer College *California* W
Plymouth State University *New Hampshire* W
Point Loma Nazarene University *California* W
Point Park University *Pennsylvania* W
Point University *Georgia* W
Polk State College *Florida* W
Polytechnic University of Puerto Rico *Puerto Rico* M & W
Pomona College *California* M & W
Pontifical Catholic University of Puerto Rico *Puerto Rico* M & W
Porterville College *California* W
Portland State University *Oregon* W
Post University *Connecticut* W
Potomac State College of West Virginia University *West Virginia* W
Prairie State College *Illinois* W
Prairie View A&M University *Texas* M & W
Pratt Community College *Kansas* W
Pratt Institute *New York* W
Presbyterian College *South Carolina* W
Presentation College *South Dakota* W
Prince George's Community College *Maryland* W
Princeton University *New Jersey* M & W
Principia College *Illinois* W
Providence College *Rhode Island* W
Providence University College & Theological Seminary *Manitoba (Canada)* M & W
Purchase College, State University of New York *New York* M & W
Purdue University *Indiana* W
Purdue University Northwest *Hammond, Indiana* W
Queens College of the City University of New York *New York* W
Queens University of Charlotte *North Carolina* W

Queen's University at Kingston *Ontario (Canada)* M & W
Queensborough Community College of the City University of New York *New York* W
Quincy University *Illinois* M & W
Quinnipiac University *Connecticut* W
Rabbinical College of America *New Jersey* M
Radford University *Virginia* W
Rainy River Community College *Minnesota* W
Ramapo College of New Jersey *New Jersey* M & W
Randolph College *Virginia* W
Randolph-Macon College *Virginia* W
Raritan Valley Community College *New Jersey* W
Redeemer University College *Ontario (Canada)* M & W
Redlands Community College *Oklahoma* W
Reedley College *California* W
Regis College *Massachusetts* M & W
Regis University *Colorado* W
Reinhardt University *Georgia* W
Rend Lake College *Illinois* W
Rensselaer Polytechnic Institute *New York* M & W
Research College of Nursing *Missouri* W
Rhode Island College *Rhode Island* W
Rhodes College *Tennessee* W
Rice University *Texas* M & W
Richland College *Texas* W
Rider University *New Jersey* M & W
Ridgewater College *Minnesota* W
Rio Hondo College *California* W
Ripon College *Wisconsin* W
Riverland Community College *Minnesota* W
Rivier University *New Hampshire* M & W
Roanoke College *Virginia* W
Robert Morris University *Pennsylvania* W
Robert Morris University Illinois *Illinois* M & W
Roberts Wesleyan College *New York* W
Rochester College *Michigan* W
Rochester Community and Technical College *Minnesota* W
Rochester Institute of Technology *New York* M & W
Rock Valley College *Illinois* W
Rockford University *Illinois* W
Rockhurst University *Missouri* W
Rockingham Community College *North Carolina* W
Rockland Community College *New York* W
Rocky Mountain College *Montana* W
Roger Williams University *Rhode Island* M & W
Rollins College *Florida* W
Roosevelt University *Illinois* W
Rose-Hulman Institute of Technology *Indiana* W
Rosemont College *Pennsylvania* W
Rowan University *New Jersey* W
Royal Military College of Canada *Ontario (Canada)* M & W
Rust College *Mississippi* M & W
Rutgers University - Camden *New Jersey* W
Rutgers University - New Brunswick *New Jersey* W
Rutgers University - Newark *New Jersey* M & W
Ryerson University *Ontario (Canada)* M & W
Sacramento City College *California* W
Sacred Heart University *Connecticut* M & W
Saddleback College *California* W
The Sage Colleges *New York* M & W
Saginaw Valley State University *Michigan* W
St. Ambrose University *Iowa* M & W
Saint Anselm College *New Hampshire* W
Saint Augustine's University *North Carolina* W
St. Catherine University *Minnesota* W
St. Clair County Community College *Michigan* W
St. Cloud State University *Minnesota* M & W
St. Cloud Technical & Community College *Minnesota* W
St. Edward's University *Texas* W
St. Francis College *New York* W
Saint Francis University *Pennsylvania* M & W
St. Francis Xavier University *Nova Scotia (Canada)* W
St. Gregory's University *Oklahoma* W
St. John Fisher College *New York* W
St. Johns River State College *Florida* W
Saint John's University *Minnesota* M
St. John's University *New York* W

M = Men; W = Women

Saint Joseph's College *Indiana* W
St. Joseph's College, Long Island Campus *New York* M & W
Saint Joseph's College of Maine *Maine* W
St. Joseph's College, New York *New York* M & W
St. Lawrence University *New York* W
Saint Leo University *Florida* W
Saint Louis Christian College *Missouri* W
St. Louis College of Pharmacy *Missouri* W
St. Louis Community College *Missouri* W
Saint Louis University *Missouri* M & W
Saint Luke's College of Health Sciences *Missouri* M & W
Saint Martin's University *Washington* W
Saint Mary's College *Indiana* W
Saint Mary's College of California *California* W
St. Mary's College of Maryland *Maryland* W
Saint Mary's University *Nova Scotia (Canada)* W
St. Mary's University *Texas* W
Saint Mary's University of Minnesota *Minnesota* W
Saint Michael's College *Vermont* W
St. Norbert College *Wisconsin* W
St. Olaf College *Minnesota* W
Saint Peter's University *New Jersey* W
St. Petersburg College *Florida* W
St. Thomas Aquinas College *New York* W
St. Thomas University *Florida* W
St. Thomas University *New Brunswick (Canada)* M & W
Saint Vincent College *Pennsylvania* W
Saint Xavier University *Illinois* W
Salem College *North Carolina* W
Salem International University *West Virginia* W
Salem State University *Massachusetts* W
Salisbury University *Maryland* W
Salt Lake Community College *Utah* W
Salve Regina University *Rhode Island* W
Sam Houston State University *Texas* W
Samford University *Alabama* W
San Bernardino Valley College *California* W
San Diego Christian College *California* W
San Diego City College *California* M & W
San Diego Mesa College *California* M & W
San Diego State University *California* W
San Francisco State University *California* W
San Jacinto College District *Texas* W
San Joaquin Delta College *California* W
San Jose City College *California* W
San Jose State University *California* W
Sandhills Community College *North Carolina* W
Santa Ana College *California* W
Santa Barbara City College *California* M & W
Santa Clara University *California* M & W
Santa Fe College *Florida* W
Santa Monica College *California* M & W
Santa Rosa Junior College *California* W
Sarah Lawrence College *New York* M & W
Savannah State University *Georgia* W
Schoolcraft College *Michigan* W
Schreiner University *Texas* W
Scottsdale Community College *Arizona* W
Scripps College *California* W
Seattle Pacific University *Washington* W
Seattle University *Washington* W
Seminole State College *Oklahoma* W
Seton Hall University *New Jersey* M & W
Seton Hill University *Pennsylvania* W
Sewanee: The University of the South *Tennessee* W
Seward County Community College and Area Technical School *Kansas* W
Shasta College *California* W
Shaw University *North Carolina* W
Shawnee State University *Ohio* W
Shenandoah University *Virginia* W
Shepherd University *West Virginia* W
Sheridan College *Wyoming* W
Shippensburg University of Pennsylvania *Pennsylvania* W
Shoreline Community College *Washington* W
Shorter University *Georgia* W
Siena College *New York* M & W
Siena Heights University *Michigan* M & W
Sierra College *California* W

Silver Lake College of the Holy Family *Wisconsin* W
Simmons College *Massachusetts* W
Simon Fraser University *British Columbia (Canada)* W
Simpson College *Iowa* W
Simpson University *California* W
Sinclair Community College *Ohio* W
Skagit Valley College *Washington* W
Skidmore College *New York* W
Skyline College *California* W
Slippery Rock University of Pennsylvania *Pennsylvania* M & W
Smith College *Massachusetts* W
Snead State Community College *Alabama* W
Snow College *Utah* W
Solano Community College *California* W
Sonoma State University *California* W
South Carolina State University *South Carolina* W
South Dakota School of Mines and Technology *South Dakota* W
South Dakota State University *South Dakota* W
South Florida State College *Florida* W
South Mountain Community College *Arizona* W
South Suburban College *Illinois* W
Southeast Community College, Beatrice Campus *Nebraska* W
Southeast Community College, Lincoln Campus *Nebraska* W
Southeast Community College, Milford Campus *Nebraska* W
Southeast Missouri State University *Missouri* W
Southeastern Community College *Iowa* W
Southeastern Community College *North Carolina* W
Southeastern Louisiana University *Louisiana* W
Southeastern Oklahoma State University *Oklahoma* W
Southeastern University *Florida* W
Southern Alberta Institute of Technology *Alberta (Canada)* M & W
Southern Arkansas University - Magnolia *Arkansas* W
Southern Connecticut State University *Connecticut* W
Southern Illinois University Carbondale *Illinois* W
Southern Illinois University Edwardsville *Illinois* W
Southern Methodist University *Texas* W
Southern Nazarene University *Oklahoma* W
Southern New Hampshire University *New Hampshire* W
Southern Oregon University *Oregon* W
Southern State Community College *Ohio* W
Southern University and Agricultural and Mechanical College *Louisiana* W
Southern University at New Orleans *Louisiana* M & W
Southern Utah University *Utah* W
Southern Vermont College *Vermont* M & W
Southern Virginia University *Virginia* W
Southern Wesleyan University *South Carolina* W
Southwest Baptist University *Missouri* W
Southwest Minnesota State University *Minnesota* W
Southwestern Adventist University *Texas* W
Southwestern Assemblies of God University *Texas* W
Southwestern Christian University *Oklahoma* W
Southwestern College *California* W
Southwestern College *Kansas* W
Southwestern Illinois College *Illinois* W
Southwestern Oklahoma State University *Oklahoma* W
Southwestern Oregon Community College *Oregon* W
Southwestern University *Texas* W
Spalding University *Kentucky* W
Spartanburg Methodist College *South Carolina* W
Spokane Community College *Washington* W
Spokane Falls Community College *Washington* W
Spring Arbor University *Michigan* W
Spring Hill College *Alabama* W
Springfield College *Massachusetts* M & W
Stanford University *California* M & W

State College of Florida Manatee-Sarasota *Florida* W
State University of New York College of Agriculture and Technology at Cobleskill *New York* W
State University of New York College at Cortland *New York* M & W
State University of New York College at Geneseo *New York* M & W
State University of New York College at Old Westbury *New York* W
State University of New York College at Oneonta *New York* W
State University of New York College at Potsdam *New York* W
State University of New York College of Technology at Alfred *New York* W
State University of New York College of Technology at Canton *New York* W
State University of New York College of Technology at Delhi *New York* W
State University of New York at Fredonia *New York* M & W
State University of New York Maritime College *New York* W
State University of New York at New Paltz *New York* M & W
State University of New York at Oswego *New York* W
State University of New York at Plattsburgh *New York* W
State University of New York Polytechnic Institute *New York* M & W
Stephen F. Austin State University *Texas* W
Stephens College *Missouri* W
Sterling College *Kansas* W
Stetson University *Florida* W
Stevens Institute of Technology *New Jersey* M & W
Stevenson University *Maryland* M & W
Stillman College *Alabama* W
Stockton University *New Jersey* W
Stonehill College *Massachusetts* M & W
Stony Brook University, State University of New York *New York* W
Suffolk County Community College *New York* W
Suffolk University *Massachusetts* W
Sul Ross State University *Texas* W
Sullivan County Community College *New York* W
Summit University *Pennsylvania* W
Surry Community College *North Carolina* W
Susquehanna University *Pennsylvania* M & W
Swarthmore College *Pennsylvania* M & W
Syracuse University *New York* M & W
Tabor College *Kansas* W
Tacoma Community College *Washington* W
Taft College *California* W
Tarleton State University *Texas* W
Taylor University *Indiana* W
Temple College *Texas* W
Temple University *Pennsylvania* W
Tennessee State University *Tennessee* W
Tennessee Technological University *Tennessee* W
Tennessee Wesleyan College *Tennessee* W
Texas A&M International University *Texas* W
Texas A&M University *Texas* W
Texas A&M University - Commerce *Texas* W
Texas A&M University - Corpus Christi *Texas* W
Texas A&M University - Kingsville *Texas* W
Texas Christian University *Texas* M & W
Texas College *Texas* W
Texas Lutheran University *Texas* W
Texas Southern University *Texas* M & W
Texas Southmost College *Texas* W
Texas State University *Texas* W
Texas Tech University *Texas* W
Texas Wesleyan University *Texas* W
Texas Woman's University *Texas* W
Thiel College *Pennsylvania* M & W
Thomas More College *Kentucky* W
Thompson Rivers University *British Columbia (Canada)* M & W
Tiffin University *Ohio* W
Toccoa Falls College *Georgia* W
Tompkins Cortland Community College *New York* W

M = Men; W = Women

Tougaloo College *Mississippi* W
Towson University *Maryland* M & W
Transylvania University *Kentucky* W
Treasure Valley Community College *Oregon* W
Trent University *Ontario (Canada)* M & W
Trevecca Nazarene University *Tennessee* W
Trine University *Indiana* W
Trinidad State Junior College *Colorado* W
Trinity Baptist College *Florida* W
Trinity Bible College *North Dakota* W
Trinity Christian College *Illinois* M & W
Trinity College *Connecticut* W
Trinity College of Florida *Florida* W
Trinity International University *Illinois* W
Trinity University *Texas* M & W
Trinity Valley Community College *Texas* W
Trinity Washington University *District of Columbia* W
Trinity Western University *British Columbia (Canada)* M & W
Triton College *Illinois* W
Troy University *Alabama* W
Truett-McConnell College *Georgia* W
Truman State University *Missouri* M & W
Tufts University *Massachusetts* M & W
Tulane University *Louisiana* M & W
Tusculum College *Tennessee* W
Tuskegee University *Alabama* W
Tyler Junior College *Texas* W
Tyndale University College & Seminary *Ontario (Canada)* M & W
Ulster County Community College *New York* W
Umpqua Community College *Oregon* W
Union College *Kentucky* W
Union College *Nebraska* W
Union College *New York* W
Union County College *New Jersey* W
Union University *Tennessee* W
United States Air Force Academy *Colorado* M & W
United States Coast Guard Academy *Connecticut* W
United States Merchant Marine Academy *New York* W
United States Military Academy *New York* M & W
United States Naval Academy *Maryland* M & W
Unity College *Maine* W
Universidad del Este *Puerto Rico* M & W
Universidad Metropolitana *Puerto Rico* M & W
Universidad del Turabo *Puerto Rico* M & W
Université Laval *Quebec (Canada)* M & W
Université de Moncton *New Brunswick (Canada)* W
Université de Montréal *Quebec (Canada)* M & W
Université du Québec à Chicoutimi *Quebec (Canada)* M & W
Université du Québec en Outaouais *Quebec (Canada)* W
Université Sainte-Anne *Nova Scotia (Canada)* M & W
The University of Akron *Ohio* W
The University of Akron Wayne College *Ohio* W
The University of Alabama *Alabama* M & W
The University of Alabama at Birmingham *Alabama* W
The University of Alabama in Huntsville *Alabama* W
University of Alaska Anchorage *Alaska* W
University of Alaska Fairbanks *Alaska* W
University at Albany, State University of New York *New York* W
University of Alberta *Alberta (Canada)* M & W
The University of Arizona *Arizona* W
University of Arkansas *Arkansas* W
University of Arkansas - Fort Smith *Arkansas* W
University of Arkansas at Little Rock *Arkansas* W
University of Arkansas for Medical Sciences *Arkansas* M & W
University of Arkansas at Pine Bluff *Arkansas* W
University of Bridgeport *Connecticut* W
The University of British Columbia *British Columbia (Canada)* M & W
The University of British Columbia - Okanagan Campus *British Columbia (Canada)* M & W
University at Buffalo, the State University of New York *New York* W
University of Calgary *Alberta (Canada)* M & W

University of California, Berkeley *California* W
University of California, Davis *California* W
University of California, Irvine *California* M & W
University of California, Los Angeles *California* M & W
University of California, Merced *California* W
University of California, Riverside *California* W
University of California, San Diego *California* M & W
University of California, Santa Barbara *California* M & W
University of California, Santa Cruz *California* M & W
University of Central Arkansas *Arkansas* W
University of Central Florida *Florida* W
University of Central Missouri *Missouri* W
University of Central Oklahoma *Oklahoma* W
University of Charleston *West Virginia* M & W
University of Chicago *Illinois* W
University of Cincinnati *Ohio* W
University of Cincinnati Clermont College *Ohio* W
University of Colorado Boulder *Colorado* W
University of Colorado Colorado Springs *Colorado* W
University of Colorado Denver *Colorado* M & W
University of Connecticut *Connecticut* W
University of the Cumberlands *Kentucky* W
University of Dallas *Texas* W
University of Dayton *Ohio* W
University of Delaware *Delaware* W
University of Denver *Colorado* W
University of Dubuque *Iowa* W
University of Evansville *Indiana* W
The University of Findlay *Ohio* W
University of Florida *Florida* M & W
University of Georgia *Georgia* W
University of Great Falls *Montana* W
University of Guelph *Ontario (Canada)* M & W
University of Hartford *Connecticut* M & W
University of Hawaii at Hilo *Hawaii* W
University of Hawaii at Manoa *Hawaii* M & W
University of Houston *Texas* W
University of Idaho *Idaho* W
University of Illinois at Chicago *Illinois* W
University of Illinois at Springfield *Illinois* W
University of Illinois at Urbana - Champaign *Illinois* W
University of the Incarnate Word *Texas* W
University of Indianapolis *Indiana* W
The University of Iowa *Iowa* M & W
University of Jamestown *North Dakota* W
The University of Kansas *Kansas* W
University of Kentucky *Kentucky* W
University of King's College *Nova Scotia (Canada)* M
University of La Verne *California* W
University of Louisiana at Lafayette *Louisiana* W
University of Louisiana at Monroe *Louisiana* W
University of Louisville *Kentucky* W
University of Maine at Fort Kent *Maine* W
University of Maine at Machias *Maine* W
University of Maine at Presque Isle *Maine* W
University of Manitoba *Manitoba (Canada)* M & W
University of Mary *North Dakota* W
University of Mary Hardin-Baylor *Texas* W
University of Mary Washington *Virginia* M & W
University of Maryland, Baltimore County *Maryland* M & W
University of Maryland, College Park *Maryland* W
University of Maryland Eastern Shore *Maryland* W
University of Massachusetts Boston *Massachusetts* W
University of Massachusetts Dartmouth *Massachusetts* W
University of Massachusetts Lowell *Massachusetts* W
University of Memphis *Tennessee* W
University of Miami *Florida* W
University of Michigan *Michigan* M & W
University of Michigan - Dearborn *Michigan* W
University of Minnesota, Crookston *Minnesota* W
University of Minnesota, Duluth *Minnesota* M & W
University of Minnesota, Morris *Minnesota* W

University of Minnesota, Twin Cities Campus *Minnesota* W
University of Mississippi *Mississippi* M & W
University of Missouri *Missouri* W
University of Missouri - Kansas City *Missouri* W
University of Missouri - St. Louis *Missouri* W
University of Mobile *Alabama* W
University of Montana *Montana* W
The University of Montana Western *Montana* W
University of Montevallo *Alabama* W
University of Mount Olive *North Carolina* M & W
University of Mount Union *Ohio* W
University of Nebraska at Kearney *Nebraska* W
University of Nebraska - Lincoln *Nebraska* W
University of Nebraska at Omaha *Nebraska* W
University of Nevada, Las Vegas *Nevada* W
University of Nevada, Reno *Nevada* W
University of New Brunswick Fredericton *New Brunswick (Canada)* M & W
University of New Brunswick Saint John *New Brunswick (Canada)* M & W
University of New England *Maine* W
University of New Hampshire *New Hampshire* M & W
University of New Haven *Connecticut* M & W
University of New Mexico *New Mexico* W
University of New Orleans *Louisiana* W
University of North Alabama *Alabama* W
University of North Carolina at Asheville *North Carolina* W
The University of North Carolina at Chapel Hill *North Carolina* M & W
The University of North Carolina at Charlotte *North Carolina* W
The University of North Carolina at Greensboro *North Carolina* W
The University of North Carolina at Pembroke *North Carolina* W
The University of North Carolina Wilmington *North Carolina* W
University of North Dakota *North Dakota* W
University of North Florida *Florida* W
University of North Texas *Texas* M & W
University of Northern Colorado *Colorado* W
University of Northern Iowa *Iowa* W
University of Northwestern - St. Paul *Minnesota* M & W
University of Notre Dame *Indiana* W
University of Oklahoma *Oklahoma* W
University of Oregon *Oregon* W
University of Ottawa *Ontario (Canada)* M & W
University of the Pacific *California* M & W
University of Pennsylvania *Pennsylvania* W
University of Pikeville *Kentucky* W
University of Pittsburgh *Pennsylvania* W
University of Pittsburgh at Bradford *Pennsylvania* W
University of Pittsburgh at Greensburg *Pennsylvania* W
University of Pittsburgh at Johnstown *Pennsylvania* W
University of Pittsburgh at Titusville *Pennsylvania* W
University of Portland *Oregon* W
University of Prince Edward Island *Prince Edward Island (Canada)* W
University of Puerto Rico in Arecibo *Puerto Rico* M & W
University of Puerto Rico in Bayamón *Puerto Rico* M & W
University of Puerto Rico in Carolina *Puerto Rico* M & W
University of Puerto Rico in Cayey *Puerto Rico* M & W
University of Puerto Rico in Humacao *Puerto Rico* M & W
University of Puerto Rico, Mayagüez Campus *Puerto Rico* M & W
University of Puerto Rico in Ponce *Puerto Rico* M & W
University of Puerto Rico, Río Piedras Campus *Puerto Rico* M & W
University of Puerto Rico in Utuado *Puerto Rico* M & W

M = Men; W = Women

University of Puget Sound *Washington* W
University of Redlands *California* W
University of Regina *Saskatchewan* (Canada) M & W
University of Rhode Island *Rhode Island* W
University of Richmond *Virginia* M & W
University of Rio Grande *Ohio* W
University of Rochester *New York* M & W
University of the Sacred Heart *Puerto Rico* M & W
University of St. Francis *Illinois* W
University of Saint Francis *Indiana* W
University of Saint Joseph *Connecticut* W
University of Saint Mary *Kansas* W
University of St. Thomas *Minnesota* W
University of St. Thomas *Texas* W
University of San Diego *California* M & W
University of San Francisco *California* M & W
University of Saskatchewan *Saskatchewan* (Canada) M & W
University of Science and Arts of Oklahoma *Oklahoma* W
University of the Sciences *Pennsylvania* W
The University of Scranton *Pennsylvania* M & W
University of Sioux Falls *South Dakota* W
University of South Alabama *Alabama* W
University of South Carolina *South Carolina* W
University of South Carolina Aiken *South Carolina* W
University of South Carolina Upstate *South Carolina* W
The University of South Dakota *South Dakota* W
University of South Florida *Florida* M & W
University of Southern California *California* M & W
University of Southern Indiana *Indiana* W
University of Southern Maine *Maine* W
University of Southern Mississippi *Mississippi* W
University of the Southwest *New Mexico* W
The University of Tampa *Florida* W
The University of Tennessee *Tennessee* W
The University of Tennessee at Chattanooga *Tennessee* W
The University of Tennessee at Martin *Tennessee* W
The University of Texas at Arlington *Texas* W
The University of Texas at Austin *Texas* M & W
The University of Texas at Dallas *Texas* W
The University of Texas at El Paso *Texas* W
The University of Texas Medical Branch *Texas* M & W
The University of Texas of the Permian Basin *Texas* W
The University of Texas Rio Grande Valley *Texas* W
The University of Texas at San Antonio *Texas* M & W
The University of Texas at Tyler *Texas* W
The University of Toledo *Ohio* W
University of Toronto *Ontario (Canada)* M & W
The University of Tulsa *Oklahoma* W
University of Utah *Utah* W
University of Valley Forge *Pennsylvania* W
University of Vermont *Vermont* M & W
University of Virginia *Virginia* W
The University of Virginia's College at Wise *Virginia* W
University of Washington *Washington* W
University of Waterloo *Ontario (Canada)* M & W
The University of West Alabama *Alabama* W
University of West Florida *Florida* W
University of West Georgia *Georgia* W
The University of Western Ontario *Ontario (Canada)* M & W
University of Windsor *Ontario (Canada)* M & W
The University of Winnipeg *Manitoba* (Canada) M & W
University of Wisconsin - Baraboo/Sauk County *Wisconsin* W
University of Wisconsin - Eau Claire *Wisconsin* W
University of Wisconsin - Fond du Lac *Wisconsin* W
University of Wisconsin - Fox Valley *Wisconsin* M & W
University of Wisconsin - Green Bay *Wisconsin* W
University of Wisconsin - La Crosse *Wisconsin* W

University of Wisconsin - Madison *Wisconsin* M & W
University of Wisconsin - Manitowoc *Wisconsin* W
University of Wisconsin - Marinette *Wisconsin* W
University of Wisconsin - Marshfield/Wood County *Wisconsin* W
University of Wisconsin - Milwaukee *Wisconsin* M & W
University of Wisconsin - Oshkosh *Wisconsin* W
University of Wisconsin - Parkside *Wisconsin* W
University of Wisconsin - Platteville *Wisconsin* M & W
University of Wisconsin - Richland *Wisconsin* W
University of Wisconsin - River Falls *Wisconsin* M & W
University of Wisconsin - Sheboygan *Wisconsin* W
University of Wisconsin - Stevens Point *Wisconsin* W
University of Wisconsin - Stout *Wisconsin* M & W
University of Wisconsin - Superior *Wisconsin* W
University of Wisconsin - Washington County *Wisconsin* W
University of Wisconsin - Waukesha *Wisconsin* W
University of Wisconsin - Whitewater *Wisconsin* M & W
University of Wyoming *Wyoming* W
Upper Iowa University *Iowa* W
Urbana University *Ohio* W
Ursinus College *Pennsylvania* W
Ursuline College *Ohio* W
Utah State University *Utah* M & W
Utah Valley University *Utah* W
Utica College *New York* W
Valdosta State University *Georgia* W
Valley City State University *North Dakota* W
Valparaiso University *Indiana* W
Vanguard University of Southern California *California* W
Vassar College *New York* M & W
Ventura College *California* W
Vermilion Community College *Minnesota* W
Vernon College *Texas* W
Victor Valley College *California* W
Victoria College *Texas* W
Villanova University *Pennsylvania* M & W
Vincennes University *Indiana* W
Virginia Commonwealth University *Virginia* W
Virginia Polytechnic Institute and State University *Virginia* W
Virginia State University *Virginia* W
Virginia Union University *Virginia* W
Virginia Wesleyan College *Virginia* W
Viterbo University *Wisconsin* W
Wake Forest University *North Carolina* W
Waldorf College *Iowa* W
Walla Walla Community College *Washington* W
Walla Walla University *Washington* W
Wallace State Community College *Alabama* W
Walsh University *Ohio* W
Walters State Community College *Tennessee* W
Warner Pacific College *Oregon* W
Warner University *Florida* W
Wartburg College *Iowa* W
Washburn University *Kansas* W
Washington College *Maryland* W
Washington & Jefferson College *Pennsylvania* M & W
Washington and Lee University *Virginia* W
Washington State University *Washington* M & W
Washington State University - Tri-Cities *Washington* W
Washington University in St. Louis *Missouri* M & W
Waubonsee Community College *Illinois* W
Wayland Baptist University *Texas* W
Wayne County Community College District *Michigan* W
Wayne State College *Nebraska* W
Wayne State University *Michigan* W
Waynesburg University *Pennsylvania* W
Webb Institute *New York* M & W
Webber International University *Florida* W
Weber State University *Utah* M & W
Webster University *Missouri* W
Welch College *Tennessee* W

Wellesley College *Massachusetts* W
Wells College *New York* M & W
Wenatchee Valley College *Washington* W
Wentworth Institute of Technology *Massachusetts* M & W
Wentworth Military Academy and College *Missouri* W
Wesleyan College *Georgia* W
Wesleyan University *Connecticut* M & W
West Chester University of Pennsylvania *Pennsylvania* M & W
West Hills Community College *California* W
West Liberty University *West Virginia* W
West Los Angeles College *California* W
West Texas A&M University *Texas* W
West Valley College *California* M & W
West Virginia State University *West Virginia* W
West Virginia University *West Virginia* W
West Virginia University Institute of Technology *West Virginia* W
West Virginia Wesleyan College *West Virginia* W
Westchester Community College *New York* W
Western Carolina University *North Carolina* W
Western Connecticut State University *Connecticut* W
Western Illinois University *Illinois* W
Western Kentucky University *Kentucky* W
Western Michigan University *Michigan* M & W
Western Nebraska Community College *Nebraska* W
Western New England University *Massachusetts* W
Western New Mexico University *New Mexico* W
Western Oregon University *Oregon* W
Western State Colorado University *Colorado* M & W
Western Technical College *Wisconsin* W
Western Texas College *Texas* W
Western Washington University *Washington* W
Western Wyoming Community College *Wyoming* W
Westfield State University *Massachusetts* W
Westminster College *Missouri* W
Westminster College *Pennsylvania* W
Westminster College *Utah* W
Westmont College *California* M & W
Westmoreland County Community College *Pennsylvania* W
Wharton County Junior College *Texas* W
Whatcom Community College *Washington* W
Wheaton College *Illinois* M & W
Wheaton College *Massachusetts* W
Wheeling Jesuit University *West Virginia* W
Whitman College *Washington* M & W
Whittier College *California* W
Whitworth University *Washington* W
Wichita State University *Kansas* M & W
Widener University *Pennsylvania* W
Wiley College *Texas* W
Wilfrid Laurier University *Ontario (Canada)* M & W
Wilkes Community College *North Carolina* W
Wilkes University *Pennsylvania* W
Willamette University *Oregon* W
William Jessup University *California* W
William Jewell College *Missouri* W
William Paterson University of New Jersey *New Jersey* W
William Peace University *North Carolina* W
William Penn University *Iowa* W
William Woods University *Missouri* W
Williams Baptist College *Arkansas* W
Williams College *Massachusetts* M & W
Williston State College *North Dakota* W
Wilmington College *Ohio* W
Wilmington University *Delaware* W
Wilson College *Pennsylvania* M
Wingate University *North Carolina* W
Winona State University *Minnesota* W
Winston-Salem State University *North Carolina* W
Winthrop University *South Carolina* W
Wisconsin Lutheran College *Wisconsin* W
Wittenberg University *Ohio* M & W
Wofford College *South Carolina* W
Worcester Polytechnic Institute *Massachusetts* W
Worcester State University *Massachusetts* W
Wright State University *Ohio* W

M = Men; W = Women

Wytheville Community College *Virginia* W
Xavier University *Ohio* M & W
Yakima Valley Community College *Washington* W
Yale University *Connecticut* M & W
Yavapai College *Arizona* W
Yeshiva University *New York* M
York College *Nebraska* W
York College of the City University of New York *New York* M & W
York College of Pennsylvania *Pennsylvania* W
York University *Ontario (Canada)* M & W
Youngstown State University *Ohio* W
Yuba College *California* W

Water Polo

American River College *California* M & W
Amherst College *Massachusetts* M & W
Arizona State University at the Downtown Phoenix campus *Arizona* W
Arizona State University at the Polytechnic campus *Arizona* W
Arizona State University at the Tempe campus *Arizona* W
Arizona State University at the West campus *Arizona* W
Augustana College *Illinois* M & W
Azusa Pacific University *California* W
Ball State University *Indiana* M & W
Barnard College *New York* W
Bates College *Maine* M & W
Baylor University *Texas* M & W
Boston University *Massachusetts* M & W
Bowdoin College *Maine* M & W
Brown University *Rhode Island* M & W
Bucknell University *Pennsylvania* M & W
Cabrillo College *California* M & W
California Baptist University *California* M & W
California Institute of Technology *California* M & W
California Lutheran University *California* M & W
California Maritime Academy *California* M & W
California State University, Bakersfield *California* W
California State University, East Bay *California* W
California State University, Fullerton *California* M & W
California State University, Long Beach *California* M & W
California State University, Monterey Bay *California* W
Carleton College *Minnesota* M & W
Carleton University *Ontario (Canada)* M & W
Carnegie Mellon University *Pennsylvania* M & W
Carthage College *Wisconsin* W
Central Washington University *Washington* M & W
Cerritos College *California* M
Chabot College *California* W
Chaffey College *California* M & W
Chapman University *California* M & W
Citrus College *California* M & W
Claremont McKenna College *California* M & W
Colby College *Maine* M & W
Colgate University *New York* M & W
College of Marin *California* M & W
College of San Mateo *California* W
College of the Sequoias *California* M
The Colorado College *Colorado* W
Colorado State University *Colorado* M & W
Columbia University *New York* M & W
Columbia University, School of General Studies *New York* M & W
Concordia University Irvine *California* M & W
Connecticut College *Connecticut* M & W
Cornell University *New York* M & W
Cuesta College *California* M & W
Cypress College *California* W
Dartmouth College *New Hampshire* M & W
De Anza College *California* M
Diablo Valley College *California* M & W
Duke University *North Carolina* W
Eastern Illinois University *Illinois* M & W
El Camino College *California* M
Emory University *Georgia* M & W
Florida Institute of Technology *Florida* M & W
Foothill College *California* W
Fordham University *New York* M

Fresno City College *California* W
Fresno Pacific University *California* M & W
Fullerton College *California* M & W
Gannon University *Pennsylvania* M & W
The George Washington University *District of Columbia* W
Georgetown University *District of Columbia* M
Golden West College *California* M & W
Grand Valley State University *Michigan* M & W
Grossmont College *California* M & W
Grove City College *Pennsylvania* M & W
Hamilton College *New York* M
Hartwick College *New York* M & W
Harvard University *Massachusetts* M & W
Harvey Mudd College *California* M & W
Illinois Wesleyan University *Illinois* M
Indiana University Bloomington *Indiana* W
Iona College *New York* M & W
Johns Hopkins University *Maryland* M
La Salle University *Pennsylvania* M & W
Lake Forest College *Illinois* M & W
Lehigh University *Pennsylvania* M & W
Lehman College of the City University of New York *New York* M
Lewis University *Illinois* M & W
Lindenwood University *Missouri* M & W
Long Beach City College *California* M & W
Los Angeles Pierce College *California* M
Los Angeles Valley College *California* M & W
Loyola Marymount University *California* M & W
Lycoming College *Pennsylvania* M & W
Macalester College *Minnesota* M & W
Marist College *New York* W
Massachusetts Institute of Technology *Massachusetts* M
McKendree University *Illinois* M & W
McMaster University *Ontario (Canada)* M & W
Merced College *California* M
Mercyhurst University *Pennsylvania* M & W
Miami University *Ohio* M & W
Michigan State University *Michigan* M & W
Michigan Technological University *Michigan* M & W
Modesto Junior College *California* M & W
Monmouth College *Illinois* M & W
Mt. San Antonio College *California* M & W
North Carolina State University *North Carolina* M & W
Northeastern University *Massachusetts* M & W
Oberlin College *Ohio* M & W
Occidental College *California* M & W
Ohlone College *California* M
Orange Coast College *California* M & W
Palomar College *California* M & W
Pasadena City College *California* W
Penn State Erie, The Behrend College *Pennsylvania* M & W
Pepperdine University *California* M
Pitzer College *California* M & W
Pomona College *California* M & W
Princeton University *New Jersey* M & W
Queen's University at Kingston *Ontario (Canada)* M & W
Rensselaer Polytechnic Institute *New York* M & W
Rice University *Texas* M & W
Rio Hondo College *California* M & W
Rochester Institute of Technology *New York* M & W
Sacramento City College *California* W
Saddleback College *California* M & W
St. Francis College *New York* M & W
Saint John's University *Minnesota* M
Saint Louis University *Missouri* M & W
Saint Mary's College of California *California* M & W
Salem International University *West Virginia* M & W
San Diego Mesa College *California* M & W
San Diego Miramar College *California* M & W
San Diego State University *California* W
San Joaquin Delta College *California* M & W
San Jose State University *California* M & W
Santa Ana College *California* M
Santa Clara University *California* M & W
Santa Monica College *California* M & W
Santa Rosa Junior College *California* M & W
Scripps College *California* W
Siena College *New York* W

Sierra College *California* M & W
Solano Community College *California* M & W
Sonoma State University *California* W
Southwestern College *California* M & W
Stanford University *California* M & W
Swarthmore College *Pennsylvania* M & W
Syracuse University *New York* M & W
Texas Christian University *Texas* M & W
Texas State University *Texas* M & W
Trinity College *Connecticut* M & W
Trinity University *Texas* M & W
Tufts University *Massachusetts* M & W
Tulane University *Louisiana* M & W
United States Air Force Academy *Colorado* M & W
United States Coast Guard Academy *Connecticut* M & W
United States Military Academy *New York* M
United States Naval Academy *Maryland* M
The University of Arizona *Arizona* M & W
University of California, Berkeley *California* M & W
University of California, Davis *California* M & W
University of California, Irvine *California* M & W
University of California, Los Angeles *California* M & W
University of California, San Diego *California* M & W
University of California, Santa Barbara *California* M & W
University of California, Santa Cruz *California* M & W
University of Colorado Boulder *Colorado* M & W
University of Denver *Colorado* M & W
University of Georgia *Georgia* M & W
University of Hawaii at Manoa *Hawaii* W
University of La Verne *California* M & W
University of Maryland, College Park *Maryland* W
University of Michigan *Michigan* M & W
University of Minnesota, Duluth *Minnesota* M & W
The University of North Carolina at Chapel Hill *North Carolina* M & W
University of Ottawa *Ontario (Canada)* M & W
University of the Pacific *California* M & W
University of Puerto Rico, Mayagüez Campus *Puerto Rico* M
University of Puerto Rico, Río Piedras Campus *Puerto Rico* M & W
University of Puget Sound *Washington* M & W
University of Redlands *California* M & W
University of Richmond *Virginia* M & W
University of Rochester *New York* M & W
University of Southern California *California* M & W
The University of Texas at Austin *Texas* M & W
University of Utah *Utah* M & W
University of Vermont *Vermont* M & W
The University of Western Ontario *Ontario (Canada)* M
University of Wisconsin - Madison *Wisconsin* M & W
University of Wisconsin - Whitewater *Wisconsin* M & W
University of Wyoming *Wyoming* M
Utica College *New York* W
Ventura College *California* M & W
Villanova University *Pennsylvania* M & W
Virginia Military Institute *Virginia* W
Wagner College *New York* M & W
Washington College *Maryland* M & W
Washington & Jefferson College *Pennsylvania* M & W
Washington State University *Washington* M & W
Washington University in St. Louis *Missouri* M & W
Wesleyan University *Connecticut* W
West Chester University of Pennsylvania *Pennsylvania* W
West Valley College *California* M
Western Michigan University *Michigan* M & W
Whitman College *Washington* M & W
Whittier College *California* M & W
Williams College *Massachusetts* M & W
Worcester Polytechnic Institute *Massachusetts* M & W
Xavier University *Ohio* M & W
Yale University *Connecticut* M & W
York University *Ontario (Canada)* M & W

M = Men; W = Women

Weight Lifting

Bayamón Central University *Puerto Rico* M & W
Bucknell University *Pennsylvania* M & W
Clemson University *South Carolina* M & W
Coastal Carolina University *South Carolina* M & W
Crossroads College *Minnesota* M & W
Davidson College *North Carolina* M & W
Emory University *Georgia* M & W
Furman University *South Carolina* M & W
Illinois Central College *Illinois* M & W
Inter American University of Puerto Rico, Aguadilla Campus *Puerto Rico* M & W
Inter American University of Puerto Rico, Barranquitas Campus *Puerto Rico* M & W
Inter American University of Puerto Rico, Bayamón Campus *Puerto Rico* M
Inter American University of Puerto Rico, Ponce Campus *Puerto Rico* M & W
Inter American University of Puerto Rico, San Germán Campus *Puerto Rico* M
Lafayette College *Pennsylvania* M & W
Lindenwood University *Missouri* M & W
Louisiana Tech University *Louisiana* M & W
McKendree University *Illinois* M & W
Miami University *Ohio* M & W
Northeastern University *Massachusetts* M & W
Norwich University *Vermont* M & W
Polytechnic University of Puerto Rico *Puerto Rico* M & W
Pontifical Catholic University of Puerto Rico *Puerto Rico* M & W
Rensselaer Polytechnic Institute *New York* M & W
Texas State University *Texas* M & W
Truman State University *Missouri* M & W
United States Air Force Academy *Colorado* M & W
United States Naval Academy *Maryland* M & W
Universidad del Este *Puerto Rico* M
Universidad Metropolitana *Puerto Rico* M & W
Universidad del Turabo *Puerto Rico* M & W
The University of Alabama *Alabama* M & W
University of Puerto Rico in Aguadilla *Puerto Rico* M & W
University of Puerto Rico in Arecibo *Puerto Rico* M & W
University of Puerto Rico in Cayey *Puerto Rico* M & W
University of Puerto Rico in Humacao *Puerto Rico* M & W
University of Puerto Rico in Ponce *Puerto Rico* M & W
University of Puerto Rico, Río Piedras Campus *Puerto Rico* M & W
University of Puerto Rico in Utuado *Puerto Rico* M & W
University of the Sacred Heart *Puerto Rico* M & W
The University of Texas at Austin *Texas* M & W
The University of Texas at San Antonio *Texas* M & W
University of Utah *Utah* M & W
University of Wisconsin - Whitewater *Wisconsin* M & W
Washington State University *Washington* M & W
Weber State University *Utah* M & W

Wrestling

Adams State University *Colorado* M
Alderson Broaddus University *West Virginia* M & W
Alma College *Michigan* M
American International College *Massachusetts* M
American University *District of Columbia* M
Amherst College *Massachusetts* M & W
Ancilla College *Indiana* M
Anderson University *South Carolina* M
Appalachian State University *North Carolina* M
Arizona State University at the Downtown Phoenix campus *Arizona* M
Arizona State University at the Polytechnic campus *Arizona* M
Arizona State University at the Tempe campus *Arizona* M
Arizona State University at the West campus *Arizona* M
Ashland University *Ohio* M

M = Men; W = Women

Augsburg College *Minnesota* M
Augustana College *Illinois* M
Augustana University *South Dakota* M
Baker University *Kansas* M
Bakersfield College *California* M
Baldwin Wallace University *Ohio* M
Ball State University *Indiana* M
Barton County Community College *Kansas* M
Belmont Abbey College *North Carolina* M
Benedictine College *Kansas* M
Bergen Community College *New Jersey* M
Bethany College *Kansas* M
Binghamton University, State University of New York *New York* M
Bloomsburg University of Pennsylvania *Pennsylvania* M
Boise State University *Idaho* M
Brewton-Parker College *Georgia* M
Briar Cliff University *Iowa* M
Bridgewater College *Virginia* M
Bridgewater State University *Massachusetts* M
Brock University *Ontario (Canada)* M & W
Brown University *Rhode Island* M
Bucknell University *Pennsylvania* M
Buena Vista University *Iowa* M
California Baptist University *California* M
California Polytechnic State University, San Luis Obispo *California* M
California State University, Bakersfield *California* M
Calumet College of Saint Joseph *Indiana* M
Campbell University *North Carolina* M
Campbellsville University *Kentucky* M & W
Caribbean University *Puerto Rico* M & W
Case Western Reserve University *Ohio* M
Centenary College *New Jersey* M
Central Baptist College *Arkansas* M
Central College *Iowa* M
Central Michigan University *Michigan* M
Central Washington University *Washington* M & W
Cerritos College *California* M
Chabot College *California* M
Chadron State College *Nebraska* M
The Citadel, The Military College of South Carolina *South Carolina* M
City Colleges of Chicago, Kennedy-King College *Illinois* M
City Colleges of Chicago, Wilbur Wright College *Illinois* M
Clackamas Community College *Oregon* M
Clarion University of Pennsylvania *Pennsylvania* M
Clemson University *South Carolina* M
Cleveland State University *Ohio* M
Coastal Carolina University *South Carolina* M
Coe College *Iowa* M
Coker College *South Carolina* M
Colby Community College *Kansas* M
The College at Brockport, State University of New York *New York* M
College of Mount Saint Vincent *New York* M
The College of New Jersey *New Jersey* M
Colorado Mesa University *Colorado* M
Colorado School of Mines *Colorado* M
Colorado State University *Colorado* M & W
Colorado State University - Pueblo *Colorado* M
Columbia University *New York* M
Columbia University, School of General Studies *New York* M
Concordia College *Minnesota* M
Concordia University *Quebec (Canada)* M & W
Concordia University, Nebraska *Nebraska* M
Concordia University Wisconsin *Wisconsin* M
Cornell College *Iowa* M
Cornell University *New York* M
Cuesta College *California* M
Cumberland University *Tennessee* M
Dakota Wesleyan University *South Dakota* M
Daniel Webster College *New Hampshire* M
Dartmouth College *New Hampshire* M
Darton State College *Georgia* M
Davidson College *North Carolina* M
Delaware Valley University *Pennsylvania* M
Dickinson State University *North Dakota* M
Drexel University *Pennsylvania* M
Drury University *Missouri* M

Duke University *North Carolina* M
East Los Angeles College *California* M
East Stroudsburg University of Pennsylvania *Pennsylvania* M
Eastern Illinois University *Illinois* M & W
Eastern Michigan University *Michigan* M
Edinboro University of Pennsylvania *Pennsylvania* M
El Camino College *California* M
Elizabethtown College *Pennsylvania* M
Ellsworth Community College *Iowa* M
Elmhurst College *Illinois* M
Embry-Riddle Aeronautical University - Prescott *Arizona* M
Emmanuel College *Georgia* M & W
Florida State University *Florida* M & W
Fort Lewis College *Colorado* M & W
Franklin & Marshall College *Pennsylvania* M
Fresno City College *California* M
Furman University *South Carolina* M
Gannon University *Pennsylvania* M
Gardner-Webb University *North Carolina* M
George Mason University *Virginia* M
Gettysburg College *Pennsylvania* M
Graceland University *Iowa* M
Grand Canyon University *Arizona* M
Grand Valley State University *Michigan* M
Grand View University *Iowa* M
Greensboro College *North Carolina* M
Hampden-Sydney College *Virginia* M
Hannibal-LaGrange University *Missouri* M
Harper College *Illinois* M
Harvard University *Massachusetts* M
Hastings College *Nebraska* M
Haverford College *Pennsylvania* M
Heidelberg University *Ohio* M
Highline College *Washington* M
Hofstra University *New York* M
Hunter College of the City University of New York *New York* M
Huntingdon College *Alabama* M
Indiana Tech *Indiana* M
Indiana University Bloomington *Indiana* M
Inter American University of Puerto Rico, Aguadilla Campus *Puerto Rico* M
Inter American University of Puerto Rico, Barranquitas Campus *Puerto Rico* M & W
Inter American University of Puerto Rico, Ponce Campus *Puerto Rico* M
Iowa Central Community College *Iowa* M
Iowa Lakes Community College *Iowa* M
Iowa State University of Science and Technology *Iowa* M
Itasca Community College *Minnesota* M
Ithaca College *New York* M
Jamestown Community College *New York* M
John Carroll University *Ohio* M
Johns Hopkins University *Maryland* M
Johnson & Wales University *Rhode Island* M
Kansas Wesleyan University *Kansas* M
Kent State University *Ohio* M
King University *Tennessee* M & W
King's College *Pennsylvania* M
Kutztown University of Pennsylvania *Pennsylvania* M
Labette Community College *Kansas* M
Lafayette College *Pennsylvania* M
Lake Erie College *Ohio* M
Lakehead University *Ontario (Canada)* M & W
Lakeland College *Wisconsin* M
Lassen Community College District *California* M
Laurentian University *Ontario (Canada)* M & W
Lehigh University *Pennsylvania* M
Lehman College of the City University of New York *New York* M
Life University *Georgia* M & W
Limestone College *South Carolina* M
Lindenwood University *Missouri* M & W
Lindsey Wilson College *Kentucky* M
Lock Haven University of Pennsylvania *Pennsylvania* M
Long Island University - LIU Post *New York* M
Loras College *Iowa* M
Lourdes University *Ohio* M

Luther College *Iowa* M
Lycoming College *Pennsylvania* M
Lyon College *Arkansas* M & W
MacMurray College *Illinois* M & W
Madison Area Technical College *Wisconsin* M
Manchester University *Indiana* M
Maranatha Baptist University *Wisconsin* M
Marietta College *Ohio* M & W
Maryville University of Saint Louis *Missouri* M
McDaniel College *Maryland* M
McGill University *Quebec (Canada)* M & W
McKendree University *Illinois* M & W
McMaster University *Ontario (Canada)* M & W
Memorial University of Newfoundland *Newfoundland and Labrador (Canada)* M & W
Menlo College *California* M & W
Mercyhurst North East *Pennsylvania* M
Mercyhurst University *Pennsylvania* M
Mesa Community College *Arizona* M
Messiah College *Pennsylvania* M
Miami University *Ohio* M & W
Michigan State University *Michigan* M
Middlesex County College *New Jersey* M
Millersville University of Pennsylvania *Pennsylvania* M
Millikin University *Illinois* M
Milwaukee School of Engineering *Wisconsin* M
Minnesota State University Mankato *Minnesota* M
Minnesota State University Moorhead *Minnesota* M
Minnesota West Community and Technical College *Minnesota* M
Minot State University *North Dakota* M
Missouri Baptist University *Missouri* M & W
Missouri State University *Missouri* M
Missouri Valley College *Missouri* M & W
Modesto Junior College *California* M
Montana State University - Northern *Montana* M
Moorpark College *California* M
Moravian College *Pennsylvania* M
Morningside College *Iowa* M
Mount St. Joseph University *Ohio* M
Mt. San Antonio College *California* M
Muhlenberg College *Pennsylvania* M
Muskegon Community College *Michigan* M
Muskingum University *Ohio* M
Napa Valley College *California* M
Nassau Community College *New York* M
New York University *New York* M
Newberry College *South Carolina* M
Newman University *Kansas* M
Niagara County Community College *New York* M
North Carolina State University *North Carolina* M
North Central College *Illinois* M
North Dakota State University *North Dakota* M
North Idaho College *Idaho* M
North Iowa Area Community College *Iowa* M
Northeastern University *Massachusetts* M
Northern Illinois University *Illinois* M
Northern State University *South Dakota* M
Northland Community and Technical College *Minnesota* M
Northwest College *Wyoming* M
Northwestern College *Iowa* M
Norwich University *Vermont* M
Oberlin College *Ohio* M
Ohio Northern University *Ohio* M
The Ohio State University *Ohio* M
Ohio University *Ohio* M
Ohio Valley University *West Virginia* M
Oklahoma City University *Oklahoma* M & W
Oklahoma State University *Oklahoma* M
Old Dominion University *Virginia* M
Olivet College *Michigan* M
Oral Roberts University *Oklahoma* M
Oregon State University *Oregon* M
Otero Junior College *Colorado* M
Ouachita Baptist University *Arkansas* M
Pacific University *Oregon* M & W
Palomar College *California* M
Penn State University Park *Pennsylvania* M
Pennsylvania College of Technology *Pennsylvania* M
Plymouth State University *New Hampshire* M

Pontifical Catholic University of Puerto Rico *Puerto Rico* M
Pratt Community College *Kansas* M
Princeton University *New Jersey* M
Purdue University *Indiana* M
Queen's University at Kingston *Ontario (Canada)* M & W
Rhode Island College *Rhode Island* M
Rider University *New Jersey* M
Ridgewater College *Minnesota* M
Rio Hondo College *California* M
Rochester Community and Technical College *Minnesota* M
Rochester Institute of Technology *New York* M
Roger Williams University *Rhode Island* M
Rowan College at Gloucester County *New Jersey* M
Rutgers University - New Brunswick *New Jersey* M
Sacramento City College *California* M
Sacred Heart University *Connecticut* M
Saginaw Valley State University *Michigan* M
St. Andrews University *North Carolina* M
St. Cloud State University *Minnesota* M
Saint John's University *Minnesota* M
St. Olaf College *Minnesota* M
San Bernardino Valley College *California* M
San Francisco State University *California* M
San Joaquin Delta College *California* M
Santa Ana College *California* M
Santa Rosa Junior College *California* M
Seton Hill University *Pennsylvania* M
Shippensburg University of Pennsylvania *Pennsylvania* M
Sierra College *California* M
Simon Fraser University *British Columbia (Canada)* M & W
Simpson College *Iowa* M
Simpson University *California* M
Skyline College *California* M
South Dakota State University *South Dakota* M
Southeastern University *Florida* M
Southern Illinois University Edwardsville *Illinois* M
Southern Methodist University *Texas* M
Southern Oregon University *Oregon* M
Southern Virginia University *Virginia* M
Southwest Minnesota State University *Minnesota* M
Southwestern Oregon Community College *Oregon* M & W
Spartanburg Methodist College *South Carolina* M
Springfield College *Massachusetts* M
Springfield Technical Community College *Massachusetts* M
Stanford University *California* M
State University of New York College at Cortland *New York* M
State University of New York College at Oneonta *New York* M
State University of New York College of Technology at Alfred *New York* M
State University of New York at Oswego *New York* M
Stevens Institute of Technology *New Jersey* M
Stonehill College *Massachusetts* M
Sullivan County Community College *New York* M
Syracuse University *New York* M
Texas Christian University *Texas* M & W
Texas State University *Texas* M & W
Thaddeus Stevens College of Technology *Pennsylvania* M
Thiel College *Pennsylvania* M
Thomas More College *Kentucky* M
Tiffin University *Ohio* M
Trine University *Indiana* M
Trinity Bible College *North Dakota* M
Trinity College *Connecticut* M
Triton College *Illinois* M
Truett-McConnell College *Georgia* M
Truman State University *Missouri* M
United States Air Force Academy *Colorado* M
United States Coast Guard Academy *Connecticut* M
United States Merchant Marine Academy *New York* M
United States Military Academy *New York* M

United States Naval Academy *Maryland* M
The University of Alabama *Alabama* M
University of Alberta *Alberta (Canada)* M & W
University at Buffalo, the State University of New York *New York* M
University of Calgary *Alberta (Canada)* M & W
University of California, Irvine *California* M
University of Central Missouri *Missouri* M
University of Central Oklahoma *Oklahoma* M
University of Chicago *Illinois* M
University of Colorado Boulder *Colorado* M
University of the Cumberlands *Kentucky* M & W
University of Delaware *Delaware* M
University of Dubuque *Iowa* M
The University of Findlay *Ohio* M
University of Georgia *Georgia* M
University of Great Falls *Montana* M
University of Guelph *Ontario (Canada)* M & W
University of Illinois at Urbana - Champaign *Illinois* M
University of Indianapolis *Indiana* M
The University of Iowa *Iowa* M
University of Jamestown *North Dakota* M & W
University of Mary *North Dakota* M
University of Maryland, Baltimore County *Maryland* M
University of Maryland, College Park *Maryland* M
University of Maryland Eastern Shore *Maryland* M
University of Michigan *Michigan* M
University of Michigan - Dearborn *Michigan* M
University of Minnesota, Duluth *Minnesota* M
University of Minnesota, Twin Cities Campus *Minnesota* M
University of Missouri *Missouri* M
University of Mount Union *Ohio* M
University of Nebraska at Kearney *Nebraska* M
University of Nebraska - Lincoln *Nebraska* M
University of New Brunswick Fredericton *New Brunswick (Canada)* M & W
University of New Hampshire *New Hampshire* M & W
University of New Haven *Connecticut* M
The University of North Carolina at Chapel Hill *North Carolina* M
The University of North Carolina at Pembroke *North Carolina* M
University of North Georgia *Georgia* M
University of North Texas *Texas* M
University of Northern Colorado *Colorado* M
University of Northern Iowa *Iowa* M
University of Oklahoma *Oklahoma* M
University of Pennsylvania *Pennsylvania* M
University of Pittsburgh *Pennsylvania* M
University of Pittsburgh at Johnstown *Pennsylvania* M
University of Puerto Rico in Arecibo *Puerto Rico* M
University of Puerto Rico in Cayey *Puerto Rico* M
University of Puerto Rico in Humacao *Puerto Rico* M
University of Puerto Rico, Mayagüez Campus *Puerto Rico* M
University of Puerto Rico, Río Piedras Campus *Puerto Rico* M & W
University of Regina *Saskatchewan (Canada)* M & W
University of Saskatchewan *Saskatchewan (Canada)* M & W
The University of Scranton *Pennsylvania* M
University of Sioux Falls *South Dakota* M
University of Southern Maine *Maine* M
The University of Tennessee at Chattanooga *Tennessee* M
The University of Texas at Austin *Texas* M & W
University of Toronto *Ontario (Canada)* M
University of Utah *Utah* M
University of Virginia *Virginia* M
The University of Western Ontario *Ontario (Canada)* M & W
University of Wisconsin - Eau Claire *Wisconsin* M
University of Wisconsin - La Crosse *Wisconsin* M
University of Wisconsin - Madison *Wisconsin* M
University of Wisconsin - Oshkosh *Wisconsin* M
University of Wisconsin - Parkside *Wisconsin* M
University of Wisconsin - Platteville *Wisconsin* M

M = Men; W = Women

University of Wisconsin - River Falls *Wisconsin* M
University of Wisconsin - Stevens Point *Wisconsin* M
University of Wisconsin - Whitewater *Wisconsin* M
University of Wyoming *Wyoming* M
Upper Iowa University *Iowa* M
Ursinus College *Pennsylvania* M
Utah Valley University *Utah* M
Valley Forge Military College *Pennsylvania* M
Victor Valley College *California* M
Virginia Military Institute *Virginia* M
Wabash College *Indiana* M
Waldorf College *Iowa* M & W
Warner Pacific College *Oregon* M & W
Wartburg College *Iowa* M
Washington & Jefferson College *Pennsylvania* M
Washington and Lee University *Virginia* M
Washington State University *Washington* M

Washington University in St. Louis *Missouri* M
Waubonsee Community College *Illinois* M
Wayland Baptist University *Texas* M & W
Wayne State College *Nebraska* M
Waynesburg University *Pennsylvania* M
Weber State University *Utah* M
Wentworth Military Academy and College *Missouri* M
Wesleyan University *Connecticut* M
West Chester University of Pennsylvania *Pennsylvania* M
West Liberty University *West Virginia* M
West Valley College *California* M
West Virginia University *West Virginia* M
West Virginia University Institute of Technology *West Virginia* M
Western Carolina University *North Carolina* M
Western New England University *Massachusetts* M

Western State Colorado University *Colorado* M & W
Western Wyoming Community College *Wyoming* M
Wheaton College *Illinois* M
Wheeling Jesuit University *West Virginia* M
Wichita State University *Kansas* M & W
Wilkes University *Pennsylvania* M
William Penn University *Iowa* M
Williams Baptist College *Arkansas* M
Williams College *Massachusetts* M
Williamson College of the Trades *Pennsylvania* M
Wilmington College *Ohio* M
Worcester Polytechnic Institute *Massachusetts* M
Yakima Valley Community College *Washington* M
Yale University *Connecticut* M & W
Yeshiva University *New York* M
York College *Nebraska* M
York College of Pennsylvania *Pennsylvania* M

M = Men; W = Women

AACSB International-The Association to Advance Collegiate Schools of Business (AACSB)

Abilene Christian University *Texas*
Adelphi University *New York*
Alfred University *New York*
American University *District of Columbia*
Appalachian State University *North Carolina*
Arizona State University at the Tempe campus *Arizona*
Arkansas State University *Arkansas*
Arkansas Tech University *Arkansas*
Auburn University *Alabama*
Auburn University at Montgomery *Alabama*
Augusta University *Georgia*
Babson College *Massachusetts*
Ball State University *Indiana*
Barry University *Florida*
Baruch College of the City University of New York *New York*
Baylor University *Texas*
Bellarmine University *Kentucky*
Belmont University *Tennessee*
Bentley University *Massachusetts*
Berry College *Georgia*
Binghamton University, State University of New York *New York*
Birmingham-Southern College *Alabama*
Black Hills State University *South Dakota*
Bloomsburg University of Pennsylvania *Pennsylvania*
Boise State University *Idaho*
Boston College *Massachusetts*
Boston University *Massachusetts*
Bowling Green State University *Ohio*
Bradley University *Illinois*
Brandeis University *Massachusetts*
Brigham Young University *Utah*
Brock University *Ontario (Canada)*
Bryant University *Rhode Island*
Butler University *Indiana*
California Polytechnic State University, San Luis Obispo *California*
California State Polytechnic University, Pomona *California*
California State University, Bakersfield *California*
California State University, Chico *California*
California State University, East Bay *California*
California State University, Fresno *California*
California State University, Fullerton *California*
California State University, Long Beach *California*
California State University, Los Angeles *California*
California State University, Northridge *California*
California State University, Sacramento *California*
California State University, San Bernardino *California*
California State University, Stanislaus *California*
Canisius College *New York*
Carnegie Mellon University *Pennsylvania*
Case Western Reserve University *Ohio*
Central Michigan University *Michigan*
Central Washington University *Washington*
Chapman University *California*

Christopher Newport University *Virginia*
The Citadel, The Military College of South Carolina *South Carolina*
Clarion University of Pennsylvania *Pennsylvania*
Clark Atlanta University *Georgia*
Clark University *Massachusetts*
Clarkson University *New York*
Clayton State University *Georgia*
Clemson University *South Carolina*
Cleveland State University *Ohio*
Coastal Carolina University *South Carolina*
The College at Brockport, State University of New York *New York*
College of Charleston *South Carolina*
The College of New Jersey *New Jersey*
The College of William and Mary *Virginia*
Colorado State University *Colorado*
Colorado State University - Pueblo *Colorado*
Columbia University *New York*
Columbus State University *Georgia*
Concordia University *Quebec (Canada)*
Cornell University *New York*
Creighton University *Nebraska*
Dalhousie University *Nova Scotia (Canada)*
Dalton State College *Georgia*
Dartmouth College *New Hampshire*
Delaware State University *Delaware*
DePaul University *Illinois*
Dominican University *Illinois*
Drake University *Iowa*
Drexel University *Pennsylvania*
Drury University *Missouri*
Duke University *North Carolina*
Duquesne University *Pennsylvania*
East Carolina University *North Carolina*
East Tennessee State University *Tennessee*
Eastern Illinois University *Illinois*
Eastern Kentucky University *Kentucky*
Eastern Michigan University *Michigan*
Eastern Washington University *Washington*
Elizabeth City State University *North Carolina*
Elon University *North Carolina*
Emory University *Georgia*
Emporia State University *Kansas*
Fairfield University *Connecticut*
Fairleigh Dickinson University, College at Florham *New Jersey*
Fairleigh Dickinson University, Metropolitan Campus *New Jersey*
Fayetteville State University *North Carolina*
Florida Atlantic University *Florida*
Florida Gulf Coast University *Florida*
Florida International University *Florida*
Florida State University *Florida*
Fordham University *New York*
Fort Lewis College *Colorado*
Francis Marion University *South Carolina*
Frostburg State University *Maryland*
George Mason University *Virginia*
The George Washington University *District of Columbia*
Georgetown University *District of Columbia*
Georgia College & State University *Georgia*
Georgia Institute of Technology *Georgia*

Georgia Southern University *Georgia*
Georgia Southwestern State University *Georgia*
Georgia State University *Georgia*
Gonzaga University *Washington*
Grambling State University *Louisiana*
Grand Valley State University *Michigan*
Harvard University *Massachusetts*
HEC Montreal *Quebec (Canada)*
Henderson State University *Arkansas*
Hofstra University *New York*
Howard University *District of Columbia*
Idaho State University *Idaho*
Illinois Institute of Technology *Illinois*
Illinois State University *Illinois*
Indiana State University *Indiana*
Indiana University Bloomington *Indiana*
Indiana University Kokomo *Indiana*
Indiana University Northwest *Indiana*
Indiana University of Pennsylvania *Pennsylvania*
Indiana University - Purdue University Fort Wayne *Indiana*
Indiana University - Purdue University Indianapolis *Indiana*
Indiana University South Bend *Indiana*
Indiana University Southeast *Indiana*
Iona College *New York*
Iowa State University of Science and Technology *Iowa*
Ithaca College *New York*
Jackson State University *Mississippi*
Jacksonville State University *Alabama*
Jacksonville University *Florida*
James Madison University *Virginia*
John Carroll University *Ohio*
Kansas State University *Kansas*
Kennesaw State University *Georgia*
Kent State University *Ohio*
King's College *Pennsylvania*
Kutztown University of Pennsylvania *Pennsylvania*
La Salle University *Pennsylvania*
Lamar University *Texas*
Lander University *South Carolina*
Le Moyne College *New York*
Lehigh University *Pennsylvania*
Long Island University - LIU Post *New York*
Longwood University *Virginia*
Louisiana State University and Agricultural & Mechanical College *Louisiana*
Louisiana State University in Shreveport *Louisiana*
Louisiana Tech University *Louisiana*
Loyola Marymount University *California*
Loyola University Chicago *Illinois*
Loyola University Maryland *Maryland*
Loyola University New Orleans *Louisiana*
Manhattan College *New York*
Marist College *New York*
Marquette University *Wisconsin*
Marshall University *West Virginia*
Massachusetts Institute of Technology *Massachusetts*
McMaster University *Ontario (Canada)*
McNeese State University *Louisiana*
Memorial University of Newfoundland *Newfoundland and Labrador (Canada)*

Mercer University *Georgia*
Meredith College *North Carolina*
Miami University *Ohio*
Michigan State University *Michigan*
Michigan Technological University *Michigan*
Middle Tennessee State University *Tennessee*
Midwestern State University *Texas*
Millsaps College *Mississippi*
Minnesota State University Mankato *Minnesota*
Minnesota State University Moorhead *Minnesota*
Mississippi State University *Mississippi*
Missouri State University *Missouri*
Missouri Western State University *Missouri*
Monmouth University *New Jersey*
Montana State University *Montana*
Montana State University Billings *Montana*
Montclair State University *New Jersey*
Morehead State University *Kentucky*
Morehouse College *Georgia*
Morgan State University *Maryland*
Murray State University *Kentucky*
New Jersey Institute of Technology *New Jersey*
New Mexico State University *New Mexico*
New York Institute of Technology *New York*
New York University *New York*
Niagara University *New York*
Nicholls State University *Louisiana*
Norfolk State University *Virginia*
North Carolina Agricultural and Technical State University *North Carolina*
North Carolina Central University *North Carolina*
North Carolina State University *North Carolina*
North Dakota State University *North Dakota*
Northeastern University *Massachusetts*
Northern Arizona University *Arizona*
Northern Illinois University *Illinois*
Northern Kentucky University *Kentucky*
Northern Michigan University *Michigan*
Northwestern State University of Louisiana *Louisiana*
Northwestern University *Illinois*
Oakland University *Michigan*
Ohio Northern University *Ohio*
The Ohio State University *Ohio*
Ohio University *Ohio*
Oklahoma City University *Oklahoma*
Oklahoma State University *Oklahoma*
Old Dominion University *Virginia*
Oregon State University *Oregon*
Ouachita Baptist University *Arkansas*
Pace University *New York*
Pacific Lutheran University *Washington*
Penn State Erie, The Behrend College *Pennsylvania*
Penn State Harrisburg *Pennsylvania*
Penn State University Park *Pennsylvania*
Pepperdine University *California*
Pittsburg State University *Kansas*
Portland State University *Oregon*
Prairie View A&M University *Texas*
Purdue University *Indiana*
Queens University of Charlotte *North Carolina*
Queen's University at Kingston *Ontario (Canada)*
Quinnipiac University *Connecticut*
Radford University *Virginia*
Ramapo College of New Jersey *New Jersey*
Rensselaer Polytechnic Institute *New York*
Rhode Island College *Rhode Island*
Rice University *Texas*
Rider University *New Jersey*
Robert Morris University *Pennsylvania*
Rochester Institute of Technology *New York*
Rockhurst University *Missouri*
Roger Williams University *Rhode Island*
Rollins College *Florida*
Rowan University *New Jersey*
Rutgers University - Camden *New Jersey*
Rutgers University - Newark *New Jersey*
Sacred Heart University *Connecticut*
Saginaw Valley State University *Michigan*
St. Bonaventure University *New York*
St. Cloud State University *Minnesota*
St. John Fisher College *New York*
St. John's University *New York*
Saint Joseph's University *Pennsylvania*
Saint Louis University *Missouri*
Saint Mary's College of California *California*

Saint Mary's University *Nova Scotia (Canada)*
St. Mary's University *Texas*
Saint Xavier University *Illinois*
Salisbury University *Maryland*
Sam Houston State University *Texas*
Samford University *Alabama*
San Diego State University *California*
San Francisco State University *California*
San Jose State University *California*
Santa Clara University *California*
Savannah State University *Georgia*
Seattle Pacific University *Washington*
Seattle University *Washington*
Seton Hall University *New Jersey*
Shenandoah University *Virginia*
Shippensburg University of Pennsylvania *Pennsylvania*
Siena College *New York*
Simmons College *Massachusetts*
Simon Fraser University *British Columbia (Canada)*
Sonoma State University *California*
South Carolina State University *South Carolina*
Southeast Missouri State University *Missouri*
Southeastern Louisiana University *Louisiana*
Southeastern Oklahoma State University *Oklahoma*
Southern Arkansas University - Magnolia *Arkansas*
Southern Illinois University Carbondale *Illinois*
Southern Illinois University Edwardsville *Illinois*
Southern Methodist University *Texas*
Southern University and Agricultural and Mechanical College *Louisiana*
Southern Utah University *Utah*
Stanford University *California*
State University of New York College at Geneseo *New York*
State University of New York College at Oneonta *New York*
State University of New York at Oswego *New York*
State University of New York at Plattsburgh *New York*
State University of New York Polytechnic Institute *New York*
Stephen F. Austin State University *Texas*
Stetson University *Florida*
Suffolk University *Massachusetts*
Susquehanna University *Pennsylvania*
Syracuse University *New York*
Temple University *Pennsylvania*
Tennessee State University *Tennessee*
Tennessee Technological University *Tennessee*
Texas A&M International University *Texas*
Texas A&M University *Texas*
Texas A&M University - Commerce *Texas*
Texas A&M University - Corpus Christi *Texas*
Texas Christian University *Texas*
Texas Southern University *Texas*
Texas State University *Texas*
Texas Tech University *Texas*
Texas Wesleyan University *Texas*
Towson University *Maryland*
Trinity University *Texas*
Truman State University *Missouri*
Tulane University *Louisiana*
Tuskegee University *Alabama*
United States Air Force Academy *Colorado*
United States Coast Guard Academy *Connecticut*
Université Laval *Quebec (Canada)*
The University of Akron *Ohio*
The University of Alabama *Alabama*
The University of Alabama at Birmingham *Alabama*
The University of Alabama in Huntsville *Alabama*
University of Alaska Anchorage *Alaska*
University of Alaska Fairbanks *Alaska*
University at Albany, State University of New York *New York*
University of Alberta *Alberta (Canada)*
The University of Arizona *Arizona*
University of Arkansas *Arkansas*
University of Arkansas at Little Rock *Arkansas*
University of Baltimore *Maryland*
The University of British Columbia *British Columbia (Canada)*
University at Buffalo, the State University of New York *New York*
University of Calgary *Alberta (Canada)*
University of California, Berkeley *California*

University of California, Davis *California*
University of California, Irvine *California*
University of California, Los Angeles *California*
University of California, Riverside *California*
University of California, San Diego *California*
University of Central Arkansas *Arkansas*
University of Central Florida *Florida*
University of Central Missouri *Missouri*
University of Chicago *Illinois*
University of Cincinnati *Ohio*
University of Colorado Boulder *Colorado*
University of Colorado Colorado Springs *Colorado*
University of Colorado Denver *Colorado*
University of Connecticut *Connecticut*
University of Dayton *Ohio*
University of Delaware *Delaware*
University of Denver *Colorado*
University of Detroit Mercy *Michigan*
University of Evansville *Indiana*
University of Florida *Florida*
University of Georgia *Georgia*
University of Hartford *Connecticut*
University of Hawaii at Hilo *Hawaii*
University of Hawaii at Manoa *Hawaii*
University of Houston *Texas*
University of Houston - Clear Lake *Texas*
University of Houston - Downtown *Texas*
University of Houston - Victoria *Texas*
University of Idaho *Idaho*
University of Illinois at Chicago *Illinois*
University of Illinois at Springfield *Illinois*
University of Illinois at Urbana - Champaign *Illinois*
The University of Iowa *Iowa*
The University of Kansas *Kansas*
University of Kentucky *Kentucky*
University of Louisiana at Lafayette *Louisiana*
University of Louisiana at Monroe *Louisiana*
University of Louisville *Kentucky*
University of Maine *Maine*
University of Manitoba *Manitoba (Canada)*
University of Maryland, College Park *Maryland*
University of Maryland Eastern Shore *Maryland*
University of Maryland University College *Maryland*
University of Massachusetts Amherst *Massachusetts*
University of Massachusetts Boston *Massachusetts*
University of Massachusetts Dartmouth *Massachusetts*
University of Massachusetts Lowell *Massachusetts*
University of Memphis *Tennessee*
University of Miami *Florida*
University of Michigan *Michigan*
University of Michigan - Dearborn *Michigan*
University of Michigan - Flint *Michigan*
University of Minnesota, Duluth *Minnesota*
University of Minnesota, Twin Cities Campus *Minnesota*
University of Mississippi *Mississippi*
University of Missouri *Missouri*
University of Missouri - Kansas City *Missouri*
University of Missouri - St. Louis *Missouri*
University of Montana *Montana*
University of Montevallo *Alabama*
University of Nebraska at Kearney *Nebraska*
University of Nebraska - Lincoln *Nebraska*
University of Nebraska at Omaha *Nebraska*
University of Nevada, Las Vegas *Nevada*
University of Nevada, Reno *Nevada*
University of New Hampshire *New Hampshire*
University of New Haven *Connecticut*
University of New Mexico *New Mexico*
University of New Orleans *Louisiana*
University of North Carolina at Asheville *North Carolina*
The University of North Carolina at Chapel Hill *North Carolina*
The University of North Carolina at Charlotte *North Carolina*
The University of North Carolina at Greensboro *North Carolina*
The University of North Carolina Wilmington *North Carolina*
University of North Dakota *North Dakota*
University of North Florida *Florida*
University of North Georgia *Georgia*
University of North Texas *Texas*

Accreditation Board for Engineering and Technology (ABET)

Index of Professional Accreditations

DeVry University *Arlington, Virginia*
DeVry University Online *Illinois*
Dordt College *Iowa*
Drexel University *Pennsylvania*
Duke University *North Carolina*
East Carolina University *North Carolina*
East Stroudsburg University of Pennsylvania *Pennsylvania*
East Tennessee State University *Tennessee*
Eastern Kentucky University *Kentucky*
Eastern Washington University *Washington*
Edinboro University of Pennsylvania *Pennsylvania*
Elizabethtown College *Pennsylvania*
Embry-Riddle Aeronautical University - Daytona *Florida*
Embry-Riddle Aeronautical University - Prescott *Arizona*
Erie Community College *New York*
Erie Community College, North Campus *New York*
Essex County College *New Jersey*
Excelsior College *New York*
Fairfield University *Connecticut*
Fairleigh Dickinson University, Metropolitan Campus *New Jersey*
Fairmont State University *West Virginia*
Farmingdale State College *New York*
Fayetteville State University *North Carolina*
Fayetteville Technical Community College *North Carolina*
Ferris State University *Michigan*
Fitchburg State University *Massachusetts*
Florence-Darlington Technical College *South Carolina*
Florida Agricultural and Mechanical University *Florida*
Florida Atlantic University *Florida*
Florida Gulf Coast University *Florida*
Florida Institute of Technology *Florida*
Florida International University *Florida*
Florida Memorial University *Florida*
Florida State University *Florida*
Forsyth Technical Community College *North Carolina*
Fort Lewis College *Colorado*
Fort Valley State University *Georgia*
Franklin W. Olin College of Engineering *Massachusetts*
Gannon University *Pennsylvania*
Gaston College *North Carolina*
Gateway Community College *Connecticut*
Geneva College *Pennsylvania*
George Fox University *Oregon*
George Mason University *Virginia*
The George Washington University *District of Columbia*
Georgia Institute of Technology *Georgia*
Georgia Piedmont Technical College *Georgia*
Georgia Southern University *Georgia*
Gonzaga University *Washington*
Grambling State University *Louisiana*
Grand Valley State University *Michigan*
Greenville Technical College *South Carolina*
Grove City College *Pennsylvania*
Hampton University *Virginia*
Harding University *Arkansas*
Harvard University *Massachusetts*
Harvey Mudd College *California*
Hocking College *Ohio*
Hofstra University *New York*
Hope College *Michigan*
Horry-Georgetown Technical College *South Carolina*
Houston Community College *Texas*
Howard University *District of Columbia*
Hudson County Community College *New Jersey*
Hudson Valley Community College *New York*
Humboldt State University *California*
Hunter College of the City University of New York *New York*
Idaho State University *Idaho*
Illinois Institute of Technology *Illinois*
Illinois State University *Illinois*
Indiana State University *Indiana*
Indiana Tech *Indiana*
Indiana University of Pennsylvania *Pennsylvania*
Indiana University - Purdue University Fort Wayne *Indiana*

Indiana University - Purdue University Indianapolis *Indiana*
Inter American University of Puerto Rico, Bayamón Campus *Puerto Rico*
Iona College *New York*
Iowa State University of Science and Technology *Iowa*
Iowa Western Community College *Iowa*
Jackson State University *Mississippi*
Jacksonville State University *Alabama*
James A. Rhodes State College *Ohio*
James Madison University *Virginia*
John Brown University *Arkansas*
Johns Hopkins University *Maryland*
Kansas State University *Kansas*
Kennesaw State University *Georgia*
Kent State University at Tuscarawas *Ohio*
Kettering University *Michigan*
Lafayette College *Pennsylvania*
Lake Superior State University *Michigan*
Lakeland Community College *Ohio*
Lamar University *Texas*
Lawrence Technological University *Michigan*
Lehigh University *Pennsylvania*
LeTourneau University *Texas*
Lipscomb University *Tennessee*
Lorain County Community College *Ohio*
Louisiana State University and Agricultural & Mechanical College *Louisiana*
Louisiana State University Health Sciences Center *Louisiana*
Louisiana State University in Shreveport *Louisiana*
Louisiana Tech University *Louisiana*
Loyola Marymount University *California*
Loyola University Maryland *Maryland*
Maine Maritime Academy *Maine*
Manhattan College *New York*
Marietta College *Ohio*
Marquette University *Wisconsin*
Marshall University *West Virginia*
Massachusetts Institute of Technology *Massachusetts*
McNeese State University *Louisiana*
Mercer University *Georgia*
Merrimack College *Massachusetts*
Messiah College *Pennsylvania*
Metropolitan State University of Denver *Colorado*
Miami University *Ohio*
Michigan State University *Michigan*
Michigan Technological University *Michigan*
Middle Georgia State University *Georgia*
Middle Tennessee State University *Tennessee*
Middlesex County College *New Jersey*
Midlands Technical College *South Carolina*
Midwestern State University *Texas*
Millersville University of Pennsylvania *Pennsylvania*
Milwaukee School of Engineering *Wisconsin*
Minnesota State University Mankato *Minnesota*
Mississippi State University *Mississippi*
Mississippi Valley State University *Mississippi*
Missouri Southern State University *Missouri*
Missouri State University *Missouri*
Missouri University of Science and Technology *Missouri*
Missouri Western State University *Missouri*
Mohawk Valley Community College *New York*
Monmouth University *New Jersey*
Monroe Community College *New York*
Montana State University *Montana*
Montana State University - Northern *Montana*
Montana Tech of The University of Montana *Montana*
Montclair State University *New Jersey*
Morgan State University *Maryland*
Morrison Institute of Technology *Illinois*
Morrisville State College *New York*
Murray State University *Kentucky*
Nashua Community College *New Hampshire*
Nashville State Community College *Tennessee*
Nassau Community College *New York*
Naugatuck Valley Community College *Connecticut*
New England Institute of Technology *Rhode Island*
New Jersey Institute of Technology *New Jersey*
New Mexico Institute of Mining and Technology *New Mexico*
New Mexico State University *New Mexico*

New York City College of Technology of the City University of New York *New York*
New York Institute of Technology *New York*
NHTI, Concord's Community College *New Hampshire*
Nicholls State University *Louisiana*
Norfolk State University *Virginia*
North Carolina Agricultural and Technical State University *North Carolina*
North Carolina State University *North Carolina*
North Dakota State University *North Dakota*
Northeast Wisconsin Technical College *Wisconsin*
Northeastern University *Massachusetts*
Northern Arizona University *Arizona*
Northern Illinois University *Illinois*
Northern Kentucky University *Kentucky*
Northern Michigan University *Michigan*
Northwest State Community College *Ohio*
Northwestern State University of Louisiana *Louisiana*
Northwestern University *Illinois*
Norwich University *Vermont*
Oakland University *Michigan*
Ohio Northern University *Ohio*
The Ohio State University *Ohio*
Ohio University *Ohio*
Oklahoma Christian University *Oklahoma*
Oklahoma City Community College *Oklahoma*
Oklahoma State University *Oklahoma*
Oklahoma State University Institute of Technology *Oklahoma*
Old Dominion University *Virginia*
Olivet Nazarene University *Illinois*
Onondaga Community College *New York*
Oral Roberts University *Oklahoma*
Orangeburg-Calhoun Technical College *South Carolina*
Oregon Institute of Technology *Oregon*
Oregon State University *Oregon*
Owens Community College *Ohio*
Pace University *New York*
Pacific Lutheran University *Washington*
Passaic County Community College *New Jersey*
Paul Smith's College *New York*
Pellissippi State Community College *Tennessee*
Penn State Altoona *Pennsylvania*
Penn State Beaver *Pennsylvania*
Penn State Berks *Pennsylvania*
Penn State DuBois *Pennsylvania*
Penn State Erie, The Behrend College *Pennsylvania*
Penn State Fayette, The Eberly Campus *Pennsylvania*
Penn State Harrisburg *Pennsylvania*
Penn State Hazleton *Pennsylvania*
Penn State New Kensington *Pennsylvania*
Penn State Schuylkill *Pennsylvania*
Penn State Shenango *Pennsylvania*
Penn State University Park *Pennsylvania*
Penn State Wilkes-Barre *Pennsylvania*
Penn State Worthington Scranton *Pennsylvania*
Penn State York *Pennsylvania*
Pennsylvania College of Technology *Pennsylvania*
Philadelphia University *Pennsylvania*
Piedmont Technical College *South Carolina*
Pittsburg State University *Kansas*
Point Park University *Pennsylvania*
Portland State University *Oregon*
Prairie View A&M University *Texas*
Prince George's Community College *Maryland*
Princeton University *New Jersey*
Purdue University *Indiana*
Purdue University Northwest *Hammond, Indiana*
Purdue University Northwest *Westville, Indiana*
Queensborough Community College of the City University of New York *New York*
Quinnipiac University *Connecticut*
Radford University *Virginia*
Regis University *Colorado*
Rensselaer Polytechnic Institute *New York*
Rice University *Texas*
Robert Morris University *Pennsylvania*
Rochester Institute of Technology *New York*
Roger Williams University *Rhode Island*
Rose-Hulman Institute of Technology *Indiana*
Rowan College at Burlington County *New Jersey*
Rowan University *New Jersey*

Rutgers University - New Brunswick *New Jersey*
Saginaw Valley State University *Michigan*
St. Ambrose University *Iowa*
St. Cloud State University *Minnesota*
Saint Louis University *Missouri*
Saint Martin's University *Washington*
St. Mary's University *Texas*
Salem State University *Massachusetts*
Sam Houston State University *Texas*
San Diego State University *California*
San Francisco State University *California*
San Jose State University *California*
San Juan College *New Mexico*
Santa Clara University *California*
Savannah State University *Georgia*
Savannah Technical College *Georgia*
Seattle Pacific University *Washington*
Seattle University *Washington*
Shippensburg University of Pennsylvania *Pennsylvania*
Sinclair Community College *Ohio*
Slippery Rock University of Pennsylvania *Pennsylvania*
Smith College *Massachusetts*
South Carolina State University *South Carolina*
South Dakota School of Mines and Technology *South Dakota*
South Dakota State University *South Dakota*
Southeast Missouri State University *Missouri*
Southeastern Louisiana University *Louisiana*
Southern Adventist University *Tennessee*
Southern Connecticut State University *Connecticut*
Southern Illinois University Carbondale *Illinois*
Southern Illinois University Edwardsville *Illinois*
Southern Methodist University *Texas*
Southern University and Agricultural and Mechanical College *Louisiana*
Southern Utah University *Utah*
Southwest Tennessee Community College *Tennessee*
Southwestern Oklahoma State University *Oklahoma*
Spartanburg Community College *South Carolina*
Springfield Technical Community College *Massachusetts*
Stanford University *California*
Stark State College *Ohio*
State Technical College of Missouri *Missouri*
State University of New York College of Environmental Science and Forestry *New York*
State University of New York College of Technology at Alfred *New York*
State University of New York College of Technology at Canton *New York*
State University of New York Maritime College *New York*
State University of New York at New Paltz *New York*
State University of New York Polytechnic Institute *New York*
Stephen F. Austin State University *Texas*
Stevens Institute of Technology *New Jersey*
Stony Brook University, State University of New York *New York*
Suffolk University *Massachusetts*
Swarthmore College *Pennsylvania*
Sweet Briar College *Virginia*
Syracuse University *New York*
Tarleton State University *Texas*
Taylor University *Indiana*
TCI - College of Technology *New York*
Temple University *Pennsylvania*
Tennessee State University *Tennessee*
Tennessee Technological University *Tennessee*
Texas A&M University *Texas*
Texas A&M University - Commerce *Texas*
Texas A&M University - Corpus Christi *Texas*
Texas A&M University - Kingsville *Texas*
Texas Christian University *Texas*
Texas Southern University *Texas*
Texas Southmost College *Texas*
Texas State University *Texas*
Texas Tech University *Texas*
Three Rivers Community College *Connecticut*
Towson University *Maryland*
Tri-County Technical College *South Carolina*
Trident Technical College *South Carolina*
Trine University *Indiana*

Trinidad State Junior College *Colorado*
Trinity College *Connecticut*
Trinity University *Texas*
Troy University *Alabama*
Tufts University *Massachusetts*
Tulane University *Louisiana*
Tuskegee University *Alabama*
Union College *New York*
Union University *Tennessee*
United States Air Force Academy *Colorado*
United States Coast Guard Academy *Connecticut*
United States Merchant Marine Academy *New York*
United States Military Academy *New York*
United States Naval Academy *Maryland*
The University of Akron *Ohio*
The University of Alabama *Alabama*
The University of Alabama at Birmingham *Alabama*
The University of Alabama in Huntsville *Alabama*
University of Alaska Anchorage *Alaska*
University of Alaska Fairbanks *Alaska*
The University of Arizona *Arizona*
University of Arkansas *Arkansas*
University of Arkansas at Little Rock *Arkansas*
University of Bridgeport *Connecticut*
University at Buffalo, the State University of New York *New York*
University of California, Berkeley *California*
University of California, Davis *California*
University of California, Irvine *California*
University of California, Los Angeles *California*
University of California, Riverside *California*
University of California, San Diego *California*
University of California, Santa Barbara *California*
University of California, Santa Cruz *California*
University of Central Arkansas *Arkansas*
University of Central Florida *Florida*
University of Central Missouri *Missouri*
University of Central Oklahoma *Oklahoma*
University of Cincinnati *Ohio*
University of Colorado Boulder *Colorado*
University of Colorado Colorado Springs *Colorado*
University of Colorado Denver *Colorado*
University of Connecticut *Connecticut*
University of Dayton *Ohio*
University of Delaware *Delaware*
University of Denver *Colorado*
University of Detroit Mercy *Michigan*
University of the District of Columbia *District of Columbia*
University of Evansville *Indiana*
The University of Findlay *Ohio*
University of Florida *Florida*
University of Georgia *Georgia*
University of Hartford *Connecticut*
University of Hawaii at Manoa *Hawaii*
University of Houston *Texas*
University of Houston - Clear Lake *Texas*
University of Houston - Downtown *Texas*
University of Idaho *Idaho*
University of Illinois at Chicago *Illinois*
University of Illinois at Urbana - Champaign *Illinois*
The University of Iowa *Iowa*
The University of Kansas *Kansas*
University of Kentucky *Kentucky*
University of Louisiana at Lafayette *Louisiana*
University of Louisiana at Monroe *Louisiana*
University of Louisville *Kentucky*
University of Maine *Maine*
University of Maryland, Baltimore County *Maryland*
University of Maryland, College Park *Maryland*
University of Massachusetts Amherst *Massachusetts*
University of Massachusetts Boston *Massachusetts*
University of Massachusetts Dartmouth *Massachusetts*
University of Massachusetts Lowell *Massachusetts*
University of Memphis *Tennessee*
University of Miami *Florida*
University of Michigan *Michigan*
University of Michigan - Dearborn *Michigan*
University of Minnesota, Duluth *Minnesota*
University of Minnesota, Twin Cities Campus *Minnesota*
University of Mississippi *Mississippi*
University of Missouri *Missouri*
University of Missouri - Kansas City *Missouri*

University of Missouri - St. Louis *Missouri*
University of Montana *Montana*
University of Nebraska - Lincoln *Nebraska*
University of Nebraska at Omaha *Nebraska*
University of Nevada, Las Vegas *Nevada*
University of Nevada, Reno *Nevada*
University of New Hampshire *New Hampshire*
University of New Haven *Connecticut*
University of New Mexico *New Mexico*
University of New Orleans *Louisiana*
University of North Alabama *Alabama*
University of North Carolina at Asheville *North Carolina*
The University of North Carolina at Chapel Hill *North Carolina*
The University of North Carolina at Charlotte *North Carolina*
The University of North Carolina at Greensboro *North Carolina*
The University of North Carolina Wilmington *North Carolina*
University of North Dakota *North Dakota*
University of North Florida *Florida*
University of North Texas *Texas*
University of Northern Iowa *Iowa*
University of Notre Dame *Indiana*
University of Oklahoma *Oklahoma*
University of Oklahoma Health Sciences Center *Oklahoma*
University of the Pacific *California*
University of Pennsylvania *Pennsylvania*
University of Pittsburgh *Pennsylvania*
University of Pittsburgh at Johnstown *Pennsylvania*
University of Portland *Oregon*
University of Puerto Rico in Arecibo *Puerto Rico*
University of Puerto Rico in Bayamón *Puerto Rico*
University of Puerto Rico, Río Piedras Campus *Puerto Rico*
University of Rhode Island *Rhode Island*
University of Rochester *New York*
University of St. Thomas *Minnesota*
University of San Diego *California*
The University of Scranton *Pennsylvania*
University of South Alabama *Alabama*
University of South Carolina *South Carolina*
University of South Carolina Upstate *South Carolina*
University of South Florida *Florida*
University of Southern California *California*
University of Southern Indiana *Indiana*
University of Southern Maine *Maine*
University of Southern Mississippi *Mississippi*
The University of Tampa *Florida*
The University of Tennessee *Tennessee*
The University of Tennessee at Chattanooga *Tennessee*
The University of Tennessee at Martin *Tennessee*
The University of Texas at Arlington *Texas*
The University of Texas at Austin *Texas*
The University of Texas at Dallas *Texas*
The University of Texas at El Paso *Texas*
The University of Texas Health Science Center at Houston *Texas*
The University of Texas Rio Grande Valley *Texas*
The University of Texas at San Antonio *Texas*
The University of Texas at Tyler *Texas*
The University of Toledo *Ohio*
The University of Tulsa *Oklahoma*
University of Utah *Utah*
University of Vermont *Vermont*
University of Virginia *Virginia*
The University of Virginia's College at Wise *Virginia*
University of Washington *Washington*
University of Washington, Tacoma *Washington*
University of West Florida *Florida*
University of West Georgia *Georgia*
University of Wisconsin - Eau Claire *Wisconsin*
University of Wisconsin - Madison *Wisconsin*
University of Wisconsin - Milwaukee *Wisconsin*
University of Wisconsin - Oshkosh *Wisconsin*
University of Wisconsin - Platteville *Wisconsin*
University of Wisconsin - Stevens Point *Wisconsin*
University of Wisconsin - Stout *Wisconsin*
University of Wyoming *Wyoming*
Utah State University *Utah*
Utah Valley University *Utah*
Valparaiso University *Indiana*

Vanderbilt University *Tennessee*
Vaughn College of Aeronautics and Technology *New York*
Vermont Technical College *Vermont*
Villanova University *Pennsylvania*
Virginia Commonwealth University *Virginia*
Virginia Military Institute *Virginia*
Virginia Polytechnic Institute and State University *Virginia*
Virginia State University *Virginia*
Wake Technical Community College *North Carolina*
Walla Walla Community College *Washington*
Walla Walla University *Washington*
Washington State University *Washington*
Washington State University - Vancouver *Washington*
Washington University in St. Louis *Missouri*
Waukesha County Technical College *Wisconsin*
Wayne State University *Michigan*
Webb Institute *New York*
Weber State University *Utah*
Wentworth Institute of Technology *Massachusetts*
West Chester University of Pennsylvania *Pennsylvania*
West Texas A&M University *Texas*
West Virginia State University *West Virginia*
West Virginia University *West Virginia*
West Virginia University Institute of Technology *West Virginia*
Western Carolina University *North Carolina*
Western Kentucky University *Kentucky*
Western Michigan University *Michigan*
Western New England University *Massachusetts*
Western Washington University *Washington*
Westfield State University *Massachusetts*
Wichita State University *Kansas*
Widener University *Pennsylvania*
Wilkes University *Pennsylvania*
William Paterson University of New Jersey *New Jersey*
Winona State University *Minnesota*
Winston-Salem State University *North Carolina*
Winthrop University *South Carolina*
Worcester Polytechnic Institute *Massachusetts*
Wright State University *Ohio*
Yale University *Connecticut*
York College of Pennsylvania *Pennsylvania*
York Technical College *South Carolina*
Youngstown State University *Ohio*
Zane State College *Ohio*

Academy of Nutrition and Dietetics (AND)

Alcorn State University *Mississippi*
Andrews University *Michigan*
Appalachian State University *North Carolina*
Arizona State University at the Polytechnic campus *Arizona*
Ball State University *Indiana*
Bastyr University *Washington*
Baylor University *Texas*
Benedictine University *Illinois*
Boston University *Massachusetts*
Bowling Green State University *Ohio*
Brigham Young University *Utah*
Brooklyn College of the City University of New York *New York*
Buffalo State College, State University of New York *New York*
California State Polytechnic University, Pomona *California*
California State University, Chico *California*
California State University, Fresno *California*
California State University, Long Beach *California*
California State University, Los Angeles *California*
California State University, Northridge *California*
California State University, Sacramento *California*
Case Western Reserve University *Ohio*
Central Michigan University *Michigan*
Central Washington University *Washington*
Clemson University *South Carolina*
College of Saint Benedict *Minnesota*
College of Saint Elizabeth *New Jersey*
Colorado State University *Colorado*
Concordia College *Minnesota*
Cornell University *New York*

Delta State University *Mississippi*
Drexel University *Pennsylvania*
D'Youville College *New York*
East Carolina University *North Carolina*
East Tennessee State University *Tennessee*
Eastern Illinois University *Illinois*
Eastern Kentucky University *Kentucky*
Eastern Michigan University *Michigan*
Edinboro University of Pennsylvania *Pennsylvania*
Emory University *Georgia*
Florida International University *Florida*
Florida State University *Florida*
Framingham State University *Massachusetts*
Gannon University *Pennsylvania*
Georgia State University *Georgia*
Goldfarb School of Nursing at Barnes-Jewish College *Missouri*
Harvard University *Massachusetts*
Howard University *District of Columbia*
Hunter College of the City University of New York *New York*
Idaho State University *Idaho*
Illinois State University *Illinois*
Immaculata University *Pennsylvania*
Indiana State University *Indiana*
Indiana University of Pennsylvania *Pennsylvania*
Indiana University - Purdue University Indianapolis *Indiana*
Iowa State University of Science and Technology *Iowa*
James Madison University *Virginia*
Johns Hopkins University *Maryland*
Kansas State University *Kansas*
Keene State College *New Hampshire*
Kent State University *Ohio*
La Salle University *Pennsylvania*
Lamar University *Texas*
Lehman College of the City University of New York *New York*
Life University *Georgia*
Lipscomb University *Tennessee*
Loma Linda University *California*
Long Island University - LIU Post *New York*
Louisiana State University and Agricultural & Mechanical College *Louisiana*
Louisiana Tech University *Louisiana*
Loyola University Chicago *Illinois*
Marshall University *West Virginia*
Marywood University *Pennsylvania*
McNeese State University *Louisiana*
Medical University of South Carolina *South Carolina*
Mercyhurst University *Pennsylvania*
Meredith College *North Carolina*
Michigan State University *Michigan*
Mississippi State University *Mississippi*
Montclair State University *New Jersey*
Morehead State University *Kentucky*
Mount Carmel College of Nursing *Ohio*
Mount Marty College *South Dakota*
Mount Mary University *Wisconsin*
Murray State University *Kentucky*
New York Institute of Technology *New York*
New York University *New York*
Nicholls State University *Louisiana*
North Carolina Central University *North Carolina*
North Dakota State University *North Dakota*
Northern Illinois University *Illinois*
Oakwood University *Alabama*
The Ohio State University *Ohio*
Oklahoma State University *Oklahoma*
Oregon Health & Science University *Oregon*
Penn State University Park *Pennsylvania*
Prairie View A&M University *Texas*
Purdue University *Indiana*
Queens College of the City University of New York *New York*
Radford University *Virginia*
Rush University *Illinois*
The Sage Colleges *New York*
Saint Louis University *Missouri*
Sam Houston State University *Texas*
San Diego State University *California*
San Francisco State University *California*
San Jose State University *California*
Seton Hill University *Pennsylvania*
Simmons College *Massachusetts*

Southeast Missouri State University *Missouri*
Southern Illinois University Carbondale *Illinois*
Southern University and Agricultural and Mechanical College *Louisiana*
State University of New York College at Oneonta *New York*
Stephen F. Austin State University *Texas*
Stony Brook University, State University of New York *New York*
Syracuse University *New York*
Texas A&M University *Texas*
Texas A&M University - Kingsville *Texas*
Texas Christian University *Texas*
Texas State University *Texas*
Texas Tech University *Texas*
Texas Woman's University *Texas*
Tufts University *Massachusetts*
Tulane University *Louisiana*
The University of Akron *Ohio*
The University of Alabama *Alabama*
The University of Alabama at Birmingham *Alabama*
University of Alaska Anchorage *Alaska*
The University of Arizona *Arizona*
University of Arkansas for Medical Sciences *Arkansas*
University at Buffalo, the State University of New York *New York*
University of California, Berkeley *California*
University of California, Davis *California*
University of California, Los Angeles *California*
University of Central Arkansas *Arkansas*
University of Central Oklahoma *Oklahoma*
University of Cincinnati *Ohio*
University of Connecticut *Connecticut*
University of Delaware *Delaware*
University of Florida *Florida*
University of Georgia *Georgia*
University of Houston *Texas*
University of Idaho *Idaho*
University of Illinois at Chicago *Illinois*
University of Illinois at Urbana - Champaign *Illinois*
University of the Incarnate Word *Texas*
The University of Iowa *Iowa*
The University of Kansas *Kansas*
University of Kentucky *Kentucky*
University of Louisiana at Lafayette *Louisiana*
University of Maine *Maine*
University of Maryland, College Park *Maryland*
University of Maryland Eastern Shore *Maryland*
University of Massachusetts Amherst *Massachusetts*
University of Memphis *Tennessee*
University of Michigan *Michigan*
University of Minnesota, Twin Cities Campus *Minnesota*
University of Mississippi *Mississippi*
University of Missouri *Missouri*
University of Nebraska - Lincoln *Nebraska*
University of Nebraska Medical Center *Nebraska*
University of Nevada, Reno *Nevada*
University of New Hampshire *New Hampshire*
University of New Mexico *New Mexico*
The University of North Carolina at Chapel Hill *North Carolina*
The University of North Carolina at Greensboro *North Carolina*
University of North Dakota *North Dakota*
University of North Florida *Florida*
University of Northern Colorado *Colorado*
University of Oklahoma Health Sciences Center *Oklahoma*
University of Pittsburgh *Pennsylvania*
University of Puerto Rico, Medical Sciences Campus *Puerto Rico*
University of Rhode Island *Rhode Island*
University of Saint Joseph *Connecticut*
The University of South Dakota *South Dakota*
University of Southern California *California*
University of Southern Mississippi *Mississippi*
The University of Tennessee *Tennessee*
The University of Tennessee at Martin *Tennessee*
The University of Texas at Austin *Texas*
The University of Texas Health Science Center at Houston *Texas*
The University of Texas Rio Grande Valley *Texas*
University of Utah *Utah*

University of Vermont *Vermont*
University of Virginia *Virginia*
University of Washington *Washington*
University of Wisconsin - Green Bay *Wisconsin*
University of Wisconsin - Madison *Wisconsin*
University of Wisconsin - Stout *Wisconsin*
Utah State University *Utah*
Vanderbilt University *Tennessee*
Virginia Commonwealth University *Virginia*
Virginia Polytechnic Institute and State University *Virginia*
Virginia State University *Virginia*
Viterbo University *Wisconsin*
Washington State University *Washington*
Washington State University - Spokane *Washington*
Wayne State University *Michigan*
West Virginia University *West Virginia*
Western Carolina University *North Carolina*
Western Michigan University *Michigan*
Winthrop University *South Carolina*
Yale University *Connecticut*
Youngstown State University *Ohio*

Accreditation Commission for Acupuncture and Oriental Medicine (ACAOM)

Bastyr University *Washington*
Mercy College *New York*
New York College of Health Professions *New York*
Swedish Institute, College of Health Sciences *New York*
University of Bridgeport *Connecticut*

Accreditation Commission for Education in Nursing (ACEN)

Abraham Baldwin Agricultural College *Georgia*
Adelphi University *New York*
Adirondack Community College *New York*
Adventist University of Health Sciences *Florida*
Aiken Technical College *South Carolina*
Alabama Southern Community College *Alabama*
Albany State University *Georgia*
Alcorn State University *Mississippi*
Alderson Broaddus University *West Virginia*
Allegany College of Maryland *Maryland*
Allen College *Iowa*
Alvin Community College *Texas*
Amarillo College *Texas*
Andrews University *Michigan*
Angelo State University *Texas*
Anna Maria College *Massachusetts*
Anne Arundel Community College *Maryland*
Anoka-Ramsey Community College *Minnesota*
Aquinas College *Tennessee*
Arizona Western College *Arizona*
Arkansas Northeastern College *Arkansas*
Arkansas State University *Arkansas*
Arkansas Tech University *Arkansas*
Ashland Community and Technical College *Kentucky*
Athens Technical College *Georgia*
Atlantic Cape Community College *New Jersey*
Aultman College of Nursing and Health Sciences *Ohio*
Austin Community College District *Texas*
Austin Peay State University *Tennessee*
Bacone College *Oklahoma*
Bainbridge State College *Georgia*
Baltimore City Community College *Maryland*
Barton College *North Carolina*
Barton County Community College *Kansas*
Bay de Noc Community College *Michigan*
Becker College *Massachusetts*
The Belanger School of Nursing *New York*
Bellevue College *Washington*
Bergen Community College *New Jersey*
Berkshire Community College *Massachusetts*
Bethel College *Indiana*
Bethune-Cookman University *Florida*
Bevill State Community College *Alabama*
Big Bend Community College *Washington*
Bill and Sandra Pomeroy College of Nursing at Crouse Hospital *New York*
Bishop State Community College *Alabama*
Black Hawk College *Illinois*
Blackhawk Technical College *Wisconsin*

Blinn College *Texas*
Blue Ridge Community College *Virginia*
Blue Ridge Community and Technical College *West Virginia*
Bluefield State College *West Virginia*
Bluegrass Community and Technical College *Kentucky*
Boise State University *Idaho*
Borough of Manhattan Community College of the City University of New York *New York*
Bowie State University *Maryland*
Bradley University *Illinois*
Brenau University *Georgia*
Briar Cliff University *Iowa*
BridgeValley Community and Technical College *South Charleston, West Virginia*
Brigham Young University - Idaho *Idaho*
Bristol Community College *Massachusetts*
Bronx Community College of the City University of New York *New York*
Brookdale Community College *New Jersey*
Brookhaven College *Texas*
Broome Community College *New York*
Broward College *Florida*
Bryan College of Health Sciences *Nebraska*
Bryant & Stratton College - Eastlake Campus *Ohio*
Bryant & Stratton College - Wauwatosa Campus *Wisconsin*
Bucks County Community College *Pennsylvania*
Bunker Hill Community College *Massachusetts*
Butler Community College *Kansas*
Butler County Community College *Pennsylvania*
Cabarrus College of Health Sciences *North Carolina*
Calhoun Community College *Alabama*
California State University, East Bay *California*
Cape Cod Community College *Massachusetts*
Cape Fear Community College *North Carolina*
Capital Community College *Connecticut*
Cardinal Stritch University *Wisconsin*
Carl Albert State College *Oklahoma*
Carl Sandburg College *Illinois*
Carolinas College of Health Sciences *North Carolina*
Case Western Reserve University *Ohio*
Casper College *Wyoming*
Castleton University *Vermont*
Catawba Valley Community College *North Carolina*
Cayuga County Community College *New York*
Cecil College *Maryland*
Cedar Crest College *Pennsylvania*
Centra College of Nursing *Virginia*
Central Alabama Community College *Alabama*
Central Arizona College *Arizona*
Central Carolina Technical College *South Carolina*
Central Maine Community College *Maine*
Central New Mexico Community College *New Mexico*
Central Ohio Technical College *Ohio*
Central Texas College *Texas*
Central Wyoming College *Wyoming*
Century College *Minnesota*
Cerritos College *California*
Chaffey College *California*
Chamberlain College of Nursing *Missouri*
Chandler-Gilbert Community College *Arizona*
Charleston Southern University *South Carolina*
Chattanooga State Community College *Tennessee*
Chemeketa Community College *Oregon*
Chesapeake College *Maryland*
Chicago State University *Illinois*
Chippewa Valley Technical College *Wisconsin*
Cincinnati State Technical and Community College *Ohio*
Cisco College *Texas*
City Colleges of Chicago, Harry S. Truman College *Illinois*
City Colleges of Chicago, Richard J. Daley College *Illinois*
Clarion University of Pennsylvania *Pennsylvania*
Clark College *Washington*
Clark State Community College *Ohio*
Clarkson College *Nebraska*
Cleveland State Community College *Tennessee*
Clinton Community College *New York*
Cloud County Community College *Kansas*
Clovis Community College *New Mexico*

Cochran School of Nursing *New York*
Colby Community College *Kansas*
Colegio Universitario de San Juan *Puerto Rico*
College of the Canyons *California*
College of Central Florida *Florida*
College of Coastal Georgia *Georgia*
College of the Desert *California*
College of Lake County *Illinois*
College of the Mainland *Texas*
College of Marin *California*
College of Menominee Nation *Wisconsin*
College of Saint Elizabeth *New Jersey*
College of Saint Mary *Nebraska*
College of Southern Idaho *Idaho*
College of Southern Maryland *Maryland*
College of Southern Nevada *Nevada*
College of Staten Island of the City University of New York *New York*
College of The Albemarle *North Carolina*
Collin County Community College District *Texas*
Colorado State University - Pueblo *Colorado*
Columbia Basin College *Washington*
Columbia College of Nursing *Wisconsin*
Columbia-Greene Community College *New York*
Columbia State Community College *Tennessee*
Columbia University *New York*
Columbus State Community College *Ohio*
Columbus State University *Georgia*
Columbus Technical College *Georgia*
Community College of Allegheny County *Pennsylvania*
Community College of Baltimore County *Maryland*
Community College of Beaver County *Pennsylvania*
Community College of Philadelphia *Pennsylvania*
Community College of Rhode Island *Rhode Island*
Connors State College *Oklahoma*
Copiah-Lincoln Community College *Mississippi*
Coppin State University *Maryland*
Corning Community College *New York*
County College of Morris *New Jersey*
Cox College *Missouri*
Cumberland County College *New Jersey*
Cumberland University *Tennessee*
Cuyahoga Community College *Ohio*
Cypress College *California*
Dabney S. Lancaster Community College *Virginia*
Daemen College *New York*
Dakota Wesleyan University *South Dakota*
Dalton State College *Georgia*
Darton State College *Georgia*
Davidson County Community College *North Carolina*
Davis & Elkins College *West Virginia*
Daytona State College *Florida*
Del Mar College *Texas*
Delaware County Community College *Pennsylvania*
Delaware State University *Delaware*
Delaware Technical & Community College, Jack F. Owens Campus *Delaware*
Delaware Technical & Community College, Stanton/Wilmington Campus *Delaware*
Delaware Technical & Community College, Terry Campus *Delaware*
Delgado Community College *Louisiana*
Delta College *Michigan*
Des Moines Area Community College *Iowa*
DeSales University *Pennsylvania*
Dickinson State University *North Dakota*
Dillard University *Louisiana*
Dixie State University *Utah*
Dodge City Community College *Kansas*
Doña Ana Community College *New Mexico*
Drake University *Iowa*
Drexel University *Pennsylvania*
Durham Technical Community College *North Carolina*
Dutchess Community College *New York*
Dyersburg State Community College *Tennessee*
East Arkansas Community College *Arkansas*
East Carolina University *North Carolina*
East Central Community College *Mississippi*
East Central University *Oklahoma*
East Stroudsburg University of Pennsylvania *Pennsylvania*
Eastern Kentucky University *Kentucky*
Eastern Maine Community College *Maine*

Eastern Michigan University *Michigan*
Eastern New Mexico University *New Mexico*
Eastern New Mexico University - Roswell *New Mexico*
Eastern Oklahoma State College *Oklahoma*
ECPI University *Virginia Beach, Virginia*
Edison Community College *Ohio*
El Camino College *California*
El Centro College *Texas*
El Paso Community College *Texas*
Elgin Community College *Illinois*
Elizabethtown Community and Technical College *Kentucky*
Elmira College *New York*
Emporia State University *Kansas*
Endicott College *Massachusetts*
Erie Community College, North Campus *New York*
Essex County College *New Jersey*
Estrella Mountain Community College *Arizona*
Everett Community College *Washington*
Excelsior College *New York*
Fairmont State University *West Virginia*
Farmingdale State College *New York*
Fayetteville Technical Community College *North Carolina*
Ferris State University *Michigan*
Finger Lakes Community College *New York*
Finger Lakes Health College of Nursing *New York*
Fiorello H. LaGuardia Community College of the City University of New York *New York*
Florence-Darlington Technical College *South Carolina*
Florida Agricultural and Mechanical University *Florida*
Florida Atlantic University *Florida*
Florida Gateway College *Florida*
Florida SouthWestern State College *Florida*
Florida State College at Jacksonville *Florida*
Fort Scott Community College *Kansas*
Fortis College *Centerville, Ohio*
Fox Valley Technical College *Wisconsin*
Framingham State University *Massachusetts*
Francis Marion University *South Carolina*
Franciscan University of Steubenville *Ohio*
Franklin Pierce University *New Hampshire*
Frederick Community College *Maryland*
Gadsden State Community College *Alabama*
Galveston College *Texas*
Garden City Community College *Kansas*
Gardner-Webb University *North Carolina*
GateWay Community College *Arizona*
Gateway Community College *Connecticut*
Gateway Technical College *Wisconsin*
Genesee Community College *New York*
George C. Wallace Community College *Alabama*
George Corley Wallace State Community College *Alabama*
Georgia College & State University *Georgia*
Georgia Highlands College *Georgia*
Georgia Northwestern Technical College *Georgia*
Georgia Southwestern State University *Georgia*
Glendale Community College *Arizona*
Golden West College *California*
Good Samaritan College of Nursing and Health Science *Ohio*
Goodwin College *Connecticut*
Gordon State College *Georgia*
Governors State University *Illinois*
Grambling State University *Louisiana*
Grand Rapids Community College *Michigan*
Grays Harbor College *Washington*
Grayson College *Texas*
Great Basin College *Nevada*
Great Bay Community College *New Hampshire*
Greenfield Community College *Massachusetts*
Greenville Technical College *South Carolina*
Grossmont College *California*
Gulf Coast State College *Florida*
Gwynedd Mercy University *Pennsylvania*
Hampton University *Virginia*
Hannibal-LaGrange University *Missouri*
Harcum College *Pennsylvania*
Harding University *Arkansas*
Harford Community College *Maryland*
Harper College *Illinois*
Harrisburg Area Community College *Pennsylvania*

Hawaii Community College *Hawaii*
Hawai'i Pacific University *Hawaii*
Heartland Community College *Illinois*
Helene Fuld College of Nursing *New York*
Henderson Community College *Kentucky*
Henry Ford College *Michigan*
Herzing University *Madison, Wisconsin*
Hesston College *Kansas*
Highline College *Washington*
Hillsborough Community College *Florida*
Hinds Community College *Mississippi*
Hocking College *Ohio*
Holmes Community College *Mississippi*
Holyoke Community College *Massachusetts*
Hopkinsville Community College *Kentucky*
Horry-Georgetown Technical College *South Carolina*
Houston Baptist University *Texas*
Howard College *Texas*
Howard Community College *Maryland*
Hudson Valley Community College *New York*
Hutchinson Community College *Kansas*
Idaho State University *Idaho*
Illinois Central College *Illinois*
Illinois Eastern Community Colleges, Olney Central College *Illinois*
Illinois Valley Community College *Illinois*
Indian River State College *Florida*
Indiana State University *Indiana*
Indiana University East *Indiana*
Indiana University Northwest *Indiana*
Indiana University - Purdue University Fort Wayne *Indiana*
Indiana University - Purdue University Indianapolis *Indiana*
Inter American University of Puerto Rico, Arecibo Campus *Puerto Rico*
Inter American University of Puerto Rico, Metropolitan Campus *Puerto Rico*
Inver Hills Community College *Minnesota*
Iowa Wesleyan University *Iowa*
Itawamba Community College *Mississippi*
Ivy Tech Community College - Central Indiana *Indiana*
J. Sargeant Reynolds Community College *Virginia*
Jackson State Community College *Tennessee*
James A. Rhodes State College *Ohio*
James H. Faulkner State Community College *Alabama*
Jamestown Community College *New York*
Jefferson Community College *New York*
Jefferson Community and Technical College *Kentucky*
Jefferson Davis Community College *Alabama*
Jefferson State Community College *Alabama*
John Tyler Community College *Virginia*
Johns Hopkins University *Maryland*
Johnson County Community College *Kansas*
Joliet Junior College *Illinois*
Jones County Junior College *Mississippi*
Kansas City Kansas Community College *Kansas*
Kansas Wesleyan University *Kansas*
Kapiolani Community College *Hawaii*
Kaskaskia College *Illinois*
Kauai Community College *Hawaii*
Kean University *New Jersey*
Keiser University *Florida*
Kennebec Valley Community College *Maine*
Kentucky State University *Kentucky*
Kettering College *Ohio*
Keuka College *New York*
Kilgore College *Texas*
Kingsborough Community College of the City University of New York *New York*
Kutztown University of Pennsylvania *Pennsylvania*
La Roche College *Pennsylvania*
Labette Community College *Kansas*
Labouré College *Massachusetts*
LaGrange College *Georgia*
Lake Land College *Illinois*
Lake Michigan College *Michigan*
Lake-Sumter State College *Florida*
Lake Superior State University *Michigan*
Lakeland Community College *Ohio*
Lakeshore Technical College *Wisconsin*
Lakeview College of Nursing *Illinois*
Lamar University *Texas*

Lander University *South Carolina*
Langston University *Oklahoma*
Lansing Community College *Michigan*
Laramie County Community College *Wyoming*
Laredo Community College *Texas*
Lawson State Community College *Alabama*
Lee College *Texas*
Lehigh Carbon Community College *Pennsylvania*
Lewis and Clark Community College *Illinois*
Lincoln Land Community College *Illinois*
Lincoln Memorial University *Tennessee*
Lincoln University *Missouri*
Lipscomb University *Tennessee*
Lock Haven University of Pennsylvania *Pennsylvania*
Lone Star College - CyFair *Texas*
Lone Star College - Kingwood *Texas*
Lone Star College - Montgomery *Texas*
Lone Star College - North Harris *Texas*
Lone Star College - Tomball *Texas*
Long Beach City College *California*
Lorain County Community College *Ohio*
Los Angeles Harbor College *California*
Los Angeles Pierce College *California*
Los Angeles Valley College *California*
Louisiana State University at Alexandria *Louisiana*
Louisiana State University at Eunice *Louisiana*
Louisiana Tech University *Louisiana*
Lower Columbia College *Washington*
Loyola University Chicago *Illinois*
Loyola University New Orleans *Louisiana*
Lubbock Christian University *Texas*
Lurleen B. Wallace Community College *Alabama*
Luzerne County Community College *Pennsylvania*
Macomb Community College *Michigan*
Madison Area Technical College *Wisconsin*
Madisonville Community College *Kentucky*
Maine College of Health Professions *Maine*
Manchester Community College *New Hampshire*
Manhattan Area Technical College *Kansas*
Mansfield University of Pennsylvania *Pennsylvania*
Maria College *New York*
Marion Technical College *Ohio*
Marshall University *West Virginia*
Marymount University *Virginia*
Marywood University *Pennsylvania*
Massachusetts Bay Community College *Massachusetts*
Massasoit Community College *Massachusetts*
McLennan Community College *Texas*
McNeese State University *Louisiana*
Medgar Evers College of the City University of New York *New York*
Medical University of South Carolina *South Carolina*
Mercer County Community College *New Jersey*
Mercy College of Health Sciences *Iowa*
Mercy College of Ohio *Ohio*
Mercyhurst University *Pennsylvania*
Meridian Community College *Mississippi*
Mesa Community College *Arizona*
Metropolitan Community College *Nebraska*
Metropolitan State University of Denver *Colorado*
Miami Dade College *Florida*
Miami University Hamilton *Ohio*
Mid-Plains Community College *Nebraska*
Mid-State Technical College *Wisconsin*
Middle Georgia State University *Georgia*
Middle Tennessee State University *Tennessee*
Middlesex Community College *Massachusetts*
Middlesex County College *New Jersey*
Midland College *Texas*
Midland University *Nebraska*
Midlands Technical College *South Carolina*
Midway University *Kentucky*
Miles Community College *Montana*
Millersville University of Pennsylvania *Pennsylvania*
Milwaukee Area Technical College *Wisconsin*
Minneapolis Community and Technical College *Minnesota*
Minnesota West Community and Technical College *Minnesota*
Minot State University *North Dakota*
Mississippi Delta Community College *Mississippi*
Mississippi Gulf Coast Community College *Mississippi*
Mississippi University for Women *Mississippi*

Missouri Southern State University *Missouri*
Missouri State University - West Plains *Missouri*
Mitchell Community College *North Carolina*
Mohave Community College *Arizona*
Mohawk Valley Community College *New York*
Monroe Community College *New York*
Monroe County Community College *Michigan*
Montana State University - Northern *Montana*
Montana Tech of The University of Montana *Montana*
Montefiore School of Nursing *New York*
Monterey Peninsula College *California*
Montgomery College *Maryland*
Montgomery County Community College *Pennsylvania*
Moorpark College *California*
Moraine Park Technical College *Wisconsin*
Moraine Valley Community College *Illinois*
Morehead State University *Kentucky*
Morgan Community College *Colorado*
Morrisville State College *New York*
Motlow State Community College *Tennessee*
Mott Community College *Michigan*
Mount Aloysius College *Pennsylvania*
Mount Wachusett Community College *Massachusetts*
Murray State College *Oklahoma*
Muskegon Community College *Michigan*
Nashua Community College *New Hampshire*
Nassau Community College *New York*
National American University *Kansas City, Missouri*
National Park College *Arkansas*
Naugatuck Valley Community College *Connecticut*
Navarro College *Texas*
Nebraska Wesleyan University *Nebraska*
Neosho County Community College *Kansas*
Neumann University *Pennsylvania*
New Jersey City University *New Jersey*
New Mexico Junior College *New Mexico*
New Mexico State University - Alamogordo *New Mexico*
New Mexico State University - Carlsbad *New Mexico*
New York City College of Technology of the City University of New York *New York*
New York Institute of Technology *New York*
New York University *New York*
NHTI, Concord's Community College *New Hampshire*
Niagara County Community College *New York*
Nicholls State University *Louisiana*
Nicolet Area Technical College *Wisconsin*
Norfolk State University *Virginia*
Normandale Community College *Minnesota*
North Arkansas College *Arkansas*
North Carolina Agricultural and Technical State University *North Carolina*
North Carolina Central University *North Carolina*
North Central Kansas Technical College *Kansas*
North Central State College *Ohio*
North Central Texas College *Texas*
North Hennepin Community College *Minnesota*
North Idaho College *Idaho*
North Iowa Area Community College *Iowa*
North Seattle College *Washington*
North Shore Community College *Massachusetts*
Northampton Community College *Pennsylvania*
Northcentral Technical College *Wisconsin*
Northeast Alabama Community College *Alabama*
Northeast Community College *Nebraska*
Northeast Mississippi Community College *Mississippi*
Northeast State Community College *Tennessee*
Northeast Wisconsin Technical College *Wisconsin*
Northeastern Oklahoma Agricultural and Mechanical College *Oklahoma*
Northeastern State University *Oklahoma*
Northern Essex Community College *Massachusetts*
Northern Kentucky University *Kentucky*
Northern Maine Community College *Maine*
Northern Oklahoma College *Oklahoma*
Northern Virginia Community College *Virginia*
Northland Community and Technical College *Minnesota*
Northland Pioneer College *Arizona*
Northwest College *Wyoming*

Northwest Mississippi Community College *Mississippi*
Northwest-Shoals Community College *Alabama*
Northwest State Community College *Ohio*
Northwestern Oklahoma State University *Oklahoma*
Northwestern State University of Louisiana *Louisiana*
Norwalk Community College *Connecticut*
Norwich University *Vermont*
Notre Dame of Maryland University *Maryland*
Oakland Community College *Michigan*
Oakton Community College *Illinois*
Oakwood University *Alabama*
Ocean County College *New Jersey*
Odessa College *Texas*
Ohio University *Ohio*
Ohlone College *California*
Oklahoma Baptist University *Oklahoma*
Oklahoma City Community College *Oklahoma*
Oklahoma City University *Oklahoma*
Oklahoma Panhandle State University *Oklahoma*
Oklahoma State University Institute of Technology *Oklahoma*
Oklahoma State University, Oklahoma City *Oklahoma*
Olympic College *Washington*
Onondaga Community College *New York*
Orange County Community College *New York*
Orangeburg-Calhoun Technical College *South Carolina*
Oregon Health & Science University *Oregon*
Otero Junior College *Colorado*
Otterbein University *Ohio*
Our Lady of the Lake College *Louisiana*
Pacific Union College *California*
Palm Beach State College *Florida*
Palomar College *California*
Panola College *Texas*
Paradise Valley Community College *Arizona*
Paris Junior College *Texas*
Park University *Missouri*
Parkland College *Illinois*
Pasco-Hernando State College *Florida*
Passaic County Community College *New Jersey*
Patrick Henry Community College *Virginia*
Pearl River Community College *Mississippi*
Peninsula College *Washington*
Penn State University Park *Pennsylvania*
Pennsylvania College of Health Sciences *Pennsylvania*
Pennsylvania College of Technology *Pennsylvania*
Pensacola State College *Florida*
Phillips Beth Israel School of Nursing *New York*
Phillips Community College of the University of Arkansas *Arkansas*
Phoenix College *Arizona*
Piedmont College *Georgia*
Piedmont Technical College *South Carolina*
Piedmont Virginia Community College *Virginia*
Pierce College at Puyallup *Washington*
Pima Community College *Arizona*
Pitt Community College *North Carolina*
Polk State College *Florida*
Pontifical Catholic University of Puerto Rico *Puerto Rico*
Portland Community College *Oregon*
Prairie State College *Illinois*
Prairie View A&M University *Texas*
Pratt Community College *Kansas*
Presentation College *South Dakota*
Prince George's Community College *Maryland*
Provo College *Utah*
Pueblo Community College *Colorado*
Purdue University Northwest *Hammond, Indiana*
Purdue University Northwest *Westville, Indiana*
Queens University of Charlotte *North Carolina*
Queensborough Community College of the City University of New York *New York*
Quincy College *Massachusetts*
Quinnipiac University *Connecticut*
Quinsigamond Community College *Massachusetts*
Ramapo College of New Jersey *New Jersey*
Randolph Community College *North Carolina*
Raritan Valley Community College *New Jersey*
Reading Area Community College *Pennsylvania*
Redlands Community College *Oklahoma*

Regis College *Massachusetts*
Richland Community College *Illinois*
Ridgewater College *Minnesota*
River Valley Community College *New Hampshire*
Riverland Community College *Minnesota*
Riverside City College *California*
Rivier University *New Hampshire*
Roane State Community College *Tennessee*
Robert Morris University Illinois *Illinois*
Rochester Community and Technical College *Minnesota*
Rockford University *Illinois*
Rockland Community College *New York*
Rogers State University *Oklahoma*
Rose State College *Oklahoma*
Rowan-Cabarrus Community College *North Carolina*
Rowan College at Burlington County *New Jersey*
Rowan College at Gloucester County *New Jersey*
Roxbury Community College *Massachusetts*
Rush University *Illinois*
Rutgers University - Newark *New Jersey*
Saddleback College *California*
St. Catherine University *Minnesota*
St. Charles Community College *Missouri*
St. Elizabeth College of Nursing *New York*
Saint Francis Medical Center College of Nursing *Illinois*
St. John's College *Illinois*
St. Joseph School of Nursing *New Hampshire*
St. Joseph's College, New York *New York*
Saint Louis University *Missouri*
St. Luke's College *Iowa*
Saint Mary's College *Indiana*
Saint Paul College - A Community & Technical College *Minnesota*
St. Petersburg College *Florida*
St. Philip's College *Texas*
St. Vincent's College *Connecticut*
Salem Community College *New Jersey*
Salem State University *Massachusetts*
Salish Kootenai College *Montana*
Salt Lake Community College *Utah*
Salve Regina University *Rhode Island*
San Antonio College *Texas*
San Bernardino Valley College *California*
San Diego City College *California*
San Joaquin Delta College *California*
San Juan College *New Mexico*
Santa Ana College *California*
Santa Barbara City College *California*
Santa Fe College *Florida*
Santa Fe Community College *New Mexico*
Santa Monica College *California*
Savannah Technical College *Georgia*
Scottsdale Community College *Arizona*
Seattle Central College *Washington*
Seminole State College *Oklahoma*
Seminole State College of Florida *Florida*
Seton Hall University *New Jersey*
Seward County Community College and Area Technical School *Kansas*
Shawnee State University *Ohio*
Shelton State Community College *Alabama*
Shepherd University *West Virginia*
Sheridan College *Wyoming*
Shoreline Community College *Washington*
Sinclair Community College *Ohio*
Skagit Valley College *Washington*
Slippery Rock University of Pennsylvania *Pennsylvania*
Snead State Community College *Alabama*
Somerset Community College *Kentucky*
Sonoma State University *California*
South College *Tennessee*
South Georgia State College *Georgia*
South Plains College *Texas*
South Puget Sound Community College *Washington*
South Suburban College *Illinois*
Southeast Arkansas College *Arkansas*
Southeast Community College, Beatrice Campus *Nebraska*
Southeast Community College, Lincoln Campus *Nebraska*
Southeast Kentucky Community and Technical College *Kentucky*

Southeast Missouri Hospital College of Nursing and Health Sciences *Missouri*
Southern Adventist University *Tennessee*
Southern Arkansas University - Magnolia *Arkansas*
Southern Maine Community College *Maine*
Southern Regional Technical College *Georgia*
Southern State Community College *Ohio*
Southern Union State Community College *Alabama*
Southern University and Agricultural and Mechanical College *Louisiana*
Southern University at Shreveport *Louisiana*
Southern Vermont College *Vermont*
Southern West Virginia Community and Technical College *West Virginia*
Southwest Baptist University *Missouri*
Southwest Mississippi Community College *Mississippi*
Southwest Tennessee Community College *Tennessee*
Southwest Wisconsin Technical College *Wisconsin*
Southwestern College *California*
Southwestern Illinois College *Illinois*
Southwestern Oklahoma State University *Oklahoma*
Spartanburg Community College *South Carolina*
Springfield Technical Community College *Massachusetts*
Stark State College *Ohio*
State College of Florida Manatee-Sarasota *Florida*
State University of New York College of Technology at Alfred *New York*
State University of New York College of Technology at Canton *New York*
State University of New York College of Technology at Delhi *New York*
State University of New York Empire State College *New York*
Stephen F. Austin State University *Texas*
Stevens-Henager College *West Haven, Utah*
Stevenson University *Maryland*
Suffolk County Community College *New York*
Sullivan County Community College *New York*
Syracuse University *New York*
Tacoma Community College *Washington*
Tarrant County College District *Texas*
Technical College of the Lowcountry *South Carolina*
Temple College *Texas*
Tennessee State University *Tennessee*
Texarkana College *Texas*
Texas A&M International University *Texas*
Texas Southmost College *Texas*
Thomas Edison State University *New Jersey*
Thomas More College *Kentucky*
Thomas Nelson Community College *Virginia*
Thomas University *Georgia*
Three Rivers Community College *Connecticut*
Three Rivers Community College *Missouri*
Tidewater Community College *Virginia*
Tompkins Cortland Community College *New York*
Tri-County Technical College *South Carolina*
Trident Technical College *South Carolina*
Trinity College of Nursing and Health Sciences *Illinois*
Trinity Valley Community College *Texas*
Triton College *Illinois*
Trocaire College *New York*
Troy University *Alabama*
Truckee Meadows Community College *Nevada*
Tulsa Community College *Oklahoma*
Tuskegee University *Alabama*
Ulster County Community College *New York*
Umpqua Community College *Oregon*
Union County College *New Jersey*
Universidad Adventista de las Antillas *Puerto Rico*
Universidad Metropolitana *Puerto Rico*
University of Alaska Anchorage *Alaska*
University of Arkansas Community College at Batesville *Arkansas*
University of Arkansas - Fort Smith *Arkansas*
University of Arkansas at Little Rock *Arkansas*
University of Arkansas at Monticello *Arkansas*
University of Arkansas at Pine Bluff *Arkansas*
University of Central Oklahoma *Oklahoma*
University of Charleston *West Virginia*
University of Cincinnati Blue Ash College *Ohio*
University of Colorado Denver *Colorado*
University of Delaware *Delaware*

University of the District of Columbia *District of Columbia*
University of Evansville *Indiana*
University of Guam *Guam*
University of Hawaii at Hilo *Hawaii*
University of Hawaii Maui College *Hawaii*
University of Holy Cross *Louisiana*
University of Indianapolis *Indiana*
University of Jamestown *North Dakota*
University of Kentucky *Kentucky*
University of Maine at Augusta *Maine*
University of Mary *North Dakota*
University of Massachusetts Dartmouth *Massachusetts*
University of Minnesota, Twin Cities Campus *Minnesota*
University of Mobile *Alabama*
University of Nevada, Las Vegas *Nevada*
University of New England *Maine*
The University of North Carolina at Chapel Hill *North Carolina*
The University of North Carolina at Greensboro *North Carolina*
The University of North Carolina Wilmington *North Carolina*
University of North Georgia *Georgia*
University of Oklahoma Health Sciences Center *Oklahoma*
University of Pennsylvania *Pennsylvania*
University of Phoenix - Phoenix Campus *Arizona*
University of Pittsburgh at Bradford *Pennsylvania*
University of Pittsburgh at Titusville *Pennsylvania*
University of Puerto Rico in Arecibo *Puerto Rico*
University of Puerto Rico in Humacao *Puerto Rico*
University of Puerto Rico, Mayagüez Campus *Puerto Rico*
University of Rio Grande *Ohio*
University of the Sacred Heart *Puerto Rico*
University of Saint Francis *Indiana*
University of South Carolina Aiken *South Carolina*
University of South Carolina Lancaster *South Carolina*
University of South Carolina Upstate *South Carolina*
The University of South Dakota *South Dakota*
The University of Tampa *Florida*
The University of Tennessee at Martin *Tennessee*
The University of Texas Health Science Center at Houston *Texas*
The University of Texas Medical Branch *Texas*
The University of Toledo *Ohio*
The University of Tulsa *Oklahoma*
University of the Virgin Islands *United States Virgin Islands*
The University of West Alabama *Alabama*
Utah Valley University *Utah*
Utica College *New York*
Valencia College *Florida*
Vanderbilt University *Tennessee*
Vermont Technical College *Vermont*
Victoria College *Texas*
Vincennes University *Indiana*
Virginia Commonwealth University *Virginia*
Virginia Western Community College *Virginia*
Wagner College *New York*
Walla Walla University *Washington*
Wallace State Community College *Alabama*
Walsh University *Ohio*
Walters State Community College *Tennessee*
Warren County Community College *New Jersey*
Washington Adventist University *Maryland*
Washington State University *Washington*
Washtenaw Community College *Michigan*
Waukesha County Technical College *Wisconsin*
Wayland Baptist University *Texas*
Wayne Community College *North Carolina*
Wayne State University *Michigan*
Weatherford College *Texas*
Weber State University *Utah*
Webster University *Missouri*
Wenatchee Valley College *Washington*
Wesley College *Delaware*
West Georgia Technical College *Georgia*
West Kentucky Community and Technical College *Kentucky*
West Virginia Northern Community College *West Virginia*

West Virginia University at Parkersburg *West Virginia*
West Virginia Wesleyan College *West Virginia*
Western Kentucky University *Kentucky*
Western Nebraska Community College *Nebraska*
Western Nevada College *Nevada*
Western New Mexico University *New Mexico*
Western Oklahoma State College *Oklahoma*
Western Piedmont Community College *North Carolina*
Western Technical College *Wisconsin*
Western Wyoming Community College *Wyoming*
Westmoreland County Community College *Pennsylvania*
Whatcom Community College *Washington*
Wichita Area Technical College *Kansas*
Wisconsin Indianhead Technical College *Wisconsin*
Wytheville Community College *Virginia*
Yakima Valley Community College *Washington*
Yavapai College *Arizona*
York College of the City University of New York *New York*
York College of Pennsylvania *Pennsylvania*
York Technical College *South Carolina*
Youngstown State University *Ohio*

Accreditation Committee for Perfusion Education (ACPeE)

Barry University *Florida*
Drexel University *Pennsylvania*
Medical University of South Carolina *South Carolina*
Milwaukee School of Engineering *Wisconsin*
Northeastern University *Massachusetts*
The Ohio State University *Ohio*
Rush University *Illinois*
State University of New York Upstate Medical University *New York*
University of Nebraska Medical Center *Nebraska*

Accreditation Council for Business Schools and Programs (ACBSP)

Adirondack Community College *New York*
Aiken Technical College *South Carolina*
Alabama State University *Alabama*
Albany State University *Georgia*
Alcorn State University *Mississippi*
Alvernia University *Pennsylvania*
American InterContinental University Atlanta *Georgia*
American InterContinental University Houston *Texas*
American InterContinental University Online *Illinois*
American Public University System *West Virginia*
Anderson University *Indiana*
Anderson University *South Carolina*
Angelo State University *Texas*
Arcadia University *Pennsylvania*
Argosy University, Chicago *Illinois*
Argosy University, Hawai'i *Hawaii*
Argosy University, Inland Empire *California*
Argosy University, Los Angeles *California*
Argosy University, Nashville *Tennessee*
Argosy University, Orange County *California*
Argosy University, Phoenix *Arizona*
Argosy University, Salt Lake City *Utah*
Argosy University, San Diego *California*
Argosy University, San Francisco Bay Area *California*
Argosy University, Sarasota *Florida*
Argosy University, Schaumburg *Illinois*
Argosy University, Seattle *Washington*
Argosy University, Tampa *Florida*
Argosy University, Twin Cities *Minnesota*
Argosy University, Washington DC *Virginia*
Ashland University *Ohio*
Athens State University *Alabama*
Athens Technical College *Georgia*
Atlanta Metropolitan State College *Georgia*
Augsburg College *Minnesota*
Austin Community College District *Texas*
Baker University *Kansas*
Baltimore City Community College *Maryland*
Baton Rouge Community College *Louisiana*
Benedict College *South Carolina*
Bergen Community College *New Jersey*
Bethune-Cookman University *Florida*
Biola University *California*

Bishop State Community College *Alabama*
Bluefield State College *West Virginia*
Bowie State University *Maryland*
Brenau University *Georgia*
British Columbia Institute of Technology *British Columbia (Canada)*
Bronx Community College of the City University of New York *New York*
Bucks County Community College *Pennsylvania*
Butler Community College *Kansas*
Butler County Community College *Pennsylvania*
Cabrini University *Pennsylvania*
Caldwell University *New Jersey*
Calhoun Community College *Alabama*
California Baptist University *California*
California State University, Dominguez Hills *California*
Cameron University *Oklahoma*
Campbell University *North Carolina*
Capella University *Minnesota*
Capilano University *British Columbia (Canada)*
Capital University *Ohio*
Cardinal Stritch University *Wisconsin*
Carl Albert State College *Oklahoma*
Carlos Albizu University, Miami Campus *Florida*
Carlow University *Pennsylvania*
Casper College *Wyoming*
Catawba College *North Carolina*
Cedar Crest College *Pennsylvania*
Cedarville University *Ohio*
Centennial College *Ontario (Canada)*
Central New Mexico Community College *New Mexico*
Chadron State College *Nebraska*
Chattanooga State Community College *Tennessee*
Chicago State University *Illinois*
City Colleges of Chicago, Harold Washington College *Illinois*
City Colleges of Chicago, Wilbur Wright College *Illinois*
City University of Seattle *Washington*
Claflin University *South Carolina*
Cleveland State Community College *Tennessee*
College of Mount Saint Vincent *New York*
The College of Saint Rose *New York*
College of Southern Maryland *Maryland*
College of Southern Nevada *Nevada*
Colorado Technical University Colorado Springs *Colorado*
Columbia State Community College *Tennessee*
Columbus State Community College *Ohio*
Community College of Baltimore County *Maryland*
Community College of Rhode Island *Rhode Island*
Concord University *West Virginia*
Concordia University *Oregon*
Concordia University, St. Paul *Minnesota*
Cossatot Community College of the University of Arkansas *Arkansas*
County College of Morris *New Jersey*
Cumberland University *Tennessee*
Dakota State University *South Dakota*
Dallas Baptist University *Texas*
Delaware Technical & Community College, Jack F. Owens Campus *Delaware*
Delaware Technical & Community College, Stanton/Wilmington Campus *Delaware*
Delaware Technical & Community College, Terry Campus *Delaware*
Delaware Valley University *Pennsylvania*
Delgado Community College *Louisiana*
Delta State University *Mississippi*
Denmark Technical College *South Carolina*
Des Moines Area Community College *Iowa*
DeSales University *Pennsylvania*
DeVry University *Mesa, Arizona*
DeVry University *Alhambra, California*
DeVry University *Anaheim, California*
DeVry University *Fremont, California*
DeVry University *Long Beach, California*
DeVry University *Oakland, California*
DeVry University *Oxnard, California*
DeVry University *Palmdale, California*
DeVry University *San Diego, California*
DeVry University *Colorado Springs, Colorado*
DeVry University *Jacksonville, Florida*
DeVry University *Alpharetta, Georgia*

DeVry University *Decatur, Georgia*
DeVry University *Duluth, Georgia*
DeVry University *Chicago, Illinois*
DeVry University *Downers Grove, Illinois*
DeVry University *Elgin, Illinois*
DeVry University *Gurnee, Illinois*
DeVry University *Naperville, Illinois*
DeVry University *Tinley Park, Illinois*
DeVry University *Indiana*
DeVry University *Kansas City, Missouri*
DeVry University *Nevada*
DeVry University *North Brunswick, New Jersey*
DeVry University *Paramus, New Jersey*
DeVry University *North Carolina*
DeVry University *Columbus, Ohio*
DeVry University *Seven Hills, Ohio*
DeVry University *Fort Washington, Pennsylvania*
DeVry University *King of Prussia, Pennsylvania*
DeVry University *Tennessee*
DeVry University *Irving, Texas*
DeVry University *Arlington, Virginia*
DeVry University *Chesapeake, Virginia*
DeVry University *Manassas, Virginia*
Dominican University *Illinois*
Doña Ana Community College *New Mexico*
Drury University *Missouri*
Dyersburg State Community College *Tennessee*
East Central University *Oklahoma*
Eastern New Mexico University *New Mexico*
Edgewood College *Wisconsin*
Edinboro University of Pennsylvania *Pennsylvania*
Elizabethtown College *Pennsylvania*
Embry-Riddle Aeronautical University - Daytona *Florida*
Embry-Riddle Aeronautical University - Prescott *Arizona*
Embry-Riddle Aeronautical University - Worldwide *Florida*
Evangel University *Missouri*
Fairmont State University *West Virginia*
Ferris State University *Michigan*
Florence-Darlington Technical College *South Carolina*
Florida Agricultural and Mechanical University *Florida*
Florida Memorial University *Florida*
Florida State College at Jacksonville *Florida*
Fontbonne University *Missouri*
Freed-Hardeman University *Tennessee*
Friends University *Kansas*
Gadsden State Community College *Alabama*
Gallaudet University *District of Columbia*
Gannon University *Pennsylvania*
Gardner-Webb University *North Carolina*
Gaston College *North Carolina*
Geneva College *Pennsylvania*
George Fox University *Oregon*
Georgian Court University *New Jersey*
Goldey-Beacom College *Delaware*
Governors State University *Illinois*
Grand Canyon University *Arizona*
Great Bay Community College *New Hampshire*
Greensboro College *North Carolina*
Greenville Technical College *South Carolina*
Grove City College *Pennsylvania*
Guilford College *North Carolina*
Gwynedd Mercy University *Pennsylvania*
Hardin-Simmons University *Texas*
Harding University *Arkansas*
Harper College *Illinois*
Harris-Stowe State University *Missouri*
Harrisburg Area Community College *Pennsylvania*
Haskell Indian Nations University *Kansas*
Heidelberg University *Ohio*
Hennepin Technical College *Minnesota*
Herzing University *Madison, Wisconsin*
Hocking College *Ohio*
Holy Family University *Pennsylvania*
Hood College *Maryland*
Horry-Georgetown Technical College *South Carolina*
Houston Baptist University *Texas*
Huston-Tillotson University *Texas*
Hutchinson Community College *Kansas*
Immaculata University *Pennsylvania*
Indiana University East *Indiana*

Inter American University of Puerto Rico, Guayama Campus *Puerto Rico*
Inter American University of Puerto Rico, Ponce Campus *Puerto Rico*
Inver Hills Community College *Minnesota*
Ivy Tech Community College - Bloomington *Indiana*
Ivy Tech Community College - Central Indiana *Indiana*
Ivy Tech Community College - Columbus *Indiana*
Ivy Tech Community College - East Central *Indiana*
Ivy Tech Community College - Kokomo *Indiana*
Ivy Tech Community College - Lafayette *Indiana*
Ivy Tech Community College - North Central *Indiana*
Ivy Tech Community College - Northeast *Indiana*
Ivy Tech Community College - Northwest *Indiana*
Ivy Tech Community College - Richmond *Indiana*
Ivy Tech Community College - Southeast *Indiana*
Ivy Tech Community College - Southern Indiana *Indiana*
Ivy Tech Community College - Southwest *Indiana*
Ivy Tech Community College - Wabash Valley *Indiana*
Jackson College *Michigan*
Jackson State Community College *Tennessee*
James A. Rhodes State College *Ohio*
Jarvis Christian College *Texas*
Jefferson State Community College *Alabama*
John Brown University *Arkansas*
Johnson C. Smith University *North Carolina*
Johnson County Community College *Kansas*
Joliet Junior College *Illinois*
Jones County Junior College *Mississippi*
Kansas City Kansas Community College *Kansas*
Kaplan University, Davenport Campus *Iowa*
Keiser University *Florida*
Kennebec Valley Community College *Maine*
Kent State University *Ohio*
Kent State University at Ashtabula *Ohio*
Kent State University at East Liverpool *Ohio*
Kent State University at Geauga *Ohio*
Kent State University at Salem *Ohio*
Kent State University at Trumbull *Ohio*
Kent State University at Tuscarawas *Ohio*
Kentucky State University *Kentucky*
Kettering University *Michigan*
King University *Tennessee*
Kirkwood Community College *Iowa*
La Roche College *Pennsylvania*
LaGrange College *Georgia*
Lake Superior State University *Michigan*
Langston University *Oklahoma*
Lasell College *Massachusetts*
Lawrence Technological University *Michigan*
Lawson State Community College *Alabama*
Lebanon Valley College *Pennsylvania*
Lee University *Tennessee*
Lehigh Carbon Community College *Pennsylvania*
Lenoir-Rhyne University *North Carolina*
Lewis University *Illinois*
Liberty University *Virginia*
LIM College *New York*
Lincoln Memorial University *Tennessee*
Lincoln University *Missouri*
Lindenwood University *Missouri*
Lipscomb University *Tennessee*
Lock Haven University of Pennsylvania *Pennsylvania*
Louisiana College *Louisiana*
Luzerne County Community College *Pennsylvania*
Lynchburg College *Virginia*
Malone University *Ohio*
Manchester Community College *New Hampshire*
Manor College *Pennsylvania*
Marymount University *Virginia*
Maryville University of Saint Louis *Missouri*
Marywood University *Pennsylvania*
Medgar Evers College of the City University of New York *New York*
Mercy College *New York*
Messiah College *Pennsylvania*
Methodist University *North Carolina*
Metropolitan College of New York *New York*
Metropolitan Community College *Nebraska*
MidAmerica Nazarene University *Kansas*
Midlands Technical College *South Carolina*
Midstate College *Illinois*

Millersville University of Pennsylvania *Pennsylvania*
Milligan College *Tennessee*
Millikin University *Illinois*
Mississippi College *Mississippi*
Mississippi University for Women *Mississippi*
Mississippi Valley State University *Mississippi*
Missouri Southern State University *Missouri*
Monroe College *New York*
Moravian College *Pennsylvania*
Morris College *South Carolina*
Morrisville State College *New York*
Motlow State Community College *Tennessee*
Mott Community College *Michigan*
Mount Aloysius College *Pennsylvania*
Mount Saint Mary's University *California*
Mount Vernon Nazarene University *Ohio*
Mountwest Community & Technical College *West Virginia*
Nashville State Community College *Tennessee*
Nebraska Wesleyan University *Nebraska*
Neosho County Community College *Kansas*
Neumann University *Pennsylvania*
New Jersey City University *New Jersey*
New Mexico Highlands University *New Mexico*
NHTI, Concord's Community College *New Hampshire*
Normandale Community College *Minnesota*
North Arkansas College *Arkansas*
North Carolina Central University *North Carolina*
North Central State College *Ohio*
North Hennepin Community College *Minnesota*
Northampton Community College *Pennsylvania*
Northcentral University *Arizona*
Northeast State Community College *Tennessee*
Northeastern State University *Oklahoma*
Northern Arizona University *Arizona*
Northern Maine Community College *Maine*
Northern New Mexico College *New Mexico*
Northern Oklahoma College *Oklahoma*
Northern State University *South Dakota*
NorthWest Arkansas Community College *Arkansas*
Northwest Missouri State University *Missouri*
Northwest Nazarene University *Idaho*
Northwest State Community College *Ohio*
Northwest University *Washington*
Northwestern College - Chicago Campus *Illinois*
Northwestern Oklahoma State University *Oklahoma*
Northwood University, Michigan Campus *Michigan*
Norwich University *Vermont*
Notre Dame de Namur University *California*
Oakwood University *Alabama*
Ohio Dominican University *Ohio*
Okanagan College *British Columbia (Canada)*
Oklahoma Baptist University *Oklahoma*
Oklahoma Christian University *Oklahoma*
Oklahoma City Community College *Oklahoma*
Oklahoma City University *Oklahoma*
Oral Roberts University *Oklahoma*
Orange County Community College *New York*
Orangeburg-Calhoun Technical College *South Carolina*
Our Lady of the Lake University of San Antonio *Texas*
Owens Community College *Ohio*
Owensboro Community and Technical College *Kentucky*
Paine College *Georgia*
Park University *Missouri*
Peirce College *Pennsylvania*
Pellissippi State Community College *Tennessee*
Pennsylvania College of Technology *Pennsylvania*
Philander Smith College *Arkansas*
Phillips Community College of the University of Arkansas *Arkansas*
Piedmont College *Georgia*
Plymouth State University *New Hampshire*
Point Loma Nazarene University *California*
Post University *Connecticut*
Pratt Community College *Kansas*
Purdue University Northwest *Westville, Indiana*
Queens University of Charlotte *North Carolina*
Queensborough Community College of the City University of New York *New York*
Rasmussen College Appleton *Wisconsin*
Rasmussen College Aurora *Illinois*
Rasmussen College Blaine *Minnesota*

Rasmussen College Brooklyn Park *Minnesota*
Rasmussen College Eagan *Minnesota*
Rasmussen College Fargo *North Dakota*
Rasmussen College Fort Myers *Florida*
Rasmussen College Green Bay *Wisconsin*
Rasmussen College Lake Elmo/Woodbury *Minnesota*
Rasmussen College Mankato *Minnesota*
Rasmussen College Mokena/Tinley Park *Illinois*
Rasmussen College Ocala *Florida*
Rasmussen College Rockford *Illinois*
Rasmussen College Romeoville/Joliet *Illinois*
Rasmussen College St. Cloud *Minnesota*
Rasmussen College Tampa/Brandon *Florida*
Rasmussen College Wausau *Wisconsin*
Regent University *Virginia*
River Valley Community College *New Hampshire*
Riverland Community College *Minnesota*
Roane State Community College *Tennessee*
Roanoke College *Virginia*
Roosevelt University *Illinois*
St. Ambrose University *Iowa*
Saint Leo University *Florida*
Saint Paul College - A Community & Technical College *Minnesota*
St. Petersburg College *Florida*
Saint Vincent College *Pennsylvania*
Saint Xavier University *Illinois*
Salt Lake Community College *Utah*
San Juan College *New Mexico*
Schenectady County Community College *New York*
Seward County Community College and Area Technical School *Kansas*
Sinclair Community College *Ohio*
Skyline College *California*
Slippery Rock University of Pennsylvania *Pennsylvania*
Snow College *Utah*
South Texas College *Texas*
South University *Alabama*
South University *Royal Palm Beach, Florida*
South University *Tampa, Florida*
South University *Georgia*
South University *Michigan*
South University *North Carolina*
South University *Ohio*
South University *South Carolina*
South University *Texas*
South University *Glen Allen, Virginia*
South University *Virginia Beach, Virginia*
Southeast Community College, Lincoln Campus *Nebraska*
Southeastern Oklahoma State University *Oklahoma*
Southern Nazarene University *Oklahoma*
Southern New Hampshire University *New Hampshire*
Southern Oregon University *Oregon*
Southern Utah University *Utah*
Southwest Baptist University *Missouri*
Southwest Tennessee Community College *Tennessee*
Spartanburg Community College *South Carolina*
Stark State College *Ohio*
Sullivan County Community College *New York*
Tarleton State University *Texas*
Technical College of the Lowcountry *South Carolina*
Texas A&M University - Kingsville *Texas*
Texas Lutheran University *Texas*
Texas Wesleyan University *Texas*
Texas Woman's University *Texas*
Thomas Edison State University *New Jersey*
Thomas More College *Kentucky*
Three Rivers Community College *Connecticut*
Three Rivers Community College *Missouri*
Tiffin University *Ohio*
Tri-County Technical College *South Carolina*
Trident Technical College *South Carolina*
Trine University *Indiana*
Trinity Christian College *Illinois*
Troy University *Alabama*
Tunxis Community College *Connecticut*
Universidad del Este *Puerto Rico*
Universidad Metropolitana *Puerto Rico*
The University of Akron *Ohio*
University of Arkansas at Monticello *Arkansas*
University of Bridgeport *Connecticut*

University of Central Oklahoma *Oklahoma*
University of Dallas *Texas*
University of the District of Columbia *District of Columbia*
The University of Findlay *Ohio*
University of the Incarnate Word *Texas*
University of Indianapolis *Indiana*
University of Mobile *Alabama*
University of Mount Olive *North Carolina*
University of New England *Maine*
University of North Alabama *Alabama*
University of Northwestern Ohio *Ohio*
University of Phoenix - Augusta Campus *Georgia*
University of Phoenix - Central Valley Campus *California*
University of Phoenix - Charlotte Campus *North Carolina*
University of Phoenix - Colorado Springs Downtown Campus *Colorado*
University of Phoenix - Columbus Georgia Campus *Georgia*
University of Phoenix - Dallas Campus *Texas*
University of Phoenix - Hawaii Campus *Hawaii*
University of Phoenix - Houston Campus *Texas*
University of Phoenix - Jersey City Campus *New Jersey*
University of Phoenix - Las Vegas Campus *Nevada*
University of Phoenix - New Mexico Campus *New Mexico*
University of Phoenix - North Florida Campus *Florida*
University of Phoenix - Online Campus *Arizona*
University of Phoenix - Phoenix Campus *Arizona*
University of Phoenix - Sacramento Valley Campus *California*
University of Phoenix - San Antonio Campus *Texas*
University of Phoenix - San Diego Campus *California*
University of Phoenix - South Florida Campus *Florida*
University of Phoenix - Southern Arizona Campus *Arizona*
University of Phoenix - Southern California Campus *California*
University of Puerto Rico in Aguadilla *Puerto Rico*
University of Puerto Rico in Arecibo *Puerto Rico*
University of Puerto Rico in Bayamón *Puerto Rico*
University of Puerto Rico in Carolina *Puerto Rico*
University of Puerto Rico in Cayey *Puerto Rico*
University of Puerto Rico in Humacao *Puerto Rico*
University of Puerto Rico in Ponce *Puerto Rico*
University of Puerto Rico, Río Piedras Campus *Puerto Rico*
University of Puerto Rico in Utuado *Puerto Rico*
University of the Sacred Heart *Puerto Rico*
University of St. Francis *Illinois*
University of Saint Francis *Indiana*
University of St. Thomas *Texas*
University of South Carolina Lancaster *South Carolina*
University of the Virgin Islands *United States Virgin Islands*
The University of West Alabama *Alabama*
University of Wisconsin - Stout *Wisconsin*
Vancouver Island University *British Columbia (Canada)*
Vincennes University *Indiana*
Virginia Union University *Virginia*
Virginia Western Community College *Virginia*
Viterbo University *Wisconsin*
Volunteer State Community College *Tennessee*
Voorhees College *South Carolina*
Wagner College *New York*
Walden University *Minnesota*
Walla Walla University *Washington*
Wallace State Community College *Alabama*
Walsh College of Accountancy and Business Administration *Michigan*
Walters State Community College *Tennessee*
Webster University *Missouri*
West Georgia Technical College *Georgia*
West Kentucky Community and Technical College *Kentucky*
West Liberty University *West Virginia*
West Virginia State University *West Virginia*
West Virginia Wesleyan College *West Virginia*

Western New Mexico University *New Mexico*
Westminster College *Utah*
Wheeling Jesuit University *West Virginia*
Wiley College *Texas*
Wilkes University *Pennsylvania*
Williamsburg Technical College *South Carolina*
Wingate University *North Carolina*
Woodbury University *California*
Xavier University of Louisiana *Louisiana*
York College of Pennsylvania *Pennsylvania*
York Technical College *South Carolina*
Zane State College *Ohio*

Accreditation Council for Pharmacy Education (ACPE)

Albany College of Pharmacy and Health Sciences *New York*
Auburn University *Alabama*
Belmont University *Tennessee*
Butler University *Indiana*
Campbell University *North Carolina*
Chicago State University *Illinois*
Creighton University *Nebraska*
Drake University *Iowa*
Duquesne University *Pennsylvania*
D'Youville College *New York*
East Tennessee State University *Tennessee*
Ferris State University *Michigan*
Florida Agricultural and Mechanical University *Florida*
Hampton University *Virginia*
Harding University *Arkansas*
Howard University *District of Columbia*
Husson University *Maine*
Idaho State University *Idaho*
Lipscomb University *Tennessee*
Loma Linda University *California*
Long Island University - LIU Brooklyn *New York*
MCPHS University *Massachusetts*
Medical University of South Carolina *South Carolina*
Mercer University *Georgia*
North Dakota State University *North Dakota*
Northeastern University *Massachusetts*
Nova Southeastern University *Florida*
Ohio Northern University *Ohio*
The Ohio State University *Ohio*
Oregon State University *Oregon*
Pacific University *Oregon*
Palm Beach Atlantic University *Florida*
Purdue University *Indiana*
Regis University *Colorado*
Roosevelt University *Illinois*
Rutgers University - New Brunswick *New Jersey*
St. John Fisher College *New York*
St. John's University *New York*
St. Louis College of Pharmacy *Missouri*
Samford University *Alabama*
Shenandoah University *Virginia*
South Dakota State University *South Dakota*
South University *Georgia*
Southern Illinois University Edwardsville *Illinois*
Southwestern Oklahoma State University *Oklahoma*
Temple University *Pennsylvania*
Texas A&M University *Texas*
Texas Southern University *Texas*
Thomas Jefferson University *Pennsylvania*
The University of Arizona *Arizona*
University of Arkansas for Medical Sciences *Arkansas*
University at Buffalo, the State University of New York *New York*
University of California, San Diego *California*
University of Charleston *West Virginia*
University of Cincinnati *Ohio*
University of Colorado Denver *Colorado*
University of Connecticut *Connecticut*
The University of Findlay *Ohio*
University of Florida *Florida*
University of Georgia *Georgia*
University of Hawaii at Hilo *Hawaii*
University of Houston *Texas*
University of the Incarnate Word *Texas*
The University of Iowa *Iowa*
The University of Kansas *Kansas*
University of Kentucky *Kentucky*

University of Louisiana at Monroe *Louisiana*
University of Michigan *Michigan*
University of Minnesota, Twin Cities Campus *Minnesota*
University of Mississippi *Mississippi*
University of Missouri - Kansas City *Missouri*
University of Montana *Montana*
University of Nebraska Medical Center *Nebraska*
University of New England *Maine*
University of New Mexico *New Mexico*
The University of North Carolina at Chapel Hill *North Carolina*
University of Oklahoma Health Sciences Center *Oklahoma*
University of the Pacific *California*
University of Pittsburgh *Pennsylvania*
University of Puerto Rico, Medical Sciences Campus *Puerto Rico*
University of Rhode Island *Rhode Island*
University of Saint Joseph *Connecticut*
University of the Sciences *Pennsylvania*
University of South Carolina *South Carolina*
University of South Florida *Florida*
University of Southern California *California*
The University of Texas at Austin *Texas*
The University of Toledo *Ohio*
University of Utah *Utah*
University of Washington *Washington*
University of Wisconsin - Madison *Wisconsin*
University of Wyoming *Wyoming*
Virginia Commonwealth University *Virginia*
Washington State University *Washington*
Wayne State University *Michigan*
West Virginia University *West Virginia*
Western New England University *Massachusetts*
Wilkes University *Pennsylvania*
Wingate University *North Carolina*
Xavier University of Louisiana *Louisiana*

Accreditation Review Committee on Education for the Anesthesiologist Assistant (ARCEAA)

Case Western Reserve University *Ohio*
Emory University *Georgia*

Accreditation Review Committee on Education in Surgical Technology (ARCST)

Amarillo College *Texas*
Ashland Community and Technical College *Kentucky*
Augusta Technical College *Georgia*
Austin Community College District *Texas*
Baker College *Michigan*
Baltimore City Community College *Maryland*
Bismarck State College *North Dakota*
Bunker Hill Community College *Massachusetts*
Cabarrus College of Health Sciences *North Carolina*
Central Ohio Technical College *Ohio*
Central Wyoming College *Wyoming*
Cincinnati State Technical and Community College *Ohio*
City Colleges of Chicago, Malcolm X College *Illinois*
Coastal Carolina Community College *North Carolina*
Columbus State Community College *Ohio*
Columbus Technical College *Georgia*
Community College of Allegheny County *Pennsylvania*
Community College of Denver *Colorado*
Cuyahoga Community College *Ohio*
Del Mar College *Texas*
Delaware County Community College *Pennsylvania*
Delta College *Michigan*
East Central Community College *Mississippi*
Eastern Idaho Technical College *Idaho*
El Paso Community College *Texas*
Frederick Community College *Maryland*
Gateway Technical College *Wisconsin*
Henry Ford College *Michigan*
Holmes Community College *Mississippi*
Itawamba Community College *Mississippi*
Ivy Tech Community College - Central Indiana *Indiana*
Ivy Tech Community College - Columbus *Indiana*
Ivy Tech Community College - East Central *Indiana*

Ivy Tech Community College - Lafayette *Indiana*
Ivy Tech Community College - Northwest *Indiana*
Ivy Tech Community College - Southwest *Indiana*
Ivy Tech Community College - Wabash Valley *Indiana*
James H. Faulkner State Community College *Alabama*
Kilgore College *Texas*
Kirkwood Community College *Iowa*
Lakeland Community College *Ohio*
Lamar State College - Port Arthur *Texas*
Loma Linda University *California*
Lorain County Community College *Ohio*
Luzerne County Community College *Pennsylvania*
Macomb Community College *Michigan*
Manchester Community College *Connecticut*
Manchester Community College *New Hampshire*
McCann School of Business & Technology *Monroe, Louisiana*
Mercy College of Health Sciences *Iowa*
Miller-Motte College *Wilmington, North Carolina*
Milwaukee Area Technical College *Wisconsin*
Montgomery College *Maryland*
Mount Aloysius College *Pennsylvania*
Mt. Hood Community College *Oregon*
Nassau Community College *New York*
New England Institute of Technology *Rhode Island*
Niagara County Community College *New York*
North Arkansas College *Arkansas*
Northwest Technical College *Minnesota*
Odessa College *Texas*
Our Lady of the Lake College *Louisiana*
Owens Community College *Ohio*
Parkland College *Illinois*
Pearl River Community College *Mississippi*
Presentation College *South Dakota*
Renton Technical College *Washington*
Richland Community College *Illinois*
Rochester Community and Technical College *Minnesota*
St. Cloud Technical & Community College *Minnesota*
San Joaquin Valley College *Visalia, California*
Seward County Community College and Area Technical School *Kansas*
Sinclair Community College *Ohio*
Skyline College *California*
Southeast Arkansas College *Arkansas*
Southeast Community College, Lincoln Campus *Nebraska*
Southern Crescent Technical College *Georgia*
Southern University at Shreveport *Louisiana*
Southern West Virginia Community and Technical College *West Virginia*
Southwestern College *California*
Spokane Community College *Washington*
Springfield Technical Community College *Massachusetts*
Stevens-Henager College *West Haven, Utah*
Trinity Valley Community College *Texas*
Trocaire College *New York*
Tyler Junior College *Texas*
The University of Akron *Ohio*
University of Arkansas - Fort Smith *Arkansas*
University of Arkansas for Medical Sciences *Arkansas*
University of Saint Francis *Indiana*
Vincennes University *Indiana*
Waukesha County Technical College *Wisconsin*
Wayne County Community College District *Michigan*
West Virginia Northern Community College *West Virginia*
Wichita Area Technical College *Kansas*

Accreditation Review Committee for the Medical Illustrator (ARCMI)

Augusta University *Georgia*
Johns Hopkins University *Maryland*
University of Illinois at Chicago *Illinois*
University of Michigan *Michigan*
University of Toronto *Ontario (Canada)*

Accrediting Bureau of Health Education Schools (ABHES)

American Career College *Anaheim, California*
American Career College *Ontario, California*

American Medical Academy *Florida*
American Medical Sciences Center *California*
AmeriTech College *Utah*
Angeles College *California*
Arizona College *Arizona*
Arizona College - Mesa *Arizona*
ATA Career Education *Florida*
ATA College *Kentucky*
Bay State College *Massachusetts*
Cambridge Institute of Allied Health and Technology *Florida*
Carrington College - Boise *Idaho*
Carrington College - Mesa *Arizona*
Carrington College - Phoenix North *Arizona*
Carrington College - Phoenix West *Arizona*
Carrington College - Spokane *Washington*
Carrington College - Tucson *Arizona*
Casa Loma College - Van Nuys *California*
The College of Health Care Professions *Austin, Texas*
The College of Health Care Professions *Fort Worth, Texas*
The College of Health Care Professions *Houston, Texas*
The College of Health Care Professions *San Antonio, Texas*
CollegeAmerica - Flagstaff *Arizona*
Community Care College *Oklahoma*
Dallas Nursing Institute *Texas*
Fortis College *Mobile, Alabama*
Fortis College *Montgomery, Alabama*
Fortis College *Georgia*
Fortis College *Cincinnati, Ohio*
Fortis College *Westerville, Ohio*
Fortis College *South Carolina*
Fortis Institute *Fort Lauderdale, Florida*
Fortis Institute *Palm Springs, Florida*
Fortis Institute *Pensacola, Florida*
Fortis Institute *Port Saint Lucie, Florida*
Fortis Institute *Nashville, Tennessee*
Gurnick Academy of Medical Arts *California*
Heritage College *Kansas*
Heritage Institute *Fort Myers, Florida*
Heritage Institute *Jacksonville, Florida*
IBMC College *Colorado Springs, Colorado*
Jefferson Regional Medical Center School of Nursing *Arkansas*
Keiser University *Florida*
Lincoln Technical Institute *Florida*
Mandl School *New York*
Midwest Institute *Saint Louis, Missouri*
Milwaukee Career College *Wisconsin*
National Career College *California*
Nightingale College *Utah*
Northwest Career College *Nevada*
Orion College *Florida*
Pima Medical Institute *Mesa, Arizona*
Pima Medical Institute *Tucson, Arizona*
Pima Medical Institute *California*
Pima Medical Institute *Aurora, Colorado*
Pima Medical Institute *Colorado Springs, Colorado*
Pima Medical Institute *Denver, Colorado*
Pima Medical Institute *Nevada*
Pima Medical Institute *Albuquerque, New Mexico*
Pima Medical Institute *Texas*
Pima Medical Institute *Renton, Washington*
Pima Medical Institute *Seattle, Washington*
Professional Skills Institute *Ohio*
Riverside School of Health Careers *Virginia*
St. Louis College of Health Careers *Fenton, Missouri*
St. Louis College of Health Careers *Saint Louis, Missouri*
St. Paul's School of Nursing *Staten Island, New York*
Southwest University at El Paso *Texas*
Southwestern Oklahoma State University at Sayre *Oklahoma*
Standard Healthcare Services, College of Nursing *Virginia*
Ultimate Medical Academy Clearwater *Florida*
Ultimate Medical Academy Online *Florida*
Ultimate Medical Academy Tampa *Florida*
Universal College of Healing Arts *Nebraska*
Valley College of Medical Careers *California*
WellSpring School of Allied Health *Missouri*

Accrediting Commission of Career Schools and Colleges (ACCSC)

Advance Science Institute *Florida*
Advanced Technology Institute *Virginia*
All-State Career School - Essington Campus *Pennsylvania*
American Academy of Art *Illinois*
American Institute of Alternative Medicine *Ohio*
American Trade School *Missouri*
Antonelli College *Hattiesburg, Mississippi*
Antonelli College *Jackson, Mississippi*
Antonelli College *Ohio*
Antonelli Institute *Pennsylvania*
Arizona Automotive Institute *Arizona*
The Art Institute of California - San Diego, a campus of Argosy University *California*
The Art Institute of Cincinnati *Ohio*
Atenas College *Puerto Rico*
Aviator College of Aeronautical Science & Technology *Florida*
Baton Rouge School of Computers *Louisiana*
Bel - Rea Institute of Animal Technology *Colorado*
Berks Technical Institute *Pennsylvania*
Bidwell Training Center *Pennsylvania*
Blue Cliff College - Gulfport *Mississippi*
Blue Cliff College - Shreveport *Louisiana*
Brightwood Career Institute, Broomall Campus *Pennsylvania*
Brightwood Career Institute, Philadelphia Mills Campus *Pennsylvania*
Brightwood College, Baltimore Campus *Maryland*
Brightwood College, Beltsville Campus *Maryland*
Brightwood College, Chula Vista Campus *California*
Brightwood College, Dayton Campus *Ohio*
Brightwood College, Fresno Campus *California*
Brightwood College, Las Vegas Campus *Nevada*
Brightwood College, North Hollywood Campus *California*
Brightwood College, Palm Springs Campus *California*
Brightwood College, Riverside Campus *California*
Brightwood College, San Diego Campus *California*
Brightwood College, Towson Campus *Maryland*
Broadview University - Layton *Utah*
Broadview University - West Jordan *Utah*
Brown Mackie College - Hopkinsville *Kentucky*
Bryan College *California*
California College San Diego *National City, California*
California College San Diego *San Diego, California*
California College San Diego *San Marcos, California*
Career College of Northern Nevada *Nevada*
Career Training Academy *Lower Burrell, Pennsylvania*
Career Training Academy *Monroeville, Pennsylvania*
Career Training Academy *Pittsburgh, Pennsylvania*
Careers Unlimited *Utah*
Carrington College - San Jose *California*
The Center of Cinematography, Arts and Television *Puerto Rico*
Centro de Estudios Multidisciplinarios *Bayamon, Puerto Rico*
Centro de Estudios Multidisciplinarios *Humacao, Puerto Rico*
Centro de Estudios Multidisciplinarios *Mayaguez, Puerto Rico*
Centro de Estudios Multidisciplinarios *Rio Piedras, Puerto Rico*
Centura College *South Carolina*
Centura College *Chesapeake, Virginia*
Centura College *Newport News, Virginia*
Centura College *Norfolk, Virginia*
Centura College *North Chesterfield, Virginia*
Centura College *Virginia Beach, Virginia*
Chattanooga College - Medical, Dental and Technical Careers *Tennessee*
CollegeAmerica - Cheyenne *Wyoming*
CollegeAmerica - Colorado Springs *Colorado*
CollegeAmerica - Denver *Colorado*
CollegeAmerica - Flagstaff *Arizona*
CollegeAmerica - Fort Collins *Colorado*
CollegeAmerica - Phoenix *Arizona*
Colorado School of Healing Arts *Colorado*
Colorado School of Trades *Colorado*
Columbia College Hollywood *California*

Commonwealth Technical Institute *Pennsylvania*
Compass College of Cinematic Arts *Michigan*
Concorde Career College *Garden Grove, California*
Concorde Career College *North Hollywood, California*
Concorde Career College *San Bernardino, California*
Concorde Career College *San Diego, California*
Concorde Career College *Colorado*
Concorde Career College *Missouri*
Concorde Career College *Oregon*
Concorde Career College *Dallas, Texas*
Concorde Career College *Grand Prairie, Texas*
Concorde Career College *San Antonio, Texas*
Concorde Career Institute *Jacksonville, Florida*
Concorde Career Institute *Miramar, Florida*
Concorde Career Institute *Orlando, Florida*
Concorde Career Institute *Tampa, Florida*
Coyne College *Illinois*
Creative Center *Nebraska*
The Culinary Institute of America *New York*
Culinary Institute LeNotre *Texas*
Daytona College *Florida*
Dean Institute of Technology *Pennsylvania*
DigiPen Institute of Technology *Washington*
Eastern International College *Belleville, New Jersey*
Eastern International College *Jersey City, New Jersey*
L'Ecole Culinaire - Kansas City *Missouri*
L'Ecole Culinaire - Memphis *Tennessee*
L'Ecole Culinaire - St. Louis *Missouri*
ECPI University *Raleigh, North Carolina*
ECPI University *Glen Allen, Virginia*
ECPI University *Richmond, Virginia*
Erie Institute of Technology *Pennsylvania*
ETI Technical College of Niles *Ohio*
Everest Institute *Georgia*
Everglades University *Boca Raton, Florida*
Everglades University *Maitland, Florida*
Everglades University *Sarasota, Florida*
Ex'pression College for Digital Arts *California*
Florida College of Natural Health *Maitland, Florida*
Florida College of Natural Health *Miami, Florida*
Florida College of Natural Health *Pompano Beach, Florida*
Fortis College *Arizona*
Fortis College *Cutler Bay, Florida*
Fortis College *Largo, Florida*
Fortis College *Winter Park, Florida*
Fortis College *Indiana*
Fortis College *Centerville, Ohio*
Fortis College *Cuyahoga Falls, Ohio*
Fortis College *Utah*
Fortis Institute *Forty Fort, Pennsylvania*
Fortis Institute *Scranton, Pennsylvania*
Fountainhead College of Technology *Tennessee*
Fremont College *Cerritos, California*
Fremont College *Los Angeles, California*
Full Sail University *Florida*
Great Lakes Institute of Technology *Pennsylvania*
Hallmark University *Texas*
Hamilton Technical College *Iowa*
Heritage College *Colorado*
Heritage College *Missouri*
Heritage College *Oklahoma*
Herzing University *Alabama*
Herzing University *Minnesota*
Herzing University *Madison, Wisconsin*
Hussian College, School of Art *Pennsylvania*
ICDC College *California*
The Illinois Institute of Art - Chicago *Illinois*
Independence University *Utah*
The Institute of Production and Recording *Minnesota*
Institute of Technology *California*
IntelliTec College *Colorado Springs, Colorado*
IntelliTec College *Grand Junction, Colorado*
IntelliTec College *Pueblo, Colorado*
IntelliTec College *New Mexico*
Interior Designers Institute *California*
International College of Broadcasting *Ohio*
Island Drafting and Technical Institute *New York*
ITI Technical College *Louisiana*
JNA Institute of Culinary Arts *Pennsylvania*
Johnson College *Pennsylvania*
Keystone Technical Institute *Pennsylvania*

The Landing School *Maine*
Lincoln College of Technology *Colorado*
Lincoln College of Technology *Indiana*
Lincoln College of Technology *Maryland*
Lincoln College of Technology *Tennessee*
Lincoln Technical Institute *Allentown, Pennsylvania*
Lincoln Technical Institute *Philadelphia, Pennsylvania*
Los Angeles Film School *California*
Madison Media Institute *Wisconsin*
MediaTech Institute *Texas*
Meridian College *Florida*
Metropolitan Career Center Computer Technology Institute *Pennsylvania*
MIAT College of Technology *Michigan*
Minneapolis Media Institute *Minnesota*
Missouri College *Missouri*
Mt. Sierra College *California*
Myotherapy Institute *Nebraska*
National Polytechnic College *California*
New Castle School of Trades *Pennsylvania*
New England Culinary Institute *Vermont*
North-West College *California*
Northwest College of Art & Design *Washington*
Northwest School of Wooden Boatbuilding *Washington*
Nossi College of Art *Tennessee*
Ohio College of Massotherapy *Ohio*
Ohio Technical College *Ohio*
O'More College of Design *Tennessee*
Pacific College *California*
Paier College of Art, Inc. *Connecticut*
Pennco Tech *Pennsylvania*
Pima Medical Institute *Mesa, Arizona*
Pinnacle Career Institute *Kansas City, Missouri*
Pittsburgh Career Institute *Pennsylvania*
Pittsburgh Institute of Aeronautics *Pennsylvania*
Platt College *Alhambra, California*
Platt College *Ontario, California*
Platt College *Riverside, California*
Platt College *Colorado*
Platt College *Moore, Oklahoma*
Platt College *Oklahoma City, Oklahoma*
Platt College *Tulsa, Oklahoma*
Platt College San Diego *California*
Ponce Paramedical College *Puerto Rico*
Provo College *Utah*
Redstone College - Denver *Colorado*
The Refrigeration School *Arizona*
Remington College - Baton Rouge Campus *Louisiana*
Remington College - Cleveland Campus *Ohio*
Remington College - Dallas Campus *Texas*
Remington College - Fort Worth Campus *Texas*
Remington College - Heathrow Campus *Florida*
Remington College - Honolulu Campus *Hawaii*
Remington College - Houston Southeast Campus *Texas*
Remington College - Lafayette Campus *Louisiana*
Remington College - Little Rock Campus *Arkansas*
Remington College - Memphis Campus *Tennessee*
Remington College - Mobile Campus *Alabama*
Remington College - Nashville Campus *Tennessee*
Remington College - North Houston Campus *Texas*
Remington College - Shreveport *Louisiana*
The Restaurant School at Walnut Hill College *Pennsylvania*
Rockford Career College *Illinois*
Rosedale Technical Institute *Pennsylvania*
SAE Institute Chicago *Illinois*
SAE Institute Nashville *Tennessee*
St. Joseph School of Nursing *New Hampshire*
School of Advertising Art *Ohio*
School of Automotive Machinists *Texas*
Southeastern College - Jacksonville *Florida*
Southeastern College - West Palm Beach *Florida*
Southern California Institute of Technology *California*
Southwest Institute of Healing Arts *Arizona*
Southwest University of Visual Arts *Arizona*
Spartan College of Aeronautics and Technology *California*
Spartan College of Aeronautics and Technology *Oklahoma*
Stanbridge College *California*
Stevens-Henager College *Boise, Idaho*
Stevens-Henager College *Idaho Falls, Idaho*

Stevens-Henager College *Logan, Utah*
Stevens-Henager College *Orem, Utah*
Stevens-Henager College *Saint George, Utah*
Stevens-Henager College *Salt Lake City, Utah*
Stevens-Henager College *West Haven, Utah*
Swedish Institute, College of Health Sciences *New York*
Triangle Tech, Bethlehem *Pennsylvania*
Triangle Tech, DuBois *Pennsylvania*
Triangle Tech, Erie *Pennsylvania*
Triangle Tech, Greensburg *Pennsylvania*
Triangle Tech, Pittsburgh *Pennsylvania*
Triangle Tech, Sunbury *Pennsylvania*
Tulsa Welding School *Oklahoma*
Unitek College *California*
Universal Technical Institute *Arizona*
Vatterott College *Fairview Heights, Illinois*
Vatterott College *Iowa*
Vatterott College *Kansas*
Vatterott College *Berkeley, Missouri*
Vatterott College *Joplin, Missouri*
Vatterott College *Kansas City, Missouri*
Vatterott College *Saint Charles, Missouri*
Vatterott College *Saint Joseph, Missouri*
Vatterott College *Springfield, Missouri*
Vatterott College *Sunset Hills, Missouri*
Vatterott College *Ohio*
Vatterott College *Tulsa, Oklahoma*
Vatterott College *Warr Acres, Oklahoma*
Vatterott College *Memphis, Tennessee*
Vet Tech Institute *Pennsylvania*
Virginia Marti College of Art and Design *Ohio*
Vista College *Utah*
West Coast Ultrasound Institute *California*
Western Technical College *El Paso, Texas*
Wichita Technical Institute *Kansas*
Williamson College of the Trades *Pennsylvania*
WyoTech Blairsville *Pennsylvania*
WyoTech Daytona *Florida*
WyoTech Laramie *Wyoming*
YTI Career Institute - Altoona *Pennsylvania*
YTI Career Institute - York *Pennsylvania*

Accrediting Council on Education in Journalism and Mass Communications (ACEJMC)

Abilene Christian University *Texas*
American University *District of Columbia*
Arizona State University at the Tempe campus *Arizona*
Arkansas State University *Arkansas*
Auburn University *Alabama*
Ball State University *Indiana*
Baylor University *Texas*
Bowling Green State University *Ohio*
Brigham Young University *Utah*
California State University, Chico *California*
California State University, Fullerton *California*
California State University, Northridge *California*
Central Michigan University *Michigan*
Colorado State University *Colorado*
Columbia University *New York*
Drake University *Iowa*
East Tennessee State University *Tennessee*
Eastern Illinois University *Illinois*
Florida Agricultural and Mechanical University *Florida*
Florida International University *Florida*
Grambling State University *Louisiana*
Hampton University *Virginia*
Hofstra University *New York*
Howard University *District of Columbia*
Indiana University Bloomington *Indiana*
Iona College *New York*
Iowa State University of Science and Technology *Iowa*
Jackson State University *Mississippi*
Kansas State University *Kansas*
Kent State University *Ohio*
Louisiana State University and Agricultural & Mechanical College *Louisiana*
Marquette University *Wisconsin*
Marshall University *West Virginia*
Michigan State University *Michigan*
Middle Tennessee State University *Tennessee*
Murray State University *Kentucky*

New Mexico State University *New Mexico*
New York University *New York*
Nicholls State University *Louisiana*
Norfolk State University *Virginia*
Northwestern State University of Louisiana *Louisiana*
Northwestern University *Illinois*
Ohio University *Ohio*
Oklahoma State University *Oklahoma*
Penn State University Park *Pennsylvania*
St. Cloud State University *Minnesota*
San Francisco State University *California*
San Jose State University *California*
South Dakota State University *South Dakota*
Southern Illinois University Carbondale *Illinois*
Southern University and Agricultural and Mechanical College *Louisiana*
Syracuse University *New York*
Temple University *Pennsylvania*
Texas A&M University *Texas*
Texas Christian University *Texas*
Texas State University *Texas*
Texas Tech University *Texas*
The University of Alabama *Alabama*
University of Alaska Anchorage *Alaska*
University of Alaska Fairbanks *Alaska*
The University of Arizona *Arizona*
University of Arkansas *Arkansas*
University of California, Berkeley *California*
University of Colorado Boulder *Colorado*
University of Connecticut *Connecticut*
University of Florida *Florida*
University of Georgia *Georgia*
University of Hawaii at Manoa *Hawaii*
University of Illinois at Urbana - Champaign *Illinois*
The University of Iowa *Iowa*
The University of Kansas *Kansas*
University of Kentucky *Kentucky*
University of Louisiana at Lafayette *Louisiana*
University of Louisiana at Monroe *Louisiana*
University of Maryland, College Park *Maryland*
University of Memphis *Tennessee*
University of Miami *Florida*
University of Minnesota, Twin Cities Campus *Minnesota*
University of Mississippi *Mississippi*
University of Missouri *Missouri*
University of Montana *Montana*
University of Nebraska - Lincoln *Nebraska*
University of Nevada, Reno *Nevada*
The University of North Carolina at Chapel Hill *North Carolina*
University of North Texas *Texas*
University of Oklahoma *Oklahoma*
University of Oregon *Oregon*
University of South Carolina *South Carolina*
The University of South Dakota *South Dakota*
University of South Florida *Florida*
University of Southern California *California*
University of Southern Mississippi *Mississippi*
The University of Tennessee *Tennessee*
The University of Tennessee at Chattanooga *Tennessee*
The University of Tennessee at Martin *Tennessee*
The University of Texas at Austin *Texas*
University of Utah *Utah*
University of Washington *Washington*
University of Wisconsin - Eau Claire *Wisconsin*
University of Wisconsin - Oshkosh *Wisconsin*
University of Wisconsin - River Falls *Wisconsin*
Washington and Lee University *Virginia*
West Virginia University *West Virginia*
Western Kentucky University *Kentucky*
Winthrop University *South Carolina*

Accrediting Council for Independent Colleges and Schools (ACICS)

Academy of Art University *California*
Academy College *Minnesota*
Academy of Couture Art *California*
Ambria College of Nursing *Illinois*
American College for Medical Careers *Florida*
American National University *Danville, Kentucky*
American National University *Florence, Kentucky*
American National University *Lexington, Kentucky*
American National University *Louisville, Kentucky*

American National University *Pikeville, Kentucky*
American National University *Richmond, Kentucky*
American National University *Canton, Ohio*
American National University *Cincinnati, Ohio*
American National University *Cleveland, Ohio*
American National University *Columbus, Ohio*
American National University *Kettering, Ohio*
American National University *Stow, Ohio*
American National University *Youngstown, Ohio*
American National University *Charlottesville, Virginia*
American National University *Danville, Virginia*
American National University *Harrisonburg, Virginia*
American National University *Lynchburg, Virginia*
American National University *Martinsville, Virginia*
American National University *Salem, Virginia*
American University of Health Sciences *California*
The Art Institute of California - Hollywood, a campus of Argosy University *California*
The Art Institute of California - Los Angeles, a campus of Argosy University *California*
The Art Institute of California - Orange County, a campus of Argosy University *California*
The Art Institute of California - Sacramento, a campus of Argosy University *California*
The Art Institute of California - San Francisco, a campus of Argosy University *California*
The Art Institute of Colorado *Colorado*
The Art Institute of Fort Lauderdale *Florida*
The Art Institute of Indianapolis *Indiana*
The Art Institute of Las Vegas *Nevada*
The Art Institute of Philadelphia *Pennsylvania*
The Art Institute of Phoenix *Arizona*
The Art Institute of Pittsburgh *Pennsylvania*
The Art Institute of St. Louis *Missouri*
The Art Institute of Tucson *Arizona*
The Art Institute of Vancouver *British Columbia (Canada)*
ASA College *New York*
Atlantic University College *Puerto Rico*
ATS Institute of Technology *Ohio*
Beal College *Maine*
Beckfield College *Kentucky*
Beckfield College *Ohio*
Bergin University of Canine Studies *California*
Berks Technical Institute *Pennsylvania*
Bon Secours Memorial College of Nursing *Virginia*
Bradford School *Ohio*
Bradford School *Pennsylvania*
Brightwood Career Institute, Broomall Campus *Pennsylvania*
Brightwood Career Institute, Harrisburg Campus *Pennsylvania*
Brightwood Career Institute, Philadelphia Campus *Pennsylvania*
Brightwood Career Institute, Philadelphia Mills Campus *Pennsylvania*
Brightwood Career Institute, Pittsburgh Campus *Pennsylvania*
Brightwood College, Arlington Campus *Texas*
Brightwood College, Bakersfield Campus *California*
Brightwood College, Baltimore Campus *Maryland*
Brightwood College, Beaumont Campus *Texas*
Brightwood College, Beltsville Campus *Maryland*
Brightwood College, Brownsville Campus *Texas*
Brightwood College, Charlotte Campus *North Carolina*
Brightwood College, Chula Vista Campus *California*
Brightwood College, Corpus Christi Campus *Texas*
Brightwood College, Dallas Campus *Texas*
Brightwood College, Dayton Campus *Ohio*
Brightwood College, El Paso Campus *Texas*
Brightwood College, Fort Worth Campus *Texas*
Brightwood College, Fresno Campus *California*
Brightwood College, Friendswood Campus *Texas*
Brightwood College, Hammond Campus *Indiana*
Brightwood College, Houston Campus *Texas*
Brightwood College, Indianapolis Campus *Indiana*
Brightwood College, Laredo Campus *Texas*
Brightwood College, Las Vegas Campus *Nevada*
Brightwood College, McAllen Campus *Texas*
Brightwood College, Modesto Campus *California*
Brightwood College, Nashville Campus *Tennessee*
Brightwood College, North Hollywood Campus *California*
Brightwood College, Palm Springs Campus *California*

Brightwood College, Riverside Campus *California*
Brightwood College, Sacramento Campus *California*
Brightwood College, San Antonio Ingram Campus *Texas*
Brightwood College, San Antonio San Pedro Campus *Texas*
Brightwood College, San Diego Campus *California*
Brightwood College, Towson Campus *Maryland*
Brightwood College, Vista Campus *California*
Bristol University *California*
Broadview Entertainment Arts University *Utah*
Broadview University - Boise *Idaho*
Broadview University - Layton *Utah*
Broadview University - West Jordan *Utah*
Brookline College *Phoenix, Arizona*
Brookline College *Tempe, Arizona*
Brookline College *Tucson, Arizona*
Brookline College *New Mexico*
Brooks Institute *California*
Brown Mackie College - Akron *Ohio*
Brown Mackie College - Hopkinsville *Kentucky*
Brown Mackie College - North Canton *Ohio*
Brown Mackie College - Quad Cities *Iowa*
Bryan University *Arkansas*
Bryan University *California*
Bryan University *Kansas*
Bryan University *Columbia, Missouri*
Bryan University *Springfield, Missouri*
California Miramar University *California*
California University of Management and Sciences *California*
Cambria-Rowe Business College *Indiana, Pennsylvania*
Cambria-Rowe Business College *Johnstown, Pennsylvania*
Cambridge Junior College *California*
Career Point College *Oklahoma*
Career Point College *Texas*
Carrington College - Las Vegas *Nevada*
Carrington College - Reno *Nevada*
Charter College *Alaska*
Charter College *California*
City College *Altamonte Springs, Florida*
City College *Fort Lauderdale, Florida*
City College *Gainesville, Florida*
City College *Hollywood, Florida*
City College *Miami, Florida*
Clary Sage College *Oklahoma*
Coleman University *California*
College of Business and Technology - Cutler Bay Campus *Florida*
College of Business and Technology - Flagler Campus *Florida*
College of Business and Technology - Hialeah Campus *Florida*
College of Business and Technology - Main Campus *Florida*
College of Business and Technology - Miami Gardens *Florida*
College of Court Reporting *Indiana*
Colorado Heights University *Colorado*
Columbia Centro Universitario *Caguas, Puerto Rico*
Columbia Centro Universitario *Yauco, Puerto Rico*
Columbia College *Virginia*
Community Care College *Oklahoma*
Consolidated School of Business *Lancaster, Pennsylvania*
Consolidated School of Business *York, Pennsylvania*
Court Reporting Institute of St. Louis *Missouri*
Daymar College *Bellevue, Kentucky*
Daymar College *Bowling Green, Kentucky*
Daymar College *Madisonville, Kentucky*
Daymar College *Owensboro, Kentucky*
Daymar College *Ohio*
Daymar College *Clarksville, Tennessee*
Daymar College *Murfreesboro, Tennessee*
Daymar College *Nashville, Tennessee*
Delta School of Business and Technology *Louisiana*
Design Institute of San Diego *California*
Dewey University - Arroyo *Puerto Rico*
Dewey University - Bayamón *Puerto Rico*
Dewey University - Carolina *Puerto Rico*
Dewey University - Fajardo *Puerto Rico*
Dewey University - Hato Rey *Puerto Rico*
Dewey University - Juana Diaz *Puerto Rico*

Dewey University - Manati *Puerto Rico*
Dewey University - Mayaguez *Puerto Rico*
Digital Media Arts College *Florida*
Douglas Education Center *Pennsylvania*
DuBois Business College *DuBois, Pennsylvania*
DuBois Business College *Huntingdon, Pennsylvania*
DuBois Business College *Oil City, Pennsylvania*
Duluth Business University *Minnesota*
Eagle Gate College *Layton, Utah*
Eagle Gate College *Murray, Utah*
Ecotech Institute *Colorado*
EDIC College *Puerto Rico*
EDP University of Puerto Rico *Puerto Rico*
EDP University of Puerto Rico - San Sebastian *Puerto Rico*
Elmira Business Institute *New York*
Empire College *California*
Everest College *Colorado Springs, Colorado*
Everest College *Thornton, Colorado*
Everest College *Missouri*
Everest College *Nevada*
Everest College *Arlington, Texas*
Everest College *Fort Worth, Texas*
Everest College *Virginia*
Everest College *Washington*
Everest University *Largo, Florida*
Everest University *Orange Park, Florida*
Everest University *Orlando, Florida*
Everest University *Tampa, Florida*
Florida Career College *Florida*
Florida Technical College *DeLand, Florida*
Florida Technical College *Orlando, Florida*
Forrest College *South Carolina*
Fortis College *Orange Park, Florida*
Fortis College *Maryland*
Fortis College *Ravenna, Ohio*
Fortis College *Norfolk, Virginia*
Fortis College *Richmond, Virginia*
Fortis Institute *Alabama*
Fortis Institute *Erie, Pennsylvania*
Fox College *Illinois*
Gallipolis Career College *Ohio*
Global Health College *Virginia*
Globe Institute of Technology *New York*
Globe University - Appleton *Wisconsin*
Globe University - Eau Claire *Wisconsin*
Globe University - Green Bay *Wisconsin*
Globe University - La Crosse *Wisconsin*
Globe University - Madison East *Wisconsin*
Globe University - Madison West *Wisconsin*
Globe University - Minneapolis *Minnesota*
Globe University - Sioux Falls *South Dakota*
Globe University - Wausau *Wisconsin*
Globe University - Woodbury *Minnesota*
Golf Academy of America *Arizona*
Golf Academy of America *California*
Golf Academy of America *Florida*
Golf Academy of America *South Carolina*
Golf Academy of America *Texas*
Goodwin College *Connecticut*
Gwinnett College *Georgia*
Harrison College *Indiana*
Harrison College *Ohio*
Herzing University *Florida*
Herzing University *Georgia*
Herzing University *Louisiana*
Hickey College *Missouri*
Hondros College *Ohio*
Huertas Junior College *Puerto Rico*
Humacao Community College *Puerto Rico*
IBMC College *Fort Collins, Colorado*
IGlobal University *Virginia*
International Business College *Fort Wayne, Indiana*
International Business College *Indianapolis, Indiana*
International Business College *El Paso, Texas*
Jones College *Florida*
Jose Maria Vargas University *Florida*
Kaplan University, Hagerstown Campus *Maryland*
Kaplan University, Lincoln *Nebraska*
Kaplan University, Omaha *Nebraska*
Key College *Florida*
King's College *North Carolina*
Lansdale School of Business *Pennsylvania*
Laurel Business Institute *Pennsylvania*
Laurel Technical Institute *Pennsylvania*
Laurus College *California*

Learnet Academy *California*
Lincoln College of Technology *Florida*
Lincoln College of Technology *Georgia*
Lincoln Technical Institute *Philadelphia, Pennsylvania*
Lincoln University *California*
Living Arts College *North Carolina*
Long Island Business Institute *New York*
Marconi International University *Florida*
McCann School of Business & Technology *Monroe, Louisiana*
McCann School of Business & Technology *Shreveport, Louisiana*
McCann School of Business & Technology *Hazleton, Pennsylvania*
McCann School of Business & Technology *Lewisburg, Pennsylvania*
McCann School of Business & Technology *Pottsville, Pennsylvania*
Medtech College *Florida*
Medtech College *Fort Wayne, Indiana*
Medtech College *Greenwood, Indiana*
Medtech College *Indianapolis, Indiana*
Medtech College *Kentucky*
Metro Business College *Cape Girardeau, Missouri*
Metro Business College *Jefferson City, Missouri*
Metro Business College *Rolla, Missouri*
Miami-Jacobs Career College *Columbus, Ohio*
Miami-Jacobs Career College *Dayton, Ohio*
Miami-Jacobs Career College *Independence, Ohio*
Miami-Jacobs Career College *Sharonville, Ohio*
Miami-Jacobs Career College *Springboro, Ohio*
Miami-Jacobs Career College *Troy, Ohio*
Michigan Jewish Institute *Michigan*
Mildred Elley - New York City *New York*
Mildred Elley School *New York*
Millennia Atlantic University *Florida*
Miller-Motte College *Cary, North Carolina*
Miller-Motte College *Fayetteville, North Carolina*
Miller-Motte College *Greenville, North Carolina*
Miller-Motte College *Jacksonville, North Carolina*
Miller-Motte College *Raleigh, North Carolina*
Miller-Motte College *Wilmington, North Carolina*
Miller-Motte Technical College *Augusta, Georgia*
Miller-Motte Technical College *Columbus, Georgia*
Miller-Motte Technical College *Macon, Georgia*
Miller-Motte Technical College *Mississippi*
Miller-Motte Technical College *Conway, South Carolina*
Miller-Motte Technical College *North Charleston, South Carolina*
Miller-Motte Technical College *Chattanooga, Tennessee*
Miller-Motte Technical College *Clarksville, Tennessee*
Miller-Motte Technical College *Madison, Tennessee*
Miller-Motte Technical College *Lynchburg, Virginia*
Miller-Motte Technical College *Roanoke, Virginia*
Minneapolis Business College *Minnesota*
Minnesota School of Business - Blaine *Minnesota*
Minnesota School of Business - Brooklyn Center *Minnesota*
Minnesota School of Business - Elk River *Minnesota*
Minnesota School of Business - Lakeville *Minnesota*
Minnesota School of Business - Plymouth *Minnesota*
Minnesota School of Business - Richfield *Minnesota*
Minnesota School of Business - Rochester *Minnesota*
Minnesota School of Business - St. Cloud *Minnesota*
Missouri College *Missouri*
Mountain State College *West Virginia*
National College *Bristol, Tennessee*
National College *Knoxville, Tennessee*
National College *Nashville, Tennessee*
National University College *Bayamón, Puerto Rico*
Neumont University *Utah*
NewSchool of Architecture and Design *California*
North American University *Texas*
Northwestern Polytechnic University *California*
Ohio Business College *Hilliard, Ohio*
Ohio Business College *Sandusky, Ohio*
Ohio Business College *Sheffield Village, Ohio*
Ohio Valley College of Technology *Ohio*

Oklahoma Technical College *Oklahoma*
Pacific States University *California*
Penn Commercial Business and Technical School *Pennsylvania*
Pennsylvania Institute of Health and Technology *Pennsylvania*
Pinnacle Career Institute *Kansas*
Pinnacle Career Institute *Kansas City, Missouri*
Pioneer Pacific College *Oregon*
Pioneer Pacific College - Eugene/Springfield Branch *Oregon*
Pittsburgh Career Institute *Pennsylvania*
Professional Golfers Career College *California*
Provo College *Utah*
Radians College *District of Columbia*
Rasmussen College Bloomington *Minnesota*
Rasmussen College Eagan *Minnesota*
Rasmussen College Fargo *North Dakota*
Rasmussen College Mankato *Minnesota*
Rasmussen College New Port Richey *Florida*
Rasmussen College Ocala *Florida*
Rasmussen College St. Cloud *Minnesota*
Redstone College - Denver *Colorado*
Remington College - Baton Rouge Campus *Louisiana*
Remington College - Honolulu Campus *Hawaii*
Remington College - Lafayette Campus *Louisiana*
Rockford Career College *Illinois*
SAE Institute Atlanta *Georgia*
Sage College *California*
Salter College *Chicopee, Massachusetts*
Salter College *West Boylston, Massachusetts*
Santa Barbara Business College *Ventura, California*
Schiller International University *Florida*
Sentara College of Health Sciences *Virginia*
Silicon Valley University *California*
Solex College *Illinois*
South Coast College *California*
South College - Asheville *North Carolina*
South Hills School of Business & Technology *Altoona, Pennsylvania*
South Hills School of Business & Technology *State College, Pennsylvania*
Southern Technical College *Fort Myers, Florida*
Southern Technical College *Orlando, Florida*
Southern Technical College *Tampa, Florida*
Spencerian College *Kentucky*
Spencerian College - Lexington *Kentucky*
Stautzenberger College *Brecksville, Ohio*
Stautzenberger College *Maumee, Ohio*
Stevens - The Institute of Business & Arts *Missouri*
Stratford University *Maryland*
Stratford University *Alexandria, Virginia*
Stratford University *Falls Church, Virginia*
Stratford University *Glen Allen, Virginia*
Stratford University *Newport News, Virginia*
Stratford University *Virginia Beach, Virginia*
Stratford University *Woodbridge, Virginia*
Sullivan College of Technology and Design *Kentucky*
Sumner College *Oregon*
Taylor Business Institute *Illinois*
Texas County Technical College *Missouri*
Tribeca Flashpoint College *Illinois*
Trumbull Business College *Ohio*
University of Advancing Technology *Arizona*
University of Antelope Valley *California*
Valley College *West Virginia*
Vet Tech Institute of Houston *Texas*
Virginia College in Augusta *Georgia*
Virginia College in Austin *Texas*
Virginia College in Baton Rouge *Louisiana*
Virginia College in Biloxi *Mississippi*
Virginia College in Birmingham *Alabama*
Virginia College in Charleston *South Carolina*
Virginia College in Chattanooga *Tennessee*
Virginia College in Columbia *South Carolina*
Virginia College in Columbus *Georgia*
Virginia College in Florence *South Carolina*
Virginia College in Fort Pierce *Florida*
Virginia College in Greensboro *North Carolina*
Virginia College in Greenville *South Carolina*
Virginia College in Huntsville *Alabama*
Virginia College in Jackson *Mississippi*
Virginia College in Jacksonville *Florida*
Virginia College in Knoxville *Tennessee*

Virginia College in Lubbock *Texas*
Virginia College in Macon *Georgia*
Virginia College in Mobile *Alabama*
Virginia College in Montgomery *Alabama*
Virginia College in Pensacola *Florida*
Virginia College in Richmond *Virginia*
Virginia College in Savannah *Georgia*
Virginia College in Shreveport/Bossier City *Louisiana*
Virginia College in Spartanburg *South Carolina*
Virginia College in Tulsa *Oklahoma*
Virginia International University *Virginia*
West Coast University *North Hollywood, California*
West Virginia Business College *Nutter Fort, West Virginia*
West Virginia Business College *Wheeling, West Virginia*
West Virginia Junior College - Bridgeport *West Virginia*
West Virginia Junior College - Charleston *West Virginia*
West Virginia Junior College - Morgantown *West Virginia*

American Academy for Liberal Education (AALE)

Ave Maria University *Florida*
Baylor University *Texas*
Michigan State University *Michigan*
Northeast Catholic College *New Hampshire*
Patrick Henry College *Virginia*
Soka University of America *California*
Southern Virginia University *Virginia*
Thomas Aquinas College *California*
Thomas More College of Liberal Arts *New Hampshire*
University of Dallas *Texas*

American Association of Blood Banks (AABB)

The George Washington University *District of Columbia*
University of Cincinnati *Ohio*
University of Illinois at Chicago *Illinois*
The University of Texas Health Science Center at San Antonio *Texas*

American Association of Colleges of Nursing (AACN)

Abilene Christian University *Texas*
Adams State University *Colorado*
Adelphi University *New York*
Alcorn State University *Mississippi*
Allen College *Iowa*
Alvernia University *Pennsylvania*
Alverno College *Wisconsin*
American International College *Massachusetts*
American Sentinel University *Colorado*
Anderson University *Indiana*
Appalachian State University *North Carolina*
Arizona State University at the Tempe campus *Arizona*
Armstrong State University *Georgia*
Ashland University *Ohio*
Aspen University *Colorado*
Auburn University *Alabama*
Auburn University at Montgomery *Alabama*
Augsburg College *Minnesota*
Augusta University *Georgia*
Augustana University *South Dakota*
Aurora University *Illinois*
Avila University *Missouri*
Azusa Pacific University *California*
Baker University *Kansas*
Ball State University *Indiana*
The Baptist College of Florida *Florida*
Baptist College of Health Sciences *Tennessee*
Barry University *Florida*
Baylor University *Texas*
Bellarmine University *Kentucky*
Bellin College *Wisconsin*
Belmont University *Tennessee*
Bemidji State University *Minnesota*
Benedictine University *Illinois*
Berea College *Kentucky*

Rabbinical Academy Mesivta Rabbi Chaim Berlin *New York*
Rabbinical College of America *New Jersey*
Rabbinical College Beth Shraga *New York*
Rabbinical College Bobover Yeshiva B'nei Zion *New York*
Rabbinical College Ch'san Sofer *New York*
Rabbinical College of Long Island *New York*
Rabbinical College of Ohr Shimon Yisroel *New York*
Rabbinical College of Telshe *Ohio*
Rabbinical Seminary of America *New York*
Sh'or Yoshuv Rabbinical College *New York*
Talmudic University *Florida*
Talmudical Academy of New Jersey *New Jersey*
Talmudical Institute of Upstate New York *New York*
Talmudical Seminary of Bobov *New York*
Talmudical Seminary Oholei Torah *New York*
Talmudical Yeshiva of Philadelphia *Pennsylvania*
Telshe Yeshiva - Chicago *Illinois*
Torah Temimah Talmudical Seminary *New York*
United Talmudical Seminary *New York*
U.T.A. Mesivta of Kiryas Joel *New York*
Yeshiva Beth Moshe *Pennsylvania*
Yeshiva Beth Yehuda - Yeshiva Gedolah of Greater Detroit *Michigan*
Yeshiva College of the Nation's Capital *Maryland*
Yeshiva Derech Chaim *New York*
Yeshiva D'Monsey Rabbinical College *New York*
Yeshiva of Far Rockaway Derech Ayson Rabbinical Seminary *New York*
Yeshiva Gedolah Imrei Yosef D'Spinka *New York*
Yeshiva Gedolah Rabbinical College *Florida*
Yeshiva Gedolah Zichron Leyma *New Jersey*
Yeshiva Karlin Stolin Rabbinical Institute *New York*
Yeshiva and Kolel Bais Medrash Elyon *New York*
Yeshiva and Kollel Harbotzas Torah *New York*
Yeshiva of Machzikai Hadas *New York*
Yeshiva of Nitra Rabbinical College *New York*
Yeshiva Ohr Elchonon Chabad/West Coast Talmudical Seminary *California*
Yeshiva Shaar Hatorah Talmudic Research Institute *New York*
Yeshiva Shaarei Torah of Rockland *New York*
Yeshiva of the Telshe Alumni *New York*
Yeshiva Toras Chaim *New Jersey*
Yeshiva Toras Chaim Talmudical Seminary *Colorado*
Yeshivas Be'er Yitzchok *New Jersey*
Yeshivas Novominsk *New York*
Yeshivat Mikdash Melech *New York*
Yeshivath Viznitz *New York*
Yeshivath Zichron Moshe *New York*

Association of American Law Schools (AALS)

American University *District of Columbia*
Arizona State University at the Tempe campus *Arizona*
Baylor University *Texas*
Boston College *Massachusetts*
Boston University *Massachusetts*
Brigham Young University *Utah*
Capital University *Ohio*
Case Western Reserve University *Ohio*
The Catholic University of America *District of Columbia*
Cleveland State University *Ohio*
The College of William and Mary *Virginia*
Columbia University *New York*
Cornell University *New York*
Creighton University *Nebraska*
DePaul University *Illinois*
Drake University *Iowa*
Duke University *North Carolina*
Duquesne University *Pennsylvania*
Emory University *Georgia*
Florida State University *Florida*
Fordham University *New York*
George Mason University *Virginia*
The George Washington University *District of Columbia*
Georgetown University *District of Columbia*
Georgia State University *Georgia*
Golden Gate University *California*
Gonzaga University *Washington*
Hamline University *Minnesota*
Harvard University *Massachusetts*

Hofstra University *New York*
Howard University *District of Columbia*
Illinois Institute of Technology *Illinois*
Lewis & Clark College *Oregon*
Louisiana State University and Agricultural & Mechanical College *Louisiana*
Loyola Marymount University *California*
Loyola University Chicago *Illinois*
Loyola University New Orleans *Louisiana*
Marquette University *Wisconsin*
Mercer University *Georgia*
Mississippi College *Mississippi*
New York University *New York*
Northeastern University *Massachusetts*
Northern Illinois University *Illinois*
Northern Kentucky University *Kentucky*
Northwestern University *Illinois*
Nova Southeastern University *Florida*
Ohio Northern University *Ohio*
The Ohio State University *Ohio*
Oklahoma City University *Oklahoma*
Pace University *New York*
Pepperdine University *California*
Quinnipiac University *Connecticut*
Rutgers University - Camden *New Jersey*
Rutgers University - Newark *New Jersey*
St. John's University *New York*
Saint Louis University *Missouri*
St. Mary's University *Texas*
St. Thomas University *Florida*
Samford University *Alabama*
Santa Clara University *California*
Seattle University *Washington*
Seton Hall University *New Jersey*
Southern Illinois University Carbondale *Illinois*
Southern Methodist University *Texas*
Stanford University *California*
Stetson University *Florida*
Suffolk University *Massachusetts*
Syracuse University *New York*
Temple University *Pennsylvania*
Texas Tech University *Texas*
Touro College *New York*
Tulane University *Louisiana*
The University of Akron *Ohio*
The University of Alabama *Alabama*
The University of Arizona *Arizona*
University of Arkansas *Arkansas*
University of Arkansas at Little Rock *Arkansas*
University of Baltimore *Maryland*
University at Buffalo, the State University of New York *New York*
University of California, Berkeley *California*
University of California, Davis *California*
University of California, Los Angeles *California*
University of Chicago *Illinois*
University of Cincinnati *Ohio*
University of Colorado Boulder *Colorado*
University of Connecticut *Connecticut*
University of Dayton *Ohio*
University of Denver *Colorado*
University of Detroit Mercy *Michigan*
University of Florida *Florida*
University of Georgia *Georgia*
University of Hawaii at Manoa *Hawaii*
University of Houston *Texas*
University of Idaho *Idaho*
University of Illinois at Urbana - Champaign *Illinois*
The University of Iowa *Iowa*
The University of Kansas *Kansas*
University of Kentucky *Kentucky*
University of Louisville *Kentucky*
University of Maine *Maine*
University of Memphis *Tennessee*
University of Miami *Florida*
University of Michigan *Michigan*
University of Minnesota, Twin Cities Campus *Minnesota*
University of Mississippi *Mississippi*
University of Missouri *Missouri*
University of Missouri - Kansas City *Missouri*
University of Montana *Montana*
University of Nebraska - Lincoln *Nebraska*
University of Nevada, Las Vegas *Nevada*
University of New Mexico *New Mexico*

The University of North Carolina at Chapel Hill *North Carolina*
University of North Dakota *North Dakota*
University of Notre Dame *Indiana*
University of Oklahoma *Oklahoma*
University of Oregon *Oregon*
University of the Pacific *California*
University of Pennsylvania *Pennsylvania*
University of Pittsburgh *Pennsylvania*
University of Puerto Rico, Río Piedras Campus *Puerto Rico*
University of Richmond *Virginia*
University of San Diego *California*
University of San Francisco *California*
University of South Carolina *South Carolina*
The University of South Dakota *South Dakota*
University of Southern California *California*
The University of Tennessee *Tennessee*
The University of Texas at Austin *Texas*
The University of Toledo *Ohio*
The University of Tulsa *Oklahoma*
University of Utah *Utah*
University of Virginia *Virginia*
University of Washington *Washington*
University of Wisconsin - Madison *Wisconsin*
University of Wyoming *Wyoming*
Valparaiso University *Indiana*
Vanderbilt University *Tennessee*
Villanova University *Pennsylvania*
Wake Forest University *North Carolina*
Washburn University *Kansas*
Washington and Lee University *Virginia*
Washington University in St. Louis *Missouri*
Wayne State University *Michigan*
West Virginia University *West Virginia*
Western New England University *Massachusetts*
Whittier College *California*
Widener University *Pennsylvania*
Willamette University *Oregon*
Yale University *Connecticut*
Yeshiva University *New York*

Association for Biblical Higher Education (ABHE)

Alaska Bible College *Alaska*
Alaska Christian College *Alaska*
Allegheny Wesleyan College *Ohio*
Ambrose University *Alberta (Canada)*
American Baptist College *Tennessee*
Appalachian Bible College *West Virginia*
Arlington Baptist College *Texas*
Baptist Bible College *Missouri*
Baptist University of the Americas *Texas*
Barclay College *Kansas*
Bethany Global University *Minnesota*
Bethel College *Virginia*
Bethesda University *California*
Beulah Heights University *Georgia*
Boise Bible College *Idaho*
Briercrest College *Saskatchewan (Canada)*
Cairn University *Pennsylvania*
Calvary Bible College and Theological Seminary *Missouri*
Carolina Christian College *North Carolina*
Carolina College of Biblical Studies *North Carolina*
Carver College *Georgia*
Central Christian College of the Bible *Missouri*
Cincinnati Christian University *Ohio*
Clear Creek Baptist Bible College *Kentucky*
College of Biblical Studies - Houston *Texas*
Columbia Bible College *British Columbia (Canada)*
Columbia International University *South Carolina*
Crossroads Bible College *Indiana*
Dallas Christian College *Texas*
Davis College *New York*
Ecclesia College *Arkansas*
Emmanuel Bible College *Ontario (Canada)*
Emmaus Bible College *Iowa*
Eston College *Saskatchewan (Canada)*
Faith Baptist Bible College and Theological Seminary *Iowa*
Family of Faith College *Oklahoma*
God's Bible School and College *Ohio*
Grace Bible College *Michigan*
Grace College of Divinity *North Carolina*
Grace Mission University *California*

Grace University *Nebraska*
Great Lakes Christian College *Michigan*
Heritage Christian University *Alabama*
Heritage College and Seminary *Ontario (Canada)*
Hobe Sound Bible College *Florida*
Hope International University *California*
Horizon College & Seminary *Saskatchewan (Canada)*
Horizon University *California*
Huntsville Bible College *Alabama*
John Wesley University *North Carolina*
Johnson University *Tennessee*
Johnson University Florida *Florida*
Kentucky Mountain Bible College *Kentucky*
Kingswood University *New Brunswick (Canada)*
Kuyper College *Michigan*
Lancaster Bible College *Pennsylvania*
Life Pacific College *California*
Lincoln Christian University *Illinois*
Luther Rice College & Seminary *Georgia*
Manhattan Christian College *Kansas*
Master's College and Seminary *Ontario (Canada)*
Mid-South Christian College *Tennessee*
Midwest University *Missouri*
Montana Bible College *Montana*
Moody Bible Institute *Illinois*
Multnomah University *Oregon*
Nazarene Bible College *Colorado*
Nebraska Christian College *Nebraska*
New Hope Christian College *Oregon*
Northpoint Bible College *Massachusetts*
Oak Hills Christian College *Minnesota*
Ohio Christian University *Ohio*
Ozark Christian College *Missouri*
Pacific Rim Christian University *Hawaii*
Pillar College *New Jersey*
Prairie Bible Institute *Alberta (Canada)*
Providence University College & Theological Seminary *Manitoba (Canada)*
Rio Grande Bible Institute *Texas*
Rocky Mountain College *Alberta (Canada)*
Rosedale Bible College *Ohio*
Saint Louis Christian College *Missouri*
Selma University *Alabama*
Simmons College of Kentucky *Kentucky*
South Florida Bible College and Theological Seminary *Florida*
Southeastern Baptist College *Mississippi*
Southeastern Bible College *Alabama*
Steinbach Bible College *Manitoba (Canada)*
SUM Bible College & Theological Seminary *California*
Summit Pacific College *British Columbia (Canada)*
Summit University *Pennsylvania*
Theological University of the Caribbean *Puerto Rico*
Tri-State Bible College *Ohio*
Trinity Bible College *North Dakota*
Trinity College of Florida *Florida*
Tyndale University College & Seminary *Ontario (Canada)*
Universidad Pentecostal Mizpa *Puerto Rico*
Vanguard College *Alberta (Canada)*
Welch College *Tennessee*
Williamson College *Tennessee*
World Mission University *California*

Association for Clinical Pastoral Education, Inc. (ACIPE)

Anderson University *Indiana*
Baylor University *Texas*
Boston University *Massachusetts*
Drew University *New Jersey*
Duke University *North Carolina*
Eastern Mennonite University *Virginia*
Eastern University *Pennsylvania*
Emory University *Georgia*
Gardner-Webb University *North Carolina*
George Fox University *Oregon*
Georgetown University *District of Columbia*
Gonzaga University *Washington*
Harvard University *Massachusetts*
Howard University *District of Columbia*
Indiana University - Purdue University Indianapolis *Indiana*
The Jewish Theological Seminary *New York*
Johns Hopkins University *Maryland*

Liberty University *Virginia*
Loma Linda University *California*
Loyola University Chicago *Illinois*
Mount Angel Seminary *Oregon*
New Orleans Baptist Theological Seminary *Louisiana*
New York University *New York*
The Ohio State University *Ohio*
Regent University *Virginia*
Rush University *Illinois*
Sacred Heart Major Seminary *Michigan*
St. John's University *New York*
Saint Louis University *Missouri*
Seton Hall University *New Jersey*
Sewanee: The University of the South *Tennessee*
Southeastern Baptist Theological Seminary *North Carolina*
The Southern Baptist Theological Seminary *Kentucky*
Southern Methodist University *Texas*
Stanford University *California*
Texas Christian University *Texas*
Thomas Jefferson University *Pennsylvania*
The University of Alabama at Birmingham *Alabama*
University of Arkansas for Medical Sciences *Arkansas*
University of California, Davis *California*
University of California, Los Angeles *California*
University of Chicago *Illinois*
University of Dubuque *Iowa*
The University of Iowa *Iowa*
University of Kentucky *Kentucky*
University of Louisville *Kentucky*
University of Minnesota, Twin Cities Campus *Minnesota*
The University of North Carolina at Chapel Hill *North Carolina*
University of Notre Dame *Indiana*
University of Oklahoma Health Sciences Center *Oklahoma*
University of Pennsylvania *Pennsylvania*
University of Rochester *New York*
University of St. Thomas *Minnesota*
University of St. Thomas *Texas*
The University of Tennessee *Tennessee*
The University of Texas Health Science Center at Houston *Texas*
University of Virginia *Virginia*
Vanderbilt University *Tennessee*
Virginia Commonwealth University *Virginia*
Virginia Union University *Virginia*
Wake Forest University *North Carolina*
Washington University in St. Louis *Missouri*
West Virginia University *West Virginia*
Yale University *Connecticut*

The Association of Technology, Management, and Applied Engineering (ATMAE)

Alcorn State University *Mississippi*
Arizona State University at the Polytechnic campus *Arizona*
Bowling Green State University *Ohio*
Butler County Community College *Pennsylvania*
California Polytechnic State University, San Luis Obispo *California*
California State University, Chico *California*
Central Connecticut State University *Connecticut*
Cleveland State Community College *Tennessee*
College of the Redwoods *California*
Crowder College *Missouri*
Delgado Community College *Louisiana*
East Carolina University *North Carolina*
Eastern Illinois University *Illinois*
Eastern Kentucky University *Kentucky*
Eastern Michigan University *Michigan*
Elizabeth City State University *North Carolina*
Georgia Southern University *Georgia*
Illinois State University *Illinois*
Indiana State University *Indiana*
Iowa State University of Science and Technology *Iowa*
Ivy Tech Community College - Central Indiana *Indiana*
Ivy Tech Community College - Lafayette *Indiana*
Ivy Tech Community College - Northeast *Indiana*

Ivy Tech Community College - Richmond *Indiana*
Ivy Tech Community College - Southern Indiana *Indiana*
Ivy Tech Community College - Southwest *Indiana*
Ivy Tech Community College - Wabash Valley *Indiana*
Jackson State Community College *Tennessee*
Jackson State University *Mississippi*
Jacksonville State University *Alabama*
Kean University *New Jersey*
Middle Tennessee State University *Tennessee*
Millersville University of Pennsylvania *Pennsylvania*
Minnesota State University Moorhead *Minnesota*
Missouri State University *Missouri*
Moberly Area Community College *Missouri*
Morehead State University *Kentucky*
Norfolk State University *Virginia*
North Carolina Agricultural and Technical State University *North Carolina*
Northeast State Community College *Tennessee*
Northern Illinois University *Illinois*
Northern Michigan University *Michigan*
Nunez Community College *Louisiana*
Ozarks Technical Community College *Missouri*
Purdue University *Indiana*
San Jose State University *California*
Sinclair Community College *Ohio*
Southeast Missouri State University *Missouri*
Southeastern Louisiana University *Louisiana*
Southern Illinois University Carbondale *Illinois*
Southern University at Shreveport *Louisiana*
State Fair Community College *Missouri*
State Technical College of Missouri *Missouri*
Tennessee Technological University *Tennessee*
Texas A&M University - Commerce *Texas*
Texas A&M University - Kingsville *Texas*
Texas Southern University *Texas*
University of Arkansas at Pine Bluff *Arkansas*
University at Buffalo, the State University of New York *New York*
University of Central Missouri *Missouri*
University of Louisiana at Lafayette *Louisiana*
University of Nebraska at Kearney *Nebraska*
University of North Dakota *North Dakota*
University of Northern Iowa *Iowa*
University of Southern Maine *Maine*
The University of Texas at Tyler *Texas*
University of Wisconsin - Platteville *Wisconsin*
University of Wisconsin - Stout *Wisconsin*
Walters State Community College *Tennessee*
Western Kentucky University *Kentucky*

Association of Theological Schools in the United States and Canada (ATS)

Abilene Christian University *Texas*
Acadia University *Nova Scotia (Canada)*
Ambrose University *Alberta (Canada)*
Anderson University *Indiana*
Andrews University *Michigan*
Ashland University *Ohio*
Azusa Pacific University *California*
Baptist Missionary Association Theological Seminary *Texas*
Barry University *Florida*
Baylor University *Texas*
Bethel University *Minnesota*
Biola University *California*
Boston College *Massachusetts*
Boston University *Massachusetts*
Briercrest College *Saskatchewan (Canada)*
Brock University *Ontario (Canada)*
California Lutheran University *California*
Campbell University *North Carolina*
The Catholic University of America *District of Columbia*
Cincinnati Christian University *Ohio*
Columbia International University *South Carolina*
Drew University *New Jersey*
Duke University *North Carolina*
Eastern Mennonite University *Virginia*
Eastern University *Pennsylvania*
Emory University *Georgia*
Freed-Hardeman University *Tennessee*
Fresno Pacific University *California*
Gardner-Webb University *North Carolina*
George Fox University *Oregon*

Georgia Christian University *Georgia*
Grace College *Indiana*
Grace School of Theology *Texas*
Hardin-Simmons University *Texas*
Harvard University *Massachusetts*
Heritage College and Seminary *Ontario (Canada)*
Howard University *District of Columbia*
Indiana Wesleyan University *Indiana*
La Sierra University *California*
Lancaster Bible College *Pennsylvania*
Lenoir-Rhyne University *North Carolina*
Lincoln Christian University *Illinois*
Lipscomb University *Tennessee*
Loyola Marymount University *California*
Lubbock Christian University *Texas*
McGill University *Quebec (Canada)*
McMaster University *Ontario (Canada)*
Mercer University *Georgia*
Milligan College *Tennessee*
Moody Bible Institute *Illinois*
Mount Angel Seminary *Oregon*
Mount St. Mary's University *Maryland*
Multnomah University *Oregon*
New Orleans Baptist Theological Seminary *Louisiana*
Newman University *Kansas*
Nyack College *New York*
Oakland City University *Indiana*
Oral Roberts University *Oklahoma*
Pontifical College Josephinum *Ohio*
Providence University College & Theological Seminary *Manitoba (Canada)*
Queen's University at Kingston *Ontario (Canada)*
Regent University *Virginia*
Sacred Heart Major Seminary *Michigan*
Saint Charles Borromeo Seminary, Overbrook *Pennsylvania*
St. John Vianney College Seminary *Florida*
Saint John's University *Minnesota*
Saint Paul University *Ontario (Canada)*
St. Thomas University *Florida*
Saint Vincent College *Pennsylvania*
Samford University *Alabama*
Santa Clara University *California*
Seattle Pacific University *Washington*
Seattle University *Washington*
Seton Hall University *New Jersey*
Sewanee: The University of the South *Tennessee*
Shaw University *North Carolina*
Shepherd University *California*
Southeastern Baptist Theological Seminary *North Carolina*
The Southern Baptist Theological Seminary *Kentucky*
Southern Methodist University *Texas*
Texas Christian University *Texas*
Trinity International University *Illinois*
Trinity Western University *British Columbia (Canada)*
Tyndale University College & Seminary *Ontario (Canada)*
University of Chicago *Illinois*
University of Dubuque *Iowa*
University of Notre Dame *Indiana*
University of St. Thomas *Minnesota*
University of St. Thomas *Texas*
University of Toronto *Ontario (Canada)*
The University of Western Ontario *Ontario (Canada)*
The University of Winnipeg *Manitoba (Canada)*
Vanderbilt University *Tennessee*
Virginia Union University *Virginia*
Wake Forest University *North Carolina*
Wilfrid Laurier University *Ontario (Canada)*
World Mission University *California*
Yale University *Connecticut*

Aviation Accreditation Board International (AABI)

Arizona State University at the Polytechnic campus *Arizona*
Auburn University *Alabama*
Daniel Webster College *New Hampshire*
Embry-Riddle Aeronautical University - Daytona *Florida*
Embry-Riddle Aeronautical University - Prescott *Arizona*

Florida Institute of Technology *Florida*
Hampton University *Virginia*
Louisiana Tech University *Louisiana*
Mercer County Community College *New Jersey*
Middle Tennessee State University *Tennessee*
North Shore Community College *Massachusetts*
Purdue University *Indiana*
St. Cloud State University *Minnesota*
Saint Louis University *Missouri*
University of Central Missouri *Missouri*
University of Nebraska at Omaha *Nebraska*
University of North Dakota *North Dakota*
Western Michigan University *Michigan*

Commission on Accreditation of Healthcare Management Education (CAHME)

Arizona State University at the Tempe campus *Arizona*
Armstrong State University *Georgia*
Baruch College of the City University of New York *New York*
Baylor University *Texas*
Boston University *Massachusetts*
California State University, Long Beach *California*
Columbia University *New York*
Cornell University *New York*
Dalhousie University *Nova Scotia (Canada)*
Duke University *North Carolina*
Florida International University *Florida*
George Mason University *Virginia*
The George Washington University *District of Columbia*
Georgia State University *Georgia*
Governors State University *Illinois*
Indiana University - Purdue University Indianapolis *Indiana*
Johns Hopkins University *Maryland*
King's College *Pennsylvania*
Marymount University *Virginia*
Medical University of South Carolina *South Carolina*
New York University *New York*
Northwestern University *Illinois*
The Ohio State University. *Ohio*
Penn State University Park *Pennsylvania*
Rush University *Illinois*
Saint Louis University *Missouri*
San Diego State University *California*
Seton Hall University *New Jersey*
Simmons College *Massachusetts*
Temple University *Pennsylvania*
Texas State University *Texas*
Texas Tech University *Texas*
Texas Woman's University *Texas*
Trinity University *Texas*
Tulane University *Louisiana*
Université de Montréal *Quebec (Canada)*
The University of Alabama at Birmingham *Alabama*
University of Arkansas at Little Rock *Arkansas*
University of California, Berkeley *California*
University of California, Los Angeles *California*
University of Central Florida *Florida*
University of Colorado Denver *Colorado*
University of Florida *Florida*
University of Houston - Clear Lake *Texas*
University of the Incarnate Word *Texas*
The University of Iowa *Iowa*
The University of Kansas *Kansas*
University of Kentucky *Kentucky*
University of Memphis *Tennessee*
University of Miami *Florida*
University of Michigan *Michigan*
University of Minnesota, Twin Cities Campus *Minnesota*
University of Missouri *Missouri*
The University of North Carolina at Chapel Hill *North Carolina*
The University of North Carolina at Charlotte *North Carolina*
University of Oklahoma Health Sciences Center *Oklahoma*
University of Ottawa *Ontario (Canada)*
University of Pennsylvania *Pennsylvania*
University of Pittsburgh *Pennsylvania*
University of Puerto Rico, Medical Sciences Campus *Puerto Rico*

University of St. Thomas *Minnesota*
The University of Scranton *Pennsylvania*
University of South Carolina *South Carolina*
University of South Florida *Florida*
University of Southern California *California*
University of Southern Maine *Maine*
University of Toronto *Ontario (Canada)*
University of Utah *Utah*
University of Washington *Washington*
University of Wisconsin - Madison *Wisconsin*
Virginia Commonwealth University *Virginia*
Washington State University *Washington*
Washington State University - Spokane *Washington*
Washington University in St. Louis *Missouri*
Weber State University *Utah*
Widener University *Pennsylvania*
Xavier University *Ohio*
Yale University *Connecticut*

Commission on Opticianry Accreditation (COA)

Camden County College *New Jersey*
College of Southern Nevada *Nevada*
Durham Technical Community College *North Carolina*
El Paso Community College *Texas*
Erie Community College *New York*
Essex County College *New Jersey*
Georgia Piedmont Technical College *Georgia*
Hillsborough Community College *Florida*
Holyoke Community College *Massachusetts*
Indiana University Bloomington *Indiana*
J. Sargeant Reynolds Community College *Virginia*
Miami Dade College *Florida*
Middlesex Community College *Connecticut*
Milwaukee Area Technical College *Wisconsin*
New York City College of Technology of the City University of New York *New York*
Ogeechee Technical College *Georgia*
Raritan Valley Community College *New Jersey*
Roane State Community College *Tennessee*
Seattle Central College *Washington*
Southwestern Indian Polytechnic Institute *New Mexico*
Tyler Junior College *Texas*

Committee on Accreditation of Education Programs in Kinesiotherapy (CoA-KT)

California State University, Long Beach *California*
Norfolk State University *Virginia*
San Diego State University *California*
Shaw University *North Carolina*
University of Southern Mississippi *Mississippi*
The University of Toledo *Ohio*

Committee on Accreditation for Respiratory Care (CoARC)

Allegany College of Maryland *Maryland*
Alvin Community College *Texas*
Amarillo College *Texas*
American River College *California*
Angelina College *Texas*
Armstrong State University *Georgia*
Ashland Community and Technical College *Kentucky*
Athens Technical College *Georgia*
Augusta Technical College *Georgia*
Augusta University *Georgia*
Baltimore City Community College *Maryland*
Baptist College of Health Sciences *Tennessee*
Bellarmine University *Kentucky*
Bergen Community College *New Jersey*
Berkshire Community College *Massachusetts*
Black River Technical College *Arkansas*
Bluegrass Community and Technical College *Kentucky*
Boise State University *Idaho*
Borough of Manhattan Community College of the City University of New York *New York*
Bossier Parish Community College *Louisiana*
Bowling Green State University *Ohio*
Brookdale Community College *New Jersey*
Broward College *Florida*
Butte College *California*

Carrington College - Mesa *Arizona*
Carrington College - Phoenix North *Arizona*
Carteret Community College *North Carolina*
Catawba Valley Community College *North Carolina*
Central New Mexico Community College *New Mexico*
Central Piedmont Community College *North Carolina*
Champlain College *Vermont*
Chattanooga State Community College *Tennessee*
Cincinnati State Technical and Community College *Ohio*
College of DuPage *Illinois*
College of Southern Nevada *Nevada*
Collin County Community College District *Texas*
Columbia State Community College *Tennessee*
Columbus State Community College *Ohio*
Community College of Allegheny County *Pennsylvania*
Community College of Aurora *Colorado*
Community College of Baltimore County *Maryland*
Community College of Philadelphia *Pennsylvania*
Community College of Rhode Island *Rhode Island*
Concorde Career College *North Hollywood, California*
Concorde Career College *Missouri*
Crafton Hills College *California*
Cuyahoga Community College *Ohio*
Dakota State University *South Dakota*
Darton State College *Georgia*
Daytona State College *Florida*
Del Mar College *Texas*
Delaware County Community College *Pennsylvania*
Delaware Technical & Community College, Jack F. Owens Campus *Delaware*
Delaware Technical & Community College, Stanton/Wilmington Campus *Delaware*
Delgado Community College *Louisiana*
Delta College *Michigan*
Des Moines Area Community College *Iowa*
Doña Ana Community College *New Mexico*
Durham Technical Community College *North Carolina*
East Los Angeles College *California*
East Tennessee State University *Tennessee*
Eastern Florida State College *Florida*
Eastern Gateway Community College *Ohio*
Eastern New Mexico University - Roswell *New Mexico*
Edgecombe Community College *North Carolina*
El Camino College *California*
El Centro College *Texas*
El Paso Community College *Texas*
Erie Community College, North Campus *New York*
Fayetteville Technical Community College *North Carolina*
Ferris State University *Michigan*
Florence-Darlington Technical College *South Carolina*
Florida Agricultural and Mechanical University *Florida*
Florida SouthWestern State College *Florida*
Florida State College at Jacksonville *Florida*
Foothill College *California*
Forsyth Technical Community College *North Carolina*
Frederick Community College *Maryland*
Fresno City College *California*
Front Range Community College *Colorado*
Gannon University *Pennsylvania*
GateWay Community College *Arizona*
Genesee Community College *New York*
George C. Wallace Community College *Alabama*
Georgia State University *Georgia*
Great Falls College Montana State University *Montana*
Greenville Technical College *South Carolina*
Grossmont College *California*
Gulf Coast State College *Florida*
Gwinnett Technical College *Georgia*
Gwynedd Mercy University *Pennsylvania*
Hannibal-LaGrange University *Missouri*
Harrisburg Area Community College *Pennsylvania*
Hawkeye Community College *Iowa*
Henry Ford College *Michigan*
Highline College *Washington*

Hillsborough Community College *Florida*
Hinds Community College *Mississippi*
Houston Community College *Texas*
Hudson Valley Community College *New York*
Illinois Central College *Illinois*
Independence University *Utah*
Indian River State College *Florida*
Indiana University Northwest *Indiana*
Indiana University of Pennsylvania *Pennsylvania*
Indiana University - Purdue University Indianapolis *Indiana*
Itawamba Community College *Mississippi*
Ivy Tech Community College - Central Indiana *Indiana*
Ivy Tech Community College - Lafayette *Indiana*
Ivy Tech Community College - Northeast *Indiana*
Ivy Tech Community College - Northwest *Indiana*
J. Sargeant Reynolds Community College *Virginia*
Jackson State Community College *Tennessee*
James A. Rhodes State College *Ohio*
Jefferson College of Health Sciences *Virginia*
Jefferson Community and Technical College *Kentucky*
Johnson County Community College *Kansas*
Kalamazoo Valley Community College *Michigan*
Kankakee Community College *Illinois*
Kansas City Kansas Community College *Kansas*
Kapiolani Community College *Hawaii*
Kaskaskia College *Illinois*
Kennebec Valley Community College *Maine*
Kettering College *Ohio*
Kirkwood Community College *Iowa*
Labette Community College *Kansas*
Lake Superior College *Minnesota*
Lakeland Community College *Ohio*
Lamar Institute of Technology *Texas*
Lane Community College *Oregon*
Lincoln Land Community College *Illinois*
Loma Linda University *California*
Lone Star College - Kingwood *Texas*
Long Island University - LIU Brooklyn *New York*
Los Angeles Valley College *California*
Louisiana State University at Eunice *Louisiana*
Louisiana State University Health Sciences Center *Louisiana*
Macomb Community College *Michigan*
Madison Area Technical College *Wisconsin*
Madisonville Community College *Kentucky*
Manchester Community College *Connecticut*
Mansfield University of Pennsylvania *Pennsylvania*
Marygrove College *Michigan*
Massachusetts Bay Community College *Massachusetts*
Massasoit Community College *Massachusetts*
Maysville Community and Technical College *Maysville, Kentucky*
Maysville Community and Technical College *Morehead, Kentucky*
McLennan Community College *Texas*
Metropolitan Community College *Nebraska*
Miami Dade College *Florida*
Mid-State Technical College *Wisconsin*
Middle Georgia State University *Georgia*
Midland College *Texas*
Midlands Technical College *South Carolina*
Midwestern State University *Texas*
Millersville University of Pennsylvania *Pennsylvania*
Milwaukee Area Technical College *Wisconsin*
Mississippi Gulf Coast Community College *Mississippi*
Missouri Southern State University *Missouri*
Modesto Junior College *California*
Mohawk Valley Community College *New York*
Molloy College *New York*
Monroe County Community College *Michigan*
Moraine Valley Community College *Illinois*
Morehead State University *Kentucky*
Mott Community College *Michigan*
Mt. Hood Community College *Oregon*
Mt. San Antonio College *California*
Mountain Empire Community College *Virginia*
Muskegon Community College *Michigan*
Napa Valley College *California*
Nashua Community College *New Hampshire*
Nassau Community College *New York*
National Louis University *Illinois*

Naugatuck Valley Community College *Connecticut*
Nebraska Methodist College *Nebraska*
Newman University *Kansas*
Nicholls State University *Louisiana*
North Central State College *Ohio*
North Dakota State University *North Dakota*
North Shore Community College *Massachusetts*
Northeast Iowa Community College *Iowa*
Northeast Mississippi Community College *Mississippi*
Northeast Wisconsin Technical College *Wisconsin*
Northeastern University *Massachusetts*
Northern Essex Community College *Massachusetts*
Northern Kentucky University *Kentucky*
Northern Virginia Community College *Virginia*
NorthWest Arkansas Community College *Arkansas*
Northwest Mississippi Community College *Mississippi*
Northwest Technical College *Minnesota*
Norwalk Community College *Connecticut*
Oakland Community College *Michigan*
Odessa College *Texas*
The Ohio State University *Ohio*
Ohlone College *California*
Oklahoma City Community College *Oklahoma*
Onondaga Community College *New York*
Orange Coast College *California*
Ozarks Technical Community College *Missouri*
Palm Beach State College *Florida*
Parkland College *Illinois*
Passaic County Community College *New Jersey*
Pearl River Community College *Mississippi*
Pensacola State College *Florida*
Piedmont Technical College *South Carolina*
Pima Community College *Arizona*
Pima Medical Institute *Mesa, Arizona*
Pima Medical Institute *Tucson, Arizona*
Pima Medical Institute *Denver, Colorado*
Pitt Community College *North Carolina*
Pittsburgh Career Institute *Pennsylvania*
Prince George's Community College *Maryland*
Pueblo Community College *Colorado*
Pulaski Technical College *Arkansas*
Quinnipiac University *Connecticut*
Quinsigamond Community College *Massachusetts*
Reading Area Community College *Pennsylvania*
Roane State Community College *Tennessee*
Robeson Community College *North Carolina*
Rochester Community and Technical College *Minnesota*
Rock Valley College *Illinois*
Rogue Community College *Oregon*
Rose State College *Oklahoma*
Rowan College at Gloucester County *New Jersey*
St. Augustine College *Illinois*
Saint Paul College - A Community & Technical College *Minnesota*
St. Petersburg College *Florida*
St. Philip's College *Texas*
Salisbury University *Maryland*
San Joaquin Valley College *Visalia, California*
Sandhills Community College *North Carolina*
Santa Fe College *Florida*
Santa Monica College *California*
Seattle Central College *Washington*
Seminole State College of Florida *Florida*
Seward County Community College and Area Technical School *Kansas*
Shawnee State University *Ohio*
Shelton State Community College *Alabama*
Shenandoah University *Virginia*
Sinclair Community College *Ohio*
Skyline College *California*
South Plains College *Texas*
Southcentral Kentucky Community and Technical College *Kentucky*
Southeast Community College, Lincoln Campus *Nebraska*
Southeast Kentucky Community and Technical College *Kentucky*
Southern Illinois University Carbondale *Illinois*
Southern Maine Community College *Maine*
Southern Regional Technical College *Georgia*
Southern University at Shreveport *Louisiana*
Southwest Virginia Community College *Virginia*
Southwestern Community College *North Carolina*

Southwestern Illinois College *Illinois*
Spartanburg Community College *South Carolina*
Spokane Community College *Washington*
Springfield Technical Community College *Massachusetts*
Stanly Community College *North Carolina*
Stark State College *Ohio*
State College of Florida Manatee-Sarasota *Florida*
State University of New York Upstate Medical University *New York*
Stony Brook University, State University of New York *New York*
Tacoma Community College *Washington*
Tallahassee Community College *Florida*
Tarrant County College District *Texas*
Temple College *Texas*
Tennessee State University *Tennessee*
Texas Southern University *Texas*
Texas Southmost College *Texas*
Texas State University *Texas*
Tidewater Community College *Virginia*
Trident Technical College *South Carolina*
Triton College *Illinois*
Tulsa Community College *Oklahoma*
Tyler Junior College *Texas*
Union County College *New Jersey*
Universidad Adventista de las Antillas *Puerto Rico*
The University of Akron *Ohio*
The University of Alabama at Birmingham *Alabama*
University of Arkansas Community College at Hope *Arkansas*
University of Arkansas for Medical Sciences *Arkansas*
University of Central Florida *Florida*
University of Charleston *West Virginia*
University of the District of Columbia *District of Columbia*
University of Hartford *Connecticut*
University of Holy Cross *Louisiana*
The University of Kansas *Kansas*
University of Mary *North Dakota*
University of Missouri *Missouri*
University of Montana *Montana*
University of Pittsburgh at Johnstown *Pennsylvania*
University of South Alabama *Alabama*
University of Southern Indiana *Indiana*
The University of Texas Health Science Center at San Antonio *Texas*
The University of Texas Medical Branch *Texas*
The University of Toledo *Ohio*
Valencia College *Florida*
Victor Valley College *California*
Victoria College *Texas*
Vincennes University *Indiana*
Volunteer State Community College *Tennessee*
Wallace State Community College *Alabama*
Walters State Community College *Tennessee*
Washburn University *Kansas*
Washington Adventist University *Maryland*
Washington State Community College *Ohio*
Wayne County Community College District *Michigan*
Weatherford College *Texas*
Weber State University *Utah*
West Chester University of Pennsylvania *Pennsylvania*
West Virginia Northern Community College *West Virginia*
West Virginia University Institute of Technology *West Virginia*
Westchester Community College *New York*
Western Technical College *Wisconsin*
Western Wyoming Community College *Wyoming*
Wheeling Jesuit University *West Virginia*
York College of Pennsylvania *Pennsylvania*
Youngstown State University *Ohio*

Council on Chiropractic Education (CCE)

Cleveland University - Kansas City *Kansas*
D'Youville College *New York*
Life University *Georgia*
Logan University *Missouri*
Palmer College of Chiropractic *Iowa*
University of Bridgeport *Connecticut*

Council on Education for Public Health (CEPH)

Arizona State University at the Tempe campus *Arizona*
Armstrong State University *Georgia*
Boston University *Massachusetts*
Bowling Green State University *Ohio*
Brooklyn College of the City University of New York *New York*
Brown University *Rhode Island*
California State University, Fresno *California*
California State University, Long Beach *California*
California State University, Northridge *California*
Cleveland State University *Ohio*
Columbia University *New York*
Dartmouth College *New Hampshire*
Drexel University *Pennsylvania*
East Stroudsburg University of Pennsylvania *Pennsylvania*
East Tennessee State University *Tennessee*
Emory University *Georgia*
Florida Agricultural and Mechanical University *Florida*
Florida International University *Florida*
The George Washington University *District of Columbia*
Harvard University *Massachusetts*
Hunter College of the City University of New York *New York*
Idaho State University *Idaho*
Indiana University Bloomington *Indiana*
Indiana University - Purdue University Indianapolis *Indiana*
Johns Hopkins University *Maryland*
Kent State University *Ohio*
Loma Linda University *California*
Louisiana State University Health Sciences Center *Louisiana*
Morgan State University *Maryland*
New Jersey Institute of Technology *New Jersey*
New Mexico State University *New Mexico*
New York University *New York*
Northern Arizona University *Arizona*
Northern Illinois University *Illinois*
Northwestern University *Illinois*
Nova Southeastern University *Florida*
The Ohio State University *Ohio*
Old Dominion University *Virginia*
Oregon Health & Science University *Oregon*
Oregon State University *Oregon*
Portland State University *Oregon*
Saint Louis University *Missouri*
San Diego State University *California*
San Francisco State University *California*
San Jose State University *California*
Southern Connecticut State University *Connecticut*
Temple University *Pennsylvania*
Tufts University *Massachusetts*
Tulane University *Louisiana*
The University of Akron *Ohio*
The University of Alabama at Birmingham *Alabama*
University at Albany, State University of New York *New York*
The University of Arizona *Arizona*
University of Arkansas for Medical Sciences *Arkansas*
University of California, Berkeley *California*
University of California, Los Angeles *California*
University of Hawaii at Manoa *Hawaii*
University of Illinois at Chicago *Illinois*
The University of Iowa *Iowa*
The University of Kansas *Kansas*
University of Maryland, College Park *Maryland*
University of Massachusetts Amherst *Massachusetts*
University of Miami *Florida*
University of Michigan *Michigan*
University of Minnesota, Twin Cities Campus *Minnesota*
University of Nebraska Medical Center *Nebraska*
University of Nebraska at Omaha *Nebraska*
University of New Mexico *New Mexico*
The University of North Carolina at Chapel Hill *North Carolina*
The University of North Carolina at Greensboro *North Carolina*

University of Northern Colorado *Colorado*
University of Oklahoma Health Sciences Center *Oklahoma*
University of Pittsburgh *Pennsylvania*
University of Puerto Rico, Medical Sciences Campus *Puerto Rico*
University of Rochester *New York*
University of South Carolina *South Carolina*
University of South Florida *Florida*
University of Southern California *California*
University of Southern Mississippi *Mississippi*
The University of Tennessee *Tennessee*
The University of Texas Health Science Center at Houston *Texas*
The University of Texas Medical Branch *Texas*
The University of Toledo *Ohio*
University of Utah *Utah*
University of Washington *Washington*
University of Wisconsin - La Crosse *Wisconsin*
Virginia Commonwealth University *Virginia*
West Chester University of Pennsylvania *Pennsylvania*
West Virginia University *West Virginia*
Western Kentucky University *Kentucky*
Wichita State University *Kansas*
Yale University *Connecticut*
Youngstown State University *Ohio*

Council for Interior Design Accreditation (CIDA)

Academy of Art University *California*
Arizona State University at the Tempe campus *Arizona*
The Art Institute of Atlanta *Georgia*
The Art Institute of Dallas, a campus of South University *Texas*
Auburn University *Alabama*
Boston Architectural College *Massachusetts*
Brenau University *Georgia*
Brigham Young University - Idaho *Idaho*
Buffalo State College, State University of New York *New York*
California College of the Arts *California*
California State Polytechnic University, Pomona *California*
California State University, Fresno *California*
California State University, Northridge *California*
California State University, Sacramento *California*
Chatham University *Pennsylvania*
Colorado State University *Colorado*
Columbus College of Art & Design *Ohio*
Cornell University *New York*
Dakota County Technical College *Minnesota*
Design Institute of San Diego *California*
Drexel University *Pennsylvania*
East Carolina University *North Carolina*
Eastern Michigan University *Michigan*
El Centro College *Texas*
Endicott College *Massachusetts*
Fashion Institute of Technology *New York*
Florida International University *Florida*
Florida State University *Florida*
The George Washington University *District of Columbia*
Georgia Southern University *Georgia*
The Illinois Institute of Art - Chicago *Illinois*
The Illinois Institute of Art - Schaumburg *Illinois*
Illinois State University *Illinois*
Indiana University Bloomington *Indiana*
Interior Designers Institute *California*
Iowa State University of Science and Technology *Iowa*
James Madison University *Virginia*
Kansas State University *Kansas*
Kean University *New Jersey*
Kent State University *Ohio*
La Roche College *Pennsylvania*
Lawrence Technological University *Michigan*
Louisiana State University and Agricultural & Mechanical College *Louisiana*
Louisiana Tech University *Louisiana*
Marymount University *Virginia*
Maryville University of Saint Louis *Missouri*
Meredith College *North Carolina*
Miami University *Ohio*
Michigan State University *Michigan*

Middle Tennessee State University *Tennessee*
Mississippi State University *Mississippi*
Moore College of Art & Design *Pennsylvania*
Mount Ida College *Massachusetts*
Mount Mary University *Wisconsin*
New York Institute of Technology *New York*
New York School of Interior Design *New York*
Newbury College *Massachusetts*
North Dakota State University *North Dakota*
The Ohio State University *Ohio*
Ohio University *Ohio*
Oklahoma State University *Oklahoma*
O'More College of Design *Tennessee*
Philadelphia University *Pennsylvania*
Pratt Institute *New York*
Purdue University *Indiana*
Ringling College of Art and Design *Florida*
Rochester Institute of Technology *New York*
Rocky Mountain College of Art + Design *Colorado*
Ryerson University *Ontario (Canada)*
Samford University *Alabama*
School of Visual Arts *New York*
Southern Illinois University Carbondale *Illinois*
Southwest University of Visual Arts *Arizona*
Stephen F. Austin State University *Texas*
Suffolk University *Massachusetts*
Syracuse University *New York*
Texas Christian University *Texas*
Texas State University *Texas*
Texas Tech University *Texas*
The University of Akron *Ohio*
The University of Alabama *Alabama*
University of Arkansas *Arkansas*
University of California, Berkeley *California*
University of California, Los Angeles *California*
University of Central Oklahoma *Oklahoma*
University of Cincinnati *Ohio*
University of Florida *Florida*
University of Georgia *Georgia*
University of Kentucky *Kentucky*
University of Louisiana at Lafayette *Louisiana*
University of Louisville *Kentucky*
University of Manitoba *Manitoba (Canada)*
University of Memphis *Tennessee*
University of Minnesota, Twin Cities Campus *Minnesota*
University of Missouri *Missouri*
University of Nebraska - Lincoln *Nebraska*
University of Nevada, Las Vegas *Nevada*
The University of North Carolina at Greensboro *North Carolina*
University of North Texas *Texas*
University of Oklahoma *Oklahoma*
University of Oregon *Oregon*
University of Southern Mississippi *Mississippi*
The University of Tennessee *Tennessee*
The University of Tennessee at Chattanooga *Tennessee*
The University of Texas at Arlington *Texas*
The University of Texas at Austin *Texas*
The University of Texas at San Antonio *Texas*
University of Wisconsin - Madison *Wisconsin*
University of Wisconsin - Stevens Point *Wisconsin*
University of Wisconsin - Stout *Wisconsin*
Utah State University *Utah*
Virginia Commonwealth University *Virginia*
Virginia Polytechnic Institute and State University *Virginia*
Washington State University *Washington*
Watkins College of Art, Design, & Film *Tennessee*
Wentworth Institute of Technology *Massachusetts*
West Valley College *California*
West Virginia University *West Virginia*
Western Carolina University *North Carolina*
Western Michigan University *Michigan*
Winthrop University *South Carolina*
Woodbury University *California*

Council on Occupational Education (COE)

Academy for Nursing and Health Occupations *Florida*
Advanced College *California*
Advanced Computing Institute *California*
Advanced Training Associates *California*
Albany Technical College *Georgia*

Ashland Community and Technical College *Kentucky*
Atlanta Technical College *Georgia*
Auguste Escoffier School of Culinary Arts *Texas*
Aviation & Electronic Schools of America *California*
Big Sandy Community and Technical College *Kentucky*
Blake Austin College *California*
Brightwood College, Arlington Campus *Texas*
Brightwood College, Dallas Campus *Texas*
Brightwood College, Nashville Campus *Tennessee*
Brown College of Court Reporting *Georgia*
Burnett International College *Florida*
Cameron College *Louisiana*
Center for Advanced Legal Studies *Texas*
Central Georgia Technical College *Georgia*
Central Louisiana Technical Community College *Louisiana*
Coastal Pines Technical College *Georgia*
College of Business and Technology - Main Campus *Florida*
Colorado Academy of Veterinary Technology *Colorado*
Columbia College *Virginia*
Concorde Career College *Tennessee*
East San Gabriel Valley Regional Occupational Program & Technical Center *California*
Eastern Virginia Career College *Virginia*
Elizabethtown Community and Technical College *Kentucky*
Fletcher Technical Community College *Louisiana*
Flint Hills Technical College *Kansas*
Fortis College *Louisiana*
Fortis Institute *Palm Springs, Florida*
Fortis Institute *Cookeville, Tennessee*
Gateway Community and Technical College *Kentucky*
Georgia Northwestern Technical College *Georgia*
H. Councill Trenholm State Community College *Alabama*
Interactive College of Technology *Chamblee, Georgia*
Interactive College of Technology *Gainesville, Georgia*
Interactive College of Technology *Kentucky*
Interactive College of Technology *Houston, Texas*
Interactive College of Technology *Pasadena, Texas*
J. F. Drake State Community and Technical College *Alabama*
J F Ingram State Technical College *Alabama*
Jersey College *New Jersey*
Lancaster County Career and Technology Center *Pennsylvania*
Lanier Technical College *Georgia*
Lincoln College of Technology *Florida*
Lincoln Culinary Institute *Florida*
Living Arts College *North Carolina*
Louisiana Culinary Institute *Louisiana*
Management Resources College *Florida*
Maysville Community and Technical College *Morehead, Kentucky*
McCann School of Business & Technology *Monroe, Louisiana*
Medtech College *Georgia*
Medtech College *Virginia*
Midwestern Career College *Illinois*
Morrison Institute of Technology *Illinois*
North Central Institute *Tennessee*
North Georgia Technical College *Georgia*
Northshore Technical Community College *Louisiana*
Northwest Kansas Technical College *Kansas*
Northwest Louisiana Technical College *Louisiana*
Oconee Fall Line Technical College *Georgia*
Ogeechee Technical College *Georgia*
Owensboro Community and Technical College *Kentucky*
Praxis Institute *Florida*
Professional Hands Institute *Florida*
Quest College *Texas*
Reid State Technical College *Alabama*
SABER College *Florida*
Somerset Community College *Kentucky*
South Central Louisiana Technical College *Louisiana*
South Georgia Technical College *Georgia*

Southcentral Kentucky Community and Technical College *Kentucky*
Southeastern Technical College *Georgia*
Southern Crescent Technical College *Georgia*
Southern Regional Technical College *Georgia*
Sowela Technical Community College *Louisiana*
Spartan College of Aeronautics and Technology *California*
Stratford University *Falls Church, Virginia*
Sullivan and Cogliano Training Center *Florida*
Universal Career School *Florida*
Vista College *Texas*
West Georgia Technical College *Georgia*
West Kentucky Community and Technical College *Kentucky*
Wichita Area Technical College *Kansas*
Wiregrass Georgia Technical College *Georgia*

Council on Rehabilitation Education (CORE)

Alabama Agricultural and Mechanical University *Alabama*
Alabama State University *Alabama*
Arkansas State University *Arkansas*
Assumption College *Massachusetts*
Auburn University *Alabama*
Ball State University *Indiana*
Boston University *Massachusetts*
Bowling Green State University *Ohio*
California State University, Fresno *California*
California State University, Los Angeles *California*
California State University, Sacramento *California*
California State University, San Bernardino *California*
Coppin State University *Maryland*
Drake University *Iowa*
East Carolina University *North Carolina*
East Central University *Oklahoma*
Edinboro University of Pennsylvania *Pennsylvania*
Emporia State University *Kansas*
Florida State University *Florida*
Fort Valley State University *Georgia*
The George Washington University *District of Columbia*
Georgia State University *Georgia*
Hofstra University *New York*
Hunter College of the City University of New York *New York*
Illinois Institute of Technology *Illinois*
Jackson State University *Mississippi*
Kent State University *Ohio*
Langston University *Oklahoma*
Louisiana State University Health Sciences Center *Louisiana*
Maryville University of Saint Louis *Missouri*
Michigan State University *Michigan*
Minnesota State University Mankato *Minnesota*
Mississippi State University *Mississippi*
Montana State University Billings *Montana*
New York University *New York*
Northeastern University *Massachusetts*
Northern Illinois University *Illinois*
The Ohio State University *Ohio*
Ohio University *Ohio*
Penn State University Park *Pennsylvania*
Pontifical Catholic University of Puerto Rico *Puerto Rico*
Portland State University *Oregon*
Rutgers University - Newark *New Jersey*
St. Cloud State University *Minnesota*
St. John's University *New York*
Salve Regina University *Rhode Island*
San Diego State University *California*
San Francisco State University *California*
South Carolina State University *South Carolina*
Southern Illinois University Carbondale *Illinois*
Southern University and Agricultural and Mechanical College *Louisiana*
Springfield College *Massachusetts*
Stephen F. Austin State University *Texas*
Syracuse University *New York*
Thomas University *Georgia*
Troy University *Alabama*
The University of Alabama *Alabama*
The University of Alabama at Birmingham *Alabama*

University at Albany, State University of New York *New York*
The University of Arizona *Arizona*
University of Arkansas *Arkansas*
University of Arkansas at Little Rock *Arkansas*
University of Buffalo, the State University of New York *New York*
University of Florida *Florida*
University of Hawaii at Manoa *Hawaii*
University of Idaho *Idaho*
University of Illinois at Urbana - Champaign *Illinois*
The University of Iowa *Iowa*
University of Kentucky *Kentucky*
University of Maryland, College Park *Maryland*
University of Maryland Eastern Shore *Maryland*
University of Massachusetts Boston *Massachusetts*
University of Memphis *Tennessee*
University of Missouri *Missouri*
The University of North Carolina at Chapel Hill *North Carolina*
University of North Florida *Florida*
University of North Texas *Texas*
University of Northern Colorado *Colorado*
University of Pittsburgh *Pennsylvania*
University of Puerto Rico, Río Piedras Campus *Puerto Rico*
The University of Scranton *Pennsylvania*
University of South Carolina *South Carolina*
University of South Florida *Florida*
University of Southern Maine *Maine*
The University of Tennessee *Tennessee*
The University of Texas at Austin *Texas*
The University of Texas at El Paso *Texas*
The University of Texas Rio Grande Valley *Texas*
University of Wisconsin - Madison *Wisconsin*
University of Wisconsin - Stout *Wisconsin*
Utah State University *Utah*
Virginia Commonwealth University *Virginia*
Wayne State University *Michigan*
West Virginia University *West Virginia*
Western Michigan University *Michigan*
Western Oregon University *Oregon*
Western Washington University *Washington*
Wilberforce University *Ohio*
Winston-Salem State University *North Carolina*
Wright State University *Ohio*

Council on Social Work Education (CSWE)

Abilene Christian University *Texas*
Adelphi University *New York*
Alabama Agricultural and Mechanical University *Alabama*
Alabama State University *Alabama*
Albany State University *Georgia*
Alvernia University *Pennsylvania*
Anderson University *Indiana*
Andrews University *Michigan*
Anna Maria College *Massachusetts*
Appalachian State University *North Carolina*
Arizona State University at the Tempe campus *Arizona*
Arizona State University at the West campus *Arizona*
Arkansas State University *Arkansas*
Asbury University *Kentucky*
Ashland University *Ohio*
Auburn University *Alabama*
Augsburg College *Minnesota*
Augustana University *South Dakota*
Aurora University *Illinois*
Austin Peay State University *Tennessee*
Avila University *Missouri*
Azusa Pacific University *California*
Ball State University *Indiana*
Barry University *Florida*
Barton College *North Carolina*
Baylor University *Texas*
Belmont University *Tennessee*
Bemidji State University *Minnesota*
Benedict College *South Carolina*
Bennett College *North Carolina*
Bethany College *Kansas*
Bethany College *West Virginia*
Bethel College *Kansas*
Bethel University *Minnesota*

Binghamton University, State University of New York *New York*
Bloomsburg University of Pennsylvania *Pennsylvania*
Bluffton University *Ohio*
Boise State University *Idaho*
Boston College *Massachusetts*
Boston University *Massachusetts*
Bowie State University *Maryland*
Bowling Green State University *Ohio*
Bradley University *Illinois*
Brescia University *Kentucky*
Briar Cliff University *Iowa*
Bridgewater State University *Massachusetts*
Brigham Young University *Utah*
Brigham Young University - Hawaii *Hawaii*
Bryn Mawr College *Pennsylvania*
Buena Vista University *Iowa*
Buffalo State College, State University of New York *New York*
Cabrini University *Pennsylvania*
Cairn University *Pennsylvania*
California State University, Bakersfield *California*
California State University, Chico *California*
California State University, Dominguez Hills *California*
California State University, East Bay *California*
California State University, Fresno *California*
California State University, Fullerton *California*
California State University, Long Beach *California*
California State University, Los Angeles *California*
California State University, Northridge *California*
California State University, Sacramento *California*
California State University, San Bernardino *California*
California State University, Stanislaus *California*
California University of Pennsylvania *Pennsylvania*
Calvin College *Michigan*
Campbell University *North Carolina*
Campbellsville University *Kentucky*
Capital University *Ohio*
Carlow University *Pennsylvania*
Carthage College *Wisconsin*
Case Western Reserve University *Ohio*
Castleton University *Vermont*
The Catholic University of America *District of Columbia*
Cedar Crest College *Pennsylvania*
Cedarville University *Ohio*
Central Connecticut State University *Connecticut*
Central Michigan University *Michigan*
Chadron State College *Nebraska*
Chatham University *Pennsylvania*
Chicago State University *Illinois*
Christopher Newport University *Virginia*
Clark Atlanta University *Georgia*
Clarke University *Iowa*
Cleveland State University *Ohio*
The College at Brockport, State University of New York *New York*
The College of New Rochelle *New York*
College of Saint Benedict *Minnesota*
The College of Saint Rose *New York*
The College of St. Scholastica *Minnesota*
Colorado State University *Colorado*
Colorado State University - Pueblo *Colorado*
Columbia College *Missouri*
Columbia College *South Carolina*
Columbia University *New York*
Concord University *West Virginia*
Concordia College *Minnesota*
Concordia College - New York *New York*
Concordia University Wisconsin *Wisconsin*
Coppin State University *Maryland*
Cornerstone University *Michigan*
Creighton University *Nebraska*
Daemen College *New York*
Defiance College *Ohio*
Delaware State University *Delaware*
Delta State University *Mississippi*
DePaul University *Illinois*
Dominican College *New York*
Dominican University *Illinois*
Dordt College *Iowa*
East Carolina University *North Carolina*
East Central University *Oklahoma*

East Tennessee State University *Tennessee*
Eastern Connecticut State University *Connecticut*
Eastern Kentucky University *Kentucky*
Eastern Mennonite University *Virginia*
Eastern Michigan University *Michigan*
Eastern Nazarene College *Massachusetts*
Eastern University *Pennsylvania*
Eastern Washington University *Washington*
Edinboro University of Pennsylvania *Pennsylvania*
Elizabethtown College *Pennsylvania*
Elms College *Massachusetts*
Evangel University *Missouri*
Fayetteville State University *North Carolina*
Ferris State University *Michigan*
Ferrum College *Virginia*
Florida Agricultural and Mechanical University *Florida*
Florida Atlantic University *Florida*
Florida Gulf Coast University *Florida*
Florida International University *Florida*
Florida State University *Florida*
Fordham University *New York*
Fort Hays State University *Kansas*
Freed-Hardeman University *Tennessee*
Frostburg State University *Maryland*
Gallaudet University *District of Columbia*
Gannon University *Pennsylvania*
George Fox University *Oregon*
George Mason University *Virginia*
Georgia State University *Georgia*
Georgian Court University *New Jersey*
Gordon College *Massachusetts*
Goshen College *Indiana*
Governors State University *Illinois*
Grace College *Indiana*
Grambling State University *Louisiana*
Grand Valley State University *Michigan*
Hardin-Simmons University *Texas*
Harding University *Arkansas*
Hawai'i Pacific University *Hawaii*
Heritage University *Washington*
Hood College *Maryland*
Hope College *Michigan*
Howard Payne University *Texas*
Howard University *District of Columbia*
Humboldt State University *California*
Hunter College of the City University of New York *New York*
Idaho State University *Idaho*
Illinois State University *Illinois*
Indiana State University *Indiana*
Indiana University Bloomington *Indiana*
Indiana University East *Indiana*
Indiana University Northwest *Indiana*
Indiana University - Purdue University Indianapolis *Indiana*
Indiana University South Bend *Indiana*
Indiana Wesleyan University *Indiana*
Inter American University of Puerto Rico, Arecibo Campus *Puerto Rico*
Inter American University of Puerto Rico, Metropolitan Campus *Puerto Rico*
Iona College *New York*
Jackson State University *Mississippi*
Jacksonville State University *Alabama*
James Madison University *Virginia*
Johnson C. Smith University *North Carolina*
Juniata College *Pennsylvania*
Kansas State University *Kansas*
Kean University *New Jersey*
Kennesaw State University *Georgia*
Kentucky Christian University *Kentucky*
Kentucky State University *Kentucky*
Keuka College *New York*
Kutztown University of Pennsylvania *Pennsylvania*
La Salle University *Pennsylvania*
La Sierra University *California*
Lamar University *Texas*
Lehman College of the City University of New York *New York*
Lewis-Clark State College *Idaho*
Limestone College *South Carolina*
Lincoln Memorial University *Tennessee*
Lipscomb University *Tennessee*
Livingstone College *North Carolina*

Lock Haven University of Pennsylvania *Pennsylvania*
Loma Linda University *California*
Long Island University - LIU Brooklyn *New York*
Long Island University - LIU Post *New York*
Longwood University *Virginia*
Loras College *Iowa*
Louisiana College *Louisiana*
Louisiana State University and Agricultural & Mechanical College *Louisiana*
Lourdes University *Ohio*
Loyola University Chicago *Illinois*
Lubbock Christian University *Texas*
Luther College *Iowa*
MacMurray College *Illinois*
Madonna University *Michigan*
Malone University *Ohio*
Manchester University *Indiana*
Mansfield University of Pennsylvania *Pennsylvania*
Marian University *Wisconsin*
Marist College *New York*
Mars Hill University *North Carolina*
Marshall University *West Virginia*
Marygrove College *Michigan*
Marywood University *Pennsylvania*
McDaniel College *Maryland*
Mercy College *New York*
Mercyhurst University *Pennsylvania*
Meredith College *North Carolina*
Methodist University *North Carolina*
Metropolitan State University *Minnesota*
Metropolitan State University of Denver *Colorado*
Miami University *Ohio*
Michigan State University *Michigan*
Middle Tennessee State University *Tennessee*
Midwestern State University *Texas*
Miles College *Alabama*
Millersville University of Pennsylvania *Pennsylvania*
Minnesota State University Mankato *Minnesota*
Minnesota State University Moorhead *Minnesota*
Minot State University *North Dakota*
Misericordia University *Pennsylvania*
Mississippi College *Mississippi*
Mississippi State University *Mississippi*
Mississippi Valley State University *Mississippi*
Missouri State University *Missouri*
Missouri Western State University *Missouri*
Molloy College *New York*
Monmouth University *New Jersey*
Morehead State University *Kentucky*
Morgan State University *Maryland*
Mount Mary University *Wisconsin*
Mount Mercy University *Iowa*
Mount St. Joseph University *Ohio*
Murray State University *Kentucky*
Nazareth College of Rochester *New York*
New Mexico Highlands University *New Mexico*
New Mexico State University *New Mexico*
New York University *New York*
Newman University *Kansas*
Niagara University *New York*
Norfolk State University *Virginia*
North Carolina Agricultural and Technical State University *North Carolina*
North Carolina Central University *North Carolina*
North Carolina State University *North Carolina*
Northeastern Illinois University *Illinois*
Northeastern State University *Oklahoma*
Northern Arizona University *Arizona*
Northern Kentucky University *Kentucky*
Northern Michigan University *Michigan*
Northwest Nazarene University *Idaho*
Northwestern College *Iowa*
Northwestern State University of Louisiana *Louisiana*
Oakwood University *Alabama*
The Ohio State University *Ohio*
Ohio University *Ohio*
Olivet Nazarene University *Illinois*
Oral Roberts University *Oklahoma*
Our Lady of the Lake University of San Antonio *Texas*
Pacific Lutheran University *Washington*
Pacific Union College *California*
Philander Smith College *Arkansas*
Pittsburg State University *Kansas*

Plymouth State University *New Hampshire*
Pontifical Catholic University of Puerto Rico *Puerto Rico*
Portland State University *Oregon*
Prairie View A&M University *Texas*
Presentation College *South Dakota*
Providence College *Rhode Island*
Radford University *Virginia*
Ramapo College of New Jersey *New Jersey*
Regis College *Massachusetts*
Rhode Island College *Rhode Island*
Roberts Wesleyan College *New York*
Rochester Institute of Technology *New York*
Rust College *Mississippi*
Rutgers University - Camden *New Jersey*
Rutgers University - New Brunswick *New Jersey*
Rutgers University - Newark *New Jersey*
Sacred Heart University *Connecticut*
Saginaw Valley State University *Michigan*
St. Ambrose University *Iowa*
St. Catherine University *Minnesota*
St. Cloud State University *Minnesota*
St. Edward's University *Texas*
Saint Francis University *Pennsylvania*
Saint John's University *Minnesota*
Saint Leo University *Florida*
Saint Louis University *Missouri*
Saint Mary's College *Indiana*
St. Olaf College *Minnesota*
Salem State University *Massachusetts*
Salisbury University *Maryland*
Salve Regina University *Rhode Island*
San Diego State University *California*
San Francisco State University *California*
San Jose State University *California*
Savannah State University *Georgia*
Seton Hall University *New Jersey*
Seton Hill University *Pennsylvania*
Shepherd University *West Virginia*
Shippensburg University of Pennsylvania *Pennsylvania*
Siena College *New York*
Simmons College *Massachusetts*
Skidmore College *New York*
Slippery Rock University of Pennsylvania *Pennsylvania*
Smith College *Massachusetts*
South Carolina State University *South Carolina*
Southeast Missouri State University *Missouri*
Southeastern Louisiana University *Louisiana*
Southern Adventist University *Tennessee*
Southern Arkansas University - Magnolia *Arkansas*
Southern Connecticut State University *Connecticut*
Southern Illinois University Carbondale *Illinois*
Southern Illinois University Edwardsville *Illinois*
Southern University and Agricultural and Mechanical College *Louisiana*
Southern University at New Orleans *Louisiana*
Southwest Minnesota State University *Minnesota*
Southwestern Adventist University *Texas*
Southwestern Oklahoma State University *Oklahoma*
Spalding University *Kentucky*
Spring Arbor University *Michigan*
Springfield College *Massachusetts*
State University of New York at Fredonia *New York*
State University of New York at Plattsburgh *New York*
Stephen F. Austin State University *Texas*
Stockton University *New Jersey*
Stony Brook University, State University of New York *New York*
Syracuse University *New York*
Talladega College *Alabama*
Tarleton State University *Texas*
Taylor University *Indiana*
Temple University *Pennsylvania*
Tennessee State University *Tennessee*
Texas A&M University - Commerce *Texas*
Texas A&M University - Kingsville *Texas*
Texas Christian University *Texas*
Texas Southern University *Texas*
Texas State University *Texas*
Texas Tech University *Texas*
Texas Woman's University *Texas*
Troy University *Alabama*
Tulane University *Louisiana*

Tuskegee University *Alabama*
Union University *Tennessee*
The University of Akron *Ohio*
The University of Alabama *Alabama*
The University of Alabama at Birmingham *Alabama*
University of Alaska Anchorage *Alaska*
University of Alaska Fairbanks *Alaska*
University at Albany, State University of New York *New York*
University of Arkansas *Arkansas*
University of Arkansas at Little Rock *Arkansas*
University of Arkansas at Monticello *Arkansas*
University of Arkansas at Pine Bluff *Arkansas*
University at Buffalo, the State University of New York *New York*
University of California, Berkeley *California*
University of California, Los Angeles *California*
University of Central Florida *Florida*
University of Central Missouri *Missouri*
University of Chicago *Illinois*
University of Cincinnati *Ohio*
University of Connecticut *Connecticut*
University of Denver *Colorado*
University of Detroit Mercy *Michigan*
University of the District of Columbia *District of Columbia*
The University of Findlay *Ohio*
University of Georgia *Georgia*
University of Guam *Guam*
University of Hawaii at Manoa *Hawaii*
University of Houston *Texas*
University of Illinois at Chicago *Illinois*
University of Illinois at Springfield *Illinois*
University of Illinois at Urbana - Champaign *Illinois*
University of Indianapolis *Indiana*
The University of Iowa *Iowa*
The University of Kansas *Kansas*
University of Kentucky *Kentucky*
University of Louisiana at Monroe *Louisiana*
University of Louisville *Kentucky*
University of Maine *Maine*
University of Maine at Presque Isle *Maine*
University of Mary *North Dakota*
University of Mary Hardin-Baylor *Texas*
University of Maryland, Baltimore County *Maryland*
University of Memphis *Tennessee*
University of Michigan *Michigan*
University of Michigan - Flint *Michigan*
University of Minnesota, Duluth *Minnesota*
University of Minnesota, Twin Cities Campus *Minnesota*
University of Mississippi *Mississippi*
University of Missouri *Missouri*
University of Missouri - Kansas City *Missouri*
University of Missouri - St. Louis *Missouri*
University of Montana *Montana*
University of Montevallo *Alabama*
University of Nebraska at Kearney *Nebraska*
University of Nebraska at Omaha *Nebraska*
University of Nevada, Las Vegas *Nevada*
University of Nevada, Reno *Nevada*
University of New England *Maine*
University of New Hampshire *New Hampshire*
University of North Alabama *Alabama*
The University of North Carolina at Chapel Hill *North Carolina*
The University of North Carolina at Charlotte *North Carolina*
The University of North Carolina at Greensboro *North Carolina*
The University of North Carolina at Pembroke *North Carolina*
The University of North Carolina Wilmington *North Carolina*
University of North Dakota *North Dakota*
University of North Texas *Texas*
University of Northern Iowa *Iowa*
University of Oklahoma *Oklahoma*
University of Pennsylvania *Pennsylvania*
University of Pittsburgh *Pennsylvania*
University of Puerto Rico in Humacao *Puerto Rico*
University of Puerto Rico, Río Piedras Campus *Puerto Rico*
University of Rio Grande *Ohio*
University of the Sacred Heart *Puerto Rico*
University of St. Francis *Illinois*

University of Saint Francis *Indiana*
University of Saint Joseph *Connecticut*
University of St. Thomas *Minnesota*
University of Sioux Falls *South Dakota*
The University of South Dakota *South Dakota*
University of South Florida *Florida*
University of Southern California *California*
University of Southern Indiana *Indiana*
University of Southern Maine *Maine*
University of Southern Mississippi *Mississippi*
The University of Tennessee *Tennessee*
The University of Tennessee at Chattanooga *Tennessee*
The University of Tennessee at Martin *Tennessee*
The University of Texas at Arlington *Texas*
The University of Texas at Austin *Texas*
The University of Texas at El Paso *Texas*
The University of Texas Rio Grande Valley *Texas*
The University of Texas at San Antonio *Texas*
The University of Toledo *Ohio*
University of Utah *Utah*
University of Vermont *Vermont*
University of Washington *Washington*
University of West Florida *Florida*
University of Wisconsin - Eau Claire *Wisconsin*
University of Wisconsin - Green Bay *Wisconsin*
University of Wisconsin - Madison *Wisconsin*
University of Wisconsin - Milwaukee *Wisconsin*
University of Wisconsin - Oshkosh *Wisconsin*
University of Wisconsin - River Falls *Wisconsin*
University of Wisconsin - Superior *Wisconsin*
University of Wisconsin - Whitewater *Wisconsin*
University of Wyoming *Wyoming*
Ursuline College *Ohio*
Utah State University *Utah*
Valdosta State University *Georgia*
Valparaiso University *Indiana*
Virginia Commonwealth University *Virginia*
Virginia Union University *Virginia*
Walla Walla University *Washington*
Warren Wilson College *North Carolina*
Wartburg College *Iowa*
Washburn University *Kansas*
Washington University in St. Louis *Missouri*
Wayne State University *Michigan*
Weber State University *Utah*
West Chester University of Pennsylvania *Pennsylvania*
West Texas A&M University *Texas*
West Virginia State University *West Virginia*
West Virginia University *West Virginia*
Western Carolina University *North Carolina*
Western Connecticut State University *Connecticut*
Western Illinois University *Illinois*
Western Kentucky University *Kentucky*
Western Michigan University *Michigan*
Western New England University *Massachusetts*
Western New Mexico University *New Mexico*
Westfield State University *Massachusetts*
Wheelock College *Massachusetts*
Whittier College *California*
Wichita State University *Kansas*
Widener University *Pennsylvania*
William Woods University *Missouri*
Winona State University *Minnesota*
Winthrop University *South Carolina*
Wright State University *Ohio*
Xavier University *Ohio*
Yeshiva University *New York*
York College of the City University of New York *New York*
Youngstown State University *Ohio*

Distance Education Accrediting Commission (DEAC)

Allied American University *California*
American Business & Technology University *Missouri*
American College of Healthcare Sciences *Oregon*
American Sentinel University *Colorado*
APT College *California*
Ashworth College *Georgia*
Aspen University *Colorado*
California Coast University *California*
California Intercontinental University *California*

California National University for Advanced Studies *California*
City Vision University *Missouri*
Columbia Southern University *Alabama*
Dunlap-Stone University *Arizona*
EC-Council University *New Mexico*
Ellis University *Illinois*
Global University *Missouri*
Grantham University *Kansas*
Harrison Middleton University *Arizona*
Henley-Putnam University *California*
Huntington College of Health Sciences *Tennessee*
INSTE Bible College *Iowa*
National Paralegal College *Arizona*
New Charter University *California*
The Paralegal Institute at Brighton College *Arizona*
Penn Foster College *Arizona*
Sessions College for Professional Design *Arizona*
Shiloh University *Iowa*
Southwest University *Louisiana*
University of Management and Technology *Virginia*

Joint Commission on Allied Health Personnel in Ophthalmology (JCAHPO)

Emory University *Georgia*
Lakeland Community College *Ohio*
Louisiana State University Health Sciences Center *Louisiana*
Old Dominion University *Virginia*
Portland Community College *Oregon*
Pueblo Community College *Colorado*
Triton College *Illinois*

Joint Review Committee on Education in Cardiovascular Technology (JRCECT)

Augusta Technical College *Georgia*
El Centro College *Texas*
Florida SouthWestern State College *Florida*
Geneva College *Pennsylvania*
Grossmont College *California*
Gwynedd Mercy University *Pennsylvania*
Milwaukee Area Technical College *Wisconsin*
Orange Coast College *California*
Southeast Technical Institute *South Dakota*
Spokane Community College *Washington*
The University of Toledo *Ohio*

Joint Review Committee on Education in Diagnostic Medical Sonography (JRCEDMS)

Adventist University of Health Sciences *Florida*
Augusta University *Georgia*
Austin Community College District *Texas*
Baptist College of Health Sciences *Tennessee*
Bellevue College *Washington*
Bergen Community College *New Jersey*
Boise State University *Idaho*
Broward College *Florida*
Bunker Hill Community College *Massachusetts*
Caldwell Community College and Technical Institute *North Carolina*
Central Ohio Technical College *Ohio*
Chippewa Valley Technical College *Wisconsin*
College of Southern Nevada *Nevada*
Community College of Allegheny County *Pennsylvania*
Cuyahoga Community College *Ohio*
Del Mar College *Texas*
Delaware Technical & Community College, Stanton/Wilmington Campus *Delaware*
Delta College *Michigan*
El Centro College *Texas*
Forsyth Technical Community College *North Carolina*
The George Washington University *District of Columbia*
Hillsborough Community College *Florida*
Jackson College *Michigan*
Keiser University *Florida*
Kettering College *Ohio*
Lorain County Community College *Ohio*
Mercy College of Health Sciences *Iowa*
Miami Dade College *Florida*
Middlesex Community College *Massachusetts*

Nebraska Methodist College *Nebraska*
New York University *New York*
Oakland Community College *Michigan*
Orange Coast College *California*
Owens Community College *Ohio*
Pitt Community College *North Carolina*
Pittsburgh Career Institute *Pennsylvania*
Rochester Institute of Technology *New York*
Rowan College at Gloucester County *New Jersey*
St. Catherine University *Minnesota*
Seattle University *Washington*
Springfield Technical Community College *Massachusetts*
State University of New York Downstate Medical Center *New York*
Thomas Jefferson University *Pennsylvania*
Triton College *Illinois*
Tyler Junior College *Texas*
University of Nebraska Medical Center *Nebraska*
University of Oklahoma Health Sciences Center *Oklahoma*
Valencia College *Florida*
Wallace State Community College *Alabama*

Joint Review Committee on Education in Electroneurodiagnostic Technology (JRCEND)

Kirkwood Community College *Iowa*
Labouré College *Massachusetts*
Niagara County Community College *New York*
Orange Coast College *California*
Scott Community College *Iowa*
Southwestern Community College *North Carolina*
Western Technical College *Wisconsin*

Joint Review Committee on Education in Radiologic Technology (JRCERT)

Adventist University of Health Sciences *Florida*
Aims Community College *Colorado*
Albany Technical College *Georgia*
Allegany College of Maryland *Maryland*
Allen College *Iowa*
Amarillo College *Texas*
Angelina College *Texas*
Anne Arundel Community College *Maryland*
Argosy University, Twin Cities *Minnesota*
Arkansas State University *Arkansas*
Armstrong State University *Georgia*
Asheville-Buncombe Technical Community College *North Carolina*
Athens Technical College *Georgia*
Augusta University *Georgia*
Austin Community College District *Texas*
Avila University *Missouri*
Bacone College *Oklahoma*
Bakersfield College *California*
Ball State University *Indiana*
Bellevue College *Washington*
Bergen Community College *New Jersey*
Blackhawk Technical College *Wisconsin*
Blinn College *Texas*
Bluefield State College *West Virginia*
Boise State University *Idaho*
Bronx Community College of the City University of New York *New York*
Brookdale Community College *New Jersey*
Broome Community College *New York*
Bunker Hill Community College *Massachusetts*
Cabrillo College *California*
Caldwell Community College and Technical Institute *North Carolina*
California State University, Long Beach *California*
California State University, Northridge *California*
Cañada College *California*
Capital Community College *Connecticut*
Carl Sandburg College *Illinois*
Carrington College - Spokane *Washington*
Carteret Community College *North Carolina*
Casper College *Wyoming*
Central Ohio Technical College *Ohio*
Central Virginia Community College *Virginia*
Chaffey College *California*
Champlain College *Vermont*
Charles R. Drew University of Medicine and Science *California*
Chesapeake College *Maryland*

CHI Health School of Radiologic Technology *Nebraska*
Chippewa Valley Technical College *Wisconsin*
City College of San Francisco *California*
City Colleges of Chicago, Malcolm X College *Illinois*
City Colleges of Chicago, Wilbur Wright College *Illinois*
Clarkson College *Nebraska*
Cleveland Community College *North Carolina*
Clovis Community College *New Mexico*
College of Coastal Georgia *Georgia*
College of DuPage *Illinois*
College of Lake County *Illinois*
Colorado Mesa University *Colorado*
Columbia State Community College *Tennessee*
Columbus State Community College *Ohio*
Community College of Allegheny County *Pennsylvania*
Community College of Baltimore County *Maryland*
Community College of Denver *Colorado*
Community College of Philadelphia *Pennsylvania*
Community College of Rhode Island *Rhode Island*
Copiah-Lincoln Community College *Mississippi*
County College of Morris *New Jersey*
Cumberland County College *New Jersey*
Cuyahoga Community College *Ohio*
Cypress College *California*
Del Mar College *Texas*
Delaware Technical & Community College, Jack F. Owens Campus *Delaware*
Delaware Technical & Community College, Stanton/Wilmington Campus *Delaware*
Delgado Community College *Louisiana*
Delta College *Michigan*
Doña Ana Community College *New Mexico*
East Tennessee State University *Tennessee*
Eastern Florida State College *Florida*
Eastern Gateway Community College *Ohio*
Eastern Maine Community College *Maine*
Edgecombe Community College *North Carolina*
El Camino College *California*
El Centro College *Texas*
Emory University *Georgia*
Erie Community College *New York*
Essex County College *New Jersey*
Eugenio María de Hostos Community College of the City University of New York *New York*
Fayetteville Technical Community College *North Carolina*
Ferris State University *Michigan*
Florence-Darlington Technical College *South Carolina*
Florida SouthWestern State College *Florida*
Foothill College *California*
Forsyth Technical Community College *North Carolina*
Fort Hays State University *Kansas*
Fresno City College *California*
Gadsden State Community College *Alabama*
Galveston College *Texas*
Gannon University *Pennsylvania*
GateWay Community College *Arizona*
Gateway Community College *Connecticut*
George C. Wallace Community College *Alabama*
Goldfarb School of Nursing at Barnes-Jewish College *Missouri*
Grand Rapids Community College *Michigan*
Greenville Technical College *South Carolina*
Gulf Coast State College *Florida*
Gwinnett Technical College *Georgia*
Gwynedd Mercy University *Pennsylvania*
Hagerstown Community College *Maryland*
Hazard Community and Technical College *Kentucky*
Hillsborough Community College *Florida*
Hinds Community College *Mississippi*
Holy Family University *Pennsylvania*
Holyoke Community College *Massachusetts*
Horry-Georgetown Technical College *South Carolina*
Houston Community College *Texas*
Howard University *District of Columbia*
Hudson Valley Community College *New York*
Hutchinson Community College *Kansas*
Illinois Central College *Illinois*
Illinois Eastern Community Colleges, Olney Central College *Illinois*
Indian Hills Community College *Iowa*

Indian River State College *Florida*
Indiana University Northwest *Indiana*
Indiana University - Purdue University Indianapolis *Indiana*
Indiana University South Bend *Indiana*
Iowa Central Community College *Iowa*
Itawamba Community College *Mississippi*
Ivy Tech Community College - Central Indiana *Indiana*
Ivy Tech Community College - Wabash Valley *Indiana*
Jackson State Community College *Tennessee*
James A. Rhodes State College *Ohio*
Jefferson State Community College *Alabama*
Johnston Community College *North Carolina*
Jones County Junior College *Mississippi*
Kapiolani Community College *Hawaii*
Kaskaskia College *Illinois*
Keiser University *Florida*
Kellogg Community College *Michigan*
Kent State University at Salem *Ohio*
Kettering College *Ohio*
Kilgore College *Texas*
Kishwaukee College *Illinois*
Labette Community College *Kansas*
Labouré College *Massachusetts*
Lake Michigan College *Michigan*
Lakeland Community College *Ohio*
Lakeshore Technical College *Wisconsin*
Lamar University *Texas*
Lansing Community College *Michigan*
Laramie County Community College *Wyoming*
Laredo Community College *Texas*
Lincoln Land Community College *Illinois*
Loma Linda University *California*
Long Beach City College *California*
Long Island University - LIU Post *New York*
Lorain County Community College *Ohio*
Los Angeles City College *California*
Louisiana State University at Eunice *Louisiana*
Madison Area Technical College *Wisconsin*
Mansfield University of Pennsylvania *Pennsylvania*
Marion Technical College *Ohio*
Marygrove College *Michigan*
Massachusetts Bay Community College *Massachusetts*
Massasoit Community College *Massachusetts*
McLennan Community College *Texas*
McNeese State University *Louisiana*
Merced College *California*
Mercer County Community College *New Jersey*
Mercy College of Ohio *Ohio*
Meridian Community College *Mississippi*
Merritt College *California*
Miami Dade College *Florida*
Mid Michigan Community College *Michigan*
Middlesex Community College *Connecticut*
Middlesex Community College *Massachusetts*
Middlesex County College *New Jersey*
Midland College *Texas*
Midlands Technical College *South Carolina*
Milwaukee Area Technical College *Wisconsin*
Misericordia University *Pennsylvania*
Mississippi Delta Community College *Mississippi*
Mississippi Gulf Coast Community College *Mississippi*
Missouri Southern State University *Missouri*
Monroe Community College *New York*
Moorpark College *California*
Moraine Valley Community College *Illinois*
Morehead State University *Kentucky*
Mt. San Antonio College *California*
Nassau Community College *New York*
National Louis University *Illinois*
National Park College *Arkansas*
Naugatuck Valley Community College *Connecticut*
New York City College of Technology of the City University of New York *New York*
Newman University *Kansas*
NHTI, Concord's Community College *New Hampshire*
Niagara County Community College *New York*
North Arkansas College *Arkansas*
North Central State College *Ohio*
North Country Community College *New York*
North Shore Community College *Massachusetts*

Northampton Community College *Pennsylvania*
Northcentral Technical College *Wisconsin*
Northeast Mississippi Community College *Mississippi*
Northern Essex Community College *Massachusetts*
Northern Kentucky University *Kentucky*
Northern New Mexico College *New Mexico*
Northwest Technical College *Minnesota*
Northwestern State University of Louisiana *Louisiana*
Oakland Community College *Michigan*
Odessa College *Texas*
Orange Coast College *California*
Orangeburg-Calhoun Technical College *South Carolina*
Oregon Health & Science University *Oregon*
Oregon Institute of Technology *Oregon*
Our Lady of the Lake College *Louisiana*
Owens Community College *Ohio*
Owensboro Community and Technical College *Kentucky*
Palm Beach State College *Florida*
Parkland College *Illinois*
Pasadena City College *California*
Passaic County Community College *New Jersey*
Pearl River Community College *Mississippi*
Penn State New Kensington *Pennsylvania*
Penn State Schuylkill *Pennsylvania*
Pennsylvania College of Technology *Pennsylvania*
Pensacola State College *Florida*
Piedmont Technical College *South Carolina*
Pima Community College *Arizona*
Pima Medical Institute *Mesa, Arizona*
Pima Medical Institute *Tucson, Arizona*
Pima Medical Institute *Denver, Colorado*
Pima Medical Institute *Albuquerque, New Mexico*
Pima Medical Institute *Seattle, Washington*
Pitt Community College *North Carolina*
Pittsburgh Career Institute *Pennsylvania*
Polk State College *Florida*
Portland Community College *Oregon*
Presentation College *South Dakota*
Prince George's Community College *Maryland*
Quinnipiac University *Connecticut*
Quinsigamond Community College *Massachusetts*
Riverland Community College *Minnesota*
Roane State Community College *Tennessee*
Robert Morris University *Pennsylvania*
Rose State College *Oklahoma*
Rowan-Cabarrus Community College *North Carolina*
St. Philip's College *Texas*
Salt Lake Community College *Utah*
Sandhills Community College *North Carolina*
Santa Barbara City College *California*
Santa Fe College *Florida*
Santa Rosa Junior College *California*
Sauk Valley Community College *Illinois*
Scott Community College *Iowa*
Shawnee State University *Ohio*
Sinclair Community College *Ohio*
South Arkansas Community College *Arkansas*
South Plains College *Texas*
South Suburban College *Illinois*
Southeast Arkansas College *Arkansas*
Southeast Community College, Lincoln Campus *Nebraska*
Southern Maine Community College *Maine*
Southern Union State Community College *Alabama*
Southern University at Shreveport *Louisiana*
Southern West Virginia Community and Technical College *West Virginia*
Southwest Tennessee Community College *Tennessee*
Southwest Virginia Community College *Virginia*
Southwestern Community College *North Carolina*
Southwestern Illinois College *Illinois*
Southwestern Oklahoma State University at Sayre *Oklahoma*
Spartanburg Community College *South Carolina*
Springfield Technical Community College *Massachusetts*
State College of Florida Manatee-Sarasota *Florida*
State University of New York Upstate Medical University *New York*
Tacoma Community College *Washington*
Tarrant County College District *Texas*

Texas Southmost College *Texas*
Texas State University *Texas*
Thomas Jefferson University *Pennsylvania*
Tidewater Community College *Virginia*
Trident Technical College *South Carolina*
Triton College *Illinois*
Trocaire College *New York*
Truckee Meadows Community College *Nevada*
Tulsa Community College *Oklahoma*
Tyler Junior College *Texas*
Universidad Central del Caribe *Puerto Rico*
The University of Alabama at Birmingham *Alabama*
University of Arkansas - Fort Smith *Arkansas*
University of Arkansas for Medical Sciences *Arkansas*
University of Central Florida *Florida*
University of Charleston *West Virginia*
University of Cincinnati Blue Ash College *Ohio*
University of the District of Columbia *District of Columbia*
University of Hartford *Connecticut*
University of Louisiana at Monroe *Louisiana*
University of Louisville *Kentucky*
University of Michigan - Flint *Michigan*
University of Missouri *Missouri*
University of Nebraska Medical Center *Nebraska*
The University of North Carolina at Chapel Hill *North Carolina*
University of Oklahoma Health Sciences Center *Oklahoma*
University of Puerto Rico, Medical Sciences Campus *Puerto Rico*
University of Saint Francis *Indiana*
University of Southern Indiana *Indiana*
The University of Texas Health Science Center at Houston *Texas*
University of Wisconsin - La Crosse *Wisconsin*
Valencia College *Florida*
Vance-Granville Community College *North Carolina*
Virginia Commonwealth University *Virginia*
Virginia Highlands Community College *Virginia*
Virginia Western Community College *Virginia*
Volunteer State Community College *Tennessee*
Wake Technical Community College *North Carolina*
Wallace State Community College *Alabama*
Washburn University *Kansas*
Washtenaw Community College *Michigan*
Wayne State University *Michigan*
Wenatchee Valley College *Washington*
Westchester Community College *New York*
Western Oklahoma State College *Oklahoma*
Western Technical College *Wisconsin*
Wharton County Junior College *Texas*
Wiregrass Georgia Technical College *Georgia*
Wor-Wic Community College *Maryland*
Xavier University *Ohio*
Yakima Valley Community College *Washington*
York Technical College *South Carolina*
Yuba College *California*
Zane State College *Ohio*

Joint Review Committee on Educational Programs in Athletic Training (JRCAT)

Alvernia University *Pennsylvania*
Anderson University *Indiana*
Appalachian State University *North Carolina*
Arkansas State University *Arkansas*
Augustana University *South Dakota*
Azusa Pacific University *California*
Ball State University *Indiana*
Barry University *Florida*
Bethel University *Minnesota*
Boise State University *Idaho*
Boston University *Massachusetts*
Bridgewater State University *Massachusetts*
Brigham Young University *Utah*
California State University, Fresno *California*
California State University, Fullerton *California*
California State University, Northridge *California*
California State University, Sacramento *California*
California University of Pennsylvania *Pennsylvania*
Campbell University *North Carolina*
Canisius College *New York*
Capital University *Ohio*
Castleton University *Vermont*

Catawba College *North Carolina*
Central Connecticut State University *Connecticut*
Central Methodist University *Missouri*
Central Michigan University *Michigan*
Colby-Sawyer College *New Hampshire*
The College at Brockport, State University of New York *New York*
College of Charleston *South Carolina*
Dakota Wesleyan University *South Dakota*
DePauw University *Indiana*
Duquesne University *Pennsylvania*
East Carolina University *North Carolina*
East Stroudsburg University of Pennsylvania *Pennsylvania*
Eastern Illinois University *Illinois*
Eastern Kentucky University *Kentucky*
Eastern Michigan University *Michigan*
Elon University *North Carolina*
Emory & Henry College *Virginia*
Emporia State University *Kansas*
Endicott College *Massachusetts*
Florida Southern College *Florida*
Fort Lewis College *Colorado*
George Fox University *Oregon*
The George Washington University *District of Columbia*
Georgia Southern University *Georgia*
Grand Valley State University *Michigan*
Gustavus Adolphus College *Minnesota*
High Point University *North Carolina*
Hofstra University *New York*
Hope College *Michigan*
Illinois State University *Illinois*
Indiana State University *Indiana*
Indiana University Bloomington *Indiana*
Indiana University of Pennsylvania *Pennsylvania*
Iowa State University of Science and Technology *Iowa*
Ithaca College *New York*
James Madison University *Virginia*
Kansas State University *Kansas*
Kean University *New Jersey*
Keene State College *New Hampshire*
King's College *Pennsylvania*
Lasell College *Massachusetts*
Lenoir-Rhyne University *North Carolina*
Lincoln Memorial University *Tennessee*
Linfield College *Oregon*
Lipscomb University *Tennessee*
Lock Haven University of Pennsylvania *Pennsylvania*
Longwood University *Virginia*
Manchester University *Indiana*
Marietta College *Ohio*
Mars Hill University *North Carolina*
Marshall University *West Virginia*
Mercyhurst University *Pennsylvania*
Merrimack College *Massachusetts*
Messiah College *Pennsylvania*
Methodist University *North Carolina*
Miami University *Ohio*
Minnesota State University Mankato *Minnesota*
Missouri State University *Missouri*
New Mexico State University *New Mexico*
North Dakota State University *North Dakota*
Northeastern University *Massachusetts*
Northern Illinois University *Illinois*
Ohio Northern University *Ohio*
Ohio University *Ohio*
Oklahoma State University *Oklahoma*
Oregon State University *Oregon*
Otterbein University *Ohio*
Park University *Missouri*
Penn State University Park *Pennsylvania*
Plymouth State University *New Hampshire*
Purdue University *Indiana*
Roanoke College *Virginia*
Rowan University *New Jersey*
Sacred Heart University *Connecticut*
Salem State University *Massachusetts*
Salisbury University *Maryland*
Samford University *Alabama*
San Diego State University *California*
San Jose State University *California*
Slippery Rock University of Pennsylvania *Pennsylvania*

South Dakota State University *South Dakota*
Southeast Missouri State University *Missouri*
Southern Connecticut State University *Connecticut*
Southern Illinois University Carbondale *Illinois*
Southwestern University *Texas*
Springfield College *Massachusetts*
State University of New York College at Cortland *New York*
Stetson University *Florida*
Temple University *Pennsylvania*
Texas Christian University *Texas*
Texas State University *Texas*
Towson University *Maryland*
Troy University *Alabama*
Truman State University *Missouri*
The University of Alabama *Alabama*
University of Central Florida *Florida*
University of Charleston *West Virginia*
University of Cincinnati *Ohio*
University of Delaware *Delaware*
University of Florida *Florida*
University of Georgia *Georgia*
University of Illinois at Urbana - Champaign *Illinois*
University of Indianapolis *Indiana*
The University of Iowa *Iowa*
University of Mary *North Dakota*
University of Montana *Montana*
University of Mount Union *Ohio*
University of Nebraska at Kearney *Nebraska*
University of Nebraska at Omaha *Nebraska*
University of Nevada, Las Vegas *Nevada*
University of New Hampshire *New Hampshire*
University of New Mexico *New Mexico*
The University of North Carolina at Chapel Hill *North Carolina*
University of North Dakota *North Dakota*
University of North Florida *Florida*
University of Northern Colorado *Colorado*
University of Northern Iowa *Iowa*
University of Pittsburgh *Pennsylvania*
University of South Carolina *South Carolina*
University of Southern Maine *Maine*
University of Southern Mississippi *Mississippi*
The University of Toledo *Ohio*
The University of Tulsa *Oklahoma*
University of Utah *Utah*
University of Vermont *Vermont*
The University of West Alabama *Alabama*
University of Wisconsin - La Crosse *Wisconsin*
University of Wisconsin - Madison *Wisconsin*
Valdosta State University *Georgia*
Vanguard University of Southern California *California*
Washington State University *Washington*
Waynesburg University *Pennsylvania*
West Chester University of Pennsylvania *Pennsylvania*
West Virginia University *West Virginia*
West Virginia Wesleyan College *West Virginia*
Western Illinois University *Illinois*
Westfield State University *Massachusetts*
Whitworth University *Washington*
William Paterson University of New Jersey *New Jersey*
Wilmington College *Ohio*
Wingate University *North Carolina*
Winona State University *Minnesota*
Wright State University *Ohio*
Xavier University *Ohio*

Joint Review Committee on Educational Programs for the EMT-Paramedic (JRCEMTP)

Austin Community College District *Texas*
Bismarck State College *North Dakota*
Borough of Manhattan Community College of the City University of New York *New York*
Broward College *Florida*
Capital Community College *Connecticut*
Catawba Valley Community College *North Carolina*
Central Washington University *Washington*
Century College *Minnesota*
Chemeketa Community College *Oregon*
College of Central Florida *Florida*
Columbia Basin College *Washington*
Columbia College *California*

Columbia State Community College *Tennessee*
Columbus State Community College *Ohio*
Crafton Hills College *California*
Creighton University *Nebraska*
Daytona State College *Florida*
Delaware Technical & Community College, Terry Campus *Delaware*
Delgado Community College *Louisiana*
Dixie State University *Utah*
Doña Ana Community College *New Mexico*
Eastern Florida State College *Florida*
Eastern Kentucky University *Kentucky*
Eastern New Mexico University - Roswell *New Mexico*
Florida Gateway College *Florida*
Florida SouthWestern State College *Florida*
Florida State College at Jacksonville *Florida*
Gadsden State Community College *Alabama*
Galveston College *Texas*
George C. Wallace Community College *Alabama*
Greenville Technical College *South Carolina*
Gulf Coast State College *Florida*
Harrisburg Area Community College *Pennsylvania*
Hillsborough Community College *Florida*
Holmes Community College *Mississippi*
Houston Community College *Texas*
Hudson Valley Community College *New York*
Indian River State College *Florida*
Ivy Tech Community College - Southwest *Indiana*
Jackson State Community College *Tennessee*
Jefferson College of Health Sciences *Virginia*
Johnson County Community College *Kansas*
Jones County Junior College *Mississippi*
Lansing Community College *Michigan*
Lee College *Texas*
Lurleen B. Wallace Community College *Alabama*
Miami Dade College *Florida*
Mississippi Gulf Coast Community College *Mississippi*
Monroe Community College *New York*
NHTI, Concord's Community College *New Hampshire*
Nicholls State University *Louisiana*
Northeast Alabama Community College *Alabama*
Northern Virginia Community College *Virginia*
NorthWest Arkansas Community College *Arkansas*
Oklahoma City Community College *Oklahoma*
Palm Beach State College *Florida*
Pasco-Hernando State College *Florida*
Pennsylvania College of Technology *Pennsylvania*
Pensacola State College *Florida*
Polk State College *Florida*
Pueblo Community College *Colorado*
St. Petersburg College *Florida*
Santa Fe College *Florida*
Seminole State College of Florida *Florida*
Southern Union State Community College *Alabama*
Tacoma Community College *Washington*
Tallahassee Community College *Florida*
Texas Tech University *Texas*
Tidewater Community College *Virginia*
The University of Alabama at Birmingham *Alabama*
University of Arkansas for Medical Sciences *Arkansas*
University of Maryland, Baltimore County *Maryland*
University of New Mexico *New Mexico*
University of Pittsburgh *Pennsylvania*
University of South Alabama *Alabama*
The University of Texas Health Science Center at San Antonio *Texas*
Valencia College *Florida*
Volunteer State Community College *Tennessee*
Wallace State Community College *Alabama*
Weber State University *Utah*
Western Carolina University *North Carolina*
Youngstown State University *Ohio*

Joint Review Committee on Educational Programs in Nuclear Medicine Technology (JRCNMT)

Adventist University of Health Sciences *Florida*
Amarillo College *Texas*
Augusta University *Georgia*
Baptist College of Health Sciences *Tennessee*
BridgeValley Community and Technical College *South Charleston, West Virginia*

Bronx Community College of the City University of New York *New York*
Broward College *Florida*
Caldwell Community College and Technical Institute *North Carolina*
Cedar Crest College *Pennsylvania*
Community College of Allegheny County *Pennsylvania*
Cuyahoga Community College *Ohio*
Delaware Technical & Community College, Stanton/Wilmington Campus *Delaware*
Ferris State University *Michigan*
Forsyth Technical Community College *North Carolina*
Galveston College *Texas*
Gateway Community College *Connecticut*
Hillsborough Community College *Florida*
Houston Community College *Texas*
Indiana University - Purdue University Indianapolis *Indiana*
Kent State University at Salem *Ohio*
MCPHS University *Massachusetts*
Molloy College *New York*
Old Dominion University *Virginia*
Prince George's Community College *Maryland*
Rochester Institute of Technology *New York*
Rowan College at Gloucester County *New Jersey*
Saint Louis University *Missouri*
Saint Mary's University of Minnesota *Minnesota*
Salem State University *Massachusetts*
Santa Fe College *Florida*
Southeast Technical Institute *South Dakota*
Springfield Technical Community College *Massachusetts*
Triton College *Illinois*
The University of Alabama at Birmingham *Alabama*
University of Arkansas for Medical Sciences *Arkansas*
University at Buffalo, the State University of New York *New York*
University of Cincinnati *Ohio*
The University of Findlay *Ohio*
University of the Incarnate Word *Texas*
The University of Iowa *Iowa*
University of Missouri *Missouri*
University of Nebraska Medical Center *Nebraska*
University of Nevada, Las Vegas *Nevada*
University of Oklahoma Health Sciences Center *Oklahoma*
University of Puerto Rico, Medical Sciences Campus *Puerto Rico*
The University of Tennessee *Tennessee*
University of Vermont *Vermont*
Vanderbilt University *Tennessee*
Virginia Commonwealth University *Virginia*
Wheeling Jesuit University *West Virginia*
Worcester State University *Massachusetts*

Liaison Committee on Medical Education/American Medical Association (LCME/AMA)

Augusta University *Georgia*
Boston University *Massachusetts*
Brown University *Rhode Island*
Case Western Reserve University *Ohio*
Columbia University *New York*
Creighton University *Nebraska*
Dalhousie University *Nova Scotia (Canada)*
Dartmouth College *New Hampshire*
Drexel University *Pennsylvania*
Duke University *North Carolina*
East Carolina University *North Carolina*
East Tennessee State University *Tennessee*
Emory University *Georgia*
Florida International University *Florida*
Florida State University *Florida*
The George Washington University *District of Columbia*
Georgetown University *District of Columbia*
Harvard University *Massachusetts*
Hofstra University *New York*
Howard University *District of Columbia*
Indiana University - Purdue University Indianapolis *Indiana*
Johns Hopkins University *Maryland*
Lakehead University *Ontario (Canada)*

Laurentian University *Ontario (Canada)*
Loma Linda University *California*
Louisiana State University Health Sciences Center *Louisiana*
Louisiana State University in Shreveport *Louisiana*
Loyola University Chicago *Illinois*
Marshall University *West Virginia*
McGill University *Quebec (Canada)*
McMaster University *Ontario (Canada)*
Medical University of South Carolina *South Carolina*
Memorial University of Newfoundland *Newfoundland and Labrador (Canada)*
Mercer University *Georgia*
Michigan State University *Michigan*
New York University *New York*
Northwestern University *Illinois*
The Ohio State University *Ohio*
Oregon Health & Science University *Oregon*
Queen's University at Kingston *Ontario (Canada)*
Quinnipiac University *Connecticut*
Rush University *Illinois*
Rutgers University - New Brunswick *New Jersey*
Rutgers University - Newark *New Jersey*
Saint Louis University *Missouri*
Southern Illinois University Carbondale *Illinois*
Stanford University *California*
State University of New York Downstate Medical Center *New York*
State University of New York Upstate Medical University *New York*
Stony Brook University, State University of New York *New York*
Temple University *Pennsylvania*
Texas A&M University *Texas*
Thomas Jefferson University *Pennsylvania*
Tufts University *Massachusetts*
Tulane University *Louisiana*
Universidad Central del Caribe *Puerto Rico*
Université Laval *Quebec (Canada)*
Université de Montréal *Quebec (Canada)*
Université de Sherbrooke *Quebec (Canada)*
The University of Alabama at Birmingham *Alabama*
University of Alberta *Alberta (Canada)*
The University of Arizona *Arizona*
University of Arkansas for Medical Sciences *Arkansas*
The University of British Columbia *British Columbia (Canada)*
University at Buffalo, the State University of New York *New York*
University of Calgary *Alberta (Canada)*
University of California, Davis *California*
University of California, Irvine *California*
University of California, Los Angeles *California*
University of California, San Diego *California*
University of Central Florida *Florida*
University of Chicago *Illinois*
University of Cincinnati *Ohio*
University of Colorado Denver *Colorado*
University of Florida *Florida*
University of Hawaii at Manoa *Hawaii*
University of Illinois at Chicago *Illinois*
The University of Iowa *Iowa*
The University of Kansas *Kansas*
University of Kentucky *Kentucky*
University of Louisville *Kentucky*
University of Manitoba *Manitoba (Canada)*
University of Miami *Florida*
University of Michigan *Michigan*
University of Minnesota, Duluth *Minnesota*
University of Minnesota, Twin Cities Campus *Minnesota*
University of Mississippi Medical Center *Mississippi*
University of Missouri *Missouri*
University of Missouri - Kansas City *Missouri*
University of Nebraska Medical Center *Nebraska*
University of Nevada, Reno *Nevada*
University of New Mexico *New Mexico*
The University of North Carolina at Chapel Hill *North Carolina*
University of North Dakota *North Dakota*
University of Oklahoma Health Sciences Center *Oklahoma*
University of Ottawa *Ontario (Canada)*
University of Pennsylvania *Pennsylvania*
University of Pittsburgh *Pennsylvania*

University of Puerto Rico, Medical Sciences Campus *Puerto Rico*
University of Rochester *New York*
University of Saskatchewan *Saskatchewan (Canada)*
University of South Alabama *Alabama*
University of South Carolina *South Carolina*
The University of South Dakota *South Dakota*
University of South Florida *Florida*
University of Southern California *California*
The University of Texas Health Science Center at Houston *Texas*
The University of Texas Health Science Center at San Antonio *Texas*
The University of Texas Medical Branch *Texas*
The University of Toledo *Ohio*
University of Toronto *Ontario (Canada)*
University of Utah *Utah*
University of Vermont *Vermont*
University of Virginia *Virginia*
University of Washington *Washington*
The University of Western Ontario *Ontario (Canada)*
University of Wisconsin - Madison *Wisconsin*
Vanderbilt University *Tennessee*
Virginia Commonwealth University *Virginia*
Wake Forest University *North Carolina*
Washington University in St. Louis *Missouri*
Wayne State University *Michigan*
West Virginia University *West Virginia*
Wright State University *Ohio*
Yale University *Connecticut*
Yeshiva University *New York*

Midwifery Education Accreditation Council (MEAC)

Bastyr University *Washington*
Birthingway College of Midwifery *Oregon*
The Florida School of Traditional Midwifery *Florida*
Miami Dade College *Florida*
Midwives College of Utah *Utah*
National College of Midwifery *New Mexico*

Montessori Accreditation Council for Teacher Education (MACTE)

Barry University *Florida*
Chaminade University of Honolulu *Hawaii*
Chestnut Hill College *Pennsylvania*
Contra Costa College *California*
Eastern Florida State College *Florida*
Fort Valley State University *Georgia*
Indiana University South Bend *Indiana*
Lander University *South Carolina*
Lone Star College - North Harris *Texas*
New York University *New York*
Oklahoma City University *Oklahoma*
Palm Beach State College *Florida*
Saint Mary's College of California *California*
Three Rivers Community College *Connecticut*
Tidewater Community College *Virginia*
Xavier University *Ohio*

National Accrediting Agency for Clinical Laboratory Sciences (NAACLS)

Alamance Community College *North Carolina*
Alexandria Technical and Community College *Minnesota*
Allegany College of Maryland *Maryland*
Amarillo College *Texas*
Andrews University *Michigan*
Arapahoe Community College *Colorado*
Argosy University, Twin Cities *Minnesota*
Arizona State University at the Tempe campus *Arizona*
Arkansas State University *Arkansas*
Arkansas State University - Beebe *Arkansas*
Armstrong State University *Georgia*
Asheville-Buncombe Technical Community College *North Carolina*
Auburn University at Montgomery *Alabama*
Augusta University *Georgia*
Austin Community College District *Texas*
Austin Peay State University *Tennessee*
Barton County Community College *Kansas*
Beaufort County Community College *North Carolina*
Bellarmine University *Kentucky*

Bergen Community College *New Jersey*
Bevill State Community College *Alabama*
Bismarck State College *North Dakota*
Bowling Green State University *Ohio*
Brigham Young University *Utah*
Bristol Community College *Massachusetts*
Broome Community College *New York*
California State University, Dominguez Hills *California*
Camden County College *New Jersey*
Carolinas College of Health Sciences *North Carolina*
Central Community College - Hastings Campus *Nebraska*
Central Georgia Technical College *Georgia*
Central Maine Community College *Maine*
Central New Mexico Community College *New Mexico*
Central Piedmont Community College *North Carolina*
Central Texas College *Texas*
Central Virginia Community College *Virginia*
Chippewa Valley Technical College *Wisconsin*
Cincinnati State Technical and Community College *Ohio*
Clark State Community College *Ohio*
Clinton Community College *New York*
Clover Park Technical College *Washington*
Coastal Carolina Community College *North Carolina*
Coastal Pines Technical College *Georgia*
College of Coastal Georgia *Georgia*
College of Southern Nevada *Nevada*
Columbus State Community College *Ohio*
Community College of Allegheny County *Pennsylvania*
Community College of Philadelphia *Pennsylvania*
Community College of Rhode Island *Rhode Island*
Copiah-Lincoln Community College *Mississippi*
Dalton State College *Georgia*
Darton State College *Georgia*
Davidson County Community College *North Carolina*
Del Mar College *Texas*
Delaware Technical & Community College, Jack F. Owens Campus *Delaware*
Delaware Technical & Community College, Stanton/Wilmington Campus *Delaware*
Delgado Community College *Louisiana*
Des Moines Area Community College *Iowa*
Dutchess Community College *New York*
East Carolina University *North Carolina*
East Tennessee State University *Tennessee*
Eastern Florida State College *Florida*
Eastern Gateway Community College *Ohio*
Eastern Kentucky University *Kentucky*
Eastern Michigan University *Michigan*
El Centro College *Texas*
El Paso Community College *Texas*
Elgin Community College *Illinois*
Erie Community College, North Campus *New York*
Farmingdale State College *New York*
Felician University *New Jersey*
Ferris State University *Michigan*
Fitchburg State University *Massachusetts*
Florence-Darlington Technical College *South Carolina*
Florida Gateway College *Florida*
Florida Gulf Coast University *Florida*
Florida State College at Jacksonville *Florida*
Fortis College *Louisiana*
Fortis Institute *Cookeville, Tennessee*
Gadsden State Community College *Alabama*
The George Washington University *District of Columbia*
Georgia Piedmont Technical College *Georgia*
Goldfarb School of Nursing at Barnes-Jewish College *Missouri*
Grand Valley State University *Michigan*
Grayson College *Texas*
Greenville Technical College *South Carolina*
Halifax Community College *North Carolina*
Harcum College *Pennsylvania*
Harford Community College *Maryland*
Harrisburg Area Community College *Pennsylvania*
Hartnell College *California*
Hawkeye Community College *Iowa*

Hazard Community and Technical College *Kentucky*
Henderson Community College *Kentucky*
Hibbing Community College *Minnesota*
Hinds Community College *Mississippi*
Housatonic Community College *Connecticut*
Houston Community College *Texas*
Idaho State University *Idaho*
Illinois Central College *Illinois*
Illinois State University *Illinois*
Indian River State College *Florida*
Indiana University Northwest *Indiana*
Indiana University - Purdue University Indianapolis *Indiana*
Inter American University of Puerto Rico, Metropolitan Campus *Puerto Rico*
Inter American University of Puerto Rico, San Germán Campus *Puerto Rico*
Iowa Central Community College *Iowa*
Ivy Tech Community College - North Central *Indiana*
Ivy Tech Community College - Wabash Valley *Indiana*
J. Sargeant Reynolds Community College *Virginia*
Jackson State Community College *Tennessee*
Jefferson State Community College *Alabama*
John A. Logan College *Illinois*
Kankakee Community College *Illinois*
Kapiolani Community College *Hawaii*
Keiser University *Florida*
Kellogg Community College *Michigan*
Kilgore College *Texas*
Lake Area Technical Institute *South Dakota*
Lake Superior College *Minnesota*
Lakeland Community College *Ohio*
Lamar State College - Orange *Texas*
Lanier Technical College *Georgia*
Lansing Community College *Michigan*
Laredo Community College *Texas*
Lincoln Memorial University *Tennessee*
Loma Linda University *California*
Long Island University - LIU Post *New York*
Lorain County Community College *Ohio*
Louisiana State University at Alexandria *Louisiana*
Louisiana State University Health Sciences Center *Louisiana*
Madison Area Technical College *Wisconsin*
Manchester Community College *Connecticut*
Marion Technical College *Ohio*
Marist College *New York*
Marquette University *Wisconsin*
Marshall University *West Virginia*
McLennan Community College *Texas*
McNeese State University *Louisiana*
Mercer County Community College *New Jersey*
Mercy College of Ohio *Ohio*
Meridian Community College *Mississippi*
Miami Dade College *Florida*
Michigan State University *Michigan*
Mid-Plains Community College *Nebraska*
Middlesex County College *New Jersey*
Midlands Technical College *South Carolina*
Milwaukee Area Technical College *Wisconsin*
Minnesota State Community and Technical College *Minnesota*
Minnesota West Community and Technical College *Minnesota*
Mississippi Delta Community College *Mississippi*
Mississippi Gulf Coast Community College *Mississippi*
Mitchell Technical Institute *South Dakota*
Montgomery County Community College *Pennsylvania*
Morgan State University *Maryland*
Mt. San Antonio College *California*
Nashua Community College *New Hampshire*
National Park College *Arkansas*
Navarro College *Texas*
Neumann University *Pennsylvania*
New Mexico State University - Alamogordo *New Mexico*
Norfolk State University *Virginia*
North Arkansas College *Arkansas*
North Georgia Technical College *Georgia*
North Hennepin Community College *Minnesota*
Northeast Mississippi Community College *Mississippi*
Northeast State Community College *Tennessee*

Northeast Wisconsin Technical College *Wisconsin*
Northeastern Oklahoma Agricultural and Mechanical College *Oklahoma*
Northeastern University *Massachusetts*
Northern Illinois University *Illinois*
Northern Michigan University *Michigan*
Northern Virginia Community College *Virginia*
Northwest Technical College *Minnesota*
Oakton Community College *Illinois*
Odessa College *Texas*
The Ohio State University *Ohio*
Old Dominion University *Virginia*
Orange County Community College *New York*
Orangeburg-Calhoun Technical College *South Carolina*
Oregon Health & Science University *Oregon*
Oregon Institute of Technology *Oregon*
Our Lady of the Lake College *Louisiana*
Pearl River Community College *Mississippi*
Penn State Hazleton *Pennsylvania*
Penn State New Kensington *Pennsylvania*
Phillips Community College of the University of Arkansas *Arkansas*
Pierpont Community & Technical College *West Virginia*
Pontifical Catholic University of Puerto Rico *Puerto Rico*
Portland Community College *Oregon*
Presentation College *South Dakota*
Quinnipiac University *Connecticut*
Reading Area Community College *Pennsylvania*
Rend Lake College *Illinois*
Rose State College *Oklahoma*
Rush University *Illinois*
Saint Louis University *Missouri*
Saint Paul College - A Community & Technical College *Minnesota*
St. Petersburg College *Florida*
St. Philip's College *Texas*
Salisbury University *Maryland*
Salt Lake Community College *Utah*
San Francisco State University *California*
Sandhills Community College *North Carolina*
Seminole State College *Oklahoma*
Seward County Community College and Area Technical School *Kansas*
Shawnee Community College *Illinois*
Shawnee State University *Ohio*
Shoreline Community College *Washington*
Somerset Community College *Kentucky*
South Arkansas Community College *Arkansas*
South Central College *Minnesota*
Southeast Community College, Lincoln Campus *Nebraska*
Southeast Kentucky Community and Technical College *Kentucky*
Southeastern Community College *North Carolina*
Southeastern Illinois College *Illinois*
Southern Illinois University Carbondale *Illinois*
Southern Illinois University Edwardsville *Illinois*
Southern Regional Technical College *Georgia*
Southern University at Shreveport *Louisiana*
Southern West Virginia Community and Technical College *West Virginia*
Southwest Tennessee Community College *Tennessee*
Southwestern Community College *North Carolina*
Southwestern Illinois College *Illinois*
Spartanburg Community College *South Carolina*
Springfield Technical Community College *Massachusetts*
Stark State College *Ohio*
State University of New York College of Agriculture and Technology at Cobleskill *New York*
State University of New York Upstate Medical University *New York*
Stevenson University *Maryland*
Stony Brook University, State University of New York *New York*
Tarleton State University *Texas*
Temple College *Texas*
Tennessee State University *Tennessee*
Texas A&M University - Corpus Christi *Texas*
Texas Southern University *Texas*
Texas Southmost College *Texas*
Texas State University *Texas*

Thomas Jefferson University *Pennsylvania*
Thomas Nelson Community College *Virginia*
Three Rivers Community College *Missouri*
Tri-County Technical College *South Carolina*
Trident Technical College *South Carolina*
Tulsa Community College *Oklahoma*
Tuskegee University *Alabama*
Tyler Junior College *Texas*
The University of Alabama at Birmingham *Alabama*
University of Alaska Anchorage *Alaska*
The University of Arizona *Arizona*
University of Arkansas for Medical Sciences *Arkansas*
University at Buffalo, the State University of New York *New York*
University of California, Davis *California*
University of California, Irvine *California*
University of Central Florida *Florida*
University of Cincinnati *Ohio*
University of Connecticut *Connecticut*
University of Delaware *Delaware*
University of Hartford *Connecticut*
University of Hawaii at Manoa *Hawaii*
University of Illinois at Springfield *Illinois*
The University of Iowa *Iowa*
The University of Kansas *Kansas*
University of Kentucky *Kentucky*
University of Maine at Augusta *Maine*
University of Maine at Presque Isle *Maine*
University of Massachusetts Dartmouth *Massachusetts*
University of Massachusetts Lowell *Massachusetts*
University of Minnesota, Twin Cities Campus *Minnesota*
University of Mississippi Medical Center *Mississippi*
University of Nebraska Medical Center *Nebraska*
University of Nevada, Las Vegas *Nevada*
University of New Hampshire *New Hampshire*
University of New Mexico *New Mexico*
University of New Mexico - Gallup *New Mexico*
The University of North Carolina at Chapel Hill *North Carolina*
University of North Dakota *North Dakota*
University of Pikeville *Kentucky*
University of Puerto Rico, Medical Sciences Campus *Puerto Rico*
University of Rio Grande *Ohio*
University of the Sacred Heart *Puerto Rico*
University of South Alabama *Alabama*
University of Southern Mississippi *Mississippi*
The University of Tennessee *Tennessee*
The University of Texas at El Paso *Texas*
The University of Texas Health Science Center at Houston *Texas*
The University of Texas Health Science Center at San Antonio *Texas*
The University of Texas Medical Branch *Texas*
The University of Texas Rio Grande Valley *Texas*
University of Utah *Utah*
University of Vermont *Vermont*
University of Washington *Washington*
University of West Florida *Florida*
University of Wisconsin - La Crosse *Wisconsin*
University of Wisconsin - Madison *Wisconsin*
University of Wisconsin - Milwaukee *Wisconsin*
University of Wisconsin - Stevens Point *Wisconsin*
Vanderbilt University *Tennessee*
Victoria College *Texas*
Virginia Commonwealth University *Virginia*
Wake Forest University *North Carolina*
Wake Technical Community College *North Carolina*
Wallace State Community College *Alabama*
Washington State Community College *Ohio*
Wayne State University *Michigan*
Weber State University *Utah*
Wenatchee Valley College *Washington*
West Liberty University *West Virginia*
West Virginia Northern Community College *West Virginia*
West Virginia University *West Virginia*
Western Carolina University *North Carolina*
Western Piedmont Community College *North Carolina*
Western Technical College *Wisconsin*
Wichita Area Technical College *Kansas*
Wichita State University *Kansas*

Winston-Salem State University *North Carolina*
Wiregrass Georgia Technical College *Georgia*
Wright State University *Ohio*
Wytheville Community College *Virginia*
York Technical College *South Carolina*
Youngstown State University *Ohio*
Zane State College *Ohio*

National Architectural Accrediting Board, Inc. (NAAB)

Arizona State University at the Tempe campus *Arizona*
Auburn University *Alabama*
Ball State University *Indiana*
Boston Architectural College *Massachusetts*
California College of the Arts *California*
California Polytechnic State University, San Luis Obispo *California*
California State Polytechnic University, Pomona *California*
Carnegie Mellon University *Pennsylvania*
The Catholic University of America *District of Columbia*
City College of the City University of New York *New York*
Clemson University *South Carolina*
Columbia University *New York*
Cooper Union for the Advancement of Science and Art *New York*
Cornell University *New York*
Drexel University *Pennsylvania*
Drury University *Missouri*
Florida Agricultural and Mechanical University *Florida*
Georgia Institute of Technology *Georgia*
Hampton University *Virginia*
Harvard University *Massachusetts*
Howard University *District of Columbia*
Illinois Institute of Technology *Illinois*
Iowa State University of Science and Technology *Iowa*
Kansas State University *Kansas*
Kent State University *Ohio*
Lawrence Technological University *Michigan*
Louisiana State University and Agricultural & Mechanical College *Louisiana*
Louisiana Tech University *Louisiana*
Massachusetts Institute of Technology *Massachusetts*
Miami University *Ohio*
Mississippi State University *Mississippi*
Montana State University *Montana*
Morgan State University *Maryland*
New Jersey Institute of Technology *New Jersey*
New York Institute of Technology *New York*
NewSchool of Architecture and Design *California*
North Carolina State University *North Carolina*
North Dakota State University *North Dakota*
Norwich University *Vermont*
The Ohio State University *Ohio*
Oklahoma State University *Oklahoma*
Parsons School of Design *New York*
Penn State University Park *Pennsylvania*
Philadelphia University *Pennsylvania*
Pratt Institute *New York*
Princeton University *New Jersey*
Rensselaer Polytechnic Institute *New York*
Rhode Island School of Design *Rhode Island*
Rice University *Texas*
Roger Williams University *Rhode Island*
Savannah College of Art and Design *Georgia*
Southern California Institute of Architecture *California*
Syracuse University *New York*
Temple University *Pennsylvania*
Texas A&M University *Texas*
Texas Tech University *Texas*
Tulane University *Louisiana*
Tuskegee University *Alabama*
The University of Arizona *Arizona*
University of Arkansas *Arkansas*
University at Buffalo, the State University of New York *New York*
University of California, Berkeley *California*
University of California, Los Angeles *California*
University of Cincinnati *Ohio*

University of Colorado Denver *Colorado*
University of Detroit Mercy *Michigan*
University of the District of Columbia *District of Columbia*
University of Florida *Florida*
University of Hawaii at Manoa *Hawaii*
University of Houston *Texas*
University of Idaho *Idaho*
University of Illinois at Chicago *Illinois*
University of Illinois at Urbana - Champaign *Illinois*
The University of Kansas *Kansas*
University of Kentucky *Kentucky*
University of Louisiana at Lafayette *Louisiana*
University of Maryland, College Park *Maryland*
University of Miami *Florida*
University of Michigan *Michigan*
University of Minnesota, Twin Cities Campus *Minnesota*
University of Nebraska - Lincoln *Nebraska*
University of Nevada, Las Vegas *Nevada*
University of New Mexico *New Mexico*
The University of North Carolina at Charlotte *North Carolina*
University of Notre Dame *Indiana*
University of Oklahoma *Oklahoma*
University of Oregon *Oregon*
University of Pennsylvania *Pennsylvania*
University of Puerto Rico, Río Piedras Campus *Puerto Rico*
University of South Florida *Florida*
University of Southern California *California*
The University of Tennessee *Tennessee*
The University of Texas at Arlington *Texas*
The University of Texas at Austin *Texas*
University of Utah *Utah*
University of Virginia *Virginia*
University of Washington *Washington*
University of Wisconsin - Milwaukee *Wisconsin*
Virginia Polytechnic Institute and State University *Virginia*
Washington University in St. Louis *Missouri*
Wentworth Institute of Technology *Massachusetts*
Woodbury University *California*
Yale University *Connecticut*

National Association of Nurse Practitioners in Women's Health (NPWH)

Emory University *Georgia*

National Association of Schools of Art and Design (NASAD)

Academy of Art University *California*
Alfred University *New York*
Anderson University *South Carolina*
Appalachian State University *North Carolina*
Arcadia University *Pennsylvania*
Arizona State University at the Tempe campus *Arizona*
Arkansas State University *Arkansas*
Art Academy of Cincinnati *Ohio*
Art Center College of Design *California*
The Art Institute of Atlanta *Georgia*
The Art Institute of Dallas, a campus of South University *Texas*
Auburn University *Alabama*
Austin Peay State University *Tennessee*
Azusa Pacific University *California*
Ball State University *Indiana*
Belhaven University *Mississippi*
Biola University *California*
Bloomsburg University of Pennsylvania *Pennsylvania*
Boise State University *Idaho*
Bowling Green State University *Ohio*
Bradley University *Illinois*
Brigham Young University *Utah*
Bucks County Community College *Pennsylvania*
Buffalo State College, State University of New York *New York*
California College of the Arts *California*
California Institute of the Arts *California*
California Polytechnic State University, San Luis Obispo *California*
California State Polytechnic University, Pomona *California*
California State University, Chico *California*

California State University, East Bay *California*
California State University, Fullerton *California*
California State University, Long Beach *California*
California State University, Los Angeles *California*
California State University, Northridge *California*
California State University, Sacramento *California*
California State University, San Bernardino *California*
California State University, Stanislaus *California*
California University of Pennsylvania *Pennsylvania*
Carnegie Mellon University *Pennsylvania*
Carson-Newman University *Tennessee*
Casper College *Wyoming*
Central Michigan University *Michigan*
Central State University *Ohio*
Clarion University of Pennsylvania *Pennsylvania*
Clemson University *South Carolina*
Cleveland Institute of Art *Ohio*
Coastal Carolina University *South Carolina*
College for Creative Studies *Michigan*
College of DuPage *Illinois*
The College of Saint Rose *New York*
Columbia College *South Carolina*
Columbia College Hollywood *California*
Columbus College of Art & Design *Ohio*
Columbus State University *Georgia*
Converse College *South Carolina*
Cooper Union for the Advancement of Science and Art *New York*
Cornish College of the Arts *Washington*
Del Mar College *Texas*
Delaware College of Art and Design *Delaware*
Delta State University *Mississippi*
Drake University *Iowa*
Drexel University *Pennsylvania*
East Carolina University *North Carolina*
East Tennessee State University *Tennessee*
Eastern Illinois University *Illinois*
Edinboro University of Pennsylvania *Pennsylvania*
Emporia State University *Kansas*
Endicott College *Massachusetts*
Escuela de Artes Plasticas y Diseño de Puerto Rico *Puerto Rico*
Fashion Institute of Technology *New York*
Ferris State University *Michigan*
FIDM/Fashion Institute of Design & Merchandising, Los Angeles Campus *California*
FIDM/Fashion Institute of Design & Merchandising, Orange County Campus *California*
FIDM/Fashion Institute of Design & Merchandising, San Diego Campus *California*
FIDM/Fashion Institute of Design & Merchandising, San Francisco Campus *California*
Florida International University *Florida*
Florida State University *Florida*
Francis Marion University *South Carolina*
George Mason University *Virginia*
The George Washington University *District of Columbia*
Georgia Institute of Technology *Georgia*
Georgia Southern University *Georgia*
Georgia State University *Georgia*
Grand Rapids Community College *Michigan*
Grand Valley State University *Michigan*
Hartwick College *New York*
Hope College *Michigan*
Howard University *District of Columbia*
Humboldt State University *California*
Illinois State University *Illinois*
Indiana State University *Indiana*
Indiana University Bloomington *Indiana*
Indiana University of Pennsylvania *Pennsylvania*
Indiana University - Purdue University Indianapolis *Indiana*
Institute of American Indian Arts *New Mexico*
Iowa State University of Science and Technology *Iowa*
Ivy Tech Community College - Columbus *Indiana*
Ivy Tech Community College - North Central *Indiana*
Jackson State University *Mississippi*
Jacksonville State University *Alabama*
James Madison University *Virginia*
Kansas City Art Institute *Missouri*
Kansas State University *Kansas*
Kean University *New Jersey*
Kennesaw State University *Georgia*

Kent State University *Ohio*
Kutztown University of Pennsylvania *Pennsylvania*
La Roche College *Pennsylvania*
Laguna College of Art & Design *California*
Lander University *South Carolina*
Lawrence Technological University *Michigan*
Lorain County Community College *Ohio*
Louisiana State University and Agricultural & Mechanical College *Louisiana*
Louisiana Tech University *Louisiana*
Loyola Marymount University *California*
Maine College of Art *Maine*
Maryland Institute College of Art *Maryland*
Maryville University of Saint Louis *Missouri*
Marywood University *Pennsylvania*
Massachusetts College of Art and Design *Massachusetts*
McNeese State University *Louisiana*
Memphis College of Art *Tennessee*
Mercy College *New York*
Messiah College *Pennsylvania*
Metropolitan State University of Denver *Colorado*
Miami University *Ohio*
Middle Tennessee State University *Tennessee*
Millersville University of Pennsylvania *Pennsylvania*
Milwaukee Institute of Art and Design *Wisconsin*
Minneapolis College of Art and Design *Minnesota*
Minnesota State University Mankato *Minnesota*
Minnesota State University Moorhead *Minnesota*
Mississippi State University *Mississippi*
Mississippi University for Women *Mississippi*
Mississippi Valley State University *Mississippi*
Montana State University *Montana*
Montana State University Billings *Montana*
Montclair State University *New Jersey*
Montserrat College of Art *Massachusetts*
Moore College of Art & Design *Pennsylvania*
Mount Ida College *Massachusetts*
Murray State University *Kentucky*
New Hampshire Institute of Art *New Hampshire*
New Jersey City University *New Jersey*
New World School of the Arts *Florida*
New York Film Academy *California*
New York School of Interior Design *New York*
Nicholls State University *Louisiana*
North Carolina State University *North Carolina*
North Dakota State University *North Dakota*
Northeastern Illinois University *Illinois*
Northern Illinois University *Illinois*
Northwestern State University of Louisiana *Louisiana*
The Ohio State University *Ohio*
Ohio University *Ohio*
Old Dominion University *Virginia*
Oregon College of Art & Craft *Oregon*
Otis College of Art and Design *California*
Pacific Northwest College of Art *Oregon*
Parsons School of Design *New York*
Penn State University Park *Pennsylvania*
Pennsylvania Academy of the Fine Arts *Pennsylvania*
Pennsylvania College of Art & Design *Pennsylvania*
Philadelphia University *Pennsylvania*
Pratt Institute *New York*
Purchase College, State University of New York *New York*
Purdue University *Indiana*
Rhode Island College *Rhode Island*
Rhode Island School of Design *Rhode Island*
Ringling College of Art and Design *Florida*
Roberts Wesleyan College *New York*
Rochester Institute of Technology *New York*
Rocky Mountain College of Art + Design *Colorado*
Rowan University *New Jersey*
The Sage Colleges *New York*
St. Cloud State University *Minnesota*
Saint Mary's College *Indiana*
Salem State University *Massachusetts*
Salve Regina University *Rhode Island*
San Diego State University *California*
San Francisco Art Institute *California*
San Francisco State University *California*
San Jose State University *California*
School of the Art Institute of Chicago *Illinois*
School of the Museum of Fine Arts, Boston *Massachusetts*

School of Visual Arts *New York*
Siena Heights University *Michigan*
Sinclair Community College *Ohio*
Skidmore College *New York*
Slippery Rock University of Pennsylvania *Pennsylvania*
Sonoma State University *California*
South Carolina State University *South Carolina*
Southeastern Louisiana University *Louisiana*
Southern Illinois University Carbondale *Illinois*
Southern Methodist University *Texas*
Southern University and Agricultural and Mechanical College *Louisiana*
Southern Utah University *Utah*
State University of New York at New Paltz *New York*
State University of New York at Oswego *New York*
Stephen F. Austin State University *Texas*
Suffolk University *Massachusetts*
Syracuse University *New York*
Temple University *Pennsylvania*
Tennessee State University *Tennessee*
Tennessee Technological University *Tennessee*
Texas Christian University *Texas*
Texas Tech University *Texas*
Union University *Tennessee*
The University of Akron *Ohio*
The University of Alabama *Alabama*
The University of Alabama at Birmingham *Alabama*
The University of Alabama in Huntsville *Alabama*
University of Alaska Anchorage *Alaska*
The University of Arizona *Arizona*
University of Arkansas at Little Rock *Arkansas*
University of Arkansas at Pine Bluff *Arkansas*
The University of the Arts *Pennsylvania*
University of Bridgeport *Connecticut*
University of Central Arkansas *Arkansas*
University of Central Missouri *Missouri*
University of Central Oklahoma *Oklahoma*
University of Cincinnati *Ohio*
University of Cincinnati Blue Ash College *Ohio*
University of Connecticut *Connecticut*
University of Dayton *Ohio*
University of Denver *Colorado*
University of Florida *Florida*
University of Georgia *Georgia*
University of Hartford *Connecticut*
University of Idaho *Idaho*
University of Illinois at Chicago *Illinois*
University of Illinois at Urbana - Champaign *Illinois*
University of Indianapolis *Indiana*
The University of Kansas *Kansas*
University of Kentucky *Kentucky*
University of Louisiana at Lafayette *Louisiana*
University of Maine *Maine*
University of Massachusetts Dartmouth *Massachusetts*
University of Massachusetts Lowell *Massachusetts*
University of Memphis *Tennessee*
University of Michigan *Michigan*
University of Mississippi *Mississippi*
University of Montana *Montana*
University of Montevallo *Alabama*
University of Nebraska - Lincoln *Nebraska*
University of Nebraska at Omaha *Nebraska*
University of Nevada, Las Vegas *Nevada*
University of New Orleans *Louisiana*
University of North Alabama *Alabama*
University of North Dakota *North Dakota*
University of North Texas *Texas*
University of Northern Iowa *Iowa*
University of Notre Dame *Indiana*
University of Oregon *Oregon*
University of the Pacific *California*
University of St. Francis *Illinois*
University of Saint Francis *Indiana*
University of South Carolina *South Carolina*
University of South Carolina Upstate *South Carolina*
The University of South Dakota *South Dakota*
University of South Florida *Florida*
University of Southern Maine *Maine*
University of Southern Mississippi *Mississippi*
The University of Tennessee *Tennessee*
The University of Tennessee at Chattanooga *Tennessee*
The University of Texas at Arlington *Texas*
The University of Texas at Austin *Texas*

The University of Texas of the Permian Basin *Texas*
The University of Texas at San Antonio *Texas*
The University of Toledo *Ohio*
University of West Georgia *Georgia*
University of Wisconsin - Madison *Wisconsin*
University of Wisconsin - Stevens Point *Wisconsin*
University of Wisconsin - Stout *Wisconsin*
University of Wisconsin - Whitewater *Wisconsin*
Valdosta State University *Georgia*
Vincennes University *Indiana*
Virginia Commonwealth University *Virginia*
Virginia Polytechnic Institute and State University *Virginia*
Virginia State University *Virginia*
Washburn University *Kansas*
Washington University in St. Louis *Missouri*
Watkins College of Art, Design, & Film *Tennessee*
Wayne State College *Nebraska*
Weber State University *Utah*
Wentworth Institute of Technology *Massachusetts*
West Virginia University *West Virginia*
Western Carolina University *North Carolina*
Western Illinois University *Illinois*
Western Kentucky University *Kentucky*
Western Michigan University *Michigan*
Western Washington University *Washington*
Wichita State University *Kansas*
William Paterson University of New Jersey *New Jersey*
Winthrop University *South Carolina*
Woodbury University *California*
Youngstown State University *Ohio*

National Association of Schools of Dance (NASD)

Ball State University *Indiana*
Barnard College *New York*
Belhaven University *Mississippi*
Brenau University *Georgia*
Brigham Young University *Utah*
Butler University *Indiana*
California Institute of the Arts *California*
California State University, Fullerton *California*
California State University, Long Beach *California*
Chapman University *California*
The College at Brockport, State University of New York *New York*
Columbia College *South Carolina*
Florida State University *Florida*
Hope College *Michigan*
Jacksonville University *Florida*
James Madison University *Virginia*
Kent State University *Ohio*
Loyola Marymount University *California*
Mercyhurst University *Pennsylvania*
Montclair State University *New Jersey*
New World School of the Arts *Florida*
Oakland University *Michigan*
The Ohio State University *Ohio*
Ohio University *Ohio*
Point Park University *Pennsylvania*
Rutgers University - New Brunswick *New Jersey*
St. Olaf College *Minnesota*
San Jose State University *California*
Slippery Rock University of Pennsylvania *Pennsylvania*
Southern Methodist University *Texas*
Southern Utah University *Utah*
Temple University *Pennsylvania*
Texas Christian University *Texas*
Texas Woman's University *Texas*
Towson University *Maryland*
The University of Akron *Ohio*
The University of Alabama *Alabama*
The University of Arizona *Arizona*
University of California, Santa Barbara *California*
University of Cincinnati *Ohio*
University of Florida *Florida*
University of Georgia *Georgia*
University of Illinois at Urbana - Champaign *Illinois*
The University of Iowa *Iowa*
University of Michigan *Michigan*
University of Minnesota, Twin Cities Campus *Minnesota*
University of Missouri - Kansas City *Missouri*
University of New Mexico *New Mexico*

The University of North Carolina at Greensboro *North Carolina*
University of Southern Mississippi *Mississippi*
The University of Texas at Austin *Texas*
University of Utah *Utah*
University of Wisconsin - Milwaukee *Wisconsin*
University of Wisconsin - Stevens Point *Wisconsin*
Virginia Commonwealth University *Virginia*
Wayne State University *Michigan*
Western Kentucky University *Kentucky*
Western Michigan University *Michigan*
Wichita State University *Kansas*
Winthrop University *South Carolina*

National Association of Schools of Music (NASM)

Abilene Christian University *Texas*
Adams State University *Colorado*
Alabama State University *Alabama*
Albion College *Michigan*
Alcorn State University *Mississippi*
Alma College *Michigan*
Alverno College *Wisconsin*
Amarillo College *Texas*
American University *District of Columbia*
Anderson University *Indiana*
Anderson University *South Carolina*
Andrews University *Michigan*
Angelo State University *Texas*
Anna Maria College *Massachusetts*
Appalachian State University *North Carolina*
Arizona State University at the Tempe campus *Arizona*
Arkansas State University *Arkansas*
Arkansas Tech University *Arkansas*
Armstrong State University *Georgia*
Asbury University *Kentucky*
Ashland University *Ohio*
Auburn University *Alabama*
Augsburg College *Minnesota*
Augustana College *Illinois*
Augustana University *South Dakota*
Austin Peay State University *Tennessee*
Azusa Pacific University *California*
Baker University *Kansas*
Baldwin Wallace University *Ohio*
Ball State University *Indiana*
The Baptist College of Florida *Florida*
Baylor University *Texas*
Belhaven University *Mississippi*
Belmont University *Tennessee*
Bemidji State University *Minnesota*
Benedictine College *Kansas*
Berry College *Georgia*
Bethany College *Kansas*
Bethel College *Indiana*
Binghamton University, State University of New York *New York*
Biola University *California*
Birmingham-Southern College *Alabama*
Black Hills State University *South Dakota*
Bloomsburg University of Pennsylvania *Pennsylvania*
Bluffton University *Ohio*
Boise State University *Idaho*
Boston University *Massachusetts*
Bowling Green State University *Ohio*
Bradley University *Illinois*
Brevard College *North Carolina*
Bridgewater State University *Massachusetts*
Brigham Young University *Utah*
Brigham Young University - Idaho *Idaho*
Broward College *Florida*
Bucknell University *Pennsylvania*
Bucks County Community College *Pennsylvania*
Buffalo State College, State University of New York *New York*
Butler University *Indiana*
Cairn University *Pennsylvania*
California Baptist University *California*
California Institute of the Arts *California*
California Polytechnic State University, San Luis Obispo *California*
California State University, Chico *California*
California State University, Dominguez Hills *California*

California State University, East Bay *California*
California State University, Fresno *California*
California State University, Fullerton *California*
California State University, Long Beach *California*
California State University, Los Angeles *California*
California State University, Northridge *California*
California State University, Sacramento *California*
California State University, San Bernardino *California*
California State University, Stanislaus *California*
Calvin College *Michigan*
Cameron University *Oklahoma*
Campbellsville University *Kentucky*
Capital University *Ohio*
Carnegie Mellon University *Pennsylvania*
Carson-Newman University *Tennessee*
Carthage College *Wisconsin*
Case Western Reserve University *Ohio*
Casper College *Wyoming*
The Catholic University of America *District of Columbia*
Cedarville University *Ohio*
Centenary College of Louisiana *Louisiana*
Central College *Iowa*
Central Connecticut State University *Connecticut*
Central Methodist University *Missouri*
Central Michigan University *Michigan*
Central State University *Ohio*
Central Washington University *Washington*
Chapman University *California*
Charleston Southern University *South Carolina*
Chicago State University *Illinois*
Chowan University *North Carolina*
Christopher Newport University *Virginia*
Cincinnati Christian University *Ohio*
Claflin University *South Carolina*
Clarion University of Pennsylvania *Pennsylvania*
Clarke University *Iowa*
Clayton State University *Georgia*
Cleveland Institute of Music *Ohio*
Cleveland State University *Ohio*
Coastal Carolina University *South Carolina*
Coe College *Iowa*
Coker College *South Carolina*
The Colburn School Conservatory of Music *California*
College of Charleston *South Carolina*
The College of New Jersey *New Jersey*
College of Saint Benedict *Minnesota*
The College of Saint Rose *New York*
The College of Wooster *Ohio*
Colorado Christian University *Colorado*
Colorado Mesa University *Colorado*
Colorado State University *Colorado*
Colorado State University - Pueblo *Colorado*
Columbia College *South Carolina*
Columbus State University *Georgia*
Community College of Baltimore County *Maryland*
Concordia College *Minnesota*
Concordia University Chicago *Illinois*
Concordia University, Nebraska *Nebraska*
Conservatorio de Musica de Puerto Rico *Puerto Rico*
Converse College *South Carolina*
Cornerstone University *Michigan*
Cottey College *Missouri*
Culver-Stockton College *Missouri*
Curtis Institute of Music *Pennsylvania*
Dallas Baptist University *Texas*
Del Mar College *Texas*
Delta State University *Mississippi*
DePaul University *Illinois*
DePauw University *Indiana*
Dickinson State University *North Dakota*
Drake University *Iowa*
Drury University *Missouri*
Duquesne University *Pennsylvania*
East Carolina University *North Carolina*
East Central University *Oklahoma*
East Tennessee State University *Tennessee*
East Texas Baptist University *Texas*
Eastern Illinois University *Illinois*
Eastern Kentucky University *Kentucky*
Eastern Michigan University *Michigan*
Eastern New Mexico University *New Mexico*
Eastern Washington University *Washington*

Edinboro University of Pennsylvania *Pennsylvania*
Elizabeth City State University *North Carolina*
Elizabethtown College *Pennsylvania*
Emporia State University *Kansas*
Evangel University *Missouri*
Fayetteville State University *North Carolina*
Fisk University *Tennessee*
Florida Atlantic University *Florida*
Florida College *Florida*
Florida International University *Florida*
Florida Memorial University *Florida*
Florida State University *Florida*
Fort Hays State University *Kansas*
Fort Lewis College *Colorado*
Friends University *Kansas*
Furman University *South Carolina*
Gardner-Webb University *North Carolina*
George Fox University *Oregon*
George Mason University *Virginia*
The George Washington University *District of Columbia*
Georgia College & State University *Georgia*
Georgia Southern University *Georgia*
Georgia State University *Georgia*
Gordon College *Massachusetts*
Grambling State University *Louisiana*
Grand Rapids Community College *Michigan*
Grand Valley State University *Michigan*
Greensboro College *North Carolina*
Gustavus Adolphus College *Minnesota*
Hamline University *Minnesota*
Hampton University *Virginia*
Hardin-Simmons University *Texas*
Harding University *Arkansas*
Harper College *Illinois*
Hartwick College *New York*
Hastings College *Nebraska*
Heidelberg University *Ohio*
Henderson State University *Arkansas*
Hendrix College *Arkansas*
Hillsborough Community College *Florida*
Hiram College *Ohio*
Holyoke Community College *Massachusetts*
Hope College *Michigan*
Houghton College *New York*
Howard Community College *Maryland*
Howard Payne University *Texas*
Howard University *District of Columbia*
Humboldt State University *California*
Huntingdon College *Alabama*
Idaho State University *Idaho*
Illinois Central College *Illinois*
Illinois State University *Illinois*
Illinois Wesleyan University *Illinois*
Immaculata University *Pennsylvania*
Indiana State University *Indiana*
Indiana University Bloomington *Indiana*
Indiana University of Pennsylvania *Pennsylvania*
Indiana University - Purdue University Fort Wayne *Indiana*
Indiana University - Purdue University Indianapolis *Indiana*
Indiana Wesleyan University *Indiana*
Iowa State University of Science and Technology *Iowa*
Ithaca College *New York*
Jackson State University *Mississippi*
Jacksonville State University *Alabama*
Jacksonville University *Florida*
James Madison University *Virginia*
Johns Hopkins University *Maryland*
Joliet Junior College *Illinois*
Judson College *Alabama*
Kansas State University *Kansas*
Kean University *New Jersey*
Keene State College *New Hampshire*
Kennesaw State University *Georgia*
Kent State University *Ohio*
Kentucky State University *Kentucky*
Kutztown University of Pennsylvania *Pennsylvania*
La Sierra University *California*
Lamar University *Texas*
Lander University *South Carolina*
Lawrence University *Wisconsin*
Lebanon Valley College *Pennsylvania*
Lee University *Tennessee*

Limestone College *South Carolina*
Lincoln University *Missouri*
Linfield College *Oregon*
Lipscomb University *Tennessee*
Longwood University *Virginia*
Louisiana State University and Agricultural & Mechanical College *Louisiana*
Louisiana Tech University *Louisiana*
Loyola Marymount University *California*
Loyola University New Orleans *Louisiana*
Luther College *Iowa*
Lynchburg College *Virginia*
Lynn University *Florida*
Mansfield University of Pennsylvania *Pennsylvania*
Mars Hill University *North Carolina*
Marshall University *West Virginia*
Marylhurst University *Oregon*
Maryville College *Tennessee*
Maryville University of Saint Louis *Missouri*
Marywood University *Pennsylvania*
The Master's College and Seminary *California*
McNally Smith College of Music *Minnesota*
McNeese State University *Louisiana*
Mercer University *Georgia*
Mercyhurst University *Pennsylvania*
Meredith College *North Carolina*
Messiah College *Pennsylvania*
Metropolitan State University of Denver *Colorado*
Miami University *Ohio*
Michigan State University *Michigan*
MidAmerica Nazarene University *Kansas*
Middle Tennessee State University *Tennessee*
Midwestern State University *Texas*
Millersville University of Pennsylvania *Pennsylvania*
Millikin University *Illinois*
Minnesota State University Mankato *Minnesota*
Minnesota State University Moorhead *Minnesota*
Minot State University *North Dakota*
Mississippi College *Mississippi*
Mississippi State University *Mississippi*
Mississippi University for Women *Mississippi*
Mississippi Valley State University *Mississippi*
Missouri Baptist University *Missouri*
Missouri State University *Missouri*
Missouri Western State University *Missouri*
Montana State University *Montana*
Montana State University Billings *Montana*
Montclair State University *New Jersey*
Montgomery College *Maryland*
Moody Bible Institute *Illinois*
Moravian College *Pennsylvania*
Morehead State University *Kentucky*
Morehouse College *Georgia*
Morgan State University *Maryland*
Morningside College *Iowa*
Mount St. Joseph University *Ohio*
Mount Vernon Nazarene University *Ohio*
Murray State University *Kentucky*
Musicians Institute *California*
Muskingum University *Ohio*
Nassau Community College *New York*
Nazareth College of Rochester *New York*
Nebraska Wesleyan University *Nebraska*
New England Conservatory of Music *Massachusetts*
New Jersey City University *New Jersey*
New Mexico State University *New Mexico*
New Orleans Baptist Theological Seminary *Louisiana*
New World School of the Arts *Florida*
Newberry College *South Carolina*
Nicholls State University *Louisiana*
Norfolk State University *Virginia*
Normandale Community College *Minnesota*
North Carolina Agricultural and Technical State University *North Carolina*
North Dakota State University *North Dakota*
North Greenville University *South Carolina*
North Park University *Illinois*
Northeastern Illinois University *Illinois*
Northeastern State University *Oklahoma*
Northern Arizona University *Arizona*
Northern Illinois University *Illinois*
Northern Kentucky University *Kentucky*
Northern Michigan University *Michigan*
Northern State University *South Dakota*
Northwest College *Wyoming*

University of Wisconsin - Milwaukee *Wisconsin*
University of Wisconsin - Oshkosh *Wisconsin*
University of Wisconsin - Platteville *Wisconsin*
University of Wisconsin - River Falls *Wisconsin*
University of Wisconsin - Stevens Point *Wisconsin*
University of Wisconsin - Superior *Wisconsin*
University of Wisconsin - Whitewater *Wisconsin*
University of Wyoming *Wyoming*
Utah State University *Utah*
Valdosta State University *Georgia*
Valley City State University *North Dakota*
Valparaiso University *Indiana*
Vanderbilt University *Tennessee*
VanderCook College of Music *Illinois*
Virginia Commonwealth University *Virginia*
Virginia Polytechnic Institute and State University *Virginia*
Virginia State University *Virginia*
Viterbo University *Wisconsin*
Walla Walla University *Washington*
Wartburg College *Iowa*
Washburn University *Kansas*
Washington State University *Washington*
Wayland Baptist University *Texas*
Wayne State College *Nebraska*
Wayne State University *Michigan*
Weber State University *Utah*
Webster University *Missouri*
Wesleyan College *Georgia*
West Chester University of Pennsylvania *Pennsylvania*
West Liberty University *West Virginia*
West Texas A&M University *Texas*
West Virginia University *West Virginia*
West Virginia Wesleyan College *West Virginia*
Western Carolina University *North Carolina*
Western Connecticut State University *Connecticut*
Western Illinois University *Illinois*
Western Kentucky University *Kentucky*
Western Michigan University *Michigan*
Western Oregon University *Oregon*
Western State Colorado University *Colorado*
Western Washington University *Washington*
Westfield State University *Massachusetts*
Westminster College *Pennsylvania*
Westmont College *California*
Wheaton College *Illinois*
Whitworth University *Washington*
Wichita State University *Kansas*
Willamette University *Oregon*
William Carey University *Mississippi*
William Jewell College *Missouri*
William Paterson University of New Jersey *New Jersey*
Wingate University *North Carolina*
Winona State University *Minnesota*
Winston-Salem State University *North Carolina*
Winthrop University *South Carolina*
Wittenberg University *Ohio*
Wright State University *Ohio*
Xavier University *Ohio*
Xavier University of Louisiana *Louisiana*
Yale University *Connecticut*
York College of Pennsylvania *Pennsylvania*
Young Harris College *Georgia*
Youngstown State University *Ohio*

National Association of Schools of Theatre (NAST)

American Academy of Dramatic Arts - Los Angeles *California*
American Academy of Dramatic Arts - New York *New York*
American Musical and Dramatic Academy, Los Angeles *California*
Appalachian State University *North Carolina*
Auburn University *Alabama*
Ball State University *Indiana*
Baylor University *Texas*
Boise State University *Idaho*
Bowling Green State University *Ohio*
Bradley University *Illinois*
Brigham Young University *Utah*
Butler University *Indiana*
California Institute of the Arts *California*

California State University, Dominguez Hills *California*
California State University, Fresno *California*
California State University, Fullerton *California*
California State University, Long Beach *California*
California State University, Northridge *California*
California State University, Sacramento *California*
California State University, San Bernardino *California*
California State University, Stanislaus *California*
Casper College *Wyoming*
College of the Holy Cross *Massachusetts*
Columbus State University *Georgia*
Community College of Baltimore County *Maryland*
Dartmouth College *New Hampshire*
Davis & Elkins College *West Virginia*
Del Mar College *Texas*
Florida International University *Florida*
Florida State University *Florida*
Francis Marion University *South Carolina*
Grambling State University *Louisiana*
Hope College *Michigan*
Howard University *District of Columbia*
Humboldt State University *California*
Idaho State University *Idaho*
Illinois State University *Illinois*
Indiana University Bloomington *Indiana*
Indiana University of Pennsylvania *Pennsylvania*
Ithaca College *New York*
Jacksonville State University *Alabama*
James Madison University *Virginia*
Kansas State University *Kansas*
KD Conservatory College of Film and Dramatic Arts *Texas*
Kean University *New Jersey*
Kennesaw State University *Georgia*
Kent State University *Ohio*
Lander University *South Carolina*
Lehigh University *Pennsylvania*
Longwood University *Virginia*
Louisiana State University and Agricultural & Mechanical College *Louisiana*
Loyola Marymount University *California*
Loyola University Chicago *Illinois*
Mars Hill University *North Carolina*
Miami University *Ohio*
Missouri State University *Missouri*
Montclair State University *New Jersey*
New World School of the Arts *Florida*
North Carolina Agricultural and Technical State University *North Carolina*
North Carolina Central University *North Carolina*
North Dakota State University *North Dakota*
Northern Illinois University *Illinois*
Northwestern State University of Louisiana *Louisiana*
Northwestern University *Illinois*
Oakland University *Michigan*
The Ohio State University *Ohio*
Ohio University *Ohio*
Oklahoma State University *Oklahoma*
Old Dominion University *Virginia*
Otterbein University *Ohio*
Penn State University Park *Pennsylvania*
Portland State University *Oregon*
Purdue University *Indiana*
Radford University *Virginia*
Rowan University *New Jersey*
St. Cloud State University *Minnesota*
St. Olaf College *Minnesota*
Salem State University *Massachusetts*
San Diego State University *California*
San Francisco State University *California*
San Jose State University *California*
Southern Illinois University Carbondale *Illinois*
Southern Methodist University *Texas*
State University of New York at Fredonia *New York*
State University of New York at New Paltz *New York*
Stephen F. Austin State University *Texas*
Temple University *Pennsylvania*
Texas Tech University *Texas*
Towson University *Maryland*
The University of Alabama *Alabama*
The University of Arizona *Arizona*
University of Arkansas at Little Rock *Arkansas*
University of California, Los Angeles *California*

University of Central Arkansas *Arkansas*
University of Cincinnati *Ohio*
University of Connecticut *Connecticut*
University of Florida *Florida*
University of Georgia *Georgia*
University of Illinois at Urbana - Champaign *Illinois*
University of the Incarnate Word *Texas*
The University of Iowa *Iowa*
University of Kentucky *Kentucky*
University of Louisville *Kentucky*
University of Maryland, College Park *Maryland*
University of Memphis *Tennessee*
University of Minnesota, Twin Cities Campus *Minnesota*
University of Mississippi *Mississippi*
University of Missouri - Kansas City *Missouri*
University of Montana *Montana*
University of Nebraska - Lincoln *Nebraska*
University of Nevada, Las Vegas *Nevada*
University of New Mexico *New Mexico*
University of New Orleans *Louisiana*
The University of North Carolina at Greensboro *North Carolina*
University of North Dakota *North Dakota*
University of Oklahoma *Oklahoma*
University of Pittsburgh *Pennsylvania*
University of Portland *Oregon*
University of South Carolina *South Carolina*
The University of South Dakota *South Dakota*
University of South Florida *Florida*
University of Southern Mississippi *Mississippi*
The University of Tennessee *Tennessee*
The University of Texas at Austin *Texas*
The University of Texas Rio Grande Valley *Texas*
University of Virginia *Virginia*
University of West Georgia *Georgia*
University of Wisconsin - Madison *Wisconsin*
University of Wisconsin - Stevens Point *Wisconsin*
University of Wisconsin - Whitewater *Wisconsin*
Valdosta State University *Georgia*
Vincennes University *Indiana*
Virginia Commonwealth University *Virginia*
Virginia Polytechnic Institute and State University *Virginia*
Wayne State University *Michigan*
West Virginia University *West Virginia*
Western Illinois University *Illinois*
Western Michigan University *Michigan*
Winona State University *Minnesota*
Winthrop University *South Carolina*
Youngstown State University *Ohio*

National Commission on Orthotic and Prosthetic Education (NCOPE)

California State University, Dominguez Hills *California*
University of Washington *Washington*

National Council for Accreditation of Teacher Education (NCATE)

Adelphi University *New York*
Alabama Agricultural and Mechanical University *Alabama*
Alabama State University *Alabama*
Alaska Pacific University *Alaska*
Albany State University *Georgia*
Alcorn State University *Mississippi*
Alverno College *Wisconsin*
American University *District of Columbia*
Anderson University *Indiana*
Anderson University *South Carolina*
Andrews University *Michigan*
Angelo State University *Texas*
Antioch University Midwest *Ohio*
Appalachian State University *North Carolina*
Arkansas State University *Arkansas*
Arkansas Tech University *Arkansas*
Armstrong State University *Georgia*
Asbury University *Kentucky*
Ashland University *Ohio*
Athens State University *Alabama*
Auburn University *Alabama*
Auburn University at Montgomery *Alabama*
Augsburg College *Minnesota*
Augusta University *Georgia*
Augustana College *Illinois*

Augustana University *South Dakota*
Aurora University *Illinois*
Austin Peay State University *Tennessee*
Azusa Pacific University *California*
Baker University *Kansas*
Baldwin Wallace University *Ohio*
Ball State University *Indiana*
Barton College *North Carolina*
Baylor University *Texas*
Bellarmine University *Kentucky*
Belmont University *Tennessee*
Bemidji State University *Minnesota*
Benedict College *South Carolina*
Benedictine College *Kansas*
Bennett College *North Carolina*
Berea College *Kentucky*
Berry College *Georgia*
Bethany College *Kansas*
Bethany College *West Virginia*
Bethel College *Indiana*
Bethel College *Kansas*
Bethune-Cookman University *Florida*
Birmingham-Southern College *Alabama*
Black Hills State University *South Dakota*
Bloomsburg University of Pennsylvania *Pennsylvania*
Bluefield State College *West Virginia*
Bluffton University *Ohio*
Boise State University *Idaho*
Boston College *Massachusetts*
Bowie State University *Maryland*
Bowling Green State University *Ohio*
Bradley University *Illinois*
Brenau University *Georgia*
Brewton-Parker College *Georgia*
Bridgewater State University *Massachusetts*
Brigham Young University *Utah*
Brooklyn College of the City University of New York *New York*
Buffalo State College, State University of New York *New York*
Butler University *Indiana*
California Lutheran University *California*
California Polytechnic State University, San Luis Obispo *California*
California State University, Bakersfield *California*
California State University, Chico *California*
California State University, Dominguez Hills *California*
California State University, East Bay *California*
California State University, Fresno *California*
California State University, Fullerton *California*
California State University, Long Beach *California*
California State University, Los Angeles *California*
California State University, Monterey Bay *California*
California State University, Northridge *California*
California State University, San Bernardino *California*
California State University, San Marcos *California*
California State University, Stanislaus *California*
California University of Pennsylvania *Pennsylvania*
Cameron University *Oklahoma*
Campbell University *North Carolina*
Campbellsville University *Kentucky*
Canisius College *New York*
Capella University *Minnesota*
Capital University *Ohio*
Cardinal Stritch University *Wisconsin*
Carson-Newman University *Tennessee*
Castleton University *Vermont*
Catawba College *North Carolina*
The Catholic University of America *District of Columbia*
Cedarville University *Ohio*
Centenary College of Louisiana *Louisiana*
Central Connecticut State University *Connecticut*
Central Michigan University *Michigan*
Central State University *Ohio*
Central Washington University *Washington*
Chadron State College *Nebraska*
Chaminade University of Honolulu *Hawaii*
Charleston Southern University *South Carolina*
Chicago State University *Illinois*
Chowan University *North Carolina*
Christian Brothers University *Tennessee*

The Citadel, The Military College of South Carolina *South Carolina*
City College of the City University of New York *New York*
Claflin University *South Carolina*
Clarion University of Pennsylvania *Pennsylvania*
Clark Atlanta University *Georgia*
Clayton State University *Georgia*
Clemson University *South Carolina*
Cleveland State University *Ohio*
Coastal Carolina University *South Carolina*
The College at Brockport, State University of New York *New York*
College of Charleston *South Carolina*
The College of New Jersey *New Jersey*
College of Saint Benedict *Minnesota*
The College of Saint Rose *New York*
College of Staten Island of the City University of New York *New York*
The College of William and Mary *Virginia*
The College of Wooster *Ohio*
Colorado Mesa University *Colorado*
Columbia College *South Carolina*
Columbus State University *Georgia*
Concord University *West Virginia*
Concordia College *Minnesota*
Concordia College - New York *New York*
Concordia University Ann Arbor *Michigan*
Concordia University Chicago *Illinois*
Concordia University, Nebraska *Nebraska*
Concordia University, St. Paul *Minnesota*
Converse College *South Carolina*
Coppin State University *Maryland*
Creighton University *Nebraska*
Cumberland University *Tennessee*
Dakota State University *South Dakota*
Dalton State College *Georgia*
Defiance College *Ohio*
Delaware State University *Delaware*
Delta State University *Mississippi*
DePaul University *Illinois*
DePauw University *Indiana*
Dickinson State University *North Dakota*
Doane University *Nebraska*
Dominican University *Illinois*
Drury University *Missouri*
Duke University *North Carolina*
Duquesne University *Pennsylvania*
D'Youville College *New York*
East Carolina University *North Carolina*
East Central University *Oklahoma*
East Stroudsburg University of Pennsylvania *Pennsylvania*
East Tennessee State University *Tennessee*
Eastern Connecticut State University *Connecticut*
Eastern Illinois University *Illinois*
Eastern Kentucky University *Kentucky*
Eastern Mennonite University *Virginia*
Eastern Michigan University *Michigan*
Eastern New Mexico University *New Mexico*
Eastern Washington University *Washington*
Edgewood College *Wisconsin*
Edinboro University of Pennsylvania *Pennsylvania*
Elizabeth City State University *North Carolina*
Elon University *North Carolina*
Emory University *Georgia*
Emporia State University *Kansas*
Erskine College *South Carolina*
Evangel University *Missouri*
Fairfield University *Connecticut*
Fairmont State University *West Virginia*
Faulkner University *Alabama*
Fayetteville State University *North Carolina*
Ferris State University *Michigan*
Fitchburg State University *Massachusetts*
Five Towns College *New York*
Florida Agricultural and Mechanical University *Florida*
Florida Atlantic University *Florida*
Florida International University *Florida*
Florida State University *Florida*
Fontbonne University *Missouri*
Fordham University *New York*
Fort Hays State University *Kansas*
Fort Valley State University *Georgia*
Francis Marion University *South Carolina*

Franciscan University of Steubenville *Ohio*
Franklin College *Indiana*
Freed-Hardeman University *Tennessee*
Friends University *Kansas*
Frostburg State University *Maryland*
Furman University *South Carolina*
Gallaudet University *District of Columbia*
Gardner-Webb University *North Carolina*
George Fox University *Oregon*
George Mason University *Virginia*
The George Washington University *District of Columbia*
Georgetown College *Kentucky*
Georgia College & State University *Georgia*
Georgia Southern University *Georgia*
Georgia Southwestern State University *Georgia*
Georgia State University *Georgia*
Glenville State College *West Virginia*
Gonzaga University *Washington*
Goshen College *Indiana*
Governors State University *Illinois*
Grace College *Indiana*
Graceland University *Iowa*
Grambling State University *Louisiana*
Grand Canyon University *Arizona*
Grand Valley State University *Michigan*
Greensboro College *North Carolina*
Gustavus Adolphus College *Minnesota*
Hamline University *Minnesota*
Hampton University *Virginia*
Hanover College *Indiana*
Harding University *Arkansas*
Harris-Stowe State University *Missouri*
Hastings College *Nebraska*
Heidelberg University *Ohio*
Henderson State University *Arkansas*
Hendrix College *Arkansas*
High Point University *North Carolina*
Hiram College *Ohio*
Hofstra University *New York*
Hood College *Maryland*
Howard University *District of Columbia*
Hunter College of the City University of New York *New York*
Huntington University *Indiana*
Idaho State University *Idaho*
Illinois State University *Illinois*
Indiana State University *Indiana*
Indiana University Bloomington *Indiana*
Indiana University East *Indiana*
Indiana University Kokomo *Indiana*
Indiana University Northwest *Indiana*
Indiana University of Pennsylvania *Pennsylvania*
Indiana University - Purdue University Fort Wayne *Indiana*
Indiana University South Bend *Indiana*
Indiana University Southeast *Indiana*
Indiana Wesleyan University *Indiana*
Iona College *New York*
Jackson State University *Mississippi*
Jacksonville State University *Alabama*
James Madison University *Virginia*
John Brown University *Arkansas*
John Carroll University *Ohio*
Johns Hopkins University *Maryland*
Johnson C. Smith University *North Carolina*
Kansas State University *Kansas*
Kansas Wesleyan University *Kansas*
Kean University *New Jersey*
Keene State College *New Hampshire*
Kennesaw State University *Georgia*
Kent State University *Ohio*
Kentucky State University *Kentucky*
King's College *Pennsylvania*
Kutztown University of Pennsylvania *Pennsylvania*
Lake Erie College *Ohio*
Lamar University *Texas*
Lander University *South Carolina*
Langston University *Oklahoma*
Lee University *Tennessee*
Lehman College of the City University of New York *New York*
LeMoyne-Owen College *Tennessee*
Lenoir-Rhyne University *North Carolina*
Lewis & Clark College *Oregon*
Lewis University *Illinois*

Liberty University *Virginia*
Limestone College *South Carolina*
Lincoln University *Missouri*
Lindenwood University *Missouri*
Lipscomb University *Tennessee*
Livingstone College *North Carolina*
Lock Haven University of Pennsylvania *Pennsylvania*
Longwood University *Virginia*
Louisiana College *Louisiana*
Louisiana State University and Agricultural & Mechanical College *Louisiana*
Louisiana State University at Alexandria *Louisiana*
Louisiana State University in Shreveport *Louisiana*
Louisiana Tech University *Louisiana*
Loyola Marymount University *California*
Loyola University Chicago *Illinois*
Loyola University Maryland *Maryland*
Luther College *Iowa*
Lyon College *Arkansas*
Madonna University *Michigan*
Malone University *Ohio*
Manchester University *Indiana*
Manhattanville College *New York*
Mansfield University of Pennsylvania *Pennsylvania*
Marian University *Indiana*
Marian University *Wisconsin*
Marietta College *Ohio*
Marquette University *Wisconsin*
Mars Hill University *North Carolina*
Marshall University *West Virginia*
Marygrove College *Michigan*
Marymount University *Virginia*
Maryville University of Saint Louis *Missouri*
Marywood University *Pennsylvania*
Mayville State University *North Dakota*
McDaniel College *Maryland*
McKendree University *Illinois*
McMaster University *Ontario (Canada)*
McNeese State University *Louisiana*
McPherson College *Kansas*
Medgar Evers College of the City University of New York *New York*
Mercer University *Georgia*
Meredith College *North Carolina*
Methodist University *North Carolina*
Metropolitan College of New York *New York*
Metropolitan State University of Denver *Colorado*
Miami University *Ohio*
MidAmerica Nazarene University *Kansas*
Middle Georgia State University *Georgia*
Middle Tennessee State University *Tennessee*
Miles College *Alabama*
Millersville University of Pennsylvania *Pennsylvania*
Milligan College *Tennessee*
Millikin University *Illinois*
Millsaps College *Mississippi*
Minnesota State University Mankato *Minnesota*
Minnesota State University Moorhead *Minnesota*
Minot State University *North Dakota*
Misericordia University *Pennsylvania*
Mississippi College *Mississippi*
Mississippi State University *Mississippi*
Mississippi University for Women *Mississippi*
Mississippi Valley State University *Mississippi*
Missouri Baptist University *Missouri*
Missouri Southern State University *Missouri*
Missouri State University *Missouri*
Missouri Western State University *Missouri*
Molloy College *New York*
Monmouth University *New Jersey*
Montana State University Billings *Montana*
Montana State University - Northern *Montana*
Montclair State University *New Jersey*
Montreat College *North Carolina*
Morehead State University *Kentucky*
Morgan State University *Maryland*
Morris College *South Carolina*
Mount Saint Mary College *New York*
Mount St. Mary's University *Maryland*
Mount Vernon Nazarene University *Ohio*
Murray State University *Kentucky*
Muskingum University *Ohio*
National Louis University *Illinois*
Nebraska Wesleyan University *Nebraska*
New Jersey City University *New Jersey*

New Mexico Highlands University *New Mexico*
New Mexico State University *New Mexico*
New York City College of Technology of the City University of New York *New York*
New York Institute of Technology *New York*
Newberry College *South Carolina*
Newman University *Kansas*
Niagara University *New York*
Nicholls State University *Louisiana*
Norfolk State University *Virginia*
North Carolina Agricultural and Technical State University *North Carolina*
North Carolina Central University *North Carolina*
North Carolina State University *North Carolina*
North Carolina Wesleyan College *North Carolina*
North Dakota State University *North Dakota*
North Greenville University *South Carolina*
Northeastern Illinois University *Illinois*
Northeastern State University *Oklahoma*
Northern Arizona University *Arizona*
Northern Illinois University *Illinois*
Northern Kentucky University *Kentucky*
Northern State University *South Dakota*
Northwest Missouri State University *Missouri*
Northwest Nazarene University *Idaho*
Northwestern College *Iowa*
Northwestern Oklahoma State University *Oklahoma*
Northwestern State University of Louisiana *Louisiana*
Notre Dame College *Ohio*
Notre Dame of Maryland University *Maryland*
Nova Southeastern University *Florida*
Nyack College *New York*
Oakland City University *Indiana*
Oakwood University *Alabama*
Ohio Dominican University *Ohio*
Ohio Northern University *Ohio*
The Ohio State University *Ohio*
Ohio University *Ohio*
Ohio Valley University *West Virginia*
Ohio Wesleyan University *Ohio*
Oklahoma Baptist University *Oklahoma*
Oklahoma Christian University *Oklahoma*
Oklahoma Panhandle State University *Oklahoma*
Oklahoma State University *Oklahoma*
Oklahoma Wesleyan University *Oklahoma*
Old Dominion University *Virginia*
Olivet Nazarene University *Illinois*
Oral Roberts University *Oklahoma*
Oregon State University *Oregon*
Ottawa University *Kansas*
Otterbein University *Ohio*
Ouachita Baptist University *Arkansas*
Pace University *New York*
Pacific Lutheran University *Washington*
Pacific University *Oregon*
Paine College *Georgia*
Penn State Harrisburg *Pennsylvania*
Penn State University Park *Pennsylvania*
Peru State College *Nebraska*
Pfeiffer University *North Carolina*
Philander Smith College *Arkansas*
Pittsburg State University *Kansas*
Plymouth State University *New Hampshire*
Point University *Georgia*
Portland State University *Oregon*
Prairie View A&M University *Texas*
Presbyterian College *South Carolina*
Purdue University *Indiana*
Purdue University Northwest *Hammond, Indiana*
Purdue University Northwest *Westville, Indiana*
Queens College of the City University of New York *New York*
Queens University of Charlotte *North Carolina*
Quinnipiac University *Connecticut*
Radford University *Virginia*
Rhode Island College *Rhode Island*
Rider University *New Jersey*
Roosevelt University *Illinois*
Rowan University *New Jersey*
Sacred Heart University *Connecticut*
The Sage Colleges *New York*
Saginaw Valley State University *Michigan*
St. Andrews University *North Carolina*
Saint Augustine's University *North Carolina*
St. Bonaventure University *New York*

St. Cloud State University *Minnesota*
St. John Fisher College *New York*
Saint John's University *Minnesota*
Saint Joseph's College *Indiana*
Saint Joseph's University *Pennsylvania*
Saint Louis University *Missouri*
Saint Mary-of-the-Woods College *Indiana*
Saint Mary's College *Indiana*
St. Olaf College *Minnesota*
St. Thomas Aquinas College *New York*
Saint Xavier University *Illinois*
Salem College *North Carolina*
Salem State University *Massachusetts*
Salisbury University *Maryland*
Sam Houston State University *Texas*
Samford University *Alabama*
San Diego State University *California*
San Francisco State University *California*
San Jose State University *California*
Seattle Pacific University *Washington*
Seattle University *Washington*
Seton Hall University *New Jersey*
Shaw University *North Carolina*
Shawnee State University *Ohio*
Shepherd University *West Virginia*
Shippensburg University of Pennsylvania *Pennsylvania*
Siena College *New York*
Slippery Rock University of Pennsylvania *Pennsylvania*
Sonoma State University *California*
South Carolina State University *South Carolina*
South Dakota State University *South Dakota*
Southeast Missouri State University *Missouri*
Southeastern Louisiana University *Louisiana*
Southeastern Oklahoma State University *Oklahoma*
Southern Adventist University *Tennessee*
Southern Arkansas University - Magnolia *Arkansas*
Southern Connecticut State University *Connecticut*
Southern Illinois University Carbondale *Illinois*
Southern Illinois University Edwardsville *Illinois*
Southern Nazarene University *Oklahoma*
Southern New Hampshire University *New Hampshire*
Southern University and Agricultural and Mechanical College *Louisiana*
Southern University at New Orleans *Louisiana*
Southern Wesleyan University *South Carolina*
Southwestern Adventist University *Texas*
Southwestern College *Kansas*
Southwestern Oklahoma State University *Oklahoma*
Spalding University *Kentucky*
Spelman College *Georgia*
Stanford University *California*
State University of New York College at Cortland *New York*
State University of New York College at Geneseo *New York*
State University of New York College at Old Westbury *New York*
State University of New York College at Oneonta *New York*
State University of New York College at Potsdam *New York*
State University of New York at Fredonia *New York*
State University of New York at New Paltz *New York*
State University of New York at Oswego *New York*
Stephen F. Austin State University *Texas*
Sterling College *Kansas*
Stetson University *Florida*
Stevenson University *Maryland*
Stillman College *Alabama*
Stony Brook University, State University of New York *New York*
Syracuse University *New York*
Tabor College *Kansas*
Taylor University *Indiana*
Tennessee State University *Tennessee*
Tennessee Technological University *Tennessee*
Texas A&M University *Texas*
Texas Tech University *Texas*
Towson University *Maryland*
Transylvania University *Kentucky*
Trevecca Nazarene University *Tennessee*
Trine University *Indiana*
Trinity University *Texas*

Trinity Washington University *District of Columbia*
Troy University *Alabama*
Truman State University *Missouri*
Tuskegee University *Alabama*
Union College *Nebraska*
Union University *Tennessee*
The University of Akron *Ohio*
The University of Alabama *Alabama*
The University of Alabama at Birmingham *Alabama*
The University of Alabama in Huntsville *Alabama*
University of Alaska Anchorage *Alaska*
University of Alaska Fairbanks *Alaska*
University of Alaska Southeast *Alaska*
University of Arkansas *Arkansas*
University of Arkansas - Fort Smith *Arkansas*
University of Arkansas at Little Rock *Arkansas*
University of Arkansas at Monticello *Arkansas*
University of Arkansas at Pine Bluff *Arkansas*
The University of British Columbia *British Columbia (Canada)*
University of Central Arkansas *Arkansas*
University of Central Florida *Florida*
University of Central Missouri *Missouri*
University of Central Oklahoma *Oklahoma*
University of Cincinnati *Ohio*
University of Colorado Boulder *Colorado*
University of Colorado Colorado Springs *Colorado*
University of Colorado Denver *Colorado*
University of Connecticut *Connecticut*
University of Dayton *Ohio*
University of Delaware *Delaware*
University of Denver *Colorado*
University of the District of Columbia *District of Columbia*
University of Evansville *Indiana*
The University of Findlay *Ohio*
University of Florida *Florida*
University of Georgia *Georgia*
University of Guam *Guam*
University of Hartford *Connecticut*
University of Hawaii at Hilo *Hawaii*
University of Hawaii at Manoa *Hawaii*
University of Holy Cross *Louisiana*
University of Houston *Texas*
University of Houston - Clear Lake *Texas*
University of Idaho *Idaho*
University of Indianapolis *Indiana*
The University of Kansas *Kansas*
University of Kentucky *Kentucky*
University of La Verne *California*
University of Louisiana at Lafayette *Louisiana*
University of Louisiana at Monroe *Louisiana*
University of Louisville *Kentucky*
University of Maine *Maine*
University of Maine at Farmington *Maine*
University of Maryland, Baltimore County *Maryland*
University of Maryland, College Park *Maryland*
University of Maryland Eastern Shore *Maryland*
University of Maryland University College *Maryland*
University of Massachusetts Amherst *Massachusetts*
University of Massachusetts Boston *Massachusetts*
University of Massachusetts Lowell *Massachusetts*
University of Memphis *Tennessee*
University of Miami *Florida*
University of Minnesota, Duluth *Minnesota*
University of Minnesota, Morris *Minnesota*
University of Minnesota, Twin Cities Campus *Minnesota*
University of Mississippi *Mississippi*
University of Missouri - Kansas City *Missouri*
University of Missouri - St. Louis *Missouri*
University of Montana *Montana*
The University of Montana Western *Montana*
University of Montevallo *Alabama*
University of Mount Union *Ohio*
University of Nebraska at Kearney *Nebraska*
University of Nebraska - Lincoln *Nebraska*
University of Nebraska at Omaha *Nebraska*
University of Nevada, Las Vegas *Nevada*
University of Nevada, Reno *Nevada*
University of New Mexico *New Mexico*
University of New Orleans *Louisiana*
University of North Alabama *Alabama*
University of North Carolina at Asheville *North Carolina*

The University of North Carolina at Chapel Hill *North Carolina*
The University of North Carolina at Charlotte *North Carolina*
The University of North Carolina at Greensboro *North Carolina*
The University of North Carolina at Pembroke *North Carolina*
The University of North Carolina Wilmington *North Carolina*
University of North Dakota *North Dakota*
University of North Florida *Florida*
University of North Georgia *Georgia*
University of North Texas *Texas*
University of Northern Colorado *Colorado*
University of Oklahoma *Oklahoma*
University of the Ozarks *Arkansas*
University of the Pacific *California*
University of Pittsburgh *Pennsylvania*
University of Portland *Oregon*
University of Puerto Rico in Aguadilla *Puerto Rico*
University of Puerto Rico in Arecibo *Puerto Rico*
University of Puerto Rico in Bayamón *Puerto Rico*
University of Puerto Rico in Cayey *Puerto Rico*
University of Puerto Rico in Humacao *Puerto Rico*
University of Puerto Rico, Mayagüez Campus *Puerto Rico*
University of Puerto Rico in Ponce *Puerto Rico*
University of Puerto Rico, Río Piedras Campus *Puerto Rico*
University of Puerto Rico in Utuado *Puerto Rico*
University of Puget Sound *Washington*
University of Rhode Island *Rhode Island*
University of Rio Grande *Ohio*
University of Rochester *New York*
University of St. Francis *Illinois*
University of Saint Francis *Indiana*
University of Saint Mary *Kansas*
University of St. Thomas *Minnesota*
University of San Diego *California*
University of Science and Arts of Oklahoma *Oklahoma*
The University of Scranton *Pennsylvania*
University of Sioux Falls *South Dakota*
University of South Alabama *Alabama*
University of South Carolina *South Carolina*
University of South Carolina Aiken *South Carolina*
University of South Carolina Beaufort *South Carolina*
University of South Carolina Upstate *South Carolina*
The University of South Dakota *South Dakota*
University of South Florida *Florida*
University of South Florida, St. Petersburg *Florida*
University of Southern Indiana *Indiana*
University of Southern Maine *Maine*
University of Southern Mississippi *Mississippi*
The University of Tennessee *Tennessee*
The University of Tennessee at Chattanooga *Tennessee*
The University of Tennessee at Martin *Tennessee*
The University of Texas at Arlington *Texas*
The University of Texas of the Permian Basin *Texas*
The University of Toledo *Ohio*
The University of Tulsa *Oklahoma*
University of Vermont *Vermont*
University of Virginia *Virginia*
The University of West Alabama *Alabama*
University of West Florida *Florida*
University of West Georgia *Georgia*
University of Wisconsin - La Crosse *Wisconsin*
University of Wisconsin - Platteville *Wisconsin*
University of Wisconsin - River Falls *Wisconsin*
University of Wisconsin - Stout *Wisconsin*
University of Wisconsin - Whitewater *Wisconsin*
University of Wyoming *Wyoming*
Ursuline College *Ohio*
Valdosta State University *Georgia*
Valley City State University *North Dakota*
Valparaiso University *Indiana*
Vanderbilt University *Tennessee*
Virginia Commonwealth University *Virginia*
Virginia Polytechnic Institute and State University *Virginia*
Virginia State University *Virginia*
Virginia Union University *Virginia*
Viterbo University *Wisconsin*

Wabash College *Indiana*
Wagner College *New York*
Wake Forest University *North Carolina*
Walden University *Minnesota*
Walsh University *Ohio*
Wartburg College *Iowa*
Washburn University *Kansas*
Washington State University *Washington*
Washington University in St. Louis *Missouri*
Wayne State College *Nebraska*
Weber State University *Utah*
Webster University *Missouri*
Wesley College *Delaware*
West Chester University of Pennsylvania *Pennsylvania*
West Liberty University *West Virginia*
West Virginia State University *West Virginia*
West Virginia University *West Virginia*
West Virginia University at Parkersburg *West Virginia*
West Virginia Wesleyan College *West Virginia*
Western Carolina University *North Carolina*
Western Connecticut State University *Connecticut*
Western Governors University *Utah*
Western Illinois University *Illinois*
Western Kentucky University *Kentucky*
Western Michigan University *Michigan*
Western New Mexico University *New Mexico*
Western Oregon University *Oregon*
Western Washington University *Washington*
Westfield State University *Massachusetts*
Wheaton College *Illinois*
Wheelock College *Massachusetts*
Whitworth University *Washington*
Wichita State University *Kansas*
Widener University *Pennsylvania*
Willamette University *Oregon*
William Carey University *Mississippi*
William Paterson University of New Jersey *New Jersey*
Williams Baptist College *Arkansas*
Wilmington University *Delaware*
Wingate University *North Carolina*
Winona State University *Minnesota*
Winston-Salem State University *North Carolina*
Winthrop University *South Carolina*
Wittenberg University *Ohio*
Wright State University *Ohio*
Xavier University of Louisiana *Louisiana*
Yeshiva University *New York*
York College *Nebraska*
York College of the City University of New York *New York*
Youngstown State University *Ohio*

National Recreation and Park Association (NRPA)

Appalachian State University *North Carolina*
Arizona State University at the Tempe campus *Arizona*
Arizona State University at the West campus *Arizona*
Arkansas Tech University *Arkansas*
Aurora University *Illinois*
Bowling Green State University *Ohio*
Brigham Young University *Utah*
California Polytechnic State University, San Luis Obispo *California*
California State University, Chico *California*
California State University, Fresno *California*
California State University, Long Beach *California*
California State University, Northridge *California*
California State University, Sacramento *California*
Central Michigan University *Michigan*
Clemson University *South Carolina*
The College at Brockport, State University of New York *New York*
Colorado State University *Colorado*
East Carolina University *North Carolina*
East Stroudsburg University of Pennsylvania *Pennsylvania*
Eastern Illinois University *Illinois*
Eastern Kentucky University *Kentucky*
Eastern Michigan University *Michigan*
Eastern Washington University *Washington*
Ferris State University *Michigan*

Ferrum College *Virginia*
Florida International University *Florida*
Florida State University *Florida*
Frostburg State University *Maryland*
Gallaudet University *District of Columbia*
Georgia Southern University *Georgia*
Grambling State University *Louisiana*
Green Mountain College *Vermont*
Illinois State University *Illinois*
Indiana State University *Indiana*
Indiana University Bloomington *Indiana*
Ithaca College *New York*
Kansas State University *Kansas*
Kent State University *Ohio*
Lincoln University *Pennsylvania*
Longwood University *Virginia*
Lyndon State College *Vermont*
Marshall University *West Virginia*
Metropolitan State University of Denver *Colorado*
Michigan State University *Michigan*
Middle Tennessee State University *Tennessee*
Minnesota State University Mankato *Minnesota*
Missouri State University *Missouri*
Montclair State University *New Jersey*
North Carolina Central University *North Carolina*
North Carolina State University *North Carolina*
Northern Arizona University *Arizona*
Ohio University *Ohio*
Oklahoma State University *Oklahoma*
Old Dominion University *Virginia*
Radford University *Virginia*
San Diego State University *California*
San Francisco State University *California*
San Jose State University *California*
Slippery Rock University of Pennsylvania *Pennsylvania*
Southeast Missouri State University *Missouri*
Southern Illinois University Carbondale *Illinois*
Springfield College *Massachusetts*
State University of New York College at Cortland *New York*
Temple University *Pennsylvania*
Texas A&M University *Texas*
Texas State University *Texas*
University of Arkansas *Arkansas*
University of Florida *Florida*
University of Georgia *Georgia*
University of Idaho *Idaho*
University of Illinois at Urbana - Champaign *Illinois*
The University of Iowa *Iowa*
University of Maine at Machias *Maine*
University of Maine at Presque Isle *Maine*
University of Minnesota, Twin Cities Campus *Minnesota*
University of Mississippi *Mississippi*
University of Missouri *Missouri*
University of Montana *Montana*
University of New Hampshire *New Hampshire*
The University of North Carolina at Chapel Hill *North Carolina*
The University of North Carolina at Greensboro *North Carolina*
The University of North Carolina Wilmington *North Carolina*
University of North Texas *Texas*
University of Northern Iowa *Iowa*
University of Ottawa *Ontario (Canada)*
University of St. Francis *Illinois*
University of Southern Mississippi *Mississippi*
The University of Tennessee *Tennessee*
The University of Toledo *Ohio*
University of Utah *Utah*
University of Wisconsin - La Crosse *Wisconsin*
Utah State University *Utah*
Virginia Commonwealth University *Virginia*
Virginia Wesleyan College *Virginia*
West Virginia State University *West Virginia*
West Virginia University *West Virginia*
Western Illinois University *Illinois*
Western Kentucky University *Kentucky*
Western Washington University *Washington*
Winston-Salem State University *North Carolina*
York College of Pennsylvania *Pennsylvania*

Network of Schools of Public Policy, Affairs, and Administration (NASPAA)

Albany State University *Georgia*
American University *District of Columbia*
Appalachian State University *North Carolina*
Arizona State University at the Tempe campus *Arizona*
Arkansas State University *Arkansas*
Auburn University *Alabama*
Auburn University at Montgomery *Alabama*
Baruch College of the City University of New York *New York*
Binghamton University, State University of New York *New York*
Boise State University *Idaho*
Bowie State University *Maryland*
Bridgewater State University *Massachusetts*
Brigham Young University *Utah*
California State Polytechnic University, Pomona *California*
California State University, Bakersfield *California*
California State University, Chico *California*
California State University, Dominguez Hills *California*
California State University, East Bay *California*
California State University, Fresno *California*
California State University, Fullerton *California*
California State University, Long Beach *California*
California State University, Los Angeles *California*
California State University, San Bernardino *California*
California State University, Stanislaus *California*
Carnegie Mellon University *Pennsylvania*
Central Michigan University *Michigan*
Clark Atlanta University *Georgia*
Cleveland State University *Ohio*
The College at Brockport, State University of New York *New York*
College of Charleston *South Carolina*
Columbia University *New York*
DePaul University *Illinois*
East Carolina University *North Carolina*
Eastern Kentucky University *Kentucky*
Eastern Michigan University *Michigan*
Florida Atlantic University *Florida*
Florida Gulf Coast University *Florida*
Florida International University *Florida*
Florida State University *Florida*
George Mason University *Virginia*
The George Washington University *District of Columbia*
Georgia College & State University *Georgia*
Georgia Southern University *Georgia*
Georgia State University *Georgia*
Governors State University *Illinois*
Grambling State University *Louisiana*
Grand Valley State University *Michigan*
Howard University *District of Columbia*
Indiana University Bloomington *Indiana*
Indiana University Northwest *Indiana*
Indiana University - Purdue University Fort Wayne *Indiana*
Indiana University - Purdue University Indianapolis *Indiana*
Indiana University South Bend *Indiana*
Jackson State University *Mississippi*
James Madison University *Virginia*
John Jay College of Criminal Justice of the City University of New York *New York*
Kansas State University *Kansas*
Kean University *New Jersey*
Kennesaw State University *Georgia*
Kent State University *Ohio*
Kentucky State University *Kentucky*
Long Island University - LIU Brooklyn *New York*
Long Island University - LIU Post *New York*
Louisiana State University and Agricultural & Mechanical College *Louisiana*
Michigan State University *Michigan*
Mississippi State University *Mississippi*
Missouri State University *Missouri*
Morehead State University *Kentucky*
New Mexico State University *New Mexico*
New York University *New York*
North Carolina Central University *North Carolina*
North Carolina State University *North Carolina*

Northeastern University *Massachusetts*
Northern Illinois University *Illinois*
Northern Kentucky University *Kentucky*
Oakland University *Michigan*
The Ohio State University *Ohio*
Old Dominion University *Virginia*
Penn State Harrisburg *Pennsylvania*
Portland State University *Oregon*
Rutgers University - Camden *New Jersey*
Rutgers University - New Brunswick *New Jersey*
Rutgers University - Newark *New Jersey*
Saint Louis University *Missouri*
San Diego State University *California*
San Francisco State University *California*
San Jose State University *California*
Savannah State University *Georgia*
Seattle University *Washington*
Seton Hall University *New Jersey*
Southern Illinois University Carbondale *Illinois*
Southern Illinois University Edwardsville *Illinois*
Southern University and Agricultural and Mechanical College *Louisiana*
Suffolk University *Massachusetts*
Syracuse University *New York*
Tennessee State University *Tennessee*
Texas A&M University *Texas*
Texas Southern University *Texas*
Texas State University *Texas*
Texas Tech University *Texas*
Troy University *Alabama*
The University of Alabama at Birmingham *Alabama*
University at Albany, State University of New York *New York*
The University of Arizona *Arizona*
University of Arkansas at Little Rock *Arkansas*
University of Baltimore *Maryland*
University of Central Florida *Florida*
University of Colorado Colorado Springs *Colorado*
University of Colorado Denver *Colorado*
University of Connecticut *Connecticut*
University of Dayton *Ohio*
University of Delaware *Delaware*
University of Georgia *Georgia*
University of Illinois at Chicago *Illinois*
University of Illinois at Springfield *Illinois*
The University of Kansas *Kansas*
University of Kentucky *Kentucky*
University of La Verne *California*
University of Louisville *Kentucky*
University of Maine *Maine*
University of Maryland, Baltimore County *Maryland*
University of Maryland, College Park *Maryland*
University of Memphis *Tennessee*
University of Minnesota, Twin Cities Campus *Minnesota*
University of Missouri *Missouri*
University of Missouri - Kansas City *Missouri*
University of Missouri - St. Louis *Missouri*
University of Nebraska at Omaha *Nebraska*
University of Nevada, Las Vegas *Nevada*
University of New Mexico *New Mexico*
University of New Orleans *Louisiana*
The University of North Carolina at Chapel Hill *North Carolina*
The University of North Carolina at Charlotte *North Carolina*
The University of North Carolina at Greensboro *North Carolina*
The University of North Carolina Wilmington *North Carolina*
University of North Dakota *North Dakota*
University of North Florida *Florida*
University of North Texas *Texas*
University of Oregon *Oregon*
University of Pittsburgh *Pennsylvania*
University of San Francisco *California*
University of South Carolina *South Carolina*
The University of South Dakota *South Dakota*
University of South Florida *Florida*
University of Southern California *California*
University of Southern Maine *Maine*
The University of Tennessee *Tennessee*
The University of Tennessee at Chattanooga *Tennessee*
The University of Texas at Arlington *Texas*
The University of Texas at Austin *Texas*

The University of Texas at Dallas *Texas*
The University of Texas at El Paso *Texas*
The University of Texas at San Antonio *Texas*
The University of Toledo *Ohio*
University of Utah *Utah*
University of Vermont *Vermont*
University of Washington *Washington*
University of West Florida *Florida*
University of West Georgia *Georgia*
Valdosta State University *Georgia*
Villanova University *Pennsylvania*
Virginia Commonwealth University *Virginia*
Virginia Polytechnic Institute and State University *Virginia*
Wayne State University *Michigan*
West Virginia University *West Virginia*
Western Kentucky University *Kentucky*
Western Michigan University *Michigan*
Wichita State University *Kansas*
Willamette University *Oregon*
Wright State University *Ohio*

New York State Board of Regents (NYSBR)

Bramson ORT College *New York*
Globe Institute of Technology *New York*
Holy Trinity Orthodox Seminary *New York*
Memorial Hospital School of Nursing *New York*
New York Career Institute *New York*
TCI - College of Technology *New York*
Utica School of Commerce *New York*
Wood Tobe - Coburn School *New York*

Northwest Commission on Colleges and Universities (NCCU)

Aaniiih Nakoda College *Montana*
Alaska Pacific University *Alaska*
The Art Institute of Portland *Oregon*
The Art Institute of Seattle *Washington*
Bastyr University *Washington*
Bates Technical College *Washington*
Bellevue College *Washington*
Bellingham Technical College *Washington*
Big Bend Community College *Washington*
Blackfeet Community College *Montana*
Blue Mountain Community College *Oregon*
Boise State University *Idaho*
Brigham Young University *Utah*
Brigham Young University - Idaho *Idaho*
Capilano University *British Columbia (Canada)*
Carroll College *Montana*
Cascadia College *Washington*
Central Oregon Community College *Oregon*
Central Washington University *Washington*
Centralia College *Washington*
Chemeketa Community College *Oregon*
Chief Dull Knife College *Montana*
City University of Seattle *Washington*
Clackamas Community College *Oregon*
Clark College *Washington*
Clatsop Community College *Oregon*
Clover Park Technical College *Washington*
The College of Idaho *Idaho*
College of Southern Idaho *Idaho*
College of Southern Nevada *Nevada*
College of Western Idaho *Idaho*
Columbia Basin College *Washington*
Columbia Gorge Community College *Oregon*
Concordia University *Oregon*
Corban University *Oregon*
Cornish College of the Arts *Washington*
Dawson Community College *Montana*
Dixie State University *Utah*
Eastern Idaho Technical College *Idaho*
Eastern Oregon University *Oregon*
Eastern Washington University *Washington*
Edmonds Community College *Washington*
Everett Community College *Washington*
The Evergreen State College *Washington*
Flathead Valley Community College *Montana*
Fort Peck Community College *Montana*
George Fox University *Oregon*
Gonzaga University *Washington*
Grays Harbor College *Washington*
Great Basin College *Nevada*

Great Falls College Montana State University *Montana*
Green River College *Washington*
Helena College University of Montana *Montana*
Heritage University *Washington*
Highline College *Washington*
Idaho State University *Idaho*
Ilisagvik College *Alaska*
Klamath Community College *Oregon*
Lake Washington Institute of Technology *Washington*
Lane Community College *Oregon*
LDS Business College *Utah*
Lewis & Clark College *Oregon*
Lewis-Clark State College *Idaho*
Linfield College *Oregon*
Linn-Benton Community College *Oregon*
Little Big Horn College *Montana*
Lower Columbia College *Washington*
Marylhurst University *Oregon*
Miles Community College *Montana*
Montana State University *Montana*
Montana State University Billings *Montana*
Montana State University - Northern *Montana*
Montana Tech of The University of Montana *Montana*
Mount Angel Seminary *Oregon*
Mt. Hood Community College *Oregon*
Multnomah University *Oregon*
Nevada State College *Nevada*
North Idaho College *Idaho*
North Seattle College *Washington*
Northwest Christian University *Oregon*
Northwest Indian College *Washington*
Northwest Nazarene University *Idaho*
Northwest University *Washington*
Olympic College *Washington*
Oregon College of Art & Craft *Oregon*
Oregon Health & Science University *Oregon*
Oregon Institute of Technology *Oregon*
Oregon State University *Oregon*
Oregon State University - Cascades *Oregon*
Pacific Lutheran University *Washington*
Pacific Northwest College of Art *Oregon*
Pacific University *Oregon*
Peninsula College *Washington*
Pierce College at Fort Steilacoom *Washington*
Pierce College at Puyallup *Washington*
Portland Community College *Oregon*
Portland State University *Oregon*
Reed College *Oregon*
Renton Technical College *Washington*
Rocky Mountain College *Montana*
Rogue Community College *Oregon*
Saint Martin's University *Washington*
Salish Kootenai College *Montana*
Salt Lake Community College *Utah*
Seattle Central College *Washington*
Seattle Pacific University *Washington*
Seattle University *Washington*
Shoreline Community College *Washington*
Sierra Nevada College *Nevada*
Simon Fraser University *British Columbia (Canada)*
Skagit Valley College *Washington*
Snow College *Utah*
South Puget Sound Community College *Washington*
South Seattle College *Washington*
Southern Oregon University *Oregon*
Southern Utah University *Utah*
Southwestern Oregon Community College *Oregon*
Spokane Community College *Washington*
Spokane Falls Community College *Washington*
Stone Child College *Montana*
Tacoma Community College *Washington*
Tillamook Bay Community College *Oregon*
Treasure Valley Community College *Oregon*
Truckee Meadows Community College *Nevada*
Umpqua Community College *Oregon*
University of Alaska Anchorage *Alaska*
University of Alaska Anchorage, Kenai Peninsula College *Alaska*
University of Alaska Anchorage, Kodiak College *Alaska*
University of Alaska Anchorage, Matanuska-Susitna College *Alaska*
University of Alaska Fairbanks *Alaska*

University of Alaska, Prince William Sound College *Alaska*
University of Alaska Southeast *Alaska*
University of Alaska Southeast, Ketchikan Campus *Alaska*
University of Alaska Southeast, Sitka Campus *Alaska*
University of Great Falls *Montana*
University of Idaho *Idaho*
University of Maryland Eastern Shore *Maryland*
University of Montana *Montana*
The University of Montana Western *Montana*
University of Nevada, Las Vegas *Nevada*
University of Nevada, Reno *Nevada*
University of Oregon *Oregon*
University of Portland *Oregon*
University of Puget Sound *Washington*
University of Utah *Utah*
University of Washington *Washington*
University of Washington, Bothell *Washington*
University of Washington, Tacoma *Washington*
Utah State University *Utah*
Utah Valley University *Utah*
Walla Walla Community College *Washington*
Walla Walla University *Washington*
Warner Pacific College *Oregon*
Washington State University *Washington*
Washington State University - Global Campus *Washington*
Washington State University - Spokane *Washington*
Washington State University - Tri-Cities *Washington*
Washington State University - Vancouver *Washington*
Weber State University *Utah*
Wenatchee Valley College *Washington*
Western Governors University *Utah*
Western Nevada College *Nevada*
Western Oregon University *Oregon*
Western Washington University *Washington*
Westminster College *Utah*
Whatcom Community College *Washington*
Whitman College *Washington*
Whitworth University *Washington*
Willamette University *Oregon*
Yakima Valley Community College *Washington*

Society of American Foresters (SAF)

Alabama Agricultural and Mechanical University *Alabama*
Auburn University *Alabama*
California Polytechnic State University, San Luis Obispo *California*
Clemson University *South Carolina*
Colorado State University *Colorado*
Duke University *North Carolina*
Humboldt State University *California*
Iowa State University of Science and Technology *Iowa*
Louisiana State University and Agricultural & Mechanical College *Louisiana*
Louisiana Tech University *Louisiana*
Michigan State University *Michigan*
Michigan Technological University *Michigan*
Mississippi State University *Mississippi*
North Carolina State University *North Carolina*
Northern Arizona University *Arizona*
The Ohio State University *Ohio*
Oklahoma State University *Oklahoma*
Oregon State University *Oregon*
Penn State University Park *Pennsylvania*
Purdue University *Indiana*
Southern Illinois University Carbondale *Illinois*
State University of New York College of Environmental Science and Forestry *New York*
Stephen F. Austin State University *Texas*
Texas A&M University *Texas*
University of Alaska Fairbanks *Alaska*
University of Arkansas at Monticello *Arkansas*
University of California, Berkeley *California*
University of Florida *Florida*
University of Georgia *Georgia*
University of Idaho *Idaho*
University of Illinois at Urbana - Champaign *Illinois*
University of Kentucky *Kentucky*
University of Maine *Maine*

University of Massachusetts Amherst *Massachusetts*
University of Michigan *Michigan*
University of Minnesota, Twin Cities Campus *Minnesota*
University of Missouri *Missouri*
University of Montana *Montana*
University of New Hampshire *New Hampshire*
The University of Tennessee *Tennessee*
University of Vermont *Vermont*
University of Washington *Washington*
University of Wisconsin - Madison *Wisconsin*
University of Wisconsin - Stevens Point *Wisconsin*
Utah State University *Utah*
Virginia Polytechnic Institute and State University *Virginia*
Washington State University *Washington*
West Virginia University *West Virginia*
Yale University *Connecticut*

Teacher Education Accreditation Council (TEAC)

Abilene Christian University *Texas*
Alfred University *New York*
American InterContinental University Online *Illinois*
Aquinas College *Michigan*
Baker University *Kansas*
Bard College *New York*
Bayamón Central University *Puerto Rico*
Bethel College *Indiana*
Bethel University *Minnesota*
Binghamton University, State University of New York *New York*
Bluefield College *Virginia*
Boston College *Massachusetts*
Brigham Young University *Utah*
Caldwell University *New Jersey*
Calvin College *Michigan*
Cambridge College *Massachusetts*
Case Western Reserve University *Ohio*
Centenary College *New Jersey*
Centenary College of Louisiana *Louisiana*
Central Michigan University *Michigan*
Chapman University *California*
Colgate University *New York*
College of Mount Saint Vincent *New York*
The College of St. Scholastica *Minnesota*
Colorado State University *Colorado*
Colorado State University - Pueblo *Colorado*
Cornell University *New York*
Daemen College *New York*
Dominican College *New York*
Drew University *New Jersey*
Fairleigh Dickinson University, Metropolitan Campus *New Jersey*
Felician University *New Jersey*
Ferris State University *Michigan*
Florida Atlantic University *Florida*
Georgian Court University *New Jersey*
Hawai'i Pacific University *Hawaii*
Hofstra University *New York*
Hollins University *Virginia*
Holy Family University *Pennsylvania*
Inter American University of Puerto Rico, Arecibo Campus *Puerto Rico*
Inter American University of Puerto Rico, Barranquitas Campus *Puerto Rico*

Inter American University of Puerto Rico, Metropolitan Campus *Puerto Rico*
Inter American University of Puerto Rico, San Germán Campus *Puerto Rico*
Lake Erie College *Ohio*
Lakeland College *Wisconsin*
Le Moyne College *New York*
Lesley University *Massachusetts*
Lindenwood University *Missouri*
Long Island University - LIU Brooklyn *New York*
Long Island University - LIU Post *New York*
Lourdes University *Ohio*
Manhattan College *New York*
Mary Baldwin College *Virginia*
Marygrove College *Michigan*
Medaille College *New York*
Michigan State University *Michigan*
Michigan Technological University *Michigan*
Montana State University *Montana*
Mount St. Joseph University *Ohio*
Nazareth College of Rochester *New York*
New Jersey City University *New Jersey*
New York University *New York*
Northern Michigan University *Michigan*
Oakland University *Michigan*
Ohio Valley University *West Virginia*
Olivet College *Michigan*
Pontifical Catholic University of Puerto Rico *Puerto Rico*
Pratt Institute *New York*
Randolph College *Virginia*
Regent University *Virginia*
Regis University *Colorado*
Rice University *Texas*
Robert Morris University *Pennsylvania*
Roberts Wesleyan College *New York*
Rochester Institute of Technology *New York*
Rockhurst University *Missouri*
Rutgers University - New Brunswick *New Jersey*
St. Ambrose University *Iowa*
Saint Francis University *Pennsylvania*
St. John's University *New York*
St. Joseph's College, New York *New York*
St. Lawrence University *New York*
Saint Martin's University *Washington*
Saint Peter's University *New Jersey*
Shenandoah University *Virginia*
Siena Heights University *Michigan*
Southern Utah University *Utah*
Spring Arbor University *Michigan*
State University of New York Empire State College *New York*
State University of New York at Plattsburgh *New York*
Stockton University *New Jersey*
Temple University *Pennsylvania*
Texas State University *Texas*
Touro College *New York*
Tulane University *Louisiana*
Universidad del Turabo *Puerto Rico*
University at Albany, State University of New York *New York*
University at Buffalo, the State University of New York *New York*
University of Detroit Mercy *Michigan*
University of Hawaii at Hilo *Hawaii*
University of Houston - Victoria *Texas*
University of Massachusetts Boston *Massachusetts*

University of Miami *Florida*
University of Michigan *Michigan*
University of Michigan - Dearborn *Michigan*
University of Missouri *Missouri*
University of Nebraska - Lincoln *Nebraska*
University of New Hampshire *New Hampshire*
University of Pittsburgh *Pennsylvania*
University of St. Thomas *Texas*
The University of Scranton *Pennsylvania*
University of Southern Maine *Maine*
The University of Texas at Tyler *Texas*
The University of Tulsa *Oklahoma*
University of Utah *Utah*
University of Virginia *Virginia*
Utah State University *Utah*
Utah Valley University *Utah*
Utica College *New York*
Wayne State University *Michigan*
Weber State University *Utah*
Westminster College *Utah*
Wilmington College *Ohio*
Worcester State University *Massachusetts*
Xavier University *Ohio*
Yeshiva University *New York*

Transnational Association of Christian Colleges and Schools (TRACS)

Apex School of Theology *North Carolina*
Bethesda University *California*
Beulah Heights University *Georgia*
Bob Jones University *South Carolina*
Boston Baptist College *Massachusetts*
California Christian College *California*
Charlotte Christian College and Theological Seminary *North Carolina*
Christian Life College *Illinois*
Clinton College *South Carolina*
Community Christian College *California*
Crossroads College *Minnesota*
Epic Bible College *California*
Faith Theological Seminary *Maryland*
Georgia Christian University *Georgia*
Gutenberg College *Oregon*
Heritage Bible College *North Carolina*
Hillsdale Free Will Baptist College *Oklahoma*
Hiwassee College *Tennessee*
International Baptist College and Seminary *Arizona*
The King's University *Texas*
Luther Rice College & Seminary *Georgia*
Manthano Christian College *Michigan*
Maple Springs Baptist Bible College and Seminary *Maryland*
Messenger College *Texas*
Morthland College *Illinois*
New Saint Andrews College *Idaho*
Pacific Islands University *Guam*
Patrick Henry College *Virginia*
Paul Quinn College *Texas*
Piedmont International University *North Carolina*
Shasta Bible College *California*
Shorter College *Arkansas*
Southern California Seminary *California*
Trinity Baptist College *Florida*
University of Fort Lauderdale *Florida*
Virginia Baptist College *Virginia*
Virginia University of Lynchburg *Virginia*
Visible Music College *Tennessee*
World Mission University *California*

Index of U.S. Colleges

Index of U.S. Colleges